LIVING IN FEAR

A History of Horror in the Mass Media

BY LES DANIELS

CHARLES SCRIBNER'S SONS
•NEW YORK•

ACKNOWLEDGMENTS

To Edward Arnold Ltd., for "Rats" by M. R. James, from *The Collected Ghost Stories*; to Alfred A. Knopf, Inc., for "Novel of the White Powder" by Arthur Machen, from *The Three Impostors*; to Arkham House Publishers, for "The Outsider" by H. P. Lovecraft, from *The Outsider and Others*; to Scott Meredith Literary Agency, Inc., for "Slime" by Joseph Payne Brennan, from *Weird Tales*; and to Harold Matson Co., Inc., for "Blood Son" by Richard Matheson, from *The Shores of Space*.

The author also wishes to express his gratitude to the following individuals, whose cooperation, advice, and encouragement contributed to the completion of this book: Norma Asbornsen, H. L. P. Beckwith, Jr., Syd Blazar, Alec Chalmers, Desi De Simone, Harris Dienstfrey; William Gaines, Al Feldstein, and Jerry De Fuccio; Donald Grant, John King, Ellen Mayer, Mad Peck Studios, Barry Smith, Robert Somma, Barton L. St. Armand, Flo Steinberg, James Warren, Kenny Weinstein, and Marshall Wyatt. Special thanks also to two people who have spent a long time living in fear: my agent, Max Gartenberg, and my editor, Patricia Cristol.

Library of Congress Cataloging in Publication Data

Daniels, Les, 1943–
Living in fear.

Includes The imp of the perverse, by E. A. Poe; My favorite murder, by A. Bierce; Rats, by M. R. James; Novel of the white powder, by A. Machen; The outsider, by H. P. Lovecraft; Slime, by J. P. Brennan; Model nephew, by J. Davis; Blood son, by R. Matheson; and index.
1. Horror in mass media. 2. Horror tales, American.
3. Horror tales, English. I. Title.
P96.H65D3 823'.0872 75-16392
ISBN 0-684-14342-9

1 3 5 7 9 11 13 15 17 19 MD/C 20 18 16 14 12 10 8 6 4 2

Printed in the United States of America

CONTENTS

LIVING IN FEAR

·1·

THE PLAGUE YEARS: A BACKGROUND OF BELIEF

It might seem that there are enough things to be afraid of in real life. Poverty and pain, crime and corruption, oppression and depression, disease and death—all these lurk in the shadows, and sooner or later they pounce on everybody. And yet, for a substantial audience, purely imaginary terrors represent an authentic attraction. A fondness for fabricated fright is almost a universal human characteristic, although there are those who reject it, either because they find expressions of this impulse too terrifying or because they consider the whole genre crude and degrading. A possibility exists that the latter sort of disdain actually conceals the former sort of distress, but most people at least occasionally overcome both attitudes enough to experience some enjoyment from fictitious fears. There is an almost irresistible impulse to speculate on what may lie beyond our mortal miseries; this inclination may count for more than the wish to be terrified, since devotees of the macabre often continue to indulge their interest long after they are too jaded to be authentically unnerved.

Innumerable essays have been written attempting to explain the fascination for terror tales; there are enough theories to fill a book, but none of them are completely convincing. The fact is that the muse of the macabre has inspired more variations in style and subject than many glib commentators have encountered. It is commonplace to picture prehistoric people huddled in the darkness, making up stories to explain the bewildering world around them. This is an interesting image, but it fails to acknowledge that primitive myths were as likely to involve benevolent forces as brutal ones. It also ignores the fact that stories of the sinister supernatural really began to come into their own after belief in the uncanny had been almost extinguished. The myths and legends of ancient days are often full of horrors, but these are presented in a context where marvels are commonplace, so much so that virtually all of the narratives that have survived from the distant past have some fantastic element. The horror story as a distinct entity is a relatively recent invention, only a few centuries old, and it developed almost simultaneously with the idea of fiction. Modern audiences are so accustomed to tales which are obvious inventions that they fail to realize the extent to which their ancestors expected and believed their stories to be gospel truth. Even the terrifying tragedies of the relatively sophisticated Elizabethan era were usually presented as biographies of historical characters, and the pioneering novelists of the seventeenth and eighteenth centuries took great pains to disguise their fictions as fact so that they would not be accused of spreading lies.

So interest in fearsome fantasies cannot be completely explained as the result of a desire to understand the unknown. Still, the legends of the past provided many of the monsters that haunt the literature of the present, and part of the modern enthusiasm for the macabre may be attributed to ancestral memories of the days when demons were almost expected to put in an occasional appearance. The theory that ancient ideas survive in modern minds is one of the explanations that psychologists offer for the present prevalence of occult entertainments, but this interpretation is not as widespread as the psychoanalytical one which asserts that supernatural events symbolize neurotic personal problems. Sigmund Freud, in his essay "The Uncanny," calls it "that class of the terrifying which leads us back to something long known to us, once very familiar"; these, he asserts, are not recollections of primitive cultural attitudes but of "repressed infantile complexes." Thus, for instance, the hungry fiends that haunt so many horror tales may be taken to represent the oral stage of infant development, and many menaces have been analyzed as embodiments of maladjusted sexuality. Such suggestions may have some validity, but they fail to account for the intensity of the audience's vicarious experience. A skillful presentation is engrossing enough to create a sense of participation, and the imaginary horrors produce something like the dismay they would elicit if they were real, regardless of their symbolic value. An attack by a werewolf would be sufficient cause for alarm, even without the victim pausing to contemplate a misspent youth. The Freudian theory offers some insights, but is insufficient as a complete explanation, like the "collective unconscious" theory of Freud's disciple Carl Jung, which might account for the continued validity of motifs based on superstition but not for the effect of the new science fiction concepts which have demonstrated their chilling power in recent decades.

A quasi-psychological theory frequently offered by less knowledgeable commentators than Freud or Jung suggests that the appeal of the macabre exists primarily for masochists, or, alternatively, for sadists. In brief, this is an accusation that devotees take a depraved pleasure either in their own painful emotions or in the suffering of various imaginary victims. These assertions represent an obvious oversimplification, since sadism and masochism are diametrically opposed states of mind. The two explanations largely cancel out each other, and attempts to reconcile them through the use of the fatuous phrase "sadomasochism" can only further muddy the waters. Some works may appeal to one attitude or the other, but many more do not. The terms when properly used refer to states of sexual excitement caused by inflicting or experiencing pain; most suffering has more obvious motivation and does not include these special emotions. Ascribing exclusively sexual interests of a debatable nature to the artists and audiences who appreciate the awesome is primarily a tactic to discredit the genre by those who find it distressing.

Arguments about the relative tastefulness of various approaches have often been based on questions of terminology. Such important contributors as actors Boris Karloff and Christopher Lee have insisted that the word *terror* should be employed, since its strict definition implies a spiritual state of fear, whereas *horror* suggests a physical revulsion bordering on nausea. They may well be correct in designating the ideal description, but this semantic issue is largely technical: phrases like *horror film* and *horror story* have gained such popular acceptance that quibbling is irrelevant. The attempt to differentiate derives from a desire to distinguish between acceptable and unacceptable entries in the field, but such classifications are inevitably a matter of taste. Each individual has an opinion regarding the limits of taste, yet it must be acknowledged that the appeal of the macabre is dependent in large measure on the way in which it violates decorum. Discretion is one of the genre's minor virtues, and while it is possible to feel that certain episodes are excessively grim, no rigid code of restrictions could be devised that would be anything less than ludicrous.

Some aesthetic justification for the portrayal of terrifying events was offered by the ancient Greek philosopher Aristotle, whose *Poetics* includes the theory of catharsis. Aristotle held that the frequently frightening tragedies written and performed by his contemporaries served to purge the emotions through pity and terror, leaving the audience less likely to behave horribly because they had experienced the results vicariously. Perhaps the most gruesome of the classic Greek tragedies were the work of Aeschylus, whose masterpiece is the *Oresteia* (458 B.C.). This series of three plays chronicles the bloody history of the House of Atreus in the aftermath of the Trojan War. King Agamemnon has sacrificed his daughter's life to ensure victory; upon his return he is murdered by his wife Clytemnestra, and she in turn is slain by their son Orestes. As punishment, he is haunted by the Furies, hideous female spirits with serpents in their hair who weep bloody tears. While the traditions of the formalized Greek theater dictated that the murders, and indeed all action, should take place offstage, the Furies themselves were permitted to tread the boards; they are among the earliest examples of the vengeful spirits that have reappeared in literature ever since.

An even earlier narrative form than the drama is the epic poem. The legendary blind bard Homer produced the two great Greek epics; *The Iliad* is a tale of war, but *The Odyssey* includes many uncanny creatures and incidents in its hero's ten-year voyage home: the one-eyed giant cannibal Polyphemus, the seductive Sirens whose songs drive men to destruction, the sorceress Circe who turns sailors into swine, and the descent of Odysseus into Hades, where he converses with the spirits of the dead, feeding them with the blood of rams. Like the early tragedies, epics were considered to be historical records. They survive as literature because of the brilliant interpreters who set them down; but the lore of ancient Greece contains a myriad of memorable monsters, usually provided to prove a hero's prowess, but not so often blessed by the touch of a literary luminary.

That part of Western culture not derived from the Greeks owes most to the Judeo-Christian tradition represented by the Holy Bible, which contains many incidents involving sinister manifestations of the supernatural, most obviously in the person of the fallen angel Lucifer, who is credited with controlling most of the malignant entities that have infested literature since the dawn of time. Also worth noting are the stories of Enoch and the Witch of Endor, not to mention the awesome visions described in the Book of Revelation. The Bible offers glimpses of the Assyrian and Egyptian civilizations which were storehouses of the occult; little survives in the form of melodramatic narratives, but the lore of Egypt especially has proved an inspiration to modern authors in search of an idea. It seems a pity that comparatively few writers have drawn material from the equally fascinating American cultures of the Aztecs and the Mayas; not much more has been done than a couple of poor films.

The arts in ancient Rome followed the lead of the Greeks; Virgil's epic *The Aeneid* contains several weird scenes based on Homer's example. The Roman drama made some innovations, involving more action on stage, in the lurid tragedies of Seneca. The real development, though, was in the appearance of comparatively casual prose tales, like the werewolf story written by Petronius and the tale of a haunted house from Pliny's *Letters*, both fascinating in that they are full of stock incidents (such as clanking chains) that have survived two thousand years without alteration.

The whole world is full of tales like these; but it is impossible to recount them all, and it seems wisest to concentrate on what has proved to be the most flourishing branch of this universal tree. A powerful and persuasive tradition of terror tales has grown up among English-speaking people, first in Britain and later in America. Many of the creations conjured up in this milieu have spread to other nations with a thoroughness that no other culture has been able to duplicate. Even essentially alien concepts such as the vampire legend have received their definitive treatment in Anglo-American hands. This ability to assimilate the uncanny lore of all nations is exemplified by indefatigable researchers like the eccentric twentieth-century Englishman Montague Summers who, clad in a black cloak and buckled shoes, ravaged the archives of Europe to produce purportedly factual compilations like *The History of Witchcraft and Demonology* (1926) and *The Vampire, His Kith and Kin* (1928). Such efforts helped to preserve traditions of the past that had yet to be presented in artistic form.

The first great appearance of the uncanny in English literature is the epic adventure *Beowulf.* This poem, written down over a thousand years ago and presumably composed even earlier, recounts the adventures of Beowulf, a fighter of monsters who slays Grendel, a terrible troll, and is then drawn into combat with the creature's even more menacing mother. He survives this struggle but gives his life to defeat a dragon. This tale of heroism and horror is told in Old English, a form of the language so archaic that it is impossible for the modern reader to understand it.

Old English was succeeded by the comparatively intelligible Middle English, the development of which coincided with the period when printing became feasible. The greatest work of this era is Geoffrey Chaucer's *Canterbury Tales*, written over several years near the end of the fourteenth century (the precise dates of composition for works of this period are uncertain). This narrative poem includes many tales told by religious pilgrims to relieve the tedium of their journey; several of the stories are supernatural. "The Prioress's Tale" describes a murdered boy who sings his favorite hymn after his throat has been cut, leading to the discovery of his corpse and the punishment of his killers; "The Nun's Priest's Tale" includes uncanny anecdotes on the power of dreams. In one of them, a man has a nightmare in which his traveling companion reveals the facts of his murder, and in another a nightmare saves the life of a man who envisions a shipwreck.

This was also the era when the legends of King Arthur and his knights began to achieve literary permanence. The anonymous poem *Sir Gawain and the Green Knight* recounts the strange bargain between Sir Gawain and his grotesque green adversary, who offers the hero three opportunities to strike him in exchange for submission to the same conditions a year later. Although Sir Gawain beheads his opponent, the Green Knight gathers up his head and rides away, leaving Gawain in an agony of suspense for a year before the Green Knight decides to spare him. Sir Thomas Malory's definitive collection of Arthurian lore, *Le Morte d'Arthur*, is full of supernatural sequences; but they are submerged in an essentially heroic narrative and frequently involve benevolent entities. Malory's prose romance was published in 1485, several years after the author's death, by William Caxton, who had set up England's first printing press in 1476. Caxton was also responsible for the first edition of the *Canterbury Tales*, and his pioneering efforts marked the beginning of mass media in the English-speaking world. Ironically, the press came into being at a period when the best writers were moving toward the theater, so

Divers kinds of Tortures exercised on the Primitive Martyrs during the 10th Roman Persecution.
Cruelties inflicted on the Primitive Christians, their Bodies being tied to Stakes, thrust through with Spears, & others thrust under their nails with Thorns.
B. Tanner Sc.

An eighteenth-century illustration for John Foxe's *Book of Martyrs*, popular for centuries after its original appearance in 1563.

The Tragicall Hiſtorie of the Life and Death of Doctor Fauſtus.

With new Additions.

Written by Ch. Mar.

Printed at London for *Iohn Wright*, and are to be ſold at his ſhop without Newgate. 1631.

This 1631 title page includes the oldest known illustration for Christopher Marlowe's play about a tragic deal with devils, *Doctor Faustus* (1588).

that books provided less of the important literature of succeeding centuries than might have been expected. Still, most of the important plays were preserved for posterity by the press.

English drama began with "mystery plays," religious spectacles performed under church auspices and based on Bible stories. These gave way to "morality plays," allegorical dramas portraying personified vices and virtues. These culminated around 1500 with the anonymous masterpiece *Everyman*, in which the title character is visited by Death and discovers how little of his life he can bring with him to the grave. This short, stark piece is still a disturbing drama, perhaps the only work of its era that can still be performed effectively.

Everyman remained the greatest English play for nearly a century, until it was superseded by the robust and realistic drama of the Elizabethans. The tragedies of this period are full of violence, villains, and visions. The first important innovator in the field was Thomas Kyd, whose *Spanish Tragedy* was first produced around 1585. It proved to be the biggest hit of its day and was revived for decades. Kyd's most influential idea was to abandon the technique of ancient drama, in which all important action took place out of sight while the stage was occupied by static figures who discussed the situation. His sensational approach included the presentation of eight death scenes, along with assorted maniacs, ghosts, and such gory details as the removal of a man's tongue. The plot, in which a spirit incites the hero Hieronimo to punish his murderer, inspired the Elizabethan tradition of "revenge tragedy"; in fact, Revenge is one of the characters, a relic from the morality plays. Historical perspective and discreet scholarship have caused modern audiences to regard the drama of this age as something elegant and effete, but in truth it was an age of lurid thrillers. Actors wore bladders of sheep's blood under their clothing to make the slaughter more convincing; real weapons were used, and a performer would sometimes be so carried away that he would actually kill a colleague or even a member of the audience.

Surpassing Kyd in both style and substance was Christopher Marlowe, whose *Doctor Faustus*, even in the faulty transcriptions that have survived, is a masterpiece of the macabre. Marlowe transformed fragmentary legends into the definitive treatment on the subject of selling one's soul to Satan; he also created archetypal characters in the mocking Mephistopheles and his victim Faust, who trades eternity for youth, knowledge, power, and passion. Doctor Faustus, who as an alchemist is a cross between a scientist and a magician, is the model for the hero of hundreds of horror stories, not only because he deals with devils, but because his thirst for achievement leaves him blind to its chilling consequences.

Of course, William Shakespeare overshadows all his contemporaries. Many of his supernatural scenes are familiar, but his first tragedy, written under the influence of Kyd, is not so well known. *Titus Andronicus* (1594) contains so many ghastly incidents that some scholars have labored, in vain, to prove that Shakespeare did not write it. Titus is a conquering general of ancient Rome whose daughter is raped by the sons of the queen he has defeated. Her tongue and hands are removed to prevent accusation, but Titus discovers the culprits regardless. Insane with rage, he butchers the sons and feeds them to their mother, who discovers the nature of the feast just before Titus stabs her. He also kills his daughter at the same banquet of blood and is slaughtered himself along with several other characters, one of them by being buried up to his neck in an anthill. There are no scenes involving the uncanny, but the play is certainly horrifying enough without them.

Vicemq; nostris: redde me inferis precor
Vmbris reductum meq; subiectum tuis
Restitue uinclis: ille me abscondet locus
Sed & ille nouit. The. Nr̃a te tellus manet
Illic solutam cede gradiuus manum
Restituit armis. illa te alcide uocat.
Facere inocẽtes terra quæ superos solet.

Tragœdia secunda. Thyestes.

Actꝰ. i. Tãta. & Mege. Tãtalus loq̃t
Quis me furor nũc sedab ĩfausta abstra
Auido fugaces ore captãtẽ cibos(hit
Quis male deorum tantalo uias domos
Ostendit iterum peius est inuentum siti
Arente in undis aliquid. & peius fame
Hiante semper sisyphi nunquid lapis
Gestandus humeris lubricus nostris uenit
Aut membra celeri deferens cursu rota
Aut pœna Tytii se per accrescens iecur

A woodcut, ca. 1510, illustrating *Thiestes*, by the ancient Roman dramatist Seneca, whose scenes of cannibalism influenced Shakespeare's *Titus Andronicus*.

Lucifer, improbably dressed in the garb of a Roman soldier, rakes over damned souls in John Baptist Medina's 1688 illustration for John Milton's *Paradise Lost*.

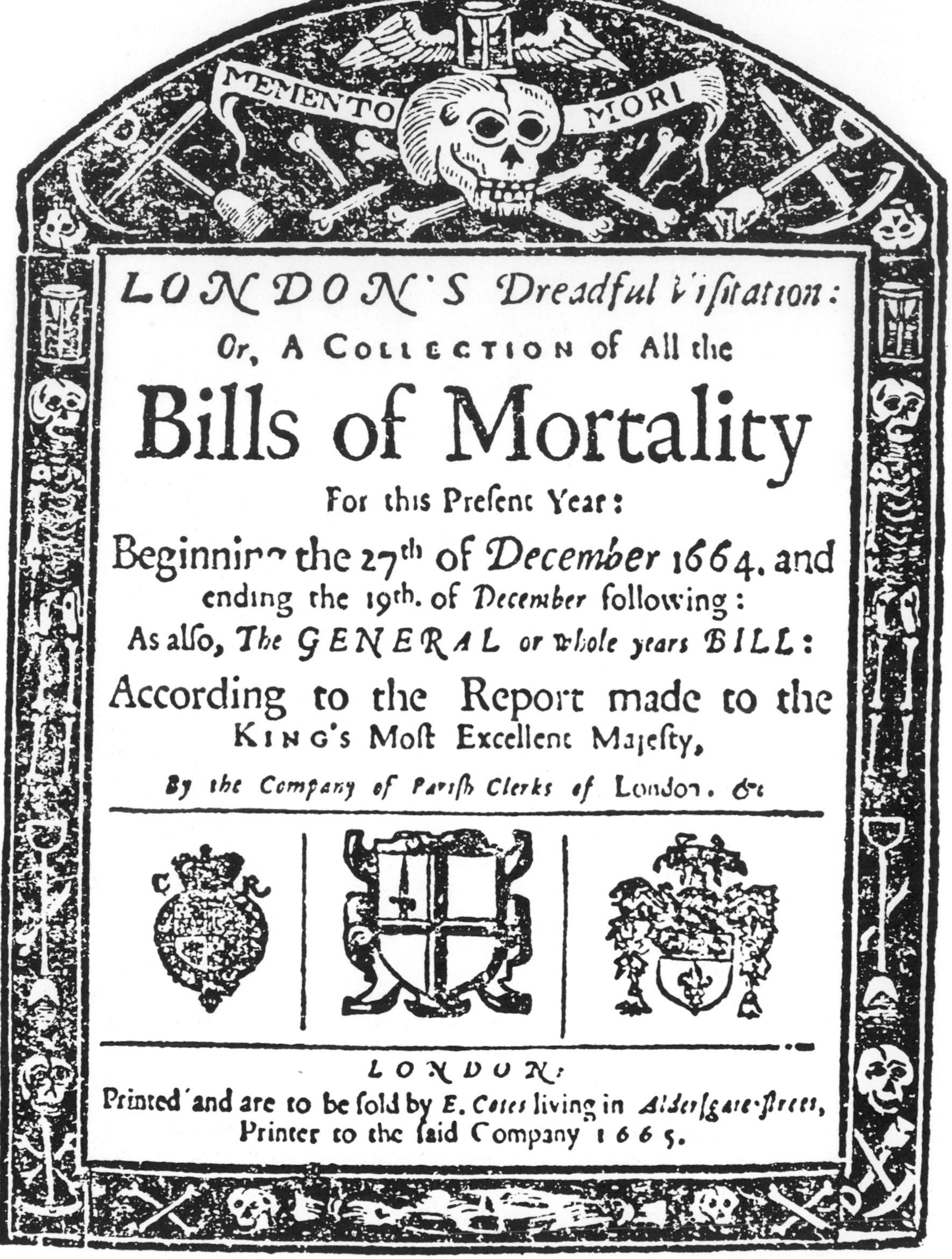
MEMENTO MORI

LONDON'S Dreadful Visitation:
Or, A COLLECTION of All the
Bills of Mortality
For this Present Year:
Beginning the 27th of December 1664. and
ending the 19th. of December following:
As also, The GENERAL or whole years BILL:
According to the Report made to the
KING's Most Excellent Majesty,
By the Company of Parish Clerks of London. &c.

LONDON:
Printed and are to be sold by E. Cotes living in Aldersgate-street,
Printer to the said Company 1665.

Gravestones inspired the design for the title page of this report to royalty on the plague of 1665, immortalized in Daniel Defoe's *Journal of the Plague Year*.

Most of Shakespeare's succeeding tragedies contain some elements of terror, if nothing as intense as *Titus Andronicus.* Even *Romeo and Juliet* (1596) has its macabre moments as Juliet imagines and then experiences her awakening among the corpses in her family crypt. In *Julius Caesar* (1599), the emperor appears as a ghost who helps drive his killers to suicide, and it is the spirit of his father that drives Hamlet to madness and murder in Shakespeare's finest and final revenge tragedy, the ultimate refinement of Kyd's theme. The later tragedies are free from such fantastic elements, with the notable exception of *Macbeth* (1606). His tragedy is precipitated by the enigmatic prophecies and visions provided by three witches, and he is haunted by the ghost of his victim, Banquo.

It was inevitable that the theater should decline somewhat from the heights attained by its greatest genius, but the stage and indeed all the arts in England suffered a terrible setback from the civil war which brought the Puritans to power. In 1642, a scant quarter of a century after Shakespeare's death, a grim and narrow-minded Puritan Parliament banned the performance of plays "to appease and avert the wrath of God." The greatest author of this gray period was the blind poet John Milton, whose *Paradise Lost* (1667) contains a portrait of a defiant Lucifer so powerful that Milton unwittingly inspired devilish sentiments in the poets of a less devout age more than a century later.

Literature recovered slowly from the effects of repression, and the trend for decades, even after the defeat of the Puritans, was away from extravagant tales of the marvelous and the macabre. Fantasy would find a foothold only after the idea of fiction had been firmly established. The turning point proved to be the birth of the novel, which evolved slowly from embellished accounts of actual events, or at least of reasonable facsimiles. Daniel Defoe has perhaps the best claim to the title of first English novelist, yet all his works were presented to the public as statements of fact. His nervousness about the new form was expressed in a piece he wrote debating whether or not the perusal of fiction was sinful. Originally a journalist, Defoe published a pamphlet in 1706 now known as "The Apparition of Mrs. Veal." It was purportedly a true ghost story, and research has indicated that the characters were real persons; but the idea persists that it was written to help the sales of a treatise on the afterlife prominently mentioned in the text. Defoe's most powerful work in the vein of terror is *A Journal of the Plague Year* (1722), a grippingly convincing eyewitness account of the London plague of 1665. It seems almost impossible to believe that it is a work of the imagination, loaded as it is with vivid details and exhausting documentation. The scenes of carts full of victims rolling away to mass graves amid the awful command "Bring out your dead!" are truly grim, all the more so because although the story was concocted, the plague was real.

These years, and the ones before them, were the years when diseases did destroy multitudes, when executions were public spectacles, when accusations of sorcery were commonplace. It is customary to regard our times as the most violent and dangerous of all, not without some justice; but modern civilization, for all its faults, has built a buffer between the average individual and the brutal realities of death and destruction. Perhaps it is because there has been less and less horror to confront face to face that we have embraced it more and more in synthetic forms. The root of many contemporary problems may be buried in the recent centuries of spiritual skepticism, yet the left-handed religious sentiments that inspire tales of demons and doom have survived.

Perhaps it is more than a coincidence that 1717, the year of England's last witchcraft trial, saw the birth of Horace Walpole, the man whose nostalgia for the bad old days of tyranny and terror ushered in the modern method of living in fear.

2

STRAWBERRY HILL: GOTHIC GHOSTS

The first modern horror story, like so many of its successors, was inspired by a dream. Its author wrote: "I waked one morning, in the beginning of last June, from a dream, of which all I could recover was, that I had thought myself in an ancient castle (a very natural dream for a head like mine filled with Gothic story) and that on the uppermost banister of a great staircase I saw a gigantic hand in armour. In the evening I sat down, and began to write, without knowing in the least what I intended to say or relate. The work grew on my hands and I grew so fond of it that one evening, I wrote from the time I had drunk my tea, about six o'clock, till half an hour after one in the morning, when my hands and fingers were so weary that I could not hold the pen to finish the sentence."

The dreamer was Horace Walpole, describing in a letter to a friend how he came to write *The Castle of Otranto.* It may seem strange to describe this short novel, now over two centuries old, as the beginning of the "modern" mainstream of macabre imaginings; but it marked a distinct departure from the tales of supernatural doings that had been told in the past centuries. By 1764, when Walpole made a book out of his nightmare, belief in forces beyond man's control or understanding had begun to fade away. The eighteenth century was the Age of Reason, and the best minds in the most influential circles were dismissing the idea of the supernatural as nonsense. Even those who stopped short of atheism held that creation had been so perfectly planned as to exclude the intervention of forces from beyond, whether they represented light or darkness. Of course, this skepticism was far from universal; but it represented a cultural attitude that has continued to expand its influence, so that stories like *Otranto* are now classified as fantasies, to be enjoyed rather than believed.

In this sense, the whole field of macabre fantasy is reactionary, basing its appeal on subjects that were still compelling, even if they had ceased to be convincing. Walpole, whose tale of ghostly vengeance in medieval days was based on his personal interests, discovered a large audience who, if they did not believe in ghosts, could still be frightened by them and could find the fright enjoyable. The wealthy and eccentric English aristocrat was doubtless surprised at his book's popularity. Who would have thought so many people were willing to spend even an imaginary night in a Gothic castle—especially since Walpole was the only man in England who had built one for centuries?

No present-day nostalgia buff can compare with Walpole, who devoted two decades and a considerable fortune to the construction of archaic architecture on his estate, Strawberry Hill. In this strange sort of private Disneyland he was free to indulge his passion for the romance of bygone days, and the unusual atmosphere finally inspired his novel, whose setting was patterned after Walpole's bizarre home. *The Castle of Otranto* proved to be so successful and influential that it gave birth to countless imitators over the next half-century—so many, in fact, that it inaugurated an entire school of English literature: the Gothic novel.

A handful of these Gothic novels are still remembered as part of the history of English literature, and more specifically as landmarks in the field of fantasy. Most have been completely forgotten, despite their status as the most widely read works of their era. They were the eighteenth century's best sellers, and they achieved that status despite a general lack of critical acclaim. Indeed, the Gothic novel might be said to have brought in its wake the whole concept of mass culture, of works of art that have won great popularity despite their lack of official sanction. What they failed to produce in the way of serious themes or elegant style was replaced by their sensational effects.

Walpole established the formula with his tale of madness, murder, and family intrigue. His principal character is Manfred, master of the Castle of Otranto, who has gained his position by poisoning the former prince, Alfonso. Although this crime is not revealed

Horace Walpole, the originator of the Gothic novel, built this imitation medieval castle on his estate, Strawberry Hill.

until the end of the tale, it is Alfonso's ghost, clad in armor and grown to enormous stature, who perpetrates most of the story's eerie events. Manfred's son is crushed to death on his wedding day by a gigantic helmet, and Manfred decides to provide himself with a new heir by pursuing Isabella, the disappointed bride. She succeeds in keeping him at arm's length with the help of Manfred's distressed wife Hippolita and their daughter, Matilda. Further obstructions are provided by a mysterious young man named Theodore and by the ghost, who continues to appear piecemeal, once as the hand of Walpole's dream and most ludicrously as an overgrown, ironclad foot. There is also a fairly ridiculous incident in which a statue of Alfonso expresses its indignation by developing a bloody nose.

Such are the horrors of *The Castle of Otranto*, climaxing when the ghost finally collects itself into a titanic figure and bursts out of the walls of its dwelling, leaving only ruins. Declaring the stranger Theodore to be the true heir to the castle it has so thoughtlessly destroyed, the spirit rises slowly into the clouds and disappears. Manfred, who has just mistakenly murdered his daughter in an attempt on Theodore, confesses and repents. The usurper and his luckless wife join religious orders, and Theodore weds Isabella, on the less than gallant grounds that she may console him in his grief over his true love, the murdered Matilda.

The ghost is perhaps the most believable character in this conglomeration of quaint dialogue and stilted action, which is filled with sentiments and motivations of the most naïve and melodramatic type. Walpole's intentions provide an explanation if not an excuse: the book was originally published not as his own work, but as a translation of an Italian manuscript from the twelfth century. He even invented a pseudonym for the translator and wrote a tongue-in-cheek introduction, praising the work for "the piety that reigns throughout, the lessons of virtue that are inculcated, and the rigid purity of the sentiments." These were offered as compensation for the supernatural events, "exploded now even from romances." Thus Walpole continued to work in the tradition of the early English novelists who claimed historical accuracy and uplifting morality in order to justify their excursions into the suspicious field of fiction. His anonymity may also have been motivated by doubts about the reception that might be given to such an excursion into the archaic. Yet Walpole's interest in the antique and the uncanny struck a responsive chord in thousands of readers, so that he was ready to acknowledge his authorship for the second edition. The book was published abroad in several languages and freely adapted as a play, *The Count of Narbonne*, by Robert Jephson.

The Castle of Otranto was a deliberate reaction to the realistic and detailed books that are the classic examples of the eighteenth-century novel. In his preface to the first edition, Walpole praised the book for its adherence to the rules of drama, which traditionally prescribed a single setting and a concentrated passage of time. This contrasts his book with the famous novels of the preceding quarter-century, which ranged over wide stretches of geography and allowed for the passage of many years. The resulting tight construction is most obviously seen in the length of his story, which runs barely a hundred pages, while many of his predecessors come closer to a thousand. His low opinion of those considered to be his superiors is a matter of record: he called Richardson "deplorably tedious," Fielding "perpetually disgusting," and Sterne "tiresome."

Such judgments put Walpole at odds with the serious literary historians of today, but there is little doubt that he spoke for many of his contemporaries. His "Gothic" formula gradually attracted more and more followers, while realistic fiction suffered a serious

"The sleep of reason breeds monsters," the title of this work by Francisco de Goya, sums up the Gothic reaction to Rationalism. The artist, whose productions became increasingly morbid, spent his last years studying magic.

decline. For over a generation, novels based on *Otranto* were to dominate English literature, and their preeminence continued well into the nineteenth century. The public gleefully abandoned the sensible for the sensational, and the result was an apparently endless wave of "trash," of works that were despised by critics but were nevertheless enjoyed by huge audiences.

Yet the triumph of the Gothic novel was a gradual process. The world of eighteenth-century letters was a leisurely one, and it was thirteen years before Walpole's first disciple got into print. This was Clara Reeve, whose novel *The Old English Baron* was published in 1777 under the less atmospheric title *The Champion of Virtue.* Again, it was published anonymously; the author's name appeared with the new title in 1780. Somewhat longer and far more restrained than *The Castle of Otranto*, this novel retained the Gothic setting but reduced the uncanny occurrences to three consecutive "dismal hollow" groans heard as the hero uncovers evidence of a murder committed years before. Stripped to its essentials, the plot is virtually the same as Walpole's, involving a young man, Edmund, who recovers his birthright and deposes a murderous usurper. Poorly constructed, so that it trails off in a monotonous discussion of claims to the estate, this novel is hardly worth considering as an example of macabre literature. Yet it is important as a transition between Walpole's early effort and the flood that was to follow.

The author declared that it was her purpose to create a "literary offspring" of *Otranto*, "written upon the same plan" but devoid of the fantastic elements that "instead of attention, excite laughter." The result is something like the historical novel of today, not even especially mysterious or suspenseful within its naturalistic framework. All in all, *The Old English Baron* surpasses its predecessor only in the exaggerated priggishness of its virtuous characters. A disgusted Horace Walpole wrote, "The work is a professed imitation of mine, only stripped of the marvellous, and so entirely stripped, except in the one awkward attempt at a ghost or two, that it is the most insipid dull thing you can read. It certainly does not make me laugh; for what makes one doze, seldom makes one merry."

The problem of providing thrills while maintaining plausibility found a solution of sorts in the work of Ann Radcliffe, the most widely read of all the Gothic novelists. Her technique involved describing weird events that were explained at the end of the book as villainous tricks which, however contrived and unlikely, were definitely not supernatural. This recipe allowed skeptical readers to have their cake and eat it too, a fact that may have helped account for Mrs. Radcliffe's popularity, as well as for her comparatively high standing with the more serious-minded critics. Yet such devices are likely to exasperate the present-day enthusiast of macabre fiction. Similarly, her considerable gifts as a stylist are more likely to irritate than to entertain, since she employed them in elaborate descriptions of largely irrelevant landscapes or in conjuring up mysterious atmospheres in which, ultimately, nothing much happens. She was, in short, the mistress of anticlimax, and all the more annoying because her books are very long. Her major contribution was to shift the focus of her tales so that villains and spooks were pushed into the background. Instead, her novels are presented largely through the eyes of terror's intended victim. In all of Mrs. Radcliffe's novels, the heroine stands at the center of the stage. She may be threatened, pursued, harassed, or imprisoned, but no real harm ever comes to her, so that the plots are sequences of events that almost happen.

Born in the same year the first Gothic novel appeared, Ann Radcliffe had five novels published during her lifetime: *The Castles of Athlin and Dunbayne* (1789), *A Sicilian Romance* (1790), *The Romance of the Forest* (1792), *The Mysteries of Udolpho* (1794), and *The Italian*

(1797). The last two are generally considered her best, but *Udolpho* represents the apex of her career. This is the story of Emily de St. Aubert, who is persecuted by her aunt's sinister spouse, Montoni. (Mrs. Radcliffe's insistence on Italian villains, if duplicated today, would doubtless inspire action from an antidefamation league.) A classic example of Radcliffean terror occurs when Emily, having worked herself up into a highly nervous condition, pulls aside a tapestry and promptly swoons. A healthy chunk of the novel must be perused before the reader discovers that Emily saw a corpse, and another decent interval elapses before said corpse is exposed as a wax dummy, left lying around on a flimsy pretext.

This sort of hemming and hawing apparently provided thrills aplenty for Ann Radcliffe's predominantly female, middle-class, middlebrow followers, who were delighted to imagine themselves as persecuted aristocrats of exquisite beauty and unsullied virtue, fleeing from ambiguous dangers that might have been death or the fate worse than death. The genteel paranoia of maiden ladies dreaming of demon lovers pervades these works, driving such a literary luminary as Jane Austen to parody them in her earliest novel, *Northanger Abbey*. Yet even she excepted the Radcliffe sagas from her general mockery of such works, reinforcing the opinion that these were the best of a bad lot, most of them mercifully forgotten.

If some of the Gothic novels seem a trifle insipid, there were others of a more colorful cast, less concerned with the tribulations of the innocent than with the transgressions of the depraved. One such volume is *Vathek*. Written by an Englishman, William Beckford, it was originally composed in French and only later translated into the author's native tongue. This unique and delightful book virtually defies classification. Witches, demons, and ghouls wander through its pages; yet it is far from frightening, and not because Beckford lacks skill. His book is a fantasy with an Arabian Nights flavor, describing the sins and damnation of Vathek, ninth caliph of the race of the Abassides. Although such a theme is appropriate to the Gothic tradition, Beckford's luxuriant imagery and sly humor create a mood totally antithetical to that suggested by the gray castles and black deeds of medieval Europe.

Much of the action of *Vathek* takes place in a gigantic tower, eleven thousand steps high, where the caliph's wicked mother casts spells and performs human sacrifices to guide him on a pilgrimage to an underworld of demons. There he seeks power and glory, but he finds only the torture of a heart set eternally aflame. William Beckford was to build a tower too, though the results were less spectacular. Perhaps inspired by Horace Walpole's success with Strawberry Hill, Beckford personally designed a huge and elaborate structure which, upon completion, promptly fell over. Undaunted, Beckford tried again with somewhat better results, only at tremendous expense. Indeed, his life's work was the dissipation of the fortune he had inherited from his father, who had been Lord Mayor of London. It took him most of his eighty-four years to spend the money; but he did it, and he declared that he was never bored for a moment of his life.

Vathek included enough entertaining Oriental outrages to make Beckford a prime contender for the title of most decadent artist in eighteenth-century England; but the crown was snatched away from him in 1796 by one Matthew Gregory Lewis, who also took Beckford's seat in Parliament. The sensational Lewis novel, *The Monk*, which appeared with its author's government credentials firmly affixed, was the most morbidly erotic and morally exotic product of the Gothic period. *The Monk* also defined the archetypal horror hero, half-saint and half-Satanist, in the person of its protagonist, who runs amok in an orgy of rape and murder.

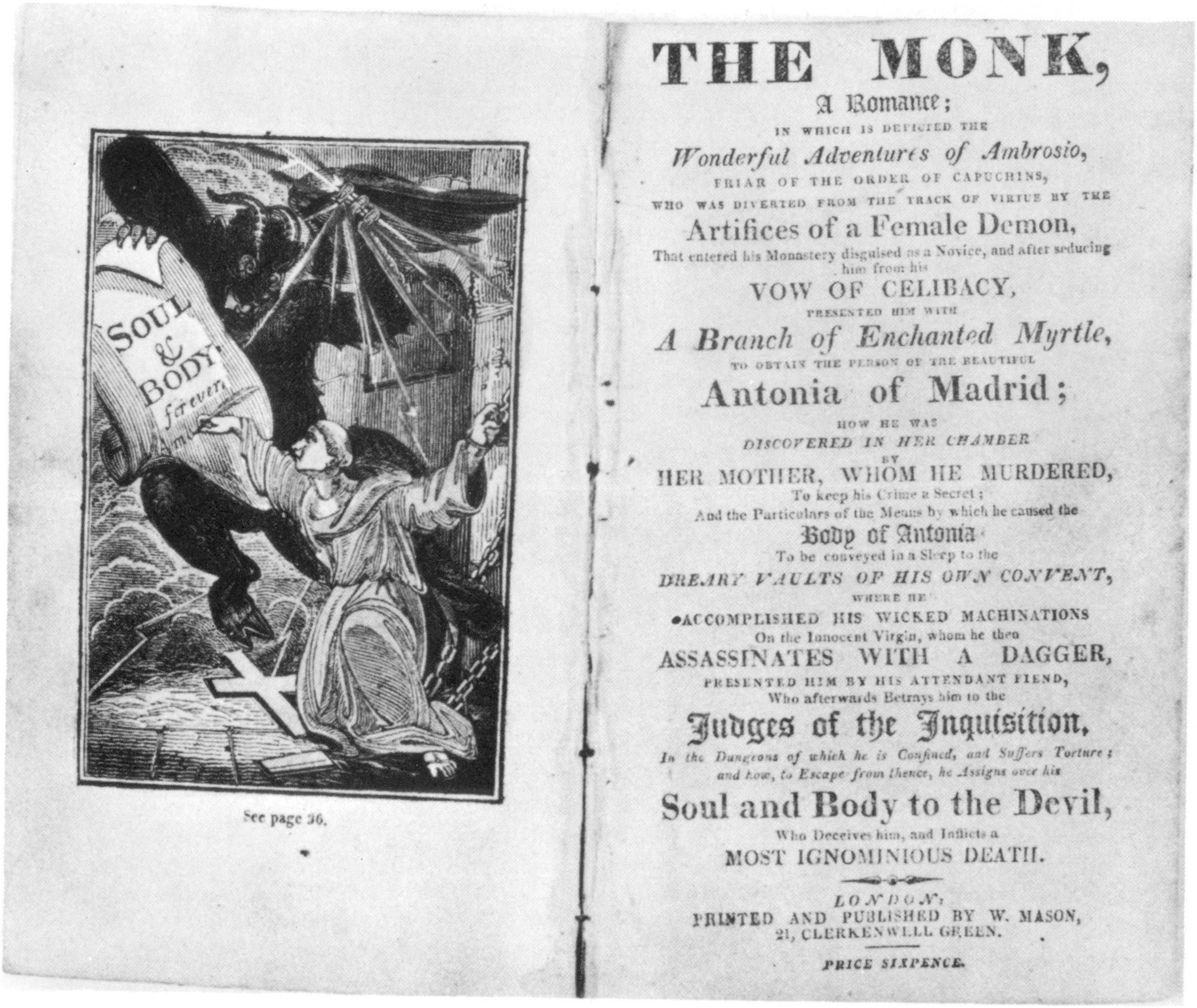

THE MONK,
A Romance;
IN WHICH IS DEPICTED THE
Wonderful Adventures of Ambrosio,
FRIAR OF THE ORDER OF CAPUCHINS,
WHO WAS DIVERTED FROM THE TRACK OF VIRTUE BY THE
Artifices of a Female Demon,
That entered his Monastery disguised as a Novice, and after seducing him from his
VOW OF CELIBACY,
PRESENTED HIM WITH
A Branch of Enchanted Myrtle,
TO OBTAIN THE PERSON OF THE BEAUTIFUL
Antonia of Madrid;
HOW HE WAS
DISCOVERED IN HER CHAMBER
BY
HER MOTHER, WHOM HE MURDERED,
To keep his Crime a Secret;
And the Particulars of the Means by which he caused the
Body of Antonia
To be conveyed in a Sleep to the
DREARY VAULTS OF HIS OWN CONVENT,
WHERE HE
ACCOMPLISHED HIS WICKED MACHINATIONS
On the Innocent Virgin, whom he then
ASSASSINATES WITH A DAGGER,
PRESENTED HIM BY HIS ATTENDANT FIEND,
Who afterwards Betrays him to the
Judges of the Inquisition,
In the Dungeons of which he is Confined, and Suffers Torture; and how, to Escape from thence, he Assigns over his
Soul and Body to the Devil,
Who Deceives him, and Inflicts a
MOST IGNOMINIOUS DEATH.

LONDON:
PRINTED AND PUBLISHED BY W. MASON,
21, CLERKENWELL GREEN.

PRICE SIXPENCE.

The frontispiece and title page for an abridged edition of the controversial Gothic novel *The Monk* by Matthew Gregory Lewis.

Ambrosio, the abbot of the Capuchins, is a foundling raised by the monks, whose extraordinary piety has made him the leader of his order and the most respected clergyman in Madrid at the time of the Spanish Inquisition. He meets temptation in the form of the beautiful Matilda, a young woman who, disguised as the novice Rosario, enters the monastery to seduce the abbot. Ambrosio breaks his vow of chastity and is led by Matilda into a whirlpool of greater and greater sin. When he tires of her charms, he conceives a passion for an innocent girl, Antonia, and attempts to force himself upon her, encouraged and aided by Matilda, who reveals herself as a sorceress. His first attempt to rape Antonia is frustrated by her mother, whom Ambrosio murders while the girl, under a spell, is unconscious. Later, he succeeds in kidnapping Antonia, rapes her, then murders her in a vain effort to avoid discovery. He and Matilda are finally taken prisoner by the Inquisition. Employing black arts to escape, Matilda appears to Ambrosio in his cell and convinces him to sell his soul in order to avoid execution. A devil transports Ambrosio from prison, as agreed, but then callously hurls the monk from a precipice, after revealing to him the terrible truth that Antonia had been his sister and her mother, his own.

This was stronger stuff than any of Lewis's predecessors had attempted, and the book created a scandal, aggravated by the fact that the author was identified on the title page as a member of Parliament. An organization called the Society for the Suppression of Vice succeeded in having the book banned, and later editions were printed with some of the more lurid scenes of sex and violence removed, as well as certain passages smacking of blasphemy. While there is nothing in *The Monk* that would be censored today, its overall tone is still sufficient to disturb a sensitive reader. In fact, Lewis has been accused of most of Ambrosio's mental attitudes, although there is nothing in his biography to support such charges. On the contrary, it seems clear that Lewis had made a clever and calculated attempt to shock the public, and in that he did not fail.

He also carried many of the themes of the Gothic novel to their logical conclusions. If writers of the Radcliffe school could titillate their readers with the prospect of dastardly crimes, why not go all the way and show what they constantly suggested? If the mere suggestion of the supernatural could thrill an audience, why not present it as a tangible reality? This direct approach makes *The Monk* the most dramatic and readable product of its school, and its vivid details were to become standard fare in subsequent tales of the macabre. Lewis even influenced Ann Radcliffe, whose *Mysteries of Udolpho* had inspired him to try his hand at Gothic fiction. Her novel *The Italian*, which appeared a year after *The Monk*, is about a girl-chasing monk, Schedoni, who ends up in the hands of the Inquisition.

The Monk's exaggerated treatment of conventional material helps to explain the Age of Reason's fascination with Gothic novels; it also anticipated the ideas that were to prevail among creative artists in the Romantic movement. In fact, Lewis is a pivotal figure in the transition between these two antithetical views of life and art; he employed a standard fictional formula to promote the causes of liberty and libertinism. The dark, forbidding edifices in which horrors were perpetrated came to symbolize established corruption, while the authoritarian figure of the monk took on the colors of rebellion by releasing his passions in defiance of reason and propriety. Drawn larger than life, Ambrosio's self-indulgence and damnation influenced the melancholy, posturing heroes of the great Romantic poet Lord Byron. Unchecked emotions in conflict with absolute power were not merely literary concerns, as the French Revolution had so recently demonstrated, and *The Monk* includes a scene in which a furious mob storms a stronghold of the Inquisition to tear its proprietors limb from limb.

The book made Lewis an overnight celebrity at the age of twenty, and for the rest of his life he was known as "Monk" Lewis. He was never to have comparable success with a work of fiction, although he adapted a number of German stories whose explicit horrors had influenced his approach to the Gothic novel. Yet he was to create a few more sensations before he stopped writing at thirty-three by writing a series of spectacular works for the stage. Some of his plays were tragedies and comedies of the standard type; but he made his reputation as a dramatist with supernatural melodramas which were, in effect, the horror movies of their era. As such, they were distinguished less by ingenious plotting or effective dialogue than by clever staging. Lewis excelled in the use of lighting, music, and mechanical devices which, in combination, produced uncanny scenes of real power. It appears that he supervised such technical effects personally and that they accounted for most of his reputation as a playwright.

His most popular play was *The Castle Spectre* (1797). This featured a strangely familiar plot revolving around the treacherous Osmond who murders his brother and sister-in-law in order to become an earl. He has lecherous designs on his niece but is frustrated by her mother's ghost. Lewis had to struggle with his producers, who wanted to keep the ghost offstage; but he finally had his way, and the apparition in his fourth act had a suitably chilling effect on the audience. In fact, it is generally credited with making *The Castle Spectre* a hit. Some credit may also be due to the author's sister, Maria. Fearing a recurrence of the legal problems that had plagued *The Monk* just a year before, he had employed her to censor the play.

Lewis seems to have saved some of his most outlandish ideas for one of his last dramatic efforts, *The Wood Daemon* (1807). A window flies open in the midst of a thunderstorm to reveal a witch flying through flames in a dragon-powered chariot. Later, a magician's cave—complete with two huge snakes breathing blue fire, four demons, and a bloodstained altar—is suddenly transformed into a castle's barren hall. Such special effects kept audiences enthralled; but Lewis had had enough, and he gave up literature the next year, confessing that he was bored and convinced that his work would never improve.

Two decades after *The Monk* appeared, Lewis undertook a new project which some of his contemporaries must have found even more shocking. He had inherited a family plantation in Jamaica, and he embarked on a series of hazardous ocean voyages to examine his estate. He was shocked by the desperate condition under which his slaves were struggling, and he embarked on a series of reforms that scandalized his neighbors. Such changes as he made may seem inadequate today (decently fed and clothed slaves are slaves nonetheless); but his humanitarian policies were far ahead of their time and gave him more satisfaction than his fame as an author. The strain of traveling from Europe to the tropics finally proved too much for him, however, and he died of a fever on a ship bound for Jamaica. His funeral was grotesque enough to have appeared in one of his stories: he was buried at sea, but his coffin refused to sink and was last seen floating off across the Atlantic.

Lewis's last visit to Europe found him exchanging ghost stories with a group of expatriate English writers that included the great Romantic poets Byron and Shelley. Thus he was coincidentally present during the composition of the most famous and influential Gothic novel, *Frankenstein.* This classic horror novel was the best entry in a four-way contest. The losers included Percy Bysshe Shelley, Lord Byron, and Byron's physician, Dr. John Polidori; the winner was Mary Wollstonecraft Shelley, whose prize was literary immortality. Indeed, nothing written by either of her more respected competitors is more widely known or recognized today. There are few fictional characters whose names so readily conjure an image and a plot summary in the average person's mind—perhaps only *Romeo and Juliet* or *Robinson Crusoe* can be compared to *Frankenstein* as "household words."

When it was proposed at Geneva in 1816 that each member of the ingenious quartet write a ghost story, only Mrs. Shelley found herself at a loss. The others began in earnest but soon abandoned their projects. The germ of her plot finally appeared in a nightmare, which seems to have been inspired by discussions between Byron and her husband about the possibility of creating or restoring life through the use of galvanic batteries.

That night, as she wrote in her introduction, "I saw—with shut eyes, but acute mental vision—I saw the pale student of unhallowed arts kneeling beside the thing he had put together. I saw the hideous phantasm of a man stretched out, and then, on the working of some powerful engine, show signs of life, and stir with an uneasy, half vital motion. . . .

Frankenstein at work on his monster's ill-fated mate, as depicted by the twentieth-century American artist Lynd Ward.

His success would terrify the artist; he would rush away from his odious handiwork, horror-stricken. He would hope that, left to itself, the slight spark of life which he had communicated would fade; that this thing, which had received such imperfect animation, would subside into dead matter; and he might sleep in the belief that the silence of the grave would quench forever the transient existence of the hideous corpse which he had looked upon as the cradle of life. He sleeps; but he is awakened; he opens his eyes; behold the horrid thing stands at his bedside, opening his curtains, and looking on him with yellow, watery, but speculative eyes."

This is the story in a nutshell; in the experimenter's dismay is foreshadowed all the terrors that will follow. In fact, it was some version of this brief sketch that Mary Shelley originally wrote; her enthusiastic husband convinced her to expand it into a novel. In the process, it was changed from a vivid thriller into an elaborate, sometimes clumsy discussion of problems involving education and morality. *Frankenstein* is perhaps the most serious and high-minded horror story ever written, and the monster is no inarticulate brute, but a literate, introspective individual, fond of debate and given to long-winded philosophical discourses. No popular adaptation has captured the flavor of this bizarre character, who narrates a large portion of the book in the best oratorical fashion.

The novel is the story of Victor Frankenstein, a young Swiss student who leaves his family to attend the university at Ingolstadt. His mother dies of scarlet fever just before his departure, and a later dream suggests that this loss may have helped inspire his determination to conquer death. Surviving are his father, two younger brothers—Ernest and William—and Elizabeth Lavena, ward of the family, who is engaged to Frankenstein. After two years of intense study and effort, the young scientist succeeds in fulfilling his ambition by discovering the secret of life. The result is a gigantic and grotesque monster, which escapes from his creator's quarters while the young man suffers a nervous collapse.

As Frankenstein is being nursed back to health by his devoted friend Henry Clerval, the monster attempts to find companionship and sympathy but is rebuffed and mistreated by the horrified human beings he encounters. He flees to a forest, where he has his most significant experience with the De Laceys, a family of cottagers on whom he spies for over a year, attempting to learn their language and their ways. He finally attempts to approach them; however, his appearance disgusts everyone but the father, who is blind, and he is driven away by violence.

Embittered and enraged, the monster decides to seek out his creator and demand some sort of release from his lonely torment. He first encounters Frankenstein's little brother William and murders him, infuriated by the child's fear. The family's servant Justine is executed for the crime. The monster finally meets his maker, and after telling his story, he demands that a mate be created for him. Guilty and fearful, Frankenstein attempts the task in the hope of placating the monster but is finally unwilling to continue, fearing that he may unleash an entire race of loathsome creatures.

The monster, who has threatened revenge for the destruction of his half-completed mate, murders Clerval and, on their wedding night, Frankenstein's bride, Elizabeth. Frankenstein's father dies of shock, and the young man takes it upon himself to pursue the monster and destroy him. After a protracted chase in which the monster leads his creator into the icy regions of the north, the exhausted and half-mad Frankenstein is taken aboard the ship of an Arctic explorer, Robert Walton. He describes his adventures to Walton and dies. The monster finds his body aboard the ship and vows to burn himself alive, his life purposeless now that his vengeance is complete.

Boris Karloff as the Frankenstein monster in a scene from the 1931 film that comes close to capturing the Gothic mood of the original novel. From *Frankenstein* (1931). *Courtesy of Universal Pictures.*

When the book was published in 1818, Percy Bysshe Shelley published an anonymous review declaring that the book had a moral, "and it is perhaps the most important, and of the most universal application of any moral that can be enforced by example. Treat a person ill, and he will become wicked." This is something of a simplification, since the monster can scarcely be considered a person. His appearance makes it obvious that he is something unnatural: "His yellow skin scarcely covered the work of muscles and arteries beneath; his hair was of a lustrous black, and flowing; his teeth of a pearly whiteness; but these luxuriances only formed a more horrid contrast with his watery eyes, that seemed almost of the same colour as the dun white sockets in which they were set, his shrivelled complexion and straight black lips."

Nevertheless the attempts of this walking corpse to become human do strike a genuine note of pathos that make him something unique in the history of the Gothic novel. The best villains have a certain ambiguity about them; but if the monster's predecessors inspire sympathy, it is only because the reader can identify with the lusts for power, wealth, and passion which they embody. Mary Shelley created a new mood, one that would be frequently imitated, by imagining a character who could excite pity and terror in equal proportions.

She has also been credited with writing the first science fiction novel. This seems a fair claim, despite the lack of any significant scientific details in the story. Frankenstein, who narrates the section of the book dealing with the life-giving process, reveals nothing of his technique because he wants to discourage imitators; but there are hints in the second chapter that lightning may have supplied the spark of life. Yet this reticence does not invalidate the book's status as science fiction, since its horrors spring from an experiment and not from the demons or deceptions that characterize the Gothic novel. Thus it stands apart from its predecessors and is traditionally included among them only because of its publication date.

The era in which *Frankenstein* appeared was one in which scientific advancement had hardly made a dent in the solid traditions of the past. Yet technological advances were in the wind, and the Industrial Revolution was working permanent changes in the fabric of society. On one level, the story mirrors the transformations that were to create displaced, dehumanized people in the name of progress. More to the point, *Frankenstein* is prophetic in symbolizing modern problems like pollution and nuclear power, which demonstrate the drawbacks inherent in scientific achievements. The book has yet to lose its relevance as a fable of human fallibility.

Mrs. Shelley's concern with social issues came to her naturally. Her father, William Godwin, was a radical political theorist and writer whose novel *The Adventures of Caleb Williams* (1794) includes a long chase after a murderer which may have inspired the protracted pursuit at the end of *Frankenstein.* Her mother, Mary Wollstonecraft, was an early feminist, the author of a tract called *Vindication of the Rights of Women.* Both of Mrs. Shelley's parents, however, were surpassed by her husband, whose ideas about changing the world took some remarkably bizarre forms. He once distributed copies of a political pamphlet by attaching them to small balloons and releasing them over a city, and on another occasion he demonstrated his distress over cruelty to animals by sneaking out one night and slaughtering his neighbor's entire flock of sheep. Especially in the light of Mrs. Shelley's dream, there seems little doubt that this eccentric idealist was the model for Victor Frankenstein.

With this character, Mrs. Shelley inaugurated another important tradition in nightmarish narratives, that of the "mad scientist." Most of those who followed

Frankenstein into this line of work were considerably more unscrupulous but continued to share his obsessiveness and shortsightedness. The theme of an experimenter whose work destroys him degenerated into a melodrama in which the scientist "deserves" his punishment because he has been wicked; his well-intentioned counterpart usually succeeds in rectifying his errors and emerging more or less unscathed. Only a few of Frankenstein's more distinguished colleagues, like Stevenson's Dr. Jekyll, take on the tinge of tragedy. They have more than a little in common with the medieval Faust, who destroys himself in a search for forbidden knowledge. In fact, Frankenstein confesses that he devoted much of his study to the ancient alchemists, which gives his story supernatural overtones and at the same time suggests the dark and mysterious sources from which modern science has grown.

If *Frankenstein* is immortal because of its compelling theme, it is still readable largely because of the strange relationship between the man and his monster. Both are rebels; the creator defies nature, and his creature defies society. They represent diametrically opposed causes of antisocial behavior: the monster, desperate because his condition is so miserable; his maker, arrogant because he has had every advantage. When mass murder has reduced Frankenstein to a suitable degree of desperation, a strange feeling of fellowship grows between the two, so that the monster even leaves food for Frankenstein to prolong their chase through the wilderness. Before death overtakes them, each has become the other's only reason for living.

Mary Shelley wrote one other novel in a fantastic vein, *The Last Man* (1826). This is even further than *Frankenstein* from the Gothic tradition and even closer to modern concepts of science fiction. It depicts the end of the human race in a futuristic world complete with airships and other imaginary devices that have since become real. *The Last Man* may have been the first book to describe the end of civilization, with the exception of religious works predicting an apocalypse. It is less frightening than melancholic, however, and seems intended less to thrill the reader than to describe allegorically the author's distress at the death of so many of her contemporaries, including her husband. She had been less than twenty when she composed her first novel; when *The Last Man* appeared a decade later, most of the brilliant poets of the Romantic era had died prematurely: Shelley by drowning, Keats from consumption, and Byron in a Greek revolution. Wildly praised and condemned in their time, these men were labeled "The Satanic School" by England's conservative poet laureate Robert Southey, because of the self-indulgent quality of their characters and work and more specifically because of the sympathy they expressed for Satan as portrayed in Milton's *Paradise Lost.* Not too coincidentally, this was one of the few books read by Frankenstein's monster, who also counted himself among the devil's party.

Lord Byron's misanthropic, occasionally incestuous heroes show the strongest influence of the Gothic attitude on any of these poets; but it was Samuel Taylor Coleridge who penned the undisputed masterpiece among macabre poems of the era, *The Rime of the Ancient Mariner* (1798). The story of the sailor who cursed himself and his ship by defying superstition still remains one of the most powerful and popular poems in the English language. Coleridge was equally important as a critic, and his suggestion that readers should approach works of the imagination with a "willing suspension of disbelief" is particularly relevant to tales with supernatural themes. To those who remain completely locked in the world of rationality against which Gothic and Romantic artists revolted, the realm of fantasy is a closed book.

The Gothic novel had pretty well played itself out as a literary form by the time

Frankenstein appeared; its innovations might be said to be the death knell of a type that had already begun to repeat itself shamelessly, as such imitative titles as the anonymous *Monks of Otranto* indicate. The last gasp came in 1820 when an Irish clergyman named Charles Robert Maturin produced the ponderous but powerful *Melmoth the Wanderer.* It was wildly praised by literary titans like Poe, Balzac, and Baudelaire, who saw the legend of the Wandering Jew submerged beneath the author's shifting subplots. Maturin's high critical reputation rests on his compilation and renovation of many stock devices that characterized the Gothic novel, set in a new framework that gave them a unique perspective. Melmoth is a man who has sold his soul to the devil in exchange for prolonged life and forbidden knowledge. Unlike the standard document, his contract contains an escape clause: Melmoth can avoid damnation if he can induce someone else to take his place. It seems to be an unusually bad bargain even for this sort of thing, since Melmoth uses his long life and magical powers almost exclusively to search for the substitute, as if he has made his deal with the devil only to help himself in backing out of it. The novel consists of a number of episodes in which the immortal wanderer seeks out wretched individuals in situations so grim that they will welcome temporary relief at whatever cost. Yet none of them accepts his offer, and he disappears over the edge of a cliff after a last visit to his ancestral home.

This most ambitious and complicated of the Gothic novels is clumsily constructed in a series of interlocking flashbacks, so that each episode is interrupted by the next. Only an unusually alert and patient reader can encounter such a structure without annoyance, and persons of this type were doubtless more common in the nineteenth century than they are today. Although the novel as a whole is somewhat tedious, many of the incidents are handled with superior skill. Melmoth's most likely prospects are discovered in typical Gothic predicaments: one is trapped in a primitive insane asylum; another, almost inevitably, is a victim of the Inquisition. But the most eerie and unusual scene occurs when the wanderer takes time out from temptations to woo and win an innocent young woman; their wedding is performed and witnessed by reanimated corpses.

Melmoth the Wanderer was not Maturin's only work in the Gothic vein; in addition to a number of conventional plays and novels, he had previously produced a derivative tale of treachery and parricide called *The Fatal Revenge*, or *The Family of Montorio* (1807). The villain, Orazio, makes his intentions clear to even the dullest reader by disguising himself as a monk named Schemoli. *Melmoth* was quite a bit more original, especially in the treatment of its grim, tormented hero-villain who, although he tries his damnedest, never really manages to destroy anyone but himself. Forced by his quest to seek out the most tragic victims of injustice and inhumanity, he is more a witness to horrors than a perpetrator of them, conscious all the time that something worse is in store for him. Balzac was so moved by his plight that he wrote a frivolous sequel, *Melmoth Reconciled*, in which the curse is passed on to an embezzler.

Although the Gothic novel had run its course by the second decade of the nineteenth century, it continued to influence the mainstream literature of the years to come, most obviously in the case of Emily Brontë's *Wuthering Heights* and her sister Charlotte's *Jane Eyre*, both published as late as 1847. Of course, the influence of this style on future tales of the macabre is incalculable. Never again, though, would studies in terror so completely dominate the imagination of a mass audience.

The twentieth century has seen a resurrection of the term "Gothic" applied to works quite distinct from the horror stories that it originally inspired. The term has been adopted by Mrs. Radcliffe's sorority of successors, generally to its discredit, although

This vision of angels and corpses was created by Gustave Doré to illustrate Samuel Taylor Coleridge's classic macabre poem *The Rime of the Ancient Mariner*.

there are tasteful exceptions like Daphne Du Maurier, author of *Rebecca.* In general, these books, now accounting for a considerable share of the paperback market, concern an unlikely multitude of young ladies married to men who seem bent on murdering them. The so-called Gothic novel of the twentieth century is debased currency, with the menaced heroine (always rescued) at the center of the stage, the supernatural (always explained away) in the background, and the damned soul of the defiant villain who inspired these stories imprisoned in the body of a cheap cad.

· 3 ·

IMPS OF THE PERVERSE: AFRAID IN AMERICA

If the British horror tradition was a reaction against widespread rationalism, expressing itself in a nostalgic and somewhat frivolous attitude toward traditional religious beliefs, the situation in colonial America was considerably less sophisticated. The grim Puritan philosophy, which proved to be little more than a brief phase in the progress of English history, became the bedrock upon which colonial culture was based. The earliest American publications were fundamentalist religious tracts that treated witches and devils as tangible threats. In 1693, the year after the accused Salem witches had been executed, the immensely powerful clergyman Cotton Mather published his most hair-raising work, *The Wonders of the Invisible World*, describing a supernatural conspiracy abroad in the land. He explained that Satan was particularly anxious to cause trouble in the colonies, because the land had been, until a few years before, a heathen stronghold under the dominion of hell.

As Mather explained the situation, "We have been advised by some Credible Christians yet alive, that a Malefactor, accused of *Witchcraft* as well as *Murder*, and Executed in this place more than Forty Years ago, did then give Notice, of *An Horrible* PLOT *against the Country by* WITCHCRAFT, *and a Foundation of* WITCHCRAFT *then Laid, which if it were not seasonably Discovered, would probably Blow up, and pull down all the Churches in the Country*. And we have now with Horror seen the *Discovery* of such a *Witchcraft!* An Army of *Devils* is horribly broke in upon the place which is the *Center,* and after a sort, the *First-born* of our *English* Settlements: and the Houses of the Good People there, are fill'd with the doleful Shrieks of their Children and Servants, Tormented by Invisible Hands, with Tortures altogether preternatural."

With this sort of thing available to give them nightmares, early Americans had no need to fall back on fiction. And for generations, there would be none to fall back on. Political and historical documents began to pour off the printing presses along with the sermons, but literature designed to entertain as well as edify was still a long way off. The first American play was produced in 1767, and the first novel in 1789. Meanwhile, readers in search of morbid thrills did the best they could with Cotton Mather's later works like the quaintly titled *Death Made Easy and Happy* (1701). Hell-fire and damnation found another expert witness in Jonathan Edwards, who achieved his first great success in 1741 with *Sinners in the Hands of an Angry God.* Of course, works like these were appearing simultaneously in Europe, which also had its share of witchcraft trials; but there they were counterbalanced by a wide range of opinions and entertainments that served to create a more humane atmosphere.

Given such a background, it is not too surprising that America's first major novelist had a bit of a morbid streak and made a murderous religious fanatic the title character of his most famous novel. The author was Charles Brockden Brown, who transferred the mood and tone of the British Gothic novels to a new continent. By setting his stories in his own country, Brown abandoned the ready-made air of medieval mystery on which his English contemporaries depended so much. Instead, he dwelt on the fragility of the new civilization, threatened as it was by the wilderness it had so recently replaced and by the strange personalities drifting through an infant society. Although his efforts are better remembered by historians than by the general public, the books had a definite influence on writers who followed him.

Wieland; or, *The Transformation* (1798) is generally considered to be his best work; it is also his most effective excursion into the domain of the macabre. Wieland is a farmer living with his wife, children, and sister near a grotesque temple constructed by his father, a retired missionary. Old Wieland, who had invented his own religion, died mysteriously after an unexplained incident in the temple that left him delirious, with his clothing burned away. Wieland and his sister Clara are never able to forget this puzzling tragedy, especially when disembodied voices are heard near the scene. At first the voices warn people to stay away from the temple; later they speak in the house to terrify Clara and then to alienate the affections of her fiancé. There are enough witnesses to convince Wieland that the voices represent a genuine supernatural manifestation, and when they finally order him to kill his wife and their four children, he does so. He is arrested, but he escapes and returns to the farm to murder Clara. There he is confronted with the all-too-human source of the instructions which he had interpreted as divine. They have been produced by Carwin, a wandering stranger who has been visiting the family. Unknown to the others, Carwin is a ventriloquist, or, in the author's terminology, a biloquist. This seems to be a typical explanation in the style of Ann Radcliffe, but Brown introduces a significant variation. Carwin, although mischievous and even malicious, is not a murderous character. He had warned the family away from the temple because he had been using it as a lovers' rendezvous, and he had interfered with Clara's romance just to see how much more he could get away with; but he had never ordered the killings. What he had done was to drive Wieland, already haunted by the memory of his father, into a form of madness in which the orders he received came from his own troubled mind. Confronted with the proof that what had seemed to be indisputably divine inspiration was actually inherited insanity, Wieland commits suicide.

Brown's use of mental aberration as the cause of frightening incidents was to be repeated in the works of many American authors, most notably Poe, who praised Brown's novels highly. Brown returned to the theme in *Edgar Huntly;* or, *Memoirs of a Sleep-Walker* (1799). This book is narrated by the title character, whose mind fails after the death of a friend and the loss of a fortune. His illness first takes the form of bouts of somnambulism; at one point he blacks out and wakes up trapped in a cave which is also the den of a panther. For a long nightmarish portion of the novel, Huntly is lost in the wilderness, delirious, fighting off wild animals and hostile Indians, and simultaneously suffering from the delusion that his entire family is dead. He finally recovers his reason, but another sleepwalker whom Huntly has attempted to help is less fortunate: he goes completely mad and, after an attempted murder, kills himself.

A third novel, *Arthur Mervyn*, has a more ordinary plot involving the career of a young man seeking his fortune; but the first half contains some gruesome incidents based on Brown's personal experiences during the yellow fever epidemic of 1773. Much of the material indicates that Brown was familiar with Defoe's *Journal of the Plague Year*, but he achieves an intimacy his predecessor had not even attempted. His details were the result of his own observation rather than historical records, and he intensified his effectiveness by letting his hero fall victim to the dread disease, which nearly kills him. Perhaps the most horrible scenes occur in the hospitals staffed by desperate and greedy men who ignore their patients to avoid infection, leaving the dead and the dying together in dark and desolate wards. Arthur Mervyn also witnesses the brutality of hardened corpse collectors who do not even wait until men are dead to load them onto their carrion carts; he barely escapes being buried alive himself, regaining consciousness just before he is put in a coffin.

Charles Brockden Brown published several other books and countless articles or pamphlets on political and historical subjects; but his fame rests on these three novels, all written in the space of one year. They established him as the first American master of frightening fiction. A considerably larger reputation in this field was achieved with a much smaller output by Washington Irving, the first American author to achieve wide fame abroad as well as at home. Like Brown, Irving was trained as a lawyer; but he soon abandoned that profession to pursue a career in literature. He did, however, have the distinct advantage of a wealthy background which permitted him to work without haste or distraction. His sophistication and sense of humor make his spectral tales unique and have endeared them to a wider audience than can be found for the grim narratives he sometimes seemed to be mocking.

Although he published books on geographical and historical subjects, including a biography of George Washington, most of Irving's reputation came from the short pieces collected in *The Sketch Book of Geoffrey Crayon, Gent.* (1819), more commonly known simply as *The Sketch Book.* This included his most celebrated stories, "Rip Van Winkle" and "The Legend of Sleepy Hollow," as well as "The Spectre Bridegroom," about a man who did not let his death interfere with his forthcoming wedding.

Irving, who toured the capitals of Europe as a traveler and a diplomat, treats terror and the supernatural from a comfortable distance, as quaint relics of an almost forgotten folklore. In "The Legend of Sleepy Hollow," he describes Ichabod Crane, the foolish schoolmaster who is scared out of town by the imaginary ghost of the Headless Horseman, as a devoted reader of Cotton Mather. In fact, it is Ichabod's fondness for repeating the old preacher's spook stories that inspires his rival in love to impersonate Sleepy Hollow's legendary horror. The fact that the Horseman's dreaded head turns out to be a humble pumpkin is perhaps a Radcliffean echo, but it is primarily a piece of comic relief and represents an implied attack on the naïve credulity of the Puritan era. In spite of this, the "galloping Hessian of the Hollow" remains a splendid vision, a relic of overthrown authority which is no longer a cause for alarm.

The idea that the Headless Horseman represents the regime defeated by the American Revolution is reinforced by "Rip Van Winkle." It can hardly be a coincidence that Rip's twenty-year nap encompasses the struggle to remove a government and replace it with another, so that he wakes up pledging his loyalty to King George instead of President George. That Rip misses the bloody conflict and finds life very much the same under the

Ichabod Crane is pursued by the Headless Horseman in this scene from Washington Irving's "The Legend of Sleepy Hollow," drawn during the author's lifetime by Felix O. C. Darley.

new order serves only to reinforce the impression that his enchanted sleep has been enchanting as well. Even the picture of the president over Rip's favorite inn is indistinguishable from the old one of the king. Losing two decades of one's life, which should be a shocking experience, is treated as a blessing, especially since it separates the hero from his nagging wife. Thus Irving helped to inaugurate the literary tradition of solving domestic difficulties by bizarre if not bloodcurdling methods. And the drunken, bowling ghosts who offer Rip the magic brew are predominately figures of fun, further establishing Irving's reputation as the man who made foolish phantoms fashionable.

At least one more of Irving's stories is worth mentioning: "The Devil and Tom Walker," from the later collection *Tales of a Traveller* (1824). Tom trades his soul to Satan for success in business and enjoys a brilliant career as a moneylender until he is dragged away screaming. The usual light, mocking tone predominates; but Irving has some telling points to make about crooked commercial practices and strikes even closer to home when the devil describes his special interests in America: "Since the red men have been exterminated by you white savages, I amuse myself by presiding at the persecutions of Quakers and Anabaptists; I am the great patron and prompter of slave dealers, and the grand-master of the Salem witches."

Growing up in America when Irving was publishing his best work was Edgar Allan Poe, without doubt the most important author to make his name as a delineator of the demonic. Many great writers have touched on terrifying themes, but Poe stands alone as one who achieved worldwide recognition while concentrating almost entirely on the inhuman side of human nature. It was an uphill struggle.

Although he is arguably the most significant writer, critic, and literary theorist in the history of the United States, Poe has been almost consistently under attack since he first set pen to paper. Engaged in controversies with powerful and influential figures like Longfellow, whom he accused of plagiarism, during his lifetime Poe suffered from bad luck compounded by his own irascibility and intemperance. His worst mistake in this vein came when he put his posthumous literary affairs in the hands of one Rufus

The dwarfish spirits who cast a spell on Rip Van Winkle, as imagined by the modern English illustrator Arthur Rackham.

Griswold, who used his position to blacken Poe's reputation in every possible way. Griswold obviously never forgot that Poe had attacked him years before in a critical article. His authorized edition of Poe's work contained a maliciously distorted biography, and he even altered the text of Poe's letters to create a convincingly ugly portrait of the man who had entrusted him with his life's work.

It took the best part of a century for responsible scholars to undo the damage Griswold had done, but Poe had hardly been cleared of these charges when he was subjected to a new sort of slander. Certain psychological critics, more familiar with Freudian analysis than literary artifice, treated his tales as if they were the unconsidered outpourings of a subconsciousness run wild, rather than the carefully crafted products of a skillful technician. Starting with Marie Bonaparte, who published a huge volume called *The Life and Works of Edgar Allan Poe: A Psycho-Analytic Interpretation*, it became fashionable to use his artistic symbols to construct theories about his private life and personal behavior that were unsupported by any convincing historical evidence. Poe was accused of most of the sins of which his characters were guilty, or at least of having wished to commit them, and he had shortcomings ascribed to him that he had never even mentioned in his stories. All this was done on the apparent assumption that the writer did not really know what he was talking about, that his work was somehow over his own head. And this happened to a man who was unusually self-conscious about what went into his writing and who even published a group of essays explaining how all the incidents and details in his tales and poems were calculated to produce deliberate effects.

There can be little doubt that Poe was a troubled individual. Indeed, he once described himself as "insane, with long intervals of horrible sanity." Nevertheless, his published works do not constitute a case history, nor should they be considered as such. Neither can the impact of his writing be explained in terms of hypothetical abnormalities. Freudian critics might be well advised to consider these lines from his "Sonnet—To Science":

Science! true daughter of Old Time thou art!
Who alterest all things with thy peering eyes.
Why preyest thou thus upon the poet's heart,
Vulture, whose wings are dull realities?

Poe began his career as a poet, although his most famous poem, "The Raven" (1845), did not appear until four years before his death. But, strangely enough, the earliest prose efforts of this master of the macabre were in a humorous vein. These were the "Tales of the Folio Club," a collection of parodies and satires which he hoped to publish as a book. Although this ambition was never realized, several of these stories were printed separately in *The Philadelphia Saturday Courier* in 1832. Throughout his career Poe continued to produce comic sketches; many of them made light of the same themes that were treated seriously in his more famous tales. He demonstrated an awareness of the ludicrous side of horror tales, as well as a knowledge of his era's requirements for popular entertainment, in a pair of pieces entitled "How to Write a *Blackwood's* Article" and "A Predicament." *Blackwood's* was a popular British magazine which increased its circulation with a series of sensational stories of the hair-raising variety. Poe mocked the convention of a narrator who continues to record impressions while involved in the most perilous situations by describing the plight of Psyche Zenobia. Seeking atmosphere in an old clock tower, she gets caught in the works and finally is decapitated by the "huge, glittering, scimitar-like minute-hand of the clock." Even this does not dissuade her from taking elaborate notes on her condition, her head watching her body from the street below.

This sort of black humor occurs in many of Poe's lesser-known tales, such as "The Man That Was Used Up," describing a war hero turned political candidate. He has sustained so many injuries in becoming a celebrity that his body is almost completely destroyed, and he can appear in public only with the help of four false limbs, a wig, false teeth, and an unbelievable variety of artificial devices. Apparently the "manufactured" political candidate was invented before the twentieth century. In "Some Words with a Mummy," an ancient Egyptian named Count Allamistakeo is revived with an electric shock (possibly the first use of this popular resurrected-mummy theme) and proves to be a genial fellow with a low opinion of certain American political practices. When Poe was not having fun with his readers, he might be making fun of them instead, as in the case of the piece now known as "The Balloon Hoax," in which he managed to convince the *New York Sun* and its readers that a pair of Welsh balloonists had flown across the Atlantic almost a century before the feat was actually to be accomplished.

Even his grimmest tales were sometimes inspired by apparently frivolous motives. For instance, "Berenice" (1835) is often cited as an example of Poe's bad taste and of his personal obsessions. The hero of this tale blacks out after his sweetheart's death and wakes up to discover that he has broken open her tomb and removed all of her teeth. Those who search for deep meaning or even common sense in this wildly overwritten little epic are apparently unaware of the commonplace explanation: the author claimed to have written it on a bet with an acquaintance who was convinced that it would be impossible to write a story on such a theme and get it published. Poe won.

Dead ladies of one sort or another are, it must be admitted, among Poe's most common themes. The reason is not much of a mystery. His mother, a traveling actress who had been deserted by her husband, died in her son's presence just before he turned three. He was almost immediately adopted by Mr. and Mrs. John Allan of Richmond, Virginia, largely on the insistence of Mrs. Allan. She died when he was twenty, thus dissolving the somewhat shaky relationship between John Allan and Edgar Allan Poe, who was finally disowned and disinherited. He married his cousin, Virginia Clemm, who came down with tuberculosis, the same disease that had killed Mrs. Poe and Mrs. Allan. She lingered between life and death, constantly recovering and relapsing, for five years. And finally she died, too.

The impact of these three tragic coincidences permanently colored Poe's view of life and had considerable influence on his art as well. Many of his tales and most of his poems deal with the loss of a beloved woman; he even argues in "The Philosophy of Composition" that the death of a beautiful woman "is, unquestionably, the most poetical topic in the world." This conclusion is drawn from the premise that tragedy produces the greatest emotional effects, but it still seems debatable at best. Nevertheless, Poe almost makes it convincing, at least in his poems. Even the bald statement of policy was probably not too shocking to the readers of his era, who were well versed in a tradition of sentimental sadness. Their willingness to go along with the idea made "The Raven" his most popular work, the one that made his reputation. In fact, "The Philosophy of Composition" was an article about how he came to write the poem, an effort to get a little more mileage out of his greatest success, for which he was paid the lordly sum of twenty-five dollars. Poe did at least have the satisfaction of selling the article to a former employer who had rejected the poem while slipping its author a few dollars as an act of kindness.

No doubt Poe needed the money. Raised in the expectation of becoming a wealthy southern gentleman, he spent his entire adult life in poverty. It was next to impossible for an American in the first half of the nineteenth century to make a living with a pen; most of his contemporaries had other sources of income, but the best Poe ever got was a few short-lived, ill-paying editorial positions, terminated by clashes over policy, his occasional bouts of alcoholism, or the collapse of the business. His principal ambition was to start his own magazine, but he could never raise the capital. None of his books realized any profit—he was lucky when he didn't have to finance the printing, and received a few free copies for his trouble. One collection of poems that he couldn't give away is now a rare item valued at fifty thousand dollars; but Poe isn't getting any of the money.

Perhaps it was because of Poe's precarious financial position, coupled with his disappointment at not inheriting a fortune, that he decided to place so many of his characters in the idle aristocracy. Yet they are rarely happy in their lot, and more likely to be the tormented, dissolute remnants of a once proud family. A case in point is Roderick Usher, protagonist of the story that is generally regarded as Poe's best, "The Fall of the House of Usher" (1839). Usher's senses have become so unnaturally acute that ordinary sounds, smells, textures, tastes, and lights have become intolerable to him. He has been refined almost completely out of existence, perhaps symbolizing a class whose days, like his own, were numbered. The collapsing "house" is, of course, not only the building but Roderick and his dying sister Madeline as well, all inextricably linked together so that the end of one means the end of all and of the dynasty they represent. Thus, Roderick's apparently unmotivated decision to bury Madeline alive is, in effect, a kind of suicide. He dies when she returns from the tomb to confront him, and their ancestral mansion disintegrates almost immediately, the result of a fissure in its walls which is a visual emblem of personalities hopelessly split or, in common parlance, "cracked."

The hint of the supernatural in this coincidental collapse is relatively rare in Poe's tales, which characteristically find their frightening aspects in madness and murder. The major stories in which uncanny events play a significant part include "Morella" (1835), "Ligeia" (1838), "William Wilson" (1839), "The Masque of the Red Death" (1842), and "The Facts in the Case of M. Valdemar" (1845). Even in most of these, the ghostly elements are sufficiently subtle to be open to interpretation. In "Morella," the narrator's wife dies, but her spirit apparently returns to possess the body of their dying daughter. A variation on this theme occurs in Poe's favorite of his tales, "Ligeia," in which a widower remarries, only to discover that his fatally ill second wife has somehow been replaced by her predecessor. Both stories are written so that it is possible to suspect that the narrator is hallucinating, haunted by his own mind rather than by the spirits of the dead. A sentimental counterpoint to "Ligeia" appears in the story "Eleonora" (1842). The heroine returns not to demand a love that transcends the grave but to whisper approval of her husband's new marriage.

"William Wilson" is the story of a man haunted by his double, who has been with him since childhood and even bears the same name. At first it seems no more than a grotesque coincidence, but the double has an intimate knowledge of all Wilson's actions, especially the deplorable ones. He is so intent upon detecting and frustrating vice that he appears to be an embodied conscience; when Wilson finally murders him, he destroys himself as well. Indeed, the censorious superego seems to be the source for most of Poe's horrors, especially when coupled with a senseless desire to do wrong. This even seems to

The most intense and terrifying illustrations for the tales of Edgar Allan Poe were done seventy years after the author's death by Harry Clarke; this drawing is for "The Masque of the Red Death."

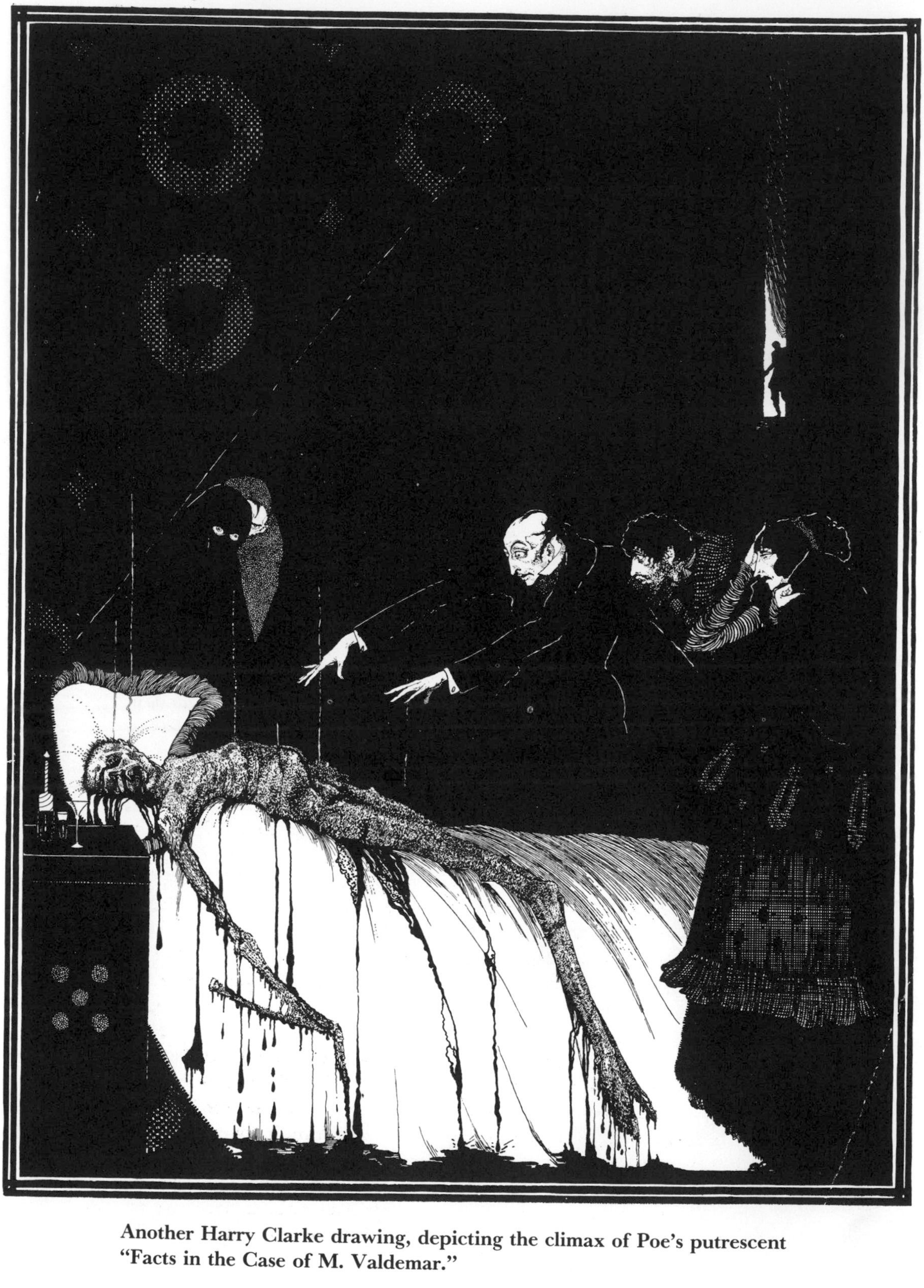

Another Harry Clarke drawing, depicting the climax of Poe's putrescent "Facts in the Case of M. Valdemar."

be true of the extravagant Gothic fantasy "The Masque of the Red Death," in which Prince Prospero and his aristocratic friends revel in a locked abbey while awaiting the passing of a terrible plague. Their masquerade ball is invaded by the personification of the pestilence, whose presence seems to reprimand their selfish seclusion and their special privileges as well.

A very different sort of fear is at issue in "The Facts in the Case of M. Valdemar." On the point of dying from tuberculosis (Poe calls it "phthisis"), Valdemar is hypnotized and remains in the trance for seven months after he announces his own death. The documentary style of the narrative, complete with clinical descriptions of the patient's condition and the hypnotist's techniques, makes Valdemar's living death truly awe inspiring. The climax of the story, in which the trance is broken and Valdemar instantly decays, is perhaps the most gruesome Poe ever conceived.

If Poe was fascinated with the mystery of what might lie beyond the life we know, he could do no more than hint at its solution. He had better luck with mysteries of his own devising, and he became known as the father of the detective story because of his stories of "ratiocination." The first of these, "The Murders in the Rue Morgue" (1841), contains the terrifying image of a razor-wielding, homicidal "Ourang-Outang"; but the rest are more restrained or, in the case of the treasure-hunting "Gold-Bug," almost idyllic. Poe wrote of these tales that "people think them more ingenious than they are—on account of their method and air of method. In the 'Murders in the Rue Morgue,' for instance, where is the ingenuity of unravelling a web which you (the author) have woven for the express purpose of unravelling?"

Such stories did, however, lend themselves to Poe's critical theory on the construction of short fiction, which demanded that every word be calculated to produce a climactic effect, a "pre-established design." The involuted structure of the detective story, putting first things last, is the logical result of this theory; but Poe's real triumph was living up to his criteria in tales told in a more straightforward manner. His delvings into the minds of detectives were comparatively easy for others to imitate, but his compelling explorations of the criminal mind have rarely been duplicated.

Deranged murderers had been a commonplace in Gothic fiction, but Poe offered a new perspective on such characters by making them the narrators of their own adventures. This first-person technique caused readers to identify so completely with the killers that they were less likely to be shocked by the crime than by the subsequent capture. And the realization that insanity could be so infectious was most frightening of all. By making his audience aware of the darker side of their own natures, Poe added a different dimension to the literature of fear.

Poe's major works in this vein include "The Black Cat" (1843), "The Tell-Tale Heart" (1843), and "The Cask of Amontillado" (1846). The last tale is a bit different in that the narrator seems to be getting away with murder; but then again the story itself is a confession, delivered by a man who is still reliving his crime fifty years later. Here again the victim is buried alive; this was a fate that Poe apparently considered the most horrible imaginable; he even wrote a piece on the subject, "The Premature Burial" (1844), which is really an essay giving factual accounts of "the ultimate woe," with a fictional tag in which the narrator is cured of his obsessive fear. Amusingly enough, one aspect of the cure involved giving up the reading of "bugaboo tales—*such as this.*"

The narrator of "The Cask of Amontillado" claims revenge as a motive, although no details of his injuries are provided; but the killer in "The Tell-Tale Heart" says his morbid distaste for the appearance of his victim's blind eye is reason enough. When the

Clarke's ornate illustration for the final scene of "The Black Cat" contrasts strongly with a starker scene by Aubrey Beardsley (opposite page), whose techniques were nonetheless a discernible influence on the later artist.

old man has been buried beneath the floorboards, his murderer places his chair on the spot while being interviewed by the police and is driven to confession by a sound that he takes to be his victim's heartbeat but is surely his own. Similarly, "The Black Cat" describes a man who reveals his wife's corpse to the police when he raps on the cellar wall that hides her, driven by "the mere phrenzy of bravado." His knock is answered by the cat he had meant to kill and had inadvertently walled up alive. The hysterical self-assurance with which these characters seal their own dooms suggests that they subconsciously desire to be found out and that their crimes, like Roderick Usher's, are more than half-suicidal.

"The Black Cat" contains a passage that gives a clue to the psychology at work in these stories. "Perverseness," the killer claims, "is one of the primitive impulses of the human heart," and the realization that an act is senseless or dangerous can in fact become a compelling reason for committing it. This idea, which anticipates Freud's theory of the "death wish," receives its fullest discussion in one of Poe's lesser-known tales, "The Imp of the Perverse." This story, reprinted here, first appeared in the July 1845 issue of *Graham's Magazine*, a publication that Poe had edited for a year in 1841–42. It may have been Poe's own "imp" that caused him to lose the position, probably the best he ever had, by too much drinking and arguing with the publisher. Nevertheless, *Graham's* continued to be one of his best markets, although it was George Graham who rejected "The Raven" and was later forced to eat crow by publishing the spin-off "Philosophy of Composition."

Although it is far from his best efforts as an artistically finished work of fiction, "The Imp of the Perverse" is significant for the light it casts on the major tales. Like "The Premature Burial" and many other minor Poe tales, this begins with a long essay to which a much shorter narrative is attached. The psychological theorizing has its basis in the now discarded system of phrenology, which attempted to analyze character on the basis of the head's shape. Certain traits were assigned to various portions of the skull, and their comparative prominence was purportedly a key to the subject's personality. It has been reported that Poe had a particular fondness for this system (then considered perfectly scientific) because the dimensions of his own dome reportedly indicated a man of unusual talent and intelligence. Maybe there was something to it after all.

The contrast between the verbose theorizing and the terse narrative is readily apparent; each successive paragraph moves at a quicker pace, so that the story steadily accelerates. Poe even includes a passage about the perversity of circumlocution, suggesting that the long-winded opening to his tale may have been written tongue in cheek. Those critics who have discussed this story generally attribute these opening remarks directly to Poe rather than to the fictional character he created to deliver them. Yet the confession that the Imp forces from the criminal is not exactly the equivalent of the foolish or wicked acts the narrator discusses so glibly. The Imp here is the conscience, and all the murderer's rationalizations cannot disguise the moral blindness of a man who sees harmony in homicide and cacophony in confession. The man who wrote this story may have been aware of his own weaknesses, but that does not make him wicked. The fact is that in this story, as in most of these tales of madness and murder, Poe-etic justice has struck again.

Unfortunately, life is not often as just as art. Poe's crimes were all imaginary, but his punishment was painfully real. His wife's inevitable death finally came in 1847, when he was at the peak of his powers. He never really recovered from the shock of losing her; two years later, after increasingly heavy drinking and at least one attempted suicide, he gave

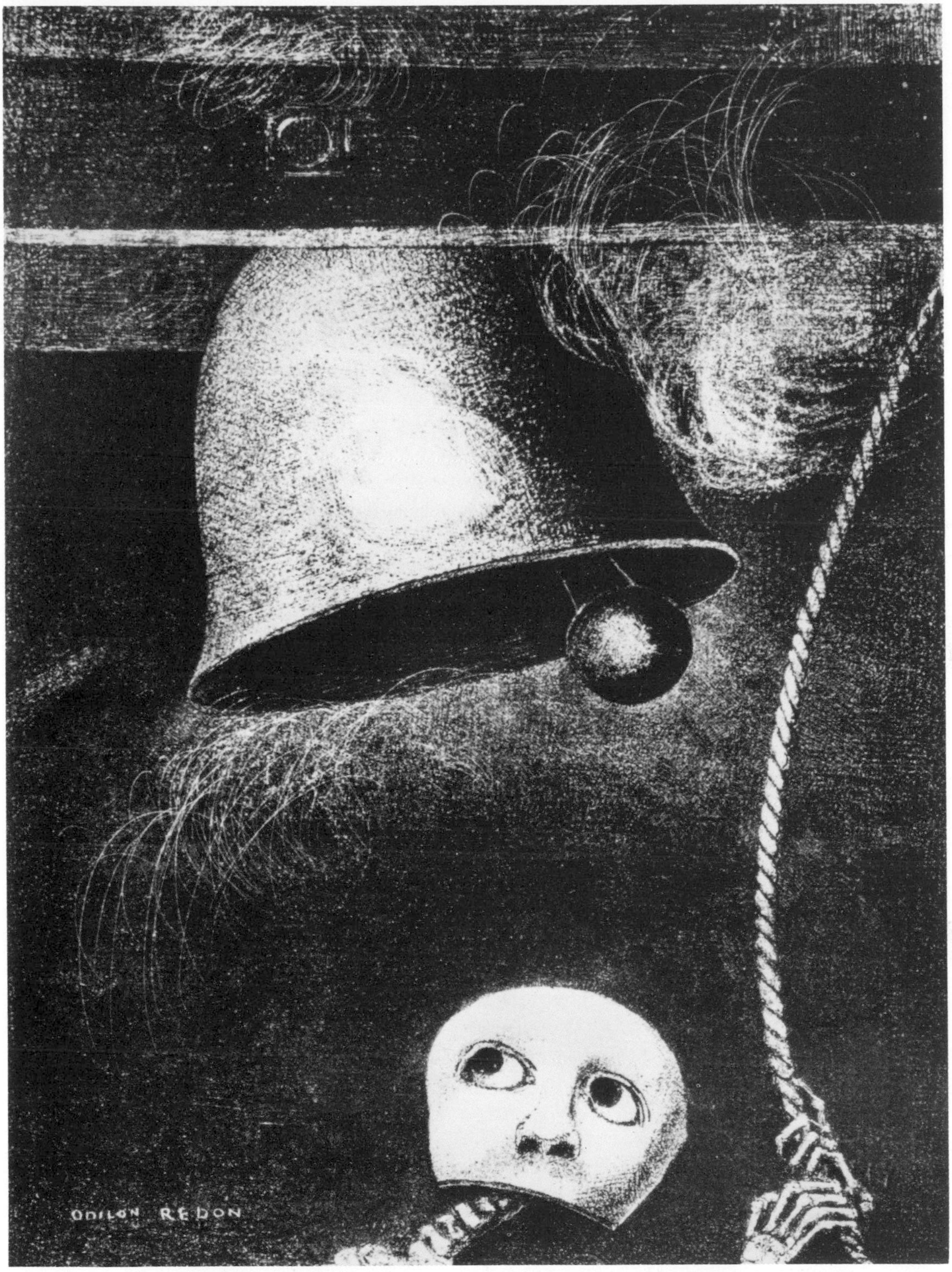

Odilon Redon's "Mask Tolling the Hour of Death" is one of a series of lithographs which the French Symbolist attributed to the influence of Poe, who was recognized abroad before he was appreciated in his native land.

up the ghost under mysterious circumstances. He was found unconscious in the streets of Baltimore and died four days later without ever really coming around. Although it can never be proved beyond doubt, it seems likely that he was the victim of dirty work at the ballot box. It was not uncommon for ward heelers to round up inebriated individuals and drive them from poll to poll until they collapsed, after racking up as many votes as possible. The fact that Poe was found in such poor condition on an election day suggests that he may have given his all for the democracy he professed to despise. Baltimore's most bizarre tribute to Poe's memory is a school for unwed mothers which, inexplicably, bears his name.

Poe had only one contemporary with a comparable talent for the construction of macabre fiction: the gloomy New Englander Nathaniel Hawthorne. Poe's review of Hawthorne's *Twice-Told Tales* gave him the opportunity to expound his famous theory on the construction of the short story; he also saw fit to describe Hawthorne as "a man of the truest genius." There was undoubtedly a distinct sympathy between the two men; Hawthorne's subjects are often bizarre or uncanny, although his tone is very different from Poe's. Hawthorne is primarily a moralist, and his stories inevitably tend toward allegory. His themes and characters never entirely lose their abstract quality, and they never achieve the breathless terror that is characteristic of Poe at his best. There is something cold and calculating about Hawthorne's approach; the author and his attitudes are always very much in the foreground, and the reader is more likely to contemplate the meaning of the fiction than to be swept along by its dramatic intensity.

A trio of his best tales exemplify Hawthorne's approach to the macabre: "Young Goodman Brown" (1835), "Rappaccini's Daughter" (1844), and "Ethan Brand" (1851). Young Goodman Brown is a colonist who comes upon a meeting of devil worshipers while traveling through a forest. He discovers to his dismay that they include friends and neighbors from his village, which is the notorious Salem. There is no melodramatic climax; rather, Brown returns home and resumes his life, not knowing whether or not his experience was a dream. Nevertheless, his values have been so shattered that he becomes hostile and suspicious, and he remains miserable until his death many years later. The story is not really about Satanism but rather about the dangers of hypocrisy and self-righteousness: Brown destroys himself when he is unable to accept the idea that all mortals are touched by sin.

"Rappaccini's Daughter" is the story of an Italian scientist who specializes in the cultivation of exquisitely beautiful but poisonous plants. His zeal and possessiveness have caused him to raise his daughter Beatrice among his other creations, so that she is equally deadly. When an aspiring lover administers an antidote in an attempt to restore her to a normal condition, the cure proves fatal. The story in synopsis seems like a scenario for dozens of twentieth-century "mad scientist" epics; but Hawthorne's style makes it clear that this is another moral fable, with both the poisons and the antidote representing the selfishness of those who attempt to manipulate innocence for their own ends.

Perhaps Hawthorne's most typically Gothic effort is "Ethan Brand," which he subtitled "A Chapter from an Abortive Romance." It would appear to be the last chapter of this nonexistent novel, since it ends with the death of the hero, who has returned home after a long and successful search for the "Unpardonable Sin." This sin is never identified, but Ethan Brand's pride and isolation are emphasized in such exaggerated terms that his story almost seems to be a spoof of works like Maturin's

Melmoth the Wanderer. Vague allusions to the events in previous "chapters" are so instantly identifiable that further details are unnecessary; in fact, Hawthorne has created a miniature Gothic novel through a compendium of the genre's most typical clichés. Brand burns himself alive in a limekiln, and the taciturn tender is pleased to discover that the skeleton left behind will increase his haul of lime by half a bushel. Such are the practical results of a romantic quest for exotic damnation.

Hawthorne wrote many more tales with supernatural subjects. Some are serious, and many are almost whimsical; but the author's apparent intention to create moral fables generally overcomes the eerie atmosphere. His novels also contain some supernatural overtones. *The House of the Seven Gables* (1851) seems to be slightly haunted, and *The Marble Faun* (1860) hints at revenants from classical mythology, but both books are principally concerned with other topics. The innate idealism in his apparently irresistible tendency toward allegory had a counterpart in real life when Hawthorne joined an early experiment in communal living at Brook Farm. The community was not a success, but at least it provided material for another novel.

Herman Melville, the third great figure in mid-nineteenth-century American literature, is even further than Hawthorne from the dark, demonic world of Poe; but his great novel *Moby Dick* (1851) is in many respects a Gothic story all at sea. The obsessed tyrant Captain Ahab would have been right at home in a medieval castle, and the giant white whale he pursues so feverishly looks at times like a monster from hell. The book is many other things, but it is at least half a horror story. It has more than a few features in common with Poe's only novel, *The Narrative of Arthur Gordon Pym* (1838), in which a shipwrecked sailor is driven to cannibalism before drifting to the South Pole, where he is confronted, as the book ends, by a huge figure whose skin is "of the perfect whiteness of the snow."

Several of Melville's shorter pieces have terrifying aspects. His *Billy Budd*, with its personifications of good and evil, has the grim tone of an old morality play. A more typical horror tale is "The Bell-Tower," in which a master workman murders one of his assistants in his enthusiasm to complete work on a gigantic clock and is killed in turn by his own mechanism, flawed as it is by the blood of his victim, which has weakened the metal he had cast. Melville also envisioned some stranger menaces drawn from the burgeoning American free enterprise system. One was "Bartleby the Scrivener," who creates chaos and despair in an office full of go-getters by being the one man there who, whatever is proposed to him, "would prefer not to." At the opposite end of the spectrum is "The Lightning-Rod Man," a traveling salesman who roams the country deliberately instilling paranoia in his customers so that he can drum up a little business.

One writer of this period who concentrated almost exclusively on the macabre was Fitz-James O'Brien, an Irish immigrant to the United States who concocted some surprisingly original concepts during a tragically short career. "The Diamond Lens" describes a miniature world discovered through a microscopic device, and "The Wondersmith" depicts a menacing mannequin who may as well be a robot. Both of these stories anticipated themes that were to become stock devices in a later era, as did O'Brien's most famous tale, "What Was It?" This compelling piece concerns the discovery of a mute, invisible man who dies in captivity, leaving no clue to his origin. "The Lost Room" disappears when its tenant gambles for possession of it with a band of spirits and loses. O'Brien's ingenuity might have brought him greater fame if he had lived long enough to write even a few more stories. As it was, poverty induced him to hire himself out as a military substitute for the sentimental writer Thomas Bailey Aldrich, whose success had made it possible for him to fulfill his military obligation with cash (this was perfectly legal at the time). The result was O'Brien's death in a Civil War skirmish.

One writer who lived through this conflict was Ambrose Bierce, who was to make an even more impressive contribution to the literature of the uncanny. He wrote *The Devil's Dictionary* at the top of his voice; everybody quotes him, but few know his name. And nobody knows how he died.

THE IMP OF THE PERVERSE

By Edgar Allan Poe

In the consideration of the faculties and impulses—of the *prima mobilia* of the human soul, the phrenologists have failed to make room for a propensity which, although obviously existing as a radical, primitive, irreducible sentiment, has been equally overlooked by all the moralists who have preceded them. In the pure arrogance of the reason, we have all overlooked it. We have suffered its existence to escape our senses solely through want of belief—of faith;—whether it be faith in Revelation, or faith in the Kabbala. The idea of it has never occurred to us, simply because of its supererogation. We saw no *need* of impulse—for the propensity. We could not perceive its necessity. We could not understand, that is to say, we could not have understood, had the notion of this *primum mobile* ever obtruded itself;—we could not have understood in what manner it might be made to further the objects of humanity, either temporal or eternal. It cannot be denied that phrenology and, in great measure, all metaphysicianism have been concocted *a priori.* The intellectual or logical man, rather than the understanding or observant man, set himself to imagine designs—to dictate purposes to God. Having thus fathomed, to his satisfaction, the intentions of Jehovah, out of these intentions he built his innumerable systems of mind. In the matter of phrenology, for example, we first determined, naturally enough, that it was the design of the Deity that man should eat. We then assigned to man an organ of alimentiveness, and this organ is the scourge with which the Deity compels man, will-I nill-I, into eating. Secondly, having settled it to be God's will that man should continue his species, we discovered an organ of amativeness, forthwith. And so with combativeness, with ideality, with causality, with constructiveness,—so, in short, with every organ, whether representing a propensity, a moral sentiment, or a faculty of the pure intellect. And in these arrangements of the *principia* of human action, the Spurzheimites, whether right or wrong, in part, or upon the whole, have but followed, in principle, the footsteps of their predecessors; deducing and establishing everything from the preconceived destiny of man, and upon the ground of the objects of his Creator.

It would have been wiser, it would have been safer, to classify (if classify we must) upon the basis of what man usually or occasionally did, and was always occasionally doing, rather than upon the basis of what we took it for granted the Deity intended him to do. If we cannot comprehend God in his visible works, how then in his inconceivable thoughts, that call the works into being? If we cannot understand him in his objective creatures, how then in his substantive moods and phases of creation?

Induction, *a posteriori,* would have brought phrenology to admit, as an innate and primitive principle of human action, a paradoxical something, which we may call *perverseness,* for want of a more characteristic term. In the sense I intend, it is, in fact, a *mobile* without motive, a motive not *motivirt.* Through its promptings we act without comprehensible object; or, if this shall be understood as a contradiction in terms, we may so far modify the proposition as to say, that through its promptings we act, for the reason that we should *not.* In theory, no reason can be more unreasonable; but, in fact, there is none more strong. With certain minds, under certain conditions it becomes absolutely irresistible. I am not more certain that I breathe, than that the assurance of the wrong or error of any action is often the one unconquerable *force* which impels us, and alone impels us to its prosecution. Nor will this overwhelming tendency to do wrong for the wrong's sake, admit of analysis, or resolution into ulterior elements. It is radical, a primitive impulse—elementary. It will be said, I am aware, that when we persist in acts because we feel we should *not* persist in them, our conduct is but a modification of that which ordinarily springs from the *combativeness* of phrenology. But a glance will show the fallacy of this idea. The phrenological combativeness has, for its essence, the necessity of self-defence. It is our safeguard against injury. Its principle regards our well-being; and thus the desire to be well is excited simultaneously with its development. It follows, that the desire to be well must be excited simultaneously with any principle which shall be merely a modification of combativeness, but in the case of that something which I term *perverseness,* the desire to be well is not only not aroused, but a strongly antagonistical sentiment exists.

An appeal to one's own heart is, after all, the best reply to the sophistry just noticed. No one who trustingly consults and thoroughly questions his own soul will be disposed to deny the entire radicalness of the propensity in question. It is not more incomprehensible than distinctive. There lives no man who at some period has not been tormented, for example, by an earnest desire to tantalise a listener by circumlocution. The speaker is aware that he displeases; he has every intention to please; he is usually curt, precise, and clear; the most laconic and luminous language is struggling for utterance upon his tongue; it is only with difficulty that he restrains himself from giving it flow; he dreads and deprecates the anger of him whom he addresses; yet, the thought strikes him, that by certain involutions and parentheses this anger may be engendered. That single thought is enough. The impulse increases to a wish, the wish to a desire, the desire to an uncontrollable longing, and the longing (to the deep regret and mortification of the speaker, and in defiance of all consequences) is indulged.

We have a task before us which must be speedily performed. We know that it will be ruinous to make delay. The most important crisis of our life calls, trumpet-tongued, for immediate energy and action. We glow, we are consumed with eagerness to commence the work, with the anticipation of whose glorious result our whole souls are on fire. It must, it shall be undertaken to-day, and yet we put it off until to-morrow; and why? There is no answer, except that we feel *perverse,* using the word with no comprehension of the principle. To-morrow arrives, and with it a more impatient anxiety to do our duty, but with this very increase of anxiety arrives, also, a nameless, a positively fearful, because unfathomable, craving for delay. This craving gathers strength as the moments fly. The last hour for action is at hand. We tremble with the violence of the conflict within us,—of the definite with the indefinite—of the substance with the shadow. But, if the contest has proceeded thus far, it is the shadow which prevails,—we struggle in vain. The clock strikes, and is the knell of our welfare. At the same time, it is the chanticleer-note to the ghost that has so long overawed us. It flies—it disappears—we are free. The old energy returns. We will labour *now.* Alas, it is *too late!*

We stand upon the brink of a precipice. We peer into the abyss—we grow sick and dizzy. Our first impulse is to shrink from the danger. Unaccountably we remain. By slow degrees our sickness and dizziness and horror become merged in a cloud of unnamable feeling. By gradations, still more imperceptible, this cloud assumes shape, as did the vapour from the bottle out of which arose the genius in the *Arabian Nights.* But out of this *our* cloud upon the precipice's edge, there grows into palpability, a shape, far more terrible than any genius or any demon of a tale, and yet it is but a thought, although a fearful one, and one which chills the very marrow of our bones with the fierceness of the delight of its horror. It is merely the idea of what would be our sensations during the sweeping precipitancy of a fall from such a height. And this fall—this rushing annihilation—for the very reason that it involves that one most ghastly and loathsome of all the most ghastly and loathsome images of death and suffering which have ever presented themselves to our imagination—for this very cause do we now the most vividly desire it. And because our reason violently deters us from the brink, *therefore* do we the most impetuously approach it. There is no passion in nature so demoniacally impatient as that of him who, shuddering upon the edge of a precipice, thus meditates a plunge. To indulge, for a moment, in any attempt at *thought,* is to be inevitably lost; for reflection but urges us to forbear, and *therefore* it is, I say, that we *cannot.* If there be no friendly arm to check us, or if we fail in a sudden effort to prostrate ourselves backward from the abyss, we plunge, and are destroyed.

Examine these and similar actions as we will, we shall find them resulting solely from the spirit of the *Perverse.* We perpetrate them merely because we feel that we should *not.* Beyond or behind this there is no intelligible principle; and we might, indeed, deem this perverseness a direct instigation of the arch-fiend, were it not occasionally known to operate in furtherance of good.

I have said thus much, that in some measure I may answer your question—that I may explain to you why I am here—that I may assign to you something that shall have at least the faint aspect of a cause for my wearing these fetters, and for my tenanting this cell of the condemned. Had I not been thus prolix, you might either have misunderstood me altogether, or, with the rabble, have fancied me mad. As it is, you will easily perceive that I am one of the many uncounted victims of the Imp of the Perverse.

It is impossible that any deed could have been wrought with a more thorough deliberation. For weeks, for months, I pondered upon the means of the murder. I rejected a thousand schemes, because their accomplishment involved a *chance* of detection. At length, in reading some French memoirs, I found an account of a nearly fatal illness that occurred to Madame Pilau, through the agency of a candle accidentally poisoned. The idea struck my fancy at once. I knew my victim's habit of reading in bed. I knew, too, that his apartment was narrow and ill-ventilated. But I need not vex you with impertinent details. I need not describe the easy artifices by which I substituted, in his bed-room candle stand, a wax-light of my own making for the one which I there found. The next morning he was discovered dead in his bed, and the coroner's verdict was—"Death by the visitation of God."

Having inherited his estate, all went well with me for years. The idea of detection never once entered my brain. Of the remains of the fatal taper I had myself carefully disposed. I had left no shadow of a clue by which it would be possible to convict, or even suspect, me of the crime. It is inconceivable how rich a sentiment of satisfaction arose in my bosom as I reflected upon my absolute security. For a very long period of time I was accustomed to revel in this sentiment. It afforded me more real delight than all the mere worldly advantages accruing from my sin. But there arrived at length an epoch, from which the pleasurable feeling grew, by scarcely perceptible gradations, into a haunting and harassing thought. It harassed me because it haunted. I could scarcely get rid of it for an instant. It is quite a common thing to be thus annoyed with the ringing in our ears, or rather in our memories, of the burthen of some ordinary song, or some unimpressive snatches from an opera. Nor will we be the less tormented if the song in itself be good, or the opera air meritorious. In this manner, at last, I would perpetually catch myself pondering upon my security, and repeating, in a low under-tone, the phrase, "I am safe."

One day, whilst sauntering along the streets, I arrested myself in the act of murmuring, half aloud, these customary syllables. In a fit of petulance I re-modelled them thus: "I am safe—I am safe—yes—if I be not fool enough to make open confession."

No sooner had I spoken these words, than I felt an icy chill creep to my heart. I had had some experience in these fits of perversity (whose nature I have been at some trouble to explain), and I remembered well that in no instance I had successfully resisted their attacks. And now my own casual self-suggestion, that I might possibly be fool enough to confess the murder of which I had been guilty, confronted me, as if the very ghost of him whom I had murdered—and beckoned me on to death.

At first, I made an effort to shake off this nightmare of the soul. I walked vigorously—faster—still faster—at length I ran. I felt a maddening desire to shriek aloud. Every succeeding wave of thought overwhelmed me with new terror, for, alas! I well, too well, understood that to *think,* in my situation, was to be lost. I still quickened my pace. I bounded like a madman through the crowded thoroughfares. At length, the populace took the alarm and pursued me. I felt *then* the consummation of my fate. Could I have torn out my tongue, I would have done it—but a rough voice resounded in my ears—a rougher grasp seized me by the shoulder. I turned—I gasped for breath. For a moment I experienced all the pangs of suffocation; I became blind, and deaf, and giddy; and then some invisible fiend, I thought, struck me with his broad palm upon the back. The long-imprisoned secret burst forth from my soul.

They say that I spoke with a distinct enunciation, but with marked emphasis and passionate hurry, as if in dread of interruption before concluding the brief but pregnant sentences that consigned me to the hangman and to hell.

Having related all that was necessary for the fullest judicial conviction, I fell prostrate in a swoon.

But why shall I say more? To-day I wear these chains, and am *here!* To-morrow I shall be fetterless!—*but where?*

·4·

MY FAVORITE MURDER: VICTORIAN VILLAINY

The second half of the nineteenth century was an era in which ghostly tales flourished. A growing number of writers achieved success as specialists in the spectral, and many serious "mainstream" novelists took an occasional stab at the supernatural. Yet what Poe's followers produced were not exactly, in his phrase, "Tales of the Grotesque and the Arabesque." His dreamworld of mysterious madness was engulfed by a rising tide of restraint called Victorianism in Britain and industrialism in the United States. The era of romantics and revolutionaries was over, passions had cooled, and finance became the principal motive for the use of force, in fact and in fiction. Poe's more frankly morbid stories were ultimately to have less effect on his followers than his studies in ratiocination, which became increasingly popular as bloodthirsty individuals took to the printed page and created murder for fun and profit. The intellectual air of the detective story, with its inverted logic and deductive substructure, brought all sorts of lurid details to light that previously might have been considered illegitimate, at least in respectable literature. "Mysteries" seemed more intelligent and uplifting than tales of terror, even though their subject matter was often as grim as that of the more despised genre. By the beginning of the twentieth century, there were hordes of mystery fans who would never be caught dead with anything as tasteless as a horror story.

On the other side of the coin, it became possible for at least one man to construct a humor of homicide. This was Ambrose Bierce, who employed an ironic tone and some outrageous incidents to create the cruel comedy of stories like "My Favorite Murder," which in its title alone is a commentary on the growing popularity of literary crimes. Born in 1842, Bierce fought on the Union side in the Civil War and wrote what may well be the best war stories in American literature, although they will never be recognized as such by those who imagine that battles are anything but brutal and bloody. He also wrote some brilliant tales of psychic phenomena, including such famous works as "An Occurrence at Owl Creek Bridge" and "The Damned Thing." In addition he was a gifted wit and satirist, author of the sardonic *Fantastic Fables* (1899) and *The Devil's Dictionary* (originally *The Cynic's Word Book*), a series of sarcastic definitions that more or less inaugurated this popular form. Many of Bierce's grim wisecracks, now almost a century old, are still current among people who may have no idea of their source.

The apparent contrast between the two fields in which Bierce gained his reputation becomes less striking when his works are read. His humor is cold and cutting, and it exhibits the same hostility toward humanity to be found in his short stories. Bierce is beyond melancholy or even morbidity; his characteristic attitude is misanthropy, born of an idealism outraged by people's failure to live up to their professed principles. His wartime experiences demonstrated the hollowness of conventions about the glory of war, and his innocent involvement in some shady business deals made him skeptical about the sources of financial success. Many of his tales reflect the vicious behavior prevalent during the settlement of the West, which he experienced firsthand as a surveyor and a miner.

Although he lived for a few years in England, Bierce spent most of his literary career in San Francisco, where he was associated with several regional periodicals. Book publication and widespread recognition did not come until years after he had begun to write fiction. His first book in the vein of the macabre appeared in 1892; it was unfortunately *The Monk and the Hangman's Daughter*, a tired Gothic novel translated by G. A. Danziger from a German text and rendered into proper English by Bierce. Danziger, whose literary ambitions would involve him, decades later, after he had changed his name to Adolphe de Castro, in collaborations with the twentieth-century spine chiller H. P. Lovecraft, proved very troublesome about dividing the profits, and the matter was not really settled until their publisher went bankrupt. Both men ended up with nothing, though the book was not as bad as all that.

Luckily for Bierce, the same year also saw the publication of his fine collection of Civil War stories, *Tales of Soldiers and Civilians*, now better known under its British title, *In the Midst of Life*. This book is so much better than *The Monk and the Hangman's Daughter* that it almost justifies Bierce's definition of a novel, in *The Devil's Dictionary*, as "a short story padded." Bierce went on to defend short fiction in a manner very reminiscent of Poe, and there seems little doubt that their arguments are justified, at least with regard to tales of terror. After the decline of the Gothic novel, few of the best stories in the graveyard genre were of book length. It is not inappropriate to consider *In the Midst of Life* in this context; some of the tales in the volume are as harrowing as anything in English. Bierce's grim realism demonstrates by misdirection that the appeal of the horror tale depends on an understanding between reader and writer that they are playing a frivolous game and that too much truth makes for the wrong sort of mood. Such is the case with stories like "Chickamauga," in which a deaf child, too young to comprehend his situation, wanders through a battlefield and rides on the backs of hideously wounded men who are crawling away to die. The collection also includes the celebrated tour de force "An Occurrence at Owl Creek Bridge," in which a spy about to be hanged seems to escape when the rope breaks and has almost made his way to safety when he suddenly dies of a broken neck; all his adventures are revealed as hallucinations experienced in the second before his execution.

The "Civilians" section of this volume features a pair of tales on the psychology of fear, "A Watcher by the Dead" and "The Suitable Surroundings." Both treat wagers based on a character's avowed ability to withstand scary situations, and both men end up dead of fright. In "A Watcher by the Dead," a man bets that he can spend a night locked in an empty house with a corpse. He expires when the "corpse," actually a friend of his opponent, comes to life; and the unfortunate practical joker, now trapped with the man he has killed, proceeds to go mad. In "The Suitable Surroundings," a writer of ghost stories challenges an acquaintance to read some of his work in a supposedly haunted house. The story contains the information that the author intends to kill himself and then visit his victim. When a frightened boy looking for ghosts peers through the window at the appalled reader, nature takes its course.

A year later, in 1893, Bierce published his ghostly tales under the title *Can Such Things Be?* Among them is "The Damned Thing," about an invisible monster that terrorizes and finally kills a lonely farmer. Speculation that the creature is of a color outside the spectrum visible to the human eye gives the story a science fiction flavor. Like many of Bierce's best efforts, "The Damned Thing" has a complicated structure. Although only a few pages long, it is divided into four sections, narrated from different points of view and not in chronological order. The first section describes a coroner's inquest on the dead man, the second is an eyewitness account of his fatal encounter with the unseen beast, the third relates the jury's rejection of the testimony, and the fourth is an excerpt from the victim's diary in which he discusses the nature of his killer. This elaborate technique serves to create an air of mystery and enables Bierce to withhold his most shocking material until the end of the story, so that by roundabout means he follows Poe's advice about building to a final climax of horror. The breakdown into "chapters" also allows Bierce to slip a bit of cruel comedy into his serious work; the sections frequently have facetious titles like "One Does Not Always Eat What Is on the Table," used to introduce the description of a corpse laid out for the coroner's inspection.

Bierce's convoluted construction sometimes invokes a supernatural aura only to dispel it with an interpretation that is more plausible and equally unpleasant. In "The Death of Halpin Frayser," a man long separated from his family falls asleep unwittingly on the grave of his mother and has a nightmare in which her ghost attacks him. He is found strangled the next morning; but he has actually been murdered not by his mother's ghost but by her second husband, a maniac who guards her grave. Ingenious arrangement and the powerful symbolism of the nightmare join to make this combination of coincidences more effective than they should be, and in fact the coincidences become uncanny rather than merely unbelievable. Several of Bierce's tales employ spectral vengeance as an antidote to racial prejudice; both "The Haunted Valley" and "The Night-Doings at 'Deadman's' " describe murdered Chinese immigrants who rise to destroy their bigoted butchers. Bierce also gave the Frankenstein theme a wry rehash in "Moxon's Master," the story of a mechanical chess player driven to homicide by his creator's plot to win the game by cheating. "A Psychological Shipwreck" is perhaps the best fictional treatment of the wraith, the spirit of a living person released to provide a warning of impending disaster.

Bierce's tales of morbid mirth were not published as separate books, but they appear in his collected works under the titles *Negligible Tales* and *The Parenticide Club*. They are to some extent offshoots of pioneer America's fondness for "tall tales"; by combining perfectly outrageous descriptions of villainy with ironic understatement he anticipated the twentieth century's fondness for "sick" comedy. The fact that these stories so often involve interfamilial infamies need not provide a field day for Freudians; Bierce was obviously making a calculated effort to be as offensive as possible. A hint of his method can be found in the first sentence of "An Imperfect Conflagration": "Early one June morning in 1872 I murdered my father—an act which made a deep impression on me at the time." No summary can do justice to tales like "A Bottomless Grave" or "Oil of Dog"; but "My Favorite Murder," reprinted at the end of this chapter, shows Bierce at his most hideously hilarious.

In 1913, the seventy-one-year-old writer took it into his head to visit Mexico, where a revolution was in progress. He disappeared without a trace. More than one author has been tempted into imagining an appropriate end for this colorful character, but nothing could really improve on the mystery he himself left behind him. A man who could describe a hearse as "Death's baby-carriage" should be entitled to have the last laugh on his readers.

He had a successor of sorts in the person of Stephen Crane, who spiritualized Bierce's war stories into *The Red Badge of Courage* (1895). Most of Crane's tales deal with men facing fear in a variety of situations. He rarely touches on the uncanny, but several pieces describe men adrift in the wilderness who are driven to regard their bleak surroundings as omens of supernatural malignancy. Perhaps his most shocking story is "The Monster" (1898) in which a black servant is hideously mutilated while rescuing a white child from a burning building. His injury also leaves him slightly if not dangerously insane, so that he does not acknowledge his deformity and insists on attempting to socialize with people who find his appearance horrifying. His employer is morally obligated to retain his services and finds his business ruined and his family ostracized as a result. "The Monster" ends on a note of despair; there is no solution to what is presented as an intolerable situation. All the more frightening because it seems so perfectly plausible, the story is at once a powerful piece of realism and a parable on the pernicious effects of prejudice.

Bierce really stands alone in this period as the major American master of the macabre, but the British Isles seemed to be teeming with ghost stories. One of the most important figures in the development of a British tradition was Joseph Sheridan Le Fanu, whose influence on later writers was so great that some have compared him to Poe. He is certainly not as fine an artist, but his work defined a tradition that many of his followers found invaluable in the construction of their own tales. His major achievement was to make a transition between the ponderous Gothic novel and the short story, which is now generally regarded as the most appropriate form for frightening fiction.

Born in 1814, Le Fanu was, like Bierce, a successful journalist. He wrote several novels, all pervaded with a gloomy Gothic atmosphere, of which the most impressive is *Uncle Silas*. They were very popular in their time but today are almost completely overshadowed by his briefer works, which are more concentrated and more frankly supernatural. The majority of these were composed during the last few years of his life when, after the death of his wife, he became a recluse and an invalid. He began to retire early and wake after midnight, writing in bed by candlelight until dawn, fortified with strong tea. This habit became the subject of one of his finest tales, "Green Tea," the story of a clergyman whose use of that stimulant induces horrible visions of a monkey-demon which torments him until he is driven to suicide. The tale is an early example of what has been called the "psychological" ghost story, one in which apparitions can be interpreted either as genuine spirits or as the products of disordered minds. A third explanation is offered by one of the characters: abnormal mental states may produce a susceptibility to dangerous spiritual forces whose existence normally goes undetected. This theory is propounded by a Dr. Hesselius, who represents another of Le Fanu's innovations: that of the psychic investigator who is consulted in cases involving supernatural manifestations. Such figures became increasingly popular as ghost stories began to compete with detective fiction; Hesselius is the father of such characters as Algernon Blackwood's Dr. John Silence, William Hope Hodgson's Carnacki, Dennis Wheatley's Duke de Richleau, Seabury Quinn's Jules de Grandin, and Joseph Payne Brennan's Lucius Leffing.

Le Fanu's work is distinguished by a leisurely pace and a certain subtlety in the introduction of his uncanny effects. His tone is not as feverish as Poe's nor as grim as

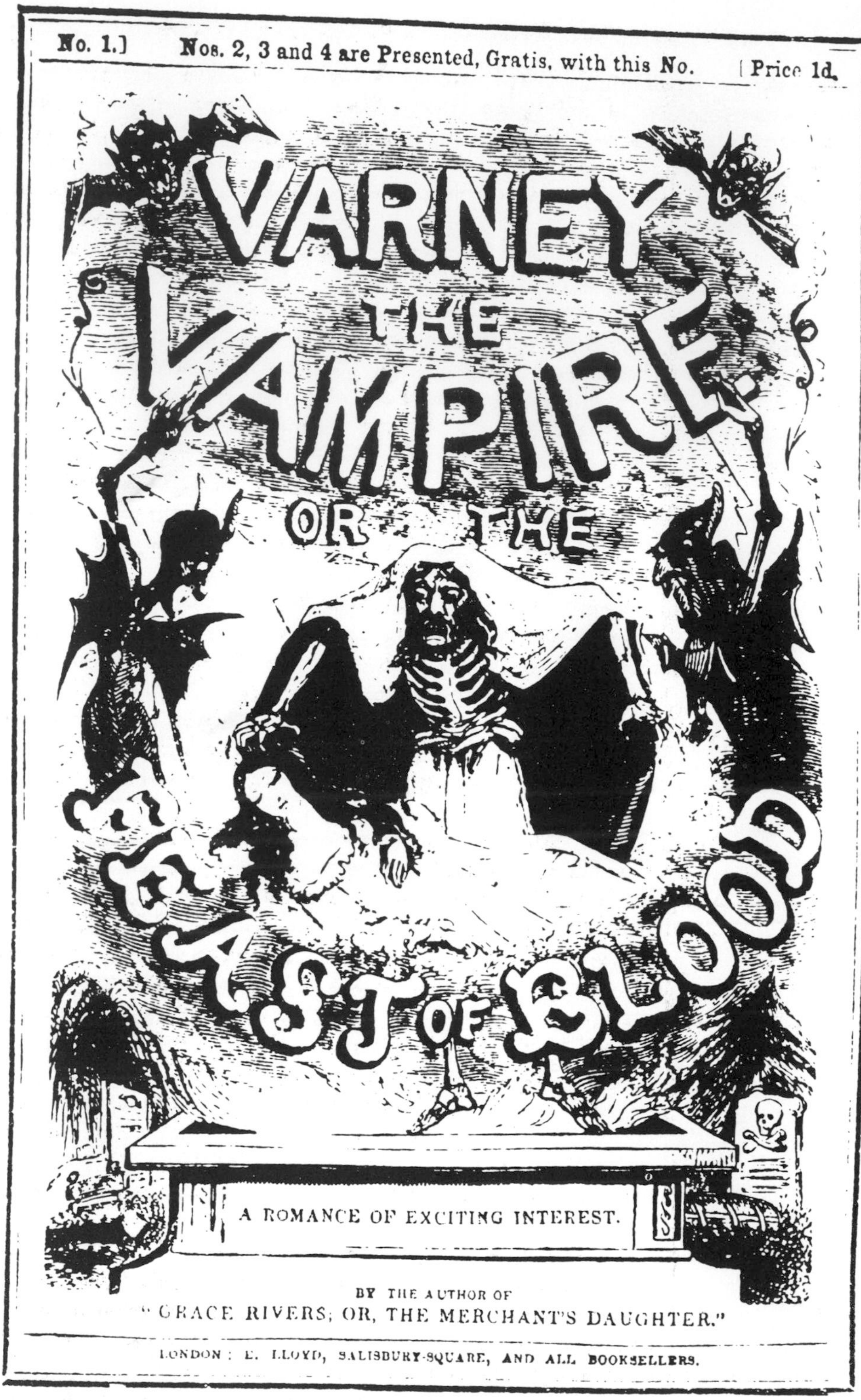

An anonymous artist designed this cover for the anonymously published *Varney the Vampire*, usually ascribed to Thomas Peckett Prest but more recently attributed by some authorities to James Malcolm Rymer.

Bierce's, and he usually begins by describing normal events in the lives of his protagonists, only gradually allowing the nature of his story to emerge. Often the ghostly manifestations are preceded by some disturbing but natural event that throws the characters off balance and leaves them open to the forces described by Dr. Hesselius. He used many stock situations like the vengeful ghost and the deal with the devil, but he told them better than they had ever been told before. And many of his stories inaugurated traditions, like "Narrative of the Ghost of a Hand," an incident from a novel, whose title should be self-explanatory.

The imaginative Irish author's most impressive tale may well be "Carmilla" (1871), a vampire story, which its proponents suggest is the most outstanding presentation of its theme, although it has been overshadowed by the enormous success of Bram Stoker's *Dracula.* The legend of the reanimated corpse that feeds on the blood of the living had been exposed before in two markedly inferior literary productions by John Polidori and Thomas Peckett Prest. Polidori, who had failed to produce anything for the contest that inspired Mary Shelley to write *Frankenstein,* abandoned his first idea and adapted one of Lord Byron's to produce "The Vampyre," originally published under Byron's name, in 1819. An improbable plot, in which the hero allows his sister to marry the vampire rather than break a promise to keep the fiend's identity a secret, pretty well destroys whatever effect the story might have had. Prest's novel, *Varney the Vampire,* or *The Feast of Blood* (1847) was one of a series of melodramatic potboilers with which Prest entertained vast audiences before sinking into well-deserved obscurity. This book, recently reprinted, has a reputation that a perusal of the text will not sustain. Even a dedicated devotee would be hard pressed to wade through its eight hundred pages of thinly connected incidents to watch Varney fling himself into the mouth of Mount Vesuvius. Prest is perhaps best remembered by the extravagant title of one of his forgotten epics: *The Skeleton Clutch,* or *The Goblet of Gore.*

"Carmilla" is far superior to either of these earlier efforts. Le Fanu takes great pains with the character of his vampire, a beautiful young woman who prefers seduction to violence and makes a specialty of becoming the houseguest of her victims. A note of perversity is struck by her preference for female conquests, a contravention of the literary convention that vampires prefer to inflict themselves on the opposite sex. An atmosphere of barely subdued eroticism pervades the relationship between Carmilla and the lady who narrates the story, creating a mood that has few parallels in Victorian literature. The fact that the scenes of stifled passion occur before Carmilla's bloodthirsty motives are exposed only serves to make them more remarkable.

Le Fanu died in 1873 after a prolonged illness that was characterized by terrible nightmares, many of which may have worked their way into his fiction. He was particularly upset by a recurrent dream in which an old house collapsed on him, so much so that the doctor who pronounced him dead said only, "I feared this; that house fell at last."

The "Green Tea" theme of a drug that produces horror received its most famous treatment at the hands of Robert Louis Stevenson, whose *Strange Case of Dr. Jekyll and Mr. Hyde* was published in 1886. This short novel, about a doctor whose potion transforms him into a being with all his worst traits intensified, is unfortunately a victim of its own notoriety. There can hardly be a person alive who does not know the outline of the plot; but Stevenson shrouds it in mystery, introducing Jekyll and Hyde as separate characters and withholding the secret of their single identity and origin until the last few pages. As a result of the story's success, Stevenson's carefully contrived air of confusion and suspense is lost, and it is virtually impossible to give it a fair reading. Such is the price of fame.

A magazine illustration by D. H. Friston for the first publication of Joseph Sheridan Le Fanu's classic tale of a female vampire, "Carmilla."

Nevertheless, the tale is a classic, and Stevenson, for all his brilliant romances, is probably best remembered as its author. The circumstances of its composition are almost as remarkable as the story itself. Stevenson, never in the best of health, was seriously ill when the germ of the plot came to him in the form of a dream. "All I dreamt of *Dr. Jekyll and Mr. Hyde*," he wrote later, "was that a man was being pressed into a cabinet, where he swallowed a drug and changed into another being." Inspired by this visionary fragment, he wrote the entire book in three days, all the while suffering from severe hemorrhages. When he read it to his wife, she criticized him for neglecting the plot's moral implications, insisting that what he had treated as a thriller was really a powerful allegory. Furious, the writer stormed out of the room. He returned a moment later, cried "You are right!" and threw the manuscript into the fire. He then proceeded to write another version from scratch, again taking a mere three days to complete the task.

A few critics have bemoaned the loss of the first version, which they imagine to have been more exciting if less edifying; but such speculations can never be proved. In its final form the book created a sensation and still contained enough moral sentiment to become the subject for numerous sermons. It was immediately adapted for the stage and later became one of the most frequently filmed stories in the history of motion pictures. These popularized versions have obscured many of the details of the original, giving rise, for instance, to the notion that Hyde is a hideous monster, complete with fangs and claws. In fact, he is perfectly human and not at all deformed physically, distinguished from Jekyll by being smaller and younger. The characters who describe him as horrible admit that it is his attitude, rather than his appearance, which frightens them. The idea of a hideous Hyde seems to be an unconscious recognition that the story is a science fiction version of

Mr. Hyde was described by Stevenson as an individual of comparatively presentable appearance; the concept that he was a monster seems to derive from Frederic March's Oscar-winning film performance in 1932. From *Dr. Jekyll and Mr. Hyde* (1932). *Courtesy of MGM.*

the werewolf legend. It is also worth noting that Jekyll is not quite the noble seeker after truth usually portrayed on the screen but rather a man fully aware of his sinful side and rather fond of it. His confessed intention was to embody his evil impulses so that they could be expressed without guilt or shame. Of course, Hyde overpowers Jekyll and begins to appear without chemical aid, and it is Hyde who commits suicide when he runs out of the ingredient that permits him to disguise himself.

Stevenson created almost a mirror image of Jekyll and Hyde in his short story "Markheim," concerning a murderer haunted by his double, who seems at first to be a devil but is ultimately portrayed as a guardian angel, driving Markheim to despair so that he will repent and confess. A powerful portrayal of the criminal's growing panic makes this slightly strained parable palatable. Stevenson also incited quite a bit of late-blooming controversy with "The Body Snatcher," which has been cited as the definitive example of supernatural elements introduced too abruptly into a basically straightforward story. Yet his is the best treatment of the grim "resurrection" trade, which provided stolen corpses for purposes of medical instruction during the nineteenth century. The criminal who had serviced the doctors is murdered to seal his lips, but his dissected body inexplicably ends up among their spoils when they begin grave robbing on their own. Those who find the first part of the tale unnerving will scarcely be put off by its uncanny resolution.

Stevenson was just one of the many successful authors whose fiction included sinister sidelines. Sir Walter Scott had been a serious student of the occult and wrote a factual history of the subject, as well as fictional efforts like "Wandering Willie's Tale" and "The Tapestried Chamber." Charles Dickens, well known for his whimsical Christmas ghost stories like "A Christmas Carol" (1843) and for chilling scenes in novels like *Oliver Twist* and *Great Expectations*, wrote a pair of fine out-and-out chillers in "The Signal-Man" and "To Be Taken with a Grain of Salt" (or "Trial for Murder"), both describing premonitions of death. These stories were published in *All the Year Round*, a magazine Dickens edited in a manner that revealed his lively interest in spooky stories. Among his contributors was Edward Bulwer-Lytton, best remembered today for *The Last Days of Pompeii.* A true believer in worlds beyond our ken, Bulwer-Lytton infused most of his popular novels with weird atmosphere and produced one of the finest accounts of a haunted house in "The Haunted and the Haunters, or the House and the Brain" (1857), which suggested that ghosts are the revenants not of personalities but of their powerful thoughts and emotions, which have taken on an independent existence. Wilkie Collins, who occasionally collaborated with Dickens, undercut the tradition of uncanny fiction with the first major detective novel, *The Moonstone* (1868), which nevertheless inspired many eerie tales with its theme of a desecrated Oriental idol whose worshipers demand vengeance. Some of his shorter works, like "The Dream Woman" and "A Terribly Strange Bed," are still effective tales of terror.

In later decades, Rudyard Kipling, who chronicled the rise of British imperialism in India, used the same exotic setting for "The Phantom 'Rickshaw" (1888), in which a faithless lover is haunted by the ghost of the woman he has betrayed; and "The Mark of the Beast," in which a soldier is cursed for defiling a sacred statue. And the subtle and brilliant Henry James, an American expatriate who settled in England, took time off from his more serious work to concoct several eerie tales, including one that may outlive everything else he wrote, *The Turn of the Screw* (1898). Told from the viewpoint of a young governess who is convinced that her young charges are influenced by the spirits of two sinister servants, it is fashioned so that it is impossible to tell whether the ghosts are genuine or merely a product of the lady's overworked imagination. Both interpretations

Edward Bulwer-Lytton's novel of a magician's quest for eternal life, *Zanoni* (1842), was illustrated by C. T. Deblois.

are equally unnerving, since one of the children is finally scared to death; but the popularity of Freudian criticism has given the psychological theory the upper hand in recent years, despite the author's clear intention to leave the point ambiguous. Elaborately written, *The Turn of the Screw* has the dubious distinction of being the favorite ghost story of people who dislike ghost stories.

A few writers have suffered the irony of having their major efforts virtually forgotten, while the thrillers they have tossed off in idle moments have brought them a small measure of immortality. Such is the case with F. Marion Crawford, whose novels made him the best-selling author in turn-of-the-century America. Hardly anyone reads them today, but the stories collected in *Wandering Ghosts* (1894) include some minor classics in the domain of the weird that seem likely to survive as long as such things are read. "The Upper Berth" is a chilling account of a drowned man whose clammy presence fills the stateroom in which he made his last voyage, and "The Screaming Skull" is the skillfully presented monologue of a man haunted by a skull found in his house in a hatbox. This tale seems to have inaugurated the now popular tradition of a doomed character whose

An impressionistic illustration for Robert W. Chambers's "The Yellow Sign," done decades after the story's original appearance by the popular pulp magazine artist Hannes Bok. *Courtesy of Sisu Publishers.*

narration points to an inevitable climax supplied by a newspaper account of his death. A depraved old man who arranges for a brother and sister to marry is the owner of "The Dead Smile"; his plot is foiled only when a document is removed from his coffin in an exceptionally gruesome scene.

Crawford's career is paralleled by that of Robert W. Chambers, a popular and prolific novelist who specialized in fashionable love stories. His reputation today rests almost entirely on one of his earliest books, *The King in Yellow* (1895). This macabre collection included a few trivial and sentimental pieces; but the best selections were not only effective but also extremely influential on his successors in the United States. Chambers dropped fascinating hints of a new kind of horror, not based on fear of death or the devil, but rather on a vague awareness of other worlds and dimensions threatening to overwhelm our own. More suggested than specified, the menace of *The King in Yellow* fascinated many later writers like H. P. Lovecraft, who attempted to detail the nameless forces lurking in the background of this book. The most famous Chambers story is "The Yellow Sign," describing an artist who innocently acquires a talisman of strange design, then finds it is a symbol of the evil lore described in a blasphemous book called *The King in Yellow*. Already shocked to the point of madness by the secrets of the forbidden volume, he is hardly even surprised when a living corpse comes to reclaim the talisman, leaving death in its wake. More fascinating, if more clumsily told, is "The Repairer of Reputations," whose hero has also read the deadly book. He encounters an agent of the King in Yellow, a deformed old man with a pointed head, missing fingers, and wax ears, whose uncanny sources of information make him a master blackmailer. He promises to make the maddened narrator ruler of the earth; but the plan is frustrated when the blackmailer's cat, which has a great fondness for scratching him, finally tears his throat out. It almost seems that the visions of power are no more than the plans of lunatics, but evidence of the old man's powers reveals that the world has narrowly escaped a catastrophe. The story is set in a futuristic 1920, overshadowed by the presence of a government "lethal chamber" in which legal suicides are permitted.

More traditional, and far more popular, were the menaces imagined by the Anglo-Irish author Bram Stoker, who made himself immortal with *Dracula* (1897). Not a professional writer, Stoker made his living as the manager of the distinguished actor Sir Henry Irving. His interest in the macabre, however, may have been encouraged in part by Irving's roof-raising performance in his production of *The Bells*, a play about a murderer haunted by the sound of his victim's sleigh bells who is finally brought to justice by an ingenious hypnotist. Irving's other eerie efforts on the stage included a version of Faust and a treatment of the legend of a haunted ship, The Flying Dutchman.

Stoker claimed that *Dracula*, in the grand tradition, had been inspired by a nightmare. It had also entailed a fair amount of research. Stoker based his vampire character on a historical personage, a fifteenth-century Romanian warlord named Vlad Tepes, notorious for his acts of wanton cruelty. The nickname Dracula meant "son of the dragon." The author picked up historical and geographical details from Arminius Vambery of Budapest University; but his references to the medieval character are slight, and Dracula might as well have been the fictional character he was generally assumed to be.

The book has been frequently condemned without a fair reading (often with none at all); but it is nevertheless a vivid and gripping melodrama, on an epic scale never suggested by the hastily contrived stage version or the many film adaptations, all apparently based on the play's confined settings. An irresistible combination of

John Carradine, with his gray hair and moustache, came closer than most actors to Bram Stoker's description of Dracula. From *The House of Dracula* (1945). *Courtesy of Universal Pictures.*

repression and mayhem, rife with sexual and religious symbolism, *Dracula* is probably the best out-and-out horror novel ever written.

Narrated by various characters in their letters and diaries, the novel tells the now familiar tale of the "undead" nobleman from Transylvania who travels to London in search of new blood but is finally destroyed by a band of men with the knowledge and courage to oppose him. The early scenes are set in Dracula's mountain castle, where the vampire-count is visited by Jonathan Harker, who has come to sell him a home in England. This section, in which Harker gradually realizes what a strange household he is in, is probably the best part of the book. In the closing chapters, Dracula is pursued across Europe and killed outside the castle after a wild battle with his Gypsy servants. In the contrast between these medieval scenes and the main action in Victorian London, Stoker devised a method for bringing the Gothic novel up to date. The malevolent aristocrat who literally feeds upon the people of his domain is a more powerful symbol of predatory privilege than anything devised by Stoker's eighteenth-century predecessors, and his attempt to emigrate has all the implications of a foreign invasion.

The story is so well known that it has become the authoritative source on the care and feeding of vampires; Stoker's decisions regarding the legendary attributes of these lecherous leeches have been accepted as gospel truth. Unlike most of the vampires described in the purportedly factual manuscripts of olden days, Dracula can transform himself into a mist, a wolf, or a bat. He has a marked aversion for symbols of Christianity and a chauvinistic fondness for female victims. Other debatable points include Stoker's declaration that this cursed condition is contagious and that the proper cure is a wooden stake through the monster's heart (vampires were most commonly burned by those who believed in them). At any rate, Stoker's deviations from tradition were dramatically sound, and they helped ensure his book's success.

Dracula is a particularly fascinating monster because, unlike the equally famous creations of Dr. Frankenstein and Dr. Jekyll, he is almost completely remorseless. Rich, immortal, irresistible, and nearly omnipotent, he is the embodiment of an unleashed id, sleeping all day and spending his nights creeping into bedrooms. The sexual side of his ungentlemanly behavior undoubtedly titillated Victorian readers; this is particularly evident in the incident of his first English victim, Lucy Westerna, who keeps three suitors at arm's length while Dracula is turning her into a lustful fiend like himself. The highly charged scene in which her frustrated admirers converge on her coffin to hammer a stake into her has overtones of a symbolic rape.

Dracula is not the only colorful character in the book; some effectively eerie moments are provided by Renfield, a lunatic with a fondness for eating insects who hopes to work up to bigger things with the count's cooperation. Unaccountably forgotten in virtually every adaptation of the novel is Quincey Morris, a visiting American cowboy with an incredible vocabulary who sacrifices his life to kill Dracula and save the heroine, Harker's wife, Mina. Stoker also contributed to the growing tradition of psychic detectives with Dr. Abraham Van Helsing, the wily old Dutch physician who provides the necessary expertise to defeat the Transylvanian terror.

The author of *Dracula* produced several other books in the same vein, but none of them had a comparable impact. *The Jewel of Seven Stars* (1903) is a tale of Egyptian horrors involving the resurrection of a queen dead for thousands of years, and *The Lady of the Shroud* features a woman who poses as a vampire to thwart an international plot. Stoker died in 1912, just after completing *The Lair of the White Worm*. This novel, about a giant slug who lives beneath the earth and projects itself into the form of a mysterious woman, has more potential than perfection. The clumsy style shows all too clearly the effects of the severe illness from which Stoker was suffering. His last year recalled the debility of his childhood, when he was so weak that he did not leave his bed until the age of eight. *Dracula's Guest* (1914) was a posthumous collection of stories that included a fragment excised from *Dracula* as well as a pair of anthologist's favorites, "The Judge's House" and "The Squaw." The former is a good haunted-house story in which the ghost appears as a rat; the latter depicts a foolhardy American tourist who dies in an iron maiden which he has insisted on entering just for the thrill of it.

Dracula's history as a play commenced a few days after its publication, when it was read in a theater to protect the stage rights. The distinction of portraying the title character went to a Mr. Jones. A real adaptation was finally done in 1924 by actor Hamilton Deane, who played Van Helsing to Raymond Huntley's Dracula. Unanimously despised by the critics, the play was a huge success with the public.

A popularity surpassing even that of Stoker's famous character was enjoyed by Arthur

Conan Doyle's Sherlock Holmes, the fictional investigator who established the detective story as the favorite form for the consumption of pen-and-ink corpses. He handled many a gruesome case, including a few with supernatural overtones. Of course Holmes always found a logical explanation for apparently uncanny events, but many of the tales were effectively eerie. The most famous example is *The Hound of the Baskervilles*, in which the detective discovers a murderous canine ghost to be a well-trained animal covered with phosphorus. Similar cases include "The Adventure of the Devil's Foot," in which a rare poison creates the impression that its victims have died of fright; and "The Adventure of the Sussex Vampire," in which a woman caught sucking the blood of her child turns out to be drawing the poison from a wound administered by the real culprit.

One reaction to this sort of challenge was provided by the collected exploits of *Carnacki the Ghost-Finder* (1910) by William Hope Hodgson. A few of Carnacki's cases, like "The Horse of the Invisible," involve felonious fraud; but his investigations are usually concerned with genuine supernatural manifestations, often of the most grotesque type. "The Whistling Room," haunted by the spirit of a murdered jester, has a floor in which gigantic lips appear to produce hideous music. And "The Hog" is a filthy grunting force from another world which Carnacki keeps at bay with the use of an electric pentacle. This sort of detection had an interesting similarity to the life of Arthur Conan Doyle, who spent his last years seriously and hopefully investigating the possibility of communicating with the dead.

Hodgson, whose brief career was cut short by his death in the First World War, specialized not only in tales of psychic detection, but also in ghostly yarns about the sea. He had been a sailor for several years and later became an expert at conjuring up the mood of mystery and isolation of men adrift on the vast expanses of uncharted oceans. His most famous short stories of the sea are "The Derelict," in which an abandoned ship is covered with a strange mold that consumes any living creature coming into contact with the vessel; and "The Voice in the Night," in which two castaways feed on a fungus which eventually takes over their bodies, reducing them to shapeless gray masses, still unfortunately retaining their human intelligence. When potential rescuers approach, the sufferers are obliged to send them away, lest their affliction prove contagious. Other tales concern haunted ships and sea monsters.

Hodgson is most renowned for his four novels, *The Boats of the "Glen Carig," The House on the Borderland, The Ghost Pirates,* and *The Night Land*, all written between 1907 and 1912. Two of these consolidated the themes of his best sea stories, while *The House on the Borderland* and *The Night Land* moved in a new direction. Like *The King in Yellow*, these books sought to portray a different sort of horror, one that had considerable effect on later writers. They might technically be called science fiction, but Hodgson's intention was to express the mysteries of space and time, rather than to imagine the results of new discoveries or inventions. The idea of invaders from another dimension gets a persuasive and powerful treatment in *The House on the Borderland.* A manuscript found in a remote area tells the tale of a man whose isolated home is besieged by monsters. His defense of his house and his underground search for the creatures produce a mood of claustrophobic terror, while his vision of their source in an awesome infinity creates a breathless sense of wonder. This is probably his best novel, although many connoisseurs prefer *The Night Land*, a maddening combination of wild imagination, insufferable sentimentality, and tortured syntax. Presented as the work of a seventeenth-century man who dreams that he is living millions of years in the future, the book is written in a ridiculous and infuriating style that purports to indicate the narrator's era but in fact has no equivalent in the

Lee Brown Coye, a pulp magazine artist whose apparently simple work has a haunting long-term effect, drew this scene from William Hope Hodgson's story "The Hog" in 1946. *Courtesy of Lee Brown Coye.*

English language. In the world he describes, humanity is nearly extinct. The sun has gone out, the earth is alive with horrifying beings of every shape and size, and the few people left alive hide from an utterly inimical environment in a huge metal pyramid. Telepathically contacted by another colony of desperate people, the hero ventures out to bring them aid and encounters the most staggering array of outlandish adversaries ever committed to print. He finds love at the second pyramid, and the reader is apt to shudder anew at the maudlin excesses inspired in this encounter. Still, in its overall conception and in its best incidents, *The Night Land* is a compelling literary nightmare.

Horrors of a much more traditional sort were produced by the last great master of the Victorian ghost story, M. R. James. Without really breaking any new ground, the scholarly antiquarian brought to his work a sense of style and structure that has rarely been surpassed in macabre fiction. His academic work took most of his time, and he seems to have tossed off his dozens of cobwebby yarns to amuse himself and his friends. James was a devoted disciple of Le Fanu and shared his fondness for a slow beginning to set the scene and lull the reader. He wrote that "two ingredients most valuable in the concocting of a ghost story are, to me, the atmosphere and the nicely managed crescendo."

The first of his tales was written in 1894, and he continued to concoct them for more than thirty years. They were published in four volumes: *Ghost Stories of an Antiquary* (1904), *More Ghost Stories* (1911), *A Thin Ghost and Others* (1919), and *A Warning to the*

James McBryde was the artist for the first short story collection by M. R. James. "Oh, Whistle and I'll Come to You, My Lad" describes an unseen ghost that erupts from the victim's bedsheets.

Curious (1925). A few previously uncollected pieces were added to all the above to produce *Collected Ghost Stories* in 1931. The first two books are the best known and have supplied dozens of anthologies. They include such gems as "The Mezzotint," about a haunted picture that changes to portray the ghastly history of the house it depicts; "Oh, Whistle, and I'll Come to You, My Lad," concerning a musical instrument that calls up the spirits of the dead; and "Casting the Runes," in which a sorcerer sends a demon to punish a critic who gave his book on witchcraft a bad review. Most of the stories are enhanced by James's knowledge of English history; they are frequently set in old cathedrals or venerable country houses, or else they involve the discovery of curious relics. His ghosts, which appear only briefly, take some unusual forms. The one in "The Diary of Mr. Poynter" has a human shape but crawls on all fours and has a face entirely covered with hair; the one in "The Rose Garden" is just a face, "large, smooth and pink," with only one tooth. These unpleasant creatures have a way of getting uncomfortably close to their victims; as H. P. Lovecraft noted, they are often touched before they are seen. One that is heard before it is seen is the subject of "Rats," a seldom seen tale, one of the author's last, which is reprinted here from *Collected Ghost Stories.*

M. R. James, along with the rest of the men discussed in this survey of Victorian chillers, was an isolated toiler in his own literary graveyard. But the turn of the century saw a new development as a whole group of uncanny authors banded together to form a secret society. It was their solemn purpose to become masters of the lost art of magic.

MY FAVORITE MURDER

By Ambrose Bierce

Having murdered my mother under circumstances of singular atrocity, I was arrested and put upon my trial, which lasted seven years. In charging the jury, the judge of the Court of Acquittal remarked that it was one of the most ghastly crimes that he had ever been called upon to explain away.

At this, my attorney rose and said:

"May it please your Honor, crimes are ghastly or agreeable only by comparison. If you were familiar with the details of my client's previous murder of his uncle you would discern in his later offense (if offense it may be called) something in the nature of tender forbearance and filial consideration for the feelings of the victim. The appalling ferocity of the former assassination was indeed inconsistent with any hypothesis but that of guilt; and had it not been for the fact that the honorable judge before whom he was tried was the president of a life insurance company that took risks on hanging, and in which my client held a policy, it is hard to see how he could decently have been acquitted. If your Honor would like to hear about it for instruction and guidance of your Honor's mind, this unfortunate man, my client, will consent to give himself the pain of relating it under oath."

The district attorney said: "Your Honor, I object. Such a statement would be in the nature of evidence, and the testimony in this case is closed. The prisoner's statement should have been introduced three years ago, in the spring of 1881."

"In a statutory sense," said the judge, "you are right, and in the Court of Objections and Technicalities you would get a ruling in your favor. But not in a Court of Acquittal. The objection is overruled."

"I except," said the district attorney.

"You cannot do that," the judge said. "I must remind you that in order to take an exception you must first get this case transferred for a time to the Court of Exceptions on a formal motion duly supported by affidavits. A motion to that effect by your predecessor in office was denied by me during the first year of this trial. Mr. Clerk, swear the prisoner."

The customary oath having been administered, I made the following statement, which impressed the judge with so strong a sense of the comparative triviality of the offense for which I was on trial that he made no further search for mitigating circumstances, but simply instructed the jury to acquit, and I left the court, without a stain upon my reputation:

"I was born in 1856 in Kalamakee, Mich., of honest and reputable parents, one of whom Heaven has mercifully spared to comfort me in my later years. In 1867 the family came to California and settled near Nigger Head, where my father opened a road agency and prospered beyond the dreams of avarice. He was a reticent, saturnine man then, though his increasing years have now somewhat relaxed the austerity of his disposition, and I believe that nothing but his memory of the sad event for which I am now on trial prevents him from manifesting a genuine hilarity.

"Four years after we had set up the road agency an itinerant preacher came along, and having no other way to pay for the night's lodging that we gave him, favored us with an exhortation of such power that, praise God, we were all converted to religion. My father at once sent for his brother, the Hon. William Ridley of Stockton, and on his arrival turned over the agency to him, charging him nothing for the franchise nor plant—the latter consisting of a Winchester rifle, a sawed-off shotgun, and an assortment of masks made out of flour sacks. The family then moved to Ghost Rock and opened a dance house. It was called 'The Saints' Rest Hurdy-Gurdy,' and the proceedings each night began with prayer. It was there that my now sainted mother, by her grace in the dance, acquired the *sobriquet* of 'The Bucking Walrus.'

"In the fall of '75 I had occasion to visit Coyote, on the road to Mahala, and took the stage at Ghost Rock. There were four other passengers. About three miles beyond Nigger Head, persons whom I identified as my Uncle William and his two sons held up the stage. Finding nothing in the express box, they went through the passengers. I acted a most honorable part in the affair, placing myself in line with the others, holding up my hands and permitting myself to be deprived of forty dollars and a gold watch. From my behavior no one could have suspected that I knew the gentlemen who gave the entertainment. A few days later, when I went to Nigger Head and asked for the return of my money and watch my uncle and cousins swore they knew nothing of the matter, and they affected a belief that my father and I had done the job ourselves in dishonest violation of commercial good faith. Uncle William even threatened to retaliate by starting an opposition dance house at Ghost Rock. As 'The Saints' Rest' had become rather unpopular, I saw that this would assuredly ruin it and prove a paying enterprise, so I told my uncle that I was willing to overlook the past if he would take me into the scheme and keep the partnership a secret from my father. This fair offer he rejected, and I then perceived that it would be better and more satisfactory if he were dead.

"My plans to that end were soon perfected, and communicating them to my dear parents I had the gratification of receiving their approval. My father said he was proud of me, and my mother promised that although her religion forbade her to assist in taking human life I should have the advantage of her prayers for my success. As a preliminary measure looking to my security in case of detection I made an application for membership in that powerful order, the Knights of Murder, and in due course was received as a member of the Ghost Rock commandery. On the day that my probation ended I was for the first time permitted to inspect the records of the order and learn who belonged to it—all the rites of initiation having been conducted in masks. Fancy my delight when, in looking over the roll of membership, I found the third name to be that of my uncle, who indeed was junior vice-chancellor of the order! Here was an opportunity exceeding my wildest dreams—to murder I could add insubordination and treachery. It was what my good mother would have called 'a special Providence.'

"At about this time something occurred which caused my cup of joy, already full, to overflow on all sides, a circular cataract of bliss. Three men, strangers in that locality, were arrested for the stage robbery in which I had lost my money and watch. They were brought to trial and, despite my efforts to clear them and fasten the guilt upon three of the most respectable and worthy citizens of Ghost Rock, convicted on the clearest proof. The murder would now be as wanton and reasonless as I could wish.

"One morning I shouldered my Winchester rifle, and going over to my uncle's house, near Nigger Head, asked my Aunt Mary, his wife, if he were at home, adding that I had come to kill him. My aunt replied with her peculiar smile that so many gentlemen called on that errand and were afterward carried away without having performed it that I must excuse her for doubting my good faith in the matter. She said I did not look as if I would kill anybody, so, as a proof of good faith I leveled my rifle and wounded a Chinaman who happened to be passing the house. She said she knew whole families that could do a thing of that kind, but Bill Ridley was a horse of another color. She said, however, that I would find him over on the other side of the creek in the sheep lot; and she added that she hoped the best man would win.

"My Aunt Mary was one of the most fair-minded women that I have ever met.

"I found my uncle down on his knees engaged in skinning a sheep. Seeing that he had neither gun nor pistol handy I had not the heart to shoot him, so I approached him, greeted him pleasantly and struck him a powerful blow on the head with the butt of my rifle. I have a very good delivery and Uncle William lay down on his side, then rolled over on his back, spread out his fingers and shivered. Before he could recover the use of his limbs I seized the knife that he had been using and cut his hamstrings. You know, doubtless, that when you sever the *tendo Achillis* the patient has no further use of his leg; it is just the same as if he had no leg. Well, I parted them both, and when he revived he was at my service. As soon as he comprehended the situation, he said:

" 'Samuel, you have got the drop on me and can afford to be generous. I have only one thing to ask of you, and that is that you carry me to the house and finish me in the bosom of my family.'

"I told him I thought that a pretty reasonable request and I would do so if he would let me put him into a wheat sack; he would be easier to carry that way and if we were seen by the neighbors *en route* it would cause less remark. He agreed to that, and going to the barn I got a sack. This, however, did not fit him; it was too short and much wider than he; so I bent his legs, forced his knees up against his breast and got him into it that way, tying the sack above his head. He was a heavy man and I had all that I could do to get him on my back, but I staggered along for some distance until I came to a swing that some of the children had suspended to the branch of an oak. Here I laid him down and sat upon him to rest, and the sight of the rope gave me a happy inspiration. In twenty minutes my uncle, still in the sack, swung free to the sport of the wind.

"I had taken down the rope, tied one end tightly about the mouth of the bag, thrown the other across the limb and hauled him up about five feet from the ground. Fastening the other end of the rope also about the mouth of the sack, I had the satisfaction to see my uncle converted into a large, fine pendulum. I must add that he was not himself entirely aware of the nature of the change that he had undergone in his relation to the exterior world, though in justice to a good man's memory I ought to say that I do not think he would in any case have wasted much of my time in vain remonstrance.

"Uncle William had a ram that was famous in all that region as a fighter. It was in a state of chronic constitutional indignation. Some deep disappointment in early life had soured its disposition and it had declared war upon the whole world. To say that it would butt anything accessible is but faintly to express the nature and scope of its military activity: the universe was its antagonist; its methods that of a projectile. It fought like the angels and devils, in mid-air, cleaving the atmosphere like a bird, describing a parabolic curve and descending upon its victim at just the exact angle of incidence to make the most of its velocity and weight. Its momentum, calculated in foot-tons, was something incredible. It had been seen to destroy a four year old bull by a single impact upon that animal's gnarly forehead. No stone wall had ever been known to resist its downward swoop; there were no trees tough enough to stay it; it would splinter them into matchwood and defile their leafy honors in the dust. This irascible and implacable brute—this incarnate thunderbolt—this monster of the upper deep, I had seen reposing in the shade of an adjacent tree, dreaming dreams of conquest and glory. It was with a view to summoning it forth to the field of honor that I suspended its master in the manner described.

"Having completed my preparations, I imparted to the avuncular pendulum a gentle oscillation, and retiring to cover behind a contiguous rock, lifted up my voice in a long rasping cry whose diminishing final note was drowned in a noise like that of a swearing cat, which emanated from the sack. Instantly that formidable sheep was upon its feet and had taken in the military situation at a glance. In a few moments it had approached, stamping, to within fifty yards of the swinging foeman, who, now retreating and anon advancing, seemed to invite the fray. Suddenly I saw the beast's head drop earthward as if depressed by the weight of its enormous horns; then a dim, white, wavy streak of sheep prolonged itself from that spot in a generally horizontal direction to within about four yards of a point immediately beneath the enemy. There it struck sharply upward, and before it had faded from my gaze at the place whence it had set out I heard a horrid thump and a piercing scream, and my poor uncle shot forward, with a slack rope higher than the limb to which he was attached. Here the rope tautened with a jerk, arresting his flight, and back he swung in a breathless curve to the other end of his arc. The ram had fallen, a heap of indistinguishable legs, wool and horns, but pulling itself together and dodging as its antagonist swept downward it retired at random, alternately shaking its head and stamping its fore-feet. When it had backed about the same distance as that from which it had delivered the assault it paused again, bowed its head as if in prayer for victory and again shot forward, dimly visible as before—a prolonging white streak with monstrous undulations, ending with a sharp ascension. Its course this time was at a right angle to its former one, and its impatience so great that it struck the enemy before he had nearly reached the lowest point of his arc. In consequence he went flying round and round in a horizontal circle whose radius was about equal to half the length of the rope, which I forgot to say was nearly twenty feet long. His shrieks, *crescendo* in approach and *diminuendo* in recession, made the rapidity of his revolution more obvious to the ear than to the eye. He had evidently not yet been struck in a vital spot. His posture in the sack and the distance from the ground at which he hung compelled the ram to operate upon his lower extremities and the end of his back. Like a plant that has struck its root into some poisonous mineral, my poor uncle was dying slowly upward.

"After delivering its second blow the ram had not again retired. The fever of battle burned hot in its heart; its brain was intoxicated with the wine of strife. Like a pugilist who in his rage forgets his skill and fights ineffectively at half-arm's length, the angry beast endeavored to reach its fleeting foe by awkward vertical leaps as he passed overhead, sometimes, indeed, succeeding in striking him feebly, but more frequently overthrown by its own misguided eagerness. But as the impetus was exhausted and the man's circles narrowed in scope and diminished in speed, bringing him nearer to the ground, these tactics produced better results, eliciting a superior quality of screams, which I greatly enjoyed.

"Suddenly, as if the bugles had sung truce, the ram suspended hostilities and walked away, thoughtfully wrinkling and smoothing its great aquiline nose, and occasionally cropping a bunch of grass and slowly munching it. It seemed to have tired of war's alarms and resolved to beat the sword into a plowshare and cultivate the arts of peace. Steadily it held its course away from the field of fame until it had gained a distance of nearly a quarter of a mile. There it stopped and stood with its rear to the foe, chewing its cud and apparently half asleep. I observed, however, an occasional slight turn of its head, as if its apathy were more affected than real.

"Meantime Uncle William's shrieks had abated with his motion, and nothing was heard from him but long, low moans, and at long intervals my name, uttered in pleading tones exceedingly grateful to my ear. Evidently the man had not the faintest notion of what was being done to him, and was inexpressibly terrified. When Death comes cloaked in mystery he is terrible indeed. Little by little my uncle's oscillations diminished, and finally he hung motionless. I went to him and was about to give him the *coup de grâce,* when I heard and felt a succession of smart shocks which shook the ground like a series of light earthquakes, and turning in the direction of the ram, saw a long cloud of dust approaching me with inconceivable rapidity and alarming effect! At a distance of some thirty yards away it stopped short, and from the near end of it rose into the air what I at first thought a great white bird. Its ascent was so smooth and easy and regular that I could not realize its extraordinary celerity, and was lost in admiration of its grace. To this day the impression remains that it was a slow, deliberate movement, the ram—for it was that animal—being upborne by some power other than its own impetus, and supported through the successive stages of its flight with infinite tenderness and care. My eyes followed its progress through the air with unspeakable pleasure, all the greater by contrast with my former terror of its approach by land. Onward and upward the noble animal sailed, its head bent down almost between its knees, its fore-feet thrown back, its hinder legs trailing to rear like the legs of a soaring heron.

"At a height of forty or fifty feet, as fond recollection presents it to view, it attained its zenith and appeared to remain an instant stationary; then, tilting suddenly forward without altering the relative position of its parts, it shot downward on a steeper and steeper course with augmenting velocity, passed immediately above me with a noise like the rush of a cannon shot and struck my poor uncle almost squarely on the top of the head! So frightful was the impact that not only the man's neck was broken, but the rope too; and the body of the deceased, forced against the earth, was crushed to pulp beneath the awful front of that meteoric sheep! The concussion stopped all the clocks between Lone Hand and Dutch Dan's, and Professor Davidson, a distinguished authority in matters seismic, who happened to be in the vicinity, promptly explained that the vibrations were from north to southwest.

"Altogether, I cannot help thinking that in point of artistic atrocity my murder of Uncle William has seldom been excelled."

RATS

By M. R. James

"And if you was to walk through the bedrooms now, you'd see the ragged, mouldy bedclothes a-heaving and a-heaving like seas." "And a-heaving and a-heaving with what?" he says. "Why, with the rats under 'em."

But was it with the rats? I ask, because in another case it was not. I cannot put a date to the story, but I was young when I heard it, and the teller was old. It is an ill-proportioned tale, but that is my fault, not his.

It happened in Suffolk, near the coast. In a place where the road makes a sudden dip and then a sudden rise; as you go northward, at the top of that rise, stands a house on the left of the road. It is a tall red-brick house, narrow for its height; perhaps it was built about 1770. The top of the front has a low triangular pediment with a round window in the centre. Behind it are stables and offices, and such garden as it has is behind them. Scraggy Scotch firs are near it: an expanse of gorse-covered land stretches away from it. It commands a view of the distant sea from the upper windows of the front. A sign on a post stands before the door; or did so stand, for though it was an inn of repute once, I believe it is so no longer.

To this inn came my acquaintance, Mr. Thomson, when he was a young man, on a fine spring day, coming from the University of Cambridge, and desirous of solitude in tolerable quarters and time for reading. These he found, for the landlord and his wife had been in service and could make a visitor comfortable, and there was no one else staying in the inn. He had a large room on the first floor commanding the road and the view, and if it faced east, why, that could not be helped; the house was well built and warm.

He spent very tranquil and uneventful days: work all the morning, an afternoon perambulation of the country round, a little conversation with country company or the people of the inn in the evening over the then fashionable drink of brandy and water, a little more reading and writing, and bed; and he would have been content that this should continue for the full month he had at disposal, so well was his work progressing, and so fine was the April of that year—which I have reason to believe was that which Orlando Whistlecraft chronicles in his weather record as the "Charming Year."

One of his walks took him along the northern road, which stands high and traverses a wide common, called a heath. On the bright afternoon when he first chose this direction his eye caught a white object some hundreds of yards to the left of the road, and he felt it necessary to make sure what this might be. It was not long before he was standing by it, and found himself looking at a square block of white stone fashioned somewhat like the base of a pillar, with a square hole in the upper surface. Just such another you may see at this day on Thetford Heath. After taking stock of it he contemplated for a few minutes the view, which offered a church tower or two, some red roofs of cottages and windows winking in the sun, and the expanse of sea—also with an occasional wink and gleam upon it—and so pursued his way.

In the desultory evening talk in the bar, he asked why the white stone was there on the common.

"A old-fashioned thing, that is," said the landlord (Mr. Betts), "we was none of us alive when that was put there." "That's right," said another. "It stands pretty high," said Mr. Thomson, "I dare say a sea-mark was on it some time back." "Ah! yes," Mr. Betts agreed, "I 'ave 'eard they could see it from the boats; but whatever there was, it's fell to bits this long time." "Good job too," said a third, " 'twarn't a lucky mark, by what the old men used to say; not lucky for the fishin', I mean to say." "Why ever not?" said Thomson. "Well, I never see it myself," was the answer, "but they 'ad some funny ideas, what I mean, peculiar, them old chaps, and I shouldn't wonder but what they made away with it theirselves."

It was impossible to get anything clearer than this: the company, never very voluble, fell silent, and when next someone spoke it was of village affairs and crops. Mr. Betts was the speaker.

Not every day did Thomson consult his health by taking a country walk. One very fine afternoon found him busily writing at three o'clock. Then he stretched himself and rose, and walked out of his room into the passage. Facing him was another room, then the stair-head, then two more rooms, one looking out to the back, the other to the south. At the south end of the passage was a window, to which he went, considering with himself that it was rather a shame to waste such a fine afternoon. However, work was paramount just at the moment; he thought he would just take five minutes off and go back to it, and those five minutes he would employ—the Bettses could not possibly object—to looking at the other rooms in the passage, which he had never seen. Nobody at all, it seemed, was indoors; probably, as it was market day, they were all gone to the town, except perhaps a maid in the bar. Very still the house was, and the sun shone really hot; early flies buzzed in the window-panes. So he explored. The room facing his own was undistinguished except for an old print of Bury St. Edmunds; the two next him on his side of the passage were gay and clean, with one window apiece, whereas his had two. Remained the south-west room, opposite to the last which he had entered. This was locked; but Thomson was in a mood of quite indefensible curiosity, and feeling confident that there could be no damaging secrets in a place so easily got at, he proceeded to fetch the key of his own room, and when that did not answer, to collect the keys of the other three. One of them fitted, and he opened the door. The room had two windows looking south and west, so it was as bright and the sun as hot upon it as could be. Here there was no carpet, but bare boards; no pictures, no washing-stand, only a bed, in the farther corner: an iron bed, with mattress and bolster, covered with a bluish check counterpane. As featureless a room as you can well imagine, and yet there was something that made Thomson close the door very quickly and yet quietly behind him and lean against the window-sill in the passage, actually quivering all over. It was this, that under the counterpane someone lay, and not only lay, but stirred. That it was some *one* and not some *thing* was certain, because the shape of a head was unmistakable on the bolster; and yet it was all covered, and no one lies with covered head but a dead person; and this was not dead, not truly dead, for it heaved and shivered. If he had seen these things in dusk or by the light of a flickering candle, Thomson could have comforted himself and talked of fancy. On this bright day that was impossible. What was to be done? First, lock the door at all costs. Very gingerly he approached it and bending down listened, holding his breath; perhaps there might be a sound of heavy breathing, and a prosaic explanation. There was absolute silence. But as, with a rather tremulous hand, he put the key into its hole and turned it, it rattled, and on the instant a stumbling padding tread was heard coming towards the door. Thomson fled like a rabbit to his room and locked himself in: futile enough, he knew it was; would doors and locks be any obstacle to what he suspected? but it was all he could think of at the moment, and in fact nothing happened; only there was a time of acute suspense—followed by a misery of doubt as to what to do. The impulse, of course, was to slip away as soon as possible from a house which contained such an inmate. But only the day before he had said he should be staying for at least a week more, and how if he changed plans could he avoid the suspicion of having pried into places where he certainly had no business? Moreover, either the Bettses knew all about the inmate, and yet did not leave the house, or knew nothing, which equally meant that there was nothing to be afraid of, or knew just enough to make them shut up the room, but not enough to weigh on their spirits: in any of these cases it seemed that not much was to be feared, and certainly so far he had had no sort of ugly experience. On the whole the line of least resistance was to stay.

Well, he stayed out his week. Nothing took him past that door, and, often as he would pause in a quiet hour of day or night in the passage and listen, and listen, no sound whatever issued from that direction. You might have thought that Thomson would have made some attempt at ferreting out stories connected with the inn—hardly perhaps from Betts, but from the parson of the parish, or old people in the village; but no, the reticence which commonly falls on people who have had strange experiences, and believe in them, was upon him. Nevertheless, as the end of his stay drew near, his yearning after some kind of explanation grew more and more acute. On his solitary walks he persisted in planning out some way, the least obtrusive, of getting another daylight glimpse into that room, and eventually arrived at this scheme. He would leave by an afternoon train—about four o'clock. When his fly was waiting, and his luggage on it, he would make one last expedition upstairs to look round his own room and see if anything was left unpacked, and then, with that key, which he had contrived to oil (as if that made any difference!), the door should once more be opened, for a moment, and shut.

So it worked out. The bill was paid, the consequent small talk gone through while the fly was loaded: "pleasant part of the country—been very comfortable, thanks to you and Mrs. Betts—hope to come back some time," on one side: on the other, "very glad you've found satisfaction, sir, done our best—always glad to 'ave your good word—very much favoured we've been with the weather, to be sure." Then, "I'll just take a look upstairs in case I've left a book or something out—no, don't trouble, I'll be back in a minute." And as noiselessly as possible he stole to the door and opened it. The shattering of the illusion! He almost laughed aloud. Propped, or you might say sitting, on the edge of the bed was—nothing in the round world but a scarecrow! A scarecrow out of the garden, of course, dumped into the deserted room. . . . Yes; but here amusement ceased. Have scarecrows bare bony feet? Do their heads loll on to their shoulders? Have they iron collars and links of chain about their necks? Can they get up and move, if never so stiffly, across a floor, with wagging head and arms close at their sides? and shiver?

The slam of the door, the dash to the stair-head, the leap downstairs, were followed by a faint. Awaking, Thomson saw Betts standing over him with the brandy bottle and a very reproachful face. "You shouldn't a done so, sir, really you shouldn't. It ain't a kind way to act by persons as done the best they could for you." Thomson heard words of this kind, but what he said in reply he did not know. Mr. Betts, and perhaps even more Mrs. Betts, found it hard to accept his apologies and his assurances that he would say no word that could damage the good name of the house. However, they *were* accepted. Since the train could not now be caught, it was arranged that Thomson should be driven to the town to sleep there. Before he went the Bettses told him what little they knew. "They says he was landlord 'ere a long time back, and was in with the 'ighwaymen that 'ad their beat about the 'eath. That's how he come by his end: 'ung in chains, they say, up where you see that stone what the gallus stood in. Yes, the fishermen made away with that, I believe, because they see it out at sea and it kep' the fish off, according to their idea. Yes, we 'ad the account from the people that 'ad the 'ouse before we come. 'You keep that room shut up,' they says, 'but don't move the bed out, and you'll find there won't be no trouble.' And no more there 'as been; not once he haven't come out into the 'ouse, though what he may do now there ain't no sayin'. Anyway, you're the first I know on that's seen him since we've been 'ere: I never set eyes on him myself, nor don't want. And ever since we've made the servants' rooms in the stablin', we ain't 'ad no difficulty that way. Only I do 'ope, sir, as you'll keep a close tongue, considerin' 'ow an 'ouse do get talked about": with more to this effect.

The promise of silence was kept for many years. The occasion of my hearing the story at last was this: that when Mr. Thomson came to stay with my father it fell to me to show him to his room, and instead of letting me open the door for him, he stepped forward and threw it open himself, and then for some moments stood in the doorway holding up his candle and looking narrowly into the interior. Then he seemed to recollect himself and said: "I beg your pardon. Very absurd, but I can't help doing that, for a particular reason." What that reason was I heard some days afterwards, and you have heard now.

5

THE GOLDEN DAWN: A SECRET SOCIETY

The end of the nineteenth century brought with it a reaction against rationality similar to that of the Romantics but smaller in scope. There were sporadic outbreaks of interest in the uncanny, perhaps as a reaction to the scientific discoveries that distinguished the era. Numerous groups banded together for the study of psychic phenomena, some shamefully gullible and some strictly investigative; but none had such an impact on the world of fantastic fictions as the Order of the Golden Dawn. This secret society was unique, possibly because of the metaphysical lore it professed, but most certainly for the talented and influential writers that it inspired. Whether or not the Order of the Golden Dawn truly possessed a magical doctrine, there is something almost uncanny in the sheer number of its members who found fame as the authors of supernatural stories. And, considering that the purpose of the order was to achieve spiritual elevation, there is something a trifle disturbing in the fact that most of these men who wrote of the unknown dwelt on its terrors.

A veil of mystery still clings to the ghost of this extinguished organization. Not only were its teachings esoteric, but membership itself was rarely a public affair; even those who are positively known to have been members often chose to remain silent on the subject. Various volumes have appeared through the years purporting to expose the rituals of the order, but a definitive list of the men who practiced them seems unlikely to emerge. Among the more prominent occultists can certainly be included S. L. MacGregor Mathers, the group's founder; Aleister Crowley, perhaps the most notorious self-styled magician of modern times; and A. E. Waite, the designer of a rectified Tarot deck which has since become the standard. Among the authors enlightened by the Golden Dawn are the distinguished Irish poet William Butler Yeats, as well as such important tellers of terror tales as Arthur Machen and Algernon Blackwood. To these can be added, with varying degrees of certainty, the names of such writers as Sax Rohmer, Lord Dunsany, G. K. Chesterton, H. Rider Haggard, Talbot Mundy, and even, according to one source, Bram Stoker. A list like this suggests that nearly every British author of the uncanny in this generation was initiated into the Order of the Golden Dawn. And the proceedings acquire an appropriately grim tone when it is noted that one of the charter members was the coroner for the City of London.

It is somewhat surprising that among all these literary figures, the one least associated with the bizarre should have been the least reticent about his occult experiences. This was William Butler Yeats, the respectable Nobel Prize winner, who was introduced into the society by its leader, Mathers, in 1887. Yeats described a gaunt, autocratic individual who had the ability to induce visions in his followers. Mathers handed a small symbol to the poet, and "there rose before me mental images that I could not control: a desert and black Titan raising himself up by his two hands from the middle of a heap of ancient ruins." This strange picture, which Mathers described as a fire elemental, seems to have inspired a later poem, "The Second Coming," in which Yeats depicts a stone colossus rising out of the Holy Land to herald a millennium of horror. Immersed since boyhood in Irish myth, Yeats found it easy to master the symbolism of the Golden Dawn's rituals, which apparently played no small part in the formulation of the mystical philosophy he described in *A Vision* (1925).

The birth of the order seems to have been inspired by the discovery of certain ancient books and manuscripts on the subject of magic, which in turn brought Mathers into contact with magical societies already established in Europe. All of this might have been sufficiently mysterious, but Mathers was not above suggesting that he had been personally instructed by a spiritual figure from the distant past. Other members became increasingly annoyed by his aloof and arrogant manner, especially the one who had

"Resistance—The Black Idol," by the Czech artist Frantisek Kupka, might almost be an illustration for the William Butler Yeats poem "The Second Coming," which seems to have been inspired by a vision received from the Order of the Golden Dawn.

Two cards from the major arcana of Waite's Tarot. The design for Death is original (tradition shows a naked skeleton walking with a scythe); the Devil is close to the decks of previous centuries. The cards represent, respectively, Scorpio and Capricorn.

brought him the first of those magical manuscripts. Eventually arguments about authority were to tear the Order of the Golden Dawn apart, amid hurled curses that were intended to be deadly. But if Mathers could be a grim and forbidding character, he also had a warmer side, manifested in such disparate activities as housing and instructing his followers without charge or releasing mice from traps to keep them as pets. He also had some eccentricities (besides the obvious one of wishing to be a wizard): he became unaccountably enamored of Scotland, which led him to adopt the name MacGregor and to wear kilts. He also fancied himself a military strategist and looked forward with some enthusiasm to the world war he predicted. Yet, despite his affectations, he was not entirely devoid of humor, especially when dismissing neurotic seekers of free advice. To a woman who complained of rotting corpses who visited her at night and attempted to climb into her bed, he merely commented, "Very bad taste on both sides."

Mathers had the personality to keep the group going for as long as it lasted, but the most permanent contribution to the spread of occult studies was made by Arthur Edward Waite. He was only one of several who published surveys of the unknown territory, but the deck of Tarot cards he designed has, with the expiration of copyright, gone into universal circulation. It has, at least for popular consumption, superseded the decks of previous centuries and has influenced most of the cards and commentaries that have appeared subsequently. Indeed, several purportedly authoritative works on the occult have made the error of assuming an ancient history for variations that appear only in Waite's comparatively modern work. The artist who executed his plans was Pamela Coleman Smith; several other experts have followed this arrangement—that the cards should be designed by a man and drawn by a woman. The Tarot, which was vital to the teachings of the Golden Dawn, is most widely known as a pack of cards for telling fortunes, but occultists claim that this is little more than a legend designed to keep the cards in circulation while disguising their true purpose. The Tarot is in fact a picture book of seventy-eight pages, drawn to depict the secrets of creation in symbolic form. The four suits represent the four elements of alchemy: wands (clubs) are fire, swords (spades) are air, cups (hearts) are water, and coins (diamonds) are earth. The value of the cards can be determined, at least in part, by juxtaposing their alchemical and numerological significances. More important than these cards, called the minor arcana, from which the modern poker deck evolved, are the major arcana, a series of twenty-two "jokers" which are richer in meaning, bearing such resonant titles as Death, the Devil, the Magician,

Waite's Seven of Cups and Three of Swords. His most important innovation was the creation of pictures for the minor arcana, which formerly consisted of only a number of pips, like modern playing cards.

the High Priestess, and the Hanged Man. Each of these represents a number of things: a planet or sign of the zodiac, a color, a direction, a bodily function, a musical note, a state of mind, and a letter of the Hebrew alphabet. These correspondences seem to suggest hidden relationships, and contemplation of the Tarot is said to set the mind in tune with higher forces. Occult lore, now apparently confirmed by science, teaches that all matter is composed of the same stuff, which is, in essence, energy. Thought is said to be another manifestation of the same energy, making it theoretically possible to alter the material world by concentration and willpower. There is little doubt that some people have been able to do surprising things by working along these lines, although the technique is less likely to produce a sudden miracle than a gradual change in conditions. Those who are sufficiently advanced to work faster are usually assumed to be too spiritual to supply themselves spontaneously with palaces or piles of pearls. At any rate, study of the cards and their symbolism purportedly prepares the mind for such interesting activities. There is something irresistibly fascinating in their mere appearance and something a bit uncanny in their attributions: how did their creators, centuries ago, know exactly how many cards would be needed to account for all the planets in our solar system, three of which had yet to be discovered? The most impressive contemporary commentary on this intriguing topic is by Paul Foster Case, who claims, strangely enough, to have received his information via the Order of the Golden Dawn.

Not to be outdone by Waite, another member of the secret society created his own Tarot, although the designs are so eccentric that they have never been widely accepted. This was Aleister Crowley, the most famous and flamboyant magician of the group and the one who seems most to blame for its disintegration. He was first a sort of lieutenant to Mathers, who hoped that the energetic newcomer would help him to assert his control over rebellious members of the order. Rarely has one man so grossly underestimated another. Crowley certainly succeeded in alienating the rival factions, but it was only the first step in his plans to achieve control himself. He declared that a vision he had experienced in Egypt included instructions that he should become leader of the Golden Dawn. Mathers was furious. Each accused the other of attempted murder by magic and began casting sinister spells in retaliation. This long-distance duel continued for years, and when Mathers finally died in 1918, numerous persons (Yeats at least temporarily among them) were convinced that Crowley's curses had finally proved fatal. Previously, Crowley had started his own organization, the Silver Star, with rituals based on those of the Golden Dawn. Similar splinter groups, each claiming to possess the "most truthful" truth of all, caused the collapse of the original order, and matters hardly improved when Crowley spitefully published its secret rituals in his magazine, *The Equinox.*

Crowley in fact was a great one for publishing things. Yet few of his works can be classified as fantasy fiction, unless it is assumed that all his volumes of instruction in magic are merely the result of an overactive imagination. In a sense, this may be an accurate assessment, since he acknowledges in his do-it-yourself books that the rituals he describes are primarily aids to concentration and that the real work is done by the magician's mental processes. At any rate, most of his own efforts, like those of his former colleagues, seem to have been directed not toward performing miracles but rather in attempting to communicate with spirits. Consequently, results tended to be subjective and difficult to assess. What was obvious about Crowley is that he was a wild man. He shaved his head, sharpened his teeth, and relished his reputation as the wickedest man in the world. "Do what thou wilt shall be the whole of the law" became his motto, and he traveled from country to country indulging in orgies featuring bizarre sex and numerous drugs. Rumors that he was a killer and cannibal were never supported by hard evidence, but he could hardly be described as a good influence. Several of his followers lost their minds or committed suicide. He wrote pornographic poetry as well as instruction books, but when it came to describing in fiction what he called "Magick," he was oddly restrained. His *Diary of a Drug Fiend* shows a mystical figure not unlike himself benevolently giving addicts the strength to cure themselves, although it was his own policy to increase his intake constantly, thus demonstrating his superiority to any outside influence. His one occult novel, *Moonchild* (1917), is disappointingly tame; his colorful reputation is better served by W. Somerset Maugham's uneven novel *The Magician*, which offers a fictionalized Crowley bent on the creation of artificial life through witchcraft.

In an atmosphere created by men like Mathers, Crowley, and Waite, it is hardly surprising that the writers around them made the supernatural their subject. Perhaps the most important, and certainly the most controversial, of these authors was Arthur Machen. He has been described by various critics as the best and the worst author in the genre. His rich, resonant style is something of an acquired taste, and his themes are as dramatic to some as they are disgusting to others. Born in Wales in 1863, Machen lived to be eighty-four; but most of his best writing was done before the turn of the century. He came to London as a young man, changed his name from Arthur Jones, and settled down to a life of loneliness and poverty. The Golden Dawn apparently supplied him with companionship as well as source material, and he also drew on Welsh legends about the mysterious powers of primeval nature. Never able to make a decent living with his pen, he became a traveling actor in 1901, abandoning literature for years. His brief moment of glory as a writer came in 1914, through a maddening set of circumstances not devoid of supernatural overtones. On September 29 of that year, a newspaper printed a brief tale by Machen called "The Bowmen." It was a story of the First World War and of how British troops had been aided in the battle of Mons by the ghostly arrows of their ancestors. The story created a sensation, not so much because of its merits as because it was believed to be true! Reports were circulated by participants in the battle that St. George and an army of angels had indeed fought for England, and Machen's little fantasy became fact for thousands. It was a great morale builder, and nobody paid much attention to the author's plaintive insistence that he had imagined the whole thing. It is possible to construct a theory demonstrating that both Machen and the men at Mons were telling the truth by assuming that the miraculous tale had been transmitted to the writer by some sort of telepathy. In any case, it was a shattering experience for Machen, who put the story in a book that sold better than anything he had done before, and he continued to refer to the incident in his later works as a bewildering example of human gullibility.

Many of Machen's best terror tales appeared within the space of a year. Two 1894 stories, "The Great God Pan" and "The Inmost Light," represent his debut in the field; they were followed in 1895 by the dazzling episodic novel *The Three Impostors,* which was actually written several years earlier. This novel, which contains some of his most vivid horrors, takes the form of a detective story in which two gentlemen of leisure entertain themselves by attempting to unravel a mystery concerning an ancient coin and a stranger who appears to be in mortal danger. They encounter three impostors, who tell them astounding stories about why they, too, are seeking the desperate young man wearing spectacles. But these three are finally revealed as members of a sinister secret society, although not in time to prevent them from destroying their prey. The bulk of the book is devoted to the tales with which the amateur detectives are beguiled; the best of them, "Novel of the White Powder," is reprinted at the end of this chapter.

This chronicle of demonic disintegration includes suggestions of Machen's major theme, the ancient evil still alive in the backwaters of Britain. Here it is presented through the motif of a preternatural potion, indicating the influence of Le Fanu and Stevenson. Another of the fabulous yarns from *The Three Impostors*, "The Novel of the Black Seal," features the same theme of reversion as an anthropologist discovers that myths about fairies and goblins hide a hideous truth about primitive and malignant beings lurking in the English countryside. The supernatural that Machen portrays is subhuman rather than superhuman, not exotically gifted but crude, stunted, and bestial. Animals themselves are the source of *The Terror* (1917); they revolt against the human race and its overwhelming war. Stories like "The Great God Pan" and "The White People" suggest the revolting results of crossbreeding humans and these loathsome throwbacks; the implications seem to have distressed Machen's detractors. He has been criticized by some for relying too much on gruesome physical details and conversely because he relies too much on the idea of unspeakable, indescribable horrors. Perhaps some indication of his value as a writer can be gained from the realization that he was supported in his old age with funds raised by such distinguished men of letters as T. S. Eliot and George Bernard Shaw.

An interesting contrast to Machen's career is provided by Algernon Blackwood, his chief rival as a creator of supernatural short stories among the members of the Golden Dawn. Blackwood matched Machen's longevity, surviving from 1869 until 1951; but instead of giving up literature at an early age, he was a late bloomer whose first fiction was published when he was thirty-six. He achieved his greatest recognition through readings on British Broadcasting Company programs, which he did long past the age when most men retire. Many of his terror tales, like Machen's, are set in the wilds of a primitive nature; but Blackwood was less concerned with the brutishness at the edge of civilization, concentrating instead on the idea of awe-inspiring spiritual entities that rule the lands beyond man's domain. His best stories have a mystical flavor, deriving their most powerful effects from the suggestion that spirits are seductive, capable of absorbing human souls into an unearthly ecstasy.

"These stories, I think," wrote Blackwood, "were the accumulated repressed results of dreams, yearnings, hopes, and fears due to early Evangelical upbringing, ecstasies tasted in wild nature, draughts of bitter kind in New York's underworld life, and a wild certainty, if still half a dream, that human consciousness holds illimitable possibilities now only latent." He was raised in a zealously religious household and grew up with a fear of damnation which was finally allayed by his occult studies. At twenty he emigrated to Canada, where he failed as a farmer. He then traveled to the United States, where he was, among other things, a gold prospector, and he finally ended up in New York where he endured periods of terrible poverty occasionally relieved by employment as a newspaper reporter. He returned to England after ten years and became known as an author after an enthusiastic friend took some of his tales to a publisher. His most famous stories appeared within a few years of his debut, but he continued to write for decades.

Blackwood's first book, *The Empty House* (1906), is a collection of comparatively ordinary ghost stories; but his second, *The Listener* (1907), includes "The Willows," a long story generally regarded as his masterpiece. It depicts the adventures of two vacationers boating on the Danube who are trapped on an island and menaced by strange, shadowy figures. It is a compelling example of Blackwood's ability to create atmosphere and to describe subjective experiences in which the supernatural is sensed rather than seen. Based on his own impressions during a similar trip, "The Willows" ends with the travelers escaping after the spirits around them claim another victim, whose corpse they discover floating in the river. When Blackwood took the same trip again after writing this story, he and his companion found a body in the water at the same point described in the story. As Blackwood commented wryly, "A coincidence, of course!"

In fact, Blackwood claimed that most of his tales had their origin in his own strange experiences and that it was virtually impossible for him to write a story unless his mystical faculties were stimulated. Among the stories in *John Silence, Physician Extraordinary* (1908) is "Secret Worship," describing a man who returns to the boarding school in Germany that he attended as a boy, only to learn that it has fallen into the hands of devil worshipers. Blackwood asserted that this is what had happened to his own school in the Black Forest. "Ancient Sorceries," in the same volume, describes a French town where Blackwood had had a vision that all the inhabitants could transform themselves into cats. The hero of these stories, John Silence, is the author's most famous character and perhaps the best example of the occult detective, although he is less likely to participate in adventures than to observe them. Silence's experiences include one with a werewolf in Canada, but it does not compare with "The Wendigo" (1910), about a legendary demon of the Canadian backwoods with which the author claimed a nodding acquaintance. What is important in his work, however, is less the variety of plots than the absolute conviction with which Blackwood infuses them. He is without peer in expressing the mental processes of men in the presence of the uncanny and in making his apparitions seem to be experiences rather than events. He is the rare writer in the field who can be subtle without losing impact.

At the opposite end of the spectrum is Blackwood's flamboyant colleague Arthur Sarsfield Ward, who wrote under the name Sax Rohmer. His gift for outlandish melodrama brought him greater financial success than anyone else in the Order of the Golden Dawn, so much so that in later years he signed himself $ax Rohmer. "I couldn't keep track of the money," he declared. "I just gave up and spent it." Most of his fortune was due to the creation of Dr. Fu Manchu, a fiendish Oriental villain who is estimated to have earned Rohmer more than two million dollars, although books about him constitute only a small part of the author's works, a mere dozen volumes. Fu Manchu was the subject of Rohmer's first book, in 1913, and his last, published just before he died in 1959 at the age of seventy-six. The original volume, *The Mystery of Dr. Fu-Manchu* (Rohmer soon eliminated the hyphen), appeared in America as *The Insidious Dr. Fu-Manchu.* Like the next two books, it was a collection of short stories that had originally appeared in magazines. The villain dies at the end of each; the third death was expected to prove fatal; but Fu Manchu was revived after thirteen years to appear in a series of full-fledged novels that are artistically superior to the original tales, although they lack period charm. In fact the sinister Chinese mastermind lasts so long that he eventually runs into trouble with his homeland's new Communist government, becoming a quasi-hero in the process. He is more effective when his motives are unmixedly malicious. Tall, gaunt, and bald, with green eyes like a cat's, Dr. Fu Manchu is the world's champion mad scientist, employing wild inventions combined with a touch of old-style sorcery. Zombies, giant spiders, plagues, untraceable poisons, and an elixir of youth are the devices against which struggled the doctor's dauntless opponent, Nayland Smith.

In his last decade Rohmer attempted to rival this outrageous but enthralling series with one about a powerful villainess, Sumuru, bent, like Fu Manchu, on conquering the

world, but employing an army of women. Sumuru does not really compare with her male predecessor, but she is an improvement on the character introduced and abandoned in Rohmer's second novel, *The Sins of Severac Bablon* (1914). Bablon was in effect a Jewish Fu Manchu, a descendant of the ancient kings of Israel described by Rohmer as a "Jewish Robin Hood." Too dignified to take over the planet, Bablon is content to chastise or reform wealthy Jews who sully the name of his people.

Rohmer's third book and his sole venture into nonfiction was *The Romance of Sorcery* (1914), a history of magic and magicians that seems to have been heavily influenced by his Golden Dawn indoctrination, although he does not refer directly to personal experience. His third novel, and probably his best, appeared the same year as a magazine serial and four years later in book form. This was *Brood of the Witch Queen*, a supernatural thriller devoid of the author's usual pseudoscientific explanations, concerning a young man who is a revitalized relic of ancient Egypt at large in modern England. Rohmer's occult lore was never as well employed as in this tale of a malevolent magician's use of elemental spirits, and he never equaled the claustrophobic chills of the scenes in the bowels of a pyramid. His other books with predominantly uncanny themes include *The Dream Detective* (1920), the adventures of psychic detective Moris Klaw; *The Green Eyes of Bast* (1920), about a lycanthropic cat-woman; *Grey Face* (1924), about a modern alchemist who has discovered the secret of making gold and prolonging life; and *The Bat Flies Low* (1935), which is particularly interesting because of the way the author uses occult lore to anticipate the theories of nuclear physics. The book describes a secret process for producing power, guarded since time immemorial by an Egyptian cult. An American utility company steals the secret, but the attempt to try it out produces an explosion that rocks the world.

Rohmer could hardly pass for a stylist; most of his works are fast-paced action tales, not really very well written. Thus he stands in contrast to Edward John Moreton Drax Plunkett, eighteenth Baron Dunsany, known to his readers as Lord Dunsany. He remarked near the end of his career with some truth and more egotism, "I can't think of any great prose writers who have come up to the standards I have set for prose." He was equally adept at lyrical evocations of mythical domains or at caustically witty commentaries on modern culture, and his writing is impressive, if not quite as good as he thought. His themes are usually supernatural, and a note of terror is frequently sounded; but his work is characterized by the contrasting qualities of mystical beauty and ironic humor. The Irish baron first achieved fame as a dramatist; his first play was produced in 1909 at Dublin's Abbey Theatre, where the great poetic plays of Yeats were presented. Dunsany made his debut with *The Glittering Gate*, a typical piece of whimsy about burglars who attempt the job of breaking and entering into Heaven. Thieves were among his favorite characters, appearing again in his most frightening and effective play, *A Night at an Inn*. This employed the device of an idol's stolen eye; but in this case it is not his agents who recover the gem, but the great stone god himself.

Dunsany's first book was *The Gods of Pegana* (1905), which began his creation of an original mythology. This series of stories or sketches describes the universe as originating with Mana-Yood-Sushai, who created lesser gods and then retired. In stately, almost biblical language, Dunsany depicts an artificial religion that is the background for his

Boris Karloff as Sax Rohmer's insidious Oriental, and Myrna Loy as his daughter, from the 1932 film *The Mask of Fu Manchu*. *Courtesy of MGM.*

later tales of heroes and rogues in *The Sword of Welleran* (1908) and *The Book of Wonder* (1912). His inventiveness proved very influential in later decades, as a number of writers, among them H. P. Lovecraft and Clark Ashton Smith, adopted the idea of inventing their own supernatural entities instead of dealing with those that had traditionally existed. Dunsany's private life contrasted starkly to his literary work; he was a bluff, hearty man, a professional soldier who fought in two wars and devoted most of his later years to hunting. Almost the epitome of the old-style British aristocrat, he claimed that his writing was done rapidly without revision during his spare time. Later stories, like those in *Tales of Wonder* (1916), brought the fantastic into the modern world, with increasing doses of comedy. This tendency culminated in the appearance of his best-known character, who narrated five books beginning with *Travel Tales of Mr. Joseph Jorkens* in 1931. Jorkens, the alcoholic member of a staid English club, specializes in spinning outrageous tall tales in exchange for free drinks. Dunsany used his own extensive travels to provide backgrounds for these frequently hilarious yarns of the occult. Of all Dunsany's stories, the most widely known is the atypical and unnerving "Two Bottles of Relish," in which investigators gradually realize, without ever actually saying so, that they cannot find the corpse they are seeking because the murderer, normally a vegetarian, has eaten it. Dunsany lived to the age of seventy-nine, suggesting, as with Blackwood, Machen, and Rohmer, that one of the Golden Dawn's secrets may have had something to do with longevity.

Dunsany's glib pen was rivaled by that of G. K. Chesterton, a prolific master of paradox who devoted most of his time to essays but is now remembered almost exclusively for his fiction. In 1911 he published the first of five books of detective stories, *The Innocence of Father Brown.* Considered by connoisseurs to be nearly the equal of Poe's Dupin and Doyle's Sherlock Holmes, Chesterton's detective is a small, rotund priest who solves mysteries by intuition and induction. Chesterton specialized in the description of terrifying, apparently supernatural crimes which are finally revealed to have rational explanations. Among Father Brown's classic cases are "The Invisible Man," in which a murderer passes unseen before witnesses by the simple but ingenious expedient of posing as a mailman; and "The Hammer of God," in which a deathblow of apparently superhuman strength is delivered by a killer who drops the weapon from a church tower. Chesterton himself was the model for Dr. Gideon Fell, the obese, blustering, mustachioed detective created by John Dickson Carr, the modern master of the macabre mystery. Chesterton's ventures into fantasy were less frequent than his detective tales, but on one occasion at least he created a minor classic: *The Man Who Was Thursday* (1908). This novel, subtitled *A Nightmare*, is a brilliant example of Chesterton's ability to shift ground beneath the reader's feet, each apparent conception of the plot astoundingly giving way to another without any loss of coherence or excitement. The story concerns an idealist who infiltrates an anarchist organization only to discover that everyone else there is also a spy, except the jovial leader Sunday, who is revealed as a practical joker with all the powers of time and space at his command. Chesterton, like Arthur Machen, converted to Roman Catholicism, apparently inspired less by the doctrine of the church than by a love of mysticism and ritual which may have been echoed by the Order of the Golden Dawn.

The bookish, urbane Chesterton produced literature in keeping with his character; a type with wider appeal came from the pens of two more adventurous authors, Sir Henry Rider Haggard and Talbot Mundy. Haggard spent much of his early life in Africa as secretary to the governor of Natal. He later became interested in agriculture and at one

"Mung and the Beast of Mung," sinister supernatural figures from Lord Dunsany's *Gods of Pegana*, illustrated by S. H. Sime.

Another fearsome figure from Dunsany's synthetic mythology, enigmatically entitled "It." The artist, Sime, worked so closely with the author that his pictures often became the inspiration for the stories.

time was an ostrich farmer in Pretoria. Despite what might appear to be the strange nature of that venture, he was an expert in his field and earned his knighthood through research and writing on farming techniques. Yet greater fame and a larger income came from his romantic novels of Africa. His first success was *King Solomon's Mines* (1886), the enthralling tale of a jungle treasure hunt; but both Haggard and his audience seem to have had a special fondness for his novel of a lost African civilization, *She* (1887), which spawned several sequels over the next four decades. *She* is the story of explorers who discover the city ruled by Ayesha, an immortal queen called She-Who-Must-Be-Obeyed. Ayesha, domineering and beautiful, recognizes one of the men as the incarnation of her lover, Kallikrates, dead for thousands of years. She offers to share her throne with him and reveals the secret of her longevity, a magical flame whose touch preserves life. When her lover is reluctant to enter the fire, Ayesha impatiently precedes him, but a second exposure to the flame proves to be her undoing, and she dies, a hideously withered hag. The deathless love of a dynamic lady proved to be a compelling concept for countless Victorian readers, and numerous novels appeared subsequently that were variations on the same theme; some of the best were written by the twentieth-century American A. Merritt. Haggard himself made a comeback in 1905 with *Ayesha,* or *The Return of She*, which shows Leo Vincey, the hero of the first novel, meeting the reincarnation of Ayesha in the form of an Asian priestess. Neither survives this encounter, although readers are assured that they will meet in another world, if not another novel. Instead, Haggard went further into the past for *She and Allan* (1921), recounting previous adventures of Ayesha with the hero of other Haggard novels. *Wisdom's Daughter* (1923) must have disappointed all but the most devoted admirers of Ayesha, because it was merely an elaborate retelling of her origin, already described in the other books. Still, there is something intriguing about Haggard's idea, at least in the original version, and *She* became something of a minor classic, later inspiring several motion pictures.

A writer who handled the theme of occult adventure in exotic settings with considerably more skill was Talbot Mundy. Like Haggard, he was for a time in the British Empire's colonial service; although he spent most of his time in India, he also traveled in Tibet, Africa, and Australia. Particularly enthralled by the magic and mystery of these lands, Mundy made an extensive study of the subject and declared that while he found some fraud, he also found enough evidence to confirm his belief in the supernatural. He emigrated to the United States in 1911 and almost immediately embarked on a career as an author, most of his work appearing in popular magazines before book publication. Often Mundy's occult inclinations provided little more than the spice for an action saga, as in the case of his early success, *King of the Khyber Rifles* (1916). This is primarily concerned with efforts to frustrate an Indian rebellion during the First World War; but the hero, Athelstan King, is aided by the beautiful Yasmini, whose powers include the ability to see the past and the future in a crystal. She tries unsuccessfully to lure King into a liaison of passion and political power, foreshadowing Mundy's typical use of the supernatural not as a threat, but as a temptation to abandon the stern demands of duty. Another of Mundy's British Secret Service heroes is James Grim, known as Jimgrim, who Mundy claimed was based on an intelligence officer he had met in Palestine, "who very kindly introduced me to the lewder fellows of the baser sort with whom it was his business to deal." Jimgrim and his shady entourage were teamed with King to investigate *The Nine Unknown* (1922), a group possessing untold knowledge who secretly control the destiny of the human race. The adventurers never uncover the Nine, but they do manage to defeat nine impostors who are using the reputation of their betters for nefarious purposes, and they also get a glimpse of the

The immortal queen Ayesha bathing in her magical fire in a scene from Haggard's *She*, illustrated by Maurice Greiffenhagen.

Nine's process for converting gold into an elixir of life which flows into a sacred river. In *The Devil's Guard* (1926), Jimgrim and his men venture into the Tibetan Himalayas where they become involved with a band of wicked wizards, one of whom is a former friend who wishes to corrupt the dauntless band. In *Jimgrim* (1931), the hero again ventures into the mystic mountains to defeat a magician who has gained the knowledge of lost Atlantis. Jimgrim resorts to the use of a magical drug to battle this almost omnipotent opponent, yielding at last to the lure of the uncanny and sacrificing his life to save the world from destruction. Mundy's other novels of the unknown India include *Om* (1923) and *Full Moon* (1935); but he is perhaps best remembered for the series of sagas that began in 1934 with *Tros of Samothrace*, huge novels about a warrior in the days of Caesar and Cleopatra which are almost completely devoid of supernatural incidents.

The conviction that the writers from the Order of the Golden Dawn brought to their work, combined with their long careers, enabled them virtually to dominate the literature of the supernatural for decades. Of course, they were not alone. Even in the golden days of the Golden Dawn, around the turn of the century, other artists were banding together, albeit in less formalized organizations, whose purposes included the description of the uncanny and the evil. Decades before, the poet and painter Dante Gabriel Rossetti and his associates had formed the Pre-Raphaelite Brotherhood, dedicated to principles of mysticism, symbolism, and medievalism in the arts. A macabre air hovers around the work of these men, exemplified by incidents in Rossetti's life that might have been imagined by Poe. Rossetti was so passionately attached to his wife and model that when she died, he had the manuscripts of his best poems buried in her coffin. Seven years later she was exhumed so that he could recover his work and have it published. Afterward, he became convinced that she was haunting him, embodied in the form of birds. Rossetti's sister Christina produced a poem, "Goblin Market" (1862), that anticipated and may have influenced Arthur Machen's view of the little folk as sinister tempters. Perhaps the greatest of the group was William Morris, a Renaissance man who achieved remarkable results in various fields of creative endeavor. He wrote numerous fantasies in poetry and prose, but the horrific element is largely lacking.

The Pre-Raphaelites did not survive into the twentieth century, but their influence continued, in a somewhat decadent form, through a younger group centered around the flamboyant figure of Oscar Wilde. The chief outlet for their work was the controversial periodical *The Yellow Book*, which seemed dedicated to outraging Victorian sensibilities. Wilde claimed that art should not be bound by morality, and he and his colleagues delighted in exploring the possibilities of evil, at least in their works. Wilde produced a macabre masterpiece in *The Picture of Dorian Gray* (1891), which was considered a shocking book by conservative critics not because it was frightening, but because it contained suggestions of wickedness and sin. The novel concerns a young man whose portrait absorbs all the effects of his debauched existence while he remains young and fresh in appearance, for no other reason than that he wished aloud that it might be so. After years of this unnatural career, he attacks the portrait with a knife in a fit of fury, with his own transformation and destruction as the result. Although usually praised for its witty dialogue and titillating hints of depravity, *Dorian Gray* is also a powerful terror tale, recognizable, at least in summary, to a wider public than the author's celebrated comedies. The illustrator of some of Wilde's work was Aubrey Beardsley, the exquisite black-and-white delineator whose principal subject seemed to be corruption in all its forms. Beardsley also did some drawings for Poe's stories and designed several remarkably restrained title pages for books by Arthur Machen.

A drawing by Aubrey Beardsley for a tale of terror which is also generally regarded as the world's first detective story, Poe's "Murders in the Rue Morgue."

The Order of the Golden Dawn, influenced in part by these illustrious predecessors, exemplified the English tradition of superior stories of the supernatural. While it might be said to have represented the finest flowering of the genre within a narrow span of space and time, it was by no means the end of English expression in the field. A number of skillful writers continued to make important contributions, some of them achieving a modest sort of immortality with but a single short tale. Such was the case with W. W. Jacobs, who wrote "The Monkey's Paw" (1902) in which three wishes, used to revive a dead son, turn from a blessing into a curse. This later became a popular play. Oliver Onions and Robert Hichens are well remembered for "The Beckoning Fair One" (1911) and "How Love Came to Professor Guildea" (1905), two chilling accounts of lovelorn female spirits who drive their victims mad. W. F. Harvey contributed at least two minor masterpieces: "August Heat" (1910) describes two men whose premonitions of each other's deaths drive them irresistibly toward murder, and "The Beast with Five Fingers," published in 1925, is the definitive treatment of the crawling-hand theme. The distinguished poet Walter de la Mare is responsible for several atmospheric pieces like "Seaton's Aunt," "A Recluse," and "Out of the Deep" which are so subtly done that the presence of the uncanny must be intuited from insufficient evidence.

The eccentric style of M. P. Shiel has produced several chilling short stories; his most famous work is a novel about the last survivor of the human race, *The Purple Cloud* (1901). Such serious novelists as L. P. Hartley and John Metcalfe have contributed to a more lurid literature; Hartley's "The Travelling Grave" is among the most grotesque tales in English, and Metcalfe's collection *The Smoking Leg* contains a wide variety of uncanny effects. Working in the tradition of Le Fanu and M. R. James, H. R. Wakefield has produced several volumes of fine ghost stories, including *They Return at Evening, The Clock Strikes Twelve,* and the beautifully titled *Imagine a Man in a Box.*

Among those who have devoted a larger portion of their careers to the field, no two authors more vividly exemplify its potential range than John Collier and Dennis Wheatley. Collier is a superb stylist and imaginative innovator whose short stories are polished gems of black comedy, more disturbing than many comparatively impassioned works because of their cruelly aloof and ironic tone. No summary can do justice to his tales; but among his classic conceptions are "The Chaser," in which infallible love potions are sold cheaply by a shrewd sorcerer who realizes that he is merely establishing a clientele for his very expensive but undetectable poisons; "Evening Primrose," in which a young man seeks refuge from society by moving into a luxurious department store, only to find that he is but one of many such misfits whose lives are more dreadful than the ones they abandoned; and "Green Thoughts," in which a man-eating plant gives evidence against a killer when its blossoms duplicate the heads of his victims. Most of his best stories have been collected in the book *Fancies and Goodnights* (1951).

Dennis Wheatley, whose books have sold many millions of copies all over the world, can hardly compare with Collier as a master of the language, but his sprawling novels of action and intrigue are compelling reading. Among thrillers of nearly every type, his tales of black magic are the most impressive. Beginning with *The Devil Rides Out* (1935), Wheatley has written a series of novels in which the suave Duke de Richleau combats energetic bands of Satanists. While his novels are more exciting than atmospheric, Wheatley displays a thorough knowledge of his subject, and many of his books contain a note cautioning readers against dabbling in magic. *Strange Conflict* (1941) contains his most unusual plot, as de Richleau fights the Second World War on the astral plane to defeat those enemies who are using the supernatural for purposes of espionage. The same theme appears in *They Used Dark Forces* (1964); it represents more than a writer's pipe dream, for Hitler is known to have employed magicians, fraudulent or not, and British Intelligence, with which Wheatley was connected, used its own astrologers to anticipate Axis plans in order to counter them.

Frightening fiction has continued unabated to the present day, and it is in many respects the most satisfactory medium for the creation of macabre moods. Yet even as the Golden Dawn was instructing its initiates in the secrets that produced so many sinister stories, a new miracle was in the offing that cast a blinding shadow over the printed page. It was the motion picture, which, even without the magic of words, would bring more monsters to more millions than ever before.

NOVEL OF THE WHITE POWDER

By Arthur Machen

My name is Leicester; my father, Major-General Wyn Leicester, a distinguished officer of artillery, succumbed five years ago to a complicated liver complaint acquired in the deadly climate of India. A year later my only brother, Francis, came home after an exceptionally brilliant career at the University, and settled down with the resolution of a hermit to master what has been well called the great legend of the law. He was a man who seemed to live in utter indifference to everything that is called pleasure; and though he was handsomer than most men, and could talk as merrily and wittily as if he were a mere vagabond, he avoided society, and shut himself up in a large room at the top of the house to make himself a lawyer. Ten hours a day of hard reading was at first his allotted portion; from the first light in the east to the late afternoon he remained shut up with his books, taking a hasty half-hour's lunch with me as if he grudged the wasting of the moments, and going out for a short walk when it began to grow dusk. I thought that such relentless application must be injurious, and tried to cajole him from the crabbed textbooks, but his ardour seemed to grow rather than diminish, and his daily tale of hours increased. I spoke to him seriously, suggesting some occasional relaxation, if it were but an idle afternoon with a harmless novel; but he laughed, and said that he read about feudal tenures when he felt in need of amusement, and scoffed at the notions of theatres, or a month's fresh air. I confessed that he looked well, and seemed not to suffer from his labours, but I knew that such unnatural toil would take revenge at last, and I was not mistaken. A look of anxiety began to lurk about his eyes, and he seemed languid, and at last he avowed that he was no longer in perfect health; he was troubled, he said, with a sensation of dizziness, and awoke now and then of nights from fearful dreams, terrified and cold with icy sweats. "I am taking care of myself," he said, "so you must not trouble; I passed the whole of yesterday afternoon in idleness, leaning back in that comfortable chair you gave me, and scribbling nonsense on a sheet of paper. No, no; I will not overdo my work; I shall be well enough in a week or two depend upon it."

Yet in spite of his assurances I could see that he grew no better, but rather worse; he would enter the drawing-room with a face all miserably wrinkled and despondent, and endeavour to look gaily when my eyes fell on him, and I thought such symptoms of evil omen, and was frightened sometimes at the nervous irritation of his movements, and at glances which I could not decipher. Much against his will, I prevailed on him to have medical advice, and with an ill grace he called in our old doctor.

Dr. Haberden cheered me after examination of his patient.

"There is nothing really much amiss," he said to me. "No doubt he reads too hard and eats hastily, and then goes back again to his books in too great a hurry, and the natural sequence is some digestive trouble and a little mischief in the nervous system. But I think—I do indeed, Miss Leicester—that we shall be able to set this all right. I have written him a prescription which ought to do great things. So you have no cause for anxiety."

My brother insisted on having the prescription made up by a chemist in the neighbourhood. It was an odd, old-fashioned shop, devoid of the studied coquetry and calculated glitter that make so gay a show on the counters and shelves of the modern apothecary; but Francis liked the old chemist, and believed in the scrupulous purity of his drugs. The medicine was sent in due course, and I saw that my brother took it regularly after lunch and dinner. It was an innocent-looking white powder, of which a little was dissolved in a glass of cold water; I stirred it in, and it seemed to disappear, leaving the water clear and colorless. At first Francis seemed to benefit greatly; the weariness vanished from his face, and he became more cheerful than he had ever been since the time when he left school; he talked gaily of reforming himself, and avowed to me that he had wasted his time.

"I have given too many hours to law," he said, laughing; "I think you have saved me in the nick of time. Come, I shall be Lord Chancellor yet, but I must not forget life. You and I will have a holiday together before long; we will go to Paris and enjoy ourselves, and keep away from the Bibliothèque Nationale."

I confessed myself delighted with the prospect.

"When shall we go?" I said. "I can start the day after to-morrow if you like."

"Ah! that is perhaps a little too soon; after all, I do not know London yet, and I suppose a man ought to give the pleasures of his own country the first choice. But we will go off together in a week or two, so try and furbish up your French. I only know law French myself, and I am afraid that wouldn't do."

We were just finishing dinner, and he quaffed off his medicine with a parade of carousal as if it had been wine from some choicest bin.

"Has it any particular taste?" I said.

"No; I should not know I was not drinking water," and he got up from his chair and began to pace up and down the room as if he were undecided as to what he should do next.

"Shall we have coffee in the drawing-room?" I said; "or would you like to smoke?"

"No, I think I will take a turn; it seems a pleasant evening. Look at the afterglow; why, it is as if a great city were burning in flames, and down there between the dark houses it is raining blood fast. Yes, I will go out; I may be in soon, but I shall take my key; so good-night, dear, if I don't see you again."

The door slammed behind him, and I saw him walk lightly down the street, swinging his malacca cane, and I felt grateful to Dr. Haberden for such an improvement.

I believe my brother came home very late that night, but he was in a merry mood the next morning.

"I walked on without thinking where I was going," he said, "enjoying the freshness of the air, and livened by the crowds as I reached more frequented quarters. And then I met an old college friend, Orford, in the press of the pavement, and then—well, we enjoyed ourselves. I have felt what it is to be young and a man; I find I have blood in my veins, as other men have. I made an appointment with Orford for to-night; there will be a little party of us at the restaurant. Yes; I shall enjoy myself for a week or two, and hear the chimes at midnight, and then we will go for our little trip together."

Such was the transmutation of my brother's character that in a few days he became a lover of pleasure, a careless and merry idler of western pavements, a hunter out of snug restaurants, and a fine critic of fantastic dancing; he grew fat before my eyes, and said no more of Paris, for he had clearly found his paradise in London. I rejoiced, and yet wondered a little; for there was, I thought, something in his gaiety that indefinitely displeased me, though I could not have defined my feeling. But by degrees there came a change; he returned still in the cold hours of the morning, but I heard no more about his pleasures, and one morning as we sat at breakfast together I looked suddenly into his eyes and saw a stranger before me.

"Oh, Francis!" I cried. "Oh, Francis, Francis, what have you done?" and rending sobs cut the words short. I went weeping out of the room; for though I knew nothing, yet I knew all, and by some odd play of thought I remembered the evening when he first went abroad, and the picture of the sunset sky glowed before me; the clouds like a city in burning flames, and the rain of blood. Yet I did battle with such thoughts, resolving that perhaps, after all, no great harm had been done, and in the evening at dinner I resolved to press him to fix a day for our holiday in Paris. We had talked easily enough, and my brother had just taken his medicine, which he continued all the while. I was about to begin my topic when the words forming in my mind vanished, and I wondered for a second what icy and intolerable weight oppressed my heart and suffocated me as with the unutterable horror of the coffin-lid nailed down on the living.

We had dined without candles; the room had slowly grown from twilight to gloom, and the walls and corners were indistinct in the shadow. But from where I sat I looked out into the street; and as I thought of what I would say to Francis, the sky began to flush and shine, as it had done on a well-remembered evening, and in the gap between two dark masses that were houses an awful pageantry of flame appeared—lurid whorls of writhed cloud, and utter depths burning, grey masses like the fume blown from a smoking city, and an evil glory blazing far above shot with tongues of more ardent fire, and below as if there were a deep pool of blood. I looked down to where my brother sat facing me, and the words were shaped on my lips, when I saw his hand resting on the table. Between the thumb and forefinger of the closed hand there was a mark, a small patch about the size of a sixpence, and somewhat of the colour of a bad bruise. Yet, by some sense I cannot define, I knew that what I saw was no bruise at all; oh! if human flesh could burn with flame, and if flame could be black as pitch, such was that before me. Without thought or fashioning of words grey horror shaped within me at the sight, and in an inner cell it was known to be a brand. For the moment the stained sky became dark as midnight, and when the light returned to me I was alone in the silent room, and soon after I heard my brother go out.

Late as it was, I put on my hat and went to Dr. Haberden, and in his great consulting room, ill lighted by a candle which the doctor brought in with him, with stammering lips, and a voice that would break in spite of my resolve, I told him all, from the day on which my brother began to take the medicine down to the dreadful thing I had seen scarcely half an hour before.

When I had done, the doctor looked at me for a minute with an expression of great pity on his face.

"My dear Miss Leicester," he said, "you have evidently been anxious about your brother; you have been worrying over him, I am sure. Come, now, is it not so?"

"I have certainly been anxious," I said. "For the last week or two I have not felt at ease."

"Quite so; you know, of course, what a queer thing the brain is?"

"I understand what you mean; but I was not deceived. I saw what I have told you with my own eyes."

"Yes, yes of course. But your eyes had been staring at that very curious sunset we had tonight. That is the only explanation. You will see it in the proper light to-morrow, I am sure. But, remember, I am always ready to give any help that is in my power; do not scruple to come to me, or to send for me if you are in any distress."

I went away but little comforted, all confusion and terror and sorrow, not knowing where to turn. When my brother and I met the next day, I looked quickly at him, and noticed, with a sickening at heart, that the right hand, the hand on which I had clearly seen the patch as of a black fire, was wrapped up with a handkerchief.

"What is the matter with your hand, Francis?" I said in a steady voice.

"Nothing of consequence. I cut a finger last night, and it bled rather awkwardly. So I did it up roughly to the best of my ability."

"I will do it neatly for you, if you like."

"No, thank you, dear; this will answer very well. Suppose we have breakfast; I am quite hungry."

We sat down and I watched him. He scarcely ate or drank at all, but tossed his meat to the dog when he thought my eyes were turned away; there was a look in his eyes that I had never yet seen, and the thought flashed across my mind that it was a look that was scarcely human. I was firmly convinced that awful and incredible as was the thing I had seen the night before, yet it was no illusion, no glamour of bewildered sense, and in the course of the evening I went again to the doctor's house.

He shook his head with an air puzzled and incredulous, and seemed to reflect for a few minutes.

"And you say he still keeps up the medicine? But why? As I understand, all the symptoms he complained of have disappeared long ago; why should he go on taking the stuff when he is quite well? And by the by, where did he get it made up? At Sayce's? I never send any one there; the old man is getting careless. Suppose you come with me to the chemist's; I should like to have some talk with him."

We walked together to the shop; old Sayce knew Dr. Haberden, and was quite ready to give any information.

"You have been sending that in to Mr. Leicester for some weeks, I think, on my prescription," said the doctor, giving the old man a pencilled scrap of paper.

The chemist put on his great spectacles with trembling uncertainty, and held up the paper with a shaking hand.

"Oh, yes," he said, "I have very little of it left; it is rather an uncommon drug, and I have had it in stock some time. I must get in some more, if Mr. Leicester goes on with it."

"Kindly let me have a look at the stuff," said Haberden, and the chemist gave him a glass bottle. He took out the stopper and smelt the contents, and looked strangely at the old man.

"Where did you get this?" he said, "and what is it? For one thing, Mr. Sayce, it is not what I prescribed. Yes, yes, I see the label is right enough, but I tell you this is not the drug."

"I have had it a long time," said the old man in feeble terror; "I got it from Burbage's in the usual way. It is not prescribed often, and I have had it on the shelf for some years. You see there is very little left."

"You had better give it to me," said Haberden. "I am afraid something wrong has happened."

We went out of the shop in silence, the doctor carrying the bottle neatly wrapped in paper under his arm.

"Dr. Haberden," I said, when we had walked a little way—"Dr. Haberden."

"Yes," he said, looking at me gloomily enough.

"I should like you to tell me what my brother has been taking twice a day for the last month or so."

"Frankly, Miss Leicester, I don't know. We will speak of this when we get to my house."

We walked on quickly without another word till we reached Dr. Haberden's. He asked me to sit down, and began pacing up and down the room, his face clouded over, as I could see, with no common fears.

"Well," he said at length, "this is all very strange; it is only natural that you should feel alarmed, and I must confess that my mind is far from easy. We will put aside, if you please, what you told me last night and this morning, but the fact remains that for the last few weeks Mr. Leicester has been impregnating his system with a drug which is completely unknown to me. I tell you, it is not what I ordered; and what the stuff in the bottle really is remains to be seen."

He undid the wrapper, and cautiously tilted a few grains of the white powder on to a piece of paper, and peered curiously at it.

"Yes," he said, "it is like the sulphate of quinine, as you say; it is flaky. But smell it."

He held the bottle to me, and I bent over it. It was a strange, sickly smell, vaporous and overpowering, like some strong anaesthetic.

"I shall have it analysed," said Haberden; "I have a friend who has devoted his whole life to chemistry as a science. Then we shall have something to go upon. No, no; say no more about that other matter; I cannot listen to that; and take my advice and think no more about it yourself."

That evening my brother did not go out as usual after dinner.

"I have had my fling," he said with a queer laugh, "and I must go back to my old ways. A little law will be quite a relaxation after so sharp a dose of pleasure," and he grinned to himself, and soon after went up to his room. His hand was still all bandaged.

Dr. Haberden called a few days later.

"I have no special news to give you," he said. "Chambers is out of town, so I know no more about that stuff than you do. But I should like to see Mr. Leicester, if he is in."

"He is in his room," I said; "I will tell him you are here."

"No, no, I will go up to him; we will have a little quiet talk together. I dare say that we have made a good deal of fuss about a very little; for, after all, whatever the powder may be, it seems to have done him good."

The doctor went upstairs, and standing in the hall I heard his knock, and the opening and shutting of the door; and then I waited in the silent house for an hour, and the stillness grew more and more intense as the hands of the clock crept round. Then there sounded from above the noise of a door shut sharply, and the doctor was coming down the stairs. His footsteps crossed the hall, and there was a pause at the door; I drew a long, sick breath with difficulty, and saw my face white in a little mirror, and he came in and stood at the door. There was an unutterable horror shining in his eyes; he steadied himself by holding the back of a chair with one hand, his lower lip trembled like a horse's, and he gulped and stammered unintelligible sounds before he spoke.

"I have seen that man," he began in a dry whisper. "I have been sitting in his presence for the last hour. My God! And I am alive and in my senses! I, who have dealt with death all my life, and have dabbled with the melting ruins of the earthly tabernacle. But not this, oh! not this," and he covered his face with his hands as if to shut out the sight of something before him.

"Do not send for me again, Miss Leicester," he said with more composure. "I can do nothing in this house. Good-bye."

As I watched him totter down the steps, and along the pavement towards his house, it seemed to me that he had aged by ten years since the morning.

My brother remained in his room. He called out to me in a voice I hardly recognized that he was very busy, and would like his meals brought to his door and left there, and I gave the order to the servants. From that day it seemed as if the arbitrary conception we call time had been annihilated for me; I lived in an ever-present sense of horror, going through the routine of the house mechanically, and only speaking a few necessary words to the servants. Now and then I went out and paced the streets for an hour or two and came home again; but whether I were without or within, my spirit delayed before the closed door of the upper room, and, shuddering, waited for it to open. I have said that I scarcely reckoned time; but I suppose it must have been a fortnight after Dr. Haberden's visit that I came home from my stroll a little refreshed and lightened. The air was sweet and pleasant, and the hazy form of green leaves, floating cloud-like in the square, and the smell of blossoms, had charmed my senses, and I felt happier and walked more briskly. As I delayed a moment at the verge of the pavement, waiting for a van to pass by before crossing over to the house, I happened to look up at the windows, and instantly there was the rush and swirl of deep cold waters in my ears, my heart leapt up and fell down, down as into a deep hollow, and I was amazed with a dread and terror without form or shape. I stretched out a hand blindly through the folds of thick darkness, from the black and shadowy valley, and held myself from falling, while the stones beneath my feet rocked and swayed and tilted, and the sense of solid things seemed to sink away from under me. I had glanced up at the window of my brother's study, and at that moment the blind was drawn aside, and something that had life stared out into the world. Nay, I cannot say I saw a face or any human likeness; a living thing, two eyes of burning flame glared at me, and they were in the midst of something as formless as my fear, the symbol and presence of all evil and all hideous corruption. I stood shuddering and quaking as with the grip of ague, sick with unspeakable agonies of fear and loathing, and for five minutes I could not summon force or motion to my limbs. When I was within the door, I ran up the stairs to my brother's room and knocked.

"Francis, Francis," I cried, "for Heaven's sake, answer me. What is the horrible thing in your room? Cast it out, Francis; cast it from you."

I heard a noise as of feet shuffling slowly and awkwardly, and a choking, gurgling sound, as if some one was struggling to find utterance, and then the noise of a voice, broken and stifled, and words that I could scarcely understand.

"There is nothing here," the voice said. "Pray do not disturb me. I am not very well to-day."

I turned away, horrified, and yet helpless. I could do nothing, and I wondered why Francis had lied to me, for I had seen the appearance beyond the glass too plainly to be deceived, though it was but the sight of a moment. And I sat still, conscious that there had been something else, something I had seen in the first flash of terror, before those burning eyes had looked at me. Suddenly I remembered; as I lifted my face the blind was being drawn back, and I had had an instant's glance of the thing that was moving it, and in my recollection I knew that a hideous image was engraved forever on my brain. It was not a hand; there were no fingers that held the blind, but a black stump pushed it aside, the mouldering outline and the clumsy movement as of a beast's paw had glowed into my senses before the darkling waves of terror had overwhelmed me as I went down quick into the pit. My mind was aghast at the thought of this, and of the awful presence that dwelt with my brother in his room; I went to his door and cried to him again, but no answer came. That night one of the servants came up to me and told me in a whisper that for three days food had been regularly placed at the door and left untouched; the maid had knocked but had received no answer; she had heard the noise of shuffling feet that I had noticed. Day after day went by, and still my brother's meals were brought to his door and left untouched; and though I knocked and called again and again, I could get no answer. The servants began to talk to me; it appeared they were as alarmed as I; the cook said that when my brother first shut himself up in his room she used to hear him come out at night and go about the house; and once, she said, the hall door had opened and closed again, but for several nights she had heard no sound. The climax came at last; it was in the dusk of the evening, and I was sitting in the darkening dreary room when a terrible shriek jarred and rang harshly out of the silence, and I heard a frightened scurry of feet dashing down the stairs. I waited, and the servant-maid staggered into the room and faced me, white and trembling.

"Oh, Miss Helen!" she whispered; "oh! for the Lord's sake, Miss Helen, what has happened? Look at my hand, miss; look at that hand!"

I drew her to the window, and saw there was a black wet stain upon her hand.

"I do not understand you," I said. "Will you explain to me?"

"I was doing your room just now," she began. "I was turning down the bed-clothes, and all of a sudden there was something fell upon my hand, wet, and I looked up, and the ceiling was black and dripping on me."

I looked hard at her and bit my lip.

"Come with me," I said. "Bring your candle with you."

The room I slept in was beneath my brother's, and as I went in I felt I was trembling. I looked up at the ceiling, and saw a patch, all black and wet, and a dew of black drops upon it, and a pool of horrible liquor soaking into the white bed-clothes.

I ran upstairs and knocked loudly.

"Oh, Francis, Francis, my dear brother," I cried, "what has happened to you?"

And I listened. There was a sound of choking, and a noise like water bubbling and regurgitating, but nothing else, and I called louder, but no answer came.

In spite of what Dr. Haberden had said, I went to him; with tears streaming down my cheeks I told him all that had happened, and he listened to me with a face set hard and grim.

"For your father's sake," he said at last, "I will go with you, though I can do nothing."

We went out together; the streets were dark and silent, and heavy with heat and a drought of many weeks. I saw the doctor's face white under the gas-lamps, and when we reached the house his hand was shaking.

We did not hesitate, but went upstairs directly. I held the lamp, and he called out in a loud, determined voice—

"Mr. Leicester, do you hear me? I insist on seeing you. Answer me at once."

There was no answer, but we both heard that choking noise I have mentioned.

"Mr. Leicester, I am waiting for you. Open the door this instant, or I shall break it down." And he called a third time in a voice that rang and echoed from the walls—

"Mr. Leicester! For the last time I order you to open the door."

"Ah!" he said, after a pause of heavy silence, "we are wasting time here. Will you be so kind as to get me a poker, or something of the kind?"

I ran into a little room at the back where odd articles were kept, and found a heavy adze-like tool that I thought might serve the doctor's purpose.

"Very good," he said, "that will do, I dare say. I give you notice, Mr. Leicester," he cried loudly at the keyhole, "that I am now about to break into your room."

Then I heard the wrench of the adze, and the woodwork split and cracked under it; with a loud crash the door suddenly burst open, and for a moment we started back aghast at a fearful screaming cry, no human voice, but as the roar of a monster, that burst forth inarticulate and struck at us out of the darkness.

"Hold the lamp," said the doctor, and we went in and glanced quickly round the room.

"There it is," said Dr. Haberden, drawing a quick breath; "look, in that corner."

I looked, and a pang of horror seized my heart as with a white-hot iron. There upon the floor was a dark and putrid mass, seething with corruption and hideous rottenness, neither liquid nor solid, but melting and changing before our eyes, and bubbling with unctuous oily bubbles like boiling pitch. And out of the midst of it shone two burning points like eyes, and I saw a writhing and stirring as of limbs, and something moved and lifted up what might have been an arm. The doctor took a step forward, raised the iron bar and struck at the burning points; he drove in the weapon, and struck again and again in the fury of loathing.

A week or two later, when I had recovered to some extent from the terrible shock, Dr. Haberden came to see me.

"I have sold my practice," he began, "and to-morrow I am sailing on a long voyage. I do not know whether I shall ever return to England; in all probability I shall buy a little land in California, and settle there for the remainder of my life. I have brought you this packet, which you may open and read when you feel able to do so. It contains the report of Dr. Chambers on what I submitted to him. Good-bye, Miss Leicester, good-bye."

When he was gone I opened the envelope; I could not wait, and proceeded to read the papers within. Here is the manuscript, and if you will allow me, I will read you the astounding story it contains.

"My dear Haberden," the letter began, "I have delayed inexcusably in answering your questions as to the white substance you sent me. To tell you the truth, I have hesitated for some time as to what course I should adopt, for there is a bigotry and orthodox standard in physical science as in theology, and I knew that if I told you the truth I should offend rooted prejudices which I once held dear myself. However, I have determined to be plain with you, and first I must enter into a short personal explanation.

"You have known me, Haberden, for many years as a scientific man; you and I have often talked of our profession together, and discussed the hopeless gulf that opens before the feet of those who think to attain to truth by any means whatsoever except the beaten way of experiment and observation in the sphere of material things. I remember the scorn with which you have spoken to me of men of science who have dabbled a little in the unseen, and have timidly hinted that perhaps the senses are not, after all, the eternal, impenetrable bounds of all knowledge, the everlasting walls beyond which no human being has ever passed. We have laughed together heartily, and I think justly, at the 'occult' follies of the day, disguised under various names—the mesmerisms, spiritualisms, materializations, theosophies, all the rabble rout of imposture, with their machinery of poor tricks and feeble conjuring, the true back-parlour of shabby London streets. Yet, in spite of what I have said, I must confess to you that I am no materialist, taking the word of course in its usual signification. It is now many years since I have convinced myself—convinced myself, a sceptic, remember—that the old ironbound theory is utterly and entirely false. Perhaps this confession will not wound you so sharply as it would have done twenty years ago; for I think you cannot have failed to notice that for some time hypotheses have been advanced by men of pure science which are nothing less than transcendental, and I suspect that most modern chemists and biologists of repute would not hesitate to subscribe the *dictum* of the old Schoolman, *Omnia exeunt in mysterium*, which means, I take it, that every branch of human knowledge if traced up to its source and final principles vanishes into mystery. I need not trouble you now with a detailed account of the painful steps which led me to my conclusions; a few simple experiments suggested a doubt as to my then standpoint, and a train of thought that rose from circumstances comparatively trifling brought me far; my old conception of the universe has been swept away, and I stand in a world that seems as strange and awful to me as the endless waves of the ocean seen for the first time, shining, from a peak in Darien. Now I know that the walls of sense that seemed so impenetrable, that seemed to loom up above the heavens and to be founded below the depths, and to shut us in for evermore, are no such everlasting impassable barriers as we fancied, but thinnest and most airy veils that melt away before the seeker, and dissolve as the early mist of the morning about the brooks. I know that you never adopted the extreme materialistic position; you did not go about trying to prove a universal negative, for your logical sense withheld you from that crowning absurdity; but I am sure that you will find all that I am saying strange and repellent to your habits of thought. Yet, Haberden, what I tell you is the truth, nay, to adopt our common language, the sole and scientific truth, verified by experience; and the universe is verily more splendid and more awful than we used to dream. The whole universe, my friend, is a tremendous sacrament; a mystic, ineffable force and energy, veiled by an outward form of matter; and man, and the sun and the other stars, and the flower of the grass, and the crystal in the test-tube, are each and every one as spiritual, as material, and subject to an inner working.

"You will perhaps wonder, Haberden, whence all this tends; but I think a little thought will make it clear. You will understand that from such a standpoint the whole view of things is changed, and what we thought incredible and absurd may be possible enough. In short, we must look at legend and belief with other eyes, and be prepared to accept tales that had become mere fables. Indeed this is no such great demand. After all, modern science will concede as much, in a hypocritical manner; you must not, it is true, believe in witchcraft, but you may credit hypnotism; ghosts are out of date, but there is a good deal to be said for the theory of telepathy. Give superstition a Greek name, and believe in it, should almost be a proverb.

"So much for my personal explanation. You sent me, Haberden, a phial, stoppered and sealed, containing a small quantity of flaky white powder, obtained from a chemist who has been dispensing it to one of your patients. I am not surprised to hear that this powder refused to yield any results to your analysis. It is a substance which was known to a few many hundred years ago, but which I never expected to have submitted to me from the shop of a modern apothecary. There seems no reason to doubt the truth of the man's tale; he no doubt got, as he says, the rather uncommon salt you prescribed from the wholesale chemist's; and it has probably remained on his shelf for twenty years, or perhaps longer. Here what we call chance and coincidence begin to work; during all these years the salt in the bottle was exposed to certain recurring variations of temperature, variations probably ranging from 40° to 80°. And, as it happens, such changes, recurring year after year at irregular intervals, and with varying degrees of intensity and duration, have constituted a process, and a process, so complicated and so delicate, that I question whether modern scientific apparatus directed with the utmost precision could produce the same result. The white powder you sent me is something very different from the drug you prescribed; it is the powder from which the wine of the Sabbath, the *Vinum Sabbati*, was prepared. No doubt you have read of the Witches' Sabbath, and have laughed at the tales which terrified our ancestors; the black cats, and the broomsticks, and dooms pronounced against some old woman's cow. Since I have known the truth I have often reflected that it is on the whole a happy thing that such burlesque as this is believed, for it serves to conceal much that it is better should not be known generally. However, if you care to read the appendix to Payne Knight's monograph, you will find that the true Sabbath was something very different, though the writer has very nicely refrained from printing all he knew. The secrets of the true Sabbath were the secrets of remote times surviving into the Middle Ages, secrets of an evil science which existed long before Aryan man entered Europe. Men and women, seduced from their homes on specious pretences, were met by beings well qualified to assume, as they did assume, the part of devils, and taken by their guides to some desolate and lonely place, known to the initiate by long tradition, and unknown to all else. Perhaps it was a cave in some bare and wind-swept hill, perhaps some inmost recess of a great forest, and there the Sabbath was held. There, in the blackest hour of night, the *Vinum Sabbati* was prepared, and this evil graal was poured forth and offered to the neophytes, and they partook of an infernal sacrament; *sumentes calicem principis inferorum*, as an old author well expresses it. And suddenly, each one that had drunk found himself attended by a companion, a share of glamour and unearthly allurement, beckoning him apart, to share in joys more exquisite, more piercing than the thrill of any dream, to the consummation of the marriage of the Sabbath. It is hard to write of such things as these, and chiefly because that shape that allured with loveliness was no hallucination, but, awful as it is to express, the man himself. By the power of that Sabbath wine, a few grains of white powder thrown into a glass of water, the house of life was riven asunder and the human trinity dissolved, and the worm which never dies, that which lies sleeping within us all, was made tangible and an external thing, and clothed with a garment of flesh. And then, in the hour of midnight, the primal fall was repeated and re-presented, and the awful thing veiled in the mythos of the Tree in the Garden was done anew. Such was the *nuptiæ Sabbati.*

"I prefer to say no more; you, Haberden, know as well as I do that the most trivial laws of life are not to be broken with impunity; and for so terrible an act as this, in which the very inmost place of the temple was broken open and defiled, a terrible vengeance followed. What began with corruption ended also with corruption."

Underneath is the following in Dr. Haberden's writing:—

"The whole of the above is unfortunately strictly and entirely true. Your brother confessed all to me on that morning when I saw him in his room. My attention was first attracted to the bandaged hand, and I forced him to show it to me. What I saw made me, a medical man of many years' standing, grow sick with loathing, and the story I was forced to listen to was infinitely more frightful than I could have believed possible. It has tempted me to doubt the Eternal Goodness which can permit nature to offer such hideous possibilities; and if you had not with your own eyes seen the end, I should have said to you—disbelieve it all. I have not, I think, many more weeks to live, but you are young, and may forget all this.

"JOSEPH HABERDEN, M.D."

In the course of two or three months I heard that Dr. Haberden had died at sea shortly after the ship left England.

·6·

THE SILVER KEY: MASS MARKETS

The birth of the twentieth century gave fantasies of fear a new look. Within the space of a generation, science showered mankind with such surprising devices as electric lights, telegraphs, telephones, horseless carriages, airplanes, and cornflakes. Among the results were opportunities for expression in media innovations like motion pictures, phonograph records, and even comic strips. Old monsters are never far behind new mediums, and the brain behind half of this wild pioneering, Thomas Alva Edison, was also responsible for the first *Frankenstein* film, now lost, in 1910.

Actually, movies with macabre motives had begun to appear years earlier. The French director Georges Méliès had begun making bizarre motion pictures in the last decade of the nineteenth century. He was the first great innovator in the field of camera trickery, and he delighted especially in stopping the film to change somebody or something into something else. He used double exposures to create gigantic figures and pioneered the use of specially constructed sets for his fantastic featurettes. Although he frequently used supernatural or science fiction subjects, the tone of his work was essentially light and playful. He made little attempt to induce a mood of menace but rather communicated the fabulous fun of playing with a new toy. His *Trip to the Moon* is still especially enjoyable, but his principal contribution was proving that motion pictures were capable of visualizing the incredible in a way that had never been possible before.

Many silent films have been lost to posterity, some so completely that no one is aware that they ever existed. For the first few years they tended to steer clear of anything too shocking—audiences were horrified to see guns fired out of the screen at them, or trains rushing toward the camera. Nothing much stronger seems to have been required or even tolerated. Gradually a few films began to touch on the grim or the grotesque, but it is difficult to determine which, if any, should be regarded as the first "horror movie." The title might as well go to one of countless versions of *Dr. Jekyll and Mr. Hyde.* The first American production, made in 1908, was a photographic record of a stage play. Two years later the Edison *Frankenstein* appeared, with Charles Ogle as a monster who looks a bit foolish in the few remaining stills. The story was shortened almost beyond recognition and provided with a happy ending in which the monster is improbably destroyed by the love between Frankenstein and his bride. Whoever wrote the script had unwittingly set the pattern for almost every future film in the genre. In contravention of the literary

Conscience (1914), an appropriately titled Poe adaptation loosely based on "The Tell-Tale Heart" in which the hero escapes punishment for murder by the standard route: he wakes up.

The majority of the masterpieces in the silent cinema of the sinister were made in Germany, where the public seemed more willing to play the game. German films produced the first actors to specialize in repulsive roles, among them Paul Wegener and Conrad Veidt. In 1913 Wegener starred in *The Student of Prague*, who is haunted by his double after selling his soul to the devil. He codirected and played the title role in *The Golem* (1915), an adaptation of a Jewish legend, hundreds of years old. The Golem is a statue brought to life by a rabbi to protect his people from religious persecution. The film portrays it as being discovered and revived in modern times. Predictably, the monster

Paul Wegener directed and starred in *The Golem* (1920), the best of his three films about the legendary living statue.

Conrad Veidt and Lil Dagover in the influential German film *The Cabinet of Dr. Caligari.* The expressionistic sets were designed by Hermann Warm, Walter Reimann, and Walter Röhrig.

runs amok, but is destroyed when the heroine removes the magical symbol that has animated its clay body. A sequel two years later, *The Golem and the Dancing Girl*, was a comedy in which Wegener played himself, impersonating his famous character for a practical joke. He returned to the role in a 1920 film, again called *The Golem*, which is probably the best of the lot, based as it was on the original story with its medieval setting and strong motivation. The fact that the character lasted through three movies anticipated the great successes of the talking picture's monsters, who were hardly worth their salt unless they could spawn a sequel or two.

Conrad Veidt surpassed Wegener by landing the role of the sinister somnambulist Cesare in *The Cabinet of Dr. Caligari* (1919), still usually cited in lists of the most important films ever made. Directed by Robert Wiene, from a screenplay by Carl Mayer and Hans Janowitz, this expressionist film went a long way toward proving that movies in general, and horror movies in particular, could be substantial works of art. The plot concerns a wandering showman, Dr. Caligari (Werner Krauss), who keeps the black-clad Cesare in a coffin, waking him periodically so that he may tell fortunes for crowds. At night he sends the creature out to commit murders, apparently only so that the dire predictions of the day will come true. Cesare kidnaps the heroine, but he collapses after a grueling chase, and Caligari is revealed to be the proprietor of a local madhouse. The story is less important than its treatment; the film made startling use of grotesque sets that were like nothing ever seen on the screen before. There was no attempt at realism. Rather, the twisted, contorted backgrounds through which the actors moved were extensions of the mood of madness and murder. Ingeniously arranged false perspectives made the somnambulist's flight a dizzy demonstration of geometry gone wild. Veidt looks very much like a walking corpse, and the scene in which he slowly comes to life, his nostrils twitching as if they had never smelled fresh air before, is a small gem of pantomime. His later work in macabre movies included a dual role in the Jekyll-Hyde imitation *The Head of Janus* (1920) and the lead in Wiene's *Hands of Orlac* (1925), about a man who has his amputated hands replaced by surgery and becomes convinced that he has lost control over them when he discovers that they are those of a murderer. As if to emphasize the similarity in their careers, Veidt next took Paul Wegener's role in a 1926 remake of *The Student of Prague.*

Germans also produced the first Dracula film, *Nosferatu* (1922). Like *The Head of Janus*, this movie changed some names and details of the literary work from which it was lifted; but the deception was unsuccessful. Bram Stoker's widow sued the production company, which promptly went bankrupt, and the movie was withdrawn from circulation, although a few copies escaped the court order that they be destroyed. F. W. Murnau directed the adaptations of both Stevenson's and Stoker's classics. *Nosferatu* is a grotesque film, about half terrifying and half just terrible. The vampire Orlock, played under a pseudonym by one Max Schreck (his last name means "terror"), has such an outrageous appearance that he could never pass for normal as Dracula did. A bald, snaggle-toothed fiend with pointed ears and huge claws, he is accompanied by a retinue of rats. There is nothing suave about him, but some of his appearances are startling. When he crosses the sea in search of new victims, his coffin is opened by a curious sailor, and Schreck pops up like a jack-in-the-box. Murnau has some feeling for the workaday world of the vampire, as in one quaint shot of Orlock entering a new town, scurrying through the twilit streets, bent double by the weight of the coffin he carries on his back. The adapter, Henrik Galeen, seems to have invented the idea that a vampire could be destroyed by sunlight. This concept was to be repeated in many later films, although Stoker's Dracula could walk abroad at noon without ill effect.

Max Schreck was the first film Dracula, in F. W. Murnau's *Nosferatu* (1922), a German adaptation that gave the vampire an incredibly bizarre look.

Fritz Lang, whose career spanned several decades and two continents, directed several important fantasy films during the great era of Germany's silent screen. None of them seems intended primarily to frighten the audience, but many of them have their awe-inspiring moments. *Dr. Mabuse* (1922) depicts a master criminal who plots to dominate the world through hypnotism, and *Siegfried* (1924) features a fight with a dragon. Lang's most elaborately produced and vividly realized film is *Metropolis* (1926), a science fiction spectacle written, like most of his early movies, by his wife Thea von Harbou. The story is based in a city of the future where tremendous advances have been made possible by the toil of workers underground. They revolt, and the leader of the city floods their subterranean homes; but he finally relents and promises a new order. Some sensational scenery and the creation of a treacherous female robot are among the highlights of *Metropolis*, a movie that pleases the eye more than the intellect.

Many of these German films had limited distribution abroad because of the problems of wartime, but their innovations went a long way toward defining the ingredients and attitudes that were to become characteristic of the sinister cinema. And movies, during the silent era, had no real language barrier. Still, the great tradition of the horror film is largely an American phenomenon. The first prestige production there was yet another version of *Dr. Jekyll and Mr. Hyde* (1920), this one starring the distinguished actor John Barrymore. He played Hyde as a dirty old man with an elongated head. The screenplay by Clara Berenger elaborated on Stevenson's story by adding a pair of young women for him to threaten; no subsequent version was considered complete without them. Barrymore's most impressive scenes relied on his stage ability, which permitted him to contort his features sufficiently to portray the transformation without makeup or special

In many ways the first important American horror film was John Barrymore's *Dr. Jekyll and Mr. Hyde.* The accomplished actor is shown here in the more entertaining of the two roles.

photography. The film is not as good as its star, but it certainly surpasses the version released in the same year that featured Sheldon Lewis and seems to have been designed to confuse audiences into believing it was the Barrymore picture.

America finally produced the first full-fledged horror star in Lon Chaney, the "Man of a Thousand Faces," who more or less inaugurated the tradition of elaborate screen makeup, even becoming an authority on the subject for an edition of *The Encyclopaedia Britannica.* Chaney's parents were both deaf-mutes, and his gift for pantomime made him one of the most expressive actors of the silent screen. Although his macabre roles brought him his greatest fame, they constitute a distinct minority of his motion picture performances, which were largely character parts. He played villains of every stripe, using his skills as a makeup artist in several Oriental characterizations and contorting his limbs to portray an unlikely succession of amputees. His first fantastic role came in *A Blind Bargain* (1922), when he portrayed a low-browed ape-man, the victim of experiments in gland transplantations performed by a crackpot scientist, who was also played by Chaney. The film proved popular enough to lead to bigger and better things.

His next two films were his greatest, *The Hunchback of Notre Dame* (1923) and *The Phantom of the Opera* (1925), both made at Universal, a company that was well on its way to becoming the world's most productive monster factory. Both films were based on French novels, Victor Hugo's *Notre Dame de Paris* and Gaston Leroux's *Phantom of the Opera*; both were set in a Paris reconstructed on Hollywood back lots. The first featured Chaney as the deformed foundling who grows up to be the bell ringer of the greatest church in Paris, which he transforms into a fort to protect a Gypsy girl condemned to death. The story had been filmed before, but never on such a grand scale. Hugo's plot appears almost as twisted as Quasimodo's spine: Chaney saves Esmeralda at the cost of his own life, while in the book his efforts were frustrated and he survived the doomed heroine. The film thus avoids the tragedy and irony of Hugo's original conception, substituting for it a mood of pathos, the burden of which falls on Quasimodo's ungainly shoulders. Chaney rose to the occasion, infusing his role with a sense of suffering that was probably not all acting, since the disguise he designed for himself was extremely uncomfortable. He not only covered his face with putty, applied a fake blind eye, false teeth, and a fright wig, but he also constructed a rubber torso that made the hunchback convincing even when he was stripped to the waist for a whipping. Chaney's tortured air was to become stock-in-trade for later monsters, few of whom would achieve stardom unless they could evoke a little sympathy.

Hugo's novel was not really a horror story; but the film almost succeeded in turning it into one, and it is regarded today as something along those lines. Working with a plot that was frankly intended to raise goose bumps, Chaney enjoyed his greatest triumph as Erik, the mysterious figure who haunts the Paris Opera. A patron of the arts who extends his critic's prerogative to include the killing of unworthy performers and unappreciative audiences, the masked Phantom takes a young singer as his protégée and leads her to his home in the grottoes beneath the opera house. He releases her when she promises not to reveal his secret but kidnaps her after she betrays him. She is finally rescued by the bumbling hero and an intelligent detective; the Phantom is killed by an inexplicably incensed mob, who may perhaps have had relatives among the wealthy music lovers obliterated when Erik released a huge chandelier hanging over the heads of the opera audience.

The Phantom of the Opera suffers hardly at all from its weak motivation and shaky plotting; although the story is preposterous even by horror movie standards, its

Lon Chaney distorted his body as well as his face to portray Quasimodo in *The Hunchback of Notre Dame* (1923), a free adaptation of Hugo's novel directed by Wallace Worsley. *Courtesy of Universal Pictures.*

Rupert Julian's *Phantom of the Opera*, with Lon Chaney and Mary Philbin, was the film that launched Carl Laemmle's Universal studio as the primary producer of American horror movies, a position it retained for decades. *Courtesy of Universal Pictures.*

simple-mindedness conveys an irresistible charm. Later versions lost the magic mood when, for instance, they attempted to explain the Phantom's origin as a disfigured musician or a swindled composer. Chaney's Erik has no such pedestrian background; he simply is the Phantom and always has been. It is his career, and he is a professional. When the heroine creeps up behind him to remove his mask and he leaps up from his organ to reveal his hideous visage, Erik's life seems to have reached a peak. Certainly Chaney's had; the scene is remembered with mingled awe and affection as one of the great thrills in the annals of the cinema. The makeup is Chaney's masterpiece. A domed skull, hollow eyes, high cheekbones, distended nostrils, and jagged teeth make it the face of death itself. The beauty of later monsters was only skin deep, but Chaney probed beneath the surface of his own body, stretching his mouth with fish hooks, shoving lumps of celluloid high up into his cheeks and, according to some reports, using chemicals to distort the appearance of his eyes. The disguise was still flexible enough to permit some emoting, and the actor gave his all, shifting from the despair of the unloved to the bravado of the unremorseful. He has a wonderful last moment when he turns on his pursuers and holds them at bay with a threatening gesture, as if he were about to throw a bomb. As the mob cowers, he contemptuously opens his hand to reveal that it is empty.

By the time this movie was released, the genre had become sufficiently well established to be parodied; so Chaney appeared in *The Monster*, a haunted-house comedy in which he played a demented doctor defeated by a correspondence-school detective. His last great horror role came two years later in *London after Midnight* (1927), directed by Tod Browning, who was to be responsible for some of the best frightening features of the sound era. Chaney played a vampire who turns out to be a detective who scares a murderer into confessing. He was planning to play Dracula in Browning's film version when he died, in 1930.

Meanwhile, the popular success of recorded music preserved more than a few weird songs for posterity. Regional markets opened up as local performers were sought out, and shellac 78s recorded a number of morbid traditions in native ballads and blues, songs considerably less sentimental than their Tin Pan Alley counterparts. Nearby murders and disasters were frequently described in the lyrics of new songs, while many Elizabethan songs on supernatural subjects survived a transatlantic passage to emerge in new versions among Appalachian folk singers.

Certainly more influential than the new music market, at least as far as fearsome fantasies were concerned, was the extraordinary expansion of the press during the same period. Nobody guessed that electric devices were about to replace the printed word as the principal means for communicating ideas. Formal literary decorum was mislaid as mass public education led inevitably to mass-oriented periodicals. The most vivid and apparently reprehensible of these were known as "pulp" magazines, after the inexpensive, eminently biodegradable material on which they were printed. The pulps became the primary depository for lurid fantasies in the United States, unleashing dozens of apparently immortal characters like Tarzan, the Shadow, Buck Rogers, Doc Savage, and the Spider, thus initiating a pantheon of heroes into the mythology of a new but tenacious "lowbrow" culture.

In fact, the creation of a blatantly fraudulent mythology became the main concern of many of the writers associated with the most consistently literate of the pulps, *Weird Tales*, which began publication in 1923. Published by Jacob Clark Henneberger and edited—for its first few issues—by Edwin Baird, who was soon replaced by Farnsworth Wright, its editor for its formative years, *Weird Tales* was a labor of love that managed to stay afloat for more than thirty years even though it never showed a profit. Its most important author was Howard Phillips Lovecraft, who since his death in 1937 has become one of the most popular and imitated men in his field.

A sickly child prodigy who was writing a professional astronomy column while still a teenager, Lovecraft's mature work managed to combine ancient demonology with the recent Einsteinian theories of space, time, and relativity, which he apparently found fully intelligible. The result was what is now called the "Cthulhu Mythos," named for the most famous of the hideous entities which he portrays both as the monsters of yore and the masters of a fourth dimension which science has yet to reveal. Many of his stories have autobiographical overtones and are set in the history-haunted regions of New England that he knew so well. Both qualities appear in "The Silver Key," a nostalgic piece in which a family relic enables the protagonist to transcend chronology by returning to his own childhood, creating a closed cycle of growth and return without the intervening traumas of birth and death.

Lovecraft was a favorite not only with the readers of *Weird Tales*, but also with a sizable group of writers whom he encouraged to imitate the style and subjects that were his own. The most prominent members of this coterie were Robert E. Howard, Clark Ashton Smith, Robert Bloch, Frank Belknap Long, August Derleth, and Donald Wandrei. Wandrei and particularly Derleth did the most to establish their mentor's reputation through Arkham House, a publishing company started in 1939 for the express purpose of preserving Lovecraft's work in permanent form. Their first volume, *The Outsider and Others*, a fat book containing almost all of Lovecraft's important work, would be the ideal introduction to his strange world if not for the fact that this rare item now commands prices ranging upward from a hundred dollars.

There are several qualities that set Lovecraft apart from the average pulp magazine writer. His style is remarkably stately for the periodicals in which his stories appeared, his plots suggest a new source of strange atmosphere, and his eccentric but endearing personality has become almost legendary. In fact, one commentator called Lovecraft himself "his own most fantastic creation," which is quite an achievement for an author whose most famous character is a gigantic green glob of tentacled terror called Cthulhu.

It is as the creator of the Cthulhu mythos that Lovecraft is most widely recognized. The title refers to the group of stories he wrote toward the end of his life, creating implicitly if not deliberately a mythology in which beings from outside our universe wait on the edge of human experience for a chance to recapture the planet that was once their domain. These stories gain their power not so much from the descriptions or activities of the extraterrestrial monsters as from the implications to be drawn from their presence: that the universe is not essentially benign or humanistic and that mankind represents an accident rather than a triumph of nature. Lovecraft's terrors have little to do with the essentially egocentric topics of death and return from the grave. Although some of his early stories do involve these more traditional devices, a typical Lovecraft character is less likely to lose his life than his life-style, less in danger of a broken neck than a snapped mind. The emblem of the Lovecraft cosmos is the blind idiot-god Azathoth, king of creation, who cackles in chaos to the music of frantic flute players; and the ultimate shock in his tales comes from the unwelcome ability to see the universe through Azathoth's eyes. Lovecraft described his stories as attempts to create the effect of "dislocations in space and time," and his success in some efforts makes his work the literary equivalent of a psychedelic trip, which may in part account for his recent popularity with a new generation of readers.

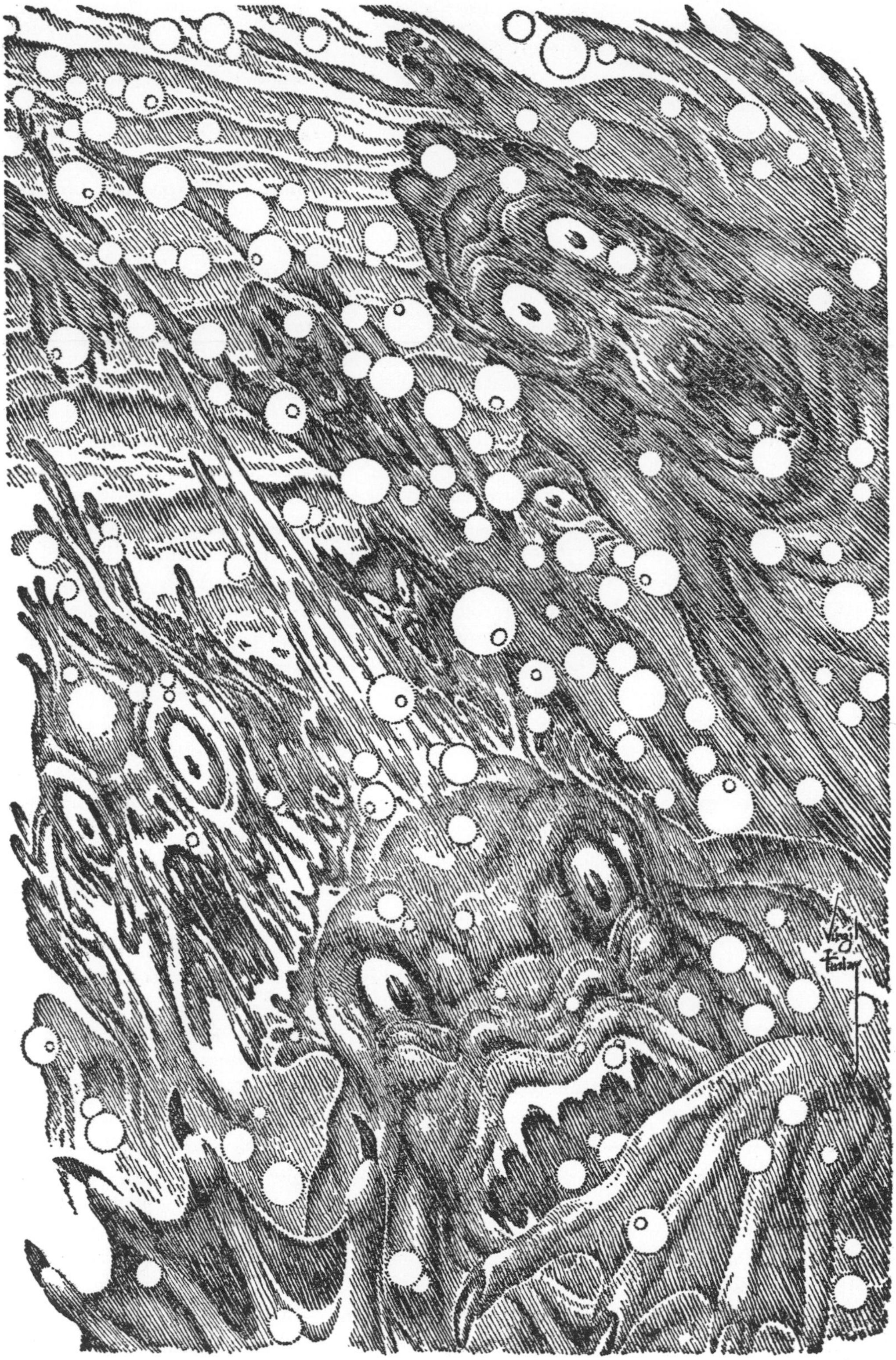

Virgil Finlay, the most renowned *Weird Tales* artist, began his career with the magazine shortly before death ended Lovecraft's, but Finlay later illustrated several Cthulhu stories, including "The House in the Valley" by Lovecraft's disciple August Derleth.

Lovecraft, however, denied any interest in drugs, although some of his characters take to opium to blot out intolerable memories. He even scorned the use of alcohol and tobacco, finding his greatest stimulation and inspiration in his own dreams, which were vivid and often organized enough to form the basis for some of his best stories. Dreams and darkness were his domain in life as well as in literature; he was a "night person" who roamed the streets after midnight and kept his shades drawn during the daylight hours to maintain an appropriately gloomy atmosphere.

Born in Providence, Rhode Island, in 1890, H. P. Lovecraft lived there all his life, excepting a few excursions and a short, ill-fated marriage that brought him briefly to New York. He grew up in a strange atmosphere amid the declining fortunes of a once distinguished family; both his parents died in a local mental hospital. Most of his adult life was spent in residence with his two elderly aunts. He was a recluse with relatively few personal contacts except those maintained through his huge correspondence by which he communicated with kindred spirits, mostly aspiring authors. His incredible letters, some of which have been published in several Arkham House volumes, accounted for an incredible amount of his time and energy. It was not unusual for one of these elaborate letters in his infinitesimal script to be the equivalent of one hundred typed pages, longer than almost any of his stories.

Equally demanding was his work in revising and ghostwriting, activities that provided most of his meager income. His most famous client was the magician Harry Houdini, but there were a number of lesser lights whose work might never have been published without Lovecraft's extensive efforts. One was Providence writer C. M. Eddy, Jr., whose scandalous story of an undertaking necrophile, "The Loved Dead," helped to make *Weird Tales* famous. But all of these activities restricted Lovecraft's own work and made him something less than a prolific writer. The list of his tales was expanded after his death in a somewhat grotesque manner, through a series of "posthumous collaborations" with August Derleth. These do not involve messages from beyond but are stories worked up by Derleth from notes and fragments left at Lovecraft's death. Unfortunately the stories are presented as Lovecraft's work despite the fact that in most cases his contribution consists of but one or two sentences or, in the case of the novel *The Lurker at the Threshold* (1945), a few pages. The essentially derivative nature of Derleth's writing in these tales makes them a poor introduction to Lovecraft.

Perhaps his most typical performance, and his most famous, is the story "The Call of Cthulhu," written in 1927. This tale of an elemental force rising out of the Pacific after eons of imprisonment was the first major exposition of the myth pattern that made Lovecraft's horrors unique. As usual, the tale is told in the first person by a narrator whose main characteristic is an overwhelming curiosity. His investigations into the legends and lore of the Cthulhu cult, conducted at a discreet scholarly distance, produce a body of information that leaves the hero stricken with horror from afar. The story begins with the line "The most merciful thing in the world, I think, is the inability of the human mind to correlate all its contents." This is a fair statement of Lovecraft's principal theme, a sophisticated prefiguration of the later monster movie cliché, "There are some things man was not meant to know." But his heroes are not mad scientists bent on unholy experiments so much as they are jaded intellectuals morbidly drawn to bizarre events already in progress.

The generally investigative form of Lovecraft's fiction often leads to a sort of shock ending that is not exactly a twist, but rather the logical culmination of suggestions scattered throughout the story. The tales are organized so that the final phrase, often in italics, reveals a detail that provides the cornerstone for a construction of events with staggering implications. This technique seems to be Lovecraft's interpretation of Poe's principle concerning unity of effect.

Utilizing what was essentially a nineteenth-century form to present his unnerving version of twentieth-century speculations about the cosmos, Lovecraft employed a prose style that was straight out of the eighteenth century. This was his favorite period in history, the era in which he felt he belonged. His preference for it was also expressed in his love for colonial architecture and in his frequently stated desire to dress in the costume of the period, which was apparently fulfilled only in his most famous portrait, by *Weird Tales* artist Virgil Finlay. Lovecraft's attachment to the eighteenth century was a result of a precocious childhood spent largely among the old books in his grandfather's library, where his interests in literature and escapism were encouraged by the formal prose of a bygone era.

Stylistically, Lovecraft's writing set him immediately apart from his contemporaries in pulp magazines, who with rare exceptions wrote in punchy phrases loaded with contemporary slang. Perhaps it was snob appeal that accounted for the respect he earned at *Weird Tales.* On the other hand, many critics have accused him of overwriting and of relying too heavily on adjectives. It is true that many of his stories seem stilted, and they are often more impressive when recalled than when they are being read. The best example of the way in which Lovecraft's stories retrospectively overcome their own faults

Finlay's whimsical portrait of Lovecraft shows the author in the attire of his beloved eighteenth century. Lovecraft never really used a quill pen, but his mentor, Lord Dunsany, did.

may be found in the case of Colin Wilson, the British critic who wrote a scathing attack on Lovecraft a few years ago, then turned around and wrote several stories and a novel as contributions to the Cthulhu mythos.

The whole business of this story cycle has some amusing aspects. Lovecraft and his followers were aware of the humor inherent in some of their extravagant visions and would occasionally include gags and in-jokes among their gruesome incidents. For instance, Lovecraft was fond of referring to nonexistent books that purportedly contained evil lore. One of these, the *Necronomicon* of Abdul Alhazred, was such a successful hoax that several collectors have offered astronomical prices for a copy. The frequently cited *Cultes des Ghouls* by the Comte d'Erlette was a tribute to August Derleth, and the dreaded high priest Klarkash-Ton, mentioned in several stories, was Lovecraft's California colleague Clark Ashton Smith. The most extravagant example of this kind of kidding around came about in 1934 when Robert Bloch, now most famous as the author of *Psycho*, wrote "The Shambler from the Stars," a story set in Providence which describes Lovecraft falling victim to one of his own demons. Lovecraft responded with "The Haunter of the Dark," in which a certain Robert Blake meets an equally grim fate while investigating a haunted church. This in turn set Bloch to work on "The Shadow from the Steeple."

Like Bloch, many of the writers Lovecraft inspired began when they were teenagers, but he himself did not write his first serious terror tale until the age of twenty-seven, when he produced "Dagon," a story of a sea monster suggestive of the later "Call of Cthulhu." The late-blooming author had a sickly constitution that prevented him from receiving a complete formal education; but his extensive reading made him the master of a number of historical and scientific subjects which stood him in good stead during a career that moved from brief, dreamlike fantasies to complex, lengthy tales bordering on science fiction. With a few exceptions, each story he wrote was longer than the last, as he progressively intensified his atmosphere and elaborated his plots. His work can be divided into three periods, of which the last was to prove the most popular and influential. His earliest tales, written in the manner of Lord Dunsany, were brief, slight, suggestive pieces only a few pages long, prose poems too vague for any real shock value, although some of them, like "Celephais" and "The Cats of Ulthar," do succeed in evoking the aura of imaginary ancient civilizations.

More important was a second group of stories, written in the early twenties, frequently set in New England, and often considered to have been inspired by the works of Poe, although the importance of this influence has been exaggerated. The best of these tales include "The Outsider," "The Rats in the Walls," "Pickman's Model," and "In the Vault." More effective than most of Lovecraft's more ambitious Cthulhu epics, "The Outsider" creates an authentic sense of dislocation as the amnesiac protagonist, lost in a tenantless structure with a haunting atmosphere, climbs an abandoned tower for a view of his surroundings and discovers, when he reaches the top, that he is not where he expected to be at all. This story, reprinted at the end of this chapter, is arguably the author's finest work. "Pickman's Model," which has been widely imitated, describes a Boston artist with a fondness for supernatural subjects who is discovered to be painting from life. The picture of ghouls at work in a subway sounds especially unnerving. "In the Vault" is the story of a degenerate New England undertaker who shortens a corpse to fit an undersized coffin and lives to regret it. This seems to have inspired a number of stories about reprehensible individuals in the same profession. The unusually gruesome "Rats in the Walls" features a hero who returns to his ancestral home where he discovers that his ancestors were cannibals. He immediately reverts to type.

This theme of inherited weirdness occurs in a number of Lovecraft's lesser tales like "Arthur Jermyn" and "The Lurking Fear." It also provided the plot for his finest novel, *The Case of Charles Dexter Ward*, in which a young man is possessed by the spirit of a deceased distant relative who was a black magician. This sort of treatment seems to express Lovecraft's views on evolution, which he presented not as a form of upward mobility so much as a proof that mankind has dark origins and impulses that can never be wholly eradicated.

His concept of inhuman forces at work in heredity was one manifestation of the general pattern that emerged during the last decade of his life to form the Cthulhu cycle. He wrote, "All my stories, unconnected as they may be, are based on the fundamental lore or legend that this world was inhabited at one time by another race who, in practicing black magic, lost their foothold and were expelled, yet live on outside ever ready to take possession of this earth again."

It should be made clear that this statement represents Lovecraft's fictional position and not a conscious personal belief. He claimed to be a skeptic, an atheist, and a materialist, and one of the most interesting features of his personality is the contrast between his philosophy and his fantasy life. It was his theory that people who believed in the supernatural would find it as dull as anything else they take for granted. Although Lovecraft never developed quite that attitude toward the inhuman entities he imagined, his last tales show the development of a strange kind of tolerance. His earlier portrayals of the Great Old Ones are uniformly ghastly, perhaps best exemplified by "The Colour Out of Space," in which a strange force blights the Massachusetts countryside, a tale remarkable for its anticipation of the horrors of radiation poisoning. His later, longer tales of the Cthulhu mythos begin to carry overtones of sympathy and even identification with the monsters, whose immortality and ability to range through space and time give them opportunities for scientific investigation, through which Lovecraft projects his own curiosity about the mysteries of the universe. The most obvious example of this kind of development occurs in *At the Mountains of Madness*, a short novel in which an Antarctic expedition uncovers the remnants of an ancient alien civilization. Lovecraft's delight with his own creations becomes so obvious that he has to drag in a new kind of monster at the last minute to alleviate an increasingly chummy atmosphere.

Perhaps the best effort among these later stories is "The Shadow Out of Time," in which an American scientist involuntarily trades bodies with an alien bent on an exchange of information. The man returns to normal with garbled memories and serious doubts about his sanity, finally realizing the appalling truth when an archaeological investigation uncovers proof of his own presence beneath mysterious ruins, left eons before his birth.

The sense of wonder that such a story can produce is Lovecraft's greatest achievement. He transformed the archaic conventions of the supernatural story into something approaching scientific speculation, achieving in his best tales a mood that exists nowhere else in literature, not even in the works of his imitators. Yet to dismiss the best of the *Weird Tales* authors as no more than pale imitations of Lovecraft would be unfair. Many of them made important contributions in their own right, and at least one has a following which today puts him in the unenviable position of being, like H. P. Lovecraft, a writer who lived close to poverty only to become a best-selling author decades after his death.

Such was the fate of Robert E. Howard, a young Texan who wrote a handful of tales in the Lovecraft manner but who specialized in combining horror with heroics. His fondness for stalwart characters who battle incredible menaces in a series of stories puts his work close to the mainstream of the pulp magazines; but his fascination with fear and

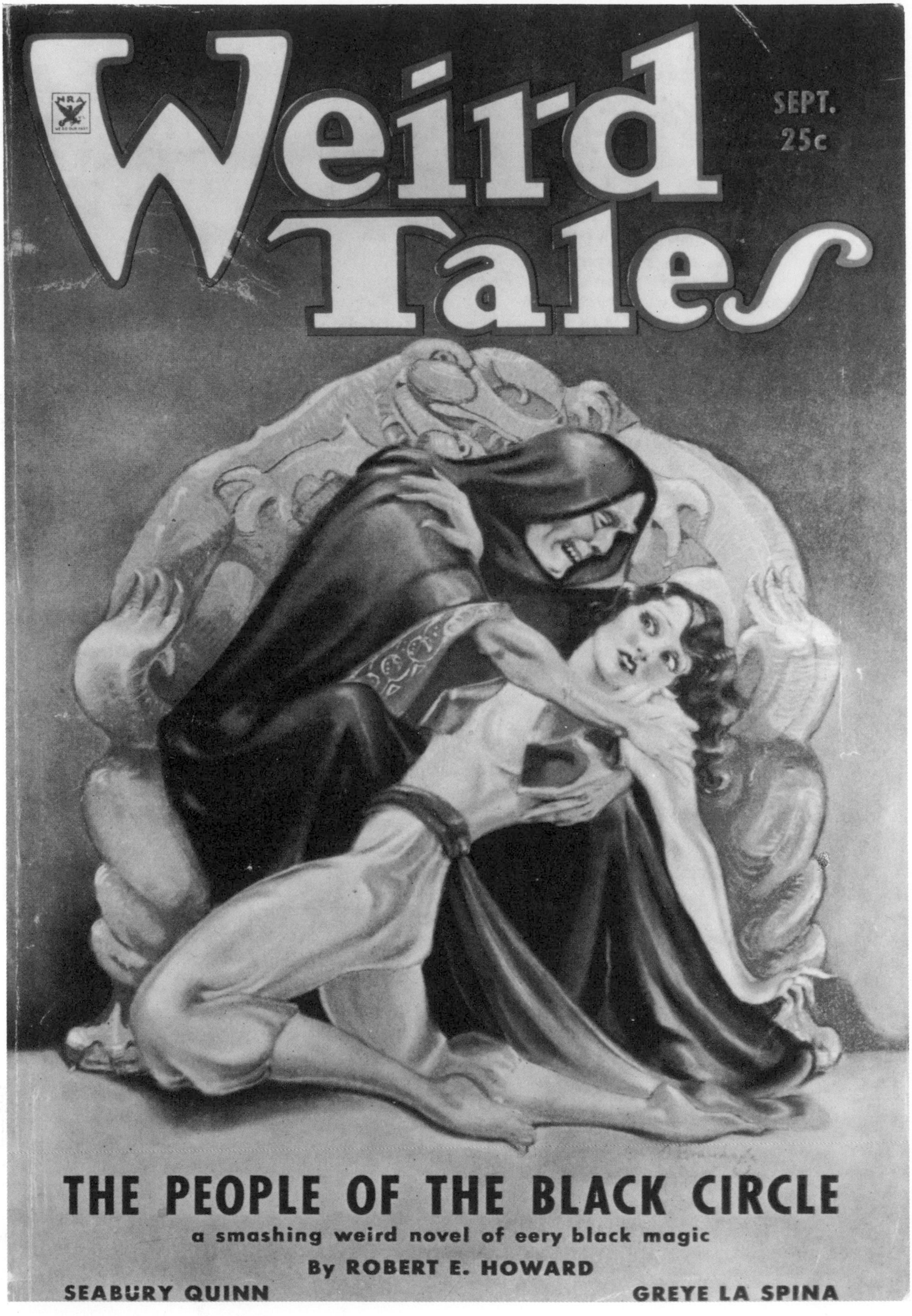
Weird Tales
NRA
SEPT.
25c
THE PEOPLE OF THE BLACK CIRCLE
a smashing weird novel of eery black magic
By ROBERT E. HOWARD
SEABURY QUINN
GREYE LA SPINA

his fondness for scenes of bloody conflict, combined with a raw talent for fast-paced storytelling, are more than enough to set him apart. One of Howard's most impressive heroes is Solomon Kane, a seventeenth-century Puritan swordsman who made his debut in 1928 with the story "Red Shadows." Kane, who contends with supernatural forces in a kind of one-man crusade, has some of his wildest adventures with black magic in Africa. He is almost completely overshadowed, though—as are such other Howard creations as King Kull and Bran Mak Morn—by the appearance in 1932 of Conan, a barbaric soldier of fortune struggling for spoils and survival in a world full of sorcery and seduction. Conan's wild adventures, which eventually bring him the crown of a mythical kingdom called Aquilonia, created a sensation in *Weird Tales* for three years, cut short by Howard's suicide in 1936. Like Lovecraft's Cthulhu cycle, the Conan epic proved irresistible to later writers, several of whom have carried on Conan's career with mixed results.

The only writer to vie consistently with Howard and Lovecraft for first place in the hearts of *Weird Tales* readers was Seabury Quinn, creator of the psychic detective Jules de Grandin. Virtually unknown today, de Grandin is a fast-talking Frenchman whose accent is somewhat more preposterous than his adventures. He appears in almost a hundred solidly plotted encounters with the uncanny, beginning in 1925 with "Terror on the Links," about an ape-man running amok on a golf course. Quinn may have acquired some background information for these tales while he was editor of a mortician's trade paper called *Casket and Sunnyside.*

Another *Weird Tales* giant was Clark Ashton Smith, a Californian who can be compared to Lovecraft for his reclusiveness and his fondness for elaborate prose. Smith was originally a poet, as well as an artist and a sculptor, whose macabre verse helped inspire Lovecraft to write professionally. He in turn introduced Smith to the magazine, and the result was a group of macabre stories dripping with florid prose. Smith's ornately worded tales are generally lightened by a sly sense of humor. Most are set in exotic worlds of the distant past or future, where immoral characters meet quaintly appropriate dooms. His style delights some readers as much as it dismays others. The florid prose suddenly stopped flowing when Smith decided to abandon fiction, cutting his *Weird Tales* career almost as short as Lovecraft's or Howard's, although he outlived them both by decades.

The longest-running career to begin in the magazine seems to have been that of Robert Bloch, now still hard at work twenty years after *Weird Tales* gave up the ghost in 1954. His first contribution was a grim medieval tale of cannibalistic monks called "The Feast in the Abbey." It took him a few years to come out from under Lovecraft's shadow, but he eventually emerged with a style and substance all his own, specializing in wry, ironic stories in which horror is mixed with screwball humor. Many of Bloch's best tales are narrated in a modern slang that far removes them from the sedate solemnity of his mentor.

Strangely enough, the one who stayed closest to Lovecraft was August Derleth. A serious writer of considerable ability who wrote a number of excellent novels outside the domain of the dreadful, Derleth continued to produce supernatural stories in the Lovecraftian manner throughout his long career, in an obvious tribute to the man who inspired him to try his hand at fiction. Lovecraft and his other colleagues were more than repaid by Derleth's indefatigable efforts on their behalf, especially through publication by Arkham House, which rescued their work from obscurity and made their reputations.

This *Weird Tales* cover illustrates one of Robert E. Howard's Conan tales. The artist, Margaret Brundage, used her daughters for models. Her fondness for the female form embarrassed H. P. Lovecraft, who used to remove the covers and dispose of them.

Clark Ashton Smith, best remembered for his stories, was also a poet and a self-taught sculptor and artist. This pencil drawing, which reflects some of the flavor of his prose, depicts the head of a magician hovering over a clawed demon.

The only pulp with an influence comparable to that of *Weird Tales* was *Black Mask*, which altered the flavor of the mystery story with the "hard-boiled," hardworking, nonintellectual detectives of Dashiell Hammett and Raymond Chandler. Still, the eerie and inexplicable crime found its greatest champion during this period in the person of the Anglo-American author John Dickson Carr. His specialty is the locked-room mystery, in which there seems to be no explanation for the method of the criminal except a supernatural one. He creates an effectively macabre atmosphere in novels like *The Three Coffins* and *Castle Skull*, and his solutions, while dissipating the uncanny overtones, are often as frightening as his puzzles. Ellery Queen, another major mystery author, handled creepy cases like *The Greek Coffin Mystery* and *The Egyptian Cross Mystery*, in which the crime proves especially puzzling because all of the victims have been decapitated. Thrillers like these helped to keep the tradition of the horror story alive while detective stories were well on their way to becoming the most popular type of novel in the English-speaking world.

By this time, mysteries and horror stories were becoming so well established that parodies and comedy treatments of the mode were developing into a separate genre. The classic stage examples include *The Bat* by Mary Roberts Rinehart and Avery Hopwood, and *The Cat and the Canary* by John Willard, which was made into an excellent silent film by Paul Leni in 1927. Both concern crazed killers with animal pseudonyms, and both are set in supposedly haunted houses where comic relief is provided by the exaggerated panic of potential victims. And in October 1927, Broadway audiences got a taste of something a little stronger when the stage version of *Dracula* opened at the Fulton Theater, where it ran for almost a year. Playing the title role was a Hungarian actor, Bela Lugosi. He would repeat the role in a talking motion picture four years later, when tales of terror were beginning to reach new heights of popularity as Hollywood created images and intonations to embody the fantasies of yesterday for generations yet unborn.

THE OUTSIDER

By H. P. Lovecraft

That night the Baron dreamt of many a wo;
And all his warrior-guests, with shade and form
Of witch, and demon, and large coffin-worm,
Were long be-nightmared.

—KEATS

Unhappy is he to whom the memories of childhood bring only fear and sadness. Wretched is he who looks back upon lone hours in vast and dismal chambers with brown hangings and maddening rows of antique books, or upon awed watches in twilight groves of grotesque, gigantic, and vine-encumbered trees that silently wave twisted branches far aloft. Such a lot the gods gave to me—to me, the dazed, the disappointed; the barren, the broken. And yet I am strangely content and cling desperately to those sere memories, when my mind momentarily threatens to reach beyond to *the other.*

I know not where I was born, save that the castle was infinitely old and infinitely horrible, full of dark passages and having high ceilings where the eye could find only cobwebs and shadows. The stones in the crumbling corridors seemed always hideously damp, and there was an accursed smell everywhere, as of the piled-up corpses of dead generations. It was never light, so that I used sometimes to light candles and gaze steadily at them for relief, nor was there any sun outdoors, since the terrible trees grew high above the topmost accessible tower. There was one black tower which reached above the trees into the unknown outer sky, but that was partly ruined and could not be ascended save by a well-nigh impossible climb up the sheer wall, stone by stone.

I must have lived years in this place, but I can not measure the time. Beings must have cared for my needs, yet I can not recall any person except myself, or anything alive but the noiseless rats and bats and spiders. I think that whoever nursed me must have been shockingly aged, since my first conception of a living person was that of something mockingly like myself, yet distorted, shriveled, and decaying like the castle. To me there was nothing grotesque in the bones and skeletons that strewed some of the stone crypts deep down among the foundations. I fantastically associated these things with everyday events, and thought them more natural than the colored pictures of living beings which I found in many of the moldy books. From such books I learned all that I know. No teacher urged or guided me, and I do not recall hearing any human voice in all those years—not even my own; for although I had read of speech, I had never thought to try to speak aloud. My aspect was a matter equally unthought of, for there were no mirrors in the castle, and I merely regarded myself by instinct as akin to the youthful figures I saw drawn and painted in the books. I felt conscious of youth because I remembered so little.

Outside, across the putrid moat and under the dark mute trees, I would often lie and dream for hours about what I read in the books; and would longingly picture myself amidst gay crowds in the sunny world beyond the endless forests. Once I tried to escape from the forest, but as I went farther from the castle the shade grew denser and the air more filled with brooding fear; so that I ran frantically back lest I lose my way in a labyrinth of nighted silence.

So through endless twilights I dreamed and waited, though I knew not what I waited for. Then in the shadowy solitude my longing for light grew so frantic that I could rest no more, and I lifted entreating hands to the single black ruined tower that reached above the forest into the unknown outer sky. And at last I resolved to scale that tower, fall though I might; since it were better to glimpse the sky and perish, than to live without ever beholding day.

In the dank twilight I climbed the worn and aged stone stairs till I reached the level where they ceased, and thereafter clung perilously to small footholds leading upward. Ghastly and terrible was that dead, stairless cylinder of rock; black, ruined, and deserted, and sinister with startled bats whose wings made no noise. But more ghastly and terrible still was the slowness of my progress; for climb as I might, the darkness overhead grew no thinner, and a new chill as of haunted and venerable mold assailed me. I shivered as I wondered why I did not reach the light, and would have looked down had I dared. I fancied that night had come suddenly upon me, and vainly groped with one free hand for a window embrasure, that I might peer out and above, and try to judge the height I had attained.

All at once, after an infinity of awesome, sightless crawling up that concave and desperate precipice, I felt my head touch a solid thing, and knew I must have gained the roof, or at least some kind of floor. In the darkness I raised my free hand and tested the barrier, finding it stone and immovable. Then came a deadly circuit of the tower, clinging to whatever holds the slimy wall could give; till finally my testing hand found the barrier yielding, and I turned upward again, pushing the slab or door with my head as I used both hands in my fearful ascent. There was no light revealed above, and as my hands went higher I knew that my climb was for the nonce ended; since the slab was the trap-door of an aperture leading to a level stone surface of greater circumference than the lower tower, no doubt the floor of some lofty and capacious observation chamber. I crawled through carefully, and tried to prevent the heavy slab from falling back into place, but failed in the latter attempt. As I lay exhausted on the stone floor I heard the eerie echoes of its fall, but hoped when necessary to pry it up again.

Believing I was now at prodigious height, far above the accursed branches of the wood, I dragged myself up from the floor and fumbled about for windows, that I might look for the first time upon the sky, and the moon and stars of which I had read. But on every hand I was disappointed; since all that I found were vast shelves of marble, bearing odious oblong boxes of disturbing size. More and more I reflected, and wondered what hoary secrets might abide in this high apartment so many eons cut off from the castle below. Then unexpectedly my hands came upon a doorway, where hung a portal of stone, rough with strange chiseling. Trying it, I found it locked; but with a supreme burst of strength I overcame all obstacles and dragged it open inward. As I did so there came to me the purest ecstasy I have ever known; for shining tranquilly through an ornate grating of iron, and down a short stone passageway of steps that ascended from the newly found doorway, was the radiant full moon, which I had never before seen save in dreams and in vague visions I dared not call memories.

Fancying now that I had attained the very pinnacle of the castle, I commenced to rush up the few steps beyond the door; but the sudden veiling of the moon by a cloud caused me to stumble, and I felt my way more slowly in the dark. It was still very dark when I reached the grating—which I tried carefully and found unlocked, but which I did not open for fear of falling from the amazing height to which I had climbed. Then the moon came out.

Most demoniacal of all shocks is that of the abysmally unexpected and grotesquely unbelievable. Nothing I had before undergone could compare in terror with what I now saw; with the bizarre marvels that sight implied. The sight itself was as simple as it was stupefying, for it was merely this: instead of a dizzying prospect of treetops seen from a lofty eminence, there stretched around me on the level through the grating nothing less than *the solid ground,* decked and diversified by marble slabs and columns, and overshadowed by an ancient stone church, whose ruined spire gleamed spectrally in the moonlight.

Half unconscious, I opened the grating and staggered out upon the white gravel path that stretched away in two directions. My mind, stunned and chaotic as it was, still held the frantic craving for light; and not even the fantastic wonder which had happened could stay my course. I neither knew nor cared whether my experience was insanity, dreaming, or magic; but was determined to gaze on brilliance and gayety at any cost. I knew not who I was or what I was, or what my surroundings might be; though as I continued to stumble along I became conscious of a kind of fearsome latent memory that made my progress not wholly fortuitous. I passed under an arch out of that region of slabs and columns, and wandered through the open country; sometimes following the visible road, but sometimes leaving it curiously to tread across meadows where only occasional ruins bespoke the ancient presence of a forgotten road. Once I swam across a swift river where crumbling, mossy masonry told of a bridge long vanished.

Over two hours must have passed before I reached what seemed to be my goal, a venerable ivied castle in a thickly wooded park, maddeningly familiar, yet full of perplexing strangeness to me. I saw that the moat was filled in, and that some of the well-known towers were demolished; whilst new wings existed to confuse the beholder. But what I observed with chief interest and delight were the open windows—gorgeously ablaze with light and sending forth sound of the gayest revelry. Advancing to one of these I looked in and saw an oddly dressed company, indeed; making merry, and speaking brightly to one another. I had never, seemingly, heard human speech before and could guess only vaguely what was said. Some of the faces seemed to hold expressions that brought up incredibly remote recollections, others were utterly alien.

I now stepped through the low window into the brilliantly lighted room, stepping as I did so from my single bright moment of hope to my blackest convulsion of despair and realization. The nightmare was quick to come, for as I entered, there occurred immediately one of the most terrifying demonstrations I had ever conceived. Scarcely had I crossed the sill when there descended upon the whole company a sudden and unheralded fear of hideous intensity, distorting every face and evoking the most horrible screams from nearly every throat. Flight was universal, and in the clamor and panic several fell in a swoon and were dragged away by their madly fleeing companions. Many covered their eyes with their hands, and plunged blindly and awkwardly in their race to escape, overturning furniture and stumbling against the walls before they managed to reach one of the many doors.

The cries were shocking; and as I stood in the brilliant apartment alone and dazed, listening to their vanishing echoes, I trembled at the thought of what might be lurking near me unseen. At a casual inspection the room seemed deserted, but when I moved toward one of the alcoves I thought I detected a presence there—a hint of motion beyond the golden-arched doorway leading to another and somewhat similar room. As I approached the arch I began to perceive the presence more clearly; and then, with the first and last sound I ever uttered—a ghastly ululation that revolted me almost as poignantly as its noxious cause—I beheld in full, frightful vividness the inconceivable, indescribable, and unmentionable monstrosity which had by its simple appearance changed a merry company to a herd of delirious fugitives.

I can not even hint what it was like, for it was a compound of all that is unclean, uncanny, unwelcome, abnormal, and detestable. It was the ghoulish shade of decay, antiquity, and dissolution; the putrid, dripping eidolon of unwholesome revelation, the awful baring of that which the merciful earth should always hide. God knows it was not of this world—or no longer of this world—yet to my horror I saw in its eaten-away and bone-revealing outlines a leering, abhorrent travesty on the human shape; and in its moldy, disintegrating apparel an unspeakable quality that chilled me even more.

I was almost paralyzed, but not too much so to make a feeble effort toward flight; a backward stumble which failed to break the spell in which the nameless, voiceless monster held me. My eyes, bewitched by the glassy orbs which stared loathsomely into them, refused to close; though they were mercifully blurred, and showed the terrible object but indistinctly after the first shock. I tried to raise my hand to shut out the sight, yet so stunned were my nerves that my arm could not fully obey my will. The attempt, however, was enough to disturb my balance; so that I had to stagger forward several steps to avoid falling. As I did so I became suddenly and agonizingly aware of the *nearness* of the carrion thing, whose hideous hollow breathing I half fancied I could hear. Nearly mad, I found myself yet able to throw out a hand to ward off the fetid apparition which pressed so close; when in one cataclysmic second of cosmic nightmarishness and hellish accident *my fingers touched the rotting outstretched paw of the monster beneath the golden arch.*

I did not shriek, but all the fiendish ghouls that ride the night wind shrieked for me as in that same second there crashed down upon my mind a single and fleeting avalanche of soul-annihilating memory. I knew in that second all that had been; I remembered beyond the frightful castle and the trees, and recognized the altered edifice in which I now stood; I recognized, most terrible of all, the unholy abomination that stood leering before me as I withdrew my sullied fingers from its own.

But in the cosmos there is balm as well as bitterness, and that balm is nepenthe. In the supreme horror of that second I forgot what had horrified me, and the burst of black memory vanished in a chaos of echoing images. In a dream I fled from that haunted and accursed pile, and ran swiftly and silently in the moonlight. When I returned to the churchyard place of marble and went down the steps I found the stone trap-door immovable; but I was not sorry, for I had hated the antique castle and the trees. Now I ride with the mocking and friendly ghouls on the night wind, and play by day amongst the catacombs of Nephren-Ka in the sealed and unknown valley of Hadoth by the Nile. I know that light is not for me, save that of the moon over the rock tombs of Neb, nor any gayety save the unnamed feasts of Nitokris beneath the Great Pyramid; yet in my new wildness and freedom I almost welcome the bitterness of alienage.

For although nepenthe has calmed me, I know always that I am an outsider; a stranger in this century and among those who are still men. This I have known ever since I stretched out my fingers to the abomination within that great gilded frame; stretched out my fingers and touched *a cold and unyielding surface of polished glass.*

7

THE INVISIBLE RAY: MASS MEDIA

The sound of terror brought a new dimension to worlds of weirdness in the third decade of the twentieth century, arriving just in time to startle a public weighted down by a massive worldwide depression. Films, at last able to speak and even to scream, unleashed a stream of horrors, and the "monster movie" became one of the safest investments in the cutthroat world called Hollywood. Simultaneously, the burgeoning business of radio broadcasting brought a new kind of drama into millions of homes, and sinister stories were among the most welcome additions to the family circle. Horror had found a voice at last.

Of course, deadly dialogue had been available for centuries to the fortunate minority that patronized the theater, but the new media were available on a mass scale. Motion pictures in particular provided strange sights and sounds that seem to have embedded themselves permanently in the modern consciousness. The first attempt to terrify moviegoers was entitled, appropriately enough, *The Terror*, a 1928 effort from Warner Brothers, which had released the first important talking picture, *The Jazz Singer.* Directed by Roy Del Ruth from a play by England's popular mystery author Edgar Wallace, the film was just another thriller about a masked murderer on the loose in an old house, and it failed to create a sensation. The real birth of talking terror was postponed until 1931, when Universal released its version of *Dracula*, a tremendous success that set the studio on the road to becoming the major producer of macabre motion pictures for the next quarter of a century.

Director Tod Browning apparently had originally planned to feature Lon Chaney in the title role, especially after Chaney's success in the talking remake of the mystery story *The Unholy Three* (1930); but the actor's unexpected death necessitated a change of plans. Eventually, Browning recruited Bela Lugosi, who had taken the part on Broadway, and thus a legend was born. Lugosi, with his slicked-back black hair, piercing eyes, predatory profile, and rich Hungarian accent, became permanently identified with the role, even though he played it only twice in films (and on one of these occasions, at that, in a comedy). He looked almost nothing like the white-haired, mustachioed old man described by Bram Stoker; but Lugosi's highly theatrical performance was so effective that his face has become Dracula's face and his voice, Dracula's voice. His stately, slightly overripe readings of lines like "I never drink . . . wine" and "I am taking with me only three . . . boxes" come perilously close to comedy; but he makes an impressively sinister figure nonetheless.

Although there were a few slight changes, the film *Dracula* was closely based on actor Hamilton Deane's stage version. The unfortunate decision to use the play was understandable in view of its considerable success, but it made the movie less vivid than it should have been. As it was, the film coasted on the strength of its first few minutes, set amid the grim gray mountains of Transylvania. The script replaced the traveling real-estate salesman Jonathan Harker with Renfield, the madman who comes under Dracula's power in the book; he is here at least given a good reason for losing his grip on reality. His ride to Castle Dracula in a coach whose driver is suddenly replaced by a bat, his confrontation with the Count who passes through a giant spider web without disturbing it, and his climactic encounter with Dracula's three undead wives all build to an appropriately creepy crescendo. He travels with Dracula on the ship bound for

Bela Lugosi carries Helen Chandler into his lair in this scene from the climax of Tod Browning's 1931 film *Dracula. Courtesy of Universal Pictures.*

England and is completely batty by the time he is discovered as the only man alive among a crew of corpses. The lunatic laughter coming from the ship's hold remains one of the most haunting sounds in the history of horror movies. Renfield, who has some of the best moments later in the film as the man who knows more about Dracula than anybody wants to hear, was portrayed by Dwight Frye. This actor was subsequently cast in several famous films as a half-witted apprentice fiend, but *Dracula* gave him his meatiest role.

Another actor who had his work cut out for him after appearing in the film was Edward Van Sloan, who played the wise old enemy of evil, Dr. Van Helsing. Stern and inflexible, the white-haired gentleman with the wire-rimmed spectacles would return to do battle with many of Hollywood's most menacing monsters. His cat-and-mouse scenes with Lugosi provide most of the tension in the lackluster later portions of the film. The script seems to shy away from what should be its most shocking moments. The fact that Lucy has become a vampire is passed over in a few lines of limp dialogue, and Dracula's death scene is shown only in a shot of the heroine Mina (Helen Chandler) experiencing sympathy pains that look like a mild case of heartburn. The only blood in this film version of the bloodiest of all horror tales is the sample that Renfield squeezes out of his finger after cutting it accidentally on a paper clip. Still, Dracula's approving smile as Renfield sucks on the wounded finger is one of the film's best moments.

Dracula's merits for today's audiences may rest almost entirely on the performances of Lugosi, Frye, and Van Sloan; but it thrilled the public in 1931 and pointed the way for Universal to save itself from the hard times that threatened many major studios during the dark days of the early thirties, when economic chaos was complicated by the technical problem of transition to "talkies." The next obvious step was a follow-up film, which proved to be considerably better. In fact, it is the most famous film in its field, although admittedly *Dracula* remains a close second.

Frankenstein (1931) was a free, modernized adaptation of Mary Shelley's novel; it made a star of its monster, Boris Karloff (born William Henry Pratt). The plot of this picture, which leaves Frankenstein alive and explains his creation's hostility away as the result of an accidental "criminal brain" transplant, may leave something to be desired; but solid supporting players and sensitive direction by James Whale helped to save it. What makes it a classic, though, is the vivid yet understated performance of Karloff, who somehow infuses the character of the mute brute with a sensitive, almost poetic spirit. Another decisive factor is the shocking disguise designed for Karloff by Jack Pierce who, as Universal's makeup man, would create some of the world's most famous faces out of whole cloth. The square-skulled, bleary-eyed creature with the scar on his forehead and the electrodes in his throat has become a piece of visual folklore, although it remains protected by Universal's copyright. The face was very much designed for Karloff's features; it was considerably less effective in some of the numerous sequels when applied to other actors, among them, eventually, Bela Lugosi, who rejected this plum of a part in the original version either because he objected to the heavy makeup it would entail or because the monster had no lines. (Both explanations have been offered for his refusal to play the role; possibly it was the combination of drawbacks that convinced him it would hurt his career.)

Frankenstein himself was played with appropriate hysteria by Colin Clive; the screenplay by Garrett Fort and Francis Faragoh inexplicably changed his name to Henry and made his best friend Victor. Clive's most memorable scene occurs when the monster is vitalized after a pyrotechnical display of lightning flashes and electrical equipment. The monster is entirely swathed in bandages except for an indecently naked hand which twitches spasmodically as Clive screams "It's alive! It's alive!" His handiwork is revealed the next morning dressed in an undersized black suit; Karloff makes an unlikely entrance by backing through a door, apparently only so he can turn slowly to reveal his fearsome face. A skylight opens in the ceiling and the monster bathes himself in the light, raising his arms to the sun as though in worship; the scene recalls his creator's earlier lines about the discovery of a mysterious ray, the one that brought life into the world.

Dwight Frye and Edward Van Sloan returned in this film; Frye as Fritz, Frankenstein's hunchbacked assistant who so goads the monster by beating it that it finally murders him; and Van Sloan as Frankenstein's teacher, who becomes the second victim when he attempts to dissect the monster, rendered unconscious all too temporarily by a powerful drug. This leaves the monster free to roam the country, but his liberty is short. After murdering a few peasants and making a pass at Frankenstein's fiancée, he is chased back to Frankenstein's laboratory in an abandoned windmill by an army of torch-bearing villagers and is there consumed in flames. The combination of fire and an indignant population proved impressive; it was used again to end dozens of later films, including several more with the same monster. The final scene of *Frankenstein* shows the hero's relieved father preparing for his son's wedding with a toast: "Here's to a son to the house of Frankenstein!" He was to get his wish—and more. The film launched a series of seven sequels from Universal alone, to say nothing of the many others that emerged from other studios in later decades.

Universal's next effort was considerably less impressive. Directed by Robert Florey, who had almost been put in charge of *Frankenstein*, *The Murders in the Rue Morgue* (1932) starred Bela Lugosi as a nineteenth-century mad scientist who conducts a series of fruitless experiments having something to do with blood transfusions between people and his pet gorilla. Some evocative sets and a curly-headed Lugosi could hardly compensate for the fact that an actor in a monkey suit is rarely awe inspiring.

Karloff fared considerably better with his second effort into the uncanny, *The Mummy* (1932), a powerful tale of a reanimated Egyptian that had no direct literary source but was concocted out of nothing in particular by light humorist Nina Wilcox Putnam. This subtle film featured only a few minutes of Karloff as a half-decayed figure wrapped in bandages. After being resurrected by a foolhardy archaeologist reading an ancient scroll, the mummy Im-Ho-Tep disappears, showing up years later as a comparatively presentable modern Egyptian. Only extreme close-ups reveal his glowing eyes and dehydrated flesh. He plans to revive the ancient princess for whose love he had been buried alive thousands of years before; but her preserved body collapses in the museum where he finds it, and he is forced to seek out her reincarnation. The young lady in question responds by calling on an ancient goddess for protection from his unwelcome advances. A statue answers her plea with a beam of unearthly light, and Karloff disintegrates into dust in a pioneering piece of camera wizardry by Universal's special-effects artist, John P. Fulton. He was finally honored with an Academy Award in 1956 when, after years of brilliant work, he parted the Red Sea for Cecil B. De Mille's *Ten Commandments*. *The Mummy* was directed by Karl Freund, a cameraman who had photographed *Dracula* as well as most of Fritz Lang's silent fantasies in Germany. Featured in the cast as an expert on ancient curses was, not too surprisingly, Edward Van Sloan.

Universal had uncovered a box office bonanza with its horror films, and its rival studios were quick to get in on the action. None succeeded better than Paramount, which

Zita Johann confronts Boris Karloff who, despite his efforts to disguise his wizened visage, can only be *The Mummy* (1932). *Courtesy of Universal Pictures.*

scored a tremendous coup by releasing a monster movie that won an Oscar for its star, Fredric March, performing the dual role in the finest version of the frequently filmed *Dr. Jekyll and Mr. Hyde* (1932). Director Rouben Mamoulian's version of the story remains the only film in the genre to have received such a major Academy Award, although March's performance is not really the best ever offered in a macabre motion picture. Nevertheless, March created quite an impression by overplaying both parts, making Jekyll cold and dull and Hyde a rambunctious brute whose outrageously ugly appearance created a new convention at odds with the literary source. This version continued the tradition of the 1920 Barrymore film, focusing on affairs with two women, one representing vice and the other, virtue. This emphasis served to provide a spurious sort of suspense involving the fate of the new characters while shifting attention away from the more complex topic of Jekyll's dilemma. The movie is most impressive in its visual effects. The transformations from Jekyll to Hyde surpassed anything ever seen on the screen in the way of technical wizardry, and the photography throughout conveys a feeling of menace and dislocation through a variety of unusual perspectives.

The same year saw the release of one of the most disturbing and controversial films ever made: *Freaks*, from Metro-Goldwyn-Mayer. It was directed by Tod Browning, fresh from his lucrative adaptation of *Dracula*; but it proved to be anything but a money-maker. Audiences proved as queasy as distributors when confronted with this bizarre look at the world of circus sideshows in which most of the cast consisted of actual freaks. The plot involves a physically normal performer named Cleopatra who seduces a midget into marriage to get her hands on his inheritance. The freaks accept her into their community, only to discover that she and her strong man lover plan to murder her little husband. The freaks take up arms, killing Cleopatra's confederate and turning her, improbably enough, into a chicken with the head of a woman. This transformation, which could hardly have been accomplished by any natural method, seems to imply that the freaks have supernatural powers; but it is introduced so abruptly that it appears merely absurd. The film's power lies in the way Browning manipulates audience reactions: pinheaded or limbless characters overcome the viewers' initial dismay and engage their sympathy; but as the freaks pursue the larcenous lovers through a thunderstorm they once again become sources of shock. One brief shot of an armless, legless man crawling rapidly through the mud with a knife in his teeth, emerging from under a circus wagon like a gigantic worm, is particularly dismaying. This sort of material puts *Freaks* in a very different category from the mainstream of horror films, which, however gruesome or depraved, are clearly works of the imagination.

The MGM studio was far better served, commercially speaking, by its second 1932 venture into the grotesque, a corny but engaging adaptation of Sax Rohmer's *Mask of Fu Manchu*, with Boris Karloff in the title role. In the same year, Karloff also appeared in Universal's *Old Dark House*, playing a brutish, bearded butler in this haunted-house thriller directed by James Whale.

Bela Lugosi, who generally chose his roles less carefully than his horror colleague, got a fairly good part for a preposterously small fee in the independently produced *White Zombie*. This tale of black magic in Haiti has a poetic charm generated in large measure by its unsophisticated melodramatics. It is, at least, the best of the low-budget productions that emanated from the minor Hollywood studios during the depression and the Second World War.

Among the other major studios that took a stab at scaring money out of their customers during 1932 were RKO, with *The Most Dangerous Game*; and Warner Brothers, with *Dr. X*. The former, based on a famous short story by Richard Connell, concerns a hunter (Leslie Banks) who stages shipwrecks to bring human prey to his island home; the latter depicts a series of stranglings committed by a one-armed scientist who has concocted a formula for building a new limb out of "synthetic flesh." *Dr. X* was the first horror film shot in color, although there had been a few color scenes in Lon Chaney's silent *Phantom of the Opera*. There was an unrelated "sequel," *The Return of Dr. X*, in 1939, interesting only because the role of the sinister scientist, who in this incarnation kept himself alive with constant blood transfusions, was played by Humphrey Bogart.

Warner Brothers followed *Dr. X* with another color film, *The Mystery of the Wax Museum* (1933). It featured the same heroine, Fay Wray, as well as Doctor X himself, Lionel Atwill. This sauve, sinister actor was to enliven many a morbid movie with his icy intensity. In the 1932 film he had been a red herring dragged across the trail of the real killer; but he is definitely up to no good in the wax museum as its crazed proprietor who makes dummies of all his victims. His antisocial behavior is attributed to a fire that destroyed an earlier exhibition as well as most of his face; the climax of the film comes when the struggling heroine punches Atwill in the nose, shattering the wax mask that has disguised him from her as well as the audience. The unexpected revelation of his disfigured features is still remembered as a moment of true terror by those who have seen *The Mystery of the Wax Museum*. Atwill reported an ironic result of his care in performing the part: having read the script and realizing that his face was supposed to be a mask, he was careful to keep his features as immobile as possible. The result was so effective that the producers, anxious to preserve their surprise ending, removed almost all his close-ups from the final print.

Fay Wray had already begun to establish a reputation as the screen's shrillest screamer; she was to have her finest hour in the hands of Hollywood's most lovable monster, a fifty-foot gorilla named Kong. The special effects in this 1933 RKO release have never been duplicated. Since *King Kong* appeared there have been dozens of films about oversized creatures wreaking havoc; but few have benefited from such time and care as technician Willis O'Brien expended, and none has been able to endow the central character with the vividly expressed personality that made Kong such a delight. O'Brien had begun his experiments with miniature models to be enlarged by double exposures back in the silent era, when he engineered a troupe of dinosaurs for the 1925 production *The Lost World.* Adapted from a novel by Arthur Conan Doyle, the plot of this film, in which prehistoric animals are discovered and brought back to civilization, is similar to that of *King Kong.* What the newer film provided was a sympathetic menace and a disheveled blond heroine whose tempestuous affair really deserved the publicity campaign that had described Browning's version of *Dracula* as the "Strangest Love Story of All." What Kong might have in mind for the lady can only be imagined; he seems to be content to carry her around clenched in his hairy fist—or so it seems, since the scene in which he curiously removes her clothes was eliminated by the studio censor. After all, she was a movie star (the expedition that uncovered Kong was a search for some spectacular film footage), and the giant ape may have been no more than the world's biggest Fay Wray fan. There are some interesting similarities between the roles assigned to the monster and the heroine; they first meet when she is trussed up as a sacrifice by the mob of savages who worship Kong, and his first appearance in Manhattan finds him in the same sort of predicament, displayed in chains for the benefit of a jaded theater audience. His sudden escape to wreak havoc upon the metropolis may well be what killed vaudeville. Kong's climactic battle against modern civilization is the most memorable portion of this famous film; audiences depressed by economic disaster were apparently delighted to watch a brute force assaulting their disappointing civilization. The great ape destroys an elevated train as if it were one of the hapless dinosaurs of his island home, and he meets his end when an attack by a squadron of biplanes with machine guns turns his last stand atop the Empire State Building into an aviator's shooting gallery. Kong's death scene, while a trifle hammy, is one of the most famous in the history of the cinema.

The popular success of the film led almost immediately to a sequel, *Son of Kong* (1933), a movie that must bear the responsibility for inaugurating the tradition of naming sequels after the relatives of successful monsters. Kong, Jr., proved to be a smaller but still impressive white gorilla named Kiko, considerably more sociable than his father. He watches over the crew who returns to Kong's island (including actor Robert Armstrong, who had discovered Junior's more impressive forebear) and eventually sacrifices his life to save his human acquaintances from a flood. Kong's son was the most altruistic monster ever presented on the screen, but that seems to have counted against him. The primary function of a fictional fiend is to express the audience's suppressed hostility; by this standard, *Son of Kong* was somewhat disappointing.

Universal retaliated in the same year with a more subtle but nevertheless impressive adaptation of H. G. Wells's novel *The Invisible Man.* The special effects by John P. Fulton were less spectacular than those in the *Kong* films; but they were still eerie and effective, especially when augmented by James Whale's witty direction and an intense vocal

Above, Kong battles a pterodactyl for the privilege of escorting Fay Wray around Skull Island in *King Kong*, a film enriched by Max Steiner's musical score, one of the first supplied for a sound horror film. *RKO Radio Pictures.*

Right, Claude Rains contemplates his troubles in *The Invisible Man* (1933). The beautiful detail of the artificial nose poking out from the bandages was ignored in subsequent treatments of the subject. *Courtesy of Universal Pictures.*

performance by Claude Rains. The scene in which Rains unwraps the bandages around his head to reveal a visual vacancy is still amazing, especially because Fulton took the trouble to show the back of the wrapping encircling the invisible head—the kind of detail overlooked by later imitators. Rains became one of a number of performers who used fantasy films to establish themselves as serious actors.

The Invisible Man demonstrated the eminent adaptability of the short science fiction novels by Wells, many of which seem to have been written for the screen. Further proof was offered by Paramount's 1933 production *The Island of Lost Souls*, a version of his *Island of Dr. Moreau.* Charles Laughton plays the demented doctor whose jungle retreat is an experimental laboratory for attempts to turn beasts into human beings through surgery; Bela Lugosi plays the leader of the beast-men who turn on their creator when they realize that he is ignoring the commandments he has given them.

The fact that *The Island of Lost Souls* featured a whole menagerie of monsters may have inspired Universal to costar its two major menaces, Karloff and Lugosi, in the 1934 feature *The Black Cat.* Only the title was retained from a story by Poe; the new plot concerned a Hungarian Satanist (Karloff) tormenting a comparatively normal physician who finally goes mad when he realizes that his wife and daughter have been stuffed in his enemy's cellar. As the doctor, Lugosi finally proves himself to be more offensive by skinning the devil worshiper alive. The unlikely events are justified principally by the performances of the stars, whose scenes together communicate a convincing mood of mounting conflict.

The natural result of the successful collaboration was another effort along the same lines, complete with another spurious Poe title, *The Raven* (1935). Lugosi portrayed a plastic surgeon who seeks revenge when a young woman he has cured spurns his love. He coerces a fugitive killer (Karloff) into assisting him with an operation which turns the gangster into a revolting mutant, and he embarks on a preposterous course of vengeance based on a series of torture devices, most of them derived from Poe's story of the Spanish Inquisition, "The Pit and the Pendulum." The surgeon is a fairly incompetent fiend, since he fails to eliminate any of the victims he has invited to his house for a weekend of terror; but the film almost overcomes its own shortcomings by the entertainment value of its outrageous melodramatics.

The best of the Karloff-Lugosi features is *The Invisible Ray* (1936), directed by Lambert Hillyer. This was the first film to suggest the possibility of radiation poisoning, as a

Universal's top horror stars, Karloff and Lugosi, meet across a chessboard in their elegant but insubstantial first encounter, *The Black Cat*, stylishly directed by Edgar G. Ulmer.

Elsa Lanchester meets Boris Karloff and wishes she had never been built in this scene from the tragicomic *Bride of Frankenstein* (1935).
Courtesy of Universal Pictures.

scientist, portrayed by Karloff, is contaminated by a new element he discovers in a meteorite. As a result, he glows in the dark and his very touch is fatal. The ray has power for good as well as evil; it can kill, but it also cures blindness, and it seems to be closely allied with the mysterious force described in the 1931 *Frankenstein.* The film comes closer than most of its genre to a serious consideration of science's strange trials and temptations, although Karloff inevitably goes "mad" and eliminates a good portion of the cast, including a sympathetic colleague played by Lugosi. Eventually the protagonist meets one of the most ignominious ends in the history of film fiends: he is destroyed like a naughty child by his own mother, who deprives him of the formula that keeps his crazy chemistry in balance.

A year earlier, in 1935, Universal had released the first in a long string of sequels, James Whale's *Bride of Frankenstein.* Many consider it to be superior to the original, and it is a vastly entertaining film, but one that replaces the grim mood of *Frankenstein* with considerable amounts of comedy and pathos. The monster escapes from the burning windmill, but his awesome appearance is almost immediately undercut by the humorously exaggerated reactions of the old lady who witnesses his resurrection. Subsequent scenes of his flight through a forest reproduce the tone and some of the incidents of the original novel. The monster saves a shepherdess from drowning and is wounded by hunters for his pains, and he finds temporary refuge in the cottage of an old blind man, who welcomes him as a friend. The scenes with the hermit (O. P. Heggie) contain some embarrassingly sentimental moments as the old man thanks God for sending him a friend, weeping while his grotesque guest pats him on the back and strains of "Ave Maria" swell up on the sound track. He also teaches the creature a few words, and the unfortunate effect of the subsequent dialogue is that the monster seems more a stupid brute than the uncanny figure of his first appearances. Karloff delivers his clumsy lines as well as can be expected; only years after the film was made did he reveal his distress at the changes in the character that had brought him fame.

The real point of *The Bride of Frankenstein* is the creation of the monster's mate; but this is delayed until the last few minutes, while Frankenstein (again Colin Clive) teeters between terror and the temptation to try again. Providing most of the impetus is a crackpot old scientist named Dr. Praetorius, portrayed with sinister glee by Ernest Thesiger. Introduced as Frankenstein's former teacher, he sparks the young scientist's imagination with a display of his own handiwork, a group of miniature humans wearing fanciful costumes and living in bottles. This ludicrous collection is not as persuasive as the monster who, on orders from Dr. Praetorius, kidnaps Frankenstein's bride, thus ensuring the young man's cooperation in the creation of a female monster. One nasty-minded writer came up with the idea that parts of Mrs. Frankenstein might be used to manufacture the monster's mate; but this notion was Universally rejected. Instead, anonymous donors provide the raw material for film history's most famous femme fatale, who is spectacularly animated in a fantastic electrical laboratory designed by Kenneth Strickfaden. As played by Elsa Lanchester (who also portrayed Mary Shelley in the film's brief prologue), the monstress is considerably more presentable than her intended spouse. Looking almost human beneath a wild hairdo that still seems charged with lightning, she loses no time in expressing disgust for her pathetically eager suitor; he responds fatalistically by blowing up the laboratory with a switch conveniently, if improbably, designed for just that purpose. Mr. and Mrs. Frankenstein are allowed to escape, to provide the stock Hollywood ending and some offspring to populate future sequels.

The Bride of Frankenstein marked the climax of the depression's Hollywood horror cycle and the beginning of the end as well. Its horrors were too fully humanized, and while such a technique might work once, it became self-defeating when employed as standard operating procedure. A spate of similarly self-conscious productions left frightening films as dead as Dracula by 1936. Universal's *Werewolf of London* (1935) attempted without much success to capitalize on the legends of lycanthropy. It concentrated largely on the hero's efforts to cure his condition, and even in his bestial form Henry Hull seems incapable of much enthusiasm. Even the expert technicians seemed asleep at the switch: Jack Pierce's makeup job was sketchy, and John Fulton's shaky special effects required Hull to pass behind a row of pillars as each stage of the transformation from man to monster was revealed. The film did at least establish the motion picture tradition that werewolves are not men who turn into wolves, but men who turn into hairy men with fangs and claws.

Equally disappointing was MGM's *Mark of the Vampire* (1935), Tod Browning's remake of the silent *London after Midnight.* What makes the film so infuriating is that it contains a

Carol Borland yields to Bela Lugosi in a bloodsucking scene that turns out to be only playacting, from Tod Browning's tricky *Mark of the Vampire* (1935). *Courtesy of MGM.*

few minutes of the most eerie and evocative vampire scenes ever filmed, but they are interspersed with great stretches of dull exposition, and the conclusion of the film reveals that the supernatural manifestations are only a hoax. Bela Lugosi and Carol Borland are impressive in what are, unfortunately, no more than bit parts.

The last nail in the coffin of fearsome film fare was provided by Universal's 1936 offering, *Dracula's Daughter.* The plot was not really based, as the studio claimed, on Bram Stoker's short story "Dracula's Guest," which was an early portion of the original novel excised before the first printing. Rather, *Dracula's Daughter* was a sequel to the Lugosi film, in which the count's vampiric heiress appears in London to claim her father's body. The sequel makes up for the telescoped version of the novel by returning most of the characters to Transylvania for the climax, something its predecessor had failed to do; but it is, for the most part, an anemic effort. Perhaps out of misguided deference to the "weaker sex," the script depicts its title character (Gloria Holden) as a reluctant leech who spends most of her time bemoaning her condition and seeking medical advice. Her backsliding is so apparent that she is eliminated, not by the forces of good, but by a disgusted underling with a bow and arrow. This ingenious variation on the obligatory wooden stake passed almost unnoticed for decades, but it was to become a cliché of latter-day vampire epics.

For audiences of the depressing thirties, and perhaps for all followers of the genre, much of the pleasure to be derived from horror films depends on the presence of a purposeful menace, rather than one plagued by doubt and indecision or explained away as part of a rational plan as in *Mark of the Vampire.* And so in 1936 the movie monsters crawled back into their crypts, only to be resurrected three years later when a revival of the original *Dracula* and *Frankenstein* demonstrated that the right kind of macabre motion picture was more popular than ever.

Meanwhile, radio broadcasting had developed into a successful commercial enterprise. Just as the movies were discovering sound, the public discovered radio, and a new medium for drama was born, one that soon proved eminently suitable for the presentation of mysterious melodramas. The earliest and most successful radio series with a macabre theme was "The Shadow." Perhaps the best-remembered program in the history of radio drama, "The Shadow" was on the airwaves in one form or another for a quarter of a century, covering nearly all the years in which plays were broadcast. The program and the title character evolved gradually from a primitive effort in the late twenties called "Street and Smith's Detective Story Magazine Hour." Originally, the program consisted of no more than an actor reading stories from the popular pulp magazine, but writer Harry Charlot suggested that the narrator (James La Curto) should be called the Shadow, and a character gradually evolved to become the principal figure in the stories he had been designed to tell. He soon became so impressive that publishers Street and Smith inaugurated a new magazine named after him. The Shadow in print, however, was a different character than the one on the radio. In his magazine incarnation, as conceived by writer Walter Gibson under the pseudonym Maxwell Grant, the Shadow was a black-clad crime fighter whose principal weapons were a pair of huge revolvers. The radio Shadow was above such crude tactics, preferring to torment the wicked into betraying themselves through a more subtle use of supernatural powers. He had learned in the Orient how to "cloud men's minds" so that he was, in effect, invisible. Common criminals were obviously no match for him, so script writers frequently pitted him against more exotic menaces like werewolves, vampires, zombies, mad scientists, and even beings from outer space. Somehow, none of them was as frightening as the Shadow himself, even though he seemed perfectly personable in his secret identity as a wealthy playboy named Lamont Cranston. The Shadow's most popular lines were "The weed of crime bears bitter fruit" and "Who knows what evil lurks in the hearts of men? The Shadow knows!" They were followed by bursts of maniacal laughter which strongly suggested that his knowledge of evil was based on personal experiences never revealed to the public. Actors who assumed the role included Frank Readick, Robert Hardy Andrews, Bill Johnstone, Bret Morrison, and, for a two-year stretch beginning in 1937, a young actor named Orson Welles, who would soon be involved in a broadcast that must be counted as the most successful attempt to scare audiences in the history of mass communications.

A crew of less exotic heroes confronted a similar series of bizarre villains in a radio series called "I Love a Mystery." A trio of fun-loving adventurers operating out of a detective agency, Jack Packard, Doc Long, and Reggie York were the creations of Carlton E. Morse, a pioneer in radio drama whose offerings were usually a bit more sedate. The "I Love a Mystery" crew handled many a bizarre case, including one, "The Decapitation of Jefferson Monk," that was made into a movie. Their most notorious adventure, "The Temple of the Vampires," was frequently revived during the program's run from 1939 to 1952.

In addition to the weird adversaries that some of radio's popular heroes encountered, broadcasting unleashed on the public a plethora of preternatural personalities whose horrors went virtually unopposed. A surprising number of programs took to the air with no regular characters to sustain them, only the promise of a series of unrelated sinister stories. Yet the programs that were dramatic anthologies of terror tales enjoyed considerable success during the decades of radio's finest hours. Among them were "Inner Sanctum," "Suspense," "Superstition," "The Hermit's Cave," "The Haunting Hour," "The Weird Circle," "The Sealed Book," "The Witch's Tales," "Stay Tuned for Terror," "Starring Boris Karloff," "Lights Out," and even, briefly, the redundantly titled "The Strange Dr. Weird," starring Maurice Tarplin.

The most memorable of the group was "Inner Sanctum," which began in January 1941 under the more evocative title "The Squeaking Door." The original title contained the key to the program's success. The stories were frequently mechanical murder mysteries; but they basked in the uncanny aura created by a sound-effects man and the show's host, Raymond Edward Johnson, who introduced himself simply as Raymond. His slow, sardonic introductions invited the listeners into the dark room of their own imaginations, accompanied by the sound of a massive portal creaking on rusty hinges. When the door finally slammed shut at the end of the half-hour, cutting short Raymond's insincere farewell ("Good night, and pleasant dreams"), the audience was ready for nightmares. Johnson and his producer Himan Brown more or less created the tradition of the horror story hosted by a sinister, sarcastic spokesman; the technique was subsequently used in films, in comic books, and on television. Indeed, "Inner Sanctum" was one of the few radio programs of any type to make a successful transition to video, showing the squeaking door in all its splendor while Raymond remained modestly off camera.

Most of the other programs were pale imitations of these. "The Hermit's Cave" made more of an impression than most because its cantankerous caretaker came across as a convincing character and because most of his narratives eschewed simple or even complicated murder stories in favor of tales with a more uncanny flavor. "Lights Out," a spin-off from an earlier program called "Everyman's Theater," showcased the works of writer Arch Oboler, who had an unusual grasp of the techniques that could turn sounds and the spoken word into a compelling dramatic experience. Among his best efforts were

"Two" (with Joan Crawford and Raymond Edward Johnson), a play about the end of the earth; and "The Ugliest Man in the World," a surprisingly sentimental offering that was repeated five times by popular request. The most notorious "Lights Out" program concerned a scientist whose experiments with cell structure accidentally produce a chicken heart that grows until it threatens to absorb the entire planet.

Not as well known but equally skillful were the scripts prepared by Robert Bloch for "Stay Tuned for Terror." Bloch, a *Weird Tales* author who began as a disciple of Lovecraft, had found his own style in the years after his mentor's death. His specialty was a sort of gallows humor that bore some resemblance to that employed by Ambrose Bierce, but Bloch's work was distinguished by a particularly modern flavor, in which the skepticism and slang of twentieth-century life were contrasted with ancient terrors. His most famous story, "Yours Truly, Jack the Ripper," became the most renowned offering of "Stay Tuned for Terror." Virtually unrelieved by Bloch's usual comic touches, the script hypothesized that the murders perpetrated by the nineteenth century's notorious mass killer were part of a ritual by which he achieved immortality, forcing him to enact a similar series of crimes at regular intervals in his endless career. It seemed as reasonable a theory as any to account for the sporadic outbreaks of senseless slaughter that have plagued contemporary civilization.

Despite their merits, all these efforts to unnerve radio listeners pale beside what was achieved by "The Mercury Theater" on October 30, 1938. Its version of the H. G. Wells novel *The War of the Worlds* scared more people more thoroughly than any work of the imagination ever created. Most of the credit (or blame) must go to actor and coproducer Orson Welles, who conceived the plan to modernize the 1898 novel, shift the locale from England to the United States, and, most important, to present the story as a series of news announcements interrupting a musical program. Several announcements during the program explaining its fictional nature were missed or ignored by thousands of radio fans who became firmly convinced that their planet had in fact been attacked by monsters from Mars. The result was a mass panic, especially in New Jersey, where scriptwriter Howard Koch had decided the Martians would land first. The most common extreme reaction was to jump into a car and flee from the invaders. Fortunately no one was seriously injured, and within a few days the broadcast was accepted by most Americans as a great joke, while a few serious thinkers paused to analyze public impressionability to official-sounding statements. Welles and his coproducer John Houseman claimed that their intentions were perfectly innocent; but they were soon on their way, along with writer Howard Koch, to distinguished careers in the motion picture industry. If any of them had any idea of the sensation they would cause, they have never admitted it.

On a much more modest scale, pulp magazines continued their campaign to keep readers on the edges of their seats. *Weird Tales* struggled on, producing some excellent fiction and no profits; yet its grim financial condition failed to discourage competition. Inspired by the success of Hollywood horrors, several pulp publishers ventured into the domain of the macabre, usually with motives somewhat less lofty than those that kept *Weird Tales* afloat. An outfit modestly designated as Culture Publications started a new slant on the literature of terror with its magazine *Spicy Mystery.* This was just one of a whole line of "spicy" titles, dedicated to the proposition that sex, or as much of it as the censors would allow, could sell magazines. The term "mystery" was used here to designate uncanny events rather than criminal cases; but the principal emphasis was on the "spicy," and the thrust of the stories was toward sadism. Elements of this sort of eroticism are present, of course, in many artistically accomplished works of the macabre,

Weird Tales
is on the air . . . . in
STAY TUNED FOR TERROR
This programme is adapted by ROBERT BLOCH from his stories which have appeared in WEIRD TALES, the narrator being Craig Dennis.
STAY TUNED FOR TERROR is produced by Neblett Radio Productions, with the active cooperation of WEIRD TALES MAGAZINE . . . for the enjoyment of fantasy fans everywhere.
LOOK FOR ANNOUNCEMENTS IN YOUR LOCAL NEWSPAPER giving the broadcast time and dates in your area.
~*~
And remember to . . . .
Stay Tuned for Terror!

Boris Dolgov designed this ad to inform *Weird Tales* readers that Robert Bloch's stories were also available on the radio.

but the offerings in *Spicy Mystery* were crude and monotonous. The same sort of hackwork formula was repeated in *Dime Mystery*, *Horror Stories*, and *Terror Tales*, all the products of Popular Publications. Other publishers followed suit, and the slightly perverted horror pulps flourished for a decade, finally dying out during the Second World War when many of their producers began converting to comic books. This new type of magazine became a major factor in the decline and eventual disappearance of the pulps.

Bucking the tide was the one pulp magazine to rival the esteem in which aficionados of fantasy held *Weird Tales*. This was Street and Smith's *Unknown*, edited by John W. Campbell, Jr. *Unknown*, whose title was later changed to *Unknown Worlds*, appeared in the midst of a failing market and only lasted from 1939 until 1943. Yet in those few short years it managed to acquire a reputation that still survives. Regular *Unknown* authors developed a characteristically light, whimsical mood. There were darker moments; but the typical tale recognized the humorous incongruity of the supernatural in urban life and demonstrated that even magical intervention in the affairs of men was unlikely to relieve the frustration of the human condition. Wisecracks worked hand in hand with hexes, creating a hybrid horror style that juxtaposed legendary legerdemain with contemporary complications. Among the writers who helped to establish the flavor of this short-lived but influential publication was L. Sprague de Camp who specialized in novels like *Lest Darkness Fall*, a tale of a modern historian adrift in ancient Rome which owed something of its concept to Mark Twain's *Connecticut Yankee in King Arthur's Court.* Fritz Leiber, Jr., created a lighthearted variation on Robert E. Howard's sword-and-sorcery

Unknown World's chief artist, Edd Cartier, came up with this vision of Fritz Leiber's "Smoke Ghost," a sinister spirit of the sooty city. _Copyright © 1941 by Street and Smith Publications, Inc. Copyright © (renewed) 1969 by The Condé Nast Publications Inc._

One of Edd Cartier's illustrations for Henry Kuttner's "A Gnome There Was," an apparently humorous story that, with typical *Unknown* duplicity, slips suddenly into stark horror. ***Copyright © 1941 by Street and Smith Publications, Inc. Copyright © (renewed) 1969 by The Condé Nast Publications Inc.***

sagas with a series of stories about the ancient adventurers Fafhrd and the Gray Mouser; more characteristic of the *Unknown* forum were pieces like "Smoke Ghost," in which Leiber attempted with considerable success to conjure up a new sort of spirit, one that haunted the dark and dirty recesses of a modern metropolis. He also brought witchcraft to a modern college campus with his celebrated novel *Conjure Wife.*

Perhaps the best representative of the magazine was Theodore Sturgeon, who excelled in screwball conceptions such as "Yesterday Was Monday," in which the hero discovers a gang of little men whose strange task it is to shift scenery from one day to the next, preparing the stage for the drama of mortal existence. In a change of pace, Sturgeon penned the magazine's best-known horror tale, "It," about a mindless creature spontaneously formed on the skeleton of a murdered man. Another eminently successful chiller was "The Devil We Know," by Henry Kuttner, in which a man makes what seems to be a successful deal with a demon, only to discover that in the process he has inherited his demon's demon, a hideous entity totally beyond human comprehension. Perhaps the magazine's most celebrated contributor is L. Ron Hubbard, who wrote whimsical adventure fantasies like *Triton* and *Slaves of Sleep* years before he propounded the theories which brought him fame and fortune as the creator of the controversial self-improvement programs Dianetics and Scientology. All of these writers were later to achieve fame in the field of science fiction; after Lovecraft's experimental fusion of that genre with fantasy, it was not uncommon for authors to work in both fields. Some *Unknown* authors, like Fredric Brown and Anthony Boucher, were equally adept in the field of the detective story. Boucher's novelette *The Compleat Werewolf*, about a lovable lycanthrope who ends up working as an undercover investigator, is a classic example of the *Unknown* style. The magazine demonstrated the extent to which traditionally frightening fantasies had become commonplace and thus fair game for parodists.

Hollywood was discovering that its monsters, too, had become tolerable. Universal started off a new cycle of sinister cinema well enough in 1939 with *Son of Frankenstein*; in retrospect it was a transition point between the comparatively sincere efforts of the thirties and the more mechanical productions of the forties. Solidly directed by Rowland V. Lee, it featured Boris Karloff's last appearance in the role that had made him a star. The monster is silent again, but *Bride of Frankenstein* had established the precedent that he should be a tool in the hands of a superior intelligence, devoid of the unpredictability that had made him such a fascinating figure in the first film. On the other hand, Bela Lugosi got his best role since *Dracula*, portraying a homicidal peasant named Ygor who had survived the hangman's noose with a broken neck. Ygor discovers the monster, dormant but intact after the previous film's explosion, and convinces the original Frankenstein's son (Basil Rathbone) to revive his father's creation. The monster becomes Ygor's pawn in a plan of revenge against the men who had sent the depraved old codger to the gallows; the son of Frankenstein comes to regret his scientific curiosity and assuages his guilt by swinging Tarzan-style from a rope to kick the monster in a pool of boiling sulfur. Well acted and lavishly produced, *Son of Frankenstein* is an exciting film that nevertheless fails almost completely to evoke an aura of the uncanny. Even the addition of an extra menace in the person of the deformed Ygor failed to recall the eerie atmosphere of earlier efforts; but it was becoming apparent that the horror film was established as a genre that audiences were prepared to enjoy even when it failed to produce a strong emotional impact.

Universal was not the only studio to show a revived interest in horror in 1939; most of the other Hollywood studios sensed the trend. Paramount perhaps came closest to an assessment of the general trend by releasing a totally humorous version of that old standby *The Cat and the Canary*, designed as a vehicle for comedian Bob Hope. RKO remade *The Hunchback of Notre Dame* with Charles Laughton in the title role, playing down the frightening features of the story and, as in Lon Chaney's silent version, ignoring the novel's downbeat conclusion.

A series of slightly more thoughtful mad-scientist melodramas began to emerge from Columbia, including *The Man They Could Not Hang* (1939), *Before I Hang* (1940), and *The Man with Nine Lives* (1940). These were concocted from the formula of a well-meaning doctor whose experiments are interrupted by the authorities, resulting in the death of a volunteer subject, the doctor's execution for murder, and his return for revenge through the very device that had caused all the trouble. All starred Boris Karloff, and they are especially interesting today because so many of the outlandish devices he struggles with, such as artificial hearts and frozen patients, have become medical realities since the films were made.

Parody continued in 1940 with the Bob Hope feature *The Ghost Breakers*, successful enough to be remade in the next decade as a Dean Martin and Jerry Lewis feature, *Scared Stiff*. Meanwhile, Universal decided to revive two of its most successful unemployed monsters, the Mummy and the Invisible Man. Each suffered in comparison with the original conception. *The Mummy's Hand* was not a sequel to the 1932 film but a new story about a different mummy, Kharis, who was revived by Egyptian priests to guard a royal tomb. Tom Tyler played Kharis, reanimated by a brew of Tanna leaves, as an efficient but characterless killing machine. *The Invisible Man Returns* featured Vincent Price as an embattled hero who uses invisibility to track down a murderer. The role was a feeble version of the megalomaniac originally enacted by Claude Rains, noteworthy only because it gave Price his first opportunity in the sort of film that would, in later decades, provide him with his greatest fame.

A more immediate but shorter-lived success came to the actor who, beginning in 1941, was to carry Universal's horror films for the next five years, portraying most of their famous fiends and a few new ones besides. This was Lon Chaney, Jr. Born Creighton Chaney, the son of the silent film star had given a powerful performance in 1939 as a simpleminded killer in *Of Mice and Men.* His first Universal horror feature, *Man-Made Monster*, gave Chaney a similar role, as a bewildered circus performer who becomes supercharged with electric current.

Bewilderment became Chaney's principal expression in those performances in which his features were fairly free of makeup. Lacking the dynamic presence of his predecessors, he usually managed to carry his weight through his evident sincerity and dedication. He got his best part almost immediately in the 1941 feature *The Wolf Man* directed by George Waggner. As reluctant werewolf Larry Talbot, Chaney displayed his dismay within an appropriate context, and the role became a sort of minor classic which he would repeat in four more films (although never without the support of a more reliable monster). Curt Siodmak's screenplay for *The Wolf Man* established the Hollywood version of the werewolf myth, in which the lycanthrope must be killed with a silver weapon. The deathblow is finally delivered by Talbot's father (Claude Rains); the curse had originally

Lon Chaney, Jr., had his best and favorite role as Larry Talbot, the Wolf Man (1941), in the screen's most famous treatment of the lycanthropy legend. ***Courtesy of Universal Pictures.***

been inflicted on him by another sort of father figure, Bela Lugosi, who plays the cameo role of a Gypsy werewolf. Jack Pierce and John Fulton came through with what they had failed to provide for *The Werewolf of London*: Pierce's makeup work was appropriately menacing, and Fulton handled the transformation scenes with a skill that would increase with each new Wolf Man saga.

The same year saw a more familiar series of transformations as *Dr. Jekyll and Mr. Hyde* was dragged out once again, this time by MGM. Spencer Tracy played the dual role with minimal makeup and considerable restraint, but this careful film is decidedly inferior to the occasionally ludicrous but always lively Fredric March version.

In 1942, RKO launched a new series of horror movies to be produced by Val Lewton, whose strong hand seems to have had more influence on the character of his films than the directors he employed. His productions included *The Cat People* (1942), *I Walked with a Zombie* (1943), *The Seventh Victim* (1943), *The Curse of the Cat People* (1944), *Isle of the Dead* (1945), *The Body Snatcher* (1945), and *Bedlam* (1946). As a group they were distinguished by subtlety and psychological overtones; they hint at the supernatural, while other motion pictures of the decade exploited its entertainment value. They are well liked by critics who deplore the usual movie of this type, being in this sense at least the cinematic equivalent of *The Turn of the Screw*. Unfortunately some of them seem only halfhearted attempts, more respectable than entertaining.

Perhaps the most widely known and praised of Lewton's movies is *The Cat People*, a variation on the werewolf theme in which a young woman (Simone Simon) is transformed into a black panther. Director Jacques Tourneur manages to sustain doubt about whether or not the changes are really taking place until the end of the film, when the woman dies after the unseen beast has been wounded by one of its victims. The ambiguity about the nature of the heroine's problem creates a kind of suspense, but it leaves open until the last moment the truly horrifying possibility that *The Cat People* may be, like *Mark of the Vampire*, one of those horror films that degenerate at the end into implausible murder mysteries. Even its devotees should have been disappointed by the movie's spurious sequel *The Curse of the Cat People*. This tale of a small girl and her imaginary playmates is totally devoid of terror and may well be the most inaccurately titled production in the history of the cinema.

Lewton's subsequent productions abandoned the uncanny element almost entirely. For instance, the "zombie" in *I Walked with a Zombie*, also directed by Tourneur, is not one of the resurrected corpses employed as slave laborers by Caribbean sorcerers but a woman whose unusual disease makes her look like a zombie to her superstitious neighbors. Yet even after a logical explanation is offered the ambiguity remains, providing most of the tension and a haunting mood most fully expressed when a backsliding nurse escorts the patient through the night to a forbidden voodoo ceremony.

Eventually Lewton acquired the services of a prominent performer in the field, Boris Karloff. Bigger budgets also allowed more elaborate productions, perhaps shown to best advantage in an adaptation of Stevenson's *Body Snatcher*. Nineteenth-century Edinburgh is convincingly evoked in this story of physicians and grave robbers, and Karloff's excellent performance as a body snatcher who graduates to murder is matched by that of Henry Daniell as a sanctimonious doctor whose quest for specimens leads him down the road to disaster. The conflict between the two makes the whole film grim and suspenseful; it achieves an authentic moment of supernatural shock when the doctor, driven to the murder of his unscrupulous supplier, visits a cemetery himself and discovers that he has carted off the corpse of his vengeful victim. Karloff's other features for Lewton, lacking the fine hand of director Robert Wise, were less successful. *Isle of the Dead* showed the unpleasant predicament of a group of war refugees quarantined by a plague that sends one of their number to a premature burial; *Bedlam* presented Karloff as the brutal proprietor of an insane asylum who is finally murdered by one of his charges.

A film with a similarly subtle approach to the supernatural was Paramount's *The Uninvited* (1944). This genteel ghost story featured Ray Milland and Ruth Hussey as the owners of a haunted house. Based on a popular novel by Dorothy Macardle, and directed by Lewis Allen, it was a capable effort which also made more money than most of the mainstream monster movies. It was, in fact, so far removed from the typical Hollywood treatment that it almost seems to belong to a different genre.

While these productions were making some impressive attempts to unnerve audiences, the mainstream efforts at Universal seemed less intent on frightening the fans than on providing them with a rousing good time. The tone of the studio's later films suggests that the intention was to let the viewers identify with the increasingly outrageous antics of their favorite monsters, most of them played by Lon Chaney, Jr. In 1942 he got his chance at the monster in *Ghost of Frankenstein*, probably the worst of the studio's series, lacking both the conviction of the first three films and the wild action of those that were to follow. It did at least establish a nice sense of continuity, for the monster is released from the now hardened sulfur pit where he had been in retirement since *Son of Frankenstein.* He is once again in the hands of Ygor (still Lugosi) who has overcome his apparent death in the previous episode with no explanation at all. Their adventures take them to visit another son of Frankenstein (Cedric Hardwicke), who is persuaded to replace the monster's objectionable criminal brain with that of a colleague. With the help of a corrupt assistant, Ygor succeeds in having his own brain placed in the gigantic body, and he enjoys a brief moment of triumph before succumbing to the inevitable conflagration. No mention is made of this startling transformation in later sequels, although the monster was played in the next film by none other than Bela Lugosi.

In the same year, Chaney made a somewhat overweight Kharis in *The Mummy's Tomb*, searching America without much success for the reincarnation of his lost Egyptian love. The 1944 sequel, *The Mummy's Ghost*, seemed to be cut from the same moldy bandage, as Kharis discovers a familiar face (Ramsay Ames) on a college campus and makes several attempts to carry her off. Incredibly, he finally gets away with it, slinking off into a swamp with the heroine who tacitly admits the wisdom of his choice as her hair turns white and she is transformed into an ancient mummified crone. It took three writers, Griffin Jay, Henry Sucher, and Brenda Weisberg, to come up with this downbeat ending, apparently the first in the history of the commercial horror film. Unfortunately the series did not end on this surprising note but concluded in the same year with still another sequel, *The Mummy's Curse*, in which Kharis and his lady love are dredged out of the swamp (mysteriously transported from New England to Louisiana) and put through their paces one more time.

Chaney inherited another set of antisocial characteristics in 1943 when he appeared as *Son of Dracula.* He made a rather too solid and stolid vampire, but the film provided a field day for John Fulton by elaborating on some of the more obscure powers of the undead. For the first time a man was shown changing himself into a bat (always photographed from the rear, so that the long black cloak could be transformed by animation), and Chaney also appeared as a mobile cloud of mist. In one particularly impressive scene, the vampire floats across a lake standing upright on his coffin. The film also must bear the responsibility for firmly establishing the cinematic tradition (contrary to most previously published accounts, but also present in the silent film *Nosferatu*) that sunlight is poison to Dracula and his descendants.

The Mummy's Tomb (1942) featured Lon Chaney, Jr., as the walking mass of mold and bandages, Kharis, whose adventures filled four films. *Courtesy of Universal Pictures.*

This imaginative outing was overshadowed, though, by 1943's spectacular social event, *Frankenstein Meets the Wolf Man.* Chaney returned to his best role as Larry Talbot, carrying most of the movie's weight as he inexplicably returns from the dead, complete with his curious affliction. Seeking expert medical advice from Dr. Frankenstein, he encounters the monster (Bela Lugosi) instead. After decorous maneuvering, Talbot becomes the Wolf Man just as the monster receives his annual dose of electricity, and the two engage in a fight to the finish, staged with less relish than might be desired. Before a winner can be declared, civic-minded villagers blow up a dam, flooding the castle where the monsters are earning their keep and slowing them down for several months.

They were back in 1944, along with Count Dracula and other assorted fiends; the film was *House of Frankenstein.* Boris Karloff and J. Carrol Naish were featured as a mad scientist and a hunchback awaiting execution when a fortuitous lightning bolt demolishes their prison. On their journey back to the doctor's abandoned laboratory, they join a traveling chamber of horrors whose chief attraction is the skeleton of Dracula, a stake still planted in its ribs. Karloff removes the stake and, contrary to all traditional lore, revives the vampire. Appearing in a rather mechanical series of double exposures which includes the formation of a dress suit, Dracula is incarnated in the person of John Carradine, a fine actor whose tall, gaunt appearance, complete with white hair and moustache, duplicates the description in the original novel more accurately than any other performer. Unfortunately, he has only a few minutes of screen time before he is eliminated by the rays of the sun. The two linking characters continue their journey, discovering the Wolf Man and the Frankenstein monster encased in ice after the previous film's flood. Chaney emerges in human form and enlists the doctor's help in ending his affliction; but the unconscious monster captures Karloff's interest, and the Wolf Man is eliminated with a silver bullet. The monster is finally revived in the film's climax, hardly getting on his feet before he is driven into a pool of quicksand by the inevitable band of torch-bearing villagers. A former wrestler named Glenn Strange portrayed Hollywood's most famous horror. Coached by Karloff, he was to play the role three times, duplicating his master's record, if not his artistic accomplishment. Still, his brief appearance did not allow for a very profound performance. *House of Frankenstein* strained credibility, even by the standards of its genre; but the story by Curt Siodmak made for an entertaining free-for-all, demonstrating that the monsters were now stars in their own right who had only to appear and take a bow to satisfy their clearly unfrightened followers.

Inevitably, 1945 brought a new house party, *House of Dracula.* Another scientist (Onslow Stevens), provided the focal point as he is visited by the Wolf Man (still Chaney) and Dracula (again Carradine), both seeking a cure for their conditions. The doctor tries transfusions on the vampire, but he ends up infected himself and decides to shove the count's coffin out into the daylight. The Wolf Man, on one of his rampages, finds his old friend the monster unconscious in a cavern, apparently beneath the last film's quicksand. The doctor, of course, is anxious to give Glenn Strange another dose of voltage, but he finds time to cure Larry Talbot by altering the shape of his skull. The monster walks again, for just long enough to go up in flames with the doctor. As a variation on the previous film, *House of Dracula* has a female hunchback as the scientist's assistant. Nonetheless, the movie signaled the end of the line for the long cycle of Hollywood horrors.

Numerous other movies of less consequence were released during the same period, many by poverty-row studios like Monogram and P.R.C. Occasionally good performers like John Carradine and Bela Lugosi ended up in deadly productions from these outfits such as *Revenge of the Zombies* or *The Devil Bat*; the best actor to emerge from this school was bald, beady-eyed George Zucco, a threatening thespian who eventually graduated to supporting roles in some of Universal's later productions. In some ways the most remarkable star of the sinister cinema was Rondo Hatton, whose total lack of acting ability found cruel compensation in his naturally distorted features. He appeared in second-rate efforts like *The Brute Man* and *House of Horrors*, in which he played a creature called the Creeper. Universal kept a bad concept going for three films (to allow for double features), in a series begun when a demented doctor creates an ape-woman in *Captive Wild Woman* (1943), *Jungle Woman* (1944), and *Jungle Captive* (1945).

While Hollywood was running out of steam, England came up with one of the most accomplished films on supernatural subjects, *Dead of Night* (1945). Several directors were involved in this project, which was a compendium of six stories told by guests at a house and linked together by the story of a visitor who had dreamed that he would arrive there. Some of the sequences are light in tone or sketchy in execution, but they provide a sense of the range of uncanny effects which the standard "monster" movies had ignored. The most morbid of the lot involves a schizophrenic ventriloquist (Michael Redgrave) whose dummy acquires a life of its own; variations on this plot became a stock device in various media.

In general, fearsome films were a rare occurrence in Europe during the same period when they flourished most fantastically in the United States. One exception was Carl Dreyer's unrecognizably free adaptation of Le Fanu's "Carmilla" entitled *Vampyr* (1932). This moody, impressionistic film, shot entirely through gauze and available in several versions, has proved to be of more interest to the critics than to the public. The increasingly Kafkaesque air of depression Germany is captured in Fritz Lang's *M* (1931), in which criminals supplant the regular police force to unearth a homicidal maniac. The director and his star, Peter Lorre, soon emigrated to the United States, where their melancholy talents were well employed. Lorre shaved his head to appear in MGM's *Mad Love* (1935), directed by Karl Freund, as a surgeon who grafts a murderer's hands onto a crippled musician. In one remarkably bizarre scene, he attempts to prove his skill by masquerading as a guillotined killer whose head has been replaced with the aid of a grotesque steel brace. Lorre also had the distinction of starring in the last serious Hollywood horror film of the forties, the Warner Brothers adaptation of William Fryer Harvey's story, *The Beast with Five Fingers* (1947).

Universal finally threw in the towel in 1948 with its last monster rally, which might have been entitled *House of the Wolf Man*; instead, it was *Abbott and Costello Meet Frankenstein.* Sometimes very funny, and never as bad as purists might imagine, this was the film in which Bela Lugosi donned his famous cape again for his second and last portrayal of the bloodthirsty Dracula, although he had played a similar role in Columbia's 1944 *Return of the Vampire.* The popular comedy team of Abbott and Costello made expository scenes more entertaining than many more serious performers had been able to do, and the Wolf Man (Chaney), the Frankenstein monster (Strange), and Count Dracula were all allowed to play it straight. This time Dracula is in charge, planning to make the monster more malleable by giving him Costello's addled brain. The Wolf Man is something of a hero when in human form, and he even sacrifices his life to destroy Dracula by jumping over a ledge to crush the vampire bat in his hairy paws. It was the end of the line for Larry Talbot and for the Universal version of the monster as well. Sizzling in the fourth fire of his seventeen-year career, Frankenstein's brainchild decided to retire permanently. There was one brief moment of hope: having destroyed the three

Comedians Bud and Lou in *Abbott and Costello Meet Frankenstein* (Glenn Strange), to say nothing of Dracula (Bela Lugosi) and the Wolf Man (Lon Chaney, Jr.). *Courtesy of Universal Pictures.*

most durable demons in Hollywood history, the heroes had only a moment's peace at the end of the movie before the voice of Vincent Price informed them that the Invisible Man was on the job.

It was a prophetic moment; Price was one of the few movie menaces to survive the next decade with his credentials intact. The huge harvest of horrors unleashed in the thirties and forties seemed to have exhausted both creators and consumers, and the fortunes of fiends were failing. There were, however, a few keepers of the flame who worked unacknowledged wonders while waiting for lightning to strike again.

8

SLIME: THE RETREAT TO REALITY

The Second World War, climaxing with the explosion of nuclear weapons and capped by the hideous revelations unearthed in a beaten Germany, had temporarily exhausted the public's appetite for horrors of any kind. The continuing series of Abbott and Costello parodies were all that remained of the frightening films that had resurrected so many fictional fiends; the comedy team went on to *Meet Dr. Jekyll and Mr. Hyde* and *Meet the Invisible Man* in 1953 and *Meet the Mummy* in 1954. None of them could hold a candle to the duo's original encounter with the uncanny in 1948.

By 1950, however, there were a few signs of new blood. Viewed historically, these were temporary phenomena, highlights of a low period for fearsome fantasies. Some significant creations emerged, though; in fact, two different art forms came up with innovative structures for raising the hair of the mass audience, each to have a significant effect during the few years of its existence. In the cinema, monster movies got a new lease on life through a transfusion of "science fiction," which came to mean that mutation and invasion from outer space were the sources for new horrors constructed around old plot outlines. The apparently greater plausibility of the "scientific" over the supernatural served to keep the genre alive until a new generation of out-and-out thrill seekers could grow into an economic bloc. More extraordinary and unexpected was the brutally graphic and remarkably literate group of comic books that helped to turn a commercial enterprise into a budding art form, one whose importance has only begun to be appreciated.

The comic book publisher was William Gaines, a fear fancier who inherited Entertaining Comics with some misgivings, then decided to promote horror material as a serious proposition. The resulting E.C. comic books were *Tales from the Crypt*, *The Vault of Horror*, and *The Haunt of Fear*. They were not exactly the first in their field to play on the emotion of fear, but they concentrated on it with new intensity, building on a tradition that stretched back for years.

The comic book was an outgrowth of the newspaper comic strips which were close to half a century old before they began to appear successfully in magazine form. The original newspaper strips were predominantly humorous, but they grew grimmer with the advent of the depression. Adventure material began to appear, and there were occasional touches of terror in works like *Tarzan* (adapted from the Edgar Rice Burroughs sagas by Hal Foster, later by Burne Hogarth), *Buck Rogers* (by Phil Nowland

and Dick Calkins), *Flash Gordon* (by Alex Raymond), and *Dick Tracy* (by Chester Gould). Gould's detective strip was the grimmest of the lot, more than once running into censorship problems because of the creator's insistence on violent deaths and grotesquely deformed villains. Writer Lee Falk came up with two characters with subdued supernatural suggestions: Mandrake the Magician, who used hocus-pocus to right wrongs; and the Phantom, a masked hero who preserved the illusion that he was immortal by training successive generations of offspring to inherit his disguise.

Comic books began by reprinting newspaper material, but they came into their own in 1938 when the debut of Superman in *Action Comics* demonstrated that new characters could be even more successful. Amid the wide variety of costumed heroes that sprang up to follow this example, there were several whose demeanor had macabre overtones. The most popular came from Superman's publishers, National Periodicals. This was Batman, a creation of Bob Kane, Jerry Robinson, and Bill Finger who bowed in 1939 in *Detective Comics.* An enemy of crime who was inspired by the murder of his mother and father, Bruce Wayne adopted the grotesque gray guise of a bat to frighten superstitious felons. His early adventures depicted the Batman as a merciless menace; but he was gradually humanized, and the uncanny atmosphere of the original stories was dissipated. Another major character with a weird background was Will Eisner's Spirit, who got his start in 1940. Another masked avenger, though considerably less flamboyant, the Spirit was a detective who faked his own death to solve a case and enjoyed his new role as a mystery man so much that he adopted it permanently, setting up headquarters in Wildwood Cemetery. Drawn and written with unusual flair, *The Spirit* did not really emphasize its hero's supposedly supernatural origin; Eisner achieved most of his effects through wit and an unusual degree of naturalism.

There was a comic book policeman who was actually killed but managed to come back anyway as the Spectre. Written by Jerry Siegel, the author of the original Superman stories, *The Spectre*'s title character had powers surpassing those of every other comic book hero. In fact, the forbidding white figure wrapped in a green cloak was absolutely omnipotent, battling felonious plots with a limitless array of sensational stunts. One of his favorite tricks was scaring his adversaries to death. Most of his adventures took place in National's *More Fun Comics*, where he lasted for five years despite his lack of human warmth and weaknesses. Slightly less spectacular magicians were a commonplace in the early days of comic books; most of them, like Fred Guardineer's Zatara, were similar to Lee Falk's Mandrake. The exception, who lasted longer than any of his rivals, was Fawcett Publications' Ibis the Invincible, who began his thirteen-year career in 1940. Ibis, a resurrected Egyptian prince, woke up from a four-thousand-year sleep to discover himself in twentieth-century America. He wore a turban instead of a top hat and performed his miracles with the aid of a magic wand called the Ibistick. Created by Bill Parker and drawn during his best period by Mac Raboy, Ibis distinguished himself during his *Whiz Comics* appearances by battling not the usual crew of gangsters, but a series of bloodcurdling supernatural fiends. For a decade, this feature was as close as comic books came to creating an authentically macabre atmosphere.

The search for bizarre superheroes in the early days of comic books unleashed a number of short-lived characters who were more or less monsters in their own right. Among the strangest was Russ Cochran's Eye, who was just what his name implied; his appearance inspired the Hand, who appeared with the slogan "The hand is quicker than the eye." Other unattractive heroes included the Hunchback, the Black Dwarf, the Banshee, and Blackout, who fought crime even after having been burned to a crisp. None of them became a great popular favorite, but monsters of almost every description were commonplace as opponents for almost every comic book character. Throughout the 1940s, the whole medium featured healthy doses of blood and thunder. Inevitably, the best box office attraction of all the monsters became a comic book star in his own right when Dick Briefer's version of Frankenstein began in a 1941 issue of *Prize Comics.* In this incarnation, the well-intentioned monster soon became a pawn of Nazi masterminds. After the war, Briefer began a new *Frankenstein* comic book, a comedy treatment in which the monster was a lovable lout. A few years later he reverted back to his antisocial habits, doubtless inspired by the success of William Gaines and his E.C. horror comic books.

A similar series of personality changes was undergone by the most outlandish of comic book creatures, the Heap. A downed German ace from the First World War, he rose again to aid the Nazis, his body fused by some odd osmosis with a vast mass of grass. The gigantic green walking vegetable started his career as a villain for the heroic Sky Wolf in Hillman Publications' *Air Fighters.* He was soon converted into an aid to the Allies, then set loose on the civilian population as the star of his own series. Always menacing, the Heap still did his share of good deeds, at least by efficiently eliminating more mortal evildoers. He was the creation of writer Harry Stein and artist Mort Leav.

Any one of these characters from the golden age of comic books was capable of creating nightmares, but they all paled beside the gruesome graphics of E.C.'s *Tales from the Crypt*, *Vault of Horror*, and *Haunt of Fear.* These three titles were launched in 1950, as part of what publisher Gaines called a "new trend," different from what had been attempted before because the magazines featured short stories related only by theme, without the crutch of continuing characters. As a result, the basically optimistic outcome of the traditional comic book tale was no longer required. In fact, E.C. specialized in unhappy endings. Editor Albert Feldstein, who wrote the scripts from the publisher's suggestions, brought a new level of sophistication to comic book stories in vocabulary, mood, tone, and plot. His skill was matched by the witchcraft of the artists. The chief chefs around this cauldron of ink were Jack Davis, Johnny Craig, and Graham Ingels, each identified with one of the terror titles by virtue of his skill in depicting its master of ceremonies. These were, respectively, the Crypt-Keeper *(Tales from the Crypt)*, the Vault-Keeper *(The Vault of Horror)*, and the Old Witch *(The Haunt of Fear)*. They functioned like the horror hosts of earlier radio shows, opening and closing the stories with lurid leers and pungent puns.

Occasionally, the artists appeared in their stories, as in the case of an early effort that purported to explain the origin of the comic books themselves. Publisher Gaines and editor Feldstein were depicted as a pair of innocent young fellows with a fondness for love comics who were kidnapped by the terrible trio. They saved their lives by signing contracts promising permanent employment to the sinister storytellers. Other tales in the same ludicrous vein offered origins for the nasty narrators: "A Little Stranger" depicted the Old Witch as the daughter of a werewolf and a vampire, while "Lower Berth" revealed that the Crypt-Keeper was the offspring of an elopement by two sideshow exhibits, an ancient mummy and a two-headed man who climbed out of a jar of formaldehyde to express his love. The scurrilous sexual suggestions inherent in these tales were just an example of the outrages against decorum of which the E.C. horror line made a specialty.

These publications were most outrageous, however, in their graphically detailed depiction of the gruesome and the grotesque. Revenge from beyond the grave was the most standard plot device, and those who returned were not the pale and dignified ghosts so common in literature but half-decayed corpses, dragging themselves from their coffins to enact their ghastly retribution. The vividly rendered features of the walking dead

Ibis the Invincible and his companion, Taia, fend off the forces of evil on this dramatic comic book cover by Mac Raboy.

Dick Briefer's humorous treatment of Frankenstein, referred to during this comic book incarnation as "the merry monster."

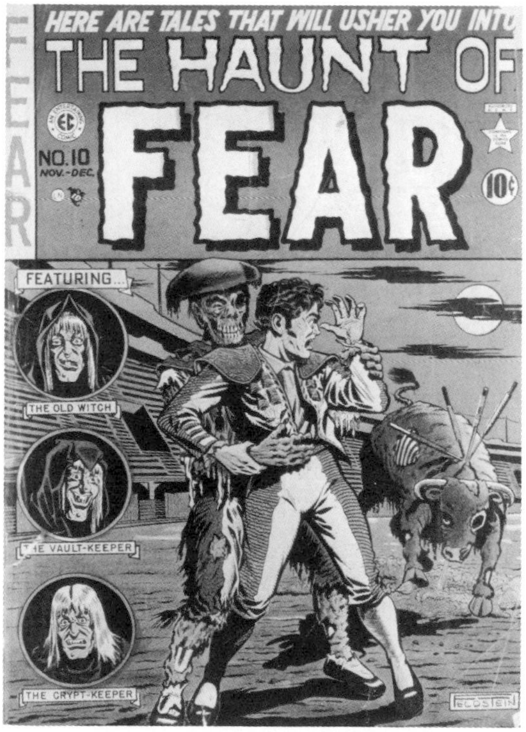

Editor and writer Al Feldstein also did artwork for the early E.C. comics, as in the case of this cover for a 1951 *Haunt of Fear*. © *1975 William M. Gaines.*

Graham Ingels, known to his fans as "Ghastly," did this cover, illustrating a scene from the story "Nobody There." There is also a notice that E.C. had acquired the services of the distinguished fantasy author Ray Bradbury. © *1975 William M. Gaines.*

surpassed anything seen before in the mass media. Among the astounding variations employed on this theme was a story in which the vengeful rotten remnants were those of a circus elephant, lovingly depicted by the most morbid of the staff artists, "Ghastly" Graham Ingels. Such bizarre extensions of more or less traditional plots were a specialty at E.C., where the fine line between horror and hilarity was crossed with impunity. Many of the best tales had the quality of "shaggy dog" stories, and it was apparent that many readers were not only willing to suspend their disbelief, but actually were beyond being frightened. Producers and their public alike took a fiendish glee in each new atrocity, abetting the advancement of a new aesthetic of artistic terror. Audiences with a palate for this sort of fare were recognizing the implausibility of the whole genre, were quite aware that it was concocted for their amusement, and were impressed by ingenuity and technical expertise rather than by their own emotional reactions. This sort of attitude, which distinguishes the hardened horror fan from the ordinary citizen, may have been encouraged by the obvious overkill in some of the multimonster movies like *Frankenstein Meets the Wolf Man*; but it was never more evident than in *Tales from the Crypt*, *Vault of Horror*, and *Haunt of Fear*.

Exposed to this sort of material without previous conditioning, serious thinkers were apt to be appalled, especially when the giddy ghoulishness appeared in a format that was presumed to be intended for young children. The final result was a carefully orchestrated demand for comic book censorship, which succeeded in driving horror comics out of business and at the same time inaugurated the whole concept of sociological dismay over macabre themes in the popular arts. Fuel for the flames of moral indignation was provided by the countless imitations of E.C. that flooded the market. Without exception they were inferior to the originals, but the dozens of miscellaneous titles made horror comics a bigger target and justified critical disdain with their crude scripts and artwork.

Still, E.C. had five years to build a reputation that has grown steadily since the company was forced into its untimely retreat from the world of the weird. Considerable credit should go to artist Johnny Craig, whose clean-cut characters ended up in messy situations that were only the more gruesome because of the vivid contrast. Craig began early to work on his own scripts, and ended up writing all the stories for *Vault of Horror.* At the opposite end of the spectrum was Graham Ingels, whose every line seemed touched with corruption, producing a powerful cumulative effect by a process of progressive putrefaction. Somewhere between the two was Jack Davis, whose speed and incisiveness have since made him one of the most popular commercial artists in the United States. His work now appears on the covers of wholesome middle-class magazines, but he got his start committing atrocities in ink as introduced by the Crypt-Keeper. Somehow he seemed to end up with the wildest scripts, perhaps best exemplified by the notorious "Foul Play" from the June 1953 *Haunt of Fear.* This tale about a murderous baseball player ended with the killer's indignant colleagues dismembering him and using his remains as equipment for a night game, shown in gory detail. Stories like this seem to have been designed to further offend those already critical of comic books, and indeed, the last page of "Foul Play" was reprinted in Dr. Frederic Wertham's *Seduction of the Innocent*, a 1954 book that sealed the doom of horror comics, at least for the foreseeable future. Davis himself seems to have preferred something a bit more subtle. His favorite tale from the crypt was "Country Clubbing," a bloodless and humorous 1954 tall tale from the South which, according to editor Al Feldstein, was the artist's own idea. In keeping with his choice of restrained treatment, but considerably more chilling, is the Davis story reproduced at the end of this chapter. "Model Nephew," from *Haunt of Fear,*

This cover by Johnny Craig, who also wrote and edited *Vault of Horror*, shows a highlight from his wrenching little epic "Till Death" about a man who revives his beloved wife with voodoo but cannot prevent her decomposition. © *1975 William M. Gaines.*

number 22, is one of the ingenious and infinite variations on the theme of supernatural vengeance which were the E.C. specialty.

Although Davis, Ingels, and Craig were the artists most consistently identified with the E.C. horror line, there were a number of others, including Feldstein, who drew the original versions of the hosts before overwork kicked him upstairs into the editor's chair. Two talented realists, Reed Crandall and George Evans, and a controversial impressionist, Bernie Krigstein, helped enliven the later issues. The generally grim attitude of the trend-setting terror offerings spilled over into other E.C. publications, such as *Shock Suspenstories* and *Crime Suspenstories*, and took some spectacular new directions with the monstrous aliens depicted by Al Williamson, Wallace Wood, and Joe Orlando for the science fiction comic books *Weird Science* and *Weird Fantasy*.

All of them were abandoned simultaneously in 1954 as the result of the Comics Code Authority. This censorship body, created with mixed disgust and delight by comic book publishers of various persuasions, made it impossible to get distribution without a seal of approval. Getting the seal meant eliminating anything that might prove objectionable to almost anyone. The most telling charge against comic books, promulgated with debatable logic in *Seduction of the Innocent* and adopted by hordes of self-righteous citizens, was that the depiction of crime was contributing to juvenile delinquency. Macabre material was banned almost as an afterthought but in such specific terms that it became impossible to market. Crime and criminals, on the other hand, continued to be involved in the plots of most publications, simply because the standard superheroes had to have somebody to fight. Nobody ever seriously suggested that fictional werewolves had led to even a slight increase in the werewolf population, but stories along these lines stood accused of the more nebulous transgression of warping minds. Perhaps for the first time in human history, tales of terror were being declared unfit for human consumption, slimy throwbacks from an ignorant past that could be jettisoned without remorse from a scientific, psychoanalyzed civilization.

The last of the pulp magazines was wiped out in the same magazine distribution cleanup of 1954–55. A few of these publications survived by converting to the more sedate digest format; but none of these was a terror title, although there had been dozens in the previous decade. Fantasy became a poor relation, occasionally admitted out of pity into the sanctified pages of the science fiction magazines, which had begun to enjoy a new prestige after the appearance of such astounding devices as the atomic bomb.

The pulps had been twice betrayed by comic books, which first had absorbed much of their audience and then had become involved in a scandalous situation that made the sale of any magazine with a lurid cover just about impossible. The venerable *Weird Tales* was one of the last to go, in September 1954, shortly after converting to a smaller size. Yet the last years of the magazine were far from vacant. It provided early opportunities for the considerable talents of Ray Bradbury, the first American science fiction writer to receive wide recognition from conservative critics. Bradbury began his career with a group of gruesome and remarkably original weird tales, and many of them were adapted with his consent by the E.C. comic book men. His first book, *Dark Carnival* (1947), was a collection of horror stories, and all of his subsequent collections have included something stranger than science fiction. His *October Country* is a revised and amended version of *Dark Carnival*, and the novel *Something Wicked This Way Comes* is a supernatural story about a sinister circus. As an avowed fan, Bradbury was driven to new heights by his dismay at the simultaneous destruction of both pulp magazines and the most imaginative comic book lines. The result was the novel *Fahrenheit 451*, in which the "firemen" of the future are sanitary-minded book burners. The same scorn for suppressors was expressed in stories like "Usher II," in which a lunatic builds a replica of Poe's fancied mansion on Mars and invites a party of censors there to be destroyed in a mechanical chamber of horrors. "The Exiles," a poignant variation on the same theme, depicts the saddened spirits of all earth's fantasy authors, each disintegrating in turn as the last volume of his works is consigned to the flames.

Such proselytizing aside, Bradbury brought a distinctively personal touch to his stories, delivering them in an effusively rhapsodic style that has been a subject of much controversy. Among his most memorable offerings is "The Handler," in which a disgruntled undertaker avenges snubs by playing grim practical jokes with the bodies of his customers. The heroine of "There Was an Old Woman" rises out of her coffin, consumed with righteous indignation, and goes home to finish her knitting. Like this one, many of his best tales seem to be told from the viewpoint of a naïve and fascinated child. A counterpoint is offered by "The Small Assassin," in which an infant expresses his resentment at being born by engineering the death of his parents.

Among the most significant stories printed in the twilight of *Weird Tales* was Joseph Payne Brennan's "Slime," a fantasy of living, growing, moving, omnivorous protoplasm. The structure is so solid and the description so vivid that this tale, reprinted at the end of this chapter, became the inspiration for many fictions and films, some of them shameless plagiarisms. Yet because the copyright holder, *Weird Tales*, was legally defunct, the author has gone virtually unrewarded. "Slime" in fact epitomized, if it did not single-handedly imagine, the plot that became a formula for fifties monster movies, in which a titanic creature threatens to destroy civilization. Instead of expressing human aberrations, monsters became symbols of impersonal forces; the conflict would be not between good and evil, but between survival and annihilation. Brennan has written many other memorable terror tales, including the haunting short-short story "Levitation," about a hypnotist's demonstration gone awry, and several adventures of a psychic detective collected in *The Casebook of Lucius Leffing*. Yet he is most concerned with his work as a poet; many of his best poems in the vein of the macabre appeared in the volume *Nightmare Need* (1964).

Macabre fiction did survive in the United States, largely because of the presence of two new magazines, both discreetly of digest size to distinguish them from the moribund pulps. The first was *The Magazine of Fantasy*, which first appeared in 1949, edited by Anthony Boucher and J. Francis McComas. This was a sincere effort to establish the literary credentials of fantastic fiction, relying for its selections on writers from the past as well as on new contributors. The stories were well chosen, and the magazine avoided the lurid graphics that so often characterized pulp magazines and comic books; but it survived only by changing its title and contents to *The Magazine of Fantasy and Science Fiction*, with a distinct emphasis on the latter. Nevertheless, the fantasy element was not entirely abandoned, and some fine stories of the supernatural have appeared from this source, especially welcome during the era when science fiction enthusiasts had only sneers for that genre's ancient ancestor. *Fantasy and Science Fiction* scored an especially impressive blow by publishing Robert Bloch's ingenious tale "That Hell Bound Train," which was good enough to win a best-short-story award from science fiction professionals, despite the fact that it was an unscientific variation on the deal-with-the-devil theme.

The other principal market for supernatural fiction was provided by *Fantastic*, which began promisingly in 1952 under the editorship of Howard Browne. Among the features that established the magazine's lineage were a series of beautifully rendered drawings by Virgil Finlay, who had established a reputation in *Weird Tales* as the most proficient American illustrator in fantasy periodicals. One of the finest of his remarkably detailed

Fantastic employed Virgil Finlay to create this scene for "The Lighthouse," a fragmentary Poe tale completed for the magazine by the prolific Robert Bloch.

and painstaking pieces appeared in conjunction with a unique posthumous collaboration, when Robert Bloch completed an unfinished Edgar Allan Poe tale, "The Lighthouse," for a 1953 issue of *Fantastic.* The magazine has also provided a home for further adventures of Fritz Leiber's *Unknown* characters, Fafhrd and the Gray Mouser. A series of changes in editors and publishers has varied the quality of *Fantastic* over the years, but it has published many fine stories in the supernatural tradition. Recently, the increasingly popular Robert E. Howard character, Conan, has been revived in its pages by Howard enthusiasts L. Sprague de Camp and Lin Carter. Still, science fiction dominated the magazine, as it did virtually all of the Hollywood horror films released in the decade between 1947 and 1957.

Actual events provided the inspiration for the new breed of monsters, which were generally by-products of atomic energy or the pilots of "flying saucers." Unidentified flying objects were sighted with increasing frequency in the postwar world; it was only a matter of time before they showed up on the motion picture screen. The first and in many respects the most impressive of the alien invaders was the parasitic vegetable man who, eulogized in song by Phil Harris, became the most famous monster of the decade: *The Thing* (1951). It lands near the North Pole, where its spaceship is discovered by a group of American soldiers. Perhaps the most telling scene in this Howard Hawks production is the first appearance of this strange object buried in the ice; as the men fan out on its perimeter to determine its shape and size, they and the audience realize simultaneously that they are standing around a huge disk, the dreaded flying saucer. Once its ice-covered passenger is moved to an Arctic station and thawed out, the action becomes very familiar, as the Thing stalks its victims in the approved monster tradition. Electricity eliminates the menace and presumably ends the threat of alien invasion, thus establishing the cost-conscious concept that invaders from space usually show up as solo scouts whose defeat will forestall a mass attack. The space being's appearance is far from exotic; he is just an oversized man with a vaguely featureless face, a far cry from the creature originally described in the source story, John W. Campbell's "Who Goes There?" In fact, the film has just about nothing to do with this much more subtle and complex piece of fiction.

Serious followers of literary science fiction found little satisfaction in most of the movies that followed in the wake of *The Thing.* The rare exceptions included monsterless movies like George Pal's documentary-style *Destination Moon* (1950) and the evangelistic *Day the Earth Stood Still* (1951). There were a few minutes of cataclysmic horror in Pal's serious-minded follow-up, *When Worlds Collide* (1952). The story by Philip Wylie and Edwin Balmer, already twenty years old, is about a rocket-powered attempt to escape from the title's astronomical catastrophe. There are some spectacular scenes of destruction, but the most frightening aspect of the film is the sanctimonious air radiating from the small band of self-appointed survivors.

Still, a more typical example of things to come was provided by *The Man from Planet X* (1951), a lackluster invader who is content to sit in his spaceship sending out menacing thought waves. Some extremely inept and childish films followed the early entries; the worst of the lot, which shall remain nameless here but was actually shown under several titles, features an alien dressed in the prop department's old gorilla suit, topped with a comical toy space helmet. He demonstrates his scientific sophistication with a machine that blows soap bubbles.

By 1953 at least a few efforts were being made to produce a quality product. The most obvious triumph was George Pal's production of *War of the Worlds*, featuring some spectacular special effects and, at last, a full-scale attack by the men from Mars. It was less convincing than the 1938 radio version, but it was more entertaining because the audience could watch. Apparently audiences took a real delight in seeing urban sprawl crumbling under the onslaught of a hostile intelligence. Actors, writers, and directors all played second fiddle to the technicians who engineered the destruction. One of the best, Ray Harryhausen, breathed life into *The Beast from 20,000 Fathoms*, a city-crushing dinosaur revived by nuclear experiments. This was based on Ray Bradbury's comparatively nonviolent short story "The Foghorn," in which a lonely sea monster falls in love with a lighthouse. Bradbury was perhaps more accurately represented by *It Came from Outer Space*, depicting a hideous visitor who panics the population but turns out to be, as the hero has insisted, just a tourist. This comparatively thoughtful approach unfortunately made for a dull film, and the screenplay adapted from Bradbury's original story failed to approach the style that is his essence.

Probably the most entertaining thing about *It Came from Outer Space* (and a dozen other films of 1953) is that it was made in a new three-dimensional process. Polaroid glasses made it possible for patrons of the arts to enjoy a convincing illusion of depth, but they also doomed the process because nobody wanted to wear them after the novelty had worn off. The first 3-D feature, a jungle adventure called *Bwana Devil*, was produced by radio writer Arch Oboler. Films of every identifiable genre were made in 3-D, which even temporarily revived the old-school horror film. The best of the bunch, in fact the best deep drama of all, was *House of Wax*, a new version of the old Warner Brothers thriller *Mystery of the Wax Museum.* Vincent Price played the artist in wax who turns to murder after he is disfigured in a fire; his enthusiastic performance made him a star of the sinister cinema, although his real reputation came later, when morbid melodramas were more firmly back in fashion. *House of Wax* itself was engagingly corny, with a restrained use of color and photographic gimmicks. The same studio got its monkey suit out of mothballs for *The Phantom of the Rue Morgue,* with Karl Malden; then Price was put through his paces again as *The Mad Magician.* Neither of these 1954 features would have been especially impressive in only two dimensions.

Universal finally got back into monster movies the same year with their 3-D black-and-white film *The Creature from the Black Lagoon.* This proved to be a prehistoric fish-man discovered by a scientific expedition to the tropics. This rather ordinary little film, directed in pedestrian style by Jack Arnold, remains lodged in the memory solely because of the beautifully designed creature whose sleek, finny structure was a joy to behold. He proved to be a winner and was annually revived in *Revenge of the Creature* and *The Creature Walks among Us*, the first of his breed in a decade to be so honored. In the former film he is shipped to the United States with predictable results; in the latter a team of surgeons alter his appearance to emphasize his human characteristics. He lost his good looks, and was so chagrined that he retired.

Warner Brothers came up with a new kind of mutant, the giant insect, with 1954's *Them!* Named by a horrified child who is the first surviving witness to their might, "Them" are several colonies of oversized ants. They are only about twice as tall as a man, but there are hundreds of them. They perform their share of mean feats in the streets; yet the film is most impressive in the claustrophobic scenes underground, where armed men seek to destroy the nests of the mutants.

One of the heroes of *Them* had also been the portrayer of the Thing. The heavily disguised actor was James Arness, whose towering strength found a more expressive range when he became the star of television's perennial western program "Gunsmoke." The new stature he gained on the picture tube typified what was in many ways the definitive trend of the fifties. Television conquered all, with terrible economic effects on

Vincent Price goes up in flames along with his museum in Andre deToth's *House of Wax*, the best of the three-dimensional movies and one that gave a big boost to the actor's career as a film fiend. *Courtesy of Warner Bros. Inc. Copyright © 1953.*

Intrepid investigators go underground to discover a nest of oversized, atomically mutated ants in this scene from the pioneering insect adventure *Them! Courtesy of Warner Bros. Inc. Copyright © 1954.*

The Creature from the Black Lagoon, portrayed by Ricou Browning, was an aquatic menace with the usual crush on a human heroine. *Courtesy of Universal Pictures.*

every other means of communication. Advertising deserted big-time radio, which in turn abandoned drama for a format of news and recorded music. Even those publishers in no immediate danger of being censored out of existence felt the pinch, and several major magazines folded, although there was some reassurance in the burgeoning sales of paperback novels. The motion picture, which had held its own against radio, seemed in danger of complete extinction, or at least absorption, by TV. Once proud studios like Warner Brothers and Universal found themselves reduced to producing film footage for the new medium. The talents of "quickie" or "B" movie artists were particularly appropriate for feeding the ravenous "idiot box," and a whole new pantheon of culture heroes appeared. The overkill effect of TV's embarrassment of tarnished riches soon altered almost everyone's concepts of art and entertainment.

The dark muse soon found her niche in this new black-and-white world, with shows like "Inner Sanctum" and "Suspense," transferred from radio, and a number of "mystery" anthology programs like "Climax." There were also numerous lurid literary adaptations on the more high-minded dramatic programs like "Studio One" and "Lux Video Theater." Still, most fantasy came packaged as science fiction. Purportedly plausible menaces were standard fare on the late-night series "Tales of Tomorrow" and its juvenile equivalents "Captain Video," "Space Patrol," and "Tom Corbett, Space Cadet." Nevertheless, the most forward-looking program in the field got most of its material from the past. It was a local effort, in which a slinky California actress donned a fright wig and dubbed herself Vampira. She hosted the presentation of the few horror films already released to television. Few of them were very good, but Vampira pioneered a style of programming that would become wildly popular a few years later, when Hollywood's major monsters were unleashed on the home screen.

Meanwhile, the mutants marched on across theater screens. 1955 brought *It Came from Beneath the Sea*, which introduced a mammoth octopus whose construction proved so expensive that it was only equipped with five tentacles. Universal's *Tarantula* featured a giant spider, with a couple of mutant men thrown in for good measure. The same studio's *This Island Earth* was a bit more imaginative, involving a planned invasion of earth that fails to come off when the alien agent of a doomed planet takes pity on the human race. Despite the reprieve, there are some frightening minutes for the people who become guests on the dying world of Metaluna, as they barely escape the climax of an atomic war and the loathsome monstrosities it has already spawned.

The most significant filmed fantasies of 1955, however, were a pair of films from abroad. They came from England and Japan, two countries that would soon be major producers in the field. The Japanese entry was *Godzilla*, another atomically reactivated lizard. He stood out from the competition, however, by being bigger than any of his rivals and also more destructive. King Kong had punched a train, but Godzilla could eat one. He also breathed fire and appeared to be totally invulnerable. The average monster got stopped before he had inflicted more than token damage, but Godzilla virtually wiped

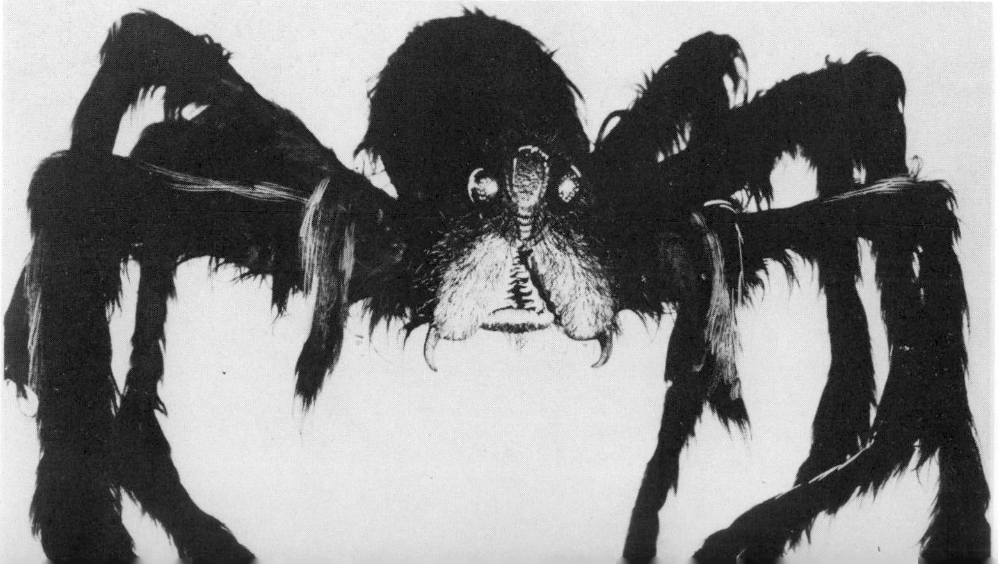

The bugs kept getting bigger, as in the mutated *Tarantula* (1955). The film also featured the usually dignified Leo G. Carroll as a mad scientist whose experiments leave him almost as ugly as the overgrown spider. *Courtesy of Universal Pictures.*

The best of the giant monsters made in Japan was the first, Godzilla. Not a puppet animated by stop-motion techniques, Godzilla was a man in a lizard suit stomping miniature sets. *Courtesy of Jewell Enterprises.*

Tokyo off the map. The plots of movies of this school generally revolved around attempts to stop the monster; Godzilla was overpowering enough to demand a new invention, explained in appropriately "scientific" gibberish, which reduced him to a skeleton. A bit of footage featuring American actor Raymond Burr was added to increase audience identification in the United States, and the film made a killing. Godzilla, billed as "King of the Monsters," pretty well capped the trend toward giant monsters. The costs of technical effects were skyrocketing, and the comparatively small expenses at the Japanese studio Toho would soon make them the principal producers of mammoth menaces.

The Creeping Unknown was one of the earliest efforts from a studio that soon became extremely influential in the production of horror movies, England's Hammer Films. This movie, atypical of Hammer's later work, concerns a rocket pilot who returns to earth infected with a fungus. It covers his whole body, turning him into the title character who is electrocuted for his antisocial behavior. Originally titled *The Quatermass Experiment*, this was the first of a series about the cantankerous scientist Quatermass, played by Brian Donlevy. As in the case of *Godzilla*, an American actor seems to have been used to encourage exportation. Donlevy is the major incongruity in a generally plausible, low-key production, although the astronaut's wife, who continually refers to the murderous fungoid mass as "Victor," is equally dispensable.

In 1956 the science fiction sweepstakes included only two major entries, but they were among the best of the breed. MGM's *Forbidden Planet* was a lavish look at another world, embellished by special effects from Walt Disney Studios. The tone was predominantly light, with a good deal of comic relief provided by the sophisticated Robbie the Robot; but there was a monster too, its presence explained by an engaging premise. The civilization that had inhabited Altair-4 had created a technology that would instantly embody its conscious desires and, in the process, had destroyed itself with an invisible embodiment of the id. At the other end of the spectrum from this colorful, slick production was *Invasion of the Body Snatchers*, directed by Don Siegel from a story by Jack Finney. There were no titanic terrors here, but something far more insidious. These invaders are inert vegetable forms that have the power to reduplicate human beings while their victims sleep; the plan is not to wipe out the human race but to replace it. There is something a bit illogical about this plot, but it comes off with all the conviction of a nightmare, as the horrified inhabitants of a small town discover half-formed effigies of themselves lying in their homes and gradually succumb to sleep and supplantation. Only one exhausted man (Kevin McCarthy) escapes. Far from destroying the duplicators, he achieves his most triumphant moment at the film's end when he finally convinces the stolid authorities of a nearby city that the peril may indeed exist.

In the same year, there were some signs of renewed interest in the more traditional type of horror film, but they appeared within a depressing context. Three movies appeared featuring Bela Lugosi; one was none too good, and the other two were truly terrible. Lugosi's star had sunk almost steadily since his initial portrayal of Dracula. In 1955 he voluntarily committed himself to a hospital to be treated for a medically induced narcotics problem that had plagued him for twenty years. Having cured himself by a tremendous act of will at the age of seventy-three, he played a small part in United Artists' *Black Sleep*, a film about a nineteenth-century surgeon (Basil Rathbone) who makes monsters almost accidentally while searching for a miracle cure. Lugosi is his butler. His next two outings were probably the two worst horror films made up to that time, *Bride of the Monster* and *Plan 9 from Outer Space (Grave Robbers from Outer Space)*. Incredibly cheap and incompetent, featuring cardboard sets and wooden dialogue, they were significantly inferior to even the worst quickies of the previous decade. Lugosi died during the filming of *Plan 9*, which depicted aliens raising the dead to form an army, and his role was completed by a nameless extra holding a black cloak over his face.

Lugosi's death seemed to symbolize the end of an era. Science fiction-style horrors seemed to have gone about as far as they could, and old-school efforts like *Bride of the Monster* indicated that the genre was as dead as Dracula. Horror comics had come and gone, the pulps were finished, and it looked very much like the fictional fiends who had plagued humanity since the dawn of time were ready to call it a night. There was definite need for new blood.

SLIME

By Joseph Payne Brennan

It was a great gray-black hood of horror moving over the floor of the sea. It slid through the soft ooze like a monstrous mantle of slime obscenely animated with questing life. It was by turns viscid and fluid. At times it flattened out and flowed through the carpet of mud like an inky pool; occasionally it paused, seeming to shrink in upon itself, and reared up out of the ooze until it resembled an irregular cone or a gigantic hood. Although it possessed no eyes, it had a marvelously developed sense of touch, and it possessed a sensitivity to minute vibrations which was almost akin to telepathy. It was plastic, essentially shapeless. It could shoot out long tentacles, until it bore a resemblance to a nightmare squid or a huge starfish; it could retract itself into a round flattened disc, or squeeze into an irregular hunched shape so that it looked like a black boulder sunk on the bottom of the sea.

It had prowled the black water endlessly. It had been formed when the earth and the seas were young; it was almost as old as the ocean itself. It moved through a night which had no beginning and no dissolution. The black sea basin where it lurked had been dark since the world began—an environment only a little less inimical than the stupendous gulfs of interplanetary space.

It was animated by a single, unceasing, never-satisfied drive: a voracious, insatiable hunger. It could survive for months without food, but minutes after eating it was as ravenous as ever. Its appetite was appalling and incalculablc.

On the icy ink-black floor of the sea the battle for survival was savage, hideous—and usually brief. But for the shape of moving slime there was no battle. It ate whatever came its way, regardless of size, shape or disposition. It absorbed microscopic plankton and giant squid with equal assurance. Had its surface been less fluid, it might have retained the circular scars left by the grappling suckers of the wildly threshing deep-water squid, or the jagged toothmarks of the anachronistic frillshark, but as it was, neither left any evidence of its absorption. When the lifting curtain of living slime swayed out of the mud and closed upon them, their fiercest death throes came to nothing.

The horror did not know fear. There was nothing to be afraid of. It ate whatever moved, or tried not to move, and it had never encountered anything which could in turn eat it. If a squid's sucker, or a shark's tooth, tore into the mass of its viscosity, the rent flowed in upon itself and immediately closed. If a segment was detached, it could be retrieved and absorbed back into the whole.

The black mantle reigned supreme in its savage world of slime and silence. It groped greedily and endlessly through the mud, eating and never sleeping, never resting. If it lay still, it was only to trap food which might otherwise be lost. If it rushed with terrifying speed across the slimy bottom, it was never to escape an enemy, but always to flop its hideous fluidity upon its sole and inevitable quarry—food.

It had evolved out of the muck and slime of the primitive sea floor, and it was as alien to ordinary terrestrial life as the weird denizens of some wild planet in a distant galaxy. It was an anachronistic experiment of nature compared to which the saber-toothed tiger, the woolly mammoth and even Tyrannosaurus, the slashing, murderous king of the great earth reptiles, were as tame, weak entities.

Had it not been for a vast volcanic upheaval on the bottom of the ocean basin, the black horror would have crept out its entire existence on the silent sea ooze without ever manifesting its hideous powers to mankind.

Fate, in the form of a violent subterranean explosion, covering huge areas of the ocean's floor, hurled it out of its black slime world and sent it spinning towards the surface.

Had it been an ordinary deep-water fish, it never would have survived the experience. The explosion itself, or the drastic lessening of water pressure as it shot towards the surface, would have destroyed it. But it was no ordinary fish. Its viscosity, or plasticity, or whatever it was that constituted its essentially amoebic structure, permitted it to survive.

It reached the surface slightly stunned and flopped on the surging waters like a great blob of black blubber. Immense waves stirred up by the subterranean explosion swept it swiftly towards shore, and because it was somewhat stunned it did not try to resist the roaring mountains of water.

Along with scattered ash, pumice, and the puffed bodies of dead fish, the black horror was hurled towards a beach. The huge waves carried it more than a mile inland, far beyond the strip of sandy shore, and deposited it in the midst of a deep brackish swamp area.

As luck would have it, the submarine explosion and subsequent tidal wave took place at night, and therefore the slime horror was not immediately subjected to a new and hateful experience—light.

Although the midnight darkness of the storm-lashed swamp did not begin to compare with the stygian blackness of the sea bottom where even violet rays of the spectrum could not penetrate, the marsh darkness was nevertheless deep and intense.

As the water of the great wave receded, sluicing through the thorn jungle and back out to sea, the black horror clung to a mudbank surrounded by a rank growth of cattails. It was aware of the sudden, startling change in its environment, and for some time it lay motionless, concentrating its attention on obscure internal readjustment which the absence of crushing pressure and a surrounding cloak of frigid sea water demanded. Its adaptability was incredible and horrifying. It achieved in a few hours what an ordinary creature could have attained only through a process of gradual evolution. Three hours after the titanic wave flopped it onto the mudbank, it had undergone swift organic changes which left it relatively at ease in its new environment.

In fact, it felt lighter and more mobile than it ever had before in its sea basin existence.

As it flung out feelers and attuned itself to the minutest vibrations and emanations of the swamp area, its pristine hunger drive reasserted itself with overwhelming urgency. And the tale which its sensory apparatus returned to the monstrous something which served it as a brain, excited it tremendously. It sensed at once that the swamp was filled with luscious tidbits of quivering food—more food, and food of a greater variety than it had ever encountered on the cold floor of the sea.

Its savage, incessant hunger seemed unbearable. Its slimy mass was swept by a shuddering wave of anticipation.

Sliding off the mudbank, it slithered over the cattails into an adjacent area consisting of deep black pools interspersed with waterlogged tussocks. Weed stalks stuck up out of the water and the decayed trunks of fallen trees floated half-submerged in the larger pools.

Ravenous with hunger, it sloshed into the bog area, flicking its tentacles about. Within minutes it had snatched up several fat frogs and a number of small fish. These, however, merely titillated its appetite. Its hunger turned into a kind of ecstatic fury. It commenced a systematic hunt, plunging to the bottom of each pool and quickly but carefully exploring every inch of its oozy bottom. The first creature of any size which it encountered was a muskrat. An immense curtain of adhesive slime suddenly swept out of the darkness, closed upon it—and squeezed.

Heartened and whetted by its find, the hood of horror rummaged the rank pools with renewed zeal. When it surfaced, it carefully probed the tussocks for anything that might have escaped it in the water. Once it snatched up a small bird nesting in some swamp grass. Occasionally it slithered up the crisscrossed trunks of fallen trees, bearing them down with its unspeakable slimy bulk, and hung briefly suspended like a great dripping curtain of black marsh mud.

It was approaching a somewhat less swampy and more deeply wooded area when it gradually became aware of a subtle change in its new environment. It paused, hesitating, and remained half in and half out of a small pond near the edge of the nearest trees.

Although it had absorbed twenty-five or thirty pounds of food in the form of frogs, fish, water snakes, the muskrat, and a few smaller creatures, its fierce hunger had not left it. Its monstrous appetite urged it on, and yet something held it anchored in the pond.

What it sensed, but could not literally see, was the rising sun spreading a gray light over the swamp. The horror had never encountered any illumination except that generated by the grotesque phosphorescent appendages of various deep-sea fishes. Natural light was totally unknown to it.

As the dawn light strengthened, breaking through the scattering storm clouds, the black slime monster fresh from the inky floor of the sea sensed that something utterly unknown was flooding in upon it. Light was hateful to it. It cast out quick feelers, hoping to catch and crush the light. But the more frenzied its efforts became, the more intense became the abhorred aura surrounding it.

At length, as the sun rose visibly above the trees, the horror, in baffled rage rather than in fear, grudgingly slid back into the pond and burrowed into the soft ooze of its bottom. There it remained while the sun shone and the small creatures of the swamp ventured forth on furtive errands.

A few miles away from Wharton's Swamp, in the small town of Clinton Center, Henry Hossing sleepily crawled out of the improvised alley shack which had afforded him a degree of shelter for the night and stumbled into the street. Passing a hand across his rheumy eyes, he scratched the stubble on his cheek and blinked listlessly at the rising sun. He had not slept well; the storm of the night before had kept him awake. Besides, he had gone to bed hungry, and that never agreed with him.

Glancing furtively along the street, he walked slouched forward, with his head bent down, and most of the time he kept his eyes on the walk or on the gutter in the hopes of spotting a chance coin.

Clinton Center had not been kind to him. The handouts were sparse, and only yesterday he had been warned out of town by one of the local policemen.

Grumbling to himself, he reached the end of the street and started to cross. Suddenly he stooped quickly and snatched up something from the edge of the pavement.

It was a crumpled green bill, and as he frantically unfolded it, a look of stupefied rapture spread across his bristly face. Ten dollars! More money than he had possessed at any one time in months!

Stowing it carefully in the one good pocket of his seedy gray jacket, he crossed the street with a swift stride. Instead of sweeping the sidewalks, his eyes now darted along the rows of stores and restaurants.

He paused at one restaurant, hesitated, and finally went on until he found another less pretentious one a few blocks away.

When he sat down, the counterman shook his head. "Get goin', bud. No free coffee today."

With a wide grin, the hobo produced his ten-dollar bill and spread it on the counter. "That covers a good breakfast here, pardner?"

The counterman seemed irritated. "Okay, okay. What'll you have?" He eyed the bill suspiciously.

Henry Hossing ordered orange juice, toast, ham and eggs, oatmeal, melon and coffee.

When it appeared, he ate every bit of it, ordered three additional cups of coffee, paid the check as if two-dollar breakfasts were customary with him, and then sauntered back to the street.

Shortly after noon, after his three-dollar lunch, he saw the liquor store. For a few minutes he stood across the street from it, fingering his five-dollar bill. Finally he crossed with an abstracted smile, entered and bought a quart of rye.

He hesitated on the sidewalk, debating whether or not he should return to the little shack in the side alley. After a minute or two of indecision, he decided against it and struck out instead for Wharton's Swamp. The local police were far less likely to disturb him there, and since the skies were clearing and the weather mild, there was little immediate need of shelter.

Angling off the highway which skirted the swamp several miles from town, he crossed a marshy meadow, pushed through a fringe of bush, and sat down under a sweet gum tree which bordered a deeply wooded area.

By late afternoon he had achieved a quite cheerful glow, and he had little inclination to return to Clinton Center. Rousing himself from reverie, he stumbled about collecting enough wood for a small fire and went back to his sylvan seat under the sweet gum.

He slept briefly as dusk descended, but finally bestirred himself again to build a fire, as deeper shadows fell over the swamp. Then he returned to his swiftly diminishing bottle. He was suspended in a warm net of inflamed fantasy when something abruptly broke the spell and brought him back to earth.

The flickering flames of his fire had dwindled down until now only a dim eerie glow illuminated the immediate area under the sweet gum. He saw nothing and at the moment heard nothing, and yet he was filled with a sudden and profound sense of lurking menace.

He stood up, staggering, leaned back against the sweet gum and peered fearfully into the shadows. In the deep darkness beyond the waning arc of firelight he could distinguish nothing that had any discernible form or color.

Then he detected the stench and shuddered. In spite of the reek of cheap whiskey which clung around him, the smell was overpowering. It was heavy, fulsome, fetid, alien, and utterly repellent. It was vaguely fishlike, but otherwise beyond any known comparison.

As he stood trembling under the sweet gum, Henry Hossing thought of something dead which had lain for long ages at the bottom of the sea.

Filled with mounting alarm, he looked around for some wood which he might add to the dying fire. All he could find nearby, however, were a few twigs. He threw these on and the flames licked up briefly and subsided.

He listened and heard—or imagined he heard—an odd sort of slithering sound in the nearby bushes. It seemed to retreat slightly as the flames shot up.

Genuine terror took possession of him. He knew that he was in no condition to flee—and now he came to the horrifying conclusion that whatever unspeakable menace waited in the surrounding darkness was temporarily held at bay only by the failing gleam of his little fire.

Frantically he looked around for more wood. But there was none. None, that is, within the faint glow of firelight. And he dared not venture beyond.

He began to tremble uncontrollably. He tried to scream, but no sound came out of his tightened throat.

The ghastly stench became stronger, and now he was sure that he could hear a strange sliding, slithering sound in the black shadows beyond the remaining spark of firelight.

He stood frozen in absolute helpless panic as the tiny fire smoldered down into darkness.

At the last instant a charred bit of wood broke apart, sending up a few sparks, and in that flicker of final light he glimpsed the horror.

It had already glided out of the bushes, and now it rushed across the small clearing with nightmare speed. It was a final incarnation of all the fears, shuddering apprehensions, and bad dreams which Henry Hossing had ever known in his life. It was a fiend from the pit of Hell come to claim him at last.

A terrible ringing scream burst from his throat, but it was smothered before it was finished as the black shape of slime fastened upon him with irresistible force.

Giles Gowse—"Old Man" Gowse—got out of bed after eight hours of fitful tossing and intermittent nightmares and grouchily brewed coffee in the kitchen of his dilapidated farmhouse on the edge of Wharton's Swamp. Half the night, it seemed, the stench of stale seawater had permeated the house. His interrupted sleep had been full of foreboding, full of shadowy and evil portents.

Muttering to himself, he finished breakfast, took a milk pail from the pantry, and started for the barn where he kept his single cow.

As he approached the barn, the strange offensive odor which had plagued him during the night assailed his nostrils anew.

"Wharton's Swamp! That's what it is!" he told himself. And he shook his fist at it.

When he entered the barn the stench was stronger than ever. Scowling, he strode towards the rickety stall where he kept the cow, Sarey.

Then he stood still and stared. Sarey was gone. The stall was empty.

He reentered the barnyard. "Sarey!" he called.

Rushing back into the barn, he inspected the stall. The rancid reek of the sea was strong here, and now he noticed a kind of shine on the floor. Bending closer, he saw that it was a slick coat of glistening slime, as if some unspeakable creature covered with ooze had crept in and out of the stall.

This discovery, coupled with the weird disappearance of Sarey, was too much for his jangled nerves. With a wild yell he ran out of the barn and started for Clinton Center, two miles away.

His reception in the town enraged him. When he tried to tell people about the disappearance of his cow, Sarey, about the reek of sea and ooze in his barn the night before, they laughed at him. The more impolite ones, that is. Most of the others patiently heard him out—and then winked and touched their heads significantly when he was out of sight.

One man, the druggist, Jim Jelinson, seemed mildly interested. He said that as he was coming through his backyard from the garage late the previous evening, he had heard a fearful shriek somewhere in the distant darkness. It might, he averred, have come from the direction of Wharton's Swamp. But it had not been repeated and eventually he had dismissed it from his mind.

When Old Man Gowse started for home late in the afternoon he was filled with sullen, resentful bitterness. They thought he was crazy, eh? Well, Sarey *was* gone; they couldn't explain *that* away, could they? They explained the smell by saying it was dead fish cast up by the big wave which had washed into the swamp during the storm. Well—maybe. And the slime on his barn floor they said was snails. *Snails!* As if any he'd ever seen could cause that much slime!

As he was nearing home, he met Rupert Barnaby, his nearest neighbor. Rupert was carrying a rifle and he was accompanied by Jibbe, his hound.

Although there had been an element of bad blood between the two bachelor neighbors for some time, Old Man Gowse, much to Barnaby's surprise, nodded and stopped.

"Evenin' hunt, neighbor?"

Barnaby nodded. "Thought Jibbe might start up a coon. Moon later, likely."

"My cow's gone," Old Man Gowse said abruptly. "If you should see her—" He paused. "But I don't think you will. . . ."

Barnaby, bewildered, stared at him. "What you gettin' at?"

Old Man Gowse repeated what he had been telling all day in Clinton Center.

He shook his head when he finished, adding, "I wouldn't go huntin' in that swamp tonight fur—ten thousand dollars!"

Rupert Barnaby threw back his head and laughed. He was a big man, muscular, resourceful, and levelheaded—little given to even mild flights of the imagination.

"Gowse," he laughed, "no use you givin' me those spook stories! Your cow got loose and wandered off. Why, I ain't even seen a bobcat in that swamp for over a year!"

Old Man Gowse set his lips in a grim line. "Maybe," he said, as he turned away, "you'll see suthin' worse than a wildcat in that swamp tonight!"

Shaking his head, Barnaby took after his impatient hound. Old Man Gowse was getting queer all right. One of these days he'd probably go off altogether and have to be locked up.

Jibbe ran ahead, sniffing, darting from one ditch to another. As twilight closed in, Barnaby angled off the main road onto a twisting path which led into Wharton's Swamp.

He loved hunting. He would rather tramp through the brush than sit home in an easy chair. And even if an evening's foray turned up nothing, he didn't particularly mind.

Actually he made out quite well; at least half his meat supply consisted of the rabbits, racoons, and occasional deer which he brought down in Wharton's Swamp.

When the moon rose, he was deep in the swamp. Twice Jibbe started off after rabbits, but both times he returned quickly, looking somewhat sheepish.

Something about his actions began to puzzle Barnaby. The dog seemed reluctant to move ahead; he hung directly in front of the hunter. Once Barnaby tripped over him and nearly fell headlong.

The hunter paused finally, frowning, and looked ahead. The swamp appeared no different than usual. True, a rather offensive stench hung over it, but that was merely the result of the big waves which had splashed far inland during the recent storm. Probably an accumulation of seaweed and the decaying bodies of some dead fish lay rotting in the stagnant pools of the swamp.

Barnaby spoke sharply to the dog. "What ails you, boy? Git, now! You trip me again, you'll get a boot!"

The dog started ahead some distance, but with an air of reluctance. He sniffed the clumps of marsh grass in a perfunctory manner and seemed to have lost interest in the hunt.

Barnaby grew exasperated. Even when they discovered the fresh track of a racoon in the soft mud near a little pool, Jibbe manifested only slight interest.

He did run on ahead a little further, however, and Barnaby began to hope that, as they closed in, he would regain his customary enthusiasm.

In this he was mistaken. As they approached a thickly wooded area, latticed with tree thorns and covered with a heavy growth of cattails, the dog suddenly crouched in the shadows and refused to budge.

Barnaby was sure that the racoon had taken refuge in the nearby thickets. The dog's unheard-of conduct infuriated him.

After a number of sharp cuffs, Jibbe arose stiffly and moved ahead, the hair on his neck bristled up like a lion's mane.

Swearing to himself, Barnaby pushed into the darkened thickets after him.

It was quite black under the trees, in spite of the moonlight, and he moved cautiously in order to avoid stepping into a pool.

Suddenly, with a frantic yelp of terror, Jibbe literally darted between his legs and shot out of the thickets. He ran on, howling weirdly as he went.

For the first time that evening Barnaby experienced a thrill of fear. In all his previous experience, Jibbe had never turned tail. On one occasion he had even plunged in after a sizeable bear.

Scowling into the deep darkness, Barnaby could see nothing. There were no baleful eyes glaring at him.

As his own eyes tried to penetrate the surrounding blackness, he recalled Old Man Gowse's warning with a bitter grimace. If the old fool happened to spot Jibbe streaking out of the swamp, Barnaby would never hear the end of it.

The thought of this angered him. He pushed ahead now with a feeling of sullen rage for whatever had terrified the dog. A good rifle shot would solve the mystery.

All at once he stopped and listened. From the darkness immediately ahead, he detected an odd sound, as if a large bulk were being dragged over the cattails.

He hesitated, unable to see anything, stoutly resisting an idiotic impulse to flee. The black darkness and the slimy stench of stagnant pools here in the thickets seemed to be suffocating him.

His heart began to pound as the slithering noise came closer. Every instinct told him to turn and run, but a kind of desperate stubbornness held him rooted to the spot.

The sound grew louder, and suddenly he was positive that something deadly and formidable was rushing towards him through the thickets with accelerated speed.

Throwing up his rifle, he pointed at the direction of the sound and fired.

In the brief flash of the rifle he saw something black and enormous and glistening, like a great flapping hood, break through the final thicket. It seemed to be *rolling* towards him, and it was moving with nightmare swiftness.

He wanted to scream and run, but even as the horror rushed forward, he understood that flight at this point would be futile. Even though the blood seemed to have congealed in his veins, he held the rifle pointed up and kept on firing.

The shots had no more visible effect than so many pebbles launched from a slingshot. At the last instant his nerve broke and he tried to escape, but the monstrous hood lunged upon him, flapped over him, and squeezed, and his attempt at a scream turned into a tiny gurgle in his throat.

Old Man Gowse got up early, after another uneasy night, and walked out to inspect the barnyard area. Nothing further seemed amiss, but there was still no sign of Sarey. And that detestable odor arose from the direction of Wharton's Swamp when the wind was right.

After breakfast, Gowse set out for Rupert Barnaby's place, a mile or so distant along the road. He wasn't sure himself what he expected to find.

When he reached Barnaby's small but neat frame house, all was quiet. Too quiet. Usually Barnaby was up and about soon after sunrise.

On a sudden impulse, Gowse walked up the path and rapped on the front door. He waited and there was no reply. He knocked again, and after another pause, stepped off the porch.

Jibbe, Barnaby's hound, slunk around the side of the house. Ordinarily he would bound about and bark. But today he stood motionless—or nearly so—he was trembling—and stared at Gowse. The dog had a cowed, frightened, guilty air which was entirely alien to him.

"Where's Rup?" Gowse called to him. "Go get Rup!"

Instead of starting off, the dog threw back his head and emitted an eerie, long-drawn howl.

Gowse shivered. With a backward glance at the silent house, he started off down the road.

Now maybe they'd listen to him, he thought grimly. The day before they had laughed about the disappearance of Sarey. Maybe they wouldn't laugh so easily when he told them that Rupert Barnaby had gone into Wharton's Swamp with his dog—and that the dog had come back alone!

When Police Chief Miles Underbeck saw Old Man Gowse come into headquarters in Clinton Center, he sat back and sighed heavily. He was busy this morning and undoubtedly Old Man Gowse was coming in to inquire about the infernal cow of his that had wandered off.

The old eccentric had a new and startling report, however. He claimed that Rupert Barnaby was missing. He'd gone into the swamp the night before, Gowse insisted, and had not returned.

When Chief Underbeck questioned him closely, Gowse admitted that he wasn't *positive* Barnaby hadn't returned. It was barely possible that he had returned home very early in the morning and then left again before Gowse arrived.

But Gowse fixed his flashing eyes on the chief and shook his head. "He never came out, I tell ye! That dog of his knows! Howled, he did, like a dog howls for the dead! Whatever come took Sarey—got Barnaby in the swamp last night!"

Chief Underbeck was not an excitable man. Gowse's burst of melodrama irritated him and left him unimpressed.

Somewhat gruffly he promised to look into the matter if Barnaby had not turned up by evening. Barnaby, he pointed out, knew the swamp better than anyone else in the county. And he was perfectly capable of taking care of himself. Probably, the chief suggested, he had sent the dog home and gone elsewhere after finishing his hunt the evening before. The chances were he'd be back by suppertime.

Old Man Gowse shook his head with a kind of fatalistic skepticism. Vouching that events would soon prove his fears well founded, he shambled grouchily out of the station.

The day passed and there was no sign of Rupert Barnaby. At six o'clock, Old Man Gowse grimly marched into the Crown, Clinton Center's second-rung hotel, and registered for a room. At seven o'clock Chief Underbeck dispatched a prowl car to Barnaby's place. He waited impatiently for its return, drumming on the desk, disinterestedly shuffling through a sheaf of reports which had accumulated during the day.

The prowl car returned shortly before eight. Sergeant Grimes made his report. "Nobody there, sir. Place locked up tight. Searched the grounds. All we saw was Barnaby's dog. Howled and ran off as if the devil were on his tail!"

Chief Underbeck was troubled. If Barnaby *was* missing, a search should be started at once. But it was already getting dark, and portions of Wharton's Swamp were very nearly impassable even during the day. Besides, there was no proof that Barnaby had not gone off for a visit, perhaps to nearby Stantonville, for instance, to call on a crony and stay overnight.

By nine o'clock he had decided to postpone any action till morning. A search now would probably be futile in any case. The swamp offered too many obstacles. If Barnaby had not turned up by morning, and there was no report that he had been seen elsewhere, a systematic search of the marsh could begin.

Not long after he had arrived at this decision, and as he was somewhat wearily preparing to leave headquarters and go home, a new and genuinely alarming interruption took place.

Shortly before nine thirty, a car braked to a sudden stop outside headquarters. An elderly man hurried in, supporting by thc arm a sobbing, hysterical young girl. Her skirt and stockings were torn and there were a number of scratches on her face.

After assisting her to a chair, the man turned to Chief Underbeck and the other officers who gathered around.

"Picked her up on the highway out near Wharton's Swamp. Screaming at the top of her lungs!" He wiped his forehead. "She ran right in front of my car. Missed her by a miracle. She was so crazy with fear I couldn't make sense out of what she said. Seems like something grabbed her boyfriend in the bushes out there. Anyway, I got her in the car without much trouble and I guess I broke a speed law getting here."

Chief Underbeck surveyed the man keenly. He was obviously shaken himself, and since he did not appear to be concealing anything, the chief turned to the girl.

He spoke soothingly, doing his best to reassure her, and at length she composed herself sufficiently to tell her story.

Her name was Dolores Rell and she lived in nearby Stantonville. Earlier in the evening she had gone riding with her fiancé, Jason Bukmeist of Clinton Center. As Jason was driving along the highway adjacent to Wharton's Swamp, she had remarked that the early evening moonlight looked very romantic over the marsh. Jason had stopped the car, and after they had surveyed the scene for some minutes, he suggested that, since the evening was warm, a brief "stroll in the moonlight" might be fun.

Dolores had been reluctant to leave the car, but at length had been persuaded to take a short walk along the edge of the marsh where the terrain was relatively firm.

As the couple were walking along under the trees, perhaps twenty yards or so from the car, Dolores became aware of an unpleasant odor and wanted to turn back. Jason, however, told her she only imagined it and insisted on going farther. As the trees grew closer together, they walked Indian file, Jason taking the lead.

Suddenly, she said, they both heard something swishing through the brush towards them. Jason told her not to be frightened, that it was probably someone's cow. As it came closer, however, it seemed to be moving with incredible speed. And it didn't seem to be making the kind of noise a cow would make.

At the last second Jason whirled with a cry of fear and told her to run. Before she could move, she saw a monstrous something rushing under the trees in the dim moonlight. For an instant she stood rooted with horror; then she turned and ran. She thought she heard Jason running behind her. She couldn't be sure. But immediately after she heard him scream.

In spite of her terror, she turned and looked behind her.

At this point in her story she became hysterical again, and several minutes passed before she could go on.

She could not describe exactly what she had seen as she looked over her shoulder. The thing which she had glimpsed rushing under the trees had caught up with Jason. It almost completely covered him. All she could see of him was his agonized face and part of one arm, low near the ground, as if the thing were squatting astride him. She could not say what it was. It was black, formless, bestial and yet not bestial. It was the dark gliding kind of indescribable horror which she had shuddered at when she was a little girl alone in the nursery at night.

She shuddered now and covered her eyes as she tried to picture what she had seen. "O God—*the darkness came alive! The darkness came alive!*"

Somehow, she went on presently, she had stumbled through the trees into the road. She was so terrified she hardly noticed the approaching car. There could be no doubt that Dolores Rell was in the grip of a genuine terror. Chief Underbeck acted with alacrity. After the white-faced girl had been driven to a nearby hospital for treatment of her scratches and the administration of a sedative, Underbeck rounded up all available men on the force, equipped them with shotguns, rifles, and flashlights, hurried them into four prowl cars, and started off for Wharton's Swamp.

Jason Bukmeist's car was found where he had parked it. It had not been disturbed. A search of the nearby swamp area, conducted in the glare of flashlights, proved fruitless. Whatever had attacked Bukmeist had apparently carried him off into the farthest recesses of the sprawling swamp.

After two futile hours of brush breaking and marsh sloshing, Chief Underbeck wearily rounded up his men and called off the hunt until morning.

As the first faint streaks of dawn appeared in the sky over Wharton's Swamp, the search began again. Reinforcements, including civilian volunteers from Clinton Center, had arrived, and a systematic combing of the entire swamp commenced.

By noon, the search had proved fruitless—or nearly so. One of the searchers brought in a battered hat and a rye whiskey bottle which he had discovered on the edge of the marsh under a sweet gum tree. The shapeless felt hat was old and worn, but it was dry. It had, therefore, apparently been discarded in the swamp since the storm of a few days ago. The whiskey bottle looked new; in fact, a few drops of rye remained in it. The searcher reported that the remains of a small campfire were also found under the sweet gum.

In the hope that this evidence might have some bearing on the disappearance of Jason Bukmeist, Chief Underbeck ordered a canvass of every liquor store in Clinton Center in an attempt to learn the names of everyone who had recently purchased a bottle of the particular brand of rye found under the tree.

The search went on, and midafternoon brought another, more ominous discovery. A diligent searcher, investigating a trampled area in a large growth of cattails, picked a rifle out of the mud.

After the slime and dirt had been wiped away, two of the searchers vouched that it belonged to Rupert Barnaby. One of them had hunted with him and remembered a bit of scrollwork on the rifle stock.

While Chief Underbeck was weighing this unpalatable bit of evidence, a report of the liquor store canvass in Clinton Center arrived. Every recent purchaser of a quart bottle of the particular brand in question had been investigated. Only one could not be located—a tramp who had hung around the town for several days and had been ordered out.

By evening most of the exhausted searching party were convinced that the tramp, probably in a state of homicidal viciousness brought on by drink, had murdered both Rupert Barnaby and Jason and secreted their bodies in one of the deep pools of the swamp. The chances were the murderer was still sleeping off the effects of drink somewhere in the tangled thickets of the marsh.

Most of the searchers regarded Dolores Rell's melodramatic story with a great deal of skepticism. In the dim moonlight, they pointed out, a frenzied, wild-eyed tramp bent on imminent murder might very well have resembled some kind of monster. And the girl's hysteria had probably magnified what she had seen.

As night closed over the dismal morass, Chief Underbeck reluctantly suspended the hunt. In view of the fact that the murderer probably still lurked in the woods, however, he decided to establish a system of night-long patrols along the highway which paralleled the swamp. If the quarry lay hidden in the treacherous tangle of trees and brush, he would not be able to escape onto the highway without running into one of the patrols. The only other means of egress from the swamp lay miles across the mire where the open sea washed against a reedy beach. And it was quite unlikely that the fugitive would even attempt escape in that direction.

The patrols were established in three-hour shifts, two men to a patrol, both heavily armed, and both equipped with powerful searchlights. They were ordered to investigate every sound or movement which they detected in the brush bordering the highway. After a single command to halt, they were to shoot to kill. Any curious motorists who stopped to inquire about the hunt were to be swiftly waved on their way, after being warned not to give rides to anyone and to report all hitchhikers.

Fred Storr and Luke Matson, on the midnight to three o'clock patrol, passed an uneventful two hours on their particular stretch of the highway. Matson finally sat down on a fallen tree stump a few yards from the edge of the road.

"Legs givin' out," he commented wryly, resting his rifle on the stump. "Might as well sit a few minutes."

Fred Storr lingered nearby. "Guess so, Luke. Don't look like—" Suddenly he scowled into the black fringes of the swamp. "You hear something, Luke?"

Luke listened, twisting around on the stump. "Well, maybe," he said finally, "kind of a little scratchy sound like."

He got up, retrieving his rifle.

"Let's take a look," Fred suggested in a low voice. He stepped over the stump and Luke followed him towards the tangle of brush which marked the border of the swamp jungle.

Several yards farther along they stopped again. The sound became more audible. It was a kind of slithering, scraping sound, such as might be produced by a heavy body dragging itself over uneven ground.

"Sounds like—a snake," Luke ventured. "A damn big snake!"

"We'll get a little closer," Fred whispered. "You be ready with that gun when I switch on my light!"

They moved ahead a few more yards. Then a powerful yellow ray stabbed into the thickets ahead as Fred switched on his flashlight. The ray searched the darkness, probing in one direction and then another.

Luke lowered his rifle a little, frowning. "Don't see a thing," he said. "Nothing but a big pool of black scum up ahead there."

Before Fred had time to reply, the pool of black scum reared up into horrible life. In one hideous second it hunched itself into an unspeakable glistening hood and rolled forward with fearful speed.

Luke Matson screamed and fired simultaneously as the monstrous scarf of slime shot forward. A moment later it swayed above him. He fired again and the thing fell upon him.

In avoiding the initial rush of the horror, Fred Storr lost his footing. He fell headlong—and turned just in time to witness a sight which slowed the blood in his veins.

The monster had pounced upon Luke Matson. Now, as Fred watched, literally paralyzed with horror, it spread itself over and around the form of Luke until he was completely enveloped. The faint writhing of his limbs could still be seen. Then the thing squeezed, swelling into a hood and flattening itself again, and the writhing ceased.

As soon as the thing lifted and swung forward in his direction, Fred Storr, goaded by frantic fear, overcame the paralysis of horror which had frozen him.

Grabbing the rifle which had fallen beside him, he aimed it at the shape of living slime and started firing. Pure terror possessed him as he saw that the shots were having no effect. The thing lunged towards him, to all visible appearances entirely oblivious to the rifle slugs tearing into its loathsome viscid mass.

Acting out of some instinct which he himself could not have named, Fred Storr dropped the rifle and seized his flashlight, playing its powerful beam directly upon the onrushing horror.

The thing stopped, scant feet away, and appeared to hesitate. It slid quickly aside at an angle, but he followed it immediately with the cone of light. It backed up finally and flattened out, as if trying by that means to avoid the light, but he trained the beam on it steadily, sensing with every primitive fiber which he possessed that the yellow shaft of light was the one thing which held off hideous death.

Now there were shouts in the nearby darkness and other lights began stabbing the shadows. Members of the adjacent patrols, alarmed by the sound of rifle fire, had come running to investigate.

Suddenly the nameless horror squirmed quickly out of the flashlight's beam and rushed away in the darkness.

In the leaden light of early dawn Chief Underbeck climbed into a police car waiting on the highway near Wharton's Swamp and headed back for Clinton Center. He had made a decision and he was grimly determined to act on it at once.

When he reached headquarters, he made two telephone calls in quick succession, one to the governor of the state and the other to the commander of the nearby Camp Evans Military Reservation.

The horror in Wharton's Swamp—he had decided—could not be coped with by the limited men and resources at his command.

Rupert Barnaby, Jason Bukmeist, and Luke Matson had without any doubt perished in the swamp. The anonymous tramp, it now began to appear, far from being the murderer, had been only one more victim. And Fred Storr—well, he hadn't disappeared. But the other patrol members had found him sitting on the ground near the edge of the swamp in the clutches of a mind-warping fear which had, temporarily at least, reduced him to near idiocy. Hours after he had been taken home and put to bed, he had refused to loosen his grip on a flashlight which he squeezed in one hand. When they switched the flashlight off, he screamed, and they had to switch it on again. His story was so wildly melodramatic it could scarcely be accepted by rational minds. And yet—they had said as much about Dolores Rell's hysterical account. And Fred Storr was no excitable young girl; he had a reputation for levelheadedness, stolidity, and verbal honesty which was touched with understatement rather than exaggeration. As Chief Underbeck arose and walked out to his car in order to start back to Wharton's Swamp, he noticed Old Man Gowse coming down the block.

With a sudden thrill of horror he remembered the eccentric's missing cow. Before the old man came abreast, he slammed the car door and issued crisp directions to the waiting driver. As the car sped away, he glanced in the rearview mirror.

Old Man Gowse stood grimly motionless on the walk in front of Police Headquarters.

"Old Man Cassandra," Chief Underbeck muttered. The driver shot a swift glance at him and stepped on the gas.

Less than two hours after Chief Underbeck arrived back at Wharton's Swamp, the adjacent highway was crowded with cars—state police patrol cars, cars of the local curious, and Army trucks from Camp Evans.

Promptly at nine o'clock over three hundred soldiers, police, and citizen volunteers, all armed, swung into the swamp to begin a careful search.

Shortly before dusk most of them had arrived at the sea on the far side of the swamp. Their exhaustive efforts had netted nothing. One soldier, noticing fierce eyes glaring out of a tree, had bagged an owl, and one of the state policemen had flushed a young bobcat. Someone else had stepped on a copperhead and been treated for snakebite. But there was no sign of a monster, a murderous tramp, nor any of the missing men.

In the face of mounting skepticism, Chief Underbeck stood firm. Pointing out that, so far as they knew to date, the murderer prowled only at night, he ordered that after a four-hour rest and meal period the search should continue.

A number of helicopters which had hovered over the area during the afternoon landed on the strip of shore, bringing food and supplies. At Chief Underbeck's insistence, barriers were set up on the beach. Guards were stationed along the entire length of the highway; powerful searchlights were brought up. Another truck from Camp Evans arrived with a portable machine gun and several flamethrowers.

By eleven o'clock that night the stage was set. The beach barriers were in place, guards were at station, and huge searchlights, erected near the highway, swept the dismal marsh with probing cones of light.

At eleven fifteen the night patrols, each consisting of ten strongly-armed men, struck into the swamp again.

Ravenous with hunger, the hood of horror reared out of the mud at the bottom of a rancid pool and rose towards the surface. Flopping ashore in the darkness, it slid quickly away over the clumps of scattered swamp grass. It was impelled, as always, by a savage and enormous hunger.

Although hunting in its new environment had been good, its immense appetite knew no appeasement. The more food it consumed, the more it seemed to require.

As it rushed off, alert to the minute vibrations which indicated food, it became aware of various disturbing emanations. Although it was the time of darkness in this strange world, the darkness at this usual hunting period was oddly pierced by the monster's hated enemy—light. The food vibrations were stronger than the shape of slime had ever experienced. They were on all sides, powerful, purposeful, moving in many directions all through the lower layers of puzzling, light-riven darkness.

Lifting out of the ooze, the hood of horror flowed up a latticework of gnarled swamp snags and hung motionless, while drops of muddy water rolled off its glistening surface and dripped below. The thing's sensory apparatus told it that the maddening streaks of lack of darkness were everywhere.

Even as it hung suspended on the snags like a great filthy carpet coated with slime, a terrible touch of light slashed through the surrounding darkness and burned against it.

It immediately loosened its hold on the snags and fell back into the ooze with a mighty *plop.* Nearby, the vibrations suddenly increased in intensity. The maddening streamers of light shot through the darkness on all sides.

Baffled and savage, the thing plunged into the ooze and propelled itself in the opposite direction.

But this proved to be only a temporary respite. The vibrations redoubled in intensity. The darkness almost disappeared, riven and pierced by bolts and rivers of light.

For the first time in its incalculable existence, the thing experienced something vaguely akin to fear. The light could not be snatched up and squeezed and smothered to death. It was an alien enemy against which the hood of horror had learned only one defence—flight, hiding.

And now as its world of darkness was torn apart by sudden floods and streamers of light, the monster instinctively sought the refuge afforded by that vast black cradle from which it had climbed.

Flinging itself through the swamp, it headed back for sea.

The guard patrols stationed along the beach, roused by the sound of gunfire and urgent shouts of warning from the interior of the swamp, stood or knelt with ready weapons as the clamor swiftly approached the sea.

The dismal reedy beach lay fully exposed in the harsh glare of searchlights. Waves rolled in towards shore, splashing white crests of foam far up the sands. In the searchlights' illumination the dark waters glistened with an oily iridescence.

The shrill cries increased. The watchers tensed, waiting. And suddenly across the long dreary flats clotted with weed stalks and sunken drifts there burst into view a nightmare shape which froze the shore patrols in their tracks.

A thing of slimy blackness, a thing which had no essential shape, no discernible earthly features, rushed through the thorn thickets and onto the flats. It was a shape of utter darkness, one second a great flapping hood, the next a black viscid pool of living ooze which flowed upon itself, sliding forward with incredible speed.

Some of the guards remained rooted where they stood, too overcome with horror to pull the triggers of their weapons. Others broke the spell of terror and began firing. Bullets from half a dozen rifles tore into the black monster speeding across the mud flats.

As the thing neared the end of the flats and approached the first sand dunes of the open beach, the patrol guards who had flushed it from the swamp broke into the open.

One of them paused, bellowing at the beach guards. "It's heading for sea! For God's sake don't let it escape!"

The beach guards redoubled their firing, suddenly realizing with a kind of sick horror that the monster was apparently unaffected by the rifle slugs. Without a single pause, it rolled through the last fringe of cattails and flopped onto the sands.

As in a hideous nightmare, the guards saw it flap over the nearest sand dune and slide towards the sea. A moment later, however, they remembered the barbed wire beach barrier which Chief Underbeck had stubbornly insisted on their erecting.

Gaining heart, they closed in, running over the dunes towards the spot where the black horror would strike the wire.

Someone in the lead yelled in sudden triumph. "It's caught! It's stuck on the wire!"

The searchlights concentrated swaths of light on the barrier.

The thing had reached the barbed wire fence and apparently flung itself against the twisted strands. Now it appeared to be hopelessly caught; it twisted and flopped and squirmed like some unspeakable giant jellyfish snared in a fisherman's net.

The guards ran forward, sure of their victory. All at once, however, the guard in the lead screamed a wild warning. "It's squeezing through! It's getting away!"

In the glare of light they saw with consternation that the monster appeared to be *flowing* through the wire, like a blob of liquescent ooze.

Ahead lay a few yards of downward slanting beach and, beyond that, rolling breakers of the open sea.

There was a collective gasp of horrified dismay as the monster, with a quick forward lurch, squeezed through the barrier. It tilted there briefly, twisting, as if a few last threads of itself might still be entangled in the wire.

As it moved to disengage itself and rush down the wet sand into the black sea, one of the guards hurled himself forward until he was almost abreast of the barrier. Sliding to his knees, he aimed at the escaping hood of horror.

A second later a great searing spout of flame shot from his weapon and burst in a smoky red blossom against the thing on the opposite side of the wire.

Black oily smoke billowed into the night. A ghastly stench flowed over the beach. The guards saw a flaming mass of horror grope away from the barrier. The soldier who aimed the flamethrower held it remorselessly steady.

There was a hideous bubbling, hissing sound. Vast gouts of thick, greasy smoke swirled into the night air. The indescribable stench became almost unbearable.

When the soldier finally shut off the flamethrower, there was nothing in sight except the white-hot glowing wires of the barrier and a big patch of blackened sand.

With good reason the mantle of slime had hated light, for its ultimate source was fire—the final unknown enemy which even the black hood could not drag down and devour.

MODEL NEPHEW

By Jack Davis, Albert Feldstein, and William M. Gaines

UNCLE'S HANDS BEGIN TO SHAKE SO THAT HE DROPS THE TINY MIZZEN MAST HE HOLDS WITH THE LONG SLENDER TWEEZERS...
YOU'LL GET IT ALL, SIDNEY... WHEN I'M DEAD! BUT NOT ONE MINUTE BEFORE...
I KNOW, UNCLE...
HE TURNS TO ME, AND THERE IS A FEAR IN HIS OLD EYES... THE FEAR OF A MAN WHO HAS SUDDENLY REALIZED THAT HE IS FACE TO FACE WITH DEATH. I MOVE TOWARD HIM...
YOU WOULDN'T...
OH, WOULDN'T I, UNCLE...?
HIS JAW DROPS OPEN AND HE STARTS TO CRY OUT. I CLAP MY HAND OVER HIS MOUTH... HIS NOSE... CUTTING OFF HIS AIR...
DON'T STRUGGLE, UNCLE. IT WILL ALL BE OVER IN A MOMENT...
G-G-G-GH...
I WATCH AS UNCLE'S FACE TURNS RED... THEN BLUE... AND HIS EYES FAIRLY POP FROM HIS HEAD AS THE LAST DROP OF OXYGEN IN HIS BLOODSTREAM IS ABSORBED...
SUFFOCATION CAN LOOK SO MUCH LIKE A HEART ATTACK, UNCLE! ONE CAN RARELY TELL THE DIFFERENCE... ESPECIALLY IN AN AGED PERSON...
UNCLE STIFFENS AS HIS LIFE EBBS AND DISSOLVES. AS HE DIES, HE SWINGS HIS ARMS BEFORE HIM, SWEEPING THE BOTTLE CONTAINING THE SHIP MODEL HE'D BEEN WORKING ON FROM HIS DESK...
DRAT IT...
THE BOTTLE SMASHES INTO A THOUSAND JAGGED FRAGMENTS WITH A SPLITTING CRASH AND THE TINY SHIP SPLINTERS INTO A SMALL PILE OF STRING AND TOOTHPICKS AND BALSA WOOD...
THAT'S SURE TO BRING THE SERVANTS. I'VE GOT TO GET OUT OF HERE.
I RELEASE MY UNCLE'S LIFELESS BODY, AND I DART FROM THE LIBRARY, OUT OF THE FRENCH DOORS, CLOSING THEM BEHIND ME. FROM A SAFE HIDING-PLACE AMONG THE BUSHES BEYOND THE PATIO, I WATCH THE SERVANT ENTER AND STAND DUMBFOUNDED AS HE VIEWS UNCLE'S CORPSE...
2

A FEW DAYS LATER, AT THE LAWYER'S OFFICE, MY LATE UNCLE'S WILL IS READ AND I LISTEN TO THE WORDS THAT MAKE ME A WEALTHY MAN...
...AND SO, TO MY NEPHEW SIDNEY, I LEAVE MY ENTIRE ESTATE, SAVE THOSE POSSESSIONS THAT ARE NEAR AND DEAR TO ME...MY OLD SEA CAPTAIN'S UNIFORM AND MY COLLECTION OF SHIPS-IN-BOTTLES. THESE, I REQUEST, BE INTERRED WITH MY BONES...
UNCLE'D MADE HIS FORTUNE WITH SHIPS. HE'D STARTED AS A SAILOR, WORKED HIS WAY UP TO SHIP'S CAPTAIN, AND EVENTUALLY BOUGHT HIS OWN FREIGHTER. FROM THERE, A WHOLE SHIPPING LINE HAD GROWN. WHEN UNCLE RETIRED, HE'D SOLD EVERYTHING. BUT HE NEVER COULD FORGET THE SEA ENTIRELY. I REMEMBER, AS A BOY, HIS TELLING ME STORIES OF HIS SEA ADVENTURES...
SHE WAS THE SWEETEST FOUR-MASTER THAT EVER SAILED THE SEA, SIDNEY.
AND THIS IS WHAT SHE LOOKED LIKE, UNCLE?
YEP, SIDNEY. THAT'S HER...EVERY SPAR AND LANYARD. MADE THAT MODEL MYSELF.
HOW'D YOU GET IT IN THE BOTTLE, UNCLE?
HEH, HEH. THAT'S A SECRET, BOY! A SECRET.
AW, I DON'T CARE, ANYWAY!
BUT I DID CARE. I REMEMBER STEALING TO THE LIBRARY ONE NIGHT AND WATCHING, FASCINATED, AS UNCLE CAREFULLY FITTED THE TINY SECTIONS OF HIS SHIP MODELS IN THROUGH THE NARROW NECK OF THE BOTTLE AND GLUED THEM INTO PLACE...
AND AS I GREW INTO MATURITY, AND I DISCOVERED HOBBIES OF MY OWN...CARS, AND WOMEN, AND HORSE RACES...THINGS THAT REQUIRED MONEY... I REMEMBER COMING TO MY UNCLE, AND BEGGING FOR A HANDOUT, AND HIM WORKING ON THOSE MISERABLE SHIP MODELS...
UNCLE, I...
SH-H-H-H! NOT NOW! THIS IS A TICKLISH PART...
BUT NOW ALL THAT IS OVER. I WILL NEVER HAVE TO BEG FOR ANOTHER CENT. IT IS ALL MINE...EVERYTHING. THE LAWYER, READING THE WILL, TELLS ME THAT...
...AND THAT I BE PLACED IN THE MAUSOLEUM I HAVE BUILT FOR MYSELF IN FAIRHAVEN CEMETERY, ALONG WITH THESE NEAR AND DEAR POSSESSIONS...
GOOD RIDDANCE...
3

THE FUNERAL IS A SIMPLE AFFAIR. I HAVE SEEN TO THAT. AFTER ALL, WHY WASTE MONEY ON THE DEAD OLD GOAT. BUT I HAVE TO KEEP MYSELF FROM LAUGHING, AS THE SERVANTS FILE INTO THE MAUSOLEUM AND PLACE HIS STUPID SHIP-MODELS BESIDE HIS COFFIN...
ASHES TO ASHES... DUST TO DUST...
...AND DRAPE HIS MOTH-EATEN OLD UNIFORM AND CAP OVER THE SILENT SOMBER COFFIN...
AS SOON AS MY LATE UNCLE'S AFFAIRS ARE PUT IN ORDER AND HIS ESTATE IS TURNED OVER TO ME, I GO ON A WILD SPENDING BINGE...NO HOLDS BARRED. I GET RID OF ALL MY INHIBITIONS IN ONE MAD CONTINUOUS SPREE OF WINE, WOMEN, AND SONG...
ONE NIGHT, RETURNING HOME FROM MY LATEST FUN-SEEKING ESCAPADE, I FIND MYSELF DOWN BY THE WATER-FRONT, A LITTLE HIGH, WALKING DOWN A DESERTED, WINDING, FOG-BLANKETED, COBBLE-STONED STREET. AS I STAGGER ALONG, I HEAR A VOICE...
SIDNEY! I'VE BEEN LOOKING FOR YOU!
HUH?
A FIGURE STANDS BEFORE ME, SILHOUETTED IN THE HAZY LIGHT FROM A DISTANT STREET LAMP... A FIGURE IN A SEA-CAPTAIN'S UNIFORM...
COME, SIDNEY! I NEED A CREW. MY SHIP IS WAITING. COME...
WHO...WHO IS IT?
4

I TRY TO PEER INTO THE GLOOM, TO MAKE OUT THE FEATURES OF THE STOOPED FIGURE STANDING BEFORE ME, BUT THE LIQUOR I HAVE CONSUMED DULLS MY SENSES...
WE MUST HURRY, SIDNEY!
KEEP AWAY FROM ME! KEEP AWAY...
HE COMES TOWARD ME, SHAMBLING OVER THE COBBLESTONES. SUDDENLY AN ICY FEAR GRIPS MY HEART. THERE IS SOMETHING FAMILIAR ABOUT THAT FIGURE. HIS WALK. HIS VOICE...
WHO... WHO ARE YOU?
DON'T YOU KNOW, SIDNEY?
I BEGIN TO RUN. I AM TERRORIZED. MY HEART BEATS IN MY CHEST LIKE A TRIP HAMMER RUN WILD. HE STUMBLES AFTER ME...
NO! NO! STAY AWAY...
I RUN THROUGH THE DESERTED WATERFRONT ALLEYS, THE PERSPIRATION POURING FROM MY FACE. BUT NO MATTER HOW FAST I RUN, THE SHUFFLING FIGURE BEHIND GAINS ON ME. AND THEN, SUDDENLY, THE ROAD ENDS. I HAVE RUN OUT ONTO A PIER...
OUR SHIP IS WAITING, SIDNEY!
OH, LORD...
HE IS ALMOST UPON ME. I STAND, FROZEN, BENEATH THE DIM LAMP AT THE PIER'S END. AND THEN I SMELL IT...THE ODOR...THE ODOR OF DRIFTWOOD AND ROTTING SEAWEED...THE VILE AND NAUSEATING STENCH OF DECAY...
HE REACHES OUT TO ME, AND I INHALE THE FOULNESS OF HIS AURA, THE PUTRID REEK OF HIS FETOR. AND THEN THE LIGHT ABOVE US FALLS UPON HIS FACE...
CHOKE... UNCLE...
THE FOG CLOSES IN ABOUT ME...FIRST GREY, THEN BLACK... AND I SLIP INTO THE MERCIFUL ESCAPE OF UNCONSCIOUSNESS, FALLING TO THE ROTTED BRINE-IMPREGNATED PIER BOARDS...
5

THE SOUND OF THE SEA AWAKENS ME. IT IS A HOLLOW ROARING SOUND, LIKE THE SOUND YOU HEAR WHEN YOU PLACE A SEA SHELL TO YOUR EAR. I STIR, SIT UP, AND LOOK ABOUT ME...
GOOD LORD! I'M ON A SHIP!
THE SKY ABOVE ME AS BLACK AS TAR, AND AN INKY, GREEN SEA, CALM AND STILL, STRETCHES AWAY TOWARD IT. I STAND ON THE DECK AND I CALL...
YOU'VE GOT TO TAKE ME BACK! HELP ME... SOMEBODY. YOU'VE GOT TO TAKE ME BACK TO LAND! I'LL PAY...I'LL PAY ANYTHING!
I LISTEN. NO SOUND. ONLY THE EMPTY FAR AWAY ROAR... ECHOING. I STAGGER ACROSS THE DECK TO THE CABIN DOOR, SCREAMING...
ANYBODY ON BOARD? ANYBODY?
I PULL AT THE DOOR LATCH. THE DOOR STICKS FAST. AND THEN I SEE THAT IT'S NO DOOR AT ALL, BUT MERELY A DOOR PAINTED ON THE CABIN WALL...
WHAT IS THIS? WHAT KIND OF SHIP IS THIS?
I PEER INTO THE BLACK PORT HOLES...
ANYBODY IN THERE?
AND THEN I REALIZE THAT THEY ARE MERELY BLACK CIRCLES PAINTED TO RESEMBLE PORTHOLES...
GOOD LORD!
I AM ALONE... ALONE ON A DERELICT SHIP... A SHIP FLOATING IN THE MIDDLE OF NOWHERE... WITH FAKE CABINS AND PAINTED PORT HOLES AND DUMMY DOORS. OH, GOD... SAVE ME!
6

MY CRIES OF ANGUISH DRIFT INTO THE NIGHT, AND THEIR ECHOES COME BACK, TAUNTING, LAUGHING AT ME. FRANTICALLY, I PEER OUT ACROSS THE STILL SEA TO THE GLOW IN THE EAST THAT IS THE COMING DAWN...
DAYLIGHT! PERHAPS... PERHAPS...
AND THEN I SEE THAT THE OCEAN BELOW ME DOES NOT MOVE. ITS CALM SWELLS HANG FROZEN, PARALYZED, A MOTIONLESS MASS THAT STRETCHES AWAY SILENTLY TO THE... THE...
THE HORIZON! IT'S ONLY A SHORT DISTANCE AWAY!
SUDDENLY MY BLOOD FREEZES. I SWING DOWN THE SHIP'S SIDE, BURNING MY HANDS AS I SLIDE DOWN THE HEAVY ROPE...
OH, LORD! NO! NO!
...I DASH MADLY ACROSS THE SOLID SEA, STAMPING OVER THE FROZEN WAVES...
IT CAN'T BE...
AND I REACH THE WALL...THE WALL OF GLASS THAT RISES UPWARD AROUND AND OVER MY DERELICT SHIP AND DOWN TO THE DISTANT OPPOSITE HORIZON...
GLASS! IT'S GLASS! OH, GOD...
I STARE OUT OF MY BOTTLE PRISON AT THE DISTANT COFFIN LOOMING IN THE DAWN LIGHT FILTERING THROUGH THE MAUSOLEUM WINDOW. AND I SEE THE STILL-DAMP CAPTAIN'S UNIFORM DRAPED UPON IT... STILL DAMP FROM THE FOG OF THE NIGHT BEFORE. AND I KNOW THAT I AM DOOMED... DOOMED TO SPEND ETERNITY ON THE DECKS OF THIS SHAM VESSEL... THIS SHIP-IN-A-BOTTLE FOREVER LOCKED BESIDE ITS MAKER'S BIER...
CHOKE...
HEH, HEH. WELL, HIDIOTS! THAT ABOUT CORKS UP O.W.'S MORBID MESS-MAG FOR THIS ISSUE. WE'LL ALL SEE YOU NEXT IN MY HUMBLE HORROR HEDITION OF TALES FROM THE CRYPT. IN THE MEANTIME, IF YOU WANT TO MEET MORE FIENDS LIKE YOURSELF, CORRESPOND WITH OTHER CREEPS, WEAR PINS AND PATCHES, CARRY IDENTIFICATION CARDS, FRAME CERTIFICATES, AND GENERALLY ACT THE FOOL, THEN JOIN THE E.C. FAN-ADDICT CLUB! IF YOU WANT TO REMAIN REASONABLY SANE, DON'T DO IT! 'BYE, NOW.

·9·

BLOOD SONS: A RUTHLESS REVIVAL

The onslaught of fearsome fantasies which constituted a definable and still viable horror revival may be dated at 1957, a year in which the sensitive and knowing might reasonably have expected the last monster to retire. The idea of expressing supernatural terror in works of the imagination had been so generally condemned that its exorcism was taken for granted. Moralists and do-gooders soon found new targets in television and in electronically amplified music, which soon replaced the comic book as the whipping boy of the arts. The flames of indignation were stoked by the morbid lyrics of the many popular songs like "Teen Angel" and "Endless Sleep," now classified by humorous historians as "death rock." Meanwhile, less sentimental images of mortality waited in the shadows.

It was a two-pronged attack. Two new film companies simultaneously rediscovered the commercial value of traditional terror tales; in the same year television unleashed a horde of Hollywood's hoary horrors. Screen Gems acquired the rights to the backlog of Universal's monster movie classics (and their numerous sequels), which were released to the public in a financial and cultural coup known to the trade as "Shock Theater." Syndicated to local stations throughout the United States for late-night viewing, these films introduced to a new generation such figures as Dracula, Frankenstein, the Wolf Man, the Mummy, and the Invisible Man, to say nothing of their offspring. The package proved to be eminently marketable, and it was followed in 1958 by more of the same, offered under the whimsical banner "Son of Shock."

The motion picture outfits that contributed most dramatically to the horror revival were Hammer Films of England and American International Pictures in the United States. Their rise to prominence foreshadowed forthcoming trends in the commercial cinema. This was most immediately obvious in the case of American International, whose first important release in the genre was *I Was a Teenage Werewolf* (1957). The title alone, by combining the dreaded blood lust of the monster movie with the equally menacing and relentless rhythm of "teenage" rock-and-roll music, jolted middle-aged taste makers and jaded adolescents as well, thus contributing in a small way to the contemporary generation gap. As the millions of kids from the war and postwar baby booms grew into a measure of financial freedom, they began to repaint the face of the entertainment industry. Mass communication made them infuriatingly sophisticated at an early age, and, raised in the shadow of nuclear annihilation, they began to look on society-smashing monstrosities as heroic rebels. The undead villains of an earlier day were transformed mirthfully into immortal monsters, as youth attempted to forge an ethic out of iconoclasm. The aesthetics of "camp" and "pop" are based on a similar awareness of the ironies inherent in the projections of another era's mentality.

In short, *I Was a Teenage Werewolf* seemed as absurd to its devotees as to its detractors, but the absurdity in no way interfered with their enjoyment. The story introduced a variation on legendary lycanthropy, as the title character was converted into his bestial form by a scientific experiment in regression. This plot device emphasized the film's slight but self-evident vein of social significance, with the monster emerging as a victim of an indifferent establishment, his troubles increased by the malevolent authority figure who offers to relieve them. There were also less esoteric elements of adolescent fantasy, such as the scene in which the protagonist unleashes his animal passions in the girl's gymnasium of his high school. Although clearly never intended as a serious work of art, the film had more energy and momentum than many of its more pretentious competitors. The teenage terror was portrayed by Michael Landon who, like James Arness, later achieved less ephemeral fame as the star of a western television series ("Bonanza").

The concept of the awesome adolescent was the work of producer Herman Cohen, who concluded after a demographic survey that such a subject could hardly fail at the box office. The movie did indeed make an impressive profit on a small investment and was rapidly followed by *I Was a Teenage Frankenstein*, another 1957 Cohen production for American International. Whit Bissell played the sinister scientist, as he had in the previous outing, and Gary Conway was his creature, decked out in makeup so improbably putrescent that he looked as if he had just been hit in the face with a pie. More intentionally outrageous than its predecessor, this effort emphasized the humor and incongruity in the plot, becoming paradoxically less amusing because of its self-conscious efforts to transcend itself. Still, the image of the monster being irresistibly drawn to a rock-and-roll party remains etched in the memory. Cohen completed a trilogy in the same year with the release of *Blood of Dracula*, which really should have been called *I Was a Teenage Vampire*, since it features a heroine at a school for problem girls who is transformed into a bloodsucking monster by one of her treacherous teachers. Once again, traditional terrors were modified to accommodate the theme of puberty betrayed. Although a few other motion pictures were to appear in the same vein *(Teenage Caveman, Teenage Monster, Teenage Zombies)*, a longer-lasting theme was inaugurated in American International's *Invasion of the Saucermen.* Here the kids are the heroes, defeating a menace that their obtuse elders have insisted on ignoring.

A somewhat more dignified but equally controversial approach was adopted by England's Hammer Films. Rather than updating the classic stories, Hammer restored them to their nineteenth-century settings, filming them in color with casts of excellent if unknown performers. Ingenuity and the English economy made it possible to produce impressively mounted movies at minimal cost, and the use of color film helped to give some old bodies a new lease on life.

Transformed by time and television, Karloff and Lugosi had begun to take on the aura of lovable father figures; a new menace was discovered just in the nick of time when a gaunt character actor named Christopher Lee was cast as both monsters in the Hammer remakes of *Frankenstein* and *Dracula.* Lee's classical training, comparative youth, and commanding physical presence produced the great horror star of the day. At one point he was reported to be receiving more fan letters from women than any other actor in Europe, indicating that his portrayals were flavored with a perverse sort of sex appeal. A

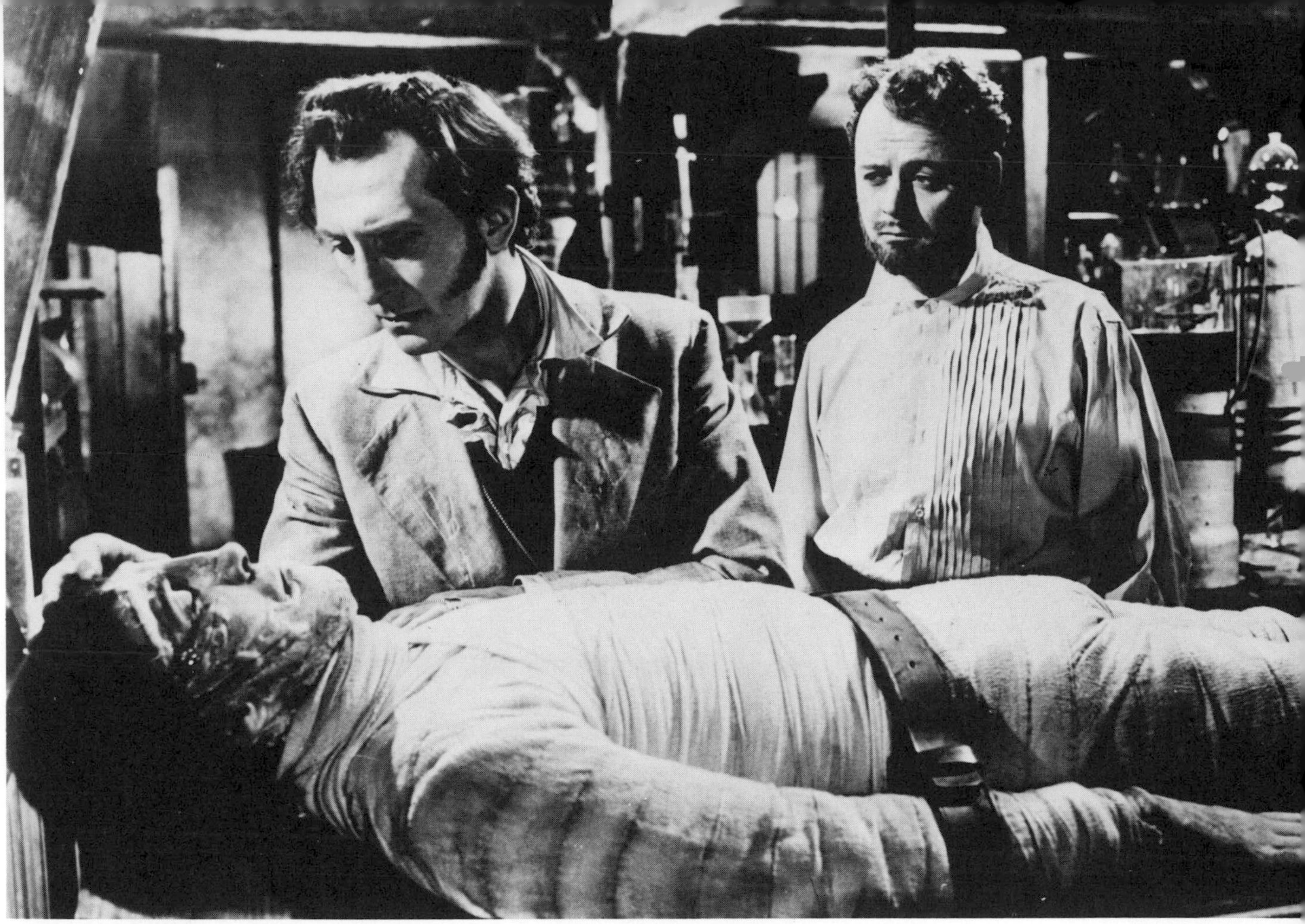

Peter Cushing goes to work on his creation, Christopher Lee, while Robert Urquhart looks on skeptically. The trend-setting Hammer film *The Curse of Frankenstein* was the first of a series following the career of the creator rather than his creature. *Courtesy of Warner Bros. Inc. Copyright © 1957.*

perfect foil for Lee's grim vitality was found in the cool, intellectual performances of Peter Cushing, who played the scientists responsible for creating the first monster and destroying the second. Sequels and spin-offs followed like flies, for Hammer had discovered a formula for converting crimson carnage into the long green. Their first color horror film, *The Curse of Frankenstein* (1957), grossed millions of pounds worldwide on a budget of a mere hundred thousand. The follow-up, released in America as *Horror of Dracula* (1958), was equally successful, and no thing from this organization has finished in the red.

The most identifiable ingredient in this bubbling vat of viciousness was its frankness. The demonic, sometimes sadistic strain of the true Gothic found in authors like Walpole, Maturin, and especially "Monk" Lewis was here in full flower. While the 1931 *Dracula* had featured a virginal heroine and only as much blood as could be drawn from a cut finger, the Hammer version offered a superfluity of statuesque starlets and gallons of gore flowing from torn throats and transfixed hearts. Some critics carped and cringed; but the public had no such reservations, and, within a decade, Hammer's ruddy realism had become a cinema standard. Equally important as an indicator of future trends was the company's financial position. An independent producer, Hammer released through a

Christopher Lee achieved stardom with Hammer Films' version of *Dracula*, released in the United States as *Horror of Dracula* (1958). In the opinion of some observers, his intense performance overshadowed that of Bela Lugosi. *Courtesy of Universal Pictures.*

variety of American studios which, caught in a cross fire between TV and the maverick menace mongers, were on their way to conversion into holding companies, video producers, or distribution directors.

The Curse of Frankenstein was no more faithful to the novel than previous adaptations, but the screenplay by Jimmy Sangster offered some new variations. Frankenstein is portrayed as a ruthless monomaniac, committing murders to obtain organs for his creation, which he deliberately uses for further crimes after bringing it to life. The sympathetic side of the original character is represented by a more scrupulous assistant who attempts to destroy the monster, only to discover that Frankenstein has revived it again. Billed as "the creature," Christopher Lee was a shambling, scarred, green-faced wreck who gives the unpleasant impression that he may fall apart at any moment. He is finally dissolved in a vat of acid, and Frankenstein, unable to prove that any such being has ever existed, is condemned to death for the monster's crimes.

Horror of Dracula, despite its cumbersome title, was a distinct improvement. Almost certainly Hammer's finest film, its adherents cite it as one of the genre's finest moments, while dissidents curse it for inaugurating a tradition in which subtlety and atmosphere counted less than shock and action. Director Terence Fisher was in this, as in the previous film, a very direct storyteller, abandoning the elaborate photographic tricks that can create a mood of mystery and concentrating instead on detailed scenes of sheer physical horror. Decked out in oversized canine teeth and crimson contact lenses, Christopher Lee makes Dracula a ferocious figure, far removed from the stately stalkers in earlier screen versions. His performance is effective enough to overshadow many of Bela Lugosi's most memorable mannerisms, and Lee went on to play the vampire in half a dozen sequels, becoming the premier interpreter of this most durable of horror roles. *Horror of Dracula* has an especially gruesome climax. The vampire's disintegration in the sunlight is not depicted in the usual series of sedate double exposures but in a rapid succession of violent action shots that make the transformation more effective than any amount of careful process photography.

Emboldened by the success of his compressed adaptations of the original novels, screenwriter Jimmy Sangster concocted a new story for Hammer's next effort, a sequel called *Revenge of Frankenstein* (1958). This witty little black comedy inaugurated a series that concentrated on the further adventures of the mad scientist, in contrast to the old Universal series that had considered his monster to be a much more marketable commodity. The film depicts Dr. Frankenstein (still Peter Cushing) escaping from a condemned cell to resume his experiments under an alias. Work in a charity hospital provides an endless supply of spare parts, and a new creature is soon under construction, its brain volunteered by a cripple who is anxious for a new lease on life. The result is an eminently presentable young man, at least until the brain begins to reproduce symptoms of paralysis in its new body. Frustration drives the creature to murder, and Frankenstein's identity is exposed. Before he can flee, he is attacked by his resentful charity patients and beaten to a pulp. Dying, Frankenstein instructs his assistant to take appropriate measures, and he is wheeled into a laboratory where a new host body is waiting for its creator's brain. An epilogue depicts a resurrected Dr. Frankenstein, with a new name and a new body, arranging his hair to hide a slight scar as he prepares to embark on a new experiment.

Released on the same program with *Revenge of Frankenstein* was one of the better horror films of the decade, a modest black-and-white non-Hammer offering entitled *Curse of the*

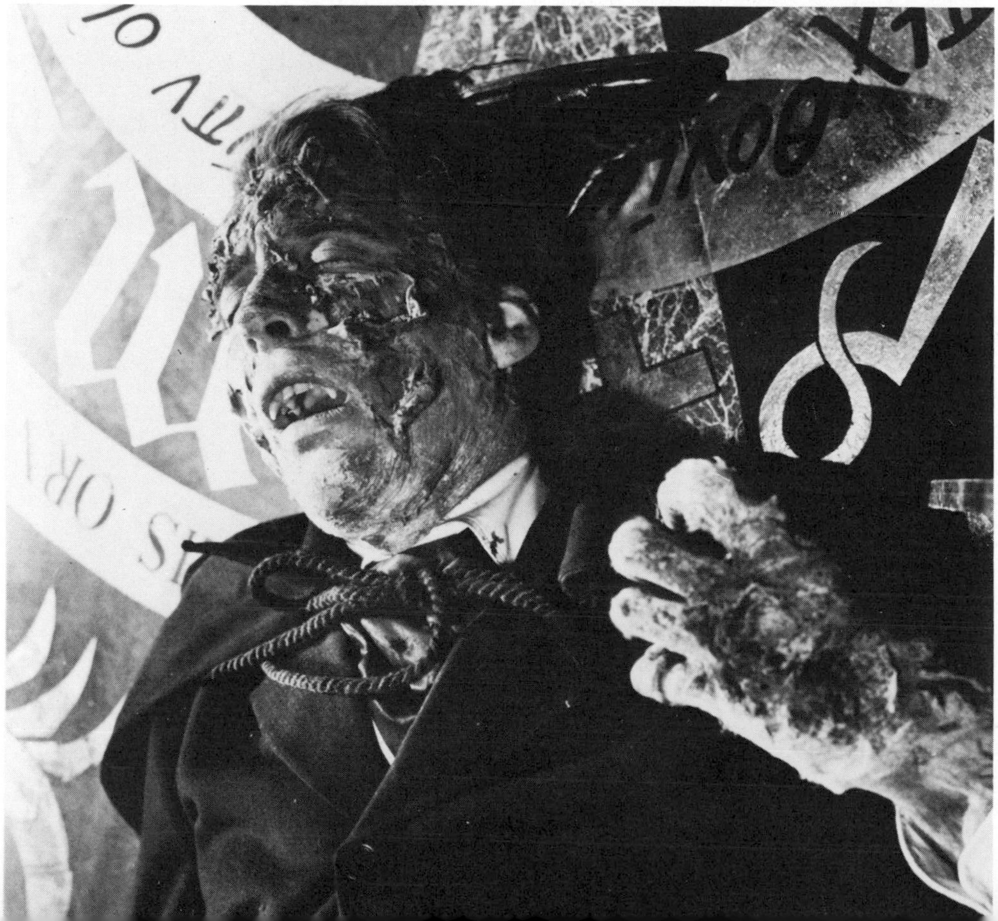

The gruesome climax of *Horror of Dracula*, in which Christopher Lee disintegrates into dust, exemplified director Terence Fisher's decision to provide maximum shock value. *Courtesy of Universal Pictures.*

Demon. Directed by Jacques Tourneur, *Curse of the Demon* retained much of the eerie atmosphere he had conjured up for the Val Lewton productions of an earlier era. Based on the M. R. James short story "Casting the Runes," the elaborated screenplay came closer to themes described by H. P. Lovecraft, especially in the appearance of a titanic entity from beyond. Despite a brief visit from this overpowering individual, the prevalent tone was tense and intimate, and the film came closer than most of its contemporaries to evoking an authentic sense of the supernatural.

The resurgence of interest in the macabre represented by these films and others of less importance was also reflected by broadcasters. Televised terrors began to come into their own. A leader in the field was Columbia Broadcasting System's "Alfred Hitchcock Presents," which bowed late in 1956. The famous motion picture director's fame was based on mystery and suspense films of a comparatively normal sort, but the television program rapidly acquired a somewhat ghoulish character. Amid stories of more common crimes, there appeared tales like Stanley Ellin's "Speciality of the House," in which an exclusive club for gourmets is revealed to be feeding its members human flesh; and John Keir Cross's "The Glass Eye," in which a spinster conceives an affection for a reclusive ventriloquist, only to discover that he is a life-sized dummy manipulated by a dwarf sitting on his knee. Occasionally the tales were frankly supernatural. In "Banquo's Chair," a detective plans to make a murderer confess by arranging for an actor to impersonate the victim's ghost. The actor is delayed, but the ghost appears right on cue. This episode and a few others were directed by Hitchcock himself, but for the most part he was content to serve as a sardonic master of ceremonies. In this capacity alone he broke a number of precedents. The rotund Englishman invariably introduced commercial messages with cutting remarks about his sponsor, a remarkably tolerant manufacturer of patent medicines. Furthermore, he subverted a cherished broadcasting rule which insisted that criminals should be punished for their misdeeds. More often than not, the teleplays left the villains triumphant, and Hitchcock would appear at the end of the program to reassure his viewers, with obvious insincerity, that justice had eventually triumphed.

The same network offered another program that intermittently touched on the macabre: Rod Serling's "Twilight Zone." Serling, a television writer who made his reputation with several social problem dramas like "Patterns" and "Requiem for a Heavyweight," was the host and chief scriptwriter for this series of dramas on fantasy themes. Although whimsy and science fiction were featured more frequently than tales of terror, "Twilight Zone" pioneered the concept of imaginative drama on prime-time television, making material of its type available on a wider scale than ever before. The themes were sometimes a trifle familiar to those already conversant with the literature in the field, but Serling's undeniable skill in dramatic construction provided considerable compensation. Perhaps his most frightening conception was "The Monsters Are Due on Maple Street," which depicted a small town degenerating into mass madness and murder under the threat of an invasion from outer space. A final twist suggests that spreading such panic is the form an actual invasion would take. A minor tour de force in a familiar tradition was provided by an adaptation of Charles Beaumont's short story "Perchance to Dream." Here a man with a weak heart visits a psychiatrist because his nightmares have become so horrible he is convinced that falling asleep will kill him. The session with the doctor turns out to be but another dream, for the patient falls asleep on the couch and dies from the terrors in his own mind. Perhaps the most unusual feature of "Twilight Zone" was Serling's behavior as the host. In contrast to the humorous approach that had become almost obligatory for masters of ceremonies on similar programs, Serling's demeanor was uniformly grim and earnest.

Supernatural stories of a different sort were presented on the American Broadcasting Company's "One Step Beyond." Produced, directed, and introduced by John Newland, this program was devoted exclusively to purportedly authentic accounts of uncanny events. Psychic phenomena of every sort were given a very restrained treatment which compared unfavorably with the melodramatics that audiences had come to expect in presentations of this kind, while the documentation was usually too scanty to produce a deep sense of conviction. Nevertheless there were a few interesting shows, especially one that abandoned the usual dramatic format to present a study of hallucinogenic drugs. Newland himself partook of some peyote to test its effect on extrasensory perception. This segment is especially noteworthy in retrospect, since drugs like these, although virtually unknown when the program first appeared, were to become an important factor in the occult revival of later years.

Perhaps the most ambitious of television's excursions into the unknown was the National Broadcasting Company's "Thriller." Its weekly offerings were a full hour in length, offering at least quantitatively twice as much as its rival programs, although both "Twilight Zone" and "Alfred Hitchcock Presents" made disappointing efforts to expand their time segments during their last days. "Thriller" acquired the services of the venerable Boris Karloff, already in his eighth decade but still more than able to perform as the program's host and, on occasion, its principal actor. For nearly half a century, Karloff's name had been synonymous with horror, and his presence in a production invariably added a note of dignity even though he appeared, especially in the years just before "Thriller," in some distinctly second-rate films. This program, however, maintained a solid level of quality, although it was not entirely free from clichés. As usual, crime dramas shared the screen with offerings of a more outré nature, but the macabre was represented here in greater proportion than on any previous television series. A number of the stories were drawn from the pages of the old *Weird Tales* magazine; an important contributor in this regard was veteran author Robert Bloch, whose previous credentials also included a stint as a radio dramatist. Among the most powerful of the program's productions was an adaptation of Bloch's story "The Spectacles," an episodic tale in which a pair of specially ground glasses permit the wearer to view the world as it really is. After a series of dreadful disillusionments, the protagonist glances into a mirror and, discovering the loathsomeness of his own reflection, destroys the spectacles and then himself. Another outstanding effort was a version of Robert E. Howard's improbably titled haunted-house tale, "Pigeons from Hell."

A lamentably short-lived excursion into the bizarre was provided by the CBS summer replacement series "Way Out." For a few weeks, some literate and ingenious half-hour dramas were presented by English author Roald Dahl, whose ironic tales have made him one of the modern masters of the macabre. Makeup artist Dick Smith made an important contribution to the effectiveness of the show's most striking segment, in which a photographer acquires the ability to alter the appearance of his subjects by retouching their portraits. When a drop of the enchanted liquid he uses accidentally falls on his own picture, he is horribly transformed, but not into the typical Hollywood monster. Instead, one side of his face is transformed into a flat, featureless surface, just as it had been blotted out in the photograph.

Each of these television programs had its moments, but none could compare with the old theatrical productions released to television by "Shock Theater." These films, seen by millions more than in their original appearances, established a permanent monster mythology for the mass audience. At the same time they provided a platform for dozens of new performers in the genre. The hideous host or hostess had become a staple ingredient in broadcasts of this character, and a multitude of characters found employment introducing the old movies to new audiences. Most of these "monsters of ceremonies" were crude and unimaginative, but at least one, John Zacherle, emerged as a first-rate parodist whose antics were more entertaining than all but the best of the films he introduced.

Working under the name of Roland for one season in Philadelphia, Zacherle was transferred to New York where, as Zacherley, he brought his strange profession to new heights of gory glory. Unlike many of his colleagues, Zacherley watched the movies he was presenting, and he made a specialty of building his routines around the premise of the evening's film. A "mummy" movie would find him involved in a scheme for do-it-yourself embalming, while a "mad scientist" feature would inspire him to transplant a brain (usually impersonated by a totally unconvincing cauliflower). He also injected himself directly into the films themselves, redeeming the clichés by replacing them. Confronted with the inevitable morgue scene in which a sheet would be pulled back to reveal a body for identification, Zacherley would arrange for his director to cut to a shot of Zacherley on a slab, waving at the viewers. On several occasions, he donned an Alpine hat to replace the leader of the indignant peasants out to destroy the monster in what he referred to as a "torchlight parade." As the quality of the movies declined, he became increasingly ruthless. Forced to contend with a particularly lame jungle epic, climaxed by a battle between two totally unconvincing gorillas, Zacherley killed the sound track and substituted a saccharine waltz. At the end of an interminable haunted-house mystery, the detective's elaborate explanations were drowned out by the crescendo strains of a Sousa march. One series of Zacherley's programs concluded with the gleeful ghoul being dragged away by the men in white suits; but the character has never really died, and its creator, now a comparatively subdued disc jockey, is still ready to don his white face and black coat at the drop of a head.

The shot of adrenaline provided by such video vultures encouraged motion picture producers to embark on a campaign of creature features. A solid market for such fare was indubitably present, and it seemed that any horror film could show a profit, regardless of

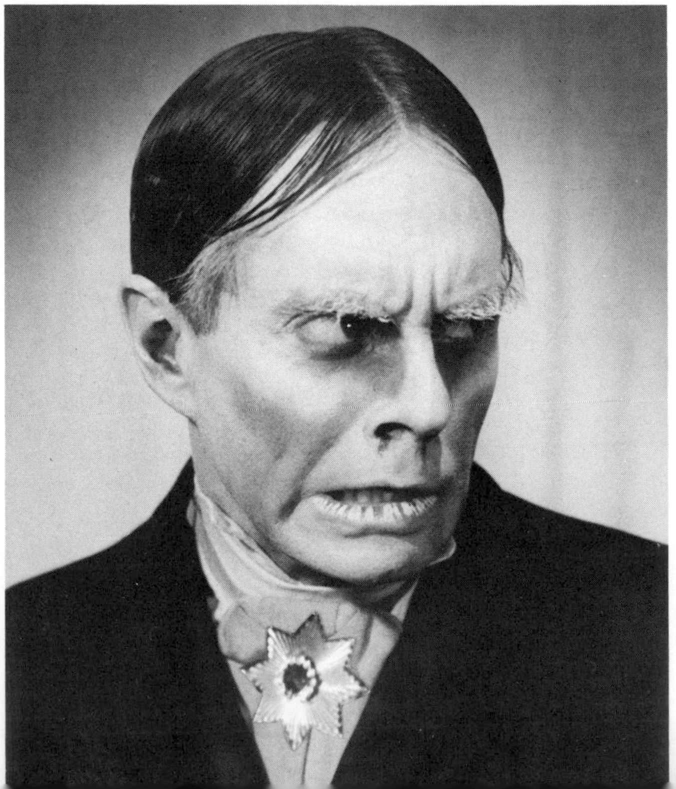

John Zacherle, who appeared in this guise under the names "Roland" and "Zacherley," was the best of television's horror hosts, a clever comedian whose monstrous mockery made light of dark doings.

its merits, provided that its budget was kept within certain limits. Drive-in theaters, at their peak during this era, helped to guarantee the profits on a number of films which, in all likelihood, were not even seen by their adolescent audiences. At any rate, some of the worst films ever made appeared, beside which even the poverty-row productions of the previous decade took on a certain dignity. Every connoisseur has his own favorite candidates for oblivion, but few were worse than Astor's *Frankenstein's Daughter* (1958), which disgraced a once proud name with a thoroughly inept effort about a male monster with a blonde's head attached. Equally incompetent were Allied Artists' *Attack of the Fifty-Foot Woman* (1958), featuring a disgruntled giantess knocking over papier-mâché buildings in a search for her estranged spouse while groaning "Harry! Harry!" in an overamplified monotone; and Astor's *She-Demons*, in which an unregenerated Nazi scientist conducts improbable experiments on the inhabitants of a tropical island.

One way for motion pictures to set themselves apart from this herd of monstrosities involved the use of publicity stunts. The leader in this field was producer-director William Castle, who used promotional gimmicks like heart-attack insurance policies and electric joy buzzers to keep crowds coming to see his films, providing enough ballyhoo to turn fairly ordinary flicks into sinister circuses. Strangely enough, the quality of Castle's films increased while his ingenuity kept him in business. An early outing, *Macabre* (1958), was a jumbled tale of premature burial that had little to offer except the promise that any patron dying of fright while in the theater would be eligible to collect a thousand dollars. The film's quality made this offer tolerably safe. A bit more shocking was *The Tingler* (1959), especially since Castle arranged to wire theater seats to keep his audience on the edges of them. This made about as much sense as the plot, in which a scientist discovers that fear manifests itself in the form of an oversized insect on the victim's spinal cord. The improbable was made somewhat more palatable by the presence of Vincent Price, whose brisk overplaying of the doctor helped establish him as the leading American actor in cinema shockers. Price was also on hand for Castle's prime achievement of the gadget period, *The House on Haunted Hill* (1958). This featured a process called Emergo, which consisted of a skeleton on a wire zooming over the heads of the audience, effectively disrupting the film's more authentic jolts. Still, it was a capable thriller, with some nasty ghosts explained away as the machinations of an equally nasty murderer. The Emergo device was vaguely tied into the action, since one of the killer's tricks involved the use of a marionette made out of bones; but several of his more interesting illusions went unexposed in the general rush to wind up the details of the plot.

Vincent Price also made an innocuous appearance as a well-intentioned onlooker in one of the period's most sensational science fiction shockers, *The Fly* (1958). This Twentieth Century-Fox production contravened normal expectations by not being about a giant insect. Instead, it concerned a young scientist who invents a device for transporting matter by disintegrating it in a transmitter and reintegrating it in a receiver. When he transports himself there is a fly hidden in the machine, and the result is a man with the oversized head of a fly. Most of the subsequent proceedings are devoted to his dismay at this revolting development, until he is finally put out of his misery by his wife. What rescued the film from oblivion was its grotesque climax, when the pesky fly is discovered in a spider's web, complete with a human head that screams for help in a buzzing falsetto. The story, by George Langelaan, had appeared previously in *Playboy*, a men's magazine which, against all likelihood, became an important forum for frightening fiction. Much of the responsibility for this rested with one of the editors, Ray Russell, whose own story "Sardonicus" was filmed in 1962 by William Castle.

Another science fiction effort that acquired an enduring reputation was Paramount's *The Blob* (1958). A weak script, lackadaisical direction, and bored actors could not detract from the charm of this colorful alien invader, which grew from a mere handful of goo by absorbing citizens of an all-American town. Sliding under doors, oozing through ventilators, emptying a theater at a midnight horror show, the Blob was a joy to behold, a lovable character that deserved more than its eventual destruction by the inevitable band of quick-witted teenagers, led by a slightly embarrassed Steve McQueen.

All this renewed flurry of interest in cinema and video manifestations of the macabre culminated in the emergence of a house organ for devotees of demonic drama. This was *Famous Monsters of Filmland*, an apparently inexplicable but undeniably durable magazine which, since its debut in 1958, has documented the past and present of fearsome films. Published against considerable odds by a tough-minded fantasy fancier named James Warren, *Famous Monsters* outlasted the dismay of social critics and the dissent of serious cinema scholars and eventually became something of an institution to succeeding generations of American kids. Competitors have come and gone, but the magazine's combination of wide-eyed enthusiasm and wisecracking ennui has proved unbeatable. The editor and principal writer is longtime monster lover Forrest J. Ackerman, whose credentials stretch back to the days of *Weird Tales*, when he was affectionately satirized, in a pamphlet anonymously circulated among members of the Lovecraft circle, for his unflagging devotion to the cause of fantasy fandom. Ackerman's tongue-in-cheek approach, deliberately aimed at a preadolescent audience, has contributed considerably to the concept that imaginary horrors are just good clean fun. His more serious endeavor is a gigantic collection of fantasy and science fiction material, to be housed for posterity in a Hollywood mansion.

Warren's brainchild rapidly became a rallying point and a marketplace for the fun-loving forces of fear, promoting and even inspiring not only films, but also a wide array of novelty merchandise dedicated to the proposition that every child, at heart, is a little monster. Rubber masks reproducing the features of filmland's famous fiends, glow-in-the-dark plastic vampire fangs, monster T-shirts, and similar accouterments now adorn the forms of countless children. Reportedly the Frankenstein mask alone has been worn by over a million satisfied customers. Aurora Products, a firm purveying model kits that usually ran to boats and planes, was persuaded to produce a series of scale-model monster kits, and millions of otherwise idle hands were soon employed in creating their own monsters.

No story captures this mood of monster madness more vividly than Richard Matheson's "Blood Son," even though it was written several years before the craze took hold. Originally published in an obscure 1951 pulp magazine, it surfaced in Matheson's 1957 collection *The Shores of Space.* Reprinted at the end of this chapter, this touching tale of a boy who wants to be a vampire when he grows up shifts through satire, schizophrenia, and the supernatural with telling effect. Of course, the fate of its protagonist is considerably more dramatic than that of his real-life counterparts. There may possibly be some justice in the argument that fictional crimes may inspire the impressionable to go and do likewise; but it seems reasonably clear that horror movies and similar fare do not increase the population of homicidal maniacs. Surely if a young Frankenstein fan had run amok, the media would have made the public painfully aware of it. Rather, it appears to be the repressed model of decorum who poses the real threat. Similarly, the creators of fearsome fantasies often seem to delight in depicting themselves and their fellows as dangerous lunatics, although the disappointing fact is that they are mild mannered to a fault, never inflicting tortures on anyone, occasionally excepting

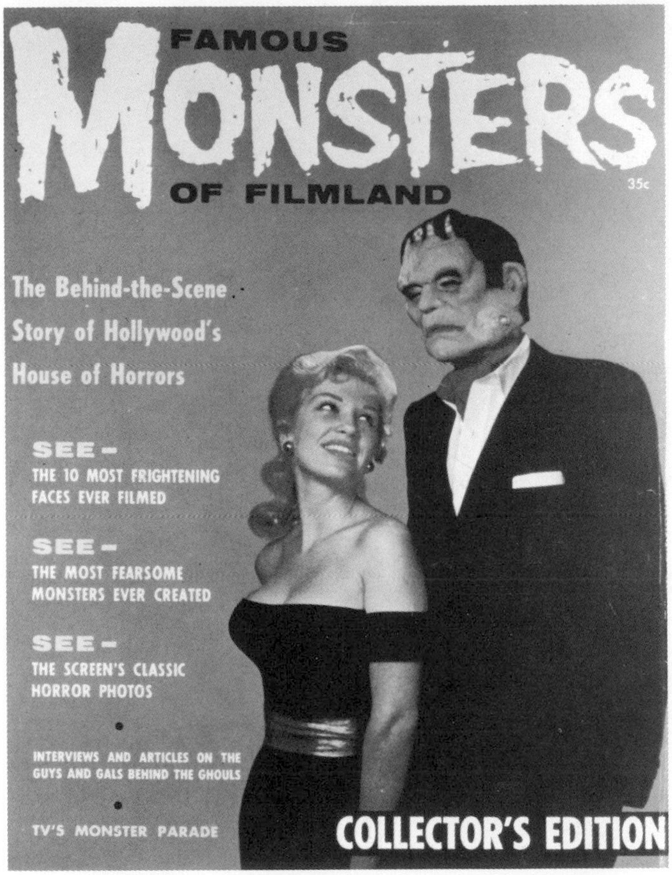

James Warren inaugurated the return of horror magazines with *Famous Monsters of Filmland* in 1958 (Warren is wearing the Frankenstein mask on the cover), and he revived horror comics a few years later with *Creepy*; the first issue's cover is by Jack Davis.

The modern master of special effects is Ray Harryhausen, whose best techniques are demonstrated in a series of adventure epics like *The Seventh Voyage of Sinbad* (1958), in which this duel takes place between Kerwin Matthews and a skeleton who surpasses the usual oversized beasts.

themselves. All this suggests, theories to the contrary, that an interest in imaginary horrors is a sort of safety valve, creating catharsis rather than corruption.

Richard Matheson is a leader of that group of fantasy writers who, perhaps partly inspired by the indefatigable Robert Bloch, have fattened their traditionally feeble finances by finding work in films. His 1954 novel, *I Am Legend*, which offers a scientifically plausible explanation for a future plague of vampirism, was filmed twice within a decade, though neither version approached the intensity of the original. It is a grim and compelling chronicle of the last mortal on the planet, hunted by night and a hunter by day, finally eradicated by creatures who regard him as an anachronistic freak. An expert on vampire variations, Matheson is also responsible for the short story "The Funeral," a wildly comic look at an undertaker who loses his grip at the last rites of a sentimental vampire with some troublesome friends. Matheson's novel *The Shrinking Man*, about a radiation casualty who dwindles into infinity, became a tastefully low-key 1957 Universal film, *The Incredible Shrinking Man*, directed by Jack Arnold.

In contrast to this diminutive individual were the titans released with monotonous regularity by the Japanese studio Toho. After *Godzilla* came *Rodan*, an oversized prehistoric bird whose wings create cataclysmic air currents; *Gigantis, the Fire Monster*; and

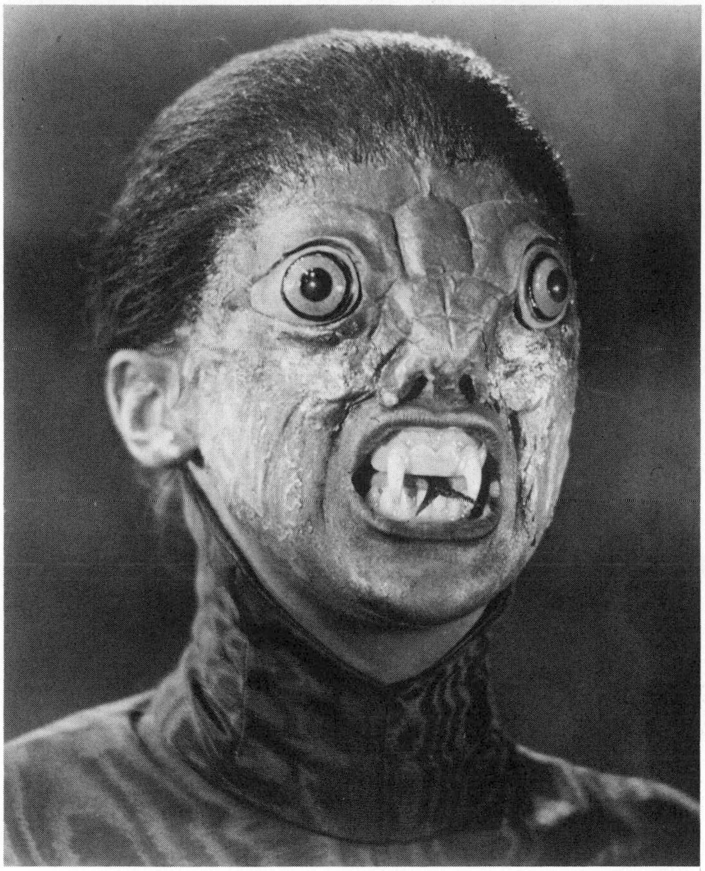

Jacqueline Pearce portrayed an unusual sort of monster, a snake woman, in the 1966 Hammer production *The Reptile*, directed by John Gilling. © *1966 Hammer Film Productions Ltd. All rights reserved. Courtesy of Twentieth Century-Fox.*

Mothra, a big, benevolent butterfly under the control of insipid twin pixies. The films became increasingly juvenile and the special effects, increasingly incompetent, and they were never aided by the atrocious dubbing they received for American release. Eventually the monsters were teamed up, often under American titles that were misleading at best. *Godzilla vs. the Thing* might have conjured up images of the famous science fiction film of an earlier day, but the "thing" turns out to be Mothra. *King Kong vs. Godzilla* particularly outraged purists by offering an actor in a shoddy ape suit as a substitute for the beautifully articulated animated model of 1933.

Other monster factories continued their onslaught with somewhat more respectable results. In 1959, Hammer Films released nicely mounted color remakes of *The Mummy* and *The Hound of the Baskervilles*, directed by Terence Fisher and costarring Peter Cushing and Christopher Lee. They slipped a bit in 1960 with *House of Fright*, an ingenious but inept variation on the Jekyll and Hyde story. In this one the doctor is rather homely, while his evil alter ego is a handsome devil; but coming up with this idea seems to have exhausted everyone connected with the project. More to the point was a sharp little fang-and-stake epic, rather deceptively entitled *Brides of Dracula* (1960). The count himself is nowhere in sight, but his old nemesis Dr. Van Helsing is on hand (Peter Cushing) to keep a crew of his followers at bay. Better yet was *Curse of the Werewolf* (1961), a relatively restrained (for Hammer) treatment of the lycanthropy legend based on a novel by Guy Endore. A surprising amount of attention was paid to the psychology of the afflicted party (Oliver Reed), who did not even show his furry face until the film's finish. On the other hand, the studio slipped in 1962 (as had Universal in 1943) by attempting to remake *The Phantom of the Opera.* The original's mythic proportions were lost when the Phantom (Herbert Lom) was explained away as a disgruntled composer with a scarred face.

The macabre motion picture gained a new aura of legitimacy in 1960 when director Alfred Hitchcock released *Psycho* on an unsuspecting public. Hitchcock's films had traditionally featured murder and mayhem of a fairly tasteful nature (with the possible exception of his 1926 silent Jack the Ripper film, *The Lodger*); but *Psycho*, perhaps inspired by the success of his intermittently morbid television show, was a thoroughgoing shocker. It also proved to be the most lucrative film produced in the genre up to the time, and it launched enough imitators to create a whole new subclassification of the horror film, one that has continued to the present day. Adapted from a novel by Robert Bloch, *Psycho* kept audiences off guard by devoting its first half to a typical Hitchcockian situation involving the adventures of a secretary (Janet Leigh) who has absconded with a small fortune. Since she serves as the sole focus for so much of the film, audiences are hardly prepared to see her brutally murdered shortly after her arrival at a seedy motel. She is ferociously stabbed to death while taking a shower, and the scene is jolting not only because of the juxtaposition of nudity and brutality, but also because of the photography and editing. The scene is a series of quick cuts from various angles, evoking a sense of frenzied violence without a direct depiction of its effects. The sequence is so revolutionary that the film is arguably among the most technically influential in the history of the medium. Hitchcock had more gore in store for his viewers, as well as the shocking revelation that the murders have not been committed by the motel keeper's mother, but rather by her crazed son (Anthony Perkins), who impersonates the old lady while keeping her mummified corpse in the cellar. Inferior variations have made this plot a trifle familiar, but in its day it was mind boggling.

A different sort of depravity reared its lovely head almost simultaneously. Virtually unnoticed by discreet students of the cinema, the glamorous English actress Barbara Steele broke new ground by emerging as the first full-time female fiend in films. Apparently regardless of writer or director, her movies display an outrageous spirit of depravity that transcends itself in self-mockery and sensible sensuality, perhaps most vividly displayed when, during the course of one obligatory love scene, she demonstrates an excess of passion by biting not her partner's but her own shoulder. A strange sort of submerged star status has enabled her to have an influence on cinema styles that far surpasses her public profile. She received star billing as an addled actress in Federico Fellini's classic *8½*, but the most clear-cut example of her work is in Mario Bava's atmospheric vampire film *Black Sunday* (1960), in which she characteristically plays the dual roles of haunter and haunted. This stylish Italian effort was one of the first European horror films to reach large American audiences since the days of the silent screen, but imports were to become increasingly common as the Hollywood studio system lost its stranglehold. Indeed, most of Barbara Steele's films have been European; the best of them include the Italian *Nightmare Castle* (1965), in which she portrayed an alternately seductive and vindictive ghost as well as her own victim; and *She-Beast* (1965), a combined Italian-Yugoslav production that juxtaposed some sinister Slavic legendry with the problems of Communist bureaucracy to produce some unexpected if not totally incongruous satire. In her only American film she was considerably overshadowed by a strong producer-director, one whose career requires separate comment.

The man in question, Roger Corman, did more than his share to upgrade the quality of the American horror film as well as that of his studio, American International. Until

1960, AI had been content with low-budget, black-and-white shockers perhaps best exemplified by the *Teenage* series. Increased capital and perhaps the example of Hammer Films led them in 1960 to a more dignified if less lively sort of production, *House of Usher*, which proved to be the first of a long series of free Poe adaptations. Corman was entrusted with this project after working wonders in the fifties with a series of inexpensive thrillers such as *It Conquered the World* (1956) and *The Wasp Woman* (1959). The best of earlier efforts were a pair of black comedies, *Bucket of Blood* (1959) and *The Little Shop of Horrors* (1960). The former concerned an ambitious if simpleminded "beatnik" who wins renown as a sculptor through the familiar device of covering corpses with clay. What made the story entertaining was the protagonist's mixture of dismay and delight as a series of accidents sets him off on a career of carnage. *The Little Shop of Horrors* featured a young florist's assistant with a prize plant that develops into a man-eater. The voracious vegetable's improbable but insistent demand "Feed me! Feed me!" seems to be firmly embedded in the minds of viewers who do not even remember the film's title.

Corman was finally rewarded with a substantial budget and a clever, accomplished actor in the person of veteran villain Vincent Price. Price created a new sort of movie "monster," a depraved mortal who struggles almost pathetically to avoid moral responsibility for past misdeeds, usually represented by a terribly tangible female corpse. In *House of Usher* he portrayed Poe's most striking character, a conception only slightly enfeebled by the inevitable elaborations on the plot which became necessary in order to turn a short tale into a full-length motion picture. Later adaptations were almost entirely original stories; but this first effort was fairly faithful to Poe's conception, although it added an improbable love affair for the doomed Madeline Usher. Still, the film did not have the proverbial Hollywood happy ending in which a pair of young lovers flee unscathed from the general disaster, and in fact almost all of Corman's Poe films have been free of this expendable cliché. This audience-identification device did not seem necessary to Corman, who has theorized that the success of his stories is based directly on the delight with which young audiences view the collapse of a corrupt establishment.

The next in the series, *The Pit and the Pendulum* (1961), retained only the title torture devices from Poe's famous tale, appending them to an original narrative by Richard Matheson (who had also adapted *House of Usher*) in which a medieval Spanish nobleman is driven mad by apparitions of his dead wife. Barbara Steele played the lady in question, who turns out to be very much alive, at least until the end of the film, and Price was in good form as the anguished aristocrat. Included in this outing, as in its predecessor, was a dream sequence in phosphorescent shades of green and blue. Such scenes were to become an inevitable part of the Corman formula. *Tales of Terror* (1962) managed to stay a bit closer to Poe by employing three of his stories; it also employed not only Vincent Price, but Peter Lorre and Basil Rathbone as well. The same year's *Premature Burial* starred Ray Milland and featured a screenplay by authors Ray Russell and Charles Beaumont. The obliquely titled *Haunted Palace* (1963) used the name of a Poe poem to disguise Beaumont's adaptation of H. P. Lovecraft's *Case of Charles Dexter Ward.* Though far from flawless, *The Haunted Palace* is not only the first but also the best filmed version of Lovecraft; Price played the possessed New Englander with characteristic aplomb, and the brief evocation of the ancient gods was appropriately awesome. This outing also included Lon Chaney, Jr., in a small role, and Corman continued his policy of hiring Hollywood's finest fiends by featuring Boris Karloff along with Price and Peter Lorre in *The Raven* (1963). Unfairly promoted as a serious shocker, this was a parody, not so much of Poe as of Corman, and not so funny as foolish, although there are some entertaining

Vincent Price loses his mind at the sight of Barbara Steele, who has convinced him of her death and will soon live to regret it, in the second of Roger Corman's Poe series, *The Pit and the Pendulum. Courtesy of American International.*

moments in a climactic magician's duel between Price and Karloff. Corman took a vacation from Poe and Price for the remainder of the year, directing Boris Karloff in an original story, *The Terror*, and casting Ray Milland as *X, the Man with the X-Ray Eyes.* The latter, written by Ray Russell and Robert Dillon, had an interesting premise and some good moments as a physician improves his vision for medical purposes and discovers that he can see through everything. Maddened by endless views of infinity, he finally tears out his glistening black eyeballs. In 1964, Corman traveled to England for his climactic endeavors, *The Masque of the Red Death* and *The Tomb of Ligeia. Masque* is his most lavish display, complete with the famous colored chambers of Prince Prospero's plague-besieged castle. It even offered Price a change of pace by allowing him to play a dedicated villain who does not spend all his time shying away from his own shadow. The film fails only in its attempts at profundity: when the Red Death appears he has Prospero's face, inspiring the dying guests to a limp and ludicrous dance, while the personified plague retreats to a

Roger Corman's spoof *The Raven* was distinguished mainly by its cast: Boris Karloff, Peter Lorre, and Vincent Price. Also present was Hazel Court, whose frequent work as a harassed heroine paralleled that of Evelyn Ankers twenty years previously. *Courtesy of American International.*

hillside to discuss the meaning of life with a group of similarly cowled figures—presumably the Yellow Death, the Green Death, and so on. All this is a long way from the petulant talking plant of *The Little Shop of Horrors*, and not necessarily in the right direction. Corman may have sensed as much himself, for *The Tomb of Ligeia* proved to be his last horror film. It was a highly polished reworking of those that had gone before, complete with perturbed Price and spectral spouse and even including fire footage from *House of Usher.* Before retiring from the field, Corman had not only made some solid films; he had also raised (at least in comparison to the previous decade) the level of competence that audiences would expect from American horror movies, and he had firmly established Vincent Price in the public's mind as the reigning master of the macabre.

A parallel development to this improvement of genre films was the increased output of what might be termed "serious" horror films—those that attempted to transcend a despised form by employing performers and attitudes generally considered too dignified for this sort of cinema. Perhaps they were inspired by *Psycho*, which had made a remarkable amount of money. *The Innocents* (1961) was an adaptation of Henry James's *Turn of the Screw*, featuring a performance by Deborah Kerr, direction by Jack Clayton, and a script by Truman Capote. The whole affair was so tasteful that it became tedious, and Capote's insistence on the psychological interpretation of the story banished the ghosts to limbo. More successful, if on a less ethereal level, was Robert Aldrich's *Whatever Happened to Baby Jane?* (1962). Bette Davis and Joan Crawford, rival queens from Hollywood's heyday, consented to appear as a pair of has-been hags who drive each other crazy in a decaying old mansion. It worked out so well that both women went on to appear in several more movies of the same type, though never together and never with the zany zest of this first encounter. In 1963 Robert Wise, who later achieved his greatest fame for directing the saccharine *Sound of Music*, served up his last morbid morsel, *The Haunting*, starring Julie Harris and Claire Bloom. Although the camera could not capture all the interior undertones of Shirley Jackson's novel, *The Haunting of Hill House*, Wise nevertheless managed to conjure up one of the most effective haunted-house atmospheres in screen history, most effective when one of the heroines realizes the hand she has been holding in the dark does not belong to anybody.

Alfred Hitchcock returned to horror of a sort in his 1963 film *The Birds*, a version of Daphne Du Maurier's enigmatic short story in which our feathered friends turn against mankind. Although much was made of the attack of the birds and its possible philosophical implications, the most shocking scene was a gratuitously introduced incident in which a carelessly dropped cigarette results in the explosion of a gas station.

At the opposite end of the spectrum from these prestige productions were the pictures released by an outfit called Box Office Spectaculars, including *Blood Feast* (1963), *2000 Maniacs* (1964), and *Color Me Blood Red* (1964). These films were truly horrible, not so much because of their renowned gruesomeness as because of their total ineptitude regarding production, performance, writing, directing, and decor. Principal responsibility for these deplorable efforts must rest with one Herschell G. Lewis, who wrote, photographed, and directed them, displaying an inordinate fondness for graphic scenes of dismemberment and disembowelment. These Box Office Spectaculars, it must be admitted, do have their adherents, if only among those who find the total lack of taste and talent to be hilarious.

Meanwhile, more orthodox producers of frightening films continued on their merry way. Hammer Films slipped a bit in 1964 with *The Evil of Frankenstein* (coming up with new titles was just one of the problems). This episode in the series retained Peter Cushing in the title role but made precious little sense as a sequel to previous films, since the plot involved the revival of a monster who had not appeared in any earlier outings. As played by Kiwi Kingston, he looked suspiciously like the old Universal monster, suggesting that this movie was an attempt to curry favor with nostalgic fans. As such, it did not succeed. Directed by Freddie Francis, this was a far cry from Don Sharp's pointed *Kiss of the Vampire* (1963), a well-mounted variation on familiar themes, featuring a whole convention of vampires and some new methods of dealing with them.

Hammer was also acquiring some British rivals, principally an organization called Amicus, which acquired the services of Peter Cushing and Christopher Lee for an anthology of short shockers called *Dr. Terror's House of Horrors* (1964). It proved to be a compendium of clichés; but Amicus stuck by its guns and in later years produced some increasingly capable chillers in the anthology style. Another outfit, Anglo-Amalgamated, revived Sax Rohmer's immortal villain in the person of Christopher Lee and came up

Dracula, Prince of Darkness* continued the Hammer policy of showing horrors in gory detail. The punctured person is actress Barbara Shelley. © *1965 Hammer Film Productions Ltd. Courtesy of Twentieth Century-Fox.

with *The Face of Fu Manchu* (1965). It worked surprisingly well under Don Sharp's capable direction, especially in its evocation of Edwardian England. Later films in the series proved to be comparatively slipshod.

Perhaps spurred on by this competition, Hammer rallied in 1965 with *Dracula, Prince of Darkness.* Christopher Lee returned in his best role, directed by Terence Fisher, and much of the excitement of *Horror of Dracula* was recaptured. A bizarre combination of history and horror was in evidence when Hammer presented *Rasputin, the Mad Monk*; it was held together entirely by Christopher Lee's dynamic performance as the hypnotic Russian. And the company attempted something like a big-budget spectacle with a version of H. Rider Haggard's *She*, with Cushing and Lee supporting Ursula Andress as the ageless Ayesha.

Still, the most interesting cinema shocker of 1965 was a black-and-white sleeper called *Dark Intruder.* Originally intended as a pilot film for an unproduced television series called "Black Cloak," it was released theatrically by Universal without creating much of a stir. Yet Barre Lyndon's Lovecraftian screenplay, involving transmigration of souls, and twins under the terrible curse of ancient gods, was unusually imaginative, and the direction by Harvey Hart was appropriately weird and compelling. Based on this small sample, the projected series would have been far superior to any of the exercises in televised terror that have actually made it onto the TV screen.

Frank Frazetta, who has since largely abandoned comics for book cover work, did this painting for "Rock God," a story by science fiction writer Harlan Ellison.

Reed Crandall, one of the deans of comic book illustration, created this panel of medieval wizardry for the *Creepy* story "Castle Carrion," written by Archie Goodwin.

That year also saw an undeniable sign that the macabre was back in full flower: the reappearance of the horror comic book, after an enforced absence of more than a decade. The publisher was James Warren, of *Famous Monsters of Filmland* fame. He had published some one-shot comic book adaptations of films, combining motion picture stills with comic strip speech balloons to produce versions of such films as the original Hammer Frankenstein and Dracula movies, as well as such minor efforts as *Horror of Party Beach.* The success of these and various comics in the monster magazines led in 1965 to the release of *Creepy*, an oversized black-and-white comic book featuring some of the best artists in the business. Al Williamson, Reed Crandall, Frank Frazetta, and Jack Davis were among those represented in the first issue, which was written and edited by Archie Goodwin. An artistic and commercial success, *Creepy* was soon followed by more Warren horror titles and a host of imitators as well. Warren's bold move had successfully defied the industry's Comics Code Authority, all-powerful since its inception in 1954; when even the least respected of the arts was allowed to traffic in blood and thunder, it was certain that the vultures had come home to roost for good.

Yet there was more to come. The generation that had grown up insisting that death and decay were good clean fun finally reached its majority. And the artists who became spokesmen for this group began to whisper, against all common sense, that there might be something supernatural behind all this claptrap, that there might be more truth than poetry to this business of living in fear.

BLOOD SON

By Richard Matheson

The people on the block decided definitely that Jules was crazy when they heard about his composition.

There had been suspicions for a long time.

He made people shiver with his blank stare. His coarse gutteral tongue sounded unnatural in his frail body. The paleness of his skin upset many children. It seemed to hang loose around his flesh. He hated sunlight.

And his ideas were a little out of place for the people who lived on the block.

Jules wanted to be a vampire.

People declared it common knowledge that he was born on a night when winds uprooted trees. They said he was born with three teeth. They said he'd used them to fasten himself on his mother's breast drawing blood with the milk.

They said he used to cackle and bark in his crib after dark. They said he walked at two months and sat staring at the moon whenever it shone.

Those were things that people said.

His parents were always worried about him. An only child, they noticed his flaws quickly.

They thought he was blind until the doctor told them it was just a vacuous stare. He told them that Jules, with his large head, might be a genius or an idiot. It turned out he was an idiot.

He never spoke a word until he was five. Then, one night coming up to supper, he sat down at the table and said "Death."

His parents were torn between delight and disgust. They finally settled for a place in between the two feelings. They decided that Jules couldn't have realized what the word meant.

But Jules did.

From that night on, he built up such a large vocabulary that everyone who knew him was astonished. He not only acquired every word spoken to him, words from signs, magazines, books; he made up his own words.

Like—nightouch. Or—killove. They were really several words that melted into each other. They said things Jules felt but couldn't explain with other words.

He used to sit on the porch while the other children played hopscotch, stickball and other games. He sat there and stared at the sidewalk and made up words.

Until he was twelve Jules kept pretty much out of trouble.

Of course there was the time they found him undressing Olive Jones in an alley. And another time he was discovered dissecting a kitten on his bed.

But there were many years in between. Those scandals were forgotten.

In general he went through childhood merely disgusting people.

He went to school but never studied. He spent about two or three terms in each grade.

The teachers all knew him by his first name. In some subjects like reading and writing he was almost brilliant.

In others he was hopeless.

One Saturday when he was twelve, Jules went to the movies. He saw "Dracula."

When the show was over he walked, a throbbing nerve mass, through the little girl and boy ranks.

He went home and locked himself in the bathroom for two hours.

His parents pounded on the door and threatened but he wouldn't come out.

Finally he unlocked the door and sat down at the supper table. He had a bandage on his thumb and a satisfied look on his face.

The morning after he went to the library. It was Sunday. He sat on the steps all day waiting for it to open. Finally he went home.

The next morning he came back instead of going to school.

He found *Dracula* on the shelves. He couldn't borrow it because he wasn't a member and to be a member he had to bring in one of his parents.

So he stuck the book down his pants and left the library and never brought it back.

He went to the park and sat down and read the book through. It was late evening before he finished.

He started at the beginning again, reading as he ran from street light to street light, all the way home.

He didn't hear a word of the scolding he got for missing lunch and supper. He ate, went in his room and read the book to the finish. They asked him where he got the book. He said he found it.

As the days passed Jules read the story over and over. He never went to school.

Late at night, when he had fallen into an exhausted slumber, his mother used to take the book into the living room and show it to her husband.

One night they noticed that Jules had underlined certain sentences with dark shaky pencil lines.

Like: "The lips were crimson with fresh blood and the stream had trickled over her chin and stained the purity of her lawn death robe."

Or: "When the blood began to spurt out, he took my hands in one of his, holding them tight and, with the other seized my neck and pressed my mouth to the wound. . . ."

When his mother saw this, she threw the book down the garbage chute.

In the next morning when Jules found the book missing he screamed and twisted his mother's arm until she told him where the book was.

Then he ran down to the cellar and dug in the piles of garbage until he found the book.

Coffee grounds and egg yolk on his hands and wrists, he went to the park and read it again.

For a month he read the book avidly. Then he knew it so well he threw it away and just thought about it.

Absence notes were coming from school. His mother yelled. Jules decided to go back for a while.

He wanted to write a composition.

One day he wrote it in class. When everyone was finished writing, the teacher asked if anyone wanted to read their composition to the class.

Jules raised his hand.

The teacher was surprised. But she felt charity. She wanted to encourage him. She drew in her tiny jab of a chin and smiled.

"All right," she said, "Pay attention children. Jules is going to read us his composition."

Jules stood up. He was excited. The paper shook in his hands.

"My Ambition by . . ."

"Come to the front of the class, Jules, dear."

Jules went to the front of the class. The teacher smiled lovingly. Jules started again.

"My Ambition by Jules Dracula."

The smile sagged.

"When I grow up I want to be a vampire."

The teacher's smiling lips jerked down and out. Her eyes popped wide.

"I want to live forever and get even with everybody and make all the girls vampires. I want to smell of death."

"Jules!"

"I want to have a foul breath that stinks of dead earth and crypts and sweet coffins."

The teacher shuddered. Her hands twitched on her green blotter. She couldn't believe her ears. She looked at the children. They were gaping. Some of them were giggling. But not the girls.

"I want to be all cold and have rotten flesh with stolen blood in the veins."

"That will . . . hrrumph!"

The teacher cleared her throat mightily.

"That will be all Jules," she said.

Jules talked louder and desperately.

"I want to sink my terrible white teeth in my victims' necks. I want them to . . ."

"Jules! Go to your seat this instant!"

"I want them to slide like razors in the flesh and into the veins," read Jules ferociously.

The teacher jolted to her feet. Children were shivering. None of them were giggling.

"Then I want to draw my teeth out and let the blood flow easy in my mouth and run hot in my throat and . . ."

The teacher grabbed his arm. Jules tore away and ran to a corner. Barricaded behind a stool he yelled:

"And drip off my tongue and run out my lips down my victims' throats! I want to drink girls' blood!"

The teacher lunged for him. She dragged him out of the corner. He clawed at her and screamed all the way to the door and the principal's office.

"That is my ambition! That is my ambition! *That is my ambition!*"

It was grim.

Jules was locked in his room. The teacher and the principal sat with Jules' parents. They were talking in sepulchral voices.

They were recounting the scene.

All along the block parents were discussing it. Most of them didn't believe it at first. They thought their children made it up.

Then they thought what horrible children they'd raised if the children could make up such things.

So they believed it.

After that everyone watched Jules like a hawk. People avoided his touch and look. Parents pulled their children off the street when he approached. Everyone whispered tales of him.

There were more absence notes.

Jules told his mother he wasn't going to school anymore. Nothing would change his mind. He never went again.

When a truant officer came to the apartment Jules would run over the roofs until he was far away from there.

A year wasted by.

Jules wandered the streets searching for something; he didn't know what. He looked in alleys. He looked in garbage cans. He looked in lots. He looked on the east side and the west side and in the middle.

He couldn't find what he wanted.

He rarely slept. He never spoke. He stared down all the time. He forgot his special words.

Then.

One day in the park, Jules strolled through the zoo.

An electric shock passed through him when he saw the vampire bat.

His eyes grew wide and his discolored teeth shone dully in a wide smile.

From that day on, Jules went daily to the zoo and looked at the bat. He spoke to it and called it the Count. He felt in his heart it was really a man who had changed.

A rebirth of culture struck him.

He stole another book from the library. It told all about wild life.

He found the page on the vampire bat. He tore it out and threw the book away.

He learned the selection by heart.

He knew how the bat made its wound. How it lapped up the blood like a kitten drinking cream. How it walked on folded wing stalks and hind legs like a black furry spider. Why it took no nourishment but blood.

Month after month Jules stared at the bat and talked to it. It became the one comfort in his life. The one symbol of dreams come true.

One day Jules noticed that the bottom of the wire covering the cage had come loose.

He looked around, his black eyes shifting. He didn't see anyone looking. It was a cloudy day. Not many people were there.

Jules tugged at the wire.

It moved a little.

Then he saw a man come out of the monkey house. So he pulled back his hand and strolled away whistling a song he had just made up.

Late at night, when he was supposed to be asleep he would walk barefoot past his parents' room. He would hear his father and mother snoring. He would hurry out, put on his shoes and run to the zoo.

Everytime the watchman was not around, Jules would tug at the wiring.

He kept on pulling it loose.

When he was finished and had to run home, he pushed the wire in again. Then no one could tell.

All day Jules would stand in front of the cage and look at the Count and chuckle and tell him he'd soon be free again.

He told the Count all the things he knew. He told the Count he was going to practice climbing down walls head first.

He told the Count not to worry. He'd soon be out. Then, together, they could go all around and drink girls' blood.

One night Jules pulled the wire out and crawled under it into the cage.

It was very dark.

He crept on his knees to the little wooden house. He listened to see if he could hear the Count squeaking.

He stuck his arm in the black doorway. He kept whispering.

He jumped when he felt a needle jab in his finger.

With a look of great pleasure on his thin face, Jules drew the fluttering hairy bat to him.

He climbed down from the cage with it and ran out of the zoo; out of the park. He ran down the silent streets.

It was getting late in the morning. Light touched the dark skies with grey. He couldn't go home. He had to have a place.

He went down an alley and climbed over a fence. He held tight to the bat. It lapped at the dribble of blood from his finger.

He went across a yard and into a little deserted shack.

It was dark inside and damp. It was full of rubble and tin cans and soggy cardboard and excrement.

Jules made sure there was no way the bat could escape.

Then he pulled the door tight and put a stick through the metal loop.

He felt his heart beating hard and his limbs trembling. He let go of the bat. It flew to a dark corner and hung on the wood.

Jules feverishly tore off his shirt. His lips shook. He smiled a crazy smile.

He reached down into his pants pocket and took out a little pen knife he had stolen from his mother.

He opened it and ran a finger over the blade. It sliced through the flesh.

With shaking fingers he jabbed at his throat. He hacked. The blood ran through his fingers.

"Count! Count!" he cried in frenzied joy. "Drink my red blood! Drink me! Drink me!"

He stumbled over the tin cans and slipped and felt for the bat. It sprang from the wood and soared across the shack and fastened itself on the other side.

Tears ran down Jules' cheeks.

He gritted his teeth. The blood ran across his shoulders and across his thin hairless chest.

His body shook in fever. He staggered back toward the other side. He tripped and felt his side torn open on the sharp edge of a tin can.

His hands went out. They clutched the bat. He placed it against his throat. He sank on his back on the cool wet earth. He sighed.

He started to moan and clutch at his chest. His stomach heaved. The black bat on his neck silently lapped his blood.

Jules felt his life seeping away.

He thought of all the years past. The waiting. His parents. School. Dracula. Dreams. For this. This sudden glory.

Jules' eyes flickered open.

The inside of the reeking shack swam about him.

It was hard to breathe. He opened his mouth to gasp in the air. He sucked it in. It was foul. It made him cough. His skinny body lurched on the cold ground.

Mists crept away in his brain.

One by one like drawn veils.

Suddenly his mind was filled with terrible clarity.

He felt the aching pain in his side.

He knew he was lying half naked on garbage and letting a flying bat drink his blood.

With a strangled cry, he reached up and tore away the furry throbbing bat. He flung it away from him. It came back, fanning his face with its vibrating wings.

Jules staggered to his feet.

He felt for the door. He could hardly see. He tried to stop his throat from bleeding so.

He managed to get the door open.

Then, lurching into the dark yard, he fell on his face in the long grass blades.

He tried to call out for help.

But no sounds save a bubbling mockery of words came from his lips.

He heard the fluttering wings.

Then, suddenly they were gone.

Strong fingers lifted him gently. Through dying eyes Jules saw the tall dark man whose eyes shone like rubies.

"My son," the man said.

·10·

HEAVEN AND HELL: INNER SPACE

The late 1960s proved to be an extraordinary period for the promulgation of fearsome fantasies. The monstrous movement of the preceding years continued to gain momentum, and it was augmented by a new wave of mysticism which, while ostensibly directed toward sweetness and light, displayed a darker side as well. The extreme intensity of this new belief in the supernatural proved to be comparatively short-lived, but it left in its wake an atmosphere more favorable to occultism than there had been for two centuries. Ironically, if not too surprisingly, subsequent disillusionment with dabblings in the divine did not dramatically diminish the plausibility of the demonic, and many who had trouble believing in heaven found hell comparatively credible.

The cultural tone of this era was largely the product of the young people who were just coming of age. What happened to this generation has been described in many terms, some positive and some negative but all inadequate. To some observers (and participants) they were a "psychedelic" generation, and certainly the fascination with hallucinogens provided much of the imagery employed by emerging artists; but there was a simultaneous increase in the use of narcotics and depressants that produce a diametrically opposed effect. Such extremism was the order of the day, producing as many bright-eyed "Jesus freaks" as bleary-orbed devil worshipers. Those inclined toward the rediscovered art of astrology attribute such unorthodox behavior to the presence of Pluto in Leo and the reversals in mentality and morality, to the coming "Age of Aquarius," expected momentarily to replace the Piscean or Christian bimillennium that has occupied human attention since the year one. Searching for heights and depths beyond the range of more earthbound mortals, those creators who attempted to express the new consciousness often referred to themselves as members of the "Underground" or as advocates of the "Revolution," which might not be a war and might not even happen at all. For the most part, they were attempting to alter the human condition by burrowing from within, not from within the established system—that would be too traditional—but from within the individual's mind and, if there is one, from within the soul.

The well-received black music of the period is in fact described as "soul music," but this seems to define its level of sincerity rather than its spirituality. Yet there certainly is a search for some sorts of spirits being conducted in today's popular songs, especially among the British composers and performers whose translation of American "rock and

roll" has led some observers to suspect that the combination of electric tone and lyric poetry is the most significant art form of the sixties and seventies. The range of expression employed proved wide enough to make horrors right at home.

There had been a few foreshadowings of such monstrous music, but only in burlesque form. In 1958, television horror host John Zacherle had moderate success with "Dinner with Drac," a spoken recitation delivered over a rock-and-roll background. Considerably more successful was "The Monster Mash," recorded a few years later by Bobby Pickett, imitating the inflections of Boris Karloff. This song broke some sort of precedent when it was released in the original version for the second time in 1973; it proved even more popular than in its first outing, and was for a time the most popular record in the United States.

A more serious sort of sinister strain made its appearance in the works of the London-based band the Rolling Stones, whose stance, generally hostile and antisocial, became positively morbid with the song "Paint It Black" (1966), a minor-key tribute to death and despair with a droning sitar accompaniment. It was very well received, and subsequent Stones albums have usually included at least one song with a similarly sinister theme. Lyricist and lead singer Mick Jagger has frequently indicated an interest in occult subjects; he is, for instance, an Arthur Machen enthusiast who cites "Novel of the White Powder" in arguing that no drug should be consumed unless its ingredients are ascertained. The 1967 album *Their Satanic Majesties Request* was indicative in its title alone, and the impression was intensified by the cover photograph, depicting the Rolling Stones in the costumes of medieval magicians. Most of the songs on the album had science fiction or supernatural subjects, and there is a long passage of primitive chanting that seems to suggest some unholy ritual. The 1968 album *Beggar's Banquet* contained a number that crystallized the band's image as spokesmen for the supernatural: "Sympathy for the Devil." Complex, hypnotic rhythms accompanied this dramatic monologue by no less a personage than Lucifer himself, recounting his triumphs and soliciting souls with a mixture of charm and threats. This powerful piece also provided the basis for a Jean-Luc Godard film, originally titled *One Plus One* but generally released in the United States under the more marketable *Sympathy for the Devil* (1970). Pieces like "Let It Bleed" (1969) and "Sister Morphine" continued in the same vicious vein, and 1973 found the Rolling Stones doing a duet with death in "Dancing with Mr. D."

The only English group whose reputation exceeded that of the Stones was the Beatles (John Lennon, Paul McCartney, George Harrison, and Ringo Starr). Their early image defined them as lovable moppets, but a few years after their debut in 1964 they began to pen some psychically suggestive songs like "Tomorrow Never Knows" (1966), "Strawberry Fields" (1967), "I Am the Walrus" (1967), and "Glass Onion." Harrison's increasingly frequent compositions revealed him as a melancholy mystic, while Lennon displayed the greatest fondness for the grotesque.

No pop group has done more to explore bizarre states of mind than The Who, whose full-length and coherent but barely comprehensible "rock opera" *Tommy* (1969) has even been performed at the Metropolitan Opera. *Tommy* is very likely the magnum opus of electric music. The plot, involving the private regeneration and public rejection of a modern messiah, is indicative of the hard-nosed and probing mysticism of its composer, Peter Townshend. More immediately macabre are the songs of his colleague, bassist John Entwistle, whose "Boris the Spider" was the first authentically frightening rock tune, a combination of throbbing bass and quavering treble which achieved a hair-raising sonic range. Entwistle's first solo album, *Smash Your Head against the Wall* (1970), is an unadulterated horror show, with songs like "External Youth" and "Heaven

and Hell" exposing the simplemindedness of traditional dualistic morality in a manner that can only be described as Mephistophelean. His second album, *Whistle Rhymes* (1972), is equally morbid in a slightly more mortal manner, although the disconcerting sounds of "Nightmare" are as effective as anything he has accomplished. Followed by bands like Procul Harum, Pink Floyd, and King Crimson, these British rock revisionists have made fearful fantasy a permanent part of the music market.

The only American artist of comparable stature is singer-songwriter Bob Dylan, whose lyrics come closest of all to the standards of traditional poetry. His middle and most powerful period (postprotest and preprettification) contained some shattering images of urban despair, complete with characters like Jack the Ripper, Captain Ahab, and the Phantom of the Opera. His nerve-racking nihilism is perhaps most impressive in songs like "It's All Right Ma, I'm Only Bleeding" and "Desolation Row." The same sickness of the soul pervades his three best albums, *Highway 61 Revisited* (1965), *Blonde on Blonde* (1966), and *John Wesley Harding* (1967). Dylan's influence is most obvious on such fine American performers as the Byrds and the Band, and his negativism had its West Coast counterpart in the apocalyptic visions of "psychedelic" groups like the Grateful Dead, the Jefferson Airplane, the Mothers, and the Doors. The last of these, under the leadership of Jim Morrison, showed a special fondness for psychological melodrama.

Some bands have attempted to make horrors the sole focus of their performances. There was, for instance, a short-lived outfit that named itself H. P. Lovecraft, but it failed to live up to its namesake's standards. The most popular group of this type, in fact one of the most successful in recent years, is Alice Cooper. Not only do they specialize in sinister songs like "Halo of Flies," "Dead Babies," and "Dwight Frye" (a tribute to the character actor who appeared in *Dracula* and *Frankenstein*), but they also incorporate various forms of visual nastiness into their stage act. Starting with minor atrocities like dismembering dolls, they have worked up to the point where Alice (the lead vocalist) has, with the aid of professional conjurers, arranged to hang himself on stage and to be decapitated by a trick guillotine.

A radical crew with similar sentiments has also invaded the comics. By working with a despised and therefore accessible medium, a dedicated band of young cartoonists has altered the values of an art form, just as their more richly rewarded brothers have polarized popular music. The subject matter of "underground comix" is deliberately shocking, graphically depicting taboo forms of sex, of violence, and of political opinion, the last of which is presented as being inextricably bound up with the other two subjects. The most prominent artist in underground comics is Robert Crumb, whose *Zap* comic books began to appear in 1968. Crumb is conducting an all-out assault on our culture in which horrors are only part of the picture; but everything he portrays is grotesque, and some of his subjects are quite gruesome. All of his characters are mad, either by society's standards or those of the creator, who has described himself as a purveyor of "psychological sadism, with you, the reader, as the victim." Several of his heroes, like Nuts Boy and Forky McDonald, are psychopathic killers. Even more outlandish are the frantic figures of Crumb's cohort S. Clay Wilson, who are all practicing sadists or masochists, often members of cult groups; they are not much surprised to find demons in their midst. Wilson specializes in vivid renderings of appalling acts of perverted violence. The science-fantasy strip *Trashman* by Spain depicts the struggle of urban guerrillas against authorities who practice cannibalism and human sacrifice. Underground horror comic books were formalized by Rory Hayes and Gary Arlington with *Bogeyman* (1969), and since then almost every artist in this field has worked in the genre, acknowledging the inspiration of E.C. comics such as *Tales from the Crypt*. Some of the better titles in the

character, Mia Farrow gave a performance as hollow as her role, while better actors like John Cassavetes and Maurice Evans were obliged to stand in her shadow trying to avoid looking embarrassed. The story was derived from Ira Levin's best-selling 1967 novel, which utilized long passages about the tragic state of current events to add credence to the idea that Satan was up and about. Yet even granting the premise that the father of evil was ready to unleash a half-human offspring on the world, it still seems implausible that he would choose the neurotic and reluctant Rosemary to be the mother, especially considering the number of followers he had in her apartment building alone. The devil worshipers were portrayed against type as individuals both normal and boring; Ruth Gordon won an Oscar for enacting one of them as a perfectly lovable old lady.

Rosemary's Baby is just one of a number of novels with bizarre themes to enjoy wide popularity during this era, the first such literary period since the heyday of the Gothic novel almost two centuries ago. Perhaps the most talented author to mix the macabre with mass appeal was John Fowles, whose suspenseful debut *The Collector* appeared in 1963 and was capably adapted for the screen in 1965 by veteran director William Wyler. The story concerns a repressed young clerk who buys an isolated house with his huge lottery winnings, then kidnaps a young woman he has admired with the hope that she will fall in love with him. Avoiding the obvious melodramatics, Fowles paints an exquisite portrait of the butterfly-collecting psychopath, whose plan idealistically eschews such predictable devices as rape or murder. The result is a terrific tension concerning whether or not he will completely lose control, only intensified by the realization that the character is not entirely unsympathetic and that a disaster for his victim will be one for him as well. The conflict degenerates into sickening horror as the girl contracts pneumonia and the collector, torn between pity and paranoia, allows her to die before he can bring himself to seek medical help. The motion picture version, although unable to reproduce all the insight of the original, was one of the most accurate film adaptations of high-quality terror tales, and best acting awards at the Cannes Film Festival went to the principal performers, Terence Stamp and Samantha Eggar.

In 1966 Fowles followed *The Collector* with a more ambitious if less perfectly controlled novel, *The Magus*. The plot involved a visitor to a Greek island who comes half-voluntarily under the power of its mysterious proprietor, a man whose odd behavior and odder entourage suggest that he is a magician who has mastered the secrets of life and death. Illusion and reality become hopelessly scrambled for the hero, who sometimes suspects that he is the victim of an elaborate hoax but sometimes toys with the conviction that he is in the presence of the supernatural. The puzzle is never perfectly solved; while some of the bizarre manifestations are explained away as theatrical trickery, a tantalizing residue of doubt remains. The question is not only whether the "magus" is a magician or a fraud but, regardless, whether he should be considered a sadistic madman or a profound teacher. All of this proved a little too subtle and complex for the 1968 film version, which was nonetheless handsomely mounted and well played by a cast including Michael Caine and Anthony Quinn.

A moderately successful actor named Tom Tryon managed to become a popular author with nerve-racking novels like *The Other* (1971) and *Harvest Home* (1973). *The Other* was almost immediately adapted into a motion picture; its narrative of children involved in murder and possession is another embodiment of the almost obligatory theme (as in *Rosemary's Baby* and later *The Exorcist*) which, by outraging maternal instincts, appeals to the predominantly matronly audience for best-selling novels.

A different sort of audience, predominantly students, constituted a considerable market for fantasy novels in inexpensive paperback editions. Wonders of the most unpredictable nature appear in the works of Kurt Vonnegut, Jr., whose sarcastic despair somehow brought hope to a vast throng of young science fiction readers. His novel *Cat's Cradle*, originally published in 1963 but increasingly popular in later years, might qualify as a tale of terror, since its subject was the destruction of the planet by a chemical that solidifies the water supply; but the book is so fashioned that its tone implies no more than a wry dismay over human stupidity. Many of Vonnegut's adherents also read J. R. R. Tolkien's elfin epic *The Lord of the Rings*, a revived trilogy from an earlier era which, although it was devoid of the dreadful, did at least demonstrate the continued growth of a market for the literature of fantasy. A somewhat grimmer picture was provided by science fiction author Robert Heinlein's *Stranger in a Strange Land*, about an extraterrestrial messiah executed for excessive humanism. More to the point were at least some of the tales collected in Harlan Ellison's anthology of original science fiction stories, *Dangerous Visions* (1967). Fascinated by Robert Bloch's famous story "Yours Truly, Jack the Ripper," Ellison solicited a story from Bloch in which that tale's immortal protagonist would be transported into the future. The result, "A Toy for Juliette," was good enough, but Ellison had ideas of his own that led to a sequel to the sequel entitled "The Prowler in the City at the Edge of the World." This immensely powerful picture of a maniac's mental processes also provided some wrenchingly realistic descriptions of his unsavory behavior, but it was most effective in its vision of a degenerate postatomic society so cold-bloodedly degenerate that even the Ripper finds it unbearable.

Less widely known, but more accomplished than many modern books in the genre, were two fine novels by James Blish and Brock Brower. Blish, renowned for his science fiction, created an impressive picture of satanism in *Black Easter* (1968). This tale of an attempt to unleash all the forces of evil upon an unsuspecting world includes some convincing demonology, and a pessimistic conclusion which is likely to rattle even the most hardened reader. Brower's *The Late Great Creature* (1971) is the story of an imaginary horror movie star who slips into madness with a bit of method to it. This piece of frightening fun contains interesting background on the preparation of monstrous motion pictures, as well as some unflattering portraits of slightly disguised celebrities in the field.

Of course no literary effort enjoyed the vast audiences that were commonplace for television, where programs with a sinister slant were spreading like plague. Not too surprisingly, the early symptoms included a pair of shows with a parody flavor. Televised terror remained a tricky problem, because the medium is subjected to heavy censorship and because commercial and household interruptions are not conducive to a sustained mood. A comedy treatment appeared to be a painless way for video producers to get in on the burgeoning monster boom, and Universal studios, by now heavily involved in television film work, revived its heavily copyrighted Frankenstein makeup and unleashed "The Munsters." This was a typical television situation comedy series, expressed through the clichés of the old-school horror film. The basic gag was that a family of monsters could be completely sociable and totally unaware of the effect they have on the public at large. As the head of the family, Herman Munster (Fred Gwynne) was a dead ringer for Universal's Frankenstein monster; his son was a budding werewolf, his father-in-law a vampire, and his wife Lily (Yvonne De Carlo) some sort of undifferentiated zombie. The show was pretty predictable, but it managed to survive for more than one season, and it even spawned a lackluster theatrical feature, *Munster Go Home*, in 1966.

"The Munsters" of 1964 spawned "The Addams Family" of 1965, although the new program had another origin a quarter of a century older, which may in fact have been an inspiration to the producers of "The Munsters." "The Addams Family" was derived from the cartoons of Charles Addams, which had been for years a popular feature of the

A holiday scene at the home of the fiendish family created by Charles Addams, whose work delighted readers of *The New Yorker* for years before getting a wider, if weaker, exposure through a television series. *Drawing by Chas. Addams. Copyright 1946, 1974 The New Yorker Magazine, Inc.*

New Yorker magazine. Virtually every cartoon Addams has done derives its humor from a macabre premise, and many of them have featured a household of nameless ghouls residing in a decrepit mansion, complete with a butler who bears a striking resemblance to Boris Karloff, as the actor himself noticed in his introduction to a collection of Addams drawings, *Drawn and Quartered* (1942). Although the television version was somewhat restrained (there was never anything approaching the Addams cartoon in which the family prepared to pour boiling oil on a crew of Christmas carolers), the series improved somewhat on "The Munsters" by offering a group, portrayed by John Astin, Carolyn Jones, and Jackie Coogan among others, that was, if not actually fiendish, at least entertainingly depraved.

Science fiction also provided a share of rather oblique televised terror. The ABC network offered a variety of programs in this vein; the longest run was enjoyed by producer Irwin Allen's "Voyage to the Bottom of the Sea," the saga of a futuristic atomic submarine crew who encounter monstrous menaces as regularly as clockwork. "The Time Tunnel" featured a group of scientists experiencing anxiety on journeys to the past which seemed to be made up of old feature film footage, and "Land of the Giants" portrayed the adventures of a group of space travelers in a place where the people are ten times their size. "The Invaders" pitted actor Roy Thinnes against a horde of aliens who, disguised as human beings, contemplated the conquest of our planet in what appeared to

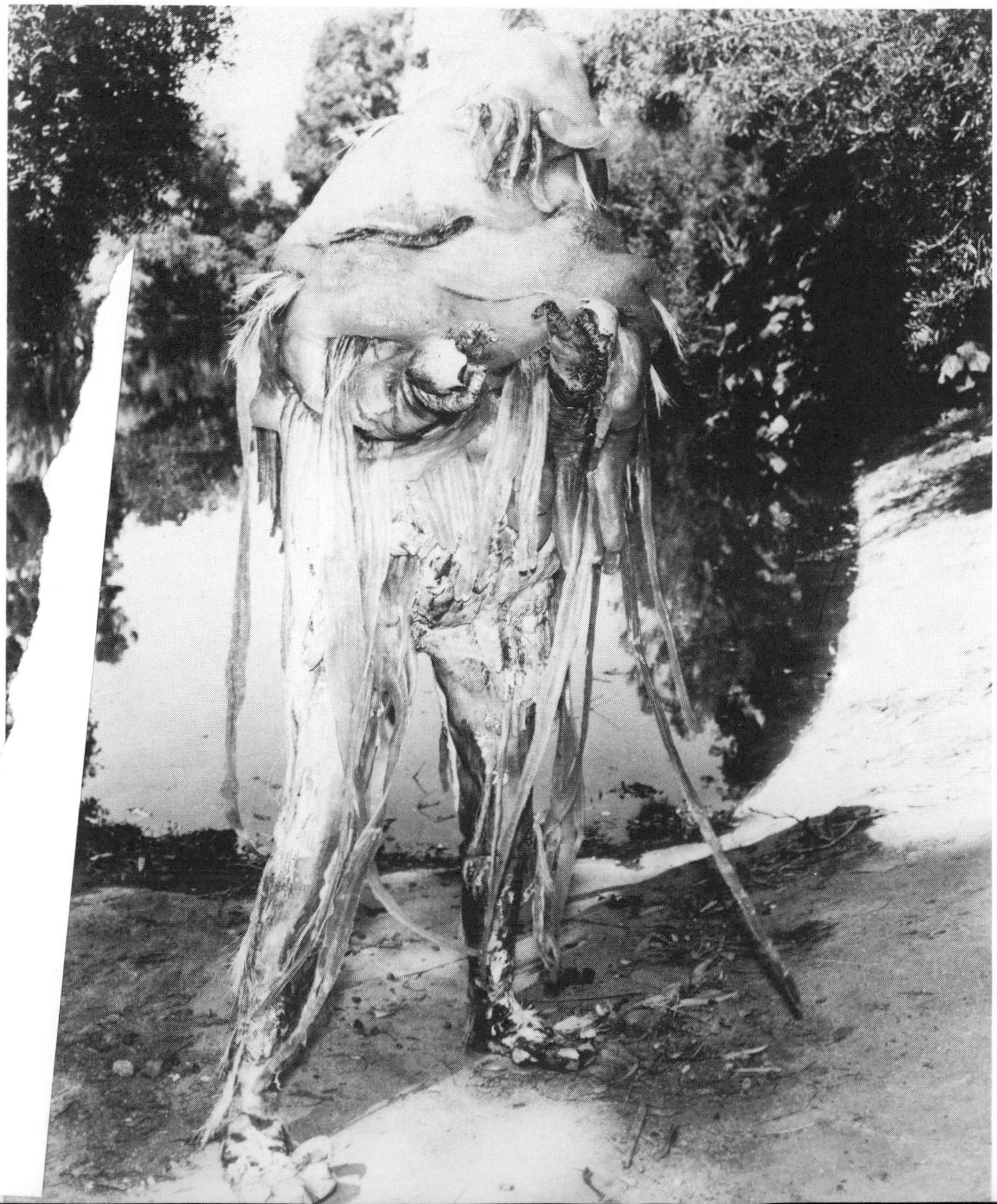

One of the unearthly beings that slithered through Gene Roddenberry's science fiction television series "The Outer Limits." Perhaps the best episode is "Demon with the Glass Hand," by Harlan Ellison.

Peering through the cobwebs is Jonathan Frid, who portrayed the vampire on the daytime television serial "Dark Shadows."

be a singularly uninspired fashion. The program did not last long enough for them to inflict any serious damage.

The best work in this video vein was done by producer Gene Roddenberry, whose science fiction anthology series "The Outer Limits" enjoyed a respectable run in the early sixties. It was perhaps most noteworthy for the variety of outlandish creatures from outer space who paraded through its episodes. In 1966 Roddenberry and the NBC network launched what must be considered as the most successful science fiction program, "Star Trek." This saga of an exploratory mission through space lasted for three years, its life extended by an unprecedented viewer demand for its continuation. Even its eventual demise did nothing to discourage its fanatical followers, who even have annual conventions to celebrate their favorite TV fare. The program had, not surprisingly, its share of unearthly incidents and individuals, not the least of which was Mr. Spock (Leonard Nimoy), a half-human, half-alien member of the spaceship's crew whose pointed logic and pointed ears endeared him to millions.

A similar cult following was enjoyed by Jonathan Frid, who portrayed Barnabas Collins on that most improbable of television shows "Dark Shadows." It was ostensibly a soap opera, one of those sentimental daytime dramas with which networks hope to entertain housewives; but "Dark Shadows" soon developed into something quite different. Producer Dan Curtis hit upon the idea of a soap opera in the mode of the so-called Gothic novels that are enjoying current popularity; but the show rapidly became a frankly supernatural melodrama, complete with a werewolf named Quentin and Barnabas, the reluctant vampire. The program was broadcast by ABC late enough in the day to acquire an after-school juvenile audience, and it experienced several years of wild popularity, giving rise to such spin-offs as a series of novels and bubble-gum cards.

The horror content was somewhat subdued, but there was some compensation for bloodthirsty fans in the MGM motion picture version, the gory *House of Dark Shadows* (1970).

Writer Rod Serling, whose "Twilight Zone" had etherealized the airwaves a decade earlier, returned in 1970 as the host of "Night Gallery," a program that abandoned science fiction and fantasy to concentrate on hard-core chills. "Night Gallery" had a unique origin, beginning experimentally as one of a group of four rotating programs and becoming a full-fledged series in the next season. This NBC offering was perhaps the first network show to commit itself completely to the macabre, rather than gingerly introducing that element into a format built around a more general theme such as mystery or imagination. As such, it had its ups and downs, sometimes coming up with a good moment but usually falling victim to its own heavy-handedness, attempting to maintain suspense with a plot whose outcome was obvious before the exposition was over. Serling was no longer writing most of the scripts; a number of stories were adapted from writers like H. P. Lovecraft and Richard Matheson. The best effort was "They're Tearing Down Tim Riley's Bar," a tale involving the nostalgic hallucinations of a middle-aged man (William Windom) which was more poignant than petrifying.

Less sincere and less successful were such short-lived shows as "The Sixth Sense" and "Ghost Story." The former featured Gary Rhodes as a colorless psychic investigator; the latter was an anthology with Sebastian Cabot as the inevitable host. The failure of "Ghost Story" was especially surprising in that its producer was William Castle, whose motion pictures usually displayed expertise and enthusiasm. As it was, the series evidenced little more than someone's inexplicable enthusiasm for stories about animal ghosts. An attempt was made to stir up interest by changing the title to "Circle of Fear," but no other alterations were apparent. In 1973 the three major networks had abandoned this sort of programming, although syndicated shows included revivals of many of these morbid moments. There were also two British productions, "Touch of Evil" and "Great Mysteries," which occasionally touched on the terrifying, usually without much effect.

Television has hardly abandoned horror, however. Instead, the networks have promoted the genre with what would appear to be an ever increasing number of special one-shot productions. The demand for televised theatrical feature films has become so great that the supply is in danger of being exhausted; as a result several companies, notably Universal, have begun production of made-for-TV "movies," which have since become a network staple, especially on ABC. Inevitably there have been a few stabs at the supernatural, and a trend was inaugurated when one of them broke the ratings record for television movies. This was *The Night Stalker*, a contemporary vampire tale made for ABC's "Movie of the Week." It was, in its modest way, a clever and capable production. Produced by Dan Curtis of "Dark Shadows" fame, with a script by Richard Matheson based on a story by Jeff Rice, *The Night Stalker* featured Darren McGavin as a Las Vegas reporter who deduces that a series of murders are the work of a vampire (Barry Atwater). The supernatural menace is equated with the corruption and commercialization of the city, where the authorities refuse to accept even the most powerful proof of the vampire's existence, apparently less awed by the unholy than by the business reversals that publicity might produce. The newspaper stories are killed along with the vampire, and the reporter is run out of town. The film was popular enough to spawn a sequel and, in 1974, a weekly ABC series featuring McGavin as the occult investigator Kolchak. The wave of films that have followed in the wake of *The Night Stalker* have generally ranged from the dull to the deplorable; but there has been at least one exception: another Richard Matheson brainchild entitled *Duel*. This unnerving little film depicted the ordeal of a motorist who is pursued by a huge truck. The truck driver is never seen, and the persecution takes on occult or allegorical overtones while remaining a tangible threat. This TV movie, starring Dennis Weaver, was good enough to be released as a theatrical feature in Europe.

ABC has also employed another format for televised thrillers, ninety-minute taped dramas produced (sometimes in England) for their late-night grab bag, "Wide World of Entertainment." The originals have largely been a lame lot based on the premise that nothing is as chilling as watching a starlet age suddenly; but there have been a few more ambitious projects based on the classics. The man behind these is Dan Curtis, certainly the past decade's busiest perpetrator of video villainy. His taped version of *Frankenstein* in 1972 ran on two successive nights for a total of three hours. Like all previous adaptations, it altered the original story; more to the point, it was a disappointingly lackluster production, slow and shoddy with a monster whose appearance and behavior suggested a village idiot rather than an uncanny creation. Curtis did far better with his two-part adaptation of Oscar Wilde's *Picture of Dorian Gray*; it was in fact comparable to the 1945 MGM treatment which had featured Hurd Hatfield and George Sanders. Much of the credit for the TV version belongs to Wilde, whose dandified dialogue makes the scriptwriter's job enviable and easy; but the direction and acting were more than capable, with unknown Shane Briant quite effective in the title role.

Curtis also concocted a two-hour TV film version of *Dracula* for CBS in 1974, but it was something less than a triumph. Richard Matheson's script surprisingly failed to draw new blood from the old chestnut; the innovations he did present were frequently embarrassing (for instance, the soft-focus flashbacks representing the prevampire count as a great lover). Veteran villain Jack Palance was a disappointing Dracula, his performance an uneasy cross between Bela Lugosi and Christopher Lee that never got off the ground. As a director, Curtis failed to provide much atmosphere, and the rigid CBS censor left little opportunity for scenes of physical horror. This network, in fact, has displayed a strangely schizophrenic attitude regarding the whole genre: it has purchased and shown innumerable theatrical features of recent vintage, but it has cut them mercilessly. The current trend in horror films, for better or worse, is to structure them around sequences leading up to scenes of a shocking nature. To cut these, as CBS invariably does, is to create a series of anticlimaxes, often incoherent and occasionally incomprehensible. If the network finds the movies tasteless, it would surely be preferable not to show them at all.

NBC surpassed its rival in prestige if not productivity by presenting two elaborately mounted and well-publicized revivals; the first featured Kirk Douglas in, of all things, a musical version of *Dr. Jekyll and Mr. Hyde*, conceived and directed by David Winters. The combination of music and the macabre proved less incongruous than might have been anticipated. The songs were hardly memorable, but neither were they intrusive, and the result was something more than a spoof, not really a bad treatment of a once frightening story that had been done to death. Douglas's enthusiasm carried the show through some shaky transitions in tone, and there was one memorably macabre if essentially silly scene: Mr. Hyde seated at a piano in a graveyard, contemplating mayhem while sardonically serenading his masochistic mistress. Almost a year later, toward the end of 1973, NBC presented the most ambitious TV horror show to date, a two-part, four-hour version of Mary Shelley's story, entitled, with more arrogance than accuracy, *Frankenstein: The True Story*. It was, in fact, no more faithful to the novel than other adaptations and perhaps violated the spirit of the original more than less elaborate versions. Scriptwriters seem to find the theme so fascinating that they cannot resist attempts to improve on its treatment. The principal conceit of this version by Christopher Isherwood and Don Bachardy was to make the monster a handsome and charming young man who even makes a debut in high society before he begins to deteriorate with what looks like a case of terminal acne. Frankenstein himself is depicted as the unwilling tool of a sinister scientist named, in tribute to the original author's acquaintance, Dr. Polidori. Since yet another experimenter is given credit for the life-giving technique, Frankenstein (Leonard Whiting) emerges as a cipher, devoid of both immorality and ingenuity. A female "monster" is duly created and proves to be a presentable if unscrupulous young lady who is destroyed by her degenerated male counterpart (Michael Sarrazin) in a fit of jealous rage. The film also suffered from pedestrian direction by Jack Smight; but on the bright side of the coin, there was an outstanding supporting cast (James Mason, John Gielgud, Ralph Richardson, Michael Wilding, Margaret Leighton, and Agnes Moorehead), and an expensive series of period costumes and settings, including the climactic ocean voyage to the Arctic (characteristically mismanaged so that Frankenstein is fleeing the monster rather than pursuing). Despite its glaring faults, this sincere and serious effort, obviously involving large expenditures of time, talent, and cash, indicated the growing respectability of the genre, and devotees considered it a good sign. It was certainly a silk purse, albeit an empty one.

Television's acceptance of macabre material has been paralleled by developments in publishing. Not only are nerve-racking novels becoming increasingly popular, but pulse-pounding periodicals are on the upswing. Still the leader in the field is publisher James Warren, whose *Famous Monsters of Filmland* revived the morbid magazine in 1958 and whose *Creepy* resurrected the horror comic book in 1965. The latter was almost immediately joined by a second title, *Eerie*, followed in 1969 by *Vampirella*, which in addition to the usual variety of stories launched the adventures of the first sustained spectral character in comic books for many years. The beautiful bloodsucker Vampirella, as conceived by *Famous Monsters* editor Forrest J. Ackerman, is a refugee from outer space. The idea that her behavior is normal on her home planet makes her something less of a villainess, if no less a vampire, and most of her adventures have found her fighting temptation and a variety of menaces less moderate than herself. The striking portrait of "Vampi" on the cover of the first issue was by Frank Frazetta; Tom Sutton illustrated the early stories, and was later succeeded by José Gonzales, and then Leopold Sanchez. The first years of Warren's horror comics were distinguished by the work of artists like Wallace Wood and Johnny Craig, who had originally made their mark in the E.C. comics of an earlier era; later issues have introduced a variety of new artists, including many who live and work in Europe. Among the most talented of the young American contributors are Berni Wrightson, a master of mood whose style is reminiscent of E.C.'s Graham Ingels; and Richard Corben, recruited from the ranks of the underground horror comic books. All of these publications are edited by William DuBay, who is also at the helm of Warren's latest publication, a revival of Will Eisner's spectral sleuth the Spirit, who delighted aficionados by returning from the dead in 1974.

There may be no way to duplicate Eisner's unique talents, but all of Warren's earlier efforts inspired a rash of imitators. Dozens of horror film magazines appeared in the wake of *Famous Monsters*, most of them halfhearted efforts that collapsed after a few issues. An exception of sorts is Calvin T. Beck's *Castle of Frankenstein*, which has managed to hang on despite an extremely erratic schedule that has yielded only twenty issues in almost as many years. It can hardly be considered an economic rival to its more popular predecessor, but it is worth noting as the one magazine in the field that has not

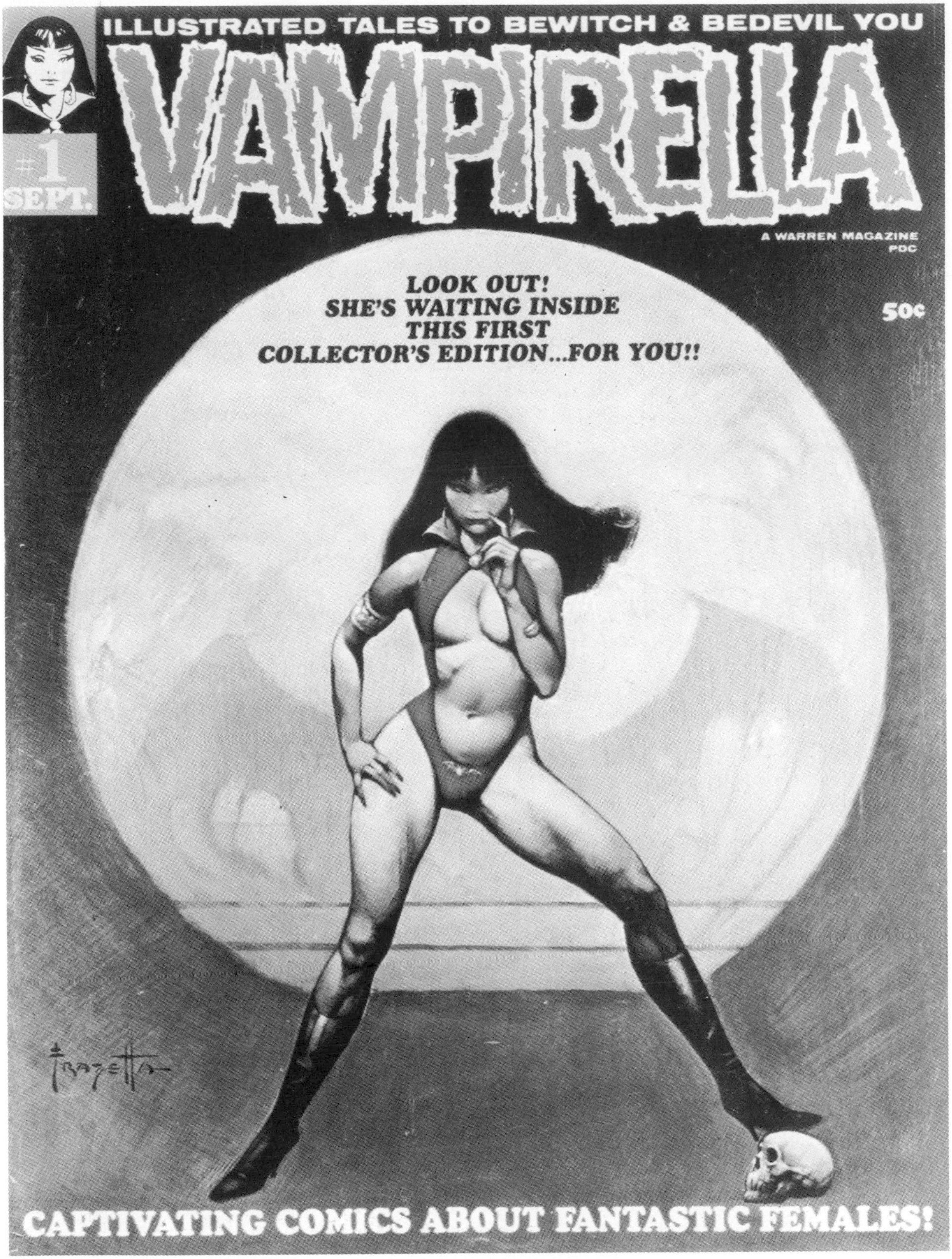

Frank Frazetta's version of the exotic Vampirella, an extraterrestrial, glamorous bloodsucker. *Copyright © 1969, 1975 by Warren Communications Corp. All rights reserved.*

Will Eisner's spectral comic book character the Spirit was recently revived for a new generation by Warren Publishing.

Barry Smith illustrated the Conan saga "Red Nails" in this striking panel from the pages of *Savage Tales. Copyright © 1973, 1974. Courtesy of the Marvel Comics Group. All rights reserved.*

attempted to follow in Ackerman's jocular footsteps, offering instead a more serious treatment that makes it an alternative instead of just an imitation. As for horror comics, they have proliferated without much success, the longest run inexplicably achieved by an outfit specializing in reprinting second-rate stories from an earlier era and, when these have been run into the ground from constant overexposure, hiring an even less capable artist to redraw them. That this miserable line has continued to perpetuate itself for over a decade is a tribute to the popularity of the genre.

Warren's horror comics (and their imitators) defied the Comics Code ban on such material by using a new format: larger, premium-priced magazines printed without color. The mainstream comics publishers have approached the genre gingerly. Marvel Comics, the best-known line of the last decade, specializes in atomically mutated heroes like Jack Kirby's *Fantastic Four* and Steve Ditko's *Amazing Spider-Man*; but editor and writer Stan Lee has featured some occult characters like the psychic investigator Dr. Strange, who bowed in 1963. Lee's successor Roy Thomas has amplified this impulse, especially since Comics Code taboos regarding the macabre were modified in early 1971. The most impressive result was an adaptation of Robert E. Howard's *Weird Tales* stories, increasingly popular through paperback book revival, which began in 1970 under the title *Conan the Barbarian.* Much of the critical and popular success of this effort was due to the young English artist Barry Smith, whose increasingly capable renderings were vividly detailed and unusually imaginative. Perhaps sensing that their adaptations seem a bit tame beside their gory, sexy source, Marvel has moved into the black-and-white uncensored format with a Conan showcase called *Savage Tales.* It was a tentative venture, with more than a year between the first and second issues; but the company eventually moved into the field with several terror titles, although only the Conan stories display suitable enthusiasm. And since Barry Smith's departure to publish his own work, even the Conan series has shown a marked decline. Marvel also made Dracula and the Frankenstein monster the heroes of their own color comic books, with mixed results, and attempted to revive the horror fiction pulp magazine with *The Haunt of Horror*, which lasted for only two issues before it was transformed into a comic book.

A much more commendable move in the same direction was made in 1973 when publisher Leo Margulies and veteran editor Sam Moskowitz revived the legendary *Weird Tales*, half a century after its original appearance and nineteen years after it had folded. The magazine has presented fiction of the highest quality, concentrating on reprints not only from its earlier incarnation but also from a variety of sources uncovered by the editor's remarkable research. A labor of love that appears to be growing in circulation, the new *Weird Tales* is a signal that the morbid imagination is experiencing its finest hour.

Nothing shows this more clearly, though, than the incredible proliferation of horror films, climaxed by the appearance of one that seems likely to become one of the most lucrative movies in motion picture history, *The Exorcist* (1973). This major production was a far cry from the growing number of cheap and lurid "exploitation" films loosely based on horror themes. Television had produced a jaded audience, and thus movies with vaguely *verboten* contents came into vogue, often making profits without showing the slightest sign of artistic achievement or even intention. While most of these deplorable grade "Z" quickies tended toward pornography, a few found financial rewards in depicting the crudest of tortures and mutations, generally rendered totally unbelievable by lack of technical ability. Occasionally sex and the supernatural were combined, as in the feeble *Orgy of the Dead* (1966). No film in this category was more thoroughly repulsive than the German export *Mark of the Devil* (1972). This catalog of the atrocities perpetrated by witch-hunters featured, at least for American audiences, the offer of a free vomit bag to anyone bored enough to attend. Thus the worst hacks of the previous generation, motivated by materialism, pursued the same extremism the young underground artists embraced in their search for artistic freedom.

Still, many of the most effective motion pictures in the genre continue to be produced not by the officially sanctioned studios on slumming expeditions, nor by their equally insincere counterparts in the lower depths of technical poverty. Most of the important work has been done, as it usually is, by those with an authentic commitment to their product. This category consists, as it has for the past decade, of American International in the United States and Hammer Films in England, although the latter has considerable competition from the newer company, Amicus, which continues to specialize in films combining several short episodes.

Some of the Amicus productions, including *Torture Garden* (1968), *The House That Dripped Blood* (1971), and *Asylum* (1972), were written by the prolific Robert Bloch, adapted from his stories. The latter two especially were well received by reviewers, presumably because they were well mounted and capably performed; but not even a Bloch screenplay could capture the wry quality of his fiction. Amicus encountered much the same problem with *Tales from the Crypt* (1972) and *The Vault of Horror* (1973), two collections from the old but increasingly reputable E.C. comic books. Screenwriter

Peter Cushing, an actor who usually plays his parts with minimal makeup, portrayed this vengeful corpse in the film adaptation of the comic book series *Tales from the Crypt. Courtesy of Cinerama Releasing.*

Milton Subotsky failed to convey the tone of the originals, a fact that was only underscored by the decision to have the staid English actor Ralph Richardson portray the formerly leering, jeering Crypt-Keeper. The only episode in either film that was really effective was "Poetic Justice," a tale from *Crypt* starring Peter Cushing, adapted from drawings by Graham Ingels. Still, the mixing of the media in these two films was an irresistible lure for horror fans.

Meanwhile, Hammer Films seems to have been experiencing some fluctuation in the quality of its production, although the quantity has remained consistently high. Most of the newer movies from Hammer have not enjoyed the services of writer Jimmy Sangster or director Terence Fisher, whose efforts made the studio's early efforts so impressive; yet it seems fair to suggest that the more recent efforts are not so much markedly inferior as overly familiar. Perhaps the outstanding production, at least partly because it was the most unusual, was *Five Million Years to Earth* (1968). This sedate yet suspenseful science fiction story, directed by Roy Ward Baker from a script by Nigel Kneale, bypassed Hammer's beloved Victorian setting to depict excavations in modern London which reveal evidence of an ancient alien invasion. The hypothesis of the story is that these visitors from space inspired the legends of demonology and altered the history of the human race.

Hammer's series characters were not on their best behavior. Christopher Lee returned in *Dracula Has Risen from the Grave* (1968), *Taste the Blood of Dracula* (1969), *Scars of Dracula* (1970), *Dracula A.D. '72* (1972), and *The Satanic Rites of Dracula* (1974). The titles alone give some indication of the increasing desperation of the writers, who found it difficult to concoct new tricks for the count and began structuring their stories so that he was more and more of a minor character. Lee, whose commanding presence gave each of these films at least a few good moments, finally announced in 1974 that he was through with the part for good, although there remains the possibility that a suitable script might tempt him. As it happened, Lee's best recent film for Hammer was *The Devil's Bride* (1967), directed by Terence Fisher with a screenplay by the busy Richard Matheson. The source was Dennis Wheatley's novel *The Devil Rides Out*, and Lee, strange as it seems, played the hero, psychic investigator de Richleau. This movie was just a bit too early to benefit from the trendy interest in Satanism, but it was superior to most of its successors; the scene in which the protagonists huddle within a pentacle while the forces of evil rage around them is authentically awesome.

Peter Cushing has carried on as Dr. Frankenstein in *Frankenstein Created Woman* (1966), *Frankenstein Must Be Destroyed* (1969), and *Frankenstein and the Monster from Hell* (1974)—none of them exactly classics, but all preferable to some of the sleazy American products that were beginning to appear using Frankenstein and Dracula. The most astounding of these were combined on a double bill in 1966: Embassy's *Jesse James Meets Frankenstein's Daughter* and *Billy the Kid vs. Dracula*, which unfortunately were not as hilarious as their titles might suggest. Hammer may have been reacting to this sort of product when it released *Horror of Frankenstein* (1970), in appearance and apparently in intention a parody of the company's germinal 1957 offering, *The Curse of Frankenstein*. Ralph Bates played the demented doctor in the 1970 film, sparing Cushing the task of burlesquing his most famous role.

The best Hammer productions of recent years, as has been indicated, were not bound by the restrictions of the series format. The vampire theme proved most durable. *The Vampire Lovers* (1970), directed by Roy Ward Baker, was a capable version of Le Fanu's "Carmilla," with the erotic elements emphasized, particularly by the performance of the star, voluptuous Ingrid Pitt. This story was rehashed a scant year later in *Lust for a Vampire*, an inferior sequel that looked like a regrettable remake. The most interesting treatment of the bloodsucking breed was *Vampire Circus* (1972), an uneven but extremely eerie effort that recaptured some of the air of mystery absent from the era's busier films. Robert Young directed this tale of a traveling troupe of terrors who descend on an isolated village, using their supernatural powers to put on a dazzling show that is also devilishly seductive.

In other areas, Hammer has offered a glut of ghouls that includes a few interesting variations on familiar themes. Ralph Bates and Martine Beswick (in appearance if not intensity a latter-day Barbara Steele) portrayed *Dr. Jekyll and Sister Hyde* (1972). The title tells the whole story; the details of the scientist's transformation were not as interesting as the concept. Hammer's lackluster mummy series was invigorated after several dull entries by *Blood from the Mummy's Tomb* (1972), which was not the usual ambulatory bandage saga but a version of Bram Stoker's novel of reincarnation, *The Jewel of the Seven Stars*. Despite the tasteless title (perhaps the inevitable result of too many movies with the same subject), the film, directed by Seth Holt, was subtle and imaginative.

American International has continued its dominance of macabre movies in the United States, even distributing many of Hammer's offerings. Although Roger Corman has abandoned the genre, his influence lingers on in the comparatively polished color productions that have replaced the black-and-white quickies of the company's earliest days. More attempts have been made to adapt the works of H. P. Lovecraft, with depressing results; *Die, Monster, Die!* (1965), directed by Daniel Haller, turned "The Colour Out of Space" into a pedestrian "mad doctor" muddle, unredeemed even by the presence of Boris Karloff. *The Dunwich Horror* (1970) was duller still, with the perennial juvenile Dean Stockwell totally miscast as the demented, demon-spawned Wilbur Whately, and Sandra Dee, unbelievable as the inevitable Hollywood heroine. Haller muddled through again, making no attempt to depict the monstrosities of the author's imagination, opting instead for a feeble attempt to turn the tale into *Rosemary's Baby.*

The studio's Poe series has continued in fits and starts; for a while it seemed that every Vincent Price film would be credited to that author. Such was the case with *The Conqueror Worm* (1968), shown in England under the more appropriate title *The Witchfinder General.* This account of the inquisitorial tactics of the historical figure Matthew Hopkins had nothing to do with Poe; but it was effectively directed by Michael Reeves, and it received high praise in some quarters, although it was a bit grim and realistic for the average "monster movie" buff. *The Cry of the Banshee* (1970), a crude elaboration of an Irish legend, was attributed to Poe without even the courtesy gesture of naming it after one of his works.

The ultimate abandonment of literary adaptations led, on the whole, to preferable productions. Vincent Price got one of his juiciest roles as *The Abominable Dr. Phibes,* playing a crazed physician who takes revenge against the colleagues who have allowed his wife to die. Presumably deceased, Phibes keeps himself in action with a quaint clockwork conglomeration, part of the art deco decor that made the film charming as well as chilling. Beneath his suspiciously stiff Vincent Price mask, the face of Phibes was foul and fearsome, giving Price one of his rare chances to play a monster instead of just a malevolent mortal. This 1971 film, directed by Robert Fuest, was so successful that it led to a sequel a year later, giving Price his first continuing character—remarkable in that few actors have received star status in the genre, as he had already done, without this kind of audience identification. Still, Price was perhaps better served by *Theater of Blood* (1973), in which he was cast as a crazed Shakespearean actor who reacts to a bad press by murdering the critics. Price's essentially comic portrayal, matched by that of Diana Rigg as his helpful daughter, was contrasted with scenes of explicit horror. Possibly fearing for their own safety, real reviewers were generous with their praise for this film, which, although released by United Artists, maintained the tone and the plot structure of American International's Dr. Phibes movies.

Featured with Price in *Dr. Phibes Rises Again* was Robert Quarry, an actor who gained some following in *Count Yorga—Vampire* (1970) and *The Return of Count Yorga* (1971). Quarry was a bit heavy-set for a hungry horror, but he looked good in contrast to the ragged production and intermittently inept performers around him. Considerably more interesting (if not entirely for artistic reasons) was the vampire series American International inaugurated in 1972 with *Blacula.* William Marshall portrayed an African prince, corrupted by Count Dracula, who is revived unexpectedly in modern Los Angeles. The racial switch was startling if not inherently implausible, and there were some political implications in the action, as "Blacula" (fortunately never addressed by this title during the course of the film) wipes out a platoon of police to express his indignation over the destruction of his mistress. The protagonist also breaks precedent when, having done his worst, he commits suicide, disdainfully exposing himself to sunlight in what appears to be a commentary upon the efforts of his opponents. Marshall had sufficient dignity and energy to keep the project afloat, resulting in plans for a number of movies in the same vein. The only one to appear, however, was *Scream, Blacula, Scream* (1973), an inferior sequel.

Although Amicus, Hammer, and American International have been manufacturing the majority of movie menaces in recent years, less sinister studios have done their worst as well. The field of fantasy films received a boost from the release of some expensive and profitable science fiction films, notably Stanley Kubrick's massive *2001: A Space Odyssey* (1968). This ambitious MGM release, presented on the huge Cinerama screen, explored the theme, by now familiar in fiction, that our planet has been under the influence of omniscient extraterrestrial forces since the dawn of time. Although the treatment was occasionally awesome, the result could hardly be classified as a "horror film." The same was true of the less impressive but more accessible *Planet of the Apes* (1968). Scripted by Rod Serling from a novel by Pierre Boulle, this depicted a voyage to a world where intelligent simians rule primitive humans, revealing in the climax that this is the earth as it will be in the future. As indicated by the presence of heroic star Charlton Heston, the movie was basically an adventure, with some small touches of social satire. It was pretty well divorced from the mood of terror, but it nevertheless appealed to the many monster lovers who seem to have an inordinate fondness for apes and were justifiably impressed with the ingenious monkey makeup. Twentieth Century-Fox did well enough in this monkey business to follow it up with four sequels in as many years, and the simian saga became, briefly, a CBS television series in 1974. Heston avoided the sequels, but he went on to appear in *The Omega Man* (1971), a slick version of Matheson's *I Am Legend* which turned the novel's vampires into presumably more respectable "mutants"; and *Soylent Green* (1973), a view of an overpopulated future in which industry provides protein for people by using the previous population. These efforts proved to be more earnest than effective, but their big budgets and intermittent moralizing created the impression that films with bizarre subjects were being taken seriously.

Of course, events such as the recent moon landing gave science fiction a sort of status with which more frankly fearsome fantasies could hardly compete, despite the burgeoning interest in the occult. Still, there were some interesting developments from unexpected sources, as producers and studios not usually associated with the macabre ventured into the domain of dread. Cinerama, usually identified with elaborate spectacles, released a small shocker called *Willard* in 1971. Much to their amazement, it proved to be a box office bonanza and even inaugurated a small cycle of imitations. Willard was a young man with a trained pack of murderous rats, and his unlikely popularity inspired a number of films featuring not overgrown monsters, but lots of little ones. There was even a sequel, *Ben*, named for the lead rodent. MGM followed the trend off the deep end with *Night of the Lepus*, about a plague of rabbits. Nobody was capable of taking this too seriously.

On the brighter side, two outstanding directorial debuts resulted in films with impressive new perspectives. *Targets* (1968) was written, directed, and produced by Peter Bogdanovich, who has since acquired an enviable reputation for work of considerably less ingenuity. *Targets* also provided an admirable swan song for Boris Karloff, who died shortly after its release. His role was virtually a self-portrait, that of an elderly horror movie star who wishes to retire, convinced that his roles are irrelevant when contrasted with the less romantic terrors of contemporary civilization. As the film progresses, his preparations for his last premiere, at a drive-in theater, are juxtaposed with adventures of an apparently normal young man who goes berserk, first murdering his family and then setting out on a career of aimless sniping. The paths of the two characters cross at the climax of the film, as Karloff arrives at the drive-in where the sniper, hidden behind the silver screen, is picking off thrill-seeking patrons in their cars. The aged actor, furious when his secretary is shot, marches mechanically toward the killer, who panics at the sight of the man whose gigantic image is also menacing him from the screen. Thus, in a contrived but powerful scene, the imaginary monster defeats a genuine menace. Although a trifle self-conscious, *Targets* is an impressive tour de force, Karloff's best film in decades, and an important landmark in the genre. Unfortunately the film was badly handled by Paramount, receiving less promotion and distribution than the most pedestrian product might be expected to deserve.

Much the same problem affected the success of *Night of the Living Dead* (1968), an independent production that got no attention at the time of its release but eventually acquired an underground reputation that kept it in circulation for years. Made on a minuscule budget, it ultimately earned millions. Directed and photographed by George Romero from a script by John Russo, *Night of the Living Dead* was the work of a television crew from Pittsburgh, Pennsylvania. Working with a cast of unknowns and limited technical facilities, they created a harrowing film, all the more effective because of its naturalistic documentary quality. The premise is that the dead have risen to devour the living (the cause, that old devil radiation, is passed over without much interest by author and audience); the plot involves a group of people besieged in an isolated house. Many effects are dependent on irony and reversed clichés: an attractive young couple who seem most likely to survive are destroyed in a rash attempt to escape. Even the film's apparent hero, a black veteran who plots strategy against the ungodly invaders, is in for his share of surprises. This man of action (Duane Jones), is opposed by a blustering, cowardly businessman (played by the film's coproducer, Karl Hardman) who argues impotently that everyone would be safe barricaded in the cellar. Finally, after all his companions have been slaughtered, Jones manages to save himself—by hiding in the cellar. He emerges when he realizes that the authorities have cleared the area of the awful army and, dazed and bedraggled, he is taken for a walking corpse; his rescuers kill him. One of the most brilliant sequences shows the group gathered around the house's television set. At first eager for information, they are gradually lulled by their role as observers, nearly oblivious to the horrors around them until the electricity suddenly fails and reality rears its ugly head. Uncompromisingly realistic, perhaps all the more so for its almost archaic use of black-and-white film, *Night of the Living Dead* generates so much clammy claustrophobia that it has become the center of a cult.

But this and all other recent frightening films have been overshadowed by the monumental impact of *The Exorcist* (1973), at once the most expensive and the most profitable production of its kind. Based on the best-selling 1971 novel by William Peter Blatty, it deals with the theme of demonic possession. What distinguishes both versions of *The Exorcist* from less popular works in the genre is, among other things, its air of conviction. Most fearsome fantasies for the past two centuries have at least indirectly

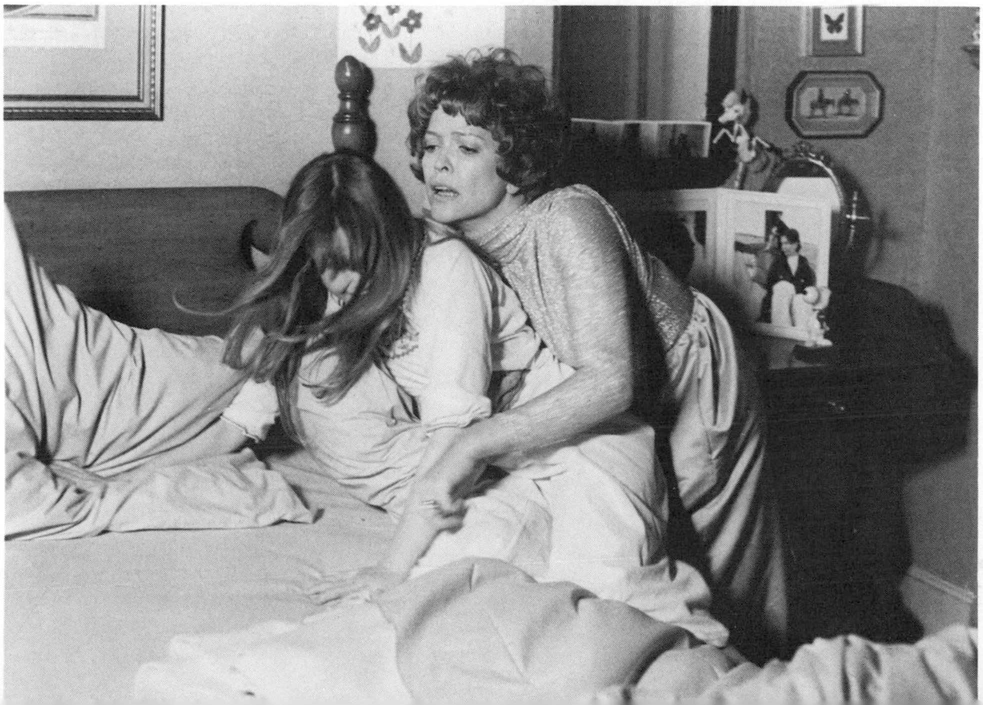

Linda Blair, as a child possessed by a demon, gives her movie star mother (Ellen Burstyn) a hard time in the controversial but undeniably effective film *The Exorcist. From the motion picture* The Exorcist *courtesy of Warner Bros. Inc. Copyright © 1974.*

acknowledged the skepticism of their audiences, making an almost playful appeal to archaic beliefs. Blatty's story is based on a sort of psychic phenomenon that major religious institutions are still inclined to take seriously, and reports of presumably authentic cases of possession and exorcism were used as part of a publicity campaign. Critics who were dumbfounded by the appeal of *The Exorcist* attempted to attribute its success to the era's renewed interest in the occult; Blatty replied with some indignation that numerous works with comparable subjects had not done nearly as well. He was better at refuting other people's suggestions than at providing his own, for there seems little doubt that what attracted sensation seekers to the book and especially to the movie was the scurrilous nature of its incidents. Blatty employed what Henry James called "the turn of the screw," the twist of having evil wreak its havoc upon an innocent child, a ploy that by now seems almost obligatory for those who wish their horrors to reach a public usually immune to them. But *The Exorcist* was not content to depict innocence threatened by death and decay; instead, it showed the possessed young girl urinating on a carpet, masturbating with a crucifix, and vomiting on a priest. These are the scenes that patrons of the film seem to find the most memorable, and they are fairly obviously distinguishable from the graphic gruesomeness that might be expected of a horror movie. In this sense at least, *The Exorcist* is more shocking than frightening. On the other hand, director William Friedkin did succeed in conjuring up some uncanny atmosphere, aided and abetted by elaborate work with the sound track, makeup, and special effects. Still, with all this effort, and with all the offensive details, it is ironic that many viewers should report themselves most disturbed by the coldly clinical scenes in which the child Regan undergoes a series of exhaustive medical tests.

A work like *The Exorcist*, with its scandalous incidents and its insistence that its subject is plausible, only serves to emphasize the essentially playful nature of most work in the field. While the new credibility of the occult has inspired a few fantasies, there is an apparently permanent audience, gleefully living in fear, who recognize imaginary terrors as projections of sublimated emotions. For this audience, an air of conviction is sufficient. The demons of the unconscious serve social purposes by expressing antisocial attitudes, and in time they become so acceptable that they can be employed in extraordinary ways. It has already been noted that these presumably frightening figures are regarded with considerable affection by children; while Blatty titillates adults with his tale of corrupted youth, the average kid finds Dracula about as disturbing as Donald Duck. In fact, the Count and his colleague the Frankenstein monster have recently been used by a large cereal concern, General Mills, to make its products more attractive to prepubescent palates. The pair appear in animated form on television, endorsing breakfast foods called Count Chocula and Frankenberry, and their pictures appear on the boxes on supermarket shelves. The monsters are among us, sugarcoated and vitamin enriched. Such a situation might be viewed with alarm; but it is really a demonstration that we have nothing to fear from these creatures, that the slight shudder they may evoke and the minor misanthropy they may express are simply safety valves that make our often grim world, if anything, a little less monstrous.

INDEX

Note: Films, television and radio programs, and comics are listed by title. Literary works appear under their authors' names.

BIOGRAPHICAL DICTIONARY OF MATHEMATICIANS

REFERENCE BIOGRAPHIES FROM THE
Dictionary of Scientific Biography

Volume 2

LEONARD DICKSON – AL-KHWĀRIZIMĪ

Charles Scribner's Sons
NEW YORK

Collier Macmillan Canada
TORONTO

Maxwell Macmillan International
NEW YORK, OXFORD, SINGAPORE, SYDNEY

Library of Congress Cataloging-in-Publication Data

Biographical Dictionary of Mathematicians: reference biographies from the Dictionary of scientific biography.
p.cm.
"Published under the auspices of the American Council of Learned Societies."
Includes bibliographical references and index.
ISBN 0-684-19282-9. – ISBN 0-684-19289-6 (v. 2)
1. Mathematicians–Biography–Dictionaries. I. American Council of Learned Societies. II. Dictionary of scientific biography.
QA28.B534 1991
510'.92'2–dc20
[B]
90-52920
CIP

Charles Scribner's Sons
Macmillan Publishing Company
866 Third Ave.
New York, New York 10022

Collier Macmillan Canada, Inc.
1200 Eglington Ave. East
Suite 200
Don Mills, Ontario M3C 3N1

1 3 5 7 9 11 13 15 17 19 20 18 16 14 12 10 8 6 4 2

Printed in the United States of America.

BIOGRAPHICAL DICTIONARY OF MATHEMATICIANS

DICKSON, LEONARD EUGENE (*b.* Independence, Iowa, 22 January 1874; *d.* Harlingen, Texas, 17 January 1954)

The son of Campbell and Lucy Tracy Dickson, Leonard Eugene Dickson had a distinguished academic career. After graduating with a B.S. in 1893 as class valedictorian from the University of Texas, he became a teaching fellow there. He received his M.S. in 1894. With the grant of a fellowship he then proceeded to the newly founded University of Chicago, where he received its first doctorate in mathematics in 1896. He spent the following year in postgraduate studies at Leipzig and Paris.

Upon his return to the United States, Dickson began his career in mathematics. After a one-year stay at the University of California as instructor in mathematics, in 1899 he accepted an associate professorship at the University of Texas. One year later he returned to the University of Chicago, where he spent the rest of his career, except for his leaves as visiting professor at the University of California in 1914, 1918, and 1922. He was assistant professor from 1900 to 1907, associate professor from 1907 to 1910, and professor from 1910 to 1939. He married Susan Davis on 30 December 1902; their children were Campbell and Eleanor. At the university his students and colleagues regarded him highly as a scholar and a teacher. He supervised the dissertations of at least fifty-five doctoral candidates and helped them obtain a start in research after graduation. In 1928 he was appointed to the Eliakim Hastings Moore distinguished professorship.

Dickson was a prolific mathematician. His eighteen books and hundreds of articles covered many areas in his field. In his study of finite linear groups, he generalized the results of Galois, Jordan, and Serret for groups over the field of p elements to groups over an arbitrary finite field. He gave the first extensive exposition of the theory of finite fields, wherein he stated and proved for $m = 2, 3$ his modified version of the Chevalley theorem: For a finite field it seems to be true that every form of degree m in $m + 1$ variables vanishes for values not all zero in the field. In linear algebra he applied arithmetical concepts and proved that a real Cayley division algebra is actually a division algebra. He also expanded upon the Cartan and Wedderburn theories of linear associative algebras. He studied the relationships between the theory of invariants and number theory.

While he believed that mathematics was the queen of the sciences, he held further that number theory was the queen of mathematics, a belief that resulted in his monumental three-volume *History of the Theory of Numbers,* in which he investigated diophantine equations, perfect numbers, abundant numbers, and Fermat's theorem. In a long series of papers after 1927 on additive number theory, he proved the ideal Waring theorem, using the analytic results of Vinogradov.

Dickson received recognition for his work. The American Mathematical Society, for which he was editor of the *Monthly* from 1902 to 1908 and of the *Transactions* from 1911 to 1916, honored him. He was its president from 1916 to 1918 and received its Cole Prize in 1928 for his book *Algebren und ihre Zahlentheorie.* Earlier, in 1924, the American Association for the Advancement of Science awarded him its thousand-dollar prize for his work on the arithmetic of algebras. Harvard in 1936 and Princeton in 1941 awarded him an honorary Sc.D. In addition to his election to the National Academy of Sciences in 1913, he was a member of the American Philosophical Society, the American Academy of Arts and Sciences, and the London Mathematical Society, and he was a correspondent of the Academy of the French Institute.

BIBLIOGRAPHY

Dickson's books are *Linear Groups With an Exposition of the Galois Field Theory* (Leipzig, 1901); *College Algebra* (New York, 1902); *Introduction to the Theory of Algebraic Equations* (New York, 1903); *Elementary Theory of Equations* (New York, 1914); *Algebraic Invariants* (New York, 1914); *Linear Algebras* (Cambridge, Mass., 1914); *Theory and Applications of Finite Groups* (New York, 1916), written with G. A. Miller and H. F. Blichfeldt; *History of the Theory of Numbers* (Washington, 1919-1923), vol. I, *Divisibility and Primality;* vol. II, *Diophantine Analysis;* vol. III, *Quadratic and Higher Forms* (with a ch. on the class number by G. H. Cresse); *A First Course in the Theory of Equations* (New York, 1922); *Plane Trigonometry With Practical Applications* (Chicago, 1922); *Algebras and Their Arithmetics* (Chicago, 1923); *Modern Algebraic Theories* (Chicago, 1926); *Algebren und ihre Zahlentheorie* (Zurich, 1927); *Introduction to the Theory of Numbers* (Chicago, 1929); *Studies in the Theory of Numbers* (Chicago, 1930); *Minimum Decompositions Into Fifth Powers,* vol. III (London, 1933); *New First Course in the Theory of Equations* (New York, 1939); and *Modern Elementary Theory of Numbers* (Chicago, 1939).

Other writings are *On Invariants and the Theory of Numbers,* American Mathematical Society Colloquium Publications, **4** (1914), 1-110; *Researches on Waring's Problem,* Carnegie Institution of Washington, pub. no. 464 (1935).

A. A. Albert, "Leonard Eugene Dickson 1874-1954," in *Bulletin of the American Mathematical Society,* **61** (1955), 331-346, contains a complete bibliography of Dickson's writings.

RONALD S. CALINGER

DICKSTEIN, SAMUEL (*b.* Warsaw, Poland, 12 May 1851; *d.* Warsaw, 29 September 1939)

Dickstein devoted his life to building up the organizational structure for Polish science, especially for mathematics. In the eighteenth century Poland's territory had been divided among Prussia, Austria, and Russia; and thus Polish science education and scientific life depended mostly on personal initiative and not on state support. In his youth Dickstein experienced the escalation of national oppression after the unsuccessful uprising of 1863. There was no Polish university in Warsaw at that time, and higher education was provided in part by the Szkola Główna, which was a teachers' college. From 1866 to 1869 Dickstein studied at the Szkola Główna, which was converted into the Russian University in Warsaw in 1869. After 1870 he continued his studies there and in 1876 received a master's degree in pure mathematics.

From 1870 Dickstein taught in Polish secondary schools, concentrating on mathematics; from 1878 to 1888 he directed his own private school in Warsaw. In 1884, with A. Czajewicz, he founded Biblioteka Matematyczno-Fizyczna, which was intended to be a series of scientific textbooks written in Polish. These books greatly influenced the development of Polish scientific literature. In 1888 Dickstein took part in the founding of the first Polish mathematical-physical magazine, *Prace matematyczno-fizyczne.* Later he founded other publications, such as *Wiadomości matematyczne* and the education journal *Ruch pedagogiczny* (1881).

The Poles' efforts after the creation of the Polish university led in 1906 to the founding of Towarzystwo Kursów Naukowych, which organized the university science courses. Dickstein was the first rector of that society. In 1905 he became a founder of the Warsaw Scientific Society, and he was instrumental in the development of the Society of Polish Mathematicians. After the revival of the Polish university in Warsaw he became professor of mathematics there in 1919. His own mathematical work was concerned mainly with algebra. His main sphere of interest besides education was the history of mathematics, and he published a number of articles on Polish mathematicians that contributed to their recognition throughout the world. Of especial note are the monograph *Hoene Wroński, jego życie i prace* (Cracow, 1896) and the edition of the Leibniz-Kochański correspondence, published in *Prace matematyczno-fizyczne,* **7** (1901), and **8** (1902). Appreciation of his historical works was shown in his election as vice-president of the International Academy of Sciences. The list of his scientific works includes more than 200 titles. Dickstein died during the bombardment of Warsaw and his family perished during the German occupation of Poland.

BIBLIOGRAPHY

I. ORIGINAL WORKS. The list of Dickstein's works up to 1917 is contained in a special issue of the magazine *Wiadomości matematyczne;* works from subsequent years are in the memorial volume *III Polski zjazd matematyczny. Jubileusz 65-lecia działalności naukowej, pedagogicznej i społecznej profesora Samuela Dicksteina* (Warsaw, 1937).

II. SECONDARY LITERATURE. Besides the memorial volume, the basic biographical data and an appreciation are contained in A. Mostowski, "La vie et l'oeuvre de Samuel Dickstein," in *Prace matematyczno-fizyczne,* **47** (1949), 5-12.

LUBOŠ NOVÝ

DIGGES, LEONARD (*b.* England, *ca.* 1520; *d.* England, 1559 [?])

Digges, a member of an ancient family in Kent, was the second son of James Digges of Barham. He was admitted to Lincoln's Inn in 1537 and, if he received the usual education of young gentlemen of the time, may also have attended a university. His works are strongly indebted to contemporary Continental sources, and it is possible that he traveled abroad in 1542.

Digges was interested in elementary practical mathematics, especially surveying, navigation, and gunnery. His almanac and prognostication (1555) contains much material useful to sailors. In 1556 he published an elementary surveying manual, *Tectonicon.* Both of these works went through many editions in the sixteenth century. In 1571 his son Thomas completed and published his more advanced practical geometry *Pantometria,* the first book of which was an up-to-date surveying text. The material in these works is based largely on Peter Apian and Gemma Frisius, but in many cases Digges was the first to describe the instruments and techniques in English.

Digges was a keen experimentalist who gained a reputation, while still quite young, for skill in ballistics. Although his military treatise *Stratioticos* (1579) is largely the work of his son, it is based partly on his notes and the results of his gunnery experiments. The genesis of *Stratioticos* may be found in Digges's association with Sir Thomas Wyatt and others in the preparation of a scheme for an organized militia for Protector Somerset in 1549.

Digges took part in Wyatt's rebellion in 1554. He was attainted and condemned to death but was pardoned for life, probably through the intercession of his kinsman Lord Clinton (later earl of Lincoln), to whom the *Prognostication* was dedicated. He completed payments for the redemption of his property on 7 May 1558 and probably died shortly thereafter.

BIBLIOGRAPHY

I. Original Works. Digges's writings are *A Prognostication of Right Good Effect* (London, 1555), enl. and retitled *A Prognostication Everlasting* (London, 1556; 11 eds. before 1600); *A Boke Named Tectonicon* (London, 1556; 8 eds. before 1600); *A Geometrical Practise Named Pantometria* (London, 1571, 1591), bk. 1, "Longimetria," repr. by R. T. Gunther as *First Book of Digges Pantometria,* Old Ashmolean Reprints, 4 (Oxford, 1927); and *An Arithmeticall Militare Treatise Named Stratioticos* (London, 1579, 1590).

II. Secondary Literature. The *Dictionary of National Biography* article on Leonard Digges is wholly unreliable. Some biographical material can be found in D. M. Loades, *Two Tudor Conspiracies* (London, 1965); and E. G. R. Taylor, *Mathematical Practitioners of Tudor and Stuart England* (Cambridge, 1954). The works on surveying are discussed in E. R. Kiely, *Surveying Instruments* (New York, 1947); and A. W. Richeson, *English Land Measuring to 1800* (Cambridge, Mass., 1967). The *Stratioticos* is discussed in Henry J. Webb, *Elizabethan Military Science* (Madison, Wis., 1965), with reference to Thomas Digges.

Joy B. Easton

DIGGES, THOMAS (*b.* Kent, England, 1546 [?]; *d.* London, England, August 1595)

Digges was the son of Leonard Digges of Wotten, Kent, and his wife, Bridget Wilford. He received his mathematical training from his father, who died when Thomas was young, and from John Dee.

Digges was the leader of the English Copernicans. In 1576 he added "A Perfit Description of the Caelestiall Orbes" to his father's *Prognostication.* This contained a translation of parts of book I of Copernicus' *De revolutionibus* and Digges's own addition of a physical, rather than a metaphysical, infinite universe in which the fixed stars were at varying distances in infinite space. He had already published his *Alae seu scalae mathematicae* (1573), containing observations on the new star of 1572 that were second only to those of Tycho Brahe in accuracy. Digges hoped to use these observations to determine whether the Copernican theory was true or needed further modifications, and he called for cooperative observations by astronomers everywhere.

In addition to his astronomical work Digges included a thorough discussion of the Platonic solids and five of the Archimedean solids in his father's *Pantometria* (1571). He also published *Stratioticos* (1579), a treatise on military organization with such arithmetic and algebra as was necessary for a soldier. To this work he appended questions relative to ballistics that were partially answered in the second editions of *Stratioticos* (1590) and *Pantometria* (1591). He was able, on the basis of his own and his father's experiments, to disprove many commonly held erroneous ideas in ballistics but was not able to develop a mathematical theory of his own. These appendixes constitute the first serious ballistic studies in England.

Digges was a member of the parliaments of 1572 (which met off and on for ten years) and 1584 and became increasingly active in public affairs. He was involved with plans for the repair of Dover harbor for several years and served as muster master general of the army in the Low Countries. Apart from his continuing studies in ballistics, his scientific writings cover only a decade; and his promised works on navigation, fortification, and artillery never appeared.

BIBLIOGRAPHY

I. Original Works. Digges's writings include "A Mathematical Discourse of Geometrical Solids," in Leonard Digges, *A Geometrical Practise Named Pantometria* (London, 1571, 1591), trans. by his grandson Dudley Digges as *Nova corpora regularia* (London, 1634); *Alae seu scalae mathematicae* (London, 1573); "A Perfit Description of the Caelestiall Orbes," in Leonard Digges, *Prognostication Everlastinge* (London, 1576, most later eds.); and *An Arithmeticall Militare Treatise Named Stratioticos* (London, 1579, 1590). For his nonmathematical publications and reports in MS, see the *Dictionary of National Biography,* V, 976–978.

II. Secondary Literature. F. R. Johnson, in a letter to the *Times Literary Supplement* (5 Apr. 1934), p. 244, gives information on the dates of Thomas' birth and Leonard's death. The *Dictionary of National Biography* is inaccurate on Thomas' early years, but the account of his later life is useful. For his parliamentary career see J. E. Neale, *Elizabeth I and Her Parliaments* (New York, 1958).

Digges's works are discussed in F. R. Johnson and S. V. Larkey, "Thomas Digges, the Copernican System, and the Idea of the Infinity of the Universe in 1576," in *Huntington Library Bulletin,* no. 5 (Apr. 1934), 69–117; and F. R. Johnson, *Astronomical Thought in Renaissance England* (Baltimore, 1937). For a different interpretation of Digges's infinite universe see A. Koyré, *From the Closed World to the Infinite Universe* (New York, 1957), pp. 34–39. For the ballistics see A. R. Hall, *Ballistics in the Seventeenth Century* (Cambridge, 1952); and for the military treatise H. J. Webb, *Elizabethan Military Science* (Madison, Wis., 1965).

Joy B. Easton

DINI, ULISSE (*b.* Pisa, Italy, 14 November 1845; *d.* Pisa, 28 October 1918)

Dini, son of Pietro and Teresa Marchionneschi Dini, came from a very modest background. He studied first in his native city, where, at the age of nineteen, he defended a thesis on applicable surfaces. Having won a competitive examination for study abroad, he left the teachers' college founded by his teacher, Enrico Betti, and went to Paris, where he studied for a year under Joseph Bertrand and Charles Hermite. Seven of his publications on the theory of surfaces date from that brief period.

In 1866 Dini taught higher algebra and theoretical geodesy at the University of Pisa; in 1871 he succeeded Betti (who preferred to direct his efforts to mathematical physics) as professor of analysis and higher geometry and, as early as 1877, also taught infinitesimal analysis. He held these two professorships for the rest of his life. Rector of the university between 1888 and 1890 and director of the teachers' college from 1908 to 1918, Dini was also one of the founders of the School of Applied Engineering in Pisa and was its interim director.

From his youth Dini took an active role in public life; he was a member of the city council of Pisa in 1871 and in various other years until 1895. He was elected to the national parliament in 1880 as a deputy from Pisa and was reelected three times. In 1892 he was appointed a senator of the kingdom.

Dini was an upright, honest, kind man who divided his life between teaching and pure research, on the one hand, and the obligations of a public career completely devoted to the well-being of his native city and his country, on the other.

Two periods of equally intense production may be noted in Dini's scientific activity. The first dealt with infinitesimal geometry and centered on studies of the properties of certain surfaces undertaken by Liouville and Meusnier in France and by Beltrami in Italy. These include surfaces of which the product or the ratio of two principal radii of curvature remains constant (helicoid surfaces to which Dini's name has been given); ruled surfaces for which one of the principal radii of curvature is a function of the other; and the problem suggested by Beltrami, and solved in its entirety by Dini, of representing, point by point, one surface on another in such manner that the geodesic curves of one correspond to the geodesic curves of the other. Dini's complete study of the conformable representation of one surface on another resembles the differential parameters introduced by Beltrami and, generally speaking, equations with partial differential coefficients.

Without losing sight of this geometric research, toward which he guided his best students (such as Luigi Bianchi), Dini preferred to devote himself, after 1871, to analytical studies, in which he was inspired by Weierstrass' and Mittag-Leffler's results on uniform functions and by Dirichlet's on series development of functions of a real variable. He discovered the properties of this development through application of an inversion formula more general than Abel's. Dini of course gave preference to the study of functions of a real variable; but his publication on uniform functions, in which he showed that Weierstrass' and Mittag-Leffler's formulas could be obtained through the method used by Betti in his theory of elliptic functions, proves that he was just as content to develop functions of a complex variable.

Dini devoted a volume to Fourier series and a long

chapter of his *Lezioni di analisi infinitesimale* to integral equations, in which many original and fruitful ideas appear. Of his last works in mathematical analysis, the greatest number concern the integration of linear differential equations and equations with partial derivatives of the second order. It must also be mentioned that he discovered a method of solving the linear equation

$$a_0 y^{(n)} + a_1 y^{(n-1)} + \cdots + a_n y = X,$$

in which the a's are given functions of x, X being a function of x. Dini also established a theorem for the upper and lower bounds for the moduli of the roots of an algebraic equation.

BIBLIOGRAPHY

I. ORIGINAL WORKS. Dini's main writings are *Fondamenti per la teoria delle funzioni di variabili reali* (Pisa, 1878), trans. into German by J. Lüroth and A. Schepp as *Grundlagen für eine Theorie der Funktionen einer veränderlichen reellen Grösse* (Leipzig, 1892); *Serie di Fourier e altre rappresentazioni analitiche delle funzioni di una variabile reale* (Pisa, 1880); *Lezioni di analisi infinitesimale,* 2 vols. (Pisa, 1907–1915); and *Lezioni sulla teoria delle funzioni sferiche e delle funzioni di Bessel* (Pisa, 1912). There are articles by Dini in *Annali di matematica pura ed applicata, Atti della Reale Accademia dei Lincei, Comptes rendus hebdomadaires des séances de l'Académie des sciences, Giornale di matematiche,* and *Rendiconti del circolo matematico di Palermo.* The work on uniform functions, "Alcuni teoremi sulle funzioni di una variabile complessa," is in *Collectanea mathematica in memoriam Dominici Chelini* (Milan, 1881), pp. 258–276.

II. SECONDARY LITERATURE. Gino Loria examined the life and works of Dini in "Gli scienziati italiani dall'inizio del medio evo ai nostri giorni," in *Repertorio . . . diretto da Aldo Mieli,* I, pt. 1 (Rome, 1921), pp. 137–150. This work includes a complete bibliography of Dini's works (62 titles), a reproduction of an autograph letter, and several details concerning his political activity. Luigi Bianchi, a student of Dini's, wrote "Commemorazione del socio Ulisse Dini," in *Atti della Reale Accademia dei Lincei,* **28** (1919), 154–163; and the article in the *Enciclopedia Treccani,* XII, 909. See also W. B. Ford, "A Brief Account of the Life and Work of the Late Professor Ulisse Dini," in *Bulletin of the American Mathematical Society,* **26** (1920), 173–177.

PIERRE SPEZIALI

DINOSTRATUS (*fl.* Athens, fourth century B.C.)

According to Proclus (*Commentary on Euclid, Book I;* Friedlein, ed., 67.8–12), "Amyclas of Heraclea, one of the associates of Plato, and Menaechmus, a pupil of Eudoxus who had also studied with Plato, and his brother Dinostratus made the whole of geometry still more perfect." Dinostratus therefore lived in the middle of the fourth century B.C., and although there is no direct evidence his Platonic associations point to Athens as the scene of his activities. He must have ranged over the whole field of geometry, although only one of his achievements is recorded and the record bristles with difficulties. This is the application of the curve known as the quadratrix to the squaring of the circle.

The evidence rests solely on Pappus (*Collection,* IV. 30; Hultsch ed., 250.33–252.3), whose account is probably derived from Sporus (third century). Pappus says: "For the squaring of the circle there was used by Dinostratus, Nicomedes and certain other later persons a certain curve which took its name from this property; for it is called by them square-forming" (τετραγωνίζουσα *sc.* γραμμή, quadratrix). The curve was not discovered by Dinostratus but by Hippias, for Proclus, whose account is derived from Eudemus, says: "Nicomedes trisected any rectilineal angle by means of the conchoidal curves, of which he had handed down the origin, order and properties, being himself the discoverer of their special characteristic. Others have done the same thing by means of the quadratrices of Hippias and Nicomedes" (Friedlein, ed., 272.3–10). It has been usual, following Bretschneider, to deduce that Hippias first discovered the curve and that Dinostratus first applied it to finding a square equal in area to a circle, whence it came to be called quadratrix. It is no objection that Proclus writes of the "quadratrix of Hippias," for we regularly speak of Dinostratus' brother Menaechmus as discovering the parabola and hyperbola, although these terms were not employed until Apollonius; nor is there any significance in the plural "quadratrices." It is a more serious objection that Proclus (Friedlein, ed., 356.11) says that different mathematicians have been accustomed to discourse about curves, showing the special property of each kind, as "Hippias with the quadratrices," for this suggests that Hippias may have written a whole treatise on such curves, and he could hardly have failed to omit the circle-squaring aspect; against this may be set the fact that the angle-dividing property of the curve is more fundamental than its circle-squaring property. It is also odd that Proclus does not mention the name of Dinostratus in connection with the quadratrix; nor does Iamblichus, as quoted by Simplicius (*On the Categories of Aristotle,* 7; Kalbfleisch, ed., 192.15–25), who writes of the quadrature of the circle as having been effected by the spiral of Archimedes, the quadratrix of Nicomedes, the "sister of the cochloid" invented by Apollonius, and a curve arising from double motion found by

Carpus. Despite all these difficulties, posterity has firmly associated the name of Dinostratus with the quadrature of the circle by means of the quadratrix.

Pappus, IV.30 (Hultsch, ed., 252.5–25), describes how the curve is formed. Let *ABCD* be a square and *BED* a quadrant of a circle with center *A*. If the radius of the circle moves uniformly from *AB* to *AD* and in the same time the line *BC* moves, parallel to its original position, from *BC* to *AD*, then at any given time the intersection of the moving radius and the moving straight line will determine a point *F*. The path traced by *F* is the quadratrix. If *G* is the point where it meets *AD*, it can be shown by *reductio per impossibile* (Pappus, IV.31–32; Hultsch, ed., 256.4–258.11) that

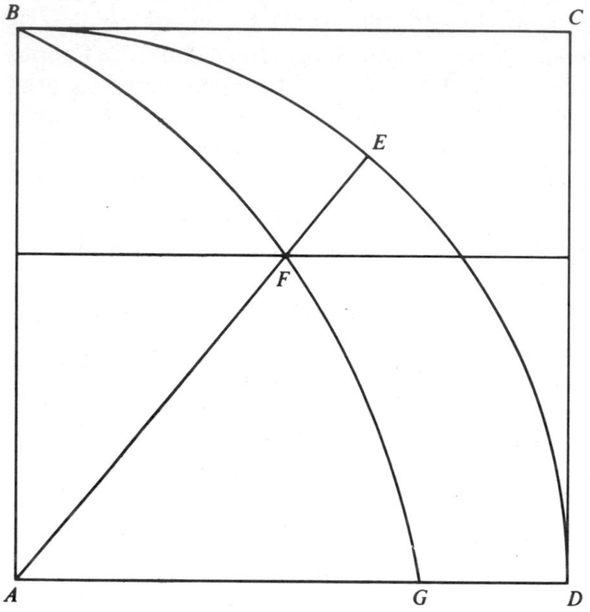

FIGURE 1

$$\text{arc } BED:AB = AB:AG.$$

This gives the circumference of the circle, the area of which may be deduced by using the proposition, later proved by Archimedes, that the area of a circle is equal to a right triangle in which the base is equal to the circumference and the perpendicular to the radius. If Dinostratus rectified the circle in the manner of Pappus' proof, it is one of the earliest examples in Greek mathematics of the indirect proof *per impossibile* so widely employed by Euclid. (Pythagoras before him is said to have used the method to prove the irrationality of $\sqrt{2}$ and Eudoxus must have used it for his proofs by exhaustion.) It is not out of the question that a mathematician of the Platonic school could have proved Archimedes, *Measurement of a Circle*, proposition 1, which is also proved *per impossibile*, but he may only have suspected its truth without a rigorous proof.

According to Pappus, IV.31 (Hultsch, ed., 252.26–256.3), Sporus was displeased with the quadrature because the very thing that the construction was designed to achieve was assumed in the hypothesis. If *G* is known, the circle can indeed be rectified and thence squared, but Sporus asks two questions: How is it possible to make the two points moving from *B* reach their destinations at the same time unless we first know the ratio of the straight line *AB* to the circumference *BED?* Since in the limit the radius and the moving line do not intersect but coincide, how can *G* be found without knowing the ratio of the circumference to the straight line? Pappus endorsed these criticisms. Most modern mathematicians have agreed that the second is valid, for *G* can be found only by closer and closer approximation, but some, such as Hultsch, have thought that modern instrument makers would have no difficulty in making the moving radius and the moving straight line reach *AD* together. It is difficult, however, as Heath argues, to see how this could be done without, at some point, a conversion of circular into rectilinear motion, which assumes a knowledge of the thing sought. Both objections would therefore seem to be valid.

BIBLIOGRAPHY

For further reading see the following, listed chronologically: C. A. Bretschneider, *Die Geometrie und die Geometer von Euklides* (Leipzig, 1870), pp. 95–96, 153–155; Paul Tannery, "Pour l'histoire des lignes et des surfaces courbes dans l'antiquité," in *Bulletin des sciences mathématiques et astronomiques,* 2nd ser., **7**, pt. 1 (1883), 278–284; G. J. Allman, *Greek Geometry From Thales to Euclid* (Dublin, 1889), pp. 180–193; Gino Loria, *Le scienze esatte nell'antica Grecia,* 2nd ed. (Milan, 1914), pp. 160–164; T. L. Heath, *A History of Greek Mathematics,* I (Oxford, 1921), 225–230; Ivor Thomas, *Selections Illustrating the History of Greek Mathematics,* I (London-Cambridge, Mass., 1939), 334–347; B. L. van der Waerden, *Science Awakening* (Groningen, 1954), pp. 191–193; and Robert Böker, in *Der kleine Pauly,* I (Stuttgart, 1964), cols. 1429–1431.

IVOR BULMER-THOMAS

DIOCLES (second century B.C. [?])

Nothing is known of the life of this Greek mathematician, but he must have lived after Archimedes (*d.* 212 B.C.) and before Geminus of Rhodes (*fl.* 70 B.C.). Eutocius, a Byzantine mathematician of the fifth and sixth centuries, preserved two fragments of Diocles' work *On Burning Mirrors* in his commentary on Archimedes' *On the Sphere and Cylinder.*

One of these fragments deals with the solution of the problem of the two mean proportionals by means of the cissoid, which Diocles invented. The problem of doubling the cube, the celebrated Delian problem of ancient geometry, had been the subject of mathematical investigation at least as early as the fifth century B.C. Hippocrates of Chios is reported to have discovered that a solution could be found if a way could be devised for finding two mean proportionals in continued proportion between two straight lines, the greater of which line is double the lesser. The question was studied by Plato's Academy and a mechanical solution is even attributed, erroneously, to Plato. Before Diocles, solutions were offered by Archytas, Eudoxus, Menaechmus, Eratosthenes, Nicomedes, Apollonius, Hero, and Philo of Byzantium. All of these, and later solutions, are preserved by Eutocius.

Proposition 4 of Book II of Archimedes' *On the Sphere and Cylinder* presents the problem of how to cut a given sphere by a plane in such a way that the volumes of the segments are in a given ratio to one another. Diocles' solution to the problem, as given in the fragment preserved by Eutocius, was an ingenious geometrical construction that satisfied, by means of the intersection of an ellipse and a hyperbola, the three simultaneous relations which hold in Archimedes' proposition.

Diocles' work *On Burning Mirrors,* judging from the time at which he lived and the work of his predecessors, must have been of considerable scope. It can be assumed that it discussed concave mirrors in the forms of a sphere, a paraboloid, and a surface described by the revolution of an ellipse about its major axis. Apollonius of Perga, a mathematician who was born about 262 B.C., had earlier written a book on burning mirrors, but Arabic tradition associated Diocles with the discovery of the parabolic burning mirror. The Greek *Fragmentum mathematicum Bobiense* contains a fragment of a treatise on the parabolic burning mirror, and some authorities have attributed this work to Diocles. Others consider this attribution very doubtful. William of Moerbeke translated into Latin the fragments of Diocles on mean proportionals and the division of the sphere as a part of his general translation from the Greek of the works of Archimedes and Eutocius' commentaries on them.

BIBLIOGRAPHY

The fragments of Diocles' work can be found in *Archimedis Opera omnia cum commentariis Eutocii iterum,* J. L. Heiberg, ed., III (Leipzig, 1915), 66–70, 160–176.

On Diocles or his work, see Moritz Cantor, *Vorlesungen über Geschichte der Mathematik,* I (Stuttgart, 1907, repr. New York, 1965), 350, 354–355; Thomas Heath, *A History of Greek Mathematics,* 2 vols. (Oxford, 1960), I, 264–266; II, 47–48, 200–203; George Sarton, *Introduction to the History of Science,* I (Baltimore, 1927), 183; Moritz Steinschneider, *Die europäischen Uebersetzungen aus dem arabischen bis Mitte des 17. Jahrhunderts* (Graz, 1965), p. 17; and E. Wiedemann, "Ibn al Haitams Schrift über parabolische Hohlspiegel," in *Bibliotheca mathematica,* 3rd ser., **10** (1909–1910), 202.

KARL H. DANNENFELDT

DIONIS DU SÉJOUR, ACHILLE-PIERRE (*b.* Paris, France, 11 January 1734; *d.* Vernou, near Fontainebleau, France, 22 August 1794)

The son of Louis-Achille Dionis du Séjour, counselor at the *cour des aides* in Paris, and of Geneviève-Madeleine Héron, Achille-Pierre studied in Paris at the Collège Louis-le-Grand and then at the Faculté de Droit. A counselor at the Parlement of Paris in 1758, he sat as a member of the Chambre des Enquêtes beginning in 1771 and in 1779 moved to the Grand Chambre, where he was appreciated for his simplicity, his liberalism, and his humanity. He devoted the bulk of his leisure time to mathematical and astronomical research, which brought him election as *associé libre* of the Académie des Sciences on 26 June 1765. (Dionis du Séjour maintained this title at the time of the reorganization of 1785 but resigned it on 14 July 1786 in order to be eligible for election as associate member of the physics section.) His cordiality, his devotion to the cause of scientific research, and his philosophic spirit brought him many friendships; and the quality of his writings earned the respect of Lagrange, Laplace, and Condorcet, among others.

With his friend and future colleague Mathieu-Bernard Goudin, Dionis du Séjour published a treatise on the analytical geometry of plane curves (1756) and a compendium of theoretical astronomy (1761). From 1764 to 1783 he wrote a series of important memoirs on the application of the most recent analytic methods to the study of the principal astronomical phenomena (eclipses, occultations, reductions of observations, determination of planetary orbits, etc.). Revised and coordinated, these memoirs were reprinted in the two-volume *Traité analytique des mouvements apparents des corps célestes* (1786–1789), of which Delambre gives a detailed analysis. The *Traité* is completed by two works, one on comets (1775), in which he demonstrates the near impossibility of a collision of one of these heavenly bodies with the earth, and the other on the varying appearance of the rings of Saturn (1776). All these works are dominated by an obvious concern for rigor and by a great familiarity with analytical methods; if the prolixity of the developments and the complexity of the calculations rendered them of little use at the time, their reexamination in the light of present possibilities of calculation would certainly be fruitful.

In pure mathematics, beyond the study of plane curves, Dionis du Séjour was interested in the theory of the solution of equations, an area where his works have been outclassed by those of his contemporaries Bézout and Lagrange. Finally, in collaboration with Condorcet and Laplace, he undertook a systematic inquiry to determine the population of France. Utilizing the list of communes appearing in the Cassini map of France and the most recent information furnished by the civil registers, this inquiry was based on the empirical hypothesis that the annual number of births in a given population is approximately one twenty-sixth of the total of that population.

The Revolution interrupted Dionis du Séjour's scientific activity. Elected a deputy of the Paris nobility on 10 May 1789, he sat in the National (later Constituent) Assembly until its duties were completed on 30 September 1791. Resigning later from the office of judge of a Paris tribunal, to which post he had been elected on 30 November 1791, he retired to his rich holdings in Argeville, a commune in Vernou, near Fontainebleau, where he died without issue almost a month after 9 Thermidor, having experienced, it seems, a period of difficulties and quite justifiable anxiety.

BIBLIOGRAPHY

I. ORIGINAL WORKS. A list of Dionis du Séjour's papers is in *Table générale des matières contenues dans l'Histoire et dans les Mémoires de l'Académie royale des sciences,* VII-X (Paris, 1768-1809).

His books are *Traité des courbes algébriques* (Paris, 1756), written with Goudin; *Recherches sur la gnomonique, les rétrogradations des planètes et les éclipses du soleil* (Paris, 1761), written with Goudin; *Recueil de problèmes astronomiques résolus analytiquement,* 3 vols. (Paris, 1769-1778), a collection of his papers on astronomy published in the *Histoire de l'Académie royale des sciences; Essai sur les comètes en général; et particulièrement sur celles qui peuvent approcher de l'orbite de la terre* (Paris, 1775); *Essai sur les phénomènes relatifs aux disparitions périodiques de l'anneau de Saturne* (Paris, 1776); *Traité analytique des mouvements apparents des corps célestes,* 2 vols. (Paris, 1786-1789); and *Traité des propriétés communes à toutes les courbes, suivi d'un mémoire sur les éclipses du soleil* (Paris, 1788), written with Goudin.

II. SECONDARY LITERATURE. It should be noted that in any alphabetical listing Dionis du Séjour's name sometimes appears as Dionis, sometimes as Du Séjour, and sometimes as Séjour. On Dionis du Séjour or his work, see the following (listed chronologically): J. S. Bailly, *Histoire de l'astronomie moderne,* III (Paris, 1782), index under Séjour; J. de Lalande, articles in *Magasin encyclopédique ou Journal des sciences, des lettres et des arts,* **1** (1795), 31-34; in *Connaissance des temps . . . pour l'année sextile VIIe de la République* (May 1797), 312-317; and in *Bibliographie astronomique* (Paris, 1803), pp. 750-752 and index; Nicollet, in Michaud, ed., *Biographie universelle,* XI (1814), 401-403, and in new ed., XI (1855), 90-91; J. B. Delambre, *Histoire de l'astronomie au XVIIIe siècle* (Paris, 1827), pp. xxiii-xxiv, 709-735; R. Grant, *History of Physical Astronomy* (London, 1852), pp. 232, 267; J. Hoefer, in *Nouvelle biographie générale,* XV (Paris, 1858), 295-296; Poggendorff, I, 574-575; A. Maury, *L'ancienne Académie des sciences* (Paris, 1864), see index; J. Bertrand, *L'Académie des sciences et les académiciens de 1666 à 1793* (Paris, 1869), pp. 311-312; J. C. Houzeau and A. Lancaster, *Bibliographie générale de l'astronomie,* 3 vols. (Brussels, 1882-1889; repr. London, 1964) I, pt. 2, 1301, 1313, 1341, II, cols. 385, 483, 1078, 1083, 1150, 1207; J. F. Robinet, A. Robert, and J. le Chapelain, *Dictionnaire historique et biographique de la Révolution et de l'Empire,* I (Paris, 1899), 643-644; F. Matagrin, *Vernou et le château d'Argeville* (Melun, 1905), pp. 128-129; A. Douarche, *Les tribunaux civils de Paris pendant la Révolution,* 2 vols. (Paris, 1905-1907), see index; N. Nielsen, *Géomètres français sous la Révolution* (Copenhagen, 1929), pp. 73-79; and Roman d'Amat, in *Dictionnaire de biographie française,* XI (1967), 390-391.

RENÉ TATON

DIONYSODORUS (*fl.* Caunus [?], Asia Minor, third-second centuries B.C.)

The Dionysodorus who is the subject of this article is recorded by Eutocius as having solved, by means of the intersection of a parabola and a hyperbola, the cubic equation to which (in effect) Archimedes had reduced the problem of so cutting a sphere by a plane that the volumes of the segments are in a given ratio. Of the many bearers of this name in Greek literature, he has usually been identified with the Dionysodorus who is described by Strabo (XII, 3,16) as a mathematician and is included among the men noteworthy for their learning who were born in the region of Amisene in Pontus, on the shore of the Black Sea. But since Wilhelm Cronert published in 1900 hitherto unknown fragments from the Herculaneum roll no. 1044, and especially since Wilhelm Schmidt commented on them in 1901, it has seemed more probable that he should be identified with Dionysodorus of

Caunus, son of a father of the same name, who was probably an Epicurean. One fragment (no. 25) indicates that this Dionysodorus succeeded Eudemus as the teacher of Philonides, and another (no. 7) that Philonides published some lectures by Dionysodorus. Eudemus is obviously the Eudemus of Pergamum to whom Apollonius dedicated the first two books of his *Conics,* and Philonides is the mathematician to whom Apollonius asked Eudemus to show the second book. When we recollect that Caunus in Caria is near Apollonius' birthplace, Perga in Pamphylia, it is clear that this Dionysodorus moved in distinguished mathematical company and would have been capable of the elegant construction that Eutocius has recorded. If this identification is correct, he would have lived in the second half of the third century B.C. If he is to be identified with Dionysodorus of Amisene, all that can be said about his date is that he wrote before Diocles, say before 100 B.C. It is clear that he is not the same person as the geometer Dionysodorus of Melos, who is mentioned by Pliny (*Natural History,* II, 112.248) as having arranged for a message to be put in his tomb saying that he had been to the center of the earth and had found the earth's radius to measure 42,000 stades. Strabo, indeed, specifically distinguishes them.

In the passage quoted by Eutocius, *Commentarii in libros II De sphaera et cylindro* (Archimedes, Heiberg ed., III, 152.28–160.2), Dionysodorus says: Let AB be a diameter of a given sphere which it is required to cut in the given ratio $CD:DE$. Let BA be produced to F so that $AF = AB/2$, let AG be drawn perpendicular to AB so that $FA:AG = CE:ED$, and let H be taken on AG produced so that $AH^2 = FA \cdot AG$. With axis FB let a parabola be drawn having AG as its parameter; it will pass through H. Let it be FHK where BK is perpendicular to AB. Through G let there be drawn a hyperbola having FB and BK as asymptotes. Let it cut the parabola at L—it will, of course, cut at a second point also—and let LM be drawn perpendicular to AB. Then, proves Dionysodorus, a plane drawn through M perpendicular to AB will cut the sphere into segments whose volumes have the ratio $CD:DE$.

It will be more instructive to turn the procedure into modern notation rather than reproduce the prolix geometrical proofs. In his treatise *On the Sphere and Cylinder,* II, 2 and 4, Archimedes proves geometrically that if r be the radius of a sphere and h the height of one of the segments into which it is divided by a plane, the volume of the segment is equal to a cone with the same base as the segment and height

$$h \cdot \frac{3r - h}{2r - h}.$$

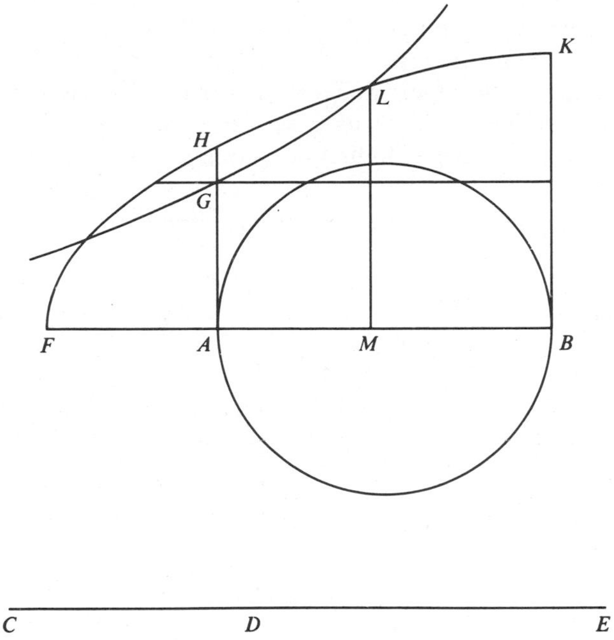

FIGURE 1

If h' is the height of the other segment, and the volumes of the segments stand in the ratio $m:n$, then

$$nh \cdot \frac{3r - h}{2r - h} = mh' \cdot \frac{3r - h'}{2r - h'}.$$

Eliminating h' by the relationship $h + h' = 2r$, we obtain the cubic equation in the usual modern form

$$h^3 - 3h^2r + \frac{4m}{m + n} r^3 = 0.$$

If we substitute $x = 2r - h (= h')$ we may put the equation in the form solved by Dionysodorus:

$$4r^2 : x^2 = (3r - x) : \frac{n}{m + n} r.$$

Dionysodorus solves it as the intersection of the parabola

$$y^2 = \frac{n}{m + n} r(3r - x)$$

and the hyperbola

$$xy = \frac{n}{m + n} 2r^2.$$

It seems probable (despite Schmidt) that this mathematician is the same Dionysodorus who is mentioned by Hero as the author of the book Περὶ τῆς σπείρας, "On the Tore" (*Heronis opera omnia,* H. Schöne, ed., III, 128.1–130.11), in which he gave a formula for the volume of a torus. If BC is a diameter of the circle $BDCE$ and if BA is perpendicular to the straight line HAG in the same plane, when AB makes a complete revolution around *HAG,* the circle generates a spire or torus whose volume, says Dionysodorus, bears to the cylinder having *HG* for its axis and *EH* for the radius of its base the same ratio as the circle *BDCE* bears to half the parallelogram *DEHG.*

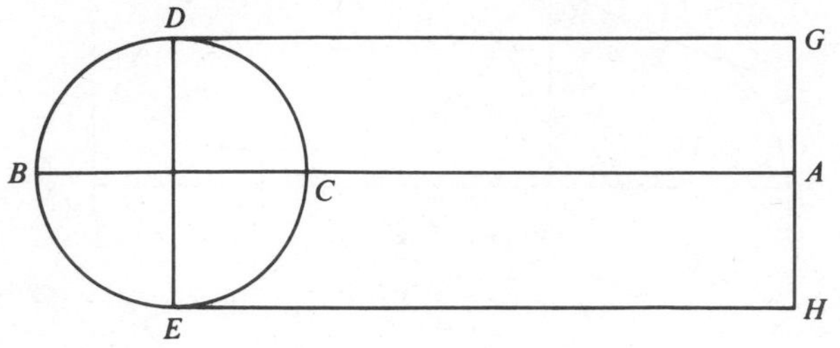

FIGURE 2

That is to say, if r is the radius of the circle and $EH = a$,

$$\frac{\text{Volume of torus}}{\pi a^2 \cdot 2r} = \frac{\pi r^2}{a/2 \cdot 2r},$$

whence

$$\text{Volume of torus} = 2\pi a \cdot \pi r^2.$$

In an example, apparently taken from Dionysodorus, $r = 6$ and $a = 14$, and Hero notes that if the torus be straightened out and treated as a cylinder, it will have 12 as the diameter of its base and 88 as its length, so that its volume is $9956\tfrac{4}{7}$. This is equivalent to saying that the volume of the torus is equal to the area of the generating circle multiplied by the length of the path traveled by its center of gravity, and it is the earliest example of what we know as Guldin's theorem (although originally enunciated by Pappus).

Among the inventors of different forms of sundials in antiquity Vitruvius (IX, 8; Krohn, ed., 218.8) mentions a Dionysodorus as having left a conical form of sundial—"Dionysodorus conum (reliquit)." It would no doubt, as Frank W. Cousins asserts, stem from the hemispherical sundial of Berossus, and the cup would be a portion of a right cone, with the nodal point of the style on the axis pointing to the celestial pole. Although there can be no certainty, there seems equally no good reason for not attributing this invention to the same Dionysodorus; it would fit in with his known use of conic sections.

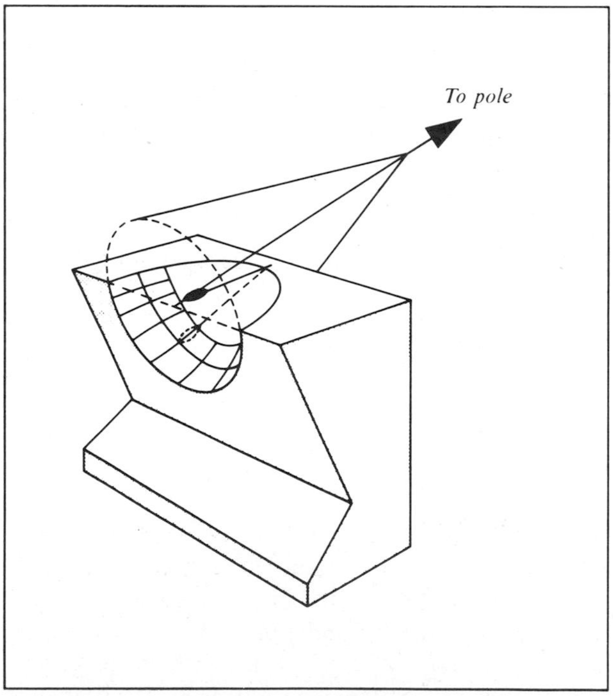

FIGURE 3. Conjectural reconstruction of Dionysodorus' conical sundial.

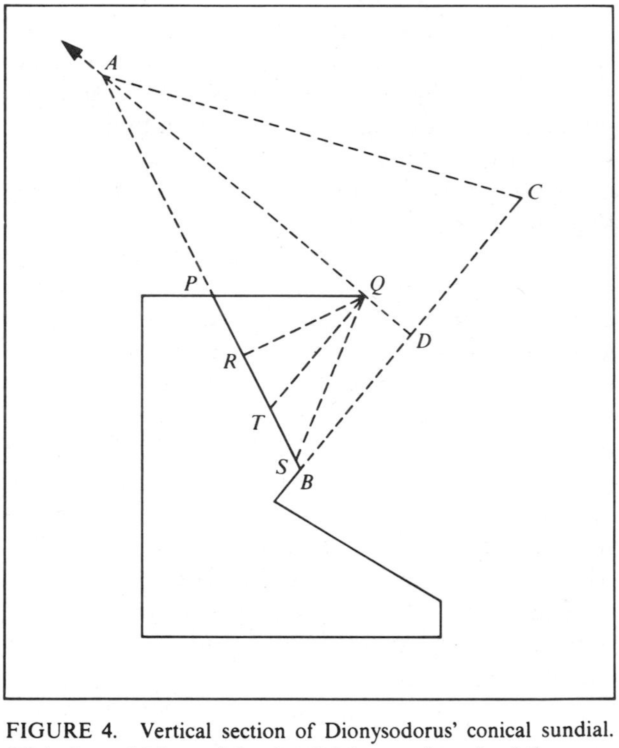

FIGURE 4. Vertical section of Dionysodorus' conical sundial. *PQ* is the style, its nodal point *Q* lying on the axis of the cone, which points to the celestial pole. When the sun is overhead at the equator, the nodal point casts a shadow at *T*, when farthest south at *R*, and when farthest north at *S*.

BIBLIOGRAPHY

On Dionysodorus or his work, see Eutocius, *Commentarii in libros II De sphaera et cylindro,* in Archimedes, Heiberg ed., III, 152.27–160.2; Hero of Alexandria, *Metrica,* II, 13—*Heronis opera omnia,* H. Schöne, ed., III, 128.1–130.11; Wilhelm Cronert, "Der Epikur Philonides," in *Sitzungsberichte der K. Preussischen Akademie der Wissenschaften zu Berlin* (1900), 942–959, esp. frag. 7, p. 945, and frag. 25, p. 952. Wilhelm Schmidt, "Über den griechischen Mathematiker Dionysodorus," in *Bibliotheca mathematica,* 3rd ser., **4** (1904), 321–325; Sir Thomas Heath, *A History of Greek Mathematics,* II (Oxford, 1921), 46, 218–219, 334–335; Ivor Thomas, *Selections Illustrating the History of Greek Mathematics,* II (London–Cambridge, Mass., 1941), pp. 135, 163, 364, 481; René R. J. Rohr, *Les cadrans solaires* (Paris, 1965), pp. 31–32, trans. by G. Godin as *Sundials: History, Theory and Practice* (Toronto–Buffalo, 1970), pp. 12, 13; and Frank W. Cousins, *Sundials* (London, 1969), pp. 13, 30 (correcting Cdynus to Caunus).

IVOR BULMER-THOMAS

DIOPHANTUS OF ALEXANDRIA (*fl.* A.D. 250)

We know virtually nothing about the life of Diophantus. The dating of his activity to the middle of the third century derives exclusively from a letter of Michael Psellus (eleventh century). The letter reports that Anatolius, the bishop of Laodicea since A.D. 270, had dedicated a treatise on Egyptian computation to his friend Diophantus. The subject was one to which, as Psellus states, Diophantus himself had given close attention.[1] This dating is in accord with the supposition that the Dionysius to whom Diophantus dedicated his masterpiece, *Arithmetica,* is St. Dionysius, who, before he became bishop of Alexandria in A.D. 247, had led the Christian school there since 231.[2] An arithmetical epigram of the *Greek Anthology* provides the only further information (if the data correspond to facts): Diophantus married at the age of thirty-three and had a son who died at forty-two, four years before his father died at the age of eighty-four.[3] That is all we can learn of his life, and relatively few of his writings survive. Of these four are known: *Moriastica, Porismata, Arithmetica,* and *On Polygonal Numbers.*

Moriastica. The *Moriastica,* which must have treated computation with fractions, is mentioned only once, in a scholium to Iamblichus' commentary on Nicomachus' *Arithmetica.*[4] Perhaps the *Moriastica* does not constitute an original treatise but only repeats what Diophantus wrote about the symbols of fractions and how to calculate with them in his *Arithmetica.*

Porismata. In several places in the *Arithmetica* Diophantus refers to propositions which he had proved "in the *Porismata.*" It is not certain whether it was—as seems more probable—an independent work, as Hultsch and Heath assume, or whether such lemmas were contained in the original text of the *Arithmetica* and became lost with the commentators; the latter position is taken by Tannery, to whom we owe the critical edition of Diophantus.

Arithmetica. The *Arithmetica* is not a work of theoretical arithmetic in the sense understood by the Pythagoreans or Nicomachus. It deals, rather, with logistic, the computational arithmetic used in the solution of practical problems. Although Diophantus knew elementary number theory and contributed new theorems to it, his *Arithmetica* is a collection of problems. In the algebraic treatment of the basic equations, Diophantus, by a sagacious choice of suitable auxiliary unknowns and frequently brilliant artifices, succeeded in reducing the degree of the equation (the unknowns reaching as high as the sixth power) and the number of unknowns (as many as ten) and thus in arriving at a solution. The *Arithmetica* is therefore essentially a logistical work, but with the difference that Diophantus' problems are purely numerical with the single exception of problem V, 30.[5] In his solutions Diophantus showed himself a master in the field of indeterminate analysis, and apart from Pappus he was the only great mathematician during the decline of Hellenism.

Extent of the Work. At the close of the introduction, Diophantus speaks of the thirteen books into which he had divided the work; only six, however, survive. The loss of the remaining seven books must have occurred early, since the oldest manuscript (in Madrid), from the thirteenth century, does not contain them. Evidence for this belief may be found in the fact that Hypatia commented on only the first six books (end of the fourth century). A similarity may be found in the *Conics* of Apollonius, of which Eutocius considered only the first four books. But whereas the latter missing material can be supplied in great part from Arabic sources, there are no such sources for the *Arithmetica,* although it is certain that Arabic versions did exist.

Western Europe learned about a Diophantus manuscript for the first time through a letter to Bianchini from Regiomontanus (15 February 1464), who reported that he had found one in Venice; it contained, however, not the announced thirteen books but only six. In his inaugural address at Padua at about the same time, Regiomontanus spoke of the great importance of this find, since it contained the whole "flower of arithmetic, the *ars rei et census,* called algebra by the Arabs."

Reports concerning the supposed existence of the complete *Arithmetica* are untrustworthy.[6] The question, then, is where one should place the gap: after the sixth book or within the existing books? The quadratic equations with one unknown are missing; Diophantus promised in the introduction to treat them, and many examples show that he was familiar with their solution. A section dealing with them seems

DIOPHANTUS OF ALEXANDRIA

to be missing between the first and second books. Here and at other places[7] a great deal has fallen into disorder through the commentators or transcription. For example, the first seven problems of the second book fit much better with the problems of the first, as do problems II, 17, and II, 18. As for what else may have been contained in the missing books, there is no precise information, although one notes the absence, for example, of the quadratic equation system (1) $x^2 \pm y^2 = a$; (2) $xy = b$, which had already appeared in Babylonian mathematics. Diophantus could surely solve this as well as the system he treated in problems I, 27, 30: (1) $x \pm y = a$; (2) $xy = b$, a system likewise known by the Babylonians.

Since in one of the manuscripts the six books are apportioned into seven and the writing on polygonal numbers could be counted as the eighth, it has been supposed that the missing portion was not particularly extensive. This is as difficult to determine as how much—considering the above-mentioned problems, which are not always simple—Diophantus could have increased the difficulty of the problems.[8]

Introduction to the Techniques of Algebra. In the introduction, Diophantus first explains for the beginner the structure of the number series and the names of the powers up to n^6. They are as follows:

n^2 is called square number, *τετράγωνος* (*ἀριθμός*)
n^3 is called cube number, *κύβος*
n^4 is called square-square number, *δυναμοδύναμις*
n^5 is called square-cube number, *δυναμόκυβος*
n^6 is called cube-cube number, *κυβόκυβος*

The term n^1, however, is expressed as the side of a square number, *πλευρὰ τοῦ τετραγώνου*.[9]

Diophantus introduced symbols for these powers; they were also used—with the exception of the second power—for the powers of the unknowns. The symbols are: for x^2, Δ^{Υ}(*δύναμις*); for x^3, K^{Υ}; for x^4, $\Delta^{\Upsilon}\Delta$; for x^5, ΔK^{Υ}; and for x^6, $K^{\Upsilon}K$. The unknown x, "an indeterminate multitude of units," is simply called "number" (*ἀριθμός*); it is reproduced as an s-shaped symbol, similar to the way it appears in the manuscripts.[10] No doubt the symbol originally appeared as a final sigma with a cross line, approximately like this: ϛ; a similar sign is found (before Diophantus) in a papyrus of the early second century.[11] Numbers which are not coefficients of unknowns are termed "units" (*μοναδες*) and are indicated by $\overset{\circ}{M}$. The symbols for the powers of the unknowns are also employed for the reciprocal values $1/x$, $1/x^2$, etc., in which case an additional index, $^{\chi}$, marks them as fractions. Their names are patterned on those of the ordinals: for example, $1/x$ is the xth (*ἀριθμοστόν*), $1/x^2$ the x^2th (*δυναμοστόν*), and so on. All these symbols—among which is one for the "square number," $\square^{os}$(*τετράγωνος*)—were read as the full words for which they stand, as is indicated by the added grammatical endings, such as ϛ^{οι} and ϛϛ^{οι} = *ἀριθμοί*. Diophantus then sets forth in tabular form for the various species (*εἶδος*) of powers multiplication rules for the operations $x^m \cdot x^n$ and $x^m \cdot x^{1/n}$; thus—as he states—the divisions of the species are also defined. The sign for subtraction, ⋔, is also new; it is described in the text as an inverted "psi." The figure is interpreted as the paleographic abbreviation of the verb *λείπειν* ("to want").

Since Diophantus did not wish to write a textbook, he gives only general indications for computation: one should become practiced in all operations with the various species and "should know how to add positive ('forthcoming') and negative ('wanting') terms with different coefficients to other terms, themselves either positive or likewise partly positive and partly negative, and how to subtract from a combination of positive and negative terms other terms either positive or likewise partly positive and partly negative."[12] Only two rules are stated explicitly: a "wanting" multiplied by a "wanting" yields a "forthcoming" and a "forthcoming" multiplied by a "wanting" yields a "wanting." Only in the treatment of the linear equations does Diophantus go into more detail: one should "add the negative terms on both sides, until the terms on both sides are positive, and then again . . . subtract like from like until one term only is left on each side."[13] It is at this juncture that he promised that he would later explain the technique to be used if two species remain on one side. There is no doubt that he had in mind here the three forms of the quadratic equation in one unknown.

Diophantus employs the usual Greek system of numerals, which is grouped into myriads; he merely—as the manuscripts show—separates the units place of the myriads from that of the thousands by means of a point. One designation of the fractions, however, is new; it is used if the denominator is a long number or a polynomial. In this case the word *μορίου* (or *ἐν μορίῳ*), in the sense of "divided by" (literally, "of the part"), is inserted between numerator and denominator. Thus, for example, our expression $(2x^3 + 3x^2 + x)/(x^2 + 2x + 1)$ appears (VI, 19) as

$$K^{\Upsilon}\bar{\beta}\ \Delta^{\Upsilon}\ \bar{\gamma}\ ϛ\ \bar{\alpha}\ \textit{ἐν μορίῳ}\ \Delta^{\Upsilon}\bar{\alpha}\ ϛ\ \bar{\beta}\ \overset{\circ}{M}\ \bar{\alpha}.$$

One sees that the addends are simply juxtaposed without any plus sign between them. Similarly, since brackets had not yet been invented, the negative members had to be brought together behind the minus symbol: thus, $12 - 1/x - 14x = \overset{\circ}{M}\overline{\iota\beta}$ ⋔ ϛ$^{\chi}$ $\bar{\alpha}$ϛ $\overline{\iota\delta}$

DIOPHANTUS OF ALEXANDRIA

(VI, 22). The symbolism that Diophantus introduced for the first time, and undoubtedly devised himself, provided a short and readily comprehensible means of expressing an equation: for example, $630x^2 + 73x = 6$ appears as $\Delta^{\Upsilon}\overline{\chi\lambda}$ ϛ $\overline{o\gamma}$ ἴσ. $\overset{o}{M}\bar{\varsigma}$ (VI, 8). Since an abbreviation is also employed for the word "equals" (ἴσος),[14] Diophantus took a fundamental step from verbal algebra toward symbolic algebra.

The Problems of the Arithmetica. The six books of the *Arithmetica* present a collection of both determinate and (in particular) indeterminate problems, which are treated by algebraic equations and also by algebraic inequalities. Diophantus generally proceeds from the simple to the more difficult, both in the degree of the equation and in the number of unknowns. However, the books always contain exercises belonging to various groups of problems. Only the sixth book has a unified content. Here all the exercises relate to a right triangle; without regard to dimension, polynomials are formed from the surface, from the sides, and once even from an angle bisector. The first book, with which exercises II, 1–7, ought to be included, contains determinate problems of the first and second degrees. Of the few indeterminate exercises presented there, one (I, 14: $x + y = k \cdot xy$) is transformed into a determinate exercise by choosing numerical values for y and k. The indeterminate exercises I, 22–25, belong to another group; these are the puzzle problems of "giving and taking," such as "one man alone cannot buy"—formulated, to be sure, in numbers without units of measure.[15] The second and all the following books contain only indeterminate problems, beginning with those of the second degree but, from the fourth book on, moving to problems of higher degrees also, which by a clever choice of numerical values can be reduced to a lower degree.[16]

The heterogeneity of the 189 problems treated in the *Arithmetica* makes it impossible to repeat the entire contents here. Many who have worked on it have divided the problems into groups according to the degree of the determinate and indeterminate equations. The compilations of all the problems made by Tannery (II, 287–297), by Loria (pp. 862–874), and especially by Heath (*Diophantus,* pp. 260–266) provide an introductory survey. However, the method of solution that Diophantus adopts often yields new problems that are not immediately evident from the statement of the original problem and that should be placed in a different position by any attempted grouping of the entire contents. Nevertheless, certain groups of exercises clearly stand out, although they do not appear together but are dispersed throughout the work. Among the exercises of indeterminate analysis—Diophantus' own achievements lie in this area—certain groups at least should be cited with individual examples:

I. Polynomials (or other algebraic expressions) to be represented as squares. Among these are:

1. One equation for one unknown:

(II, 23; IV, 31) $ax^2 + bx + c = u^2.$

(VI, 18) $ax^3 + bx^2 + cx + d = u^2.$

(V, 29) $ax^4 + b = u^2.$

(VI, 10) $ax^4 + bx^3 + cx^2 + dx + e = u^2.$

(IV, 18) $x^6 - ax^3 + x + b^2 = u^2.$

One equation for two unknowns:

(V, 7, lemma 1) $xy + x^2 + y^2 = u^2.$

One equation for three unknowns:

(V, 29) $x^4 + y^4 + z^4 = u^2.$

2. Two equations for one unknown ("double equation"):

(II, 11) $a_1x + b_1 = u^2,$ $a_2x + b_2 = v^2.$

(VI, 12) $a_1x^2 + b_1x = u^2,$ $a_2x^2 + b_2x = v^2.$

Two equations for two unknowns:

(II, 24) $(x + y)^2 + x = u^2,$ $(x + y)^2 + y = v^2.$

3. Three equations for three unknowns:

(IV, 19) $xy + 1 = u^2,$ $yz + 1 = v^2,$ $xz + 1 = w^2.$

(II, 34) $x_i^2 + \sum_{k=1}^{3} x_k = u_i^2 \quad (i = 1 \cdots 3).$

(IV, 23) $\prod_{i=1}^{3} x_i - x_k = u_k^2 \quad (k = 1 \cdots 3).$

(V, 21) $\prod_{i=1}^{3} x_i^2 + x_k^2 = u_k^2 \quad (k = 1 \cdots 3).$

4. Four equations for four unknowns:

(III, 19) $\left(\sum_{i=1}^{4} x_i\right)^2 \pm x_k = u_k^2 \quad (k = 1 \cdots 4).$

5. Further variations: In V, 5,[17] to construct six squares for six expressions with three unknowns or six squares for six expressions with four unknowns (IV, 20), etc.

 DIOPHANTUS OF ALEXANDRIA

II. Polynomials to be represented as cube numbers.

1. One equation for one unknown:
   (VI, 17) $x^2 + 2 = u^3$.
   (VI, 1) $x^2 - 4x + 4 = u^3$.
2. Two equations for two unknowns:
   (IV, 26) $xy + x = u^3$, $xy + y = v^3$.
3. Three equations for three unknowns:

$$\text{(V, 15)}\quad \left(\sum_{i=1}^{3} x_i\right)^3 + x_k = u_k^3 \quad (k = 1 \cdots 3).$$

III. To form two polynomials such that one is a square and the other a cube.

1. Two equations for two unknowns:
   (IV, 18) $x^3 + y = u^3$, $y^2 + x = v^2$.
   (VI, 21) $x^3 + 2x^2 + x = u^3$, $2x^2 + 2x = v^2$.
2. Two equations for three unknowns:
   (VI, 17) $xy/2 + z = u^2$, $x + y + z = v^3$.

IV. Given numbers to be decomposed into parts.

1. From the parts to form squares according to certain conditions:
   (V, 9) $1 = x + y$; it is required that $x + 6 = u^2$ and $y + 6 = v^2$.
   (II, 14) $20 = x + y$; it is required that $x + u^2 = v^2$ and $y + u^2 = w^2$.
   (IV, 31) $1 = x + y$; it is required that $(x + 3)\cdot(y + 5) = u^2$.
   (V, 11) $1 = x + y + z$; it is required that $x + 3 = u^2$, $y + 3 = v^2$, and $z + 3 = w^2$.
   (V, 13) $10 = x + y + z$; it is required that $x + y = u^2$, $y + z = v^2$, and $z + x = w^2$.
   (V, 20) $1/4 = \sum_{i=1}^{3} x_i$; it is required that

$$x_i - \left(\sum_{k=1}^{3} x_k\right)^3 = u_i^2 \ (i = 1 \cdots 3).$$

2. From the parts to form cubic numbers:
   (IV, 24) $6 = x + y$; it is required that $xy = u^3 - u$.
   (IV, 25) $4 = x + y + z$; it is required that $xyz = u^3$, whereby $u = (x - y) + (y - z) + (x - z)$.

V. A number is to be decomposed into squares.
(II, 8) $16 = x^2 + y^2$.
(II, 10) $60 = x^2 - y^2$.
(IV, 29) $12 = x^2 + y^2 + z^2 + u^2 + x + y + z + u$.
(V, 9) $13 = x^2 + y^2$, whereby $x^2 > 6$ and $y^2 > 6$.

In the calculation of the last problem Diophantus arrives at the further exercise of finding two squares that lie in the neighborhood of $(51/20)^2$. He terms such a case an "approximation" (παρισότης) or an "inducement of approximation" (ἀγωγὴ τῆς παρισότητος). Further examples of solution by approximation are:

(V, 10) $9 = x^2 + y^2$, whereby $2 < x^2 < 3$. This is the only instance in which Diophantus represents (as does Euclid) a number by a line segment.
(V, 12) $10 = x + y + z$, where $x > 2$, $y > 3$, and $z > 4$.
(V, 13) $20 = x + y + z$, whereby each part <10.
(V, 14) $30 = x^2 + y^2 + z^2 + u^2$, whereby each square <10.

VI. Of the problems formulated in other ways, the following should be mentioned.

(IV, 36) $xy/(x + y) = a$, $yz/(y + z) = b$, and $xz/(x + z) = c$.

(IV, 38) The products

$$x_k \cdot \sum_{i=1}^{3} x_i \quad (k = 1 \cdots 3)$$

are to be a triangular number $u(u + 1)/2$, a square v^2, and a cube w^3, in that order.

(IV, 29) $\sum x_i^2 + \sum x_i = 12 \quad (i = 1 \cdots 4)$.

(IV, 30) $\sum x_i^2 - \sum x_i = 4 \quad (i = 1 \cdots 4)$.

(V, 30) This is the only exercise with units of measure attached to the numbers. It concerns a wine mixture composed of x jugs of one type at five drachmas and y jugs of a better type at eight drachmas. The total price should be $5x + 8y = u^2$, given that $(x + y)^2 = u^2 + 60$.

Methods of Problem-solving. In only a few cases can one recognize generally applicable methods of solution in the computations that Diophantus presents, for he considers each case separately, often obtaining an individual solution by means of brilliant stratagems. He is, however, well aware that there are many solutions. When, as in III, 5 and 15, he obtains two solutions by different means, he is satisfied and does not arrange them in a general solution—which, in any case, it was not possible for him to do.[18] Of course a solution could not be negative, since negative numbers did not yet exist for Diophantus. Thus, in V, 2, he says of the equation $4 = 4x + 20$ that it is absurd (ἄτοπον). The solution need not be a whole number. Such a solution is therefore not a "Diophantine" solution. The only restriction is that the solution must be rational.[19] In the equation $3x + 18 = 5x^2$ (IV, 31), where such is not the case, Diophantus notes: "The equation is not rational" (οὐκ ἔστιν ἡ ἴσωσις ῥητή); and he ponders how the number 5 could be changed so that the quadratic equation would have a rational solution.

There are two circumstances that from the very beginning hampered or even prevented the achievement of a general solution. First, Diophantus can symbolically represent only one unknown; if the problem contains several, he can carry them through the text as "first, second, etc." or as "large, medium, small," or even express several unknowns by means of one. Mostly, however, definite numbers immediately take the place of the unknowns and particularize the problem. The process of calculation becomes particularly opaque because newly appearing unknowns are again and again designated by the same symbol for x.

Second, Diophantus lacked, above all else, a symbol for the general number n. It is described, for example, as "units, as many as you wish" (V, 7, lemma 1; $\overset{\circ}{M}$ ὅσων θέλεις). For instance, nx is termed "x, however great" (II, 9; ϛ ὅσος δήποτε) or "any x" (IV, 39; ἀριθμός τις). Nevertheless, Diophantus did succeed, at least in simple cases, in expressing a general number—in a rather cumbersome way, to be sure. Thus in IV, 39, the equation $3x^2 + 12x + 9 = (3 - nx)^2$ yields $x = (12 + 6n)/(n^2 - 3)$; the description reads "x is a sixfold number increased by twelve, which is divided by the difference by which the square of the number exceeds 3."

Among the paths taken by Diophantus to arrive at his solutions, one can clearly discern several methods:

1. For the determinate linear and quadratic equations there are the usual methods of balancing and completion (see, for example, the introduction and II, 8); in determinate systems, Diophantus solves for one unknown in terms of the other by the first equation and then substitutes this value in the second. For the quadratic equation in two unknowns, he employs the Babylonian normal forms; for the equation in one unknown, the three forms $ax^2 + bx = c$, $ax^2 = bx + c$, and $ax^2 + c = bx$. Moreover, his multiplication of the equation by a can be seen from the criterion for rationality $(b/2)^2 + ac = \square$ or, as the case may be, $(b/2)^2 - ac = \square$.[20]

2. The number of unknowns is reduced. This often happens through the substitution of definite numbers at the beginning, which in linear equations corresponds to the method of "false position." If a sum is to be decomposed into two numbers, for example $x + y = 10$, then Diophantus takes $x = 5 + X$ and $y = 5 - X$. This is also the case with the special cubic equations in IV, 1 and 2.[21]

3. The degree of the equation is reduced. Either a definite number is substituted for one or more unknowns or else a function of the first unknown is substituted.

(V, 7, lemma 1) $xy + x^2 + y^2 = u^2$; y is taken as 1 and u as $x - 2$; this gives $x^2 + x + 1 = (x - 2)^2$; therefore $x = 3/5$ and $y = 1$, or $x = 3$ and $y = 5$.

(V, 29) $x^4 + y^4 + z^4 = u^2$, with $y^2 = 4$ and $z^2 = 9$; therefore $x^4 + 97 = u^2$. With $u = x^2 - 10$ this yields $20x^2 = 3$. Since $20/3$ is not a square, the method of reckoning backward (see below) is employed.

(IV, 37) $60u^3 = v^2$, with $v = 30u$.

(II, 8) $16 - x^2 = (nx - 4)^2$, with $n = 2$. The "cancellation of a species" (see II, 11, solution 2) is possible with $ax^2 + bx + c = u^2$, for example, by substituting $mx + n$ for u and determining the values of m and n for which like powers of x on either side have the same coefficient. Expressions of higher degree are similarly simplified.

(VI, 18) $x^3 + 2 = u^2$, with $x = (X - 1)$, yields $(X - 1)^3 + 2 = u^2$; if $u = (3X/2) + 1$, then $X^3 - 3X^2 + 3X + 1 = (9X^2/4) + 3X + 1$, and hence a first-degree equation.

(VI, 10) $x^4 + 8x^3 + 18x^2 + 12x + 1 = u^2$, where $u = 6x + 1 - x^2$.

4. The double equation. (II, 11) (1) $x + 3 = u^2$, (2) $x + 2 = v^2$; the difference yields $u^2 - v^2 = 1$. Diophantus now employs the formula for right triangles, $m \cdot n = [(m + n)/2]^2 - [(m - n)/2]^2$ and sets the difference $1 = 4 \cdot 1/4$; thus the following results: $u = 17/8$, $v = 15/8$, and $x = 97/64$. Similarly, in II, 13, the difference 1 is given as $2 \cdot 1/2$; in III, 15, $5x + 5 = 5(x + 1)$; and in III, 13, $16x + 4 = 4(4x + 1)$.

5. Reckoning backward is employed if the computation has resulted in an impasse, as above in V, 29; here Diophantus considers how in $20x^2 = 3$ the numbers 20 and 3 have originated. He sets $20 = 2n$ and $3 = n^2 - (y^4 + z^4)$. With $n = y^2 + 4$ and $z^2 = 4$, $3 = 8y^2$ and $20/3 = (y^2 + 4)/4y^2$. Now only $y^2 + 4$ remains to be evaluated as a square. Similar cases include IV, 31, and IV, 18.

6. Method of approximation to limits (V, 9–14). In V, 9, the problem is $13 = u^2 + v^2$, with $u^2 > 6$ and

$v^2 > 6$. First, a square is sought which satisfies these conditions. Diophantus takes $u^2 = 6\frac{1}{2} + (1/x)^2$. The quadruple $26 + 1/y^2$ (with $y = x/2$) should also become a square. Setting $26 + 1/y^2 = (5 + 1/y)^2$ yields $y = 10$, $x^2 = 400$, and $u = 51/20$. Since $13 = 3^2 + 2^2$, Diophantus compares 51/20 with 3 and 2. Thus, $51/20 = 3 - 9/20$ and $51/20 = 2 + 11/20$. Since the sum of the squares is not 13 (but 13 1/200), Diophantus sets $(3 - 9x)^2 + (2 + 11x)^2 = 13$ and obtains $x = 5/101$. From this the two squares $(257/101)^2$ and $(258/101)^2$ result.

7. Method of limits. An example is V, 30. The conditions are $(x^2 - 60)/8 < x < (x^2 - 60)/5$. From this follow $x^2 < 8x + 60$ or $x^2 = 8x + n\ (n < 60)$, and $x^2 > 5x + 60$ or $x^2 = 5x + n\ (n > 60)$. The values (in part incorrect) assigned according to these limits were no doubt found by trial and error. In IV, 31, the condition is $5/4 < x^2 < 2$. After multiplication by 8^2, the result is $80 < (8x)^2 < 128$; consequently $(8x)^2 = 100$ is immediately apparent as a square; therefore $x^2 = 25/16$. In a similar manner, x^6 is interpolated between 8 and 16 in VI, 21.

8. Other artifices appear in the choice of designated quantities in the exercises. Well-known relations of number theory are employed. For example (in IV, 38), $8 \cdot$ triangular number $+ 1 = \square$, therefore $8[n(n + 1)/2] + 1 = (2n + 1)^2$. In IV, 29, Diophantus applies the identity $(m + n)^2 = m^2 + 2mn + n^2$ to the problem $x^2 + x + y^2 + y + z^2 + z + u^2 + u = 12$. Since $x^2 + x + 1/4$ is a square, $4 \cdot 1/4$ must be added to 12; whence the problem becomes one of decomposing 13 into four squares. Other identities employed include:

(II, 34) $[(m - n)/2]^2 + m \cdot n = [(m + n)/2]^2$

(VI, 19) $m^2 + [(m^2 - 1)/2]^2 = [(m^2 + 1)/2]^2$

(II, 30) $m^2 + n^2 \pm 2mn = \square$

(III, 19) $(m^2 - n^2)^2 + (2mn)^2 = (m^2 + n^2)^2$

(V, 15) In this exercise the expressions $(x + y + z)^3 + x$, $(x + y + z)^3 + y$, and $(x + y + z)^3 + z$ are to be transformed into perfect cubes. Hence Diophantus takes $x = 7X^3$ and $(x + y + z) = X$, so the first cube is $(2X)^3$. The other two numbers are $y = 26X^3$ and $z = 63X^3$. From this results $96X^2 = 1$. Here again reckoning backward must be introduced. In I, 22, in the indeterminate equation $2x/3 + z/5 = 3y/4 + x/3 = 4z/5 + y/4$, Diophantus sets $x = 3X$ and $y = 4$. In VI, 16, a rational bisector of an acute angle of a right triangle is to found; the segments into which the bisector divides one of the sides are set at $3x$ and $3 - 3x$, and the other side is set at $4x$. This gives a hypotenuse of $4 - 4x$, since $3x{:}4x = (3 - 3x){:}$ hypotenuse.[22]

In VI, 17, one must find a right triangle for which the area plus the hypotenuse $= u^2$ and the perimeter $= v^3$. Diophantus takes $u = 4$ and the perpendiculars equal to x and 2; therefore, the area is x, the hypotenuse $= 16 - x$, and the perimeter $= 18 = v^3$. By reckoning backward (with $u = m$, rather than $u = 4$) the hypotenuse becomes $m^2 - x$ and the perimeter $m^2 + 2 = v^3$. Diophantus then sets $m = X + 1$ and $v = X - 1$, which yields the cubic equation $X^3 - 3X^2 + 3X - 1 = X^2 + 2X + 3$, the solution of which Diophantus immediately presents (obviously after a factorization): $X = 4$.

It is impossible to give even a partial account of Diophantus' many-sided and often surprising inspirations and artifices. It is impossible, as Hankel has remarked, even after studying the hundredth solution, to predict the form of the hundred-and-first.

On Polygonal Numbers. This work, only fragmentarily preserved and containing little that is original, is immediately differentiated from the *Arithmetica* by its use of geometric proofs. The first section treats several lemmas on polygonal numbers, a subject already long known to the Greeks. The definition of these numbers is new; it is equivalent to that given by Hypsicles, which Diophantus cites. According to this definition, the polygonal number

$$p_a^n = \frac{[(a-2)\cdot(2n-1)+2]^2-(a-4)^2}{8\cdot(a-2)},$$

where a indicates the number of vertices and n the number of "sides" of the polygon.[23] Diophantus then gives the inverse formula, with which one can calculate n from p and a. The work breaks off during the investigation of how many ways a number p can be a polygonal number.

Porisms and Number-theory Lemmas. Diophantus refers explicitly in the *Arithmetica* to three lemmas in a writing entitled "The Porisms," where they were probably proved. They may be reproduced in the following manner:

1. If $x + a = u^2$, $y + a = v^2$, and $xy + a = w^2$, then $v = u + 1$ (V, 3).[24]

2. If $x = u^2$, $y = (u + 1)^2$, and $z = 2 \cdot (x + y) + 2$, then the six expressions $xy + (x + y)$, $xy + z$, $xz + (x + z)$, $xz + y$, $yz + (y + z)$, and $yz + x$ are perfect squares (V, 5).

3. The differences of two cubes are also the sums of two cubes (V, 16). In this case one cannot say whether the proposition was proved.

In solving his problems Diophantus also employs other, likewise generally applicable propositions, such as the identities cited above (see Methods of Problem-solving, §8). Among these are the proposition (III, 15) $a^2 \cdot (a + 1)^2 + a^2 + (a + 1)^2 = \square$ and the formula (III, 19) $(a^2 + b^2) \cdot (c^2 + d^2) = x^2 + y^2$, where

$x = (ac \pm bd)$ and $y = (ad \mp bc)$. The formula is used in order to find four triangles with the same hypotenuse. From the numbers chosen in this instance, $a^2 + b^2 = 5$ and $c^2 + d^2 = 13$, it has been concluded that Diophantus knew that a prime number $4n + 1$ is a hypotenuse.[25] In the examples of the decomposition of numbers into sums of squares, Diophantus demonstrates his knowledge of the following propositions, which were no doubt empirically derived: No number of the form $4n + 3$ is the sum of two square numbers (V, 9), and no number of the form $8n + 7$ is the sum of three square numbers (V, 11). Furthermore, every number is the sum of two (V, 9), three (V, 11), or four (IV, 29, and 30; V, 14) square numbers. Many of these propositions were taken up by mathematicians of the seventeenth century, generalized, and proved, thereby creating modern number theory.

In all his multifarious individual problems, in which the idea of a generalization rarely appears, Diophantus shows himself to be an ingenious and tireless calculator who did not shy away from large numbers and in whose work very few mistakes can be found.[26] One wonders what goals Diophantus had in mind in his *Arithmetica*. There was undoubtedly an irresistible drive to investigate the properties of numbers and to explore the mysteries which had grown up around them. Hence Diophantus appears in the period of decline of Greek mathematics on a lonely height as "a brilliant performer in the art of indeterminate analysis invented by him, but the science has nevertheless been indebted, at least directly, to this brilliant genius for few methods, because he was deficient in the speculative thought which sees in the True more than the Correct."[27]

Diophantus' Sources. Procedures for calculating linear and quadratic problems had been developed long before Diophantus. We find them in Babylonian and Chinese texts, as well as among the Greeks since the Pythagoreans. Diophantus' solution of the quadratic equation in two unknowns corresponds completely to the Babylonian, which reappears in the second book of Euclid's *Elements* in a geometric presentation. The treatment of the second-degree equation in one unknown is also Babylonian, as is the multiplication of the equation by the coefficient of x^2. There are a few Greek algebraic texts that we possess which are more ancient than Diophantus: the older arithmetical epigrams (in which there are indeterminate problems of the first degree), the *Epanthema* of Thymaridas of Paros, and the papyrus (Michigan 620) already mentioned. Moreover, knowledge of number theory was available to Diophantus from the Babylonians and Greeks, concerning, for example, series and polygonal numbers,[28] as well as rules for the formation of Pythagorean number triples. A special case of the decomposition of the product of two sums of squares into other sums of squares (see above, Porisms and Lemmas) had already appeared in a text from Susa.[29] One example of indeterminate analysis in an old Babylonian text corresponds to exercise II, 10, in Diophantus.[30] Diophantus studied special cases of the general Pellian equation with the "side and diagonal numbers" $x^2 - 2y^2 = \pm 1$. The indeterminate Archimedean cattle problem would have required a solution of the form $x^2 - ay^2 = 1$. Consequently, Diophantus certainly was not, as he has often been called, the father of algebra. Nevertheless, his remarkable, if unsystematic, collection of indeterminate problems is a singular achievement that was not fully appreciated and further developed until much later.

Influence. In their endeavor to acquire the knowledge of the Greeks, the Arabs—relatively late, it is true—became acquainted with the *Arithmetica*. Al-Nadīm (987/988) reports in his index of the sciences that Qusṭā ibn Lūqā (*ca.* 900) wrote a *Commentary on Three and One Half Books of Diophantus' Work on Arithmetical Problems* and that Abū'l-Wafā' (940–988) likewise wrote *A Commentary on Diophantus' Algebra*, as well as a *Book on the Proofs of the Propositions Used by Diophantus and of Those That He Himself* [Abu'l-Wafā'] *Has Presented in His Commentary*. These writings, as well as a commentary by Ibn al-Haytham on the *Arithmetica* (with marginal notations by Ibn Yūnus), have not been preserved. On the other hand, Arab texts do exist that exhibit a concern for indeterminate problems. An anonymous manuscript (written before 972) treats the problem $x^2 + n = u^2$, $x^2 - n = v^2$; a manuscript of the same period contains a treatise by al-Ḥusain (second half of tenth century) that is concerned with the theory of rational right triangles.[31] But most especially, one recognizes the influence of Diophantus on al-Karajī. In his algebra he took over from Diophantus' treatise a third of the exercises of book I; all those in book II beginning with II, 8; and almost all of book III. What portion of the important knowledge of the Indians in the field of indeterminate analysis is original and what portion they owe to the Greeks is the subject of varying opinions. For example, Hankel's view is that Diophantus was influenced by the Indians, while Cantor and especially Tannery claim just the opposite.

Problems of the type found in the *Arithmetica* first appeared in the West in the *Liber abbaci* of Leonardo of Pisa (1202); he undoubtedly became acquainted with them from Arabic sources during his journeys

DIOPHANTUS OF ALEXANDRIA

in the Mediterranean area. A Greek text of Diophantus was available only in Byzantium, where Michael Psellus saw what was perhaps the only copy still in existence.[32] Georgius Pachymeres (1240–1310) wrote a paraphrase with extracts from the first book,[33] and later Maximus Planudes (*ca.* 1255–1310) wrote a commentary to the first two books.[34] Among the manuscripts that Cardinal Bessarion rescued before the fall of Byzantium was that of Diophantus, which Regiomontanus discovered in Venice. His intention to produce a Latin translation was not realized. Then for a century nothing was heard about Diophantus. He was rediscovered by Bombelli, who in his *Algebra* of 1572, which contained 271 problems, took no fewer than 147 from Diophantus, including eighty-one with the same numerical values.[35] Three years later the first Latin translation, by Xylander, appeared in Basel; it was the basis for a free French rendering of the first four books by Simon Stevin (1585). Viète also took thirty-four problems from Diophantus (including thirteen with the same numerical values) for his *Zetetica* (1593); he restricted himself to problems that did not contradict the principle of dimension. Finally, in 1621 the Greek text was prepared for printing by Bachet de Méziriac, who added Xylander's Latin translation, which he was able to improve in many respects. Bachet studied the contents carefully, filled in the lacunae, ascertained and corrected the errors, generalized the solutions, and devised new problems. He, and especially Fermat, who took issue with Bachet's statements,[36] thus became the founders of modern number theory, which then—through Euler, Gauss,[37] and many others—experienced an unexpected development.

NOTES

1. Tannery, *Diophanti opera,* II, 38 f. As an example of "Egyptian analysis" Psellus gives the problem of dividing a number into a determined ratio.
2. Tannery, in his *Mémoires scientifiques,* II, 536 ff., mentions as a possibility that the *Arithmetica* was written as a textbook for the Christian school at the request of Dionysius and that perhaps Diophantus himself was a Christian.
3. Tannery, *Diophanti opera,* II, 60 ff.
4. *Ibid.,* p. 72.
5. V, 30, is exercise 30 of the fifth book, according to Tannery's numbering.
6. Tannery, *Diophanti opera,* II, xxxiv.
7. III, 1-4, belongs to II, 34, 35; and III, 20, 21, is the same as II, 14, 15.
8. Problems such as the "cattle problem" do not appear in Diophantus.
9. Or, as in IV, 1, of a cube number.
10. Tannery, *Diophanti opera,* II, xxxiv.
11. Michigan Papyrus 620, in J. G. Winter, *Papyri in the University of Michigan Collection,* vol. III of *Michigan Papyri* (Ann Arbor, 1936), 26–34.
12. Heath, *Diophantus of Alexandria,* pp. 130–131.
13. *Ibid.*
14. Tannery, *Diophanti opera,* II, xli. There are two parallel strokes joined together.
15. Similar problems exist in Byzantine and in Western arithmetic books since the time of Leonardo of Pisa.
16. Heath (in his *Conspectus*) considers the few determinate problems in bk. II to be spurious. Problems 1, 2, 15, and 33-37 of bk. IV become determinate only through arbitrary assumption of values for one of the unknowns.
17. $x^2y^2 + (x^2 + y^2)$, $y^2z^2 + (y^2 + z^2)$, $z^2x^2 + (z^2 + x^2)$, $x^2y^2 + z^2$, $y^2z^2 + x^2$, $z^2x^2 + y^2$.
18. Sometimes Diophantus mentions infinitely many solutions (VI, 12, lemma 2). In VI, 15, lemma, Diophantus presents, besides a well-known solution of the equation $3x^2 - 11 = y^2$ (namely, $x = 5$ and $y = 8$), a second one: $3 \cdot (5 + z)^2 - 11 = (8 - 2z)^2$.
19. Sometimes, for example in IV, 14, the integer solution is added to the rational solution.
20. For example, in VI, 6; IV, 31; and V, 10.
21. In IV, 1, the system $x^3 + y^3 = 370$, $x + y = 10$, corresponds to the quadratic system $xy = 21$, $x + y = 10$, which was a paradigm in al-Khwārizmī. Tannery (*Mémoires scientifiques,* II, 89) shows how close Diophantus was to a solution to the cubic equation $x^3 = 3px + 2q$.
22. Here one sees the application of algebra to the solution of a geometric problem.
23. The nth polygonal number has n "sides."
24. This is not a general solution; see Tannery, *Diophanti opera,* I, 317.
25. Heath, p. 107.
26. For example, IV, 25, and V, 30; see Heath, pp. 60, 186.
27. Hankel, p. 165; Heath, p. 55.
28. For example, see Hypsicles' formula used in *On Polygonal Numbers.*
29. See E. M. Bruins and M. Rutten, *Textes mathématiques de Suse,* no. 34 in the series Mémoires de la mission archéologique en Iran (Paris, 1961), p. 117.
30. See S. Gandz, in *Osiris,* **8** (1948), 13 ff.
31. See Dickson, p. 459.
32. Tannery, *Diophanti opera,* II, xviii.
33. *Ibid.,* pp. 78–122. Also in "Quadrivium de Georges Pachymère," in *Studi e testi,* CXIV (Vatican City, 1940), 44-76.
34. *Ibid.,* pp. 125-255.
35. Bombelli and Antonio Maria Pazzi prepared a translation of the first five books, but it was not printed.
36. In his copy of Bachet's edition Fermat wrote numerous critical remarks and filled in missing material. These remarks appeared as a supplement, along with selections from Fermat's letters to Jacques de Billy, in Samuel de Fermat's new edition of Diophantus of 1670.
37. The importance of Diophantus is emphasized by Gauss in the introduction to his *Disquisitiones arithmetice:* "Diophanti opus celebre, quod totum problematis indeterminatis dicatum est, multas quaestiones continet, quae propter difficultatem suam artificiorumque subtilitatem de auctoris ingenio et acumine existimationem haud mediocrem suscitant, praesertim si subsidiorum, quibus illi uti licuit, tenuitatem consideres" ("The famous work of Diophantus, which is totally dedicated to indeterminate problems, contains many questions which arouse a high regard for the genius and penetration of the author, especially when one considers the limited means available to him").

BIBLIOGRAPHY

The first Western presentation of the Diophantine problems was by Raffaele Bombelli, in his *Algebra* (Bologna, 1572; 2nd ed., 1579). A Latin translation was produced by

W. Xylander, *Diophanti Alexandrini Rerum arithmeticarum libri sex, quorum duo adjecta habent scholia Maximi Planudis. Item liber de numeris polygonis seu multangulis* (Basel, 1575). The text with a Latin translation was prepared by C.-G. Bachet de Méziriac, *Diophanti Alexandrini Arithmeticorum libri sex, et de numeris multangulis liber unus* (Paris, 1621); a new edition was published by Samuel de Fermat with notes by his father, Pierre de Fermat (Toulouse, 1670). There is also the definitive text with Latin translation by P. Tannery, *Diophanti Alexandrini opera omnia cum Graecis commentariis,* 2 vols. (Leipzig, 1893–1895). An English translation, in a modern rendering, is T. L. Heath, *Diophantus of Alexandria, A Study in the History of Greek Algebra* (Cambridge, 1885); the second edition has a supplement containing an account of Fermat's theorems and problems connected with Diophantine analysis and some solutions of Diophantine problems by Euler (Cambridge, 1910; New York, 1964). German translations are O. Schultz, *Diophantus von Alexandria arithmetische Aufgaben nebst dessen Schrift über die Polygon-Zahlen* (Berlin, 1822); G. Wertheim, *Die Arithmetik und die Schrift über die Polygonalzahlen des Diophantus von Alexandria* (Leipzig, 1890); and A. Czwalina, *Arithmetik des Diophantos von Alexandria* (Göttingen, 1952). A French translation is P. Ver Eecke, *Diophante d'Alexandrie* (Paris, 1959). A Greek text (after Tannery's), with translation into modern Greek, is E. S. Stamatis, *Διοφαντου αριθμητικα, η αλγεβρα των αρχαιων ελληνων* (Athens, 1963).

On Polygonal Numbers appears in a French trans. by G. Massoutié as *Le traité des nombres polygones* (Mâcon, 1911).

Along with the views of the authors in their text editions and translations, the following general criticisms should be consulted: M. Cantor, *Vorlesungen über Geschichte der Mathematik,* 3rd ed., I (Leipzig, 1907), 463–488; P. Cossali, *Origine, trasporto in Italia, primi progressi in essa dell' algebra* (Parma, 1797), I, 56–95; T. L. Heath, *History of Greek Mathematics* (Oxford, 1921), II, 440–517; B. L. van der Waerden, *Erwachende Wissenschaft,* 2nd ed. (Basel-Stuttgart, 1966), pp. 457–470. See also H. Hankel, *Zur Geschichte der Mathematik in Alterthum und Mittelalter* (Leipzig, 1874), 2nd ed. with foreword and index by J. E. Hofmann (Hildesheim, 1965); F. Hultsch, "Diophantus," in Pauly-Wissowa, V, pt. 1, 1051–1073; G. Loria, *Le scienze esatte nell'antica Grecia* (Milan, 1914), pp. 845–919; E. Lucas, *Recherches sur l'analyse indéterminée et l'arithmétique de Diophante,* with preface by J. Itard (Paris, 1967); G. H. F. Nesselmann, *Die Algebra der Griechen* (Berlin, 1842), pp. 244–476; and G. Sarton, *Introduction to the History of Science,* I (Baltimore, 1927), 336 ff.

Special criticism includes P. Tannery, "La perte de sept livres de Diophante," in his *Mémoires scientifiques,* II (Toulouse-Paris, 1912), 73–90; "Étude sur Diophante," *ibid.*, 367–399; and "Sur la religion des derniers mathématiciens de l'antiquité," *ibid.*, 527–539.

Historical works include I. G. Bašmakova, "Diofant i Ferma," in *Istoriko-matematicheskie issledovaniya,* **17** (1966), 185–204; L. E. Dickson, *History of the Theory of Numbers,* II, *Diophantine Analysis* (Washington, D.C., 1920); T. L. Heath, *Diophantus* (see above), ch. 6 and supplement; K. Reich, "Diophant, Cardano, Bombelli, Viète. Ein Vergleich ihrer Aufgaben," in *Rechenpfennige, Aufsätze zur Wissenschaftsgeschichte* (Munich, 1968), pp. 131–150; P. Tannery, *Diophanti opera* (see above), II, prolegomena; and P. Ver Eecke, *Diophante* (see above), introduction.

KURT VOGEL

DIRAC, PAUL ADRIEN MAURICE (*b.* Bristol, England, 8 August 1902; *d.* Miami, Florida, 20 October 1984)

Dirac was one of the greatest theoretical physicists in the twentieth century. He is best known for his important and elegant contributions to the formulation of quantum mechanics; for his quantum theory of the emission and absorption of radiation, which inaugurated quantum electrodynamics; for his relativistic equation of the electron; for his "prediction" of the positron and of antimatter; and for his "large number hypothesis" in cosmology. Present expositions of quantum mechanics largely rely on his masterpiece *The Principles of Quantum Mechanics* (1930), and a great part of the basic theoretical framework of modern particle physics originated in his early attempts at combining quanta and relativity. Not only his results but also his methods influenced the way much of theoretical physics is done today, extending or improving the mathematical formalism before looking for its systematic interpretation.

Dirac spent most of his academic career at Cambridge and received all the honors to which a British physicist may reasonably aspire. He became a fellow of St. John's College at the age of twenty-five, a fellow of the Royal Society in 1930, Lucasian professor of mathematics in 1932, a Nobel laureate in 1933 for his "discovery of new fertile forms of the theory of atoms and for its applications," a Royal Medalist in 1939, and a Copley Medalist in 1952. He was frequently invited to lecture or to do research abroad. For instance, he traveled around the world in 1929, visited the Soviet Union several times in the 1930's, and was a fellow at the Institute for Advanced Studies, Princeton, in the years 1947–1948 and 1958–1959. In 1973 he was made a member of the Order of Merit. Dirac retired in 1969 but resumed his scientific career in 1971 at Florida State University. In January 1937 Dirac married Margit Wigner, the sister of Eugene Wigner; they had two daughters.

Dirac made his mark through his scientific writings. He had few students: the fundamental problems that he tackled were not for beginners. Unlike many of his colleagues, he was little involved in war projects.

Bristol. Dirac's mother, Florence Hannah Holten, was British; his father, Charles Adrien Ladislas Dirac, was an émigré from French Switzerland. His father did not receive friends at home and forced Paul to silence by imposing French as the language spoken at the dinner table. From childhood Dirac was a loner, enjoying the contemplation of nature, long walks, or gardening more than social life. He was not much inclined to collaboration and did his best thinking by himself. At the Merchant Venturer's Technical College, where his father taught French, he excelled in science and mathematics, and neglected literary and artistic subjects.

From 1918 to 1921 Dirac trained to be an electrical engineer at Bristol University. This background, he explained later, strongly influenced his way of doing physics: he learned how to tolerate approximations when trying to describe the physical world and how to solve problems step by step. He also developed a nonrigorous constructive conception of mathematics, beautifully articulating symbols before precisely defining them, very much as the British physicist Oliver Heaviside did in his calculus.

In 1921 the postwar economic depression prevented Dirac from finding a job, so he accepted two years of free tuition from the mathematics department at Bristol. During this period he was influenced by an outstanding professor of mathematics, Peter Fraser, who convinced him that rigor was sometimes useful and imparted to him his love for projective geometry, with its derivations of complicated theorems by means of simple one-to-one correspondences.

At Bristol, Dirac also attended Charlie Dunbar Broad's philosophy course for students of science, in which Broad criticized the fundamental concepts of science on the basis of Alfred North Whitehead's principle of extensive abstraction and argued that the ideal objects of mathematics must be constructed from the mutual relations—not the inner structure—of the roughly perceived objects of nature. This genesis was supposed to explain the relevance of geometrical concepts when they were applied to the physical world, particularly the success of Einstein's theory of relativity. For Broad, theorists were best when they were their own philosophers. Dirac also read John Stuart Mill's *System of Logic* (1843), but derived the opposite conclusion: that philosophy was "just a way to think about discoveries already made."

Broad's lectures included a serious account of the theory of relativity, which immediately fascinated Dirac. Arthur S. Eddington's *Space, Time and Gravitation* (1920), written in the euphoric period after the British eclipse expedition confirming Albert Einstein's theory in 1919, made a further impression on Dirac. Evidence of epistemological comments by "the fountainhead of relativity in England" can be found in several places in Dirac's work.

Cambridge. In the fall of 1923, Dirac entered St. John's College, Cambridge, as a research student, thanks to an 1851 Exhibition studentship and a grant from the department of scientific and industrial research for work in advanced mathematics. He hoped to study relativity with Ebenezer Cunningham, but was assigned Ralph Fowler as his adviser. Fowler was not only a preeminent specialist in statistical mechanics but also the enthusiastic leader of quantum theoretical research at Cambridge. As a correspondent of Niels Bohr, he regularly got information about the latest advances or failures in atomic theory. As the son-in-law of Ernest Rutherford, he took a strong interest in the experimental work at the Cavendish Laboratory (at Cambridge, theoretical physics was part of the Faculty of Mathematics).

Because of his retiring personality and the relative isolation of the various colleges, Dirac did not have any regular scientific interlocutor but Fowler. To compensate, he joined two physicists' clubs, the $\nabla^2 V$ Club and the more casual Kapitza Club, where theorists and experimenters discussed recent problems and welcomed foreign visitors. He also attended the colloquia at the Cavendish and, to keep up with developments in fundamental mathematics, took part in the tea parties of the distinguished Cambridge mathematician Henry Frederick Baker, who was concerned primarily with projective geometry.

Before arriving in Cambridge, Dirac did not know about the Bohr atom. This gap in his knowledge was quickly and excellently filled by Fowler's detailed lectures. Dirac also read Arnold Sommerfeld's textbook *Atomic Structure and Spectral Lines* (English ed., 1923), Bohr's *On the Application of the Quantum Theory to Atomic Structure* (1923), and Max Born's *Vorlesungen über Atommechanik* (1925). These three fundamental texts involved advanced techniques of Hamiltonian dynamics (to derive the most general expression of the rules of quantization), which Dirac learned from Edmund T. Whittaker's standard text, *A Treatise on the Analytical Dynamics of Particles and Rigid Bodies*

(1904). Perhaps more than anything in quantum theory he enjoyed reading Eddington's *Mathematical Theory of Relativity* (1923), which developed the tensor apparatus of Einstein's and Hermann Weyl's theories of gravitation. They became his models of beauty in mathematical physics.

Fowler was quick to detect the qualities of his new student and began to encourage his originality. Only six months after arriving in Cambridge, Dirac started to publish substantial research papers. Whenever his subject had not been imposed by Fowler, he tried to clarify and to generalize in a relativistic way points that he had found obscure in his readings—for instance, the definition of a particle's speed according to Eddington, or the covariance of Bohr's frequency condition, or the expression of the collision probability in the then-fashionable "detailed balancing" calculations. The main characteristics of Dirac's style showed through in this early work: directness, economy in mathematical notation, and little reference to past work.

At the end of 1924, following suggestions by Fowler and Darwin, Dirac focused on the more fundamental problem of generalizing the application of Paul Ehrenfest's adiabatic principle in quantum theory. According to this principle, the quantum conditions for a complicated system could be obtained by infinitely slow ("adiabatic") deformation of a simpler system for which one knew to which variables q the Bohr-Sommerfeld rule $\int pdq = nh$ applied.

Another method, introduced by Karl Schwartzschild and systematized by Johannes Burgers, applied to the so-called multiperiodic systems, the configuration of which can be expressed in terms of s periodic functions with s incommensurable frequencies $\omega_1, \omega_2, \ldots \omega_d, \ldots \omega_s$. One had only to introduce the "angle" variables $w_\alpha = \omega_\omega t$ and the corresponding Hamiltonian conjugates, the "action" variables J_α. In the nondegenerate case for which s is also the number of degrees of freedom, the quantum conditions can simply be written $J_\alpha = n_\alpha \hbar$, where $2\pi\hbar$ is Planck's constant. Burgers showed that this procedure was equivalent to the adiabatic principle because the J's are adiabatic invariants. Dirac increased both the rigor of the demonstration and its scope, including magnetic fields and degeneracy. He also tried to remove the restriction of multiperiodicity and to calculate the energy levels of the helium atom, but he failed. Presumably he believed that a good part of the difficulties of quantum theory could be solved by extension of the adiabatic principle without facing the basic paradoxes emphasized by Bohr and the Göttingen school. Bohr's correspondence principle did not trigger Dirac's interest as a hint toward a fundamentally new quantum mechanics. His only consideration of it was purely operational, as a set of rules to derive intensities of emitted radiation in the action-angle formalism.

Commutators and Poisson Brackets. In 1925 Bohr and Werner Heisenberg both brought their revolutionary spirit to Cambridge. Bohr lectured in May after being distressed by the results of Walther Bothe and Hans Geiger's experiment confirming the light-quantum explanation of the Compton effect and making the paradoxical features of light more obvious than ever. According to Bohr, Pauli, and Born, the crisis in quantum theory had reached its climax. The world needed a new mechanics that would preserve the quantum postulates and agree asymptotically with classical mechanics. Heisenberg came to Cambridge in July 1925 with what soon proved to meet this expectation. He lectured at the Kapitza Club, on "term zoology and Zeeman botanics"—that is, on his latest theory of spectral multiplets and anomalous Zeeman effects. It is not known how much of this talk dealt with more recent ideas, nor if Dirac in fact attended it. Fowler certainly heard of Heisenberg's brand-new "quantum kinematics" in private conversations, and asked to be kept informed.

In late August or early September, Fowler gave Dirac the proof sheets of Heisenberg's fundamental paper, "A Quantum-Theoretical Reinterpretation (*Umdeutung*) of Kinematics and Mechanical Relations." Heisenberg had replaced the position x of an electron by an array $x_{nm}e^{i(E_n - E_m)t/\hbar}$ representing the amplitudes of virtual oscillators directly giving the observable properties of scattered or emitted radiation corresponding to the energy levels E_m and E_n. To keep the new kinematics as analogous as possible to the classical one, he guessed the multiplication law of two arrays x_{nm} and y_{nm} from the corresponding rule for the Fourier coefficients of x and y, and obtained $(xy)_{nl} = \sum_m x_{nm}y_{ml}$. In the same way he guessed the quantum version of the quantization rule $\int pdq = nh$ as $\sum_m |q_{nm}|^2(E_m - E_n) = \hbar^2/2\mu$ (μ being the electron mass). The dynamics—the equation of evolution for x—was taken over from classical dynamics. At that point the most advanced quantum problem that Heisenberg could solve was the weakly anharmonic oscillator. The "essential difficulty," he noticed, was the fact that, according to the new multiplication rule, $xy \neq yx$.

Since there was no familiar Hamitonian formalism

in Heisenberg's paper, it was about ten days before Dirac realized that the new multiplication law might solve the difficulties of quantum theory. He first looked for a relativistic generalization of Heisenberg's scheme, but this proved premature. More successfully, he tried to connect it to a Hamiltonian formalism. The difference $xy - yx$, once evaluated for high quantum numbers and in terms of action-angle variables J and w, gave $i\hbar \sum_{\alpha} \frac{\partial x}{\partial w_{\alpha}} \frac{\partial y}{\partial J_{\alpha}} - \frac{\partial y}{\partial w_{\alpha}} \frac{\partial x}{\partial J_{\alpha}}$, that is, the classical Poisson bracket $\{x, y\}$ times $i\hbar$. In other words, Heisenberg's strange noncommutativity had a classical counterpart in the Poisson-bracket algebra of Hamiltonian mechanics. Dirac then assumed that the relation $xy - yx = i\hbar\{x, y\}$ held in general (far from the classical limit and for nonmultiperiodic systems) and provided the proper quantum conditions. For canonically conjugate variables p and q it reduced to $qp - pq = i\hbar$, containing Heisenberg's quantization rule.

Dirac was very pleased with this close analogy between classical and quantum mechanics because it allowed him to retain the "beauty" of classical mechanics and to transfer Hamiltonian techniques to quantum mechanics. Hence he could develop very quickly a version of quantum mechanics more elegant than that developed at Göttingen.

q-Numbers. The identity between commutator and Poisson brackets led to the fundamental equations $i\hbar g = gH - Hg$ (for any dynamical variable g evolving with the Hamiltonian H) and $qp - pq = i\hbar$ (for any canonical couple), determining the formalism of quantum mechanics. Dirac thought that Heisenberg's interpretation of the quantum variables in terms of matrices giving the observable properties of radiation was provisional and too restrictive; he preferred a symbolic approach, developing the algebra of abstract undefined "q-numbers" and looking only later for those numbers' representation in terms of observable (ordinary) "c-numbers." The domain of q-numbers had to be extensible, adapting to the further progress of the theory. Some of the axiomatic properties that Dirac imposed on them—for instance, the unicity of the square root and no divisor of zero—had to be dropped later because they cannot be realized in an algebra of operators. Dirac's idea of q-numbers and his axioms for them most probably originated at Baker's tea parties. In Baker's *Principles of Geometry* there is an abstract noncommutative algebra of coefficients for linear combinations of points, which permitted elegant and condensed proofs of theorems in projective geometry (where noncommutativity means dropping Pappus's theorem).

In the case of multiperiodic systems, Dirac could show that his fundamental equations were satisfied by an algebra of matrices with rows and columns corresponding to integral values (times h) of the action variables J. In this representation the energy matrix is diagonal, which suggests that the diagonal elements represent the spectrum of the system. Through a correspondence argument Dirac identified the matrix element $x_{J'J''}$ of the electric polarization with the amplitude of the corresponding transition $J' \rightarrow J''$, in accordance with Heisenberg's original definition of the position matrix. In this representation Dirac could solve the hydrogen atom in early 1926 (a little later than Wolfgang Pauli, but independently). Within a few months he also found the basic commutation and composition rules for angular momentum in multielectron atoms, and he made the first relativistic quantum-mechanical calculation giving the characteristics of Compton scattering. Physicists in Copenhagen were impressed by this achievement, the more so because Dirac treated the field classically, without light quanta.

Dirac assembled all these bright results in his doctoral dissertation, completed in June 1926. At that time he had solved by himself about as many quantum problems as the entire Göttingen group together. In principle his q-numbers were more general and more flexible than the Göttingen matrices, which were rigidly connected to a priori observable quantities. But Dirac had been able to solve the quantum equations only insofar as action-angle variables could be introduced into the corresponding classical problem. To proceed further, he needed a new method of finding representations of q-numbers. That is exactly what Erwin Schrödinger made available in a series of papers submitted for publication between January and June 1926.

The Impact of Schrödinger's Equation. Dirac's first reaction to Schrödinger's equation was negative: Why a second quantum mechanics, since there already was one? Why propose that matter waves were analogous to light waves, since the properties of light waves were already so paradoxical? In a letter written on 26 May 1926, Heisenberg convinced him that Schrödinger's equation $H\left(q, -i\hbar\frac{\partial}{\partial q}\right)\psi_n = E_n\psi_n$ (for one degree of freedom) provided a simple and general method to calculate the matrix elements of a general function F of p and q just by forming the integrals $F_{mn} = \int\psi_m^*(q)F\left(q, -i\hbar\frac{\partial}{\partial q}\right)\psi_n(q)\ dq$.

Then, in an astonishingly short time, Dirac accumulated new essential results. The time dependence of the matrix elements could be supplied by the equation $H\psi = i\hbar\partial\psi/\partial t$, suggested by the relativistic substitution $p_\mu \rightarrow i\hbar\partial/\partial x_\mu$. A set of identical particles, following Heisenberg's idea of eliminating unobservable differences from the formalism, had to be represented by either symmetric or antisymmetric wave functions in configuration space, the first corresponding to the Bose-Einstein statistics and the second to Pauli's exclusion principle. Finally, Dirac developed the time-dependent perturbation theory to calculate Einstein's B coefficients of absorption and stimulated emission. He also improved his calculation of the Compton effect. To reach these physical results he did not subscribe to Schrödinger's picture of $|\psi|^2$ as a density of electricity; instead he relied on Heisenberg's interpretation of the polarization matrix or on Born's statistical interpretation of the ψ function.

Interpretation of Quantum Dynamics. Dirac was not satisfied by the provisional and parochial assumptions made to interpret q-numbers and the quantum formalism: according to Heisenberg, the diagonal elements of H and the elements of the polarization matrix had an immediate meaning; according to a paper by Born (June 1926), the coefficients c_n in the development $\psi = \sum_n c_n\psi_n$ over the set of eigenfunctions ψ_n gave the probability $|c_n|^2$ for the system to be in the state n; and, according to Schrödinger's fourth memoir (June 1926), $|\psi|^2$ was "a sort of weight function in configuration space." In Dirac's view, a general interpretation should be based on a transformation theory, as in the theory of relativity (and as emphasized by Eddington).

To arrive at the interpretation, Dirac first worked out the transformations connecting the various matrix representations of his fundamental equations $qp - pq = i\hbar$ and $i\hbar\dot{g} = gH - Hg$. He called ξ and α two maximal sets of commuting q-numbers; ξ' and α', corresponding eigenvalues; and (ξ'/α'), the transformation from the representation where ξ is diagonal to the one where α is diagonal, acting on the representation $g_{\xi'\xi''}$ of g according to $g_{\alpha'\alpha''} = \int(\alpha'/\xi')g_{\xi'\xi''}(\xi''/\alpha'')\,d\xi'\,d\xi''$. In this framework the solutions of the (time-independent) Schrödinger equation were nothing but a particular transformation for which α contains H and ξ contains the position. The notations, introduced for the sake of economy and in obvious analogy to tensor notation, proved to be extremely convenient and spread widely, especially after their later improvement (1939) into the "bra-ket" (or "bra" and "ket") notation. In fact, the symbolic rules were better defined than the mathematical substratum, which was made clear only much later by mathematicians. For instance, the treatment of continuous spectra on the same footing as the discrete ones necessitated singular "δ-functions" (as in $(x'/x'') = \delta(x' - x'')$, perceived by Dirac as limits of sharply peaked functions but raised today to the rank of Schwartz distributions.

To interpret his transformations, Dirac needed only a minimal assumption suggested by the correspondence principle: that for an arbitrary physical quantity g expressed in terms of ξ and the canonical conjugate η, $g_{\xi'\xi'}$ signifies the average of the corresponding classical g for $\xi = \xi'$ and η uniformly distributed. From $\delta(g - g')|_{\xi'\xi'} = |(\xi'/g')|^2$ it follows that $|(\xi'/g')|^2\,dg'$ is proportional to the probability that g is equal to g' within dg' when $\xi = \xi'$. Dirac finished this transformation theory in November 1926 at Copenhagen.

In Göttingen, Pascual Jordan obtained roughly the same results at the same time, though from a different point of view. He defined axiomatically a concept of canonical conjugation at the quantum level and looked for the transformations $(\xi, \eta) \rightarrow (\alpha, \beta)$ from one canonical couple to another. In this more general framework the quantum variables did not necessarily have a classical counterpart, and conjugation did not necessarily correspond to Poisson-bracket conjugation. In other words, Dirac's transformation theory was more constraining than Jordan's, and gave more precise directions for the future extensions of quantum mechanics.

Dirac was also original in his conception of the role of probability in quantum mechanics. He thought that probabilities entered into the description of quantum phenomena only in the determination of the initial state (still described in terms of p's and q's), and not necessarily in the behavior of an isolated system. But, as Bohr had said at the Solvay Conference in 1927, isolated systems were unobservable. Dirac then assumed that the state of the world was represented by its wave function ψ and that it changed abruptly during a measurement, whereupon "nature made a choice."

Dirac retained his basic machinery of transformations in his subsequent lectures on quantum mechanics, but he introduced a substantial change in his fundamental textbook, *The Principles of Quantum Mechanics* (1930). In the original exposition of transformation theory, he had carefully avoided the concept of quantum state, presumably to depart from Schrödinger's idea of ψ as a state. In his *Principles*, however, he presented the principle of superposition and the related concept of space of states as capturing the most essential feature of quantum theory: the interference of probabilities. It seems plausible that this move was inspired by Bohr's insistence on the superposition principle and by John von Neumann's and Hermann Weyl's formulations of quantum mechanics, in which Hilbert spaces played a central role. From this perspective transformations were just a change of base in the space of states. The correspondence with Hamiltonian formalism appeared only in a later chapter of the book.

A New Radiation Theory. Dirac liked his transformation theory because it was the outcome of a planned line of research and not a fortuitous discovery. He forced his future investigations to fit it. The first results of this strategy were almost miraculous. First came his new radiation theory, in February 1927, which quantized for the first time James Clerk Maxwell's radiation in interaction with atoms. Previous quantum-mechanical studies of radiation problems, except for Jordan's unpopular attempt, retained purely classical fields. In late 1925 Jordan had applied Heisenberg's rules of quantization to continuous free fields and obtained a light-quantum structure with the expected statistics (Bose-Einstein) and dual fluctuation properties. Dirac further demonstrated that spontaneous emission and its characteristics—previously taken into account only by special postulates—followed from the interaction between atoms and the quantum field. Essential to this success was the fact that Dirac's transformation theory eliminated from the interpretation of the quantum formalism every reference to classical emitted radiation, contrary to Heisenberg's original point of view and also to Schrödinger's concept of ψ as a classical source of field.

This work was done during Dirac's visit to Copenhagen in the winter of 1927. Presumably to please Bohr, who insisted on wave-particle duality and equality, Dirac opposed the "corpuscular point of view" to the quantized electromagnetic "wave point of view." He started with a set of massless Bose particles described by symmetric ψ waves in configuration space. As he discovered by "playing with the equations," this description was equivalent to a quantized Schrödinger equation in the space of one particle; this "second quantization" was already known to Jordan, who during 1927 extended it into the basic modern quantum field representation of matter. Dirac limited his use of second quantization electromagnetic to radiation: to establish that the corpuscular point of view, once brought into this form, was equivalent to the wave point of view.

The Dirac Equation. An even more astonishing fruit of Dirac's transformation theory was his relativistic equation of the electron. He and many other theorists had already made use of the most obvious candidate for such an equation—$(\hbar^2\partial_\mu\partial^\mu + m^2)\psi = 0$ (Klein-Gordon)—but it did not include the spin effects necessary to explain atomic spectra. More crucially for Dirac, it could not fit into the transformation theory because it could not be rewritten under the form $i\hbar\partial\psi/\partial t = H\psi$. To be both explicitly relativistic and linear in $\partial/\partial t$, the new equation had to take the form $(i\hbar\gamma^\mu\partial_\mu - m)\psi = 0$ or, more explicitly, $i\hbar\partial\psi/\partial t = \vec{\alpha} \cdot \vec{p} + \beta m$. For the spectrum to be limited to values satisfying Einstein's relation $E^2 = p^2 + m^2$, the coefficients $\vec{\alpha}$ and β had to be such that $(\vec{\alpha} \cdot \vec{p} + \beta m)^2 = p^2 + m^2$—that is, $\beta^2 = 1$, $\alpha_i\alpha_j + \alpha_j\alpha_i = 2\,\delta_{ij}$, and $\alpha_i\beta + \beta\alpha_i = 0$.

The simplest entities satisfying these relations are 4×4 matrices, as Dirac noted with the help of Pauli's $\vec{\sigma}$ matrices (such that $[\vec{\sigma} \cdot \vec{p}]^2 = p^2$). Surprisingly, the new equation included spin effects, the value 2 of the gyromagnetic factor, and the correct fine structure formula (Sommerfeld's), as worked out approximately by Dirac and exactly by Darwin and Walter Gordon. Other theorists (Pauli, Darwin, Jordan, Hendrik, Kramers) had been searching for a wave equation integrating spin and relativistic effects, but they all started by assuming the existence of spin, either as an intrinsic particle rotation or as a wave polarization. In contrast, the key to Dirac's success was his persistent adherence to the simplest classical model, the point-electron, as a basis for quantization. Spin effects, as might have been expected from their involving h, were a consequence of relativistic quantization.

Antimatter, Monopoles. The Dirac equation played an essential role not only in atomic physics but also in high-energy physics, through the Klein-Nishina and Møller formulas describing the absorption of relativistic particles in matter. Nevertheless, it presented several strange features that enhanced the "magic" of Dirac's work: a new type of relativistic covariance involving the spinor representations of the Lorentz group, soon elucidated by Göttingen mathematicians; the trembling of the electron imagined by Schrödinger to harmonize the observed electron speed and the expectation value c of the speed operator from Dirac's equation; and, above all, the negative-energy difficulty.

The equation $E^2 = p^2 + m^2$, applying to the spectrum of free Dirac electrons, has two roots: $E = \pm(p^2 + m^2)^{1/2}$; therefore a Dirac electron with an initially positive energy should fall indefinitely by spontaneous emission toward states of lower and lower energy. To avoid this, Dirac imagined in late 1929 that the states of negative energy were normally filled up according to the exclusion principle and that holes in this "sea" would represent protons. If this were true, Dirac had in hand a grandiose unification of the particle physics of his time. But he still had to explain the ratio m_p/m_e between the proton mass and the electron mass. He thought that the disparity in mass might originate in the mutual interaction between the "sea" electrons. The precise numerical value of the ratio would perhaps appear at the same time as the other dimensionless constant, $e^2/4\pi\hbar c$, as suggested by Eddington in a 1928 paper containing a mysterious derivation of this remarkable number.

Eddington believed that electromagnetic interactions could be reduced to the "exchange" interactions, the change of sign of a wave function owing to the permutation of two fermions or to a full rotation being of the same nature as the change of phase following an electromagnetic gauge transformation. At the end of his speculation, he got $e^2/4\pi\hbar c = 1/136$. In his search for a theoretical derivation of m_p/m_e and $e^2/4\pi\hbar c$, Dirac also concentrated on the phase of the wave function.

It is usually assumed that the phase of a wave function is unambiguously defined in space (for a given gauge). But a multivalued phase is also admissible, Dirac noted, as long as the variation of phase around a closed loop is the same for any wave function (to preserve the regular statistical interpretation of ψ based on quantities such as $|\int\psi_1^*(\bar{r})\psi_2(\bar{r})\, d^3r|$). To ensure the continuity of ψ, the variation of phase around an infinitesimal closed loop can only be a multiple of 2π. This determines lines of singularities starting from (gauge) invariant singular points. Now, following the relation between electromagnetic potential and phase implied by gauge invariance, the singular points must be identified with magnetic monopoles carrying the charge $g = n\hbar c/2e$. If there is only one monopole g in nature, every electric charge must be a multiple of $\hbar c/2g$. Dirac always considered this explanation of the quantization of charge in nature as the strongest argument in favor of monopoles.

Unfortunately, no other restriction on e followed from this line of reasoning and Dirac missed his targets, the derivation of $e^2/4\pi\hbar c$ and a subsequent determination of m_p/m_e. But the latter was no longer needed: in 1931 he learned from Weyl that, due to charge conjugation symmetry, the holes in his "sea" theory necessarily carried the charge $-e$. In the same year and in a single paper, he proclaimed the necessity of antielectrons (and also antiprotons) and the possibility of monopoles, and pondered the most efficient method of advance in theoretical physics. As in his quantum-theoretical work, he had first to work out the formalism in terms of abstract symbols denoting states and observables, and next to investigate the symbols' interpretation. This was, Dirac said, "like Eddington's principle of identification," according to which the interpretation of the fundamental tensors of general relativity came after their mathematical justification.

Dirac gave a full quantum-mechanical treatment of his monopoles in 1948 with the help of "nonphysical strings" allowing a Hamiltonian formulation. More recently monopoles have been shown to be necessary in any non-Abelian gauge theory, including electromagnetic interactions. But no experimental evidence has yet been found. On the other hand, the antielectron (or positron) was discovered by Carl Anderson and Patrick Blackett in the years 1932–1933, much earlier than foreseen by Dirac, although its concept faced the general prejudice against a charge-symmetric nature.

The Multitime Theory. After the discovery of the positron, most theorists agreed that the negative-energy difficulty was solved by the "sea" concept. Another fundamental difficulty, also rooted in one of Dirac's early works, his radiation theory, lasted much longer. In 1929, when working out their version of quantum electrodynamics, Heisenberg and Pauli discovered that the second order of approximation involved infinite terms, even when it was related to physical phenomena such as level shifts in atoms. The difficulty looked so serious that in the first edition of his *Principles*, Dirac omitted the quantization of the electromagnetic field and presented only the light-quantum configuration-space approach.

In 1932 Dirac tried to start a new revolution by giving up (for electrodynamics) the most basic requirement of his quantum-mechanical work: the Hamiltonian structure of dynamical equations. Imitating Heisenberg's revolutionary breakthrough, he declared that the new theory should eliminate unobservable things like the electromagnetic fields during the interaction process, and focus on their asymptotic values before and after the interaction. The electromagnetic field, he said, was nothing but a means of observation, and therefore should not be submitted to Hamiltonian treatment. On these lines he derived a set of equations that apparently were quite new; in fact, as Leon Rosenfeld soon pointed out, it differed from the theory of Heisenberg and Pauli only in the use of the interaction representation (for which the quantum fields evolve as free fields) and of a multitime configuration space for electrons (instead of Jordan's quantized waves). Nonetheless, once it had been improved with the help of Vladimir A. Fock and Boris Podolsky, Dirac's formulation had the great advantage of being explicitly covariant, a feature particularly attractive to the Japanese quantum-field theorists Hideki Yukawa and Sin-Itiro Tomonaga.

The Large-Number Hypothesis. The infinities were still there. The discovery of the positron in 1932 gave some hope that the deformations of Dirac's "sea," the "vacuum polarization," would cure them. But such was not the case (although Wendell Furry and Victor Weisskopf made the infinities "smaller"), and Dirac himself judged the "sea" theory ugly. In 1936, depressed by this state of affairs, he hastily concluded from some experimental results of Robert S. Shankland that the energy principle should be given up in relativistic quantum theory. Needing some diversion, he turned to cosmological speculation following Eddington, who believed in a grand unification of atomic physics and cosmology. Dirac also knew Edward A. Milne, the other famous Cambridge cosmologist, who had been his supervisor for a term in 1925, and he had made friends with the American astronomer Howard P. Robertson, who believed in the expansion of the universe, during a short stay at Göttingen in 1927.

Like Eddington, Dirac focused on dimensionless numbers built from the fundamental constants of both atomic and cosmic phenomena; and he observed that there was a cluster of these numbers around 10^{39}, including the age of the universe in atomic time units and the ratio of electric forces to gravitational ones inside atoms. In 1937 he proposed the "large-number hypothesis," according to which numbers in the same cluster should be simply related. Consequently, the gravitation constant had to vary in time, as in Milne's cosmology and contrary to general relativity.

Milne believed in an "extended principle of relativity," which stipulated that the universe should look the same from wherever it is observed, and completed it by the stricture that the cosmological theory should not include any constant having dimensions. To elaborate his own cosmology further, Dirac provisionally adopted Milne's first principle (he rejected it later, in 1939) but replaced the second hypothesis—which conflicted with Eddington's idea that atomic constants should play a role in cosmology—with his large-number hypothesis. As a result the spiral nebulas (then the furthest objects known, from whose behavior Edwin Hubble had deduced his recession law) had to recede in time according to $t^{1/3}$, and the curvature of the three-dimensional space had to be zero. Relativity did not enter these reasonings; Dirac expected it to play only a subsidiary role in cosmology, since Hubble's law provided a natural speed at any point of space—and therefore a natural time axis. To reconcile this position with his admiration for Einstein's theory of gravitation, Dirac introduced two different metrics for atomic and cosmic phenomena. Only the second one was ruled by Einstein's theory; the first one varied in time according to the large-number hypothesis.

Cosmology was not just a hobby for Dirac. Rather, as he explained in 1939, it embodied his notion of progress in physics—an ever increasing mathematization of the world. In the old mechanistic conception, the equations of motion were mathematical but the initial conditions were given by observation. In the new cosmology the state preceding the initial explosion (posited by Georges Lemaître) was so simple that any complexity in nature pertained to the mathematical evolution. In this context Dirac even expressed the hope that the history of the universe would be only a history of the properties of numbers from 1 to 10^{39}. From the 1970's to the end of his life he often came back to his cosmological ideas. His large-number hypothesis has been seriously considered by several astrophysicists in spite of its speculative character.

Classical Point Electron, Indefinite Metrics. The rest of Dirac's work, from the 1930's on, centered on quantum electrodynamics. Dirac remained true to the research method that he had developed in his early work. He never reached his ultimate aim, a mathematically clean theory, but left interesting by-products of his quest. All the creators of quantum mechanics attempted to deal with the disease of infinite self-energy. One possibility they discussed was a revision of the correspondence basis, the classical theory of electrodynamics, which already involved either ambiguities (dependence on the structure of a finite electron) or infinite self-energy (for point electrons). In 1938 Dirac created a finite theory of point electrons by a convenient "reinterpretation" of the Maxwell-Lorentz equations that canceled the infinite self-mass. In spite of its formal beauty, this theory involved unphysical "runaway" solutions (spontaneously accelerating electrons) that could be eliminated (at the classical level) only at the price of making supraluminal signals possible. Not fully conscious of the latter difficulty, Dirac brought his equations to the Hamiltonian form and quantized them. Unfortunately, only half the divergent integrals of quantum electrodynamics were

DIRAC

cured by this procedure. To take care of the other half, Dirac imagined in 1942 a nonpositive (he called it "indefinite") metric in Hilbert space that allowed a new natural representation of the field commutation rules but implied negative probabilities difficult to interpret physically. Pauli admired the new formalism but criticized Dirac's artificial interpretation of it, which involved a "hypothetical world" initially (before collisions occur in the real world) empty of photons and filled up with positrons (to dry out the sea).

In 1946 Dirac realized that his new equations allowed a finite nonperturbative solution; in addition, they could be connected with the regular formalism (with only positive probabilities) by a change of representation, that is, a unitary transformation in Hilbert space. Although not able to explicate this transformation (which presumably would reintroduce infinities), Dirac concluded in 1946 that the difficulties of quantum electrodynamics were purely mathematical. During the next year other theorists realized that the difficulties were connected instead with a proper definition of physical parameters like charge and mass. Nonetheless, the indefinite metric proved to be indispensable in quantum field theory for another reason: a covariant quantization of Maxwell's field requires the introduction of (unobservable) states of negative probability. In the 1960's several theorists, including Heisenberg, also developed Dirac's idea of a finite quantum electrodynamics with indefinite metrics.

Relativistic Ether, Strings. Developed by other physicists in 1947, renormalization, a way to absorb infinities in a proper redefinition of mass and charge, allowed very successful calculations of higher-order corrections to atomic and electrodynamical processes. From this resulted the best numerical agreement ever encountered between a fundamental theory and experiment. Always more concerned with internal beauty than with experimental verdict, Dirac called it a "fluke" and kept searching for a closed quantum electrodynamics purged of infinities at every stage of calculation. His point of view quickly became heterodox as more and more theorists thought that quantum electrodynamics did not have to exist by itself, but only as a part of a more general theory encompassing other types of interactions. As if to stress his originality, Dirac did not show any interest in the growing but messy field of nuclear and particle physics.

Some of Dirac's late attempts at a new quantum electrodynamics brought fundamentally new ideas. For instance, in 1951 he resurrected ether, arguing that quantum theory allowed a Lorentz invariant notion of ether for which all drift speeds at a given point of space-time are equiprobable, in analogy with the S states of the hydrogen atom, which are invariant by rotation although the underlying classical model is not. The idea had come to him after the proposal of a new electrodynamics for which the potential is restricted by $A_\mu A^\mu = k^2$, which suggests a natural ether speed $v_\mu = k^{-1}A_\mu$, even in the absence of matter.

In 1955 Dirac proposed strings as the basic representation of quantum electrodynamics, a photon corresponding to a closed string and an electron corresponding to the extremity of an open string. Originally suggested by a manifestly gauge-invariant formulation of quantum electrodynamics in which the electron is explicitly dragging an electromagnetic field with it, this picture "made inconceivable the things we do not want to have," for instance, a physically meaningless "bare" electron.

The Lagrangian in Quantum Mechanics. None of the above-mentioned attempts questioned the basic frame of quantum mechanics that Dirac had established in his younger years. But all through his scientific career he looked for alternative or more general formulations of quantum mechanics that might be more suitable for relativistic applications. Some of the products of this kind of exploration proved to be of essential importance. For instance, in 1933, exploiting a relation discovered by Jordan between quantum canonical transformations and the corresponding classical generating functions, he found that the transformation (q_{t+T}/q_t) from q taken at time t to q taken at time $t + T$ "corresponded" to $\exp i\int_t^{t+T} L(q, \dot{q})\, dt$, where L denotes the Lagrangian and $q(t)$, the classical motion between q_t and q_{t+T}. In the same paper he introduced the "generalized transformation functions," substituting the covariant motion of timelike surface of measurement for the usual hyperplanes "t = constant" in four-dimensional space. The remark about the Lagrangian, generalized by Dirac himself in 1945 to provide the amplitude of probability of a trajectory, inspired Richard Feynman in his discovery of the "Feynman-integrals," now the most efficient method of quantization. The "general transformation function" was adopted by the Japanese school to suggest, in combination with Dirac's multitime theory, Tomonaga's manifestly covariant formulation of quantum electrodynamics (1943).

The Role of Mathematics. Dirac believed in a "mathematical quality of nature." In the ideal physical theory, the whole of the description of the universe would have its mathematical counterpart. Conversely, he claimed around 1924, at one of Baker's tea parties, that any really interesting mathematical theory should find an application in the physical world. After sufficient progress, the field of mathematics would be purified and reduced to applied mathematics, that is, theoretical physics. The foundation of this belief in an asymptotic convergence of mathematics and physics is not easy to trace in Dirac's writings, since he generally avoided philosophical discussion. What could be said mathematically was clear enough to him, and he did not require, as most philosopher-physicists would, a recourse to common language to improve understanding. When circumstances compelled him to epistemological statements—for instance, in the foreword to his *Principles*—he simply borrowed them from physicist-philosophers who were "right by definition": Bohr and Eddington. From both these masters he took the rejection of mental pictures in space-time of the old physics. From Eddington he had the idea of a "nonpicturable substratum" and the recognition, through the development and justification of transformation theories, of "the part played by the observer in himself introducing the regularity that appears in his observations, and the lack of arbitrariness in the ways of nature."

It is doubtful that Dirac regarded these statements as really meaningful. When expressing his personal feelings on the role of mathematics, his leitmotiv was the idea of "mathematical beauty." For him the main reason for the successful appearance of groups of transformations in modern theories was their mathematical beauty, something no more subject to definition than beauty in art, but obvious to the connoisseur. In this perspective the mathematical quality of nature could be just the expression of its beauty. More significantly, Dirac's requirement of beauty materialized into a methodology: one had first to select the most beautiful mathematics and then, following Eddington's "principle of identification," try to connect it to the physical world.

To implement the first stage of this methodology, a more definite notion of beauty is needed. Dirac constantly refers to the museum of his early beautiful mathematical experiences. First comes the magic of projective geometry, exemplifying the power to find surprising relations between picturable mathematical objects through simple, invisible manipulations. Then follows general relativity with the appearance of symmetry transformations, and tensor calculus perceived as a symphony of symbols. At the moment of its introduction, beauty excludes rigor. Exact mathematical meaning comes after a heuristic symbolic stage, as in the introduction of the δ-function or of the q-numbers. It is less difficult, according to Dirac, to find beautiful mathematics than to interpret it in physical terms. Here is perhaps the most creative part of his work, invoking subtle analogies and correspondence with older bits of theories.

On the whole, Dirac's method sounds highly a priori, but he occasionally insisted on the necessity of a proper balance between inductive and deductive methods. A more detailed analysis would also show that where he was the most successful, he always remained securely tied to the empirically solid parts of existing theories.

BIBLIOGRAPHY

I. Original Works. A list of Dirac's publications is in the biography by Dalitz and Peierls (see below). His main works are "The Fundamental Equations of Quantum Mechanics," in *Proceedings of the Royal Society of London*, **A109** (1925), 642–653; "On the Theory of Quantum Mechanics," *ibid.*, **A112** (1926), 661–677; "The Physical Interpretation of the Quantum Dynamics," *ibid.*, **A113** (1927), 621–641; "The Quantum Theory of Emission and Absorption of Radiation," *ibid.*, **A114** (1927), 243–265; "The Quantum Theory of the Electron, I," *ibid.*, **A117** (1928), 610–624; *The Principles of Quantum Mechanics* (Oxford, 1930); "A Theory of Electrons and Protons," in *Proceedings of the Royal Society of London*, **A126** (1930), 360–365; "Quantized Singularities in the Electromagnetic Field," *ibid.*, **A133** (1931), 60–72; and "The Cosmological Constants," in *Nature*, **139** (1937), 323. Nontechnical writings include "The Relation Between Mathematics and Physics," in *Royal Society of Edinburgh, Proceedings*, **59** (1939), 122–129; "The Evolution of the Physicist's Picture of Nature," in *Scientific American*, **208**, no. 5 (1963), 45–53; *The Development of Quantum Theory* (New York, 1971); and "Recollections of an Exciting Era," in Charles Weiner, ed., *History of Twentieth-Century Physics* (New York, 1977), 109–146.

Some of Dirac's papers have been deposited at the Churchill College Archive, Cambridge. Photocopies of manuscripts and letters, and an interview by Thomas S. Kuhn, are available in the Archive for the History of Quantum Physics (Berkeley, Copenhagen, London, New York, Rome).

II. Secondary Literature. Joan Bromberg, "The Concept of Particle Creation Before and After Quantum Mechanics," in *Historical Studies in the Physical Sciences*, **7** (1976), 161–183, and "Dirac's Quantum Electrodynamics and the Wave-Particle Equivalence," in Charles Weiner, ed., *History of Twentieth-Century Physics* (New York, 1977), 147–157; Hendrik Casimir, "Paul Dirac, 1902–1984," in *Naturwissenschaftliche Rundschau*, **38** (1985), 219–223; R. H. Dalitz and Sir Rudolf Peierls, "Paul Adrien

Maurice Dirac," in *Biographical Memoirs of Fellows of the Royal Society*, **32** (1986), 137–185; Olivier Darrigol, "La genèse du concept de champ quantique," in *Annales de physique*, **9** (1984), 433–501, and "The Origins of Quantized Matter Waves," in *Historical Studies in the Physical and Biological Sciences*, **16**, no. 2 (1986), 197–253; Michelangelo de Maria and Francesco La Teana, "Schrödinger's and Dirac's Unorthodoxy in Quantum Mechanics," in *Fundamenta scientiae*, **3** (1982), 129–148; Norwood R. Hanson, *The Concept of the Positron* (Cambridge, 1963); Max Jammer, *The Conceptual Development of Quantum Mechanics* (New York, 1966); Helge Kragh, "The Genesis of Dirac's Relativistic Theory of Electrons," in *Archive for the History of Exact Sciences*, **24** (1981), 31–67, "The Concept of the Monopole," in *Studies in History and Philosophy of Science*, **12** (1981), 141–172, "Cosmo-physics in the Thirties: Towards a History of Dirac's Cosmology," in *Historical Studies in the Physical Sciences*, **13**, no. 1 (1982), 69–108, and, as editor, *Methodology and Philosophy of Science in Paul Dirac's Physics*, University of Roskilde text no. 27 (Roskilde, 1979); B. N. Kursunoglu and E. P. Wigner, eds., *Reminiscences About a Great Physicist* (Cambridge, 1987); Jagdish Mehra and Helmut Rechenberg, *The Historical Development of Quantum Theory*, IV, *The Fundamental Equations of Quantum Mechanics* (New York, 1982); Donald F. Moyer, "Origins of Dirac's Electron, 1925–1928," in *American Journal of Physics*, **49** (1981), 944–949, "Evaluation of Dirac's Electron," *ibid*., 1055–1062, and "Vindication of Dirac's Electron," *ibid*., 1120–1135; Abdus Salam and Eugene P. Wigner, eds., *Aspects of Quantum Theory* (Cambridge, 1972); and J. G. Taylor, ed., *Tribute to Paul Dirac* (Bristol, 1987).

OLIVIER DARRIGOL

DIRICHLET, GUSTAV PETER LEJEUNE (*b*. Düren, Germany, 13 February 1805; *d*. Göttingen, Germany, 5 May 1859)

Dirichlet, the son of the town postmaster, first attended public school, then a private school that emphasized Latin. He was precociously interested in mathematics; it is said that before the age of twelve he used his pocket money to buy mathematical books. In 1817 he entered the Gymnasium in Bonn. He is reported to have been an unusually attentive and well-behaved pupil who was particularly interested in modern history as well as in mathematics.

After two years in Bonn, Dirichlet was sent to a Jesuit college in Cologne that his parents preferred. Among his teachers was the physicist Georg Simon Ohm, who gave him a thorough grounding in theoretical physics. Dirichlet completed his *Abitur* examination at the very early age of sixteen. His parents wanted him to study law, but mathematics was already his chosen field. At the time the level of pure mathematics in the German universities was at a low ebb: Except for the formidable Carl Gauss in Göttingen, there were no outstanding mathematicians, while in Paris the firmament was studded by such luminaries as P.-S. Laplace, Adrien Legendre, Joseph Fourier, Siméon Poisson, Sylvestre Lacroix, J.-B. Biot, Jean Hachette, and Francoeur.

Dirichlet arrived in Paris in May 1822. Shortly afterward he suffered an attack of smallpox, but it was not serious enough to interrupt for long his attendance at lectures at the Collège de France and the Faculté des Sciences. In the summer of 1823 he was fortunate in being appointed to a well-paid and pleasant position as tutor to the children of General Maximilien Fay, a national hero of the Napoleonic wars and then the liberal leader of the opposition in the Chamber of Deputies. Dirichlet was treated as a member of the family and met many of the most prominent figures in French intellectual life. Among the mathematicians, he was particularly attracted to Fourier, whose ideas had a strong influence upon his later works on trigonometric series and mathematical physics.

Dirichlet's first interest in mathematics was number theory. This interest had been awakened through an early study of Gauss's famous *Disquisitiones arithmeticae* (1801), until then not completely understood by mathematicians. In June 1825 he presented to the French Academy of Sciences his first mathematical paper, "Mémoire sur l'impossibilité de quelques équations indéterminées du cinquième degré." It dealt with Diophantine equations of the form

$$x^5 + y^5 = A \cdot z^5$$

using algebraic number theory, Dirichlet's favorite field throughout his life. By means of the methods developed in this paper Legendre succeeded, only a few weeks later, in giving a complete proof that Fermat's equation

$$x^n + y^n = z^n$$

has no integral solutions ($x \cdot y \cdot z \neq 0$) for $n = 5$. Until then only the cases $n = 4$ (Fermat) and $n = 3$ (Euler) had been solved.

General Fay died in November 1825, and the next year Dirichlet decided to return to Germany, a plan strongly supported by Alexander von Humboldt, who worked for the strengthening of the natural sciences in Germany. Dirichlet was permitted to qualify for habilitation as *Privatdozent* at the University of Breslau; since he did not have the required doctorate, this was awarded *honoris causa* by the University of Cologne. His habilitation thesis dealt with polynomials whose prime divisors belong to special arithmetic series. A second paper from this period was inspired by Gauss's announcements on the biquadratic law of reciprocity.

Dirichlet was appointed extraordinary professor in Breslau, but the conditions for scientific work were not inspiring. In 1828 he moved to Berlin, again with the assistance of Humboldt, to become a teacher of mathematics at the military academy. Shortly afterward, at the age of twenty-three, he was appointed extraordinary (later ordinary) professor at the University of Berlin. In 1831 he became a member of the Berlin Academy of Sciences, and in the same year he married Rebecca Mendelssohn-Bartholdy, granddaughter of the philosopher Moses Mendelssohn.

Dirichlet spent twenty-seven years as a professor in Berlin and exerted a strong influence on the development of German mathematics through his lectures, through his many pupils, and through a series of scientific papers of the highest quality that he published during this period. He was an excellent teacher, always expressing himself with great clarity. His manner was modest; in his later years he was shy and at times reserved. He seldom spoke at meetings and was reluctant to make public appearances. In many ways he was a direct contrast to his lifelong friend, the mathematician Karl Gustav Jacobi.

The two exerted some influence upon each other's work, particularly in number theory. When, in 1843, Jacobi was compelled to seek a milder climate for reasons of health, Dirichlet applied for a leave of absence and moved with his family to Rome. A circle of leading German mathematicians gathered around the two. Dirichlet remained in Italy for a year and a half, visited Sicily, and spent the second winter in Florence.

Dirichlet's first paper dealing with Fermat's equation was inspired by Legendre; he returned only once to this problem, showing the impossibility of the case $n = 14$. The subsequent number theory papers dating from the early years in Berlin were evidently influenced by Gauss and the *Disquisitiones*. Some of them were improvements on Gauss's proofs and presentation, but gradually Dirichlet cut much deeper into the theory. There are papers on quadratic forms, the quadratic and biquadratic laws of reciprocity, and the number theory of fields of quadratic irrationalities, with the extensive discussion of the Gaussian integers $a + ib$, where $i = \sqrt{-1}$ and a and b are integers.

At a meeting of the Academy of Sciences on 27 July 1837, Dirichlet presented his first paper on analytic number theory. In this memoir he gives a proof of the fundamental theorem that bears his name: Any arithmetical series of integers

$$an + b, n = 0, 1, 2, \cdots,$$

where a and b are relatively prime, must include an infinite number of primes. This result had long been conjectured and Legendre had expended considerable effort upon finding a proof, but it had been established only for a few special cases, such as

$$\{4n + 1\} = 1, 5, 9, 13, 17, 21, \cdots$$
$$\{4n + 3\} = 3, 7, 11, 15, 19, 23, \cdots.$$

The paper on the primes in arithmetic progressions was followed in 1838 and 1839 by a two-part paper on analytic number theory, "Recherches sur diverses applications de l'analyse infinitésimale à la théorie des nombres." Dirichlet begins with a few general observations on the convergence of the series now called Dirichlet series. The main number theory achievement is the determination of the formula for the class number for quadratic forms with various applications. Also from this period are his studies on Gaussian sums.

These studies on quadratic forms with rational coefficients were continued in 1842 in an analogous paper on forms with coefficients that have Gaussian coefficients. It contains an attempt at a systematic theory of algebraic numbers when the prime factorization is unique, although it is restricted to Gaussian integers. It is of interest to note that here one finds the first application of Dirichlet's *Schubfachprinzip* ("box principle"). This deceptively simple argument, which plays an important role in many arguments in modern number theory, may be stated as follows: If one distributes more than n objects in n boxes, then at least one box must contain more than one object.

It is evident from Dirichlet's papers that he searched very intently for a general algebraic number theory valid for fields of arbitrary degree. He was aware of the fact that in such fields there may not be a unique prime factorization, but he did not succeed in creating a substitute for it: the ideal theory later created by Ernst Kummer and Richard Dedekind or the form theory of Leopold Kronecker.

Dirichlet approached the problem through a generalization of the quadratic forms, using the properties of decomposable forms representable as the product of linear forms, a method closely related to the method later used by Kronecker. One part of algebraic number theory, the theory of units, had its beginning in Dirichlet's work. He had earlier written a number of papers on John Pell's equation

$$x^2 - Dy = N,$$

with particular consideration of the cases in which $N = \pm 1$ corresponds to the units in the quadratic field

$K(\sqrt{D})$. But in the paper "Zur Theorie der complexen Einheiten," presented to the Berlin Academy on 30 March 1846, he succeeded in establishing the complete result for the Abelian group of units in an algebraic number field: When the field is defined by an irreducible equation with r real roots and s pairs of complex roots, the number of infinite basis elements is $r + s - 1$; the finite basis element is a root of unity.

After these fundamental papers, the importance of Dirichlet's number theory work declined. He published minor papers on the classes of ternary forms, on the representation of integers as the sum of three squares, and on number theory sums, together with simplifications and new proofs for previous results and theories.

In 1863, Dirichlet's *Vorlesungen über Zahlentheorie* was published by his pupil and friend Richard Dedekind. To the later editions of this work Dedekind most appropriately added several supplements containing his own investigations on algebraic number theory. These addenda are considered one of the most important sources for the creation of the theory of ideals, which has now become the core of algebraic number theory.

Parallel with Dirichlet's investigations on number theory was a series of studies on analysis and applied mathematics. His first papers on these topics appeared during his first years in Berlin and were inspired by the works of the French mathematicians whom he had met during his early years in Paris. His first paper on analysis is rather formal, generalizing certain definite integrals introduced by Laplace and Poisson. This paper was followed in the same year (1829) by a celebrated one published in *Crelle's Journal,* as were most of his mathematical papers: "Sur la convergence des séries trigonométriques qui servent à représenter une fonction arbitraire entre deux limites données." The paper was written under the influence of Fourier's theory of heat conduction as presented in his *Théorie analytique de la chaleur.*

Dirichlet and several other mathematicians had been impressed by the properties of the Fourier series on trigonometric series

$$\tfrac{1}{2}a_0 + (a_1 \cos x + b_1 \sin x) + (a_2 \cos 2x + b_2 \sin 2x) + \cdots,$$

particularly by their ability to represent both continuous and discontinuous functions. Such series, although now commonly named for Fourier, had already been used by Daniel Bernoulli and Leonhard Euler to examine the laws of vibrating strings. The convergence of the series had been investigated shortly before Dirichlet in a paper by Cauchy (1823). In the introduction to his own paper Dirichlet is sharply critical of Cauchy on two accounts: first, he considers Cauchy's reasoning invalid on some points; second, the results do not cover series for which the convergence had previously been established.

Dirichlet proceeds to express the sum of the first n terms in the series corresponding formally to the given function $f(x)$ and examines the case in which the difference between $f(x)$ and the integral tends to zero. In this manner he establishes the convergence to $f(x)$ of the corresponding series, provided $f(x)$ is continuous or has a finite number of discontinuities. Dirichlet's method later became classic; it has served as the basis for many later investigations on the convergence or summation of a trigonometric series to its associated function under much more general conditions.

Dirichlet returned to the same topic a few years later in the article "Über die Darstellung ganz willkürlicher Functionen durch Sinus- und Cosinusreihen," published in the *Repertorium der Physik* (1837), a collection of review articles on mathematical physics on which his friend Jacobi collaborated. An outstanding feature of this article is Dirichlet's abandonment of the until then universally accepted idea of a function as an expression formulated in terms of special mathematical symbols or operations. Instead, he introduces generally the modern concept of a function $y = f(x)$ as a correspondence that associates with each real x in an interval some unique value denoted by $f(x)$. His concept of continuity is, however, still intuitive. For his continuous functions he defines integrals by means of sums of equidistant function values and points out that the ordinary integral properties all remain valid. On this basis the theory of Fourier series is then developed. In a related paper, "Solution d'une question relative à la théorie mathématique de la chaleur" (1830), Dirichlet uses his methods to simplify the treatment of a problem by Fourier: the temperature distribution in a thin bar with given temperatures at the endpoints.

Closely related to these investigations is the paper "Sur les séries dont le terme général dépend de deux angles et qui servent à exprimer des fonctions arbitraires entre des limites données" (1837). The Fourier series can be considered as expansions of functions defined on a circle. In this paper Dirichlet examines analogously the convergence of the expansion in spherical harmonics (*Kugelfunctionen*) of functions defined on a sphere. He later applied these results in several papers on problems in theoretical physics.

Dirichlet's contributions to general mechanics began with three papers published in 1839. All three have nearly the some content; the most elaborate has the title "Über eine neue Methode zur Bestimmung vielfacher Integrale." All deal with methods based upon a so-called discontinuity factor for evaluating multiple integrals, and they are applied particularly to the problem of determining the attraction of an ellipsoid upon an arbitrary mass point outside or inside the ellipsoid.

In the brief article "Über die Stabilität des Gleichgewichts" (1846), Dirichlet considers a general problem inspired by Laplace's analysis of the stability of the solar system. He takes the general point of view that the particles attract or repel each other by forces depending only on the distance and acting along their central line; in addition, the relations connecting the coordinates shall not depend on time. Stability is defined as the property that the deviations of the coordinates and velocities from their initial values remain within fixed, small bounds. Dirichlet criticizes as unsatisfactory the previous analyses of the problem, particularly those by Lagrange and Poisson that depended upon infinite series expansions in which terms above the second order were disregarded without sufficient justification. Dirichlet avoids this pitfall by reasoning directly on the properties of the expression for the energy of the system.

One of Dirichlet's most important papers bears the long title "Über einen neuen Ausdruck zur Bestimmung der Dichtigkeit einer unendlich dünnen Kugelschale, wenn der Werth des Potentials derselben in jedem Punkte ihrer Oberfläche gegeben ist" (1850). Here Dirichlet deals with the boundary value problem, now known as Dirichlet's problem, in which one wishes to determine a potential function $V(x,y,z)$ satisfying Laplace's equation

$$\frac{\delta^2 V}{\delta x^2} + \frac{\delta^2 V}{\delta y^2} + \frac{\delta^2 V}{\delta z^2} = 0$$

and having prescribed values on a given surface, in Dirichlet's case a sphere. This type of problem plays an important role in numerous physical and mathematical theories, such as those of potentials, heat, magnetism, and electricity. Mathematically it can be extended to an arbitrary number of dimensions.

Among the later papers on theoretical mechanics one must mention "Über die Bewegung eines festen Körpers in einem incompressibeln flüssigen Medium" (1852), which deals with the motion of a sphere in an incompressible fluid; it is noteworthy for containing the first exact integration for the hydrodynamic equations. This subject occupied Dirichlet during his last years; in his final paper, "Untersuchungen über ein Problem der Hydrodynamik" (1857), he examines a related topic, but this includes only a minor part of his hydrodynamic theories. After his death, his notes on these subjects were edited and published by Dedekind in an extensive memoir.

In 1855, when Gauss died, the University of Göttingen—which had long enjoyed the reflection of his scientific fame—was anxious to seek a successor of great distinction, and the choice fell upon Dirichlet. His position in Berlin had been relatively modest and onerous, and the teaching schedule at the military academy was very heavy and without scientific appeal. Dirichlet wrote to his pupil Kronecker in 1853 that he had little time for correspondence, for he had thirteen lectures a week and many other duties to attend to. Dirichlet responded to the offer from Göttingen that he would accept unless he was relieved of the military instruction in Berlin. The authorities in Berlin seem not to have taken the threat very seriously, and only after it was too late did the Ministry of Education offer to improve his teaching load and salary.

Dirichlet moved to Göttingen in the fall of 1855, bought a house with a garden, and seemed to enjoy the more quiet life of a prominent university in a small city. He had a number of excellent pupils and relished the increased leisure for research. His work in this period was centered on general problems of mechanics. This new life, however, was not to last long. In the summer of 1858 Dirichlet traveled to a meeting in Montreux, Switzerland, to deliver a memorial speech in honor of Gauss. While there, he suffered a heart attack and was barely able to return to his family in Göttingen. During his illness his wife died of a stroke, and Dirichlet himself died the following spring.

BIBLIOGRAPHY

Many of Dirichlet's works are in L. Kronecker and L. Fuchs, eds., *G. Lejeune Dirichlets Werke, herausgegeben auf Veranlassung der Königlichen Preussischen Akademie der Wissenschaften,* 2 vols. (Berlin, 1889–1897). Included are a portrait; a biography by E. Kummer; correspondence with Gauss, Kronecker, and Alexander von Humboldt; and material from Dirichlet's posthumous papers.

Several of Dirichlet's papers have been reissued in the series Ostwalds Klassiker der exacten Wissenschaften: no. 19, *Über die Anziehung homogener Ellipsoide* (*Über eine neue Methode zur Bestimmung vielfacher Integrale*), which includes papers by other writers (1890); no. 91, *Untersuchungen über verschiedene Anwendungen der Infinitesimalanalysis auf die Zahlentheorie* (1897); and no. 116, *Die Darstellung ganz willkürlicher Functionen durch Sinus- und Cosinusreihen* (1900).

Dirichlet's lectures have been published in G. Arendt, *Vorlesungen über die Lehre von den einfachen und mehr-*

fachen bestimmten Integrale (1904); R. Dedekind, *Vorlesungen über Zahlentheorie* (1893); and F. Grube, *Vorlesungen über die im umgekehrten Verhältniss des Quadrats der Entfernung wirkenden Kräfte* (1876).

OYSTEIN ORE

DODGSON, CHARLES LUTWIDGE (*b.* Daresbury, Cheshire, England, 27 January 1832; *d.* Guildford, Surrey, England, 14 January 1898)

Dodgson was the thirdborn of the eleven offspring of Charles Dodgson, a clergyman, and his wife and cousin, the former Frances Jane Lutwidge. All the children stuttered, and Charles Lutwidge himself is said to have spoken without impediment only to the countless nymphets whom, over decades of adulthood, he befriended, wrote wonderful letters to, entertained, and photographed (often nude) with considerable artistry. The obvious inference from this attraction to young girls seems invalid, for he was strongly undersexed. (Even in the Victorian milieu his puritanism was barely credible: for instance, he nursed a project to bowdlerize Bowdler's Shakespeare, and he demanded assurance from one of his illustrators that none of the work would be done on Sundays.) He was never wholly at ease in the company of grown-ups. Friendship with the three small daughters of Dean Liddell resulted in the celebrated *Alice* books, published under a pseudonym that he had first used in 1856 as a writer of light verse—Lewis Carroll. *Alice* brought him fame, money, and the posthumous honor of becoming the most-quoted litterateur in English discursive scientific writing of the twentieth century.

In our concern here with Dodgson's professional achievements, we must bear in mind that his vocational mathematics and his avocational nonsense commingle in a vein of logic that was his salient characteristic as a thinker. For years it was fashionable to point to the gap between mathematics and ingenious nonsense (and the other nineteenth-century master of nonsense, Edward Lear, was most unmathematical); but today we are aware that, at least in some places, the gap is not that wide. The modern view, that Dodgson was all of a piece, is simpler to sustain. His analytical mind is reflected everywhere in his writings, whose quaintness by no means damages clarity. The pity is that his talents were inhibited by ignorance and introversion, for he made no attempt to keep abreast of contemporary advances in mathematics and logic or to discuss his ideas with other academics.

Dodgson's pedestrian career unfolded without hitch. Graduated from Oxford in 1854, he became master of arts there three years later. Meanwhile, in 1855, he had been appointed lecturer in mathematics at his alma mater, Christ Church College, Oxford. In 1861 he was ordained in the Church of England, although he was never to perform any ecclesiastic duties. As a young man he made a trip to Russia, but later journeyings were restricted to London and quiet seaside vacations. Marriage was unthought of, and Dodgson entered into no close friendships. (Perhaps his acquaintanceship with Ellen Terry, the great actress, most nearly qualified for "close friendship.") He took some part in the administration of his college and was proud of his finicky management of its wine cellars. A part-time inventor of trivia, he devised several aids to writing in the dark—to assuage his chronic insomnia and to help dispel the nameless "unholy thoughts" that occasionally pestered him. But generally speaking his placidity was so well rooted that he was able to make the extraordinary statement, "My life is free from all trial and trouble."

As a lecturer Dodgson was drear; and when he gave up the chore, he noted ruefully that his first lecture had been attended by nine students and his last (twenty-five years later) by two. Away from the classroom he wrote assiduously; and his publications, in book form or pamphlet (a favorite medium), are respectably numerous. His scholarly output falls into four main groups; determinants, geometry, the mathematics of tournaments and elections, and recreational logic. He was modest enough to describe his activities as being "chiefly in the lower branches of Mathematics."

Dodgson's work on determinants opened with a paper in the *Proceedings of the Royal Society* for 1866, and this was expanded into a book that appeared the following year. *An Elementary Treatise on Determinants* is good exposition, but favorable reception was prevented by the author's extensive use of ad hoc terms and symbols.

Dodgson's writings on geometry became well known; it was a subject about which he was almost passionate. His initial contribution was *A Syllabus of Plane Algebraic Geometry* (1860), a textbook whose purpose was to develop analytic geometry along rigorous Euclidean lines. He also published pamphlets on this and related themes, in one of which he introduced an original but not particularly meritorious notation for the trigonometric ratios. His most interesting effort in this genre was a five-act comedy entitled *Euclid and His Modern Rivals,* about a mathematics lecturer, Minos, in whose dreams Euclid debates his original *Elements* with such modernizers as Legendre and J. M. Wilson and, naturally, routs the opposition. The book is an attack on the changing method of teaching classical geometry and not, as is sometimes assumed, on non-Euclidean geometry. Indeed, Dodgson showed himself keenly aware of the infirmity of the fifth postulate (on parallels), and he has his oneiric Euclid admit that "some mysterious flaw lies at the root of the subject." The interesting point here is that Riemann's revolutionary geometry was well established during Dodgson's lifetime, and an English translation of the key paper was available. This is yet another instance of Dodgson's being out of touch with the mathematical research of his day. The Euclid drama (which is most engagingly written) apparently was used as ancillary reading in English schools for a number of years.

Least known but quite praiseworthy is Dodgson's work on tournaments and voting theory. His interest stemmed from two sources: the organization of tennis tournaments and the mechanism of arriving at fair decisions by administrative committees. He decided that both matters needed rethinking. As usual, he did not bother to check the literature and so was unaware that the topic had come in for learned discussion in France before and during the Revolution. However, Dodgson unwittingly improved on existing ideas. His initial publication (a pamphlet, in 1873) reviews different methods of arriving at a fair majority opinion, and he sensibly advocates the use of degrees of preference in voting schedules. His whole approach is fresh and thoughtful, and he was the first to use matrix notation in the handling of multiple decisions.

In contrast with his mathematics, Dodgson's work on logic was written entirely under his pseudonym, which clearly testifies to his view that the subject was essentially recreational. Traditional formal logic had long been a barren and overrated discipline; but during his lifetime a renaissance in technique and significance was taking place, and most of the pioneers were his countrymen. Although he was not ignorant of the new trends, their importance either escaped him or was discountenanced. Dodgson was attracted by the contemporary interest in the diagrammatization of the logic of classes, and he had read and appreciated Venn's seminal contributions. In fact, he modified Venn diagrams by making their boundaries linear and by introducing colored counters that could be moved around to signify class contents—a very simple and effective device. On these foundations Dodgson published a game of logic that featured various forms (some very amusing) of the syllogism. His casual realization of the connections between symbolic logic and mathematics might have become vivid and fruitful had he been properly acquainted with what had already been done in the area. But he did not do the necessary reading—there is, for instance, no indication that he had read Boole's *Laws of Thought,* although he owned a copy! Finally, Dodgson was a prolific composer of innocent-looking problems in logic and paradox, some of which were to engage the attention of professional logicians until well into the twentieth century.

BIBLIOGRAPHY

I. Original Works. The authoritative conspectus of Dodgson's writings, which included sixteen books (six for children) and hundreds of other items, is S. H. Williams and F. Madan, *A Handbook of the Literature of the Rev. C. L. Dodgson (Lewis Carroll)* (London, 1931; supp., 1935). Two outstanding books are *An Elementary Treatise on Determinants* (London, 1867) and *Euclid and His Modern Rivals* (London, 1879). His initial publication on election theory, *A Discussion of the Various Procedures in Conducting Elections* (Oxford, 1873), is a rare pamphlet, only one copy being known; it is at Princeton. The Morris L. Parrish Collection of Victorian Novelists, in Princeton University library, contains the biggest mass of Dodgsoniana, much of it MS. Warren Weaver, in *Proceedings of the American Philosophical Society,* **98** (1954), 377–381, tells the history of this collection and gives some examples of its mathematical items. Dodgson's two books on recreational mathematics are now available in a 1-vol. paperback: *Pillow Problems and a Tangled Tale* (New York, 1958). Similarly, his two books on logic are bound together in the paperback *Symbolic Logic, and the Game of Logic* (New York, 1958).

II. Secondary Literature. Dodgson's nephew, S. D. Collingwood, published the first biography, in the same year as his subject's death: *The Life and Letters of Lewis Carroll* (London, 1898). It remains a primary source book. Among many subsequent biographies and evaluations, Florence Becker Lennon's *Victoria Through the Looking Glass* (New York, 1945), esp. ch. 15, is notable for its perceptive treatment of Dodgson's serious side. R. L. Green, *The Diaries of Lewis Carroll* (London, 1953), is important, although many of the entries on logic and mathematics have been excised or glossed over. Two papers prepared for the centenary of Dodgson's birth are essential reading: R. B. Braithwaite, "Lewis Carroll as Logician," in *Mathematical Gazette,* **16** (1932), 174–178; and D. B. Eperson, "Lewis Carroll—Mathematician," *ibid.,* **17** (1933), 92–100. His work on tournaments and elections is examined in Duncan Black's *The Theory of Committees and Elections* (Cambridge, 1958). Martin Gardner's *New Mathematical Diversions* (New York, 1966), ch. 4, deals with Dodgson's work on games and puzzles. The same author's earlier books, *The Annotated Alice* (New York, 1960) and *The Annotated Snark* (New York, 1962), provide remarkable insights into the logico-mathematical undercurrents in Dodgson's fantasia.

Norman T. Gridgeman

DOMINICUS DE CLAVASIO, also known as **Dominicus de Clavagio, Dominicus Parisiensis,** or **Dominic de Chivasso** (*fl.* mid-fourteenth century)

Dominicus de Clavasio's birthdate is unknown, but he was born near Turin and was active in Paris from about the mid-1340's. He taught arts at Paris during 1349–1350, was head of the Collège de Constantinople at Paris in 1349, and was an M.A. by 1350. Dominicus received the M.D. by 1356 and was on the medical faculty at Paris during 1356–1357. He was astrologer at the court of John II and may have died between 1357 and 1362.

Dominicus is the author of a *Practica geometriae* written in 1346; a *questio* on the *Sphere* of Sacrobosco; a *Questiones super perspectivam;* a set of *questiones* on the first two books of the *De caelo* of Aristotle, written before 1357; and possibly a commentary on Aristotle's *Meteorology.* He mentions in the *Practica* his intention to write a *Tractatus de umbris et radiis.*

The *questiones* on the *De caelo* have not been edited, although a few that are concerned with physical problems have been examined. They reveal that Dominicus is part of the tradition established at Paris during the fourteenth century by Jean Buridan, Nicole Oresme, and Albert of Saxony. Like these Parisian contemporaries, he adopted the impetus theory as an explanation of projectile motion as well as of acceleration in free fall. Also like his colleagues at Paris, Dominicus considered impetus as a quality. As is true of the *Questiones de caelo* of Albert of Saxony, Dominicus' discussions of impetus reveal the influence of both Oresme and Buridan. If Dominicus were directly familiar with Oresme's conceptions of impetus, he most likely drew them from the latter's early Latin *questiones* on the *De caelo* and obviously not from his much later French *Du ciel.* According to Dominicus, a body in violent motion possessed both impetus and an "actual force" (*virtus actualis*), although the relationship between these factors is unclear. Also, as Nicole Oresme may have done, he may have connected impetus with acceleration rather than velocity.

The *Practica* was a popular work during the Middle Ages and has survived in numerous manuscript versions. It served, for example, as a model for a *Geometria culmensis,* written in both Latin and German near the end of the fourteenth century. The *Practica* is divided into an introduction and three books. The introduction contains arithmetical rules and the description of an instrument, the *quadratum geometricum* of Gerbert. Book I deals with problems of measurement, book II contains geometrical constructions of two-dimensional figures, and book III is concerned with three-dimensional figures. In the course of the *Practica,* Dominicus mentions Ptolemy and the thirteenth-century mathematician and astronomer Campanus of Novara.

The *Questiones super perspectivam* reveal Dominicus' familiarity with the standard authors of the medieval optical tradition, such as Witelo, al-Rāzī (Rhazes), Roger Bacon, Peckham, and Ibn al-Haytham (Alhazen). His work is not based, however, on the influential *Perspectiva communis* of Peckham but is a commentary on the *De aspectibus* of Ibn al-Haytham and the latter's Latin successor, Witelo.

Insofar as his thought has been examined, Dominicus de Clavasio appears not as an innovator but as a fairly conventional continuator of well-established medieval traditions.

BIBLIOGRAPHY

I. ORIGINAL WORKS. H. L. L. Busard, ed., "The *Practica geometriae* of Dominicus de Clavasio," in *Archives for History of Exact Sciences,* **2** (1962–1966), 520–575, contains the entire text; Graziella Federici Vescovini, "Les questions de 'perspective' de Dominicus de Clivaxo," in *Centaurus,* **10** (1964–1965), 14–28, contains an edition of questions 1 and 6.

II. SECONDARY LITERATURE. On Dominicus or his work, see A. von Braunmühl, *Vorlesungen über Geschichte der Trigonometrie,* I (Leipzig, 1900), 107–110; M. Cantor, *Vorlesungen über Geschichte der Mathematik,* II (Leipzig, 1899), 127, 150–154, 450–452; M. Clagett, *The Science of Mechanics in the Middle Ages* (Madison, Wis., 1959), pp. 635, 636, note; M. Curtze, "Über den Dominicus parisiensis der *Geometria culmensis,*" in *Bibliotheca mathematica,* 2nd ser., **9** (1895), 107–110; and "Über die im Mittelalter zur Feldmessung benutzten Instrumente," *ibid.,* **10** (1896), 69–72; G. Eneström, "Über zwei angebliche mathematische Schulen im christlicher Mittelalter," in *Bibliotheca mathematica,* 3rd ser., **7** (1907), 252–262; Anneliese Maier, *Zwei Grundprobleme der scholastischen Naturphilosophie* (Rome, 1951), pp. 241–243; *An der Grenze von Scholastik und Naturwissenschaft* (Rome, 1952), pp. 121, 209; *Metaphysische Hintergrunde der spätscholastischen Naturphilosophie* (Rome, 1955), p. 365, note; and *Zwischen Philosophie und Mechanik* (Rome, 1958), p. 218; H. Mendthal, ed., *Geometria culmensis. Ein agronomischer Tractat aus der Zeit des Hochmeisters Conrad von Jungingen, 1393–1407* (Leipzig, 1886), which contains the Latin and German texts of the *Geometria culmensis;* K. Michalski, "La physique nouvelle et les différents courants philosophiques au xive siècle," in *Bulletin international de l'Académie polonaise des sciences et des lettres. Classe d'histoire et de philosophie, et de philologie* (Cracow), *année 1927* (1928), 150; P. Tannery, *Mémoires scientifiques,* V, J. L. Heiberg, ed. (Paris, 1922), 329–330, 357–358; Lynn Thorndike, *A History of Magic and Experimental Science,* III (New York, 1934), 587–588; *The Sphere of Sacro-*

bosco and Its Commentators (Chicago, 1949), p. 37; and E. Wickersheimer, *Dictionnaire biographique des médecins en France au moyen âge* (Paris, 1936), p. 121.

CLAUDIA KREN

DOMNINUS OF LARISSA (*b.* Larissa, *fl.* fifth century A.D.)

Domninus was a Syrian Jew of Larissa on the Orontes. (In his entry in the *Suda Lexicon* Larissa is regarded as identical with Laodicea, but they appear to have been separate towns.) He became a pupil of Syrianus, head of the Neoplatonic school at Athens, and a fellow student of Proclus. He therefore lived in the fifth century of the Christian era.

Syrianus thought equally highly of Domninus and Proclus, and Marinus relates how he offered to discourse to them on either the Orphic theories or the oracles; but Domninus wanted Orphism, Proclus the oracles, and they had not agreed when Syrianus died. Marinus implies that Domninus succeeded to Syrianus' chair, but if so, he can only have shared it for a short time with Proclus. Their disagreement widened into a controversy over the true interpretation of Platonic doctrine from which Proclus emerged as the victor in the eyes of the Academy. Domninus withdrew to Larissa, and Damascius, the last head of the Neoplatonic school, while admitting Domninus' mathematical competence, accused him of being old-fashioned in philosophical matters. This may have been a partisan judgment. Nor need we pay much attention to an anecdote related by him and intended to show that Domninus lacked the true philosophic mind: When Domninus was troubled by spitting blood and the Aesculapian oracle at Athens prescribed that he should eat swine's flesh, he had no scruples about so doing despite the precept of his Jewish religion. Equally suspect are Damascius' allegations that when advanced in years Domninus loved only the conversation of those who praised his superiority and that he would not admit to his company a young man who argued with him about a point in arithmetic.

Nothing has survived of his philosophical teachings. A reference by Proclus (*In Timaeum,* I.34B; Diehl, ed., I. 109. 30–110.12) indicates that Domninus took some interest in natural science. He held that comets were composed of a dry, vapor-like substance, and he explained the myth of Phaëthon by the assumption that the earth once passed through such a comet, the substance of which was ignited by the sun's rays and which in turn set the earth on fire.

It is on his mathematical work that his claim to remembrance rests. Nothing was known of this work until 1832, when J. F. Boissonade edited from two Paris manuscripts his Ἐγχειρίδιον ἀριθμητικῆς εἰσαγωγῆς ("Manual of Introductory Arithmetic"), and it was not until 1884 that its importance was recognized. Paul Tannery, who in the following year made a critical revision of Boissonade's text, then perceived that this brief work marked a reaction from the arithmetical notions of Nicomachus and a return to the sounder principles of Euclid. It may not be without significance that, according to Marinus, Proclus had become convinced by a dream that he possessed the soul of Nicomachus of Gerasa. Whereas numbers had been represented by Euclid as straight lines, Nicomachus had departed from this convention and, when dealing with unknown quantities, was forced into clumsy circumlocutions; he also introduced highly elaborate classifications of numbers, serving no useful purpose and difficult to justify. Proclus, according to the *Suda Lexicon,* wrote a commentary on Nicomachus' work, but without openly controverting him, Domninus, in the concise and well-ordered text edited by Boissonade, quietly undermines it. As Hultsch recognized, the book is arranged in five parts: an examination of numbers in themselves, an examination of numbers in relation to other numbers, the theory of numbers both in themselves and in relation to others, the theory of means and proportions, and the theory of numbers as figures. In general Domninus follows Euclid in his classification of numbers and departs from Nicomachus. He is content with the arithmetic, geometric, and harmonic means and finds no use for Nicomachus' seven other means. Like Euclid, he admits only plane and solid numbers. In writing this manual Domninus drew not only upon Euclid and Nicomachus but upon Theon of Smyrna and upon a source used by Iamblichus that has since disappeared.

At the end of the manual Domninus avows his intention of setting forth certain subjects more fully in an Ἀριθμητικὴ στοιχείωσις ("Elements of Arithmetic"). Whether he did so is not known, but a tract with the title Πῶς ἔστι λόγον ἐκ λόγου ἀφελεῖν ("How to Take a Ratio out of a Ratio"), edited by C. E. Ruelle in 1883, is almost certainly by Domninus and may have been written as part of the projected *Elements.* "Taking a ratio out of a ratio" does not mean subtraction but manipulation of the ratio so as to get it into other forms.

BIBLIOGRAPHY

Most of what is known about the life of Domninus comes from a long entry in the *Suda Lexicon* (Eva Adler, ed.)

that seems to be derived from a lost work by Damascius. There is a short entry in Eudocia, *Violarium* 331, Flach, ed., 239. 7–10. Eudocia's source appears to be the lost *Onomatologos* of Hesychius of Miletus; see Hans Flach, *Untersuchungen ueber Eudoxia und Suidas*, p. 60. A brief notice is given by Marinus, *Vita Procli*, ch. 26, in J. F. Boissonade ed.

Domninus' *Manual of Introductory Arithmetic* may be found in J. F. Boissonade, *Anecdota graeca*, IV (Paris, 1832), 413–429. Paul Tannery commented on it in "Domninos de Larissa," in *Bulletin des sciences mathématiques et astronomiques*, 2nd ser., **8** (1884), 288–298, repr. in his *Mémoires scientifiques*, II (Paris-Toulouse, 1912), 105–117; he revised Boissonade's text at points in "Notes critiques sur Domninos," in *Revue de philologie*, **9** (1885), 129–137, repr. in *Mémoires scientifiques*, II, 211–222; he translated the work into French, with prolegomena, as "Le manuel d'introduction arithmétique du philosophe Domninos de Larissa," in *Revue des études grecques*, **19** (1906), 360–382, repr. in *Mémoires scientifiques*, III (1915), 255–281.

"How to Take a Ratio out of a Ratio" is printed with a French translation, a commentary, and additional notes by O. Riemann, in C. E. Ruelle, "Texte inédit de Domninus de Larissa sur l'arithmétique avec traduction et commentaire," in *Revue de philologie*, **7** (1883), 82–92, with an addendum by J. Dumontier explaining the mathematical import, pp. 92–94.

There is a useful summary by F. Hultsch, "Domninos," in Pauly-Wissowa, *Real-Encyclopädie*, V (1903), cols. 1521–1525.

IVOR BULMER-THOMAS

DOPPELMAYR, JOHANN GABRIEL (*b.* Nuremberg, Germany, 1671 [?]; *d.* Nuremberg, 1 December 1750)

Doppelmayr's father, Johann Siegmund Doppelmayr, was a merchant who made a hobby of experiments in physics and, according to his son, was the first to introduce into Nuremberg an air pump equipped with a lever and standing upright "like a flower vase."

After graduating from the Aegidien Gymnasium, Doppelmayr entered the University of Altdorf in 1696 with the intention of studying law; but there he heard the lectures on mathematics and physics of Johann Cristoph Sturm, founder of the Collegium Curiosum sive Experimentale and reputedly the most skilled experimenter in Germany. For a brief while in 1700 Doppelmayr attended the University of Halle, but he then decided to give up law for physics and mathematics, and spent two years traveling and studying in Germany, Holland, and England.

After Doppelmayr's return to Nuremberg, he was appointed in 1704 to the professorship of mathematics at the Aegidien Gymnasium, a post he held until his death. His life was devoted to lecturing, writing, astronomical and meteorological observation, and physical experimentation; his reputation was such as to gain him memberships in the Academia Caesarea Leopoldina, the academies of Berlin and St. Petersburg, and the Royal Society of London.

Doppelmayr's writings are not marked by originality; they do, however, provide an index of the scientific interests and information current in Germany, and particularly of the transmission of science from England, Holland, and France into Germany during the first half of the eighteenth century.

Among the astronomical works are *Kurze Erklärung der Copernicanischen Systems* (1707), *Kurze Einleitung zur Astronomie* (1708), and translations of Thomas Streete's astronomy (1705) and of John Wilkins' defense of the Copernican system (1713). His major work, however, is the *Atlas novus coelestis* (1742), a collection of diagrams with explanations intended as an introduction to the fundamentals of astronomy. Besides star charts and a selenographic map, the *Atlas* includes diagrams illustrating the planetary systems of Copernicus, Tycho, and Riccioli; the elliptic theories of Kepler, Boulliau, Seth Ward, and Mercator; the lunar theories of Tycho, Horrocks, and Newton; and Halley's cometary theory.

Doppelmayr's writings on mathematics include *Summa geometricae practicae;* a memoir on spherical trigonometry; an essay on the construction of the sundial; and a translation (with appendices by Doppelmayr) of Nicolas Bion's treatise on mathematical instruments.

Of lasting value for historians is Doppelmayr's *Historische Nachricht* (1730), a 314-page folio volume giving biographical accounts of over 360 mathematicians, artists, and instrument makers of Nuremberg. The biographies are arranged chronologically from the fifteenth to the eighteenth century.

In physics Doppelmayr continued the experimental tradition of Sturm. His *Physica experimentis illustrata* (1731) is a list, in German, of 700 experiments and demonstrations given before the Collegium Curiosum. The procedures are not described in any detail; they are designed to illustrate such topics as the "subtlety" or fineness of subdivision of various materials, electric and magnetic "effluvia," simple machines, the principles of hydrostatics, the optics of the eye, and so on.

More important is the *Neu-entdeckte Phaenomena* (1744), a well-organized and accurate summary of the electrical experiments and theories of Hawksbee, Gray, and Dufay. This work no doubt helped to create and inform the popular interest in electrical phenomena that spread through Germany in the mid-1740's.

In the last two chapters Doppelmayr proposes a hypothesis to explain away electrical attraction and repulsion as caused by air movements; Dufay's discovery of the opposite characters of vitreous and resinous electricity is reduced to a difference in electric strength of different materials; and in general Doppelmayr returns to the earlier and less promising theoretical outlook of Hawksbee.

Doppelmayr's electrical investigations continued until his death, which followed a severe shock suffered while experimenting with one of the newly invented condensers.

BIBLIOGRAPHY

I. ORIGINAL WORKS. Doppelmayr's writings include *Eclipsis solis totalis cum mora* (Nuremberg, 1706); *Kurze Erklärung der Copernicanischen Systems* (Nuremberg, 1707); *Kurze Einleitung zur Astronomie* (Nuremberg, 1708); *Neue vermehrte Welperische Gnomonica* (Nuremberg, 1708); *Neu-eroffnete mathematische Werck-Schule* (Nuremberg, 1st ed., 1712, 2nd ed., 1720, 3rd ed., 1741), a trans. of Nicolas Bion's *Traité de la construction et des principaux usages des instruments de mathématique; Johannis Wilkins Vertheidigter Copernicus* (Leipzig, 1713), a trans. of Wilkins' essay of 1640 on the probability of earth's being a planet; *Summa geometricae practicae* (Nuremberg, 1718, 1750); *Grundliche Anweisung zur Verfertigung grossen Sonnenuhren und Beschreibung derselben* (Nuremberg, 1719), also in Latin as *Nova methodus parandi sciaterica solaria;* "Animadversiones nonnullae circa eclipsium observationes," in *Academiae Caesareo-Leopoldinae Carolinae naturae curiosum ephemerides,* **2** (1715), Centuriae III et IV, app., 133–136; "Animadversiones circa usum vitrorum planorum in observationibus astronomicis," *ibid.,* **4** (1719), Centuriae VII et VIII, 457–459; "Circa trigonometriam sphaericum," in *Academiae Caesareae Leopoldina-Caroliniae naturae curiosum acta physico-medica . . . exhibentia ephemerides . . .,* **2** (1730), 177–178; *Historische Nachricht von den Nürnbergischen Mathematicis und Künstlern* (Nuremberg, 1730); *Physica experimentis illustrata* (Nuremberg, 1731); *Atlas novus coelestis* (Nuremberg, 1742); and *Neu-entdeckte Phaenomena von bewundernswürdigen Würckungen der Natur, welche bei fast allen Körper zukommenden elektrischen Krafft . . . hervorgebracht werden* (Nuremberg, 1744). J. H. von Mädler mentions as Doppelmayr's first work a Latin trans. (1705) of Streete's *Astronomia Carolina* (1661). George Hadley, in *Philosophical Transactions of the Royal Society,* **42** (1742), 245, refers to published barometrical observations by Doppelmayr for the years 1731–1735.

II. SECONDARY LITERATURE. On Doppelmayr or his work, see *Allgemeine deutsche Biographie,* V, 344–345; J. H. von Mädler, *Geschichte der Himmelskunde,* I (Brunswick, 1873), 129; J. G. Meusel, *Lexikon der vom Jahr 1750 bis 1800 verstorbenen teutschen Schriftsteller* (Leipzig, 1802–1816), II; *Neue deutsche Biographie,* IV, 76; and G. A. Will, *Nürnbergisches Gelehrter-Lexicon,* I (Nuremberg, 1755), 287–290.

CURTIS WILSON

DOPPLER, JOHANN CHRISTIAN (*b.* Salzburg, Austria, 29 November 1803; *d.* Venice, Italy, 17 March 1853)

Christian Doppler was the son of a noted master stonemason. Although he showed talent in this craft, his poor health led his father to plan a career in business for him. Doppler's mathematical abilities were recognized by the astronomer and geodesist Simon Stampfer, at whose advice Doppler attended the Polytechnic Institute in Vienna from 1822 to 1825. Finding the curriculum too one-sided, Doppler returned to Salzburg and pursued his studies privately. He completed the Gymnasium and subsequent philosophical courses in an unusually short time, while tutoring in mathematics and physics. From 1829 to 1833 he was employed as a mathematical assistant in Vienna, and wrote his first papers on mathematics and electricity. In 1835 Doppler was on the point of emigrating to America; he had sold his possessions and had reached Munich when he obtained a position as professor of mathematics and accounting at the State Secondary School in Prague. In 1841 he became professor of elementary mathematics and practical geometry at the State Technical Academy there, during the tenure of which he enunciated his famous principle. He had become an associate member of the Königliche Böhmische Gesellschaft der Wissenschaften in Prague in 1840 and was made a full member in 1843. Doppler moved to the Mining Academy at Schemnitz (Banská Štiavnica) in 1847 as *Bergrat* and professor of mathematics, physics, and mechanics. As a result of the turbulence of 1848–1849 he returned to Vienna; there, in 1850, he became director of the new Physical Institute, which was founded for the training of teachers, and full professor of experimental physics at the Royal Imperial University of Vienna, the first such position to exist in Austria. Doppler had suffered from lung disease since his years at Prague. A trip to Venice in 1852 was of no avail, and he died there the following year, survived by his wife and five children.

Doppler's scientific fame rests on his enunciation of the Doppler principle, which relates the observed frequency of a wave to the motion of the source or the observer relative to the medium in which the wave is propagated. This appears in his article "Ueber das farbige Licht der Doppelsterne und einiger anderer

Gestirne des Himmels" (read 25 May 1842). The correct elementary formula is derived for motion of source or of observer along the line between them; the extension to the motion of both at the same time appears in an article of 1846. Doppler mentions the application of this result both to acoustics and to optics, particularly to the colored appearance of double stars and to the fluctuations of variable stars and novae. The reasoning in the latter arguments was not always very cogent; for example, he believed that all stars were intrinsically white and emitted only or mainly in the visible spectrum. The colors which he believed to be characteristic of double stars, then, were to have their origin in the Doppler effect. It should be noted that Doppler worked under rather isolated circumstances, being the earliest important physicist in Austria in the nineteenth century. He was unable to justify in his own mind the application of his principle to transverse vibrations of light, an extension performed by B. Bolzano shortly afterwards.

The first experimental verification of the acoustical Doppler effect was performed by Buys Ballot at Utrecht in 1845, using a locomotive drawing an open car with several trumpeters. Buys Ballot also criticized the unsound assumptions upon which Doppler had based his astronomical applications. Doppler replied to these and similar criticisms in a rather stubborn and unconvincing fashion. The acoustical effect was also noted and commented on at the British Association meeting in 1848 by John Scott Russell and by H. Fizeau in the same year, perhaps without knowledge of Doppler's work. Fizeau pointed to the usefulness of observing spectral line shifts in the application to astronomy, a point of such importance that the principle is sometimes called the Doppler-Fizeau principle. Although in 1850 the Italian astronomer Benedict Sestini had published data on star colors apparently supporting Doppler's application of his principle to double stars, its valid astronomical use had to wait until proper spectroscopic instrumentation was available, beginning with the work of the English astronomer William Huggins in 1868. The optical effect was first confirmed terrestrially by Belopolsky in 1901. Modified by relativity theory, the Doppler principle has become a major astronomical tool.

Doppler's principle itself was criticized by the Austrian mathematician Joseph Petzval in 1852, on the basis of an incorrect mathematical argument. Doppler defended himself to good effect in this situation. Doppler also published works of less importance on related optical effects (Bradley's aberration of light; dependence of intensity on the motion of the source; the deviation of waves by a rotating medium, as, for example, an ethereal atmosphere rotating with a star), optical instruments, and topics in mathematics and physics, especially in geometry, optics, and electricity.

BIBLIOGRAPHY

I. Original Works. Doppler's papers on his principle and related topics are found in *Abhandlungen von Christian Doppler,* ed. with notes by H. A. Lorentz (Leipzig, 1907), Ostwald's Klassiker der exakten Wissenschaften, no. 161. A list of most of his publications appears in Poggendorff, I, 594–595. The statement of his principle, "Ueber das farbige Licht der Doppelsterne und einiger anderer Gestirne des Himmels," in *Abhandlungen der Konigl. Böhmischen Gesellschaft der Wissenschaften,* 5th ser., **2** (1842), 465, was also published separately (Prague, 1842). The extension of motion to both source and observer appeared in *Annalen der Physik und Chemie,* **68** (1846), 1–35.

II. Secondary Literature. See the obituary by Anton Schrötter in *Almanach der Kaiserlichen Akademie der Wissenschaften,* **4** (1854), 112–120; further information appears in Julius Scheiner, "Johann Christian Doppler und das nach ihm benannte Prinzip," in *Himmel und Erde,* **8** (1896), 260–271. Some of his ideas and accomplishments are described in B. Bolzano, "Christ. Doppler's neueste Leistungen auf dem Gebiete der physikalischen Apparatenlehre, Akustik, Optik und optischen Astronomie," in *Annalen der Physik und Chemie,* **72** (1847), 530–555.

A. E. Woodruff

DOSITHEUS (*fl.* Alexandria, second half of the third century B.C.)

He was a friend or pupil of Conon, and on the latter's death, Archimedes, who had been in the habit of sending his mathematical works from Syracuse to Conon for discussion in the scientific circles of Alexandria, chose Dositheus as the recipient of several treatises, including *On the Quadrature of the Parabola, On Spirals, On the Sphere and the Cylinder* (two books), and *On Conoids and Spheroids.* At the beginning of the first of these Archimedes says, "Having heard that Conon has died, who was a very dear friend of mine, and that you have been an acquaintance of his and are a student of geometry . . . I determined to write and send you some geometrical theorems, as I have been accustomed to write to Conon" (Heiberg, ed., II, 262). The preambles to the other works make it clear that Dositheus on his side often wrote to Archimedes requesting the proofs of particular theorems. Nothing is known about Dositheus' own mathematical work.

His astronomical work seems to have been concerned mainly with the calendar. He is cited four times in the calendar attached to Geminus' *Isagoge* (Manitius, ed., p. 210 ff.) and some forty times in Ptolemy's *Phaseis* for weather prognostications (ἐπισημασίαι) such as formed part of a *parapegma*, a type of almanac, originally engraved on stone or wood and later transmitted in manuscript form—like the two mentioned above—giving astronomical and meteorological phenomena for the days of each month (cf. A. Rehm, "Parapegmastudien," in *Abhandlungen der Bayerischen Akademie der Wissenschaften*, phil.-hist. Abt., n.s., vol. **19** [1941]). Dositheus may have made observations in the island of Cos (*Phaseis*, p. 67. 4, Heiberg, ed.—but the text here is insecure; cf. *proleg.* cliii note 1) as well as in Alexandria.

According to Censorinus (*De die natali*, 18, 5), Dositheus wrote on the *octaëteris* (an eight-year intercalation cycle) of Eudoxus, and he may be the Dositheus Pelusiotes (Pelusium, at the northeastern extremity of the Egyptian delta) mentioned as providing information about the life of Aratus (*Theonis Alexandrini vita Arati*, §2, Maas, ed.—but spelled here Δωσίθεος).

BIBLIOGRAPHY

In addition to the works cited in the text, see F. Hultsch, "Dositheos 9," in Pauly-Wissowa, *Real-Encyclopädie*, X (1905), cols. 1607–1608.

D. R. DICKS

DOUGLAS, JESSE (*b.* New York, N.Y., 3 July 1897; *d.* New York, 7 October 1965)

Douglas became interested in mathematics while he was still a high school student; in his freshman year at the City College of New York he became the youngest person ever to win the college's Belden Medal for excellence in mathematics. He graduated with honors in 1916 and began graduate studies with Edward Kasner at Columbia University. From 1917 to 1920 (in which year he was awarded the doctorate) he also participated in Kasner's seminar in differential geometry; here he developed his love for geometry and first encountered the problem of Plateau.

From 1920 to 1926 Douglas remained at Columbia College, teaching and doing research, primarily in differential geometry. Between 1926 and 1930 he was a National Research fellow at Princeton, Harvard, Chicago, Paris, and Göttingen; during this period he also devised a complete solution to the problem of Plateau, of which the essential features were published in a series of abstracts in the *Bulletin of the American Mathematical Society*, between 1927 and 1930, while a detailed presentation appeared in the *Transactions of the American Mathematical Society* for January 1931. This solution won Douglas the Fields Medal at the International Congress of Mathematicians in Oslo in 1936.

Douglas was appointed to a position at the Massachusetts Institute of Technology in 1930 and taught there until 1936; he was a research fellow at the Institute for Advanced Study at Princeton in the academic year 1938–1939 and received Guggenheim Foundation fellowships for research in analysis and geometry in 1940 and 1941. From 1942 until 1954 he taught at Brooklyn College and at Columbia University, then in 1955 returned to City College, where he spent the rest of his life.

Douglas' work with the problem of Plateau was again rewarded in 1943 when he received the Bôcher Memorial Prize of the American Mathematical Society for his memoirs "Green's Function and the Problem of Plateau" (in *American Journal of Mathematics*, **61** [1939], 545 ff.), "The Most General Form of the Problem of Plateau" (*ibid.*, **61** [1939], 590 ff.), and "Solution of the Inverse Problem of the Calculus of Variations" (in *Transactions of the American Mathematical Society*, **50** [1941], 71–128). The problem of Plateau was apparently first posed by Lagrange about 1760, and had occupied many mathematicians—most notably Riemann, Weierstrass, and Schwarz—in the period from 1860 to 1870. The problem is concerned with proving the existence of a surface of least area bounded by a given contour. Prior to Douglas' solution, mathematicians had succeeded in solving a number of special cases, as when, in the nineteenth century, a solution was obtained for a contour that is a skew quadrilateral having a plane of symmetry. Douglas' solution of 1931 is highly generalized; indeed, it is valid when the contour is any continuous, closed, nonintersecting curve whatever (Jordan curve)—it may even be in space of any number of dimensions. (R. Garnier in 1927 and T. Radó in 1930 had succeeded in solving the problem with less generality by using alternative methods.)

Having disposed of the most fundamental instance of the problem of Plateau--a single given contour and a simply connected minimal surface—Douglas went on to consider surfaces bounded by any finite number of contours and to consider surfaces of higher topological structure—as, for example, one-sided surfaces or spherical surfaces with any number of attached handles or any number of perforations. Between 1931 and 1939 he gave solutions to such problems as these and formulated and solved other general forms of the problem.

The problem of Plateau did not represent Douglas' sole mathematical interest, however. In 1941 he published a complete solution of the inverse problem of the calculus of variations for three-dimensional space—a problem unsolved until then, although in 1894 Darboux had stated and solved the problem for the two-dimensional case. In addition to publishing some fifty papers on geometry and analysis, Douglas' work in group theory is notable; in 1951, he made significant contributions to the problem of determining all finite groups on two generators, A and B, which have the property that every group element can be expressed in the form $A^r B^s$, where r and s are integers.

BIBLIOGRAPHY

I. ORIGINAL WORKS. *Scripta mathematica,* **4** (1936), 89–90, contains a bibliography of Douglas' publications prior to 1936. A complete bibliography of his works is on file in the mathematics department of the City College of New York.

II. SECONDARY LITERATURE. Some information on Douglas' life prior to 1936 may be found in *Scripta mathematica,* **4** (1936), 89–90. In the near future the National Academy of Science will publish a biography of Douglas, including a complete bibliography of his publications. An obituary of Douglas can be found in the *New York Herald Tribune* (8 Oct. 1965).

NORMAN SCHAUMBERGER

DRACH, JULES JOSEPH (*b.* Sainte-Marie-aux-Mines, near Colmar, France, 13 March 1871; *d.* Cavalaire, Var, France, 8 March 1941)

Drach was born a few months before the Treaty of Frankfurt, by which Alsace ceased to be French. His father, Joseph Louis Drach, and mother, the former Marie-Josèphe Balthazard, modest farmers from the Vosges, took refuge with their three sons at Saint-Dié. From his youth Drach had to work for an architect in order to help his family. He was, however, able to attend elementary school and, at the urging of his teachers, who obtained a scholarship for him, went on to the *collège* in Saint-Dié and then to the lycée in Nancy. Drach was admitted at the age of eighteen to the École Normale Supérieure. Without attempting to make up his failure of the *agrégation*, and encouraged by Jules Tannery, he devoted himself to research and obtained the *doctorat-ès-sciences* in 1898. He taught at the universities of Clermont-Ferrand, Lille, Poitiers (where he married Mathilde Guitton), Toulouse, and Paris (1913), where his courses in analytical mechanics and higher analysis were well received. Drach was elected to the Académie des Sciences in 1929 and was a member of many scientific commissions. His poor health obliged him to reside in Provence for most of the year. His son Pierre entered the École Normale Supérieure in 1926 and had a brilliant career as a biologist.

After retiring to his estate at Cavalaire, Drach pursued his mathematical researches and indulged his love of reading, being interested in the plastic arts as well as in the sciences. Marked by the ordeals of his youth, he always remained close to the poor and was actively involved in the improvement of land held by the peasants.

Drach's mathematical researches display great unity. Galois's algebraic theory, with its extension to linear differential equations just made by Émile Picard (1887), seemed to him to be a model of perfection. He proposed to elucidate the fundamental reason for such a success in order to be able to extend it to the study of differential equations in the most general cases, asserting that the theory of groups is inseparable from the study of the transcendental quantities of integral calculus.

To what he termed the "geometric" point of view, in which one introduces supposedly given functions whose nature is not specified, Drach opposed the "logical" problem of integration, which consists of classifying the transcendental quantities satisfying the rational system verified by the solutions. For this process he introduced the notion of the "rationality group," whose reducibility and primitiveness he investigated. This bold conception, of an absolute character, foreshadowed the axiomatic constructions that were subsequently developed. In discovering regular methods permitting one to foresee the reductions in the difficulties of integration, Drach gave an account of the results obtained before him by Sophus Lie, Émile Picard, and Ernest Vessiot. He completed these and thus extended the special studies concerning, for example, the ballistic equations and those determining families of curves in the geometry of surfaces, such as the "wave surface."

Besides numerous articles in various journals and notes published in the *Comptes rendus . . . de l'Académie des sciences* over some forty years, Drach, with his colleague and friend Émile Borel, prepared for publication a course given at the Faculté des Sciences in Paris by Henri Poincaré—*Leçons sur la théorie de l'élasticité* (Paris, 1892)—and one given by Jules Tannery at the École Normale Supérieure, *Introduction à l'étude de la théorie des nombres et de l'algèbre supérieure* (Paris, 1895). Moreover, he played a large role in preparing for publication, under the auspices of the Académie des Sciences, the works of Henri Poincaré (11 vols., 1916–1956).

BIBLIOGRAPHY

Drach's papers include "Essai sur une théorie générale de l'intégration et sur la classification des transcendantes," in *Annales de l'École normale supérieure*, 3rd ser., **15** (1898), 243–384; "Sur le problème logique de l'intégration des équations différentielles," in *Annales de la Faculté des sciences de Toulouse*, 2nd ser., **10** (1908), 393–472; "Recherches sur certaines déformations remarquables à réseau conjugué persistant," *ibid.*, pp. 125–164; "Le système complètement orthogonal de l'espace euclidien à *n* dimensions," in *Bulletin de la Société mathématique de France*, **36** (1908), 85–126; "Sur l'intégration logique des équations différentielles ordinaires," in *Cambridge International Congress of Mathematicians. 1912*, I (Cambridge, 1913), 438–497; and "Equations différentielles de la balistique extérieure," in *Annales de l'École normale supérieure*, 3rd ser., **37** (1920), 1–94.

LUCIENNE FÉLIX

DU BOIS-REYMOND, PAUL DAVID GUSTAV (*b.* Berlin, Germany, 2 December 1831; *d.* Freiburg, Germany, 7 April 1889)

Paul du Bois-Reymond was the younger brother of the famous physiologist Emil du Bois-Reymond. He studied first at the French Gymnasium in Berlin, then at the *collège* in Neuchâtel and the Gymnasium in Naumburg. Following the example of his brother, he began to study medicine at the University of Zurich in 1853 and by the next year had published four articles that dealt basically with physiological problems. But soon du Bois-Reymond began to apply his talents to the mathematical and physical sciences. He continued his studies at the University of Königsberg, where, mainly through the influence of Franz Neumann, he turned to the study of mathematical physics, joining his talent for observation with that for making theoretical analyses. He specialized in the study of liquids, especially the areas of liquidity and capillarity. In 1859 he received his doctorate at the University of Berlin on the basis of his dissertation, "De aequilibrio fluidorum." Du Bois-Reymond then became a professor of mathematics and physics at a secondary school in Berlin and continued to devote himself systematically to mathematics until his appointment at the University of Heidelberg in 1865. In 1870 he went from Heidelberg to Freiburg as a professor, and thence to the University of Tübingen, in 1874, as the successor to H. Hankel. From 1884 until the end of his scientific career he occupied a chair of mathematics at a technical college in Berlin.

Du Bois-Reymond worked almost exclusively in the field of infinitesimal calculus, concentrating on two aspects: the theory of differential equations and the theory of the functions of real variables.

Studying the problems of mathematical physics led du Bois-Reymond to the theory of differential equations. He was concerned with these problems at the start of his scientific career and returned to them in the last years of his life. His basic study, *Beiträge zur Interpretation der partiellen Differentialgleichungen mit drei Variablen* (part 1, *Die Theorie der Charakteristiken* [Leipzig 1864]), was one of the first to follow up Monge's idea of the "characteristic" of a partial differential equation. This idea, expressed by Monge for equations of the second order as early as 1784, depended on the geometric expression of the integral of a differential equation as the surface defined by a system of curves. Du Bois-Reymond generalized this for partial differential equations of the *n*th order. These ideas, such as the simple case of a study of contact transformations, led in generalized form to the studies by Lie and Scheffers.

The chief means of solving partial differential equations at that time was by Fourier series. As early as the 1820's Cauchy, Abel, and Dirichlet had pointed out some of the difficulties of the expansion of "arbitrary" function in a Fourier series and of the convergence of this series. These problems contributed substantially to the rebuilding of the foundations of mathematical analysis. One of the first to deal with them systematically was du Bois-Reymond. He published his main results toward the end of the 1860's and in the 1870's—at first under the influence of Riemann's ideas and at a time when the results of Weierstrass' work had not been published and were little known.

He achieved a number of outstanding results. As early as 1868, when he was studying some properties of integrals, du Bois-Reymond expressed both precisely and generally and demonstrated the mean-value theorem for definite integrals, which was then an important aid in the study of Fourier series. This theorem was later expressed independently by Dini (1878), who ascribed it to Weierstrass. The latter, however, developed a similar but more specialized proposition and made no claim to du Bois-Reymond's discovery.

Like other mathematicians who relied on Dirichlet, du Bois-Reymond also originally tried to show that each continuous function in a given interval is necessarily representable by its Fourier series (or another series analogous to a trigonometric one). A decisive turn came in 1873, when du Bois-Reymond published "Über die Fourier'schen Reihen." This article contains an exposition of the chief idea of a construction of a continuous function with a divergent Fourier series at any point. Later he also attempted to show the properties of this continuous function (which has a very complicated construction) using considerations, difficult to comprehend, that concern the infinitely small and the infinitely large (the so-called *Infinitärcalcul*).

Two of the other results of du Bois-Reymond's work should be mentioned. First and foremost is the solution of the problem of the integrability of Fourier series, which he proposed (but did not publish until 1883) and for which he demonstrated certain conditions that made it possible to distinguish Fourier's from other trigonometric series. The second is the solution to a question that concerned mathematicians of that time: the publication (1873) of an example and the precise demonstration of the properties of the function that is continuous in a given interval but without derivatives. This achievement was inspired by Weierstrass.

Du Bois-Reymond was then led to attempt a general exposition of the fundamental concepts of the theory of functions in his book *Die allgemeine Functionentheorie,* the first part of which was published in 1882. Among other things, this work shows that its author was aware that a precise theory of real numbers was needed for the further progress of the theory of functions, but he did not make any real contributions to that progress. Instead, he wrote of the problems of the philosophy of mathematics, recognizing the advantages of different approaches and expressing grave doubts about the usefulness of formalism.

Du Bois-Reymond's work was directed at the basic questions of the mathematical analysis of the time and is marked by both the personality of the author and the state of the mathematics of the period. It appeared before completion of the revision of the foundations of mathematical analysis for which he was striving. Led by sheer mathematical intuition, he did not hesitate to publish even vague considerations and assertions that were later shown to be false. Further developments, some while du Bois-Reymond was still alive, disclosed these weaknesses (e.g., Pringsheim's criticism) and also rapidly outdated his results, even on the main questions. Among them is his attempt to give a general theory of convergence tests. This meant that his work, which had been greatly appreciated by his contemporaries, soon sank into oblivion, although it had included very important questions and notions that were later reflected in the work of such mathematicians as W. H. Young, A. Denjoy, and H. Lebesgue.

BIBLIOGRAPHY

Du Bois-Reymond's "Über die Fourier'schen Reihen" appeared in *Nachrichten von der Gesellschaft der Wissenschaften zu Göttingen* (1873), 571–584. *Die allgemeine Functionentheorie* was translated by G. Milhaud and A. Girot as *Théorie générale des fonctions* (Paris, 1887). On du Bois-Reymond and his work, see (in chronological order), L. Kronecker, "Paul du Bois-Reymond," in *Journal für die reine und angewandte Mathematik,* **104** (1889), 352–354; "P. du Bois-Reymond's literarische Publicationen," in *Mathematische Annalen,* **35** (1890), 463–469; H. Weber, "Paul du Bois-Reymond," *ibid.,* 457–462; *Paul du Bois-Reymond, Zwei Abhandlungen über unendliche (1871) und trigonometrische Reihen (1874),* Ostwalds Klassiker, no. 185 (Leipzig, 1912); *Paul du Bois-Reymond, Abhandlungen über die Darstellung der Funktionen durch trigonometrische Reihen (1876),* Ostwalds Klassiker, no. 186 (Leipzig, 1913); and A. B. Paplauskas, *Trigonometricheskie ryady ot Eylera do Lebega* ("Trigonometrical Series from Euler to Lesbesgue," Moscow, 1966).

LUBOŠ NOVÝ

DUDITH (DUDITIUS), ANDREAS (*b.* Buda [now Budapest], Hungary, 16 February 1533; *d.* Breslau, Germany [now Wrocław, Poland], 23 February 1589)

Andreas Dudith combined political and religious activity with humanist and scientific interests in a manner fairly common in the sixteenth century. Of mixed Hungarian and Italian descent, Dudith was educated in the Hungarian tradition of Erasmian humanism. He traveled widely in Italy, France, and England from 1550 to 1560, serving for a time as secretary to Cardinal Reginald Pole. After attending the Council of Trent in 1562–1563, Dudith received the bishopric of Pécs and performed various diplomatic missions to Poland for the emperors Sigismund II and Maximilian II between 1563 and 1576. Dudith's first marriage in 1567 to Regina Strass, a Polish noblewoman, and his subsequent adherence to Lutheranism brought upon him the condemnation of Rome and weakened his position at the Viennese court. (His second marriage, in 1574, was to Elisabeth Zborowski.) After some political reverses he retired from affairs of state in 1576 and later devoted himself to scientific and theological matters at Breslau, inclining to Calvinist and Socinian doctrines.

Dudith was familiar with the leading intellectual movements of his day; his visits to Italy had acquainted him with humanists and bibliophiles like Paulus Manutius and Giovanni-Vincenzo Pinelli and also with the works of Pietro Pomponazzi and the Paduan Averroists. In the 1570's Dudith took up the study of mathematics and cultivated the friendship of the Englishmen Henry and Thomas Savile and the German Johann Praetorius. Medicine also interested Dudith; he studied Galen and corresponded with many physicians, including the imperial physician Crato. In the breadth of his intellectual interest Dudith was typical of Renaissance humanists, and his library of printed books and manuscripts reflects this encyclopedism. Like many Italians, notably his friend Pinelli, he collected Greek mathematical manuscripts for both their philological and scientific interest. Among his manuscripts were the *Arithmetic* of Diophantus (which he loaned to Xylander to use as the text for the first Latin translation published at Basel in 1575); the *Mathematical Collections* of Pappus; the *Elementa astronomiae* of Geminos (used for the *editio princeps* of 1590); and his own transcription of the *Tetrabiblos* of Ptolemy. Several of these manuscripts were lost following the dispersal of his library, but many of his manuscripts and his 5,000 printed books are now in the Vatican, Paris, Leiden, and various Swedish libraries.

Dudith is known mainly for his contribution to the controversy over the comet of 1577. (Hellman lists more than 100 publications on this comet.) He knew several of the personalities involved in the dispute, including Thomas Erastus, Thaddaeus Hagecius (Hayck), and Tycho Brahe; and a collection of tracts on the topic was dedicated to him in 1580. Although originally interested in the astrology of the *Tetrabiblos* of Ptolemy, Dudith became an opponent of the astrologers. His *De cometarum significatione* shows the influence of Erastus in its rejection of astrology as a vain pseudoscience. Both Dudith and Erastus argued that comets could appear without causing or portending natural or political calamities. (In his first letter to Hagecius, Dudith remarked that astrology was condemned by Christian authorities and, despite his own Calvinist leanings, that astrology infringed upon free will.)

Dudith accepted, however, Aristotle's physical explanation of comets as accidental exhalations of hot air from the earth that rise in the sublunar sphere. But an insistence on mathematical astronomy rather than astrology soon led Dudith to the rejection of Aristotelian physical doctrine. In 1581 Dudith learned in a letter from Hagecius, a believer in astrology, of the latter's observation that the parallax of another comet indicated that the comet was beyond the moon. In his letter of 19 January 1581 to Rafanus, Dudith argued that this observation proved the Aristotelian explanation fallacious. If the comets were terrestrial in origin they could not penetrate beyond the sublunar sphere; if, however, they originated in the immanent heavens comets could not be classified as accidental phenomena. Dudith remarked that many recently observed comets seemed to form and dissolve in the region of permanent things. This fact suggested serious flaws in the Aristotelian system. (Tycho arrived at a similar conclusion from his observation that the 1577 comet had no parallax and must therefore be farther from the earth than was the moon. Tycho also attempted to calculate the orbit of that comet.)

Dudith's use of a mathematically precise observation to criticize a general physical theory of Aristotle's betokens the same kind of dissatisfaction with Aristotelian physical doctrines that was most eloquently expounded in the works of Galileo fifty years later.

BIBLIOGRAPHY

I. ORIGINAL WORKS. Dudith's main scientific work is *De cometarum significatione commentariolus* . . . (Basel, 1579), repr. in the 2nd pt. of *De cometis dissertationes novae clariss. Virorum Th. Erasti, Andr. Duditii* . . . (Basel, 1580). Dedicated to Dudith, it includes Dudith's letter to Erastus of 1 Feb. 1579. Subsequent eds. are: Breslau, 1619; Jena, 1665; Utrecht, 1665. The first letter to Hagecius (26 Sept. 1580) is in J. E. Scheibel, *Astronomische Bibliographie,* II (Breslau, 1786), 160–182, with other materials on the comet of 1577. The second letter (1 Feb. 1581), congratulating Hagecius on his observation of a comet's parallax, appears at the beginning of Thaddaeus Hagecius, *Apodixis physica et mathematica de cometis* (Görlitz, 1581). The letter to Rafanus is in Lorenz Scholtz, *Epistolarum philosophicarum medicinalium, ac chymicarum volumen* (Frankfurt, 1598), letter 28. Details of Dudith's voluminous correspondence are given in the Costil biography cited below.

For Dudith's writings on the marriage of priests see Q. Reuter, *Andreae Dudithii orationes in concil. Trident. Habitae* . . . (Offenbach am Main, 1610). See also the references to Dudith in J. L. E. Dreyer, ed., *Tychonis Brahe opera omnia,* 15 vols. (Copenhagen, 1913–1929), IV, 453, 455; VI, 327–328; VII, 63, 123, 182, 214; VIII, 455.

II. SECONDARY LITERATURE. An excellent biography and bibliography is Pierre Costil, *André Dudith: humaniste hongrois 1533–1589, sa vie, son oeuvre et ses manuscrits grecs* (Paris, 1935). For the controversy on the comet of 1577, see Dreyer, *op. cit.,* IV, 509; C. Doris Hellman, *The Comet of 1577: Its Place in the History of Astronomy* (New York, 1944); and Lynn Thorndike, *A History of Magic and Experimental Science,* 8 vols. (New York, 1923–1958), VI, 67–98, 183–186.

PAUL LAWRENCE ROSE

DUHAMEL, JEAN-MARIE-CONSTANT (*b.* St.-Malo, France, 5 February 1797; *d.* Paris, France, 29 April 1872)

Duhamel's scientific contributions were minor but numerous and pertinent; his teaching and involvement in academic administration were probably the primary sources of his influence. Today his name is best remembered for Duhamel's principle in partial differential equations;[1] Duhamel obtained this theorem in the context of his work on the mathematical theory of heat. Using the techniques of mathematical physics he also studied topics of acoustics. In his interests and approaches Duhamel was clearly in the tradition of the French *géomètres.*

Duhamel entered the École Polytechnique in Paris in 1814, after studying at the lycée of Rennes. The political events of 1816, which caused a reorganization of the school, obliged him to return to Rennes, where he studied law. He then taught in Paris at the Institution Massin and the Collège Louis-le-Grand (probably mathematics and physics) and founded a preparatory school, later known as the École Sainte-Barbe. The subject of his first memoir, presented in 1828,[2] indicates that by this time he was quite involved in current problems of mathematical physics.

Except for one year, Duhamel taught continuously at the École Polytechnique from 1830 to 1869. He was first given provisional charge of the analysis course, replacing Coriolis. He was made assistant lecturer in geodesy in 1831, entrance examiner in 1835, professor of analysis and mechanics in 1836, permanent examiner in 1840, and director of studies in 1844. The commission of 1850 demanded his removal because he resisted a program for change, but he returned as professor of analysis in 1851, replacing Liouville. Duhamel also taught at the École Normale Supérieure and at the Sorbonne. He was known as a good teacher, and students commented especially on his ability to clarify the concept of the infinitesimal, a topic also emphasized in his text.[3] Duhamel's most famous student was his nephew by marriage, J. L. F. Bertrand.

Duhamel's earliest research dealt with the mathematical theory of heat and was based on the work of Fourier and Poisson. It was the subject of the theses, accepted in 1834,[4] that he submitted to the Faculty of Sciences. His first memoir treated heat propagation in solids of nonisotropic conductivity, and the laws that he obtained were later verified experimentally by Henri de Sénarmont.[5] In 1833 Duhamel published a solution for the temperature distribution in a solid with variable boundary temperature. He was considering the situations in which the surface radiates into a medium and in which the temperature of the medium changes according to a known law. His object was to reduce these cases to those of a surface at constant temperature. His method, based on the principle of superposition, generalized a solution by Fourier and substituted, in place of the original temperature function, the sum of a constant temperature term and an integral term (an integral of the rate of change of the temperature function).[6] This method generalizes to Duhamel's principle.

In acoustics Duhamel studied the vibrations of strings, the vibrations of air in cylindrical and conical pipes, and harmonic overtones. For an experimental check on his analysis of a weighted string Duhamel used a novel method whereby a pointer attached to the string leaves a track on a moving plane. His study of the excitation of vibration by the violin bow, based on Poisson's *Mécanique,* used the expression for friction force that had been experimentally determined by Coulomb and Morin. Duhamel was intrigued by harmonic overtones and suggested, independently of Ohm,[7] that one perceives a complex sound as the group of simultaneous sounds into which its vibrations can be decomposed.[8]

NOTES

1. For example, R. Courant and D. Hilbert, *Methods of Mathematical Physics,* II (New York, 1966), 202–204.
2. Published in 1832.
3. Commenting on the disagreement among mathematicians over definitions of the differential, Duhamel pointed out in an introductory note to the second edition of his *Cours d'analyse* (Paris, 1847) that he had changed his own approach. Instead of considering the differential as an infinitely small addition to the variable, as he had done in the first edition, he was now considering differentials as quantities whose ratios in the limit are the same as the ratios of the variables.
4. *Théorie mathématique de la chaleur* (Paris, 1834) and *De l'influence du double mouvement des planètes sur les températures de leur différents points* (Paris, 1834).
5. "Sur la conductibilité des corps cristallisés pour la chaleur," in *Annales de chimie,* **21** (1847), 457–476; "Second mémoire sur la conductibilité des corps cristallisés pour la chaleur," in *Comptes rendus hebdomadaires des séances de l'Académie des sciences,* **25** (1847), 459–461, 707–710; *Annales de chimie,* **22** (1848), 179–211.
6. For a modern discussion of Duhamel's principle and its use in solving heat problems, see H. S. Carslaw and J. C. Jaeger, *Conduction of Heat in Solids,* 2nd ed. (Oxford, 1959), 30–32.
7. G. S. Ohm, "Ueber die Definition des Tons, nebst daran geknüpfter Theorie der Sirene und ähnlicher tonbildender Vorrichtungen," in *Annalen der Physik,* **59** (1843), 513–566.
8. *Comptes rendus,* **27** (1848), 463.

BIBLIOGRAPHY

I. Original Works. A partial listing of Duhamel's textbooks includes *Cours d'analyse,* 2 vols. (Paris, 1840–1841; 2nd ed., 1847); *Cours de mécanique,* 2 vols. (Paris, 1845–1846; 2nd ed., 1853–1854); *Élements de calcul infinitésimal,* 2 vols. (Paris, 1856; 2nd ed., 1860–1861); *Des méthodes dans les sciences de raisonnement,* 3 vols. (Paris, 1865–1873).

His articles include "Sur les équations générales de la

propagation de la chaleur dans les corps solides dont la conductibilité n'est pas la même dans tous les sens," in *Journal de l'École polytechnique*, **13** (1832), *cahier* 21, 356–399; "Sur la méthode générale relative au mouvement de la chaleur dans les corps solides plongés dans des milieux dont la température varie avec le temps," in *Journal de l'École polytechnique*, **14** (1833), *cahier* 22, 20–77; "De l'action de l'archet sur les cordes," in *Comptes rendus hebdomadaires des séances de l'Académie des sciences*, **9** (1839), 567–569; **10** (1840), 855–861; *Mémoires présentés par divers savants à l'Académie des sciences*, **8** (1843) 131–162; "Mémoire sur les vibrations des gaz dans les tuyaux de diverses formes," in *Comptes rendus hebdomadaires des séances de l'Académie des sciences*, **8** (1839), 542–543; *Journal de mathématiques pures et appliquées*, **14** (1849), 49–110; "Sur les vibrations d'une corde flexible chargée d'un ou de plusieurs curseurs," in *Journal de l'École polytechnique*, **17** (1843), *cahier* 29, 1–36; "Sur la résonnance multiple des corps," in *Comptes rendus hebdomadaires des séances de l'Académie des sciences*, **27** (1848), 457–463; and "Sur la propagation de la chaleur dans les cristaux," in *Journal de l'École polytechnique*, **19** (1848), *cahier* 32, 155–188.

For an extended list of Duhamel's papers, see the *Royal Society Catalogue of Scientific Papers, 1800–1863*, II (1868), 376–377; and *1864–1873*, VII (1877), 569.

II. SECONDARY LITERATURE. Not much material is available on Duhamel. For short accounts, see Louis Figuier, *L'année scientifique et industrielle* (*1872*), XVI (Paris, 1873), 537–540; M. Maximilien Marie, *Histoire des sciences mathématiques et physiques*, XII (Paris, 1888), 220–224; and E. Sarrau, "Duhamel," in *Ecole polytechnique, livre du centenaire 1794–1894*, I (Paris, 1894–1897), 126–130.

SIGALIA DOSTROVSKY

DUPIN, PIERRE-CHARLES-FRANÇOIS (*b.* Varzy, France, 6 October 1784; *d.* Paris, France, 18 January 1873)

Dupin grew up in his native Nivernais, where his father, Charles-André Dupin, was a lawyer and legislator. His mother was Cathérine Agnès Dupin (her maiden name was also Dupin). The second of three sons, Dupin graduated in 1803 from the École Polytechnique in Paris as a naval engineer. In 1801, under the guidance of his teacher Gaspard Monge, he had made his first discovery, the cyclid (of Dupin). After assignments in Antwerp, Genoa, and Toulon, he was placed in charge of the damaged naval arsenal on Corfu in 1807. He restored the port, did fundamental research on the resistance of materials and the differential geometry of surfaces, and became secretary of the newly founded Ionian Academy. In 1810, on his way back to France, he was detained by illness at Pisa; and during his convalescence he edited a posthumous book by his friend Leopold Vacca Berlinghierri, *Examen des travaux de César au siège d'Alexia* (Paris, 1812). At the Toulon shipyard in 1813, Dupin founded a maritime museum that became a model for others, such as that at the Louvre. That year he published his *Développements de géométrie.*

In 1816, after some difficulty, Dupin was allowed to visit Great Britain to study its arsenals and other technical installations. The results were published in *Voyages dans la Grande Bretagne entrepris relativement aux services publics de la guerre, de la marine . . . depuis 1816* (1820–1824).

Settling down to a life of teaching and public service, Dupin accepted the position of professor of mechanics at the Paris Conservatoire des Arts et Métiers, a position he held until 1854. His free public lectures, dealing with mathematics and mechanics and their industrial applications, became very popular. His *Applications de géométrie et de mécanique* (1822) was a continuation of the *Développements* but placed greater stress on applications. Many of Dupin's lectures on industry and the arts were published in *Géométrie et mécanique des arts et métiers et des beaux arts* (1825); his *Sur les forces productives et commerciales de France* appeared two years later. In 1824 the king made him a baron.

The *Développements* contains many contributions to differential geometry, notably the introduction of conjugate and asymptotic lines on a surface, the so-called indicatrix of Dupin, and "Dupin's theorem," that three families of orthogonal surfaces intersect in the lines of curvature. A particular case Dupin investigated consisted of confocal quadrics. In the *Applications* we find an elaboration of Monge's theory of *déblais et remblais*—and, hence, of congruences of straight lines, with applications to geometrical optics. Here Dupin, improving on a theorem of Malus's (1807), stated that a normal congruence remains normal after reflection and refraction. He also gave a more complete theory of the cyclids as the envelopes of the spheres tangent to three given spheres and discussed floating bodies. In 1840 he introduced what is now called the affine normal of a surface at a point.

In 1828 Dupin was elected deputy for Tarn, and he continued in politics until 1870. In 1834 he was minister of marine affairs, in 1838 he became a peer, and in 1852 he was appointed to the senate. He tirelessly encouraged the establishment of schools and libraries, the founding of savings banks, the construction of roads and canals, and the use of steam power. In 1855 he reported on the progress of the arts and sciences, as represented at the Paris World Exhibition; the part of the report dealing with Massachusetts was published in English (1865).

Dupin married Rosalie Anne Joubert in 1830. He was a correspondent of the Institut de France (1813) and a member of both the Académie des Sciences (1818) and the Académie des Sciences Morales et Politiques (1832). His older brother, André, known as Dupin *aîné*, was a prominent lawyer and politician.

BIBLIOGRAPHY

I. Original Works. Among Dupin's writings are his ed. of Berlinghierri's *Examen des travaux de César* (Paris, 1812); *Développements de géométrie* (Paris, 1813); *Voyages dans la Grande Bretagne*, 3 vols. (Paris, 1820-1824); *Applications de géométrie et de mécanique des arts et métiers*, 3 vols. (Brussels, 1825); *Sur les forces productives*, 2 vols. (Paris, 1827); "Mémoire sur les éléments du troisième ordre de la courbure des lignes," in *Comptes rendus de l'Académie des sciences*, **26** (1848), 321-325, 393-398; and *Forces productives des nations de 1800 à 1851* (Paris, 1851). For his many economic and technical writings, see A. Legoyt, in *Nouvelle biographie générale*, XIV (1868), 315-326.

II. Secondary Literature. On Dupin's life, see J. Bertrand, *Éloges académiques* (Paris, 1890), pp. 221-246; and A. Morin, *Discours funéraires de l'Institut de France* (Paris, 1873). Dupin's mathematical work is discussed in J. G. Darboux, *Leçons sur la théorie générale des surfaces* (Paris, 1887-1896, see index), and *Leçons sur les systèmes orthogonaux et les coordonnées curvilignes* (Paris, 1898; 2nd ed., 1910), ch. 1.

For information on the Dupin family, I am indebted to M. Baron Romain, Corvol d'Embernard (Nièvre).

Dirk J. Struik

DUPRÉ, ATHANASE LOUIS VICTOIRE (*b.* Cerisiers, France, 28 December 1808; *d.* Rennes, France, 10 August 1869)

After early education at the Collège of Auxerre, Dupré entered the École Normale Supérieure in Paris in 1826, gained first place in science in the *agrégation* of 1829, and immediately took a post at the Collège Royal in Rennes. There he taught mathematics and physical science until, in 1847, he was appointed to the chair of mathematics in the Faculty of Science in Rennes. His last post, from 1866, was as dean of the faculty there. He received the Legion of Honor in 1863 but won no other major honor and was never a member of the Académie des Sciences. He was an ardent Catholic throughout his life.

Dupré's scientific career fell into two parts. In the first, which lasted from his years at the École Normale until about 1859, he contributed to several branches of mathematics and physics. The most important of his papers from this period was his entry of 1858 for the competition in mathematics set by the Académie des Sciences. The paper, a study of an outstanding problem in Legendre's theory of numbers, earned Dupré an honorable mention but only half the prize of 3,000 francs.

During the second period, which covered the remaining ten years of his life, Dupré concerned himself exclusively with the mechanical theory of heat, his main interest being the implications of the theory for matter on the molecular scale. He made an important contribution to the dissemination in France of the newly discovered principles of thermodynamics in nearly forty communications to the Academy, in an entry for the Academy's Prix Bordin in 1866 (which again won him only an honorable mention and half the prize money), and in a successful advanced textbook, *Théorie mécanique de la chaleur* (1869).

BIBLIOGRAPHY

I. Original Works. The most important of Dupré's papers were published in the *Annales de chimie et de physique;* those on the mechanical theory of heat were summarized in the *Théorie mécanique de la chaleur* (Paris, 1869). His entry for the 1858 competition was published as *Examen d'une proposition de Legendre relative à la théorie des nombres* (Paris, 1859).

II. Secondary Literature. The only full biographical sketch, by Simon Sirodot, Dupré's successor as dean of the Faculty of Sciences in Rennes, appeared in the annual publication *Université de France. Académie de Rennes. Rentrée solennelle des facultés des écoles préparatoires de médecine et de pharmacie et des écoles préparatoires à l'enseignement supérieur des sciences et des lettres de l'Académie de Rennes* (Rennes, 1869), pp. 52-57.

Robert Fox

DÜRER, ALBRECHT (*b.* Nuremberg, Germany, 21 May 1471; *d.* Nuremberg, 6 April 1528)

Dürer was the son of Albrecht Dürer (or Türer, as he called and signed himself) the Elder. The elder Dürer was the son of a Hungarian goldsmith and practiced that craft himself. He left Hungary, traveled through the Netherlands, and finally settled in Nuremberg, where he perfected his craft with Hieronymus Holper. He married Holper's daughter Barbara. The printer and publisher Anton Koberger stood godfather to the younger Dürer.

Dürer attended the *Lateinschule* in St. Lorenz and learned goldsmithing from his father. From 1486 to 1489 he studied painting with Michael Wolgemut (then the leading church painter of Nuremberg); in Wolgemut's workshop he was able to learn not only all the standard painting techniques but also wood- and copper-engraving. In 1490, in accordance with the custom of the painter's guild, Dürer went on his *Wanderjahre*. Until 1494 he traveled through the Upper Rhine and to Colmar, Basel, and Strasbourg, presumably making his living as a draftsman.

Dürer returned to Nuremberg and on 7 July 1494 married Agnes Frey, the daughter of Hans Frey. Frey, who had been a coppersmith, had become prosperous as a mechanician and instrument maker. He belonged to that school of craftsmen in metals for which Nuremberg was famous. The marriage brought Dürer's family increased social standing and brought Dürer a generous dowry.

As early as his *Wanderjahre* Dürer had come to appreciate the works of Mantegna and other Italian artists. He wished to learn more of the artistic and philosophical rediscoveries of the Italian Renaissance (he knew from books about the Academy of Florence, modeled on Plato's Academy). Moreover, he had become convinced that the new art must be based upon science—in particular, upon mathematics, as the most exact, logical, and graphically constructive of the sciences. It was this realization that led him to the scientific work for which he was, in his lifetime, as celebrated as for his art. He decided to travel to Italy and in 1494 left his wife in Nuremberg and set off on foot to visit Venice.

On his return to Nuremberg in 1495, Dürer began serious study of mathematics and of the theory of art as derived from works handed down from antiquity, especially Euclid's *Elements* and the *De architectura* of Vitruvius. These years were highly productive for Dürer; in 1497 he adopted his famous monogram to protect his work against being counterfeited. At about the same time he formed an important and lasting friendship with Willibald Pirckheimer, subject of one of his most famous portraits. (Dürer was fortunate in his patrons and friends; besides Pirckheimer these included such humanists as Johannes Werner, the mathematician; Johann Tscherte, the imperial architect; and Nicholas Kratzer, court astronomer to the English King Henry VIII.)

Most important, however, this period marked the beginning of Dürer's experiments with scientific perspective and mathematical proportion. The mathematical formulations of Dürer's anatomical proportion are derived both from antiquity and from the Italian rediscoveries; he drew upon both Polyclitus the Elder and Alberti, and to these he added the notion of plastic harmony after the mode of musical harmony taken from Boethius and Augustine. The earliest of Dürer's documented figure studies to be constructed in accordance with one or several strictly codified canons of proportion date from 1500 and include the study of a female nude (now in London). In addition, critics have pointed out that the head of the famous Munich self-portrait may be shown to have been constructed proportionally.

Throughout the years 1501–1504 Dürer continued to work with the problem of proportion, making numerous studies of men and horses. His copper engraving *Adam and Eve* (1504) marks the high point of his theoretical mastery—the figures were methodically constructed, he wrote, with a compass and a ruler. The preliminary studies for the *Adam and Eve* (now in Vienna) reveal Dürer's method. During this time he also mastered the techniques of linear perspective, as may be seen in his series of woodcuts, *The Life of the Virgin*.

In 1505–1507 Dürer returned to Venice. He extended his Italian travels to Bologna on this occasion, "on account," he wrote, "of secret [knowledge of] perspective." He most probably made the journey to meet with Luca Pacioli, a mathematician and theorist of art. Pacioli's book, *Divina proportione* (in which Leonardo da Vinci collaborated), propounded the notion that the *sectio aurea* (the famous "golden mean" of classical sculpture and architecture), being mathematical in nature, related art to that science exclusively. In Venice, at the close of his second Italian trip, Dürer bought Tacinus' 1505 edition of Euclid, which was henceforth to be his model for mathematical formulation. This period of Dürer's life marks the full maturity of his mathematical, philosophical, and aesthetic theory; in his painting he had begun to realize the full synthesis of late German Gothic and Italian Renaissance painting.

Between 1506 and 1512 Dürer devoted himself to the rigorous study of the problem of form, which presented itself to him in three aspects: true, mathematical form; beautiful, proportional form; and compositional form, used in an actual work of art, ideally the fusion of the preceding. In solving these problems Dürer drew upon the resources of arithmetic and geometry; it was in his achievement as a painter that his formal solutions were meaningful and expressive.

From about 1508 Dürer sketched and wrote down the substance of his theoretical studies (fragments of these notes and drawings are preserved in the notebooks in London, Nuremberg, and Dresden). Some of these fragments may have been intended for inclusion in the encyclopedic *Speis' der Malerknaben* that Dürer had planned to publish; this *Malerbuch* was to have presented his mathematical solutions to all formal problems in the plastic arts. Although the *Malerbuch* was never completed, Dürer extracted a part of it for his major "Treatise on Proportion" (*Proportionslehre*).

In 1520–1521 Dürer traveled to the Netherlands,

particularly Bruges and Ghent, where he saw the works of the early Flemish masters. He returned to Nuremberg ill with malaria; henceforth he devoted himself primarily to the composition and printing of his three major theoretical books. (He continued to paint, however; his pictures from this period include several notable portraits of his friends as well as the important diptych of the *Four Apostles*, given to the city council of Nuremberg by Dürer in 1526 and now in Munich.)

Dürer had completed the manuscript of the "Treatise on Proportion" by 1523, but he realized that a more basic mathematical text was necessary to its full comprehension. For that reason, in 1524–1525, he wrote such a text, the *Underweysung der Messung mit Zirckel und Richtscheyt in Linien, Ebnen und gantzen Corporen* ("Treatise on Mensuration With the Compass and Ruler in Lines, Planes, and Whole Bodies"), which was published by his own firm in Nuremberg in 1525.

The *Underweysung der Messung* is in four books. In the first, Dürer treats of the construction of plane curves (including the spiral of Archimedes, the logarithmic spiral, tangential spirals, conchoids, and so forth) and of helices according to the methods of descriptive geometry. In addition he includes a method for the construction of "Dürer's leaf" (the *folium Dureri*), presents the notion of affinity by the example of the ellipse as a related representation of the circle, and, most important, describes the conic sections in top and front views as well as demonstrating their construction.

In book II Dürer develops a morphological theory of regular polygons and their exact or approximate constructions. He shows how to make use of such constructions as architectural ornaments, in parquet floors, tesellated pavements, and even bull's-eye window panes. The book concludes with theoretical investigations (culminating in the Vitruvian approximation for squaring the circle, a process which had already been noted by Dürer in a proportional study made in Nuremberg in 1504 or 1505) and with the computation of π (as 3.141).

The first part of the third book includes bird's-eye and profile elevations of pyramids, cylinders, and columns of various sorts (in 1510, in Nuremberg, Dürer had already sketched a spiral column with spherical processes). The second part of the book deals with sundials and astronomical instruments; Dürer had a small observatory at his disposal in the house that he had acquired from Bernhard Walther, a student of Regiomontanus, and could also make use of Walther's scientific library, part of which he bought. In the third part of the third book Dürer is concerned with the design of letters and illustrates the construction in a printer's quad of capitals of the Roman typeface named after him as well as an upper- and lowercase *fraktur* alphabet.

In book IV Dürer presents the development of the five Platonic solids (polyhedra) and of several semiregular (Archimedean) solids. He additionally shows how to construct the surfaces of several mixed bodies and, of particular importance, presents an approximate development of the sphere (he had begun work on the last for the construction of the first globe in Nuremberg in 1490–1492; his work on other globes, celestial charts, and armillary spheres is well known). He also shows how to duplicate the cube (the Delian problem) and related bodies, demonstrates the construction of the shadows of illuminated bodies, and finally summarizes the theory of perspective.

Except for the *Geometria Deutsch* (*ca.* 1486–1487), a book of arithmetical rules for builders which Dürer knew and used, the *Underweysung der Messung* is the first mathematics book in German. With its publication Dürer could claim a place in the front ranks of Renaissance mathematicians.

Dürer's next technical publication, the *Befestigungslehre* ("Treatise on Fortifications"), was a practical work dictated by the fear of invasion by the Turks, which gripped all of central Europe. This book was published in Nuremberg in 1527; as well as summarizing the science of fortification it contains some of Dürer's chief architectural work (various other architectural drawings and models are extant). Many of his ideas were put to use; the city of Nuremberg was strengthened according to his plan (in particular the watchtowers were fortified), similar work was undertaken at Strasbourg, and the Swiss town of Schaffhausen built what might be considered a model of Dürer's design with small vaults above and below ground, casemates, and ramparts that still survive intact.

Dürer's third book, his "Treatise on Proportion," *Vier Bücher von menschlicher Proportion,* was published posthumously in 1528; Dürer himself saw the first proof sheets (there are no other details of his last illness and death) and his friends saw to the final stages of publication. This book is the synthesis of Dürer's solutions to his self-imposed formal problems; in it, he sets forth his formal aesthetic. In its simplest terms, true form is the primary mathematical figure (the straight line, the circle, conic sections, curves, surfaces, solids, and so forth), constructed geometrically or arithmetically, and made beautiful by the application of some canon of proportion. The resulting beautiful form may be varied within limits of similarity. (In the instance of human form, there should be sufficient variation to differentiate one figure from another, but never so much as that the figure becomes deformed or nonhuman.) Dürer's Platonic idea of form figures in his larger aesthetic; for him beauty was the aggregate of symmetrical, proportionate, and harmonious forms in a more highly symmetrical, proportionate, and harmonious work of art.

Dürer's aesthetic rules are firmly based in the laws of optics—indeed, he even designed special mechanical instruments to aid in the attainment of beautiful form. He used the height of the human body as the basic unit of measurement and subdivided it linearly to reach a common denominator for construction of a unified artistic plan. This canon was not inviolable; Dürer himself modified it continually in an attempt to approximate more closely the canon of Vitruvius (which was also the canon most favored by Leonardo). Thus the artist retains freedom in the act of selecting his canon. In books I and II of the *Vier Bücher* Dürer deals, once again, with the arithmetic and geometrical construction of forms; in books III and IV he considers the problems of variation and movement.

The last of the *Vier Bücher* is perhaps of greatest mathematical interest since in treating of the movement of bodies in space Dürer was forced to present new, difficult, and intricate considerations of descriptive spatial geometry; indeed, he may be considered the first to have done so. At the end of this book he summarizes and illustrates his theories in the construction of his famous "cube man."

Dürer's chief accomplishment as outlined in the *Vier Bücher* is that in rendering figures (and by extension, in the composition of the total work of art) he first solved the problem of establishing a canon, then considered the transformations of forms within that canon, altering them in accordance with a consistent idea of proportion. In so doing he considered the spatial relations of form and the motions of form within space. His triumph as a painter lay in his disposition of carefully proportioned figures in surrounding space; he thereby elevated what had been hit-or-miss solutions of an essential problem of plastic composition to a carefully worked out mathematical theory. No earlier method had been so successful, and Dürer's theoretical work was widely influential in following centuries.

BIBLIOGRAPHY

I. ORIGINAL WORKS. Editions of Dürer's works include *Underweysung der Messung mit Zirckel und Richtscheyt in Linien, Ebnen, und gantzen Corporen* (Nuremberg, 1525; 2nd ed., Nuremberg, 1538; facsimile ed. by Alvin Jaeggli and Christine Papesch, Zurich, 1966); *Etliche Underricht zu Befestigung der Stett, Schloss und Flecken* (Nuremberg, 1927), repr. as W. Waetzoldt, ed., *Dürer's Befestigungslehre* (Berlin, 1917); and *Vier Bücher von menschlicher Proportion* (Nuremberg, 1528), of which there is a facsimile ed. in 2 vols. with text and commentary, Max Steck, ed. (Zurich, 1969).

II. SECONDARY LITERATURE. Max Steck, *Dürer's Gestaltlehre der Mathematik und der bildenden Künste* (Halle–Tübingen, 1948), contains an extensive bibliography of works by and about Dürer as well as a scientific analysis of the sources of the *Underweysung der Messung;* see also Hans Rupprich, *Dürer-Schriftlicher Nachlass,* vols. I and II (Berlin, 1956–1966), vol. III (in preparation); and Max Steck, "Albrecht Dürer als Mathematiker und Kunsttheoretiker," in *Nova Acta Leopoldina,* **16** (1954), 425–434; "Albrecht Dürer als Schrifsteller," in *Forschungen und Fortschritte,* **30** (1956), 344–347; *Dürer: Eine Bildbiographie* (Munich, 1957; 2nd ed. Munich, 1958; other German eds.), trans. into English as *Dürer and His World* (London–New York, 1964); "Ein neuer Fund zum literarischen Bild Albrecht Dürer's im Schrifttum des 16. Jahrhunderts," in *Forschungen und Fortschritte,* **31** (1957), 253–255; "Drei neue Dürer-Urkunden," *ibid.,* **32** (1958), 56–58; "Grundlagen der Kunst Albrechts Dürers," in *Universitas* (1958), pp. 41–48, also trans. for English and Spanish eds.; "Theoretische Beiträge zu Dürers Kupferstich 'Melancolia I' von 1514," in *Forschungen und Fortschritte,* **32** (1958), 246–251; *Albrecht Dürer, Schriften—Tagebücher—Briefe* (Stuttgart, 1961); "Albrecht Dürer as a Mathematician," in *Proceedings of the Tenth International Congress of the History of Science,* II (Paris, 1964), 655–658; "Albrecht Dürer als Mathematiker und Kunsttheoretiker," in *Der Architekt und der Bauingenieur* (Munich, 1965), pp. 1–6; and "Albrecht Dürer: Die exaktwissenschaftlichen Grundlagen seiner Kunst," in *Scientia, Milano,* **1C** (1966), 15–20, with French trans. as "Albert Dürer: Les sciences exactes sont les bases de son art," *ibid.,* pp. 13–17.

MAX STECK

DYCK, WALTHER FRANZ ANTON VON (*b.* Munich, Germany, 6 December 1856; *d.* Munich, 5 November 1934)

Dyck was the son of Hermann Dyck, a painter and the director of the Munich Kunstgewerbeschule, and Marie Royko. He married Auguste Müller in 1886; they had two daughters.

Dyck studied mathematics in Munich, Berlin, and Leipzig. He qualified as a university lecturer in Leipzig in 1882 and was an assistant of F. Klein. In 1884 he became a professor at the Munich Polytechnikum. He made noteworthy contributions to function theory, group theory, topology, potential theory, and the formative discussion on integral curves of differential equations. He was also one of the founders of the *Encyclopädie der mathematischen Wissenschaften.* Appointed director of the Polytechnikum in 1900, he brought about its rise to university standing as the Technische Hochschule; and as rector (1903–1906, 1919–1925) he carried out a major building expansion. In 1903 he was enlisted, along with Carl von Linde, by Oskar von Miller to aid in the establishment and early development of the Deutsches Museum; he also served as its second chairman from 1906. As a dedicated member of the Bayerische Akademie der Wissenschaften (and a class secretary in 1924), he prepared the plan and organization of the complete edition of the writings and letters of Kepler, including the posthumous works (for the most part in Pulkovo, near Leningrad). Moreover, as a founder (along with F. Schmitt-Ott) of the Notgemeinschaft der Deutschen Wissenschaften, he concerned himself with assuring financial support for the edition.

Linguistically gifted and a warm, kind-hearted man of wide-ranging and liberal interests, including art and music, Dyck was an outstanding scholar and organizer and an enthusiastic and inspiring teacher.

BIBLIOGRAPHY

I. ORIGINAL WORKS. Dyck's writings include *Uber regulär verzweigte Riemannsche Flächen und die durch sie bestimmten Irrationalitäten* (Munich, 1879), his doctoral dissertation; "Gruppentheoretische Studien," in *Mathematische Annalen,* **20** (1882), 1–44; **22** (1882), 70–108; "Beiträge zur Analysis situs," in *Sitzungsberichte der Sächsischen Akademie der Wissenschaften zu Leipzig* (1885), 314–325; (1886), 53–69; (1888), 40–52; and in *Mathematische Annalen,* **32** (1888), 457–512; **37** (1890), 273–316; *Katalog math.-physik. Modelle . . .* (Munich, 1892; supp., 1893); "Beiträge zur Potentialtheorie," in *Sitzungsberichte der Bayerischen Akademie der Wissenschaften zu München* (1895), 261–277, 447–500; (1898), 203–224; *Spezialkatalog der mathematischen Austellung, Deutsche Unterrichtungsabteilung in Chicago* (Munich, 1897); L. O. Hesse, *Gesammelte Werke,* ed. with S. Gundelfinger, J. Lüroth, and M. Noether (Munich, 1897); "Nova Kepleriana," in *Abhandlungen der Bayerischen Akademie der Wissenschaften,* **25** (1910), 1–61; **26** (1912), 1–45; **28** (1915), 1–17; **31** (1927), 1–114, written with M. Caspar; n.s. **17** (1933), 1–58, written with M. Caspar; **18** (1933), 1–58; **23** (1934), 1–88; *G. von Reichenbach* (Munich, 1912), a biography; and *J. Kepler in seinen Briefen,* 2 vols. (Munich, 1930), written with M. Caspar.

II. SECONDARY LITERATURE. Obituary notices by G. Faber are in *Forschungen und Fortschritte,* **34** (1934), 423–424, *Jahresbericht der Deutschen Mathematikervereinigung,* **45** (1935), 89–98, with portrait and bibliography, and *Jahrbuch der Bayerischen Akademie der Wissenschaften* (1934); an anonymous obituary is in *Almanach. Österreichische Akademie der Wissenschaften,* **85** (1935), 269–272; see also J. E. Hofmann, in *Natur und Kultur,* **32** (1935), 61–63, with portrait; J. Zenneck, in *Mitteilungen der Gesellschaft deutscher Naturforscher und Arzte,* **11** (1935), 2–3. On his seventieth birthday see H. Schmidt, in *Denkschriften der Technische Hochschule München,* **1** (1926), 3–4, with portrait as a youth. On the centenary of his birth see R. Sauer, in *Wissenschaftliche Vorträge, gehalten bei der akademischen Jahresfeier der Technischen Hochschule München* (1957), 10–11. A short biography by G. Faber is in *Neue Deutsche Biographie,* IV (Berlin, 1959), 210. A bronze bust by Hermann Hahn, at the Technische Hochschule in Munich, was unveiled in 1926.

J. E. HOFMANN

EGOROV, DIMITRY FEDOROVICH (*b.* Moscow, Russia, 22 December 1869; *d.* Kazan, U.S.S.R., 10 September 1931)

After graduating from the Gymnasium in Moscow, Egorov entered the division of physics and mathematics of Moscow University, from which he received a diploma in 1891. After obtaining his master's degree he remained at the university to prepare for a professorship, and in 1894 he became *Privatdozent* there. In 1901 he received his doctorate with a dissertation entitled "Ob odnom klasse ortogonalnykh sistem," and two years later he was appointed extraordinary professor in the division of physics and mathematics at the University of Moscow. In 1909 Egorov was made ordinary professor and was appointed director of the Mathematical Scientific Research Institute. He was elected corresponding member of the USSR Academy titled "Ob odnom klasse ortogonalnykh sistem," and member. Egorov was a member of the Moscow Mathematical Society; in 1902 he was elected to the French Mathematical Society and the Mathematical Society of Berlin University. From 1922 almost until his death, he was president of the Moscow Mathematical Society, and from 1922 he was editor-in-chief of *Matematicheskii sbornik.*

Egorov's investigations on triply orthogonal systems and potential surfaces, i.e., surfaces *E,* contributed greatly to differential geometry. The results of these investigations were presented by Darboux in his monograph *Leçons sur les systèmes orthogonaux et les coordonnées curvilignes* (2nd ed., Paris, 1910).

Egorov considerably advanced the solution of Peterson's problem on the bending on the principal basis. In the theory of functions of a real variable, wide use is made of Egorov's theorem: Any almost-everywhere converging sequence of measurable functions converges uniformly on a closed set, the complement of which has an infinitely small measure. This theorem, as well as Egorov's scholarship in new trends, led to the creation of the Moscow school dealing with the theory of functions of a real variable. Among the mathematicians belonging to Egorov's school are the well-known Soviet mathematicians N. N. Lusin, V. V. Golubev, and V. V. Stepanov.

Egorov also worked in other areas; for instance, he initiated an investigation into the theory of integral equations. A brilliant lecturer and scholar, Egorov wrote some college textbooks on the theory of numbers, on the calculus of variations, and on differential geometry.

BIBLIOGRAPHY

Egorov's writings include "Uravnenia s chastnymi proisvodnymi vtorogo poriadka po dvum nezavisimym peremenym," in *Uchenye zapiski Moskovskogo universiteta*, **15** (1899), i-xix, 1-392; "Ob odnom klasse ortogonalnykh sistem," *ibid.*, **18** (1901), i-vi, 1-239, his doctoral diss.; "Ob izgibanii na glavnom osnovanii pri odnom semeystve ploskikh ili konicheskikh linii," in *Matematicheskii sbornik*, **28** (1911), 167-187; "Sur les suites de fonctions mesurables," in *Comptes rendus hebdomadaires des séances de l'Académie des sciences*, **152** (1911), 244-246; and "Sur l'intégration des fonctions mesurables," *ibid.*, **155** (1912), 1474-1475; *Elementy teorii chisel* (Moscow, 1923); *Differentsialnaya geometria* (Moscow-Petrograd, 1924); "Sur les surfaces, engendrées par la distribution des lignes d'une famille donnée," in *Matematicheskii sbornik*, **31** (1924), 153-184; "Sur la théorie des équations intégrales au noyau symétrique," *ibid.*, **35** (1928), 293-310; "Sur quelques points de la théorie des équations intégrales à limites fixes," in *Comptes rendus hebdomadaires des séances de l'Académie des sciences*, **186** (1928), 1703-1705.

A secondary source is V. Steklov, P. Lazarev, and A. Belopolsky, "Zapiska ob uchenykh trudakh D. F. Egorova," in *Izvestiya Rossiiskoi akademii nauk*, **18**, no. 12-18 (1924), 445-446.

A. B. PAPLAUSKAS

EHRESMANN, CHARLES (*b.* Strasbourg, France, 19 April 1905; *d.* Amiens, France, 22 September 1979)

Ehresmann's father was a gardener employed by a convent in Strasbourg. Ehresmann's parents spoke only the Alsatian dialect, and until 1918 his schooling was in German. He was educated in the Lycée Kléber at Strasbourg and entered the École Normale Supérieure in 1924. After graduation in 1927 and military service, he taught from 1928 to 1929 at the French Lycée in Rabat, Morocco. In the years 1930 and 1931 he did research at Göttingen, and between 1932 and 1934 at Princeton, earning a doctorate in mathematics at the University of Paris in 1934. From 1934 to 1939 he conducted research at the Centre Nationale de la Recherche Scientifique.

Ehresmann became a lecturer at the University of Strasbourg in 1939, and after the German invasion in 1940, he followed that university when it relocated to Clermont-Ferrand. After 1952 he traveled extensively to many countries, where he often was invited to give courses. He became a professor at the University of Paris in 1955, where a chair of topology was created for him. After his retirement in 1975, he taught at the University of Amiens (where his wife was a professor of mathematics) in a semi-official position. He was married twice and had one son by his first wife. He died of kidney failure.

Ehresmann was one of the creators of differential topology, which explores the topological properties (in homotopy and homology) of a differential manifold, in relation to its differential structure. In his dissertation and subsequent papers between 1935 and 1939, he explicitly described the homology of classical types of homogeneous manifolds, such as Grassmannians, flag manifolds, Stiefel manifolds, and classical groups. His methods were based on decomposition of these manifolds into cells, even before the general definition of CW complexes had been given. His results later became a useful tool in the theory of characteristic classes.

Between 1939 and 1956 Ehresmann participated in the creation and development of fundamental notions in differential topology: fiber spaces, connections, almost complex structures, jets, and foliations. Fiber spaces, first considered in special cases by Seifert in 1933 and Hassler Whitney in 1935, became a focus of topological research around 1940, when their importance was realized. Ehresmann approached the theory of fiber spaces from an original angle. He had become familiar with the theory of what Élie Cartan called connections (generalizing the Levi-Cività parallelism in Riemannian manifolds) and with the "generalized spaces" on which these connections are defined; very few mathematicians understood Cartan's ideas at that time. Ehresmann realized that beneath Cartan's formulas and constructions were two fundamental fiber spaces whose basis was a differential manifold: the tangent bundle and the space of frames, the mutual relations of which were the key to Cartan's theory. This gave Ehresmann a view of the general theory of fiber spaces somewhat different from that of other mathematicians in that field.

Ehresmann's theory emphasized the importance

of a group of automorphisms of a fiber and led him to the general concept of principal fiber space, where the fibers themselves are topological groups isomorphic to a fixed group. This notion has acquired a fundamental importance in differential and algebraic geometry. Ehresmann could then precisely describe what may be called a two-way correspondence between general fiber spaces and principal ones over a fixed base: with any fiber space there is associated a well-determined (up to isomorphism) principal fiber space; conversely, with any principal fiber space with fibers isomorphic to a group G, and with any action of G on a space F, there is associated a well-determined fiber space with fibers isomorphic to F. Thus, the "space of frames" with group $GL(n\mathbf{R})$ is associated to the tangent bundle of a differential manifold of dimension n as principal fiber space.

With the help of these concepts, Ehresmann could, for any fiber bundle E over a differential manifold M, give a definition (generalizing Cartan's) of a connection on E. Geometrically it amounts to defining, for each $x \in M$ and any point u_x in the fiber E_x, a vector subspace H_{u_x} of the tangent space to E at the point u_x, which is supplementary to E_x in that space and therefore projects isomorphically onto the tangent space to M at x.

When a fiber space E is associated to a principal fiber space P with group G, and G is a subgroup of a group H, it is always possible to consider E as associated to a principal fiber space with group H (extension of G to H). But when K is a subgroup of G, it is not always possible to consider E as associated with a principal fiber space with group K (restriction of G to K). Ehresmann showed that a topological condition must be satisfied: the existence of a section over M of the fiber space associated with P and with the natural action of G on the homogeneous space G/K. This explains why there are always Riemannian structures on an arbitrary manifold M. E is then the tangent bundle, $G = GL(n, \mathbf{R})$ and K the orthogonal group $O(n, \mathbf{R})$; the quotient G/K is then diffeomorphic to an $\mathbf{R}^N$; and for fiber spaces with such fibers, sections over the base always exist. But even for pseudo-Riemannian structures, topological conditions on M are necessary.

Ehresmann studied in detail the case in which M has even dimension $2m$, E is the tangent bundle so that $G = GL(2m, \mathbf{R})$, and $K = GL(m, \mathbf{C})$. When the restriction of G to K is possible, he said, the structure it defines on M is an almost complex structure. The latter term comes from the fact that when M is a complex analytic manifold of complex dimension m, the tangent bundle has fibers that are vector spaces over $\mathbf{C}$; an almost complex structure, however, does not always derive from a complex structure, and additional conditions have to be imposed on the differential structure of M. Independently, Heinz Hopf studied almost complex structures, and many other cases of restrictions to classical subgroups of $GL(n, \mathbf{R})$ were considered later.

In 1944, Ehresmann inaugurated the global theory of completely integrable systems of partial differential equations. In his local study of partial differential equations, Cartan had emphasized the advantages that derive from a geometrical conception of such systems, in contrast with their expression in nonintrinsic terms using local coordinates. For ordinary differential equations, this geometrical conception goes back to Henri Poincaré and substitutes for such an equation (with no singularities) on a manifold M a field of tangent lines on M—or, in modern terms, a line subbundle of the tangent bundle $T(M)$. The natural generalization is therefore a vector subbundle L of rank $p > 1$ of $T(M)$, and the generalization of the integral curves of a differential equation are the injective immersions $f: N \rightarrow M$ into M of a manifold N of dimension $q \leq p$, such that for $y \in N$, the image by the tangent map $T_y(f)$ of the tangent space $T_y(N)$ is contained in the fiber $L_f(y)$. Completely integrable systems are those for which there are such maps f for manifolds N of maximal dimension p, whose images $f(N)$ may contain arbitrary points of M.

The characterization of these systems by local properties was presented in the work of Rudolf Clebsch and Georg Frobenius. Ehresmann initiated the study of their global solutions, in the spirit of the "qualitative" investigations started by Poincaré for $p = 1$, which have become known as the theory of dynamical systems. There are always maximal connected solutions $f(N)$; they are called the leaves of the system, forming a partition of M, called a foliation. Ehresmann published only a few papers on that topic; the bulk of the basic notions in the theory was developed, under his guidance, in the dissertation of his pupil Georges Reeb. It was Reeb who obtained the first significant results, in particular the remarkable "Reeb foliation" of the sphere $\mathbf{S}_3$, with a single compact leaf, which later played an important part in the general theory. Until 1960 these papers of Ehresmann and Reeb did not attract much attention, but since then the theory has enjoyed a vigorous and sustained growth that has made it a main branch of differential geometry and differential topology, with recently discovered and surprising links with the theory of C^*-algebras.

The next theory pioneered by Ehresmann was

what he called the theory of jets. Two C^∞ maps f,g of a manifold M into a manifold N have a contact of order k at a point $x \in M$ where $f(x) = g(x)$ if, in local coordinates around x and $f(x)$, their Taylor expansions coincide up to order k. This is independent of the choice of local coordinates and defines an equivalence relation in the set $E(M, N)$ of C^∞ maps of M into N. Ehresmann called the equivalence class of such a map f the kth jet of f at the point x. He developed the main properties of that notion in a series of notes. It has since been recognized that this notion provides the best frame for an intrinsic conception of general systems of partial differential equations and for Lie pseudogroups (formerly called infinite Lie groups), free from cumbersome computations in local coordinates.

After 1957 Ehresmann became one of the leaders in the new theory of categories, to which he attracted many younger mathematicians and in which his fertile imagination introduced a large number of concepts and problems. Over the next twenty years, he published his papers in that field and those of his school in a periodical of which he was both editor in chief and publisher, *Cahiers de topologie et de géométrie différentielle*.

Ehresmann's personality was distinguished by forthrightness, simplicity, and total absence of conceit or careerism. As a teacher he was outstanding, not so much for the brilliance of his lectures as for the inspiration and tireless guidance he generously gave to his research students, including Reeb and Jacques Feldbau; throughout his career he supervised a large number of doctoral dissertations.

BIBLIOGRAPHY

Charles Ehresmann, *Oeuvres complètes et commentées*, Andrée Charles Ehresmann, ed., 3 vols. (Amiens, 1982–1984).

JEAN DIEUDONNÉ

EISENHART, LUTHER PFAHLER (*b*. York, Pennsylvania, 13 January 1876; *d*. Princeton, New Jersey, 28 October 1965)

Eisenhart was the second son of Charles Augustus Eisenhart and the former Emma Pfahler. His father was a dentist, a founder of the Edison Electric Light and York Telephone companies, and secretary of the Sunday school of St. Paul's Lutheran Church. Eisenhart was taught by his mother before he entered school and completed grade school in three years. He then attended York High School until, in his junior year, he was encouraged by the principal to withdraw and devote his time to the independent study of Latin and Greek for early admission to Gettysburg College, which he attended from 1892 to 1896. Being the only upper-division mathematics student, during the last two years of college Eisenhart studied mathematics through independent guided reading.

After teaching for a year at the preparatory school of the college, he began graduate study at Johns Hopkins University in 1897 and obtained the Ph.D. in 1900 with a thesis whose topic, "Infinitesimal Deformations of Surfaces," he had chosen himself. He was introduced to differential geometry through a lecture by Thomas Craig and studied the subject through the treatises of Gaston Darboux. According to his own testimony, the experience of independent study led Eisenhart to propose the four-course plan of study adopted at Princeton in 1923, which provides for independent study and the preparation of a thesis. Eisenhart's scientific career was spent at Princeton; he retired in 1945.

In 1908 Eisenhart married Anna Maria Dandridge Mitchell of Charles Town, West Virginia; she died in 1913. In 1918 he married Katharine Riely Schmidt of York, Pennsylvania. He had one son, Churchill, by his first marriage and two daughters, Anna and Katharine, by his second.

Eisenhart's work in differential geometry covers two distinct periods and fields. The first period, to about 1920, was devoted mainly to the theory of deformations of surfaces and systems of surfaces.

Modern differential geometry was founded by Gaston Darboux as a field of applications of partial differential equations. His methods were taken up by Luigi Bianchi, who created an extensive theory of the deformations of surfaces of constant negative curvature. In another direction, Claude Guichard showed between 1897 and 1899 how the partial differential equations of the deformations of triply orthogonal systems of surfaces can be interpreted in terms of the systems of lines connecting a point and its image point. These discoveries made the theory of deformations of surfaces one of the focal points of geometric research in Europe at the turn of the century. Although there were quite a number of able mathematicians working in America in the field of geometry at that time, Eisenhart was the only one to turn to the topic of deformations. His main contribution to the theory was a unifying principle: The deformation of a surface defines the congruence (two-parameter family) of lines connecting a point and its image (following Guichard). In general, a congruence contains two families of developable surfaces (a developable surface is formed by the tangent to a space curve). Eisenhart recognized that in all known cases, the intersections of these surfaces with the given surface and its image form a net of curves with special properties. This allows not only a unified treatment of many different subjects and a replacement of tricks by methods, but also leads to many new results that round off the theory. Eisenhart gave a coherent account of the theory in *Transformations of Surfaces* (1923). The book also contains most of Eisenhart's previous results either in the text or in the exercises, with references. Some aspects of the theory were taken up later in the projective setting by Eduard Čech and his students. All these investigations deal with small neighborhoods for which existence theorems for solutions of differential equations are available.

Of the few papers not dealing with deformations dating from this period, a noteworthy one is "Surfaces Whose First and Second Forms Are Respectively the Second and First Forms of Another Surface" (1901), one of the first differential geometric characterizations of the sphere, a topic started by Heinrich Liebmann in 1899. Eisenhart proved that the unit sphere is the only surface whose first and second fundamental forms are, respectively, the second and first fundamental forms of another surface.

Einstein's general theory of relativity (1916) made Riemannian geometry the center of geometric research. The analytic tools that turned Riemannian geometry from an idea into an effective instrument were Ricci's covariant differential calculus and the related notion of Levi-Civita's parallelism. These tools had been thoroughly explored in Luigi Bianchi's *Lezioni di geometria differenziale.* As a consequence, the attention of geometers immediately turned to the generalization of Riemannian geometry. Most of Eisenhart's work after 1921 was in this direction. The colloquium lectures *Non-Riemannian Geometry* (1927) contain his account of the main results obtained by him and his students and collaborators. An almost complete coverage of Eisenhart's results, with very good references, is given in Schouten's *Ricci Calculus.* Three directions of generalization of Riemannian geometry were developed in the years after 1920. They are connected with the names of Élie Cartan, Hermann Weyl, and Eisenhart. Cartan considered geometries that induce a geometry of a transitive transformation group in any tangent space. Weyl gave an axiomatic approach to the maps of tangent spaces by parallelism along any smooth curve. Eisenhart's approach, inspired by Oswald Veblen's work on the foundations of projective geometry and started in cooperation with Veblen, is the only one to deal directly with the given space. In Riemannian geometry, the measure of length is prescribed and the geodesic lines are determined as the shortest connections between nearby points. In Eisenhart's approach, the geodesics are given as the solution of a prescribed system of second-order differential equations and the non-Riemannian geometries are obtained by asking that there should exist a Levi-Civita parallelism for which the tangents are covariant constant.

While Cartan's and Weyl's generalizations have become the foundations of the fiber space theory of differentiable manifolds, Eisenhart's theory does not fit the framework of these topological theories. The reason is that the geometric objects intrinsically derived from the "paths" of the geometry, the projective parameters of Tracy Y. Thomas, have a more complicated transformation law than the generalized Christoffel symbols of Cartan and Weyl. However, there are a number of modern developments, such as the theory of Finsler spaces and the general theory of the geometric object, that fit Eisenhart's framework but not that of the algebraic-topological approach. As far as metric geometry is concerned, the most fruitful approach seems to be to give the geodesics directly as point sets and to throw out all differential equations and analytical apparatus. On the other hand, for nonmetric geometries Eisenhart proved (in "Spaces With Corresponding Paths" [1922]) that for every one of his geometries there exists a unique geometry with the same paths and for which the mapping of tangent spaces induced by the flow of tangent vectors with unit speed along the paths is volume-preserving. For the latter geometry, which would appear to give a natural setting for topological dynamics, the Cartan, Weyl, and Eisenhart approaches are equivalent.

A number of interesting avenues of development of Riemannian geometry were opened by Eisenhart. The papers "Fields of Parallel Vectors in the Geometry of Paths" (1922) and "Fields of Parallel Vectors in a Riemannian Geometry" (1925) started the topic of recurrent fields and harmonic spaces (for a report with later references, see T. J. Willmore, *An Introduction to Differential Geometry,* ch. 7, sec. 13). The so-called Eisenhart's theorem appears in "Symmetric Tensors of the Second Order Whose First Covariant Derivatives Are Zero" (1923): If a Riemannian geometry admits a second-order, symmetric, covariant constant tensor other than the metric, the space behaves locally like the product of two lower-dimensional spaces. Together with a theorem of Georges de Rham to the effect that a simply connected, locally product Riemannian space is in fact a Cartesian product of two spaces, the theorem is an important tool in global differential geometry. An extension of the theorem is given in "Parallel Vectors in Riemannian Space" (1938).

The basic equations for the vectors of a group of motions in a Riemannian space had been given by Killing in 1892. Eisenhart developed a very powerful analytical apparatus for these questions; the results are summarized in *Riemannian Geometry* (1926; ch. 6) and *Continuous Groups of Transformations* (1933). The later developments are summarized in Kentaro Yano's *Groups of Transformations in Generalized Spaces* (1949).

Eisenhart's interest in mathematical instruction found its expression in a number of influential textbooks—such as *Differential Geometry of Curves and Surfaces* (1909), *Riemannian Geometry* (1926), *Continuous Groups of Transformations* (1933), *Coordinate Geometry* (1939), *An Introduction to Differential Geometry With Use of the Tensor Calculus* (1940)—some in fields that until then had been dependent upon European monographs devoid of exercises and other student aids. His interest in history resulted in several papers: "Lives of Princeton Mathematicians" (1931), "Plan for a University of Discoverers" (1947), "Walter Minto and the Earl of Buchan" (1950), and the preface to "Historic Philadelphia" (1953).

BIBLIOGRAPHY

I. Original Works. Eisenhart's works published between 1901 and 1909 are "A Demonstration of the Impossibility of a Triply Asymptotic System of Surfaces," in *Bulletin of the American Mathematical Society,* **7** (1901), 184–186; "Possible Triply Asymptotic Systems of Surfaces," *ibid.,* 303–305; "Surfaces Whose First and Second Forms Are Respectively the Second and First Forms of Another Surface," *ibid.,* 417–423; "Lines of Length Zero on Surfaces," *ibid.,* **9** (1902), 241–243; "Note on Isotropic Congruences," *ibid.,* 301–303; "Infinitesimal Deformation of Surfaces," in *American Journal of Mathematics,* **24** (1902), 173–204; "Conjugate Rectilinear Congruences," in *Transactions of the American Mathematical Society,* **3** (1902), 354–371; "Infinitesimal Deformation of the Skew Helicoid," in *Bulletin of the American Mathematical Society,* **9** (1903), 148–152; "Surfaces Referred to Their Lines of Length Zero," *ibid.,* 242–245; "Isothermal-Conjugate Systems of Lines on Surfaces," in *American Journal of Mathematics,* **25** (1903), 213–248; "Surfaces Whose Lines of Curvature in One System Are Represented on the Sphere by Great Circles," *ibid.,* 349–364; "Surfaces of Constant Mean Curvature," *ibid.,* 383–396; "Congruences of Curves," in *Transactions of the American Mathematical Society,* **4** (1903), 470–488; "Congruences of Tangents to a Surface and Derived Congruences," in *American Journal of Mathematics,* **26** (1904), 180–208; "Three Particular Systems of Lines on a Surface," in *Transactions of the American Mathematical Society,* **5** (1904), 421–437; "Surfaces With the Same Spherical Representation of Their Lines of Curvature as Pseudospherical Surfaces," in *American Journal of Mathematics,* **27** (1905), 113–172; "On the Deformation of Surfaces of Translation," in *Bulletin of the American Mathematical Society,* **11** (1905), 486–494; "Surfaces of Constant Curvature and Their Transformations," in *Transactions of the American Mathematical Society,* **6** (1905), 473–485; "Surfaces Analogous to the Surfaces of Bianchi," in *Annali di matematica pura ed applicata,* 3rd ser., **12** (1905), 113–143; "Certain Surfaces With Plane or Spherical Lines of Curvature," in *American Journal of Mathematics,* **28** (1906), 47–70; "Associate Surfaces," in *Mathematische Annalen,* **62** (1906), 504–538; "Transformations of Minimal Surfaces," in *Annali di matematica pura ed applicata,* 3rd ser., **13** (1907), 249–262; "Applicable Surfaces With Asymptotic Lines of One Surface Corresponding to a Conjugate System of Another," in *Transactions of the American Mathematical Society,* **8** (1907), 113–134; "Certain Triply Orthogonal Systems of Surfaces," in *American Journal of Mathematics,* **29** (1907), 168–212; "Surfaces With Isothermal Representation of Their Lines of Curvature and Their Transformations (I)," in *Transactions of the American Mathematical Society,* **9** (1908), 149–177; "Surfaces With the Same Spherical Representation of Their Lines of Curvature as Spherical Surfaces," in *American Journal of Mathematics,* **30** (1908), 19–42; and *A Treatise on the Differential Geometry of Curves and Surfaces* (Boston, 1909; repub. New York, 1960).

Between 1910 and 1919 he published "The Twelve Surfaces of Darboux and the Transformation of Moutard," in *American Journal of Mathematics,* **32** (1910), 17–36; "Congruences of the Elliptic Type," in *Transactions of the American Mathematical Society,* **11** (1910), 351–372; "Surfaces With Isothermal Representation of Their Lines of Curvature and Their Transformations (II)," *ibid.,* 475–486; "A Fundamental Parametric Representation of Space Curves," in *Annals of Mathematics,* 2nd ser., **13** (1911), 17–35; "Sopra le deformazioni continue delle superficie reali applicabili sul paraboloide a parametro puramente immaginario," in *Atti dell'Accademia nazionale dei Lincei. Rendiconti,* Classe di scienze fisiche, matematiche e naturali, 5th ser., **211** (1912), 458–462; "Ruled Surfaces With Isotropic Generators," in *Rendiconti del Circolo matematico di Palermo,* **34** (1912), 29–40; "Minimal Surfaces in Euclidean Four-Space," in *American Journal of Mathematics,* **34** (1912), 215–236; "Certain Continuous Deformations of Surfaces Applicable to the Quadrics," in *Transactions of the American Mathematical Society,* **14** (1913), 365–402; "Transformations of Surfaces of Guichard and Surfaces Applicable to Quadrics," in *Annali di matematica pura ed applicata,* 3rd ser., **22** (1914), 191–248; "Transformations of Surfaces of Voss," in *Transactions of the American Mathematical Society,* **15** (1914), 245–265; "Transformations of Conjugate Systems With Equal Point Invariants," *ibid.,* 397–430; "Conjugate Systems With Equal Tangential Invariants and the Transformation of Moutard," in *Rendiconti del Circolo matematico di Palermo,* **39** (1915), 153–176; "Transformations of Surfaces Ω," in *Proceedings of the National Academy of Sciences,* **1** (1915), 62–65; "One-Parameter Families of Curves," in *American Journal of Mathematics,* **37** (1915), 179–191; "Transformations of Conjugate Systems With Equal Invariants," in *Proceedings of the National Academy of Sciences,* **1** (1915), 290–295; "Surfaces Ω and Their Transformations," in *Transactions of the American Mathematical Society,* **16** (1915), 275–310; "Sulle superficie di rotolamento e le trasformazioni di Ribaucour," in *Atti dell'Accademia nazionale dei Lincei. Rendiconti,* Classe di scienze fisiche, matematiche e naturali, 5th ser., **242** (1915), 349–352; "Surfaces With Isothermal Representation of Their Lines of Curvature as Envelopes of Rolling," in *Annals of Mathematics,* 2nd ser., **17** (1915), 63–71; "Transformations of Surfaces Ω," in *Transactions of the American Mathematical Society,* **17** (1916), 53–99; "Deformations of Transformations of Ribaucour," in *Proceedings of the National Academy of Sciences,* **2** (1916), 173–177; "Conjugate Systems With Equal Point Invariants," in *Annals of Mathematics,* 2nd ser., **18** (1916), 7–17; "Surfaces Generated by the Motion of an Invariable Curve Whose Points Describe Straight Lines," in *Rendiconti del Circolo matematico di Palermo,* **41** (1916), 94–102; "Deformable Transformations of Ribaucour," in *Transactions of the American Mathematical Society,* **17** (1916), 437–458; "Certain Surfaces of Voss and Surfaces Associated With Them," in *Rendiconti del Circolo matematico de Palermo,* **42** (1917), 145–166; "Transformations *T* of Conjugate Systems of Curves on a Surface," in *Transactions of the American Mathematical Society,* **18** (1917), 97–124; "Triads of Transformations of Conjugate Systems of Curves," in *Proceedings of the National Academy of Sciences,* **3** (1917), 453–457; "Conjugate Planar Nets With Equal Invariants," in *Annals of Mathematics,* 2nd ser., **18** (1917), 221–225; "Transformations of Applicable Conjugate Nets of Curves on Surfaces," in *Proceedings of the National Academy of Sciences,* **3** (1917), 637–640; "Darboux's Contribution to Geometry," in *Bulletin of the American Mathematical Society,* **24** (1918), 227–237; "Surfaces Which Can Be Generated in More Than One Way by the Motion of an Invariable Curve," in *Annals of Mathematics,* 2nd ser., **19** (1918), 217–230; "Transformations of Planar Nets," in *American Journal of Mathematics,* **40** (1918), 127–144; "Transformations of Applicable Conjugate Nets of Curves on Surfaces," in *Transactions of the American Mathematical Society,* **19** (1918), 167–185; "Triply Conjugate Systems With Equal Point Invariants," in *Annals of Mathematics,* 2nd ser., **20** (1919), 262–273; "Transformations of Surfaces Applicable to a Quadric," in *Transactions of the American Mathematical Society,* **20** (1919), 323–338; and "Transformations of Cyclic Systems of Circles," in *Proceedings of the National Academy of Sciences,* **5** (1919), 555–557.

Eisenhart's works published between 1920 and 1929 are "The Permanent Gravitational Field in the Einstein Theory," in *Annals of Mathematics,* 2nd ser., **22** (1920), 86–94; "The Permanent Gravitational Field in the Einstein Theory," in *Proceedings of the National Academy of Sciences,* **6** (1920), 678–682; "Sulle congruenze di sfere di Ribaucour che ammettono una deformazione finita," in *Atti dell'Accademia nazionale dei Lincei. Rendiconti,* Classe di scienze fisiche, matematiche e naturali, 5th ser., **292** (1920), 31–33; "Conjugate Systems of Curves *R* and Their Transformations," in *Comptes rendus du sixième Congrès international des mathématiciens* (Strasbourg, 1920), pp. 407–409; "Darboux's Anteil an der Geometrie," in *Acta mathematica,* **42** (1920), 275–284; "Transformations of Surfaces Applicable to a Quadric," in *Journal de mathématiques pures et appliquées,* 8th ser., **4** (1921), 37–66; "Conjugate Nets *R* and Their Transformations," in *Annals of Mathematics,* 2nd ser., **22** (1921), 161–181; "A Geometric Characterization of the Paths of Particles in the Gravitational Field of a Mass at Rest" (abstract), in *Bulletin of the American Mathematical Society,* **27** (1921), 350; "The Einstein Solar Field," *ibid.,* 432–434; "Sulle trasformazioni *T* dei sistemi tripli coniugati di superficie," in *Atti dell'Accademia nazionale dei Lincei. Rendiconti,* Classe di scienze fisiche, matematiche e naturali, **302** (1921), 399–401; "Einstein Static Fields Admitting a Group G_2 of Continuous Transformations Into Themselves," in *Proceedings of the National Academy of Sciences,* **7** (1921), 328–334, abstract in *Bulletin of the American Mathematical Society,* **28** (1922), 34; "The Riemann Geometry and Its Generalization," in *Proceedings of the National Academy of Sciences,* **8** (1922), 19–23, abstract in *Bulletin of the American Mathematical Society,* **28** (1922), 154, written with Oswald Veblen; "Ricci's Principal Directions for a Riemann Space and the Einstein Theory," in *Proceedings of the National Academy of Sciences,* **8** (1922), 24–26, abstract in *Bulletin of the American Mathematical Society,* **28** (1922), 238; "The Einstein Equations for the Solar Field From the Newtonian Point of View," in *Science,* n.s. **55** (1922), 570–572; "Fields of Parallel Vectors in the Geometry of Paths," in *Proceedings of the National Academy of Sciences,* **8** (1922), 207–212; "Spaces With Corresponding Paths," *ibid.,* 233–238; "Condition That a Tensor Be the Curl of a Vector," in *Bulletin of the American Mathematical Society,* **28** (1922), 425–427; "Affine Geometries of Paths Possessing an Invariant Integral," in *Proceedings of the National Academy of Sciences,* **9** (1923), 4–7; "Another Interpretation of the Fundamental Gauge-Vectors of Weyl's Theory of Relativity," *ibid.,* 175–178; "Orthogonal Systems of Hypersurfaces in a General Riemann Space," in *Transactions of the American Mathematical Society,* **25** (1923), 259–280, abstract in *Bulletin of the American Mathematical Society,* **29** (1923), 212; "Symmetric Tensors of the Second Order Whose First Covariant Derivatives Are Zero," in *Transactions of the American Mathematical Society,* **25** (1923), 297–306, abstract in *Bulletin of the American Mathematical Society,* **29** (1923), 213; "Einstein and Soldner," in *Science,* n.s. **58** (1923), 516–517; "The Geometry of Paths and General Relativity," in *Annals of Mathematics,* 2nd ser., **24** (1923), 367–393; *Transformations of Surfaces* (Princeton, 1923; corr. reiss. New York, 1962); "Space-Time Continua of Perfect Fluids in General Relativity," in *Transactions of the American Mathematical Society,* **26** (1924), 205–220; "Spaces of Continuous Matter in General Relativity," abstract in *Bulletin of the American Mathematical Society,* **30** (1924), 7;

"Geometries of Paths for Which the Equations of the Paths Admit a Quadratic First Integral," in *Transactions of the American Mathematical Society,* **26** (1924), 378–384, abstract in *Bulletin of the American Mathematical Society,* **30** (1924), 297; "Linear Connections of a Space Which Are Determined by Simply Transitive Continuous Groups," in *Proceedings of the National Academy of Sciences,* **11** (1925), 243–250; "Fields of Parallel Vectors in a Riemannian Geometry," in *Transactions of the American Mathematical Society,* **27** (1925), 563–573, abstract in *Bulletin of the American Mathematical Society,* **31** (1925), 292; "Einstein's Recent Theory of Gravitation and Electricity," in *Proceedings of the National Academy of Sciences,* **12** (1926), 125–129; *Riemannian Geometry* (Princeton, 1926); "Geometries of Paths for Which the Equations of the Path Admit $n(n + 1)/2$ Independent Linear First Integrals," in *Transactions of the American Mathematical Society,* **28** (1926), 330–338, abstract in *Bulletin of the American Mathematical Society,* **32** (1926), 197; "Congruences of Parallelism of a Field of Vectors," in *Proceedings of the National Academy of Sciences,* **12** (1926), 757–760; "Displacements in a Geometry of Paths Which Carry Paths Into Paths," in *Proceedings of the National Academy of Sciences,* **13** (1927), 38–42, written with M. S. Knebelman; *Non-Riemannian Geometry* (New York, 1927; 6th pr., 1968); "Affine Geometry," in *Encyclopaedia Britannica,* 14th ed. (1929), I, 279–280; "Differential Geometry," *ibid.,* VII, 366–367; "Contact Transformations," in *Annals of Mathematics,* 2nd ser., **30** (1929), 211–249; and "Dynamical Trajectories and Geodesics," *ibid.,* 591–606.

Between 1930 and 1939 Eisenhart published "Projective Normal Coordinates," in *Proceedings of the National Academy of Sciences,* **16** (1930), 731–740; "Lives of Princeton Mathematicians," in *Scientific Monthly,* **33** (1931), 565–568; "Intransitive Groups of Motions," in *Proceedings of the National Academy of Sciences,* **18** (1932), 195–202; "Equivalent Continuous Groups," in *Annals of Mathematics,* 2nd ser., **33** (1932), 665–676; "Spaces Admitting Complete Absolute Parallelism," in *Bulletin of the American Mathematical Society,* **39** (1933), 217–226; *Continuous Groups of Transformations* (Princeton, 1933; repr. New York, 1961); "Separable Systems in Euclidean 3-Space," in *Physical Review,* 2nd ser., **45** (1934), 427–428; "Separable Systems of Stäckel," in *Annals of Mathematics,* 2nd ser., **35** (1934), 284–305; "Stäckel Systems in Conformal Euclidean Space," *ibid.,* **36** (1935), 57–70; "Groups of Motions and Ricci Directions," *ibid.,* 823–832; "Simply Transitive Groups of Motions," in *Monatshefte für Mathematik und Physik,* **43** (1936), 448–452; "Invariant Theory of Homogeneous Contact Transformations," in *Annals of Mathematics,* 2nd ser., **37** (1936), 747–765, written with M. S. Knebelman; "Graduate Study and Research," in *Science,* **83** (1936), 147–150; "Riemannian Spaces of Class Greater Than Unity," in *Annals of Mathematics,* 2nd ser., **38** (1937), 794–808; "Parallel Vectors in Riemannian Space," in *Annals of Mathematics,* 2nd ser., **39** (1938), 316–321; and *Coordinate Geometry* (Boston, 1939; repr. New York, 1960).

In the 1940's Eisenhart published *An Introduction to Differential Geometry With Use of the Tensor Calculus* (Princeton, 1940); *The Educational Process* (Princeton, 1945); "The Far-Seeing Wilson," in William Starr Myers, ed., *Woodrow Wilson, Some Princeton Memories* (Princeton, 1946), pp. 62–68; "Plan for a University of Discoverers," in *The Princeton University Library Chronicle,* **8** (1947), 123–139; "Enumeration of Potentials for Which One-Particle Schrödinger Equations Are Separable," in *Physical Review,* 2nd ser., **74** (1948), 87–89; "Finsler Spaces Derived From Riemann Spaces by Contact Transformations," in *Annals of Mathematics,* 2nd ser., **49** (1948), 227–254; "Separation of the Variables in the One-Particle Schrödinger Equation in 3-Space," in *Proceedings of the National Academy of Sciences,* **35** (1949), 412–418; and "Separation of the Variables of the Two-Particle Wave Equation," *ibid.,* 490–494.

Eisenhart's publications of the 1950's are "Homogeneous Contact Transformations," in *Proceedings of the National Academy of Sciences,* **36** (1950), 25–30; "Walter Minto and the Earl of Buchan," in *Proceedings of the American Philosophical Society,* **94,** no. 3 (1950), 282–294; "Generalized Riemann Spaces," in *Proceedings of the National Academy of Sciences,* **37** (1951), 311–315; *Uvod u diferentsijalnu geometriiu* (Belgrade, 1951), translation of *Introduction to Differential Geometry . . .*; "Generalized Riemann Spaces, II," in *Proceedings of the National Academy of Sciences,* **38** (1952), 506–508; "Generalized Riemann Spaces and General Relativity," *ibid.,* **39** (1953), 546–550; Preface to "Historic Philadelphia," in *Transactions of the American Philosophical Society,* **43,** no. 1 (1953), 3; "Generalized Riemann Spaces and General Relativity, II," in *Proceedings of the National Academy of Sciences,* **40** (1954), 463–466; "A Unified Theory of General Relativity of Gravitation and Electromagnetism. I," *ibid.,* **42** (1956), 249–251; II, *ibid.,* 646–650; III, *ibid.,* 878–881; IV, *ibid.,* **43** (1957), 333–336; "Spaces for Which the Ricci Scalar R Is Equal to Zero," *ibid.,* **44** (1958), 695–698; "Spaces for Which the Ricci Scalar R Is Equal to Zero," *ibid.,* **45** (1959), 226–229; and "Generalized Spaces of General Relativity," *ibid.,* 1759–1762.

The early 1960's saw publication of the following: "The Cosmology Problem in General Relativity," in *Annals of Mathematics,* 2nd ser., **71** (1960), 384–391; "The Paths of Rays of Light in General Relativity," in *Proceedings of the National Academy of Sciences,* **46** (1960), 1093–1097; "Fields of Unit Vectors in the Four-Space of General Relativity," *ibid.,* 1589–1601; "Generalized Spaces of General Relativity II," *ibid.,* 1602–1604; "Spaces Which Admit Fields of Normal Null Vectors," *ibid.,* 1605–1608; "The Paths of Rays of Light in General Relativity of the Nonsymmetric Field V_4," *ibid.,* **47** (1961), 1822–1823; "Spaces With Minimal Geodesics," in *Calcutta Mathematical Society Golden Jubilee Commemorative Volume* (Calcutta, 1961), pp. 249–254; "Spaces in Which the Geodesics Are Minimal Curves," in *Proceedings of the National Academy of Sciences,* **48** (1962), 22; "The Paths of Rays of Light in Generalized General Relativity of the Nonsymmetric Field V_4," *ibid.,* 773–775; "Generalized Riemannian Geometry II," *ibid.,* **49** (1963), 18–19; and "The Einstein Generalized Riemannian Geometry," **50** (1963), 190–193.

II. SECONDARY LITERATURE. Biographical memoirs are Gilbert Chinard, Harry Levy, and George W. Corner, "Luther Pfahler Eisenhart (1876–1965)," in *Year Book of the American Philosophical Society* for 1966 (Philadelphia, 1967), pp. 127–134; and Solomon Lefschetz, "Luther Pfahler Eisenhart," in *Biographical Memoirs. National Academy of Sciences,* **40** (1969), 69–90.

Eisenhart's work is discussed in Luigi Bianchi, *Lezioni di geometria differenziale,* Nichola Zanichelli, ed., II, pt. 2 (Bologna, 1930); Herbert Busemann, *The Geometry of Geodesics* (New York, 1955); J. A. Schouten, *Ricci Calculus,* 2nd ed. (Berlin–Göttingen–Heidelberg, 1954); T. Y. Thomas, "On the Projective and Equi-projective Geometries of Paths," in *Proceedings of the National Academy of Sciences,* **11** (1925), 198–203; T. J. Willmore, *An Introduction to Differential Geometry* (London, 1959); and Kentaro Yano, *Groups of Transformations in Generalized Spaces* (Tokyo, 1949).

H. GUGGENHEIMER

EISENSTEIN, FERDINAND GOTTHOLD MAX (*b.* Berlin, Germany, 16 April 1823; *d.* Berlin, 11 October 1852)

Eisenstein's father, Johann Konstantin Eisenstein, and his mother, the former Helene Pollack, had converted from Judaism to Protestantism before Gotthold was born. His father, who had served eight years in the Prussian army, tried his hand at various commercial enterprises, including manufacturing, but without financial success. Not until late in life did he begin to make a decent livelihood. Eisenstein's five brothers and sisters, born after him, died in childhood, nearly all of meningitis, which he also contracted. His interest in mathematics, awakened and encouraged by a family acquaintance, began when he was about six. "As a boy of six I could understand the proof of a mathematical theorem more readily than that meat had to be cut with one's knife, not one's fork" ("Curriculum vitae," p. 150). Early, too, Eisenstein showed musical inclinations that continued throughout his life and that found expression in playing the piano and composing.

Even while he was in elementary school, his persistently poor health prompted his parents to send him for a time to board in the country. From about 1833 to 1837 he was a resident student at the Cauer academy in Charlottenburg (near Berlin), where the quasi-military discipline was little to his taste. The effects upon him of its Spartan pedagogical methods were manifested in frequent, often feverish illnesses and depression. From September 1837 to July 1842 he attended the Friedrich Wilhelm Gymnasium and then, as a senior, the Friedrich Werder Gymnasium in Berlin. In addition, he went to hear Dirichlet and others lecture at the university.

> What attracted me so strongly and exclusively to mathematics, apart from its actual content, was especially the specific nature of the mental operation by which mathematical things are dealt with. This way of deducing and discovering new truths from old ones, and the extraordinary clarity and self-evidence of the theorems, the ingeniousness of the ideas . . . had an irresistible fascination for me. . . . Starting from the individual theorems, I soon grew accustomed to pierce more deeply into their relationships and to grasp whole theories as a single entity. That is how I conceived the idea of mathematical beauty. . . . And there is such a thing as a mathematical sense or instinct that enables one to see immediately whether an investigation will bear fruit, and to direct one's thoughts and efforts accordingly ["Curriculum vitae," pp. 156–157].

Eisenstein had the good fortune to find in the meteorologist Heinrich W. Dove and the mathematician Karl Schellbach teachers who understood and encouraged him. What he learned in class and at lectures led him to deeper, independent study of the works of Euler, Lagrange, and Gauss, although it was the last who influenced him most. In the summer of 1842, before completing school, he accompanied his mother to England to join his father, who had gone there two years earlier in search of a better livelihood. In neither England, Wales, nor Ireland could the family gain a firm footing. Eisenstein used the time to steep himself in Gauss's *Disquisitiones arithmeticae* and started on his own to study forms of the third degree and the theory of elliptic functions. In Dublin in early 1843 he made the acquaintance of W. R. Hamilton, who gave him a copy of his work "On the Argument of Abel, Respecting the Impossibility of Expressing a Root of Any General Equation Above the Fourth Degree," to be presented to the Berlin Academy.

By around mid-June 1843 Eisenstein and his mother were back in Berlin. His parents were now living apart, and from then until his death Eisenstein stayed with his mother only briefly from time to time. In August 1843 he applied to the Friedrich Wilhelm Gymnasium in Berlin for permission, as a nonstudent, to take their final examinations (a prerequisite for admission to regular university study). In the brief autobiography appended to his application he mentioned (at age twenty) the "hypochondria that has been plaguing me for two years." On 22 September 1843 Eisenstein passed his final secondary school examination, and Schellbach wrote of him in his report: "His knowledge of mathematics goes far beyond the scope of the secondary-school curriculum.

His talent and zeal lead one to expect that some day he will make an important contribution to the development and expansion of science" (a remarkable opinion, compared with the wrong ones put forth by other teachers, Galois for example).

Immediately after passing his examinations, Eisenstein enrolled at the University of Berlin. In January 1844 he delivered to the Berlin Academy the copy of Hamilton's study that he had received in Dublin, using the occasion to submit a treatise of his own on cubic forms with two variables. A. L. Crelle, whom the Academy had commissioned to evaluate Eisenstein's work and make appropriate reply to him on its behalf, accepted the treatise for publication in his *Journal für die reine und angewandte Mathematik*, thus again demonstrating Crelle's keen eye for mathematical genius, which had earlier spotted Abel, Jacobi, Steiner, and, later, Weierstrass. At the same time, Crelle introduced the young author to Alexander von Humboldt, who immediately took an interest in him. Time and again Humboldt requested financial support for Eisenstein from the Prussian ministry of education, the king, and the Berlin Academy, and often helped him out of his own pocket. Eisenstein had no feeling of economic security, since these official grants were awarded only for short periods and always had to be reapplied for, with the approved extensions often arriving late and the sums involved being quite modest and certainly not owed to the recipient. His constant dependence on gifts and charity weighed heavily on him, yet he had found in Humboldt a tireless mentor and protector, the like of which few young talents are ever blessed with. And Humboldt made it clear that he valued Eisenstein not only as a promising young scholar but also as a human being, and with tact and sensitivity he tried (albeit in vain) to divert and cheer him.

The twenty-seventh and twenty-eighth volumes of Crelle's *Journal*, published in 1844, contained twenty-five contributions by Eisenstein. These testimonials to his almost unbelievable, explosively dynamic productivity rocketed him to fame throughout the mathematical world. They dealt primarily with quadratic and cubic forms, the reciprocity theorem for cubic residues, fundamental theorems for quadratic and biquadratic residues, cyclotomy and forms of the third degree, plus some notes on elliptic and Abelian transcendentals. Gauss, to whom he had sent some of his writings, praised them very highly and looked forward with pleasure to an announced visit. In June 1844, carrying a glowing letter of recommendation from Humboldt, Eisenstein went off to see Gauss. He stayed in Göttingen fourteen days. In the course of the visit he won the high respect of the "prince of mathematicians," whom he had revered all his life. The sojourn in Göttingen was important to Eisenstein for another reason: he became friends with Moritz A. Stern—the only lasting friendship he ever made. While the two were in continual correspondence on scientific matters, even Stern proved unable to dispel the melancholy that increasingly held Eisenstein in its grip. Even the sensational recognition that came to him while he was still only a third-semester student failed to brighten Eisenstein's spirits more than fleetingly. In February 1845, at the instance of Ernst E. Kummer, who was acting on a suggestion from Jacobi (possibly inspired by Humboldt), Eisenstein was awarded an honorary doctorate in philosophy by the School of Philosophy of the University of Breslau.

The year 1846 found Eisenstein suddenly involved in an unpleasant priority dispute with Jacobi, who accused him of plagiarism and of misrepresenting known results. Writing to Stern on 20 April 1846, Eisenstein explained that "the whole trouble is that, when I learned of his work on cyclotomy, I did not immediately and publicly acknowledge him as the originator, while I frequently have done this in the case of Gauss. That I omitted to do so in this instance is merely the fault of my naïve innocence." Jacobi charged him with scientific frivolity and appropriating as his own the ideas imparted to him by others, and he maintained that Eisenstein had no original achievements to his credit but had merely cleverly proved certain theorems stated by others and carried out ideas conceived by others. This was in curious contrast with Jacobi's attitude in 1845, when he had recommended Eisenstein for the honorary doctorate.

In 1846–1847 Eisenstein published various writings, mainly on the theory of elliptic functions. Humboldt, who had tried in vain in 1846 to draw the attention of Crown Prince Maximilian of Bavaria to Eisenstein, early in 1847 recommended him for a professorship at Heidelberg—even before he had earned his teaching credentials at the University of Berlin—but again without success. During the summer semester of 1847 Riemann was among those who attended Eisenstein's lecture on elliptic functions. In September 1847 a great honor came to Eisenstein: Gauss wrote the preface to a volume of his collected treatises. No longer extant, unfortunately, is the letter from Gauss to Eisenstein in which, the latter reported to Riemann, Gauss set down the essentials of his proof of the biquadratic reciprocity law with the aid of cyclotomy.

Early in 1848 Eisenstein had attended meetings of certain democratically oriented clubs, although he took no active part in the pre-March political ferment.

During the street battles on 19 March, however, he was forcibly removed from a house from which shots had been fired and was taken with other prisoners to the Citadel at Spandau, suffering severe mistreatment en route. Although he was released the next day, the experience gravely affected his health. Moreover, when word spread that he was a "republican," financial support for him dwindled, and it took Humboldt's most strenuous efforts to keep it from drying up altogether. Eisenstein's situation visibly worsened. Alienated from his family and without close friends or any real contact with other Berlin mathematicians, he vegetated. Only occasionally did he feel able to deliver his lectures as *Privatdozent,* from his bed, if he managed to lecture at all. Yet all this time he was publishing one treatise after another in Crelle's *Journal,* especially on the quadratic partition of prime numbers, on reciprocity laws, and on the theory of forms. In August 1851, on Gauss's recommendation, both Eisenstein and Kummer were elected corresponding members of the Göttingen Society, and in March 1852 Dirichlet managed his election to membership in the Berlin Academy. In late July of that year Eisenstein suffered a severe hemorrhage. Funds raised by Humboldt so that Eisenstein could spend a year convalescing in Sicily came too late: on 11 October he died of pulmonary tuberculosis. Despite all the public recognition, he ended his days in forlorn solitude. The eighty-three-year-old Humboldt accompanied the coffin to the graveside.

Eisenstein soon became the subject of legend, and the early literature about him is full of errors. Only latter-day research has illumined the tragic course of his life. For instance, no evidence at all has been found of the dissolute existence that he was frequently rumored to have led. His lectures were usually attended by more than half of Berlin's mathematics students, which was the more remarkable since Dirichlet, Jacobi, and Steiner were then teaching at Berlin. Eisenstein was ever at pains, as he himself emphasized, to bring home to his listeners the most recent research results.

His treatises were written at a time when only Gauss, Cauchy, and Dirichlet had any conception of what a completely rigorous mathematical proof was. Even a man like Jacobi often admitted that his own work sometimes lacked the necessary rigor and self-evidence of methods and proofs. Thus it is not surprising that, as Leo Koenigsberger tells us, Eisenstein's "Study of the Infinite Double Products, of Which Elliptic Functions Are Composed as Quotients" should have been criticized by Weierstrass, who, in representing his own functions in terms of infinite products, was not picking up the torch from his forerunner, Eisenstein, but was drawing directly upon Gauss. Weierstrass correctly rated Riemann over Eisenstein, who was unable to grasp Riemann's general ideas about functions of complex variables. While Klein did concede that the simplest elliptic functions are defined by Eisenstein's everywhere absolutely convergent series, he called Eisenstein a "walking formula who starts out with a calculation and then finds in it the roots of all his knowledge." Unjustly Klein attributed to him a persecution complex and megalomania. Eisenstein's oft-quoted statement to the effect that through his contributions to the theory of forms (including his finding the simplest covariant for the binary cubic form) he hoped "to become a second Newton" (letter to Humboldt, July 1847) is nothing more than a bad joke.

The development that led to the reciprocity law of *n*th-power residues will be permanently associated with Eisenstein's work on cubic and biquadratic reciprocity laws. The Eisenstein series have become an integral part of the theory of modular forms and modular functions. They and the Eisenstein irreducibility law (along with the Eisenstein polynomial and the Eisenstein equation) continue to bear his name and to assure him a position about halfway between that contemptuous assessment by Klein and the verdict of Gauss (expressed, of course, in a letter intended for display), who held Eisenstein's talents to be such as "nature bestows on only a few in each century" (letter to Humboldt, 14 April 1846).

BIBLIOGRAPHY

I. ORIGINAL WORKS. Nearly all of Eisenstein's scientific writings were published in the *Journal für die reine und angewandte Mathematik,* specifically in vols. **27** (1844) to **44** (1852); see the bibliography by Kurt-R. Biermann in *Journal für die reine und angewandte Mathematik,* **214/215** (1964), 29–30. Selected *Mathematische Abhandlungen besonders aus dem Gebiete der höhern Mathematik und der elliptischen Functionen* (Berlin, 1847) were published with a preface by Gauss; repr., with intro. by Kurt-R. Biermann (Hildesheim, 1967). An autobiography, "Curriculum vitae des Gotth. Ferdinand Eisenstein," ed. and with intro. by F. Rudio, was published in *Zeitschrift für Mathematik und Physik,* **40** (1895), supp., 143–168. The letters from Eisenstein to M. A. Stern were published by A. Hurwitz and F. Rudio in *Zeitschrift für Mathematik und Physik,* **40** (1895), supp., 169–203. A report by Eisenstein on his imprisonment is found in Adalbert Roerdansz, *Ein Freiheits-Martyrium. Gefangene Berliner auf dem Transport nach Spandau am Morgen des 19. März 1848* (Berlin, 1848), pp. 130–135. A bibliography of Eisenstein's writings is given by Kurt-R. Biermann in *Istoriko-mathematicheskie issledovaniya,* **12** (1959), 493–502.

Historical records are available primarily at the following institutions: Archiv der Deutschen Akademie der Wissenschaften zu Berlin; Archiv der Humboldt-Universität zu Berlin; Deutsche Staatsbibliothek, Berlin; Niedersächsische Staats- und Universitäts-Bibliothek, Göttingen; Archiv der Akademie der Wissenschaften, Göttingen; and Deutsches Zentralarchiv, Historische Abteilung II, Merseburg. See also the survey by Kurt-R. Biermann in *Journal für die reine und angewandte Mathematik*, **214/215** (1964), 28.

II. SECONDARY LITERATURE. See the bibliography by Kurt-R. Biermann in *Journal für die reine und angewandte Mathematik*, **214/215** (1964), 28–29. Only the literature devoted directly to Eisenstein will be cited here. See Wilhelm Ahrens, "Gotthold Eisenstein," in *Deutsche allgemeine Zeitung*, no. 177 (17 April 1923); Moritz Cantor, "Eisenstein," in *Allgemeine deutsche Biographie*, V (1877), 774, which contains errors; J. Loewenberg, "A. v. Humboldt und G. Eisenstein," in *Allgemeine Zeitung des Judenthums*, **55** (1891), 246–248; and Julius Schuster, "A. v. Humboldt und F. G. Eisenstein," in *Janus*, **26** (1922), 99.

See also the following works by Kurt-R. Biermann: "A. v. Humboldt als Protektor G. Eisensteins und dessen Wahl in die Berliner Akademie," in *Forschungen und Fortschritte*, **32** (1958), 78–81; "Zur Geschichte der Ehrenpromotion G. Eisensteins," *ibid.*, 332–335; "Die Briefe A. v. Humboldts an F. G. M. Eisenstein," in *Alexander von Humboldt, Gedenkschrift* (Berlin, 1959), 117–159; "A. L. Crelles Verhältnis zu G. Eisenstein," in *Monatsbericht der Deutschen Akademie der Wissenschaften zu Berlin*, **1** (1959), 67–72; "Eisenstein," in *Neue deutsche Biographie*, IV (1959), 420–421; "Einige neue Ergebnisse der Eisenstein-Forschung," in *Zeitschrift für Geschichte der Naturwissenschaften, Technik und Medizin*, **1**, no. 2 (1961), 1–12; and "G. Eisenstein, Die wichtigsten Daten seines Lebens und Wirkens," in *Journal für die reine und angewandte Mathematik*, **214/215** (1964), 19–30.

KURT-R. BIERMANN

ENGEL, FRIEDRICH (*b.* Lugau, near Chemnitz [now Karl-Marx-Stadt], Germany, 26 December 1861; *d.* Giessen, Germany, 29 September 1941)

The son of a Lutheran pastor, Engel attended the Gymnasium at Greiz from 1872 to 1879, studied mathematics in Leipzig and Berlin from 1879 to 1883, and received his doctorate in Leipzig in 1883 under Adolph Mayer. In 1884 and 1885 he studied with Sophus Lie in Christiania (now Oslo). In 1885 Engel qualified as a lecturer in pure mathematics at Leipzig and became an assistant professor there in 1889 and an associate professor in 1899. In 1904 he succeeded his friend Eduard Study as full professor at Greifswald, and in 1913 he went in the same capacity to Giessen, where, after his retirement in 1931, he continued to work until his death.

Although Engel was himself an important and productive mathematician he has found his place in the history of mathematics mainly because he was the closest student and the indispensable assistant of a greater figure: Sophus Lie, after N. H. Abel the greatest Norwegian mathematician. Lie was not capable of giving to the ideas that flowed inexhaustibly from his geometrical intuition the overall coherence and precise analytical form they needed in order to become accessible to the mathematical world. It was no less a mathematician than Felix Klein who recognized that the twenty-two-year-old Engel was the right man to assist Lie and who sent him to Christiania.

Shortly after Engel's return to Leipzig in 1886, Lie succeeded Klein there, and the fruitful collaboration was continued. The result was the *Theorie der Transformationsgruppen*, which appeared from 1888 to 1893 in three volumes "prepared by S. Lie with the cooperation of F. Engel."

Engel performed two further services for the great man long after the latter's death in 1899. In 1932 there appeared Engel's lectures *Die Liesche Theorie der partiellen Differentialgleichungen: Erster Ordnung*, prepared for publication by Karl Faber. For Lie the transformation groups had only been an important aid in handling differential equations; however, he never succeeded in composing a work on his theory of these differential equations. In Faber the seventy-year-old Engel had found the right person to help him in completing this work of his teacher.

Between 1922 and 1937, Engel published six volumes and prepared the seventh of the seven-volume edition of Lie's collected papers, an exceptional service to mathematics in particular and scholarship in general. Lie's peculiar nature made it necessary for his works to be elucidated by one who knew them intimately, and thus Engel's *Anmerkungen* ("Annotations") competed in scope with the text itself. The seventh volume finally appeared in 1960.

Engel's numerous independent works also are concerned primarily with topics in the fields of continuous groups and of partial differential equations: contact transformations (in his dissertation, before his meeting with Lie), Pfaffian equations, Lie's element sets and higher differential quotients, and many others. Lie's ideas were also applied to the n-body problem in mechanics (the ten general integrals).

Engel also edited the collected works of Hermann Grassmann, thus bringing posthumous fame to this great mathematician. In addition, with his friend P. Stäckel, Engel investigated the history of non-Euclidean geometry; along with this study he translated the essential works of N. I. Lobachevsky from

Russian into German, their first appearance in a Western language.

Engel was a member of the Saxon, Russian, Norwegian, and Prussian academies. He received the Lobachevsky Gold Medal and the Norwegian Order of St. Olaf and was an honorary doctor of the University of Oslo. In 1899 he married Lina Ibbeken, the daughter of a Lutheran pastor. Their only child died very young.

BIBLIOGRAPHY

On Engel's work, see "Friedrich Engel," in *Deutsche Mathematik,* **3** (1938), 701-719, which includes a detailed bibliography with a short summary of each item by Engel himself; G. Kowaleski, "Friedrich Engel zum 70sten Geburtstag," in *Forschungen und Fortschritte* (1931), p. 466; E. Ullrich, "Ein Nachruf auf Friedrich Engel," in *Mitteilungen des Mathematischen Seminars der Universität Giessen,* no. 34 (1945), which contains a supplement to the bibliography in *Deutsche Mathematik* and, with nos. 35 and 36, containing two previously unpublished works of Engel's, is bound to form *Gedenkband für Friedrich Engel;* and "Friedrich Engel, ein Nachruf," in *Nachrichten der Giessener Hochschulgesellschaft,* **20** (1951), 139-154, and in *Mitteilungen des Mathematischen Seminars der Universität Giessen,* no. 40 (1951), which also contains the bibliographical supplement that appeared in his earlier article.

Also see H. Boerner's article in *Neue deutsche Biographie,* IV (1959), 501-502.

H. BOERNER

ENRIQUES, FEDERIGO (*b.* Leghorn, Italy, 5 January 1871; *d.* Rome, Italy, 14 June 1946)

Enriques, the son of S. Giacomo and Matilda Enriques, was educated in Pisa, where the family moved during his childhood. He attended the university and the Scuola Normale with a brilliant record in mathematics and took his degree in 1891. After a year of graduate study in Pisa, a second one in Rome, and some further work in Turin with Corrado Segre, Enriques undertook the teaching of projective and descriptive geometry at the University of Bologna, where in 1896 he was elevated to a professorship in those subjects. He remained there until 1923. He was honored by the University of St. Andrews with an honorary doctorate.

Guido Castelnuovo speaks of the happy years spent at Bologna as being perhaps the most fruitful of Enriques' entire life. His intense interest in all fields of knowledge was nurtured by close contact with professors from all the faculties, and in the period 1907-1913 he served as president of the Italian Philosophical Society. In this capacity he organized the Fourth International Congress of Philosophy, held at Bologna in 1911.

In 1923 Enriques accepted the offer of the chair of higher geometry at the University of Rome. While there he founded the National Institute for the History of Science and a school dedicated to that discipline. Since his way of life and his philosophy made it impossible for him to cooperate with the dictates of a fascist regime, Enriques retired from teaching during the years 1938-1944.

As a young man Enriques studied under Betti, Dini, Bianchi, and Volterra and was influenced in his views on algebraic geometry by Segre. In 1892 he turned to Castelnuovo in Rome for advice on the direction of his work, and their many consultations led to Enriques' specialization in the theory of algebraic surfaces and to their collaboration in the field. The Turin Academy of Sciences published Enriques' first paper on the subject in June 1893.

A short summary of Enriques' contributions to this field—relating them to those of Castelnuovo, Picard, Severi, Humbert, and Baker—may be found in F. Cajori's *A History of Mathematics.*[1] Greater detail is given in each of two other accounts, both by Castelnuovo and Enriques in collaboration. The first, entitled "Sur quelques résultats nouveaux dans la théorie des surfaces algébriques,"[2] summarizes the Italian contribution up to 1906. The second, an earlier paper, carries the title "Sur quelques récents résultats dans la théorie des surfaces algébriques."[3] H. F. Baker's presidential address to the International Congress in Cambridge (12 December 1912), published as "On Some Recent Advances in the Theory of Algebraic Surfaces,"[4] also serves to highlight the contributions in that field and in so doing details Enriques' major contributions.

Enriques also contributed to the differential geometry of hyperspace. In 1907 he and Severi received the Bordin Award of the Paris Academy of Sciences for their work on hyperelliptical surfaces. The French honored him again in 1937 by making him a corresponding member of the Académie des Sciences Morales et Politiques.

As early as 1898 Enriques' interest in foundations of mathematics was reflected in his use of a system of axioms in his textbook writings. Having written, at Felix Klein's request, the article on the foundations of geometry ("Principien der Geometrie") for the *Encyklopädie der mathematischen Wissenschaften* (III, 1-129), he became instrumental in the writing of textbooks for both elementary and high schools that greatly influenced teaching in Italy. He was responsible for the publication, in Italian, of Euclid's *Ele-*

ments with historical notes and commentary, and he encouraged the publication of historical and didactic articles in *Periodico di matematiche,* which he headed for twenty years. His interest in teaching and in teachers is well reflected in his service as president of the National Association of University Professors.

By 1895 Enriques had concluded that besides the logical criteria of independence and compatibility, a psychological criterion involving the sensations and experiences that lead to the formulation of the postulates must be considered. In an 1898 paper he set up conditions justifying the introduction of coordinates on surfaces, thus supplementing Riemann's a priori approach in the assumption of such an existence. His interest in physiological psychology led to his writing studies for the *Rivista filosofica* that were later expanded into his *Problemi della scienza* (1906). Castelnuovo describes Enriques' thesis as being that topology and metrical and projective geometry are linked, respectively, to three different orders of sensations: to the general tactile-muscular, to those of the special sense of touch, and to those of vision. In the second part of the *Problemi,* a critical examination is made of the principles of mathematical, physical, and biological sciences. In the treatment of the principles of mechanics Enriques anticipated some of the foundations of Einstein's theory of relativity. His views on structure are given in *Causalité et déterminisme* (1940), and his philosophical thought is found in *Scienza e razionalismo* (1912). A causal explanation involves a "why" as well as a "how" and links effect to cause. Theory should be "plausible in itself" and "satisfy the principle of sufficient reason which is the mental aspect of causality." Determinism thus becomes a premise of scientific research. Enriques' philosophical and historical beliefs pervade *Per la storia della logica* (1922).

In the introductory note to the English translation of *Problemi della scienza* (1914), Josiah Royce writes of the pragmatistic element in Enriques' thought that brings to the thinking process an adjustment to situations; of his stress on the unifying aspect of scientific theory, the association of concepts and of scientific representation. Enriques' philosophical stance differs from that of the Comtean school. He disagrees with Mach and Pearson in their limitation of science to a simple description of physical phenomena, yet writes: "In the formation of concepts, we shall see not only an economy of thought in accordance with the views of Mach, but also a somewhat determinate mental process. . . ." He maintains a positivistic position toward the transcendental and the absolute in his emphasis on the tentative and relative character of scientific theory; yet his theory progresses toward a comprehension of the essential core concealed in every question. Enriques maintained that "It is plainly seen that scientific questions include something essential, apart from the special way in which they are conceived in a particular epoch by the scholars who study such problems."

NOTES

1. (New York, 1961), p. 316.
2. Émile Picard and George Simart, *Théorie des fonctions algébriques de deux variables indépendentes,* II (Paris, 1906), 485-522.
3. *Mathematische Annalen,* **48** (1897), 241-316.
4. *Proceedings of the London Mathematical Society,* **12** (1913), 1-40.

BIBLIOGRAPHY

I. ORIGINAL WORKS. *Federigo Enriques: Memorie scelte di geometria,* 3 vols. (Bologna, 1956-1966), is a collection of 74 papers written between 1893 and 1940 and contains a bibliography of his works. Among his writings are *Lezioni di geometria descrittiva,* J. Schimaglia, ed. (Bologna, 1893-1894; 2nd ed., 1894-1895); republished in a new ed., U. Concina, ed. (Bologna, 1902; 2nd ed., 1908); *Lezioni di geometria proiettiva,* C. Pedretti, ed. (Bologna, 1893-1894; 2nd ed., G. Serrazanetti, ed., 1894-1895); republished in a new ed. (Bologna, 1898; 4th ed., 1920); *Conferenze di geometria: Fondamenti di una geometria iperspaziale* (Bologna, 1894-1895); *Elementi di geometria ad uso delle scuole normali* (Bologna, 1903), written with U. Amaldi; *Elementi di geometria ad uso delle scuole secondarie superiori* (Bologna, 1903), written with U. Amaldi; *Problemi della scienza* (Bologna, 1906; 2nd ed., 1908; repr. 1926), trans. into English by K. Royce with introductory note by J. Royce (Chicago, 1914); *Elementi di geometria ad uso delle scuole tecniche* (Bologna, 1909), written with U. Amaldi; *Nozioni di geometria ad uso delle scuole complementari* (Bologna, 1910), written with U. Amaldi; *Nozioni di geometria ad uso dei ginnasi inferiori* (Bologna, 1910), written with U. Amaldi; *Scienza e razionalismo* (Bologna, 1912); *Nozioni di matematica ad uso dei licei moderni,* 2 vols. (Bologna, 1914-1915); *Lezioni sulla teoria geometrica delle equazioni e delle funzioni algebriche,* 4 vols. (Bologna, 1915-1934; new ed. of vol. I, 1929), written with O. Chisini; *Conferenze sulla geometria non-euclidea,* O. Fernandez, ed. (Bologna, 1918); *Per la storia della logica. I principii e l'ordine della scienza nel concetto dei pensatori matematici* (Bologna, 1922), trans. into English by J. Rosenthal (New York, 1929); *Algebra elementare,* 2 vols. (Bologna, 1931-1932), written with U. Amaldi; *Nozioni di geometria ad uso delle scuole di avviamento al lavoro* (Bologna, 1931), written with U. Amaldi; *Nozioni intuitive di geometria ad uso degli istituti magistrali inferiori* (Bologna, 1931), written with

U. Amaldi; *Lezioni sulla teoria delle superficie algebriche,* pt. 1 (Padua, 1932), written with L. Campedelli; pt. 2 was published in *Rendiconti del seminario matematico della reale università di Roma* (1934) as "Sulla classificazione delle superficie algebriche particolarmente di genere zero"; both parts were reorganized by G. Castelnuovo and published as *Le superficie algebriche* (Bologna, 1949).

See also *Storia del pensiero scientifico,* I, *Il mondo antico* (Bologna, 1932), written with G. de Santillana; *Nozioni di geometria ad uso delle scuole di avviamento professionale* (Bologna, 1934), written with U. Amaldi; *Il significato della storia del pensiero scientifico* (Bologna, 1936); *Compendio di storia del pensiero scientifico dall'antichità fino ai tempi moderni* (Bologna, 1937), written with G. de Santillana; *Le matematiche nella storia e nella cultura,* A. Frajese, ed. (Bologna, 1938); *La théorie de la connaissance scientifique de Kant à nos jours,* Actualités Scientifiques et Industrielles no. 638 (Paris, 1938); *Le superficie razionali* (Bologna, 1939), written with F. Conforto; *Causalité et déterminisme dans la philosophie et l'histoire des sciences,* Actualités Scientifiques et Industrielles no. 899 (Paris, 1940); *Elementi di trigonometria piana ad uso dei licei* (Bologna, 1947), written with U. Amaldi; *Le dottrine di Democrito d'Abdera, testi e commenti* (Bologna, 1948), written with M. Mazziotti; and *Natura, ragione e storia,* L. Lombardo Radice, ed. (Turin, 1958), a collection of his philosophical writings with a bibliography.

See also *Questioni riguardanti la geometria elementare* (Bologna, 1900), which Enriques collected and arranged; *Questioni riguardanti le matematiche elementari:* I, *Critica dei principii* (Bologna, 1912); II, *Problemi classici della geometria. Numeri primi e analisi indeterminata. Massimi e minimi* (Bologna, 1914); pt. 2, *I problemi classici della geometria e le equazioni algebriche,* 3rd ed. (Bologna, 1926); pt. 3, *Numeri primi e analisi indeterminata. Massimi e minimi,* 3rd ed. (Bologna, 1927), all collected and arranged by Enriques; and *Gli Elementi d'Euclide e la critica antica e moderna,* ed. by Enriques and many others: bks. I–IV (Rome–Bologna, 1925); bks. V–IX (Bologna, 1930); bk. X (Bologna, 1932); bks. XI–XIII (Bologna, 1935).

II. SECONDARY LITERATURE. On Enriques or his work, see H. F. Baker, "On Some Recent Advances in the Theory of Algebraic Surfaces," in *Proceedings of the London Mathematical Society,* 2nd ser., **12** (1913), 1–40; F. Baron, "Enriques, Federigo," in *Enciclopedia filosofica* (Venice–Rome, 1957), cols. 1916–1917; Guido Castelnuovo, "Commemorazione di Federigo Enriques," in *Federigo Enriques: Memorie scelte di geometria,* pp. x–xxii; Poggendorff, IV, 388–389; *Proceedings of the Fifth International Congress of Mathematicians* (Cambridge, 1912), I, 40; II, 22; Ferruccio Rossi-Landi, "Enriques, Federigo," in *Encyclopedia of Philosophy* (New York, 1967), III, 525–526; Ferruccio Rossi-Landi and Vittorio Somenzi, "La filosofia della scienza in Italia," in *La filosofia contemporanea in Italia* (Rome, 1958), pp. 407–432; and Antonio Santucci, *Il pragmatismo in Italia* (Bologna, 1963), pp. 302–322.

CAROLYN EISELE

ERATOSTHENES (*b.* Cyrene [now Shahhat, Libya], *ca.* 276 B.C.; *d.* Alexandria, *ca.* 195 B.C.)

Eratosthenes, son of Aglaos, was born in Cyrene but spent most of his working life in Alexandria, where he was head of the library attached to the famous Museum from *ca.* 235 until his death. At some period during his early manhood he went to Athens for the ancient equivalent of a university education, and there he associated with the Peripatetic Ariston of Chios, Arcesilaus and Apelles of the Academy, and Bion the Cynic (Strabo, *Geography,* 15). When he was about thirty, he was invited to Alexandria by King Ptolemy III (Euergetes I), possibly at the instigation of Eratosthenes' fellow countryman Callimachus, who had already been given a post in the library by Ptolemy II (Philadelphus). On the death of the first chief librarian, Zenodotus, *ca.* 235, Eratosthenes was appointed to the post, Callimachus having died *ca.* 240 (*Suda Lexicon, s.v.,* calls Eratosthenes a pupil of Callimachus). At some time during his stay in Alexandria he became tutor to Euergetes' son and remained in favor with the royal court until his death. (See the anecdote related in Athenaeus, *Deipnosophistai,* VII, 276a, concerning Eratosthenes and Queen Arsinoe III.)

The above represents the most probable account of Eratosthenes' life according to the consensus of scholarly opinion, but the exact dates of the stages of his career are disputed and certainty is unattainable. In particular, Knaack puts the date of his birth back to *ca.* 284, and Jacoby (*Fragmente der griechischen Historiker,* IIB [1930], 704) even as far as 296 (suggesting that in the *Suda Lexicon, s.v., ρκς′* is a copyist's error for *ρκα′*, which then refers to the 121st olympiad, i.e., 296–293, not the 126th, i.e., 276–273), while the date of his death becomes either about 203 (Knaack) or 214 (Jacoby), both scholars accepting the testimony of our sources that Eratosthenes died at eighty (the *Suda Lexicon*) or eighty-one (Censorinus, *De die natali,* p. 15) or eighty-two (Pseudo-Lucian, *Μακρόβιοι,* p. 27). The reason for supposing that he must have been born earlier than 276 is that Strabo calls him *γνώριμος* of Zeno of Citium (the founder of Stoicism), a word that often means "pupil" in such a context; but Zeno died in 262, and Eratosthenes could hardly have studied under him at the tender age of fourteen. To this it may be answered that *γνώριμος* can also mean simply "acquainted with," and that the date of Zeno's death may be as late as 256 (see Diogenes Laertius, VII, 6:28). There is also considerable doubt about the order of succession of the early librarians at Alexandria. A papyrus fragment (*Oxyrhynchus papyri,* X, 1241, col. 2) lists them as Zenodotus (whose name is presumed to have occurred at the damaged end of the previous column), Apollonius Rhodius, Eratosthenes, Aristophanes of Byzantium, Aristarchus of Samothrace, and another Apollonius; but there are several mistakes and chronological difficulties in this list (*cf.* Grenfell and Hunt, *ad loc.*), and it is by no means certain that Apollonius Rhodius succeeded Zenodotus directly—the *Suda Lexicon* (*s.v.* "Apollonius") has him succeeding Eratosthenes, although this may arise from confusion with the later Apollonius (if he is correctly placed).

Eratosthenes was one of the foremost scholars of his time and produced works (of which only fragments remain) on geography, mathematics, philosophy, chronology, literary criticism, and grammar as well as writing poetry. According to the *Suda Lexicon,* he was described as Πένταθλος ("All-Rounder"), "another Plato," and "Beta"—the last possibly because, working in so many fields (and polymathy was greatly admired by the Alexandrians), he just failed to achieve the highest rank in each (see Strabo's remark that Eratosthenes was a mathematician among geographers and a geographer among mathematicians: *Geography,* 94; *cf.* 15), or perhaps simply because he was the second chief librarian. His most enduring work was in geography (particularly notable is his measurement of the circumference of the earth), but he himself seems to have taken most pride, as regards his scientific work, in his solution to the famous problem of doubling the cube, to celebrate which he composed an epigram disparaging previous solutions and dedicated to Euergetes and his son; the authenticity of this poem has been questioned (by Hiller and by Powell), but on inadequate grounds. As a mathematician, Eratosthenes ranked high enough in the estimation of the great Archimedes to have one of the latter's treatises, the *Method,* dedicated to him and to be the recipient of a difficult problem in indeterminate analysis, known as the "Cattle Problem," for communication to the mathematicians of Alexandria. In philosophy, Eratosthenes was an eclectic and, according to Strabo (*Geography,* 15), somewhat of a dilettante. He was the first Greek writer to make a serious study of chronological questions and established the system of dating by olympiads, while as an authority on Old Comedy he is constantly cited in the scholia to Aristophanes' plays.

Eratosthenes' *Geography* (Γεωγραφικά) was in three books, as we learn from Strabo, who quotes from it frequently and is, in fact, the chief source of our knowledge of it. It long remained a prime authority on geographical matters; Julius Caesar evidently consulted it, since in his description of the Germans he mentions that Eratosthenes knew of the Hercynian Forest (*De bello Gallico,* VI, 24), and Strabo (writing around the turn of the Christian era) admits that for the southeastern quarter of the inhabited world (*oikoumene*) he has no better authority than Eratosthenes (*Geography,* 723). The work was the first scientific attempt to put geographical studies on a sound mathematical basis, and its author may be said to have been the founder of mathematical geography. It was concerned with the terrestrial globe as a whole, its division into zones, changes in its surface, the position of the *oikoumene* as then known, and the actual mapping of it, with numerous estimates of distances along a few roughly defined parallels and meridians; but it also contained a certain amount of material descriptive of peoples and places.

Strabo, who disliked the mathematical side of the subject and much preferred purely descriptive geography (see *Geographical Fragments of Hipparchus,* pp. 36, 162, 164, 171, 191), several times complains that Eratosthenes put too much emphasis on mathematical topics such as the above (*Geography,* 48–49, 62, 65). Hipparchus (second century B.C.), on the other hand, criticizes his predecessor for not making sufficient use of astronomical data in fixing the reference lines of his map and not treating the subject in a mathematical enough manner. (Hipparchus wrote a work in three books, *Against the Geography of Eratosthenes,* of which we have substantial fragments quoted by Strabo, often inextricably mingled with citations from Eratosthenes himself—see *Geographical Fragments of Hipparchus.*) One of Eratosthenes' main purposes was to correct the traditional Ionian map, which had a round *oikoumene* with Delphi at the center, wholly surrounded by a circular ocean (as envisaged, e.g., by Anaximander and Hecataeus and already ridiculed by Herodotus, *History,* IV, 36, 2), and to sketch a better one (Strabo, *Geography,* 68), making use of all the data at his command—which, as head of the largest library in antiquity, must have been considerable (*ibid.,* 69).

Eratosthenes used as his base line a parallel running from Gibraltar through the middle of the Mediterranean and Rhodes, to the Taurus Mountains (Toros Dağlari, in Turkey), which were extended due east to include the Elburz range (south of the Caspian), the Hindu Kush, and the Himalayas, which formed the northern boundary of India (such a line, approximately bisecting the known world, had already been suggested in the previous century by Dicaearchus, a pupil of Aristotle—see *Geographical Fragments of Hipparchus,* p. 30). Intersecting this main parallel at right angles was a meridian line taken as passing through Meroë, Syene (modern Aswan, on the Tropic of Cancer), Alexandria, Rhodes, and the mouth of the Borysthenes (modern Dnieper—*ibid.*, pp. 146-147). Wherever Eratosthenes found in his sources data (such as distances in stades, similarities in fauna, flora, climate, or astronomical phenomena, lengths of the longest days, etc., recorded at different places) that he could correlate with one or both of the above base lines, he was enabled to sketch in other parallels. In addition, he divided at least the southeastern quarter of the *oikoumene* (we have no information about his treatment of the remainder) into rough geometrical figures shaped like parallelograms, which he called "seals" (σφραγῖδες), forming the first "seal" out of India and working westward (*ibid.*, pp. 128-129).

Naturally, the data at his disposal, mainly travelers' estimates of days' voyages and marches, which are notoriously unreliable—the only scientific data available were the gnomon measurements of Philo, prefect of Ptolemy, at Meroë (Strabo, *Geography,* 77), of Eratosthenes himself at Alexandria, and of Pytheas at Marseilles (*ibid.,* 63), together with some sun heights recorded by the latter (*Geographical Fragments of Hipparchus,* p. 180)—were of dubious accuracy, and any mapping done on the basis of them was bound to be largely guesswork. Hipparchus has no difficulty in showing that the figures and distances given by Eratosthenes are mathematically inconsistent with each other, and he therefore rejects them, together with some of the sensible alterations proposed by Eratosthenes for the traditional map, thus demonstrating that inspired guesswork sometimes gives better results than scientific caution (*ibid.,* pp. 34-35).

It is uncertain whether the measurement of the earth's circumference was first published in the *Geography* or in a separate treatise; if the latter, it would at any rate have been mentioned in the larger work. The method is described in detail by Cleomedes (*De motu circulari,* I, 10), the only ancient source to give it. Assuming that Syene was on the Tropic of Cancer (because there, at midday on the summer solstice, the gnomon—i.e., a vertical pointer set upright on a horizontal base—cast no shadow and a well, especially dug for this purpose [according to Pliny, *Natural History*, II, 73] was illuminated to its bottom by the sun's rays), and that this town and Alexandria were on the same meridian, Eratosthenes made a measurement of the shadow cast at Alexandria at midday on the solstice by a pointer fixed in the center of a hemispherical bowl, known as a "scaphe" (σκάφη—presumably he used this form of gnomon because the shadow of a thin stylus would be better defined than that of a large pillar or post) and estimated that the shadow amounted to 1/25 of the hemisphere, and thus 1/50 of the whole circle. Since the rays of the sun can be regarded as striking any point on the earth's surface in parallel lines, and the lines produced through the vertical gnomons at each place meet at the center of the earth, the angle of the shadow at Alexandria (*ABC* in Figure 1) is equal to the alternate angle (*BCD*) subtended by the arc *BD,* which is the distance along the meridian between Alexandria and Syene, estimated by Eratosthenes at 5,000 stades; and since it is 1/50 of the whole circle, the total circumference must be 250,000 stades. This

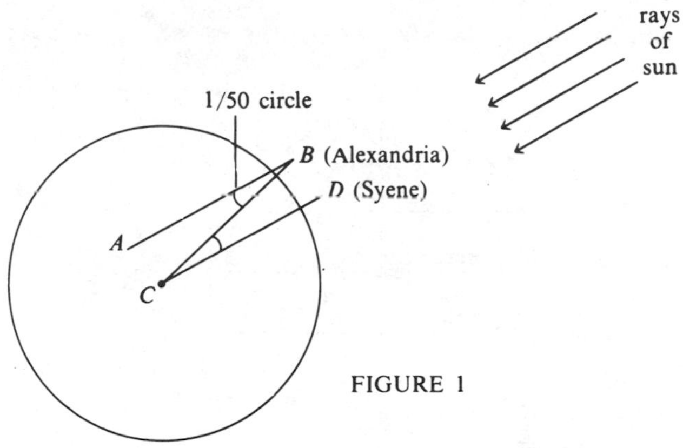

FIGURE 1

is the figure reported by Cleomedes. Hipparchus accepts a figure of 252,000 stades as Eratosthenes' measurement (Strabo, *Geography,* 132, corroborated by Pliny, *Natural History,* II, 247, whose further statement that Hipparchus added 26,000 stades to Eratosthenes' figure is incorrect—see *Geographical Fragments of Hipparchus,* p. 153), and it seems fairly certain that Eratosthenes himself added the extra 2,000 in order to obtain a number readily divisible by 60; he divided the circle into sixtieths only (Strabo, *Geography,* 113-114), the familiar division into 360° being unknown to him and first introduced into Greek science by Hipparchus (*Geographical Fragments of Hipparchus,* pp. 148-149; D. R. Dicks, "Solstices, Equinoxes, and the Pre-Socratics," in *Journal of Hellenic Studies,* **86** [1966], 27-28).

The method is sound in theory, as Hipparchus recognized, but its accuracy depends on the precision with which the basic data could be determined. The figure of 1/50 of the circle (equivalent to 7°12′) for the difference in latitude is very near the truth, but Syene (lat. 24°4′ N.) is not directly on the tropic (which in Eratosthenes' time was at 23°44′ N.), Alexandria is not on the same meridian (lying some 3° to the west), and the direct distance between the two places is about 4,530 stades, not 5,000. Probably Eratosthenes himself was aware that this last figure was doubtful (without trigonometrical methods, which he certainly did not know, it would have been impossible to measure the distance accurately), and so felt at liberty to increase his final result by 2,000. Nonetheless, the whole measurement was a very creditable achievement and one that was not bettered until modern times. On the most probable value of the stade Eratosthenes used (on this vexed question, see *Geographical Fragments of Hipparchus,* pp. 42–46), 252,000 stades are equivalent to about 29,000 English miles, which may be compared with the modern figure for the earth's circumference of a little less than 25,000 miles.

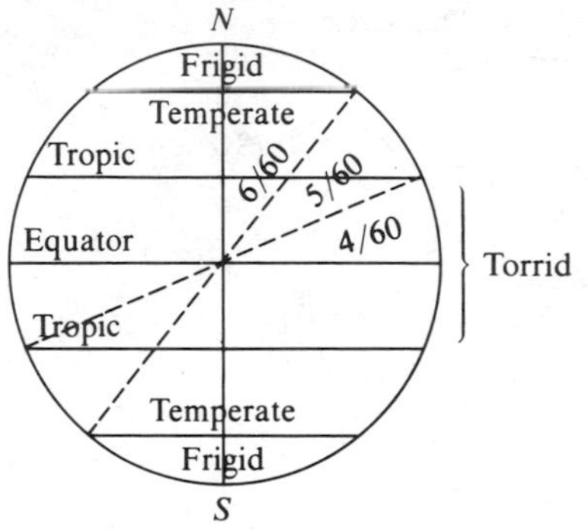

FIGURE 2

Eratosthenes also measured the obliquity of the ecliptic, which he apparently estimated as 11/83 of a circle, equivalent to 23°51′, a figure accepted as accurate by both Hipparchus and Ptolemy; how he obtained this curious ratio (if he did) is not clear *(ibid.,* fr. 41 and comment, pp. 167–168), and whether this measurement was fully described in the *Geography* or elsewhere cannot be determined—Strabo does not mention it, and he was undoubtedly writing with a copy of the *Geography* before him. What certainly would have found a place in this work was Eratosthenes' division of the terrestrial globe into zones. Of these he envisaged five (see Figure 2): a frigid zone around each pole, with a radius of 6/60 each, or 25,200 stades on the meridian circle (in his division of the circle into sixtieths, each sixtieth = 252,000 ÷ 60 = 4,200 stades), a temperate zone between each frigid zone and the tropics, with a radius of 5/60 or 21,000 stades, and a torrid zone comprising the two areas from the equator to each tropic, with a radius of 4/60 or 16,800 stades each (4/60 is equivalent to 24°, an approximate figure for the obliquity of the ecliptic known probably from the time of Eudoxus and used occasionally even by Hipparchus, e.g., *Commentarii in Arati et Eudoxi Phaenomena,* I, 10, 2)—making a total of 126,000 stades from pole to pole, i.e., half the whole circumference (see Geminus, *Isagoge,* XVI, 6 f.; V, 45 f.; Strabo, *Geography,* 113–114; *cf.* 112). The frigid zones were arbitrarily defined by the "arctic" and "antarctic" circles of an observer on the main parallel of latitude (roughly 36° N.), i.e., the circles marking the limits of the circumpolar stars that never rise or set and the stars that are never visible at that latitude (see *Geographical Fragments of Hipparchus,* pp. 165–166). Within this framework the *oikoumene,* according to Eratosthenes, has a "breadth" (north–south, as always in Greek geography) of 38,000 stades from the Cinnamon country (south of Meroë) to Thule, and a "length" (east–west) of 77,800 stades from the further side of India to beyond the Straits of Gibraltar (Strabo, *Geography,* 62–63, 64).

Although it is clear from the *Geography* that Eratosthenes was familiar with the concept of the celestial sphere, he does not seem to have done any original work in astronomy apart from the above measurements made in a geographical context; his name is not connected with any purely astronomical observation (figures for the distance and size of the sun attributed to him by Eusebius of Caesarea, *Praeparatio evangelica,* XV, 53, and Macrobius, *In somnium Scipionis,* I, 20, 9, are worthless, coming from these sources), he does not appear among the authorities cited by Ptolemy in the *Phaseis* for data relating to the parapegmata or astronomical calendars (see *Geographical Fragments of Hipparchus,* pp. 111–112), and only one astronomical title is attributed to him (and that wrongly): the fragmentary *Catasterismoi* (Robert, ed. [Berlin, 1878]; see Maass, "Analecta Eratosthenica," in *Philologische Untersuchungen,* **6** [1883], 3–55), which tells how various mythical personages were placed among the stars and gave their names to the different constellations, descriptions of which are given. It is possible that an inferior second-century compilation of the same nature, called *Poetica astronomica* (Bunte, ed. [Leipzig, 1875]) and going under the name of the Augustan scholar Hyginus, is based partly on a work of Eratosthenes, who is cited some twenty times (as against, e.g., ten times for Aratus), but this is hardly serious astronomy (see Rose, *Handbook of Latin Literature,* 3rd ed. [1954], p. 447).

In mathematics, Eratosthenes' chief work seems to have been the *Platonicus,* of which we have a few extracts given by Theon of Smyrna, who wrote in the second century (*Expositio rerum mathematicarum ad legendum Platonem utilium,* Hiller, ed. [Leipzig, 1878], pp. 2, 127, 129, 168). In this work, Eratosthenes apparently discussed from a mathematical and philosophical point of view such topics as proportion and progression (essential tools in Greek mathematics) and, arising from this, the theory of musical scales (Ptolemy, *Harmonica,* II, 14, Düring, ed. [Göteborg, 1930], pp. 70 f.; see Düring's ed. of Porphyry's commentary on this [1932], p. 91). Also in this work he gave his solution of the famous Delian problem of doubling the cube and described a piece of apparatus by which a solution could be obtained by mechanical means; the description is preserved for us by Eutocius, a sixth-century commentator on the works of Archimedes, and includes Eratosthenes' epigram (mentioned above) commemorating his achievement (*Eutocii commentarii in libros de sphaera et cylindro,* II, 1, in *Archimedes opera omnia,* Heiberg ed., III, 88 f.; epigram, p. 96); Pappus also describes the apparatus and the method (*Collectio,* III, F. Hultsch, ed. [Berlin, 1876], 22–23, 56–58). Eutocius gives his information in the form of a letter from Eratosthenes to King Ptolemy Euergetes; the "letter" is almost certainly not genuine, but there is no reason to doubt that the contents represent the matter of Eratosthenes' solution (perhaps at least partly in his own words) or that the epigram is his.

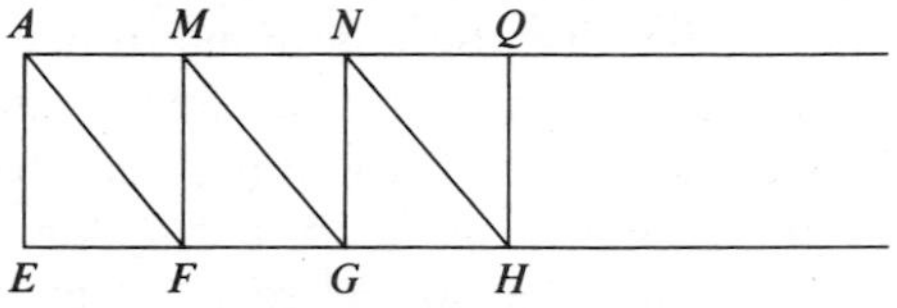

FIGURE 3

The history of the problem of doubling the cube and the various solutions proposed are fully discussed by Heath (*History of Greek Mathematics,* I, 244–270). Briefly, the problem resolves itself into finding two mean proportionals in continued proportion between two given straight lines: if a and b are the two given straight lines and we find x and y such that $a:x = x:y = y:b$, then $y = x^2/a = ab/x$; eliminating y, we have $x^3 = a^2b$, and in the case where b is twice a, $x^3 = 2a^3$, and thus the cube is doubled. Eratosthenes' mechanical solution envisaged a framework of two parallel rulers with longitudinal grooves along which could be slid three rectangular (or, according to Pappus, *loc. cit.,* triangular) plates (marked with their diagonals parallel—see Figure 3) moving independently of each other and able to overlap; if one of the plates remains fixed and the other two are moved so that they overlap as in Figure 4, it can easily be shown that points *A, B, C, D* lie on a straight line in such a way that *AE, BF, CG, DH* are in continued proportion, and *BF* and *CG* are the required mean proportionals between the given straight lines *AE* and *DH.*

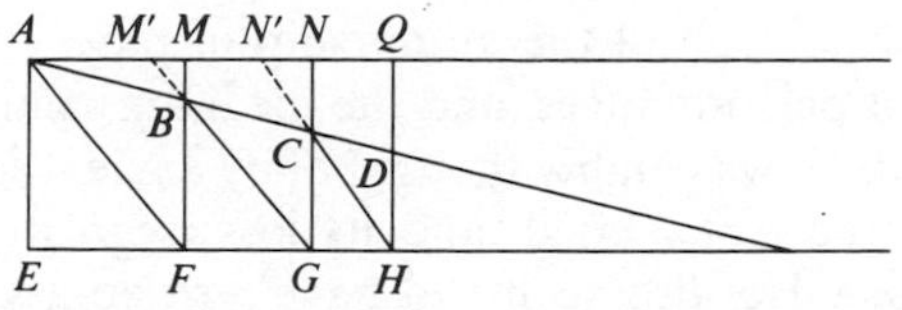

FIGURE 4. Only diagonals and righthand edges of movable plates marked.

In arithmetic Eratosthenes invented a method called the "sieve" (κόσκινον) for finding prime numbers (Nicomachus, *Introductio arithmetica,* I, 13, 2–4). According to this, one writes down consecutively the odd numbers, starting with 3 and continuing as long as desired; then, counting from 3, one passes over two numbers and strikes out the third (a multiple of 3 and hence not prime) and continues to do this until the end—thus 3 5 7 ~~9~~ 11 13 ~~15~~ 17 19 ~~21~~ 23 25 ~~27~~ 29 31 ~~33~~ 35, etc. The same process is gone through with 5, but this time passing over four numbers and striking out the fifth (a multiple of 5)—3 5 7 ~~9~~ 11 13 ~~15~~ 17 19 ~~21~~ 23 ~~25~~ ~~27~~ 29 31 ~~33~~ ~~35~~, etc. The process may be repeated with consecutive odd numbers as many times as one likes, on each occasion, if n is the odd number, n-1 numbers being passed over and the next struck out; the remaining numbers will all be prime. Pappus (late third century) also attributes to Eratosthenes a work *On Means* (Περὶ μεσοτήτων), the contents of which are a matter of conjecture but which was important enough to form part of what Heath calls the *Treasury of Analysis* (ἀναλυόμενος τόπος), comprising works by Euclid, Apollonius, Aristaeus, and Eratosthenes (Pappus, *Collectio,* Hultsch, ed., VII, 3, p. 636, 24; see Heath, *History of Greek Mathematics,* II, pp. 105, 399 ff.).

In chronology, Eratosthenes apparently wrote two works, *Chronography* (Χρονογραφίαι) and *Olympic Victors* ('Ολυμπιονίκαι); both must have entailed considerable original research (he was the first Greek writer we know to have made a scientific study of the dating of events), and the former seems to have been a popularizing work containing a number of anecdotes, several of which are repeated by Plutarch (e.g., "Demosthenes," Loeb ed., IX, 4; Teubner ed., XXX, 3; "Alexander," Loeb ed., III, 2; Teubner ed., XXXI, 2). Eratosthenes' datings remained authoritative throughout antiquity and in many cases cannot be improved upon today—e.g., the fall of Troy, 1184/1183 B.C.; the Dorian migration, 1104/1103; the first olympiad, beginning 777/776; the invasion of Xerxes, 480/479; the outbreak of the Peloponnesian War, 432/431.

In literary criticism Eratosthenes wrote a work in not less than twelve books entitled *On the Old Comedy,* the contents of which ranged over textual criticism, discussion of the authorship of plays from the dates of performances, and the meanings and usages of words; it was highly thought of by ancient scholars, being frequently cited, and its loss is greatly to be regretted. He also seems to have written a separate work on grammar. Finally, as befitted an Alexandrian polymath, he had a not inconsiderable reputation as a poet; his three main poetical works were *Hermes, Erigone,* and *Anterinys* or *Hesiod* (apparently alternative titles). The first had the same theme at the beginning as the well-known Homeric hymn but went on to draw a picture of the ascent of Hermes to the heavens and to give a vividly imaginative description of the zones of the earth as seen from there (Achilles Tatius, *Isagoge,* p. 153c in Petavius' *Uranologion* [1630]—the lines are reprinted by Hiller and by Powell); this passage was copied by Vergil (*Georgics,* I, 233–239). The *Erigone* was a star legend dealing with the story of Icarius, his daughter Erigone, and her dog, all of whom in this version were translated to the heavens as Boötes, Virgo, and Sirius, the Dog Star. The subject matter of the third poem is unknown. Only a few fragments of Eratosthenes' poetry are extant (the longest, some sixteen lines, being the passage from the *Hermes* mentioned above), and it is impossible to judge its intrinsic merit from these.

BIBLIOGRAPHY

The only published collection of all Eratosthenes' fragments is G. Bernhardy, *Eratosthenica* (Berlin, 1822), which is now greatly out of date. I have been much indebted in the preparation of this article to R. M. Bentham's unpublished Ph.D. thesis (London) entitled "The Fragments of Eratosthenes of Cyrene." It was made available to me through the kindness of his supervisor, Prof. E. H. Warmington (formerly of Birkbeck College, University of London), following the unfortunate death of the author before he submitted his thesis.

See also G. Knaack, "Eratosthenes," in Pauly-Wissowa, VI (1907), cols. 358–388; E. H. Bunbury, *History of Ancient Geography,* I (London, 1879), ch. 16; E. H. Berger, *Die geographische Fragmente des Eratosthenes* (Leipzig, 1880); A. Thalamas, *La géographie d'Ératosthène* (Versailles, 1921); D. R. Dicks, *The Geographical Fragments of Hipparchus* (London, 1960); E. Hiller, *Eratosthenis carminum reliquiae* (Leipzig, 1872); and J. U. Powell, *Collectanea Alexandrina* (Oxford, 1925).

D. R. DICKS

ERDÉLYI, ARTHUR (*b.* Budapest, Hungary, 2 October 1908; *d.* Edinburgh, Scotland, 12 December 1977)

Arthur Erdélyi was the first child of Ignác and Frieda (Roth) Diamant. After his father's death, he was adopted by his mother's second husband, Paul Erdélyi. He attended elementary school in Budapest from 1914 to 1926. After studying at the Deutsche Technische Hochschule in Brno, Czechoslovakia, he matriculated at the German University of Prague and was awarded the degree of doctor rerum naturalium in 1938. Forced by the Nazis to flee Czechoslovakia, Erdélyi managed to obtain a research grant from Edinburgh University, where in 1940 he was awarded the degree of doctor of science. In 1942 he married Eva Neuburg, and in 1949 he left Edinburgh to become a professor at the California Institute of Technology. He returned to Edinburgh in 1964 as professor of mathematics, remaining there until his death. In 1975 Erdélyi was elected a fellow of the Royal Society of London, and in 1977 he was awarded the Gunning Victoria Jubilee Prize of the Royal Society of Edinburgh.

Erdélyi began his mathematical career with a study of the confluent hypergeometric function and before arriving in Edinburgh in 1939 had already established himself as a leading expert in the area of special functions. In Edinburgh he continued to pursue his investigations, broadening his interests into generalized hypergeometric functions, classical orthogonal polynomials, and, in particular, Lamé functions, on which he published a series of fundamental papers. His career at Edinburgh University was interrupted, however, by the death at Caltech of Harry Bateman, who left behind voluminous notes on special functions that demanded editing and publication. After due consultation with leading experts, Erdélyi was appointed by Caltech in 1947 to supervise the editing and publication of the Bateman manuscripts. With him came F. G. Tricomi from the University of Turin, W. Magnus from the University of Göttingen, and F. Oberhettinger from the University of Mainz. Together they produced the three-volume *Higher Transcendental Functions* (1953–1955) and the two-volume *Tables of Integral Transforms* (1954). These books became basic reference sources for generations of applied mathematicians and physicists throughout the world, and the most important part of this work, *Higher Transcendental Functions*, remains the most scholarly and comprehensive treatment of the special functions of mathematical physics that is available.

The Bateman Manuscript Project marked a turning point in Erdélyi's development as a mathematician. As the project neared completion, he turned from an investigation of special functions for their own sake to the study of asymptotic expansions of integrals and solutions of differential equations. Erdélyi's most important contribution to this area was in the asymptotic evaluation of integrals. Fundamental to many of his investigations was the idea of an asymptotic scale and generalized asymptotic expansion, an idea that dates back at least to H. Schmidt but that Erdélyi was the first to exploit on a systematic basis. The application of these ideas yielded new theorems on the asymptotic expansion of Laplace integrals involving logarithms and exponential functions, as well as an elegant and unified treatment of Watson's lemma, Darboux's method, and the asymptotic behavior of functions in transition regions.

Erdélyi demonstrated that the Poincaré-type definition of an asymptotic expansion is much too narrow for a satisfactory discussion of the asymptotic behavior of functions depending on more than one parameter. These investigations of asymptotic analysis were influenced by the work then being undertaken in the Guggenheim Aeronautical Laboratory at Caltech on the development of an improved boundary-layer theory for viscous fluid-flow past obstacles, and Erdélyi's lifelong interest in singular perturbation theory can be traced back to this time. His book *Asymptotic Expansions* appeared in 1956 and is now regarded as one of the classic monographs on the subject of asymptotic analysis.

A third major area of Erdélyi's scientific work was in fractional integration and singular partial differential equations. His first major contribution to this area was in 1940, when together with H. Kober he introduced certain modifications of the Riemann-Liouville and Weyl fractional integrals and discussed their connection with the Hankel transform. These generalized fractional integration operators are now called Erdélyi-Kober operators. These results lay dormant for over twenty years until Erdélyi's interest was revived by the publications of Alexander Weinstein on the generalized axially symmetric potential equation. Erdélyi's first paper on this equation appeared in 1956, giving criteria for the location of singularities of solutions, and it laid the foundation for numerous later developments in the analytic theory of partial differential equations. This paper was soon followed by many others on the axially symmetric potential equation and the Euler-Poisson-Darboux equation, as well as further applications of fractional integration to dual integral equations and the theory of generalized functions. He was actively involved with this work at the time of his death.

Arthur Erdélyi was an excellent expositor, and with his broad interests he had something to say in many areas of mathematics. His reputation was based on much more than his published papers, although this alone would have sufficed to make him one of the leading analysts of his time. His combination of mathematical scholarship, an interest and enthusiasm for mathematics, a concern for younger workers, and a willingness to devote his time in aid of the mathematical community won Erdélyi the admiration and respect of an entire generation of mathematicians.

BIBLIOGRAPHY

I. ORIGINAL WORKS. *Higher Transcendental Functions*, 3 vols. (New York, 1953–1955), written with W. Magnus, F. Oberhettinger, and F. G. Tricomi; *Tables of Integral Transforms*, 2 vols. (New York, 1954), written with W. Magnus, F. Oberhettinger, and F. G. Tricomi; *Asymptotic Expansions* (New York, 1956); and *Operational Calculus and Generalized Functions* (New York, 1962).

II. SECONDARY LITERATURE. Obituaries, with bibliographies, include D. Colton, in *Bulletin of the London Mathematical Society*, **11** (1979), 191–207; and D. S. Jones, in *Biographical Memoirs of Fellows of the Royal Society*, **25** (1979), 267–286.

DAVID COLTON

ESCLANGON, ERNEST BENJAMIN (*b.* Mison, France, 17 March 1876; *d.* Eyrenville, France, 28 January 1954)

Esclangon came from a family of landed proprietors. The practical attitudes of his class are apparent in his realistic approach to problems in pure mathematics, applied celestial mechanics, relativity, observational astronomy, instrumental astronomy, astronomical chronometry, aerodynamics, interior and exterior ballistics, and aerial and underwater acoustic detection. He contributed to all of these fields to a greater or lesser degree, but always effectively.

Esclangon's first training was as a mathematician. As a student at the École Normale Supérieure (1895–1898) and an *agrégé* in mathematics (1898), he took up the problem of quasi-periodic functions. (Quasi-periodic functions, newly introduced, constitute a remarkable class among the almost periodic functions; their Fourier expansion is formed by a limited number of terms.) Esclangon elaborated a theory for these functions, studied their differentiation and integration, and examined the differential equations which allow them as coefficients. His doctoral thesis established a basis for their employment at a time when their role in mathematical physics was only beginning to be developed.

Esclangon's subsequent career as an astronomer and teacher was the result of chance—in the form of a vacant position—and of his own curiosity that led him to accept it. He was an astronomer at Bordeaux, beginning in 1899, then director of the observatories of Strasbourg (1918) and Paris (1929–1944). In addition, he taught mathematics at the Bordeaux Faculty of Science (from 1902), then became professor of astronomy at Strasbourg (in 1919) and then at Paris (1930–1946).

For fifty years Esclangon explored all the branches of fundamental astronomy. He devoted special attention to perfecting instruments, with a view to increasing the precision of observations. Of particular interest is his solution to a critical problem in positional astronomy, the rigorous definition of the axis of rotation of a transit instrument. Esclangon demonstrated that by fitting an objective in one of the extremities of this axis, which is hollow, and fitting a reticle to the other, the observer is permitted to measure the displacement of the instantaneous axis of rotation continuously throughout the course of the observation.

Esclangon's work in ballistics began in 1914 when, at the beginning of World War I, he proposed to French military authorities that they employ sound-ranging techniques to localize enemy artillery. He was charged with organizing the experimental study of this method; he was thus able to analyze the two components of the wave emitted by the projectile, the conical shock wave and the spherical wave centered on the point of emission. Esclangon then succeeded in 1916 in eliminating the registration of the shock wave and thereby assured a great precision in pinpointing enemy gun locations.

As director of the Bureau International de l'Heure (1929–1944), Esclangon was led to devote himself to problems of time. In addition to making studies on the astronomical determination of time and on its conservation and diffusion, he devised the "talking clock" (employing time signals from an observatory clock) that has made telephonic announcements of the exact time available to the Paris public since 1933.

Esclangon's practical bias and his inclination toward solid demonstrations (whether mathematical or experimental) caused him to be critical of the general theory of relativity. In a memoir of 1937, "La notion de temps. Temps physique et relativité . . .," he discusses the restrictions necessary to certain conclusions that have been stated too absolutely and states how, for example, it is possible to conceive of phenomena faster than light and why the ordinary formulas are not strictly applicable to the motion of masses at great speeds.

Esclangon was a member of the Académie des Sciences (1939) and the Bureau des Longitudes (1932). He served as president of the Union Astronomique Internationale from 1935 to 1938. He assumed his official functions with simplicity and amiability; he was affable and loved to joke, and did not deny himself leisure time. It would almost seem that he accomplished his body of important work without effort.

BIBLIOGRAPHY

I. Original Works. Esclangon published 247 memoirs, monographs, and articles, of which some of the most important are, in mathematical analysis, "Les fonctions quasi-périodiques," his doctoral thesis, in *Annales de l'Observatoire de Bordeaux,* **11** (1904), 1–276; and "Nouvelles recherches sur les fonctions quasi-périodiques," *ibid.,* **16** (1917), 51–176.

His astronomical works include "Sur les transformations de la comète Daniel . . .," in *Bulletin astronomique,* **25** (1908), 81–91; "Mémoire sur la réfraction astronomique," in *Bulletin de Comité international permanent pour l'exécution photographique de la carte du ciel,* **6** (1913), 319–389; "Sur la précision des observations méridiennes et des mesures de longitudes," in *Annales de l'Observatoire de Strasbourg,* **1** (1926), 373–405; "Mémoire sur l'amélioration des observations méridiennes," in *Bulletin astronomique,* **6** (1930), 229–260; "L'horloge parlante de l'Observatoire de Paris," in *L'astronomie,* **47** (1933), 145–155; "Horloges indiquant simultanément le temps moyen et le temps sidéral," in *Bulletin astronomique,* **11** (1938), 181–189; and "Sur la transformation en satellites permanents de la terre de projectiles auto-propulsés," in *Comptes rendus hebdomadaires des séances de l'Académie des sciences,* **225** (1947), 513–515.

In theoretical physics, Esclangon wrote "Mémoire sur les preuves astronomiques de la relativité," in *Bulletin astronomique,* **1** (1920), 303–329; and "La notion de temps. Temps physique et relativité . . .," *ibid.,* **10** (1937), 1–72.

His work in applied physics includes "Le vol plané sans force motrice," in *Comptes rendus hebdomadaires des séances de l'Académie des sciences,* **147** (1908), 496–498; "Sur un régulateur rotatif de vitesse," *ibid.,* **152** (1911), 32–35; "Sur un régulateur thermique de précision," *ibid.,* **154** (1912), 178–181, 495–497; "Sur un nouveau régulateur de température . . .," *ibid.,* **156** (1913), 1667–1670; "Mémoire sur l'intensité de la pesanteur," in *Annales de l'Observatoire de Bordeaux,* **15** (1915), 99–314; and "Le vol plané sans force motrice," in *Comptes rendus hebdomadaires des séances de l'Académie des sciences,* **177** (1923), 1102–1104.

His publications in military science comprise *Mémoire sur la détection sous-marine . . .* (Paris, 1918), in the Archives de la Marine de Guerre; and *L'acoustique des canons et des projectiles* (Paris, 1925).

II. Secondary Literature. On Esclangon and his work, see J. Chazy, "Notice nécrologique sur Ernest Esclangon," in *Comptes rendus hebdomadaires des séances de l'Académie des sciences,* **238** (1954), 629–632; and "Ernest Esclangon (1876–1954)," in *Annuaire du Bureau des longitudes* (1955), C1–C6; A. Danjon, "Obituary Notice: Ernest Esclangon," in *Monthly Notices of the Royal Astronomical Society,* **115** (1955), 124; J. Jackson, "Obituaries: Prof. E. Esclangon," in *Nature,* **173** (1954), 567; and A. Pérard, "Quelques mots de l'oeuvre scientifique d'Ernest Esclangon," in *L'astronomie,* **68** (1954), 201–204.

JACQUES R. LÉVY

EUCLID (*fl.* Alexandria [and Athens?], *ca.* 295 B.C.) The following article is in two parts: Life and Works; Transmission of the Elements.

Life and Works.

Although Euclid (Latinized as Euclides) is the most celebrated mathematician of all time, whose name became a synonym for geometry until the twentieth century,[1] only two facts of his life are known, and even these are not beyond dispute. One is that he was intermediate in date between the pupils of Plato (*d.* 347 B.C.) and Archimedes (*b. ca.* 287 B.C.); the other is that he taught in Alexandria.

Until recently most scholars would have been content to say that Euclid was older than Archimedes on the ground that Euclid, *Elements* I.2, is cited in Archimedes, *On the Sphere and the Cylinder* I.2; but in 1950 Johannes Hjelmslev asserted that this reference was a naïve interpolation. The reasons that he gave are not wholly convincing, but the reference is certainly contrary to ancient practice and is not unfairly characterized as naïve; and although it was already in the text in the time of Proclus, it looks like a marginal gloss which has crept in.[2] Although it is no longer possible to rely on this reference,[3] a general consideration of Euclid's works such as that presented here still shows that he must have written after such pupils of Plato as Eudoxus and before Archimedes.

Euclid's residence in Alexandria is known from Pappus, who records that Apollonius spent a long time with the disciples of Euclid in that city.[4] This passage is also attributed to an interpolator by Pappus' editor, Friedrich Hultsch, but only for stylistic reasons (and these not very convincing); and even if the Alexandrian residence rested only on the authority of an interpolator, it would still be credible in the light of general probabilities. Since Alexander ordered the foundation of the town in 332 B.C. and another ten years elapsed before it began to take shape, we get as a first approximation that Euclid's Alexandrian activities lay somewhere between 320 and 260 B.C. Apollonius was active at Alexandria under Ptolemy III Euergetes (acceded 246) and Ptolemy IV Philopator (acceded 221) and must have received his education about the middle of the century. It is likely, therefore, that Euclid's life overlapped that of Archimedes.

This agrees with what Proclus says about Euclid in his commentary on the first book of the *Elements.* The passage, which is contained in Proclus' summary of the history of geometry,[5] opens:

> Not much younger than these [Hermotimus of Colophon and Philippus of Medma, two disciples of Plato] is Euclid, who put together the elements, arranging in order many of Eudoxus' theorems, perfecting many of Theaetetus', and also bringing to irrefutable demonstration the things which had been only loosely proved by his predecessors. This man lived[6] in the time of the first Ptolemy;[7] for Archimedes, who followed closely upon the first [Ptolemy], makes mention of Euclid,[8] and further they say that Ptolemy once asked him if there were a shorter way to the study of geometry than the *Elements,* to which he replied that there was no royal road to geometry. He is therefore younger than Plato's circle, but older than Eratosthenes and Archimedes; for these were contemporaries, as Eratosthenes somewhere says.[9] In his aim he was a Platonist, being in sympathy with this philosophy, whence he made the end of the whole *Elements* the construction of the so-called Platonic figures.

Since Plato died in 347, Ptolemy I ruled from 323 and reigned from 304 to 285, and Archimedes was born in 287, the chronology of this passage is self-consistent but allows a wide margin according to whether Euclid flourished in Ptolemy's rule or reign. It is clear, however, that Proclus, writing over six centuries later, had no independent knowledge, obviously relying upon Archimedes for his lower date. The story about the royal road is similar to a tale that Stobaeus tells about Menaechmus and Alexander.[10] Euclid may very well have been a Platonist, for mathematics received an immense impetus from Plato's encouragement; what Proclus says about his relationship to Plato's associates, Eudoxus and Theaetetus, is borne out by his own works; and if he were a Platonist, he would have derived pleasure from making the *Elements* end with the construction of the five regular solids. The testimony of so zealous a Neoplatonist as Proclus is not, however, necessarily conclusive on this point.

Confirmation of Proclus' upper date comes from the relationship of Euclid to Aristotle, who died in 322 B.C. Euclid's postulates and axioms or "common notions" undoubtedly show the influence of Aristotle's elaborate discussion of these topics.[11] Aristotle, on the other hand, shows no awareness of Euclid, and he gives a proof of the proposition that the angles at the base of an isosceles triangle are equal which is pre-Euclidean and would hardly have been cited if *Elements* I.5 had been at hand.[12]

If exact dates could be assigned to Autolycus of Pitane, greater precision would be possible, for in his *Phaenomena* Euclid quotes (but without naming his source) propositions from Autolycus' *On the Moving Sphere.* Autolycus was the teacher of Arcesilaus, who was born about 315 B.C. It would be reasonable to suppose that Autolycus was at the height of his activities about 300 B.C., and the date that would best fit the middle point of Euclid's active career is about 295 B.C.; but the uncertainties are so great that no quarrel can be taken with the conventional round date of 300 B.C.[13]

He is therefore a totally different person from Euclid of Megara, the disciple of Plato, who lived about a hundred years earlier.[14] His birthplace is unknown,[15] and the date of his birth can only be guessed. It is highly probable, however, quite apart from what Proclus says about his Platonism, that he attended the Academy, for Athens was the great center of mathematical studies at the time; and there he would have become acquainted with the highly original work of Eudoxus and Theaetetus. He was probably invited to Alexandria when Demetrius of Phalerum, at the direction of Ptolemy Soter, was setting up the great library and museum. This was shortly after 300 B.C., and Demetrius, then an exile from Athens, where he had been the governor, would have known Euclid's reputation. It is possible that this had already been established by one or more books, but the only piece of internal or external evidence about the order in which Euclid wrote his works is that the *Optics* preceded the *Phaenomena* because it is cited in the preface of the latter. Euclid must be regarded as the founder of the great school of mathematics at Alexandria, which was unrivaled in antiquity. Pappus or an interpolator[16] pays tribute to him as "most fair and well disposed toward all who were able in any measure to advance mathematics, careful in no way to give offense, and although an exact scholar not vaunting himself," as Apollonius was alleged to do; and although the object of the passage is to denigrate Apollonius, there is no reason to reject the assessment of Euclid's character. It was presumably at Alexandria, according to a story by Stobaeus,[17] that someone who had begun to learn geometry with Euclid asked him, after the first theorem, what he got out of such things. Summoning a slave, Euclid said, "Give him three obols, since he must needs make gain out of what he learns." The place of his death is not recorded—although the natural assumption is that it was Alexandria—and the date of his death can only be conjectured. A date about 270 B.C. would accord with the fact that about the middle of the century Apollonius studied with his pupils.

Arabic authors profess to know a great deal more about Euclid's parentage and life, but what they write is either free invention or based on the assumption that the so-called book XIV of the *Elements,* written by Hypsicles, is a genuine work of Euclid.

Geometry: Elements (Στοιχεῖα). Euclid's fame rests preeminently upon the *Elements,* which he wrote in thirteen books[18] and which has exercised an influence upon the human mind greater than that of any other work except the Bible. For this reason he became known in antiquity as Ὁ Στοιχειωτής, "the Writer of the Elements," and sometimes simply as Ὁ Γεωμέτρης, "the Geometer." Proclus explains that the "elements" are leading theorems having to those which follow the character of an all-pervading principle; he likens them to the letters of the alphabet in relation to language, and in Greek they have the same name.[19] There had been *Elements* written before Euclid—notably by Hippocrates, Leo, and Theudius of Magnesia—but Euclid's work superseded them so completely that they are now known only from Eudemus' references as preserved by Proclus. Euclid's *Elements* was the subject of commentaries in antiquity by Hero, Pappus, Porphyry, Proclus, and Simplicius; and Geminus had many observations about it in a work now lost. In the fourth century Theon of Alexandria reedited it, altering the language in some places with a view to greater clarity, interpolating intermediate steps, and supplying alternative proofs, separate cases, and corollaries. All the manuscripts of the *Elements* known until the nineteenth century were derived from Theon's recension. Then Peyrard discovered in the Vatican a manuscript, known as *P,* which obviously gives an earlier text and is the basis of Heiberg's definitive edition.

Each book of the *Elements* is divided into propositions, which may be theorems, in which it is sought to prove something, or problems, in which it is sought to do something. A proposition which is complete in all its parts has a general enunciation (πρότασις); a setting-out or particular enunciation (ἔκθεσις), in which the general enunciation is related to a figure designated by the letters of the alphabet; a definition (διορισμός),[20] which is either a closer statement of the object sought, with the purpose of riveting attention, or a statement of the conditions of possibility; a construction (κατασκευή), including any necessary additions to the original figure; a proof or demonstration (ἀπόδειξις); and a conclusion (συμπέρασμα), which reverts to the language of the general enunciation and states that it has been accomplished. In many cases some of these divisions may be missing (particularly the definition or the construction) because they are not needed, but the general enunciation, proof, and conclusion are always found. The conclusion is rounded off by the formulas ὅπερ ἔδει δεῖξαι ("which was to be proved") for a theorem and ὅπερ ἔδει ποιῆσαι ("which was to be done") for a problem, which every schoolboy knows in their abbreviated Latin forms as Q.E.D. and Q.E.F. These formal divisions of a proposition in such detail are special to Euclid, for Autolycus before him—the only pre-Euclidean author to have any work survive entire—had normally given only a general enunciation and proof, although occasionally a conclusion is found; and Archimedes after him frequently omitted the general or particular enunciation.

The Greek mathematicians carefully distinguished between the analytic and the synthetic methods of proving a proposition.[21] Euclid was not unskilled in analysis, and according to Pappus he was one of the three writers—the others being Apollonius and Aristaeus the Elder—who created the special body of doctrine enshrined in the *Treasury of Analysis.* This collection of treatises included three by Euclid: his *Data, Porisms,* and *Surface Loci.* But in the *Elements* the demonstrations proceed entirely by synthesis, that is, from the known to the unknown, and nowhere is appeal made to analysis, that is, the assumption of the thing to be proved (or done) and the deduction of the consequences until we reach something already accepted or proved true. (Euclid does, however, make frequent use of *reductio ad absurdum* or *demonstratio per impossibile,* showing that if the conclusion is not accepted, absurd or impossible results follow; and this may be regarded as a form of analysis. There are also many pairs of converse propositions, and either one in a pair could be regarded as a piece of analysis for the solution of the other.) No hint is given by Euclid about the way in which he first realized the truth of the propositions that he proves. Majestically he proceeds by rigorous logical steps from one proved proposition to another, using them like stepping-stones, until the final goal is reached.

Each book (or, in the case of XI–XIII, group of books) of the *Elements* is preceded by definitions of the subjects treated, and to book I there are also prefixed five postulates (αἰτήματα) and five common notions (κοίναι ἔννοιαι) or axioms which are the foundation of the entire work. Aristotle had taught that to define an object is not to assert its existence; this must be either proved or assumed.[22] In conformity with this doctrine Euclid defines a point, a straight line, and a circle, then postulates that it is possible

1. To draw a straight line from any point to any point
2. To produce a finite straight line continuously in a straight line
3. To describe a circle with any center and radius.

In other words, he assumes the existence of points, straight lines, and circles as the basic elements of his geometry, and with these assumptions he is able to prove the existence of every other figure that he defines. For example, the existence of a square, defined in I, definition 22, is proved in I.46.

These three postulates do rather more, however, than assume the existence of the things defined. The first postulate implies that between any two points only one straight line can be drawn; and this is equivalent to saying that if two straight lines have the same extremities, they coincide throughout their length, or that two straight lines cannot enclose a space. (The latter statement is interpolated in some of the manuscripts.) The second postulate implies that a straight line can be produced in only one direction at either end, that is, the produced part in either direction is unique, and two straight lines cannot have a common segment. It follows also, since the straight line can be produced indefinitely, or an indefinite number of times, that the space of Euclid's geometry is infinite in all directions. The third postulate also implies the infinitude of space because no limit is placed upon the radius; it further implies that space is continuous, not discrete, because the radius may be indefinitely small.

The fourth and fifth postulates are of a different order because they do not state that something can be done. In the fourth the following is postulated:

4. All right angles are equal to one another.

This implies that a right angle is a determinate magnitude, so that it serves as a norm by which other angles can be measured, but it is also equivalent to an assumption of the homogeneity of space. For if the assertion could be proved, it could be proved only by moving one right angle to another so as to make them coincide, which is an assumption of the invariability of figures or the homogeneity of space. Euclid prefers to assume that all right angles are equal.

The fifth postulate concerns parallel straight lines. These are defined in I, definition 23, as "straight lines which, being in the same plane and being produced indefinitely in both directions, do not meet one another in either direction." The essential characteristic of parallel lines for Euclid is, therefore, that they do not meet. Other Greek writers toyed with the idea, as many moderns have done, that parallel straight lines are equidistant from each other throughout their lengths or have the same direction,[23] and Euclid shows his genius in opting for nonsecancy as the test of parallelism. The fifth postulate runs:

5. If a straight line falling on two straight lines makes the interior angles on the same side less than two right angles, the two straight lines, if produced indefinitely, will meet on that side on which are the angles less than two right angles.

In Figure 1 the postulate asserts that if a straight line (*PQ*) cuts two other straight lines (*AB, CD*) in *P, Q* so that the sum of the angles *BPQ, DQP* is less than two right angles, *AB, CD* will meet on the same side of *PQ* as those two angles, that is, they will meet if produced beyond *B* and *D*.

There was a strong feeling in antiquity that this postulate should be capable of proof, and attempts to prove it were made by Ptolemy and Proclus, among others.[24] Many more attempts have been made in modern times. All depend for their apparent success on making, consciously or unconsciously, an assumption which is equivalent to Euclid's postulate. It was Saccheri in his book *Euclides ab omni naevo vindicatus* (1733) who first asked himself what would be the consequences of hypotheses other than that of Euclid, and in so doing he stumbled upon the possibility of non-Euclidean geometries. Being convinced, as all mathematicians and philosophers were until the nineteenth century, that there could be no geometry besides that delineated by Euclid, he did not realize what he had done; and although Gauss had the first understanding of modern ideas, it was left to Lobachevski (1826, 1829) and Bolyai (1832), on the one hand, and Riemann (1854), on the other, to develop non-Euclidean geometries. Euclid's fifth postulate has thus been revealed for what it really is—an unprovable assumption defining the character of one type of space.

The five common notions are axioms, which, unlike the postulates, are not confined to geometry but are common to all the demonstrative sciences. The first is "Things which are equal to the same thing are also equal to one another," and the others are similar.

The subject matter of the first six books of the *Elements* is plane geometry. Book I deals with the geometry of points, lines, triangles, squares, and parallelograms. Proposition 5, that in isosceles triangles the angles at the base are equal to one another and that, if the equal straight lines are produced, the angles under the base will be equal to one another, is interesting historically as having been known (except in France) as the *pons asinorum;* this is usually taken to mean that those who are not going to be good at geometry fail to get past it, although others have seen in the figure of the proposition a resemblance to a trestle bridge with a ramp at each end which a donkey can cross but a horse cannot.

Proposition 44 requires the student "to a given straight to apply in a given rectilineal angle a parallelogram equal to a given triangle," that is, on a given straight line to construct a parallelogram equal to a given area and having one of its angles equal to a given angle. In Figure 3, *AB* is the given straight line and the parallelogram *BEFG* is constructed equal to the triangle *C* so that $\angle GBE = \angle D$. The figure is completed, and it is proved that the parallelogram

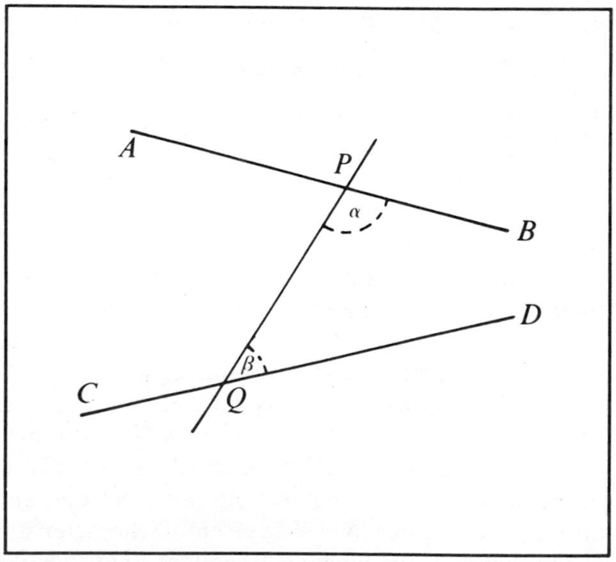

FIGURE 1. Book I, Postulate 5, $\alpha + \beta < 2$ Right Angles

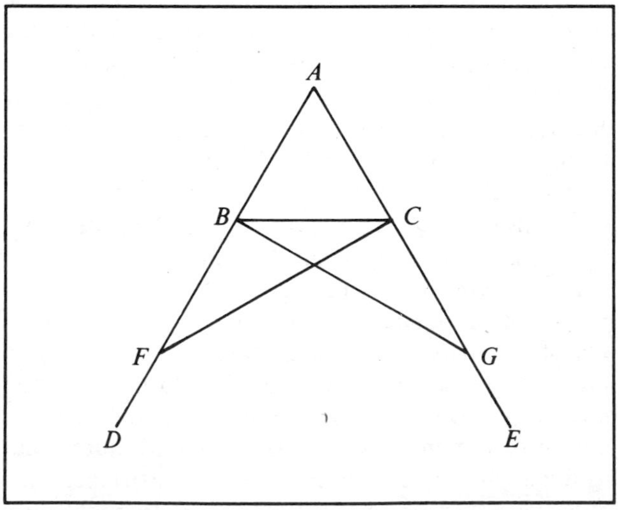

FIGURE 2. Book I, Proposition 5, Pons Asinorum

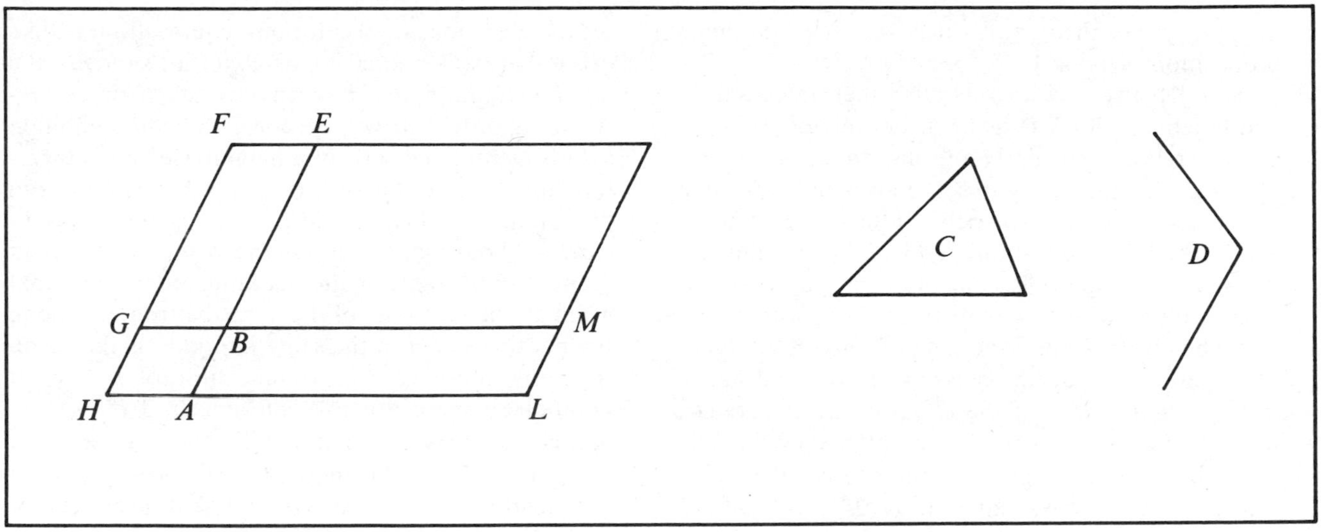

FIGURE 3. Book I, Proposition 44, Application of Areas

ABML satisfies the requirements. This is Euclid's first example of the application of areas,[25] one of the most powerful tools of the Greek mathematicians. It is a geometrical equivalent of certain algebraic operations. In this simple case, if $AL = x$, then $x \cdot AB \cos D = C$, and the theorem is equivalent to the solution of a first-degree equation. The method is developed later, as it will be shown, so as to be equivalent to the solution of second-degree equations.

Book I leads up to the celebrated proposition 47, "Pythagoras' theorem," which asserts: "In right-angled triangles the square on the side subtending the right angle is equal to the [sum of the] squares on the sides containing the right angle." In Figure 4 it is shown solely by the use of preceding propositions that the parallelogram *BL* is equal to the square *BG* and the parallelogram *CL* is equal to the square *AK,* so that the whole square *BE* is equal to the sum of the squares *BG, AK.* It is important to notice, for a reason to be given later, that no appeal is made to similarity of figures. This fundamental proposition gives Euclidean space a metric, which would be expressed in modern notation as $ds^2 = dx^2 + dy^2$. It is impossible not to admire the ingenuity with which the result is obtained, and not surprising that when Thomas Hobbes first read it he exclaimed, "By God, this is impossible."

Book II develops the transformation of areas adumbrated in I.44, 45 and is a further exercise in geometrical algebra. Propositions 5, 6, 11, and 14 are the equivalents of solving the quadratic equations $ax - x^2 = b^2$, $ax + x^2 = b^2$, $x^2 + ax = a^2$, $x^2 = ab$. Propositions 9 and 10 are equivalent to finding successive pairs of integers satisfying the equations $2x^2 - y^2 = \pm 1$. Such pairs were called by the Greeks side numbers and diameter numbers. Propositions 12 and 13 are equivalent to a proof that in any triangle with sides *a,b,c,* and angle *A* opposite *a,*

$$a^2 = b^2 + c^2 - 2\,bc \cos A.$$

It is probably not without significance that this penultimate proposition of book II is a generalization

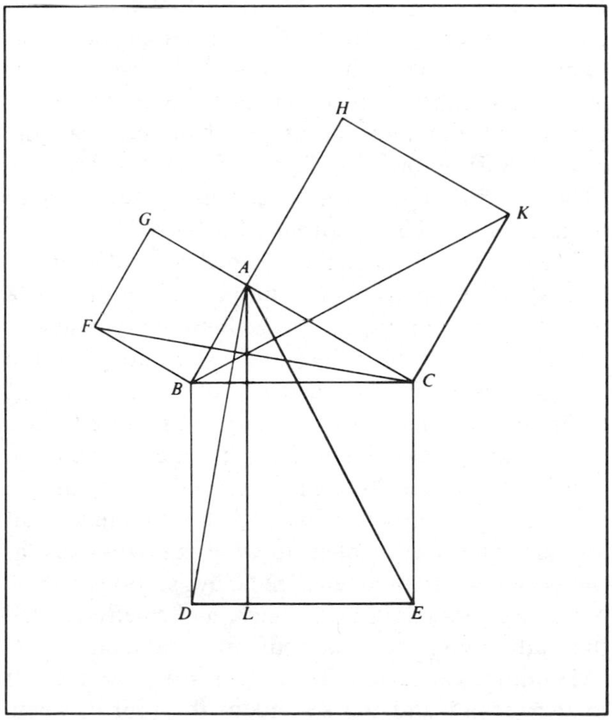

FIGURE 4. Book I, Proposition 47, "Pythagoras' Theorem," $BC^2 = CA^2 + AB^2$

of "Pythagoras' theorem," which was the penultimate proposition of book I.

Book III treats circles, including their intersections and touchings. Book IV consists entirely of problems about circles, particularly the inscribing or circumscribing of rectilineal figures. It ends with proposition 16: "In a given circle to inscribe a fifteen-angled figure which shall be both equilateral and equiangular." Proclus asserts that this is one of the propositions that Euclid solved with a view to their use in astronomy, "for when we have inscribed the fifteen-angled figure in the circle through the poles, we have the distance from the poles both of the equator and the zodiac, since they are distant from one another by the side of the fifteen-angled figure"—that is to say, the obliquity of the ecliptic was taken to be 24°, as is known independently to have been the case up to Eratosthenes.[26]

Book V develops the general theory of proportion. The theory of proportion as discovered by the Pythagoreans applied only to commensurable magnitudes because it depends upon the taking of aliquot parts, and this is all that was needed by Euclid for the earlier books of the *Elements*. There are instances, notably I.47, where he clearly avoids a proof that would depend on similitude or the finding of a proportional, because at that stage of his work it would not have applied to incommensurable magnitudes. In book V he addresses himself at length to the general theory. There is no book in the *Elements* that has so won the admiration of mathematicians. Barrow observes: "There is nothing in the whole body of the *Elements* of a more subtile invention, nothing more solidly established and more accurately handled, than the doctrine of proportionals." In like spirit Cayley says, "There is hardly anything in mathematics more beautiful than this wondrous fifth book."[27]

The heart of the book is contained in the definitions with which it opens. The definition of a ratio as "a sort of relation in respect of size between two magnitudes of the same kind" shows that a ratio, like the elephant, is easy to recognize but hard to define. Definition 4 is more to the point: "Magnitudes are said to have a ratio one to the other if capable, when multiplied, of exceeding one another." The definition excludes the infinitely great and the infinitely small and is virtually equivalent to what is now known as the axiom of Archimedes. (See below, section on book X.) But it is definition 5 which has chiefly excited the admiration of subsequent mathematicians: "Magnitudes are said to be in the same ratio, the first to the second and the second to the fourth, when, if any equimultiples whatever be taken of the first and third, and any equimultiples whatever of the second and fourth, the former equimultiples alike exceed, are alike equal to, or alike fall short of, the latter equimultiples respectively taken in corresponding order." It will be noted that the definition avoids mention of parts of a magnitude and is therefore applicable to the incommensurable as well as to the commensurable. De Morgan put its meaning very clearly: "Four magnitudes, A and B of one kind, and C and D of the same or another kind, are proportional when all the multiples of A can be distributed among the multiples of B in the same intervals as the corresponding multiples of C among those of D"; or, in notation, if m, n are two integers, and if mA lies between nB and $(n+1)B$, mC lies between nD and $(n+1)D$.[28] It can be shown that the test proposed by Euclid is both a necessary and a sufficient test of proportionality, and in the whole history of mathematics no equally satisfactory test has ever been proposed. The best testimony to its adequacy is that Weierstrass used it in his definition of equal numbers;[29] and Heath has shown how Euclid's definition divides all rational numbers into two coextensive classes and thus defines equal ratios in a manner exactly corresponding to a Dedekind section.[30]

The remaining definitions state the various kinds of transformations of ratios—generally known by their Latin names: *alternando, invertendo, componendo, separando, convertendo, ex aequali,* and *ex aequali in proportione perturbata*—and with remorseless logic the twenty-five propositions apply these various operations to the objects of Euclid's definitions.

It is a sign of the abiding fascination of book V for mathematicians that in 1967 Friedhelm Beckmann applied his own system of axioms, set up in close accordance with Euclid, in such a way as to deduce all definitions and propositions of Euclid's theory of magnitudes, especially those of books V and VI. In his view magnitudes, rather than their relation of "having a ratio," form the base of the theory of proportions. These magnitudes represent a well-defined structure, a so-called Eudoxic semigroup, with the numbers as operators. Proportion is interpreted as a mapping of totally ordered semigroups. This mapping proves to be an isomorphism, thus suggesting the application of the modern theory of homomorphism.

Book VI uses the general theory of proportion established in the previous book to treat similar figures. The first and last propositions of the book illustrate the importance of V, definition 5, for by the method of equimultiples it is proved in proposition 1 that triangles and parallelograms having the same height are to one another as their bases, and in proposition 33 it is proved that in equal circles the angles at the center or circumference are as the arcs on which they stand. There are many like propositions of equal importance. Proposition 25 sets the problem "To construct a rectilineal figure similar to one, and equal to another, given rectilineal figure."[31] In propositions 27–29 Euclid takes up again the application of areas. It has been explained above that to apply (παραβάλλειν) a parallelogram to a given straight line means to construct on that line a parallelogram equal to a given area and having a given angle. If the straight line is applied to only part of the given line, the resulting figure is said to be deficient (ἐλλείπειν); if to the straight line produced, it is said to exceed (ὑπερβάλλειν). Proposition 28 is the following problem: "To a given straight line to apply a parallelogram equal to a given rectilineal figure and deficient by a parallelogrammatic figure similar to a given one." (It has already been shown in proposition 27 that the given rectilineal figure must not be greater than the parallelogram described on half the straight line and similar to the defect.) In Figure 5 let the parallelogram TR be applied to the straight line AB so as to be equal to a given rectilineal figure having the area S and deficient by the parallelogram PB, which is similar to the given parallelogram D. Let $AB = a$, $RP = x$; let the angle of D be α and the ratio of its sides $b:c$. Let E be the midpoint of AB and let EH be drawn parallel to the sides. Then

$$\begin{aligned}(\text{the parallelogram } TR) &= (\text{the parallelogram } TB) \\ &\quad - (\text{the parallelogram } PB) \\ &= ax \sin\alpha - \frac{b}{c}x \cdot x \sin\alpha.\end{aligned}$$

If the area of the given rectilineal figure is S, this may be written

$$S = ax\sin\alpha - \frac{b}{c}x^2 \sin\alpha.$$

Constructing the parallelogram TR is therefore equivalent to solving geometrically the equation

$$ax - \frac{b}{c}x^2 = \frac{S}{\sin\alpha}.$$

It can easily be shown that Euclid's solution is equivalent to completing the square on the left-hand side. For a real solution it is necessary that

$$\frac{S}{\sin\alpha} \geq \frac{c}{b} \cdot \frac{a^2}{4}$$

$$\text{i.e., } S \geq \left(\frac{c}{b} \cdot \frac{a}{2}\right)(\sin\alpha)\left(\frac{a}{2}\right)$$

$$\text{i.e., } S \geq HE \sin\alpha \cdot EB$$

$$\text{i.e., } S \geq \text{parallelogram } HB,$$

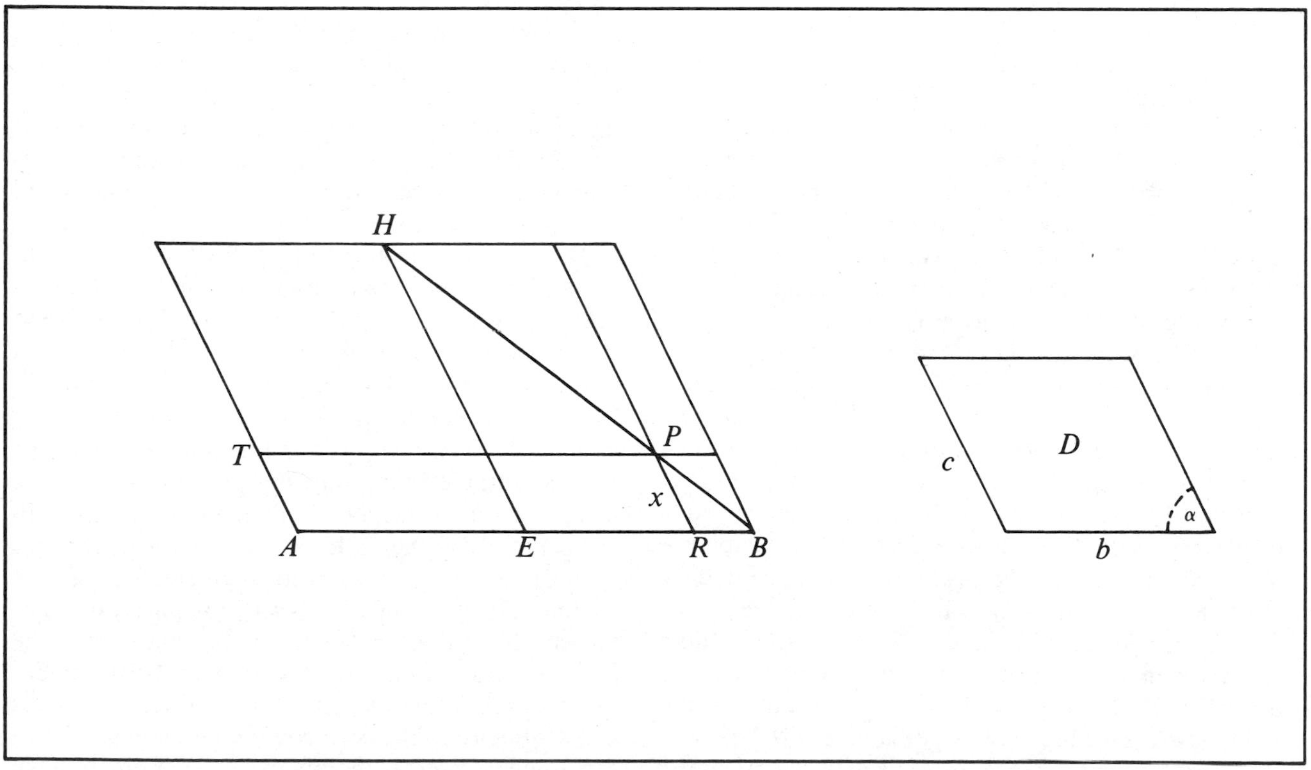

FIGURE 5. Book VI, Proposition 28

which is exactly what was proved in VI.27. Proposition 29 sets the corresponding problem for the excess: "To a given straight line to apply a parallelogram equal to a given rectilineal figure and exceeding by a parallelogrammatic figure similar to a given one." This can be shown in the same way to be equivalent to solving geometrically the equation

$$ax + \frac{b}{c}x^2 = \frac{S}{\sin \alpha}.$$

In this case there is always a real solution. No διορισμός or examination of the conditions of possibility is needed, and Euclid's solution corresponds to the root with the positive sign.

This group of propositions is needed by Euclid for his treatment of irrationals in book X, but their chief importance in the history of mathematics is that they are the basis of the theory of conic sections as developed by Apollonius. Indeed, the very words "parabola," "ellipse," and "hyperbola" come from the Greek words for "to apply," "to be deficient," and "to exceed."

It is significant that the antepenultimate proposition of the book, proposition 31, is a generalization of "Pythagoras' theorem": "In right-angled triangles any [literally "the"] figure [described] on the side subtending the right angle is equal to the [sum of the] similar and similarly described figures on the sides containing the right angle."

Books VII, VIII, and IX are arithmetical; and although the transition from book VI appears sharp, there is a logical structure in that the theory of proportion, developed in all its generality in book V, is applied in book VI to geometrical figures and in book VII to numbers. The theory of numbers is continued in the next two books. The theory of proportion in book VII is not, however, the general theory of book V but the old Pythagorean theory applicable only to commensurable magnitudes.[32] This return to an outmoded theory led both De Morgan and W. W. Rouse Ball to suppose that Euclid died before putting the finishing touches to the *Elements,*[33] but, although the three arithmetical books seem trite in comparison with those that precede and follow, there is nothing unfinished about them. It is more likely that Euclid, displaying the deference toward others that Pappus observed, thought that he ought to include the traditional teaching. This respect for traditional doctrines can be seen in some of the definitions which Euclid repeats even though he improves upon them or never uses them.[34] Although books VII–IX appear at first sight to be a reversion to Pythagoreanism, it is Pythagoreanism with a difference. In particular, the rational straight line takes the place of the Pythagorean monad;[35] but the products of numbers are also treated as straight lines, not as squares or rectangles.

After the numerical theory of proportion is established in VII.4–19, there is an interesting group of propositions on prime numbers (22–32) and a final group (33–39) on least common multiples. Book VIII deals in the main with series of numbers "in continued proportion," that is, in geometrical progression, and with geometric means. Book IX is a miscellany and includes the fundamental theorem in the theory of numbers, proposition 14: "If a number be the least that is measured by prime numbers, it will not be measured by any other prime number except those originally measuring it," that is to say, a number can be resolved into prime factors in only one way.

After the muted notes of the arithmetical books Euclid again takes up his lofty theme in book X, which treats irrational magnitudes. It opens with the following proposition (X.1): "If two unequal magnitudes be set out, and if there be subtracted from the greater a magnitude greater than its half, and from that which is left a magnitude greater than its half, and so on continually, there will be left some magnitude less than the lesser magnitude set out." This is the basis of the "method of exhaustion," as later used by Euclid in book XII. Because of the use made of it by Archimedes, either directly or in an equivalent form, for the purpose of calculating areas and volumes, it has become known, perhaps a little unreasonably, as the axiom of Archimedes. Euclid needs the axiom at this point as a test of incommensurability, and his next proposition (X.2) asserts: "If the lesser of two unequal magnitudes is continually subtracted from the greater, and the remainder never measures that which precedes it, the magnitudes will be incommensurable."

The main achievement of the book is a classification of irrational straight lines, no doubt for the purpose of easy reference. Starting from any assigned straight line which it is agreed to regard as rational—a kind of datum line—Euclid asserts that any straight line which is commensurable with it in length is rational, but he also regards as rational a straight line commensurable with it only in square. That is to say, if m, n are two integers in their lowest terms with respect to each other, and l is a rational straight line, he regards $\sqrt{m/n} \cdot l$ as rational because $(m/n)l^2$ is commensurable with l^2. All straight lines not commensurable either in length or in square with the assigned straight line he calls irrational. His fundamental proposition (X.9) is that the sides of squares are commensurable or incommensurable in length according to whether the squares have or do not have the ratio of a square number to each other, that is to say, if a, b are straight lines and m, n are two numbers, and if $a:b = m:n$, then $a^2:b^2 = m^2:n^2$ and conversely. This is easily seen in modern notation, but was far from an easy step for Euclid. The first irrational line which he isolates is the side of a square equal in area to a rectangle whose sides are commensurable in square only. He calls it a medial. If the sides of the rectangle are l, $\sqrt{k}\,l$, the medial is $k^{1/4}l$. Euclid next proceeds to define six pairs of compound irrationals (the members of each pair differing in sign only) which can be represented in modern notation as the positive roots of six biquadratic equations (reducible to quadratics) of the form

$$x^4 \pm 2alx^2 \pm bl^4 = 0.$$

The first pair are given the names "binomial" (or "biterminal") and "apotome," and Euclid proceeds to define six pairs of their derivatives which are equivalent to the roots of six quadratic equations of the form

$$x^2 + 2alx + bl^2 = 0.$$

In all, Euclid investigates in the 115 propositions of the book (of which the last four may be interpolations) every possible form of the lines which can be represented by the expression $\sqrt{(\sqrt{a} \pm \sqrt{b})}$, some twenty-five in all.[36]

The final three books of the *Elements,* XI–XIII, are devoted to solid geometry. Book XI deals largely with parallelepipeds. Book XII applies the method of exhaustion, that is, the inscription of successive figures in the body to be evaluated, in order to prove that circles are to one another as the squares on their diameters, that pyramids of the same height with triangular bases are in the ratio of their bases, that the volume of a cone is one-third of the cylinder which has the same base and equal height, that cones and cylinders having the same height are in the ratio of their bases, that similar cones and cylinders are to one another in the triplicate ratio of the diameters of their bases, and that spheres are in the triplicate ratio of their diameters. The method can be shown for the circle. Euclid inscribes a square in the circle and shows that it is more than half the circle. He bisects each arc and shows that each triangle so obtained is greater than half the segment of the circle about it. (In Figure 6, for example, triangle *EAB* is greater than half the segment of the circle *EAB* standing on *AB*.) If the process is continued indefinitely, according to X.1, we shall be left with segments of the circle smaller than some assigned magnitude, that is, the circle has been exhausted. (A little later Archimedes was to refine the method by also circumscribing a polygon, and so compressing the figure, as it were, between inscribed and circumscribed polygons.) Euclid refrains from saying that as the process is continued indefinitely, the area of the polygon will in the limit approach the area of the circle, and rigorously proves that if his proposition is not granted, impossible conclusions would follow.

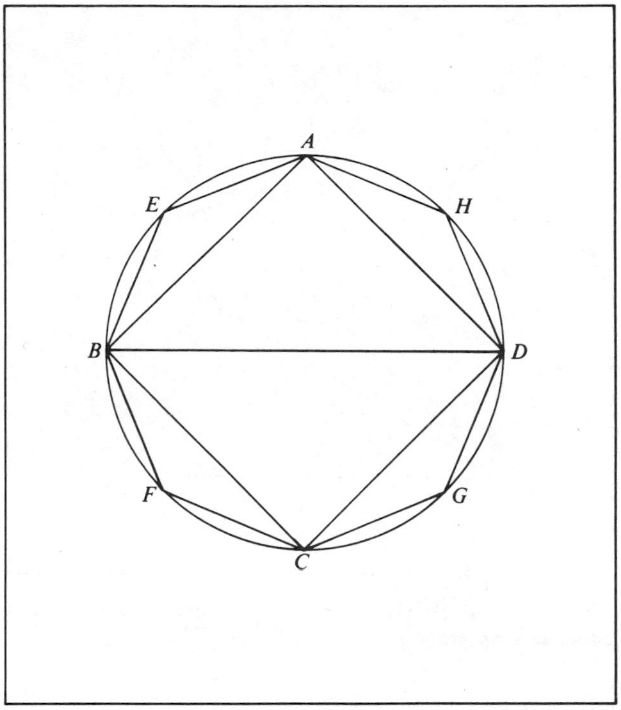

FIGURE 6. Book XII, Proposition 2, Exhaustion of a Circle

After some preliminary propositions book XIII is devoted to the construction in a sphere of the five regular solids: the pyramid (proposition 13), the octahedron (14), the cube (15), the icosahedron (16), and the dodecahedron (17). These five regular solids had been a prime subject of investigation by the Greek mathematicians, and because of the use made of them by Plato in the *Timaeus* were known as the Platonic figures.[37] The mathematical problem is to determine the edge of the figure in relation to the radius of the circumscribing sphere. In the case of the pyramid, octahedron, and cube, Euclid actually evaluates the edge in terms of the radius, and in the case of the icosahedron and dodecahedron he shows that it is one of the irrational lines classified in book X—a minor in the case of the icosahedron and an apotome in the case of the dodecahedron. In a final splendid flourish (proposition 18), Euclid sets out the sides of the five figures in the same sphere and compares them with each other, and in an addendum he shows that there can be no other regular solids. In Figure 7, $AC = CB$, $AD = 2DB$, $AG = AB$, $CL = CM$, and BF is divided in extreme and mean ratio at

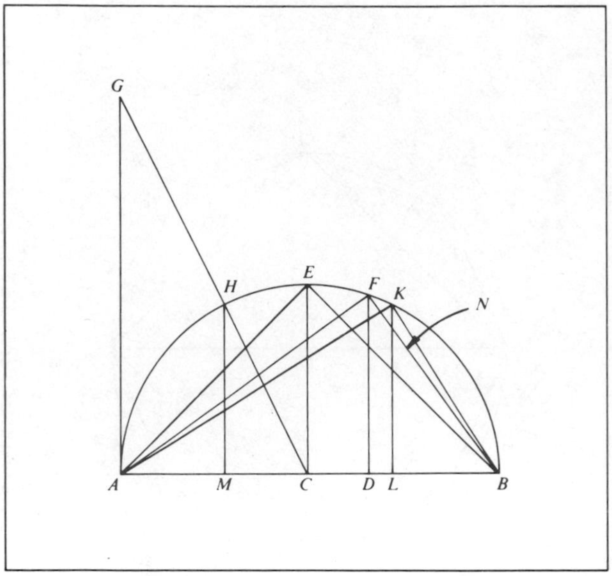

FIGURE 7. Book XIII, Proposition 18, Inscription of Regular Solids in a Sphere

$N(BF:BN = BN:NF)$. He proves that AF is the side of the pyramid, BF is the side of the cube, BE is the side of the octahedron, BK is the side of the icosahedron, and BN is the side of the dodecahedron; their values, in terms of the radius *r*, are respectively $2/3\sqrt{6}\cdot r$, $\sqrt{2}\cdot r$, $2/3\sqrt{3}\cdot r$, $r/5\sqrt{10(5-\sqrt{5})}$, $r/3(\sqrt{15}-\sqrt{3})$.

Proclus, as already noted, regarded the construction of the five Platonic figures as the end of the *Elements*, in both senses of that ambiguous word. This is usually discounted on the ground that the stereometrical books had to come last, but Euclid need not have ended with the construction of the five regular solids; and since he shows the influence of Plato in other ways, this splendid ending could easily be a grain of incense at the Platonic altar.

Proclus sums up Euclid's achievement in the *Elements* in the following words:[38]

> He deserves admiration preeminently in the compilation of his *Elements of Geometry* on account of the order and selection both of the theorems and of the problems made with a view to the elements. For he included not everything which he could have said, but only such things as were suitable for the building up of the elements. He used all the various forms of deductive arguments,[39] some getting their plausibility from the first principles, some starting from demonstrations, but all irrefutable and accurate and in harmony with science. In addition he used all the dialectical methods, the *divisional* in the discovery of figures, the *definitive* in the existential arguments, the *demonstrative* in the passages from first principles to the things sought, and the *analytic* in the converse process from the things sought to the first principles. And the various species of conversions,[40] both of the simpler (propositions) and of the more complex, are in this treatise accurately set forth and skillfully investigated, what wholes can be converted with wholes, what wholes with parts and conversely, and what as parts with parts. Further, we must make mention of the continuity of the proofs, the disposition and arrangement of the things which precede and those which follow, and the power with which he treats each detail.

This is a fair assessment. The *Elements* is on the whole a compilation of things already known, and its most remarkable feature is the arrangement of the matter so that one proposition follows on another in a strictly logical order, with the minimum of assumption and very little that is superfluous.

If we seek to know how much of it is Euclid's own work, Proclus is again our best guide. He says, as we have seen, that Euclid "put together the elements, arranging in order many of Eudoxus' theorems, perfecting many of Theaetetus', and also bringing to irrefutable demonstration the things which had been only loosely proved by his predecessors."[41] According to a scholiast of book V, "Some say that this book is the discovery of Eudoxus, the disciple of Plato."[42] Another scholiast confirms this, saying, "This book is said to be the work of Eudoxus of Cnidus, the mathematician, who lived about the times of Plato."[43] He adds, however, that the ascription to Euclid is not false, for although there is nothing to prevent the discovery from being the work of another man, "The arrangement of the book with a view to the elements and the orderly sequence of theorems is recognized by all as the work of Euclid." This is a fair division of the credit. Eudoxus also, as we can infer from Archimedes,[44] is responsible for the method of exhaustion used in book XII to evaluate areas and volumes, based upon X.1, and Archimedes attributes to Eudoxus by name the theorems about the volume of the pyramid and the volume of the cone which stand as propositions 7 and 10 of book XII of the *Elements*. Although Greek tradition credited Hippocrates with discovering that circles are to one another as the squares on their diameters,[45] we can be confident that the proof as we have it in XII.2 is also due to Eudoxus.

The interest of Theaetetus in the irrational is known from Plato's dialogue,[46] and a commentary on book X which has survived in Arabic[47] and is attributed by Heiberg[48] to Pappus credits him with discovering the different species of irrational lines known as the medial, binomial, and apotome. A scholium to X.9[49] (that squares which do not have the ratio of a square number to a square number have their sides incommensurable) attributes this theorem to Theaetetus. It would appear in this case also that the fundamental discoveries were made before Euclid but that the orderly arrangement of propositions is his work. This, indeed, is asserted in the commentary attributed to Pappus, which says:

> As for Euclid he set himself to give rigorous rules, which he established, relative to commensurability and incommensurability in general; he made precise the definitions and the distinctions between rational and irrational magnitudes, he set out a great number of orders of irrational magnitudes, and finally he clearly showed their whole extent.[50]

Theaetetus was also the first to "construct" or "write upon" the five regular solids,[51] and according to a scholiast[52] the propositions concerning the octahedron and the icosahedron are due to him. His work therefore underlies book XIII, although the credit for the arrangement must again be given to Euclid.

According to Proclus,[53] the application of areas, which, as we have seen, is employed in I.44 and 45, II.5, 6, and 11, and VI.27, 28, and 29, is "ancient, being discoveries of the muse of the Pythagoreans." A scholiast to book IV[54] attributes all sixteen theorems (problems) of that book to the Pythagoreans. It would appear, however, that the famous proof of what is universally known as "Pythagoras' theorem," I.47, is due to Euclid himself. It is beyond doubt that this property of right-angled triangles was discovered by Pythagoras, or at least in his school, but the proof was almost certainly based on proportions and therefore not applicable to all magnitudes. Proclus says:

> If we give hearing to those who relate things of old, we shall find some of them referring this discovery to Pythagoras and saying that he sacrificed an ox upon the discovery. But I, while marveling at those who first came to know the truth of this theorem, hold in still greater admiration the writer of the *Elements,* not only because he made it secure by a most clear proof, but because he compelled assent by the irrefutable reasonings of science to the still more general proposition in the sixth book. For in that book he proves generally that in right-angled triangles the figure on the side subtending the right angle is equal to the similar and similarly situated figures described on the sides about the right angle.[55]

On the surface this suggests that Euclid devised a new proof, and this is borne out by what Proclus says about the generalization. It would be an easy matter to prove VI.31 by using I.47 along with VI.22, but Euclid chooses to prove it independently of I.47 by using the general theory of proportions. This suggests that he proved I.47 by means of book I alone, without invoking proportions in order to get it into his first book instead of his sixth. The proof certainly bears the marks of genius.

To Euclid also belongs beyond a shadow of doubt the credit for the parallel postulate which is fundamental to the whole system. Aristotle had censured those "who think they describe parallels" because of a *petitio principii* latent in their theory.[56] There is certainly no *petitio principii* in Euclid's theory of parallels, and we may deduce that it was post-Aristotelian and due to Euclid himself. In nothing did he show his genius more than in deciding to treat postulate 5 as an indemonstrable assumption.

The significance of Euclid's *Elements* in the history of thought is twofold. In the first place, it introduced into mathematical reasoning new standards of rigor which remained throughout the subsequent history of Greek mathematics and, after a period of logical slackness following the revival of mathematics, have been equaled again only in the past two centuries. In the second place, it marked a decisive step in the geometrization of mathematics.[57] The Pythagoreans and Democritus before Euclid, Archimedes in some of his works, and Diophantus afterward showed that

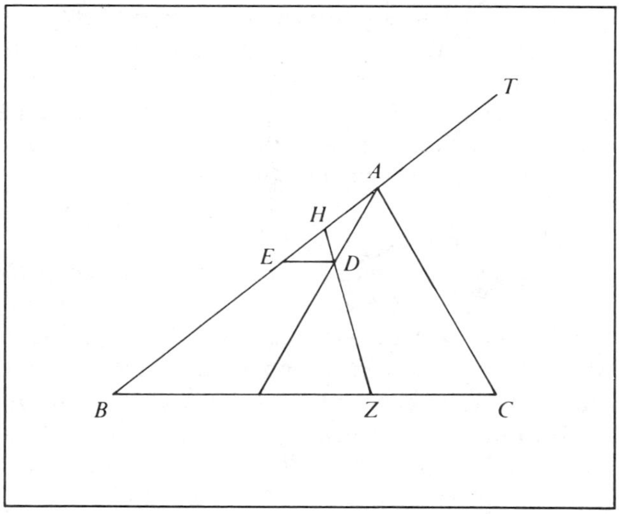

FIGURE 8. *On the Division of Figures,* Proposition 19

Greek mathematics might have developed in other directions. It was Euclid in his *Elements,* possibly under the influence of that philosopher who inscribed over the doors of the Academy "God is for ever doing geometry," who ensured that the geometrical form of proof should dominate mathematics. This decisive influence of Euclid's geometrical conception of mathematics is reflected in two of the supreme works in the history of thought, Newton's *Principia* and Kant's *Kritik der reinen Vernunft.* Newton's work is cast in the form of geometrical proofs that Euclid had made the rule even though Newton had discovered the calculus, which would have served him better and made him more easily understood by subsequent generations; and Kant's belief in the universal validity of Euclidean geometry led him to a transcendental aesthetic which governs all his speculations on knowledge and perception.

It was only toward the end of the nineteenth century that the spell of Euclidean geometry began to weaken and that a desire for the "arithmetization of mathematics" began to manifest itself; and only in the second quarter of the twentieth century, with the development of quantum mechanics, have we seen a return in the physical sciences to a neo-Pythagorean view of number as the secret of all things. Euclid's reign has been a long one; and although he may have been deposed from sole authority, he is still a power in the land.

The Data (Δεδομένα). The *Data,* the only other work by Euclid in pure geometry to have survived in Greek, is closely connected with books I–VI of the *Elements.* It is concerned with the different senses in which things are said to be given. Thus areas, straight lines, angles, and ratios are said to be "given in magnitude" when we can make others equal to them. Rectilineal figures are "given in species" or "given in form" when their angles and the ratio of their sides are given. Points, lines, and angles are "given in position" when they always occupy the same place, and so on. After the definitions there follow ninety-four propositions, in which the object is to prove that if certain elements of a figure are given, other elements are also given in one of the defined senses.

The most interesting propositions are a group of four which are exercises in geometrical algebra and correspond to *Elements* II.28, 29. Proposition 58 reads: "If a given area be applied to a given straight line so as to be deficient by a figure given in form, the breadths of the deficiency are given." Proposition 84, which depends upon it, runs: "If two straight lines contain a given area in a given angle, and if one of them is greater than the other by a given quantity, then each of them is given." This is equivalent to solving the simultaneous equations

$$y - x = a$$

$$xy = b^2,$$

and these in turn are equivalent to finding the two roots of

$$ax + x^2 = b^2.$$

Propositions 59 and 85 give the corresponding theorems for the excess and are equivalent to the simultaneous equations

$$y + x = a$$

$$xy = b^2$$

and the quadratic equation

$$ax - x^2 = b^2.$$

A clue to the purpose of the *Data* is given by its inclusion in what Pappus calls the *Treasury of Analysis.*[58] The concept behind the *Data* is that if certain things are given, other things are necessarily implied, until we are brought to something that is agreed. The *Data* is a collection of hints on analysis. Pappus describes the contents of the book as known to him;[59] the number and order of the propositions differ in some respects from the text which has come down to us.

Marinus of Naples, the pupil and biographer of Proclus, wrote a commentary on, or rather an introduction to, the *Data.* It is concerned mainly with the different senses in which the term "given" was understood by Greek geometers.

On Divisions of Figures (Περὶ διαιρεσεων βιβλίον). Proclus preserved this title along with the titles of other works of Euclid,[60] and gives an indication of its contents: "For the circle is divisible into parts unlike by definition, and so is each of the rectilineal figures; and this is indeed what the writer of the *Elements* himself discusses in his *Divisions,* dividing given figures now into like figures, now into unlike."[61] The book has not survived in Greek, but all the thirty-six enunciations and four of the propositions (19, 20, 28, 29) have been preserved in an Arabic translation discovered by Woepcke and published in 1851; the remaining proofs can be supplied from the *Practica geometriae* written by Leonardo Fibonacci in 1220, one section of which, it is now evident, was based upon a manuscript or translation of Euclid's work no longer in existence. The work was reconstructed by R. C. Archibald in 1915.

The character of the book can be seen from the first of the four propositions which has survived in Arabic (19). This is "To divide a given triangle into two equal parts by a line which passes through a point situated in the interior of the triangle." Let D be a point inside the triangle ABC and let DE be drawn parallel to CB so as to meet AB in E. Let T be taken on BA produced so that $TB \cdot DE = 1/2\, AB \cdot BC$ (that is, let TB be such that when a rectangle having TB for one of its sides is applied to DE, it is equal to half the rectangle $AB \cdot BC$). Next, let a parallelogram be applied to the line TB equal to the rectangle $TB \cdot BE$ and deficient by a square, that is, let H be taken on TB so that

$$(TB - HT) \cdot HT = TB \cdot BE.$$

HD is drawn and meets BC in Z. It can easily be

shown that *HZ* divides the triangle into two equal parts and is the line required.

The figures which are divided in Euclid's tract are the triangle, the parallelogram, the trapezium, the quadrilateral, a figure bounded by an arc of a circle and two lines, and a circle. It is proposed in the various cases to divide the given figure into two equal parts, into several equal parts, into two parts in a given ratio, or into several parts in a given ratio. The propositions may be further classified according to whether the dividing line (transversal) is required to be drawn from a vertex, from a point within or without the figure, and so on.[62]

In only one proposition (29) is a circle divided, and it is clearly the one to which Proclus refers. The enunciation is "To draw in a given circle two parallel lines cutting off a certain fraction from the circle." In fact, Euclid gives the construction for a fraction of one-third and notes a similar construction for a quarter, one-fifth, "or any other definite fraction."[63]

Porisms (Πορίσματα). It is known both from Pappus[64] and from Proclus[65] that Euclid wrote a three-book work called *Porisms.* Pappus, who includes the work in the *Treasury of Analysis,* adds the information that it contained 171 theorems and thirty-eight lemmas. It has not survived—most unfortunately, for it appears to have been an exercise in advanced mathematics;[66] but the account given by Pappus encouraged such great mathematicians as Robert Simson and Michel Chasles to attempt reconstructions, and Chasles was led thereby to the discovery of anharmonic ratios.

The term "porism" commonly means in Greek mathematics a corollary, but that is not the sense in which it is used in Euclid's title. It is clearly derived from πορίζω, "I procure," and Pappus explains that according to the older writers a porism is something intermediate between a theorem and a problem: "A theorem is something proposed with a view to the proof of what is proposed, and a problem is something thrown out with a view to the construction of what is proposed, [and] a porism is something proposed with a view to the finding [πορισμόν] of the very thing proposed."[67] Proclus reinforces the explanation. The term, he says, is used both for "such theorems as are established in the proofs of other theorems, being windfalls and bonuses of the things sought, and also for such things as are sought, but need discovery, and are neither pure bringing into being nor pure investigation."[68] As examples of a porism in this sense, Proclus gives two: first, the finding of the center of a circle, and, second, the finding of the greatest common measure of two given commensurable magnitudes.

Pappus says that it had become characteristic of porisms for the enunciation to be put in shortened form and for a number of propositions to be comprehended in one enunciation. He sets out twenty-nine different types in Euclid's work (fifteen in book I, six in book II, and eight in book III). His versions suggest that the normal form of Euclid's porisms was to find a point or a line satisfying certain conditions. Pappus says that Euclid did not normally give many examples of each case, but at the beginning of the first book he gave ten propositions belonging to one class; and Pappus found that these could be comprehended in one enunciation, in this manner:

> If in a quadrilateral, whether convex or concave, the sides cut each other two by two, and the three points in which the other three sides intersect the fourth are given, and if the remaining points of intersection save one lie on straight lines given in position, the remaining point will also lie on a straight line given in position.[69]

Pappus proceeds to generalize this theorem for any system of straight lines cutting each other two by two. In modern notation, let there be n straight lines, of which not more than two pass through one point and no two are parallel. They will intersect in $1/2n(n-1)$ points. Let the $(n-1)$ points in which one of the lines is intersected be fixed. This will leave $1/2n(n-1) - (n-1) = 1/2(n-1)(n-2)$ other points of intersection. If $(n-2)$ of these points lie on straight lines given in position, the other $1/2(n-1)(n-2) - (n-2) = 1/2(n-2)(n-3)$ points of intersection will also lie on straight lines given in position, provided that it is impossible to form with these points of intersection any triangle having for sides the sides of the polygon.[70]

Pappus adds: "It is unlikely that the writer of the *Elements* was unaware of this result, but he would have desired only to set out the first principle. For he appears in all the porisms to have laid down only the first principles and seminal ideas of the many important matters investigated."[71]

Pappus' remarks about the definition of porisms by the "older writers" have been given above. He—or an interpolator—censures more recent writers who defined a porism by an incidental characteristic: "a porism is that which falls short of a locus theorem in respect of its hypotheses."[72] What this means is far from clear, but it led Zeuthen[73] to conjecture that Euclid's porisms were a by-product of his researches into conic sections—which, if true, would be a happy combination of the two meanings of porism. Zeuthen takes the first proposition of Euclid's first book as quoted by Pappus: "If from two points given in position straight lines be drawn so as to meet on a straight line given in position, and if one of them cuts off from a straight line given in position a segment measured toward a given point on it, the other will also cut off from another straight line a segment having to the first a given ratio."[74] He notes that this proposition is true if a conic section, regarded as a "locus with respect to four lines" (see below), is substituted for the first given straight line, with the two given points as points on it.[75] It will be convenient to turn immediately to Euclid's investigations into conic sections and the "three- and four-line locus," noting that, from one point of view, his *Porisms* would appear to have been the earliest known treatise on projective geometry and transversals.

Conics. We know from Pappus that Euclid wrote a four-book work on conic sections, but it has not survived even in quotation. The relevant passage in the *Collection* reads: "Apollonius, having completed Euclid's four books of conics and added four others, handed down eight volumes of conics."[76] The work was probably lost by Pappus' time, for in the next sentence he mentions as still extant the five books of Aristaeus on "solid loci." Aristaeus preceded Euclid, for Euclid, according to Pappus or an interpolator, thought that Aristaeus deserved the credit for the discoveries in conics he had already made, and neither claimed originality nor wished to overthrow what he had already done. (It is at this point that Pappus contrasts Euclid's character with that of Apollonius, noted above.) In particular, Euclid wrote as much about the three- and four-line locus as was possible on the basis of Aristaeus' conics without claiming completeness for his proofs.[77]

Euclid doubtless shared the early Greek view that conic sections were generated by the section of a cone by a plane at right angles to a generator, and he would have used the names "section of a right-angled cone," "section of an acute-angled cone," and "section of an obtuse-angled cone," which were in use until Apollonius established the terms "parabola," "ellipse," and "hyperbola"; but he was aware that an ellipse can be obtained by any section of a cone or cylinder not parallel to the base, for in his *Phaenomena* he says: "If a cone or cylinder be cut by a plane not parallel to the base, the section is a section of an acute-angled cone which is like a shield [θυρεός]."[78]

Furthermore, Euclid was aware of the focus-directrix property (that a conic section is the locus of a point whose distance from a fixed point bears a constant relation to its distance from a fixed straight line), even though it is nowhere mentioned by Apollonius: Pappus cites the property as a lemma to Euclid's *Surface Loci,*[79] from which it is clear that it was assumed in that book without proof. It is likely, therefore, that it was proved either in Euclid's *Conics* or by Aristaeus.

Euclid was also aware that a conic may be regarded as the locus of a point having a certain relationship to three or four straight lines. He discussed this locus in his *Conics,* and he may be the original author to whom Pappus thinks Apollonius should have deferred.[80] The locus is thus defined by Pappus:

> If three straight lines be given in position, and from one and the same point straight lines be drawn to meet the three straight lines at given angles, and if the ratio of the rectangle contained by two of the straight lines toward the square on the remaining straight line be given, then the point will lie on a solid locus given in position, that is, on one of the three conic sections. And if straight lines be drawn to meet at given angles four straight lines given in position, and the ratio of the rectangle contained by two of the straight lines so drawn toward the rectangle contained by the remaining two be given, then likewise the point will lie on a conic section given in position.[81]

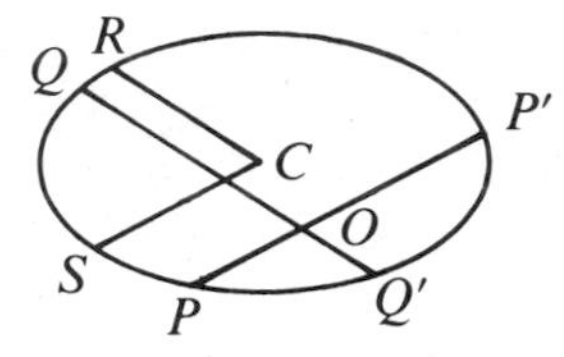

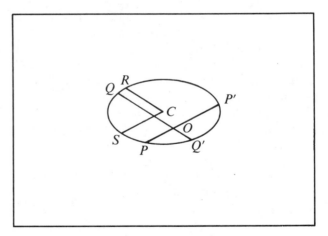

FIGURE 9. $QO \cdot OQ' : PO \cdot OP' = CR^2 : CS^2$

The three-line locus is clearly a special case of the four-line locus in which two of the straight lines coincide. The general case is the locus of a point whose distances x, y, z, u from four straight lines (which may be regarded as the sides of a quadrilateral) have the relationship $xy : zu = k$, where k is a constant.

From the property that the ratio of the rectangles under the segments of any intersecting chords drawn in fixed directions in a conic is constant (being equal to the ratio of the squares on the parallel semidiameters), it is not difficult to show that the distances of a point on a conic from an inscribed trapezium bear the above relationship $xy : zu = k$, and it is only a further step to prove that this is true of any inscribed quadrilateral. It is rather more difficult to prove the converse theorem—that the locus of a point having this relationship to the sides, first of a trapezium, then of any quadrilateral, is a conic section—but it would have been within Euclid's capacity to do so.

Apollonius says of his own *Conics:*

> The third book includes many remarkable theorems useful for the synthesis of solid loci and for determining limits of possibility. Most of these theorems, and the most elegant, are new, and it was their discovery which made me realize that Euclid had not worked out the synthesis of the locus with respect to three and four lines, but only a chance portion of it, and that not successfully; for the synthesis could not be completed without the theorems discovered by me.[82]

In the light of this passage Zeuthen conjectured that Euclid (and the other predecessors of Apollonius) saw that a point on a conic section would have the four-line property with respect first to an inscribed trapezium and then to any inscribed quadrilateral, but failed to prove the converse, even for a trapezium; they failed because they did not realize that the hyperbola is a curve with two branches.[83] It is an attractive suggestion.

Pappus exonerates Euclid from blame on the ground that "he wrote so much about the locus as was possible by means of the *Conics* of Aristaeus but did not claim finality for his proofs" and that "neither Apollonius himself nor anyone else could have added anything to what Euclid wrote, using only those properties of conics which had been proved up to Euclid's time."[84] Since Apollonius implies that he had worked out a complete theory, it is curious that he does not set it out in his treatise; but book III, propositions 53–56 of his *Conics,* when taken together, give what is in effect the converse of the three-line locus: "If from any point of a conic there be drawn three straight lines in fixed directions to meet respectively two fixed tangents to the conic and their chord of contact, the ratio of the rectangles contained by the first two lines so drawn to the square on the third is constant."

Apollonius in his first preface claims originality for his book IV and for parts of book III. He regarded the first four books as an introduction concerned with the elements of the subject. Since Pappus says that Apollonius completed the first four books of Euclid's *Conics,* we may infer from the two passages taken together that Euclid's work covered the same ground as Apollonius' first three books, but not so completely. It would appear that Euclid's work was no advance on that of Aristaeus, which would account for the fact that the latter's *Conics* was still extant, although that of Euclid had been lost, by the time of Pappus.

What Pappus calls "those properties of conics which had been proved up to Euclid's time" can be conjectured from references by Archimedes to propositions not requiring demonstration "because they are proved in the elements of conics" or simply "in the *Conics.*"[85] This would imply that the proofs were given by Aristaeus or Euclid or both. In addition, Archimedes assumes without proof the fundamental properties of the parabola, ellipse, and hyperbola in the form, for the ellipse, of

$$PN^2 : AN \cdot A'N = CB^2 : CA^2,$$

where AA' is the major axis, BB' the minor axis, C the center, P any point on the curve, and N the foot of the perpendicular from P to AA'. More generally he assumes that if QV is an ordinate of the diameter PCP of an ellipse (with corresponding formulas for the parabola and hyperbola), the ratio $QV^2 : PV \cdot P'V$ is constant. It would appear that Euclid must have treated the fundamental characteristics of the curves as proportions, and it was left to Apollonius to develop, by means of the application of areas, the fundamental properties of curves as equations between areas.[86]

Surface Loci (Τόποι πρὸς ἐπιφανείᾳ). *Surface Loci,* a work in two books, is attributed to Euclid by Pappus and included in the *Treasury of Analysis.*[87] It has not survived, and its contents can be conjectured only from remarks made by Proclus and Pappus about loci in general and two lemmas given by Pappus to Euclid's work.

Proclus defines a locus as "the position of a line or surface having one and the same property,"[88] and he says of locus theorems (τοπικά) that "some are constructed on lines and some on surfaces." It would appear that loci on lines are loci which are lines and loci on surfaces are loci which are surfaces. But Pappus says that the equivalent of a quadratrix may be obtained geometrically "by means of loci on surfaces as follows," and he proceeds to use a spiral described on a cylinder (the cylindrical helix).[89] The possibility that loci on surfaces may be curves, of a higher order than conic sections, described on surfaces gets some support from an obscure passage in which Pappus divides loci into fixed, progressive, and reversionary, and adds that linear loci are "demonstrated" (δείκνυνται) from loci on surfaces.[90]

Of the two lemmas to the *Surface Loci* which Pappus gives, the former[91] and the attached figure are unsatisfactory as they stand; but if Tannery's restoration[92] is correct, one of the loci sought by Pappus contained all the points on the elliptical parallel sections of a cylinder and thus was an oblique circular cylinder; other loci may have been cones.

It is in the second lemma that Pappus states and

proves the focus-directrix property of a conic, which implies, as already stated, that Euclid must have been familiar with it. Zeuthen, following an insight by Chasles,[93] conjectures that Euclid may have used the property in one of two ways in the *Surface Loci:* (1) to prove that the locus of a point whose distance from a given straight line is in a given ratio to its distance from a given plane is a cone; or (2) to prove that the locus of a point whose distance from a given point is in a given ratio to its distance from a given plane is the surface formed by the revolution of a conic about an axis. It seems probable that Euclid's *Surface Loci* was concerned not merely with cones and cylinders (and perhaps spheres), but to some extent with three other second-degree surfaces of revolution: the paraboloid, the hyperboloid, and the prolate (but not the oblate) spheroid. If so, he anticipated to some extent the work that Archimedes developed fully in his *On Conoids and Spheroids.*

Book of Fallacies (Ψευδαρια). Proclus mentions a book by Euclid with this title which has not survived but is clearly identical with the work referred to as *Pseudographemata* by Michael Ephesius in his commentary on the *Sophistici elenchi* of Aristotle.[94] It obviously belonged to elementary geometry and is sufficiently described in Proclus' words:

> Do you, adding or subtracting accidentally, fall away unawares from science and get carried into the opposite error and into ignorance? Since many things seem to conform with the truth and to follow from scientific principles, but lead astray from the principles and deceive the more superficial, he has handed down methods for the clear-sighted understanding of these matters also, and with these methods in our possession we can train beginners in the discovery of paralogisms and avoid being misled. The treatise in which he gave this machinery to us he entitled [the *Book of*] *Fallacies,* enumerating in order their various kinds, exercising our intelligence in each case by theorems of all sorts, setting the true side by side with the false, and combining the refutation of the error with practical illustration. This book is therefore purgative and disciplinary, while the *Elements* contains an irrefutable and complete guide to the actual scientific investigation of geometrical matters.[95]

Astronomy: Phaenomena (Φαινόμενα). This textbook of what the Greeks called *sphaeric,* intended for use by students of astronomy, survives in two recensions, of which the older must be the nearer to Euclid's own words.[96] It was included in the collection of astronomical works which Pappus calls Ὁ Ἀστρονομούμενος τόπος, *The Treasury of Astronomy,* alternatively known as *The Little Astronomy,* in contrast with Ptolemy's *Syntaxis,* or *Great Astronomy.* In the older, more authentic recension it consists of a preface and sixteen propositions.

The preface gives reasons for believing that the universe is a sphere and includes some definitions of technical terms. Euclid in this work is the first writer to use "horizon" absolutely—Autolycus had written of the "horizon (i.e., bounding) circle"—and he introduces the term "meridian circle." The propositions set out the geometry of the rotation of the celestial sphere and prove that stars situated in certain positions will rise or set at certain times. Pappus comments in detail on certain of the propositions.[97]

It is manifest that Euclid drew on Autolycus, but both of them cite without proof a number of propositions, which suggests that they had in their hands a still earlier textbook of sphaeric, which Tannery conjectured to have been the composition of Eudoxus. Many of the propositions are proved in the *Sphaerica* of Theodosius, written several centuries later. He naturally uses the theorems of Euclid's *Elements* in his proofs. By examining the propositions assumed by Autolycus, and by further considering what other propositions are needed to establish them, it is thus possible to get some idea of how much of Euclid's *Elements* was already known in the fourth century before Christ.[98]

Optics: Optica (Ὀπτικά). The *Optica,* which is attributed to Euclid by Proclus, is also attested by Pappus, who includes it, somewhat curiously, in the *Little Astronomy.*[99] It survives in two recensions; there is no reason to doubt that the earlier one is Euclid's own work, but the later appears to be a recension done by Theon of Alexandria in the fourth century, with a preface which seems to be a pupil's reproduction of explanations given by Theon at his lectures.[100]

The *Optica,* an elementary treatise in perspective, was the first Greek work on the subject and remained the only one until Ptolemy wrote in the middle of the second century.[101] It starts with definitions, some of them really postulates, the first of which assumes, in the Platonic tradition, that vision is caused by rays proceeding from the eye to the object. It is implied that the rays are straight. The second states that the figure contained by the rays is a cone which has its vertex in the eye and its base at the extremities of the object seen. Definition 4 makes the fundamental assumption that "Things seen under a greater angle appear greater, and those under a lesser angle less, while things seen under equal angles appear equal." When he comes to the text, Euclid makes a false start in proposition 1—"Of things that are seen, none is seen as a whole"—because of an erroneous assumption that the rays of light are discrete; but this does not vitiate his later work, which is sound enough. From proposition 6 it is easy to deduce that parallel lines appear to meet. In the course of proposition 8 he proves the equivalent of the theorem

$$\frac{\tan \alpha}{\tan \beta} < \frac{\alpha}{\beta},$$

where α and β are two angles and $\alpha < \beta < 1/2\pi$. There are groups of propositions relating to the appearances of spheres, cones, and cylinders. Propositions 37 and 38 prove that if a straight line moves so that it always appears to be the same size, the locus of its extremities is a circle with the eye at the center or on the circumference. The book contains fifty-eight propositions of similar character. It was written before the *Phaenomena,* for it is cited in the preface of that work. Pappus adds twelve propositions of his own based on those of Euclid.

Catoptrica (Κατοπτρικά). Proclus also attributes to Euclid a book entitled *Catoptrica,* that is, on mirrors. The work which bears that name in the editions of Euclid is certainly not by him but is a later compilation, and Proclus is generally regarded as having made a mistake. If the later compilation is the work of Theon, as may well be the case, it would have been quite easy for Proclus to have assigned it to Euclid inadvertently.

Music: Elements of Music (Αἱ κατὰ μουσικὴν στοιχειώσεις). Proclus[102] attributes to Euclid a work with this title and Marinus,[103] in his preface to Euclid's *Data,* refers to it as Μουσικῆς στοιχεῖα. Two musical treatises are included in the editions of Euclid's works, but they can hardly both be by the same author, since the *Sectio canonis,* or *Division of the Scale* (Κατατομὴ κανόνος), expounds the Pythagorean doctrine that the musical intervals are to be distinguished by the mathematical ratio of the notes terminating the interval, while the *Introduction to Harmony* (Εἰσαγωγὴ ἁρμονική) is based on the contrary theory of Aristoxenus, according to which the scale is formed of notes separated by a tone identified by the ear. It is now universally accepted that the *Introduction to Harmony* is the work of Cleonides, the pupil of Aristoxenus, to whom it is attributed in some manuscripts; but there is no agreement about the *Sectio canonis,* except that such a trite exposition of the Pythagorean theory of musical intervals is hardly worthy to be dignified with the name *Elements of Music.* The strongest argument for its authenticity is that Porphyry in his commentary on Ptolemy's *Harmonica* quotes almost the whole of it except the preface and twice, or perhaps three times, refers to Euclid's *Sectio canonis* as though it is the work he is quoting;[104] but the passages cited by Porphyry differ greatly from the text in dispute. Gregory, who was the first to question the attribution to Euclid, would have assigned it to Ptolemy,[105] along with the *Introduction to Harmony;* but his main reason, that it is not mentioned before Ptolemy, is not sufficiently strong to outweigh the primitive character of the work. Tannery thinks that the two last propositions, 19 and 20, which specially justify the title borne by the treatise, may have been added by a later editor who borrowed from Eratosthenes, but that the rest of the work must have been composed before 300 B.C. and would attribute it to the school of Plato.[106] This is not convincing, however, for we have seen how Euclid perpetuated arithmetical theories that had become outmoded, and he could have done likewise for the Pythagorean musical theory. (It is of no significance that there are three arithmetical propositions in the *Sectio canonis* not found in the *Elements.*) As for Platonism, Euclid was himself a Platonist. Jan, who included the book under Euclid's name in his *Musici scriptores Graeci,* takes the view that it was a summary of a longer work by Euclid himself.[107] Menge, who edited it for *Euclidis opera omnia,* considers that it contains some things unworthy of Euclid and is of the opinion that it was extracted by some other writer from the authentic *Elements of Music,* now lost.[108] All that it seems possible to say with certainty is that Euclid wrote a book entitled *Elements of Music* and that the *Sectio canonis* has some connection with it.

Mechanics. No work by Euclid on mechanics is extant in Greek, nor is he credited with any mechanical works by ancient writers. According to Arabic sources, however, he wrote a *Book on the Heavy and the Light,* and when Hervagius was about to publish his 1537 edition there was brought to him a mutilated fragment, *De levi et ponderoso,* which he included as one of Euclid's works. In 1900 Curtze published this side by side with a *Liber Euclidis de gravi et levi et de comparatione corporum ad invicem* which he had found in a Dresden manuscript. It is clearly the same work expressed in rather different language and, as Duhem observed, it is the most precise exposition that we possess of the Aristotelian dynamics of freely moving bodies. Duhem himself found in Paris a manuscript fragment of the same work, and in 1952 Moody and Clagett published a text, with English translation, based chiefly on a manuscript in the Bodleian Library at Oxford. A little earlier Sarton had expressed the view that "It contains the notion of specific gravity in a form too clear to be pre-Archimedean"; but it is not all that clear, and there is no reason to think that Archimedes was the first Greek writer to formulate the notion of specific gravity. It is no objection that the dynamics is Aristotelian, for, as Clagett points out, "The only dynamics that had been formulated at all, in the time in which Euclid lived, was the dynamics of Aristotle." In Clagett's judgment, "No solid evidence has been presented sufficient to determine the question of authenticity one way or the other."[109]

In 1851 Woepcke published under the title *Le livre d'Euclide sur la balance* an Arabic fragment that he had discovered in Paris. The fact that the letters used in the figures follow each other in the Greek order suggests a Greek origin. It contains a definition, two axioms, and four propositions and is an attempt to outline a theory of the lever, not on the basis of general dynamical considerations, as in Aristotle, but on the basis of axioms which may be regarded as self-evident and are confirmed by experience. It is therefore Euclidean in character; and since it falls short of the finished treatment of the subject by Archimedes, it could very well be an authentic work of Euclid, although it owes its present form to some commentator or editor. Woepcke found confirmation of its authenticity in a note in another Paris manuscript, *Liber de canonio.* After citing the proposition that the lengths of the arms of a lever parallel to the horizon are reciprocally proportional to the weights at their extremities, the author adds: "Sicut demonstratum est ab Euclide et Archimede et aliis." Heiberg and Curtze were unwilling to ascribe to the *Book on the Balance* an earlier origin than the Arabs, but Duhem accepted its authenticity. Clagett, after first allowing as "quite likely that the text was translated from the Greek and that in all probability there existed a Greek text bearing the name of Euclid," has more recently expressed the opinion that it "may be genuine and is of interest because, unlike the statement of the law of the lever in the Aristotelian *Mechanics,* its statement on the subject is proved on entirely geometrical grounds."[110]

Duhem's researches among the Paris manuscripts led him to discover a third mechanical fragment attributed to Euclid under the title *Liber Euclidis de ponderibus secundum terminorum circumferentiam.* It contains four propositions about the circles described by the ends of the lever as it rises and falls. As it stands, it is unlikely to be a direct translation of a Euclidean original, but it could derive from a work by Euclid. Duhem noticed how these three fragmentary works fill gaps in each other and conjectured that they might be the debris of a single treatise. This indeed seems probable, and although Duhem was inclined to identify the treatise with Ptolemy's lost work *On Turnings of the Scale* (Περὶ ῥοπῶν), the ultimate author from whom all three fragments spring could have been Euclid. In view of the Arabic traditions, the high probability that the work on the balance is derived from Euclid, the way in which the fragments supplement each other, and the fact that Euclid wrote on all other branches of mathematics known to him and would hardly have omitted mechanics, this is at least a hypothesis that can be countenanced.

An amusing epigram concerning a mule and an ass carrying burdens that the ass found too heavy is attributed to Euclid. It was first printed by Aldus in 1502 and is now included in the appendix to the *Palantine Anthology,* which Melancthon rendered into Latin verse.[111]

NOTES

1. The identification began in ancient times, for Aelian (second/third century), *On the Characteristics of Animals* VI.57, Scholfield ed., II (London-Cambridge, Mass., 1959), 76.26–78.10, notes that spiders can draw a circle and "lack nothing of Euclid" (Εὐκλείδου δέονται οὐδέν).
2. The reference is Archimedes, *On the Sphere and the Cylinder* I.2, Heiberg ed., I, 12.3: διὰ τὸ β του α τῶν Εὐκλείδου—"by the second [proposition] of the first of the [books] of Euclid." This is the proposition "To place at a given point a straight line equal to a given straight line." Johannes Hjelmslev, "Über Archimedes' Grössenlehre," in *Kongelige Danske Videnskabernes Selskabs Skrifter,* Matematisk-fysiske Meddelelser, **25,** 15 (1950), 7, considers that the reference should have been to Euclid I.3—"Given two unequal straight lines, to cut off from the greater a straight line equal to the less"—but the reference to Euclid I.2 is what Archimedes needed at that point. Hjelmslev also argues that the reference is inappropriate because Archimedes is dealing with magnitudes, but for Archimedes magnitudes (in this instance, at any rate) can be represented by straight lines to which Euclid's propositions apply. He is on stronger ground, however, in arguing that "Der Hinweis ist aber jedenfalls vollkommen naiv und muss von einem nicht sachkundigen Abschreiber eingesetzt worden sein." Hjelmslev receives some encouragement from E. J. Dijksterhuis, *Archimedes,* p. 150, note, who justly observes: "It might be argued against this that, all the same, Euclidean constructions can be applied to these line segments functioning as symbols. For the rest, the above doubt as to the genuineness of the reference is in itself not unjustified. Archimedes never quotes Euclid anywhere else; why should he do it all at once for this extremely elementary question?" Jean Itard, *Les livres arithmétiques d'Euclide,* pp. 9–10, accepts Hjelmslev's contentions wholeheartedly, and concludes, "Il y a certainement interpolation par quelque scoliaste ou copiste obscur."

   The reference was certainly in Proclus' text, for Proclus says that Archimedes mentions Euclid, and nowhere else does he do so. If the reference were authentic, it would be relevant that *On the Sphere and the Cylinder* was probably the fourth of Archimedes' works (T. L. Heath, *The Works of Archimedes,* p. xxxii).
3. It is possible that when Archimedes says in *On the Sphere and the Cylinder* I.6, Heiberg ed., I, 20.15–16, ταῦτα γὰρ ἐν τῇ Στοιχειώσει παραδέδοται, "for these things have been handed down in the *Elements,*" he may be referring to Euclid's *Elements,* particularly XII.2 and perhaps also X.1; but since there were other *Elements,* and the term was also applied to a general body of doctrine not attributable to a particular author, the reference cannot be regarded as certain.

4. Pappus, *Collection* VII.35, Hultsch ed., II, 678.10–12: *σχολάσας* (Hultsch *συσχολάσας*) *τοῖς ὑπὸ Εὐκλείδου μαθηταῖς ἐν ᾿Αλεξανδρείᾳ πλεῖστον χρόνον*.
5. Proclus, *In primum Euclidis,* Friedlein ed., p. 68.6–23.
6. The word is *γέγονε*. It literally means "was born"; but E. Rohde in the article "*Γέγονε* in den Biographica des Suidas," in *Rheinisches Museum für Philologie*, n.s. **33** (1878), 161–220, shows that out of 129 instances in the *Suda* it is certainly equivalent to "flourished" in eighty-eight cases, and probably in another seventeen. This must be the meaning in Proclus, for his anecdote implies that Euclid was not younger than Ptolemy.
7. This was Ptolemy I, commonly called Ptolemy Soter, who was born in 367 or 366 B.C., became ruler of Egypt in 323, declared himself king in 304, effectively abdicated in 285, and died in 283 or 282.
8. The Greek text as printed by Friedlein, p. 68.11–13 from the surviving manuscript M (Monacensis) is *γέγονε δὲ οὑτος ὁ ἀνὴρ ἐπὶ τοῦ πρώτου Πτολεμαίου· καὶ γὰρ ὁ ᾿Αρχιμήδης ἐπιβαλὼν καὶ τῶ πρώτω μνημονεύει τοῦ Εὐκλείδου*. The second *καί* is clearly superfluous, or else a miscopying of some other word (to substitute *ἐν* would ease the problem of interpretation); and *ἐπιβαλών* is not easy to understand. Grynaeus and August printed the words as *᾿Αρχιμήδης καὶ ἐν τῷ πρώτῳ* in their editions (1533; 1826), and the manuscript Z, which is the basis of Zamberti's Latin translation (1539) did not have *ἐπιβαλών*. Since Heiberg's discussion in *Litterärgeschichtliche Studien über Euklid,* pp. 18–22, the words *ὁ ᾿Αρχιμήδης ἐπιβαλὼν καὶ τῷ πρώτῳ* have generally been understood to mean "Archimedes, following closely on the first [Ptolemy]," but Peter Fraser in *Alexandria,* I, 386–388 and II, note 82, offers a new interpretation. He interprets *ἐπιβαλών* as meaning "overlapping" and thinks it refers not to Ptolemy but to Euclid, with *αὐτῷ* understood; he sees *τῷ πρώτῳ*, understood as *ἐν τῷ πρώτῳ*, as a reference to the first work in the Archimedean corpus, that is, *On the Sphere and the Cylinder.* His translation is therefore "This man flourished under the first Ptolemy; for Archimedes, who overlapped with him, refers to him in his first book [?]." The theory is attractive, but I do not agree with Fraser that there is any awkwardness in *τῷ πρώτῳ* referring to Ptolemy so soon after *ἐπὶ τοῦ πρώτου*, nor do I see any difficulty in saying that Archimedes (*b.* 287) followed closely on Ptolemy I (abdicated 285, *d.* 283/282). On the whole, therefore, I prefer Heiberg's intepretation, but Fraser's full discussion merits careful study.
9. Archimedes died in the siege of Syracuse in 212 B.C., according to Tzetzes, at the age of seventy-five; if so, he was born in 287. Eratosthenes, to whom Archimedes dedicated *The Method,* was certainly a contemporary, but the work in which he said so has not survived. The *Suda* records that he was born in the 126th olympiad (276–273 B.C.).
10. Stobaeus, *Eclogues* II, 31.115, *Anthologium,* Wachsmuth and Hense, eds., II (Berlin, 1884); 228.30–33.
11. See T. L. Heath, *The Thirteen Books of Euclid's Elements,* 2nd ed., I, 117–124, 146–151. "On the whole I think it is from Aristotle that we get the best idea of what Euclid understood by a postulate and an axiom or common notion" (*ibid.,* p. 124). See also T. L. Heath, *Mathematics in Aristotle* (Oxford, 1949), pp. 53–57.
12. Aristotle, *Prior Analytics* I, 24, 41b13–22.
13. Hultsch, in Pauly-Wissowa, VI, col. 1004, also gives 295 B.C. as the date of Euclid's *ἀκμή*. The latest and most thorough discussion is by Peter Fraser, in *Alexandria,* I, 386–388, with notes in II, especially note 82. He concludes that Euclid may have been born about 330–320 B.C. and did not live much, if at all, after about 270 B.C. This would give him a middle date of 300–295. The round figure of 300 B.C. is given by Hankel, Gow, Zeuthen, Cantor, Loria, Hoppe, Heath, and van der Waerden. Michel gives the same date "au plus tard." Thaer puts Euclid's productive period (*Wirksamkeit*) in the last decade of the fourth century B.C. Heinrich Vogt, "Die Entdeckungsgeschichte des Irrationalen nach Plato usw.," in *Biblioteca mathematica,* 3rd ser., **10** (1910), 155, and—in greater detail—in "Die Lebenzeit Euclids," *ibid.,* **13** (1913), 193–202, puts Euclid's birth at about 365 and the composition of the *Elements* at 330–320. Similar dates are given by Max Steck in his edition of P. L. Schönberger, *Proklus Diadochus* (Halle, 1945), and in *Forschungen und Fortschritte,* **31** (1957), 113; but these authors, as Fraser rightly notes, do not pay sufficient attention to the links of Euclid with Ptolemy Soter and of his pupils with Apollonius. The latest date suggested for Euclid's *floruit* is 280 B.C., given in the brief life prefixed by R. N. Adams to the twenty-first and subsequent editions of Robert Simson's *Elements* (London, 1825), but it rests on no reasoned argument.
14. It would hardly be necessary to mention this confusion, of which the first hint is found in Valerius Maximus VIII.12, Externa 1, in the reign of Tiberius (14–37), were it not common in the Middle Ages and repeated in all the printed editions of Euclid from 1482 to 1566. Karl R. Popper, *Conjectures and Refutations,* 3rd ed. (London, 1969), p. 306, has revived it ("Euclid the Geometrician . . . you don't mean the man from Megara, I presume"), but only, it must be assumed, in jest.

    Jean Itard has recently advanced the theory that Euclid may not have been an individual but a school. In *Les livres arithmétiques d'Euclide,* p. 11, he advances three hypotheses: (1) that Euclid was a single individual who composed the various works attributed to him; (2) that Euclid was an individual, the head of a school which worked under him and perhaps continued after his death to produce books to which they gave his name; (3) that a group of Alexandrian mathematicians issued their works under the name of Euclid of Megara, just as (he alleges) the chemists of the same period attributed their works to Democritus. Of these speculations he thinks the second "paraît être la plus raisonnable." Itard exaggerates "les difficultés qui surgissent à chaque instant dans la chronologie lorsque l'on admet l'existence d'un seul Euclide"; there is a lack of precise information but no difficulty about Euclid's chronology. No one has hitherto seen any reason for thinking that the author of the *Elements* could not also have been the author of the other books attributed to him. There are differences within the books of the *Elements* themselves, notably the difference between books VII–IX, with which Itard is particularly concerned, and books V and X; but these are explicable by less drastic suggestions, as will be shown later. The reason why the name of Euclid the Geometer ever came to be confused with Euclid of Megara, who lived a century earlier, is clear from the passage of Valerius Maximus cited above. Valerius says that Plato, on being asked for a solution to the problem of making an altar double a cubical altar, sent his inquiries to "Euclid the geometer." One early commentator wished to alter this to "Eudoxus," which is probably right. The first specific identification of Euclid the Geometer with Euclid of Megara does not occur until Theodorus Metochita (*d.* 1332), who writes of "Euclid of Megara, the Socratic philosopher, contemporary with Plato" as the author of works on plane and solid geometry, data, optics, and so on. Euclid was a common Greek name; Pauly-Wissowa lists no fewer than eight Eukleides and twenty Eukleidas.
15. The idea that he was born at Gela in Sicily springs from the same confusion. Diogenes Laertius II.106 says that he was "of Megara, or according to some, of Gela, as Alexander says in the *Diadochai.*"
16. The passage is bracketed by Hultsch, but he brackets with frequency and not always with convincing reason.
17. Stobaeus, *Eclogues* II, 31.114, Wachsmuth and Hense eds., II, 228.25–29.
18. The so-called books XIV and XV are not by Euclid. Book XIV is by Hypsicles, probably in the second century B.C.; book XV, by a pupil of Isidore of Miletus in the sixth century.

 EUCLID

19. Proclus, *In primum Euclidis*, Friedlein ed., p. 72.6–13.
20. This is one of two mathematical uses of the term διορισμός, the other being a determination of the conditions of possibility. In the present sense it is almost part of the particular enunciation. Proclus, Friedlein ed., pp. 203.1–205.12, explains these formal divisions of a proposition.
21. The fullest discussion is in Pappus, *Collection* VII, Pref. 1–3, Hultsch ed., II, 634.3–636.30. It was James Gow, *A Short History of Greek Mathematics*, p. 211, note 1, who first recognized that the correct translation of τόπος ἀναλυόμενος was "storehouse (or treasury) of analysis."
22. Aristotle, *Posterior Analytics* I, 10, 76a31–77a4.
23. The equidistance theory was represented in antiquity by Posidonius, as quoted by Proclus, *In primum Euclidis*, Friedlein ed., p. 176.7–10; Geminus, also as quoted by Proclus, *ibid.*, p. 177.13–16; and Simplicius as quoted by al-Nayrīzī, Curtze ed., pp. 25.8–27.14. (The "philosopher Aganis" also quoted in this passage must be Geminus.) The direction theory is represented by Philoponus in his comment on Aristotle, *Posterior Analytics* II, 16, 65a4 and was probably held by Aristotle himself.
24. For Ptolemy's attempt, see Proclus, *In primum Euclidis*, Friedlein ed., pp. 365.5–367.27; for Proclus' own attempt, *ibid.*, pp. 368.24–373.2.
25. Proclus, *In primum Euclidis*, Friedlein ed., pp. 419.15–420.23, explains at some length what is meant by the application of areas, their exceeding, and their falling short.
26. *Ibid.*, p. 269.8–21.
27. Isaac Barrow, in lecture VIII of 1666, *Lectiones habitae in scholis publicis academiae cantabrigiensis* (Cambridge, 1684), p. 336, states, "Cum hoc elegio praefixum hanc disputationem claudo, nihil extare (me judice) in toto Elementorum opere proportionalitatum doctrinam subtilius inventum, solidius stabilitum, accuratius pertractatum." The English translation is that of Robert Simson, at the end of his notes to book V of *The Elements of Euclid*, 21st ed. (London, 1825), p. 294. Simson "most readily" agrees with Barrow's judgment.
28. Augustus De Morgan, "Proportion," in *The Penny Cyclopaedia*, XIX, 51. Oskar Becker's theory (see Bibl.) that there was an earlier general theory of proportion hinted at by Aristotle is discussed in the article on Theaetetus.
29. H. G. Zeuthen, *Lehre von den Kegelschnitten im Altertum*, p. 2.
30. Heath, *The Thirteen Books of Euclid's Elements*, I, 124–126.
31. Plutarch, *Quaestiones conviviales* VIII, 2, 4.720a—compare *Non posse suaviter vivi secundum Epicurum*, 11, 1094b—says that the discovery of this proposition, rather than the one about the square on the hypotenuse of a right-angled triangle, was the occasion of a celebrated sacrifice by Pythagoras.
32. According to VII, definition 21 (20), "Numbers are proportional when the first is the same multiple, or the same part, or the same parts, of the second as the third is of the fourth." H. G. Zeuthen, *Histoire des mathématiques*, p. 128, comments: "Sans doute, en ce qui concerne l'égalité des rapports, cette définition ne renferme rien d'autre que ce qu'impliquait déjà la cinquième définition du cinquième Livre." The same author, in his article "Sur la constitution des livres arithmétiques des Éléments d'Euclide," in *Oversigt over det K. Danske Videnskabernes Selskabs Forhandlinger* (1910), 412–413, sees a point of contact between the special and general theories in VII.19, since it shows that the definition of proportion in V, definition 5, has, when applied to numbers, the same significance as in VII, definition 21 (20); and we can henceforth borrow any of the propositions proved in book V.
33. "This book has a completeness which none of the others (not even the fifth) can boast of: and we could almost suspect that Euclid, having arranged his materials in his own mind, and having completely elaborated the tenth Book, wrote the preceding books after it, and did not live to revise them thoroughly" (Augustus De Morgan, "Eucleides," in *Dictionary of Greek and Roman Biography and Mythology*, William Smith, ed., II [London, 1846], 67). See also W. W. Rouse Ball, *A Short Account of the History of Mathematics*, 3rd ed. (London, 1901), pp. 58–59.
34. After defining a point as "that which has no part" (I, definition 1), Euclid says, "The extremities of a line are points" (I, definition 3), which serves to link a line with a point but is also a concession to an older definition censured by Aristotle as unscientific. So for lines and surfaces (I, definition 6). Among unused definitions are "oblong," "rhombus," and "rhomboid," presumably taken over from earlier books.
35. Paul-Henri Michel, *De Pythagore à Euclide*, p. 92.
36. See Augustus De Morgan, "Eucleides," in *Smith's Dictionary of Greek and Roman Biography*, p. 67; and "Irrational Quantity," in *The Penny Cyclopaedia*, XIII, 35–38.
37. See Eva Sachs, *Die fünf Platonischen Körper* (Berlin, 1917).
38. Proclus, *In primum Euclidis*, Friedlein ed., p. 69.4–27.
39. In Greek, συλλογισμοί, but the word can hardly be used here in its technical sense. Two attempts have been made to turn the *Elements* into syllogisms!
40. Geometrical conversion is discussed by Proclus, *In primum Euclidis*, Friedlein ed., pp. 252.5–254.20.
41. *Ibid.*, p. 68.7–10.
42. Scholium 1, book V, *Euclidis opera omnia*, Heiberg and Menge, eds., V, 280.7–9.
43. Scholium 3, book V, *ibid.*, p. 282.13–20.
44. Archimedes, *On the Sphere and the Cylinder* I, preface, *Archimedis opera omnia*, Heiberg ed., I, 2–13; compare *Quadrature of the Parabola*, preface, *ibid.*, 262–266.
45. Simplicius, *Commentary on Aristotle's Physics* A2, 185a14, Diels ed. (Berlin, 1882), 61.8–9.
46. Plato, *Theaetetus*, 147D ff.
47. Franz Woepcke, in *Mémoires présentés à l'Académie des sciences*, **14** (1856), 658–720; W. Thomson, *Commentary of Pappus on Book X of Euclid's Elements*, Arabic text and trans., remarks, notes, glossary by G. Junge and Thomson (Cambridge, Mass., 1930; repr., 1968).
48. J. L. Heiberg, *Litterärgeschichtliche Studien über Euklid*, pp. 169–171.
49. Scholium 62, book X, *Euclidis opera omnia*, Heiberg and Menge, eds., V, 450.16.
50. T. L. Heath, *The Thirteen Books of Euclid's Elements*, III, 3–4; for Thomson's trans., see *op. cit.*, pp. 63–64.
51. *Suda Lexicon, s.v.*, Adler ed., I.2 (Leipzig, 1931), Θ93, p. 689.6–8.
52. Scholium 1, book XIII, *Euclidis opera omnia*, Heiberg and Menge, eds., V, 654.5–6.
53. Proclus, *In primum Euclidis*, Friedlein ed., p. 419.15–18.
54. Scholium 4, book IV, *Euclidis opera omnia*, Heiberg and Menge, eds., V, 273.13–15.
55. Proclus, *In primum Euclidis*, Friedlein ed., p. 426.6–18.
56. Aristotle, *Prior Analytics* II, 16, 65a4.
57. Compare Karl Popper, *Conjectures and Refutations*, 3rd ed., pp. 88–89: "Ever since Plato and Euclid, but not before, geometry (rather than arithmetic) appears as the fundamental instrument of all physical explanations and descriptions, in the theory of matter as well as in cosmology." Popper has no doubt that Euclid was a Platonist and that the closing of the *Elements* with the construction of the Platonic figures is significant.
58. Pappus, *Collection* VII.3, Hultsch ed., II, 636.19.
59. *Ibid.*, pp. 638.1–640.3.
60. Proclus, *In primum Euclidis*, Friedlein ed., p. 69.4.
61. *Ibid.*, p. 644.22–26.
62. A detailed classification is made in R. C. Archibald, *Euclid's Book on Divisions of Figures*, pp. 15–16.
63. Hero, *Metrica* III.8, Schöne ed., III, *Heronis Alexandrini opera quae supersunt omnia* (Leipzig, 1903), 172.12–174.2, considers the related problem "To divide the area of a circle into three equal parts by two straight lines." "That this problem is not rational," he notes, "is clear"; but because of its utility he proceeds to give an approximate solution.
64. Pappus, *Collection* VII.13, Hultsch ed., II, 648.18–19.

65. Proclus, *In primum Euclidis,* Friedlein ed., p. 302.12–13.
66. If it had survived, it might have led B. L. van der Waerden to modify his judgments in *Science Awakening,* 2nd ed. (Groningen, undated [1956?]), p. 197: "Euclid is by no means a great mathematician . . . Euclid is first of all a pedagogue, not a creative genius. It is very difficult to say which original discoveries Euclid added to the work of his predecessors."
67. Pappus, *Collection* VII.14, Hultsch ed., II, 650.16–20.
68. Proclus, *In primum Euclidis,* Friedlein ed., p. 301.22–26.
69. Pappus, *Collection* VII.16, Hultsch ed., II, 652.18–654. Some words have been added in the translation for the sake of clarity.
70. Robert Simson, *De porismatibus tractatus* in *Opera quaedam reliqua* (Glasgow, 1776), pp. 392–393, elucidated this passage in elegant Latin, which Gino Loria, in *Le scienze esatte nell'antica Grecia,* 2nd ed. (Milan, 1914), pp. 256–257, first put into modern notation.
71. Pappus, *Collection* VII.17, Hultsch ed., II, 654.16–19.
72. *Ibid.,* VII.14, Hultsch ed., II, 652.2.
73. H. G. Zeuthen, *Die Lehre von den Kegelschnitten im Altertum,* pp. 165–184.
74. Pappus, *Collection* VII.18, Hultsch ed., II, 656.1–4.
75. H. G. Zeuthen, *op. cit.,* p. 152.
76. Pappus, *Collection* VII.30, Hultsch ed., II, 672.18–20.
77. *Ibid.,* pp. 676.25–678.15.
78. Euclid, *Phaenomena,* preface, in *Euclidis opera omnia,* Heiberg and Menge, eds., VIII, 6.5–7.
79. Pappus, *Collection* VII.312, Hultsch ed., II, 1004.23–1006.2.
80. τῷ πρώτῳ γράψαντι, *ibid.,* p. 678.14.
81. *Ibid.,* p. 678.15–24.
82. Apollonius, *Conics* I, preface, *Apollonii Pergaei quae Graece exstant,* Heiberg ed., I (Leipzig, 1891), 4.10–17.
83. H. G. Zeuthen, *Die Lehre von den Kegelschnitten im Altertum,* pp. 136–139.
84. Pappus, *Collection* VII.35, Hultsch ed., II, 678.4–6; *ibid.,* VII.33, p. 676.21–24.
85. Archimedes, *Quadrature of a Parabola,* proposition 3, in *Archimedes opera omnia,* II, 2nd Heiberg ed. (Leipzig, 1910–1915), 268.3; *On Conoids and Spheroids,* proposition 3, Heiberg ed., I, 270.23–24; *ibid.,* p. 274.3. But when the Latin text of *On Floating Bodies,* II.6, Heiberg ed., II, 362.10–11, says of a certain proposition, "Demonstratum est enim hoc per sumpta," it probably refers to a book of lemmas rather than to Euclid's *Conics.*
86. For a full discussion of the propositions assumed by Archimedes, the following works may be consulted: J. L. Heiberg, "Die Kenntnisse des Archimedes über die Kegelschnitte," in *Zeitschrift für Mathematik und Physik,* Jahrgang 25, Hist.-lit. Abt. (1880), 41–67; and T. L. Heath, *Apollonius of Perga,* pp. l-lxvi; *The Works of Archimedes,* pp. lii–liv; *A History of Greek Mathematics,* II (Oxford, 1921), 121–125.
87. Pappus, *Collection* VII.3, Hultsch ed., II, 636.23–24.
88. Proclus, *In primum Euclidis,* Friedlein ed., p. 394.17–19.
89. Pappus, *Collection* IV.51, Hultsch ed., I, 258.20–262.2.
90. *Ibid.,* VII.21, Hultsch ed., II, 660.18–662.22. A large part of the passage is attributed to an interpolator by Hultsch, but without reasons.
91. *Ibid.,* VII.312, p. 1004.17–22.
92. Paul Tannery, review of J. L. Heiberg's *Litterärgeschichtliche Studien über Euklid,* in *Bulletin des sciences mathématiques,* 2nd ser., **6** (1882), 149–150; reprinted in *Mémoires scientifiques,* XI (Toulouse–Paris, 1931), 144–145.
93. Michel Chasles, "Aperçu historique," pp. 273–274; H. G. Zeuthen, *Die Lehre von den Kegelschnitten im Altertum,* pp. 423–431. J. L. Heiberg takes a different view in his *Litterärgeschichtliche Studien über Euklid,* p. 79.
94. Alexander (?), *Commentary on Aristotle's Sophistici elenchi,* Wallies ed., (Berlin, 1898), p. 76.23.
95. Proclus, *In primum Euclidis,* Friedlein ed., pp. 69.27–70.18.
96. The older recension is, however, best illustrated in a Vienna manuscript of the twelfth century; the later recension is found in a Vatican manuscript of the tenth century.
97. Pappus, *Collection* VI.104–130, Hultsch ed., II, 594–632.
98. The task was attempted by Hultsch, *Berichte über die Verhandlungen der Kgl. Sächsischen Gesellschaft der Wissenschaften zu Leipzig,* Phil.-hist. Classe, **38** (1886), 128–155. The method definitely establishes as known before Euclid the following propositions: I.4, 8, 17, 19, 26, 29, 47; III.1–3, 7, 10, 16 (corollary), 26, 28, 29; IV.6; XI.3, 4, 10, 11, 12, 14, 16, 19, and 38 (interpolated). But Hultsch went too far in adding the whole chain of theorems and postulates leading up to these propositions, for in some cases (e.g., I.47) Euclid worked out a novel proof.
99. Proclus, *In primum Euclidis,* Friedlein ed., p. 69.2; Pappus, *Collection* VI.80–103, Hultsch ed., II, 568.12–594.26.
100. Only the later recension was known until the end of the nineteenth century, but Heiberg then discovered the earlier one in Viennese and Florentine manuscripts. Both recensions are included in the Heiberg-Menge *Opera omnia.*
101. See A. Lejeune, *Euclide et Ptolémée: Deux stades de l'optique géométrique grecque.*
102. Proclus, *In primum Euclidis,* Friedlein ed., p. 69.3.
103. Marinus, *Commentary on Euclid's Data,* preface, in *Euclidis opera omnia,* Heiberg and Menge, eds., VIII, 254.19.
104. Καὶ αὐτὸς ὁ Στοιχειωτὴς Εὐκλείδης ἐν τῇ τοῦ Κανόνος κατατομῇ, Porphyry, *Commentary on Ptolemy's Harmonies,* Wallis ed., *Opera mathematica,* III (Oxford, 1699), 267.31–32; ἐν τῇ τοὺ Κανόνος Κατατομῇ Εὐκλείδου, *ibid.,* 272.26–27; Καὶ αὐτῷ τῷ Στ̇οιχειωτῇ καί αλλοις πολλοῖς κανονικοῖς, *ibid.,* 269.5–6.
105. David Gregory, *Euclidis quae supersunt omnia,* preface.
106. Paul Tannery, "Inauthenticité de la *Division du canon* attribuée à Euclide," in *Comptes rendus des séances de l'Académie des inscriptions et belles-lettres,* **4** (1904), 439–445; also in his *Mémoires,* III, 213–219.
107. *Excerpta potius dicas quam ipsa verba hominis sagacissimi,* in C. Jan, ed., *Musici scriptores Graeci,* p. 118.
108. *Euclidis opera omnia,* Heiberg and Menge, eds., VIII, xxxvii–xlii.
109. J. Hervagius, ed., "Euclidis de levi et ponderoso fragmentum," in *Euclidis Megarensis mathematici clarissimi Elementorum geometricorum libri xv* (Basel, 1537), pp. 585–586, and foreword; M. Curtze, "Zwei Beiträge zur Geschichte der Physik im Mittelalter," in *Biblioteca mathematica,* 3rd ser., **1** (1900), 51–54; P. Duhem, *Les origines de la statique,* I, 61–97; and George Sarton, *Introduction to the History of Science,* I, 156.
110. F. Woepcke, "Notice sur des traductions arabes de deux ouvrages perdus d'Euclide," in *Journal asiatique,* 4th ser., **18** (1851), 217–232; M. Curtze, "Das angebliche Werk des Eukleides über die Waage," in *Zeitschrift für Mathematik und Physik,* **19** (1874), 262–263; P. Duhem, *op. cit.,* pp. 61–97; Marshall Clagett, *The Science of Mechanics in the Middle Ages,* p. 28; and *Greek Science in Antiquity* (London, 1957), p. 74.
111. *Anthologia palatina, Appendix nova epigrammatum,* Cougny ed. (Paris, 1890), 7.2; *Euclidis opera omnia,* Heiberg and Menge, eds., VIII.285, with Melancthon's rendering on p. 286.

BIBLIOGRAPHY

I. Original Works. The definitive edition of Euclid's extant works is *Euclidis opera omnia,* J. L. Heiberg and H. Menge, eds., 8 vols. plus suppl., in the Teubner Classical Library (Leipzig, 1883–1916). It gives a Latin translation of Euclid's works opposite the Greek text and includes the spurious and doubtful works, the scholia, Marinus' commentary on the *Data,* and the commentary on books I-X of the *Elements* by al-Nayrīzī in Gerard of Cremona's Latin translation. The details are: I, *Elementa I–IV,* J. L. Heiberg, ed. (1883); II, *Elementa V–IX,* J. L. Heiberg, ed. (1884);

III, *Elementa X,* J. L. Heiberg, ed. (1886); IV, *Elementa XI–XIII,* J. L. Heiberg, ed. (1885); V, *Elementa qui feruntur XIV–XV. Scholia in Elementa,* J. L. Heiberg, ed. (1888); VI, *Data cum commentario Marini et scholiis antiquis,* H. Menge, ed. (1896); VII, *Optica, Opticorum recensio Theonis, Catoptrica cum scholiis antiquis,* J. L. Heiberg, ed. (1895); VIII, *Phaenomena et scripta musica,* H. Menge, ed., *Fragmenta,* collected and arranged by J. L. Heiberg (1916); suppl., *Anaritii in decem libros priores Elementorum Euclidis commentarii,* M. Curtze, ed. (1899).

The *Sectio canonis* and the (Cleonidean) *Introductio harmonica* are also included in *Musici scriptores Graeci,* C. Jan, ed. (Leipzig, 1895; repr. Hildesheim, 1962), pp. 113–166 and 167–208, respectively.

The text of Heiberg's edition of the *Elements* has been reproduced by E. S. Stamatis in four volumes (Athens, 1952–1957), with a trans. into modern Greek, introductions, and epexegeses. Stamatis is also bringing out a new edition of the *Elements* in the Teubner series reproducing Heiberg's text and variant readings. Heiberg's Latin translation is omitted but the notes to it are reproduced and assigned to the corresponding place in the Greek text. The variant readings and notes take account of critical editions later than those available to Heiberg and there are additional notes on the mathematics, ancient testimonies, a bibliography, and relevant papyrus fragments. The first vol. is *Euclidis Elementa I, Libri I–IV, cum appendicibus, post I. L. Heiberg,* E. S. Stamatis, ed. (Leipzig, 1969).

The first printed Latin translation of the *Elements* appeared at Venice in 1482; the first edition of the Greek text, edited by Simon Grynaeus, at Basel in 1533. The first complete edition of the works of Euclid in Greek, edited by David Gregory, was published at Oxford in 1703, and it remained the only complete edition until that of Heiberg and Menge. Most of the early editions and translations are listed in the following works: Thomas L. Heath, *The Thirteen Books of Euclid's Elements,* 3 vols. (Cambridge, 1905, 1925; New York, 1956), I, 91–113—97 titles from 1482 to 1820; Charles Thomas Stanford, *Early Editions of Euclid's Elements* (London, 1926)—84 titles from 1482 to 1600, with bibliographical illustrations; Max Steck, "Die geistige Tradition der frühen Euklid-Ausgaben," in *Forschungen und Fortschritte,* **31** (1957), 113–117—60 titles to 1600; F. J. Duarte, *Bibliografia in Eucleides, Arquimèdes, Newton* (Caracas, 1967)—123 titles of editions of the *Elements,* with bibliographical illustrations.

II. SECONDARY LITERATURE. Two ancient works are of prime importance: the commentary of Proclus on the first book of the *Elements* and the *Collection* of Pappus. Both are available in good editions. Proclus: *Procli Diadochi in primum Euclidis Elementorum librum commentarii,* G. Friedlein, ed. (Leipzig, 1883, repr. 1967); Thomas Taylor, *The Philosophical and Mathematical Commentaries of Proclus on the First Book of Euclid's Elements* (London, 1788–1789, 1791), is superseded by G. R. Morrow, *Proclus. A Commentary on the First Book of Euclid's Elements* (Princeton, N.J., 1970); more useful trans. of the most relevant passages are scattered T. L. Heath, *op cit.*; a German trans. and commentary, *Proklus Diadochus 410–485 Kommentar zum ersten Buch von Euklids Elementen,* P. Leander Schönberger, trans., intro. by Max Steck (Halle, 1945); and a French trans., Paul ver Eecke, *Proclus de Lycie. Les commentaires sur le premier livre des Éléments d'Euclide* (Paris–Bruges, 1948). Pappus: *Pappi Alexandrini Collectionis quae supersunt,* F. Hultsch, ed., 3 vols. (Berlin 1876–1878), with a French trans. by Paul ver Eecke, *Pappus d'Alexandrie: La Collection mathématique,* 2 vols. (Paris–Bruges, 1933).

An extensive modern literature has grown around Euclid. The older works which have not been superseded and the chief recent literature may be classified as follows:

General: J. L. Heiberg, *Litterärgeschichtliche Studien über Euklid* (Leipzig, 1882); F. Hultsch, "Autolykos und Euklid," in *Berichte der Verhandlung der Kgl. Sächsischen Gesellschaft der Wissenschaften zu Leipzig,* Phil-hist. Classe, **38** (1886), 128–155; Max Simon, "Euclid und die sechs planimetrischen Bücher," in *Abhandlungen zur Geschichte der mathematischen Wissenschaften,* **11** (1901); Thomas L. Heath, *The Thirteen Books of Euclid's Elements* (see above), I, 1–151; F. Hultsch, "Eukleides 8," in Pauly-Wissowa, II (Leipzig, 1907), cols. 1003–1052; Estelle A. DeLacy, *Euclid and Geometry* (London, 1965); E. J. Dijksterhuis, *De Elementen van Euclides,* 2 vols. (Groningen, 1929–1930); Jürgen Mau, "Eukleides 3," in *Die kleine Pauly,* II (Stuttgart, 1967), cols. 416–419.

Elements: General—Max Simon, "Euclid und die sechs planimetrischen Bücher"; T. L. Heath, *The Thirteen Books of Euclid's Elements;* E. J. Dijksterhuis, *De Elementen van Euclides;* Clemens Thaer, *Die Elemente von Euklid,* 5 pts. (Leipzig, 1933–1937); and A. Frajese and L. Maccioni, *Gli Elementi di Euclide* (Turin, 1970).

Postulates and axioms—Girolamo Saccheri, *Euclides ab omni naevo vindicatus* (Milan, 1733), and an English trans. of the part relating to postulate 5, George Bruce Halstead, *Girolamo Saccheri's Euclides Vindicatus Edited and Translated* (Chicago-London, 1920); B. L. van der Waerden, *De logische grondslagen der Euklidische meetkunde* (Groningen, 1937); A. Frenkian, *Le postulat chez Euclide et chez les modernes* (Paris, 1940); Cydwel A. Owen, *The Validity of Euclid's Parallel Postulate* (Caernarvon, 1942); A. Szabó, "Die Grundlagen in der frühgriechischen Mathematik," in *Studi italiani de filologia classica,* n.s. **30** (1958), 1–51; "Anfänge des euklidischen Axiomensystems," in *Archive for History of Exact Sciences,* **1** (1960), 37–106; "Was heisst der mathematische Terminus ἀξίωωα," in *Maia,* **12** (1960), 89–105; and "Der älteste Versuch einer definitorisch-axiomatischen Grundlegung der Mathematik," in *Osiris,* **14** (1962), 308–309; Herbert Meschkowski, *Grundlagen der Euklidischen Geometrie* (Mannheim, 1966); G. J. Pineau, *The Demonstration of Euclid's Fifth Axiom, The Treatment of Parallel Lines Without Euclid's Fifth Axiom, The Self-contradiction of Non-Euclidean Geometry, The Fault of Euclid's Geometry* (Morgan Hill, Calif.); Imre Tóth, "Das Parallelproblem in Corpus Aristotelicum," in *Archive for History of Exact Sciences,* **3** (1967), 1–422; and N. C. Zouris, *Les demonstrations du postulat d'Euclide* (Grenoble, 1968). See also Frankland (below).

Book I—William Barrett Frankland, *The First Book of Euclid's Elements With a Documentary Based Principally*

Upon That of Proclus Diadochus (Cambridge, 1905).

Book V—Augustus De Morgan, "Proportion," in *The Penny Cyclopaedia,* XIX (London, 1841), 49–53; O. Becker, "Eudoxus-Studien I. Eine voreudoxische Proportionenlehre und ihre Spuren bei Aristoteles und Euklid," in *Quellen und Studien zur Geschichte der Mathematik,* **2** (1933), 311–333; Friedhelm Beckmann, "Neue Gesichtspunkte zum 5. Buch Euklids," in *Archive for History of Exact Sciences,* **4** (1967), 1–144.

Books VII–IX—Jean Itard, *Les livres arithmétiques d'Euclide* (Paris, 1962).

Book X—[Augustus De Morgan], "Irrational Quantity," in *The Penny Cyclopaedia,* XIII (London, 1839), 35–38; H. G. Zeuthen, "Sur la constitution des livres arithmétiques des Eléments d'Euclide et leur rapport à la question de l'irrationalité," in *Oversigt over det K. Danske Videnskabernes Selskabs Forhandlinger* (1915), pp. 422 ff.; William Tomson (and Gustav Junge), *The Commentary of Pappus on Book X of Euclid's Elements: Arabic Text and Translation,* Harvard Semitic Series, VIII (Cambridge, Mass., 1930; repr. 1968).

Data: M. Michaux, *Le commentaire de Marinus* (Paris, 1947).

On Divisions of Figures: Franz Woepcke, "Notice sur des traductions arabes de deux ouvrages perdus d'Euclide," in *Journal asiatique,* 4th ser., **18** (1851), 233–247; R. C. Archibald, *Euclid's Book on Divisions of Figures With a Restoration Based on Woepcke's Text and the Practica Geometriae of Leonardo Pisano* (Cambridge, 1915).

Porisms: Robert Simson, *De Porismatibus tractatus,* in *Opera quaedam reliqua* (Glasgow, 1776), pp. 315–594; Michel Chasles, *Les trois livres de Porismes d'Euclide* (Paris, 1860); H. G. Zeuthen, *Die Lehre von den Kegelschnitten im Altertum* (Copenhagen, 1886; repr. Hildesheim, 1966), pp. 160–184.

Conics: H. G. Zeuthen, *Die Lehre von den Kegelschnitten im Altertum* (see above), pp. 129–130; T. L. Heath, *Apollonius of Perga* (Cambridge, 1896), pp. xxxi–xl.

Surface Loci: Michel Chasles, "Aperçu historique sur l'origine et le développement des méthodes en géométrie," in *Mémoires couronnés par l'Académie royale des sciences et des belles-lettres de Bruxelles,* II (Brussels, 1837), note 2, "Sur les lieux à la surface d'Euclide," 273–274; H. G. Zeuthen, *op. cit.,* pp. 423–431; T. L. Heath, *The Works of Archimedes* (Cambridge, 1897), pp. lxi–lxvi.

Optics: Giuseppe Ovio, *L'Ottica di Euclide* (Milan, 1918); Paul ver Eecke, *Euclide: L'Optique et la Catoptrique* (Paris–Bruges, 1938); Albert Lejeune, *Euclide et Ptolemée: Deux stades de l'optique géométrique grecque* (Louvain, 1948).

Catoptrica: Paul ver Eecke, *Euclide: L'Optique et la Catoptrique* (see above); Albert Lejeune, "Les 'Postulats' de la Catoptrique dite d'Euclide," in *Archives internationales d'histoires des sciences,* no. 7 (1949), 598–613.

Mechanics: Franz Woepcke, "Notice sur des traductions arabes de deux ouvrages perdus d'Euclide," in *Journal asiatique,* 4th ser., **18** (1851), 217–232; M. Curtze, "Zwei Beiträge zur Geschichte der Physik im Mittelalter," in *Biblioteca mathematica,* 3rd ser. **1** (1900), 51–54; P. Duhem, *Les origines de la statique* (Paris, 1905), pp. 61–97; E. A. Moody and Marshall Clagett, *The Medieval Science of Weights* (Madison, Wis., 1952), which includes *Liber Euclidis de ponderoso et levi et comparatione corporum ad invicem,* Marshall Clagett, ed., with intro., English trans., and notes by Ernest A. Moody; Marshall Clagett, *The Science of Mechanics in the Middle Ages* (Madison, Wis., 1959), which contains "*The Book on the Balance* Attributed to Euclid," trans. from the Arabic by Clagett.

Euclid and his works occupy a prominent place in many histories of mathematics, or Greek mathematics, including Jean Étienne Montucla, *Histoire des mathématiques,* 2nd ed., I (Paris, 1798), 204–217; Hermann Hankel, *Zur Geschichte der Mathematik in Alterthum und Mittelalter* (Leipzig, 1874), pp. 381–404; James Gow, *A Short History of Greek Mathematics* (Cambridge, 1884), pp. 195–221; Paul Tannery, *La géométrie grecque* (Paris, 1887), pp. 142–153, 165–176; H. G. Zeuthen, *Histoire des mathématiques dans l'Antiquité et le Moyen Age* (Paris, 1902)—a translation of a Danish original (Copenhagen, 1893) with additions and corrections—pp. 86–145; Moritz Cantor, *Vorlesungen über Geschichte der Mathematik,* 3rd ed., I (Leipzig, 1907), 258–294; Edmund Hoppe, *Mathematik und Astronomie im klassischen Altertum* (Heidelberg, 1911), pp. 211–239; Gino Loria, *Le scienze esatte nell' antica Grecia,* 2nd ed. (Milan, 1914), pp. 188–268; T. L. Heath, *A History of Greek Mathematics,* I (Oxford, 1921), 354–446; Paul-Henri Michel, *De Pythagore à Euclide* (Paris, 1950), pp. 85–94; and B. L. van der Waerden, *Science Awakening* (Groningen, undated [1956?])—a translation with revisions and additions of a Dutch original, *Ontwakende Wetenschap*—pp. 195–200. Shorter perceptive assessments of his work are in J. L. Heiberg, *Naturwissenschaften Mathematik und Medizin im klassischen Altertum,* 2nd ed. (Leipzig, 1920), translated by D. C. Macgregor as *Mathematics and Physical Science in Classical Antiquity* (London, 1922), pp. 53–57; J. L. Heiberg, *Geschichte der Mathematik und Naturwissenschaften im Altertum* (Munich, 1925), pp. 13–22, 75–76, 81; George Sarton, *Ancient Science and Modern Civilization* (Lincoln, Nebr., 1954); and Marshall Clagett, *Greek Science in Antiquity* (London, 1957), pp. 58–59. The text of the most important passages, with an English translation opposite and notes, is given in vol. I of the 2-vol. Loeb Classical Library *Selections Illustrating the History of Greek Mathematics* (London–Cambridge, Mass., 1939), especially pp. 436–505.

IVOR BULMER-THOMAS

EUCLID: Transmission of the Elements.

Any attempt to plot the course of Euclid's *Elements* from the third century B.C. through the subsequent history of mathematics and science is an extraordinarily difficult task. No other work—scientific, philosophical, or literary—has, in making its way from antiquity to the present, fallen under an editor's pen with anything like an equal frequency. And with good reason: it served, for almost 2,000 years, as the standard text of the core of basic mathematics. As such, the editorial attention it constantly received was to be expected as a matter of course. The complexity of the history of this attention is, moreover, not simply one of a multiplicity of translations; it includes an amazing variety of redactions, emendations, abbreviations, commentaries, scholia, and special versions for special purposes.

The Elements in Greek Antiquity. The history of the *Elements* properly begins within later Greek mathematics itself. Comments on Euclid's major work were evidently far from uncommon. Indeed, Proclus (410–485), the author of the major extant Greek commentary on the *Elements,* several times refers to similar efforts by his predecessors in a way that makes it clear that the production of works or glosses on or about Euclid was a frequent—even all too frequent and not particularly valuable—activity. It would seem that Proclus had in mind an already considerable body of scholia and remarks (largely, perhaps, in various separate philosophical and scientific works) on the *Elements,* as well as other commentaries specifically devoted to it. We know that at least four such commentaries, or at least partial commentaries, existed. The earliest was written by Hero of Alexandria, but we know of its contents only through the few references in Proclus himself and through fragments preserved in the Arabic commentary of al-Nayrīzī (*d. ca.* 922). Far more important and extensive was the commentary of Pappus of Alexandria, a work whose Greek text is also lost but of which we possess an Arabic translation of the comments on book X. Proclus also mentions the Neoplatonist Porphyry (*ca.* 232–304), although it is doubtful that his work on Euclid would have been as systematic and penetrating as those of Hero and Pappus. Finally, although he did not compose a commentary specifically on the *Elements* itself, mention should be made of Geminus of Rhodes, whose lost work on the order or doctrine of mathematics (its exact title is uncertain) so often served Proclus with valuable source material. In the period following Proclus, it should be noted that Simplicius, in addition to his well-known commentaries on a number of works of Aristotle, also wrote a *Commentary on the Premises* [or *the Proemium*] *of the Book of Euclid.* Again we are indebted to al-Nayrīzī, who preserved fragments of the work.

To these more formal works on the *Elements,* one should add the substantial number of Greek scholia. Many derive from the commentaries of Proclus and Pappus, the latter being especially significant when they derive from the lost books of his work. Others are of a much later date, to say nothing of an inferior quality, and reach all the way to the fourteenth century (where the arithmetical comments of the monk Barlaam to book II of the *Elements* stand as the most extensive so-called scholium of all).

The event, however, that had the most enduring effect within the Greek phase of the transmission of the *Elements* was the edition and slight emendation it underwent at the hands of Theon of Alexandria (fourth century; not to be confused with the second-century Neoplatonist, Theon of Smyrna). The result of Theon's efforts furnished the text for every Greek edition of Euclid until the nineteenth century. Fortunately, in his commentary to Ptolemy's *Almagest,* Theon indicates that he was responsible for an addendum to the final proposition of book VI in his "edition (ἔκδοσις) of the *Elements*"; for it was this confession that furnished scholars with their first clue in unraveling the problem of the pre-Theoninc, "pristine" Euclid. In 1808 François Peyrard noted that a Vatican manuscript (Vat. graec. 190) which Napoleon had appropriated for Paris did not contain the addition Theon had referred to. This, coupled with other notable differences from the usual Theonine editions of the *Elements,* led Peyrard to conclude that he had before him a more ancient version of Euclid's text. Accordingly, he employed the Vatican codex, as well as several others, in correcting the text presented by the *editio princeps* of Simon Grynaeus (Basel, 1533). Others, utilizing occasional additional (but always Theonine) manuscripts or earlier editions, continued to improve Peyrard's text, but it was not until J. L. Heiberg began the reconstruction of the text anew on the basis of the Vatican and almost all other known manuscripts that a critical edition of the *Elements* was finally (1883–1888) established. Heiberg not only in great measure succeeded in getting behind the numerous Theonine alterations and additions, but also was able to sift out a considerable number of pre-Theonine interpolations. In addition to the authority of the non-Theonine Vatican manuscript, he culled papyri fragments, scholia, and every known ancient quotation of, or reference to, the *Elements* for evidence in his construction of the "original" Euclid. The result still stands.

The Medieval Arabic Euclid. A most appropriate introduction to the dissemination of the *Elements* throughout the Islamic world can be had by quoting the entry on Euclid in the *Fihrist* ("Index") of the tenth-century biobibliographer Muḥammad ibn Isḥāq ibn Abī Yaʿqūb al-Nadīm:

> A geometer, he was the son of Naucrates, who was in turn the son of B[a]r[a]nīq[e]s. He taught geometry and is found as an author in this field earlier than Archimedes and others; he belonged among those called mathematical philosophers. On his book *Of the Ele-*

ments of Geometry: Its title is *στοιχεῖα*, which means "elements of geometry." It was twice translated by al-Ḥajjāj ibn Yūsuf ibn Maṭar: one translation, the first, is known under the name of Hārūnian, while the other carries the label Ma'mūnian and is the one to be relied and depended upon. Furthermore, Isḥāq ibn Ḥunayn also translated the work, a translation in turn revised by Thābit ibn Qurra al-Ḥarrānī. Moreover, Abū ʿUthman al-Dimashqī translated several books of this same work; I have seen the tenth in Mosul, in the library of ʿAlī ibn Aḥmad al-ʿImrānī (one of whose pupils was Abu'l-Ṣaqr al-Qabīṣī who in turn in our time lectures on the *Almagest*). Hero commented upon this book [i.e. the *Elements*] and resolved its difficulties. Al-Nayrīzī also commented upon it, as did al-Karābīsī, of whom further mention will be made later. Further, al-Jawharī (who will also be treated below) wrote a commentary on the whole work from beginning to end. Another commentary on book V was done by al-Māhānī. I am also informed by the physician Naẓīf that he saw the Greek of book X of Euclid and that it contained forty more propositions than that which we have (109 propositions) and that he had decided to translate it into Arabic. It is also reported by Yūḥannā al-Qass [i.e., the priest] that he saw the proposition which Thābit claimed to belong to book I, maintaining that it was in the Greek version; and Naẓīf said that he had shown it to him [Yūḥannā?]. Furthermore, Abū Jaʿfar al-Khāzin al-Khurāsānī (who will be mentioned again below) composed a commentary on Euclid's book, as did Abū'l-Wafā', although the latter did not finish his. Then a man by the name of Ibn Rāhiwayh al-Arrajānī commented on book X, while Abū'l-Qāsim al-Anṭāqī commented on the whole work and this has come out [been published?]. Further, a commentary was made by Sanad ibn ʿAlī (nine books of which, and a part of the tenth, were seen by Abū ʿAlī) and book X was commented upon by Abū Yūsuf al-Rāzī at the instance of Ibn al-ʿAmīd. In his treatise *On the Aims of Euclid's Book* al-Kindī mentioned that this book had been composed by a man by the name of Apollonius the Carpenter and that he drafted it in fifteen parts. Now, at the time when this composition had already become obsolete and in need of revision, one of the kings of Alexandria became interested in the study of geometry. Euclid was alive at this time and the king commissioned him to rework the book and comment upon it; this Euclid did and thus it came about that it was ascribed to him [as author]. Later, Hypsicles, a pupil of Euclid, discovered two further books, the fourteenth and the fifteenth; he brought them to the king and they were added to the others. And all this took place in Alexandria. Among Euclid's other writings belong: The book *On Appearances* [i.e., the *Phaenomena*]. The book *On the Difference of Images* [i.e., the *Optica*]. The book *On Given Magnitudes* [i.e., the *Data*]. The book *On Tones,* known under the title *On Music* (spurious). The book *On Division,* revised by Thābit. The book *On Practical Applications* [i.e., the *Porisma*] (spurious). The book *On the Canon.* The book *On the Heavy and the Light.* The book *On Composition* (spurious). The book *On Resolution* (spurious).

Al-Nadīm's report immediately reveals the extensive attention Euclid had already received by the end of the tenth century: two complete translations, each in turn revised, perhaps two partial translations, and an amazing variety of commentaries. What is more, this flurry of activity over the *Elements* was to continue for at least 300 years more. But before recounting the more salient aspects of this later history, it will be necessary to expand certain facets of al-Nadīm's account of the earlier efforts to work Euclid into the mainstream of Islamic mathematics. By way of introduction it may be worth indicating that the totally fanciful account reported from al-Kindī of how Euclid came to compose the *Elements* may well have derived, as Thomas Heath has maintained, from a confusing misinterpretation of the Greek preface to book XIV by Hypsicles. More important than Islamic beliefs as to the origin of the *Elements,* however, is the history of how and when this work was introduced to the Arabic-speaking world. Here al-Nadīm is more reliably informed. The first translation by al-Ḥajjāj (*fl. ca.* 786–833) to which he refers was made, as the label he assigns it indicates, under the ʿAbbāsid caliphate of Hārūn al-Rashīd (786–809), at the instance of his vizier Yaḥyā ibn Khālid ibn Barmak. We also know that a manuscript of the *Elements* was obtained from the Byzantine emperor by an earlier caliph, al-Manṣūr (754–775), although apparently without then occasioning its translation into Arabic. And this patronage of science by the ʿAbbāsid caliphs is even more in evidence in Ḥajjāj's realization that a second, shorter recension of his translation would be likely to gain the favor of Ma'mūn (813–833). It is this version alone which appears to be extant (books I–VI, XI–XIII only). The first six books exist in a Leiden manuscript conjoined with al-Nayrīzī's commentary, and from the prefatory remarks of this work we learn that, in preparing his second version of the *Elements,* Ḥajjāj "left out the superfluities, filled up the gaps, corrected or removed the errors, until he had perfected the book and made it more certain, and had summarized it, as it is found in the present version. This was done for specialists, without changing any of its substance, while he left the first version as it was for the vulgar." Although what we have of Ḥajjāj's second version has not yet undergone a thorough analysis, that it was composed with something of the notion of a school text in mind seems evident. For, to cite several instances, the tendency to distinguish separate cases of a proposition and the use of numerical examples to illustrate various proofs point toward a preoccupation with pedagogical concerns that was to become fairly characteristic of the Arabic Euclid and of the medieval Latin versions that derived from it.

The second, largely new translation of Euclid was accomplished, as al-Nadīm tells us, by Isḥāq ibn Ḥunayn, son of Ḥunayn ibn Isḥāq, the most illustrious of all translators of Greek works into Arabic. Again a second recension was prepared, in this instance by a scholar who in his own right holds a major position within the history of Islamic mathematics, Thābit ibn Qurra. Although no copies of Isḥāq's initial version appear to have survived, we do possess a number of manuscripts of the Isḥāq–Thābit recension. Further study of these manuscripts is needed to say much in detail of the character of this translation, but we do know that Thābit utilized Greek manuscripts in whatever reworking he did of the text (as stated in a marginal note to a Hebrew translation of the *Elements* and confirmed by Thābit's own reference to a Greek text). Whether Isḥāq (or even Thābit) relied to any great extent on one of the Ḥajjāj versions for any sort of guidance is problematic. For, in a comparison of a single manuscript of what are presumably books XI–XIII of Ḥajjāj with their corresponding parts in the Isḥāq–Thābit redaction, Martin Klamroth, the first scholar to examine the two translations in depth, confessed that the difference was slight. But perhaps, assuming the ascription of Klamroth's manuscript of XI–XIII to Ḥajjāj correct, this lack of variation occurs only in the later books.

It is at this point perhaps noteworthy that Klamroth was of the opinion that the Arabic tradition as a whole is closer, as we have it, to the original Euclid than the text presented by extant Greek manuscripts. Heiberg, however, marshaled a considerable amount of evidence against Klamroth's contention and clearly confirmed the superior reliability of the Greek tradition. At the same time, he established the filiation of the Isḥāq–Thābit version and a particular divergent Greek manuscript.

To complete al-Nadīm's account of translations, mention should be made that Abū ʿUthman al-Dimashqī (*fl. ca.* 908–932) not only translated parts of the *Elements* but also the commentary of Pappus to book X (the latter alone being extant). Furthermore, al-Nadīm's report of the intention of Naẓīf ibn Yumn (*d. ca.* 990) to translate book X appears to be reflected in various additions and modifications deriving from the Greek that are extant in Arabic under Naẓīf's name. Finally, although it escaped al-Nadīm's notice, the spurious books XIV and XV of the *Elements* were translated by the Baghdad mathematician and astronomer Qusṭā ibn Lūqā.

The full roster of Arabic translations of Euclid's major work only begins to sketch the program of activity concerning the *Elements* within Islamic mathematics and science. The numerous commentaries mentioned by al-Nadīm are adequate testimony to that. But even before one turns to these, attention should be drawn to yet other forms that found expression among Arabic treatments of Euclid. Quite distinct from translations proper (*naql*) there are a number of epitomes or summaries (*ikhtiṣār* or *mukhtaṣar*), recensions (*taḥrīr*), and emendations (*iṣlaḥ*) of the *Elements.*

Undoubtedly the most famous of the epitomes is that included by the Persian philosopher Avicenna (Ibn Sīnā) in the section on geometry in his voluminous philosophical encyclopedia, the *Kitāb al-Shifāʾ*. All fifteen books of the *Elements* are present, but with abbreviated proofs. Nor was Avicenna alone in his attempt to distill Euclid into a more compact dosage; we have already seen that Ḥajjāj considered one of the primary virtues of his second version of the *Elements* to be its shorter length, and other summaries were composed by Muẓaffar al-Asfuzārī (*d.* before 1122), a colleague of Omar Khayyām (al-Khayyāmi), and also, if we can believe a report by the fourteenth-century historian Ibn Khaldūn (*Muqaddima*, VI, 20), by one Ibn al-Ṣalt (presumably the Hispano-Muslim physician, astronomer, and logician Abū'l-Ṣalt [1067/1068–1134]).

More significant within the history of Islamic mathematics are the various recensions or *taḥrīr* of the *Elements.* The best known is that of the Persian philosopher and scientist Nāṣir al-Dīn al-Ṭūsī, who composed similar editions of many other Greek mathematical, astronomical, and optical works. We know that at least one *Taḥrīr Uṣūl Uqlīdis* ("Recension of Euclid's Elements") was completed by al-Ṭūsī in 1248. It covered all fifteen books and made use of both the Ḥajjāj and Isḥāq–Thābit translations. There is, however, yet another *Taḥrir* of the *Elements* that is traditionally ascribed to al-Ṭūsī. Although it covers only books I–XIII, it is considerably more detailed than the more frequently appearing 1248 version. Printed in Rome in 1594, we know of only two extant manuscripts (both at the Biblioteca Medicea-Laurenziana in Florence) of this thirteen-book *Taḥrīr.* However, one of these codices explicitly asserts that the work was completed on 10 Muḥarram 1298. Since al-Ṭūsī died in 1274, this gives grounds (and there appear to be other reasons as well) for seriously doubting the ascription to him. Yet whatever conclusion may finally be reached concerning its authorship, the preface to this *Taḥrīr* is particularly instructive with respect to the reason for composing such redactions of the *Elements* and with regard to the kind of added material they would be likely to contain. Beginning with a few remarks specifying the place of geometry within the classification of the sciences and several fanciful statements about Euclid's biography, this preface makes special note of the two previously executed translations by Ḥajjāj and (revised by) Thābit and then launches into a more elaborate description of all else Islamic scholars had done with, and to, the *Elements*. This interim "history" of Euclides Arabus tells us that much effort had been spent in removing all difficulties from the text and in clarifying its numerous obscurities. Examples were inserted to make complex things more obvious and, moving in the opposite direction, some things that were too obvious were left out. Some related propositions were combined and treated as one, implicit assumptions were made explicit, and care was taken to specify (at least by number) just which previous theorems were being utilized in a particular proof. And all of this was done, our preface continues, not just in the body of the text of these versions of the *Elements,* but everywhere in the margins and even between lines. The varieties of information produced in such a fashion are now, the author of the present *Taḥrīr* submits, sorely in need of proper arrangement and clarification, and he goes on to reveal his intention of satisfying this need through the presentation as a unified whole of the original text, together with relevant commentary. His resulting *Taḥrīr* needs much closer scrutiny in order to set forth the complete spectrum of all of the types of added material it contains, but it is clear from the preface we have been summarizing that it presumably includes, in addition to its own original contributions, many features similar to those its author has just recounted among the works of his predecessors.

One other *Taḥrīr* of the *Elements* bears specific mention: that of Muḥyi 'l-Dīn al-Maghribī (*fl.* thirteenth century), a mathematician and astronomer who worked in both Syria and Marāgha and to whom we owe editions (literally "purifications," *tahdhīb*) of Greek works on spherical trigonometry (Theodosius and Menelaeus) and of Apollonius' *Conics,* and a similar work entitled *The Essence* (*Khulāṣa*) *of the Almagest.* His *Taḥrīr* may have been written shortly after the genuine fifteen-book *Taḥrīr* of al-Ṭūsī, since it is found in a manuscript dated 1260/1261. It contains, on the other hand, a preface that is similar in many ways to that found in the later (1298) *Taḥrīr,* wrongly, it appears, ascribed to al-Ṭūsī. It also complains of the faults in previous attempts to treat Euclid, but it is more specific in assigning at least some of the blame to Avicenna, a certain al-Nīsābūrī, and Abū Ja'far al-Khāzin (cited in al-Nadīm's chronicle). Al-Maghribī's work sets out to remedy these faults and especially to explain all of the puzzles (*shukūk*) occasioned by Euclid and to supply the added lemmas (*muqaddamāt*) necessary for various proofs. In sum, one can say that al-Maghribī's *Taḥrīr,* as well as the others we have mentioned above, began from the existing translations of the *Elements* and, through the incorporation (albeit in revised form) of presumably a good many of the notions contained in earlier commentaries as well as through the creation of much original material, proceeded to the preparation of an improved Euclid that may well have been ultimately intended to serve more adequately than Euclid himself as a school text. Exactly what this improved *Elements* contains as its most salient characteristics will be revealed only after a great deal more analysis of the relevant texts. And the same must be said for the translations of Ḥajjāj and Isḥāq–Thābit.

The third type of redaction of the *Elements* mentioned above, those labeled "Emendations" (*Iṣlāḥ*), is difficult to characterize beyond what is revealed by the title, since no known copies have survived of those to which reference is made by Islamic scholars. We are told, for example, that al-Kindī composed an *Iṣlāḥ* of the *Elements* in addition to his work *On the Aims* (*Aghrāḍ*) *of Euclid's Book.* Similarly, *Iṣlāḥ*'s were written by the astronomer al-Jawharī and the Persian philosopher and scientist Athīr al-Dīn al-Abharī (*d.* 1265), but we know of them only through fragmentary quotations in other works. Further, in a way related to the emending of Euclid, it should be mentioned that the contribution of at least a few Islamic mathematicians to the transmission of the *Elements* appeared in the form of specific additions (*ziyādāt*), often merely to particular propositions within the text.

There remain the substantial number of Arabic commentaries, alternatively entitled *tafsīr* or *shurūḥ,* on Euclid. One can, indeed, extend their sequence considerably beyond that revealed in the *Fihrist.* In another passage of that work al-Nadīm notes what would be, were the reference correct, the very first such commentary on the *Elements:* one ascribed to the central figure of Arabic alchemy, Jābir ibn Ḥayyān. But this clearly seems to be an error, introduced by a later scribal addition, for the thirteenth-century astronomer Jābir ibn Aflaḥ. When we turn, however, to the list of genuine commentaries in al-Nadīm and supplement it with information drawn from later sources, the number becomes so considerable (nearly fifty, of which more than half are extant in some form or another) that only the most notable can be mentioned here. Among the most significant recorded by al-Nadīm is that by the Persian mathematician and astronomer al-Māhānī, who commented on book X and on book V, and that by the somewhat later al-Nayrīzī. The latter, which is often a source for comments from lost Greek works on Euclid, was translated into Latin in the twelfth century by Gerard of Cremona. When one pushes beyond the Euclid entry of the *Fihrist,* note should be made of the particularly astute commentary on book V written by the Andalusian mathematician Ibn Muʿādh al-Jayyānī. It contains, apart from Greek mathematics itself, the first known comprehension of the brilliant definition of the equality of ratios formulated by Eudoxus. In fact, apart from several brief glosses in the medieval Latin Euclid, this definition was seldom properly understood in the West before Isaac Barrow in the seventeenth century. Finally, some note should be made of the fact that figures in Islam who derived appreciable eminence from other pursuits also saw fit to expend time in commenting on the *Elements.* Thus, one might cite the philosophers al-Kindī and al-Fārābī, who commented on books I and V. And similar attention should be drawn to the treatises on Euclid written by Alhazen (Ibn al-Haytham), author of the extremely significant textbook on optics, *Kitāb al-Manāẓir,* and to the commentary dealing with the problems of parallels, ratios, and proportion by the even more famous Persian mathematician and poet Omar Khayyām.

A somewhat more informative outline of the commentaries can be had if one turns from their authors to the questions and subjects they treat. Although so few have been edited, to say nothing of studied, that only the most tentative attempt can be made to assay the contents of these commentaries, it is nevertheless possible to see at least some of the areas of major concern. To begin with, it should be made clear that the commentaries were more often than not on parts, and not the whole, of the *Elements.* Thus, as one expects within almost any body of Euclidean commentarial literature, considerable effort was spent in mulling over premises, i.e., definitions, postulates, and axioms (for example, in the treatises of al-Karābīsī [see al-Nadīm's report], al-Fārābī, Ibn al-Haytham, and Omar Khayyām referred to above). As a subclass of this genre of concern, emphasis should be placed upon special tracts, or passages in more general commentaries, that carried on the series of attempts already made in Greek mathematics to prove the parallels postulate (thus, to cite but a portion of the literature, we have two separate treatises on this topic written by Thābit ibn Qurra, a separate work dealing with it by al-Nayrīzī, and treatments of it in the *Taḥrīr* of both al-Maghrībi and al-Ṭūsī [both the genuine and the spurious *Taḥrīr* of the latter]).

Moving beyond the concern expressed over premises, one is immediately struck by the unusually high proportion of commentaries on books V and X. Although further investigation is needed to establish all of the motives behind the larger share of attention received by these books, a preliminary conjecture can easily be made. On the one hand, the extreme complexity of the treatment of irrational magnitudes in book X undoubtedly required more exposition and explanation to assure comprehension. On the other hand, the central role played by the theory of proportion contained in book V throughout all geometry probably caused Islamic mathematicians, rightly, to view this book as more fundamental than others. This, coupled with the consideration that some trouble was had in appreciating the Eudoxean definition of equal ratios that is included in book V, most likely gave it a position of some priority in the eyes of potential commentators.

One feature of the series of Arabic commentaries on the *Elements* should be recorded: Although the greater number of such commentators were mathematicians, astronomers, or physicians (or some combination thereof), a minority were not that, but rather philosophers. Of course, a philosopher of the mark of al-Kindī was as much concerned with things scientific as he was with things philosophical. But others, such as al-Fārābī and Avicenna, did not have his scientific interests or acumen. Yet they too commented on, or epitomized, the *Elements.* We are also informed that the philosopher and Shāfiʿite theologian Fakhr al-Dīn al-Rāzī (1149–1210) wrote on Euclid's premises and that the Cordovan philosopher, physician, and Aristotelian commentator par excellence Averroës (Ibn Rushd) wrote a treatise on what was needed from Euclid for the study of Ptolemy's *Almagest.* It is likely, to be sure, that such works on the *Elements* written by philosophers (most, unfortunately, are lost) were less penetrating and exacting than the more mathematical product of other commentators; they are, nonetheless, still significant as a measure of the extent to which the importance of Euclid had penetrated Islamic thought. In sum, the Arabic phase of the *Elements'* history may well prove to be not merely the most manifold but, even mathematically, the most creative of all.

Other medieval Near Eastern translations of the *Elements* all seem to have been based on one or another of the Arabic versions already mentioned. This is certainly the case with the Persian translation (completed in 1282–1283) of al-Ṭūsī's fifteen-book *Taḥrīr,* ostensibly made by his pupil Quṭb al-Dīn al-Shīrāzī (1236–1311). Similarly, although there are a fair number of medieval Hebrew compendia and special recensions of the *Elements,* the basic thirteenth-century Hebrew translation (or translations) appears to derive from the revised Isḥāq–Thābit version but contains marginal reference to the Ḥajjāj translation as well. It is still problematic whether we have here two distinct Hebrew translations or the collaborative effort over a number of years (*ca.* 1255–1270) of the two scholars involved: Moses ibn Tibbon and Jacob ben Maḥir ibn Tibbon.

Even more debatable is the issue of the Syriac version of Euclid. It was frequently the case that Arabic translations of Greek works were executed via a Syriac intermediary. It is, however, rather doubtful that this was true with the *Elements.* We do possess fragments of a Syriac redaction in a fifteenth- or sixteenth-century manuscript, and comparison of these fragments with the Arabic tradition clearly indicates a filiation, although without any absolute evidence of the direction in which the parentage must have run. If one asks how early the Syriac edition must be dated, present evidence necessitates moving it back to the eleventh or twelfth century. For instance, we know that the Syriac polymath Abu'l-Faraj (Bar Hebraeus, 1226–1286) lectured on Euclid at Marāgha in 1268. Furthermore, reference to a Syriac version of the *Elements* is made in the 1298 pseudo-al-Ṭūsī *Taḥrīr* and in mathematical opuscula of Ibn al-Sarī (*d.* 1153). Finally, note should be made of fragments of an Armenian version of the *Elements,* for it too appears to be related to the Arabic (Isḥāq–Thābit) tradition. It seems most probable that this Armenian Euclid was the work of Gregory Magistros (*d.* 1058), in one of whose letters we find the announcement that he had begun a translation of the *Elements.* If to this we add the fact, as one scholar has urged, that Gregory knew only Greek and Syriac, but no Arabic, it would appear that he based his translation in some way or another on the Syriac version under discussion. This gives us a terminus ante quem of the first half of the eleventh century for this version, but there is no other evidence on the basis of which we can, with any certainty, assign it an earlier date. One can merely indicate that the editor of these Syriac fragments, G. Furlani, judged them to have a very close relation to the Arabic text of Ḥajjāj and that they were, in his view, in some way derived from this text. He dismissed the apparent contrary evidence one might derive from the Syriac transcription of Greek terms, since this often occurs in Syriac works that we know were based on Arabic originals. However, the second scholar to examine the fragments, Mlle. Claire Baudoux, claimed a definite link with the Isḥāq–Thābit translation (not investigated by Furlani) and concluded that the Syriac redaction preceded Isḥāq and served as an intermediary between it and the Greek original. Nevertheless, it would seem that the issue must stand unresolved until a fresh comparison is made with both Arabic translations and all relevant evidence is presented in detail. Until then, it would seem more plausible to hold the tentative conclusion that the Syriac version had an Arabic source, and not vice versa.

As the article we have quoted above from the *Fihrist* already indicates, Euclid's other works also existed in Arabic, although al-Nadīm has omitted the names of their translators. Indeed, we are still not able to identify translators in all instances. Thus, although the original translator of *On the Division of Figures* remains unknown, we do have information that Thābit ibn Qurra revised the translation, and it is, as a matter of fact, on the basis of this revision that, together with other Latin material drawn from the work of the thirteenth-century mathematician Leonardo Fibonacci, we have been able to reconstruct the contents of this Euclidean treatise. Similarly, we know that Thābit also corrected the translation of the work *On the Heavy and the Light.* There is also a treatise extant in Arabic called *The Book of Euclid on the Balance,* but there is no further information concerning its provenance.

Three other minor works, the *Data,* the *Phaenomena,* and the *Optica* (the Arabs were not aware of the pseudo-Euclidean *Catoptrica*), have a similar Islamic history. All three were part of that collection of shorter works known as the "middle books" (*mutawassiṭāt*), which functioned as appropriate texts for the segment of mathematics falling between the *Elements* and Ptolemy's *Almagest.* Both the *Data* and the *Optica* underwent Isḥāq–Thābit translation-revisions and later *Taḥrīr* at the hands of al-Ṭūsī. Of the *Phaenomena* we are reliably informed only of the recension done by al-Ṭūsī.

The Medieval Latin Euclid: The Greek–Latin Phase. The first known Latin reference to Euclid is found in Cicero (*De oratore,* III, 132)—surely a good number of years before any attempt was made to translate the *Elements.* This latter aspect of the Latin history of Euclid begins, as far as extant sources tell us, with a fragment attributed to the third-century astrologer Censorinus. What we have in this fragment that gives excerpts from the *Elements* might also be reflected in the Euclid passages in the *De nuptiis* of Martianus Capella, although some historians feel that Martianus may have been utilizing a Greek source as well as some Latin adaptation of (or at least of parts of) the *Elements.*

The second piece of evidence in the history of Latin renditions of Euclid is found in a fifth-century palimpsest in the Biblioteca Capitolare at Verona. Treated with chemicals in the nineteenth century, it is now all but impossible to decipher. We can establish, however, that it contains fragments of a translation from books XII–XIII of the *Elements*. Very little else can be said with any surety of the translation, although its most recent editor, M. Geymonat, has urged that the palimpsest be dated slightly later and has suggested that Boethius was the author of the translation of the fragments that it contains.

Whether or not this suggestion is correct, it is to the problem of the Boethian Euclid that we must now turn. We do know that Boethius made such a translation because Cassiodorus refers to it in his *Institutiones* (II, 6, 3: "ex quibus Euclidem translatum Romanae linguae idem vir magnificus Boethius edidit") and also preserved a letter from Theodoric to Boethius himself (*Variae*, I, 45, 4) in which the existence of the translation is again attested. However, we are far less well informed of the extent and nature of this translation, for the "Boethian" geometries—or better, geometrical materials—that have come down to us are in a late fragmentary form. Basically, the excerpts we possess of Boethius' translation derive from four sources, each considerably later than the date of his actual translating efforts: (1) excerpts in the third recension of book II of Cassiodorus' *Institutiones* (eighth or ninth century); (2) excerpts in a number of manuscripts of a later redaction of the *Agrimensores*, a collection (made *ca.* 450) of materials concerned with surveying, land division, mapmaking, the rules of land tenure, etc. (*ca.* ninth century); (3) excerpts within the so-called five-book "Boethian" geometry (eighth century); (4) excerpts within the so-called two-book "Boethian" geometry (eleventh century). Special note might be taken of the full content of the last two sources, inasmuch as they appear in the literature under Boethius' name. The earlier of the two compilations, in five books, consists of gromatic material in book I and in part of book V, of excerpts from Boethius' *Arithmetica* in book II, and of excerpts from his translation of Euclid in books III–IV and in the initial section of book V. The two-book version of the "Boethian" geometry seems to have been compiled by a Lotharingian scholar without especially acute mathematical ability and contains its excerpts from Boethius' translation in book I, as well as a brief preface and a concluding section on the abacus, while book II consists largely of *Agrimensores* material. If one combines the extracts of Boethius' *Elements* from these two works with the extracts found in the Cassiodorus and *Agrimensores* sources listed above, the total schedule, as it were, of translated Euclid amounts to (a) almost all the definitions, postulates, and axioms of books I–V of the *Elements;* (b) the enunciations of almost all the propositions of books I–IV; and (c) the proofs for book I, propositions 1–3. The above four sources containing these extracts often overlap in the items they include, but it is notable that a sequence of the enunciations of propositions from book III (i.e., 7–22) is found only in the five-book "Boethian" geometry, while the definitions of book V appear only in the recension of Cassiodorus. (The relation of the four sources can be seen in the chart below.)

The ninth- through fifteenth-century manuscripts in which these sources (especially the last three) of Euclidean excerpts appear are, for the most part, collections containing other material pertinent to the quadrivium. But even when, with new and more complete translations of the *Elements* in the twelfth century, this kind of collection began to lose the dominant position it once held in medieval Latin mathematics, traces of the Boethian Euclid linger on through occasional conjunction with the newly translated material. Thus, we know of at least two different mélanges of parts of the Boethian excerpts with one of the translations of the *Elements* from the Arabic by Adelard of Bath (that labeled Adelard II below). One of these mélanges dates from about 1200 and seems to have been compiled by a North German scholar with appreciably more mathematical wit than, for example, the author of the two-book "Boethius" discussed above. It is preserved in a single thirteenth-century manuscript: Lüneburg, Ratsbücherei MS miscell. D 4°48. The second mélange occurs in four manuscripts, three of them of the twelfth century, but little has been done to attempt to determine the provenance of its author. Further, cognizance should be taken of the fact that the Boethian "source" of both mélanges seems to have been the two-book *Geometry*. Finally, although we do have these attempts to combine the Greek–Latin Boethian extracts of the *Elements* with the Arabic–Latin tradition deriving from Adelard, it should be made clear that they constituted but a minor part of the medieval Euclid in the West; the Adelardian-based tradition was soon to hold all in sway.

However, before we move to this tradition and to the Arabic–Latin Euclid in general, two other Greek–Latin medieval versions must be mentioned. Of the first we have but a fragment (I, 37–38 and II, 8–9). It exists in a single tenth-century manuscript in Munich. Although extremely literal, its translator knew little of what he was doing, since he translated as numbers the letters designating geometrical figures.

The second Greek-Latin Euclid we must discuss constitutes the most exact translation ever made of the *Elements,* being a *de verbo ad verbum* rendering in which the order of words and occasionally the syntax itself are often more Greek than Latin. Based solely on a Theonine text, the translation is known from two extant manuscripts and covers books I-XIII and XV. Neither manuscript names the translator, but a stylistic analysis of the text has established that he is identical with the anonymous twelfth-century translator of Ptolemy's *Almagest* from the Greek. A preface fortunately attached to the latter translation informs us that our nameless author was a one-time medical student at Salerno who, learning of the existence in Palermo (*ca.* 1160) of a Greek codex of Ptolemy, journeyed to Sicily in order to see this treasure and, after a period of further scientific preparation, set himself to putting it in Latin. Presumably our translator did the same for the *Elements* shortly thereafter (since no mention of such an effort is made in his description of other of his activities in his preface to his version of Ptolemy). When one turns to the translation itself, it is immediately evident that its author was extremely acute, both as an editor and as a mathematician. Not only does he give an extraordinarily exact rendering of the Greek, but on occasion he also employs brackets to indicate several passages in an alternate Greek manuscript he was using. What is more, several times he employs these same brackets to improve the logic of a proof. Unfortunately, the superb Latin Euclid he produced exerted very little, if any, influence upon his medieval successors. (It might also be indicated that one manuscript of this translation contains a pastiche of books XIV-XV in place of the missing book XIV; it too derives from Greek sources and even castigates translators from the Arabic for being insufficiently careful.)

The Greek-Latin phase of the medieval Euclid is also, perhaps, the most appropriate point at which mention should be made of the minor Euclidean works during this period. For, contrary to what proved to be true for the *Elements,* these shorter works have a medieval Latin history that derives predominantly—in all instances through anonymous translators—from the Greek. Thus, in place of the apparently lost version of the *Data* from the Arabic by Gerard of Cremona (who also translated the *Elements*), we possess several codices of an accurate rendering made in the twelfth century directly from the Greek. Similarly, although there do exist copies of Gerard's Arabic-Latin *Optica,* they are overwhelmingly outnumbered by manuscripts containing Greek-Latin translations. Indeed, there appear to be two distinct versions of the *Optica* from the Greek, some manuscripts of which are so variant as to lead one to expect an even more complicated history. There also seem to be several versions of the pseudo-Euclid *Catoptrica* made from the Greek. What is more, there is a totally separate *De speculis* translated from the Arabic (by Gerard?) and ascribed to Euclid. We know of no Greek or Arabic original from which it may have derived, although it does exist in Hebrew in several manuscripts. The *Sectio canonis* had several propositions from it transmitted through the medium of Boethius' *De institutione musica.* The *Phaenomena,* on the other hand, was not put into Latin before the Renaissance.

The Medieval Latin Euclid: The Arabic-Latin Phase. Once integral translations of the *Elements* from the Arabic were available to the medieval scholar, all Greek-Latin fragments and versions receded into the background. The new, dominant tradition was, however, twofold; one wing derived from the Ḥajjāj Euclid, the other from that of Isḥāq-Thābit, the recensions of al-Ṭūsī and al-Maghribī coming too late, of course, to enter into the competition of translating activity in the twelfth century.

The Latin *Elements* based upon the Isḥāq-Thābit text was the accomplishment of Gerard of Cremona, the most industrious of all translators of scientific, philosophical, and medical works from the Arabic. We know that he translated the *Elements* from its citation in his *Vita,* written by one of his pupils and appended to one of his translations of Galen. Identified among extant manuscripts in 1901, Gerard's Euclid was soon realized to be the closest to the Greek tradition of all Arabic-Latin versions. It alone contains Greek material—for example, the preface to the spurious book XIV—absent from the other versions. Ironically, however, it clearly seems to have been less used, and less influential, than the somewhat more inaccurate (Adelardian-based) editions. It derives its more faithful reflection of the Greek original from the fact that the Arabic of Isḥāq-Thābit, upon which it was based, is itself a more exact reproduction of the Greek. We have no explicit ascription stating that Gerard worked from this particular Arabic translation, but even the most preliminary examination of Gerard's text reveals that this was in all probability the case. For instance, the phrase "Thebit dixit" occurs frequently throughout the body of the translation. At least some of these occurrences—perhaps almost all of them—are not due to Gerard's reflecting on the text he was rendering, but to a direct translation of that text itself, since several citations that have been published by Klamroth from the Arabic and are reproduced in Gerard indicate that Thābit is named therein as well. (Third-person references by an author to himself are, of course, quite common.) While awaiting evidence that will issue from a direct comparison of the Isḥāq-Thābit and Gerard texts, note should be made of the fact that Gerard has the two propositions added after VIII, 25, and the corollaries to VIII, 14-15, which are characteristic of Isḥāq-Thābit. Yet this is not the only Arabic version Gerard had before him, at least not in its pure form. For he includes VIII, 16, which is not, according to Klamroth, in the Isḥāq-Thābit manuscripts examined. Furthermore, after having followed these manuscripts by reproducing VIII, 11-12, as two separate propositions, at the conclusion of book VIII Gerard has an addendum claiming that these two propositions were found as one *in alio libro;* the addendum continues by reproducing this combined version, proof and all. Exactly who found this combined version of VIII, 11-12, in another book is problematic; use of the first person in this passage in Gerard is not conclusive, since it could derive directly from his Arabic text. We do know, however, that the Adelardian tradition ostensibly based on the Ḥajjāj Euclid (of which book VIII is not extant) does conflate the two propositions in question. Therefore, either Gerard utilized texts of both Isḥāq-Thābit and Ḥajjāj in making his translation or, which seems more likely, he based his labors on an Isḥāq-Thābit text that contained material drawn from one or another of the Ḥajjāj versions.

Gerard also contributed to the literature of Euclides Latinus by translating the commentary of al-Nayrīzī on the *Elements*, the commentary of Muḥammad ibn ʿAbd al-Bāqī (*fl. ca.* 1100) on book X, and at least part of Dimashqī's translation of Pappus' commentary on book X.

By far the most important share of the medieval Arabic-Latin Euclid belongs to the English translator, mathematician, and philosopher Adelard of Bath. Not only was Adelard himself the author of at least three versions of the *Elements*, but he served as the point of departure for numerous offspring redactions and revisions as well. Taken together as the Adelardian tradition, they soon gained a virtual monopoly when it came to using and quoting Euclid in the Latin Middle Ages.

The first version due to Adelard himself (hereafter specified by the Roman numeral I) is the only one within the whole tradition that is, properly speaking, a translation. As such, there is clear indication that it was based on the Arabic of Ḥajjāj. Thus, the proofs in Adelard I appear to correspond quite well with what we have of Ḥajjāj. Further, Adelard I carries the same three added definitions (at least two, however, going back in some way to the Greek) to book III found in Ḥajjāj and agrees with him in reproducing the maximum of six separate cases in the proof of III, 35. But it also seems clear that Adelard I did not utilize Ḥajjāj as we have him today. The fact that he does not reproduce the arithmetical examples in books II and VI, or the added propositions in book V, that are present in the extant Ḥajjāj is not the point at issue, since these features are most likely from the commentary of al-Nayrīzī to which our Ḥajjāj text is attached. What is significant is the fact that Adelard I does contain the corollaries to II, 4, and VI, 8, which are not present in our Ḥajjāj and, even more suggestive, does not include VI, 12, which is contained in our Ḥajjāj. If one couples the latter fact with the statement in the pseudo-Ṭūsī *Taḥrīr* that Ḥajjāj did not include VI, 12, it then becomes most probable that there existed another Ḥajjāj, slightly variant from the text we possess, and that it was this Arabic version which Adelard I employed. One could argue that it would have been the first version Ḥajjāj prepared under Hārūn al-Rashīd, but we know that this earlier redaction was somewhat longer than the second version—which, presumably, is the one we possess. And Adelard I in other respects (particularly in the length and detail of the proofs) appears to correspond well enough with the second extant version to make derivation from a longer Arabic original unlikely. A variant of Ḥajjāj's second redaction seems a more plausible source.

Adelard II, on the other hand, does not give rise to similar problems, since it is not a translation but an abbreviated edition or, as Adelard himself calls it (in his version III), a *commentum*. Although the briefest of Adelard's efforts in putting Euclid into Latin, it was unquestionably the most popular. This is clear not merely on grounds of the far greater number of extant copies of Adelard II, but also because the translations given here of the "enunciations" (of definitions, postulates, axioms, and propositions) were subsequently appropriated for a good many other versions by editors other than Adelard. Indeed, the diversity thus growing out of Adelard II appears to be present within it as well, since there is considerable variation among the almost fifty manuscript copies thus far identified. The earliest extant codex (Oxford, Trinity College 47) presents, for example, a text that is more concise than any consistently presented by other manuscripts.

The characteristic feature of Adelard II lies in its proofs, which are not truly proofs at all, but *commenta* furnishing relevant directions in the event one should wish to carry out a proof. One is constantly reminded, for instance, of just which proposition or definition or axiom one is building upon, or whether the argument—should it be carried out—is direct or indirect. The *commenta* talk about the proposition and its potential proof; the language is, in our terms, metamathematical. Moreover, this talk about the proof often puts greater emphasis upon the constructions to be utilized than on the proof proper.

Adelard III, referred to by Roger Bacon as an *editio specialis,* continues this fondness for the metamathematical remark, but now embeds them within and throughout full proofs as such. In the bargain, one often finds that such reflections veer from the proposition and the proof at hand to external mathematical matters.

Adelard II and III have much in common besides their author. Both contain Arabisms; both contain Grecisms; and III quotes II. More important, however, both make use of original Latin material: they employ notions drawn from Boethian arithmetic, use classical expressions, and even (Adelard III) allude to Ovid.

A fourth major constituent of the Adelard tradition is the version of the *Elements* prepared by Campanus of Novara. It too takes over the Adelard II enunciations and, through the formulation of proofs that seem largely independent of Adelard, fashions what is, from the mathematical standpoint, the most adequate Arabic–Latin Euclid of all (its earliest dated extant copy being that of 1259). The *additiones* Campanus made to his basic Euclidean text are particularly notable. With an eye to making the *Elements* as self-contained as possible, he devoted considerable care to the elucidation and discussion of what he felt to be obscure and debatable points. He also attempted to work Euclid more into the current of thirteenth-century mathematics by relating the *Elements* to, and even supplementing it with, material drawn from the *Arithmetica* of Jordanus de Nemore.

Furthermore, Campanus and the three versions of Adelard (especially II and III) served as sources for an amazing multiplication of other versions of the *Elements.* Although the extent to which they diverge from one or another of these sources may not be great or marked with much originality, and although they frequently seem to concentrate on selected books of Euclid, one can still discern among extant manuscripts some fifteen or more additional "editions" belonging to the Adelardian tradition. They range from the thirteenth through the fifteenth centuries and none, as far as a cursory investigation has shown, bears the name of an author or a compiler.

As a whole the Adelardian tradition formed the dominant medieval Euclid. Further, although by far the greatest share of this tradition was not a strict translation from its Arabic source, the divergence from the original Greek thus occasioned caused little difficulty. The few missing propositions were easily remedied, and changes in the order of theorems gave rise to no mathematical qualms at all. Misunderstanding of what Euclid intended also seems to have been quite infrequent, save for the always problematic criterion of Eudoxus for the equality of ratios, which was ensconced in book V, definition 5. Here the most influential medieval interpretation—that of Campanus—curiously seems to have been conditioned by a strange quirk in transmission. For in place of the genuine V, definition 4, Campanus (and all other constituents of the Adelardian tradition) has another, mathematically useless, definition; and in his attempt to make sense of this, Campanus formulated a mechanics of explanation that he in turn extended to his discussion, and consequent misunderstanding, of the "Eudoxean" V, definition 5. Thus, we are witness to a unique instance in which the existence of a spurious fragment within the textual tradition seriously affected interpretation of something genuine.

The most impressive characteristic of the Adelardian–Campanus *Elements* is not, however, to be found in missing or misunderstood fragments of the text, but rather in the frequent additions made to it, additions which often take the form of supplementary propositions or premises but also occur as reflective remarks within the proofs to standard Euclidean theorems. It is not possible to tabulate even a small fraction of these additions, but it is important to realize something of the basis of their concern. To begin with, the motive behind many, indeed most, of them was to render the whole of their Euclid more didactic in tone. The trend toward a "textbook" *Elements,* noted in its Arabic history (and even, in a way, in Theon of Alexandria's new Greek redaction), was being extended. The reflections mentioned above about the structure of proofs are surely part of this increased didacticism. The labeling of the divisions within a proof, express directions as to how to carry out required constructions and how to draw three-dimensional figures, indications of what "sister" propositions can be found elsewhere in the *Elements,* and even clarifying references to notions from astronomy and music are all evidence of the same. We are also witness to the erosion (again pedagogically helpful) of the strict barrier fixed by the Greeks between number and magnitude. For the care not to employ the general propositions of book V in the arithmetical books VII–IX has been pushed out of sight, and one can find admittedly insufficient numerical proofs in propositions (especially in books V and X) dealing with general magnitude.

Of even greater interest is an ever-present preoccupation with premises and with what is fundamental. Axioms are everywhere added (even in the middle of proofs) to cover all possible gaps in the chain of reasoning, and considerable attention is paid to the logic of what is going on. Once again one sees a fit with didactic aims. But this emphasis on basic notions and assumptions was directed not only toward making the geometry of the *Elements* more accessible to those toiling in the medieval faculty of arts; it was also keyed to the bearing of issues within this geometry upon external, largely philosophical problems. Most notable in this regard is the time spent in worrying over the conceptions of incommensurability, of the so-called horn angle (between the circumference of a circle and a tangent to it), and of the divisibility of magnitudes. For these conceptions all relate, at bottom, to the problems of infinity and continuity that so often exercised the wits of medieval philosophers. The Adelardian tradition furnished, as it were, a schoolbook Euclid that admirably fit Scholastic interests both within and beyond the bounds of medieval mathematics.

There is one other medieval Latin version of the *Elements* that is connected, more tenuously to be sure, with the Adelard versions. Its connection derives from its appropriation of most of the Adelard II enunciations, although frequently with substantial change. It exists in anonymous form in a single manuscript (Paris, BN lat. 16646). We know, however, that this codex was willed to the Sorbonne in 1271 by Gérard d'Abbeville and is in all probability identical with a manuscript described in the *Biblionomia* (*ca.* 1246) of Richard de Fournival. Richard, however, identifies the manuscript as "Euclidis geometria, arismetrica et stereometria ex commentario Hermanni secundi." This version is, therefore, presumably the work of Hermann of Carinthia (*fl. ca.* 1140–1150), well-known translator of astronomical and astrological texts from the Arabic. Its proofs differ from those of the Adelardian tradition, and the occurrence of Arabisms not in this tradition has been viewed as evidence for Hermann's use of another Arabic text in compiling his redaction. The recent suggestion that this text was the Isḥāq–Thābit translation seems doubtful, however, for unlike Gerard of Cremona's version, ostensibly based on that Arabic translation, Hermann not only lacks the references to "Thebit" but also does not have the additions in book VIII (see above) characteristic of Isḥāq–Thābit. On the other hand, it is true that Hermann does show variations from the text of Ḥajjāj as we have it; but all of these, it appears, are also in Adelard I, which clearly derives, as we have seen, from some Ḥajjāj text or another. Hermann repeats the differences noted above in discussing Adelard I and with him alone, among all Latin versions, carries the full six separate cases for III, 35. One other piece of evidence might be noted: In a series of propositions (V, 20–23) dealing with proportion, the Greek Euclid specifies only one (V, 22) for "any number of magnitudes whatever," the others being stated merely for three magnitudes. Now all versions save Adelard I and Hermann, including our Ḥajjāj and, to judge from Gerard's translation, Isḥāq–Thābit, adopt the policy of stating all four propositions in general form. Hermann and Adelard I, on the other hand, retain the "three magnitudes" version of the Greek for V, 20–21, 23 but also substitute *tres* for *quotlibet* in V, 22. The filiation of these two is, therefore, quite close. One can conclude, then, that Hermann used at least both Adelard II (from which he derives many enunciations) and presumably the same version of Ḥajjāj used by Adelard I (and possibly also Adelard I itself). Finally, it has been noticed that Hermann contains the Arabicism *aelman geme* (corresponding to *ʿilm jāmiʿ*) to refer to axioms or common notions, while both Ḥajjāj and, to judge from Klamroth, Isḥāq–Thābit employ *al-ʿulūm al-mutaʿārafa.* Yet here Hermann could still be following some Ḥajjāj text, since *ʿilm jāmiʿ* (also used, incidentally, in Avicenna's epitome of Euclid) occurs as a marginal alternative in our manuscript of Ḥajjāj.

Occasional claims have also been made for two other identifiable medieval Latin versions of the *Elements.* One, purported to be by Alfred the Great, has been shown to derive from erroneous marginal ascriptions (in a single manuscript) of the Adelard II version to "Alfredus." The second, a seventeenth-century manuscript catalogue, refers to a version of the *Elements* as "ex Arab. in Lat. versa per Joan. Ocreatum." We do know of passages at the beginning of book V and in book X (props. 9, 23, 24) in certain manuscripts of Adelard II that do appeal to "Ocrea Johannis," but in such a way that this may be but a reference to separate (marginal?) comments on Euclid or to some other mathematical treatise, rather than to a distinct translation or version of the *Elements.*

If, in conclusion, one compares the very substantial amount of material constituting the Arabic–Latin Euclid with the equally extensive history the *Elements* had in Islam, several rather striking differences are apparent, even at the present, extremely preliminary stage of investigation of these two traditions. In both one finds an overwhelming number of versions, editions, and variants of Euclid proper. Although here one has a common trait, there is, on the other hand, no doubt that the number of commentaries composed in Arabic far exceeds those in Latin. Indeed, there seems to be but one "original" commentary proper in Latin, questionably ascribed to the thirteenth-century Dominican philosopher Albertus Magnus and in any event greatly dependent upon earlier translated material (notably the commentary of al-Nayrīzī). When we do find *Questiones super Euclidem,* they treat more of general problems within geometry, mathematics, or natural philosophy than they do of issues specifically tied to particular Euclidean premises or theorems. In point of fact, this bears upon a second element of contrast between the Arabic and Latin traditions—that the latter seems to have moved more rapidly toward serving the interests of philosophy, while the former remained more strictly mathematical in its concerns. One does not find, for example, anything like the Arabic debate about the parallels postulate in the Latin texts. But then Islamic mathematics itself was more lively and creative than that of the medieval Latin West.

The Renaissance and Modern Euclid. Four events seem to have been the most outstanding in determining the course of the *Elements* in the sixteenth and succeeding centuries: (1) the publication of the medieval version of Campanus of Novara, initially as the first printed Euclid at Venice (1482) by Erhard Ratdolt, and at many other places and dates in the ensuing 100 years; (2) a new Latin translation from the Greek by Bartolomeo Zamberti in 1505; (3) the *editio princeps* of the Greek text by Simon Grynaeus at Basel in 1533; (4) another Greek-Latin translation made in 1572 by Federico Commandino. The publications resulting from these four versions show their effect in almost all later translations and versions, be they Latin or vernacular.

Of Campanus we have spoken above. The printed Euclid following his was, ignoring the publication in various forms of the "Boethian" fragments, not the influential one of Zamberti but only portions of the *Elements* included in the gigantic encyclopedia *De expetendis et fugiendis rebus* (Venice, 1501) of Georgius Valla (*d.* 1499). This was not, to be sure, an easily accessible Euclid; for in addition to being an extraordinarily cumbersome book to use, the selections from the *Elements* are scattered among materials translated from other Greek mathematical and scientific texts. The first publication of a Greek-based Latin *Elements* as an integral whole was that at Venice in 1505 prepared by Bartolomeo Zamberti (*b. ca.* 1473). His translation derived from a strictly Theonine Greek text, a factor which has Zamberti attributing the proofs to this Alexandrian redactor (*cum expositione Theonis insignis mathematici*). The work also contains translations of the minor Euclidean works (which were also, in part, in Valla's encyclopedia).

Zamberti was most conscious of the advantages he believed to accrue from his working from a Greek text. This enabled him, he claimed, to add things hitherto missing and properly to arrange and prove again much found in the version of Campanus. Indeed, his animus against his medieval predecessor is far from gentle: his Euclid was, Zamberti complains, replete with "wondrous ghosts, dreams and fantasies" (*miris larvis, somniis et phantasmatibus*). Campanus himself he labels *interpres barbarissimus.*

The attack thus launched by Zamberti was almost immediately answered by new editions of Campanus, the most notable of them being that prepared at Venice in 1509 by the Franciscan Luca Pacioli. Pacioli regarded himself as a corrector (*castigator*) who freed Campanus from the errors of copyists, especially in the matter of incorrectly drawn figures. In direct reply to Zamberti, Campanus was now presented as *interpres fidissimus.*

A kind of détente was subsequently reached between the Campanus and Zamberti camps, for there was soon a series of published *Elements* reproducing the editions of both *in toto,* the first appearing at Paris in 1516. Each theorem and proof first occurs *ex Campano* and is immediately followed by its mate and proof *Theon ex Zamberto.* The *additiones* due to Campanus appear in place but are appropriately set off and indicated as such.

The end of the first third of the sixteenth century brought with it the first publication of the Greek text of the *Elements.* The German theologian Simon Grynaeus (*d.* 1541) accomplished this, working from two manuscripts, with an occasional reference to Zamberti's Latin. His edition, which included the text of Proclus' *Commentary* as well, was the only complete one of the Greek before the eighteenth century. The other Greek Euclids of the Renaissance were all partial, most frequently offering only the enunciations of the propositions in Greek (usually with accompanying translation). The most significant of such "piecemeal" *Elements* is unquestionably that of the Swiss mathematician and clockmaker Conrad Dasypodius, or Rauchfuss (1532–1600). Dasypodius makes it abundantly clear that his edition, issued in three parts at Strasbourg in 1564, was intended as a school-text Euclid. For this reason he believed it more convenient to give merely the enunciations of books III–XIII to accompany the full text of books I–II, all in Greek with Latin translation. The pedagogical design of his publication is also seen from the fact that in spite of his exclusion of a great deal of genuine Euclid, he nevertheless saw fit to include the text of the more readily comprehensible arithmetical version of book II that was composed by the

Basilian monk Barlaam (*d. ca.* 1350).

In any event, the printing of the complete Greek text in 1533, plus the earlier appearance of both Campanus and Zamberti, provided the raw material, as it were, for the first, pre-Commandino, phase of the Renaissance Euclid. The irony is that Campanus and Zamberti, and not the Greek *editio princeps*, played the dominant role. Some note of the most significant of the many early Renaissance printed editions of the *Elements* will make this clear. (The substantial, but totally uninvestigated, manuscript material of this period is here excluded from consideration.)

If one focuses, to begin with, upon Latin Euclids, the first important "new" version (Paris, 1536) is that of the French mathematician Oronce Fine (1494–1555). Yet his contribution seems to have been to insert the Greek text of the enunciations for the *libri sex priores* in the appropriate places in Zamberti's Latin translation of the whole of these books. Similarly, his compatriot Jacques Peletier du Mans brought out another six-book Latin version (Lyons, 1557), this time based, as Commandino noted, more on Campanus' Arabic–Latin edition than upon anything Greek. (It should be recorded, however, that Peletier supplemented what he took from Campanus' *additiones* with some interesting ones of his own.) At Paris in 1566 yet a third French scholar, Franciscus Flussatus Candalla (François de Foix, Comte de Candale, 1502–1594) produced a Latin *Elements*. Covering all fifteen books, and appending three more on the inscription and circumscription of solids, the appeal is once again not to the Greek text as such, but to Zamberti and Campanus. And when there is something not derived from these two, it seems as often as not to have been Candalla's own invention.

A contemporary summary view of the status of Euclid scholarship was revealed when, a few years before Candalla's expanded *Elements*, Johannes Buteo published his *De quadratura circuli* at Lyons in 1559. This work contained as an appendix Buteo's *Annotationum opuscula in errores Campani, Zamberti, Orontii, Peletarii . . . interpretum Euclidis*. Campanus was, he felt, the best of these editors, for his errors derive from his Arabic source and not from an ineptitude in mathematics. Zamberti, on the other hand, although he worked directly from the Greek, showed less acumen in geometry. Even less adequate, in Buteo's judgment, were the works of Fine and Peletier, the latter taking the greatest liberties with the text and ineptly adding or omitting as he saw fit.

We have thus far spoken merely of sixteenth-century Latin translations, but the same pattern reflecting the central impact of Campanus and Zamberti can also be discerned in the most notable vernacular renderings. The earliest of these to be printed was the Italian translation by the mathematician, mechanician, and natural philosopher Niccolò Tartaglia. Its first edition appeared at Venice in 1543. When Tartaglia submits that his redaction was made *secondo le due tradittioni*, there is no question that Campanus—who appears to be heavily favored—and Zamberti are meant. When Campanus has added propositions or premises, Tartaglia has appropriately translated them and noted their absence *nella seconda tradittione*, while things omitted by Campanus but included by Zamberti receive the reverse treatment.

The next languages to receive the privilege of displaying Euclid among their goods were French (by Pierre Forcadel at Paris in 1564) and German (at the hands of Johann Scheubel and Wilhelm Holtzmann in 1558 and 1562). We are better informed, however, of the circumstances surrounding the production of the more elaborate, first complete English edition. Yet before we describe this, it will be well to note an even earlier intrusion of Euclidean materials into English. This is found in *The Pathway to Knowledg* (London, 1551) of the Tudor mathematical practitioner Robert Recorde. Recorde fully recognized the ground he was breaking, for in anticipation of the dismay even Euclid's opening definitions would likely cause in the "simple ignorant" who were to be his readers, he cautioned: "For nother is there anie matter more straunge in the englishe tungue, then this whereof never booke was written before now, in that tungue." Recorde's purpose was distinctly practical, and he expressly mentioned the significance of geometry for surveying, land measure, and building. The *Pathway* contains the enunciations of books I–IV of Euclid, reworked and reordered to serve his practical aims.

The first proper English translation was the work of Sir Henry Billingsley, later lord mayor of London (*d.* 1606), and appeared at London in 1570 with a preface by John Dee, patron and sometime practitioner of the mathematical arts. A truly monumental folio volume, Billingsley's translation contains "manifolde additions, Scholies, Annotations and Inventions . . . gathered out of the most famous and chiefe Mathematiciens, both of old time and in our age" and even includes pasted flaps of paper that can be folded up to produce three-dimensional models for the propositions of book XI. Each book begins with a summary statement that includes considerable commentary and often an assessment of the views of Billingsley's predecessors, most notably those of Campanus and Zamberti. The role these two scholars played in Billingsley's labors is confirmed in yet another way. There exists in the Princeton University

Library a copy of the 1533 *editio princeps* of the Greek text of the *Elements* bound together with a 1558 Basel "combined" edition of Campanus and Zamberti. It is not known how these volumes came into Princeton's possession, but both contain manuscript notes in Billingsley's hand. The fact that these notes are found on only five pages of the Greek text, but on well over 200 of both Campanus and Zamberti, is clearly suggestive of Billingsley's major source. Once again, the two basic Latin versions, one medieval and one Renaissance, have exhibited the considerable extent of their influence.

However, the better part of this influence was interrupted suddenly and decisively by the fourth major version listed above: the publication at Pesaro in 1572 of the Latin translation by Federico Commandino of Urbino. Commandino—who, in addition to the place he holds in the history of physics deriving from his *Liber de centro gravitatis* (Bologna, 1565), prepared exacting Latin versions of many other Greek mathematical works—was clearly the most competent mathematician of all Renaissance editors of Euclid. He was also most astute in his scholarship, for we know that in addition to the 1533 *editio princeps,* he employed at least one other Greek manuscript in establishing the text for his translation. For the first time, save for the anonymous translation in the twelfth century, we now have a version (no matter what language) of the *Elements* that is solidly based on a tolerably critical Greek original. It even includes, also for the first time, a rendering of numerous Greek scholia. Aware, but critical, of the efforts of his predecessors, Commandino leaves no doubt of the advantage of staying closer to the Greek sources so many of them had minimized, if not ignored. The result of his labors may prove to be of less fascination than other versions, since it so closely follows the Greek we already know, but the importance it held for the subsequent modern history of the *Elements* is immeasurable. It came to serve, in sum, as the base of almost all other proper translations before Peyrard's discovery of the "pristine" Euclid in the early nineteenth century. Thus, to cite only the most notable cases in point, Greek texts of the *Elements* with accompanying Latin translation frequently based the latter on Commandino: for example, Henry Briggs's *Elementorum Euclidis libri VI priores* (London, 1620) and even David Gregory's 1703 Oxford edition of Euclid's *Opera omnia* (which was the standard, pre-nineteenth-century source for the Greek text). Commandino was also followed in later strictly Latin versions: that of Robert Simson, simultaneously issued in English at Glasgow in 1756; and even that of Samuel Horsley, appearing at London in 1802. Vernacular translations often followed a similar course, beginning with the Italian translation, revised by Commandino himself, appearing at Urbino in 1575 and extending to and beyond the English version by John Keill, Savilian professor of astronomy at Oxford, in 1708.

In all translations based heavily on Commandino, one naturally remained close to the (Theonine) Greek tradition; but there were also other efforts after, as well as before, Commandino that did not stay so nearly on course. These were the numerous commentaries on Euclid, the various schoolbook *Elements,* and, in a class by itself, the edition of Christopher Calvius.

The commentaries of the sixteenth through eighteenth centuries were almost always limited to specific books or parts of the *Elements.* We have already noted the 1559 *Annotationum opuscula* of Buteo, but a considerable amount of related commentarial literature began to flourish around the same time. Giovanni Battista Benedetti (1530–1590) brought out his *Resolutio omnium Euclidis problematum . . . una tantummodo circini data apertura* at Venice in 1553 in response to a controversy that had recently arisen out of some reflection by several Italian scholars on Euclid. Petrus Ramus, who had previously produced a Latin version of the *Elements* in 1545, published at Frankfurt in 1559 his *Scholae mathematicae,* in which he scrutinized the structure of Euclid from the standpoint of logic. Along related lines, mention might be made of the curious *Euclideae demonstrationes in syllogismos resolutae* (Strasbourg, 1564) of Conrad Dasypodius and Christianus Herlinus. Such works as these were in a way extensions, perhaps fanciful ones, of the medieval Scholastic concern with the logic of the *Elements.* Yet another development can be seen in the various attempts to reduce the *Elements* to practice. We have already noticed this standpoint in Robert Recorde, and to this one could add the first German translation of books I–VI —published by Wilhelm Holtzmann (Xylander) in 1562—which was written with the likes of painters, goldsmiths, and builders in mind; and the Italian version (1613–1625) of Antonio Cataldi, which expressly declared itself to be an *Elementi ridotti alla practica.*

On a more specific plane, commentaries on book V, and particularly upon the Eudoxean definition of equal ratios that we have already seen to be problematic, continued in the sixteenth and seventeenth centuries. Beginning with the almost totally unknown works of Giambattista Politi, *Super definitiones et propositiones quae supponuntur ab Euclide in quinto Elementorum eius* (Siena, 1529), and of Elia Vineto Santone, *Definitiones elementi quincti et sexti Euclidis*

(Bordeaux, 1575), the issue was also broached by Galileo in the added "Fifth Day" of his *Discorsi . . . a due nuove scienze* (an addendum first published at Florence in 1674 in Vincenzo Viviani's *Quinto libro degli Elementi d'Euclide*). Finally, note should be made of two of the most impressive early modern commentaries on selected aspects of Euclid. The first is Henry Savile's lectures *Praelectiones tresdecim in principium Elementorum Euclidis Oxoniae habitae MDCXX* (Oxford, 1621), which cover only the premises and first eight propositions of book I but do so in an extraordinarily penetrating, and still valuable, way. The last work to be mentioned is so famous that one often forgets that it formed part of the commentarial literature on the *Elements*—the *Euclides ab omni naevo vindicatus* (Milan, 1733) of Girolamo Saccheri, in which this Jesuit mathematician and logician fashioned the attempt to prove Euclid's parallels postulate that has won him so prominent a place in the histories of non-Euclidean geometry.

Closely connected with the commentarial literature we have sampled is the magisterial Latin version of the *Elements* composed by another, much earlier Jesuit scholar, Christopher Clavius (1537–1612). The first edition of his *Euclidis Elementorum libri XV* appeared at Rome in 1574. Not, properly speaking, a translation, as Clavius himself admitted, but a personal redaction compiled from such earlier authors as Campanus, Zamberti, and Commandino, the work is chiefly notable, to say nothing of immensely valuable, for the great amount of auxiliary material it contains. Separate *praxeis* are specified for the constructions involved in the problems, long *excursus* appear on such debatable issues as the horn angle, and virtually self-contained treatises on such topics as composite ratios, mean proportionals, the species of proportionality not treated in Euclid, and the quadratrix are inserted at appropriate places. Indeed, by Clavius' own count, to the 486 propositions he calculated in his Greek-based Euclid, he admits to adding 671 others of his own; "in universum ergo 1234 propositiones in nostro Euclide demonstrantur," he concludes. And the value of what he has compiled matches, especially for the historian, its mass.

The final segment of the modern history of Euclid that requires description is what might most appropriately be called the handbook tradition, both Latin and vernacular, of the *Elements*. Many of the briefer Renaissance versions already mentioned are properly part of this tradition, and if one sets no limit on size, editions like that of Clavius would also qualify. In point of fact, the undercurrent of didacticism we have seen to be present in the medieval Arabic and Latin versions of the *Elements* can justly be regarded as the beginning of this handbook, or school text, tradition.

In the seventeenth century, however, the tradition takes on a more definite form. Numerous examples could be cited from this period, but all of them show the tendency to shorten proofs, to leave out propositions—and even whole books—of little use, and to introduce symbols wherever feasible to facilitate comprehension. This did not mean, to be sure, the disappearance of the sorts of supplementary material characteristic of so many translations and redactions of the *Elements*. On the contrary, such material was often rearranged and retained, and even created anew, when it seemed to be fruitful from the instructional point of view. For instance, one of the most popular (some twenty editions through the first few years of the nineteenth century) handbooks, the *Elementa geometriae planae et solidae* (Antwerp, 1654) of André Tacquet (1612–1660), covers books I–VI and XI–XII, with added material from Archimedes. Its proofs are compendious, but it makes up for its gain in this regard through the addition of a substantial number of pedagogically useful corollaries and scholia. On the other hand, the *Euclidis Elementorum libri XV breviter demonstrati* (Cambridge, 1655) of Isaac Barrow (1630–1677) stubbornly holds to its status as an epitome. Producer of perhaps the shortest handbook of all of books I–XV, Barrow achieved this maximum of condensation by appropriating the symbolism of William Oughtred (1574–1660) that the latter employed in a *declaratio* of book X of Euclid in his *Clavis mathematicae* (Oxford, 1648 ff.). In his preface, Barrow claimed that his goal was "to conjoin the greatest Compendiousness of Demonstration with as much perspicuity as the quality of the subject would admit." Although his success struck some (for example, John Keill) as producing a somewhat obscure compendium, this did not prevent the appearance of numerous (some ten) editions, several of them in English. Vernacular handbooks appeared in other languages as well, perhaps the most notable being *Les Elémens d'Euclide* (Lyons, 1672) of the French Jesuit Claude-François Milliet de Chales (1621–1678). Appearing earlier in Latin (Lyons, 1660), this handbook, covering, like Tacquet's, books I–VI and XI–XII, went through some twenty-four subsequent editions, including translations into English and Italian.

The next stage in the handbook tradition belongs to the nineteenth century, where there occurred a veritable avalanche of Euclid primers, frequently radically divergent from any imaginable text of the *Elements*. Quite separate from these attempts to make Euclid proper for the grammar schools, lycées, and Gymnasia of the 1800's, the rise of classical philology carried with it the efforts to establish a sound and critical text of the *Elements.* These efforts, in turn, gave rise to the annotated translations of the present century, with an audience primarily the historian and the classicist, rather than the mathematician.

Only a paltry few of the almost innumerable versions of the *Elements* dating from the Renaissance to the present have even been mentioned above—most are merely listed in bibliographies and remain totally unexamined. Even the few titles of this period that have been cited have received little more than fleeting attention—often limited to their prefaces—from historians. Further study will, one feels certain, reveal much more of the significance this mass of Euclidean material holds for the history of mathematics and science as a whole.

BIBLIOGRAPHY

Abbreviations of frequently cited works:

Clagett, *Medieval Euclid* = Marshall Clagett, "The Medieval Latin Translations From the Arabic of the *Elements* of Euclid, With Special Emphasis on the Versions of Adelard of Bath," in *Isis,* **44** (1953), 16–42.

Curtze, *Supplementum* = *Anaritii in decem libros priores Elementorum Euclidis ex interpretatione Gherardi Cremonensis,* Maximilian Curtze, ed. (Leipzig, 1899), supplement to *Euclidis Opera omnia,* Heiberg and Menge, eds.

Heath, *Euclid* = Thomas L. Heath, *The Thirteen Books of Euclid's Elements Translated From the Text of Heiberg With Introduction and Commentary,* 3 vols. (2nd ed., Cambridge, 1925; repr. New York, 1956).

Heiberg, *Euclides* = *Euclidis Opera omnia,* J. L. Heiberg and H. Menge, eds., 8 vols. (Leipzig, 1883–1916).

Heiberg, *Litt. Stud.* = J. L. Heiberg, *Litterärgeschichtliche Studien über Euklid* (Leipzig, 1882).

Heiberg, *Paralipomena* = J. L. Heiberg, "Paralipomena zu Euklid," in *Hermes,* **38** (1903), 46–74, 161–201, 321–356.

Klamroth, *Arab. Euklid* = Martin Klamroth, "Ueber den arabischen Euklid," in *Zeitschrift der Deutschen morgenländischen Gesellschaft,* **35** (1881), 270–326, 788.

Sabra, *Simplicius* = A. I. Sabra, "Simplicius's Proof of Euclid's Parallels Postulate," in *Journal of the Warburg and Courtauld Institutes,* **32** (1969), 1–24.

Sabra, *Thābit* = A. I. Sabra, "Thābit ibn Qurra on Euclid's Parallels Postulate," in *Journal of the Warburg and Courtauld Institutes,* **31** (1968), 12–32.

General Euclidean Bibliographies

The most complete bibliography of Euclid is still that of Pietro Riccardi, *Saggio di una bibliografia Euclidea,* in 5 pts., (Bologna, 1887–1893); this work also appeared in the *Memorie della Reale Accademia delle Scienze dell' Istituto di Bologna,* 4th ser., **8** (1887), 401–523; **9** (1888), 321–343; 5th ser., **1** (1890), 27–84; **3** (1892), 639–694. More complete bibliographic information on pre-1600 eds. of the *Elements,* and works dealing with Euclid, can be found in Charles Thomas-Sanford, *Early Editions of Euclid's Elements* (London, 1926). Other bibliographies are listed in the bibliography to pt. I of the present article.

The Elements in Greek Antiquity

1. *Establishment of the "pristine" Greek text.* A history of the text in capsule form was first given in Heiberg, *Litt. Stud.,* pp. 176–186. Heiberg, *Euclides,* V (Leipzig, 1888), xxiii–lxxvi gives a more complete analysis of the Theonine and pre-Theonine texts, together with an outline of the criteria and methods used in establishing the latter. Further material relevant to the textual problem is found in Heiberg, *Paralipomena,* pp. 47–53, 59–74, 161–201. Heath, *Euclid,* I, 46–63, gives a summary of all of the Heiberg material above.

2. *Greek commentaries.* The ed. of the Greek text of Proclus by G. Friedlein is noted in pt. I of the present article, together with several trans. To this one should now add the English trans. of Glenn Morrow (Princeton, 1970). Of the literature on Proclus, the most useful to cite is J. G. van Pesch, *De Procli fontibus* (Leiden, 1900). For the commentary of Pappus, extant only in Arabic, see the following section. Heath, *Euclid,* I, 19–45, gives a convenient summary of Greek commentarial literature. To this one should add Sabra, *Simplicius,* for material on this commentary, extant only in Arabic fragments (and Latin trans. thereof). Finally, Heiberg has treated the commentaries as well as the citations of Euclid in all other later Greek authors (notably commentators on Aristotle); this material is assembled in Heiberg, *Litt. Stud.,* pp. 154–175, 186–224; and *Paralipomena,* pp. 352–354.

3. *Greek scholia.* Most of these are published in Heiberg, *Euclides,* V (Leipzig, 1888), 71–738, supplemented by Heiberg, *Paralipomena,* pp. 321–352. Scholia to the minor Euclidean works are published in vols. VI–VIII of Heiberg, *Euclides.* The most complete discussion of the scholia is J. L. Heiberg, "Om Scholierne til Euklids Elementer" (with a French résumé), in *Kongelige Danske Videnskabernes Selskabs Skrifter,* Hist.-philosofisk afdeling II, **3** (1888), 227–304. Once again there is a summary of this Danish article in Heath, *Euclid,* I, 64–74.

The Medieval Arabic Euclid

1. *General works.* Serious study of the Arabic Euclid began with J. C. Gartz, *De interpretibus et explanatoribus Euclidis arabicis schediasma historicum* (Halle, 1823) and was continued in J. G. Wenrich, *De auctorum graecorum versionibus et commentariis syriacis, arabicis, armeniacis persicisque commentatio* (Leipzig, 1842), pp. 176–189. The problem of the reports of Euclid in Arabic literature was broached in Heiberg, *Litt. Stud.,* pp. 1–21; but the major step was taken in Klamroth, *Arab. Euklid.* Klamroth's contentions concerning the superiority of the Arabic tradition were answered by Heiberg in "Die arabische Tradition

der Elemente Euklid's," in *Zeitschrift für Mathematik und Physik*, Hist.-lit. Abt., **29** (1884), 1-22. This was followed by the summary article, which included material on Arabic commentators, of Moritz Steinschneider, "Euklid bei den Arabern: Eine bibliographische Studie," in *Zeitschrift für Mathematik und Physik*, Hist.-lit. Abt., **31** (1886), 81-110. Cf. Steinschneider's *Die arabischen Uebersetzungen aus dem Griechischen* (Graz, 1960), pp. 156-164 (originally published in *Centralblatt für Bibliothekswesen*, supp. **5**, 1889). See also the article by A. G. Kapp in section 6 below. A summary view of our knowledge (as of the beginning of the present century) of the *Elements* in Islam can be found in Heath, *Euclid*, I, 75-90. M. Klamroth has also published a translation of some of the summaries of Greek works by the ninth-century historian al-Yaʿqūbī which includes a résumé of the *Elements*: "Ueber die Auszüge aus griechischen Schriftstellern bei al-Jaʿqūbī," in *Zeitschrift der Deutschen morgenländischen Gesellschaft*, **42** (1888), 3-9. The standard bibliography of Arabic mathematics and mathematicians is Heinrich Suter, *Die Mathematiker und Astronomen der Araber und ihre Werke*, *Abhandlungen zur Geschichte der mathematischen Wissenschaften*, X (Leipzig, 1900), with *Nachträge und Berichtigungen*, *op. cit.*, XIV (Leipzig, 1902), 155-185. The most recent history of Islamic mathematics, with appended bibliography, is contained in A. P. Juschkewitsch [Youschkevitch], *Geschichte der Mathematik im Mittelalter* (Basel, 1964; original Russian ed., Moscow, 1961).

2. *The translation of al-Ḥajjāj.* We know of but a single MS containing (presumably) the second Ḥajjāj version together with Nayrīzī's commentary for books I-VI (and a few lines of VII) alone: Leiden, 399, 1. This has been ed. with a modern Latin trans. by J. L. Heiberg, R. O. Besthorn, *et al.*, *Codex Leidensis 399, 1: Euclidis Elementa ex interpretatione al-Hadschdschadschii cum commentariis al-Narizii*, in 3 pts. (Copenhagen, 1893-1932). Confirmation is needed of the report of two further MSS containing a Ḥajjāj version of books XI-XII: MSS Copenhagen LXXXI and Istanbul, Fātih 3439. There is no secondary literature specifically devoted to the Ḥajjāj *Elements*, but information is contained in Klamroth, *Arab. Euklid.*

3. *The translation of Isḥāq-Thābit.* The most frequently cited MS of this version is Oxford, Bodleian Libr., MS Thurston 11 (279 in Nicoll's catalogue), dated 1238. This was one of the two basic codices employed in Klamroth, *Arab. Euklid.* The literature also makes continual reference to MS Bodl. Or. 448 (280 in Nicoll) as an Isḥāq-Thābit text; it is not this, but rather a copy of al-Maghribī's *Taḥrīr* (the error derives from a marginal misascription to Thābit that was reported by Nicoll in his catalogue). There are, however, a number of other extant copies of Isḥāq-Thābit. Intention to edit the Isḥāq-Thābit trans. was announced (but apparently abandoned) by Claire Baudoux, "Une édition polyglotte orientale des Eléments d'Euclide: La version arabe d'Ishâq et ses derivées," in *Archeion*, **19** (1937), 70-71. Of the literature on the reviser of this trans., Thābit ibn Qurra, see Eilhard Wiedemann, "Ueber Thābit, sein Leben und Wirken," in *Sitzungsberichte der physikalisch-medizinischen Sozietät zu Erlangen*, **52** (1922), 189-219; A. Sayili, "Thābit ibn Qurra's Generalization of the Pythagorean Theorem," in *Isis*, **51** (1960), 35-37; and section 7 below. An integral ed. and Russian trans. of Thābit's mathematical works is in preparation.

4. *The epitomes of Avicenna and others.* A. I. Sabra has edited Avicenna's compendium of the *Elements*, and it will appear in the Cairo ed. of Avicenna's *Kitāb al-Shifāʾ*. A brief description of this compendium was published by Karl Lokotsch, *Avicenna als Mathematiker, besonders die planimetrischen Bücher seiner Euklidübersetzung* (Erfurt, 1912). A copy of a poem praising Euclid, ascribed to Avicenna in a MS found in the Topkapi Museum at Istanbul, is the subject of A. S. Unver, "Avicenna's Praise of Euclid," in *Journal of the History of Medicine*, **2** (1947), 198-200 (other occurrences of the poem, however, disagree with this ascription). The only other Euclid compendium treated in the literature is that of al-Asfuzārī, in L. A. Sédillot, "Notice de plusieurs opuscules mathématiques: V. Quatorzième livre de l'épitome de l'Imam Muzhaffar-al-Isferledi sur les Elements d'Euclide," in *Notices et extraits des manuscrits de la Bibliothèque du Roi*, **13** (1838), 146-148.

5. *The Taḥrīr of al-Ṭūsī, pseudo-Ṭūsī, and al-Maghribī.* The genuine, fifteen-book *Taḥrīr* of al-Ṭūsī exists in an overwhelming number of MSS and has also been frequently printed (Istanbul, 1801; Calcutta, 1824; Lucknow, 1873-1874; Delhi, 1873-1874; Tehran, 1881). Indication of the spurious nature of the thirteen-book *Taḥrīr* usually ascribed to al-Ṭūsī is established by Sabra, *Thābit*, n. 11, and *Simplicius*, postscript, p. 18; doubt is also raised in B. A. Rozenfeld, A. K. Kubesov, and G. S. Sobirov, "Kto by avtorom rimskogo izdania 'Izlozhenia Evklida Nasir ad-Dina at-Tusi'" ("Who Was the Author of the Rome Edition 'Recension of Euclid by Naṣīr al-Dīn al-Ṭūsī'?"), in *Voprosy istorii estestvoznaniya i tekhniki*, **20** (1966), 51-53. The spurious *Taḥrīr* was printed at Rome in 1594, and we know of only two extant MSS: Bibl. Laur. Or. 2. and Or. 51; the latter carries the 1298 date, causing, among other factors, the problems with al-Ṭūsī's authorship. Almost all of the literature dealing with al-Ṭūsī and Euclid treats of the spurious *Taḥrīr*: H. Suter, "Einiges von Nasīr el-Dīn's Euklid-Ausgabe," in *Bibliotheca mathematica*, 2nd ser., **6** (1892), 3-6; E. Wiedemann, "Zu der Redaktion von Euklids Elementen durch *Naṣīr al Din al Ṭūsī*," in *Sitzungsberichte der physikalisch-medizinischen Sozietät zu Erlangen*, **58/59** (1926/1927), 228-236; C. Thaer, "Die Euklid-Überlieferung durch al-Ṭūsī," in *Quellen und Studien zur Geschichte der Mathematik, Astronomie und Physik*, Abt. B, Studien, **3** (1936), 116-121. More general works on al-Ṭūsī as a mathematician include an ed. of the Arabic text of the *Rasāʾil al-Ṭūsī*, 2 vols. (Hyderabad, 1939-1940); E. Wiedemann, "Naṣīr al Din al Ṭūsī," in *Sitzungsberichte der physikalisch-medizinischen Sozietät zu Erlangen*, **60** (1928), 289-316; and B. A. Rozenfeld, "O matematicheskikh rabotakh Nasireddina Ṭūsī" ("On the Mathematical Works of Naṣīr al-Dīn al-Ṭūsī"), in *Istoriko-matematicheskie issledovaniya*, **4** (1951), 489-512. See also section 7 below. The *Taḥrīr* of al-Maghribī is found in the thirteenth-century MS Bodl. Or. 448,

as well as two later codices in Istanbul. It is identified and discussed, together with the ed. and trans. of a fragment from it in Sabra, *Simplicius,* pp. 13-18, 21-24.

6. *Commentaries. The Arabic translation of the commentary of Pappus on book X.* Extracts of the Arabic text, together with a French trans., were first published by Franz Woepcke in "Essai d'une restitution de travaux perdus d'Apollonius sur les quantités irrationnelles," in *Mémoires présentés par divers savants à l'Académie des sciences,* **14** (1856), 658-720 (also published separately). Woepcke also published the full text of the commentary without date or place of publication (Paris, 1855[?]). This was in turn trans. into German with comments by H. Suter, "Der Kommentar des Pappus zum X Buche des Euklides aus der arabischen Übersetzung des Abū ʿOthmān al-Dimashḳī ins Deutsche übertragen," in *Abhandlungen zur Geschichte der Naturwissenschaften und der Medizin,* **4** (1922), 9-78. A new ed. of the Arabic text with notes and English trans. was published by William Thomson and Gustav Junge, *The Commentary of Pappus on Book X of Euclid's Elements* (Cambridge, Mass., 1930). Critical remarks on this text were published by G. Bergstrasser, "Pappos Kommentar zum Zehnten Buch von Euklid's Elementen," in *Der Islam,* **21** (1933), 195-222. A fragment of Gerard of Cremona's trans. of this Pappus text is printed in G. Junge, "Das Fragment der lateinischen Übersetzung des Pappus-Kommentars zum 10. Buche Euklids," in *Quellen und Studien zur Geschichte der Mathematik, Astronomie und Physik,* Abt. B, **3,** Studien (1936), 1-17.

Arabic commentaries. Very few of the great number of these have been published or studied. A list, quite complete in terms of present knowledge, giving brief indications of author, subject, and relevant bibliography, can be found in E. B. Plooij, *Euclid's Conception of Ratio and his Definition of Proportional Magnitudes as Criticized by Arabian Commentators* (Rotterdam, n.d.), pp. 3-13. More elaborate is A. G. Kapp, "Arabische Übersetzer und Kommentatoren Euklids, sowie deren math.-naturwiss. Werke auf Grund des Ta'rīkh al-Ḥukamā' des Ibn al-Qifṭī," in *Isis,* **22** (1934), 150-172; **23** (1935), 54-99; **24** (1935), 37-79; as the title indicates, this extensive article contains much material trans. from the biobibliographical work of Qifṭī (*ca.* 1172-1248). Arabic commentaries on book X are treated in G. P. Matvievskaya, *Uchenie o chisle na srednevekovom blizhnem i srednem vostoke* ("Studies on Number in the Medieval Near and Middle East"; Tashkent, 1967), pp. 191-229; The following commentaries (listed in approximate chronological order) have been ed. or trans. (if only partially) and analyzed: (1) al-Nayrīzī: books I-VI in Arabic in the Heiberg-Besthorn ed. of Ḥajjāj cited in section 2 above; books I-X (incomplete[?]) in the Latin trans. of Gerard of Cremona in Curtze, *Supplementum,* pp. 1-252 only (the remainder of this volume containing the commentary not of al-Nayrīzī, but of ʿAbd al-Baqi; see below). Determination through examination of al-Nayrīzī of various interpolations in the text of the *Elements* was done in Heiberg, *Paralipomena,* pp. 54-59. (2) Al-Fārābī on books I and V has been trans. into Russian on the basis of its two Hebrew copies (MSS Munich 36 and 290, not edited): M. F. Bokshteyn and B. A. Rozenfeld, "Kommentarii Abu Nasra al-Farabi k trudnostyam vo vvedeniakh k pervoy i pyatoy knigam Evklida" ("The Commentary of Abū Naṣr al-Fārābī on the Difficulties in the Introduction to Books I and V of Euclid"), in *Akademiya nauk SSR, Problemy vostokovedeniya,* no. 4 (1959), 93-104. The Arabic text of this brief work of al-Fārābī has now also apparently been discovered: Escorial MS Arab. 612, 109r-111v. A fragment of this, or of another Euclidean opusculum by al-Fārābī, is Tehran, Faculty of Theology, MS 123-D, 80v-82r. See also A. Kubesov and B. A. Rozenfeld, "On the Geometrical Treatise of al-Fārābī," in *Archives internationales d'histoire des sciences,* **22** (1969), 50. (3) Ibn al-Haytham, *On the Premises of Euclid,* has also received a (partial) Russian trans. by B. A. Rozenfeld as "Kniga kommentariev k vvedeniam knigi Evklida 'Nachala'" ("Book of Commentaries to Introductions to Euclid's *Elements*"), in *Istoriko-matematicheskie issledovaniya,* **11** (1958), 743-762. (4) Ibn Muʿādh al-Jayyānī on book V has been reproduced in facsimile with accompanying English trans. in the book of E. B. Plooij cited above. This book also contains a trans. of passages relevant to book V from the commentaries of al-Māhānī, al-Nayrīzī, Ibn al-Haytham, and Omar Khayyām. (5) Omar Khayyām's work on Euclid has received the most attention of all. A. I. Sabra has published a critical Arabic text (without trans.) as *Explanation of the Difficulties in Euclid's Postulates* (Alexandria, 1961). There is an earlier ed., on the basis of a single MS, by T. Erani (Tehran, 1936). A Russian trans., with commentary, has been published by B. A. Rozenfeld and A. P. Youschkevitch in *Istoriko-matematicheskie issledovaniya,* **6** (1953), 67-107, 143-168; repr. with a MS facsimile in Omar Khayyām, *Traktaty* (Moscow, 1961). The English trans. by Amir-Móez in *Scripta mathematica,* **24** (1959), 272-303, must be used with great care. (6) ʿAbd al-Bāqī's commentary on book X in Gerard of Cremona's Latin trans. is printed in Curtze, *Supplementum,* pp. 252-386. H. Suter has given corrections to Curtze's text in "Ueber den Kommentar des Muḥ b. ʿAbdelbāqi zum 10 Buche des Euklides," in *Bibliotheca mathematica,* 3rd ser., **7** (1907), 234-251. See the following section for literature on yet other commentarial material.

7. *On the parallels postulate.* The importance of this postulate in the history of mathematics is reflected not merely in the frequency of its discussion by Islamic authors, but also by the attention it has received from modern historians. As an introduction, see B. A. Rozenfeld and A. P. Youschkevitch, *The Prehistory of Non-Euclidean Geometry in the Middle East, XXV International Congress of Orientalists, Papers Presented by the USSR Delegation* (Moscow, 1960). Compare B. A. Rozenfeld, "The Theory of Parallel Lines in the Medieval East," in *Actes du XIe Congrès International d'Histoire des Sciences, Varsovie-Cracovie 1965,* **3** (Warsaw, etc., 1968), 175-178. More specifically, two treatments of Thābit ibn Qurra are trans. and analyzed in Sabra, *Thābit.* The problem is also the subject of Sabra, *Simplicius.* In fact, these two articles contain a mine of information pertinent to the issue throughout Islamic mathematics. The two Thābit treatises have also been

analyzed and trans. into Russian by B. A. Rozenfeld and A. P. Youschkevitch in *Istoriko-matematicheskie issledovaniya*, **14** (1961), 587–597; and **15** (1963), 363–380. Extracts from the treatments of the postulate by al-Jawharī, Qayṣar ibn Abi 'l-Qāsim, and al-Maghribī are found in the two Sabra articles. The greatest amount of attention has been paid to al-Ṭūsī's struggles with the problem, beginning with a trans. into Latin by Edward Pocock of the proof of the postulate in the pseudo-Ṭūsī *Taḥrīr;* this was printed in John Wallis, *Opera mathematica*, II (Oxford, 1693), 669–673. Both this proof and that in the genuine fifteen-book al-Ṭūsī *Taḥrīr* were published and analyzed in Arabic by A. I. Sabra, "Burhān Naṣīr al-Dīn al-Ṭūsī ʿalā muṣādarat Uqlīdis al-khāmisa," in *Bulletin of the Faculty of Arts of the University of Alexandria*, **13** (1959), 133–170. Russian treatment again occurs in G. D. Mamedbeili, *Mukhammad Nasureddin Tusi o teorii parallelnykh liny i teorii otnosheny* ("Muḥammad Naṣīr al-Dīn al-Ṭūsī on the Theory of Parallel Lines and the Theory of Proportion"; Baku, 1959), and in *Istoriko-mathematicheskie issledovaniya*, **13** (1960), 475–532. Finally, the article of H. Dilgan, "Demonstration du Ve postulat d'Euclide par Schams-ed-Din Samarkandi, Traduction de l'ouvrage Aschkal-ut-tessis de Samarkandi," in *Revue d'histoire des sciences*, **13** (1960), 191–196, does not contain a proof by Samarqandī, but rather one by Athīr al-Dīn al-Abharī that was reproduced in a commentary to Samarqandī's work.

8. *Translations into other Near Eastern languages.* The most adequate account of Hebrew versions and commentaries is in Moritz Steinschneider, *Die hebräischen Übersetzungen des Mittelalters und die Juden als Dolmetscher* (Berlin, 1893; repr. Graz, 1956), 503–513. The fragments of the Syriac version were published and trans. by G. Furlani, "Bruchstücke eine syrischen Paraphrase der 'Elemente' des Eukleides," in *Zeitschrift für Semitistik und verwandte Gebiete*, **3** (1924), 27–52, 212–235. Furlani held that the paraphrase was derived from the Arabic of Ḥajjāj. This was questioned, and the opposing view placing it before, and as a source of, the Isḥāq trans., by C. Baudoux, "La version syriaque des 'Eléments' d'Euclide," in *IIe Congrès national des sciences* (Brussels, 1935), pp. 73–75. The fragments of the early Armenian version were published and trans. (into Latin) by Maurice Leroy, "La traduction arménienne d'Euclide," in *Annuaire de l'Institut de philologie et d'histoire orientales et slaves* (*Mélanges Franz Cumont*), **4** (1936), 785–816. The letter of Gregory Magistros announcing his translating activity with respect to Euclid was published and analyzed by Leroy in the same *Annuaire*, **3** (1935), 263–294. Additional material on Armenian Euclids can be found in the article (not presently examined) by T. G. Tumanyai, "'Nachala' Evklida po drevnearmyanskim istochnikam" ("Euclid's *Elements* in Ancient Armenian Sources"), in *Istoriko-matematicheskie issledovaniya*, **6** (1953), 659–671, and in G. B. Petrosian and A. G. Abramyan, "A Newly Discovered Armenian Text of Euclid's Geometry," in *Proceedings of the Tenth International Congress of the History of Science, Ithaca, 1962*, II (Paris, 1964), 651–654.

9. *Euclid's minor works.* The Arabic trans. of the Euclidean opuscula, together with a discussion of their role as "middle books" in Islamic mathematics and astronomy, was first examined by M. Steinschneider, "Die 'mittleren' Bücher der Araber und ihre Bearbeiter," in *Zeitschrift für Mathematik und Physik*, **10** (1865), 456–498. There is little material dealing specifically with these shorter works, but in addition to the general literature in section 1 above, see Clemens Thaer, "Euklids Data in arabischer Fassung," in *Hermes*, **77** (1942), 197–205. The prolegomena in vols. VI–VIII of Heiberg, *Euclides*, also contains information on the Arabic phase of these opuscula. For literature dealing with the Islamic role in the work *On the Division of Figures* and the works on mechanics, see pt. I of the present article.

The Medieval Latin Euclid: The Greek-Latin Phase

1. *Euclidean material in Roman authors.* The fragments in Censorinus are appended in F. Hultsch's ed. (Leipzig, 1867) of the *De die natali*, pp. 60–63. For Euclid in Martianus Capella, see the *De nuptiis philologiae et mercurii*, VI, 708 ff.

2. *The Verona palimpsest.* The Euclid fragments have recently been edited, with facsimile and notes, by Mario Geymonat, *Euclidis latine facti fragmenta Veronensia* (Milan, 1964). This work contains references to all other previous literature on the palimpsest, both of paleographers and historians of mathematics.

3. *The Boethian Euclid excerpts.* The best account of all of the variables involved is the absolutely fundamental work of Menso Folkerts, *"Boethius" Geometrie II: Ein mathematisches Lehrbuch des Mittelalters* (Wiesbaden, 1970). This contains a critical ed. of (a) the two-book "Boethian" *Geometry;* (b) the Euclid excerpts preserved in all four earlier medieval sources. The Boethian-Adelard mélanges in Ratsbücherei Lüneburg MS miscell. D4° 48 have been treated and ed. by Folkerts in *Ein neuer Text des Euclides Latinus: Faksimiledruck der Handschrift Lüneburg D 4° 48, f. 13r-17v* (Hildesheim, 1970), and, together with a consideration of the mélanges in the Paris and Munich MSS (see following section), in "Anonyme lateinische Euklidbearbeitungen aus dem 12. Jahrhundert," in *Denkschriften der Österreichischen Akademie der Wissenschaften*, Math.-naturwiss. Klasse (1970), 5–42. See also Folkerts' earlier article, "Das Problem der pseudo-boethischen Geometrie," in *Sudhoff's Archiv für Geschichte der Medizin und der Naturwissenschaften*, **52** (1968), 152–161. An earlier work that also attempted, as a tangential problem, to sort out the threads of the "Boethian" Euclid is Nicolaus Bubnov, *Gerberti Opera mathematica* (Berlin, 1899; repr. Hildesheim, 1963). Before Folkerts the standard ed. of the two-book geometry was that of Gottfried Friedlein in his text of Boethius' *De institutione arithmetica . . . de institutione musica . . . accedit geometria quae fertur Boetii* (Leipzig, 1867), pp. 372–428. The five-book "Boethian" geometry still does not exist in a critical ed. The first two books have appeared, however, among Boethius' works in J. P. Migne, *Patrologia Latina*, vol. LXIII, cols. 1352–1364 (cols. 1307–1352 contain the two-book geometry now in Folkerts). Books I, III, IV, and part of V are in F. Blume, K. Lachmann, and A. Rudorff, *Die Schriften der römischen*

Feldmesser, I (Berlin, 1848), 377–412. The remaining section of book V is unedited. Although the five-book geometry has therefore not received adequate editing, a most exacting analysis of its MS sources and history has been made by C. Thulin, *Zur Überlieferungsgeschichte des Corpus Agrimensorum. Exzerptenhandschriften und Kompendien* (Göteborg, 1911). The Euclid excerpts found in Cassiodorus have been edited by R. A. B. Mynors in his text of the *Institutiones* (Oxford, 1937), pp. 169–172. A recent important article that treats of the role of "Boethian" geometry in the earlier Middle Ages is B. L. Ullman, "Geometry in the Medieval Quadrivium," in *Studi di bibliografia e di storia in onore di Tammaro de Marinis*, IV (Verona, 1964), 263–285. Among the earlier literature on the problems of Boethius and the *Elements* are H. Weissenborn, "Die Boetius-Frage," in *Abhandlungen zur Geschichte der Mathematik*, **2** (1879), 185–240; J. L. Heiberg, "Beiträge zur Geschichte der Mathematik im Mittelalter, II. Euklid's Elemente im Mittelalter," in *Zeitschrift für Mathematik und Physik*, Hist.-lit. Abt., **35** (1890), 48–58, 81–100; Georg Ernst, *De geometricis illis quae sub Boëthii nomine nobis tradita sunt, quaestiones* (Bayreuth, 1903); M. Manitius, "Collationen aus einem geometrischen Tractat," in *Hermes*, **39** (1904), 291–300, and "Collationen aus der *Ars geometrica*," *ibid.*, **41** (1906), 278–292; and several pieces by Paul Tannery, now included in his *Mémoires scientifiques*, V (Paris, 1922), 79–102, 211–228, 246–250.

4. *Boethian-Adelardian mélanges.* The Lüneburg MS mélange has been ed. by Folkerts (see above). A second mélange exists in the four MSS Paris, BN lat. 10257; Oxford, Bodl. Digby 98; Munich, CLM 13021, and CLM 23511. The Paris MS has been ed. in the unpublished dissertation of George D. Goldat, "The Early Medieval Traditions of Euclid's Elements" (Madison, Wisc., 1956).

5. *Munich manuscript fragment.* This has been ed., from MS Univ. Munich 2° 757, by Curtze, *Supplementum*, pp. xvi–xxvi. Corrections to Curtze's text can be found in Heiberg, *Paralipomena*, pp. 354–356, and *Bibliotheca mathematica*, 3rd ser., **2** (1901), 365–366. A new edition of the text has been prepared by Mario Geymonat in "Nuovi frammenti della geometria 'Boeziana' in un codice del IX secolo?" in *Scriptorium*, **21** (1967), 3–16. Geymonat dates the fragment as of the ninth century rather than the tenth; whether this be correct or not, the question that he poses of Boethius' authorship for this fragment should in all probability be answered negatively.

6. *Twelfth-century Greek–Latin translation.* This is found in only two extant MSS: Paris, BN lat. 7373, and Florence, Bib. Naz. Centr. Fondo Conventi Soppressi C I 448. The trans. has been analyzed in full in John Murdoch, "Euclides Graeco-Latinus. A Hitherto Unknown Medieval Latin Translation of the *Elements* Made Directly from the Greek," in *Harvard Studies in Classical Philology*, **71** (1966), 249–302. The Greek–Latin version of Ptolemy's *Almagest* made by the same translator is discussed, and its preface edited, in C. H. Haskins, *Studies in the History of Mediaeval Science* (Cambridge, Mass., 1924), ch. 9.

7. *Medieval Latin versions of the Euclidean opuscula.* General information on the trans. of these minor works can be found in Heiberg, *Euclides*, prolegomena to vols. VI–VIII. In fact, the text of one of the Greek–Latin renderings of the *Optica* has been ed. in Heiberg, *Euclides*, VII (1895), 3–121. The Greek–Latin version of the *Data* was first noted by A. A. Björnbo, "Die mittelalterlichen lateinischen Übersetzungen aus dem Griechischen auf dem Gebiete der mathematischen Wissenschaften," in *Festschrift Moritz Cantor* (Leipzig, 1909), p. 98. It has since been edited in the unpublished dissertation of Shuntaro Ito, "The Medieval Latin Translation of the Data of Euclid" (Madison, Wisc., 1964). The pseudo-Euclidean *De speculis*—to be distinguished from the equally spurious *Catoptrica*—has been edited in A. A. Björnbo and S. Vogl, *Alkindi, Tideus und Pseudo-Euklid. Drei optische Werke, Abhandlungen zur Geschichte der mathematischen Wissenschaften*, vol. XXVI, pt. 3 (Leipzig, 1911); cf. S. Vogl in *Festschrift Moritz Cantor* (Leipzig, 1909), pp. 127–143.

The Medieval Latin Euclid: The Arabic–Latin Phase

1. *General.* A brief resumé of our earlier knowledge of this wing of the medieval Latin Euclid can be found in Heath, *Euclid*, I, 93–96. The fundamental comprehensive description is now Clagett, *Medieval Euclid*, which includes appendices that present sample texts from all of the basic twelfth-century versions constituting the Arabic–Latin *Elements*.

2. *The translation of Gerard of Cremona.* The most complete discussion, including a listing of MSS, is Clagett, *Medieval Euclid*, pp. 27–28, 38–41. See also A. A. Björnbo, "Gerhard von Cremonas Uebersetzung von Alkwarizmis Algebra und von Euklids Elementen," in *Bibliotheca mathematica*, 3rd ser., **6** (1905), 239–248. Still useful for Gerard's life and career is B. Boncompagni, "Della vita e delle opere di Gherardo cremonense," in *Atti dell' Accademia pontificia de' Nuovi Lincei*, 1st ser., **4** (1851), 387–493. A more critical text of Gerard's *vita et libri translati* appended in a number of MSS to his trans. of Galen's *Ars parva* has been given, with annotations to the list of works trans., by F. Wüstenfeld, *Die Übersetzungen arabischer Werke in das Lateinische seit dem XI Jahrhundert. Abhandlungen der Königlichen Gesellschaft der Wissenschaften zu Göttingen* (Göttingen, 1877), pp. 57–81. For Gerard's trans. from the Arabic of commentaries on the *Elements*, see section 6 of the Arabic Euclid bibliography above.

3. *The Adelardian tradition.* The first extensive article treating of Adelard's role in the transmission of Euclid was that of Hermann Weissenborn, "Die Übersetzung des Euklid aus dem Arabischen in das Lateinische durch Adelhard von Bath . . .," in *Zeitschrift für Mathematik und Physik*, Hist.-lit. Abt., **25** (1880), 143–166. It was Clagett, *Medieval Euclid*, pp. 18–25, who first distinguished the three separate versions to be ascribed to Adelard. This article also lists a good portion of extant MSS of the three recensions. A more detailed analysis of the nature of these three versions, together with that of Campanus of Novara, is given in J. Murdoch, "The Medieval Euclid: Salient Aspects of the Translations of the *Elements* by Adelard of Bath and Campanus of Novara," in XIIe Congrès Inter-

national d'Histoire des Sciences, Colloques, in *Revue de synthèse,* **89** (1968), 67–94. For the misinterpretation within the Adelard tradition and within medieval mathematics in general of the Eudoxean definition of equal ratios, see J. Murdoch, "The Medieval Language of Proportions: Elements of the Interaction With Greek Foundations and the Development of New Mathematical Techniques," in A. C. Crombie, ed., *Scientific Change* (London, 1963), pp. 237–271, 334–343. The erroneous ascription of an Adelard version to Alfred the Great was set forth in Edgar Jorg, *Des Boetius und des Alfredus Magnus Kommentar zu den Elementen des Euklid (Nach dem Codex [Z. L. CCCXXXII] B. der Bibliotheca Nazionale di S. Marco zu Venedig), Zweities Buch* (Bottrop, 1935); that this particular MS contains merely both an Adelard II (Boethius) and an Adelard III (Alfred) version was established by M. Clagett, "King Alfred and the *Elements* of Euclid," in *Isis,* **45** (1954), 269–277. Works on Adelard himself are C. H. Haskins, *Studies in the History of Mediaeval Science* (Cambridge, Mass., 1924), ch. 2, and the frequently over-enthusiastic book of Franz Bliemetzrieder, *Adelard von Bath* (Munich, 1935). On the version of Campanus, in addition to the article of Murdoch cited above, see Hermann Weissenborn, *Die Uebersetzungen des Euklid durch Campano und Zamberti* (Halle, 1882). Further biobibliographical information on Campanus is contained in the text and trans. of his *Theorica planetarum,* as edited by Francis S. Benjamin, Jr., and G. J. Toomer (in press).

4. *The translation of Hermann of Carinthia.* See Clagett, *Medieval Euclid,* pp. 26–27, 38–42, and the ed. of books I–VI by H. L. L. Busard, "The Translation of the *Elements* of Euclid From the Arabic Into Latin by Hermann of Carinthia (?)," in *Janus,* **54** (1967), 1–142.

5. *Other translations and commentaries.* The supposed reference to a pre-Adelardian *Elements* in England "Yn tyme of good kyng Adelstones day" (as stated by a fourteenth-century verse) has been shown to apply to masonry, and not geometry, by F. A. Yeldham, "The Alleged Early English Version of Euclid," in *Isis,* **9** (1927), 234–238. For the problem of references to a trans. by Johannes Ocreat, see Clagett, *Medieval Euclid,* pp. 21–22. A commentary on books I–IV of the *Elements* that exists in a single MS (Vienna, Dominik. 80/45) and is there ascribed to Albertus Magnus is discussed by J. E. Hoffmann, "Ueber eine Euklid-Bearbeitung, die dem Albertus Magnus zuschrieben wird," in *Proceedings of the International Congress of Mathematicians, Cambridge, 1958,* pp. 554–566; and by B. Geyer, "Die mathematischen Schriften des Albertus Magnus," in *Angelicum,* **35** (1958), 159–175. An example of later medieval *questiones super Euclidem* are those of Nicole Oresme, recently edited (Leiden, 1961) by H. L. L. Busard; cf. J. E. Murdoch, in *Scripta mathematica,* **27** (1964), 67–91.

The Renaissance and Modern Euclid

1. *General.* There exists very little literature dealing with the transmission of Euclid from 1500 to the present; even bibliographies have not received much attention since the nineteenth century. And there is absolutely no work covering the fairly extensive body of MS materials from the sixteenth and seventeenth centuries. For the printed materials, the most adequate general works are the bibliographies cited above of Riccardi and Sanford, together with the brief survey of the principal eds. of the *Elements* in Heath, *Euclid,* I, 97–113. Dates and places of the versions of the *Elements* that are mentioned above have been given in the body of the text and will not be repeated here.

2. *Latin and Greek editions in the Renaissance and early modern period.* An outline of the major eds. is given in Heiberg, *Euclides,* V (1888), ci–cxiii. Heiberg has also treated of the significance for Euclid and Greek mathematics of Giorgio Valla and his encyclopedic *De expetendis et fugiendis rebus* in "Philologischen Studien zu griechischen Mathematikern: III. Die Handschriften George Vallas von griechischen Mathematikern," in *Jahrbuch für classische Philologie,* **12,** supp. (1881), 337–402; and *Beiträge zur Geschichte Georg Valla's und seiner Bibliothek, Centralblatt für Bibliothekswesen,* Beiheft 16 (Leipzig, 1896). On Zamberti see the monograph of Weissenborn on Campanus and this author that is cited in the section on the Adelardian tradition, above. There is no adequate work on Commandino or Clavius, especially concerning their role in the trans. and dissemination of Greek mathematics. Note has been taken, however, that in the seventeenth century the Jesuit Ricci, a student of Clavius, was instrumental in effecting a Chinese version of the latter's *Elements:* see L. Vanhee, "Euclide en chinois et mandchou," in *Isis,* **30** (1939), 84–88. The possibility of an earlier, thirteenth-century translation of Euclid into Chinese has been briefly discussed by Joseph Needham and Wang Ling, *Science and Civilisation in China,* III (Cambridge, 1959), 105.

Girolamo Saccheri's *Euclidis ab omni naevo vindicatus* has received a modern ed. and English trans. by G. B. Halsted (Chicago, 1920). But this contains only book I of Saccheri's treatise. For book II (dealing with the theory of proportion) see Linda Allegri, "Book II of Girolamo Saccheri's *Euclides ab omni naevo vindicatus,*" in *Proceedings of the Tenth International Congress of the History of Science, Ithaca, 1962,* II (Paris, 1964), 663–665; an English trans. is to be found in the same author's unpublished dissertation, "The Mathematical Works of Girolamo Saccheri, S. J. (1667–1733)" (Columbia University, 1960).

3. *Vernacular translations.* A recent detailed treatment of the appearance of the *Elements* in England up to *ca.* 1700 (in both English and Latin) is Diana M. Simpkins, "Early Editions of Euclid in England," in *Annals of Science,* **22** (1966), 225–249. Robert Recorde and his inclusion of Euclidean material in *The Pathway to Knowledg* is the subject of Joy B. Easton, "A Tudor Euclid," in *Scripta mathematica,* **27** (1964), 339–355. Most extensive attention has been paid to the 1570 English trans. by Sir Henry Billingsley. In addition to the work of Simpkins, above, see G. B. Halsted, "Note on the First English Euclid," in *American Journal of Mathematics,* **2** (1879), 46–48 (which contains the first notice of the volumes at Princeton with marginalia in Billingsley's hand); W. F. Shenton, "The First English Euclid," in *American Mathematical Monthly,* **35**

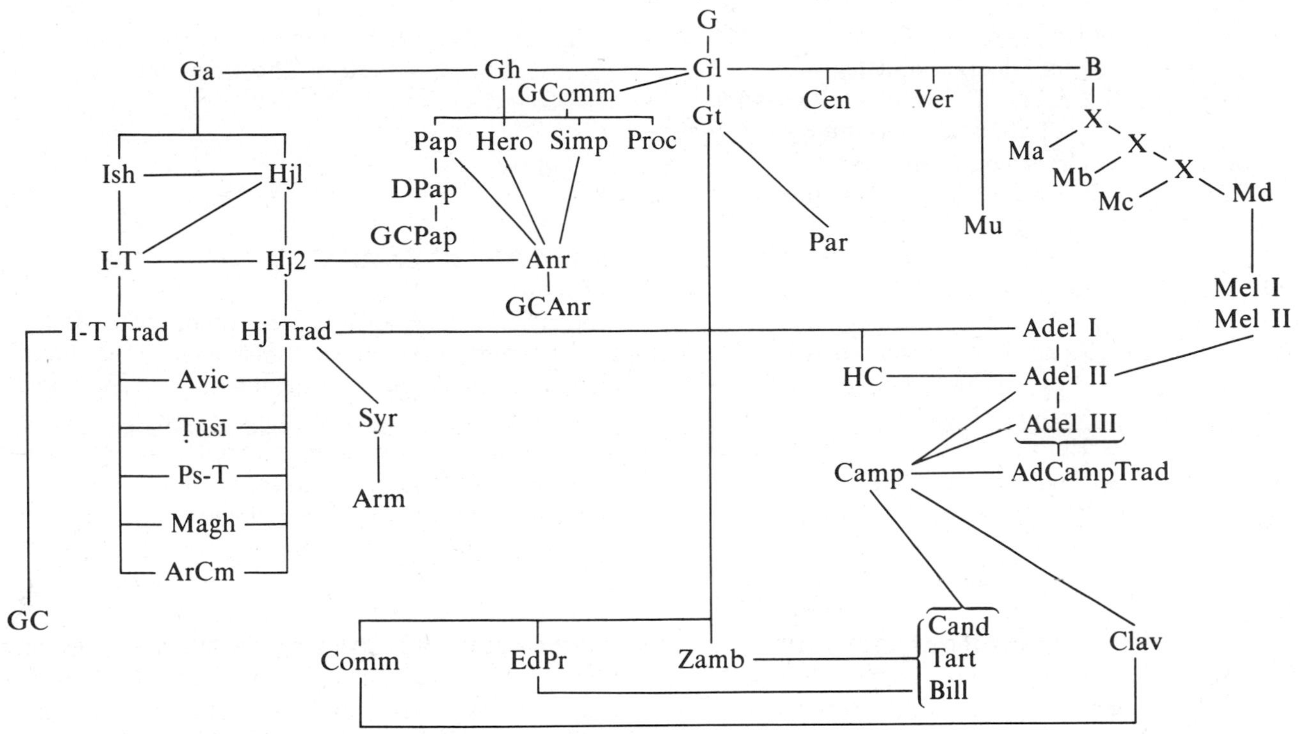

Filiation of the Major Versions of Euclid's *Elements* in the Middle Ages and the Renaissance. Note: Some of the lines of filiation indicated are conjectural. No attempt has been made to differentiate them from those definitely known to be true.

(1928), 505–512; R. C. Archibald, "The First Translation of Euclid's *Elements* Into English and Its Source," in *American Mathematical Monthly,* **57** (1950), 443–452. See also Edward Rosen, "John Dee and Commandino," in *Scripta mathematica,* **28** (1970), 325. An annotated bibliography of French trans. of Euclid is Marie Lacoarret, "Les traductions françaises des oeuvres d'Euclide," in *Revue d'histoire des sciences,* **10** (1957), 38–58. I. J. Depman has written of unnoticed Russian eds. of the *Elements* in *Istoriko-matematicheskie issledovaniya,* **3** (1950), 467–473.

4. *The nineteenth and twentieth centuries.* The most complete survey of the great number of nineteenth-century school-text Euclids is still to be found in the Riccardi bibliography (introductory section above). The most notable twentieth-century trans. that contain considerable historical and analytic annotation are, in English, Heath, *Euclid;* in Italian, Federigo Enriques, *et al.,* eds., *Gli Elementi d'Euclide e la critica antica e moderna,* 4 vols. (Rome–Bologna, 1925–1935); in Dutch, E. J. Dijksterhuis, *De Elementen van Euclides,* 2 vols. (Groningen, 1929–1930); in Russian, D. D. Morduchai-Boltovskogo, *Nachala Evklida,* 3 vols. (Moscow–Leningrad, 1948–1950); in French, of books VII–IX only, Jean Itard, *Les livres arithmétiques d'Euclide* (Paris, 1961).

AdCampTrad = Variant versions deriving from those of Adelard and Campanus
Adel I = First translation of Adelard of Bath
Adel II = *Commentum* of Adelard of Bath
Adel III = *Editio specialis* of Adelard of Bath
Anr = Commentary of al-Nayrīzī
ArCm = Arabic commentaries
Arm = Armenian version presumably made by Gregory Magistros
Avic = Epitome of Avicenna
B = Translation of Boethius
Bill = English translation of Henry Billingsley
Camp = Version of Campanus of Novara
Cand = Version of Franciscus Flussatus Candalla
Cen = Fragments in Censorinus
Clav = Edition of Christopher Clavius
Comm = Translation of Federico Commandino
DPap = Translation by al-Dimashqī of book X of Pappus' commentary
EdPr = *Editio princeps* of Greek text by Simon Grynaeus
G = Original Greek text
Gl = Pre-Theonine Greek text
Ga = Greek text employed for Arabic translations

GC	= Translation by Gerard of Cremona of Isḥāq–Thābit text
GCAnr	= Gerard of Cremona's translation of al-Nayrīzī's commentary
GComm	= Greek commentaries
GCPap	= Gerard of Cremona's translation of (part of) Dimashqī's translation of Pappus on book X
Gh	= Greek text utilized by Hero of Alexandria
Gt	= Redaction of Greek text by Theon of Alexandria
HC	= Version of Hermann of Carinthia
Hero	= Hero of Alexandria's commentary
Hj1	= First version of Ḥajjāj
Hj2	= Second version of Ḥajjāj
Hj Trad	= Ḥajjāj Arabic tradition
Ish	= Translation of Isḥāq ibn Ḥunayn
I-T	= Translation of Isḥāq as revised by Thābit ibn Qurra
I-T Trad	= Isḥāq–Thābit tradition
Ma	= Boethian excerpts preserved in Cassiodorus
Magh	= *Taḥrīr* of al-Maghribī
Mb	= Boethian excerpts preserved in *Agrimensores* material
Mc	= Boethian excerpts in five-book geometry of "Boethius"
Md	= Boethian excerpts in two-book geometry of "Boethius"
Mel I	= Boethian-Adelardian mélanges in MS Lüneburg D 4° 48
Mel II	= Boethian-Adelardian mélanges in Paris and Munich MSS
Mu	= Fragments of translation in MS Univ. Munich 2° 757
Pap	= Greek commentary of Pappus of Alexandria
Par	= Anonymous Greek–Latin translation of twelfth century
Proc	= Greek commentary of Proclus on book I
Ps-T	= Thirteen-book *Taḥrīr* erroneously ascribed to al-Ṭūsī
Simp	= Commentary of Simplicius on the premises
Syr	= Syriac redaction
Tart	= Italian translation by Niccolò Tartaglia
Ṭūsī	= Genuine fifteen-book *Taḥrīr* by al-Ṭūsī
Ver	= Verona palimpsest of fifth century
X	= Ancestors not further specified here
Zamb	= Translation of Bartolomeo Zamberti of Theonine text

JOHN MURDOCH

EUDOXUS OF CNIDUS (*b.* Cnidus, *ca.* 400 B.C.; *d.* Cnidus, *ca.* 347 B.C.)

A scholar and scientist of great eminence, Eudoxus, son of a certain Aischines, contributed to the development of astronomy, mathematics, geography, and philosophy, as well as providing his native city with laws. As a young man he studied geometry with Archytas of Tarentum, from whom he may well have taken his interest in number theory and music; in medicine he was instructed by the physician Philiston; and his philosophical inquiries were stimulated by Plato, whose lectures he attended as an impecunious student during his first visit to Athens. Later his friends in Cnidus paid for a visit to Egypt, where he seems to have had diplomatic dealings with King Nekhtanibef II on behalf of Agesilaus II of Sparta.

Eudoxus spent more than a year in Egypt, some of the time in the company of the priests at Heliopolis. He was said to have composed his *Oktaeteris,* or eight-year calendric cycle, during his sojourn with them. Next he settled at Cyzicus in northwestern Asia Minor and founded a school. He also visited the dynast Mausolus in Caria. A second visit to Athens, to which he was followed by some of his pupils, brought a closer association with Plato, but it is not easy to determine mutual influences in their thinking on ethical and scientific matters. It is unlikely that Plato had any influence upon the development of Eudoxian planetary theory or much upon the Cnidian's philosophical doctrine of forms, which recalls Anaxagoras; but it is possible that Plato's *Philebos* was written with the Eudoxian view of *hedone* (that pleasure, correctly understood, is the highest good) in mind.

Back in Cnidus, Eudoxus lectured on theology, cosmology, and meteorology, wrote textbooks, and enjoyed the respect of his fellow citizens. In mathematics his thinking lies behind much of Euclid's *Elements,* especially books V, VI, and XII. Eudoxus investigated mathematical proportion, the method of exhaustion, and the axiomatic method—the "Euclidean" presentation of axioms and propositions may well have been first systematized by him. The importance of his doctrine of proportion lay in its power to embrace incommensurable quantities.

It is difficult to exaggerate the significance of the theory, for it amounts to a rigorous definition of real

EUDOXUS OF CNIDUS

number. Number theory was allowed to advance again, after the paralysis imposed on it by the Pythagorean discovery of irrationals, to the inestimable benefit of all subsequent mathematics. Indeed, as T. L. Heath declares (*A History of Greek Mathematics,* I [Oxford, 1921], 326–327), "The greatness of the new theory itself needs no further argument when it is remembered that the definition of equal ratios in Eucl. V, Def. 5 corresponds exactly to the modern theory of irrationals due to Dedekind, and that it is word for word the same as Weierstrass's definition of equal numbers."

Eudoxus also attacked the so-called "Delian problem," the traditional one of duplicating the cube; that is, he tried to find two mean proportions in continued proportion between two given quantities. His strictly geometrical solution is lost, and he may also have constructed an apparatus with which to describe an approximate mechanical solution; an epigram ascribed to Eratosthenes (who studied the works of Eudoxus closely) refers to his use of "lines of a bent form" in his solution to the Delian problem: the "organic" demonstration may be meant here. Plato is said to have objected to the use by Eudoxus (and by Archytas) of such devices, believing that they debased pure or ideal geometry. Proclus mentions "general theorems" of Eudoxus; they are lost but may have embraced all concepts of magnitude, the doctrine of proportion included. Related to the treatment of proportion (as found in *Elements* V) was his method of exhaustion, which was used in the calculation of the volume of solids. The method was an important step toward the development of integral calculus.

Archimedes states that Eudoxus proved that the volume of a pyramid is one-third the volume of the prism having the same base and equal height and that the volume of a cone is one-third the volume of the cylinder having the same base and height (these propositions may already have been known by Democritus, but Eudoxus was, it seems, the first to prove them). Archimedes also implies that Eudoxus showed that the areas of circles are to each other as the squares on their respective diameters and that the volumes of spheres to each other are as the cubes of their diameters. All four propositions are found in *Elements* XII, which closely reflects his work. Eudoxus is also said to have added to the first three classes of mathematical mean (arithmetic, geometric, and harmonic) two more, the subcontraries to harmonic and to geometric, but the attribution to him is not quite certain.

Perhaps the most important, and certainly the most influential, part of Eudoxus' lifework was his application of spherical geometry to astronomy. In his book *On Speeds* he expounded a system of geocentric, homocentric rotating spheres designed to explain the irregularities in the motion of planets as seen from the earth. Eudoxus may have regarded his system simply as an abstract geometrical model, but Aristotle took it to be a description of the physical world and complicated it by the addition of more spheres; still more were added by Callippus later in the fourth century B.C. By suitable combination of spheres the periodic motions of planets could be represented approximately, but the system is also, as geometry, of intrinsic merit because of the hippopede, or "horse fetter," an eight-shaped curve, by which Eudoxus represented a planet's apparent motion in latitude as well as its retrogradation.

Eudoxus' model assumes that the planet remains at a constant distance from the center, but in fact, as critics were quick to point out, the planets vary in brightness and hence, it would seem, in distance from the earth. Another objection is that according to the model, each retrogradation of a planet is identical with the previous retrogradation in the shape of its curve, which also is not in accord with the facts. So, while the Eudoxian system testified to the geometrical skill of its author, it could not be accepted by serious astronomers as definitive, and in time the theory of epicycles was developed. But, partly through the blessing of Aristotle, the influence of Eudoxus on popular astronomical thought lasted through antiquity and the Middle Ages. In explaining the system, Eudoxus gave close estimates of the synodic periods of Saturn, Jupiter, Mars, Mercury, and Venus (hence the title of the book, *On Speeds*). Only the estimate for Mars is seriously faulty, and here the text of Simplicius, who gives the values, is almost certainly in error (Eudoxus, frag. 124 in Lasserre).

Eudoxus was a careful observer of the fixed stars, both during his visit to Egypt and at home in Cnidus, where he had an observatory. His results were published in two books, the *Enoptron* ("Mirror") and the *Phaenomena.* The works were criticized, in the light of superior knowledge, by the great astronomer Hipparchus two centuries later, but they were pioneering compendia and long proved useful. Several verbatim quotations are given by Hipparchus in his commentary on the astronomical poem of Aratus, which drew on Eudoxus and was also entitled *Phaenomena.* A book by Eudoxus called *Disappearances of the Sun* may have been concerned with eclipses, and perhaps with risings and settings as well. The statement in the *Suda Lexicon* that he composed an astronomical poem may result from a confusion with Aratus, but a genuine *Astronomia* in hexameters, in the Hesiodic tradition, is a possibility. A calendar of the seasonal risings and settings of constellations, together with weather signs, may have been included in the *Oktaeteris.* His observational instruments included sundials (Vitruvius, *De architectura* 9.8.1).

Eudoxus' knowledge of spherical astronomy must have been helpful to him in the geographical treatise *Ges periodos* ("Tour [Circuit] of the Earth"). About 100 fragments survive; they give some idea of the plan of the original work. Beginning with remote Asia, Eudoxus dealt systematically with each part of the known world in turn, adding political, historical, and ethnographic detail and making use of Greek mythology. His method is comparable with that of such early Ionian logographers as Hecataeus of Miletus. Egypt was treated in the second book, and Egyptian religion, about which Eudoxus could write with authority, was discussed in detail. The fourth book dealt with regions to the north of the Aegean, including Thrace. In the sixth book he wrote about mainland Hellas and, it seems, North Africa. The discussion of Italy in the seventh book included an excursus on the customs of the Pythagoreans, about whom Eudoxus may have learned much from his master Archytas of Tarentum (Eudoxus himself is sometimes called a Pythagorean).

It is greatly to be deplored that not a single work of Eudoxus is extant, for he was obviously a dominant figure in the intellectual life of Greece in the age of Plato and Aristotle (the latter also remarked on the upright and controlled character of the Cnidian, which made people believe him when he said that pleasure was the highest good).

BIBLIOGRAPHY

The biography of Eudoxus in Diogenes Laertius 8.86–8.90 is anecdotal but not worthless. The fragments have been collected, with commentary, in F. Lasserre's book *Die Fragmente des Eudoxos von Knidos* (Berlin, 1966). Eudoxian parts of Euclid's *Elements* are discussed by T. L. Heath in his edition of that work, 2nd ed., 3 vols. (Cambridge, 1926). The mathematical properties of the hippopede have been much studied; see especially O. Neugebauer, *The Exact Sciences in Antiquity,* 2nd ed. (Providence, R. I., 1957), 182–183. On the *Ges periodos,* see F. Gisinger, *Die Erdbeschreibung des Eudoxos von Knidos* (Leipzig-Berlin, 1921). A chronology of Eudoxus' life and travels is G. Huxley, "Eudoxian Topics," in *Greek, Roman and Byzantine Studies,* **4** (1963), 83–96.

See also Oskar Becker, "Eudoxos-Studien," in *Quellen und Studien zur Geschichte der Mathematik, Astronomie und Physik,* Abt. B, Studien, **2** (1933), 311–333, 369–387, and **3** (1936), 236–244, 370–410; Hans Künsberg, *Der Astronom, Mathematiker und Geograph Eudoxos von Knidos,* 2 pts. (Dinkelsbühl, 1888–1890); and G. Schiaparelli, *Scritti sulla storia della astronomia antica,* II (Bologna, 1926), 2–112.

G. L. HUXLEY

EULER, LEONHARD (*b.* Basel, Switzerland, 15 April 1707; *d.* St. Petersburg, Russia, 18 September 1783)

Life. Euler's forebears settled in Basel at the end of the sixteenth century. His great-great-grandfather, Hans Georg Euler, had moved from Lindau, on the Bodensee (Lake Constance). They were, for the most part, artisans; but the mathematician's father, Paul Euler, graduated from the theological department of the University of Basel. He became a Protestant minister, and in 1706 he married Margarete Brucker, daughter of another minister. In 1708 the family moved to the village of Riehen, near Basel, where Leonhard Euler spent his childhood.

Euler's father was fond of mathematics and had attended Jakob Bernoulli's lectures at the university; he gave his son his elementary education, including mathematics. In the brief autobiography dictated to his eldest son in 1767, Euler recollected that for several years he diligently and thoroughly studied Christoff Rudolf's *Algebra,* a difficult work (dating, in Stifel's edition, from 1553) which only a very gifted boy could have used. Euler later spent several years with his maternal grandmother in Basel, studying at a rather poor local Gymnasium; mathematics was not taught at all, so Euler studied privately with Johann Burckhardt, an amateur mathematician. In the autumn of 1720, being not yet fourteen, Euler entered the University of Basel in the department of arts to get a general education before specializing. The university was small; it comprised only a few more than a hundred students and nineteen professors. But among the latter was Johann I Bernoulli, who had followed his brother Jakob, late in 1705, in the chair of mathematics. During the academic year, Bernoulli delivered daily public lectures on elementary mathematics; besides that, for additional pay he conducted studies in higher mathematics and physics for those who were interested. Euler laboriously studied all the required subjects, but this did not satisfy him. According to the autobiography:

> . . . I soon found an opportunity to be introduced to a famous professor Johann Bernoulli. . . . True, he was very busy and so refused flatly to give me private lessons; but he gave me much more valuable advice to start reading more difficult mathematical books on my own and to study them as diligently as I could; if I

> came across some obstacle or difficulty, I was given permission to visit him freely every Saturday afternoon and he kindly explained to me everything I could not understand . . . and this, undoubtedly, is the best method to succeed in mathematical subjects.[1]

In the summer of 1722, Euler delivered a speech in praise of temperance, "De temperantia," and received his *prima laurea,* a degree corresponding to the bachelor of arts. The same year he acted as opponent (*respondens*) at the defense of two theses—one on logic, the other on the history of law. In 1723 Euler received his master's degree in philosophy. This was officially announced at a session on 8 June 1724; Euler made a speech comparing the philosophical ideas of Descartes and Newton. Some time earlier, in the autumn of 1723, he had joined the department of theology, fulfilling his father's wish. His studies in theology, Greek, and Hebrew were not very successful, however; Euler devoted most of his time to mathematics. He finally gave up the idea of becoming a minister but remained a wholehearted believer throughout his life. He also retained the knowledge of the humanities that he acquired in the university; he had an outstanding memory and knew by heart the entirety of Vergil's *Aeneid.* At seventy he could recall precisely the lines printed at the top and bottom of each page of the edition he had read when he was young.

At the age of eighteen, Euler began his independent investigations. His first work, a small note on the construction of isochronous curves in a resistant medium,[2] appeared in *Acta eruditorum* (1726); this was followed by an article in the same periodical on algebraic reciprocal trajectories (1727).[3] The problem of reciprocal trajectories was studied by Johann I Bernoulli, by his son Nikolaus II, and by other mathematicians of the time. Simultaneously Euler participated in a competition announced by the Paris Académie des Sciences which proposed for 1727 the problem of the most efficient arrangement of masts on a ship. The prize went to Pierre Bouguer, but Euler's work[4] received the *accessit.* Later, from 1738 to 1772, Euler was to receive twelve prizes from the Academy.

For mathematicians beginning their careers in Switzerland, conditions were hard. There were few chairs of mathematics in the country and thus little chance of finding a suitable job. The income and public recognition accorded to a university professor of mathematics were not cause for envy. There were no scientific magazines, and publishers were reluctant to publish books on mathematics, which were considered financially risky. At this time the newly organized St. Petersburg Academy of Sciences (1725) was looking for personnel. In the autumn of that year Johann I Bernoulli's sons, Nikolaus II and Daniel, went to Russia. On behalf of Euler, they persuaded the authorities of the new Academy to send an invitation to their young friend also.

Euler received the invitation to serve as adjunct of physiology in St. Petersburg in the autumn of 1726, and he began to study this discipline, with an effort toward applying the methods of mathematics and mechanics. He also attempted to find a job at the University of Basel. A vacancy occurred in Basel after the death of a professor of physics, and Euler presented as a qualification a small composition on acoustics, *Dissertatio physica de sono* (1727).[5] Vacancies were then filled in the university by drawing lots among the several chosen candidates. In spite of a recommendation from Johann Bernoulli, Euler was not chosen as a candidate, probably because he was too young—he was not yet twenty. But, as O. Spiess has pointed out, this was in Euler's favor;[6] a much broader field of action lay ahead of him.

On 5 April 1727 Euler left Basel for St. Petersburg, arriving there on 24 May. From this time his life and scientific work were closely connected with the St. Petersburg Academy and with Russia. He never returned to Switzerland, although he maintained his Swiss citizenship.

In spite of having been invited to St. Petersburg to study physiology, Euler was at once given the chance to work in his real field and was appointed an adjunct member of the Academy in the mathematics section. He became professor of physics in 1731 and succeeded Daniel Bernoulli, who returned to Basel in 1733 as a professor of mathematics. The young Academy was beset with numerous difficulties, but on the whole the atmosphere was exceptionally beneficial for the flowering of Euler's genius. Nowhere else could he have been surrounded by such a group of eminent scientists, including the analyst, geometer, and specialist in theoretical mechanics Jakob Hermann, a relative; Daniel Bernoulli, with whom Euler was connected not only by personal friendship but also by common interests in the field of applied mathematics; the versatile scholar Christian Goldbach, with whom Euler discussed numerous problems of analysis and the theory of numbers; F. Maier, working in trigonometry; and the astronomer and geographer J.-N. Delisle.

In St. Petersburg, Euler began his scientific activity at once. No later than August 1727 he started making reports on his investigations at sessions of the Academy; he began publishing them in the second volume of the academic proceedings, *Commentarii Academiae scientiarum imperialis Petropolitanae (1727)* (St.

Petersburg, 1729). The generous publication program of the Academy was especially important for Euler, who was unusually prolific. In a letter written in 1749 Euler cited the importance that the work at the Academy had for many of its members:

> . . . I and all others who had the good fortune to be for some time with the Russian Imperial Academy cannot but acknowledge that we owe everything which we are and possess to the favorable conditions which we had there.[7]

In addition to conducting purely scientific work, the St. Petersburg Academy from the very beginning was also obliged to educate and train Russian scientists, and with this aim a university and a Gymnasium were organized. The former existed for nearly fifty years and the latter until 1805. The Academy was also charged to carry out for the government a study of Russian territory and to find solutions for various technological problems. Euler was active in these projects. From 1733 on, he successfully worked with Delisle on maps in the department of geography. From the middle of the 1730's he studied problems of shipbuilding and navigation, which were especially important to the rise of Russia as a great sea power. He joined various technological committees and engaged in testing scales, fire pumps, saws, and so forth. He wrote articles for the popular periodical of the Academy and reviewed works submitted to it (including those on the quadrature of the circle), compiled the *Einleitung zur Rechen-Kunst*[8] for Gymnasiums, and also served on the examination board.

Euler's main efforts, however, were in the mathematical sciences. During his fourteen years in St. Petersburg he made brilliant discoveries in such areas as analysis, the theory of numbers, and mechanics. By 1741 he had prepared between eighty and ninety works for publication. He published fifty-five, including the two-volume *Mechanica.*[9]

As is usual with scientists, Euler formulated many of his principal ideas and creative concepts when he was young. Neither the dates of preparation of his works nor those of their actual publication adequately indicate Euler's intellectual progress, since a number of the plans formulated in the early years in St. Petersburg (and even as early as the Basel period) were not realized until much later. For example, the first drafts of the theory of motion of solid bodies, finished in the 1760's, were made during this time. Likewise Euler began studying hydromechanics while still in Basel, but the most important memoirs on the subject did not appear until the middle of the 1750's; he imagined a systematic exposition of differential calculus on the basis of calculus of finite differences in the 1730's but did not realize the intention until two decades later; and his first articles on optics appeared fifteen years after he began studying the subject in St. Petersburg. Only by a complete study of the unpublished Euler manuscripts would it be possible to establish the progression of his ideas more precisely.

Because of his large correspondence with scientists from many countries, Euler's discoveries often became known long before publication and rapidly brought him increasing fame. An index of this is Johann I Bernoulli's letters to his former disciple—in 1728 Bernoulli addressed the "most learned and gifted man of science Leonhard Euler"; in 1737 he wrote, the "most famous and wisest mathematician"; and in 1745 he called him the "incomparable Leonhard Euler" and *"mathematicorum princeps."* Euler was then a member of both the St. Petersburg and Berlin academies. (That certain frictions between Euler and Schumacher, the rude and despotic councillor of the St. Petersburg Academy, did Euler's career no lasting harm was due to his tact and diplomacy.) He was later elected a member of the Royal Society of London (1749) and the Académie des Sciences of Paris (1755). He was elected a member of the Society of Physics and Mathematics in Basel in 1753.

At the end of 1733 Euler married Katharina Gsell, a daughter of Georg Gsell, a Swiss who taught painting at the Gymnasium attached to the St. Petersburg Academy. Johann Albrecht, Euler's first son, was born in 1734, and Karl was born in 1740. It seemed that Euler had settled in St. Petersburg for good; his younger brother, Johann Heinrich, a painter, also worked there. His quiet life was interrupted only by a disease that caused the loss of sight in his right eye in 1738.

In November 1740 Anna Leopoldovna, mother of the infant Emperor Ivan VI, became regent, and the atmosphere in the Russian capital grew troubled. According to Euler's autobiography, "things looked rather dubious."[10] At that time Frederick the Great, who had succeeded to the Prussian throne in June 1740, decided to reorganize the Berlin Society of Sciences, which had been founded by Leibniz but allowed to degenerate during Frederick's father's reign. Euler was invited to work in Berlin. He accepted, and after fourteen years in Russia he sailed with his family on 19 June 1741 from St. Petersburg. He arrived in Berlin on 25 July.

Euler lived in Berlin for the next twenty-five years. In 1744 he moved into a house, still preserved, on the Behrenstrasse. The family increased with the birth of a third son, Christoph, and two daughters; eight other children died in infancy. In 1753 Euler bought an estate in Charlottenburg, which was then just outside the city. The estate was managed by his mother, who lived with Euler after 1750. He sold the property in 1763.

Euler's energy in middle age was inexhaustible. He was working simultaneously in two academies—Berlin and St. Petersburg. He was very active in transforming the old Society of Sciences into a large academy—officially founded in 1744 as the Académie Royale des Sciences et des Belles Lettres de Berlin. (The monarch preferred his favorite language, French, to both Latin and German.) Euler was appointed director of the mathematical class of the Academy and member of the board and of the committee directing the library and the publication of scientific works. He also substituted for the president, Maupertuis, when the latter was absent. When Maupertuis died in 1759, Euler continued to run the Academy, although without the title of president. Euler's friendship with Maupertuis enabled him to exercise great influence on all the activities of the Academy, particularly on the selection of members.

Euler's administrative duties were numerous: he supervised the observatory and the botanical gardens; selected the personnel; oversaw various financial matters; and, in particular, managed the publication of various calendars and geographical maps, the sale of which was a source of income for the Academy. The king also charged Euler with practical problems, such as the project in 1749 of correcting the level of the Finow Canal, which was built in 1744 to join the Havel and the Oder. At that time he also supervised the work on pumps and pipes of the hydraulic system at Sans Souci, the royal summer residence.

In 1749 and again in 1763 he advised on the organization of state lotteries and was a consultant to the government on problems of insurance, annuities, and widows' pensions. Some of Euler's studies on demography grew out of these problems. An inquiry from the king about the best work on artillery moved Euler to translate into German Benjamin Robins' *New Principles of Gunnery.* Euler added his own supplements on ballistics, which were five times longer than the original text (1745).[11] These supplements occupy an important place in the history of ballistics; Euler himself had written a short work on the subject as early as 1727 or 1728 in connection with the testing of guns.[12]

Euler's influence upon scientific life in Germany was not restricted to the Berlin Academy. He maintained a large correspondence with professors at numerous German universities and promoted the teaching of mathematical sciences and the preparation of university texts.

From his very first years in Berlin, Euler kept in regular working contact with the St. Petersburg Academy. This contact was interrupted only during military actions between Prussia and Russia in the course of the Seven Years' War—although even then not completely. Before his departure from the Russian capital, Euler was appointed an honorary member of the Academy and given an annual pension; on his part he pledged to carry out various assignments of the Academy and to correspond with it. During the twenty-five years in Berlin, Euler maintained membership in the St. Petersburg Academy *à tous les titres,* to quote N. Fuss. On its commission he finished the books on differential calculus and navigation begun before his departure for Berlin; edited the mathematical section of the Academy journal; kept the Academy apprised, through his letters, of scientific and technological thought in Western Europe; bought books and scientific apparatus for the Academy; recommended subjects for scientific competitions and candidates to vacancies; and served as a mediator in conflicts between academicians.

Euler's participation in the training of Russian scientific personnel was of great importance, and he was frequently sent for review the works of Russian students and even members of the Academy. For example, in 1747 he praised most highly two articles of M. V. Lomonosov on physics and chemistry; and S. K. Kotelnikov, S. Y. Rumovski, and M. Sofronov studied in Berlin under his supervision for several years. Finally, Euler regularly sent memoirs to St. Petersburg. About half his articles were published there in Latin, and the other half appeared in French in Berlin.

During this period, Euler greatly increased the variety of his investigations. Competing with d'Alembert and Daniel Bernoulli, he laid the foundations of mathematical physics; and he was a rival of both A. Clairaut and d'Alembert in advancing the theory of lunar and planetary motion. At the same time, Euler elaborated the theory of motion of solids, created the mathematical apparatus of hydrodynamics, successfully developed the differential geometry of surfaces, and intensively studied optics, electricity, and magnetism. He also pondered such problems of technology as the construction of achromatic refractors, the perfection of J. A. Segner's hydraulic turbine, and the theory of toothed gearings.

During the Berlin period Euler prepared no fewer than 380 works, of which about 275 were published, including several lengthy books: a monograph on the calculus of variations (1744);[13] a fundamental work on calculation of orbits (1745);[14] the previously mentioned work on artillery and ballistics (1745); *Intro-*

ductio in analysin infinitorum (1748);[15] a treatise on shipbuilding and navigation, prepared in an early version in St. Petersburg (1749);[16] his first theory of lunar motion (1753);[17] and *Institutiones calculi differentialis* (1755).[18] The last three books were published at the expense of the St. Petersburg Academy. Finally, there was the treatise on the mechanics of solids, *Theoria motus corporum solidorum seu rigidorum* (1765).[19] The famous *Lettres à une princesse d'Allemagne sur divers sujets de physique et de philosophie,* which originated in lessons given by Euler to a relative of the Prussian king, was not published until Euler's return to St. Petersburg.[20] Written in an absorbing and popular manner, the book was an unusual success and ran to twelve editions in the original French, nine in English, six in German, four in Russian, and two in both Dutch and Swedish. There were also Italian, Spanish, and Danish editions.

In the 1740's and 1750's Euler took part in several philosophical and scientific arguments. In 1745 and after, there were passionate discussions about the monadology of Leibniz and of Christian Wolff. German intellectuals were divided according to their opinions on monadology. As Euler later wrote, every conversation ended in a discussion of monads. The Berlin Academy announced as the subject of a 1747 prize competition an exposé and critique of the system. Euler, who was close to Cartesian mechanical materialism in natural philosophy, was an ardent enemy of monadology, as was Maupertuis. It should be added that Euler, whose religious views were based on a belief in revelation, could not share the religion of reason which characterized Leibniz and Wolff. Euler stated his objections, which were grounded on arguments of both a physical and theological nature, in the pamphlet *Gedancken von den Elementen der Cörper*... (1746).[21] His composition caused violent debates, but the decision of the Academy gave the prize to Justi, author of a rather mediocre work against the theory of monads.

In 1751 a sensational new argument began when S. König published some critical remarks on Maupertuis's principle of least action (1744) and cited a letter of Leibniz in which the principle was, in König's opinion, formulated more precisely. Submitting to Maupertuis, the Berlin Academy rose to defend him and demanded that the original of Leibniz' letter (a copy had been sent to König from Switzerland) be presented. When it became clear that the original could not be found, Euler published, with the approval of the Academy, "Exposé concernant l'examen de la lettre de M. de Leibnitz" (1752),[22] where, among other things, he declared the letter a fake. The conflict grew critical when later in the same year Voltaire published his *Diatribe du docteur Akakia, médecin du pape,* defending König and making laughingstocks of both Maupertuis and Euler. Frederick rushed to the defense of Maupertuis, quarreling with his friend Voltaire and ordering the burning of the offensive pamphlet. His actions, however, did not prevent its dissemination throughout Europe. The argument touched not only on the pride of the principal participants but also on their general views: Maupertuis and, to a lesser degree, Euler interpreted the principle of least action theologically and teleologically; König was a follower of Wolff and Voltaire—the greatest ideologist of free thought.

Three other disputes in which Euler took part (all discussed below) were much more important for the development of mathematical sciences: his argument with d'Alembert on the problem of logarithms of negative numbers, the argument with d'Alembert and Daniel Bernoulli on the solution of the equation of a vibrating string, and Euler's polemics with Dollond on optical problems.

As mentioned earlier, after Maupertuis died in 1759, Euler managed the Berlin Academy, but under the direct supervision of the king. But relations between Frederick and Euler had long since spoiled. They differed sharply, not only in their views but in their tastes, treatment of men, and personal conduct. Euler's bourgeois manners and religious zeal were as unattractive to the king as the king's passion for bons mots and freethinking was to Euler. Euler cared little for poetry, which the king adored; Frederick was quite contemptuous of the higher realms of mathematics, which did not seem to him immediately practical. In spite of having no one to replace Euler as manager of the Academy, the king, nonetheless, did not intend to give him the post of president. In 1763 it became known that Frederick wanted to appoint d'Alembert, and Euler thus began to think of leaving Berlin. He wrote to G. F. Müller, secretary of the St. Petersburg Academy, which had tried earlier to bring him back to Russia. Catherine the Great then ordered the academicians to send Euler another offer.

D'Alembert's refusal to move permanently to Berlin postponed for a time the final decision on the matter. But during 1765 and 1766 grave conflicts over financial matters arose between Euler and Frederick, who interfered actively with Euler's management of the Academy after the Seven Years' War. The king thought Euler inexperienced in such matters and relied too much on the treasurer of the Academy. For half a year Euler pleaded for royal permission to leave, but the king, well-aware that the Academy would thus lose its best worker and principal force, declined to grant his request. Finally he had to consent and vented his annoyance in crude jokes about Euler. On 9 June 1766, Euler left Berlin, spent ten days in Warsaw at the invitation of Stanislas II, and arrived in St. Petersburg on 28 July. Euler's three sons returned to Russia also. Johann Albrecht became academician in the chair of physics in 1766 and permanent secretary of the Academy in 1769. Christoph, who had become an officer in Prussia, successfully resumed his military career, reaching the rank of major-general in artillery. Both his daughters also accompanied him.

Euler settled in a house on the embankment of the Neva, not far from the Academy. Soon after his return he suffered a brief illness, which left him almost completely blind in the left eye; he could not now read and could make out only outlines of large objects. He could write only in large letters with chalk and slate. An operation in 1771 temporarily restored his sight, but Euler seems not to have taken adequate care of himself and in a few days he was completely blind. Shortly before the operation, he had lost his house and almost all of his personal property in a fire, barely managing to rescue himself and his manuscripts. In November 1773 Euler's wife died, and three years later he married her half sister, Salome Abigail Gsell.

Euler's blindness did not lessen his scientific activity. Only in the last years of his life did he cease attending academic meetings, and his literary output even increased—almost half of his works were produced after 1765. His memory remained flawless, he carried on with his unrealized ideas, and he devised new plans. He naturally could not execute this immense work alone and was helped by active collaborators: his sons Johann Albrecht and Christoph; the academicians W. L. Krafft and A. J. Lexell; and two new young disciples, adjuncts N. Fuss, who was invited in 1772 from Switzerland, and M. E. Golovin, a nephew of Lomonosov. Sometimes Euler simply dictated his works; thus, he dictated to a young valet, a tailor by profession, the two-volume *Vollständige Anleitung zur Algebra* (1770),[23] first published in Russian translation.

But the scientists assisting Euler were not mere secretaries; he discussed the general scheme of the works with them, and they developed his ideas, calculated tables, and sometimes compiled examples. The enormous, 775-page *Theoria motuum lunae . . .* (1772)[24] was thus completed with the help of Johann Albrecht, Krafft, and Lexell—all of whom are credited on the title page. Krafft also helped Euler with the three-volume *Dioptrica* (1769–1771).[25] Fuss, by his own account, during a seven-year period prepared 250 memoirs, and Golovin prepared seventy. Articles written by Euler in his later years were generally concise and particular. For example, the fifty-six works prepared during 1776 contain about the same number of pages (1,000) as the nineteen works prepared in 1751.

Besides the works mentioned, during the second St. Petersburg period Euler published three volumes of *Institutiones calculi integralis* (1768–1770),[26] the principal parts of which he had finished in Berlin, and an abridged edition of *Scientia navalis—Théorie complette de la construction et de la manoeuvre des vaisseaux* (1773).[27] The last, a manual for naval cadets, was soon translated into English, Italian, and Russian, and Euler received for it large sums from the Russian and French governments.

The mathematical apparatus of the *Dioptrica* remained beyond the practical opticist's understanding; so Fuss devised, on the basis of this work, the *Instruction détaillée pour porter les lunettes de toutes les différentes espèces au plus haut degré de perfection dont elles sont susceptibles . . .* (1774).[28] Fuss also aided Euler in preparing the *Éclaircissemens sur les établissemens publics . . .* (1776),[29] which was very important in the development of insurance; many companies used its methods of solution and its tables.

Euler continued his participation in other functions of the St. Petersburg Academy. Together with Johann Albrecht he was a member of the commission charged in 1766 with the management of the Academy. Both resigned their posts on the commission in 1774 because of a difference of opinion between them and the director of the Academy, Count V. G. Orlov, who actually managed it.

On 18 September 1783 Euler spent the first half of the day as usual. He gave a mathematics lesson to one of his grandchildren, did some calculations with chalk on two boards on the motion of balloons; then discussed with Lexell and Fuss the recently discovered planet Uranus. About five o'clock in the afternoon he suffered a brain hemorrhage and uttered only "I am dying," before he lost consciousness. He died about eleven o'clock in the evening.

Soon after Euler's death eulogies were delivered by Fuss at a meeting of the St. Petersburg Academy[30] and by Condorcet at the Paris Academy of Sciences.[31] Euler was buried at the Lutheran Smolenskoye cemetery in St. Petersburg, where in 1837 a massive monument was erected at his grave, with the inscription, "Leonhardo Eulero Academia Petropolitana." In the autumn of 1956 Euler's remains and the monument were transferred to the necropolis of Leningrad.

Euler was a simple man, well disposed and not given to envy. One can also say of him what Fontenelle said of Leibniz: "He was glad to observe the flowering in other people's gardens of plants whose seeds he provided."

Mathematics. Euler was a geometer in the wide sense in which the word was used during the eighteenth century. He was one of the most important creators of mathematical science after Newton. In his work, mathematics was closely connected with applications to other sciences, to problems of technology, and to public life. In numerous cases he elaborated mathematical methods for the direct solution of problems of mechanics and astronomy, physics and navigation, geography and geodesy, hydraulics and ballistics, insurance and demography. This practical orientation of his work explains his tendency to prolong his investigations until he had derived a convenient formula for calculation or an immediate solution in numbers or a table. He constantly sought algorithms that would be simple to use in calculation and that would also assure sufficient accuracy in the results.

But just as his friend Daniel Bernoulli was first of all a physicist, Euler was first of all a mathematician. Bernoulli's thinking was preeminently physical; he tried to avoid mathematics whenever possible, and once having developed a mathematical device for the solution of some physical problem, he usually left it without further development. Euler, on the other hand, attempted first of all to express a physical problem in mathematical terms; and having found a mathematical idea for solution, he systematically developed and generalized it. Thus, Euler's brilliant achievements in the field are explained by his regular elaboration of mathematics as a single whole. Bernoulli was not especially attracted by more abstract problems of mathematics; Euler, on the contrary, was very much carried away with the theory of numbers. All this is manifest in the distribution of Euler's works on various sciences: twenty-nine volumes of the *Opera omnia* (see Bibliography [1]) pertain to pure mathematics.

In Euler's mathematical work, first place belongs to analysis, which at the time was the most pressing need in mathematical science; seventeen volumes of the *Opera omnia* are in this area. Thus, in principle, Euler was an analyst. He contributed numerous particular discoveries to analysis, systematized its exposition in his classical manuals, and, along with all this, contributed immeasurably to the founding of several large mathematical disciplines: the calculus of variations, the theory of differential equations, the elementary theory of functions of complex variables, and the theory of special functions.

Euler is often characterized as a calculator of genius, and he was, in fact, unsurpassed in formal calculations and transformations and was even an outstanding calculator in the elementary sense of the word. But he also was a creator of new and important notions and methods, the principal value of which was in some cases properly understood only a century or more after his death. Even in areas where he, along with his contemporaries, did not feel at home, his judgment came, as a rule, from profound intuition into the subject under study. His findings were intrinsically capable of being grounded in the rigorous mode of demonstration that became obligatory in the nineteenth and twentieth centuries. Such standards were not, and could not be, demanded in the mathematics of the eighteenth century.

It is frequently said that Euler saw no intrinsic impossibility in the deduction of mathematical laws from a very limited basis in observation; and naturally he employed methods of induction to make empirical use of the results he had arrived at through analysis of concrete numerical material. But he himself warned many times that an incomplete induction serves only as a heuristic device, and he never passed off as finally proved truths the suppositions arrived at by such methods.

Euler introduced many of the present conventions of mathematical notation: the symbol e to represent the base of the natural system of logarithms (1727, published 1736); the use of letter f and of parentheses for a function $f([x/a] + c)$ (1734, published 1740); the modern signs for trigonometric functions (1748); the notation $\int n$ for the sum of divisors of the number n (1750); notations for finite differences, Δy, $\Delta^2 y$, etc., and for the sum Σ (1755); and the letter i for $\sqrt{-1}$ (1777, published 1794).

Euler had only a few immediate disciples, and none of them was a first-class scientist. On the other hand, according to Laplace, he was a tutor of all the mathematicians of his time. In mathematics the eighteenth century can fairly be labeled the Age of Euler, but his influence upon the development of mathematical sciences was not restricted to that period. The work of many outstanding nineteenth-century mathematicians branched out directly from the works of Euler.

Euler was especially important for the development of science in Russia. His disciples formed the first scientific mathematical school in the country and contributed to the rise of mathematical education. One can trace back to Euler numerous paths from Chebyshev's St. Petersburg mathematical school.

[In the following, titles of articles are not, as a rule, cited; dates in parentheses signify the year of publication.]

Theory of Numbers. Problems of the theory of

numbers had attracted mathematicians before Euler. Fermat, for example, established several remarkable arithmetic theorems but left almost no proofs. Euler laid the foundations of number theory as a true science.

A large series of Euler's works is connected with the theory of divisibility. He proved by three methods Fermat's lesser theorem, the principal one in the field (1741, 1761, 1763); he suggested with the third proof an important generalization of the theorem by introducing Euler's function $\varphi(n)$, denoting the number of positive integers less than n which are relatively prime to n: the difference $a^{\varphi(n)}-1$ is divisible by n if a is relatively prime to n. Elaborating related ideas, Euler came to the theory of n-ic residues (1760). Here his greatest discovery was the law of quadratic reciprocity (1783), which, however, he could not prove. Euler's discovery went unnoticed by his contemporaries, and the law was rediscovered, but incompletely proved, by A. M. Legendre (1788). Legendre was credited with it until Chebyshev pointed out Euler's priority in 1849. The complete proof of the law was finally achieved by Gauss (1801). Gauss, Kummer, D. Hilbert, E. Artin, and others extended the law of reciprocity to various algebraic number fields; the most general law of reciprocity was established by I. R. Shafarevich (1950).

Another group of Euler's works, in which he extended Fermat's studies on representation of prime numbers by sums of the form $mx^2 + ny^2$, where m, n, x, and y are positive integers, led him to the discovery of a new efficient method of determining whether a given large number N is prime or composite (1751, *et seq.*). These works formed the basis for the general arithmetic theory of binary quadratic forms developed by Lagrange and especially by Gauss.

Euler also contributed to so-called Diophantine analysis, that is, to the solution, in integers or in rational numbers, of indeterminate equations with integer coefficients. Thus, by means of continued fractions, which he had studied earlier (1744, *et seq.*), he gave (1767) a method of calculation of the smallest integer solution of the equation $x^2 - dy^2 = 1$ (d being a positive nonsquare integer). This had been studied by Fermat and Wallis and even earlier by scientists of India and Greece. A complete investigation of the problem was soon undertaken by Lagrange. In 1753 Euler proved the impossibility of solving $x^3 + y^3 = z^3$ in which x, y, and z are integers, $xyz \neq 0$ (a particular case of Fermat's last theorem); his demonstration, based on the method of infinite descent and using complex numbers of the form $a + b\sqrt{-3}$, is thoroughly described in his *Vollständige Anleitung zur Algebra*, the second volume of which (1769) has a large section devoted to Diophantine analysis.

In all these cases Euler used methods of arithmetic and algebra, but he was also the first to use analytical methods in number theory. To solve the partition problem posed in 1740 by P. Naudé, concerning the total number of ways the positive integer n is obtainable as a sum of positive integers $m < n$, Euler used the expansions of certain infinite products into a power series whose coefficients give the solution (1748). In particular, in the expansion

$$\prod_{r=1}^{\infty} (1 - x^r) = \sum_{k=-\infty}^{\infty} (-1)^k x^{(3k^2-k)/2}$$

the right-hand series is one of theta functions, introduced much later by C. Jacobi in his theory of elliptic functions. Earlier, in 1737, Euler had deduced the famous identity

$$\sum_{n=1}^{\infty} \frac{1}{n^s} = \prod_p \left[1\Big/\left(1 - \frac{1}{p^s}\right)\right],$$

where the sum extends over all positive integers n and the product over all primes p (1744), the left-hand side is what Riemann later called the zeta-function $\zeta(s)$.

Using summation of divergent series and induction, Euler discovered in 1749 (1768) a functional equation involving $\zeta(s)$, $\zeta(1 - s)$, and $\Gamma(s)$, which was rediscovered and established by Riemann, the first scientist to define the zeta-function also for complex values of the argument. In the nineteenth and twentieth centuries, the zeta-function became one of the principal means of analytic number theory, particularly in the studies of the laws of distribution of prime numbers by Dirichlet, Chebyshev, Riemann, Hadamard, de la Vallée-Poussin, and others.

Finally, Euler studied mathematical constants and formulated important problems relevant to the theory of transcendental numbers. His expression of the number e in the form of a continued fraction (1744) was used by J. H. Lambert (1768) in his demonstration of irrationality of the numbers e and π. F. Lindemann employed Euler's formula $\ln(-1) = \pi i$ (discovered as early as 1728) to prove that π is transcendental (1882). The hypothesis of the transcendence of a^b, where a is any algebraic number $\neq 0,1$ and b is any irrational algebraic number—formulated by D. Hilbert in 1900 and proved by A. Gelfond in 1934—presents a generalization of Euler's corresponding supposition about rational-base logarithms of rational numbers (1748).

Algebra. When mathematicians of the seventeenth century formulated the fundamental theorem that an algebraic equation of degree n with real coefficients has n roots, which could be imaginary, it was yet unknown whether the domain of imaginary roots was restricted to numbers of the form $a + bi$, which, following Gauss, are now called complex numbers. Many mathematicians thought that there existed imaginary quantities of another kind. In his letters to Nikolaus I Bernoulli and to Goldbach (dated 1742), Euler stated for the first time the theorem that every algebraic polynomial of degree n with real coefficients may be resolved into real linear or quadratic factors, that is, possesses n roots of the form $a + bi$ (1743). The theorem was proved by d'Alembert (1748) and by Euler himself (1751). Both proofs, quite different in ideas, had omissions and were rendered more precise during the nineteenth century.

Euler also aspired—certainly in vain—to find the general form of solution by radicals for equations of degree higher than the fourth (1738, 1764). He elaborated approximating methods of solutions for numerical equations (1748) and studied the elimination problem. Thus, he gave the first proof of the theorem, which was known to Newton, that two algebraic curves of degrees m and n, respectively, intersect in mn points (1748, 1750). It should be added that Euler's *Vollständige Anleitung zur Algebra,* published in many editions in English, Dutch, Italian, French, and Russian, greatly influenced nineteenth- and twentieth-century texts on the subject.

Infinite Series. In Euler's works, infinite series, which previously served mainly as an auxiliary means for solving problems, became a subject of study. One example, his investigation of the zeta-function, has already been mentioned. The point of departure was the problem of summation of the reciprocals of the squares of the integers

$$\sum_{n=1}^{\infty} \frac{1}{n^2} = \zeta(2),$$

which had been vainly approached by the Bernoulli brothers, Stirling, and other outstanding mathematicians. Euler solved in 1735 a much more general problem and demonstrated that for any even integer number $2k > 0$,

$$\zeta(2k) = a_{2k}\pi^{2k},$$

where a_{2k} are rational numbers (1740), expressed through coefficients of the Euler-Maclaurin summation formula (1750) and, consequently, through Bernoulli numbers (1755). The problem of the arithmetic nature of $\zeta(2k + 1)$ remains unsolved.

The summation formula was discovered by Euler no later than 1732 (1738) and demonstrated in 1735 (1741); it was independently discovered by Maclaurin no later than 1738 (1742). The formula, one of the most important in the calculus of finite differences, represents the partial sum of a series, $\Sigma_{n=1}^{m} u(n)$, by another infinite series involving the integral and the derivatives of the general term $u(n)$. Later Euler expressed the coefficients of the latter series through Bernoulli numbers (1755). Euler knew that although this infinite series generally diverges, its partial sums under certain conditions might serve as a brilliant means of approximating the calculations shown by James Stirling (1730) in a particular case of

$$\sum_{n=2}^{m} \log(n!).$$

By means of the summation formula, Euler in 1735 calculated (1741) to sixteen decimal places the value of Euler's constant,

$$C = 0.57721566\cdots,$$

belonging to an asymptotic formula,

$$\sum_{n=1}^{m} \frac{1}{n} \simeq \ln m + C,$$

which he discovered in 1731 (1738).

The functions studied in the eighteenth century were, with rare exceptions, analytic, and therefore Euler made great use of power series. His special merit was the introduction of a new and extremely important class of trigonometric Fourier series. In a letter to Goldbach (1744), he expressed for the first time an algebraic function by such a series (1755),

$$\frac{\pi}{2} - \frac{x}{2} = \sin x + \frac{\sin 2x}{2} + \frac{\sin 3x}{3} + \cdots.$$

He later found other expansions (1760), deducing in 1777 a formula of Fourier coefficients for expansion of a given function into a series of cosines on the interval $(0,\pi)$, pointing out that coefficients of expansion into a series of sines could be deduced analogously (1798). Fourier, having no knowledge of Euler's work, deduced in 1807 the same formulas. For his part, Euler did not know that coefficients of expansion into a series of cosines had been given by Clairaut in 1759.

Euler also introduced expansion of functions into infinite products and into the sums of elementary fractions, which later acquired great importance in the general theory of analytic functions. Numerous methods of transformation of infinite series, products, and continued fractions into one another are also his.

Eighteenth-century mathematicians distinguished

convergent series from divergent series, but the general theory of convergence was still missing. Algebraic and analytic operations on infinite series were similar to those on finite polynomials, without any restrictions. It was supposed that identical laws operate in both cases. Several tests of convergence already known found almost no application. Opinions, however, differed on the problem of admissibility of divergent series. Many mathematicians were radically against their employment. Euler, sure that important correct results might be arrived at by means of divergent series, set about the task of establishing the legitimacy of their application. With this aim, he suggested a new, wider definition of the concept of the sum of a series, which coincides with the traditional definition if the series converges; he also suggested two methods of summation (1755). Precise grounding and further development of these fruitful ideas were possible only toward the end of the nineteenth century and the beginning of the twentieth century.[32]

The Concept of Function. Discoveries in the field of analysis made in the middle of the eighteenth century (many of them his own) were systematically summarized by Euler in the trilogy *Introductio in analysin infinitorum* (1748),[15] *Institutiones calculi differentialis* (1755),[18] and *Institutiones calculi integralis* (1768–1770). The books are still of interest, especially the first volume of the *Introductio.* Many of the problems considered there, however, are now so far developed that knowledge of them is limited to a few specialists, who can trace in the book the development of many fruitful methods of analysis.

In the *Introductio* Euler presented the first clear statement of the idea that mathematical analysis is a science of functions; and he also presented a more thorough investigation of the very concept of function. Defining function as an analytic expression somehow composed of variables and constants—following in this respect Johann I Bernoulli (1718)—Euler defined precisely the term "analytic expression": functions are produced by means of algebraic operations, and also of elementary and other transcendental operations, carried out by integration. Here the classification of functions generally used today is also given; Euler speaks of functions defined implicitly and by parametric representation. Further on he states his belief, shared by other mathematicians, that all analytic expressions might be given in the form of infinite power series or generalized power series with fractional or negative exponents. Thus, functions studied in mathematical analysis generally are analytic functions with some isolated singular points. Euler's remark that functions are considered not only for real but also for imaginary values of independent variables was very important.

Even at that time, however, the class of analytic functions was insufficient for the requirements of analysis and its applications, particularly for the solution of the problem of the vibrating string. Here Euler encountered "arbitrary" functions, geometrically represented in piecewise smooth plane curves of arbitrary form—functions which are, generally speaking, nonanalytic (1749). The problem of the magnitude of the class of functions applied in mathematical physics and generally in analysis and the closely related problem of the possibility of analytic expression of nonanalytic functions led to a lengthy polemic involving many mathematicians, including Euler, d'Alembert, and Daniel Bernoulli. One of the results of this controversy over the problem of the vibrating string was the general arithmetical definition of a function as a quantity whose values somehow change with the changes of independent variables; the definition was given by Euler in *Institutiones calculi differentialis.*[18] He had, however, already dealt with the interpretation of a function as a correspondence of values in his *Introductio.*

Elementary Functions. The major portion of the first volume of the *Introductio* is devoted to the theory of elementary functions, which is developed by means of algebra and of infinite series and products. Concepts of infinitesimal and infinite quantity are used, but those of differential and integral calculus are lacking. Among other things, Euler here for the first time described the analytic theory of trigonometric functions and gave a remarkably simple, although nonrigorous, deduction of Moivre's formula and also of his own (1743),

$$e^{\pm xi} = \cos x \pm i \sin x.$$

This was given earlier by R. Cotes (1716) in a somewhat different formulation, but it was widely used only by Euler. The logarithmic function was considered by Euler in the *Introductio* only for the positive independent variable. However, he soon published his complete theory of logarithms of complex numbers (1751)—which some time before had ended the arguments over logarithms of negative numbers between Leibniz and Johann Bernoulli and between d'Alembert and Euler himself in their correspondence (1747–1748). Euler had come across the problem (1727–1728) when he discussed in his correspondence with Johann I Bernoulli the problem of the graphics of the function $y = (-1)^x$ and arrived at the equality $\ln(-1) = \pi i$.

Functions of a Complex Variable. The study of elementary functions brought d'Alembert (1747–1748)

 EULER

and Euler (1751) to the conclusion that the domain of complex numbers is closed (in modern terms) with regard to all algebraic and transcendental operations. They both also made early advances in the general theory of analytic functions. In 1752 d'Alembert, investigating problems of hydrodynamics, discovered equations connecting the real and imaginary parts of an analytic function $u(x,y) + iv(x,y)$. In 1777 Euler deduced the same equations,

$$\frac{\partial u}{\partial x} = \frac{\partial v}{\partial y}, \quad \frac{\partial u}{\partial y} = -\frac{\partial v}{\partial x},$$

from general analytical considerations, developing a new method of calculation of definite integrals $\int f(z)\,dz$ by means of an imaginary substitution

$$z = x + iy$$

(1793, 1797). He thus discovered (1794) that

$$\int_0^\infty \frac{\sin x}{x}\,dx = \frac{\pi}{2}.$$

Euler also used analytic functions of a complex variable, both in the study of orthogonal trajectories by means of their conformal mapping (1770) and in his works on cartography (1778). (The term *projectio conformis* was introduced by a St. Petersburg academician, F. T. Schubert [1789].) All of these ideas were developed in depth in the elaboration of the general theory of analytic functions by Cauchy (1825) and Riemann (1854), after whom the above-cited equations of d'Alembert and Euler are named.

Although Euler went from numbers of the form $x + iy$ to the point $u(x,y)$ and back, and used a trigonometric form $r(\cos\varphi + i\sin\varphi)$, he saw in imaginary numbers only convenient notations void of real meaning. A somewhat less than successful attempt at geometric interpretation undertaken by H. Kühn (1753) met with sharp critical remarks from Euler.

Differential and Integral Calculus. Both branches of infinitesimal analysis were enriched by Euler's numerous discoveries. Among other things in the *Institutiones calculi differentialis,* he thoroughly elaborated formulas of differentiation under substitution of variables; revealed his theorem on homogeneous functions, stated for $f(x,y)$ as early as 1736; proved the theorem of Nikolaus I Bernoulli (1721) that for $z = f(x,y)$

$$\frac{\partial^2 z}{\partial x \partial y} = \frac{\partial^2 z}{\partial y \partial x};$$

deduced the necessary condition for the exact differential of $f(x,y)$; applied Taylor's series to finding extrema of $f(x)$; and investigated extrema of $f(x,y)$, inaccurately formulating, however, sufficient conditions.

The first two chapters of the *Institutiones* are devoted to the elements of the calculus of finite differences. Euler approached differential calculus as a particular case, we would say a limiting case, of the method of finite differences used when differences of the function and of the independent variable approach zero. During the eighteenth century it was often said against differential calculus that all its formulas were incorrect because the deductions were based on the principle of neglecting infinitely small summands, e.g., on equalities of the kind $a + \alpha = a$, where α is infinitesimal with respect to a. Euler thought that such criticism could be obviated only by supposing all infinitesimals and differentials equal to zero, and therefore he elaborated an original calculus of zeroes. This concept, although not contradictory in itself, did not endure because it proved insufficient in many problems; a strict grounding of analysis was possible if the infinitesimals were interpreted as variables tending to the limit zero.

The methods of indefinite integration in the *Institutiones calculi integralis* (I, 1768) are described by Euler in quite modern fashion and in a detail that practically exhausts all the cases in which the result of integration is expressible in elementary functions. He invented many of the methods himself; the expression "Euler substitution" (for rationalization of certain irrational differentials) serves as a reminder of the fact. Euler calculated many difficult definite integrals, thus laying the foundations of the theory of special functions. In 1729, already studying interpolation of the sequence $1!, 2!, \cdots, n!, \cdots$, he introduced Eulerian integrals of the first and second kind (Legendre's term), today called the beta- and gamma-functions (1738). He later discovered a number of their properties.

Particular cases of the beta-function were first considered by Wallis in 1656. The functions B and Γ, together with the zeta-function and the so-called Bessel functions (see below), are among the most important transcendental functions. Euler's main contribution to the theory of elliptic integrals was his discovery of the general addition theorem (1768). Finally, the theory of multiple integrals also goes back to Euler; he introduced double integrals and established the rule of substitution (1770).

Differential Equations. The *Institutiones calculi integralis* exhibits Euler's numerous discoveries in the theory of both ordinary and partial differential equations, which were especially useful in mechanics.

Euler elaborated many problems in the theory of ordinary linear equations: a classical method for solving reduced linear equations with constant coefficients, in which he strictly distinguished between the general and the particular integral (1743); works on linear systems, conducted simultaneously with d'Alembert (1750); solution of the general linear equation of order n with constant coefficients by reduction to the equation of the same form of order $n - 1$ (1753). After 1738 he successfully applied to second-order linear equations with variable coefficients a method that was highly developed in the nineteenth century; this consisted of the presentation of particular solutions in the form of generalized power series. Another Eulerian device, that of expressing solutions by definite integrals that depend on a parameter (1763), was extended by Laplace to partial differential equations (1777).

One can trace back to Euler (1741) and Daniel Bernoulli the method of variation of constants later elaborated by Lagrange (1777). The method of an integrating factor was also greatly developed by Euler, who applied it to numerous classes of first-order differential equations (1768) and extended it to higher-order equations (1770). He devoted a number of articles to the Riccati equation, demonstrating its involvement with continued fractions (1744). In connection with his works on the theory of lunar motion, Euler created the widely used device of approximating the solution of the equation $dy/dx = f(x,y)$, with initial condition $x = x_0$, $y = y_0$ (1768), extending it to second-order equations (1769). This Euler method of open polygons was used by Cauchy in the 1820's to demonstrate the existence theorem for the solution of the above-mentioned equation (1835, 1844). Finally, Euler discovered tests for singular solutions of first-order equations (1768).

Among the large cycle of Euler's works on partial differential equations begun in the middle of the 1730's with the study of separate kinds of first-order equations, which he had encountered in certain problems of geometry (1740), the most important are the studies on second-order linear equations—to which many problems of mathematical physics may be reduced. First was the problem of small plane vibrations of a string, the wave equation originally solved by d'Alembert with the so-called method of characteristics. Given a general solution expressible as a sum of two arbitrary functions, the initial conditions and the boundary conditions of the problem admitted of arriving at solutions in concrete cases (1749). Euler immediately tested this method of d'Alembert's and further elaborated it, eliminating unnecessary restrictions imposed by d'Alembert upon the initial shape and velocity of the string (1749). As previously mentioned, the two mathematicians engaged in an argument which grew more involved when Daniel Bernoulli asserted that any solution of the wave equation might be expressed by a trigonometric series (1755). D'Alembert and Euler agreed that such a solution could not be sufficiently general. The discussion was joined by Lagrange, Laplace, and other mathematicians of great reputation and lasted for over half a century; not until Fourier (1807, 1822) was the way found to the correct formulation and solution of the problem. Euler later developed the method of characteristics more thoroughly (1766, 1767).

Euler encountered equations in other areas of what became mathematical physics: in hydrodynamics; in the problem of vibrations of membranes, which he reduced to the so-called Bessel equation and solved (1766) by means of the Bessel functions $J_n(x)$; and in the problem of the motion of air in pipes (1772). Some classes of equations studied by Euler for velocities close to or surpassing the velocity of sound continue to figure in modern aerodynamics.

Calculus of Variations. Starting with several problems solved by Johann and Jakob Bernoulli, Euler was the first to formulate the principal problems of the calculus of variations and to create general methods for their solution. In *Methodus inveniendi lineas curvas . . .*[13] he systematically developed his discoveries of the 1730's (1739, 1741). The very title of the work shows that Euler widely employed geometric representations of functions as flat curves. Here he introduced, using different terminology, the concepts of function and variation and distinguished between problems of absolute extrema and relative extrema, showing how the latter are reduced to the former. The problem of the absolute extremum of the function of several independent variables,

$$\int_a^b F(x, y, y')\,dx,$$

where F is the given and $y(x)$ the desired minimizing or maximizing function, is treated as the limiting problem for the ordinary extremum of the function

$$W_n(y_0, y_1, \cdots, y_n) = \sum_{k=0}^{n-1} F\left(x_k, y_k, \frac{y_{k+1} - y_k}{\Delta x}\right) \Delta x,$$

where $x_k = a + k\,\Delta x$, $\Delta x = (b - a)/n$, $k = 0, 1, \cdots, n$ (and $n \to \infty$). Thus Euler deduced the differential equation named after him to which the function $y(x)$ should correspond; this necessary condition was generalized for the case where F involves the derivatives $y', y'', \cdots, y^{(n)}$. In this way the solution of a problem in the calculus of variations might always be reduced to integration of a differential equation. A century and a half later the situation had changed. The direct method imagined by Euler, which he had employed only to obtain his differential equation, had (together with similar methods) acquired independent value for rigorous or approximate solution of variational problems and the corresponding differential equations.

In the mid-1750's, after Lagrange had created new algorithms and notations for the calculus of variations, Euler abandoned the former exposition and gave instead a detailed and lucid exposition of Lagrange's method, considering it a new calculus—which he called variational (1766). He applied the calculus of variations to problems of extreme values of double integrals with constant limits in volume III of the *Institutiones calculi integralis* (1770); soon thereafter he suggested still another method of exposition of the calculus, one which became widely used.

Geometry. Most of Euler's geometrical discoveries were made by application of the methods of algebra and analysis. He gave two different methods for an analytical exposition of the system of spherical trigonometry (1755, 1782). He showed how the trigonometry of spheroidal surfaces might be applied to higher geodesy (1755). In volume II of the *Introductio* he surpassed his contemporaries in giving a consistent algebraic development of the theory of second-order curves, proceeding from their general equation (1748). He constituted the theory of third-order curves by analogy. But Euler's main achievement was that for the first time he studied thoroughly the general equation of second-order surfaces, applying Euler angles in corresponding transformations.

Euler's studies of the geodesic lines on a surface are prominent in differential geometry; the problem was pointed out to him by Johann Bernoulli (1732, 1736, and later). But still more important were his pioneer investigations in the theory of surfaces, from which Monge and other geometers later proceeded. In 1763 Euler made the first substantial advance in the study of the curvature of surfaces; in particular, he expressed the curvature of an arbitrary normal section by principal curvatures (1767). He went on to study developable surfaces, introducing Gaussian coordinates (1772), which became widely used in the nineteenth century. In a note written about 1770 but not published until 1862 Euler discovered the necessary condition for applicability of surfaces that was independently established by Gauss (1828). In 1775 Euler successfully renewed elaboration of the general theory of space curves (1786), beginning where Clairaut had left off in 1731.

Euler was also the author of the first studies on topology. In 1735 he gave a solution to the problem of the seven bridges of Königsberg: the bridges, spanning several arms of a river, must all be crossed without recrossing any (1741). In a letter to Goldbach (1750), he cited (1758) a number of properties of polyhedra, among them the following: the number of vertices, S, edges, A, and sides, H, of a polyhedron are connected by an equality $S - A + H = 2$. A hundred years later it was discovered that the theorem had been known to Descartes. The Euler characteristic $S - A + H$ and its generalization for multidimensional complexes as given by H. Poincaré is one of the principal invariants of modern topology.

Mechanics. In an introduction to the *Mechanica* (1736) Euler outlined a large program of studies embracing every branch of the science. The distinguishing feature of Euler's investigations in mechanics as compared to those of his predecessors is the systematic and successful application of analysis. Previously the methods of mechanics had been mostly synthetic and geometrical; they demanded too individual an approach to separate problems. Euler was the first to appreciate the importance of introducing uniform analytic methods into mechanics, thus enabling its problems to be solved in a clear and direct way. Euler's concept is manifest in both the introduction and the very title of the book, *Mechanica sive motus scientia analytice exposita.*

This first large work on mechanics was devoted to the kinematics and dynamics of a point-mass. The first volume deals with the free motion of a point-mass in a vacuum and in a resisting medium; the section on the motion of a point-mass under a force directed to a fixed center is a brilliant analytical reformulation of the corresponding section of Newton's *Principia;* it was sort of an introduction to Euler's further works on celestial mechanics. In the second volume, Euler studied the constrained motion of a point-mass; he obtained three equations of motion in space by projecting forces on the axes of a moving trihedral of a trajectory described by a moving point, i.e., on the tangent, principal normal, and binormal. Motion in the plane is considered analogously. In the chapter on the motion of a point on a given surface, Euler solved a number of problems of the differential geometry of surfaces and of the theory of geodesics.

The *Theoria motus corporum solidorum,*[19] published almost thirty years later (1765), is related to the *Mechanica.* In the introduction to this work, Euler gave a new exposition of punctual mechanics and followed Maclaurin's example (1742) in projecting the forces onto the axes of a fixed orthogonal rectilinear system. Establishing that the instantaneous motion of a solid body might be regarded as composed of rectilinear translation and instant rotation, Euler devoted special attention to the study of rotatory motion. Thus, he gave formulas for projections of instantaneous angular velocity on the axes of coordinates (with application of Euler angles), and framed dynamical differential equations referred to the principal axes of inertia, which determine this motion. Special mention should be made of the problem of motion of a heavy solid body about a fixed point, which Euler solved for a case in which the center of gravity coincides with the fixed point. The law of motion in such a case is, generally speaking, expressed by means of elliptic integrals. Euler was led to this problem by the study of precession of the equinoxes and of the nutation of the terrestrial axis (1751).[33] Other cases in which the differential equations of this problem can be integrated were discovered by Lagrange (1788) and S. V. Kovalevskaya (1888). Euler considered problems of the mechanics of solid bodies as early as the first St. Petersburg period.

In one of the two appendixes to the *Methodus*...[13] Euler suggested a formulation of the principle of least action for the case of the motion of a point under a central force: the trajectory described by the point minimizes the integral $\int mv\, ds$. Maupertuis had stated at nearly the same time the principle of least action in a much more particular form. Euler thus laid the mathematical foundation of the numerous studies on variational principles of mechanics and physics which are still being carried out.

In the other appendix to the *Methodus,* Euler, at the insistence of Daniel Bernoulli, applied the calculus of variations to some problems of the theory of elasticity, which he had been intensively elaborating since 1727. In this appendix, which was in fact the first general work on the mathematical theory of elasticity, Euler studied bending and vibrations of elastic bands (either homogeneous or nonhomogeneous) and of a plate under different conditions; considered nine types of elastic curves; and deduced the famous Euler buckling formula, or Euler critical load, used to determine the strength of columns.

Hydromechanics. Euler's first large work on fluid mechanics was *Scientia navalis.* Volume I contains a general theory of equilibrium of floating bodies including an original elaboration of problems of stability and of small oscillations in the neighborhood of an equilibrium position. The second volume applies general theorems to the case of a ship.

From 1753 to 1755 Euler elaborated in detail an analytical theory of fluid mechanics in three classic memoirs—"Principes généraux de l'état d'équilibre des fluides"; "Principes généraux du mouvement des fluides"; and "Continuation des recherches sur la théorie du mouvement des fluides"—all published simultaneously (1757).[34] Somewhat earlier (1752) the "Principia motus fluidorum" was written; it was not published, however, until 1761.[35] Here a system of principal formulas of hydrostatics and hydrodynamics was for the first time created; it comprised the continuity equation for liquids with constant density; the velocity-potential equation (usually called after Laplace); and the general Euler equations for the motion of an incompressible liquid, gas, etc. As has generally been the case in mathematical physics, the main innovations were in the application of partial differential equations to the problems. At the beginning of the "Continuation des recherches" Euler emphasized that he had reduced the whole of the theory of liquids to two analytic equations and added:

> However sublime are the researches on fluids which we owe to the Messrs. Bernoulli, Clairaut and d'Alembert, they flow so naturally from my two general formulae that one cannot sufficiently admire this accord of their profound meditations with the simplicity of the principles from which I have drawn my two equations, and to which I was led immediately by the first axioms of mechanics.[36]

Euler also investigated a number of concrete problems on the motion of liquids and gases in pipes, on vibration of air in pipes, and on propagation of sound. Along with this, he worked on problems of hydrotechnology, discussed, in part, above. Especially remarkable were the improvements he introduced into the design of a hydraulic machine imagined by Segner in 1749 and the theory of hydraulic turbines, which he created in accordance with the principle of action and reaction (1752–1761).[37]

Astronomy. Euler's studies in astronomy embraced a great variety of problems: determination of the orbits of comets and planets by a few observations, methods of calculation of the parallax of the sun, the theory of refraction, considerations on the physical nature of comets, and the problem of retardation of planetary motions under the action of cosmic ether. His most outstanding works, for which he won many prizes from the Paris Académie des Sciences, are concerned with celestial mechanics, which especially attracted scientists at that time.

The observed motions of the planets, particularly of Jupiter and Saturn, as well as the moon, were evidently different from the calculated motions based on Newton's theory of gravitation. Thus, the calculations of Clairaut and d'Alembert (1745) gave the value of eighteen years for the period of revolution of the lunar perigee, whereas observations showed this value to be nine years. This caused doubts about the validity of Newton's system as a whole. For a long time Euler joined these scientists in thinking that the law of gravitation needed some corrections. In 1749 Clairaut established that the difference between theory and observation was due to the fact that he and others solving the corresponding differential equation had restricted themselves to the first approximation. When he calculated the second approximation, it was satisfactorily in accordance with the observed data. Euler did not at once agree. To put his doubts at rest, he advised the St. Petersburg Academy to announce a competition on the subject. Euler soon determined that Clairaut was right, and on Euler's recommendation his composition received the prize of the Academy (1752). Euler was still not completely satisfied, however. In 1751 he had written his own *Theoria motus lunae exhibens omnes ejus inaequalitates* (published in 1753), in which he elaborated an original method of approximate solution to the three-body problem, the so-called first Euler lunar theory. In the appendix he described another method which was the earliest form of the general method of variation of elements. Euler's numerical results also conformed to Newton's theory of gravitation.

The first Euler lunar theory had an important practical consequence: T. Mayer, an astronomer from Göttingen, compiled, according to its formulas, lunar tables (1755) that enabled the calculation of the position of the moon and thus the longitude of a ship with an exactness previously unknown in navigation. The British Parliament had announced as early as 1714 a large cash prize for the method of determination of longitude at sea with error not to exceed half a degree, and smaller prizes for less exact methods. The prize was not awarded until 1765; £3,000 went to Mayer's widow and £300 to Euler for his preliminary theoretical work. Simultaneously a large prize was awarded to J. Harrison for his construction of a more nearly perfect chronometer. Lunar tables were included in all nautical almanacs after 1767, and the method was used for about a century.

From 1770 to 1772 Euler elaborated his second theory of lunar motion, which he published in the *Theoria motuum lunae, nova methodo pertractata* (1772).[24] For various reasons, the merits of the new method could be correctly appreciated only after G. W. Hill brilliantly developed the ideas of the composition in 1877–1888.

Euler devoted numerous works to the calculation of perturbations of planetary orbits caused by the mutual gravitation of Jupiter and Saturn (1749, 1769) as well as of the earth and the other planets (1771). He continued these studies almost to his death.

Physics. Euler's principal contribution to physics consisted in mathematical elaboration of the problems discussed above. He touched upon various physical problems which would not yield to mathematical analysis at that time. He aspired to create a uniform picture of the physical world. He had been, as pointed out earlier, closer to Cartesian natural philosophy than to Newtonian, although he was not a direct representative of Cartesianism. Rejecting the notion of empty space and the possibility of action at a distance, he thought that the universe is filled up with ether—a thin elastic matter with extremely low density, like super-rarified air. This ether contains material particles whose main property is impenetrability. Euler thought it possible to explain the diversity of the observed phenomena (including electricity, light, gravitation, and even the principle of least action) by the hypothetical mechanical properties of ether. He also had to introduce magnetic whirls into the doctrine of magnetism; these are even thinner and move more quickly than ether.

In physics Euler built up many artificial models and hypotheses which were short-lived. But his main concept of the unity of the forces of nature acting deterministically in some medium proved to be important for the development of physics, owing especially to *Lettres à une princesse d'Allemagne.* Thus, his views on the nature of electricity were the prototype of the theory of electric and magnetic fields of Faraday and Maxwell. His theory of ether influenced Riemann.

Euler's works on optics were widely known and important in the physics of the eighteenth century. Rejecting the dominant corpuscular theory of light, he constructed his own theory in which he attributed the cause of light to peculiar oscillations of ether. His *Nova theoria lucis et colorum* (1746)[38] explained some, but not all, phenomena. Proceeding from certain analogies that later proved incorrect, Euler concluded that the elimination of chromatic aberration of optic lenses was possible (1747); he conducted experiments with lenses filled with water to confirm the conclusion. This provoked objections by the English optician Dollond, who, following Newton, held that dispersion was inevitable. The result of this polemic, in which both parties were partly right and partly wrong, was the creation by Dollond of achromatic telescopes (1757), a turning point in optical technology. For his part, Euler, in his *Dioptrica,* laid the foundations of the calculation of optical systems.

NOTES

All works cited are listed in the Bibliography. References to

Euler's *Opera omnia* (see [1] in Bibliography) include series and volume number.

1. 20, p. 75.
2. "Constructio linearum isochronarum in medio quocunque resistente," in 1, 2nd ser., VI, p. 1.
3. "Methodus inveniendi traiectorias reciprocas algebraicas," in 1, 1st ser., XXVII, p. 1.
4. To be published in 1, 2nd ser., XX.
5. 1, 3rd ser., I, p. 181.
6. 26, p. 51.
7. 13, II, p. 182.
8. *Einleitung zur Rechen-Kunst zum Gebrauch des Gymnasii bey der Kayserlichen Academie der Wissenschafften in St. Petersburg* (St. Petersburg, 1738–1740). See 1, 3rd ser., II, 1–303.
9. *Mechanica sive motus scientia analytice exposita,* 2 vols. (St. Petersburg, 1736). See 1, 2nd ser., I and II.
10. 20, p. 77.
11. *Neue Grundsätze der Artillerie aus dem Englischen des Herrn Benjamin Robins übersetzt und mit vielen Anmerkungen versehen* (Berlin, 1745). See 1, 2nd ser., XIV.
12. See 1, 2nd ser., XIV, 468–477.
13. *Methodus inveniendi lineas curvas maximi minimive proprietate gaudentes* (Lausanne-Geneva, 1744). Sec 1, 1st scr., XXIV.
14. *Theoria motuum planetarum et cometarum* (Berlin, 1744). See 1, 2nd ser., XXVIII, 105–251.
15. *Introductio in analysin infinitorum,* 2 vols. (Lausanne, 1748). See 1, 1st ser., VIII and IX.
16. *Scientia navalis,* 2 vols. (St. Petersburg, 1749). See 1, 2nd ser., XVIII and XIX.
17. *Theoria motus lunae* (Berlin, 1753). See 1, 2nd ser., XXIII, 64–336.
18. *Institutiones calculi differentialis cum eius usu in analysi finitorum ac doctrina serierum* (Berlin, 1755). See 1, 1st ser., X.
19. *Theoria motus corporum solidorum seu rigidorum ex primis nostrae cognitionis principiis stabilita . . .* (Rostock-Greifswald, 1765). See 1, 2nd ser., III and IV.
20. The work, which comprises 234 letters, was published at St. Petersburg in 3 vols. The first two vols. (letters 1–154) appeared in 1768; vol. III appeared in 1772. See 1, 3rd ser., XI and XII.
21. *Gedancken von den Elementen der Cörper, in welchen das Lehr-Gebäude von den einfachen Dingen und Monaden geprüfet und das wahre Wesen der Cörper entdecket wird* (Berlin, 1746). See 1, 3rd ser., II, 347–366.
22. "Exposé concernant l'examen de la lettre de M. de Leibnitz, alléguée par M. le Professeur Koenig, dans le mois de mars 1751 des Actes de Leipzig, à l'occasion du principe de la moindre action." See 1, 2nd ser., V, 64–73.
23. The work was first published at St. Petersburg in Russian (vol. I, 1768; vol. II, 1769). It then appeared in a two-volume German edition (St. Petersburg, 1770). See 1, 1st ser., I.
24. *Theoria motuum lunae, nova methodo pertractata* (St. Petersburg, 1772). See 1, 2nd ser., XXII.
25. The work was published sequentially, in 3 vols., at St. Petersburg. Vol. I deals with principles of optics (1769); vol. II with construction of telescopes (1770); and vol. III with construction of microscopes (1771). See 1, 3rd ser., III and IV.
26. The work's 3 vols. were published sequentially in St. Petersburg in 1768, 1769, and 1770. See 1, 1st ser., XI, XII, and XIII.
27. To be published in 1, 2nd ser., XXI.
28. See 1, 3rd ser., VII, 200–247.
29. *Éclaircissemens sur les établissemens publics en faveur tant des veuves que des morts, avec la déscription d'une nouvelle espèce de tontine aussi favorable au public qu'utile à l'état* (St. Petersburg, 1776). See 1, 1st ser., VII, 181–245.
30. See 17.
31. Condorcet's *éloge* was first published in *Histoire de l'Académie royale des sciences pour l'année 1783* (Paris, 1786), pp. 37–68. It is reprinted in 1, 3rd ser., XII, 287–310.
32. See 50, chs. 1–2.
33. "Recherches sur la précession des équinoxes et sur la nutation de l'axe de la terre." See 1, 2nd ser., XXIX, 92–123.
34. See 1, 2nd ser., XII, 2–132.
35. See 1, 2nd ser., XII, 133–168.
36. See 1, 2nd ser., XII, 92, for the original French.
37. See 1, 2nd ser., XV, pt. 1, 1–39, 80–104, 157–218.
38. See 1, 3rd ser., V, 1–45.

BIBLIOGRAPHY

I. ORIGINAL WORKS. Euler wrote and published more than any other mathematician. During his lifetime about 560 books and articles appeared, and he once remarked to Count Orlov that he would leave enough memoirs to fill the pages of publications of the St. Petersburg Academy for twenty years after his death. Actually the publication of his literary legacy lasted until 1862. N. Fuss published about 220 works, and then the work was carried on by V. Y. Buniakovsky, P. L. Chebyshev, and P.-H. Fuss. Other works were found still later. The list compiled by Eneström (25) includes 856 titles and 31 works by J.-A. Euler, all written under the supervision of his father.

Euler's enormous correspondence (approximately 300 addressees), which he conducted from 1726 until his death, has been only partly published. For an almost complete description, with summaries and indexes, see (37) below. For his correspondence with Johann I Bernoulli, see (2) and (3); with Nikolaus I Bernoulli (2) and (4); with Daniel Bernoulli (2) and (3); with C. Goldbach (2) and (5); with J.-N. Delisle (6); with Clairaut (7); with d'Alembert (3) and (8); with T. Mayer (9); with Lagrange (10); with J. H. Lambert (11); with M. V. Lomonosov (12); with G. F. Müller (13); with J. D. Schumacher (13); with King Stanislas II (14); and with various others (15).

1. Euler's complete works are in the course of publication in a collection that has been destined from the outset to become one of the monuments of modern scholarship in the historiography of science: *Leonhardi Euleri Opera omnia* (Berlin-Göttingen-Leipzig-Heidelberg, 1911–). The *Opera omnia* is limited for the most part to republishing works that Euler himself prepared for the press. All texts appear in the original language of publication. Each volume is edited by a modern expert in the science it concerns, and many of the introductions constitute full histories of the relevant branch of science in the seventeenth and eighteenth centuries. Several volumes are in course of preparation. The work is organized in three series. The first series (*Opera mathematica*) comprises 29 vols. and is complete. The second series (*Opera mechanica et astronomica*) is to comprise 31 vols. and still lacks vols. XVI, XVII, XIX, XX, XXI, XXIV, XXVI, XXVII, and XXXI. The third series (*Opera physica, Miscellanea, Epistolae*) is to comprise 12 vols. and still lacks vols. IX and X. Euler's correspondence is not included in this edition.

2. P.-H. Fuss, ed., *Correspondance mathématique et physique de quelques célèbres géomètres du XVIIIe siècle,* 2 vols. (St. Petersburg, 1843). See vol. I for correspondence with Goldbach. For correspondence with Johann I Bernoulli, see II, 1–93; with Nikolaus I Bernoulli, II, 679–713; and with Daniel Bernoulli, II, 407–665.

3. G. Eneström, ed., *Bibliotheca mathematica,* 3rd ser., **4** (1903), 344–388; **5** (1904), 248–291; and **6** (1905), 16–87; for correspondence with Johann I Bernoulli. For Euler's correspondence with Daniel Bernoulli, see **7** (1906–1907); 126–156. See **11** (1911), 223–226, for correspondence with d'Alembert.

4. *Opera postuma,* I (St. Petersburg, 1862), 519–549.

5. A. P. Youschkevitch and E. Winter, eds., *Leonhard Euler und Christian Goldbach. Briefwechsel 1729–1764* (Berlin, 1965).

6. A. T. Grigorian, A. P. Youschkevitch, *et. al.,* eds., *Russko-frantsuskie nauchnye svyazi* (Leningrad, 1968), pp. 119–279.

7. G. Bigourdan, ed., "Lettres inédites d'Euler à Clairaut," in *Comptes rendus du Congrès des sociétés savantes, 1928* (Paris, 1930), pp. 26–40.

8. *Bullettino di bibliografia e di storia delle scienze matematiche e fisiche,* **19** (1886), 136–148.

9. Y. K. Kopelevich and E. Forbs, eds., *Istoriko-astronomicheskie issledovania,* V (1959), 271–444; X (1969), 285–308.

10. J. L. Lagrange, *Oeuvres,* J. A. Serret and G. Darboux, eds., XIV (Paris, 1892), 135–245.

11. K. Bopp, "Eulers und J.-H. Lamberts Briefwechsel," in *Abhandlungen der Preussischen Akademie der Wissenschaften* (1924), 7–37.

12. M. V. Lomonosov, *Sochinenia,* VIII (Moscow–Leningrad, 1948); and *Polnoe sobranie sochineny,* X (Moscow–Leningrad, 1957).

13. A. P. Youschkevitch, E. Winter, *et. al.,* eds., *Die Berliner und die Petersburger Akademie der Wissenschaften im Briefwechsel Leonhard Eulers,* 2 vols. See vol. I (Berlin, 1959) for letters to G. F. Müller; vol. II (Berlin, 1961) for letters to Nartov, Schumacher, Teplov, and others.

14. T. Kłado and R. W. Wołoszyński, eds., "Korrespondencja Stanisława Augusta z Leonardem Eulerem . . ." in *Studia i materiały z dziejów nauki polskiej,* ser. C, no. 10 (Warsaw, 1965), pp. 3–41.

15. V. I. Smirnov *et. al.,* eds., *Leonard Euler. Pisma k uchenym* (Moscow–Leningrad, 1963). Contains letters to Bailly, Bülfinger, Bonnet, C. L. Ehler, C. Wolff, and others.

II. SECONDARY LITERATURE.

16. J. W. Herzog, *Adumbratio eruditorum basilensium meritis apud exteros olim hodieque celebrium* (Basel, 1778), pp. 32–60.

17. N. Fuss, *Éloge de Monsieur Léonard Euler* (St. Petersburg, 1783). A German trans. of this is in (1), 1st ser., I, xliii–xcv.

18. Marquis de Condorcet, *Éloge de M. Euler,* in *Histoire de l'Académie royale des sciences pour l'année 1783* (Paris, 1786), pp. 37–68.

19. R. Wolf, *Biographien zur Kulturgeschichte der Schweiz,* IV (Zurich, 1862), 87–134.

20. P. Pekarski, "Ekaterina II i Eyler," in *Zapiski imperatorskoi akademii nauk,* **6** (1865), 59–92.

21. P. Pekarski, *Istoria imperatorskoi akademii nauk v Peterburge,* **1** (1870), 247–308. See also index.

22. M. I. Sukhomlinov, ed., *Materialy dlya istorii imperatorskoi akademii nauk, 1716–1760,* 10 vols. (St. Petersburg, 1885–1900). See indexes.

23. *Protokoly zasedany konferentsii imperatorskoi akademii nauk s 1725 po 1803 god,* 4 vols. (St. Petersburg, 1897–1911). See indexes.

24. A. Harnack, *Geschichte der königlichen preussischen Akademie der Wissenschaften,* I–III (Berlin, 1900).

25. G. Eneström, "Verzeichnis der Schriften Leonhard Eulers," in *Jahresbericht der Deutschen Mathematiker-Vereinigung,* Ergänzungsband **4** (Leipzig, 1910–1913). An important bibliography of Euler's works in three parts, listed in order of date of publication, in order of date of composition, and by subject. The first part is reprinted in (35), I, 352–386.

26. O. Spiess, *Leonhard Euler. Ein Beitrag zur Geistesgeschichte des XVIII. Jahrhunderts* (Frauenfeld–Leipzig, 1929).

27. G. Du Pasquier, *Léonard Euler et ses amis* (Paris, 1927).

28. W. Stieda, *Die Übersiedlung Leonhard Eulers von Berlin nach Petersburg* (Leipzig, 1931).

29. W. Stieda, *J. A. Euler in seinen Briefen, 1766–1790* (Leipzig, 1932).

30. A. Speiser, *Die Basler Mathematiker* (Basel, 1939).

31. E. Fueter, *Geschichte der exakten Wissenschaften in der Schweizerischen Aufklärung, 1680–1780* (Aarau, 1941).

32. Karl Euler, *Das Geschlecht Euler-Schölpi. Geschichte einer alten Familie* (Giessen, 1955).

33. E. and M. Winter, eds., *Die Registres der Berliner Akademie der Wissenschaften, 1746–1766. Dokumente für das Wirken Leonhard Eulers in Berlin* (Berlin, 1957). With an intro. by E. Winter.

34. *Istoria akademii nauk SSSR,* I (Moscow–Leningrad, 1958). See index.

35. Y. K. Kopelevich, M. V. Krutikova, G. M. Mikhailov, and N. M. Raskin, eds., *Rukopisnye materialy Leonarda Eylera v arkhive akademii nauk SSR,* 2 vols. (Moscow–Leningrad, 1962–1965). Vol. I contains an index of Euler's scientific papers, an index of official and personal documents, summaries of proceedings of conferences of the Academy of Sciences of St. Petersburg with respect to Euler's activities, an index of Euler's correspondence, a reedited version of the first part of (24), and many valuable indexes. Vol. II contains 12 of Euler's papers on mechanics published for the first time. See especially I, 120–228.

36. G. K. Mikhailov, "K pereezdu Leonarda Eylera v Peterburg" ("On Leonhard Euler's Removal to St. Petersburg," in *Izvestiya Akademii nauk SSSR. Otdelenie tekhnicheskikh nauk,* no. 3 (1957), 10–38.

37. V. I. Smirnov and A. P. Youschkevitch, eds., *Leonard Eyler. Perepiska. Annotirovannye ukazateli* (Leningrad, 1967).

38. F. Dannemann, *Die Naturwissenschaften in ihrer Entwicklung und in ihrem Zusammenhänge,* II–III (Leipzig, 1921). See indexes.

39. R. Taton, ed., *Histoire générale des sciences,* II (Paris, 1958). See index.

40. I. Y. Timchenko, *Osnovania teorii analiticheskikh funktsy. Chast I. Istoricheskie svedenia* (Odessa, 1899).

41. M. Cantor, *Vorlesungen über Geschichte der Mathematik,* III–IV (Leipzig, 1898–1908). See indexes.
42. H. Wieleitner, *Geschichte der Mathematik,* II (Berlin–Leipzig, 1911–1921). See indexes.
43. D. J. Struik, *A Concise History of Mathematics,* 2 vols. (New York, 1948; 2nd ed., London, 1956).
44. J. E. Hofmann, *Geschichte der Mathematik,* pt. 3 (Berlin, 1957). See index.
45. A. P. Youschkevitch, *Istoria matematika v Rossii do 1917 goda* (Moscow, 1968). See index.
46. Carl B. Boyer, *A History of Mathematics* (New York, 1968).
47. L. E. Dickson, *History of the Theory of Numbers,* 3 vols. (Washington, 1919–1927; 2nd ed., 1934). See indexes.
48. D. J. Struik, "Outline of a History of Differential Geometry," in *Isis,* **19** (1933), 92–120; **20** (1933), 161–191.
49. J. L. Coolidge, *A History of Geometrical Methods* (Oxford, 1940).
50. G. H. Hardy, *Divergent Series* (Oxford, 1949).
51. A. I. Markuschevitsch, *Skizzen zur Geschichte der analytischen Funktionen* (Berlin, 1955).
52. Carl B. Boyer, *History of Analytic Geometry* (New York, 1956). See index.
53. N. I. Simonov, *Prikladnye metody analiza u Eylera* (Moscow, 1957).
54. A. T. Grigorian, *Ocherki istorii mekhaniki v Rossii* (Moscow, 1961).
55. C. Truesdell, "The Rational Mechanics of Flexible or Elastic Bodies," in (1), 2nd ser., XI, pt. 2.
56. S. Timoschenko, *History of the Strength of Materials* (New York–Toronto–London, 1953).
57. A. P. Mandryka, *Istoria ballistiki* (Moscow–Leningrad, 1964).
58. N. N. Bogolyubov, *Istoria mekhaniki mashin* (Kiev, 1964).
59. F. Rosenberger, *Die Geschichte der Physik in Grundzügen,* II (Brunswick, 1884). See index.
60. V. F. Gnucheva, *Geograficheskу departament akademii nauk XVIII veka* (Moscow–Leningrad, 1946).
61. E. Hoppe, *Die Philosophie Leonhard Eulers* (Gotha, 1904).
62. A. Speiser, *Leonhard Euler und die deutsche Philosophie* (Zurich, 1934).
63. G. Kröber, *L. Euler. Briefe an eine deutsche Prinzessin. Philosophische Auswahl* (Leipzig, 1965), pp. 5–26. See also intro.

Many important essays on Euler's life, activity, and work are in the following five memorial volumes.

64. *Festschrift zur Feier 200. Geburtstages Leonhard Eulers* (Leipzig–Berlin, 1907), a publication of the Berliner Mathematische Gesellschaft.
65. A. M. Deborin, ed., *Leonard Eyler, 1707–1783* (Moscow–Leningrad, 1935).
66. E. Winter, *et. al.,* eds., *Die deutsch-russische Begegnung und Leonhard Euler . . .* (Berlin, 1958).
67. M. A. Lavrentiev, A. P. Youschkevitch, and A. T. Grigorian, eds., *Leonard Eyler. Sbornik statey* (Moscow, 1958). See especially pp. 268–375 and 377–413 for articles on Euler's work in astronomy and his physical concepts.
68. K. Schröder, ed., *Sammelband der zu Ehren des 250. Geburtstages Leonhard Eulers . . . vorgelegten Abhandlungen* (Berlin, 1959).
69. *Istoriko-matematicheskie issledovania* (Moscow, 1949–1969). For articles on Euler, see II, V–VII, X, XII, XIII, XVI, and XVII.
70. G. K. Mikhailov, "Leonard Eyler," in *Izvestiya akademii nauk SSSR. Otdelenie teknicheskikh nauk,* no. 1 (1955), 3–26, with extensive bibliography.

A. P. YOUSCHKEVITCH

EUTOCIUS OF ASCALON (*b.* Palestine, *ca.* A.D. 480)

Eutocius was the author of commentaries on three works by Archimedes. He also edited and commented on the first four books of the *Conics* of Apollonius.

His commentary on the first book of Archimedes' *On the Sphere and Cylinder* was dedicated to Ammonius, who was a pupil of Proclus and the teacher of Simplicius and many other sixth-century philosophers, and who could not have lived long after 510. Eutocius' four commentaries on the *Conics* are dedicated to Anthemius of Tralles, the architect of Hagia Sophia in Constantinople, who died about 534. For these reasons the central point of Eutocius' activities may be put about 510, and it has become conventional to date his birth about 480.

The old belief that Eutocius flourished about fifty years later arose from a note at the end of three of his Archimedean commentaries—on *On the Sphere and Cylinder,* Books I and II, and on the *Measurement of a Circle*—to the effect that each of them was "edited by Isidorus, the mechanical engineer, our teacher." These words, bracketed by Heiberg, cannot refer to Eutocius because they are not compatible with his relationship to Ammonius, for Isidorus of Miletus continued the construction of Hagia Sophia after the death of Anthemius about 534 and could not have been Eutocius' teacher. The words are best understood as an interpolation by a pupil of Isidorus and contain the interesting information that Isidorus revised the commentaries in question. Similarly, a reference in the commentary on *On the Sphere and Cylinder,* Book II (Archimedes, Heiberg ed., III, 84.8–11) to an instrument for drawing parabolas invented by "Isidorus, the mechanical engineer, our teacher" is also best understood as an interpolation. Tannery mentions the possibility that the Isidorus in question may have been a nephew of the successor of Anthemius, who supervised the reconstruction of Hagia Sophia after an earthquake in 557. Ascalon (now Ashkelon), where Eutocius was born, lay between Azotus (now Ashdod) and Gaza on the coast of Palestine; it is the city made famous in the lament of David over Saul and Jonathan: "Tell it not in Gath, publish it not in the streets of Askelon" (II Samuel 1:20). The *Suda Lexicon* relates an unedifying story of a Thracian mercenary named Eutocius who made a lot of money and tried to buy himself into society, first at Eleutheropolis (now Beyt Guvrin, Israel), then at Ascalon, but few have followed Tannery in seeing an ancestor; it seems more probable that Ascalon has been introduced into this story by reason of the mathematician's name and fame.

In his preface to his interpretation of the *Measurement of a Circle* Eutocius refers to his earlier commentaries on *On the Sphere and Cylinder,* and in the commentary on Book I he asks Ammonius to bear with him if he should have erred through youth (Archimedes, Heiberg ed., III, 2.13). He explains that he has found no satisfactory commentaries on Archimedes before his own time and promises further elucidation of the master if his work should meet with the approval of Ammonius. Apart from the *Measurement of a Circle,* he later wrote commentaries on both books of Archimedes' treatise *On Plane Equilibria.* The commentary on Book I was dedicated to an otherwise unknown Peter, whose name reveals him to have been a Christian. It is a fair inference that Eutocius did not know the works of Archimedes entitled *Quadrature of a Parabola* and *On Spirals,* for if he had, he would have referred to them at certain points of his commentary (Archimedes, Heiberg ed., III, 228.25; 278.10; 280.4; 286.13) instead of making less suitable references. Presumably the commentaries on Apollonius' *Conics* were written later than those on Archimedes' works, but there is no direct evidence. All these commentaries have survived. It has been debated whether he also wrote a commentary on Ptolemy's *Syntaxis,* but there is no suggestion of one in a passage of his commentary on the *Measurement of a Circle* (Archimedes, Heiberg ed., III, 232.15–17), where he mentions "Pappus and Theon and many others" as having interpreted that work.

Eutocius is not known to have done any original mathematical work, and his elucidations of Archimedes and Apollonius do not add anything of mathematical significance. Nevertheless, the examples of long multiplication in his commentary on the *Measurement of a Circle* are the best available evidence of the way in which the Greeks handled such operations, and he preserves solutions of mathematical problems by the earlier Greek geometers that are sometimes the sole evidence for their existence and are therefore of major importance for the historian of mathematics.

It is through Eutocius that we have a valuable collection of solutions by Greek geometers of the problem of finding two mean proportionals to two given straight lines, that is, if a and b are two given straight lines, to find two other straight lines x and y such that $a:x = x:y = y:b$. It was to this that a problem which attracted the best Greek mathematicians for several centuries—how to find a cube double another cube—had been reduced by Hippocrates, for if $a:x = x:y = y:b$, then $a^3:x^3 = a:b$, and if $b = 2a$, then x is the side of a cube double a cube of side a. From that time the problem appears to have been attacked exclusively in this form.

The first proposition of Archimedes' *On the Sphere and Cylinder,* Book II, is "Given a cone or cylinder, to find a sphere equal to the cone or cylinder." He shows as analysis that this can be reduced to the problem of finding two mean proportionals and then, in the synthesis, says: "Between the two straight lines, let two mean proportionals be found." It is at this point that Eutocius begins an extended comment (Archimedes, Heiberg ed., III, 54.26–106.24). After noting that the method of finding two mean proportionals is in no way explained by Archimedes, he observes that he had found the subject treated by many famous men, of whom he omits Eudoxus because in his preface he said he had solved the problem by curved lines but had not used them in the proof and had, moreover, treated a certain discrete proportion as though it were continuous, which a mathematician of his caliber would not have done. In order that the thinking of those men whose solutions have been handed down might be manifest, Eutocius sets out the manner of each discovery. He gives a solution attributed to Plato (but almost certainly wrongly attributed), followed by solutions given by Hero in his *Mechanics* and *Belopoeïca,* by Philo of Byzantium, by Apollonius, by Diocles in his work *On Burning Mirrors,* by Pappus in his *Introduction to Mechanics,* by Sporus of Nicaea, by Menaechmus (two solutions), by Archytas as related by Eudemus, by Eratosthenes, and by Nicomedes in his book *On Conchoidal Lines.* (This is not a chronological order; chronologically the order would probably be Archytas, Eudoxus, Menaechmus, the pseudo-Plato, Eratosthenes, Nicomedes, Apollonius, Philo, Diocles, Hero, Sporus, and Pappus. There is, indeed, no discernible order in Eutocius' list.)

Hero's solution is given in his *Mechanics* I, 11, which has survived only in an Arabic translation, and in his *Belopoeïca,* and is reproduced by Pappus, *Collection* III, 25–26. Pappus' solution is given in *Collection* III, 27 and VIII, 26; it is the latter passage that Eutocius has in mind. The conchoid is described by Pappus, *Collection* IV, 39–40, and he mentions that

EUTOCIUS OF ASCALON

it was used by Nicomedes for finding two mean proportionals but does not give a proof. The other solutions would not be known but for their preservation by Eutocius. It is a pity that he did not include what purported to be Eudoxus' solution despite the obvious errors in transmission, but for what he has preserved he deserves the gratitude of posterity. The solution ascribed to Eratosthenes is prefaced by a letter, allegedly from Eratosthenes to Ptolemy Euergetes, giving the history of the problem of doubling the cube and its reduction to the problem of finding two mean proportionals; the letter is not authentic, but it closes with a genuine condensed proof and an epigram that Eratosthenes put on a votive monument. The solution attributed to Plato is probably not authentic because, among other reasons, it is mechanical, but the solutions of Eudoxus and Menaechmus show that the problem was studied in the Academy and may be Platonic. According to Eutocius, Nicomedes was exceedingly vain about his solution and derided that of Eratosthenes as impractical and lacking in geometrical sense. The solutions of Diocles, Sporus, and Pappus are substantially identical and so are those of Apollonius, Hero, and Philo.

It is only a little later, in commenting on the fourth proposition of *On the Sphere and Cylinder,* Book II, that Eutocius gives a further precious collection of solutions that would not otherwise be known. Proposition 4 is the problem "To cut a given sphere by a plane so that the volumes of the segments are to one another in a given ratio." In Proposition 2 Archimedes had shown that a segment of a sphere is equal to a cone with the same base as the segment and height $h(3r - h)/(2r - h)$, where r is the radius of the sphere and h is the height of the segment (LA in the figure). In Proposition 4 he proves geometrically that if h, h' are the heights of the two segments, so that $h + h' = 2r$, and they stand in the ratio $m:n$, then

$$h\frac{(3r - h)}{(2r - h)} = \frac{m}{n}h'\frac{(3r - h')}{(2r - h')}.$$

By the elimination of h' this becomes the cubic equation

$$h^3 - 3h^2r + \frac{4m}{m + n}r^3 = 0.$$

The problem is thus reduced (in modern notation) to finding the solution of a cubic equation that can be written

$$h^2(3r - h) = \frac{4m}{m + n}r^3.$$

Archimedes preferred to treat this as a particular case of a general equation

$$x^2(a - x) = bc^2,$$

where b is a given length and c^2 a given area. For a real solution it is necessary that

$$bc^2 \ngtr \frac{4}{27}a^3.$$

In the particular case of II, 4, there are always two real solutions.

Before proceeding to the synthesis of the main problem, Archimedes promised to give the analysis and synthesis of this subsidiary problem at the end, but Eutocius could not find this promise kept in any of the texts of Archimedes. He records that after an extensive search he found in an old book a discussion of some theorems that seemed relevant. They were far from clear because of errors and the figures were faulty, but they seemed to give the substance of what he wanted. The language, moreover, was in the Doric dialect and kept the names for the conic sections that had been used by Archimedes. Eutocius was therefore led to the conclusion, as we also must be, that what he had before him was in substance the missing text of Archimedes, and he proceeded to set it out in the language of his own day. The problem is solved, in modern notation, by the intersection of the parabola and rectangular hyperbola

$$x^2 = \frac{c^2}{a}y,\ (a - x)y = ab.$$

Others before Eutocius had noticed the apparent failure of Archimedes to carry out his promise, and Eutocius also reproduced solutions by Dionysodorus

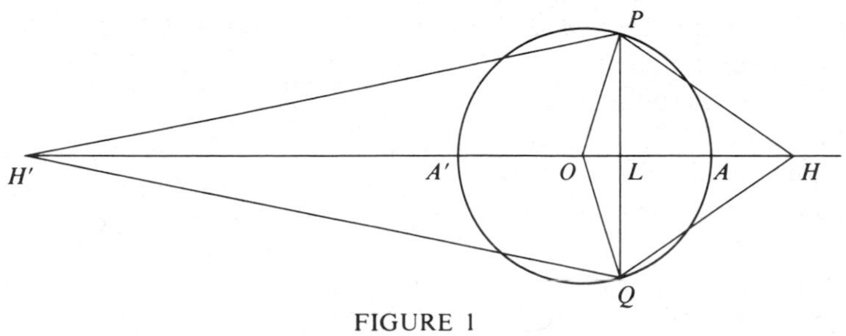

FIGURE 1

EUTOCIUS OF ASCALON

and Diocles. Dionysodorus solved the particular case of the cubic equation to which II, 4 reduces, that is,

$$(3r - x):\frac{m}{m+n}r = 4r^2:x^2.$$

His solution is the intersection of the parabola and rectangular hyperbola

$$y^2 = \frac{m}{m+n}r(3r - x) \text{ and}$$

$$xy = \frac{m}{m+n}2r^2.$$

Diocles solved not the subsidiary equation but the original problem, II, 4, by means of the intersection of an ellipse

$$(y + a - x)^2 = \frac{n}{m}\{(a+b)^2 - x^2\}$$

and the rectangular hyperbola

$$(x + a)(y + b) = 2ab.$$

It is clear that the *Measurement of a Circle* was already reduced to three propositions, with the second and third in the wrong order, when Eutocius had it before him. The chief value of his commentary is that he works out in detail the arithmetical steps where Archimedes merely gives the results. Archimedes requires a number of square roots. Eutocius excuses himself from working them out, on the ground that the method is explained by Hero and by Pappus, Theon, and other commentators on Ptolemy's *Syntaxis,* but he multiplies the square root by itself to show how close the approximation is. At the end Eutocius reveals that Apollonius in a work called Ὠκυτόκιον (*Formula for Quick Delivery*) found a closer approximation to the ratio of a circumference of a circle to its diameter than did Archimedes; and he exculpates Archimedes from the censure of Sporus of Nicaea, whose own teacher, Philo of Gadara, also found a more exact value, on the ground that Archimedes was looking for a figure useful in daily life.

Apart from what has been noted above, Eutocius' comments on Archimedes do not add much of value to the text, and occasionally he errs, as in saying that two parabolic segments in Proposition 8 of *On Plane Equilibria* are similar (Archimedes, Heiberg ed., III, 290.23-24). In a commentary on the difficult lemma that is Proposition 9 of the same book and leads to the location of the center of gravity of a portion of a parabola cut off by parallel chords, he admits himself forced to paraphrase.

The commentaries on the *Conics* display more mathematical acumen. In his preface to Book I, Apollonius explains how uncorrected copies came to be in circulation before he had completed his revision. It is therefore probable that there were variant readings and alternative proofs in the manuscripts from earliest days. It is clear that when Eutocius came to comment on Apollonius, he had before him differing versions, and he found it necessary to prepare a recension for his own purposes; in two manuscripts the four books of his comment have the heading "A Commentary of Eutocius of Ascalon on the First (Second, Third, Fourth) of the *Conics* of Apollonius as Edited by Himself." Eutocius' edition suffered at the hands of interpolators, probably in the ninth century, when mathematics had a renaissance at Constantinople under Leo the Mathematician. The best manuscript of the commentary (W, Cod. Vat. gr. 204) was copied in the tenth century, and at a number of points Eutocius' citations from Apollonius are clearly nearer to the original than is the text of the *Conics* as we have it today. In commenting on Apollonius, Eutocius had been preceded by Serenus and Hypatia. The most interesting features of the commentary are in the early pages, where Eutocius emphasizes the generality of Apollonius' method of producing conic sections from any cone.

All the books by Archimedes on which Eutocius commented have survived, and his elucidations may have contributed to their survival. There must also be some significance in the fact that the four books of the *Conics* on which he commented have survived in Greek, whereas Books V–VII have survived only in Arabic and Book VIII is entirely lost. His commentaries on Archimedes were translated into Latin along with the parent works by William of Moerbeke in 1269. The commentaries have usually been printed with the editions of Archimedes and Apollonius and have never been printed separately. The definitive text is to be found in Heiberg's editions of Archimedes and Apollonius with a Latin translation and valuable prolegomena and notes.

BIBLIOGRAPHY

I. ORIGINAL WORKS. Eutocius' commentaries can be found in *Commentarii in libros Archimedis De sphaera et cylindro, in Dimensionem circuli et in libros De planorum aequilibris,* in *Archimedis opera omnia,* J. L. Heiberg, ed., 2nd ed., III (Leipzig, 1915), 1-448; and *Commentaria in Conica,* in *Apollonii Pergaei quae graece exstant,* J. L. Heiberg, ed., II (Leipzig, 1893), 168-361.

II. SECONDARY LITERATURE. See Paul Tannery, "Sur l'histoire des lignes et surfaces courbes dans l'antiquité," in *Bulletin des sciences mathématiques,* 2nd ser., **7** (1883), 278-291; and "Eutocius et ses contemporains," *ibid.,* **8**

(1884), 315-329, repr. in *Mémoires scientifiques,* II (Toulouse–Paris, 1912), 1-47, 118-136; and Sir Thomas Heath, *A History of Greek Mathematics* (Oxford, 1921), I, 52, 57-58; II, 25, 45, 126, 518, 540-541.

IVOR BULMER-THOMAS

EVANS, GRIFFITH CONRAD (*b*. Boston, Massachusetts, 11 May 1887; *d*. Berkeley, California, 8 December 1973)

Evans was the son of George William Evans, author of such textbooks as *Algebra for Schools* and teacher of mathematics at English High School in Boston, and of Mary Taylor Evans. After graduating from English High School in 1903, he entered Harvard. He earned the A.B. degree there in 1907, the A.M. in 1908, and the Ph.D. in mathematics in 1910. Among his professors at Harvard were William Fogg Osgood, Julian Coolidge, and Maxime Bôcher. Evans was an instructor in mathematics in the academic years 1906–1907 and 1909–1910. His dissertation, "Volterra's Integral Equation of the Second Kind with Discontinuous Kernel," appeared in two parts in *Transactions of the American Mathematical Society* (1910–1911).

After receiving the doctorate, Evans went to Europe on a Sheldon Traveling Fellowship from Harvard. There he studied at the University of Rome with Vito Volterra, who exerted a lasting influence on his work; in line with his interest in the applications of mathematics, Evans also spent a summer in Berlin, working with the physicist Max Planck.

Upon his return from Europe in 1912, Evans had job offers from M.I.T., the University of California at Berkeley, and the newly founded Rice Institute in Houston. Because of its opportunities he chose Rice and, as assistant professor, began teaching there in 1912. In 1916 he was promoted to full professor of mathematics. On 20 June 1917 Evans married Isabel Mary John; they had three sons.

During World War I, Evans was commissioned a captain in the U.S. Army Signal Corps. His scientific assignments concerning bomb trajectories and sights, and antiaircraft defenses took him to England, France, and Italy. With the help of Volterra, Evans facilitated the enrollment of U.S. military personnel in special wartime courses at Italian universities.

Evans was elected vice president of the American Mathematical Society for the years 1924–1926 and held the same office in the Mathematical Association of America; he was twice elected vice president of the American Association for the Advancement of Science (for mathematics, 1931–1932, and for economics, 1936–1937). He served as an editor of the *American Journal of Mathematics* from 1927 to 1936. During his years at Rice, Evans traveled widely in the United States and Europe. He spent half a year in Belgium, France, and Italy in the period 1929–1930, and the summers of 1921 and 1928 at the University of Minnesota and at Berkeley. While at Minnesota in 1921, discussions with the British statistician R. A. Fisher encouraged Evans to promote the study of mathematical statistics in the United States. He also brought such mathematicians as Szolem Mandelbrojt, Karl Menger, and Tibor Rado as visiting professors to enrich the program at Rice.

Other institutions bid for Evans's services during these years. Harvard made several offers, and the University of California renewed its efforts to lure him to Berkeley in 1927. He declined these offers, but by 1933 he had changed his mind. The Berkeley administration had long planned a reorganization of its mathematics department upon the retirement of the department chairman, and approved the search for a new chairman and other faculty members in 1933 despite the financial difficulties confronting the university during the Great Depression. Evans was viewed as an exceptionally strong leader, and Berkeley negotiated long and hard to secure his services. Having been elected to the National Academy of Sciences in that year, he was offered a generous salary (subject to cuts applicable to all faculty salaries) and assured that he would enjoy considerable latitude in making new appointments. He extricated himself from his obligations at Rice and moved to Berkeley in the summer of 1934.

Evans's fifteen years as chairman at Berkeley marked a period of change and growth for the Mathematics Department. He had high expectations for Berkeley. As R. G. D. Richardson put it, Evans hoped "to build up [there] a great center in our subject comparable to Princeton, Harvard, and Chicago" (Richardson to E. R. Murrow, 3 May 1935, Emergency Committee Papers, box 109, New York Public Library). In building the Berkeley program, Evans at first argued against favoring displaced foreigners over unemployed Americans; as the economic picture improved, he changed his mind and added Hans Lewy, Jerzy Neyman, and Alfred Tarski to the department. Altogether Evans brought fifteen new faculty members to Berkeley between 1933 and 1949, and engineered such innovations as courses and seminars in mathematical economics (one of his own research interests), a statistical laboratory (headed by Neyman), and greater attention to the applications of mathematics. Evans later described his first few years at Berkeley as "an opportune time" for expanding and strengthening the department there (Evans to Henry Helson, 12 February 1966, Evans Papers, The Bancroft Library).

Evans assumed the presidency of the American Mathematical Society in 1938. In this capacity he encouraged the formation of the American Mathematical Society-Mathematical Association of America War Preparedness Committee (later the War Policy Committee) to guide research on problems of importance to national defense and to design mathematical training programs for the military. As president of the society until 1940, Evans served on the National Research Council committee charged with compiling a national scientific roster; after Pearl Harbor he addressed wartime issues as a member of the Mathematics Committee of the National Academy of Sciences and of the Applied Mathematics Panel of the National Defense Research Council. Between 1943 and 1947 he served as consultant for the Office of the Chief of Ordnance on gun design.

Evans continued as department chairman at Berkeley until 1949. After his retirement at the end of the 1954–1955 academic year, he continued to write and lecture for many years. In 1971 the new mathematics building on the Berkeley campus was named Evans Hall, in recognition of his contributions to mathematics and his dedication to building a world-class center of mathematical sciences at Berkeley.

Much of Evans's work built upon mathematical innovations introduced by Henri Lebesque, Vito Volterra, Maurice Frechet, and Henri Poincaré during his student years. His first paper, published in 1909, while he was still in graduate school, dealt with functional analysis, a field to which he would contribute much in the next decade. Evans's principal results concerned integrodifferential equations and integral equations with singular kernels. The American Mathematical Society invited him to deliver the Colloquium Lectures on this subject in 1916; they were published in 1918 as *Functionals and Their Applications*. These lectures illustrated the utility of integral expressions: for example, replacing second-order partial differential expressions by integral expressions for variable domains with first-order terms permitted derivation of a theorem for integral expressions analogous to Green's theorem.

Another aspect of Evans's work concerned surfaces of minimum capacity. Solution of the problem of minimal surfaces, the so-called plateau problem, depends on local properties. Evans was able to prove, however, in a series of papers beginning in 1920 that, among the surfaces with a given boundary *s*, there exists a surface of minimum (electric) capacity. In this work he used comparisons of energy integrals. The generalization of such problems led Evans to extensive research, especially in his later years, on multiple-valued harmonic functions.

Beginning with his paper on Kirckhoff's law, written while he was a graduate student and published in 1910, Evans concerned himself with the applications of mathematics. His work during both world wars evinces this interest, as does his innovative work in applying mathematics to economic theory. Evans formulated a model of the economy as a whole and posed the problem of defining an aggregate variable in terms of microeconomic components. His 1924 paper on the dynamics of monopoly, which introduced time derivatives in demand relations, was recognized as the beginning of dynamic theories of economics. Evans's textbook on mathematical economics was published in 1930 and formed the basis of his pioneering courses at Rice and Berkeley.

BIBLIOGRAPHY

I. Original Works. Evans's writings include "The Integral Equation of the Second Kind of Volterra, with Singular Kernel," in *Bulletin of the American Mathematical Society*, 2nd ser., **16** (1909), 130–136; "Note on Kirchoff's Law," in *Proceedings of the American Academy of Arts and Sciences*, **46** (1910), 97–106; "Volterra's Integral Equation of the Second Kind with Discontinuous Kernel," in *Transactions of the American Mathematical Society*, **11** (1910), 393–413, and **12** (1911), 429–472; *Functionals and Their Applications* (Providence, R.I., 1918; repr., New York, 1964); "Fundamental Points of Potential Theory," in *The Rice Institute Pamphlet*, **7** (1920), 252–329; "Problems of Potential Theory," in *Proceedings of the National Academy of Sciences*, **7** (1921), 89–98; "The Dynamics of Monopoly," in *American Mathematical Monographs*, **31** (1924), 77–83; *The Logarithmic Potential. Discontinuous Dirichlet and Neumann Problems, American Mathematical Society Colloquium Publications*, 6 (Providence, R.I., 1927); and *Mathematical Introduction to Economics* (New York, 1930); "Potentials of General Masses in Single and Double Layers. The Relative Boundary Value Problems," in *American Journal of Mathematics*, **53** (1931), 493–516, written with E. R. C. Miles; "Complements of Potential Theory," *ibid.*, **54** (1932), 213–234; "Correction and Addition to 'Complements of Potential Theory,'" *ibid.*, **57** (1935), 623–626; "On Potentials of Positive Mass., Parts I and II," in *Transactions of the American Mathematical Society*, **37** (1935), 226–253, and **38** (1935), 201–236; "Potentials and Positively Infinite Singularities of Harmonic Functions," in *Monatshefte für Mathematik und Physik*, **43** (1936), 419–424; "Modern Methods of Analysis in Potential Theory," in *Bulletin of the American Mathematical Society*,

43 (1937), 481–502; "Surfaces of Minimal Capacity" and "Surfaces of Minimum Capacity," in *Proceedings of the National Academy of Sciences*, **26** (1940), 489–491, 662–667; and "Continua of Minimum Capacity," in *Bulletin of the American Mathematical Society*, **47** (1941), 717–733.

Evans's papers at Bancroft Library, University of California, Berkeley, include twenty cartons of notebooks, journals, correspondence, course notes, and drafts and reprints of writings, as well as some papers of his father and of his son George William. Noteworthy among the unpublished materials is correspondence with American and European mathematicians and a typescript of a calculus textbook by Evans and H. E. Bray. The Bancroft collection also documents Evans's wartime activities and participation in professional organizations and university committees. The University Archives at Berkeley contain additional correspondence concerning Evans's appointment and the growth of the mathematics department under his leadership.

II. SECONDARY LITERATURE. The principal biographical notice on Evans is by a colleague at Berkeley, Charles B. Morrey, "Griffith Conrad Evans," in *Biographical Memoirs. National Academy of Sciences*, **54** (1983), 127–155. It contains a summary of Evans's major contributions to mathematics and a ninety-five-item bibliography of his publications. It is supplemented by Charles B. Morrey, Hans Lewy, R. W. Shephard, and R. L. Vaught, "Griffith Conrad Evans," in *University of California, In Memoriam* (1977), 102–103. Evans's success in building the mathematics program at Berkeley is explored in Robin E. Rider, "An Opportune Time: Griffith C. Evans and Mathematics at Berkeley," in Peter Duren, ed., *A Century of Mathematics in America*, II (Providence, R.I., 1989).

ROBIN E. RIDER

IBN EZRA, ABRAHAM BEN MEIR, also known as **Abū Isḥāq Ibrāhim al-Mājid ibn Ezra,** or **Avenare** (*b.* Toledo, Spain, *ca.* 1090; *d.* Calahorra, Spain, *ca.* 1164–1167 [?])

A versatile genius with a charming Hebrew style, Ibn Ezra disseminated rationalistic and scientific Arabic learning in France, England, and Italy. From about 1140 to 1160 he traveled continually, and it was in this last period of his life that his works were written. Ibn Ezra was a Hebrew grammarian, exegete, astrologer, translator from Arabic into Hebrew, and poet, as well as a scientist. His work as a Jewish biblical commentator was much admired by Spinoza. Ibn Ezra considered the physical sciences and astrology fundamental for every branch of Jewish learning.

Three of his treatises were devoted to numbers. *Sefer ha-eḥad* ("Book of the Unit") describes the theory of numbers from one to nine; *Sefer ha-mispar* ("Book of the Number") is on the fundamental operations of arithmetic. The latter describes the decimal system for integers with place value of the numerals from left to right, and the zero is given as *galgal* ("wheel" or "circle") in the preface. In the body of the treatise, however, Ibn Ezra returns to use of the letters of the Hebrew alphabet as numerals. The Indian influence is, nevertheless, unmistakable. The third book, *Yesod mispar* ("The Foundation of Numerals"), is concerned with grammatical peculiarities.

In Ibn Ezra's translation of al-Bīrūnī's *Ta'amē lūḥōt al-Chowārezmī* ("Commentary on the Tables of al-Khwārizmī"; the Arabic original is lost) there is interesting information on the introduction of Indian mathematics and astronomy into Arabic science during the eighth century.

Ibn Ezra was concerned with permutations and combinations, as is shown in his *Sefer ha-'olam* ("Book of the World"). In addition to treatises on the calendar, *Shalosh she'elot* ("Three Chronological Questions") and *Sefer ha-'ibbur* ("Book on Intercalation"), and the astrolabe, *Keli ha-neḥoshet* ("The Astrolabe"), Ibn Ezra wrote a number of astrological works (Steinschneider lists more than fifty) that were very popular and were translated into many languages. Two were printed in Latin in 1482 and 1485, respectively; and all of them appeared in Latin in 1507. Only two of the Hebrew originals have been printed, both in modern times. They are rich in original ideas and in the history of scientific subjects. The astrological works were translated into French in 1213 by Hagin, a Jew in the employ of Henry Bate at Malines (Mechelen), who in turn translated the French into Latin. Both the French and the Catalan translations are of great philological interest.

BIBLIOGRAPHY

Works dealing with Ibn Ezra and his writings are Henry Bate *et al.*, *De luminaribus et diebus criticis* (Padua, 1482–1483); H. Edelmann, *Keli neḥoshet* (Königsberg, 1845); J. L. Fleischer, *Sefer ha-mōrōt* (Bucharest, 1932); Yekuthiel Ginsburg, "Rabbi Ben Ezra on Permutations and Combinations," in *The Mathematics Teacher*, **15** (1922), 347–356, text from *Sefer ha-'olam;* S. J. Halberstam, *Sefer ha-'ibbur* (Lyck [Elk], Poland, 1874); D. Kahana, *Rabi Abraham ibn Ezra,* II (Warsaw, 1894), 107–111; Martin Levey, *Principles of Hindu Reckoning* (Madison, Wis., 1965), pp. 8, 35; Raphael Levy, *The Astrological Works of Abraham ibn Ezra. A Literary and Linguistic Study With Special Reference to the Old French Translation of Hagin* (Baltimore, 1927); Alexander Marx, "The Scientific Work of Some Outstanding Mediaeval Jewish Scholars," in *Essays and Studies in Memory of Linda R. Miller* (New York, 1938), pp. 138–140;

Ernst Müller, *Abraham ibn Esra Buch der Einheit aus dem Hebräischen übersetzt nebst Parallelstellen und Erläuterungen zur Mathematik Ibn Esras* (Berlin, 1921); Samuel Ochs, "Ibn Esras Leben und Werke," in *Monatsschrift für Geschichte und Wissenschaft des Judentums*, **60** (1916), 41–58, 118–134, 193–212; M. Olitzki, "Die Zahlensymbolik des Abraham ibn Esra," in *Jubelschrift Hildesheimer* (Berlin, 1890), pp. 99–120; S. Pinsker, *Yesod mispar* (Vienna, 1863), and *Abrahami Ibn Esra, Sepher ha-echad, liber de novem numeris cardinalibus cum Simchae Pinsker interpretatione primorum quatuor numerorum. Reliquorum numerorum interpretationem et proemium addidit M. A. Goldhardt* (Odessa, 1867); George Sarton, *Introduction to the History of Science*, II, pt. 1 (Baltimore, 1931), 187–189; M. Silberberg, ed., *Sefer ha-mispar. Das Buch der Zahl, ein hebräisch-arithmetisches Werk des R. Abraham ibn Esra . . .* (Frankfurt, 1895); D. E. Smith and Yekuthiel Ginsburg, "Rabbi Ben Ezra and the Hindu-Arabic Problem," in *American Mathematical Monthly*, **25** (1918), 99–108; and the following by M. Steinschneider: "Abraham Judaeus-Savasorda und Ibn Esra," in *Zeitschrift für Mathematik*, **12** (1867), 1–44, and **25** (1880), supp. 57–128; *Verzeichniss der hebräische Handschriften der K. Bibliothek zu Berlin* (Berlin, 1897; 1901); *Die hebräischen Übersetzungen . . .* (repr. Graz, 1956), p. 869; *Die arabische Literatur der Juden* (repr. Hildesheim, 1964), p. 156; and *Mathematik bei den Juden* (repr. Hildesheim, 1964), pp. 87–91.

MARTIN LEVEY

FABRI, HONORÉ, or **HONORATUS FABRIUS** (*b.* Virieu-le-Grand, Dauphiné, France, 5 April 1607; *d.* Rome, Italy, 8 March 1688)

Fabri came from a family of judges in Valromey that was probably related to the Vaugelas family.[1] Following his studies at the *institut* in Belley, he entered the Jesuit novitiate in Avignon on 18 October 1626, remaining until 1628. In the fall of that year he went to the Collège de la Trinité[2] in Lyons, where he completed his course in Scholastic philosophy under Claude Boniel. After teaching for two years at the *collège* in Roanne,[3] he returned to Lyons in 1632 in order to begin his course in theology, which he finished—following his ordination as a priest in 1635—in 1636. In the latter year he was named professor of logic at the *collège* in Arles, where for two years he gave lectures on philosophy that included natural philosophy as well. It was at this time that he discovered—independently of Harvey—the circulation of the blood, which he taught publicly.[4]

Besides being prefect at the *collège* in Aix-en-Provence (1638–1639), Fabri was leader of a sort of circle that, among other things, brought him the acquaintance of—and a long-lasting correspondence with—Gassendi. He was then recalled to Lyons to finish his third year of probation under P. Barnaud and in 1640 was promoted to professor of logic and mathematics, and also to dean, at the Collège de la Trinité.

During the following six years Fabri taught metaphysics, astronomy, mathematics, and natural philosophy. This period was the most brilliant and fruitful of his life; several books that he published later were developed from lectures delivered during this time. Fabri was the first of many famous professors produced by the Collège de la Trinité: his students included Pierre Mousnier, who later edited many of his teacher's lectures; the mathematician François de Raynaud,[5] who became famous through his friendship with Newton; Jean-Dominique Cassini; and Philippe de La Hire. Claude Dechales[6] and the astronomer and mathematician Berthet were also members of this circle. Among these scholars and the two Huygenses (father and son), Leibniz, Descartes, Mersenne, and others an active correspondence developed.

The foci of Fabri's tremendous activity were almost all urgent questions of the science of his day: heliocentrism, Saturn's rings, the theory of the tides, magnetism, optics, and kinematics. In mathematics, infinitesimal methods and the continuum problem were most prominent.

Fabri's favorable reception of certain Cartesian conceptions[7] embroiled him in an intense controversy with his superiors, which finally led to his expulsion from Lyons and his transfer to Rome, where he arrived on 12 September 1646. Although his stay was supposed to be only provisional, he was made a member in the same year of the Penitentiary College (the Inquisition). He served on that body, finally as Grand Inquisitor, for thirty-four years. Despite his important work in Church politics and theology—Fabri was considered the first expert on Jansenism—there was still time for his wide-ranging scientific research.

In mathematics, Fabri showed that despite the influence of Cavalieri and Torricelli, he was an independent and original thinker. This is clear from his principal mathematical work, *Opusculum geometricum*. Through the functional reinterpretation of Cavalieri's concept of indivisibles by means of a dynamically formulated concept of *fluxus*, Fabri approached similar ideas put forth by Newton. Fabri, however, was not able to free himself of a rather cumbersome, purely geometrical representation. In his *Synopsis geometrica* he developed a method of teaching based on his concept of *fluxus* and was not unsuccessful in using his somewhat inadequately formulated principle of homogeneity in his investigations on infinitesimals.

The *Opusculum geometricum* contains, besides an ingenious quadrature of a cycloid which Leibniz found inspiring, various quadratures and cubatures that amount to special cases of $\int x^n \sin x \, dx$, $\int \sin^p x \, dx$, and $\int\int \arcsin x \, dx \, dy$, as well as centroid determinations of sinusoidal and cycloidal segments together with their elements of rotation about both axes. The book doubtless originated in connection with the controversy over cycloids and Pascal's challenge.

In Rome, Fabri became acquainted with Michel Angelo Ricci, who recommended him to the Medici Grand Duke Leopold II. The latter made Fabri a corresponding member of the Accademia del Cimento. In 1660, with an anonymous work,[8] Fabri opened the controversy with Huygens over Saturn's rings which, after five years and a great expenditure of energy, was decided in Huygens' favor. Fabri was a fair opponent: he apologized and openly adopted Huygens' opinion. In the *Brevis annotatio* is a note that reads, more or less, "As long as no strict proof for the motion of the earth has been found, the Church is competent to decide [the issue]. If the proof, however, is found, then there should be no difficulty in explaining that the relevant passages in the Bible must be interpreted in a more symbolic sense." This statement would perhaps have been tolerated later, under Pope Clement IX, on whom Fabri had a strong influence; under Alexander VII, however, it brought Fabri (as a member of the Holy Office) fifty days in prison, and his release was effected only through the intervention of Leopold II. Yet this did not prevent the combative Jesuit from inserting into his *Dialogi physici* (1665) a chapter entitled "De motu terrae." It was also in 1665 that Fabri discovered the Andromeda nebula, which he at first thought was a new comet.

In natural philosophy Fabri was less fortunate than in mathematics. Nevertheless, the following achievements are noteworthy: the constant use of the concept of the static moment; an attempted explanation of tidal phenomena based on the action of the moon, even though it involved air pressure as the medium; an explanation of the blue color of the sky based on the principle of dispersion; and investigations on capillarity. His attempted explanation of cohesion, however, was completely unsuccessful.

In 1668 Fabri began a year's sick leave in Virieu-le-Grand, where he supervised the publication of various of his works. He continued to work in the Holy Office in Rome until 1680. The last eight years of his life he spent a short distance outside the city, devoting himself to historical studies.[9]

Aside from the individual scientific achievements mentioned, Fabri's efforts to introduce a priori methods in natural philosophy as well as in philosophy are important historically,[10] as is his lasting influence on Leibniz, who richly recompensed Fabri with his friendship. Newton, for his part, mentioned in his second paper on light and colors that he first learned of Grimaldi's experiments through the medium of "some Italian author," whom he identified as Fabri in his dialogue *De lumine.*[11]

NOTES

1. See Gassendi's letter to Mousnier of 1 October 1665, published in Fabri's *Cours de philosophie* (Lyons, 1646).
2. The Collège de la Trinité was transferred by the aldermen of Lyons to the Jesuits in 1565 but was closed in 1594, following the attempt by the Jesuits' pupil Jean Châtel on the life of Henry IV. The Jesuits were expelled from France but returned in 1604 and reestablished the college; it was not completed, however, until 1660.
3. In 1634, at the age of ten, François de La Chaise (later the Jesuit Père Lachaise) entered this *collège;* he was later bound to Fabri by close friendship and an active correspondence.
4. See *Journal des sçavans* (1666), pp. 395–400.
5. Also known as Regnauld and Reynaud.
6. Also known as de Chales.
7. See D.-G. Morhof, *Polyhistori litterarum,* II (Lübeck, 1690), 115; and Adrien Baillet, *La vie de Descartes,* II (Paris, 1691), 299.
8. *Eustachii de divinis septempedani brevis annotatio in systema Saturnium Christiani Hugenii* (Rome, 1660).
9. The manuscripts of the last creative period, most of them unpublished, are in the library of the city of Lyons.
10. See Leibniz's letter to Johann Bernoulli, dated 15 October 1710, in *Leibniz's mathematische Schriften,* C. I. G. Gerhardt, ed., III (Halle, 1856), 856.
11. Newton to Oldenburg, 7 December 1675, in H. W. Turnbull, ed., *The Correspondence of Isaac Newton,* I (Cambridge, 1959), 384.

BIBLIOGRAPHY

I. ORIGINAL WORKS. Fabri's mathematical writings include *Opusculum geometricum de linea sinuum et cycloide* (Rome, 1659), written under the pseudonym "Antimus Farbius"; and *Synopsis geometrica* (Lyons, 1669), to which is appended *De maximis et minimis in infinitum propositionum centuria,* written in 1658/1659. These works, as well as the minor *Brevis synopsis trigonometriae planae* (1658/1659) are discussed in Fellmann, below.

Fabri's works in natural philosophy are *Tractatus physicus . . .* (Lyons, 1646); *Dialogi physici . . .* (Lyons, 1665); *Synopsis optica* (Lyons, 1667); *Dialogi physici . . .* (Lyons, 1669); and *Physica* (Lyons, 1669).

II. SECONDARY LITERATURE. On Fabri's work, see Carlos Sommervogel, *Bibliothèque de la Compagnie de Jésus,* III (Paris-Brussels, 1892), 512–522, which contains an extensive bibliography; and E. A. Fellmann, "Die mathematischen Werke von Honoratus Fabry," in *Physis* (Florence), **1–2** (1959), 6–25, 69–102.

E. A. FELLMANN

FAGNANO DEI TOSCHI, GIOVANNI FRANCESCO (*b.* Sinigaglia, Italy, 31 January 1715; *d.* Sinigaglia, 14 May 1797)

Giovanni Francesco was the only child of Giulio Carlo Fagnano to show an interest in mathematics. He was ordained a priest and in 1752 was appointed canon of the cathedral of Sinigaglia. Three years later he was made archpriest. He wrote an unpublished treatise on the geometry of the triangle that was inspired by a similar work of his father's. Fagnano made several important contributions to the subject, among them the theorem that the triangle which has as its vertices the bases of the altitudes of any triangle has these altitudes as its bisectors. He also contributed several analytical communications to the *Acta eruditorum* and to other Italian and foreign reviews.

Among his most important results is that, given

$$S_n = \int x^n \sin x \, dx, \; C_n = \int x^n \cos x \, dx,$$

we obtain

$$S_n = -x^n \cos x + nC_{n-1},$$

$$C_n = x^n \sin x - nS_{n-1}.$$

He also calculated the integrals:

$$\int \tan x \, dx = -\log \cos x, \int \cot x \, dx = \log \sin x.$$

BIBLIOGRAPHY

Among Fagnano's writings is *Nova acta eruditorum* (1774), pp. 385–420. Two further sources of information on his mathematical work are *Enciclopedia delle matematiche elementari,* I, pt. 2 (1932), 491–492; and Gino Loria, *Storia delle matematiche,* 2nd ed. (Milan, 1950), p. 664.

A. NATUCCI

FAGNANO DEI TOSCHI, GIULIO CARLO (*b.* Sinigaglia, Italy, 6 December 1682; *d.* Sinigaglia, 26 September 1766)

Fagnano, the son of Francesco Fagnano and Camilla Bartolini, was born into a noble family that had included Pope Honorius II and had been established in his native town for nearly 350 years. In 1723 he was appointed *gonfaloniere* of Sinigaglia; while he held this office he was subjected to calumny by envious fellow citizens. He was the father of many children, among them Giovanni Francesco, a distinguished mathematician.

Fagnano began to study mathematics after reading the first volume of Malebranche's *Recherche de la verité*; and although he was self-educated, he soon made such progress that he became famous both in Italy and abroad. In 1721 Louis XV conferred upon him the title of count; in 1745 Pope Benedict XIV made him a marquis of Sant' Onofrio. He belonged to the Royal Society of London and the Berlin Academy of Sciences, and at his death he had been nominated for membership in the Paris Academy of Sciences. Fagnano maintained correspondence with many contemporary mathematicians, especially Grandi, Riccati, Leseur, and Jacquier; he was praised by Euler and Fontenelle, the permanent secretary of the French Academy. Lagrange, at the age of twenty, turned to him for help in publishing his first work.

Fagnano's works were published at intervals in the *Giornale dei letterati* and in the Raccolta Calogera. These were later collected and with other, unpublished works included in *Produzioni matematiche.*

In algebra Fagnano suggested new methods for the solution of equations of the second, third, and fourth degrees. He also organized in a rational manner the knowledge that scientists had of imaginary numbers, establishing for them a special algorithm that was far better than Bombelli's primitive one. In this field he established the well-known formula

$$\frac{\pi}{4} = \log\left(\frac{1-i}{1+i}\right)^{1/2}.$$

This is reminiscent of Euler's celebrated formula

$$e^{\pi i} = -1,$$

which unites the four most important numbers in mathematics.

In geometry Fagnano formulated a general theory of geometric proportions that is more noteworthy than the countless writings, published previously, that were intended to illustrate book V of Euclid's *Elements.* Much more important, however, is his work on the triangle, for which he may well be considered the founder of the geometry of the triangle. Some of the problems solved are as follows:

To find in the plane of a triangle, ABC, a point, P, that will reduce to the minimum the sum $PA + PB + PC$ or the sum $PA^2 + PB^2 + PC^2$.

To find in the plane of a quadrangle, $ABCD$, a point that will render minimum the sum $PA + PB + PC + PD$.

Two of Fagnano's major findings are (1) that the sum of the squares of the distances of the center of gravity of a triangle from the vertices equals one-third the sum of the squares of the sides and (2) that given a triangle, ABC, for every point P of BC we may construct an inscribed triangle, with its vertex at P, of minimum perimeter. He also solved the problem proposed by Simon Lhuilier: Draw through a given point the straight line on which two given straight lines cut off the minimum segment. This leads analytically to a third-degree equation.

The most important results achieved by Fagnano, however, were in analytical geometry and in integral calculus. He rectified the ellipse $x^2 + 2y^2 = a^2$, which has as its major axis the mean proportion between the minor axis and its double. The equation

$$(x^2 + y^2)^2 - 2a^2(x^2 - y^2) = 0$$

represents a fourth-degree curve that, owing to its shape, is called "lemniscate," a term derived from the Greek *lemniscata.* This was first studied by Jakob I Bernoulli (1694), but it was made famous by Fagnano's research. He established its rectification and demonstrated that each of its arcs may be divided with ruler and compass into n equal parts when n is of the form $2 \cdot 2^m$, $3 \cdot 2^m$, $5 \cdot 2^m$.

He gave the name "elliptical integrals" to integrals of the form

$$\int f\left(x_1 \sqrt{P[x]}\right) dx$$

in which $P(x)$ is a polynomial of the third or fourth degree. Euler found a basic result in their theory, known as the theorem of addition, that includes the results first found by Fagnano in the lemniscate arcs. For this reason some have considered Fagnano's work the forerunner of the theory of elliptic functions—a claim undoubtedly put forward by Legendre.

Disputes, encouraged by Fagnano's uncle Giovanni, arose over who deserved the credit of priority in these studies—Fagnano or Nikolaus I Bernoulli. On the advice of his friend Riccati, Fagnano soon put an end to these arguments.

Fagnano also found the area of the lemniscate, thus demonstrating that Tschirnhausen's opinion was erroneous and that it was impossible to square the area composed of several leaves.

In 1714 Fagnano proposed the following problem: Given a biquadratic parabola of the form $y = x^4$, and given a portion of it, determine another portion of the same curve in such a manner that the difference between the portions is rectifiable. Since no one replied, Fagnano himself published the solution, thus extending the method to infinite species of rectifiable parabolas. Fagnano also studied the problem of squaring hyperbolic spaces.

BIBLIOGRAPHY

I. Original Works. Among Fagnano's works are *Giornale dei letterati,* **19** (1714), 438; *Produzioni matematiche,* 2 vols. (Pesaro, 1750); and *Opere matematiche del marchese G. C. de' Toschi di Fagnano,* V. Volterra, G. Loria, and D. Gambioli, eds. (Rome, 1911).

II. Secondary Literature. On Fagnano or his work, see Luigi Bianchi, *Lezioni sulla teoria delle funzioni di variabile complessa e delle funzioni ellittiche* (Pisa, 1901), p. 250; Gino Loria, *Curve piane speciali algebriche e trascendenti. Teoria e storia* (Milan, 1930), I, 257 ff., and *Storia delle matematiche,* 2nd ed. (Milan, 1950), pp. 664–666; and A. Natucci, "Anton Maria Legendre inventore della teoria delle funzioni ellittiche," in *Archimede,* **4,** no. 6 (1952), 261.

There is an article on Fagnano in *Enciclopedia italiana* (1932), XIV, in which he is called Giulio Cesare. He is mentioned twice by Eugenio G. Togliatti in *Enciclopedia delle matematiche elementari:* II, pt. 1, 184, and in "Massimi e minimi," II, pt. 2. See also *Elogi e biografie d'illustri italiani del conte Giuseppe Mamiani della Rovere* (Florence, 1845), pp. 63–104.

A. Natucci

FANO, GINO (*b.* Mantua, Italy, 5 January 1871; *d.* Verona, Italy, 8 November 1952)

Fano was the son of Ugo and Angelica Fano; his father, a Garibaldian, had independent means. Gino studied from 1888 to 1892 at the University of Turin under Corrado Segre; while there, he met Guido Castelnuovo and specialized in geometry. In 1893–1894, while at Göttingen, he met Felix Klein, whose Erlangen program he had translated into Italian (*Annali di matematica,* 2nd ser., **17** [1889–1890], 307–343). From 1894 to 1899 Fano was assistant to Castelnuovo in Rome, was at Messina from 1899 to 1901, and in 1901 became professor at the University of Turin, where he taught until the Fascist laws of 1938 deprived him of his position. During World War II he taught Italian students at an international camp near Lausanne. After 1946 Fano lectured in the United States and Italy. In 1911 he married Rosetta Cassin; two sons became professors in the United States.

Fano worked mainly in projective and algebraic geometry of n-space S_n. Early studies deal with line geometry and linear differential equations with algebraic coefficients; he also pioneered in finite geometry. Later work is on algebraic and especially cubic surfaces, as well as on manifolds with a continuous group of Cremona transformations. He showed the existence of irrational involutions in three-space S_3, i.e., of "unirational" manifolds not birationally representable on S_3. He also studied birational contact transformations and non-Euclidean and non-Archimedean geometries.

BIBLIOGRAPHY

I. ORIGINAL WORKS. Among Fano's many textbooks are *Lezioni di geometria descrittiva* (Turin, 1914; 3rd ed., 1925) and *Lezioni di geometria analitica e proiettiva* (Turin, 1930; 3rd ed., 1958), written with A. Terracini. Two of his articles appeared in *Encyclopädie der mathematischen Wissenschaften* (Leipzig, 1898–1935): "Gegensatz von synthetischer und analytischer Geometrie in seiner historischen Entwicklung im XIX. Jahrhundert," in III (Leipzig, 1907), 221–288; and "Kontinuierliche geometrische Gruppen," *ibid.*, 289–388.

II. SECONDARY LITERATURE. See A. Terracini, "Gino Fano," in *Bollettino dell'Unione matematica italiana*, 3rd ser., **7** (1952), 485–490; and "Gino Fano, 1871–1952, cenni commemorative," in *Atti dell'Accademia delle scienze* (Turin), classe di scienze fisiche, **87** (1953), 350–360. A bibliography, compiled by the editorial board, is in *Rendiconti del Seminario matematico, Università e politecnico di Torino*, **9** (1950), on pp. 33–45 of this issue dedicated to Fano (with portrait).

DIRK J. STRUIK

FARRAR, JOHN (*b.* Lincoln, Massachusetts, 1 July 1779; *d.* Cambridge, Massachusetts, 8 May 1853)

Farrar was responsible for conceiving and carrying through a sweeping modernization of the science and mathematics curriculum at Harvard College, his alma mater. He brought in the best French and other European writings on introductory mathematics, most of them unknown and unused in the United States. Much of the responsibility for shifting from the Newtonian fluxional notations to Leibniz's algorithm for the calculus was his. In natural philosophy Farrar also relied heavily upon French authors. He introduced current concepts in mechanics, electricity and magnetism, optics, and astronomy.

As the foundation of his curricular reform, Farrar carried through the translation of many French works between 1818 and 1829. Published in separate, topical volumes, they became elements of two series: Cambridge Mathematics and Cambridge Natural Philosophy. He selected and combined the writings most suitable to the needs of his students. The burden of Farrar's presentation in mathematics was carried by Lacroix, Euler, Legendre, and Bézout, but he also drew from John Bonnycastle and Bowditch. In natural philosophy he relied most heavily upon Biot, but used Bézout, Poisson, Louis-Benjamin Francoeur, Gay-Lussac, Ernst Gottfried Fischer, Whewell, and Hare as well.

Farrar's translations provided an excellent introductory program that was used not only at Harvard but also at West Point and other colleges; they went through several editions. Farrar was a fine teacher and, as Hollis professor of mathematics and natural philosophy, played an important role throughout Harvard College. One of his major aspirations, the establishment of an astronomical observatory at Harvard, was not attained until after his death.

In the larger community Farrar made similar contributions. He was active in the American Academy of Arts and Sciences and occasionally translated such topical works as Arago's 1832 *Tract on Comets*, written in preparation for the comet of that year. He published essay reviews in the *North American Review* and occasional observations and a few scientific papers on astronomy, meteorology, and instruments in the *Memoirs of the American Academy of Arts and Sciences* and the *Boston Journal of Philosophy and the Arts*.

BIBLIOGRAPHY

I. ORIGINAL WORKS. Farrar wrote few scientific papers. In the *Memoirs of the American Academy of Arts and Sciences*, he published "An Account of the Violent and Destructive Storm of the 23d of September 1815," **4** (1821), 92–97, and "An Account of a Singular Electrical Phenomenon," *ibid.*, 98–102. His "Account of an Apparatus for Determining the Mean Temperature and the Mean Atmospherical Pressure for Any Period" appeared in *Boston Journal of Philosophy and the Arts*, **1** (1823–1824), 491–494. In the *North American Review* he published several review essays, all of them unsigned: **6** (1817–1818), 205–224; **8** (1818–1819), 157–168; **12** (1821), 150–174; **14** (1822), 190–230; and a few observations: **3** (1816), 36–40, 285–287; **6** (1817–1818), 149, 292.

His primary publishing activity lay in translating and combining French writings with a few others in a manner that effectively produced good college textbooks which were abreast of recent advances. Some appeared without any indication of Farrar's role; others did not name the authors on the title page but always scrupulously noted them at some point. The first editions (often of many) are a translation of S. F. Lacroix, *An Elementary Treatise on Arithmetic* (Boston, 1818); a translation of S. F. Lacroix, *Elements of Algebra* (Cambridge, Mass., 1818); a translation of L. Euler, *An Introduction to the Elements of Algebra* (Cambridge, Mass., 1818); a translation of A. M. Legendre, *Elements of Geometry* (Boston, 1819); translations of S. F. Lacroix and E. Bézout, *An Elementary Treatise on Plane and Spherical Trigonometry* (Cambridge, Mass., 1820); *An Elementary Application of Trigonometry* (Cambridge, Mass., 1822); translations of E. Bézout, *First Principles of the Differential and Integral Calculus* (Cambridge, Mass., 1824); *An Elementary Treatise on Mechanics* (Cambridge, Mass., 1825); *An Experimental Treatise on Optics* (Cambridge, Mass., 1826); *Elements of Electricity, Magnetism, and Electro-Magnetism* (Cambridge, Mass., 1826); *An Elementary Treatise on Astronomy* (Cambridge, Mass., 1827);

a translation of E. G. Fischer, *Elements of Natural Philosophy* (Boston, 1827); and a translation of F. Arago, *Tract on Comets* (Boston, 1832).

Letters and other MS records are held by the Harvard University Archives and the Massachusetts Historical Society, and a few by the Boston Public Library.

II. SECONDARY LITERATURE. On Farrar or his work, see Mrs. John Farrar, *Recollections of Seventy Years* (Boston, 1866); Dirk J. Struik, *Yankee Science in the Making* (New York, 1962), pp. 227-229, *passim;* and [John Gorham Palfrey], *Notice of Professor Farrar* (Boston, 1853).

BROOKE HINDLE

FATOU, PIERRE JOSEPH LOUIS (*b.* Lorient, France, 28 February 1878; *d.* Pornichet, France, 10 August 1929)

Fatou attended the École Normale Supérieure from 1898 to 1901. The scarcity of mathematical posts in Paris led him to accept a post at the Paris observatory, where he worked until his death. He received his doctorate in 1907 and was appointed titular astronomer in 1928. Fatou worked in practical astronomy: on determining the absolute positions of stars and planets, on instrumental constants, and on measurements of twin stars.

In order to calculate the secular perturbations produced on a planet P' through the movement of another planet, P, Gauss had had the idea of spreading the mass of P' over its orbit, so that the mass of each arc is proportional to the time it takes for the planet to trace it. This proposition is valid only when the distinction between periodic and secular perturbations does not apply, i.e., when n' is very small (n and n' are the mean motions of the planets P and P', respectively). By means of general existence theorems of solutions of differential equations, Fatou studied these motions of material systems subjected to forces whose periods tend to zero. Gauss's intuitive result had often been used in practice but had never been rigorously justified.

Fatou also studied the movement of a planet in a resistant medium. This work was based on the probability that stellar atmospheres had previously been far more extensive than they are now and would thus have given rise to capture phenomena that can be used to explain the origins of twin stars and of certain satellites.

Along with this work Fatou did both related and general mathematical research. He contributed important results on the Taylor series, the theory of the Lebesgue integral, and the iteration of rational functions of a complex variable. When studying the circle of convergence of the Taylor series, several points of view are possible: (1) one can look for criteria of convergence or divergence of the series itself on the circumference; (2) one can consider the limit values of the circle of the analytic function represented by the series and try to determine where these limit values are finite or infinite, as well as the properties of the functions of the argument represented by the real and imaginary parts of the series when these functions are well defined; (3) one can consider what points on the circumference, singular in the Weierstrass sense, also determine the analytic extension of the series. The link between these problems led Fatou to formulate a fundamental theorem in the theory of the Lebesgue integral. He found that the theory of the Lebesgue integral allowed the first two of the above problems to be treated with more precision and more generality, with the following general result: If $f_n(x) \geqslant 0$ for all values of n, $x \in E$ and $f_n(x) \rightarrow f(x)$ as $n \rightarrow \infty$, then

$$\int_E f(x)dx \leqslant \lim_{n\rightarrow\infty} \int_E f(x)dx.$$

The theorem implies that if the right-hand side is finite, then $f(x)$ is finite almost everywhere and integrable; if $f(x)$ is not integrable or is infinite in a set of positive measure, then

$$\lim_{n\rightarrow\infty} \int_E f_n(x)dx = \infty.$$

This work was advanced by Carathéodory, Friedrich and Marcel Riesz, Griffith Evans, Leon Lichtenstein, Gabor Szegö and Nicolas Lusin.

Fatou also showed ways in which the algebraic signs of a_n affect the number and character of singularities in the Taylor series. Given the series $\Sigma a_n x^n$ $0 < R < \infty$, a sequence $\{\lambda_n\}$ exists such that the series obtained by changing the signs of a_{λ_n} has the circle of convergence as a cut. This theorem was proved in general by Hurwitz and George Pólya.

BIBLIOGRAPHY

I. ORIGINAL WORKS. Fatou's writings include "Séries trigonométriques et séries de Taylor," in *Acta mathematica,* **30** (1906), 335-400; "Sur la convergence absolue des séries trigonométriques," in *Bulletin de la Société mathématique de France,* **41** (1913), 47-53; "Sur les lignes singulières des fonctions analytiques," *ibid.,* 113-119; "Sur les fonctions holomorphes et bornées à l'intérieur d'un cercle," *ibid.,* **51** (1923), 191-202; "Sur l'itération analytique et les substitutions permutables," in *Journal de mathématiques pures et appliquées,* 9th ser., **2** (1923), 343-384, and **3** (1924), 1-49; "Substitutions analytiques et équations fonctionnelles à deux variables," in *Annales scientifiques de l'École normale* *supérieure,* 3rd ser., **41** (1924), 67–142; "Sur l'itération des fonctions transcendantes entières," in *Acta mathematica,* **47** (1926), 337-370; and "Sur le mouvement d'un système soumis à des forces à courte période," in *Bulletin de la Société mathématique de France,* **56** (1928), 98–139.

The Société Mathématique de France expects to publish Fatou's papers.

II. SECONDARY LITERATURE. On Fatou or his work, see Jean Chazy, "Pierre Fatou," in *Bulletin astronomique,* **8,** fasc. 7 (1934), 379–384; Griffith Evans, *The Logarithmic Potential* (New York, 1927); P. Fatou, *Notice sur les travaux scientifiques de M. P. Fatou* (Paris, 1929); A. Hurwitz and G. Pólya, "Zwei Beweise eines von Herrn Fatou vermuteten Satzes," in *Acta mathematica,* **40** (1916), 179–183; S. Mandelbrojt, *Modern Researches on the Singularities of Functions Defined by the Taylor Series* (Houston, Tex., 1929), chs. 9, 12; and M. Riesz, "Neuer Beweis des Fatouschen Satzes," in *Göttingensche Nachrichten* (1916); and "Ein Konvergenz satz für Dirichletsche Reihen," in *Acta mathematica,* **40** (1916), 349–361.

HENRY NATHAN

FAULHABER, JOHANN (*b.* Ulm, Germany, 5 May 1580; *d.* Ulm, 1635)

The Faulhaber family lived in Ulm from the middle of the fifteenth century and had been vassals of the abbot of Fulda from 1354 to 1461. Like his father, who died in 1593, Faulhaber first learned weaving. Ursula Esslinger of Ravensburg, whom Faulhaber married in 1600, bore him nine children, several of whom distinguished themselves as mathematicians. His son Johann Matthäus, born in 1604, learned weaving from his father before he turned to mathematics. In 1622 he accompanied his father to Basel to survey the fortifications and became director of the assignment following his father's death. A second son, also named Johann, born in 1609, was captain in the Corps of Engineers at Ulm.

His natural abilities led Faulhaber from weaving to mathematics. His first teacher in Ulm was the writing and arithmetic teacher David Saelzlin. The mathematicians of the sixteenth century concerned with algebra called themselves Cossists (from the Italian *cosa,* or "thing," which was used to designate the quantity being sought). Max Jaehns calls Faulhaber one of the most significant of the Cossists and the first to take algebra into equations higher than the third degree.[1]

His education did not make Faulhaber proficient in Latin, but with laborious effort he translated the Latin texts that he needed, lent by Michael Maestlin in Tübingen, as we learn from his letter of 16 April 1617 to Matthäus Beger, in Reutlingen:

> . . . since then I have taken the trouble to get the most distinguished books in German . . . as a person who never studied Latin and only now have attained some understanding of the language . . . to translate from Latin into simple German so that I now have at hand in German the books of Euclid, Archimedes, Apollonius, Serenus, Theodosius, Regiomontanus, Cardano. . . .

After Faulhaber had helped Johann Kraft, arithmetic master in Ulm, to publish an arithmetic text, he founded his own school in Ulm in 1600.[2]

From 1604 on, Faulhaber received a salary of 30 guldens for running this school, but it was withdrawn in 1610 for a few months because he was concerning himself more and more with physical and technical inventions and developing an extensive literary activity that took him away from his pedagogic duties. Above and beyond this, he incurred the displeasure of the municipal council because he published *Neu erfundener Gebrauch eines Niederländischen Instruments zum Abmessen und Grundlegen, mit sehr geschwindem Vortheil zu practiciren* without the permission of the office responsible for supervision of the schools. About this time Faulhaber set up the formulas for the sum of the powers for natural numbers up to the thirteenth power, a problem with which Leonhard Euler was later concerned in a general way. He knew of the expression for the final difference of the arithmetic series obtained by raising the terms of an arithmetic series of the first order to a higher power.[3] More and more his school became an educational institute for higher mathematical sciences, and an artillery and engineering school was later added. In the pedagogic field Faulhaber's particular merit was in the dissemination of mathematical knowledge for general use. His arithmetic text, *Arithmetischer Wegweiser zu der hochnutzlichen freyen Rechenkunst* (1614), is a very clear textbook for the period. In the early editions he got as far as the "rule of three"; in later editions he treated all of the computations for ordinary use and even the fundamentals of equations. His writings on algebra are difficult to interpret because he used symbols that are no longer common. His particular concerns in these works are the theory of progressions, theory of magic squares, and the nature of numbers.

Like Michael Stifel, the Augustinian monk and promotor of calculation with logarithms, Faulhaber was noted for his mystical consideration of pseudomathematical problems. He attempted to interpret future events from numbers in the Bible: from Genesis, Jeremiah, Daniel, and Revelation. Together with the master baker from Ulm, Noah Kolb, he predicted the end of the world by 1605 and was put in jail for this in 1606. On the basis of his confession that he had not acted with evil intent, but from an irresistible impulse of conscience, he was released. As early as seven years later he again believed that he could see "numeri figurati"—figured numbers—in certain numbers from the Bible, and his view that God had used pyramidal numbers in the prophecies of the Bible was expressed in *Neuer mathematischer Kunstspiegel* (1612). Faulhaber meditated on the numbers 2,300 (Daniel VIII: 14), 1,335 (Daniel XII: 12), 1,290 (Daniel XII: 11), 1,260 (Revelation XI: 3), and 666 (Revelation XX: 2). These are the same numbers with which Stifel concerned himself.[4]

The extent to which this mystic arithmetic had affected Faulhaber can be seen in his books *Andeutung einer unerhörten neuen Wunderkunst* . . . (1613) and *Himmlische geheime Magia* . . . (1613). In the latter book he attempted to solve the hidden riddles of his sealed numbers by a peculiar transposition of the German, Latin, Greek, and Hebrew alphabets, a puzzle in which he refers to the tribes Gog and Magog mentioned in Revelation XX: 8. This biblical interpretation being contrary to Christian teachings, he drew the enmity of the clergy upon himself, and at their instance he was warned by the magistrate in Ulm that he should no longer print such interpretations without the knowledge and permission of the censor, upon pain of losing his civil rights. Since other theologians, such as Hasenreffer, the chancellor of Tübingen University, also sent warning letters to the Ulm city council, the prohibition of *Himmlische geheime Magia* was intensified.

Faulhaber also devoted himself to alchemy, which he practiced as a believer in Johann Valentin Andreae's *Chymische Hochzeit des Christiani Rosencreutz,* first published anonymously about 1604. On 21 January 1618 he wrote to Rudolph von Bünau: ". . . I am not sparing any efforts in inquiring about the commendable Rosicrucian Society . . ."; and on 21 March 1621, to Bünau: ". . . with the help of God, I have come to the point where I can make 2 grains of gold out of 1 grain of gold in a few days, which is why I give praise and thanks to the Almighty, and although one-tenth is supposed to become 10, up to now, I have not been able to get it any further and have worked it with my own hands."

These mysterious arts brought Faulhaber into contact with Duke Johann Friedrich von Württemberg. In 1619 he obtained permission to teach his arts and sciences freely in the duchy, and he continued to have that permission until after he again distributed his forbidden writings about Gog and Magog.

The reputation of Faulhaber's mathematics school extended so far that Descartes studied with him in 1620.[5] According to Veesenmayer, Descartes had already corresponded with Faulhaber concerning questions of plane analytic geometry[6] and had been stimulated to write *Discours sur la méthode* . . . (1637).[7] Descartes called him a "mathematicum insignem et imprimis in numerorum doctrina versatum et präceptorem."[8]

Faulhaber's lasting accomplishment was the dissemination and explanation of the logarithmic method of calculation. The dissemination of the logarithms associated with Stifel, Bürgi, and Napier occurred through his chief work, *Ingenieurs-Schul,* the *Appendix oder Anhang . . . Ingenieurs-Schul,* and the *Zehntausend Logarithmi*. . . . He gives the logarithms of the numbers 1–10,000 to seven places and the values of the six natural goniometric functions to ten places. Along with the solution of plane and spherical triangles, with the applications to fortification and astronomical geography, we find the reason in the *Appendix:* ". . . that the entire foundation and correct basis of the logarithms from which they originate and are made, arc briefly indicated and explained. . . ." In addition, it was the first publication of the Briggs logarithms in German.[9] Faulhaber devoted himself to the stereometric analogue to the Pythagorean theorem, which he found and to which he was led by an apocalyptic number, 666. He first published this theorem as a numerical example in his "Miracola arithmetica," which is part of the *Continuatio des neuen mathematischen Kunstspiegel* (1620). Descartes, who probably learned it from Faulhaber, reproduced it in 1620: "In tedraedro rectangula basis potentia aequalis est potentistrium facierum simul." If one imagines a rectangular system of coordinates intersected by an inclined plane; if A, B, and C are the areas of the right triangles that occur on the planes of the coordinates; and if D is the area of the triangle determined by the intersections of the axes on this intersecting plane, then $D^2 = A^2 + B^2 + C^2$.

Faulhaber usually gives the solutions of his mathematical problems only in hints. Among the problems treated in the first part of his *Ingenieurs-Schul,* the question concerning an irregular circle-heptagon (p. 168) attained some measure of fame because the well-known nineteenth-century mathematicians Moebius and Siebeck concerned themselves with it. Faulhaber inscribed within a circle a heptagon with sides of lengths 2,300, 1,600, 1,290, 1,000, 666, 1,260, and 1,335, then asked how the radius of this circle could be found and how many degrees and minutes each angle contained. The numbers again are those of Michael Stifel. Faulhaber does not say how he solved this problem, but in the *Ingenieurs-Schul* (ch. 13, p. 157), he gives the result according to which the radius of the circle is "found to be $1582\frac{6223}{10{,}000}$."[10]

Faulhaber's prestige as a fortifications engineer is based on his many assignments in this field. Besides

Duke August von Brunswick-Lüneburg, his services were sought by Duke Johann Friedrich von Württemberg, Cardinal Dietrichstein of Nicholsburg (near Vienna), King Gustavus Adolphus of Sweden, and the cities of Randegg, Schaffhausen, and Fürstenberg. Unfortunately, in this area too his full development was hindered by his religious fanaticism. On 5 December 1618 he entered the service of Landgrave Philipp von Butzbach, who sought him as an adviser, but he continued to live in Ulm. He wanted to make "all his inventions" known to the landgrave except his work in "munitions," i.e., in fortifications, which he was forbidden to divulge by the municipal council of Ulm.[11] Soon thereafter Faulhaber concerned himself anew with his interpretations of biblical numbers, and in April 1619 his mathematical and astronomical writings to the landgrave suddenly ended. Perhaps it was because the prince, who was firmly grounded in Christian teachings, believed that he had deceived himself about Faulhaber, or perhaps it was, as Faulhaber claims, that he was supposed to give the prince secrets which he had to consider in total confidence. In spite of this, the landgrave remained interested in his former adviser. In 1622 he received news about Faulhaber through Konrad Dietrich, superintendent in Ulm; and we learn from his letter of 23 March 1625 that Faulhaber "has been reconciled with an honorable councilman in Ulm and has promised in the name of the Almighty to let his whims fall."[12]

The full picture of Faulhaber's character is revealed from the controversies into which he was drawn. To be sure, we do not find his scientific importance reduced, but he nevertheless appears shady in view of the interplay of serious perception and speculative fantasy. Having been ordered by the municipal council of Ulm to publish an almanac for the year 1618, he used the ephemerides of Johannes Kepler. In it Kepler listed two rare constellations that were supposed to appear before and after 1 September, which means that the appearance of a comet cannot be regarded as excluded. In his almanac Faulhaber predicted a comet for 1 September 1618, on the basis of a consideration of the longitude and latitude of Mars and the moon. When one of the greatest comets of that era appeared in November 1618, Faulhaber no longer doubted the efficacy of his secret numbers and had this opinion published through his friend J. G. Goldtberg.[13] Attacked as vehemently by Hebenstreit and Zimpertus Wehe in Ulm as he was defended by Matthäus Beger in Reutlingen, Faulhaber appealed to the municipal council in Ulm and the ecclesiastical authorities, who decided in his favor.

He had a lively contact with Johannes Kepler. Upon the order of the magistrate, in 1622 he and Kepler designed a gauging kettle for the measurement of length, volume, and weight, which was cast by Hans Braun in 1627.[14]

NOTES

1. *Geschichte der Kriegswissenschaften,* vol. XXI of *Geschichte der Wissenschaften in Deutschland* (Munich-Leipzig, 1890), sec. 2, ch. 4, p. 1115, par. 118.
2. Although he was the author, it did not appear under his name. Georg Veesenmayer, *De Ulmensium in arithmeticam meritis* (Ulm, 1794), p. 6.
3. L. E. Ofterdinger, "Beiträge zur Geschichte der Mathematik in Ulm," in *Programmschrift des Königlichen Gymnasiums zu Ulm* (Ulm, 1866–1867).
4. Joseph E. Hofmann, "Michael Stifel," in *Sudhoffs Archiv für Geschichte der Medizin und Naturwissenschaften,* supp. 9 (1968), 2–5.
5. J. G. Doppelmayer, *Historische Nachricht von den Nürnbergischen Mathematicis und Künstlern* (Nuremberg, 1730), p. 209.
6. Veesenmayer, *op. cit.,* p. 7.
7. Christian Thomasius, *Historia sapientiae et stultitiae* (Halle, 1693), II, 113.
8. Ofterdinger, *op. cit.,* p. 5.
9. MS notes for and drafts of this work are in the Ulm municipal archives.
10. A. Germann, "Das irreguläre Siebeneck des Ulmer Mathematikers Joh. Faulhaber," in *Programmschrift des Königlichen Gymnasiums zu Ulm* (Ulm, 1875–1876), pp. 3–13.
11. *Ulmer Ratsprotokolle,* no. 61 (1611), fol. 674b.
12. Wilhelm Diehl, *Landgraf Philipp von Butzbach,* no. 4 of the series *Aus Butzbachs Vergangheit* (Giessen, 1922), pp. 37 ff.
13. Conrad Holzhalbius, *Herrn Faulhabers . . . Continuatio seiner neuen Wunderkunsten oder arithmetischen Wunderwerken* (Zurich, 1617).
14. K. E. Haeberle, *10,000 Jahre Waage* (Balingen, 1966), pp. 109–111.

BIBLIOGRAPHY

I. ORIGINAL WORKS. Faulhaber's writings are *Arithmetischer cubicossischer Lustgarten mit neuen Inventionibus gepflanzet* (Tübingen, 1604, 1708); *Neu erfundener Gebrauch eines Niederländischen Instruments zum Abmessen und Grundlegen . . .* (Augsburg, 1610); *Neue geometrische und perspectivische Inventiones etlicher sonderbarer Instrument . . .* (Frankfurt, 1610); *Neue geometrische und perspectivische Inventiones zu Grundrissen der Pasteyen und Vestungen* (Frankfurt, 1610); *Neuer mathematischer Kunstspiegel . . .* (Ulm, 1612); *Andeutung einer unerhörten neuen Wunderkunst . . .* (Nuremberg, 1613), Latin ed., *Ansa inauditae et novae artis . . .* (Ulm, 1613); *Himmlische geheime Magia oder neue cabalistische Kunst und Wunderrechnung vom Gog und Magog* (Nuremberg, 1613), trans. by Johannes Remmelin as *Magia arcana coelestis, sive Cabalisticus novus, artificiosus et admirandus computus de Gog et Magog . . .* (Nuremberg, 1613); *Arithmetischer Wegweiser zu der hochnutzlichen freyen Rechenkunst . . .* (Ulm, 1614, 1615, 1675, 1691, 1708, 1736, 1762, 1765), the last two eds. entitled *Arithmetischer Tausendkünstler . . . ; Neue Invention einer Haus- und Handmühle* (Ulm, 1617); *Solution, wie man die Fristen, welche ohne Interesse auf gewisse Ziel zu bezahlen verfallen* . . . (Ulm, 1618); *Continuatio des neuen mathematischen Kunstspiegel* . . . (Tübingen, 1620), which contains thirty-two inventions; *Zweiundvierzig Secreta* . . . (Augsburg, 1621), which contains the inventions in the *Continuatio* plus ten new ones; *Appendix oder Anhang der Continuation des neuen mathematischen Kunstspiegel* . . . (Augsburg, 1621); *Erste deutsche Lection . . . das Prognosticon vom Gog und Magog* . . . (Augsburg, 1621); *Tarif über das kurze und lange Brennholz* . . . (Ulm, 1625); *Ingenieurs-Schul* . . ., 4pts. (Frankfurt, 1630–1633), which is partly extracted from the works of Adrian Vlacq, John Napier, and Matthias Bernegg; *Appendix oder Anhang des ersten Theils der Ingenieurs-Schul* . . . (Augsburg, 1631); and *Zehntausend Logarithmi der absoluten oder ledigen Zahlen* . . . (Augsburg, 1631). A holograph MS of Faulhaber's, entitled "Beobachtungen von Mund- und Sonnenringen" (1619), is in the Darmstadt Landesbibliothek, 4° 3044. Ten letters from Faulhaber to Philipp von Butzbach are in the Darmstadt Staatsarchiv, 55, 1618–1619.

II. SECONDARY LITERATURE. On Faulhaber's work, see Matthias Bernegger, *Sinum, tangentium et secantium canon* . . . (Strasbourg, 1619[?]), which refers to *Neue geometrische und perspectivische Inventiones etlicher sonderbarer Instrument* . . . ; and *Phantasma qua Joh. Faulhaber de ansa inauditae et admirabilis artis* . . . (Strasbourg, 1614), a refutation of *Andeutung einer unerhörten neuen Wunderkunst;* Benjamin Bramer, *Beschreibung eines sehr leichten Perspectiv und grundreissenden Instruments auf einem Stande* . . . (Kassel, 1630), which refers to *Appendix oder Anhang der Continuation des neuen mathematischen Kunstspiegel* . . . ; Georg Galgemair, *Centiloquium circini proportionum. Ein neuer Proportionalzirkel von 4, 5, 6 oder mehr Spitzen* (Nuremberg, 1626), which refers to *Neue geometrische und perspectivische Inventiones etlicher sonderbarer Instrument* . . . ; J. G. Goldtberg, *Fama syderea nova. Gemein offentliches Ausschreiben* . . . (Nuremberg, 1618, 1619); *Expolitio famae sidereae novae Faulhabereanae* . . . (Prague, 1619); *Postulatum aequitatis plenissimum, Das ist: Ein billiges und rechtmässiges Begehren, die Expolitionem famae Faulhaberianae betreffend* . . . (Prague, 1619); *Fama syderea nova, das ist weitere Continuatio der Göttlichen neuen Wunderzeichen und grossen Miraculn* . . . (Nuremberg, 1620); and *Vindiciarium Faulhaberianum continuatio* . . . (Ulm, 1620); Conrad Holzhalbius, *Herrn Faulhabers . . . Continuatio seiner neuen Wunderkünsten oder arithmetischen Wunderwerken* (Zurich, 1617); Petrus Roth, *Arithmetica philosophica* . . ., II (Nuremberg, 1608), which refers to *Arithmetischer cubicossischer Lustgarten mit neuen Inventionibus gepflanzet;* and David Verbez, *Miracula arithmetica zu der Continuation des arithmetischen Wegweisers* (Augsburg, 1622).

Biographical literature includes C. G. Jöcher, in *Allgemeinen Gelehrten-Lexikon,* II (Leipzig, 1750), col. 527; Hermann Keefer, "Johannes Faulhaber, der bedeutendste Ulmer Mathematiker und Festungsbaumeister," in *Württembergische Schulwarte,* **4** (1928), 1–12; Emil von Loeffler, "Ein Ingenieur und Artillerie-Offizier der Festung Ulm in 30-jährigen Kriege," in *Ulmer Tagblatt* (1886), Sonntagsbeilage no. 52 and (1887), Sonntagsbeilage nos. 1–6, also in *Allgemeine Militarzeitung,* **60** (1885), which refers to Faulhaber and Joseph Furtenbach; Max Schefold, "Ein Zyklus von Faulhaberbildnissen," in *Ulmer Tagblatt* (30 Apr. and 7 May 1926); Albrecht Weyermann, *Nachrichten von Gelehrten, Künstlern und andere merkwürdigen Personen aus Ulm* (Ulm, 1798), pp. 206–215; and J. H. Zedler, in *Universal-Lexikon,* IX (Halle–Leipzig, 1735), col. 317.

Documents concerning Faulhaber are in the Darmstadt Staatsarchiv, 55 XVII. The Faulhaber family's coat of arms is reproduced in J. F. Schannat, *Fuldischer Lehnhof, sive de clientela Fuldensi beneficiaria nobili et equestri tractatus historico-iuridicus* . . . (Frankfurt, 1736), pp. 83, 91.

PAUL A. KIRCHVOGEL

FEIGL, GEORG (*b.* Hamburg, Germany, 13 October 1890; *d.* Wechselburg, Germany, 25 April 1945)

Feigl was the son of Georg Feigl, an importer, and Maria Pinl, from Bohemia. He attended the Johanneum in Hamburg and began to study mathematics and physics at the University of Jena in 1909. A severe chronic stomach disorder forced him to interrupt his studies several times, and he did not finish them until 1918, when he received the doctorate with a dissertation on conformal mapping that was supervised by Paul Koebe. In 1919 Feigl became a teaching assistant to Erhard Schmidt, a well-known mathematician at the University of Berlin. Schmidt was the scientist who most influenced Feigl and also developed his gift for teaching. Generations of students in mathematics at the University of Berlin took the introductory course "Einführung in die höhere Mathematik," which Feigl created and which after his death was published, in enlarged form, as a textbook (1953) by Hans Rohrbach.

In 1925 Feigl married Maria Fleischer, daughter of Paul Fleischer, an economist and member of the Reichstag. In 1927 he became assistant professor and in 1933 associate professor at the University of Berlin. From 1928 to 1935 he was, by appointment of the Prussian Academy of Sciences in Berlin, the managing editor of the *Jahrbuch über die Fortschritte der Mathematik,* at that time the only periodical that reviewed papers on mathematics.

Feigl's field of research was geometry, especially the foundations of geometry and topology. But his scientific activity was rather limited because of his illness, and he soon had to choose between research and teaching. His talents led Feigl to devote himself to a reform of the teaching of mathematics. He became a leading member of the National Council of German Mathematical Societies, and it was essentially through him that the new fundamental concepts of Felix Klein and David Hilbert and the modern mode of mathematical thinking based on axioms and structures were introduced into universities and even high schools.

In 1935 Feigl was called as full professor to the University of Breslau. There during World War II he formed a computing team that worked for the German Aeronautic Research Institute. In January 1945, when the Russians marched into Breslau, he moved with his team to the castle of Graf Schönburg at Wechselburg, Saxony, near Chemnitz (now Karl-Marx-Stadt). There it proved impossible to maintain his necessary medical supervision, a circumstance that led to Feigl's death a few months later.

BIBLIOGRAPHY

Feigl's writings include "Elementare Anordnungssätze der Geometrie," in *Jahresbericht der Deutschen Mathematikervereinigung,* **33** (1924), 2-24; "Zum Archimedesschen Axiom," in *Mathematische Zeitschrift,* **25** (1926), 590-601; "Eigenschaften der einfachen stetigen Kurven," *ibid.,* **27** (1927), 162-168; "Fixpunktsätze für spezielle n-dimensionale Mannigfaltigkeiten," in *Mathematische Annalen,* **98** (1927-1928), 355-398; "Erfahrungen über die mathematische Vorbildung der Mathematik-Studierenden des 1. Semesters," in *Jahresbericht der Deutschen Mathematikervereinigung,* **37** (1928), 187-199; "Geschichtliche Entwicklung der Topologie," *ibid.,* 273-286, repr. in the series Wege der Forschung, vol. CLXXVII (Darmstadt, in press); "Das Unendliche im Schulunterricht," in *Zeitschrift für mathematischen und naturwissenschaftlichen Unterricht,* **60** (1929), 385-393; "Der Übergang von der Schule zur Hochschule," in *Jahresbericht der Deutschen Mathematikervereinigung,* **47** (1937), 80-88; "Ausbildungsplan für Lehramtsanwärter in der Fächern reine Mathematik, angewandte Mathematik und Physik," in *Deutsche Mathematik,* **4** (1939), 98-108, 135-136, written with Georg Hamel; "Erfahrungen über das Mathematikstudium der Lehramtsanwärter nach der neuen Ausbildungsordnung," *ibid.,* **6** (1942), 467-471. His textbook is *Einführung in die höhere Mathematik,* Hans Rohrbach, ed. (Berlin-Göttingen-Heidelberg, 1953).

Some biographical information may be found in *Neue deutsche Biographie,* V (1961), 57.

HANS ROHRBACH

FEJÉR, LIPÓT (*b.* Pécs, Hungary, 9 February 1880; *d.* Budapest, Hungary, 15 October 1959)

Fejér became interested in mathematics while in the higher grades of the Gymnasium, and in 1897 he won a prize in one of the first mathematical competitions held in Hungary. From 1897 to 1902 he studied mathematics and physics at the universities of Budapest and Berlin. During the academic year 1899-1900 H. A. Schwarz directed his attention, through a suggestion made by C. Neumann concerning Dirichlet's problem, to the theory of Fourier series. Later in 1900 Fejér published, in the *Comptes rendus* of the Paris Academy, the fundamental summation theorem that bears his name and was also the basis of his doctoral dissertation at Budapest (1902). After participating in mathematical seminars in Göttingen and Paris, he taught at the University of Budapest from 1902 to 1905 and at that of Kolozsvár (now Cluj, Rumania) from 1905 to 1911. He was professor of higher analysis at the University of Budapest from 1911 until his death. Collaborating with F. and M. Riesz, A. Haar, G. Pólya, G. Szegö, O. Szász, and other mathematicians of international rank, Fejér became the head of the most successful Hungarian school of analysis.

Fejér was a vice-chairman of the International Congress of Mathematicians held at Cambridge in 1912. In 1933 he and Niels Bohr, two of the four European scientists invited to the Chicago World's Fair, were awarded honorary doctorates by Brown University. Fejér was elected to the Hungarian Academy of Sciences in 1908 and was also a member of several foreign academies and scientific societies. Besides receiving a number of state and academic prizes for his work, he was honorary chairman of the Bolyai Mathematical Society from its founding and the holder of an honorary doctorate from Eötvös University, Budapest (1950).

Fejér's main works deal with harmonic analysis. His classic theorem on (C, 1) summability of trigonometric Fourier series (1900) not only gave a new direction to the theory of orthogonal expansions but also, through significant applications, became a starting point for the modern general theory of divergent series and singular integrals. Through a Tauberian theorem of G. H. Hardy's the convergence theory of Fourier series was considerably affected by Fejér's theorem as well; it is closely connected with Weierstrass' approximation theorems and with the more advanced theory of power series and harmonics (potential theory), and makes possible a number of analogues for related series, such as Laplace series. In 1910 Fejér found a new method of investigating the singularities of Fourier series that was suitable for a unified discussion of various types of divergence phenomena. These results were continued and generalized in several directions by Fejér himself, by Lebesgue (1905), by M. Riesz and S. Chapman (1909-1911), by Hardy and Littlewood (1913), by T. Carleman (1921), and others.

Fejér's contributions to approximation theory and the constructive theory of functions are of great importance. In 1918 he solved Runge's problem on complex Lagrange interpolation relating to an arbitrary Jordan curve, and in the following decades he enriched the field of real Lagrange and Hermite interpolation and mechanical quadrature by introducing new procedures. His work in mechanical quadrature produced wide response in the literature (Akhiezer, Erdös, Grünwald, Natanson, Pólya, J. A. Shohat, Szegö, and Turán, among others). As for Fejér's results in complex analysis, particular stress may still be laid on a joint paper with Carathéodory (1907), of which the basic ideas influenced considerably the literature on entire functions, and a new standard proof of the fundamental theorem of conformal mappings, found in 1922 with F. Riesz.

BIBLIOGRAPHY

I. ORIGINAL WORKS. Fejér's collected works, with bilingual comments in Hungarian and German, are *Fejér Lipót Összegyüjtött Munkái / Leopold Fejér, Gesammelte Arbeiten,* 2 vols. (Budapest, 1970). The summation theorem was first printed as "Sur les fonctions bornées et intégrables," in *Comptes rendus hebdomadaires des séances de l'Académie des sciences,* **131** (1900), 984–987; the author's name is here printed incorrectly as "Tejér."

II. SECONDARY LITERATURE. The proof found with F. Riesz was published (with the permission of the authors) in T. Rado, "Über die Fundamentalabbildung schlichter Gebiete," in *Acta litterarum ac scientiarum R. Univertatis hungarica Francisco-Josephina,* **1** (1922), 240–251. See also C. Carathéodory, "Bemerkungen zu dem Existenztheorem der konformen Abbildung," in *Bulletin of the Calcutta Mathematical Society,* **20** (1930), 125–134.

Other works on Fejér are Émile Borel, *Leçons sur les séries divergentes* (Paris, 1901), p. 88, n.; the article in *Encyclopaedia Brittanica,* 12th ed. (1922), XXXI, 877; and P. Turán, "Fejér Lipót matematikai munkássága" ("The Mathematical Work of Lipót Fejér"), in *Matematikai lapok,* **1** (1950), 160–170.

An obituary by P. Szász, G. Szegö, and P. Turán is in *Magyar tudományos akadémia III osztályának közleményei,* **10** (1960), 103–148; and in *Matematikai lapok,* **11** (1960), 8–18, 225–228.

MIKLÓS MIKOLÁS

FELLER, WILLIAM (*b.* Zagreb, Yugoslavia, 7 July 1906; *d.* New York, New York, 14 January 1970)

Feller was the son of Eugene V. Feller, a wealthy owner of a chemical factory, and Ida Perc Feller. William was the tenth of twelve children, the youngest of six boys. He was educated by private tutors until he entered the University of Zagreb in 1923, from which he received the equivalent of an M.S. degree in 1925. He received his Ph.D. degree in 1926 from the University of Göttingen, where he remained until 1928. In 1928 he moved to the University of Kiel, where he headed the applied mathematics laboratory until he moved to Copenhagen in 1933, after Hitler came to power. After a year in Copenhagen, he moved to the University of Stockholm to be research associate in the probability group headed by Cramér.

During his Stockholm stay he married Clara Mary Nielsen (27 July 1938), a student of his at Kiel, who as a Danish schoolgirl had bicycled with her friends across the German border carrying anti-Nazi pamphlets. There were no children of this marriage. In 1939 the Fellers immigrated to the United States, where William became a professor at Brown University and the first executive editor of *Mathematical Reviews*. This international review, founded in 1939 because the German review had come under Nazi control, has been an invaluable mathematical tool, and much of its success is due to the policies set by Feller. In 1945 he accepted a professorship at Cornell University; he remained there until 1950, when he moved to Princeton University as Eugene Higgins professor of mathematics.

Although Feller's research was almost entirely in pure mathematics, he had more than an amateur's interest in and knowledge of several scientific fields, including statistics and genetics. He took an excited delight in applications of pure theory, and nothing pleased him more than finding new applications. He wrote several papers applying probability theory to genetics and spent the academic years 1965–1966 and 1967–1968 at Rockefeller University, where he held an appointment as permanent visiting professor and enjoyed close contacts with geneticists.

Before Kolmogorov's measure theoretic formulation (1933) of the basic concepts of probability theory, this theory was a barely respectable part of mathematics, with little interaction with other parts. Probability results were solutions to isolated mathematical problems suggested by a certain non-mathematical context. After 1933 these results took their places in an overall mathematical framework, and probability theory began a rapid development. A host of researchers, with a few great leaders such as Kolmogorov (Soviet Union), Lévy (France), and Feller, transformed mathematical probability into one of the liveliest branches of contemporary mathematics, contributing as much to the newest aspects of other branches as it drew from them.

Feller's first probability paper appeared in 1935. In this and many later papers, he discussed the properties of successive sums S_1, S_2, . . . of a sequence of independent random variables. Under what conditions does suitably normalized S_n have a nearly Gaussian distribution when n is large? What are asymptotic bounds for S_n when n is large? One of Feller's first results was a set of necessary and sufficient conditions answering the first question. One of his deepest papers answers the second, under appropriate conditions.

In 1931 Kolmogorov gave the first systematic presentation of the intimate relations between parabolic partial differential equations and the probabilistic processes now called Markov processes. Feller completely transformed this subject. First he refined and extended Kolmogorov's work. For example, he proved that the equations in question (in a more general framework than Kolmogorov's) have probabilistically meaningful solutions. Later, he put the analysis in a functional analysis framework, applying semigroup theory to the semigroups generated by Markov process transition probabilities of very general types. He linked the boundary conditions for the differential equations with the domains of the semigroup infinitesimal generators and with the conduct of the process sample paths at the boundaries of the process state spaces, incidentally defining new abstract boundaries when necessary. In particular, Feller found a beautiful form for the infinitesimal generator of the most general one-dimensional diffusion. In much of his work, Feller was a pioneer, yet he frequently obtained definitive results.

One of Feller's greatest legacies, containing research at every level, is his two-volume work *An Introduction to Probability Theory and Its Applications* (1950–1966). He never tired of revising the material in these volumes, in finding new approaches, new examples, and new applications. No other book on the subject even remotely resembles these volumes, with their combination of purest abstract mathematics and interesting applications, employing a dazzling virtuosity of analytical techniques and written in a style betraying the bubbling enthusiasm of the author. The style has made the book popular even among nonspecialists, just as its elegance and breadth have made it an inspiration for specialists.

Mathematical statistics is based on probability theory. Feller made a caustic critique of extrasensory perception experiments, and kept in touch with such statistical controversies as the effect of cigarette smoking on health. It is typical of him that what roused his ire more than the issues in such controversies was the attempt by some statisticians to strengthen weak statistics with irrelevant emotional appeals.

Those who knew him personally remember Feller best for his gusto, the pleasure with which he met life, and the excitement with which he drew on his endless fund of anecdotes about life and its absurdities, particularly the absurdities involving mathematics and mathematicians. To listen to him lecture was a unique experience, for no one else could lecture with such intense excitement.

Feller was a president of the Institute of Mathematical Statistics. He was a member of the National Academy of Sciences and of the American Academy of Arts and Sciences, a foreign associate of the Royal Danish Academy and of the Yugoslav Academy of Sciences, and a fellow of the (British) Royal Statistical Society. He was named to receive the 1969 National Medal of Science shortly before his death but died before the awards ceremony; his widow accepted the medal on his behalf.

BIBLIOGRAPHY

I. ORIGINAL WORKS. Some of Feller's early research was published under the name Willy instead of William. His writings included: "Zur Theorie der stochastischen Prozesse (Existenz- und Eindeutigkeitssätze)," in *Mathematische Annalen*, **113** (1937), 113–160; "The General Form of the So-Called Law of the Iterated Logarithm," in *Transactions of the American Mathematical Society*, **54** (1943), 373–402; "The Fundamental Limit Theorems in Probability," in *Bulletin of the American Mathematical Society*, **51** (1945), 800–832; "Diffusion Processes in One Dimension," in *Transactions of the American Mathematical Society*, **77** (1954), 1–31; "On Boundaries and Lateral Conditions for the Kolmogorov Differential Equations," in *Annals of Mathematics*, 2nd ser., **65** (1957), 527–570; and "On the Influence of Natural Selection on Population Size," in *Proceedings of the National Academy of Sciences*, **55** (1966), 733–738.

II. SECONDARY LITERATURE. See *Annals of Mathematical Statistics*, **41**, no. 6 (1970), iv–xiii, for an obituary, photograph, and complete bibliography. See *Proceedings of the Sixth Berkeley Symposium on Mathematical Statistics and Probability*, II (Berkeley, 1972), xv–xxiii, for obituaries and a very youthful picture; and see *Revue de l'institut international de statistique*, **38** (1970), 435–436, for another obituary.

J. L. DOOB

FERMAT, PIERRE DE (*b.* Beaumont-de-Lomagne, France, 20 August 1601; *d.* Castres, France, 12 January 1665)

Factual details concerning Fermat's private life are quite sparse.[1] He apparently spent his childhood and early school years in his birthplace, where his father, Dominique Fermat, had a prosperous leather business and served as second consul of the town. His uncle and godfather, Pierre Fermat, was also a merchant. To the family's firm financial position Fermat's mother, Claire de Long, brought the social status of the parliamentary *noblesse de robe.* Hence, his choice of law as his profession followed naturally from the social milieu into which he was born. Having received a solid classical secondary education locally, Fermat may have attended the University of Toulouse, although one can say with certainty only that he spent some time in Bordeaux toward the end of the 1620's before finally receiving the degree of Bachelor of Civil Laws from the University of Orleans on 1 May 1631.

Returning to Toulouse, where some months earlier he had purchased the offices of *conseiller* and *commissaire aux requêtes* in the local *parlement,* Fermat married his mother's cousin, Louise de Long, on 1 June 1631. Like his in-laws, Fermat enjoyed as *parlementaire* the rank and privileges of the *noblesse de robe;* in particular he was entitled to add the "de" to his name, which he occasionally did. Fermat's marriage contract, the price he paid for his offices, and several other documents attest to the financial security he enjoyed throughout his life.

Five children issued from Fermat's marriage. The oldest, Clément-Samuel, apparently was closest to his father. As a lawyer he inherited his father's offices in 1665 and later undertook the publication of his father's mathematical papers.[2] Fermat's other son, Jean, served as archdeacon of Fimarens. The oldest daughter, Claire, married; her two younger sisters, Catherine and Louise, took holy orders. These outward details of Fermat's family life suggest that it followed the standard pattern for men of his social status. The direct male line ended with the death of Clément-Samuel's son, Jean-François, from whom Claire's grandson inherited the offices originally bought by Fermat.

As a lawyer and *parlementaire* in Toulouse, Fermat seems to have benefited more from the high rate of mortality among his colleagues than from any outstanding talents of his own. On 16 January 1638 he rose to the position of *conseiller aux enquêtes* and in 1642 entered the highest councils of the *parlement:* the criminal court and then the Grand Chamber. In 1648 he acted as chief spokesman for the *parlement* in negotiations with the chancellor of France, Pierre Séguier. However, Fermat's letters to Séguier and to his physician and confidant, Marin Cureau de La Chambre,[3] suggest that Fermat's performance in office was often less than satisfactory; and a confidential report by the *intendant* of Languedoc to Colbert in 1664 refers to Fermat in quite deprecatory terms. A staunch Catholic, Fermat served also—again probably by reason of seniority—as member and then president of the Chambre de l'Édit, which had jurisdiction over suits between Huguenots and Catholics and which convened in the Huguenot stronghold of Castres.

In addition to his fame as a mathematician, Fermat enjoyed a modest reputation as a classical scholar. Apparently equally fluent in French, Italian, Spanish, Latin, and Greek, he dabbled in philological problems and the composition of Latin poetry (see appendixes to his *Oeuvres,* I).

Except for an almost fatal attack of the plague in 1652, Fermat seems to have enjoyed good health until the years immediately preceding his death. He died in Castres, two days after having signed his last *arrêt* for the Chambre de l'Édit there. At first buried in Castres, his remains were brought back to the family vault in the Church of the Augustines in Toulouse in 1675.

The Development of Fermat's Mathematics. Fermat's letters and papers, most of them written after 1636 for friends in Paris, provide the few available hints regarding his development as a mathematician. From them one can infer that his stay in Bordeaux in the late 1620's most decisively shaped his approach to mathematics; almost all of his later achievements derived from research begun there. It was apparently in Bordeaux that Fermat studied in depth the works of François Viète. From Viète he took the new symbolic algebra and theory of equations that served as his basic research tools. More important, however, Viète's concept of algebra as the "analytic art" and the program of research implicit in that concept largely guided Fermat's choice of problems and the manner in which he treated them. Fermat himself viewed his work as a continuation of the Viètan tradition.

From Viète, Fermat inherited the idea of symbolic algebra as a formal language or tool uniting the realms of geometry and arithmetic (number theory). An algebraic equation had meaning in both realms, depending only on whether the unknowns denoted line segments or numbers. Moreover, Viète's theory of equations had shifted attention away from solutions of specific equations to questions of the relationships between solutions and the structures of their parent equations or between the solutions of one equation and those of another. In his own study of the application of determinate equations to geometric constructions, Viète laid the groundwork for the algebraic study of solvability and constructibility. Fermat sought to build further on this foundation. An overall characteristic of his mathematics is the use of algebraic analysis to explore the relationships between problems and their solutions. Most of Fermat's research strove toward a "reduction analysis" by which a given problem could be reduced to another or identified with a class of problems for which the general solution was known. This "reduction analysis," constituted from the theory of equations, could be reversed in most cases to operate as a generator of families of solutions to problems.

At first Fermat, like Viète, looked to the Greek mathematicians for hints concerning the nature of mathematical analysis. Believing that the so-called "analytical" works cited by Pappus in book VII of the *Mathematical Collection,* most of which were no longer extant,[4] contained the desired clues, Fermat followed Viète and others in seeking to restore those lost texts, such as Apollonius' *Plane Loci* (*Oeuvres,* I, 3–51) and Euclid's *Porisms* (*Oeuvres,* I, 76–84). Another supposed source of insight was Diophantus' *Arithmetica,* to which Fermat devoted a lifetime of study. These ancient sources, together with the works of Archimedes, formed the initial elements in a clear pattern of development that Fermat's research followed. Taking his original problem from the classical sources, Fermat attacked it with the new algebraic techniques at his disposal. His solution, however, usually proved more general than the problem that had inspired it. By skillful application of the theory of equations in the form of a "reduction analysis," Fermat would reformulate the problem in its most general terms, often defining thereby a class of problems; in many cases the new problem structure lost all contact with its Greek forebear.

In Fermat's papers algebra as the "analytic art" achieved equal status with the traditional geometrical mode of ancient mathematics. With few exceptions he presented only the algebraic derivation of his results, dispensing with their classical synthetic proofs. Convinced that the latter could always be provided, Fermat seldom attempted to carry them out, with the result in several cases that he failed to see how the use of algebra had led to the introduction of concepts quite foreign to the classical tradition.

In large part Fermat's style of exposition characterized the unfinished nature of his papers, most of them brief essays or letters to friends. He never wrote for publication. Indeed, adamantly refusing to edit his work or to publish it under his own name, Fermat thwarted several efforts by others to make his results available in print. Showing little interest in completed work, he freely sent papers to friends without keeping copies for himself. Many results he merely entered in the margins of his books; e.g., his "Observations on Diophantus," a major part of his work on number theory, was published by his son on the basis of the marginalia in Fermat's copy of the Bachet edition of the *Arithmetica.* Some other work slipped into print during Fermat's lifetime, although only by virtue of honoring his demand for anonymity. This demand allows no clear or obvious explanation. Fermat knew of his reputation and he valued it. He seemed to enjoy the intellectual combat of the several controversies to which he was a party. Whatever the reason, anonymity and refusal to publish robbed him of recognition for many striking achievements and toward the end of his life led to a growing isolation from the main currents of research.

Fermat's name slipped into relative obscurity during the eighteenth century. In the mid-nineteenth century, however, renewed interest in number theory recalled him and his work to the attention of mathematicians and historians of mathematics. Various projects to publish his extant papers culminated in the four-volume edition by Charles Henry and Paul Tannery, from which the extent and importance of Fermat's achievements in fields other than number theory became clear.

Analytic Geometry. By the time Fermat began corresponding with Mersenne and Roberval in the spring of 1636, he had already composed his "Ad locos planos et solidos isagoge" (*Ouevres,* I, 91–103), in which he set forth a system of analytic geometry almost identical with that developed by Descartes in the *Géométrie* of 1637. Despite their simultaneous appearance (Descartes's in print, Fermat's in circulated manuscript), the two systems stemmed from entirely independent research and the question of priority is both complex and unenlightening. Fermat received the first impetus toward his system from an attempt to reconstruct Apollonius' lost treatise *Plane Loci* (loci that are either straight lines or circles). His completed restoration, although composed in the traditional style of Greek geometry, nevertheless gives clear evidence that Fermat employed algebraic analysis in seeking demonstrations of the theorems listed by Pappus. This application of algebra, combined with the peculiar nature of a geometrical locus and the slightly different proof procedures required by locus demonstrations, appears to have revealed to Fermat that all of the loci discussed by Apollonius could be expressed in the form of indeterminate algebraic equations in two unknowns, and that the analysis of these equations by means of Viète's theory of equations led to crucial insights into the nature and construction of the loci. With this inspiration from the *Plane Loci,* Fermat then found in Apollonius' *Conics* that the *symptomata,* or defining properties, of the conic sections likewise could be expressed as indeterminate equations in two unknowns. Moreover, the standard form in which Apollonius referred the *symptomata* to the cone on which the conic sections were generated suggested to Fermat a standard geometrical framework in which to establish the correspondence between an equation and a curve. Taking a fixed line as axis and a fixed point on that line as origin, he measured the variable length of the first unknown, *A*, from the origin along the axis. The corresponding value of the second unknown, *E*, he constructed as a line length measured from the end point of the first unknown and erected at a fixed angle to the axis. The end points of the various lengths of the second unknown then generated a curve in the *A,E* plane.

Like Descartes, then, Fermat did not employ a coordinate system but, rather, a single axis with a moving ordinate; curves were not plotted, they were generated. Within the standard framework

> Whenever two unknown quantities are found in final equality, there results a locus [fixed] in place, and the end point of one of these unknown quantities describes a straight line or a curve ["Isagoge," *Oeuvres*, I, 91].

The crucial phrase in this keystone of analytic geometry is "fixed in place";[5] it sets the task of the remainder of Fermat's treatise. Dividing the general second-degree equation $Ax^2 + By^2 + Cxy + Dx + Ey + F = 0$ into seven canonical (irreducible) forms according to the possible values of the coefficients, Fermat shows how each canonical equation defines a curve: $Dx = Ey$ (straight line), $Cxy = F$ (equilateral hyperbola), $Ax^2 \pm Cxy = By^2$ (straight lines), $Ax^2 = Ey$ (parabola), $F - Ax^2 = Ay^2$ (circle), $F - Ax^2 = By^2$ (ellipse), and $F + Ax^2 = By^2$ (axial hyperbola). In each case he demonstrates that the

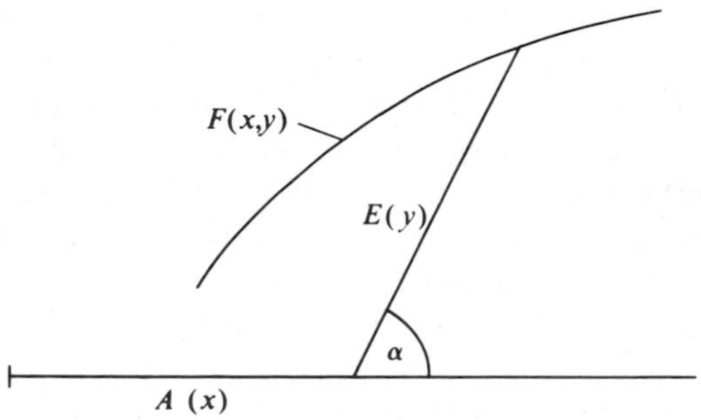

FIGURE 1

constants of the equation uniquely fix the curve defined by it, i.e., that they contain all the data necessary to construct the curve. The proof relies on the construction theorems set forth in Euclid's *Data* (for the straight line and circle, or "plane loci") or Apollonius' *Conics* (for the conic sections, or "solid loci"). In a corollary to each case Fermat employs Viète's theory of equations to establish the family of equations reducible to the canonical form and then shows how the reduction itself corresponds to a translation (or expansion) of the axis or the origin or to a change of angle between axis and ordinate. In the last theorem of the "Isagoge," for example, he reduces the equation $b^2 - 2x^2 = 2xy + y^2$ to the canonical form $2b^2 - u^2 = 2v^2$, where $u = \sqrt{2}x$ and $v = x + y$. Geometrically, the reduction shifts the orthogonal x,y system to a skew u,v system in which the u-axis forms a 45° angle with the x-axis and the v-ordinate is erected at a 45° angle on the u-axis. The curve, as Fermat shows, is a uniquely defined ellipse.

Although the analytic geometries of Descartes and Fermat are essentially the same, their presentations differed significantly. Fermat concentrated on the geometrical construction of the curves on the basis of their equations, relying heavily on the reader's knowledge of Viète's algebra to supply the necessary theory of equations. By contrast, Descartes slighted the matter of construction and devoted a major portion of his *Géométrie* to a new and more advanced theory of equations.

In the years following 1636, Fermat made some effort to pursue the implications of his system. In an appendix to the "Isagoge," he applied the system to the graphic solution of determinate algebraic equations, showing, for example, that any cubic or quartic equation could be solved graphically by means of a parabola and a circle. In his "De solutione problematum geometricorum per curvas simplicissimas et unicuique problematum generi proprie convenientes dissertatio tripartita" (*Oeuvres,* I, 118–131), he took issue with Descartes's classification of curves in the *Géométrie* and undertook to show that any determinate algebraic equation of degree $2n$ or $2n - 1$ could be solved graphically by means of curves determined by indeterminate equations of degree n.

In 1643, in a memoir entitled "Isagoge ad locos ad superficiem" (*Oeuvres,* I, 111–117), Fermat attempted to extend his plane analytic geometry to solids of revolution in space and perhaps thereby to restore the content of Euclid's *Surface Loci,* another text cited by Pappus. The effort did not meet with success because he tried to reduce the three-dimensional problem to two dimensions by determining all possible traces resulting from the intersection of a given solid by an arbitrary plane. The system required, first of all, an elaborate catalog of the possible traces for various solids. Second, the manipulation of the equation of any trace for the purpose of deriving the parameters that uniquely determine the solid requires methods that lay beyond Fermat's reach; his technique could at best define the solid qualitatively. Third, the basic system of the 1636 "Isagoge," lacking the concept of coordinates referred to two fixed orthogonal axes, presented substantial hurdles to visualizing a three-dimensional correlate.

Although Fermat never found the geometrical framework for a solid analytic geometry, he nonetheless correctly established the algebraic foundation of such a system. In 1650, in his "Novus secundarum et ulterioris ordinis radicum in analyticis usus" (*Oeuvres,* I, 181–188), he noted that equations in one unknown determine point constructions; equations in two unknowns, locus constructions of plane curves; and equations in three unknowns, locus constructions of surfaces in space. The change in the criterion of the dimension of an equation—from its degree, where the Greeks had placed it, to the number of unknowns in it—was one of the most important conceptual developments of seventeenth-century mathematics.

The Method of Maxima and Minima. The method of maxima and minima, in which Fermat first established what later became the algorithm for obtaining the first derivative of an algebraic polynomial, also stemmed from the application of Viète's algebra to a problem in Pappus' *Mathematical Collection.* In a lemma to Apollonius' *Determinate Section,* Pappus sought to divide a given line in such a way that certain rectangles constructed on the segments bore a minimum ratio to one another,[6] noting that the ratio would be "singular." In carrying out the algebraic analysis of the problem, Fermat recognized that the division of the line for rectangles in a ratio greater than the minimum corresponded to a quadratic equation that would normally yield two equally satisfactory section points. A "singular" section point for the minimum ratio, he argued, must mean that the particular values of the constant quantities of the equation allow only a single repeated root as a solution.

Turning to a simpler example, Fermat considered the problem of dividing a given line in such a way that the product of the segments was maximized. The algebraic form of the problem is $bx - x^2 = c$, where b is the length of the given line and c is the product of the segments. If c is the maximum value of all possible products, then the equation can have only one (repeated) root. Fermat then sought the value for c in terms of b for which the equation yielded that (repeated) root. To this end he applied a method of Viète's theory of equations called "syncrisis," a method originally devised to determine the relationships between the roots of equations and their constant parameters. On the assumption that his equation had two distinct roots, x and y, Fermat set $bx - x^2 = c$ and $by - y^2 = c$, whence he obtained $b = x + y$ and $c = xy$. Taking these relationships to hold generally for any quadratic equation of the above form, he next considered what happened in the case of a repeated root, i.e., when $x = y$. Then, he found, $x = b/2$ and $c = b^2/4$. Hence, the maximum rectangle results from dividing the given line in half, and that maximum rectangle has an area equal to one-quarter of the square erected on the given line b.

Amending his method in the famous "Methodus ad disquirendam maximam et minimam" (*Oeuvres,* I, 133–136), written sometime before 1636, Fermat expressed the supposedly distinct roots as A and $A + E$ (that is, x and $x + y$), where E now represented the difference between the roots. In seeking, for example, the maximum value of the expression $bx^2 - x^3$, he proceeded as follows:

$$bx^2 - x^3 = M^3$$
$$b(x + y)^2 - (x + y)^3 = M^3,$$

whence $$2bxy + by^2 - 3x^2y - 3xy^2 - y^3 = 0.$$

Division by y yields the equation

$$2bx + by - 3x^2 - 3xy - y^2 = 0,$$

which relates the parameter b to two roots of the equation via one of the roots and their difference. The relation holds for any equation of the form $bx^2 - x^3 = M^3$, but when M^3 is a maximum the equation has a repeated root, i.e., $x = x + y$, or $y = 0$. Hence, for that maximum, $2bx - 3x^2 = 0$, or $x = 2b/3$ and $M^3 = 4b^3/27$.

Fermat's method of maxima and minima, which is clearly applicable to any polynomial $P(x)$, originally rested on purely finitistic algebraic foundations.[7] It assumed, counterfactually, the inequality of two equal roots in order to determine, by Viète's theory of equations, a relation between those roots and one of the coefficients of the polynomial, a relation that was fully general. This relation then led to an extreme-value solution when Fermat removed his counterfactual assumption and set the roots equal. Borrowing a term from Diophantus, Fermat called this counterfactual equality "adequality."

Although Pappus' remark concerning the "singularity" of extreme values provided the original inspiration for Fermat's method, it may also have prevented him from seeing all its implications. Oriented toward unique extreme values and dealing with specific problems that, taken from geometrical sources and never exceeding cubic expressions, failed to yield more than one geometrically meaningful solution, Fermat never recognized the distinction between global and local extreme values or the possibility of more than one such value. This block to an overall view of the problem of maxima and minima vitiates an otherwise brilliant demonstration of Fermat's method, which he wrote for Pierre Brûlard de St.-Martin in 1643 (*Oeuvres,* supp., 120–125) and which employs the sophisticated theory of equations of Descartes's *Géométrie.* There Fermat established what today is termed the "second derivative criterion" for the nature of an extreme value ($f''(x) < 0$ for a maximum, $f''(x) > 0$ for a minimum), although his lack of a general overview forestalled investigation of points of inflection ($f''(x) = 0$).

The original method of maxima and minima had two important corollaries. The first was the method of tangents[8] by which, given the equation of a curve, Fermat could construct the tangent at any given point on that curve by determining the length of the subtangent. Given some curve $y = f(x)$ and a point (a,b) on it, Fermat assumed the tangent to be drawn and

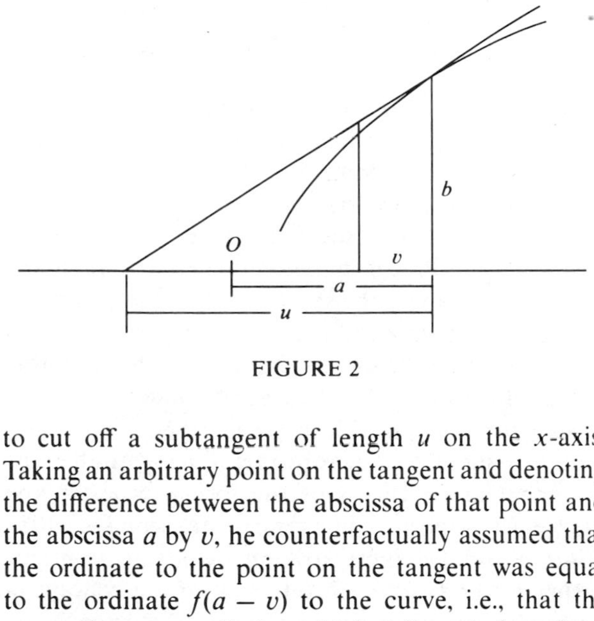

FIGURE 2

to cut off a subtangent of length u on the x-axis. Taking an arbitrary point on the tangent and denoting the difference between the abscissa of that point and the abscissa a by v, he counterfactually assumed that the ordinate to the point on the tangent was equal to the ordinate $f(a - v)$ to the curve, i.e., that the two ordinates were "adequal." It followed, then, from similar triangles that

$$\frac{b}{u} \approx \frac{f(a-v)}{u-v}.$$

Fermat removed the adequality, here denoted by $\approx$, by treating the difference v in the same manner as in the method of maxima and minima, i.e., by considering it as ultimately equal to zero. His method yields, in modern symbols, the correct result, $u = f(a)/f'(a)$, and, like the parent method of maxima and minima, it can be applied generally.

From the method of maxima and minima Fermat drew as a second corollary a method for determining centers of gravity of geometrical figures (*Oeuvres,* I, 136–139). His single example—although again the method itself is fully general—concerns the center of gravity of a paraboloidal segment. Let CAV be the generating parabola with axis AI and base CV. By symmetry the center of gravity O of the paraboloidal segment lies on axis $AI = b$ at some distance $AO = x$

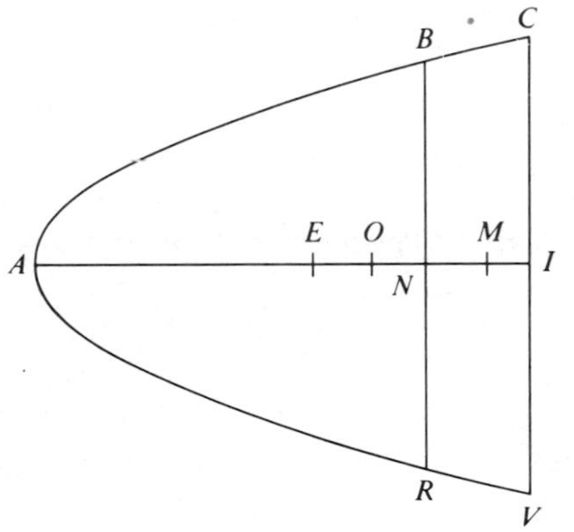

FIGURE 3

from the vertex A. Let the segment be cut by a plane parallel to the base and intersecting the axis at an arbitrary distance y from point I. Let E and M denote the centers of gravity of the two resulting subsegments. Since similar figures have similarly placed centers of gravity (Archimedes), $b/x = (b - y)/AE$, whence $EO = x - AE = xy/b$. By the definition of the center of gravity and by the law of the lever, segment $CBRV$ is to segment BAR as EO is to OM. But, by Archimedes' *Conoids and Spheroids,* proposition 26, paraboloid CAV is to paraboloid BAR as AI^2 is to AN^2, or as b^2 is to $(b - y)^2$, whence

$$\frac{EO}{OM} = \frac{CBRV}{BAR} = \frac{b^2 - (b-y)^2}{(b-y)^2}.$$

Here Fermat again employed the notion of adequality to set OM counterfactually equal to OI, whence

$$OI = b - x \approx OM = \left(\frac{xy}{b}\right)\left(\frac{b^2 - 2by + y^2}{2by - y^2}\right).$$

He removed the adequality by an application of the method of maxima and minima, i.e., by dividing through by y and then setting $y\ (= OI - OM)$ equal to zero, and obtained the result $x = 2b/3$. In applying his method to figures generated by curves of the forms

$y^q = kx^p$ and $x^p y^q = k$ (p,q positive integers), Fermat employed the additional lemma that the similar segments of the figures "have the same proportion to corresponding triangles of the same base and height, even if we do not know what that proportion is,"[9] and argued from that lemma that his method of centers of gravity eliminated the problem of quadrature as a prerequisite to the determination of centers of gravity. Such an elimination was, of course, illusory, but the method did not depend on the lemma. It can be applied to any figure for which the general quadrature is known.

Fermat's method of maxima and minima and its corollary method of tangents formed the central issue in an acrid debate between Fermat and Descartes in the spring of 1638. Viewing Fermat's methods as rivals to his own in the *Géométrie,* Descartes tried to show that the former were at once paralogistic in their reasoning and limited in their application. It quickly became clear, however, that, as in the case of their analytic geometries, Fermat's and Descartes's methods rested on the same foundations. The only substantial issue was Descartes's disapproval of mathematical reasoning based on counterfactual assumptions, i.e., the notion of adequality. Although the two men made formal peace in the summer of 1638, when Descartes admitted his error in criticizing Fermat's methods, the bitterness of the dispute, exacerbated by the deep personal hatred Descartes felt for Fermat's friend and spokesman, Roberval, poisoned any chance for cooperation between the two greatest mathematicians of the time. Descartes's sharp tongue cast a pall over Fermat's reputation as a mathematician, a situation which Fermat's refusal to publish only made worse.[10] Through the efforts of Mersenne and Pierre Hérigone, Fermat's methods did appear in print in 1642, but only as bare algorithms that, by setting the difference y of the roots equal to zero from the start, belied the careful thinking that originally underlay them. Moreover, other mathematicians soon were publishing their own, more general algorithms; by 1659, Huygens felt it necessary to defend Fermat's priority against the claims of Johann Hudde. In time, Fermat's work on maxima and minima was all but forgotten, having been replaced by the differential calculus of Newton and Leibniz.

Methods of Quadrature. Fermat's research into the quadrature of curves and the cubature of solids also had its beginnings in the research that preceded his introduction to the outside mathematical world in 1636. By that time, he had taken the model of Archimedes' quadrature of the spiral[11] and successfully extended its application to all spirals of the forms $\rho = (a\vartheta)^m$ and $R/R - \rho = (\alpha/\vartheta)^m$. Moreover, he had

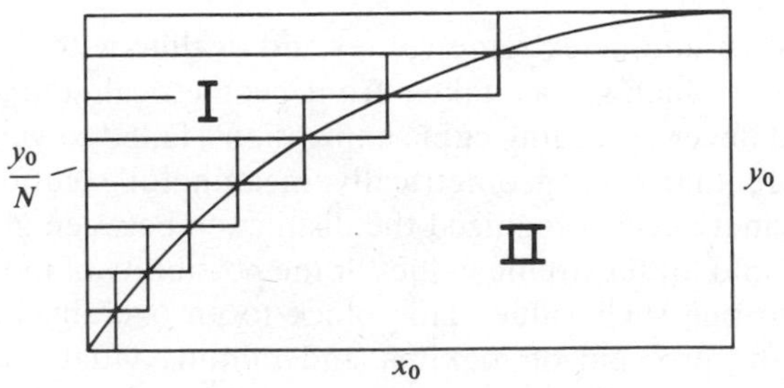

FIGURE 4

translated Archimedes' method of circumscription and inscription of sectors around and within the spiral into a rectangular framework. Dividing a given ordinate y_0 (or the corresponding abscissa x_0) of a curve $y = f(x)$ into N equal intervals and drawing lines parallel to the axis, Fermat determined that Area I in Figure 4 lay between limits $\frac{y_0}{N}\sum_{i=1}^{N} x_i$ and $\frac{y_0}{N}\sum_{i=1}^{N-1} x_i$, where x_i is the abscissa that corresponds to ordinate $(i/N)y_0$. Since he possessed a recursive formula for determining $\sum_{=1}^{N} i^m$ for any positive integer m, Fermat could prove that

$$\frac{1}{N^{m+1}}\sum_{i=1}^{N} i^m > \frac{1}{m+1} > \frac{1}{N^{m+1}}\sum_{i=1}^{N-1} i^m$$

for all values of N. In each case the difference between the bounds is $1/N$, which can be made as small as one wishes. Hence, for any curve of the form $y^m = kx$, Fermat could show that the curvilinear Area I $= [1/(m+1)]x_0 y_0$ and the curvilinear Area II $= [m/(m+1)]x_0 y_0$. As an immediate corollary, he found that he could apply the same technique to determine the volume of the solid generated by the rotation of the curve about the ordinate or axis, with the restriction in this case that m be an even integer.

Sometime before 1646 Fermat devised a substantially new method of quadrature, which permitted the treatment of all curves of the forms $y^q = kx^p$ and $x^p y^q = k$ (p,q positive integers; in the second equation $p + q > 2$). The most striking departure from the earlier method is the introduction of the concept of adequality, now used in the sense of "approximate equality" or "equality in the limiting case." In the first example given in his major treatise on quadrature[12] Fermat derives the shaded area under the curve $x^2 y = k$ in Figure 5 as follows (we use modern notation to abbreviate Fermat's lengthy verbal description while preserving its sense): the infinite x-axis is divided into intervals by the end points of a divergent geometric sequence of lengths $AG, AH, AO, \cdots$,

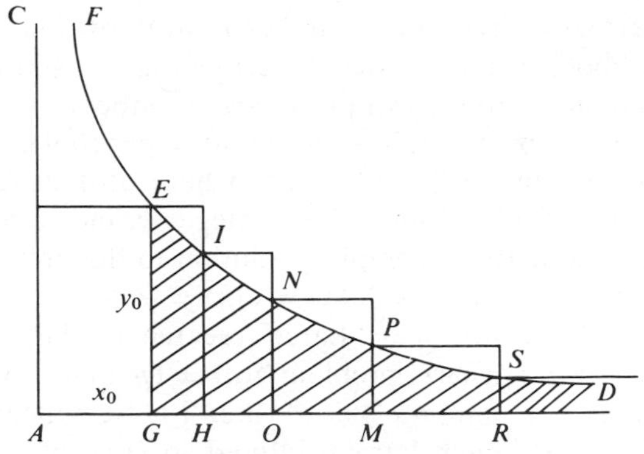

FIGURE 5

or x_0, $(m/n)x_0$, $(m/n)^2x_0, \cdots$, where $m > n$ are arbitrary integers. Since $(m/n)^i - (m/n)^{i-1} = (m/n)^{i-1}(m/n - 1)$, each interval can, by suitable choice of m and n, be made as closely equal to another as desired and at the same time can be made as small as desired. Fermat has, then, $GH \approx HO \approx OM \approx \cdots$ and $GH \rightarrow 0$. From the curve and the construction of the intervals, it follows directly that the approximating rectangles erected on the intervals form the convergent geometric series

$$(m/n - 1)x_0y_0,\ (n/m)(m/n - 1)x_0y_0,\ (n/m)^2(m/n - 1)x_0y_0, \cdots .$$

Its sum is $(m/n - 1)x_0y_0 + x_0y_0$, which is "adequal" to the shaded area. It approaches the curved area ever more closely as the size of the intervals approaches zero, i.e., as $m/n \rightarrow 1$. In the limiting case, the sum will be x_0y_0, which in turn will be the exact area of the shaded segment. Generalizing the procedure for any curve $x^py^q = k$ and a given ordinate y_0, Fermat determined that the area under the curve from y_0 on out is $[q/(p - q)]x_0y_0$. Adapting the procedure to curves $y^q = kx^p$ (by dividing the finite axis from 0 to x_0 by a convergent geometric sequence of intervals), he was also able to show that the area under the curve is $[q/(p + q)]x_0y_0$.

In the remainder of his treatise on quadrature, Fermat shifted from the geometrical style of exposition to the algebraic and, on the model of Viète's theory of equations, set up a "reduction analysis" by which a given quadrature either generates an infinite class of quadratures or can be shown to be dependent on the quadrature of the circle. To carry out the project he introduced a new concept of "application of all y^n to a given segment," by which he meant the limit-sum of the products $y^n\Delta x$ over a given segment b of the x-axis as $\Delta x \rightarrow 0$ (in the absence of any notation by Fermat, we shall borrow from Leibniz and write Omn_by^n to symbolize Fermat's concept). Fermat then showed by several concrete examples that for any curve of the form $y^n = \Sigma a_ix^i/b_jx^j$ the determination of Omn_by^n follows directly from setting $y^n = \Sigma u_i$, where $u_i = a_ix^i/b_jx^j$. For each i the resulting expression $u_i = f(x)$ will denote a curve of the form $u_i^q = kx^p$ or the form $x^pu_i^q = k$. For each curve, the determination of Omn_bu_i corresponds to the direct quadrature set forth in the first part of the treatise, and hence it is determinable. Therefore $Omn_by^n = \Sigma Omn_bu_i$ is directly determinable.

Fermat next introduced the main lemma of his treatise, an entirely novel result for which he characteristically offered no proof. For any curve $y = f(x)$ decreasing monotonically over the interval 0,b, where $f(0) = d$ and $f(b) = 0$, $Omn_by^n = Omn_dnxy^{n-1}$. This result is equivalent to the modern statement

$$\int_0^b y^n\,dx = n\int_0^d xy^{n-1}\,dy.$$

One example from Fermat's treatise on quadrature suffices to display the subtlety and power of his reduction analysis. Can the area beneath the curve $b^3 = x^2y + b^2y$ (i.e., the "witch of Agnesi") be squared algebraically? Two transformations of variable and an application of the main lemma supply the answer. From $by = u^2$ and $bv = xu$, it follows first that $Omn_xy = 1/b\ Omn_xu^2 = 2/b\ Omn_uxu = 2\ Omn_uv$. Hence, the quadrature of the original area depends on that of the transformed curve $F(u,v)$. But substitution of variables yields $b^2 = u^2 + v^2$, the equation of a circle. Therefore, the quadrature of the original area depends on the quadrature of the circle and cannot be carried out algebraically.

Fermat's treatise first circulated when it was printed in his *Varia opera* of 1679. By then much of its contents had become obsolescent in terms of the work of Newton and Leibniz. Even so, it is doubtful what effect the treatise could have had earlier. As sympathetic a reader as Huygens could make little sense of it.[13] In addition, Fermat's method of quadrature, like his method of tangents, lacks even the germ of several concepts crucial to the development of the calculus. Not only did Fermat not recognize the inverse relationship between the two methods, but both methods, conceptually and to some extent operationally, steered away from rather than toward the notion of the tangent or the area as a function of the curve.

Fermat's one work published in his lifetime, a treatise on rectification appended to a work on the cycloid by Antoine de La Loubère,[14] was a direct corollary of the method of quadrature. Cast, however, in the strictly geometrical style of classical Greek mathematics, it hid all traces of the underlying algebraic analysis. In the treatise Fermat treated the length of a curve as the limit-sum of tangential segments $\triangle S$ cut off by abscissas drawn through the end points of intervals $\triangle y$ on a given y ordinate. In essence, he showed that for any curve $y = y(x)$,

$$\frac{\triangle S^2}{\triangle y^2} = [x'(y)]^2 + 1.$$

Taking $u^2 = [x'(y)]^2 + 1$ as an auxiliary curve, Fermat used the relation $S = Omn_y u$ to reduce the problem of rectification to one of quadrature. He used the same basic procedure to determine the area of the surface generated by the rotation of the curve about an axis or an ordinate, as the results in a 1660 letter to Huygens indicate.

Number Theory. As a result of limited circulation in unpublished manuscripts, Fermat's work on analytic geometry, maxima and minima and tangents, and quadrature had only moderate influence on contemporary developments in mathematics. His work in the realm of number theory had almost none at all. It was neither understood nor appreciated until Euler revived it and initiated the line of continuous research that culminated in the work of Gauss and Kummer in the early nineteenth century. Indeed, many of Fermat's results are basic elements of number theory today. Although the results retain fundamental importance, his methods remain largely a secret known only to him. Theorems, conjectures, and specific examples abound in his letters and marginalia. But, except for a vague outline of a method he called "infinite descent," Fermat left no obvious trace of the means he had employed to find them. He repeatedly claimed to work from a method, and the systematic nature of much of his work would seem to support his claim.

In an important sense Fermat invented number theory as an independent branch of mathematics. He was the first to restrict his study in principle to the domain of integers. His refusal to accept fractional solutions to problems he set in 1657 as challenges to the European mathematics community (*Oeuvres*, II, 332–335) initiated his dispute with Wallis, Frénicle, and others,[15] for it represented a break with the classical tradition of Diophantus' *Arithmetica*, which served as his opponents' model. The restriction to integers explains one dominant theme of Fermat's work in number theory, his concern with prime numbers and divisibility. A second guiding theme of his research, the determination of patterns for generating families of solutions from a single basic solution, carried over from his work in analysis.

Fermat's earliest research, begun in Bordeaux, displays both characteristics. Investigating the sums of the aliquot parts (proper divisors) of numbers, Fermat worked from Euclid's solution to the problem of "perfect numbers"—$\sigma(a) = 2a$, where $\sigma(a)$ denotes the sum of all divisors of the integer a, including 1 and a—to derive a complete solution to the problem of "friendly" numbers—$\sigma(a) = \sigma(b) = a + b$—and to the problem $\sigma(a) = 3a$. Later research in this area aimed at the general problem $\sigma(a) = (p/q)a$, as well as $\sigma(x^3) = y^2$ and $\sigma(x^2) = y^3$ (the "First Challenge" of 1657). Although Fermat offered specific solutions to the problem $\sigma(a) = na$ for $n = 3, 4, 5, 6$, he recorded the algorithm only for $n = 3$. The central role of primeness and divisibility in such research led to several corollaries, among them the theorem (announced in 1640) that $2^k - 1$ is always a composite number if k is composite and may be composite for prime k; in the latter case, all divisors are of the form $2mk + 1$.

Fermat's interest in primeness and divisibility culminated in a theorem now basic to the theory of congruences; as set down by Fermat it read: If p is prime and a^t is the smallest number such that $a^t = kp + 1$ for some k, then t divides $p - 1$. In the modern version, if p is prime and p does not divide a, then $a^{p-1} \equiv 1 \pmod{p}$. As a corollary to this theorem, Fermat investigated in depth the divisibility of $a^k \pm 1$ and made his famous conjecture that all numbers of the form $2^{2^n} + 1$ are prime (disproved for $n = 5$ by Euler). In carrying out his research, Fermat apparently relied on an extensive factual command of the powers of prime numbers and on the traditional "sieve of Eratosthenes" as a test of primeness. He several times expressed his dissatisfaction with the latter but seems to have been unable to find a more efficient test, even though in retrospect his work contained all the necessary elements for one.

A large group of results of fundamental importance to later number theory (quadratic residues, quadratic forms) apparently stemmed from Fermat's study of the indeterminate equation $x^2 - q = my^2$ for nonsquare m. In his "Second Challenge" of 1657, Fermat claimed to have the complete solution for the case $q = 1$. Operating on the principle that any divisor of a number of the form $a^2 + mb^2$ (m not a square) must itself be of that form, Fermat established that all primes of the form $4k + 1$ (but not those of the form $4k + 3$) can be expressed as the sum of two squares, all primes of the form $8k + 1$ or $8k + 3$ as the sum of a square and the double of a square, all primes of the form $3k + 1$ as $a^2 + 3b^2$, and that the product of any two primes of the form $20k + 3$ or $20k + 7$ is expressible in the form $a^2 + 5b^2$.

Another by-product of this research was Fermat's claim to be able to prove Diophantus' conjecture that any number can be expressed as the sum of at most four squares. Extending his research on the decomposition of numbers to higher powers, Fermat further claimed proofs of the theorems that no cube could be expressed as the sum of two cubes, no quartic as the sum of two quartics, and indeed no number a^n as the sum of two powers b^n and c^n (the famous "last theorem," mentioned only once in the margin of his copy of Diophantus' *Arithmetica*). In addition, he claimed the complete solution of the so-called "four-cube problem" (to express the sum of two given cubes as the sum of two other cubes), allowing here, of course, fractional solutions of the problem.

To prove his decomposition theorems and to solve the equation $x^2 - 1 = my^2$, Fermat employed a method he had devised and called "infinite descent." The method, an inverse form of the modern method of induction, rests on the principle (peculiar to the domain of integers) that there cannot exist an infinitely decreasing sequence of integers. Fermat set down two rather vague outlines of his method, one in his "Observations sur Diophante" (*Oeuvres*, I, 340–341) and one in a letter to Carcavi (*Oeuvres*, II, 431–433). In the latter Fermat argued that no right triangle of numbers (triple of numbers a, b, c such that $a^2 + b^2 = c^2$) can have an area equal to a square ($ab/2 = m^2$ for some m), since

> If there were some right triangle of integers that had an area equal to a square, there would be another triangle less than it which had the same property. If there were a second, less than the first, which had the same property, there would be by similar reasoning a third less than the second which had the same property, and then a fourth, a fifth, etc., ad infinitum in decreasing order. But, given a number, there cannot be infinitely many others in decreasing order less than it (I mean to speak always of integers). From which one concludes that it is therefore impossible that any right triangle of numbers have an area that is a square [letter to Carcavi, *Oeuvres*, II, 431–432].

Fermat's method of infinite descent did not apply only to negative propositions. He discovered that he could also show that every prime of the form $4k + 1$ could be expressed as the sum of two squares by denying the proposition for some such prime, deriving another such prime less than the first, for which the proposition would again not hold, and so on. Ultimately, he argued, this decreasing sequence of primes would arrive at the least prime of the form $4k + 1$—namely, 5—for which, by assumption, the proposition would not hold. But $5 = 2^2 + 1^2$, which contradicts the initial assumption. Hence, the proposition must hold. Although infinite descent is unassailable in its overall reasoning, its use requires the genius of a Fermat, since nothing in that reasoning dictates how one derives the next member of the decreasing sequence for a given problem.

Fermat's letters to Jacques de Billy, published by the latter as *Doctrinae analyticae inventum novum*,[16] form the only other source of direct information about Fermat's methods in number theory. In these letters Fermat undertook a complete treatment of the so-called double equations first studied by Diophantus. In their simplest form they required the complete solution of the system $ax + b = \square$, $cx + d = \square$. By skillful use of factorization to determine the base solution and the theorem that, if a is a solution, then successive substitution of $x + a$ for x generates an infinite family of solutions, Fermat not only solved all the problems posed by Diophantus but also extended them as far as polynomials of the fourth degree.

The importance of Fermat's work in the theory of numbers lay less in any contribution to contemporary developments in mathematics than in their stimulative influence on later generations. Much of the number theory of the nineteenth century took its impetus from Fermat's results and, forced to devise its own methods, contributed to the formulation of concepts basic to modern algebra.

Other Work. *Probability*. Fermat shares credit with Blaise Pascal for laying the first foundations of the theory of probability. In a brief exchange of correspondence during the summer of 1654, the two men discussed their different approaches to the same solution of a problem originally posed to Pascal by a gambler: How should the stakes in a game of chance be divided among the players if the game is prematurely ended? In arriving at specific, detailed solutions for several simple games, Fermat and Pascal operated from the basic principle of evaluating the expectation of each player as the ratio of outcomes favorable to him to the total number of possible outcomes. Fermat relied on direct computations rather than general mathematical formulas in his solutions, and his results and methods quickly became obsolete with the appearance in 1657 of Christiaan Huygens' mathematically more sophisticated *De ludo aleae*.

Optics (*Fermat's Principle*). In 1637, when Fermat was engaged with traditional and rather pedestrian problems in geostatics, he read Descartes's *Dioptrique*. In a letter to Mersenne, which opened the controversy between Descartes and Fermat mentioned above, Fermat severely criticized the work. Methodologically, he could not accept Descartes's use of mathematics to make a priori deductions about the physical world.

Philosophically, he could not agree with Descartes that "tendency to motion" (Descartes's basic definition of light) could be understood and analyzed in terms of actual motion. Physically, he doubted both the assertion that light traveled more quickly in a denser medium (he especially questioned the meaning of such a statement together with the assertion of the instantaneous transmission of light) and Descartes's law of refraction itself. Mathematically, he tried to show that Descartes's demonstrations of the laws of reflection and refraction proved nothing that Descartes had not already assumed in his analysis, i.e., that Descartes had begged the question. The ensuing debate in the fall of 1637 soon moved to mathematics as Descartes launched a counterattack aimed at Fermat's method of tangents, and Fermat returned to the original subject of optics only in the late 1650's, when Claude Clerselier reopened the old argument while preparing his edition of Descartes's *Lettres.*

Fermat, who in his earlier years had fervently insisted that experiment alone held the key to knowledge of the physical world, nonetheless in 1662 undertook a mathematical derivation of the law of refraction on the basis of two postulates: first, that the finite speed of light varied as the rarity of the medium through which it passed and, second, that "nature operates by the simplest and most expeditious ways and means." In his "Analysis ad refractiones" (*Oeuvres,* I, 170–172), Fermat applied the second postulate (Fermat's principle) in the following manner: In Figure 6 let the upper half of the circle represent the rarer of two media and let the lower half represent the denser; further, let *CD* represent a given incident ray. If the "ratio of the resistance of the denser medium to the resistance of the rarer medium" is expressed as the ratio of the given line *DF* to some line *M*, then "the motions which occur along lines *CD* and *DI* [the refracted ray to be determined] can be measured with the aid of the lines *DF* and *M;* that is, the motion that occurs along the two lines is represented comparatively by the sum of two rectangles,

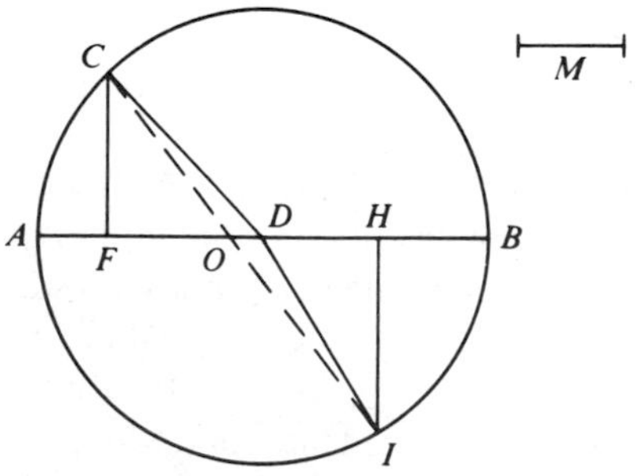

FIGURE 6

of which one is the product of *CD* and *M* and the other the product of *DI* and *DF*" ("Analysis ad refractiones," pp. 170–171). Fermat thus reduces the problem to one of determining point *H* such that that sum is minimized. Taking length *DH* as the unknown *x*, he applies his method of maxima and minima and, somewhat to his surprise (expressed in a letter to Clerselier), arrives at Descartes's law of refraction.

Although Fermat took the trouble to confirm his derived result by a formal, synthetic proof, his interest in the problem itself ended with his derivation. Physical problems had never really engaged him, and he had returned to the matter only to settle an issue that gave rise to continued ill feeling between him and the followers of Descartes.

In fact, by 1662 Fermat had effectively ended his career as a mathematician. His almost exclusive interest in number theory during the last fifteen years of his life found no echo among his junior contemporaries, among them Huygens, who were engaged in the application of analysis to physics. As a result Fermat increasingly returned to the isolation from which he had so suddenly emerged in 1636, and his death in 1665 was viewed more as the passing of a grand old man than as a loss to the active scientific community.

NOTES

1. All published modern accounts of Fermat's life ultimately derive from Paul Tannery's article in the *Grande encyclopédie,* repr. in *Oeuvres,* IV, 237–240. Some important new details emerged from the research of H. Blanquière and M. Caillet in connection with an exhibition at the Lycée Pierre de Fermat in Toulouse in 1957: *Un mathématicien de génie, Pierre de Fermat 1601–1665* (Toulouse, 1957).
2. *Diophanti Alexandrini Arithmeticorum libri sex et de numeris multangulis liber unus. Cum commentariis C. G. Bacheti V. C. et observationibus D. P. de Fermat Senatoris Tolosani* (Toulouse, 1670); *Varia opera mathematica D. Petri de Fermat Senatoris Tolosani* (Toulouse, 1679; repr. Berlin, 1861; Brussels, 1969).
3. Cureau shared Fermat's scientific interests and hence provided a special link to the chancellor. There is much to suggest that the *parlement* of Toulouse took advantage of Fermat's ties to Cureau.
4. Regarding book VII and its importance for Greek geometrical analysis, see M. S. Mahoney, "Another Look at Greek Geometrical Analysis," in *Archive for History of Exact Sciences,* **5** (1968), 318–348. On its influence in the early seventeenth century, see Mahoney, "The Royal Road" (diss., Princeton, 1967), ch. 3.
5. Fermat's original Latin reads: *fit locus loco.* The last word is not redundant, as several authors have thought; rather, the phrase is elliptic, lacking the word *datus.* Fermat's terminology here comes directly from Euclid's *Data (linea positione data:* a line given, or fixed, in position).

Regarding the algebraic symbolism that follows here and throughout the article, note that throughout his life Fermat employed the notation of Viète, which used the capital vowels for unknowns and the capital consonants for knowns or parameters. To avoid the confusion of an unfamiliar notation, this article employs Cartesian notation, translating Fermat's *A* uniformly as *x*, *E* as *y*, etc.

6. Pappus, *Mathematical Collection* VII, prop. 61. The geometrical formulation is too complex to state here without a figure and in addition requires some interpretation. In Fermat's algebraic formulation, the problem calls for the determination of the minimum value of the expression

$$\frac{bc - bx + cx - x^2}{ax - x^2},$$

where *a*, *b*, *c* are given line segments.
7. The modern foundation of Fermat's method is the theorem that if $P(x)$ has a local extreme value at $x = a$, then $P(x) = (x - a)^2R(x)$, where $R(a) \neq 0$.
8. Fermat's original version of the method is contained in the "Methodus ad disquirendam maximam et minimam" (*Oeuvres*, I, 133–136); in its most finished form it is described in a memoir sent to Descartes in June 1638 (*Oeuvres*, II, 154–162).
9. Fermat to Mersenne, 15 June 1638 (*Oeuvres*, supp., pp. 84–86).
10. Descartes's most famous remark, made to Frans van Schooten, who related it to Huygens (*Oeuvres*, IV, 122), was the following: "Monsieur Fermat est Gascon, moi non. Il est vrai, qu'il a inventé plusieurs belles choses particulières, et qu'il est homme de grand esprit. Mais quant à moi j'ai toujours étudié à considerer les choses fort généralement, afin d'en pouvoir concluire des règles, qui aient aussi ailleurs de l'usage." The connotation of "troublemaker" implicit in the term "Gascon" is secondary to Descartes's charge, believed by some of his followers, that Fermat owed his reputation to a few unsystematic lucky guesses.
11. In his treatise *On Spirals*.
12. "De aequationum localium transmutatione et emendatione ad multimodam curvilineorum inter se vel cum rectilineis comparationem, cui annectitur proportionis geometricae in quadrandis infinitis parabolis et hyperbolis usus" (*Oeuvres*, I, 255–285). The treatise was written sometime between 1657 and 1659, but at least part of it dates back to the early 1640's.
13. Huygens to Leibniz, 1 September 1691 (*Oeuvres*, IV, 137).
14. "De linearum curvarum cum lineis rectis comparatione dissertatio geometrica. Autore M.P.E.A.S." The treatise was published with La Loubère's *Veterum geometria promota in septem de cycloide libris, et in duabus adjectis appendicibus* (Toulouse, 1660).
15. The dispute is recorded in Wallis' *Commercium epistolicum de quaestionibus quibusdam mathematicis nuper habitum* (Oxford, 1658). The participants were William Brouncker, Kenelm Digby, Fermat, Bernard Frénicle, Wallis, and Frans van Schooten.
16. Published as part of Samuel Fermat's edition of Diophantus in 1670 (see note 2).

BIBLIOGRAPHY

I. Original Works. The modern edition of the *Oeuvres de Fermat*, Charles Henry and Paul Tannery, eds., 4 vols. (Paris, 1891–1912), with supp. by Cornelis de Waard (Paris, 1922), contains all of Fermat's extant papers and letters in addition to correspondence between other men concerning Fermat. The edition includes in vol. III French translations of those papers and letters that Fermat wrote in Latin and also a French translation of Billy's *Inventum novum*. English translations of Fermat's "Isagoge" and "Methodus ad disquirendam maximam et minimam" have been published in D. J. Struik's *A Source Book in Mathematics, 1200–1800* (Cambridge, Mass., 1969).

II. Secondary Literature. The two most important summaries of Fermat's career are Jean Itard, *Pierre Fermat*, Kurze Mathematiker Biographien, no. 10 (Basel, 1950); and J. E. Hofmann, "Pierre Fermat—ein Pionier der neuen Mathematik," in *Praxis der Mathematik*, **7** (1965), 113–119, 171–180, 197–203. Fermat's contributions to analytic geometry form part of Carl Boyer, *History of Analytic Geometry* (New York, 1956), ch. 5; and the place of Fermat in the history of the calculus is discussed in Boyer's *Concepts of the Calculus* (New York, 1949), pp. 154–165. The most detailed and enlightening study of Fermat's work in number theory has been carried out by J. E. Hofmann; see, in particular, "Über zahlentheoretische Methoden Fermats und Eulers, ihre Zusammenhänge und ihre Bedeutung," in *Archive for History of Exact Sciences*, **1** (1961), 122–159; and "Studien zur Zahlentheorie Fermats," in *Abhandlungen der Preussischen Akademie der Wissenschaften*, Mathematisch-Naturwissenschaftliche Klasse, no. 7 (1944). Fermat's dispute with Descartes on the law of refraction and his own derivation of the law are treated in detail in A. I. Sabra, *Theories of Light From Descartes to Newton* (London, 1967), chs. 3–5.

Michael S. Mahoney

FERRARI, LUDOVICO (*b*. Bologna, Italy, 2 February 1522; *d*. Bologna, October 1565)

Little is known of Ferrari's life. His father, Alessandro, was the son of a Milanese refugee who had settled in Bologna. Following his father's death Ferrari went to live with his uncle Vincenzo. In November 1536 he was sent to Milan by his uncle to join the household of Girolamo Cardano, replacing his uncle's son Luca, who was already in Cardano's service. Although he had not received a formal education, Ferrari was exceptionally intelligent. Cardano therefore instructed him in Latin, Greek, and mathematics and employed him as amanuensis. In Cardano's autobiography, written many years later, Ferrari is described as having "excelled as a youth all my pupils by the high degree of his learning" (*De vita propria liber* [1643], p. 156).

In 1540 Ferrari was appointed public lecturer in mathematics in Milan, and shortly afterward he defeated Zuanne da Coi, a mathematician of Brescia, at a public disputation. He also collaborated with Cardano in researches on the cubic and quartic equations, the results of which were published in the *Ars magna* (1545). The publication of this book was the cause of the celebrated feud between Ferrari and Niccolò Tartaglia of Brescia, author of *Quesiti et inventioni diverse* (1546). In the wake of the resulting public disputation, Ferrari received offers of employment from many persons of importance, including Emperor Charles V, who wanted a tutor for his son, and Ercole Gonzaga, cardinal of Mantua. He accepted Gonzaga's offer and, at the request of the cardinal's brother, Ferrante, then governor of Milan, he carried out a survey of that province. After this he was in the cardinal's service for some eight years. On his retirement because of ill health Ferrari went to Bologna to live with his sister. From September 1564 until his death in October 1565, he held the post of *lector ad mathematicam* at the University of Bologna.

When Ferrari went to live with Cardano, the latter was earning his livelihood by teaching mathematics. Although Cardano was a qualified physician, he had not yet been accepted by the College of Physicians and was then preparing his first works on medicine and mathematics for publication. It is likely that Ferrari was introduced to mathematics through Cardano's *Practica arithmetice* (1539). While this work was in preparation, news reached Cardano that a method of solving the cubic equation of the form $x^3 + ax = b$, where a and b are positive, was known to Niccolò Tartaglia of Brescia. Until then Cardano had accepted Luca Pacioli's statement in the *Summa de arithmetica, geometria, proportioni et proportionalita* (1494) that the cubic equation could not be solved algebraically. On learning that Tartaglia had solved the equation in the course of a disputation with Antonio Maria Fiore in 1535, Cardano probably tried to find the solution himself, but without success. In 1539, before his book was published, he asked Tartaglia for the solution, offering to include it in his forthcoming book under Tartaglia's name. Tartaglia refused, on the ground that he wished to publish his discovery himself. But when he visited Cardano in Milan in March 1539, he gave him the solution on the solemn promise that it would be kept secret. In 1542, however, Cardano learned that the cubic equation had been solved several years before Tartaglia by Scipione Ferro, *lector ad mathematicam* at the University of Bologna from 1496 to 1526. During a visit to Bologna, Cardano and Ferrari were shown Ferro's work, in manuscript, by his pupil and successor Annibale dalla Nave. After this Cardano did not feel obliged to keep his promise.

Having learned the method of solving one type of cubic equation, Cardano and Ferrari were encouraged to extend their researches to other types of cubics and to the quartic. Ferrari found geometrical demonstrations for Cardano's formulas for solving $x^3 + ax = bx^2 + c$ and $x^3 + ax^2 = b$; he also solved the quartic of the form $x^4 + ax^2 + b = cx$ where a, b, c, are positive. The results were embodied in Cardano's *Ars magna* (1545). In it he attributed the discovery of the method of solving the equation $x^3 + ax = b$ to Scipione Ferro and its rediscovery to Tartaglia. That this apparent breach of secrecy angered Tartaglia is evident from book IX of his *Quesiti et inventioni diverse* (1546), where he recounted the circumstances in which he had made his discovery and Cardano's attempts to obtain the solution from him. He also gave a verbatim account of the conversation at their meeting in Milan, along with his comments.

Ferrari, loyal to his master and impetuous by nature, reacted quickly. In February 1547 he wrote to Tartaglia, protesting that the latter had unjustly and falsely made statements prejudicial to Cardano. Having criticized the mathematical content of Tartaglia's work and accused him of repetition and plagiarism, Ferrari challenged him to a public disputation in geometry, arithmetic, and related disciplines. Scholarly disputations, common in those days, were often the means of testing the professional ability of the participants. Since both Ferrari and Tartaglia were engaged in the public teaching of mathematics, a disputation was a serious matter. In his reply Tartaglia, while insisting that Cardano had not kept his promise, said that he had used injurious words in order to provoke Cardano to write to him. He asked Ferrari to leave Cardano to fight his own battles; otherwise, Ferrari should admit that he was writing at Cardano's instigation. Saying that he would accept the challenge if Cardano at least countersigned Ferrari's letter, Tartaglia went on to raise objections to the conditions of the proposed disputation—the subjects, the location, the amount of caution money to be deposited, and the judges.

Twelve letters were exchanged, full of charges and insults, each party trying to justify his position. Tartaglia maintained that Cardano had broken his promise and that Ferrari was writing at Cardano's instance. Ferrari asserted that the solution of the cubic equation was known to both Scipione Ferro and Antonio Maria Fiore long before Tartaglia had discovered it and that it was magnanimous of Cardano to mention Tartaglia in the *Ars magna.* He also denied that he was writing on Cardano's behalf. In the course of this correspondence each party issued a series of thirty-one problems for the other to solve. Tartaglia sent his problems in a letter dated 21 April 1547. The problems were no more difficult than those found in Pacioli's *Summa.* On 24 May 1547 Ferrari replied with thirty-one problems of his own but did not send the solutions to those set by Tartaglia. In his reply (July 1547) Tartaglia sent the solutions to twenty-six of Ferrari's problems, leaving out those which led to cubic equations; a month later he gave his reasons for not solving these five problems. In a letter dated

October 1547 Ferrari replied, criticizing Tartaglia's solutions and giving his solutions to the problems set by the latter. Tartaglia, replying in June 1548, said he had not received Ferrari's letter until January and that he was willing to go to Milan to take part in the disputation. In July 1548 both parties confirmed their acceptance.

There is no record of what happened at the meeting except for scattered references in Tartaglia's *General trattato di numeri, et misure* (1556–1560). The parties met on 10 August 1548 in the church of Santa Maria del Giardino dei Minori Osservanti in the presence of a distinguished gathering that included Ferrante Gonzaga, governor of Milan, who had been named judge. Tartaglia says that he was not given a chance to state his case properly. Arguments over a problem of Ferrari's that Tartaglia had been unable to resolve lasted until suppertime, and everyone was obliged to leave. Tartaglia departed the next day for Brescia, and Ferrari was probably declared the winner.

Ferrari's method of solving the quartic equation $x^4 + ax^2 + b = cx$ was set out by Cardano in the *Ars magna.* It consists of reducing the equation to a cubic. The discovery was made in the course of solving a problem given to Cardano by Zuanne da Coi: "Divide 10 into three proportional parts so that the product of the first and second is 6." If the mean is x, it follows that $x^4 + 6x^2 + 36 = 60x$, or $(x^2 + 6)^2 = 60x + 6x^2$. This last equation can be put in the form

$$(x^2 + 6 + y)^2 = 6x^2 + 60x + y^2 + 12y + 2yx^2$$

or

$$(x^2 + 6 + y)^2 = (2y + 6)x^2 + 60x + (y^2 + 12y),$$

where y is a new unknown. If y is chosen so that the right-hand side of the equation is a perfect square, then y satisfies the condition

$$60^2 = 4(2y + 6)(y^2 + 12y),$$

which can be reduced to the cubic equation

$$y^3 + 15y^2 + 36y = 450.$$

That Ferrari's method of solution is applicable to all cases of the quartic equation was shown by Rafael Bombelli in his *Algebra* (1572).

BIBLIOGRAPHY

I. ORIGINAL WORKS. The letters exchanged by Ferrari and Tartaglia were printed, and copies were sent to several persons of influence in Italy. (A complete set of these letters is in the Department of Printed Books of the British Museum.) They have been published by Enrico Giordani in *I sei cartelli di matematica disfida, primamente intorno alla generale risoluzione delle equazioni cubiche, di Lodovico Ferrari, coi sei contro-cartelli in risposta di Nicolò Tartaglia, comprendenti le soluzioni de' quesiti dall'una e dall'altra parte proposti* (Milan, 1876). Ferrari's work on the cubic and quartic equations is described in Cardano's *Artis magnae, sive de regulis algebraicis* (Nuremberg, 1545).

II. SECONDARY LITERATURE. Cardano wrote a short biography of Ferrari, "Vita Ludovici Ferrarii Bononiensis," in his *Opera omnia* (Lyons, 1663), IX, 568–569. References to Ferrari in Cardano's other works are cited in J. H. Morley, *Life of Girolamo Cardano of Milan, Physician* (London, 1854), I, 148–149, 187. The history of mathematics in sixteenth-century Italy is outlined in Ettore Bortolotti, *Storia della matematica nella Università di Bologna* (Bologna, 1947), pp. 35–80. Arnaldo Masotti, "Sui cartelli di matematica disfida scambiati fra Lodovico Ferrari e Niccolò Tartaglia," in *Rendiconti dell'Istituto lombardo di scienze e lettere,* **94** (1960), 31–41, cites the important secondary literature on Ferrari.

S. A. JAYAWARDENE

FERREL, WILLIAM (*b.* Bedford [now Fulton] County, Pennsylvania, 29 January 1817; *d.* Maywood, Kansas, 18 September 1891)

After Laplace, Ferrel was the chief founder of the subject now known as geophysical fluid dynamics. He gave the first general formulation of the equations of motion for a body moving with respect to the rotating earth and drew from them the consequences for atmospheric and oceanic circulation. He contributed to meteorological and tidal theory and to the problem of "earth wobble" (changes in the axis and speed of the earth's rotation).

Born in remote south-central Pennsylvania, Ferrel was the eldest of six boys and two girls born to Benjamin Ferrel and his wife, whose maiden name was Miller. In 1829 the family moved across Maryland into what is now West Virginia, where Ferrel received the usual rudimentary education during a couple of winters in a one-room schoolhouse. A shy and solitary boy, he avidly devoured the few scientific books he acquired by arduous trips to Martinsburg, West Virginia, or Hagerstown, Maryland. Stimulated in 1832 by a partial solar eclipse, by 1835 he had taught himself, with only a crude almanac and a geography book as guides, to predict eclipses. Not until 1837, when he was twenty, did he learn "the law of gravitation, and that the moon and planets move in elliptic orbits."[1] With money saved from schoolteaching, in 1839 Ferrel entered Marshall College, Mercersburg, Pennsylvania (later merged with Franklin College in Lancaster), where he "saw

[for] the first time a treatise on algebra."[2] Lack of money forced him to leave after two years of study, and he returned home to teach school for two years. He completed his degree in 1844 at the newly founded Bethany College in Bethany, West Virginia.

Ferrel then went west to teach school, first in Missouri and then in Kentucky. In Liberty, Missouri, he found a copy of Newton's *Principia* (presumably the Glasgow edition, with the 1740 tidal papers added), and later he sent to Philadelphia for a copy of Laplace's *Mécanique céleste* (in Bowditch's translation). In 1853, aged thirty-six, Ferrel wrote his first scientific paper. He moved to Nashville, Tennessee, the first city in which he had ever lived, in 1854, and there, while teaching school, he became an important contributor to the *Nashville Journal of Medicine and Surgery*. Through Benjamin Apthorp Gould, in whose *Astronomical Journal* he had published his first and some subsequent papers, Ferrel was offered his first scientific post, on the *American Nautical Almanac* staff. He remained with the *Almanac* in Cambridge, Massachusetts, from 1858 to 1867, when Benjamin Peirce of Harvard persuaded Ferrel to go to Washington to join the U.S. Coast Survey, of which Peirce was the new superintendent. In 1882 Ferrel joined the U.S. Army's Signal Service (predecessor of the Weather Bureau), where he remained until 1886. On his retirement at age seventy he moved to Kansas City, Kansas, to be with his brother Jacob and other relatives, but the lack of "scientific associations and access to scientific libraries"[3] in the West led him to return to Martinsburg, West Virginia, in 1889 and 1890. He died in Maywood, Kansas, at the age of seventy-four.

A painfully shy man, Ferrel never married, nor did he found a school in his subject. He did not apply for any of his scientific positions, yet he became a member of the National Academy of Sciences (1868), an associate fellow of the American Academy of Arts and Sciences, an honorary member of the meteorological societies of Austria, Britain, and Germany, and a recipient of the honorary degrees of A.M. and Ph.D.

Ferrel's career as a scientist began about 1850 with his study of Newton's *Principia*. Concentrating on tidal theory—in which Newton's work had been extended in papers presented to the French Academy in 1740 by Daniel Bernoulli, Euler, and Maclaurin and published in editions of the *Principia* after Newton's death—Ferrel conjectured "that the action of the moon and sun upon the tides must have a tendency to retard the earth's rotation on its axis."[4] In his *Mécanique céleste* Laplace had discounted any effect of the tides on the earth's rate of axial rotation. In his first published paper (1853) Ferrel showed that Laplace had neglected the second-order terms that should cause tidal retardation. Since Laplace had claimed to account for all the observed acceleration in the moon's orbit without tidal friction, Ferrel suggested that the latter might be counteracted by the earth's shrinking as it cooled. When about 1860 it became clear that Laplace's theory could not account for the observed value of the moon's acceleration, Ferrel returned to the problem in a paper read to the American Academy of Arts and Sciences in 1864. Although others reached the same general conclusion independently, Ferrel's was the first quantitative treatment of tidal friction, a problem that continues to be of scientific interest.

After three more papers published locally, Ferrel returned to tidal theory in 1856 with his second paper in Gould's *Astronomical Journal*. In it he suggested that Laplace was in error when he claimed that the diurnal tide would vanish in an ocean of uniform depth. Ferrel's criticisms were parallel to Airy's, and both were strongly opposed by Kelvin. The problem of "oscillations of the second kind" to which they relate remains of current scientific interest.

In both these early papers Ferrel established the basis of his contributions to the theory of tides. Laplace had ignored fluid friction, which was not successfully treated mathematically until Navier and Poisson in the 1820's and Saint-Venant and Stokes in the 1840's inaugurated the modern theory. In tidal studies Airy (1845) assumed friction to be proportional to the first power of the velocity, in which case (as in Laplace's) the equations are linear. Thomas Young (1823), although he assumed friction to be proportional to the square of the velocity, failed to introduce the required equation of continuity. Ferrel's major contribution to tidal theory was thus to begin the full nonlinear treatment necessitated by realistic assumptions concerning friction.

After joining the Coast Survey, Ferrel made important contributions to the techniques of tidal prediction. He extended the nonharmonic developments of the tide-producing potential beyond the points reached by Laplace and Lubbock, and he gave the first reasonably complete harmonic development. Here his endeavors were parallel to those of Kelvin, who was responsible for the first tide-predicting machine (probably the earliest piece of large-scale computing machinery). In 1880 Ferrel, too, designed a tide predictor, which went into service in 1883. Although it was an analogue machine like Kelvin's, Ferrel's gave maxima and minima rather than a continuous curve as its output. Ferrel also made considerable progress in dealing with the shallow-water tidal components and in using tidal data to calculate the mass of the moon.

His studies of astronomical and geophysical tides established Ferrel's claim to a modest place in the history of science. His claim to a major place in this history lies elsewhere: He was the first to understand in mathematical detail the significance of the earth's rotation for the motion of bodies at its surface, and his application of this understanding to the motions of ocean and atmosphere opened a new epoch in meteorology. From Maury's *Physical Geography of the Sea* (1855) Ferrel learned of the belts of high pressure at 30° latitude and of low pressure at the equator and the poles. Looking for the cause of this distribution of pressure, Ferrel realized that since Laplace's tidal equations were of general application, both winds and currents must be deflected by the earth's rotation.

Pressed to write a critical review of Maury's book, Ferrel instead put his own ideas into "An Essay on the Winds and Currents of the Ocean" (*Nashville Journal,* October 1856), a precise but nonmathematical account of the general circulation, and on joining the *Nautical Almanac* staff he began to develop his ideas in mathematical form. In Gould's *Astronomical Journal* early in 1858 Ferrel made explicit the notion of an inertial circle of motion on the earth and used it to explain the gyratory nature of storms (although purely inertial motions are now known to be common in the ocean but almost absent from the atmosphere). In a series of papers published in his colleague J. D. Runkle's *Mathematical Monthly* in 1858 and 1859, then collected to form a separate pamphlet published in New York and London in 1860, Ferrel developed a general quantitative theory of relative motion on the earth's surface and applied it to winds and currents. His result, now known as Ferrel's law, was "that if a body is moving in any direction, there is a force, arising from the earth's rotation, which always deflects it to the right in the northern hemisphere, and to the left in the southern" (1858).[5] This theory and its derivation were carried to a wider audience by a summary article in the *American Journal of Science* for 1861.

Like others who treated relative motion and its geophysical consequences at about the same time, Ferrel appears to have been indebted to Foucault's pendulum (1851) and gyroscope (1852). Ferrel's treatment was remarkable for its clarity and generality, and by continuing to develop his ideas in a series of publications extending over thirty years, he pioneered in the development of meteorology from a descriptive science to a branch of mathematical physics.

When he began, meteorological thought was dominated by the unphysical ideas of Dove, who, drawing on Hadley's explanation of the trade winds (1735), insisted that the earth's rotation acted only on meridional atmospheric motions to deflect them only zonally. Although Ferrel agreed that temperature differences between equatorial and polar regions drove both atmosphere and ocean, he supported by mathematical deduction his insistence that all atmospheric motions, whatever their direction, were deflected by the earth's rotation. His application of this principle to explain both the general circulation and the rotary action of cyclonic storms began to be generally accepted in the 1870's, as weather forecasting services spread over Europe and North America. In his theory of the general circulation Ferrel developed the basic principle that on the rotating earth, convection between equator and pole must be chiefly by westerly winds. He gave the traditional three-cell diagram of the circulation, abandoned only since about 1950, as it has become clear that this scheme of an average circulation pattern along any meridian, although heuristically useful, is not supported by the data. Ferrel modified Espy's convection-condensation theory of cyclonic storms, and he gave a plausible account of the great force of tornadoes.

By 1880 meteorology seems to have caught up with Ferrel's ideas, and he was not always able to accept the advances of the following decade that built upon his innovations. The Ferrel-Espy convection-condensation theory explains tropical hurricanes but not midlatitude storms, yet about 1890 Ferrel argued vigorously against Hann's ideas on the latter type of storm. He was also unwilling to admit the role of wind stress in the generation of ocean currents. Yet Ferrel had led in bringing sound physical principles, expressed with the tools of mathematical analysis, to bear on the largest problems of oceanic and atmospheric motion: thus at his death he was called "the most eminent meteorologist and one of the most eminent scientific men that America has produced."[6] This eminence came to Ferrel for "having given to the science of meteorology a foundation in mechanics as solid as that which Newton laid for astronomy."[7]

NOTES

1. MS autobiography, printed with minor changes in *Biographical Memoirs. National Academy of Sciences,* **3** (1895), 291.
2. *Ibid.*, 292.
3. Quoted from a letter of Ferrel by Frank Waldo in *American Meteorological Journal,* **8** (1891), 360.
4. Autobiography, 294.

5. "The Influence of the Earth's Rotation Upon the Relative Motion of Bodies Near Its Surface," in *Astronomical Journal*, **5** (1858), 99.
6. W. M. Davis, *American Meteorological Journal*, **8** (1891), 359.
7. Cleveland Abbe, *Biographical Memoirs. National Academy of Sciences*, **3** (1895), 281.

BIBLIOGRAPHY

I. ORIGINAL WORKS. Ferrel's most significant paper, "The Motions of Fluids and Solids Relative to the Earth's Surface," appeared originally in *Mathematical Monthly*, **1** and **2** (Jan. 1859–Aug. 1860) and was republished with notes by Waldo as Professional Papers of the U.S. Signal Service, no. 8 (Washington, D.C., 1882). Other papers on meteorology, including his 1856 "Essay on the Winds and Currents of the Ocean," were reprinted as no. 12 of the same series (Washington, D.C., 1882). Ferrel also wrote three treatises: "Meteorological Researches for the Use of the Coast Pilot," published in three pts. as appendixes to *Report of the Superintendent of the U.S. Coast Survey for 1875* (Washington, D.C., 1878), *1878* (Washington, D.C., 1881), and *1881* (Washington, D.C., 1883); "Recent Advances in Meteorology," published as app. 71 to *Report of the Chief Signal Officer to the Secretary of War for 1885* (Washington, D.C., 1886), as Professional Papers of the Signal Service, no. 17, and as House Executive Document no. 1, pt. 2, 49th Congress, 1st session; *A Popular Treatise on the Winds* (New York, 1889). Ferrel's major work on tides is his *Tidal Researches*, appended to the *Coast Survey Report for 1874* (Washington, D.C., 1874); and he described his tide predictor in app. 10 to the *Coast Survey Report for 1883* (Washington, D.C., 1884). Ferrel's bibliography, in *Biographical Memoirs. National Academy of Sciences*, **3** (1895), 300–309, lists more than 100 items; it is preceded (287–299) by an edited version of his autobiography, the holograph MS of which is in the Harvard College Library.

II. SECONDARY LITERATURE. Cleveland Abbe's memoir, in *Biographical Memoirs. National Academy of Sciences*, **3** (1895), 267–286, is the fullest; more concise is William M. Davis' in *Proceedings of the American Academy of Arts and Sciences*, **28** (1893), 388–393. Alexander McAdie wrote a biographical article, accompanied by a portrait, in *American Meteorological Journal*, **4** (1888), 441–449; memorial articles by Simon Newcomb, Abbe, Davis, Waldo, and others are *ibid.*, **8** (1891), 337–369. K. Schneider-Carius, *Wetterkunde. Wetterforschung* (Freiburg, 1955), a sourcebook in the Orbis Academicus series, is useful on the history of meteorology. Among the older works, Frank Waldo, *Modern Meteorology* (London, 1893), in the Contemporary Science Series, gives—if anything—too much attention to Ferrel. Ferrel's place in the history of tidal theory is easier to assess, thanks to Rollin A. Harris, *Manual of Tides—Part I*, app. 8 to *Coast Survey Report for 1897* (Washington, D.C., 1898); pp. 455–462 of this excellent history are devoted to Ferrel.

HAROLD L. BURSTYN

FERRO (or FERREO, DAL FERRO, DEL FERRO), SCIPIONE (*b.* Bologna, Italy, 6 February 1465; *d.* Bologna, between 29 October and 16 November 1526)

Scipione was the son of Floriano Ferro (a papermaker by trade) and his wife, Filippa. He was a lecturer in arithmetic and geometry at the University of Bologna from 1496 to 1526, except for a brief stay in Venice during the last year. In 1513 he is recorded as an "arithmetician" by Giovanni Filoteo Achillini, in the poem *Viridario*. After Scipione's death, the same subjects were taught by his disciple, Annibale dalla Nave (or della Nave). Nave married Scipione's daughter, Filippa, and inherited his father-in-law's surname, thereby calling himself dalla Nave, alias dal Ferro. Scipione's activity as a businessman is demonstrated by various notarial documents from the years 1517–1523.

No work of Scipione's, either printed or in manuscript, is known. It is known from several sources, however, that he was a great algebraist. We are indebted to him for the solution of third-degree, or cubic, equations, which had been sought since antiquity. As late as the end of the fifteenth century, Luca Pacioli judged it "impossible" by the methods known at that time (*Summa*, I, dist. VIII, tractate 5). Scipione achieved his solution in the first or second decade of the sixteenth century, as is known from the texts of Tartaglia and Cardano. He did not print any account of his discovery, but divulged it to various people and expounded it in a manuscript that came into the possession of Nave, but which today is unknown.

In 1535 a disciple of Scipione, named Antonio Maria Fiore, in a mathematical dispute with Tartaglia proposed some problems leading to cubic equations lacking the second-degree term, of which he claimed to know the method of solution, having learned "such a secret," thirty years before, from a certain "great mathematician" (Tartaglia, *Quesiti*, bk. ix, question 25). Tartaglia (who had concerned himself with cubic equations as early as 1530) was now (1535) induced to seek and find the solution to them. Some years later, yielding to entreaties, he communicated his solution to Cardano (1539).

Still later (1542), in Bologna, Nave made known to Cardano the existence of the aforementioned manuscript by Scipione: this is attested by Ludovico Ferrari, Cardano's famous disciple, who was with the master (Ferrari to Tartaglia, *Secondo cartello*, p. 3; see also Tartaglia to Ferrari, *Seconda risposta*, p. 6). Cardano, who published the *Ars magna* (1545) somewhat later, represented the solution of cubic equations as the distinguished discovery of Scipione and Tartaglia. The following is taken from the *Ars magna* (chs. 1, 11):

> Scipione Ferro of Bologna, almost thirty years ago, discovered the solution of the cube and of things equal in number [that is, the equation $x^3 + px = q$, where p and q are positive numbers], a really beautiful and admirable accomplishment. In distinction this discovery surpasses all mortal ingenuity and all human subtlety. It is truly a gift from heaven, although at the same time a proof of the power of reason, and so illustrious that whoever attains it may believe himself capable of solving any problem. In emulation of him Niccolò Tartaglia of Brescia, a friend of ours, in order not to be conquered when he entered into competition with a disciple of Ferro, Antonio Maria Fiore, came upon the same solution, and revealed it to me because of my many entreaties to him.

The coincidence of Scipione's and Tartaglia's rules was confirmed by Ettore Bortolotti by means of an ancient manuscript (MS 595N of the Library of the University of Bologna), which reproduces Scipione's rule, which had been obtained from him by Pompeo Bolognetti, lecturer *ad praxim mathematicae* at Bologna in the years 1554–1568. Basing his conclusion on another text by Cardano and on a manuscript of the *Algebra* of Rafael Bombelli (MS B.1569 of the Library of the Archiginnasio of Bologna, assignable to about 1550), Bortolotti concludes, with plausibility, that Scipione did indeed solve both the equations $x^3 + px = q$, and $x^3 = px + q$.

How Scipione arrived at the solution of cubic equations is not known. But there is no lack of attempts at reconstructing his method. For example, in his examination of the *Liber abbaci* of Leonardo Fibonacci and of the *Algebra* of Bombelli, Giovanni Vacca seemed to be able to reproduce, in the following simple procedure, the one used by Scipione: If the sum of square roots is expressed as

$$x = \sqrt{a + \sqrt{b}} + \sqrt{a - \sqrt{b}}, \qquad (1)$$

it can be seen, by raising to the square, that this satisfies the second-degree equation (lacking the term in x)

$$x^2 = (2\sqrt{a^2 - b}) + 2a. \qquad (2)$$

Analogously, if the sum of cube roots is expressed as

$$X = \sqrt[3]{a + \sqrt{b}} + \sqrt[3]{a - \sqrt{b}}, \qquad (3)$$

then it can be seen, raising to the cube, that this satisfies the third-degree equation (lacking the term in X^2)

$$X^3 = (3\sqrt[3]{a^2 - b})X + 2a. \qquad (4)$$

Therefore, equation (4) is solved by means of (3). If one writes

$$p = 3\sqrt[3]{a^2 - b}, \quad q = 2a \qquad (a)$$

or

$$a = \frac{q}{2}, \quad b = \frac{q^2}{4} - \frac{p^3}{27}, \qquad (b)$$

the cubic equation (4) and the formula which solves it (3) assume the accustomed form:

$$X^3 = pX + q, \qquad (5)$$

$$X = \sqrt[3]{\frac{p}{2} + \sqrt{\frac{q^2}{4} - \frac{p^3}{27}}} + \sqrt[3]{\frac{p}{2} - \sqrt{\frac{q^2}{4} - \frac{p^3}{27}}}. \qquad (6)$$

This latter is called Cardano's formula, but incorrectly because Cardano does not deserve credit for having discovered it but only for having published it for the first time.

Another of Scipione's contributions to algebra concerns fractions having irrational denominators. The problem of rationalizing the denominator of such a fraction, when there are square roots intervening, goes back to Euclid. In the sixteenth century, the same problem appears with roots of greater index. And here one can single out the case of fractions of the type

$$\frac{1}{\sqrt[3]{a} + \sqrt[3]{b} + \sqrt[3]{c}},$$

which Scipione was the first to deal with, as can be seen by the manuscript of Bombelli, cited above. In that manuscript, Bombelli calls Scipione "a man uniquely gifted in this art."

Finally, it should be noted that Scipione also applied himself to the geometry of the compass with a fixed opening, although this theory was ancient, the first examples going back to Abu'l-Wafa' (tenth century). In the first half of the sixteenth century, this question arose again, particularly because of Tartaglia, Cardano, and Ferrari. And it is because of the testimony of the last-named (Ferrari to Tartaglia, *Quinto cartello,* p. 25) that we can state that Scipione also took up this problem, but we know nothing about his researches and his contributions.

BIBLIOGRAPHY

I. ORIGINAL WORKS. We possess no original works by Scipione Ferro, and the sources from which knowledge of his activity is derived are indicated in the text. Of the printed sources, the following later eds. are more accessible than the originals: Cardano, *Ars magna,* in *Opera omnia,* C. Spon, ed., vol. IV (Lyons, 1663); facs. repr. of the *Opera omnia,* with intro. by A. Buck (Stuttgart-Bad Cannstatt, 1966); Tartaglia, *Quesiti et inventioni diverse,* facsimile of the edition of 1554, sponsored by the Atheneum of Brescia, A. Masotti, ed. (Brescia, 1959); and Ferrari, *Cartelli,* and Tartaglia, *Risposte,* in the autograph ed. by E. Giordani (Milano, 1876), or in the facs. ed. of the original, sponsored by the Atheneum of Brescia, A. Masotti, ed. (in press). Concerning the two Bolognese manuscripts which have been cited, see E. Bortolotti, "L'algebra nella scuola matematica bolognese del secolo XVI," in *Periodico di matematiche,* 4th ser., **5** (1925), 147–184, as well as the collection of extracts entitled *Studi e ricerche sulla storia della matematica in Italia nei secoli XVI e XVII* (Bologna, 1928).

II. SECONDARY LITERATURE. See C. Malagola, *Della vita e delle opere di Antonio Urceo detto Codro* (Bologna, 1878), pp. 352–355, and app. XXVII, pp. 574–577, which contains "Documenti intorno a Scipione dal Ferro"; L. Frati, "Scipione dal Ferro," in *Bollettino di bibliografia e storia delle scienze matematiche,* **12** (1910), 1–5; and in *Studi e memorie per la storia dell'Università di Bologna,* **2** (1911), 193–205; E. Bortolotti, "I contributi del Tartaglia, del Cardano, del Ferrari, e della scuola matematica bolognese alla teoria algebrica delle equazioni cubiche," in *Studi e memorie per la storia dell'Università di Bologna,* **10** (1926), 55–108, thence in the aforementioned volume of *Studi e ricerche;* and G. Vacca, "Sul commento di Leonardo Pisano al Libro X degli Elementi di Euclide e sulla risoluzione delle equazioni cubiche," in *Bollettino dell'Unione matematica italiana,* **9** (1930), 59–63.

On Annibale dalla Nave, see A. Favaro, note in Eneström, *Bibliotheca mathematica,* 3rd ser., **2** (1901), 354.

On A. M. Fiore, see A. Masotti, note in *Atti* of the meeting in honor of Tartaglia, held at the Atheneum of Brescia in 1959, p. 42.

Ferro's role in the solution of cubic equations, is discussed in all histories of mathematics. See, for example, M. Cantor, *Vorlesungen über Geschichte der Mathematik;* J. Tropfke, *Geschichte der Elementar-Mathematik;* and D. E. Smith, *History of Mathematics, passim.*

Also of interest are D. E. Smith, *A Source Book in Mathematics* (New York, 1929; repr. New York, 1959), pp. 203–206, where one can read the solution of the cubic equation given in Cardano, *Ars magna,* ch. 11, English trans. by R. B. McClenon; O. Ore, *Cardano, the Gambling Scholar* (Princeton, 1953), pp. 62–107, where can be found the history of the solution of cubic equations, with English translations of various texts by Tartaglia, Cardano, and Ferrari, and various mentions of Ferro; and, finally, G. Sarton, *Six Wings: Men of Science in the Renaissance* (Bloomington, Ind., 1957), pp. 28–36, 246–249.

ARNALDO MASOTTI

FEUERBACH, KARL WILHELM (*b.* Jena, Germany, 30 May 1800; *d.* Erlangen, Germany, 12 March 1834)

Karl Wilhelm was the third of the eleven children of Eva Wilhelmine Maria Troster and the famed German jurist Paul Johann Anselm Feuerbach. By the age of twenty-two, the gifted young mathematician had been awarded the Ph.D., had made a significant contribution to a pleasant and active branch of mathematical research, and had been named professor of mathematics at the Gymnasium at Erlangen.

Feuerbach's scientific output was small, and his fame as a mathematician rests entirely upon three publications, which constitute the total output of his scientific career. His most important contribution was a theorem in Euclidean geometry, the theorem of Feuerbach:

> The circle which passes through the feet of the altitudes of a triangle touches all four of the circles which are tangent to the three sides of the triangle; it is internally tangent to the inscribed circle and externally tangent to each of the circles which touch the sides of the triangle externally [*Eigenschaften*].

In this statement one recognizes the nine-point circle of a triangle, which had been fully described though not named by Brianchon and Poncelet in 1821. The proof of this theorem was presented with a number of other conclusions on the geometry of the triangle in his small book *Eigenschaften einiger merkwürdigen Punkte . . .*, published in 1822. In this work Feuerbach developed a number of algebraic identities involving the lengths of the sides and other parts of a triangle and then proved that the two circles in question were tangent by showing that the distance between their centers was equal to the sum of their radii. He used as a model for this investigation Euler's "Solutio facilis problematum," a paper that had been published in 1765. Recognition came slowly, but many years after his death a number of papers appeared devoted to a discussion of the nine-point circle of a triangle and the theorem of Feuerbach.

In 1827 Feuerbach brought out the results of his second investigation. After an exhaustive analysis of this work, Moritz Cantor concluded that Feuerbach had proved to be an independent co-discoverer with Moebius of the theory of the homogeneous coordinates of a point in space. In the meantime, however, Feuerbach's teaching career was beset by difficulties and his health had become seriously impaired. At the age of twenty-eight he retired permanently and spent the rest of his life in Erlangen as a recluse.

BIBLIOGRAPHY

I. ORIGINAL WORKS. Feuerbach's works are *Eigenschaften einiger merkwürdigen Punkte des geradlinigen Dreiecks und mehrerer durch sie bestimmten Linien und Figuren. Eine analytisch-trigonometrische Abhandlung* (Nuremberg, 1822), a portion of which was ed. and trans. by R. A. Johnson as "Feuerbach on the Theorem Which Bears His Name," in D. E. Smith, ed., *A Source Book in Mathematics* (New York–London, 1929), paperback repr. (New York, 1959); "Einleitung zu dem Werke Analysis der dreyeckigen Pyramide durch die Methode der Coordinaten und Projectionen. Ein Beytrag zu der analytischen Geometrie," in L. Oken, *Isis,* VI (Jena, 1826), 565; and *Grundriss zu analytischen Untersuchungen der dreyeckigen Pyramide* (Nuremberg, 1827). An unpublished MS on the theory of the triangular pyramid, dated 7 July 1826, is in the Feuerbach family archives.

II. SECONDARY LITERATURE. On the man and his work, see C. J. Brianchon and J. V. Poncelet, "Géométrie des courbes: Recherches sur la détermination d'une hyperbole équilatère, au moyen de quatre conditions données," in *Annales de mathematiques,* **11** (1 Jan. 1821); M. Cantor, "Karl Wilhelm Feuerbach," in *Sitzungsberichte der Heidelberger Akademie der Wissenschaften,* Math.-naturwissen. Klasse, Abh. 25 (1910); L. Euler, "Solutio facilis problematum quorumdam geometricorum difficillimorum," in *Novi commentarii academiae scientiarum imperialis Petropolitanae,* **11** (1765), 103; H. Eulenberg, *Die Familie Feuerbach* (Stuttgart, 1924); L. Feuerbach, *Anselm Ritter von Feuerbachs biographischer Nachlass* (Leipzig, 1853); L. Guggenbuhl, "Karl Wilhelm Feuerbach, Mathematician," in *Scientific Monthly,* **81** (1955), 71; R. A. Johnson, *Modern Geometry: An Elementary Treatise on the Geometry of the Triangle and the Circle* (Boston–New York, 1929), repr. in paperback as *Advanced Euclidean Geometry* (New York, 1960); J. Lange, "Geschichte des Feuerbachschen Kreises," in *Wissenschaftliche Beilage zum Jahresbericht der Friedrichs Wederschen Ober-Realschule zu Berlin Programme No. 114* (1894); J. S. Mackay, "History of the Nine Point Circle," in *Proceedings of the Edinburgh Mathematical Society,* **11** (1892), 19; G. Radbruch, *Paul Johann Anselm Feuerbach* (Vienna, 1934) and *Gestalten und Gedanken. Die Feuerbachs, Eine geistige Dynastie* (Leipzig, 1948); T. Spoerri, *Genie und Krankheit* (Basel–New York, 1952); J. Steiner, *Die geometrischen Constructionen ausgefuhrt mittelst der geraden Linie und eines festen Kreises* (Berlin, 1833); and Olry Terquem, "Considération sur le triangle rectiligne," in *Nouvelles annales de mathématiques,* **1** (1842), 196.

LAURA GUGGENBUHL

FIBONACCI, LEONARDO, or **LEONARDO OF PISA** (*b.* Pisa, Italy, *ca.* 1170; *d.* Pisa, after 1240)

Leonardo Fibonacci, the first great mathematician of the Christian West, was a member of a family named Bonacci, whose presence in Pisa since the eleventh century is documented. His father's name is known to have been Guilielmo. It is thus that Fibonacci is to be understood as a member of the Bonacci family and not as "son of a father of the name of Bonacci," as one might suppose from the words "filio Bonacij" or "de filiis Bonacij," which appear in the titles of many manuscripts of his works. The sobriquet "Bigollo" (from *bighellone,* loafer or ne'er-do-well), used by Leonardo himself, remains unexplained. Did his countrymen wish to express by this epithet their disdain for a man who concerned himself with questions of no practical value, or does the word in the Tuscan dialect mean a much-traveled man, which he was?

Life. Leonardo himself provides exact details on the course of his life in the preface to the most extensive and famous of his works, the book on calculations entitled *Liber abbaci* (1202). His father, as a secretary of the Republic of Pisa,[1] was entrusted around 1192 with the direction of the Pisan trading colony in Bugia (now Bougie), Algeria. He soon brought his son there to have him learn the art of calculating, since he expected Leonardo to become a merchant. It was there that he learned methods "with the new Indian numerals," and he received excellent instruction (*ex mirabili magisterio*). On the business trips on which his father evidently soon sent him and which took him to Egypt, Syria, Greece (Byzantium), Sicily, and Provence, he acquainted himself with the methods in use there through zealous study and in disputations with native scholars. All these methods, however—so he reports—as well as "algorismus" and the "arcs of Pythagoras" (apparently the abacus of Gerbert) appeared to him as in "error" in comparison with the Indian methods.[2] It is quite unclear what Leonardo means here by the "algorismus" he rejects; for those writings through which the Indian methods became known, especially after Sacrobosco, a younger contemporary of Leonardo, bear that very name. Could he mean the later *algorismus linealis,* reckoning with lines, the origin of which is, to be sure, likewise obscure?

Around the turn of the century Leonardo returned to Pisa. Here for the next twenty-five years he composed works in which he presented not only calculations with Indian numerals and methods and their application in all areas of commercial activity, but also much of what he had learned of algebraic and geometrical problems. His inclusion of the latter in his own writings shows that while the instruction of his countrymen in the solution of the problems posed by everyday life was indeed his chief concern, he nevertheless also wished to provide material on theoretical arithmetic and geometry for those who were interested in more advanced questions. He even speaks once of wanting to add the "subtleties of Euclid's geometry";[3] these are the propositions from books II and X of the *Elements,* which he offers to the reader not only in proofs, in Euclid's manner, but in numerical form as well. His most important original accomplishments were in indeterminate analysis and number theory, in which he went far beyond his predecessors.

Leonardo's importance was recognized at the court of the Hohenstaufen emperor Frederick II. Leonardo's writings mention the names of many of the scholars of the circle around the emperor, including Michael Scotus, a court astrologer whom Dante (*Inferno,* XX, 115 ff.) banished to hell; the imperial philosopher, Master Theodorus; and Master Johannes of Palermo. Through a Master Dominicus, probably the Dominicus Hispanus mentioned by Guido Bonatti (see Boncompagni, *Intorno ad alcune opere di Leonardo Pisano,* p. 98, n.), Leonardo was presented to the emperor, who evidently desired to meet him, when Frederick held court in Pisa about 1225.[4] After 1228 we know almost nothing more concerning Leonardo's activity in Pisa. Only one document has survived, from 1240, in which the Republic of Pisa awards the "serious and learned Master Leonardo Bigollo" (*discretus et sapiens*) a yearly *salarium* of "libre XX denariorem" in addition to the usual allowances, in recognition of his usefulness to the city and its citizens through his teaching and devoted services. He evidently had advised the city and its officials, without payment, on matters of accounting, a service the city expected him to continue. This decree of the city, which was inscribed on a marble tablet in the Pisa city archives in the nineteenth century,[5] is the last information we have on Leonardo's life.

Writings. Five works by Leonardo are preserved:

1. The *Liber abbaci* (1202, 1228);
2. The *Practica geometriae* (1220/1221);
3. A writing entitled *Flos* (1225);
4. An undated letter to Theodorus, the imperial philosopher;
5. The *Liber quadratorum* (1225). We know of further works, such as a book on commercial arithmetic, *Di minor guisa;*[6] especially unfortunate is the loss of a tract on book X of the *Elements,* for which Leonardo promised a numerical treatment of irrationals instead of Euclid's geometrical presentation.[7]

Leonardo's works have been collected in the edition by Boncompagni; in 1838 Libri edited only one chapter of the *Liber abbaci.* Boncompagni, however, provides only the Latin text without any commentary. Hence, despite much specialized research on the *Flos* and on the *Liber quadratorum,* which Ver Eecke has translated into French, there is still no exhaustive presentation of Leonardo's problems and methods. The most detailed studies of the substance of the works are those by Cantor, Loria, and Youschkevitch.

Liber abbaci. The word *abacus* in the title does not refer to the old abacus, the sand board; rather, it means computation in general, as was true later with the Italian masters of computation, the *maestri d'abbaco.* Of the second treatment of 1228, to which "new material has been added and from which superfluous removed," there exist twelve manuscript copies from the thirteenth through the fifteenth centuries; but only three of these from the thirteenth and the beginning of the fourteenth centuries are complete. Leonardo divided this extensive work, which is dedicated to Michael Scotus, into fifteen chapters; it will be analyzed here in four sections.

Section 1 (chapters 1–7; *Scritti,* I, 1–82). Leonardo refers to Roman numerals and finger computation, which the student still needs for marking intermediate results.[8] Then the Indian numerals are introduced; following the Arabic manner, the units stand "in front" (on the right), and the fractions are on the left of the whole numbers. In addition, he introduces the fraction bar. All the computational operations are taught methodically through numerous examples and the results are checked, mostly by the method of casting out nines (seven and eleven are also used in this way). Rules are developed for the factoring of fractions into sums of unit factors. Various symbols are introduced for the representation of fractions. Thus, for example, $\frac{6\ \ 2}{7\ \ 5}$ is to be read as $\frac{2}{5}+\frac{6}{7\cdot 5}$; $0\frac{6\ \ 2}{7\ \ 5}$ means $\frac{2}{5}\cdot\frac{6}{7}$; and $\frac{6\ \ 2}{7\ \ 5}0$ is to be understood as $\frac{2}{5}+\frac{6}{7}$. Finally, $\frac{1\ 1\ 1\ 5}{5\ 4\ 3\ 9}$ signifies $\frac{5}{9}+\left(\frac{1}{3}+\frac{1}{4}+\frac{1}{5}\right)\cdot\frac{5}{9}$. The first—and the most frequently employed—of these representational methods corresponds to the ascending continued fraction $\frac{2+\frac{6}{7}}{5}$. Numerous tables (for multiplication, prime numbers, factoring numbers, etc.) complete the text.

Section 2 (chapters 8–11; *Scritti,* I, 83–165). This section contains problems of concern to merchants, such as the price of goods, calculation of profits, barter, computation of interest, wages, calculations for associations and partnerships, metal alloys, and mixture calculations; the computations of measurements and of currency conversions in particular reflect the widespread trade of the medieval city with the lands bordering the Mediterranean. One of the mixture problems included is known from Chinese mathematics, the "problem of the 100 birds"; a problem in indeterminate analysis, it requires that one purchase for 100 units of money 100 birds of different sorts, the price of each sort being different.

Section 3 (chapters 12 and 13; *Scritti,* I, 176–351). This is the most extensive section and contains problems of many types, which are called *erraticae questiones.* They are mostly puzzles, such as are found in the mathematical recreations of all times. Among them are the "cistern problems" (A spider climbing the wall of a cistern advances so many feet each day and slips back so many feet each night. How long will it take it to climb out?) and, from Egyptian mathematics, the famous so-called "hau calculations," which can be expressed in the form $ax \pm b/c \cdot x = s$. Leonardo calls them *questiones arborum* after the first example, in which a tree is supposed to stand twenty-one ells above the ground with 7/12 of its length in the earth; therefore, $x - 7/12\ x = 21$. Another group are "motion problems," involving either pursuit (as in the famous "hare and hound" problem, in which one must determine how long it will take a hound chasing a hare at a proportional speed to catch the hare) or opposite movements. In both cases the motions can be delayed through backward movements. Since in many problems the speed is not constant, but increases arithmetically, rules for the summation of series are given at the beginning of chapter 12. A group of problems that had already appeared in the epigrams of *The Greek Anthology* (a recent edition is W. R. Paton, ed. [Cambridge, Mass., 1953], V, 25 ff.) and can be designated as "giving and taking," is called by Leonardo *de personis habentibus denarios;* in these there are two or more people, each of whom demands a certain sum from one or several of the others and then states what the proportion now is between his money and that of the others. A simple example is (1) $x + 7 = 5 \cdot (y - 7)$; (2) $y + 5 = 7 \cdot (x - 5)$. In the problem of "the found purse" (*de inventione bursarum*) two or more people find a purse, and we are told for each individual what ratio the sum of his money and the total money in the purse has to the sum of the remaining individuals' monies; for example, with three people the modern arrangement would be (1) $x + b = 2 \cdot (y + z)$; (2) $y + b = 3 \cdot (x + z)$; (3) $z + b = 4(x + y)$. They are, therefore, problems in indeterminate analysis.

Another very extensive group, "one alone cannot buy," takes the form of "horse buying" (*de hominibus equum emere volentibus*). In this case it is given that one of those concerned can buy an object only if he receives from the other (or others) a portion of his (or their) cash.[9] Variations are also given that involve up to seven people and five horses; in these cases, if the price of the horse is not known, the problem is indeterminate. A problem of this type involving three people, where the equation would be

$$x + \frac{y+z}{3} = y + \frac{z+x}{4} = z + \frac{x+y}{5} = s,$$

corresponds to Diophantus II, 24. A further group treats the business trips of a merchant, which are introduced as *de viagiis.* These are the famous problems of the "gate-keeper in the apple garden." It is here that the problems involving mathematical nesting of the form $\langle[(a_1x - b_1) \cdot a_2 - b_2] \cdot a_3 - \cdots\rangle \cdot a_n - b_n = s$ are to be solved.[10] Of the multitude of other problems treated in the *Liber abbaci,* the following should be mentioned: numerous remainder problems, in which, for example, a number n is sought with the property $n \equiv 1$ (mod. 2, 3, 4, 5, and 6) $\equiv 0$ (mod. 7); the Chinese remainder problem *Ta yen,*[11] the finding of perfect numbers; the summation of a geometric series; the ancient Egyptian problem of the "seven old women" (to find $\sum_{i=1}^{n} 7^i$, the seven wives of St. Ives); the Bachet weight problem; the chess problem (to find $\sum_{i=0}^{64} 2^i$); and the rabbit problem. This last problem assumes that a pair of rabbits requires one month to mature and thereafter reproduces itself once each month. If one starts with a single pair, how many pairs will one have after n months? The answer leads to the famous Fibonacci series, the first recurrent series. Its general form for any term k_n is $k_n = k_{n-1} + k_{n-2}$; and, in this case, it can be expressed as

$$k_n = \frac{1}{\sqrt{5}} \cdot \left[\left(\frac{1+\sqrt{5}}{2}\right)^n - \left(\frac{1-\sqrt{5}}{2}\right)^n\right].$$

Leonardo demonstrates an astonishing versatility in the choice of methods of solution to be used in particular instances; he frequently employs a special procedure, for which he usually has no specific name and which has been tailored with great skill to fit the individual problem. He also shows great dexterity in the introduction of an auxiliary unknown; in this he is like Iamblichus, who demonstrated the same talent in his explanation of the *Epanthema* of Thymaridas of Paros. At other times Leonardo makes use of definitely general methods. These include the simple false position, as in the "hau calculations" and the *regula versa,* in which the calculation is made in reverse order in the nesting problems in *de viagiis;*

there is also the double false position, to which the whole of chapter 13 is devoted and which is called—as in Leonardo's Arabic models—*regula elchatayn.* With this rule, linear and pure quadratic problems can be solved with the aid of two arbitrarily chosen quantities, a_1 and a_2, of unknown magnitude and the resulting errors, f_1 and f_2. Leonardo knew this procedure, but he generally used a variation. The latter consists in ascertaining from the two errors how much closer one has come to the true answer (*veritati appropinquinare*)[12] in the second attempt and then determining the number that one must now choose in order to obtain the correct solution. A special solution for an indeterminate problem is provided by the *regula proportionis.* If, for example, in the final equation of a problem $63/600\,x = 21/200\,b$, then, according to this rule, $x = 21/200$ and $b = 63/600$ or, in whole numbers, $x = 63$ and $b = 63$.

Leonardo also employed, as easy mechanical solutions, formulas (especially in the "horse buying," "found purse," and "journey" problems) that can have been obtained only by means of algebra. He knew the algebraic methods very well; he called them *regulae rectae* and stated that they were used by the Arabs and could be useful in many ways. He called the unknown term *res* (Arabic *shai'*, "thing"); and since he used no operational symbols and no notations for further unknowns here (see, however, under *Practica geometriae*), he had to designate them as *denarii secundi* or, as the case might be, *denarii tercii hominis* and take the trouble to carry them through the entire problem. For most of the problems Leonardo provided two or more methods of solution.

An example of the "giving and taking" type is the following, in which the system named above—(1) $x + 7 = 5 \cdot (y - 7)$; (2) $7 \cdot (x - 5) = y + 5$—is involved. First, $x + y$ is presented as a line segment; at the point of contact $y = 7$ and $x = 5$ is marked off along both sides. Then the segment $y - 7$ (or $x - 5$) is equal to 1/6 (or 1/8) of the whole segment $x + y$, and together, therefore, the two segments equal $7/24 \cdot (x + y)$. The further solution is achieved by means of the simple false position $x + y = 24$. There follows still another algebraic solution, this one using the *regulae rectae.* First, $y - 7$ is designated as *res;* then (1) $x = 5$ *res* $- 7$ and (2) *res* $+ 12 = 7 \cdot (5$ *res* $- 12)$.[13]

In some cases the problem is not solvable because of mutually contradictory initial conditions. In other cases the problem is called *insolubilis, incongruum,* or *inconveniens,*[14] unless one accepts a "debit" as a solution. Leonardo is here thinking of a negative number, with which he also makes further calculations. Our operations $22 + (-9) = 22 - 9$ and $-1 + 11 = +10$ he represents with *adde denarios,* as 22 *cum debito secundi* (=9) *scilicet extrahe* 9 *de* 22 and *debitum primi* (= −1) *cum bursa* (=11) *erunt* 10.[15]

Section 4 (chapters 14 and 15; *Scritti,* I, 352–387). Leonardo here shows himself to be a master in the application of algebraic methods and an outstanding student of Euclid. Chapter 14, which is devoted to calculations with radicals, begins with a few formulas of general arithmetic. Called "keys" (*claves*), they are taken from book II of Euclid's *Elements.* Leonardo explicitly says that he is forgoing any demonstrations of his own since they are all proved there. The fifth and sixth propositions of book II are especially important; from them, he said, one could derive all the problems of the *Aliebra* and the *Almuchabala.* Square and cube roots are taught numerically according to the Indian-Arabic algorithm, which in fact corresponds to the modern one.

Leonardo also knew the procedure of adding zeros to the radicands in order to obtain greater exactness; actually, this had already been done by Johannes Hispalensis (*fl.* 1135–1153) and al-Nasawī (*fl. ca.* 1025). Next, examples are given that are illustrative of the ancient methods of approximation. For $\sqrt{A} = \sqrt{a^2 + r}$ the first approximation is $a_1 = a + r/2a$. With $r_1 = a_1^2 - A$, the second approximation is then $a_2 = a_1 - r_1/2a_1$. With the cube root $\sqrt[3]{A} = \sqrt[3]{a^3 + r}$, the first approximation is

$$a_1 = a + \frac{r}{(a+1)^3 - a^3} = a + \frac{r}{3a^2 + 3a + 1}.$$

For a second approximation Leonardo now set $r_1 = A - a_1^3$ and

$$a_2 = a_1 + \frac{r_1}{3a_1 \cdot (a+1)}.$$

He was no doubt thinking of this further approximation when he spoke of his own achievement,[16] for the first approximation was already known to al-Nasawī. The chapter then goes on systematically to carry out complete operations with Euclidean irrationals. There are expressions such as

$$a \pm \sqrt{b}, \quad \sqrt{a} \pm \sqrt{b}, \quad \sqrt{a} \cdot \sqrt{b}, \quad \sqrt{a} \cdot \sqrt[4]{b},$$

$$\sqrt[4]{a} \cdot \sqrt[4]{b}, \quad \sqrt[4]{a} \pm \sqrt[4]{b}, \quad (a + \sqrt{b}) \cdot (c \pm \sqrt{d}),$$

$$(a + \sqrt[4]{b}) \cdot (\sqrt{c} \pm \sqrt[4]{d}), \quad \frac{a - \sqrt{b}}{\sqrt{c} + \sqrt{d}}, \quad \sqrt{a + \sqrt{b}},$$

$$\frac{a}{b + \sqrt{c} + \sqrt[4]{d}}, \quad \sqrt[3]{a} + \sqrt[3]{b}.$$

The proof, which is never lacking, of the correctness of the calculations is presented geometrically. On one occasion the numbers are represented as line segments, for example, in the computation of

$$4 + \sqrt[4]{10} = \sqrt{16 + \sqrt{10} + 8 \cdot \sqrt[4]{10}},$$

where proposition 4 of book II of the *Elements* is used as a "key." On the other hand, the proof is made by means of rectangular surfaces. An example is $\sqrt{4 + \sqrt{7}} + \sqrt{4 - \sqrt{7}} = \sqrt{14}$. Here $(4 + \sqrt{7})$ is conceived as the area of a square, to which at one corner, through the elongation of the two intersecting sides, a square of area $(4 - \sqrt{7})$ is joined. Thus $\sqrt{4 + \sqrt{7}} + \sqrt{4 - \sqrt{7}}$ is the side of a larger square, which consists of the squares $4 + \sqrt{7}$ and $4 - \sqrt{7}$ and the two rectangles each equal to $\sqrt{4 + \sqrt{7}} \cdot \sqrt{4 - \sqrt{7}}$.

With respect to mathematical content Leonardo does not surpass his Arab predecessors. Nevertheless, the richness of the examples and of their methodical arrangement, as well as the exact proofs, are to be emphasized. At the end of chapter 15, which is divided into three sections, one sees particularly clearly what complete control Leonardo had over the geometrical as well as the algebraic methods for solving quadratic equations and with what skill he could use them in applied problems. The first section is concerned with proportions and their multifarious transformations. In one problem, for example, it is given that (1) $6 : x = y : 9$ and (2) $x + y = 21$. From (1) it is determined that $xy = 54$; then, using Euclid II, 5,

$$\left(\frac{x - y}{2}\right)^2 = \left(\frac{21}{2}\right)^2 - 54$$

and

$$x - y = 15.$$

From this follow the solutions 3 and 18.[17] The end points of the segments are denoted by letters of the alphabet (*abgd*$\cdots$ or *abcd*$\cdots$); for example, *.a.b* signifies a segment. Leonardo, however, also speaks about the numbers *a.b.c.d.,* by which he means $(ab) \cdot (cd)$. Sometimes, though, only a single letter is given for the entire segment.

The second section first presents applications of the Pythagorean theorem, such as the ancient Babylonian problem of a pole leaning against a wall and the Indian problem of two towers of different heights. On the given line joining them (i.e., their bases) there is a spring which shall be equally distant from the tops of the towers. The same problem was solved in chapter 13 by the method of false position. Many different types of problems follow, such as the solution of an indeterminate equation $x^2 + y^2 = 25$, given that $3^2 + 4^2 = 25$; or problems of the type *de viagiis,* in which the merchant makes the same profit on each of his journeys. Geometric and stereometric problems are also presented; thus, for example, the determination of the amount of water running out of a receptacle when various bodies, including a sphere (with $\pi = 3\frac{1}{7}$), are sunk in.

The third section contains algebraic quadratic problems (*questiones secundum modum algebre*). First, with reference made to "Maumeht," i.e., to al-Khwārizmī, the six normal forms $ax^2 = bx$, $ax^2 = c$, $bx = c$, $ax^2 + bx = c$, $ax^2 + c = bx$ (here Leonardo is acquainted with both solutions), and $ax^2 = bx + c$ are introduced; they are then exactly computed in numerous, sometimes complicated, examples. Frequently what is sought is the factorization of a number, usually 10, for example,

$$\frac{x}{10 - x} + \frac{10 - x}{x} = \sqrt{5}.$$

Another problem is $\sqrt{8x} \cdot \sqrt{3x} + 20 = x^2$, and still another is $x^2 - 2x - 4 = \sqrt{8x^2}$. Here Leonardo represents x^2 as a square divided into three rectangular parts: $\sqrt{8x^2}$, $2x$, and 4. With the aid of Euclid II, 6 he then obtains $x = \sqrt{7 + \sqrt{8}} + (1 + \sqrt{2})$. Since in the problem a "fortune" (x^2 = avere) was sought, the final solution is $x^2 = 10 + 2 \cdot \sqrt{8} + \sqrt{116 + 40 \cdot \sqrt{8}}$. Leonardo also includes equations of higher degrees that can be reduced to quadratics. For example, it is given that (1) $y = 10/x$; (2) $z = y^2/x$; and (3) $z^2 = x^2 + y^2$. This leads to $x^8 + 100x^4 = 10{,}000$. The numerical examples are taken largely from the algebra of al-Khwārizmī and al-Karajī,[18] frequently even with the same numerical values. In this fourth section of the *Liber abbaci* there also appear further names for the powers of the unknowns.

When several unknowns are involved, then (along with *radix* and *res* for x) a third unknown is introduced as *pars* ("part," Arabic, *qasm*); and sometimes the sum of two unknowns is designated as *res.* For x^2, the names *quadratus, census,* and *avere* ("wealth," Arabic, *māl*)[19] are employed; for x^3, *cubus;* for x^4, *census de censu* and *censuum census;* and for x^6, *cubus cubi.* The constant term is called *numerus, denarius,* or *dragma.*

Practica geometriae (*Scritti,* II, 1–224). This second work by Leonardo, which he composed in 1220 or 1221, between the two editions of the *Liber abbaci,* is dedicated to the Magister Dominicus mentioned above. Of the nine extant manuscripts one is in Rome, which Boncompagni used, and two are in Paris.[20] In this work Leonardo does not wish to present only measurement problems for the layman; in addition, for those with scientific interests, he considers geometry according to the method of proof. Therefore, the models are, on the one hand, Hero and the *Agrimensores,* and Euclid and Archimedes on the other. Leonardo had studied the *Liber embadorum* of Plato of Tivoli (1145) especially closely and took from it large sections and individual problems with the same numerical values. This work by Plato was a translation of the geometry of Savasorda (Abraham bar Hiyya), written in Hebrew, which in turn reproduced Arabic knowledge of the subject.

The *Practica* is divided into eight chapters (*distinctiones*), which are preceded by an introduction. In the latter the basic concepts are explained, as are the postulates and axioms of Euclid (including the spurious axioms 4, 5, 6, and 9) and the linear and surface measures current in Pisa.[21] The first chapter presents, in connection with the surfaces of rectangles, examples of the multiplication of segments, each of which is given in a sum of various units (rod, foot, ounce, etc.). The propositions of book II of the *Elements* are also recalled. The second chapter and the fifth chapter treat, as a preparation for the following problems, square and cube roots and calculation with them in a manner similar to that of the *Liber abbaci.* Next, the duplications of the cube by Archytas, Philo of Byzantium, and Plato, which are reported by Eutocius, are demonstrated, without reference to their source. The solutions of Plato and Archytas, Leonardo took from the *Verba filiorum* of the Banū Mūsā, a work translated by Gerard of Cremona. That of Philo appears also in Jordanus de Nemore's *De triangulis,* and probably both Leonardo and Jordanus took it from a common source. (See M. Clagett, *Archimedes in the Middle Ages,* I, 224, 658–660.) The third chapter provides a treatment with exact demonstrations of the calculation of segments and surfaces of plane figures: the triangle, the square, the rectangle, rhomboids (*rumboides*), trapezoids (*figurae quae habent capita abscisa*), polygons, and the circle; for the circle, applying the Archimedean polygon of ninety-six sides, π is determined as $864:275 \sim 3.141818 \cdots$. In addition, Leonardo was acquainted with quadrilaterals possessing a reentrant angle (*figura barbata*) in which a diagonal falls outside the figure.

Many of the problems lead to quadratic equations, for which the formulas of the normal forms are used. They are given verbally. Hence, for example, in the problem $4x - x^2 = 3$, we are told: If from the sum of the four sides the square surface is subtracted, then three rods remain. Attention is also drawn here to the double solution. Along with this, Leonardo gives practical directions for the surveyor and describes instrumental methods, such as can be used in finding the foot of the altitude of a triangular field or in the computation of the projection of a field lying on a hillside. Among the geodetic instruments was an archipendulum. With the help of it and a surveyor's rod, the horizontal projections of straight lines lying inclined on a hillside could be measured. For the surveyor who does not understand the Ptolemaic procedure of determining half-chords from given arcs, appropriate instructions and a table of chords are provided. This is the only place where the term *sinus versus arcus,* certainly borrowed from Arabic trigonometry, appears. The fourth chapter is devoted to the division of surfaces; it is a reworking of the *Liber embadorum,* which ultimately derives from Euclid's lost *Book on Divisions of Figures;* the latter can be reconstructed (see Archibald) from the texts of Plato of Tivoli and of Leonardo and from that of an Arabic version. In the sixth chapter Leonardo discusses volumes, including those of the regular polyhedrons, in connection with which he refers to the propositions of book XIV of Euclid. The seventh chapter contains the calculation of the heights of tall objects, for example, of a tree, and gives the rules of surveying based on the similarity of triangles; in these cases the angles are obtained by means of a quadrant.

The eighth chapter presents what Leonardo had termed "geometrical subtleties" (*subtilitates*) in the preface to the *Liber abbaci.* Among those included is the calculation of the sides of the pentagon and the decagon from the diameter of circumscribed and inscribed circles; the inverse calculation is also given, as well as that of the sides from the surfaces. There follow two indeterminate problems: $a^2 + 5 = b^2$ and $c^2 - 10 = d^2$. The *Liber quadratorum* treats a similar problem: $a^2 + 5 = b^2$, together with $a^2 - 5 = c^2$. Finally, to complete the section on equilateral triangles, a rectangle and a square are inscribed in such a triangle and their sides are algebraically calculated, with the solution given in the sexagesimal system.

Flos (*Scritti,* II, 227–247). The title of this work, which—like two following ones—is preserved in a Milanese manuscript of 1225, is *INCIPIT flos Leonardi bigoli pisani super solutionibus quarumdam questionum ad numerum et ad geometriam vel ad utrumque pertinentium.* Sent to Frederick II, it contains the elaboration of questions that Master Johannes of Palermo posed in the emperor's presence in Pisa. The work had been requested by Cardinal Raniero Capocci da Viterbo; Leonardo, moreover, provided him with additional problems of the same type. For the first problem (involving the equations $x^2 + 5 = y^2$ and $x^2 - 5 = z^2$) only the solution is presented; it is treated in the *Liber quadratorum.* The second question that Master Johannes had posed concerns the solution of the cubic equation $x^3 + 2x^2 + 10x = 20$. Leonardo, who knew book X of the *Elements* thoroughly, demonstrates that the solution can be neither a whole number, nor a fraction, nor one of the Euclidean irrational magnitudes. Consequently, he seeks an approximate solution. He gives it in sexagesimal form as $1° \, 22' \, 7'' \, 42''' \, 33^{IV} \, 4^{V} \, 40^{VI}$, the 40 being too great by about 1 1/2. We are not told how the result was found. We know only that the same problem appears in the algebra of al-Khayyāmī,[22] where it is solved by means of the intersection of a circle and a hyperbola. One may suppose that the solution follows from the Horner method, which was known to the Chinese and the Arabs.

Next Leonardo presents a series of indeterminate linear problems. If the first of these (*tres homines pecuniam communem habentes*),[23] which had already been solved by various methods in the *Liber abbaci,* was really posed by Master Johannes, then he must have taken it from the algebra of al-Karajī.[24] The following examples are well-known from the *Liber abbaci* as "the found purse" and "one alone cannot buy" problems. Here, too, negative solutions are given. In one problem with six unknowns, one of them is chosen arbitrarily, while *causa* and *res* are taken for two of the others.

Letter to Master Theodorus (undated; *Scritti,* II, 247-252). The principal subject of the letter is the "problem of the 100 birds," which Leonardo had already discussed in the *Liber abbaci.* This time, however, Leonardo develops a general method for the solution of indeterminate problems. A geometrical problem follows that is reminiscent of the conclusion of the *Practica geometriae.* A regular pentagon is to be inscribed in an equilateral triangle. Leonardo's treatment is a model for the early application of algebra in geometry. The solution is carried through to the point where a quadratic equation is reached, and then an approximate value is determined—again sexagesimally. The letter concludes with a linear problem with five unknowns; instead of a logically constructed calculation, however, only a mechanical formula is given.

Liber quadratorum (*Scritti,* II, 253-279). This work, composed in 1225, is a first-rate scientific achievement and shows Leonardo as a major number theorist. Its subject, which had already appeared among the Arabs[25] and was touched upon at the end of the *Practica geometriae* and in the introduction to the *Flos,* is the question, proposed by Master Johannes, of finding the solution of two simultaneous equations $x^2 + 5 = y^2$ and $x^2 - 5 = z^2$, or $y^2 - x^2 = x^2 - z^2 = 5$. The problem itself does not appear until late in the text; before that Leonardo develops propositions for the determination of Pythagorean triples. He knows that the sum of the odd numbers yields a square. He first considers the odd numbers from 1 to $(a^2 - 2)$ for odd a; the sum is $\left(\frac{a^2-1}{2}\right)^2$. If a^2 is added to this expression, then another square results, $\left(\frac{a^2+1}{2}\right)^2$. For even a the corresponding relation is

$$\left[1 + 3 + \cdots \left(\frac{a^2}{2}\right) - 3\right] + \left[\frac{a^2}{2} - 1 + \frac{a^2}{2} + 1\right] = \left[\left(\frac{a}{2}\right)^2 + 1\right]^2.$$

Leonardo was acquainted with still further number triples, such as the Euclidean: $2pq, p^2 - q^2, p^2 + q^2$; and he had already given another one in the *Liber abbaci.*[26]

He obtains still more triples in the following manner: if $(a^2 + b^2)$ and $(x^2 + y^2)$ are squares and if, further, $a:b \neq x:y$ and $a:b \neq y:x$, then it is true that $(a^2 + b^2) \cdot (x^2 + y^2) = (ax + by)^2 + (bx - ay)^2 = (ay + bx)^2 + (by - ax)^2$. The problem was known to Diophantus, and a special case exists in a cuneiform text from Susa. Next Leonardo introduces a special class of numbers: $n = ab \cdot (a + b) \cdot (a - b)$ for even $(a + b)$, and $n = 4\,ab \cdot (a + b) \cdot (a - b)$ for odd $(a + b)$. He names such a number *congruum* and demonstrates that it must be divisible by 24. He finds that $x^2 + h$ and $x^2 - h$ can be squares simultaneously only if h is a *congruum.* For $a = 5$ and $b = 4$, $h = 720 = 5 \cdot 12^2$. The problem now, therefore, is to obtain two differences of squares $y^2 - x^2 = x^2 - z^2 = 720$. He determines that $2401 - 1681 = 1681 - 961$, or $49^2 - 41^2 = 41^2 - 31^2$. Following division by 12^2 he gets

$$\left(3\frac{5}{12}\right)^2 + 5 = \left(4\frac{4}{12}\right)^2$$

and

$$\left(3\frac{5}{12}\right)^2 - 5 = \left(2\frac{7}{12}\right)^2.$$

One does not learn how Leonardo obtains the squares 961, 1681, and 2401; however, one can ascertain it from a procedure in Diophantus.[27] Leonardo then proves a further series of propositions in number theory, such as that a square cannot be a *congruum,* that $x^2 + y^2$ and $x^2 - y^2$ cannot simultaneously be squares, that $x^4 - y^4$ cannot be a square, etc. Next Leonardo considers expressions such as the following: $x + y + z + x^2$, $x + y + z + x^2 + y^2$, and $x + y + z + x^2 + y^2 + z^2$. They are all to be squares and they are to hold simultaneously. This was another of Master Theodorus' questions. In the questions treated in the *Liber quadratorum,* Leonardo was long without a successor.

In surveying Leonardo's activity, one sees him decisively take the role of a pioneer in the revival of mathematics in the Christian West. Like no one before him he gave fresh consideration to the ancient knowledge and independently furthered it. In arithmetic he showed superior ability in computations. Moreover, he offered material to his readers in a systematic way and ordered his examples from the easier to the more difficult. His use of the chain rule in the "Rule of Three" is a new development; and in the casting out of nines he no longer finds the remainder solely by division, but also employs the sum of digits. His rules for factoring numbers and the formation of perfect numbers are especially noteworthy, as is the recurrent series in the "rabbit problem." He treated indeterminate equations of the first and second degrees in a manner unlike that of anyone before him; ordinarily he confines himself to whole-number solutions—in contrast with Diophantus—where such are required. In geometry he demonstrates, unlike the *Agrimensores*, a thorough mastery of Euclid, whose mathematical rigor he is able to recapture, and he understands how to apply the new methods of algebra to the solution of geometric problems. Moreover, in his work a new concept of number seems to be emerging, one that recognizes negative quantities and even zero as numbers. Thus, on one occasion[28] he computes $360 - 360 = 0$ and $0:2 = 0$. Especially to be emphasized is his arithmetization of the Euclidean propositions and the employment of letters as representatives for the general number.

Leonardo's Sources. Early in his youth Leonardo already possessed the usual knowledge of a merchant of his time, as well as that preserved from the Roman tradition (abacus, surveying, formulas, etc.). Then came his journeys. What he absorbed on them cannot in most cases be determined in detail. The knowledge of the Greeks could have reached him either from the already existing Latin translations of the Arabic treatments or in Constantinople, where he had been. One can, to be sure, establish where individual problems and methods first appear, but one cannot decide whether what is involved is the recounting of another's work or an original creation of Leonardo's. The only clear cases are those in which a problem is presented with the same numerical values or when the source itself is named.

Leonardo is fully versed in the mathematics of the Arabs; for example, he writes mixed numbers with the whole numbers on the right. Algebra was available to him in the translations of the works of al-Khwārizmī by Adelard of Bath, Robert of Chester, and Gerard of Cremona or in the treatment by Johannes Hispalensis. The numerical examples are frequently taken directly from the algebra of al-Khwārizmī or from the *Liber embadorum* of Plato of Tivoli, e.g., the paradigm $x^2 + 10x = 39$. The calculation with irrationals and the relevant examples correspond to those in the commentary on Euclid by al-Nayrīzī (Anaritius), which Gerard of Cremona had translated. Countless problems are taken, in part verbatim, from the writings of Abu-Kāmil and of al-Karajī. The cubic equation in the *Flos* stems from al-Khayyāmī. Leonardo readily refers to the Arabs and to their technical words, such as *regula elchatayn* (double false position), *numerus asam* (the prime number), and *figura cata* (which he uses in connection with the chain rule); this is the "figure of transversals" in the theorem of Menelaus of Alexandria.

The geometry of the Greeks had become known through the translations from the Arabic of Euclid's *Elements* by Adelard of Bath, Hermann of Carinthia, and Gerard of Cremona, through al-Nayrīzī's commentary, and perhaps to some extent through the anonymous twelfth-century translation of the *Elements* from the Greek (see *Harvard Studies in Classical Philology,* **71** [1966], 249–302); for the measurement of circles there existed the translations of Archimedes' work by Plato of Tivoli and Gerard of Cremona.[29] For the geometric treatment of the cone and sphere, of the measurement of the circle and triangle (with Hero's formula), and of the insertion of two proportional means, the *Verba filiorum* of the Banū Mūsā was available in Gerard of Cremona's translation and was used extensively by Leonardo. On the other hand, problems from the arithmetic of Diophantus could have come only from Arabic mathematics or from Byzantium. On this subject Leonardo had obtained from the "most learned Master Muscus" a complicated problem of the type "one alone cannot buy," which is also represented in Diophantus. (That Leonardo actually had access to the Greek is shown by his rendering of ῥητοί as "riti.") Other problems that point to Byzantium are those of the type "giving and taking" and the "well problems," which had already appeared in the arithmetical epigrams of *The Greek Anthology*.

Leonardo also includes problems whose origin lies in China and India, such as the *Ta yen* rules, remainder problems, the problem of the "100 birds," and others. Concerning the course of their transmission, nothing definitive can be said. Nevertheless, they were most likely (like the "100 birds" problem found in Abū Kāmīl) transmitted through the Arabs. Problems that appeared in ancient Babylonia (quadratic equations, Pythagorean number triples) or in Egypt (unit fraction calculations, "the seven old women") had been borrowed from the Greeks.

Influence. With Leonardo a new epoch in Western mathematics began; however, not all of his ideas were immediately taken up. Direct influence was exerted only by those portions of the *Liber abbaci* and of the *Practica* that served to introduce Indian-Arabic numerals and methods and contributed to the mastering of the problems of daily life. Here Leonardo became the teacher of the masters of computation (the *maestri d'abbaco*) and of the surveyors, as one learns from the *Summa* of Luca Pacioli, who often refers to Leonardo. These two chief works were copied from the fourteenth to the sixteenth centuries. There are also extracts of the *Practica,* but they are confined to the chapters on plane figures and surveying problems; they dispense with exact proofs and with the *subtilitates* of the eighth chapter.

Leonardo was also the teacher of the "Cossists," who took their name from the word *causa,* which was used for the first time in the West by Leonardo in place of *res* or *radix.* His alphabetical designation for the general number or coefficient was first improved by Viète (1591), who used consonants for the known quantities and vowels for the unknowns.

Many of the problems treated in the *Liber abbaci,* especially some of the puzzle problems of recreational arithmetic, reappeared in manuscripts and then in printed arithmetics of later times: e.g., the problem types known as "giving and taking," "hare and hound," "horse buying," "the found purse," "number guessing," "the twins' inheritance," and the indeterminate problem of the "100 birds," which reappeared as the "rule of the drinkers" (*regula coecis, regula potatorum*) and whose solution Euler established in detail in his algebra (1767). Cardano, in his *Artis arithmeticae tractatus de integris,* mentions appreciatively Leonardo's achievements when he speaks of Pacioli's *Summa.* One may suppose, he states, that all our knowledge of non-Greek mathematics owes its existence to Leonardo, who, long before Pacioli, took it from the Indians and Arabs.[30]

In his more advanced problems of number theory, especially in the *Liber quadratorum,* Leonardo at first had no successor. This situation lasted until the work of Diophantus became available in the original text and was studied and edited by Bachet de Méziriac (1621); he, and then Fermat, laid the foundation for modern number theory. Leonardo, however, remained forgotten. Commandino's plan to edit the *Practica* was not carried out. While the historians Heilbronner (1742) and Montucla (1758) showed their ignorance of Leonardo's accomplishments, Cossali (1797) placed him once more in the proper light; however, since the texts themselves could not be found, Cossali had to rely on what was available in Pacioli. It is thanks to Libri and Boncompagni that all five of Leonardo's works are again available.

NOTES

1. In Italian his title is *deputato della patria pubblico* (Biblioteca Magliabechiana, Florence, Palchetto III, no. 25) and *pubblico cancelliere* (Biblioteca Comunale, Siena, L.IV.21).
2. *Scritti,* I, 1: "quasi errorem computavi respectu modi indorum."
3. *Ibid.:* "quedam etiam ex subtilitatibus euclidis geometrice artis apponens."
4. On the dating, see Cantor, *Vorlesungen über Geschichte der Mathematik,* II, 41.
5. Illustration in Arrighi, *Leonardo Fibonacci,* p. 15.
6. Boncompagni, *Intorno ad alcune opere di Leonardo Pisano,* p. 248.
7. *Ibid.,* p. 246: "ideo ipsum X^m librum glosare incepi, reducens intellectum ipsius ad numerum qui in eo per lineas et superficies demonstratur."
8. He should "hold the numbers in his hand" ("retinere in manu," *Scritti,* I, 7). Thus the student "should bring memory and understanding into harmony with the hands and the numerals" (*Scritti,* I, 1).
9. Youschkevitch, *Geschichte der Mathematik im Mittelalter,* p. 377; Vogel, "Zur Geschichte der linearen Gleichungen mit mehreren Unbekannten."
10. See Vogel, *Ein byzantinisches Rechenbuch des frühen 14. Jahrhunderts,* p. 157.
11. See Cantor, *op. cit.,* p. 26.
12. *Scritti,* I, 318: "adpropinquacio veritati."
13. *Ibid.,* 191: "una res et denarii 12 sunt septuplum quinque rerum et de denariis 12."
14. *Ibid.,* 228, 351.
15. *Ibid.,* 228, 352.
16. *Ibid.,* 378: "inveni hunc modum reperiendi radices."
17. *Ibid.,* 396.
18. A list of the common examples is in Woepke, *Extrait du Fakhrī, Traité d'algèbre par Aboū Bekr Mohammed ben Alhaçan Alkarkhī,* p. 29.
19. *Scritti,* I, 442 ff.
20. See Libri, *Histoire des sciences mathématiques en Italie,* II, 305.
21. See Arrighi, *op. cit.,* p. 18.
22. See Woepke, *L'algèbre d'Omar Alkayyāmī,* p. 78.
23. See Cantor, *op. cit.,* pp. 48 f.
24. See Woepke, *Extrait du Fakhrī . . .,* pp. 141 ff.
25. See Youschkevitch, *op. cit.,* p. 235.
26. *Scritti,* I, 402. The example there involves $x^2 + y^2 = 41$.
27. See Ver Eecke, *Léonard de Pise,* p. 44.
28. *Scritti,* I, 296.
29. See Clagett, *Archimedes in the Middle Ages,* I, *The Arabo-Latin Tradition,* chs. 1, 2.
30. G. Cardano, *Opera,* X (Lyons, 1663), 118, col. 2.
31. See Loria, *Storia delle matematiche,* I, 383.

BIBLIOGRAPHY

I. ORIGINAL WORKS. The only complete edition of Leonardo's works is *Scritti di Leonardo Pisano,* B. Boncompagni, ed., 2 vols. (Rome, 1857–1862). Earlier, G. Libri, in his *Histoire des sciences mathématiques en Italie,* 4 vols. (Paris, 1838–1841), published the introduction and ch. 15 of *Liber abbaci* (II, note 1, 287 ff.; note 3, 307 ff.) and the introduction of *Practica geometriae* (II, note 2, 305 f.). Also, B. Boncompagni published three short works in *Opuscoli di Leonardo Pisano* (Florence, 1852). The *Liber quadratorum* was translated into French by P. Ver Eecke as *Léonard de Pise. Le livre des nombres carrés* (Bruges, 1952). An Italian adaptation of the *Practica geometriae* of 1442 is G. Arrighi, *Leonardo Fibonacci. La pratica di geometria, volgarizzata da Cristofano di Gherardo di Dino cittadino pisano. Dal codice 2186 della Biblioteca Riccardiana di Firenze* (Pisa, 1966). There are also two Italian translations of the introduction to the *Liber abbaci* in the MSS cited in note 1.

II. SECONDARY LITERATURE. General criticism includes B. Boncompagni, "Della vita e delle opere di Leonardo Pisano matematico del secolo decimoterzo," in *Atti dell'Accademia pontificia dei Nuovi Lincei,* **5** (1851–1852), 5–91, 208–246; and *Intorno ad alcune opere di Leonardo Pisano matematico del secolo decimoterzo, notizie raccolte* (Rome, 1854); M. Cantor, *Vorlesungen über Geschichte der Mathematik,* II (Leipzig, 1913), 3–53; G. Loria, "Leonardo Fibonacci," in *Gli scienziati italiani,* Aldo Mieli, ed. (Rome, 1923), pp. 4–12; and *Storia delle matematiche,* I (Turin, 1929), 379–410; G. Sarton, *Introduction to the History of Science,* II (Baltimore, 1931), 611–613; D. E. Smith, *History of Mathematics,* 2 vols. (New York, 1958), *passim.;* J. Tropfke, *Geschichte der Elementarmathematik* (Berlin–Leipzig: I, 3rd ed., 1930; II, 3rd ed., 1933; III, 3rd ed., 1937; IV, 3rd ed., 1939; V, 2nd ed., 1923; VI, 2nd ed., 1924; VII, 2nd ed., 1924), *passim;* and A. P. Youschkevitch, *Geschichte der Mathematik im Mittelalter* (Leipzig, 1964), 371–387, trans. from the Russian (1961).

Special criticism includes the following on the *Liber abbaci:* A. Agostini, "L'uso delle lettere nel *Liber abaci* di Leonardo Fibonacci," in *Bollettino dell'Unione matematica italiana,* 3rd ser., **4** (1949), 282–287; and K. Vogel, "Zur Geschichte der linearen Gleichungen mit mehreren Unbekannten," in *Deutsche Mathematik,* **5** (1940), 217–240.

On *Practica geometriae:* R. C. Archibald, *Euclid's Book on Divisions of Figures* (Cambridge, 1915); M. Curtze, "Der *Liber embadorum* des Abraham bar Chijja Savasorda in der Übersetzung des Plato von Tivoli," in *Abhandlungen zur Geschichte der mathematischen Wissenschaften mit Einschluss ihrer Anwendungen,* **12** (1902), 3–183; and J. Millás-Vallicrosa, *Abraam bar Hiia. Llibre de Geometriá* (Barcelona, 1931).

On *Flos:* F. Woepke, "Sur un essai de déterminer la nature de la racine d'une équation du troisième degré, contenue dans un ouvrage de Léonard de Pise," in *Journal de mathématiques pures et appliquées,* **19** (1854), 401–406.

On the *Liber quadratorum* and number theory: L. E. Dickson, *History of the Theory of Numbers,* vols. I and II (1919–1920), *passim.;* F. Lucas, "Recherches sur plusieurs ouvrages de Léonard de Pise et sur diverses questions d'arithmétique supérieure," in *Bullettino di bibliografia e storia delle scienze matematiche e fisiche,* **10** (1877), 129–193, 239–293; and R. B. McClenon, "Leonardo of Pisa and His 'Liber Quadratorum,'" in *American Mathematical Monthly,* **26** (1919), 1–8.

On the history of the problems: E. Bortolotti, "Le fonti arabe di Leonardo Pisano," in *Memorie. R. Accademia delle scienze dell'Istituto di Bologna,* fis.-mat. cl., 7th ser., **8** (1929–1930), 1–30; Marshall Clagett, *Archimedes in the Middle Ages,* I, *The Arabo-Latin Tradition* (Madison, Wis., 1964), see index under "Leonardo Fibonacci"; P. Cossali, *Origine, trasporto in Italia, primi progressi in essa dell'algebra,* I (Parma, 1797), ch. 5, 96–172; II (Parma, 1799), 41, l. 16; M. Dunton and R. E. Grimm, "Fibonacci on Egyptian Fractions," in *The Fibonacci Quarterly,* **4** (1966), 339–354; V. Sanford, *The History and Significance of Certain Standard Problems in Algebra* (New York, 1927); K. Vogel, *Die Practica des Algorismus Ratisbonensis* (Munich, 1954), index, p. 267; and *Ein byzantinisches Rechenbuch des frühen 14. Jahrhunderts* (Vienna, 1968), pp. 153 ff.; J. Weinberg, *Die Algebra des Abū Kāmil Soǧā'ben Aslam* (Munich, 1935); and F. Woepke, *L'algèbre d'Omar Alkayyāmī* (Paris, 1851); *Extrait du Fakhrī, Traité d'algèbre par Aboū Bekr Mohammed ben Alhaçan Alkarkhī* (Paris, 1853); and "Recherches sur plusieurs ouvrages de Léonard de Pise et sur les rapports qui existent entre ces ouvrages et les travaux mathématiques des Arabes," in *Atti dell'Accademia pontificia dei Nuovi Lincei,* **10** (1856–1857), 236–248; **14** (1860–1861), 211–356.

See also Archibald; Boncompagni, *Opuscoli;* Ver Eecke; and G. Loria, "Leonardo Fibonacci." Sarton, II, 613, cites B. Boncompagni, *Glossarium ex libro abbaci* (Rome, 1855), not known to be in German or Italian libraries.

KURT VOGEL

FIELDS, JOHN CHARLES (*b.* Hamilton, Ontario, Canada, 14 May 1863; *d.* Toronto, Ontario, Canada, 9 August 1932)

Fields was the son of John Charles Fields and Harriet Bowes. His father died when the boy was eleven, and his mother, when he was eighteen. Fields matriculated at the University of Toronto in 1880 and received the B.A. in 1884, with a gold medal in mathematics. Johns Hopkins University awarded him a Ph.D. in 1887. He was appointed professor of mathematics at Allegheny College in 1889 and resigned in 1892 in order to continue his studies in Europe. The next decade found Fields primarily in Paris and Berlin, where associations with Fuchs, Frobenius, Hensel, Schwarz, and Max Planck contributed to his intellectual growth. In 1902 he was appointed special lecturer at the University of Toronto, where he remained until his death. He was appointed research professor in 1923.

Fields's lifelong interest in algebraic functions is first evident in his papers of 1901–1904. His treatment is completely algebraic, without recourse to geometric intuition. The structure has both elegance and generality; its machinery is simple, its parts coordinated.

His involvement in mathematical societies was of an international nature. Fields was elected a fellow of the Royal Society of Canada (1907) and of London (1913). He held various offices in the British and American Associations for the Advancement of Science and the Royal Canadian Institute (of which he was president from 1919 to 1925). He was also a corresponding member of the Russian Academy of Sciences and the Instituto de Coimbra (Portugal). The success of the International Congress of Mathematicians at Toronto in 1924 was due to his untiring efforts as president.

Fields conceived the idea of establishing an international medal for mathematical distinction and provided funds for this purpose in his will. The International Congress of Mathematicians at Zurich in 1932 adopted his proposal, and the Fields Medal was first awarded at the next congress, held at Oslo in 1936.

BIBLIOGRAPHY

I. ORIGINAL WORKS. Fields's writings include "Symbolic Finite Solutions by Definite Integrals of the Equation $d^ny/dx^n = x^my$," in *American Journal of Mathematics,* **8** (1886), 178–179, his Ph.D. thesis; and *Theory of the Algebraic Functions of a Complex Variable* (Berlin, 1906), which establishes a general plan for proving the Riemann-Roch theorem. With the assistance of J. Chapelon, Fields edited the *Proceedings* of the 1924 International Congress of Mathematicians (Toronto, 1928).

Fields's papers are held by the Rare Books and Special Collections Department of the University of Toronto. They include reprints of some of his published speeches and papers, as well as notebooks of lectures and seminars that he attended in Berlin. In addition, the collection contains two bound volumes of notes made by students of the lectures of Weierstrass, *Theorie der elliptischen Functionen* (recorded by A. Darendorff) and *Theorie der hyperelliptischen Functionen* (taken down by an anonymous auditor in the summer semester of 1887).

II. SECONDARY LITERATURE. J. L. Synge, "Obituary Notice of John Charles Fields," in *Obituary Notices of Fellows of the Royal Society of London,* **2** (1933), 129–135 (with portrait), is quite extensive. It contains a full bibliography of Fields's publications (39 titles) and an analysis of the works by his former pupil and colleague, S. Beatty. It also includes the final form of his theorems leading up to and including the proof of the Riemann-Roch theorem. See also Synge, "John Charles Fields," in *Journal of the London Mathematical Society,* **8,** pt. 2 (1933), 153–160. A short statement in *The Royal Canadian Institute Centennial Volume 1849–1949* (Toronto, 1949), William Stewart Wallace, ed., p. 163, gives evidence of Fields's personal dedication to the Royal Canadian Institute.

HENRY S. TROPP

FINE, HENRY BURCHARD (*b.* Chambersburg, Pennsylvania, 14 September 1858; *d.* Princeton, New Jersey, 22 December 1928)

Fine was the son of Lambert Suydam Fine, a Presbyterian minister. After the death of his father, his mother settled in Princeton, where Fine attended the university. During Fine's undergraduate years, his interest in mathematics was awakened by the young instructor George Halstead, who promoted the study of non-Euclidean geometry in the United States. After a year as an assistant in physics and three years as a mathematics tutor at Princeton (1880–1884), Fine, like many of his colleagues, went to Germany to study. At Leipzig he attended Felix Klein's lectures and in 1885 wrote a dissertation on an algebraic geometric problem suggested by Eduard Study, with whom he became friendly. After a summer in Berlin attending Leopold Kronecker's lectures, Fine returned to Princeton, where he taught mathematics until his death. In 1888 Fine married Philena Forbes.

In 1903, Woodrow Wilson's first year in the presidency of Princeton, Fine was appointed dean of the faculty; and when Wilson resigned to run for governor of New Jersey, Fine acted as president of the university until a successor was named in 1912. He then became dean of the departments of science, a post he held until his death. Fine was a founding member of the American Mathematical Society in 1891 and its president in 1911–1912.

Fine's impact on science lies mainly in his support of science and mathematics at Princeton. As dean of the faculty he promoted the mathematician Luther Eisenhart and brought in Oswald Veblen, G. A. Bliss, George Birkhoff, and J. H. M. Wedderburn. A professorship of mathematics and a mathematics building at Princeton were named for Fine.

Among his few contributions to mathematics were an expansion of his dissertation; several papers on differential equations; and, most important, a paper on Newton's method of approximation (1916) and an exposition of a theorem of Kronecker's on numerical equations (1914). Fine was the author of several undergraduate textbooks and an exposition of the number system of algebra.

BIBLIOGRAPHY

For a complete bibliography of Fine's publications and related secondary sources, see "Henry Burchard Fine," in *American Mathematical Society Semicentennial Publication,* I (New York, 1938), 167–169. Also consult Oswald Veblen, "Henry Burchard Fine," in *Bulletin of the American Mathematical Society,* **35** (1929), 726–730.

C. S. FISHER

FINE, ORONCE (*b.* Briançon, France, 20 December 1494; *d.* Paris, France, 6 October 1555)

Fine (Orontius Finaeus Delphinatus) was born in the Dauphiné but spent his scientific career at Paris.[1] His father, François Fine,[2] had attended the University of Paris[3] and practiced medicine in Briançon. Upon his father's death Fine was sent to Paris and was confided to the care of Antoine Silvestre, regent of the Collège de Montaigu and later of the Collège de Navarre. Although he earned his Bachelor of Medicine degree in 1522,[4] his career developed outside the university; in 1531 he was appointed to the chair of mathematics at the recently founded Collège Royal, where he taught until his death.

From 1515 Fine edited astronomical and mathematical writings for printers in Paris and abroad. Among them were Peuerbach's *Theoricae planetarum*, Sacrobosco's *De sphaera* (1516), and Gregor Reisch's *Margarita philosophica* (1535), as well as a tract by his grandfather, Michel Fine, on the plague (1522). He also was responsible for an edition of Euclid's *Elements*, of which he published only the first six books (the manuscript of the seventh book, prepared for the printer, is extant).

Fine's first book (1526) was a treatise on the equatorium, an instrument designed to determine the true positions of the planets. In this work Fine exploited the possibilities of curves traced by points (the diagrams of the equations of center), used to facilitate the placement, with respect to the equant, of the mean apsidal line (*auge*) on the epicycle. These curves, drawn on the basis of lists of the equations of center and of the proportional minutes furnished by the Alphonsine Tables, were a very ingenious innovation. At the same time Francisco Sarzosa composed a treatise on the equatorium with the same innovations.[5] It is difficult to believe that their research was independent, but it is now impossible to establish the proper priority.

Fine wrote four other treatises on the equatorium that are extant in manuscript at the library of the University of Paris (Univ. 149); three treatises are little more than outlines, and the fourth treatise describes an instrument similar to Apian's *Astronomicum Caesareum*, with the planetary instruments bound as a book (each of them simply reproduces the geometric decomposition of the Ptolemaic theory of epicycles).

Fine's further works on astronomical instruments include treatises on the new quadrant (1527, 1534) and on the astrolabe (incomplete manuscript layouts are in Paris lat. 7415 and Univ. 149). These are not innovative and offer only the standard university account. Fine also inserted a treatise on the new quadrant at the end of his work on gnomonics, *De solaribus horologiis et quadrantibus*, which first appeared in 1532 as the concluding section of his *Protomathesis*. The latter consists of four parts, each with its own title page and each separately reprinted: *De solaribus horologiis* has a separate title page dated 1531, but it is not known to exist separately, and it is unlikely that it was distributed by itself. Among the many types of sundials described in this book are a multiple dial and a *navicula*.[6] A very rare ivory *navicula* signed "Opus Orontii F. 1524"—the only scientific instrument certainly attributable to Fine, and perhaps the only one he ever constructed—is in the private Portaluppi collection at Milan.

Besides treatises on instruments, Fine's astronomical work included theoretical writings of a popular nature. These were presented at the two levels of traditional instruction: the elementary one represented by Sacrobosco's *De sphaera*, and the higher one of epicyclic astronomy. The *Cosmographia*, an elementary manual, was first published in Latin as the third part of the *Protomathesis* (1532), with a separate title page dated 1530, and was reprinted several times, both in Latin and French. It includes the description of the fixed celestial sphere used for reference, the essential ideas concerning the astronomy of the *primum mobile* (right and oblique ascensions and the duration of diurnal arcs), and a few brief notions of astronomical geography (climates and terrestrial longitudes and latitudes); but it contains no information on the motions of the planets. The latter were discussed in the *Théorique des cieux* (published anonymously in 1528), which gives a detailed exposition of the Alphonsine epicyclic theory, the first one in French. The brief *Canons . . . touchant l'usage . . . des communs almanachs* (1543) is a succinct explanation of an almanac computed for the meridian of Tübingen (undoubtedly by Johann Stöffler, which exists in editions dated 1531 and 1533).

Although Fine's interest in astronomy extended to astrology, he wrote only minor works on that subject. The *Almanach* of 1529, actually a calendar giving the dates and hours of the new moons in the nineteen-year cycle and the duration of the diurnal arcs, included a short commentary on medical astrology. *De XII coeli domiciliis* (1553) was a complete theory of the celestial houses, important for casting horoscopes. In this work Fine adopted the definition of the houses advocated by Campanus, for whom the divisions of the celestial vault, for a given horizon, are constructed on the equal divisions of its first azimuth and converge to the south and to the north of the horizon; following this definition, the one usually employed on astrolabes, the lines of the celestial houses were projected onto the astrolabe in accordance with circles passing through the points of intersection of the horizon and of the meridian. Fine also gave an original definition of the unequal hours, however, which were no longer the equal divisions of the diurnal arc and of the nocturnal arc, but the equal divisions of the ecliptic computed, at each moment, from its intersection with the horizon.

The result, for the construction of the tympana of the astrolabes, was a highly original plotting of the hourly lines – a geometric locus of these equal divisions when the ecliptic turns about the axis of the earth according to the daily movement. Although no astrolabe is known to have been constructed on the basis of this definition, it did find an application in the astrolabic dial of the planetary clock at the Bibliothèque Ste. Geneviève. The dial expressly refers to Fine, and it has therefore been assumed since the seventeenth century that the clock itself was his work. This is highly improbable.[7] It is virtually certain that the clock dates from the fifteenth century and that about 1553 one of its panels, containing the dial of the hours and the astrolabic dial, was replaced by Fine with a panel designed to illustrate his new conception of the unequal hours. The level of technical competence displayed by the mechanism of this dial is very low, for the *araignée* (the stereographic projection of the celestial vault) completes its revolution in a mean solar day and not in a sidereal day.

While the third and fourth parts of the *Protomathesis* dealt with astronomy, the first two treated arithmetic and geometry. *De arithmetica practica*, the first part, is Fine's only work on arithmetic. In accordance with the traditional schema of medieval arithmetic, the various operations carried out on the numbers were enumerated and described following a plan that distinguished whole numbers, common fractions (*fractiones vulgares*), and natural or sexagesimal fractions. The latter were of particular interest to practitioners of Alphonsine astronomy, since they were the basis of their preferred mathematical tool. Fine made it easier to work with these fractions by providing a *tabula proportionis* (so called because of its aid in computing proportional parts of the equation of the argument), or multiplication table in sexagesimal numeration, similar to the same table by John of Murs or Bianchini. The last book of the *De arithmetica*, on ratios and proportions, developed theorems established by Euclid and Ptolemy.

The two books on geometry (dated 1530 in the *Protomathesis*) treated the subject at a more elementary level. After stating the definitions of plane and solid figures, borrowed from the *Elements*, as well as the Euclidean postulates, Fine discussed the measurement of length, height, and width in the tradition of the treatises on practical geometry, of which one of the most popular aspects was geometrical canons for the use of the astrolabe. To this end he treated the geometric square, the quadrant, the cross-staff (Jacob's staff), and the mirror. The calculation of surfaces and volumes, which was the complement of the measurement of lengths, included that of circular surfaces and volumes. For the latter, Fine computed the ratio of the circumference of the circle to its diameter as 22/7.

Returning to the ratio of circumference to diameter in *De quadratura circuli* (1544), Fine offered what he believed to be a more precise value of π: $\frac{22+2/9}{7}$. In *De circuli mensura*, which follows *De quadratura*, he reduced that ratio to 47/15. Finally, in the posthumous *De rebus mathematicis* (1556), he increased the value slightly to one between the two preceding ones: $3+\frac{11}{78}$. These attempts to determine the true figure were but one aspect of his efforts to solve the quadrature of the circle, for which he examined several solutions. None of them was satisfactory; and Fine was vehemently attacked by some of his contemporaries, notably Pedro Nuñez Salaciense, in *De erratis Orontii Finaei* (1546), and Johannes Buteo (Jean Borrel), in *De quadratura circuli* (1559). It must be acknowledged that Fine's arrogance about his own accomplishments undoubtedly made his errors of logic all the more intolerable to his opponents.

Fine's work in trigonometry scarcely went beyond what was necessary to establish a table of sines: three chapters of book II of *De geometria*, included in the *Protomathesis*, and *De rectis in circuli quadrante subtensis* and *De universali quadrante*, both published in 1542 as appendixes to the first reprinting of *De mundi sphaera* (which had been included in the *Protomathesis*). Although the works of Regiomontanus and Copernicus on this subject were printed during Fine's lifetime, his writings fell entirely within the Ptolemaic tradition. For example, he limited himself to demonstrating the properties that allow successive evaluations of the half chords of arcs starting from the half chords of some other noteworthy arcs. Also, the table of sines that he constructed for intervals of fifteen minutes and a radius of sixty units is very similar to that (for example) of Fusoris.[8] Nevertheless, Fine indicated how his sines, expressed in sexagesimal notation, may be transformed into those given by Regiomontanus, which were calculated with a radius of 60,000 units.

The universal quadrant described in 1542 was the trigonometric quadrant deriving from the eleventh-century *quadrans vetustissimus*. This earlier instrument had been described and commented upon by Apian in his *Instrumentum . . . primi mobilis* (1534). Fine dealt only with the strictly trigonometric uses of the quadrant, determination of the right and versed sines of a given arc—or vice versa—and the products or ratios of two sines. Virtually ignoring the application of its properties to astronomical calculations—a task carried out by J. Bonie and by B. de Solliolis in works that Fine owned[9]—Fine did no more than enumerate these possibilities.

In his Latin thesis of 1890, L. Gallois dealt only with Fine's cartography: a large map of France on four sheets and two cordiform world maps, one of the eastern hemisphere and the other, doubly cordiform, of the northern and southern hemispheres. Gallois held that the world maps were original creations and provided the source of the similar maps executed by Schöner and Apian.[10] This hypothesis is unlikely; and in the absence of an established chronology of these maps, it may be supposed that the relations of dependence were in fact the reverse, for Fine's usual procedure was to elaborate his astronomical works on the basis of the writings of others. This was undoubtedly the case with his map of France, but the scarcity of the surviving documents does not allow its genesis to be reconstructed. Fine's map of France does not truly comprise the grid of the parallels and meridians but, rather, transfers the schema to the margins; the longitudes are computed there from *l'extremité occidentale du monde*, as in the Alphonsine Tables.

Fine's scientific work may be briefly characterized as encyclopedic, elementary, and unoriginal. It appears that the goal of his publications, which ranged in subject from astronomy to instrumental music, was to popularize the university science that he himself had been taught. In this perspective, it is perhaps his works in French (such as *Théorique des cieux*) or the French translations of his works first published in Latin (for instance, *Canons et documents très amples touchant l'usage des communs almanachs* and the *Sphère du monde*) that best illustrate his scientific career.

NOTES

1. There is disagreement as to whether the last letter of his name should be accented. Citing the Latin form Finaeus, bookkeeping records in which the name is spelled Finee, and the bad rhyme of Finé with Dauphiné and *affiné* made by André Thevet, L. Gallois (*De Orontio Finaeo*, 2) opted for the pronunciation Finé. This is the one that has generally been accepted, despite the objections of Dauphinois scholars, who, citing local usage—which ought to decide the question—prefer Fine. The form Finée probably resulted from rendering the Latin form into French. As for Thevet's rhymes, which are very late (1584), their significance is diminished by the fact that a contemporary and close friend of Fine's, Antoine Mizauld, rhymed Fine with *doctrine* in his verses. (See MS Paris fr. 1334, fol. 17.) The date of his birth is specified in an autograph note in MS Paris lat. 7147, fol. ii.
2. See E. Wickersheimer, *Dictionnaire biographique des médecins en France au moyen âge* (Paris, 1936), 553 and 154.
3. There are two MSS of a course on Aristotle given by Jean Hannon and copied by François Fine in 1472–1473 (Paris lat. 6436, 6529); see *Catalogue des manuscrits en écriture latine portant des indications de date, de lieu ou de copiste*, II (Paris, 1962), 341, 353; pl. cli.
4. *Commentaires de la Faculté de médecine de l'Université de Paris*, II, 1516–1560, M.-L. Concasty, ed. (Paris, 1964), 50b, 54a. This is in the series Collection de Documents Inédits sur l'Histoire de France.
5. E. Poulle and Fr. Maddison, "Un équatoire de Franciscus Sarzosius," in *Physis*, **5** (1963), 43–64.
6. D. J. de Solla Price, "The Little Ship of Venice, a Middle English Instrument Tract," in *Journal of the History of Medicine and Allied Sciences*, **15** (1960), 399–407; and Fr. Maddison, *Medieval Scientific Instruments and the Development of Navigational Instruments in the XVth and XVIth Centuries* (Coimbra, 1969), 14. This book is Agrupamento de Estudos de Cartografia Antiga, XXX.
7. D. Hillard and E. Poulle, "Oronce Fine et l'horloge planétaire de la Bibliothèque Sainte-Geneviève"; and E. Poulle, "Les mécanisations de l'astronomie des épicycles, l'horloge d'Oronce Fine," in *Comptes rendus des séances de l'Académie des inscriptions et belles-lettres* (1974), 59–79.
8. E. Poulle, *Un constructeur d'instruments astronomiques au XVe siècle, Jean Fusoris* (Paris, 1963), 75–80. This work is Bibliothèque de l'École Pratique des Hautes Études, IVe sect., fasc. 318.
9. E. Poulle, "Théorie des planètes et trigonométrie au XVe siècle d'après un équatoire inédit, le sexagenarium," in *Journal des savants* (1966), 129–161, esp. 131–132.
10. L. Gallois, *Les géographes allemands de la renaissance* (Paris, 1890), 92–97. This work is Bibliothèque de la Faculté des Lettres de Lyon, XIII.

BIBLIOGRAPHY

I. ORIGINAL WORKS. The list of books published by Fine is difficult to establish, for it involves sorting out many reprintings, some of them only partial, and a number of translations. There are four contemporary lists, three of them inserted in his eds. of Euclid's *Elements* of 1536, 1544, and 1551; the fourth was included by Antoine Mizauld in his ed. of Fine's *De rebus mathematicis* in 1556. All of these lists, however, pose problems. That drawn up by L. Gallois in *De Orontio Finaeo gallico geographo* (Paris, 1890), 71–79, is incomplete and has been superseded by those of R. P. Ross, in his unpublished doctoral dissertation, "Studies on Oronce Fine (1494–1555)" (Columbia University, 1971); and of D. Hillard and E. Poulle, in "Oronce Fine et l'horloge planétaire de la Bibliothèque Sainte-Geneviève," in *Bibliothèque d'humanisme et renaissance*, **33** (1971), 311–351, see 335–351. The latter list is numbered and indexed, and includes MSS. One should consult the latest findings concerning the bibliography in R. P. Ross, "Oronce Fine's Printed Works: Additions to Hillard and Poulle's Bibliography," in *Bibliothèque d'humanisme et renaissance*, **36** (1974), 83–85.

II. SECONDARY LITERATURE. Gallois's *De Orontio Finaeo* has become quite dated and presents an extremely limited picture of Fine's work. Ross's "Studies on Oronce Fine (1494–1555)" deals only with the mathematical works, among which those on astronomy are not included. It does, however, contain a recent bibliography. An overall account of Fine's work is in the exposition catalog of the Bibliothèque Ste.-Geneviève, *Science et astrologie au XVIe siècle, Oronce Fine et son horloge planétaire* (Paris, 1971). See also Richard P. Ross, "Oronce Fine's 'De sinibus libri II': The First Printed Trigonometric Treatise of the French Renaissance," in *Isis*, **66** (1975), 378–386.

EMMANUEL POULLE

FINK (FINCKE), THOMAS (*b.* Flensburg, Denmark [now Germany], 6 January 1561; *d.* Copenhagen, Denmark, 24 April 1656)

The son of Raadmand Jacob Fincke and Anna Thorsmede (who died six days after his birth), Fink studied from 1577 to 1582 in Strasbourg. Afterward he attended many universities: Jena, Wittenberg, Heidelberg (matriculated 6 February 1582), Leipzig (matriculated summer of 1582), Basel (studied medicine in 1583), and Padua (from 6 November 1583 to 1587). This varied education led to his receipt of the M.D. at Basel on 24 August 1587. After three years of traveling through Germany and Austria, Fink became physician-in-ordinary to Duke Philip of Holstein-Gottorp. When Philip died in 1591, Fink was appointed professor of mathematics at Copenhagen, his field of instruction being changed to rhetoric in 1602 and to medicine in 1603. He held high university posts and carried out his duties until only a few years before his death at the age of ninety-five.

Fink's most famous book is the *Geometriae rotundi* (1583), published when he was twenty-two. This important work is divided into fourteen books. The elementary theses on the circle are collected in the four opening books and the remaining books treat trigonometry, the last three being devoted to spherical trigonometry. A central place is occupied by Rheticus' goniometric tables, but here Fink took a step backward, giving the tables for each function separately and always from 0° to 90°, rather than using the complementary character of the functions, as Rheticus had done. In Strasbourg, Fink had been a pupil of the mathematician Dasypodius but seems to have learned mainly astrology from him. He makes it clear that he was an autodidact in mathematics. His inspiration and guide was not Euclid's *Elements*—this work disturbed him—but Ramus' *Geometria* (1569). Therefore the *Geometriae rotundi* is based mainly on Ramus, many proofs being comprehensible only after consulting the *Geometria.* Even the word "rotundum" in Fink's title, meaning both circle and sphere, was introduced by Ramus. Fink also adopted the term "radius" from him and himself introduced such terms as "tangent" and "secans." He devised new formulas, such as the law of tangents, and proved in this work that he was abreast of the mathematics of his time.

The *Geometriae rotundi* was meant as a textbook, since it treats basic formulas and refers the reader to Regiomontanus for more detail. As a textbook it was very influential. Such mathematicians as Lansbergen, Clavius, Napier, and Pitiscus recommended the work and adopted much from it. Fink's other works show his interest in astrology and astronomy. He was in contact with Tycho Brahe and Magini. But never again in a long series of publications did he reach the level of the *Geometriae rotundi.*

BIBLIOGRAPHY

I. ORIGINAL WORKS. For a bibliography see H. Ehrencron-Müller, *Forfatterlexikon omfattende Danmark . . .*, III (Copenhagen, 1926), 46–49; this work does not mention *Methodica tractatio doctrinae sphaericae* (Coburg, 1626); *Theses logicae* (Copenhagen, 1594); C. Ostenfeld, *Oratio in orbitum T. Finckii* (Copenhagen, 1656). Fink's most important works are *Geometriae rotundi libri XIIII* (Basel, 1583); and *Horoscopographia sive de inveniendo stellarum situ astrologia* (Schleswig, 1591), which includes a horoscope of Heinrich Graf von Rantzau.

II. SECONDARY LITERATURE. On Fink or his work, see Niels Nielsen, *Matematikken i Danmark 1528-1800* (Copenhagen, 1912), pp. 69–70; and H. F. Rördam, *Kjöbenhavns Universitets historie fra 1537 til 1621* (Copenhagen, 1873-1877), III, 550-562. On *Geometriae rotundi,* see A. von Braunmühl, *Vorlesungen über Geschichte der Trigonometrie,* I (Leipzig, 1900), 186–193; and J. Tropfke, *Geschichte der Elementar-Mathematik,* vols. IV (Berlin, 1922; new ed., 1940) and V (Berlin, 1923), see index in vol. VII (Berlin, 1927).

J. J. VERDONK

FISHER, RONALD AYLMER (*b*. London, England, 17 February 1890; *d*. Adelaide, Australia, 29 July 1962)

Fisher's father was a prominent auctioneer and the head of a large family; Fisher was a surviving twin. Chronic myopia probably helped channel his youthful mathematical gifts into the high order of conceptualization and intuitiveness that distinguished his mature work. At Cambridge, which he entered in 1909 and from which he graduated in 1912, Fisher studied mathematics and theoretical physics. His early postgraduate life was varied, including working for an investment house, doing farm chores in Canada, and teaching high school. Fisher soon became interested in the biometric problems of the day and in 1919 joined the staff of Rothamsted Experimental Station as a one-man statistics department charged, primarily, with sorting and reassessing a sixty-six-year accumulation of data on manurial field trials and weather records. In the following decade and a half his work there established him as the leading statistician of his era, and early in his tenure he published the epochal *Statistical Methods for Research Workers.*

Meantime, avocationally, Fisher was building a reputation as a top-ranking geneticist. He left Rothamsted in 1933 to become Galton professor of eugenics at University College, London. Ten years later he moved to Cambridge as Balfour professor of genetics. In 1959, ostensibly retired, Fisher emigrated to Australia and spent the last three years of his life working steadily and productively in the Division of Mathematical Statistics of the Commonwealth Scientific and Industrial Research Organization. Innumerable honors came to him, including election to fellowship of the Royal Society in 1929 and knighthood in 1952.

In 1917 Fisher married Ruth Eileen Guinness and, like his own parents, they had eight children—a circumstance that, according to a friend, was "a personal expression of his genetic and evolutionary convictions." Later in life he and Lady Fisher separated. Slight, bearded, eloquent, reactionary, and quirkish, Fisher made a strong impact on all who met him. The geniality and generosity with which he treated his disciples was complemented by the hostility he aimed at his dissenters. His mastery of the elegantly barbed phrase did not help dissolve feuds, and he left a legacy of unnecessary confusion in some areas of statistical theory. Nevertheless, Fisher was an authentic genius, with a splendid talent for intertwining theory and practice. He had a real feel for quantitative experimental data whose interpretation is unobvious, and throughout his career he was a happy and skillful performer on the desk calculator.

Fisher's debut in the world of mathematical statistics was occasioned by his discovery, as a young man, that all efforts to establish the exact sampling distribution of the well-known correlation coefficient had foundered. He tackled the problem in the context of points in an n-dimensional Euclidean space (n being the size of the sample), an original and, as it turned out, highly successful approach. In the following years he applied similar methods to obtain the distributions of many other functions, such as the regression coefficient, the partial and multiple correlation coefficients, the discriminant function, and a logarithmic function of the ratio of two comparable variances. Fisher also tidied up the mathematics and application of two important functions already in the literature: the Helmert-Pearson χ^2 (the sum of squares of a given number of independent standard normal variates, whose distribution is used to test the "goodness of fit" of numerical observations to expectations) and Gosset's z (the ratio of a normal sample mean, measured from a given point, in terms of its sample standard deviation). The latter was modulated by Fisher to the now familiar t, whose frequency distribution provides the simplest of all significance tests. He seized on Gosset's work to centralize the problem of making inferences from small samples, and he went on to erect a comprehensive theory of hypothesis testing.

The idea here was that many biological experiments are tests of a defined hypothesis, with the experimentalist wanting to know whether his results bolster or undermine his theorizing. If we assume, said Fisher in effect, that the scatter of results is a sample from a normal (Gaussian) distribution whose mean (suitably expressed or transformed) is the "null" hypothesis, we can, using the t distribution, compute the "tail" probability that the observed mean is a random normal sample—in much the same way that we can compute the probability of getting, say, seven or more heads in ten tosses of a fair coin. It might be thought that this probability was all an experimentalist would need, since he would subsequently make his own scientific judgment of its significance in the context of test and hypothesis. However, Fisher advocated the use of arbitrary "cutoff" points; specifically, he suggested that if the probability were $<1/20$ but $>1/100$, a weak judgment against the null hypothesis be made, and if the probability were $<1/100$ a strongly unfavorable judgment be made. This convention, helped by the publication of special tables, became popular, and it has often been used blindly. The real value of the discipline lay in its sound probabilistic structure rather than in its decision-making rules. It is noteworthy that other statistical theorists extended Fisher's ideas by introducing the power of a test, that is, its intrinsic ability, in terms of the parameters and distribution functions, to detect a given difference (between the null hypothesis and the observational estimate) at a prearranged probability level; but, for reasons never made plain, Fisher would not sanction this development.

Fisher devised his own extension of significance testing, the remarkable analysis of variance. This was bound in with his novel ideas on the wide subject of the theory of experimental design. He emphasized not merely the desirability but the logical necessity, in the design of an experiment whose results could not be freed from error, of maximizing efficiency (by devices such as blocks and confounding), and of introducing randomization in such a way as to furnish a valid estimate of the residual error. Whereas the time-honored practice in handling several factors had been to vary only one at a time during the experiment, Fisher pointed out that simultaneous variation was essential to the detection of possible interaction between factors, and that this change could be made without extra cost (in terms of experimental size and operational effort). Entrained with these innovations was the use of randomized blocks and Latin squares for the actual disposition of the test units.

Many would subscribe to the thesis that Fisher's contributions to experimental design were the most praiseworthy of all his accomplishments in statistics. It was to facilitate the interpretation of multifactor experiments carried out in the light of his ideas on design that Fisher introduced the analysis of variance (which he had originally devised to deal with hierarchical classification). In this scheme the variances due to different factors in the experiment are screened out and tested separately for statistical significance (that is, for incompatibility with the null hypothesis of "no effect"). The appeal of the analysis has been great, and here again misuses have not been uncommon among uncritical researchers—for example, some have contented themselves with, and even published, analyses of variance unaccompanied by tabulations of the group means to which the significance tests refer. This itself is a tribute, of a sort, to Fisher.

Arising out of his work on the analysis of variance was the analysis of covariance, a scheme in which the regression effect of concomitant nuisance factors could be screened out so as to purify further the significance tests. (For example, in a multifactor physiological experiment the weight of the animals might be a nuisance factor affecting response and calling for elimination or allowance by analysis of covariance.)

An early landmark in the Fisherian revolution was his long paper "On the Mathematical Foundations of Theoretical Statistics" (1922). Convinced that the subject had progressed too haphazardly and lacked a solid mathematical base, he set out to repair the situation. He drew attention to the shortcomings of the method of moments in curve fitting, stressed the importance of exact sampling distributions, and moved toward a realistic view of estimation. Discussing estimation of a parameter, he urged that a "satisfactory statistic" should be consistent (which means, roughly, unbiased), efficient (having the greatest precision), and sufficient (embracing all relevant information in the observations). His making "information" into a technical term, equatable to reciprocal variance, was a useful step (the reuse of the same word, much later, in C. E. Shannon's information theory is allied but not directly comparable).

To appreciate Fisher's handling of estimation theory, we must look upon it as a subdivision of the general problem of induction that has worried theoreticians since Hume's day. In its simplest and oldest form it is the question of how to arrive at a "best" value of a set of observations. Today we unthinkingly take the arithmetic mean, but in fact the conditions under which this procedure can be justified need careful definition. Broadly speaking, the arithmetic mean is usually the maximum likelihood estimate. This term expressed not a wholly new principle but one that Fisher transformed and named. He urged the need to recognize two kinds of uncertainty and proposed that the probability of an event, given a parameter, should be supplemented by the likelihood of a parameter, given an event. Likelihood has similarities to probability, but important differences exist (for instance, its curve cannot be integrated).

At this point, by way of illustration, we may bring in a modified form of one of Fisher's own examples. It concerns a discrete (discontinuous) distribution. We are given four counts, n_1 through n_4, of corn seedlings (each in a different descriptive category) that are hypothesized to arise from a parameter p, as shown below.

Descriptive category (i)	1	2	3	4	Σ
Fractions expected (f_i)	$(2 + p)/4$	$(1 - p)/4$	$(1 - p)/4$	$p/4$	1
Numbers observed (n_i)	1,997	906	904	32	3,839

The problem is to estimate p. Now, by definition, the likelihood, L, will be

$$(1) \qquad L = \prod_{i=1}^{4} f_i^{n_i}.$$

Instead of seeking the maximum of this, we shall find it more convenient to handle the logarithm, which is

$$(2) \quad L' = n_1 \log(2 + p) + (n_2 + n_3) \log(1 - p) + n_4 \log p.$$

Differentiating this expression with respect to p, equating the result to zero, and replacing the n_i with the actual observations yields the quadratic

$$(3) \qquad 3839p^2 + 1655p - 64 = 0,$$

from which we find $\hat{p} = 0.03571$ (the caret is widely employed nowadays to denote "an estimate of"). Therefore, among all possible values of p this is the one most likely to have given rise to the particular tetrad of observed numbers. Fisher now went further and showed that the second derivative of (2) could be equated to the variance of $\hat{p}$. This gives us

$$(4) \quad \text{var}(\hat{p}) = \frac{2p(1-p)(2+p)}{(1+2p)(n_1+n_2+n_3+n_4)}.$$

which, incidentally, is the minimum variance, indicating that the estimate of p is efficient in Fisher's special sense of that term. Substitution of $\hat{p}$ for p in (4) and insertion of the actual n_i, followed by extraction of the square root, gives us the best estimate of the standard error of $\hat{p}$. Thus we can submit $\hat{p} = 0.03571 \pm 0.00584$ as our final result.

Attachment of a standard error to an estimate, as above, is quite old in statistics, and this is yet another matter to which Fisher brought change. He was a pioneer in interval estimation, that is, the specification of numerical probability limits bracketing the point estimate. Fisher's approach is best described in the context of sampling the normal distribution. Imagine such a distribution, with mean μ and variance (second moment) σ^2, both unknown and from which we intend to draw a sample of ten items. Now, in advance of the sampling, various statements can be made about this (as yet) unknown mean, m. One such is

$$(5) \quad P\left(m < \mu - \frac{1.96}{\sqrt{10}}\,\sigma\right) = P\left(m > \mu + \frac{1.96}{\sqrt{10}}\,\sigma\right) = 0.025,$$

the factor 1.96 being taken from a table of the partial integrals of the normal function. The statement is formal, although without practical value. We draw the sample, finding, say, $m = 8.41$ with a standard deviation of $s = 6.325$; then, according to Fisher, a probability statement analogous to (5) can be cast into this form:

$$(6) \quad P\left(\mu < m - \frac{2.23}{\sqrt{10}}\,s\right) = P\left(\mu > m + \frac{2.23}{\sqrt{10}}\,s\right) = 0.025 \equiv P(\mu < 3.95) = P(\mu > 12.87) = 0.025,$$

the factor 2.23 being taken from the t table in the Gosset-Fisher theory of small samples.

Strictly speaking, this is dubious in that it involves a probable location of a parameter, which, by definition, is fixed—and unknown. But, said Fisher, the observed values of m and s have changed the "logical status" of μ, transforming it into a random variable with a "well-defined distribution." Another way of stating (6) is that the values 3.95–12.87 are the "fiducial limits" within which μ can be assigned with probability 0.95. There is no doubt that this is a credibility statement with which an experimentalist untroubled by niceties of mathematical logic should be satisfied. And indeed it might be thought that the notion of fiducialism could be rationalized in terms of a different definition of probability (leaning on credibility rather than orthodox limiting frequency). But Fisher always insisted that probability "obtained by way of the fiducial argument" was orthodox. The doctrine landed Fisher and the adherents of fiducialism in a logical morass, and the situation was worsened by the historical accident that an allied concept, the theory of confidence limits, was introduced by Jerzy Neyman about the same time (*ca.* 1930). Although it, too, had weaknesses, Neyman's theory, as the more mathematically rigorous and widely applicable, was espoused by many statisticians in preference to its rival. Battle lines were drawn, and the next few decades witnessed an extraordinarily acrimonious and indecisive fight between the schools. Fiducialism is still being explored by mathematical statisticians.

This by no means exhausts Fisher's contributions to statistics—topics such as multivariate analysis, bioassay, time series, contingency tables, and the logarithmic distribution are others that come to mind—and in fact it would be hard to do so, if only because he sometimes gave seminal ideas to colleagues to work out under their own names. We must end with some reference to another subject on which Fisher left a deep mark: genetics. In his young manhood natural selection and heredity were in a state of renewed ferment. The rediscovery in 1900 of Mendel's splendid work on particulate inheritance threw discredit not only on Karl Pearson's elaborate researches into blending inheritance but also on Darwinism itself, believed by some to be incompatible with Mendelism. Fisher thought otherwise, and in 1918 he published a paper, "The Correlation Between Relatives on the Supposition of Mendelian Inheritance," that brought powerful new mathematical tools to bear on the issue and that eventually swung informed opinion over to his views—which were, in brief, that blending inheritance is the cumulative effect of a large number of Mendelian factors that are individually insignificant. (This was to blossom into the modern discipline of biometric genetics, although Fisher himself never made any important contributions thereto.)

Fisher came to regard natural selection as a study in its own right, with evolution as but one of several sequelae. His work on the phenomenon of dominance was outstanding. He early pointed out that correlations between relatives could be made to furnish information on the dominance of the relevant genes. He demonstrated that the Mendelian selection process invariably favors the dominance of beneficial genes, and that the greater the benefit, the faster the process. Dominance, then, must play a major role in evolution by natural selection. It may here be added that Fisher's work in this area, as elsewhere, was a careful blending of theory and practice. He carried out breeding experiments with various animals (mice, poultry, and snails were some), often under trying circumstances (for example, much mouse breeding was done in his own home in Harpenden). One of his best experiments concerned the inheritance of whiteness of plumage in white leghorns: by "breeding back" into wild jungle fowl he showed that the responsible dominant gene is a result of artificial selection, and its dominance is quickly lessened when it is introduced into the ancestral wild species.

Fisher also enunciated a "fundamental theorem of natural selection" (for an idealized population) in this form: "The rate of increase in fitness of any organism at any time is equal to its genetic variance in fitness at that time." He was keenly interested in human genetics and, like most eugenicists, held alarmist views about the future of *Homo sapiens.* An important consequence of this special interest was his realization that a study of human blood groups could be instrumental in advancing both theory and practice, and in 1935 he set up a blood-grouping department in the Galton Laboratory. Many good things came out of this enterprise, including a clarification of the inheritance of Rhesus groups.

BIBLIOGRAPHY

I. Original Works. Over a period of half a century Fisher turned out an average of one paper every two months. The best listing of these is M. J. R. Healy's, in *Journal of the Royal Statistical Society,* **126A** (1963), 170–178. The earliest item, in *Messenger of Mathematics,* **41** (1912), 155–160, is a brief advocacy of the method of maximum likelihood for curve fitting; and the last, in *Journal of Theoretical Biology,* **3** (1962), 509–513, concerns the use of double heterozygotes for seeking a statistically significant difference in recombination values. Key theoretical papers are "On the Mathematical Foundations of Theoretical Statistics," in *Philosophical Transactions of the Royal Society,* **222A** (1922), 309–368; "The Theory of Statistical Estimation," in *Proceedings of the Cambridge Philosophical Society,* **22** (1925), 700–725; and "The Statistical Theory of Estimation," in *Calcutta University Readership Lectures* (Calcutta, 1938). A publication of unusual interest is "Has Mendel's Work Been Rediscovered?" in *Annals of Science,* **1** (1936), 115–137, in which Fisher finds that, probabilistically, some of Mendel's celebrated pea results were a little too good to be true, but in which he also shows that Mendel's insight and experimental skill must have been outstandingly fine. Forty-three of Fisher's most important earlier papers are reproduced in facsimile, with the author's notes and corrections, in *Contributions to Mathematical Statistics* (New York, 1950).

Fisher published five holograph books: *Statistical Methods for Research Workers* (London, 1925; 13th ed., 1958), translated into five other languages; *The Genetical Theory of Natural Selection* (London, 1930; 2nd ed., New York, 1958); *The Design of Experiments* (London, 1935; 8th ed., 1966); *The Theory of Inbreeding* (London, 1949; 2nd ed., 1965); and *Statistical Methods and Scientific Inference* (London, 1956; 2nd ed., 1959). The statistical tables in his first book were subsequently expanded and published separately, with F. Yates, as *Statistical Tables for Biological, Agricultural, and Medical Research* (London, 1938; 6th ed., 1963).

II. Secondary Literature. *Journal of the American Statistical Association,* **46** (1951), contains four informative papers by F. Yates, H. Hotelling, W. J. Youden, and K. Mather written on the occasion of the twenty-fifth anniversary of the publication of *Statistical Methods.* The principal commemorative articles published after Fisher's death will be found in *Biometrics,* **18** (Dec. 1962) and **20** (June 1964); *Biographical Memoirs of Fellows of the Royal Society of London,* **9** (1963), 92–129; *Journal of the Royal Statistical Society,* **126A** (1963), 159–170; and *Science,* **156** (1967), 1456–1462. The last contains "An Appreciation" by Jerzy Neyman, who differed with Fisher on several issues, and is therefore of special interest. The writings of Neyman and E. S. Pearson should be consulted for further information on controversial matters. Fisher's contributions to discussions at various meetings of the Royal Statistical Society are also illuminating in this regard (they are indexed in the Healy bibliography). A good philosophical study of statistical reasoning, with particular reference to Fisher's ideas, is Ian Hacking's *Logic of Statistical Inference* (London, 1965).

Norman T. Gridgeman

FONTAINE (FONTAINE DES BERTINS), ALEXIS (*b.* Claveyson, Drôme, France, 13 August 1704; *d.* Cuiseaux, Saône-et-Loire, France, 21 August 1771)

The son of Jacques, a royal notary, and of Madeleine Seytres, Fontaine studied at the Collège de Tournon before his introduction to mathematics at Paris under the guidance of Père Castel. About 1732 he acquired property in the vicinity of Paris and, having formed friendships with Clairaut and Maupertuis, presented several memoirs to the Académie des Sciences, which admitted him as *adjoint mécanicien* on 11 June 1733. Although he was promoted to geometer in 1739 and to pensionary geometer in 1742, Fontaine rarely participated in the work of the Academy and led a rather solitary existence. A difficult personality, he showed almost no interest in the work of others and incurred considerable enmity by claiming priority in certain discoveries. In 1765 he retired permanently to an estate in Burgundy, the purchase of which had almost ruined him. He broke his silence only in order to engage in an imprudent polemic with Lagrange, whom he had initially encouraged. He died before he was able to read Lagrange's reply, however.

Fontaine's work is of limited scope, often obscure, and willfully ignorant of the contributions of other mathematicians. Nevertheless, its inspiration is often original and it presents, amid confused developments, a number of ideas that proved fertile, especially in the fields of the calculus of variations, of differential equations, and of the theory of equations.

One of the first memoirs that Fontaine presented to the Academy in 1734 solved the problem of tautochrones in the case where the resistance of the medium is a second-degree function of the speed of the moving body; the method employed, more general than that of his predecessors (Huygens, Newton, Euler, Johann I Bernoulli, and others), heralds the procedures of the calculus of variations. It won deserved esteem for its author, but Fontaine erred in reconsidering the subject in 1767 and 1768 in order to criticize—unjustly—the method of variations presented by Lagrange in 1762.

On the subject of integral calculus, Fontaine was interested in the conditions of integrability of differential forms with several variables and in homogeneous functions; independently of Euler and Clairaut, he discovered the relation termed homogeneity. He gave particular attention to the problem of notation, utilizing both the Newtonian symbols of fluxions and fluents and the differential notation of Leibniz, which he usefully completed by introducing a coherent symbolism for partial differentials that was successful for a long time before being replaced by δ. One of the first to tackle the study of differential equations of the *n*th order, he failed in his ambitious plan to regroup all the types of equations that can be solved. He did, however, introduce several interesting ideas that foreshadowed in particular the theory of singular integrals.

In the theory of equations, Fontaine attempted to extend to higher degrees a method of studying equations based on their decomposition into linear factors that had shown its usefulness in the case of equations of the third and fourth degree. His memoir, complex and often unclear, was rapidly outclassed by the works of Lagrange and Vandermonde.

In his work of 1764 Fontaine included a study of dynamics dated 1739 and based on a principle closely analogous to the one that d'Alembert had made the foundation of his treatise of 1743. Although Fontaine did not raise any claim of priority, he attracted the hostility of a powerful rival who subsequently took pains to destroy the reputation of his work, which—without being of the first rank—still merits mention for its original inspiration and for certain fecund ideas that it contains.

BIBLIOGRAPHY

I. Original Works. Fontaine's works are limited to several memoirs published in the *Histoire de l'Académie royale des sciences* for 1734, 1747, 1767, and 1768 and to a volume published as M. Fontaine, *Mémoires donnés à l'Académie royale des sciences non imprimés dans leur temps* (Paris, 1764), repr., without change, as *Traité de calcul différentiel et intégral* (Paris, 1770). Actually, the two successive titles are inexact, because this collection joins to the memoirs already published in 1734 and 1747 ten others, dealing essentially with infinitesimal geometry, integral calculus, mechanics, and astronomy. Only the three memoirs inserted in the volumes of the *Histoire de l'Académie royale des sciences* for 1767 and 1768 are not included in this work.

II. Secondary Literature. On Fontaine and his work, see J. L. Boucharlat, in Michaud, ed., *Biographie universelle,* XV (Paris, 1816), 179–183, and new ed., XIV (Paris, 1856), 323–326; F. Cajori, *A History of Mathematical Notations,* II (Chicago, 1929), esp. 198–199, 206–207, 223–224; J. M. Caritat de Condorcet, "Éloge de M. Fontaine, prononcé le 13 novembre 1773," in *Histoire de l'Académie royale des sciences, 1771* (Paris, 1774), pp. 105–116; J. de Lalande, in *Bibliographie astronomique* (Paris, 1803), pp. 481, 486; M. Marie, *Histoire des sciences mathématiques et physiques,* VIII (Paris, 1886), 39–42; J. F. Montucla, in *Histoire des mathématiques,* new ed., III (Paris, 1802), 44, 177, 343, 627, 657; N. Nielsen, *Géomètres français du XVIIIe siècle* (Copenhagen-Paris, 1935), pp. 174–182; and Poggendorff, *Biographisch-literarisches Handwörterbuch,* I (Leipzig, 1863), col. 766.

René Taton

FONTENELLE, BERNARD LE BOUYER (or **BOVIER) DE** (*b.* Rouen, France, 11 February 1657; *d.* Paris, France, 9 January 1757)

Fontenelle's father, François Le Bouyer, *écuyer,* sieur de Fontenelle, was originally from Alençon; his mother, Marthe Corneille, sister of Pierre and Thomas Corneille, came from Rouen. The family was of modest means and lived in rented quarters in Rouen. His father, *sous-doyen des avocats* in the Parlement of Rouen, was "a man of quality but of mediocre fortune" and practiced his profession "with more honor than fame," according to Trublet. Fontenelle was said to resemble his mother, a woman of great intellect, who was also pious and exhorted her children to virtue. Two of them died at an early age, before Bernard was born; two more, Pierre and Joseph Alexis, were born after him—both were to become ecclesiastics. Bernard's two maternal uncles, especially his godfather Thomas Corneille, had a great influence on him; they often invited him to Paris, before he moved there permanently around 1687, and introduced him to the world of the French Academy, the theater, the salons of the *précieuses,* and the *Mercure galant,* which was directed by a friend of Thomas's, Donneau de Visé.

About 1664 the child was placed in the Jesuit *collège* in Rouen, where his uncles had studied. He was, according to his teachers, "a well-rounded child in all respects and foremost among the students." The logic and physics that he was taught seemed to him devoid of meaning: according to Trublet, "He did not find nature in them, but rather vague and abstract ideas which, so to speak, skirted the edge of things but did not really touch them at all." The Jesuits wished to make him one of their own, but Fontenelle did not have a vocation. In deference to his father he became a lawyer, but he pleaded only one case—which he lost—and quit the bar to devote himself to literature and philosophy, which were more to his taste.

Although his parents had dedicated him to St. Bernard and to the Virgin and had made him wear the habit of the Feuillants until the age of seven, Fontenelle never displayed any strong devotion. He maintained the appearance of a Catholic, however, especially toward the end of his life, and in 1684 won the Academy's prize for eloquence with a *Discours sur la patience* that would not have been out of place in a collection of sermons (but did he not take this as a joke?). Nevertheless, his scientific attitude led him to a certain skepticism toward religion. The spirit of tolerance animated him; he had, after all, Protestant paternal ancestors, and in Normandy, where Reformed churchgoers were numerous, he had friends such as the Basnages, to whom he remained faithful after the revocation of the Edict of Nantes.

Fontenelle was born with a very fragile constitution; in his childhood he spat blood and was forbidden to take any violent exercise. He was sparing and careful of himself all his life; this is undoubtedly why he was accused of egotism and of indifference toward others. Although self-centered and considering himself responsible only for his own actions, he was not at all insensitive to the needs of others; on the contrary, he was obliging toward his friends (Mlle. de Launy and Brunel, for example). He was even-tempered—perhaps that is the secret of his longevity. He loved the company of women but never married. Even as a nonagenarian he still frequented their salons, particularly that of Mme. Geoffrin, whom he made his general legatee. In his youth he had been received by Ninon de Lenclos and, from 1710 to 1733, by Mme. de Lambert, at whose home he met men of letters and scholars, such as Houdar de La Motte, Marivaux, Montesquieu, and Mairan. He also attended the duchesse du Maine at her court at Sceaux and was a frequent guest of Mme. de Tencin. He was affable and witty; his all-embracing curiosity made him an excellent listener. Above all, he prized his freedom of mind and independence in his relations with men of rank, like the regent, Philippe d'Orléans, who honored him with his friendship, lodged him in the Palais Royal (until 1730), and awarded him a pension.

Fontenelle received every possible academic honor, although he was refused four times before being accepted into the French Academy in 1691. On 9 January 1697 he entered the Académie des Sciences as *secrétaire perpétuel* and was confirmed in office on 28 January 1699. He was *sous-directeur* in 1706, 1707, 1719, and 1728; *directeur* in 1709, 1713, and 1723; and was made *pensionnaire vétéran* on 9 December 1740. He became a member of the Académie Royale des Inscriptions et Belles-Lettres in 1701 and requested veteran status in 1705. In 1733 he was elected a member of the Royal Society of London. In 1740 he contributed to the foundation of the Académie des Sciences, Belles-Lettres et Arts of Rouen, which received its charter in 1744 and of which he then became an honorary member. He became a member of the Berlin Academy on 4 December 1749, the Accademia dei Arcadi of Rome, and the Academy of Nancy. In 1702 he joined the society formed by the Abbé Bignon to direct the publication of the *Journal des sçavans.*

Commencing with his studies at the Jesuit *collège,* Fontenelle began to write poetry. In 1670 he competed for the prize of the Académie des Palinods of

Rouen, writing in Latin on the Immaculate Conception, and his work was judged worthy of printing and was published that year in the *Revue des palinods.* In 1674 he translated an ode by his teacher P. Commire, addressed to the Grand Condé "on the fact that he is subsisting only on milk" (*Mercure galant,* July 1679). In 1677 the *Mercure galant* published his "L'amour noyé" with a very flattering introduction of the author as "nephew of the two Corneille poets." On several occasions Fontenelle competed for the poetry prize of the French Academy, but without great success. His operas, written under the name of Thomas Corneille and set to music by Lully, *Psyché* (1678) and *Bellérophon* (1679), were no more successful; even less so was his tragedy *Aspar* (1680), which was ridiculed by Racine. Under the name of Donneau de Visé he produced a comedy in 1681, *La comète,* inspired by the appearance of the comet of 1680 (the same referred to in Bayle's *Pensées sur la comète*). In it Fontenelle presents—obviously, in an amusing manner—various contemporary explanations of comets, including the most popular as well as the Cartesian theory; and the antiquated notions surrounding these celestial phenomena are held up to ridicule. In the work one can see the dawn of what was to make Fontenelle famous: his taste for the exposition of scientific ideas and his censorious and mocking attitude toward everything that seemed to him to be preconception or myth.

His "Lettre sur la Princesse de Clèves," which appeared in the *Mercure* of May 1678, revealed his talent as a literary critic sensitive to feelings, although he presented himself from this time on as a *géomètre,* with a "mind completely filled with measurements and proportions." Nevertheless, the first work of his period in Rouen was not a scientific one: it was, rather, the *Nouveaux dialogues des morts,* in two volumes, which he published anonymously in 1683. This was followed in 1684 by the *Jugement de Pluton* on the two parts of the first work. Fontenelle sometimes arranged the dialogues between the ancients, sometimes between the moderns, and sometimes between members of the two groups. From occasionally comical situations he draws subtle moral observations in a lively style. One can also find interesting considerations regarding the sciences, all of which have their chimera "which they run after without being able to seize . . . but on the way they trap other very useful knowledge" (dialogue between Artemis and Ramon Lull). He also comments on the role of instruments in the field of scientific knowledge (dialogue between Marcus Apicius and Galileo) and on the difficulty of discovering the truth (dialogue between the third Pseudo-Demetrius and Descartes).

At the same time as this work, which invites serious consideration despite its light touch, there appeared the *Lettres diverses de M. le Chevalier d'Her* * * * (or *Lettres galantes . . .*, depending on the edition), which were attributed to Fontenelle, who disavowed them. No one was deceived, for they clearly bear the mark of his style and his mind and reveal his ability to scrutinize a woman's soul.

In 1685 Fontenelle displayed his taste for mathematical reflection with the publication in the *Nouvelles de la république des lettres,* under the title of "Mémoire composé par M.D.F.D.R. [M. de Fontenelle de Rouen] contenant une question d'arithmétique," of a two-part article on the properties of the number nine. It was only a simple game that did not demonstrate the author's genius in these matters. Yet, if he did not solve the problem, he did pose the question for scholars; the *Nouvelles* published a reply by de Joullieu in February 1686 and a "Démonstration générale de la question . . . touchant les nombres multiples," by J. Sauveur, in October 1686.

This first, scarcely scientific essay was followed in 1686 by Fontenelle's most famous and most frequently published and translated work, *Entretiens sur la pluralité des mondes.* In five "Evenings" (*Soirs*), then six in the 1687 edition, Fontenelle undertook to set forth to a marquise who questioned him during evening promenades in a garden the different astronomical systems: those of Ptolemy, Copernicus, and Tycho Brahe. He spoke to her of the moon and the other worlds—Venus, Mercury, Mars, Jupiter, Saturn, the fixed stars—and discussed the possibility that they might be inhabited. He explained, in terms that could be understood by an intelligent but untrained mind, recent discoveries in the world of the stars, displaying a strong Cartesian bent in his account. In choosing this subject Fontenelle was undoubtedly inspired by a growing interest in the heavenly bodies, as well as by a work that appeared in Rouen in 1655, *Le monde de la lune* (a translation of the *Discovery of a New World* of John Wilkins), and by the *Discours nouveau prouvant la pluralité des mondes* of Pierre Borel (1657), not to mention two books by Cyrano de Bergerac, *L'autre monde: L'histoire comique des états et empires de la lune* (1657) and *L'histoire comique des états et empires du soleil* (1662).

Fontenelle was not an astronomer, and the earliest editions contained a number of errors which he continued to correct until 1742 in order to bring his text into agreement with the scientific data provided him by the members of the Academy of Sciences. The book offered him an opportunity to discuss problems that fascinated him: the relativity of knowledge and the desacralization of the earth—and hence man—

attendant upon the recognition of a nongeocentric universe. Our world is not privileged: others might be inhabited, and our present knowledge is limited but grows unceasingly in the course of time. "The art of flying has only just been born; it will be brought to perfection, and someday we will go to the moon" ("Second Evening").

The work's success resulted from the author's having treated supposedly difficult subjects in a light style, playfully and with a touch of affectation that detracted nothing from the seriousness of the given explanations. All this was done in a slightly fictionalized form that permitted a certain lyricism on the enchantment of a summer evening and the immensity of the universe. It is the first example in French of a learned work placed within the reach of an educated but nonspecialized public. It is certainly to these aspects of his work that Fontenelle owed his later academic positions.

Meanwhile, he was active in other fields. He published "Éloge de Monsieur Corneille" in January 1685 in the *Nouvelles de la république des lettres.* (Revised as "Vie de Monsieur Corneille," it appeared in the 1742 edition of his *Oeuvres.*) This was followed in 1686 by *Doutes sur le système physique des causes occasionnelles,* on the theory that Malebranche had presented in the *Recherche de la vérité.* Also in 1686, the self-styled "author of the *Dialogue des morts,*" again under the veil of anonymity, published the *Histoire des oracles.* Actually, he had already set forth his reflections on history: he had sketched the treatise "Sur l'histoire," passages from which were to appear in *De l'origine des fables* (1724). Published along with them were several pages, "Sur le bonheur," also written much earlier and undoubtedly one of the best expressions of Fontenelle's practical philosophy, a human morality independent of religion.

In his reflections on history and on the origin of fables Fontenelle appears as one of the first to treat the history of religion comparatively. He espoused a critical history not only of human events but also of myths, legends, and religions. He studied their formation, showing the role of imagination and how "marvelous" phenomena can be explained by nonsupernatural causes. He found ideas similar to his in *De oraculis ethnicorum dissertationes duae,* a work published in 1683 by the Dutchman A. Van Dale, and he decided to translate it; in the end he preferred to rewrite it entirely in his own manner. This was again done under the cover of anonymity, of course, for it was dangerous to attack superstitions: it led to casting doubt on miracles—fundamental ideas of Christianity that do not agree with scientific truths discovered through reasoning and experiment. Thus, Fontenelle was later attacked by the Jesuits, in particular by Jean-François Baltus, in 1707 and 1708, following the fifth edition of the *Histoire des oracles;* in accordance with his temperamental dislike of dispute and perhaps counseled by his friends as well, he did not reply.

Fontenelle was not content, in 1686, to publish only this dangerous work. He had sent to his friend Basnage in Rotterdam (in order to forward it to Bayle, who published it in the *Nouvelles de la république des lettres* of January) a "Relation curieuse de l'Isle de Bornéo," a so-called extract from a "letter written from Batavia in the East Indies." Involved was a letter between two sisters, Mreo and Eenegu, who were, one quickly discovered, none other than Rome and Geneva. In other words, just after the revocation of the Edict of Nantes, Fontenelle stigmatized the struggle between Catholics and Protestants, besides making a clear allusion to an event of which he deeply disapproved. If he had not at this time had protectors as powerful as the lieutenant of police Marc René de Voyer de Paulmy, marquis d'Argenson, he would have received the *lettre de cachet* that Le Tellier, confessor to Louis XIV, attempted to obtain against him for his unorthodox writings.

Fontenelle settled in Paris around 1687 and resumed his literary activities, publishing in that year *Poésies pastorales de M.D.F., avec un traité sur la nature de l'églogue et une digression sur les anciens et les modernes.* Fontenelle belonged to the party of the moderns, the men of progress, together with his friend Houdar de La Motte, Charles Perrault, and the circle of the *Mercure galant,* in opposition to the party of the ancients, the men of tradition, among whom were Racine, Boileau, and La Bruyère. His relationship with the Corneille family obviously reinforced his hostility toward the partisans of Racine, but it is certain that the *Digression,* leaving aside the question of personalities, shows Fontenelle's reflections concerning science: it is owing to its progress that humanity is improved. Moreover, is not the notion of ancients and moderns really very relative?

Fontenelle wrote another libretto, for the opera *Enée et Lavinie* (1690), and a tragedy, *Brutus* (1691), under the pseudonym of Mlle. Bernard. Received into the French Academy two years before La Bruyère, who in the eighth edition of the *Caractères* (1694) was to mock him under the name of Cydias, Fontenelle published the *Recueil des plus belles pièces des poètes françois, depuis Villon jusqu'à Benserade, avec une préface et des petites vies des poètes* (1692) and the *Parallèle de Corneille et de Racine* (1693).

Thanks to his compatriot and friend Varignon, Fontenelle made the acquaintance of the Parisian scientific circle and became friendly with Nicolas de Malézieu and Guillaume de L'Hospital. For the latter's *Analyse des infiniment petits pour l'intelligence des lignes courbes* (1696), he composed a preface that might have been taken for the author's but which everyone was quite aware was by Fontenelle. In it are displayed his interest in the notion of infinity and his talent as a historian; in a few pages he retraces the history of the mathematical study of curved lines from Archimedes to Newton and Leibniz.

Fontenelle was a friend of the Abbé Bignon and of Pontchartrain, patrons of the Academy of Sciences; and his *Entretiens* was admired for its clear and elegant style, in contrast to the ponderous Latin of the Academy's secretary, Jean-Baptiste du Hamel. In 1697 Fontenelle was invited to replace the latter. The Academy's new statutes of January 1699, of which Fontenelle was in part the author, defined the role of the *secrétaire perpétuel:* he was required to publish each year the memoirs of the academicians drawn from the records, preceded by a sort of *histoire raisonnée* of the Academy's most remarkable accomplishments. He was also to deliver the *éloges* of those academicians who had died during the year and was to publish them in the *Histoire.*

Thus, under the facile pen of a writer who could simplify and clarify and who—without being a specialist—had sufficient knowledge in all areas of science to present its results without distortion, the works of the academicians could become accessible to a cultivated society that balked at Latin. From 1699 to 1740 Fontenelle devoted himself almost exclusively to his task of editing the *Histoire de l'Académie royale des sciences . . . avec les mémoires de mathématique et de physique pour la même année, tirés des registres de cette Académie.* The volume for the year 1699, which appeared in 1702, opens with an untitled preface usually called "Préface [sometimes "Discours préliminaire"] sur l'utilité des mathématiques et de la physique et sur les travaux de l'Académie," which contains essential material on the philosophy of science and is a sort of bridge between Descartes's *Discours de la méthode* and Claude Bernard's *Introduction à l'étude de la médecine expérimentale.* Here one finds the first literary expression of the idea of the interdependence of the sciences and of the constancy of the laws of nature. In 1733 there appeared the history of the early years of the Academy, under the title *Histoire de l'Académie royale des sciences. Tome Ier. Depuis son établissement en 1666, jusqu'à 1686.* Fontenelle covered only the years until 1679 but composed a preface that is an excellent history not only of the founding of the Academy but of the state of contemporary science as well.

Fontenelle eventually published forty-two volumes of the *Histoire de l'Académie,* containing sixty-nine *éloges.* He had already had some experience with this literary genre in the "Éloge de Monsieur Corneille" and especially in the "Éloge de Mons. Claude Perrault de l'Académie royale des sciences et docteur en médecine de la Faculté de Paris . . ." (*Journal des sçavans,* 28 February 1689). The first *éloges* read to the Academy were short, and one senses that Fontenelle had not yet attained complete mastery of the field in which he later proved to be without equal. His ability, evident as early as the *éloge* of Viviani (1703), was still apparent in the last one, that of Du Fay (1739).

No one before him had been able to evaluate so well the works of others nor to report on a life with such verve, nor to sprinkle his text with such subtle psychological and moral observations. The *éloges* were Fontenelle's greatest glory. They remain an astonishing—occasionally unique—source of biographical information on the scientists of the epoch. If one can sometimes reproach Fontenelle for being biased or too Cartesian at a time when science was already Newtonian, he was a good mirror of his times; and one finds in his writing what is undoubtedly the best approach in French to the works of Malebranche, Leibniz, Newton, Johann I Bernoulli, Jean-Dominique Cassini, Varignon, and Boerhaave, to cite only a few names.

The *éloges* enjoyed such success that Fontenelle saw the necessity, as early as 1708, of collecting them in a separate volume under the title *Histoire du renouvellement de l'Académie royale des sciences en M.DC.XCIX et les éloges historiques de tous les académiciens morts depuis ce renouvellement, avec un discours préliminaire sur l'utilité des mathématiques et de la physique.* In 1717 he brought out an edition with seventeen new *éloges,* in 1722 one with eleven more, and in 1733 the *Suite des éloges des académiciens . . . morts depuis l'an M.DCC.XXII.* Finally, in 1742, volumes V and VI of his *Oeuvres* contained the whole series of *éloges.*

As a member of the Academy of Sciences, Fontenelle also wished to do work of his own. In 1727, as a "Suite des mémoires de l'Académie royale des sciences," he published the *Élémens de la géométrie de l'infini.* Some doubted whether it was really the work of a mathematician, but the author believed it was and attached great value to it. He had worked on it for a long time, probably since the period of his preface to the *Analyse des infiniment petits.* The term *élémens* is to be understood in the sense of "first principles." According to Fontenelle, none of the geometers who had invented or employed the calculus of infinity had given a general theory of it; that is what he proposed to do. The work is divided into a preface relating the history of this branch of calculus and into two main parts: "Système général de l'infini" and "Différentes applications ou remarques." The author discusses "the infinite in series or in progressions of numbers" and then examines "the infinite in straight and curved lines," in the words of the Abbé Terrasson, who reviewed the work in the *Journal des sçavans* (July–October 1728).

There was a great deal of discussion in the scientific community about this work, in which mathematicians found numerous paradoxes. Johann I Bernoulli, for example, in his correspondence with Fontenelle allowed his criticisms to show through his praise: he did not understand what was meant by *finis indéterminables.* Fontenelle attempted to defend his theory and above all his distinction between metaphysical infinity and geometric infinity: one must ignore the metaphysical difficulties in order to further geometry, and the *finis indéterminables* ought to be considered "as a type of hypothesis necessary until now in order to explain several phenomena of the calculus" (letter to Johann I Bernoulli, 29 June 1729). "The orders of infinite and indeterminable quantities, like the magnitudes that they represent, are only purely relative entities, hypothetical and auxiliary. The subject matter of mathematics is only ideal," according to the terms of a "Projet de rapport" of Dortous de Mairan to the Academy on this work.

In 1731 the third edition of Thomas Corneille's *Dictionnaire des arts et des sciences* appeared, revised and augmented by Fontenelle with many scientific terms. When he retired from the Academy of Sciences, Fontenelle was feted at the French Academy on the fiftieth anniversary of his election to that body, and for this occasion he composed a "Discours sur la rime" (1741).

In 1743 a small, anonymous volume entitled *Nouvelles libertés de penser* appeared in Amsterdam; it included two articles believed to have been written by Fontenelle: "Les réflexions sur l'argument de M. Pascal et de M. Locke concernant les possibilités d'une vie à venir" and "Traité de la liberté," both of which are completely in accord with his way of thinking.

In 1752 Fontenelle published anonymously through his friend the physician Camille Falconet (who provided a preface) his *Théorie des tourbillons cartésiens avec des réflexions sur l'attraction.* Many were astonished to see the appearance at this time of a work conceived some years previously, and they tried to explain why Fontenelle had decided to present to the learned public a thoroughly outmoded scientific theory. Fontenelle agreed with Newton and the Newtonians to the degree that they did not attempt to give a meaning to "attraction" and contented themselves with calculations. Newton linked formulas with formulas; his method yielded results that corresponded to the facts, but he explained nothing in the sense that Fontenelle would wish, that is, through principles. Fontenelle wished to understand by going back to causes. It was all very well to take "attraction" as a simple word or a sign; one should not, however, endow it with content, and Newtonians who do this return to Scholastic notions and to "occult forces." If Fontenelle remained faithful to the Cartesianism of the *Entretiens,* it was certainly not owing to the stubbornness of age but to a profound conviction of the value of a mechanical explanation in Descartes's sense. This conviction, moreover, was supported by certain works that he analyzed at the Academy of Sciences, in particular those of Privat de Molières, who defended, with some modifications, the theory of vortices (*tourbillons*).

"One must always admire Descartes and on occasion follow him" (*Éloge d'Hartsoëker*): Fontenelle followed him in the matter of the vortices but not in such matters as his theory of animal machines. In his horror of systems that lull thought to sleep, he understood that the important thing is not the results acquired, which are always provisional, but the method of thinking, which consists in completely rejecting all "marvelous" facts, in questioning everything, and in believing only what reason supported by experiment clearly shows. This is the intellectual attitude inherited by the Encyclopedists that characterized the Enlightenment.

In most respects a man of the seventeenth century, Fontenelle was, in others, a man of the eighteenth—perhaps even of the twentieth—century in his unflagging intellectual curiosity and in his belief in the limitless progress of knowledge in a world in which everything must be open to rational explanation.

BIBLIOGRAPHY

I. ORIGINAL WORKS. All of Fontenelle's works have been mentioned in the article. Cited here are only the principal eds. of selected and complete works, the most recent critical eds., and several selected texts.

Editions of selected and complete works include *Oeuvres diverses de M. de Fontenelle,* 3 vols. (Amsterdam, 1701, 1716); 2 vols. (London, 1707, 1713, 1714, 1716); 8 vols. (Paris, 1715); 3 vols. (Paris, 1724); 3 vols. (The Hague, 1728–1729), with an engraving by Bernard Picart, "le Romain"; and 5 vols. (The Hague, 1736). *Oeuvres de M. de Fontenelle* appeared in several eds.: 6 vols. (Paris, 1742); 8 vols. (Paris, 1751–1752); 6 vols. (Amsterdam, 1754);

10 vols. (Paris, 1758); 11 vols. (Paris, 1761, 1766); 12 vols. (Amsterdam, 1764); and 7 vols. (London, 1785). The oft-cited Bastien ed., *Oeuvres de Fontenelle,* 8 vols. (Paris, 1790–1792), is not always faithful to Fontenelle's text and cannot be recommended. Later eds. include G. B. Depping, ed., 3 vols. (Paris, 1818), with index; and J.-B. Champagnac, ed., 5 vols. (Paris, 1825).

Critical eds. include Louis Maigron, ed., *Histoire des oracles* (Paris, 1908; repr., 1934); *De l'origine des fables* (Paris, 1932), edited with intro., notes, and commentary by J.-R. Carré; Robert Shackleton, ed., *Entretiens sur la pluralité des mondes. Digression sur les anciens et les modernes* (Oxford, 1955); and *Entretiens sur la pluralité des mondes* (Paris, 1966), with intro. and notes by Alexandre Calame.

Among selected texts are (in chronological order) A. P. Le Guay de Prémontval, ed., *L'esprit de Fontenelle, ou Recueil des pensées tirées de ses ouvrages* (The Hague, 1753); *Oeuvres choisies de Fontenelle,* 2 vols. (Liège, 1779); J. Chass, ed., *Esprit, maximes et principes de Fontenelle* (Paris, 1788); Cousin d'Avallon, ed., *Fontenelliana, ou Recueil des bons mots . . . de Fontenelle* (Paris, 1801); *Oeuvres choisies de Fontenelle,* 2 vols. (Paris, 1883), with a preface by J.-F. Thénard; Henri Pothez, ed., *Pages choisies des grands écrivains, Fontenelle* (Paris, 1909); Émile Faguet, ed., *Textes choisis et commentés* (Paris, 1912); and *Textes choisis* (Paris, 1966), with intro. and notes by Maurice Roelens, the best current ed.

II. SECONDARY LITERATURE. On Fontenelle's life, one can still profitably consult his first biographer, the Abbé Trublet, in "Mémoires pour servir à l'histoire de la vie et des ouvrages de M. de Fontenelle," a series of articles that first appeared in the *Mercure de France* (1756–1758). They were then collected in 2 vols. (Amsterdam, 1759) and were later added as vols. XI and XII of Fontenelle's *Oeuvres* (Amsterdam, 1764). They were summarized by Trublet in "Fontenelle," in Moreri's *Dictionnaire . . .* (1759).

The essential bibliography concerning Fontenelle and his work is S. Delorme, "Contribution à la bibliographie de Fontenelle," in *Revue d'histoire des sciences,* **10,** no. 4 (Oct.–Dec. 1957), 300–309.

Particularly noteworthy are Grandjeán de Fouchy, "Éloge de Fontenelle," in *Histoire de l'Académie royale des sciences, année 1757;* Louis Maigron, *Fontenelle, l'homme, l'oeuvre, l'influence* (Paris, 1906); J.-R. Carré, *La philosophie de Fontenelle, ou Le sourire de la raison* (Paris, 1932); M. Bouchard, *"L'histoire des Oracles" de Fontenelle* (Paris, 1947); John W. Cosentini, *Fontenelle's Art of Dialogue* (New York, 1952); S. Delorme, G. Martin, D. McKie, and A. Birembaut, in *Revue d'histoire des sciences,* **10,** no. 4 (1957); S. Delorme, A. Adam, A. Couder, J. Rostand, and A. Robinet, "Fontenelle, sa vie et son oeuvre, 1657–1757 (Journées Fontenelle)," in *Revue de synthèse,* 3rd ser., no. 21 (Jan.–Mar. 1961); François Grégoire, *Fontenelle, une philosophie désabusée* (Nancy, 1947); J. Rostand, *Hommes de vérité, Pasteur, Claude Bernard, Fontenelle* (Paris, 1942, 1955); and J. Vendryès, G. Canguilhem, A. Dupont-Sommer, R. Pintard, A. Adam, and A. Maurois, in *Annales de l'Université de Paris,* 27ᵉ année, no. 3 (July–Sept. 1957), p. 378 ff.

One should also consult the *Catalogue de l'Exposition Fontenelle à la Bibliothèque Nationale* (Paris, 1957), which is especially useful. See also the bibliographies in the latest critical eds. (Shackleton, Calame, and Roelens, *op. cit.*), and note, particularly from a philosophical point of view, Leonard M. Marsak, "Bernard de Fontenelle: The Idea of Science in the French Enlightenment," in *Transactions of the American Philosophical Society,* n.s. **49,** pt. 7 (1959), 1–64.

SUZANNE DELORME

FORSYTH, ANDREW RUSSELL (*b.* Glasgow, Scotland, 18 June 1858; *d.* London, England, 2 June 1942)

Forsyth was the son of John Forsyth, a marine engineer, and of Christina Glenn, of Paisley. The family moved to Liverpool, where Forsyth soon revealed his mathematical ability. He entered Trinity College, Cambridge, in 1877 and was senior wrangler in January 1881. He became a fellow of Trinity the same year with a remarkably powerful thesis on double theta functions. In 1882 he was appointed to the chair of mathematics at University College, Liverpool, but in 1884 he returned to Cambridge as a lecturer. He was elected a fellow of the Royal Society in 1886.

As a mathematician Forsyth belonged to the school of his Cambridge master, Cayley, and was outstanding in his ability to marshal complicated formulas. His importance in the history of British mathematics is due, however, to his being a great traveler and a good linguist; he was thus the first to realize the deficiencies of the Cambridge school, which was almost completely ignorant of Continental mathematics. Forsyth was determined to rectify this situation, and in 1893 he published his *Theory of Functions,* which, according to Sir Edmund Whittaker, "had a greater influence on British mathematics than any work since Newton's *Principia.*" As a result, for many years function theory dominated Cambridge mathematics.

In 1895 Forsyth succeeded Cayley as Sadlerian professor of pure mathematics but resigned in 1910 in order to marry Marion Amelia Boys, the former wife of the physicist C. V. Boys. After a short time in Calcutta, he was appointed chief professor of mathematics at Imperial College, London, in 1913. Although he retired in 1923, he continued to write mathematical treatises; but his point of view was antiquated, his work being based on manipulative skill rather than on logical processes.

Ironically, Forsyth's main achievement was having brought to Cambridge the modern style of mathematics that superseded his own, and as a result his reputation in his later years was less than it deserved to be.

BIBLIOGRAPHY

I. Original Works. Forsyth's most important books were *A Treatise on Differential Equations* (London, 1885; 6th ed., 1931), also trans. into German and Italian; *Theory of Differential Equations,* 6 vols. (Cambridge, 1890–1906); and *Theory of Functions of a Complex Variable* (Cambridge, 1893; 3rd ed., 1917). He also published *Lectures on the Differential Geometry of Curves and Surfaces* (Cambridge, 1912); *Lectures Introductory to the Theory of Functions of Two Complex Variables* (Cambridge, 1914); *Calculus of Variations* (Cambridge, 1927); *Geometry of Four Dimensions,* 2 vols. (Cambridge, 1930); and *Intrinsic Geometry of Ideal Space,* 2 vols. (London, 1935). He also contributed to British mathematical journals, *Proceedings of the Royal Society,* and other publications.

II. Secondary Literature. Biographical notices are E. H. Neville, in *Journal of the London Mathematical Society,* **17** (1942), 237–256; and E. T. Whittaker, in *Obituary Notices of Fellows of the Royal Society of London,* **4** (1942–1944), 209–227. The latter contains a complete bibliography of Forsyth's writings. See also the article on Forsyth by E. T. Whittaker, in *Dictionary of National Biography,* supp. VI (1941–1950), 267–268.

G. J. Whitrow

FOURIER, JEAN BAPTISTE JOSEPH (*b.* Auxerre, France, 21 March 1768; *d.* Paris, France, 16 May 1830)

Fourier lost both his father (Joseph, a tailor in Auxerre) and his mother (Edmée) by his ninth year and was placed by the archbishop in the town's military school, where he discovered his passion for mathematics. He wanted to join either the artillery or the engineers, which were branches of the army then generally available to all classes of society; but for some reason he was turned down, and so he was sent to a Benedictine school at St. Benoît-sur-Loire in the hope that he could later pursue his special interests at its seminary in Paris. The French Revolution interfered with these plans, however, and without regret he returned in 1789 to Auxerre and a teaching position in his old school.

During the Revolution, Fourier was prominent in local affairs, and his courageous defense of the victims of the Terror led to his arrest in 1794. A personal appeal to Robespierre was unsuccessful; but he was released after Robespierre's execution on 28 July 1794 and went as a student to the ill-fated École Normale, which opened and closed within that year. He can have spent only a short time there, but nevertheless he made a strong impression; and when the École Polytechnique started in 1795 he was appointed *administrateur de police,* or assistant lecturer, to support the teaching of Lagrange and Monge. There he fell victim of the reaction to the previous regime and was, ironically, arrested as a supporter of Robespierre (who had declined his earlier appeal). But his colleagues at the École successfully sought his release, and in 1798 Monge selected him to join Napoleon's Egyptian campaign. He became secretary of the newly formed Institut d'Égypte, conducted negotiations between Napoleon and Sitty-Nefiçah (the wife of the chief bey, Murad), and held other diplomatic posts as well as pursuing research. He does not appear to have been appointed governor of southern Egypt, however, as has often been reported.

After his return to France in 1801, Fourier wished to resume his work at the École Polytechnique; but Napoleon had spotted his administrative genius and appointed him prefect of the department of Isère, centered at Grenoble and extending to what was then the Italian border. Here his many administrative achievements included the reconciliation of thirty-seven different communities to the drainage of a huge area of marshland near Bourgoin to make valuable farming land, and the planning and partial construction of a road from Grenoble to Turin (now route N91-strada 23), which was then the quickest route between Turin and Lyons. In 1808 Napoleon conferred a barony on him.

While in Egypt, Fourier suggested that a record be made of the work of the Institut d'Égypte, and on his return to France he was consulted on its organization and deputed to write the "Préface historique" on the ancient civilization and its glorious resurrection. This he completed in 1809, but some of its historical details caused controversy. Napoleon supported it, and it appeared in the *Description de l'Égypte.*

Fourier was still at Grenoble in 1814 when Napoleon fell. By geographical accident the town was directly on the route of the party escorting Napoleon from Paris to the south and thence to Elba; to avoid an embarrassing meeting with his former chief Fourier negotiated feverishly for a detour in the route of the cortege. But no such detour was conceivable on Napoleon's return and march on Paris in 1815, and so Fourier compromised, fulfilling his duties as prefect by ordering the preparation of the defenses—which he knew to be useless—and then leaving the town for Lyons by one gate as Napoleon entered by another. He did return, however, and the two friends met at Bourgoin. Fourier need have had no fears, for Napoleon made him a count and appointed him prefect of the neighboring department of the Rhône, centered at Lyons. But before the end of Napoleon's Hundred Days, Fourier had resigned his new title and prefecture in protest against the severity of the regime and had come to Paris to try to take up research full time (it had previously been only a spare-time activity).

This was the low point of Fourier's life—he had no job, only a small pension, and a low political reputation. But a former student at the École Polytechnique and companion in Egypt, Chabrol de Volvic, was now prefect of the department of the Seine and appointed him director of its Bureau of Statistics, a post without onerous duties but with a salary sufficient for his needs.

In 1816 Fourier was elected to the reconstituted Académie des Sciences, but Louis XVIII could not forgive his having accepted the prefecture of the Rhône from Napoleon, and the nomination was refused. Diplomatic negotiation eventually cleared up the situation, and his renomination in 1817 was not opposed. He also had some trouble with the second edition of the *Description de l'Égypte* (for now his references to Napoleon needed rethinking) but in general his reputation was rising fast. He was left in a position of strength after the decline of the Société d'Arcueil, led by Laplace in the physical sciences, and gained the favor and support of the aging Laplace himself in spite of the continued enmity of Poisson. In 1822 he was elected to the powerful position of *secrétaire perpétuel* of the Académie des Sciences, and in 1827—after further protests—to the Académie Française. He was also elected a foreign member of the Royal Society.

Throughout his career, Fourier won the loyalty of younger friends by his unselfish support and encouragement; and in his later years he helped many mathematicians and scientists, including Oersted, Dirichlet, Abel, and Sturm. An unfortunate incident occurred in 1830 when he lost the second paper on the resolution of equations sent to the Academy by Evariste Galois; but this would appear to be due more to the disorganization of his papers than—as Galois believed—to deliberate suppression.

The Egyptian period of his life had one final consequence in his last years. While there he had caught some illness, possibly myxedema, which necessitated his increasing confinement to his own heated quarters. He lived at 15 rue pavée St. André des Arts (now 15 rue Séguier) until 1829, then at 19 rue d'Enfer (now the site of 73 Boulevard St. Michel) until his death. On 4 May 1830 he was struck down while descending some stairs, and he allowed the symptoms to become worse until he died twelve days later. The funeral service took place at the Église St. Jacques de Haut Pas, and he was buried in the eighteenth division of the cemetery of Père Lachaise.

Various memorials have been made to Fourier. A bust by Pierre-Alphonse Fessard was subscribed in 1831 but was destroyed during World War II. A similar fate overtook the bronze statue by Faillot erected in Auxerre in 1849; the Nazis melted it down for armaments. During the night before its destruction, however, the mayor rescued two of its bas-reliefs, which were mounted on the walls of the town hall after the war. A medallion was founded in the town in 1952, and since 1950 the *Annales de l'Institut Fourier* have been published by the University of Grenoble. In 1968 the bicentenary of his birth was celebrated and the secondary school in Auxerre was renamed the Lycée Fourier.

Heat Diffusion and Partial Differential Equations. Fourier's achievements lie in the study of the diffusion of heat and in the mathematical techniques he introduced to further that study. His interest in the problem may have begun when he was in Egypt, but the substantial work was done at Grenoble. In 1807 he presented a long paper to the Academy on heat diffusion between disjoint masses and in special continuous bodies (rectangle, annulus, sphere, cylinder, prism), based on the diffusion equation

$$\frac{\partial^2 v}{\partial x^2} + \frac{\partial^2 v}{\partial y^2} + \frac{\partial^2 v}{\partial z^2} = k \frac{\partial v}{\partial t} \tag{1}$$

(in three variables). Of the examiners, Laplace, Monge, and Lacroix were in favor of accepting his work, but Lagrange was strongly opposed to it—due, to some extent, to the Fourier series

$$f(x) = \frac{1}{2\pi} \int_{-\pi}^{\pi} f(t)\,dt + \frac{1}{\pi} \sum_{r=1}^{\infty} \left[\cos rx \int_{-\pi}^{\pi} f(t) \cos rt\,dt + \sin rx \int_{-\pi}^{\pi} f(t) \sin rt\,dt \right] \tag{2}$$

required to express the initial temperature distribution in certain of these bodies, which contradicted Lagrange's own denigration of trigonometric series in his treatment of the vibrating string problem in the 1750's. The paper was therefore never published.

A prize problem on heat diffusion was proposed in 1810, however, and Fourier sent in the revised version of his 1807 paper, together with a new analysis on heat diffusion in infinite bodies. In these cases the periodicity of the Fourier series made it incapable of expressing the initial conditions, and Fourier substituted the Fourier integral theorem, which he wrote in forms such as

$$\pi f(x) = \int_{\infty}^{\infty} f(t)\,dt \int_{0}^{\infty} \cos q(x - t)\,dq. \qquad (3)$$

The last sections of the paper dealt with more physical aspects of heat, such as the intensity of radiation, and these became more important in Fourier's thought during his later years. Fourier's paper won the competition, but the jury—probably at the insistence of Lagrange—made criticisms on grounds of "rigor and generality," which Fourier considered an unjustified reproach. He expanded the mathematical parts of the paper into his book *Théorie analytique de la chaleur.* An extended treatment of the physical aspects was first planned for further chapters of this book and then for a separate book, *Théorie physique de la chaleur,* but it was never achieved.

The history of Fourier's main work in mathematics and mathematical physics has long been confused by an exclusive concentration on only two results, Fourier series and Fourier integrals, and by the application of anachronistic standards of rigor in judgments on their derivation. Fourier's achievement is better understood if we see it as twofold: treating first the formulation of the physical problem as boundary-value problems in linear partial differential equations, which (together with his work on units and dimensions) achieved the extension of rational mechanics to fields outside those defined in Newton's *Principia;* and second, the powerful mathematical tools he invented for the solution of the equations, which yielded a long series of descendants and raised problems in mathematical analysis that motivated much of the leading work in that field for the rest of the century and beyond.

Fortunately for the historian, Fourier reproduced, nearly intact, almost all his successful results in the several versions of his basic work. A comparison of these, in correlation with unpublished sources, biographical information, and separate papers, enables a firm reconstruction of the sequence of his researches. Moreover, from this sequence and from his style of presentation, we can identify several crucial points at which he failed to solve problems as well as the reasons for his failure.

Fourier's first work in the rational mechanics of heat used a model of heat being transferred by a shuttle mechanism between discrete particles. The physical theory was a simple method of mixtures, and the mathematics was of the 1750's. Of the two problems he attacked, the second, with the n particles arranged in a ring, yielded a complete solution for the finite case. Fourier wished to extend this to the continuous case but could not, for as n increased, the time constants in the exponentials tended to zero, obliterating the time dependence of the solution. Only later did he understand how to modify his transfer model to avoid this anomaly; and by his concentration on the complete solution and its difficulties, he failed to notice that at $t = 0$ his solution gave an interpolation formula which would yield the Fourier series in the continuous case. (Lagrange's earlier failure to discover the Fourier series can be similarly explained; it had nothing to do with the scruples of rigor which are usually held to be the cause.)

Fourier's successful establishment of the equation of heat flow was probably indebted to early work of J. B. Biot on the steady temperatures in a metal bar, wherein Biot distinguished between internal conduction and external radiation. Biot's analysis was crippled by a faulty physical model for conduction which yielded an "inhomogeneous" equation $d^2v - kv\,dx = 0$; and Fourier was able to concoct a physical model which resolved the difficulty. The full time-dependent equations for one and two dimensions of the type (1) then came easily.

Fourier's masterstroke was in the choice of configuration for a problem in which to apply the equation. The semi-infinite strip, uniformly hot at one end and uniformly cold along the sides, combines the utmost simplicity with physical meaning, in the tradition of rational mechanics deriving from the Bernoullis and Euler. The steady-state case is simply Laplace's equation in Cartesian coordinates. Fourier probably tried complex-variable methods (a solution along these lines, probably retrospective, is in the *Théorie*) but then used separation of variables to yield a series solution and thus the boundary-condition equation

$$1 = \sum_{r=0}^{\infty} a_r \cos rx. \qquad (4)$$

The solution of the equation and its generalization for an arbitrary function $f(x)$ by infinite-matrix methods have been analyzed and criticized many times. It is well to remember that this work was done several decades before the Cauchy-Weierstrass orthodoxy was established. Fourier was not a naive formalist: he could handle problems of convergence quite competently, as in his discussion of the series for the sawtooth function. The leading technical ideas of several basic proofs, such as that of Dirichlet on the convergence of the Fourier series, can be found in his work. Moreover, he saw, long before anyone else, that term-by-term integration of a given trigonometric series, to evaluate the coefficients, is no guarantee of its correctness; the completeness of a series is not to be assumed. The great shock caused by his trigonometric expansions was due to his demonstration of a paradoxical property of equality over a finite interval between algebraic expressions of totally different form. Corresponding to any function in a very wide class, there could be constructed a trigonometric series whose values, on an assigned interval, are the same as those of the function. As he showed by example, the given function could even be a mixture of different algebraic expressions, each defined on disjoint subintervals of the basic one. Both trigonometric expansions and arbitrary functions had been used by others (including Poisson); but the former were restricted to problems involving periodic phenomena, and the latter, when they appeared in the solutions of partial differential equations, were assumed by their nature to be incapable of an algebraic expression.

The earliest records of this first successful investigation show its exploratory character and Fourier's excitement with his achievement. Also, in this work there are traces of the influence of Monge in the notation, in the representation of the solution as a surface, and in the separate expression of boundary values in determining the solution of a differential equation. Thenceforth, Fourier proceeded into new territory with assuredness. The three-dimension case caused some difficulties, which were resolved by splitting the original equation into two, one for interior conduction and the other relating radiation to the temperature gradient at the surface. Applied to the sphere, in spherical coordinates, this gave a nonharmonic trigonometric expansion, where the eigenvalues are the roots of a transcendental equation. Fourier used his knowledge of the theory of equations (see below) to argue for the reality of all roots, but the question caused him trouble for many years. The problem of heat conduction in a cylinder gave rise to a further generalization. Fourier's solution was in what are now called Bessel functions—derived several years before Friedrich Bessel—by techniques made fully general in the theory created by Fourier's later associates, J. Charles François Sturm and Joseph Liouville.

The study of diffusion along an infinite line, involving the development of the Fourier integral theorem, probably depended on the idea of Laplace of expressing the solution of the heat equation as an integral transform of an arbitrary function representing the initial temperature distribution. Fourier derived the cosine and sine transforms separately for configurations symmetrical and antisymmetrical about the origin, by the extension of the finite-interval expansion. Only gradually did he come to appreciate the generality of the odd-and-even decomposition of a given function.

Fourier's last burst of creative work in this field came in 1817 and 1818, when he achieved an effective insight into the relation between integral-transform solutions and operational calculus. There was at that time a three-cornered race with Poisson and Cauchy, who had started using such techniques by 1815. In a crushing counterblow to a criticism by Poisson, Fourier exhibited integral-transform solutions of several equations which had long defied analysis, and gave the lead to a systematic theory. This was later achieved by Cauchy, en route to the calculus of residues.

As a mathematician, Fourier had as much concern for practical problems of rigor as anyone in his day except Cauchy and N. H. Abel, but he could not conceive of the theory of limiting processes as a meaningful exercise in its own right. The famous referees' criticisms of the 1811 prize essay, concerning its defects of rigor and generality, have long been misinterpreted. Much of the motivation for them was political; Poisson and Biot, outclassed rivals in the theory of heat diffusion, tried for years to denigrate Fourier's achievements. The criticism of rigor was probably based on Poisson's point that the eigenvalues in the sphere problem were not proven to be all real; and complex roots would yield a physically impossible solution. (Poisson himself solved the problem for Fourier years later.) The supposed lack of generality in Fourier's series solution (2) was probably by way of contrast to an integral solution already achieved by Laplace, in which the arbitrary function was neatly encased in the integrand.

Fourier's sensibility was that of rational mechanics. He had a superb mastery of analytical technique and notation ($\int_a^b$ is his invention, for example); and this power, guided by his physical intuition, brought him success. Before him, the equations used in the leading problems in rational mechanics were usually nonlinear, and they were solved by ad hoc approximation methods. Similarly, the field of differential equations was a jungle without pathways. Fourier created and explained a coherent method whereby the different components of an equation and its series solution were neatly identified, with the different aspects of the physical situation being analyzed. He also had a uniquely sure instinct for interpreting the asymptotic properties of the solutions of his equations for their physical meaning. So powerful was his approach that a full century passed before nonlinear differential equations regained prominence in mathematical physics.

For Fourier, every mathematical statement (although not all intermediate stages in a formal argument) had to have a physical meaning, both in exhibiting real motions and in being capable, in principle, of measurement. He always interpreted his solutions so as to obtain limiting cases which could be tested against experiment, and he performed such experiments at the earliest opportunity. He rejected the prevailing Laplacian orthodoxy of analyzing physical phenomena through the assumption of imperceptible molecules connected by local Newtonian forces; because of his approach to physical theory, together with his enmity to Poisson, he was adopted as philosophical patron by Auguste Comte in the development and popularization of *philosophie positive.*

Although the physical models of his earliest drafts were very sketchy, by the time of the 1807 paper he had fully incorporated physical constants into his theory of heat. The concern for physical meaning enabled him to see the potential in his formal technique for checking the coherence of the clumps of physical constants appearing in the exponentials of the Fourier integral solutions. From this came the full theory of units and dimensions (partly anticipated by Lazare Carnot), the first effective advance since Galileo in the theory of the mathematical representation of physical quantities. A comparison with the confused struggles of contemporaries such as Biot with the same problem illuminates Fourier's achievement.

Although Fourier studied the physical theory of heat for many years, his contributions, based primarily on the phenomena of radiation, did not long survive. His concern for applying his theory produced an analysis of the action of the thermometer, of the heating of rooms, and, most important, the first scientific estimate of a lower bound for the age of the earth. It is puzzling that in spite of his faith in the importance of heat as a primary agent in the universe, Fourier seems to have had no interest in the problem of the motive power of heat; and so, along with nearly all his contemporaries, he remained in ignorance of the essay on that topic by Lazare Carnot's son, Sadi.

On the side of real-variable analysis, the problems suggested especially by Fourier series lead directly through Dirichlet, Riemann, Stokes, and Heine to Cantor, Lebesgue, F. Riesz, and Ernst Fischer. Such deep results are not the chance products of algebraic doodling. None of Fourier's predecessors or contemporaries did—or could—exploit trigonometric expansions of arbitrary functions to their full effectiveness, nor could they recognize and accept their implications for the foundations of pure and applied analysis. Such achievements required a great master craftsman of mathematics, endowed with a lively imagination and holding a conscious philosophy of mathematics appropriate for his work. For Fourier, this was expressed in his aphorism, "Profound study of nature is the most fertile source of mathematical discoveries."

Theory of Equations. In contrast with his famous work on heat diffusion, Fourier's interest in the theory of equations is remarkably little known. Yet it has a much longer personal history, for it began in his sixteenth year when he discovered a new proof of Descartes's rule of signs and was just as much in progress at the time of his death. This rule may be stated as follows:

$$\text{Let } f(x) = x^m + a_1x^{m-1} + \cdots + a_{m-1}x + a_m.$$

Then there will be a sequence of signs to the coefficients of $f(x)$. If we call a pair of adjacent signs of the same type (i.e., $+\ +$ or $-\ -$) a preservation and a pair of the opposite type a variation, then the number of positive (or negative) roots of $f(x)$ is at most the number of variations (or preservations) of sign in the sequence. Fourier's proof was based on multiplying $f(x)$ by $(x + p)$, thus creating a new polynomial which contained one more sign in its sequence and one more positive (or negative) root, according as p was less (or greater) than zero, and showing that the number of preservations (or variations) in the new sequence was not increased relative to the old sequence. Hence the number of variations (or preservations) is increased by at least one, and the theorem follows. The details of the proof may be seen in any textbook dealing with the rule, for Fourier's youthful achievement quickly became the standard proof, even if its authorship appears to be virtually unknown.

Fourier generalized Descartes's rule to estimate the number of real roots $f(x)$ within a given interval $[a,b]$, by taking the signs of the terms in the sequence

$$f^{(m)}(x), f^{(m-1)}(x), \cdots, f''(x), f'(x), f(x).$$

When $x = -\infty$ the series will be made up totally of the variations

$$+ - + - \cdots\cdots$$

while at $x = +\infty$ it is entirely preservations:

$$+ + + + \cdots\cdots.$$

Fourier showed that as x passes from $-\infty$ to $+\infty$ the variations are lost by the crossing of a real (possibly multiple) root, or the skirting of a pair of complex conjugate roots, and that the number of real roots within $[a,b]$ is at most the difference between the number of variations in the sequence when $x = a$ and the number when $x = b$. This theorem received an important extension in Fourier's own lifetime by Sturm, who showed in 1829 that the number of real roots is exactly the difference in the number of variations formulated above for the sequence of functions

$$f_m(x), f_{m-1}(x), \cdots, f_2(x), f'(x), f(x)$$

where $f_2(x), \cdots$ are defined algorithmically from $f(x)$ and $f'(x)$. This is the famous Sturm's theorem.

Fourier appears to have proved his own theorem while in his teens and he sent a paper to the Academy in 1789. However, it disappeared in the turmoil of the year in Paris, and the pressure of administrative and other scientific work delayed publication of the results until the late 1810's. Then he became involved in a priority row with Ferdinand Budan de Bois-Laurent, a part-time mathematician who had previously published similar but inferior results. At the time of his death, Fourier was trying to prepare these and many other results for a book to be called *Analyse des équations déterminées;* he had almost finished only the first two of its seven *livres.* His friend Navier edited it for publication in 1831, inserting an introduction to establish from attested documents (including the 1789 paper) Fourier's priority on results which had by then become famous. Perhaps Fourier was aware that he would not live to finish the work, for he wrote a synopsis of the complete book which also appeared in the edition. The synopsis indicated his wide interests in the subject, of which the most important not yet mentioned were various means of distinguishing between real and imaginary roots, refinements to the Newton-Raphson method of approximating to the root of an equation, extensions to Daniel Bernoulli's rule for the limiting value of the ratio of successive terms of a recurrent series, and the method of solution and applications of linear inequalities. Fourier's remarkable understanding of the last subject makes him the great anticipator of linear programming.

Fourier's other mathematical interests included a general search for problems in dynamics and mechanics, shown by a published paper on the principle of virtual work. In his later years his directorship of the Bureau of Statistics brought him in touch with the problems of probability and errors, and he wrote important papers on estimating the errors of measurement from a large number of observations, published in the Bureau's reports for 1826 and 1829.

BIBLIOGRAPHY

I. ORIGINAL WORKS. Fourier's most famous work is *Théorie analytique de la chaleur* (Paris, 1822; repr. Breslau, 1883). An English trans. was prepared by A. Freeman (Cambridge, 1878; repr. New York, 1955). A 2nd French ed. appeared in 1888 as vol. I of the *Oeuvres* of Fourier, Gaston Darboux, ed. Vol. II, containing the majority of the rest of Fourier's published works, appeared in 1890. The list of works given by Darboux in the intro. to this vol. shows that his principal omission was the *Analyse des équations déterminées* (Paris, 1831). Two German trans. of this book have been made: by C. H. Schnuse (Brunswick, 1836; notes added in 1846), and by A. Loewy, Ostwald's Klassiker, no. 127 (Leipzig, 1902). The other main omissions from Darboux's ed. were the first 79 articles of the 1811 prize paper on heat diffusion, in *Mémoires de l'Académie des sciences,* **4** (1819–1820), 185–555, which were largely in common with secs. of the book, and a joint paper with H. C. Oersted on thermoelectric effects, in *Annales de chimie et de physique,* **12** (1823), 375–389. Darboux's list also omitted the papers read by Fourier at the Institut d'Égypte, which are listed in Cousin's obit. of Fourier cited below and partially in Navier's introduction to the *Analyse.* As *secrétaire perpétuel* of the Académie des Sciences, Fourier wrote the *Analyse des travaux* (1823–1827), and *éloges* on Delambre, Herschel, Breguet, Charles, and Laplace. The references are in Darboux's list.

The main source of unpublished MSS is the twenty-nine vols. in the Bibliothèque Nationale (MSS fonds franç. 22501–22529), totaling about 5,200 sheets. Of these, 22501 is a set of miscellaneous studies and letters; 22502–22516 deal with the theory of equations, including topics only summarized in the *Analyse;* 22517–22522 cover extended work in mechanics, dynamics, and errors of measurement, etc.; and 22523–22529 are concerned with various aspects of heat diffusion and its associated mathematics and experimental work, including, in 22525, fols. 107–149, the "first draft" of his 1807 paper on heat diffusion. This paper itself was discovered by Darboux in the library of the École Nationale des Ponts et Chaussées (MS 267, now numbered 1851), which also contains several *cahiers* of lecture notes, totaling 386 pp., given by Fourier at the École Polytechnique in 1795–1796 (MS 668, and 1852). Another set of lecture notes, partly in common with this set, is in a vol. of 559 pp. in the Bibliothèque de l'Institut de France (MS 2044) where an early four-page article on Descartes's rule (MS 2038) may also be found. There is a scattering of letters in connection with his secretaryship of the Academy and his prefectures in various public MS collections in France and in the archives of various learned institutions.

With regard to his extrascientific writings, his notebook of the Egyptian campaign may be read in *Bibliothèque Égyptologique,* VI (Paris, 1904), 165–214. The various versions of the "Préface historique" are best compared on pp. 88–172 of the book by J. J. Champollion-Figeac cited below. Fourier wrote an article in the *Description* on the government of Egypt, and another on the astronomical monuments of the country (including a discussion of the

Zodiacs). Details are given in the bibliographical account and collation of the *Description de l'Égypte* (London, 1838). He also contributed notes to a trans. by A. de Grandsagne of Pliny's *Natural History* and, although they are unsigned, it is clear that he annotated Pliny's discussion of Egypt, in *Histoire naturelle,* 20 vols. (Paris, 1829–1840), IV, 190–209. He also wrote the articles "Rallier des Ourmes," "Viète," and "Jean Wallis" in the *Biographie universelle,* 52 vols. (Paris, 1811–1829).

II. SECONDARY LITERATURE. The main biographical work is by the archaeologist Jacques Joseph Champollion-Figeac, who was encouraged by Fourier at Grenoble: *Fourier, Napoléon, l'Égypte et les cent jours* (Paris, 1844). The other primary sources of biography are Victor Cousin, *Notes biographiques sur M. Fourier* (Paris, 1831), with an addition; also in his *Fragments et souvenirs,* 3rd ed. (Paris, 1857), 283–392; François Arago, "Éloge historique de Joseph Fourier," in *Mémoires de l'Académie des Sciences,* **14** (1838), lxix–cxxxviii; also in his *Oeuvres* (Paris, 1854), V, 295–369, and in an English trans. in *Biographies of Distinguished Scientific Men* (London, 1857), 242–286; and in *Annual Reports of the Smithsonian Institution* (1871), 137–176. See also Aimé-Louis Champollion-Figeac, *Chroniques dauphinoises. Les savants du département de l'Isère . . .* (Vienne, 1880) and *Seconde période historique 1794–1810* (Vienne, 1881); Victor Parisot, "Fourier," in *Biographie universelle,* XIV (Paris, 1856), 525–534; and Georges Mauger, "Joseph Fourier," in *Annuaire statistique de l'Yonne* (1837), 270–276.

Some discussion of Fourier's work is to be found in Heinrich Burkhardt, "Entwicklungen nach oscillierenden Functionen . . .," in *Jahresbericht der Deutschen Mathematikervereinigung,* **10,** pt. 2 (1901–1908), esp. chs. 7 and 8; Gaston Bachelard, *Étude sur l'évolution d'un problème de physique . . .* (Paris, 1928), esp. chs. 2–4; and Ivor Grattan-Guinness in collaboration with Jerome Ravetz, *Joseph Fourier 1768–1830* (in press), which contains the full text of the 1807 paper on heat diffusion.

JEROME R. RAVETZ

I. GRATTAN-GUINNESS

FRAENKEL, ADOLF ABRAHAM (*b.* Munich, Germany, 17 February 1891; *d.* Jerusalem, Israel, 15 October 1965)

Fraenkel studied at the universities of Munich, Marburg, Berlin, and Breslau. From 1916 to 1921 he was a lecturer at the University of Marburg, where he became a professor in 1922. In 1928 he taught at the University of Kiel, and then from 1929 to 1959 he taught at the Hebrew University of Jerusalem. A fervent Zionist with a deep interest in Jewish culture, he engaged in many social activities. His interest in the history of mathematics appears in his papers "Zahlbegriff und Algebra bei Gauss" (1920), "Georg Cantor" (1930), and "Jewish Mathematics and Astronomy" (1960). As a mathematician he was interested in the axiomatic foundation of mathematical theories. His first works were on algebra, notably on the axiomatics of Hensel's p-adic numbers and on the theory of rings. He soon turned to the theory of sets, and in 1919 his remarkable *Einleitung in die Mengenlehre* appeared, which was reprinted several times. Engaged in a proof of the independence of the axiom system of Ernst Zermelo (1908), Fraenkel noticed that the system did not suffice for a foundation of set theory and required stronger axioms of infinity. At the same time he found a way to avoid Zermelo's imprecise notion of definite property.

Briefly stated, Zermelo's set theory is about a system B of objects closed under certain principles of set production (axioms). One of these axioms, the axiom of subsets, states that if a property E is definite in a set M, then there is a subset consisting precisely of those elements x of M for which $E(x)$ is true. Property E is definite for x if it can be decided systematically whether $E(x)$ is true or false. Another one is the famous axiom of choice, stating that the union of a set T of nonvoid disjoint sets contains a subset that has precisely one element in common with the sets of T.

Instead of Zermelo's notion of definite property Fraenkel used a notion of function, introduced by definition; and he replaced Zermelo's axiom of subsets by the following: If M is a set and ϕ and ψ are functions, then there are subsets M_E and $M_{E'}$ consisting of those elements x of M for which $\phi(x)$ is an element of $\psi(x)$, and $\phi(x)$ is not an element of $\psi(x)$ respectively. Using this axiom Fraenkel proved the independence of the axiom of choice, having recourse to an infinite set of objects that are not sets themselves. A proof avoiding such an extraneous assumption proved to be far more difficult and was given in 1963 by P. J. Cohen for a slightly revised system, ZFS, named after Zermelo, Fraenkel, and Thoralf Skolem. This system derives from a modification proposed by Skolem in 1922, consisting in the interpretation of definite property as property expressible in first-order logic.

In a series of papers Fraenkel developed ZF set theory to include theories of order and well-order. His encyclopedic knowledge of set theory is preserved in his works *Abstract Set Theory* (1953) and *Foundations of Set Theory* (1958). As early as 1923 he emphasized the importance of a thorough investigation of predicativism, based on ideas of H. Poincaré and undertaken much later by G. Kreisel, S. Feferman, and K. Schütte, among others.

BIBLIOGRAPHY

I. ORIGINAL WORKS. Fraenkel's writings include "Axiomatische Begründung von Hensels p-adischen Zahlen," in *Journal für die reine und angewandte Mathematik,* **141** (1912), 43–76; "Über die Teiler der Null und die Zerlegung von Ringen," *ibid.,* **145** (1915), 139–176; *Einleitung in die Mengenlehre* (Berlin, 1919); "Zahlbegriff und Algebra bei Gauss," in *Nachrichten von der Königlichen Gesellschaft der Wissenschaften zu Göttingen,* Math.-phys. Kl. (1920), pp. 1–49; "Über einfache Erweiterungen zerlegbarer Ringe," in *Journal für die reine und angewandte Mathematik,* **151** (1921), 121–167; "Über die Zermelosche Begründung der Mengenlehre," in *Jahresbericht der Deutschen Mathematikervereinigung,* **30** (1921), 97–98; "Zu den Grundlagen der Cantor-Zermeloschen Mengenlehre," in *Mathematische Annalen,* **86** (1922), 230–237; "Axiomatische Begründung der transfiniten Kardinal-zahlen. I," in *Mathematische Zeitschrift,* **13** (1922), 153–188; "Der Begriff 'definit' und die Unabhängigkeit des Auswahl-axioms," in *Sitzungsberichte der Preussischen Akademie der Wissenschaften,* Math.-phys. Kl. (1922), pp. 253–257; "Die neueren Ideen zur Grundlegung der Analysis und Mengenlehre," in *Jahresbericht der Deutschen Mathematikervereinigung,* **33** (1924), 97–103; "Untersuchungen über die Grundlagen der Mengenlehre," in *Mathematische Zeitschrift,* **22** (1925), 250–273; "Axiomatische Theorie der geordneten Mengen," in *Journal für die reine und angewandte Mathematik,* **55** (1926), 129–158; *Zehn Vorlesungen über die Grundlegung der Mengenlehre* (Leipzig-Berlin, 1927); "Georg Cantor," in *Jahresbericht der Deutschen Mathematikervereinigung,* **39** (1930), 189–226; "Das Leben Georg Cantors," in *Georg Cantor Gesammelte Abhandlungen,* E. Zermelo, ed. (Berlin, 1932; Hildesheim, 1966), pp. 452–483; "Axiomatische Theorie der Wohlordnung," in *Journal für die reine und angewandte Mathematik,* **167** (1932), 1–11; *Abstract Set Theory* (Amsterdam, 1953); *Axiomatic Set Theory* (Amsterdam, 1958), written with P. Bernays; *Foundations of Set Theory* (Amsterdam, 1958), written with Y. Bar-Hillel; "Jewish Mathematics and Astronomy," in *Scripta mathematica,* **25** (1960), 33–47; and *Lebenskreise, aus den Erinnerungen eines jüdischen Mathematikers* (Stuttgart, 1967).

II. SECONDARY LITERATURE. On Fraenkel and his work, see (in chronological order) T. Skolem, "Einige Bemerkungen zur axiomatischen Begründung der Mengenlehre," in *Wiss. Vorträge gehalten auf dem 5. Kongress der skandinav. Mathematiker in Helsingfors 1922* (1923), pp. 217–232; J. von Neumann, "Über die Definition durch transfinite Induktion und verwandte Fragen der allgemeinen Mengenlehre," in *Mathematische Annalen,* **99** (1928), 373-391; G. Kreisel, "La prédicativité," in *Bulletin de la Société mathématique de France,* **88** (1960), 371–391; K. Schütte, *Beweistheorie* (Berlin, 1960); S. Feferman, "Systems of Predicative Analysis," in *Journal of Symbolic Logic,* **29** (1964), 1–30; P. J. Cohen, *Set Theory and the Continuum Hypothesis* (New York, 1966); and J. van Heijenoort, *From Frege to Gödel* (Cambridge, Mass., 1967).

B. VAN ROOTSELAAR

FRANÇAIS, FRANÇOIS (JOSEPH) (*b.* Saverne, Bas-Rhin, France, 7 April 1768; *d.* Mainz, Germany, 30 October 1810); **FRANÇAIS, JACQUES FRÉDÉRIC** (*b.* Saverne, Bas-Rhin, France, 20 June 1775; *d.* Metz, France, 9 March 1833)

The mathematical works of the Français brothers, François and Jacques Frédéric, are so poorly distinguished by most authors and their biographies so imprecise that it is necessary to devote a common article to the two of them. Sons of Jacques Frédéric Français, a grocer, and of Maria Barbara Steib, they were both born at Saverne, seven years apart. In 1789, François, the elder, became a seminarist. Named professor at the *collège* in Colmar in June 1791, he assumed the chair of mathematics at the *collège* in Strasbourg in September 1792. He participated actively in political life and was a secretary of the *société populaire* of Strasbourg. He took part in the Vendée campaign from May to October 1793 and, after a brief return to civilian life, went back to the army as an officer until October 1797, when he was named professor of mathematics at the École Centrale du Haut-Rhin in Colmar. He left this position in September 1803 to teach mathematics, first at the lycée in Mainz, then at the École d'Artillerie at La Fère (1804), and, finally, at the École d'Artillerie in Mainz. At his death he left four small children, whom his younger brother adopted soon afterward.

Jacques Frédéric Français, after having been an outstanding student at the *collège* of Strasbourg, enrolled as a volunteer in 1793 and was named assistant in the corps of engineers in September 1794. He was admitted to the École Polytechnique on 30 December 1797, and from there he went, in March 1800, to the École du Génie. A first lieutenant in January 1801, he participated in the expedition sent by Napoleon to attempt to save the French army in Egypt. On his return he was quartered at Toulon and was named captain of the sappers in December 1801; in November 1802, he became second in command of the staff headquarters of the corps of engineers. In this capacity he participated, with Admiral Villeneuve's squadron, in the expedition to the Antilles and in the naval battles of Cape Finisterre and Trafalgar (1805). Beginning at the end of that year, he was successively assigned to garrisons at Condé-sur-Escaut; then Kehl (1806); Strasbourg (1807), under the command of Malus; and Metz (from 1808), to the staff headquarters of the École d'Application. Promoted to first in command in July 1810, he was named, at the beginning of 1811, professor of military art at the École d'Application du Génie et de l'Artillerie in Metz. He held this last position until his death.

In July 1795 François Français presented a memoir

on the integration of partial differential equations; a new version of this paper, addressed to the Académie des Sciences in 1797, is mentioned by S. F. Lacroix (*Traité du calcul différential et du calcul intégral,* III, 598) as an important contribution to the theory of these equations. According to the testimony of Biot (*Procès-verbaux de l'Académie des sciences,* III, 204–205), Français then assisted "his uncle" Louis-François Arbogast in the elaboration of the "calculus of derivations" and in the preparation of a treatise that he devoted to this subject (1800). Having inherited Arbogast's papers in April 1803, he continued to work on the development of the calculus of derivations and its applications; thus, in a memoir presented to the Academy in November 1804, he applied this calculus to the movement of projectiles in a resistant medium. Highly esteemed by the mathematicians of the Paris Academy—Lagrange, Legendre, Lacroix, and Biot—François Français pursued original mathematical investigations, but without publishing anything. Following his death his brother Jacques Frédéric included several brief extracts in the *Annales de mathématiques* from his unpublished papers (the application of the calculus of derivations; formulas concerning polygons and polyhedra; and a study of a special curve, the tractrix); these papers were, moreover, a precious source of inspiration to him.

After having presented a memoir, now lost, on the complete integral of first-order partial differential equations in 1800, Jacques Frédéric Français did not return to mathematics until 1807–1808. He then published, on the urging of Malus, two memoirs on analytic geometry; they treated the equation of the straight line and of the plane in oblique coordinates and the transformation of the systems of oblique coordinates. Applying his method to the famous problem of finding a sphere tangent to four given spheres, he gave a solution to it in 1808, which he corrected immediately before completing it in 1812.

The study of his brother's papers attracted him once more to infinitesimal calculus and especially to the development of the calculus of derivations, to which he in turn devoted two important memoirs: one in 1811 (published in 1813) on the separation of the scales of differentiation and the integration of those functions which they determine; and the other in 1815, on the principles of this calculus. In April 1811 he presented a memoir to the Academy, published in 1812 and 1813 in the *Annales de mathématiques,* in which he put forth an unusual example in the theory of the extrema of functions of several variables. In 1813 he published a rather fully developed study on the rotation of solid bodies, in which, in the words of Cauchy (*Procès-verbaux de l'Académie des sciences,* VIII, 523–525), "interesting research is mixed with several errors."

In September 1813 Français published in the *Annales de mathématiques* a resounding article in which he presents the principles of the geometric representation of complex numbers and draws from them several applications. However, in the final paragraph, he acknowledges having taken a portion of his ideas from a letter of 1806 in which Legendre gave his brother François information about a manuscript study on this same subject that had been entrusted to him by an anonymous young author, and he requested that this author reveal himself. In fact, in the following issue of the *Annales de mathématiques,* this author, Jean-Robert Argand, whose study, although printed, had remained practically unknown, replied with a summary of the main conceptions of his work (*Essai sur une manière de représenter les quantités imaginaires dans les constructions géométriques* [Paris, 1806]). A polemic then arose in the *Annales,* in 1813 and 1814, between Argand himself, Français, and François-Joseph Servois: the first two attempted to justify the principle itself of this geometric representation, while Servois was concerned above all else to preserve the rigor and purity of algebra. These publications had the great merit of widely diffusing an innovation whose essence, although presented by Caspar Wessel in Copenhagen in 1797 (and published in 1799), by the Abbé Adrien-Quentin Buée in London in 1805, and by Argand in Paris in 1806, had remained unnoticed by the leading mathematicians.

Although Jacques Frédéric Français's mathematical publications were interrupted rather suddenly at the end of 1815, it does not seem that his curiosity was extinguished, and Poncelet's long stay in Metz certainly contributed to maintaining it. While not of the first rank, the mathematical activity of the Français brothers merits mention for its originality and diversity.

J. F. Soleirol, in his *Éloge de Monsieur Français . . . prononcé sur sa tombe le 11 mars 1833 . . .* (Metz, 1833), points out that Français also composed a course on military art, a course on geodesy, and two memoirs, one on permanent fortifications and the other on the thrust of the earth.

A final point remains to be made. Upon the death of Arbogast in April 1803, his writings, his important mathematical library, and the rich collection of scientific manuscripts that he had gathered passed to his "nephew," François Français. When François died, he bequeathed this collection of manuscripts and books, augmented by his own writings, to his brother Jacques Frédéric, who announced in December 1823 that they were being placed on sale (see *Bulletin général et universel des annonces* . . . I, fasc. 3 [1823], 493–495). Upon the latter's death the essential portion of the collection, not yet sold, passed into the hands of a bookseller in Metz, at whose shop Count Libri was still able to find various valuable manuscripts in 1839. With the sale of Libri's library, these items were dispersed; some are now in the Biblioteca Medicea-Laurenziana in Florence (in particular, certain papers of François Français) and in the Bibliothèque Nationale de Paris, while others, which are very precious, have not yet been found. It is hoped that a thorough investigation will be undertaken in order to locate them.

BIBLIOGRAPHY

I. ORIGINAL WORKS.

(1) François Français. His work amounts to four posthumous memoirs published by his brother in the *Annales de mathématiques pures et appliquées.* They deal with an aspect of the "Calcul des dérivations" ("Méthode de différentiation indépendante du développement des fonctions en séries," in *Annales,* **2** [May 1812], 325–331); with theorems concerning polyhedra and polygons (*ibid.,* **3** [Dec. 1812], 189–191, and **5** [May 1815], 341–350); and with the tractrix (**4** [Apr. 1814], 305–319). Two important memoirs presented to the Académie des Sciences remain unpublished but were known and utilized by different authors—the memoir on the integration of partial differential equations, presented in 1797 (see S. F. Lacroix, *Traité du calcul différentiel et du calcul intégral,* 2nd ed., III [Paris, 1819], 598); and the memoir on the movement of projectiles in resisting media, presented on 26 Nov. 1804, which, moreover, was the object of a flattering report by Biot on 22 April 1805 (*Procès-verbaux de l'Académie des sciences* . . ., III [Hendaye, 1913], 159, 204–205).

(2) Jacques Frédéric Français. His work includes an individual publication, *Mémoire sur le mouvement de rotation d'un corps solide libre autour de son centre de masse* (Paris, 1813); and a series of memoirs published in the *Correspondance sur l'École polytechnique* (*C.E.P.*), the *Journal de l'École polytechnique* (*J.E.P.*), and the *Annales de mathématiques pures et appliquées* of Gergonne (*Annales*). They are listed below by subject and in chronological order.

Analytic Geometry: letter to Hachette, in *C.E.P.,* **1,** no. 8 (May 1807), 320–321; on the straight line and the plane in oblique coordinates, in *C.E.P.,* **1,** no. 9 (Jan. 1808), 337–346; on a sphere tangent to four spheres in the following issues of *C.E.P.:* **1,** no. 9 (Jan. 1808), 346–349; **1,** no. 10 (Apr. 1808), 418–421; **2,** no. 2 (Jan. 1810), 63–66; **2,** no. 5 (Jan. 1813), 409–410; and in *Annales,* **3** (Nov. 1812), 158–161; on the transformation of oblique coordinates, in *J.E.P.,* **7,** *cahier* 14 (Apr. 1808), 182–190; and on various problems, in *C.E.P.,* **2,** no. 2 (Jan. 1810), 60–70.

Infinitesimal Calculus: on a singular case of the theory of the extrema of functions of several variables, in *Annales,* **3** (Oct. 1812), 132–137; and *ibid.,* **3** (June 1813), 197–206; on scales of differentiation and integration, *ibid.,* **3** (Feb. 1813), 244–272; on the calculus of derivations derived from its true principles, *ibid.,* **6** (Sept. 1815), 61–111.

Solid Mechanics: on rotation of solid bodies, in *Annales,* **3** (Jan. 1813), 197–206.

Geometric Representation of Imaginary Numbers: articles in *Annales,* **4** (Sept. 1813), 61–71; **4** (Jan. 1814), 222–227; **4** (June 1814), 364–366; and articles repr. in J. Hoüel, ed. (see below), pp. 63–74, 96–101, 109–110.

Other Topics: problems concerning the calendar, in *Annales,* **4** (Mar. 1814), 273–276, and *ibid.,* **4** (May 1814), 337–338; remarks on the tractrix, *ibid.,* 332–336; and a problem involving the pendulum and the flying bridge, *ibid.,* **6** (Oct. 1815), 126–129.

II. SECONDARY LITERATURE. On the brothers Français, see M. Chasles, *Rapport sur les progrès de la géométrie* (Paris, 1870), p. 57 (on François), pp. 35, 61 (on Jacques Frédéric); S. F. Lacroix, *Traité du calcul différentiel et du calcul intégral* (Paris, 1819), II, pp. 656–658, 789, III, p. 598, 726, 752 (on François), pp. 631–632, 752 (on Jacques Frédéric); N. Nielsen, *Géomètres français sous la Révolution* (Copenhagen, 1929), pp. 96–97 (on François), pp. 97–103 (on Jacques Frédéric); and the Royal Society *Catalogue of Scientific Papers,* II (London, 1868), 694–695: nos. 4, 7, 14, and 16 are on François, the others on Jacques Frédéric. Baptism records may be found in the municipal archives of Saverne.

On François Français, see (in chronological order), *Almanach national* (later *Almanach impérial*) for *an* VII (1798–1799) to 1810; *Procès-verbaux du Comité d'instruction publique de la convention nationale,* VI (Paris, 1907), 452; *Procès-verbaux de l'Académie des sciences,* III (Hendaye, 1913), 59, 159, 204–205, 262, 504; and J. Joachim, *L'école centrale du Haut-Rhin* (Colmar, 1934), esp. pp. 151–155, where there is partial confusion with Louis François Français, war commissioner. See also the archives of the Département du Haut-Rhin.

On Jacques Frédéric Français, see R. Argand, *Essai sur une nouvelle manière de représenter les quantités imaginaires dans les constructions géométriques,* 2nd ed. (Paris, 1874), pp. v–xvi, 63–74, 96–101, 109–110; S. Bachelard, *La représentation géométrique des quantités imaginaires au début du XIXe siècle* (Paris, 1966), pp. 11–13, 30; C. B. Boyer, *History of Analytic Geometry* (New York, 1956), pp. 222–223; A. Fourcy, *Histoire de l'École polytechnique* (Paris, 1828), p. 403; G. Libri, in *Comptes rendus hebdomadaires des séances de l'Académie des sciences,* **9** (1839), 357–358, and "Fermat," in *Revue des deux mondes* (15 May 1845), pp. 679–707; G. Loria, "Origines, perfectionnement et développement de la notion de coordonnées," in *Osiris,* **8** (1948), esp. 220–223, where there is confusion with Frédéric Louis Lefrançois; and J. V. Poncelet, *Applications d'analyse et de géométrie,* II (Paris, 1864), 592–595; and J. F. Soleirol, *Éloge de Monsieur Français . . . prononcé sur sa tombe le 11 mars 1833* . . . (Metz, 1833). Further material may be found in *Almanach national* (later *Almanach impérial,* then *Almanach royal*) for *an* VII (1798–1799) to 1833; Férussac, ed., *Bulletin général et universel des annonces et des nou-*

velles scientifiques, **1,** fasc. 3 (1823), 493–495; and *Procès-verbaux de l'Académie des sciences,* III–V (Hendaye, 1913–1914), III, 265; IV, 475, 554; V, 152, 168, 524.

Part of the original documentation of this article comes from the archives of the École Polytechnique, the Service Historique de l'Armée, and the archives of the Legion of Honor.

RENÉ TATON

FRANCESCA, PIERO DELLA (or **Piero dei Franceschi**), also known as **Petrus Borgensis** (*b.* Borgo San Sepolcro [now Sansepolcro], Italy, between 1410 and 1420; *d.* Sansepolcro, 12 October 1492)

Vasari's reason (in *Lives of the Artists*) for the adoption of the feminine form "Francesca" in Piero's name has been invalidated by the authentication of his father as "dei Franceschi" and his mother as Romana di Perino da Monterchi. Of Piero's early life—as the wide uncertainty of his birthdate reveals—nothing is known until 7 September 1439, when he was an associate of Domenico Veneziano at Florence. He is not named by Alberti in the famous dedication to his colleagues in *Della pittura* (1436), but Alberti's influence is revealed in the clearest manner in the architectural studies from Piero's workshop at Urbino.

Piero's value to science lay in his pioneering efforts to explore the nature of space and to construct it by his sophisticated study of linear perspective and masterly juxtaposition of color masses. Although his major work on the mathematics of painting, *De prospettiva pingendi,* was written only after his career as an artist was at an end, it can hardly be doubted that the diminution in the successive members of the black and white pavement in the *Flagellation* at Urbino must have been achieved by such complex calculations as are subsequently displayed in the *Prospettiva.* These represent a synthesis of the two operational diagrams that he probably learned from Alberti.

But a more strikingly original contribution of Piero's was his measuring of the distances between successive surfaces of a human head and transferring the plane sections thus obtained into a contoured plan. Luca Pacioli, whose influence in spreading the study of mathematics in the early *cinquecento* is well known, testified to the assistance of his fellow townsman but later paid him the dubious compliment of including (unacknowledged) in his *De divina proportione* a large part of Piero's last work, *De quinque corporibus regolaribus.*

BIBLIOGRAPHY

I. ORIGINAL WORKS. The *De prospettiva pingendi* was written in the vernacular; a transcript exists in the Palatina at Parma and forms the basis of the definitive text edited by G. Fasola (Florence, 1942). There is a transcript of the (contemporary) Latin trans. in the Ambrosian Library at Milan. Piero's *De quinque corporibus regolaribus* exists in a transcript (with figs. by him) in the Vatican Library (Urbinas 632). Excerpts from the original works (in English) are available in E. G. Holt, ed., *A Documentary History of Art,* I (New York, 1957), 256–267.

II. SECONDARY LITERATURE. A detailed and analytical study of Piero's life and work is Roberto Longhi, *Piero della Francesca* (London, 1930), Leonard Penlock, trans. The Introduction by Sir Kenneth Clark to the Phaidon review of his pictures, *Piero della Francesca* (London, 1951), is both readable and scholarly.

WILLIAM P. D. WIGHTMAN

FRANK, PHILIPP (*b.* Vienna, Austria, 20 March 1884; *d.* Cambridge, Massachusetts, 21 July 1966)

Frank obtained his doctorate in physics in 1907 from the University of Vienna as a student under Ludwig Boltzmann. Frank later wrote of this period:

> . . . the domain of my most intensive interest was the philosophy of science. I used to associate with a group of students who assembled every Thursday night in one of the old Viennese coffee houses. . . . We returned again and again to our central problem: How can we avoid the traditional ambiguity and obscurity of philosophy? How can we bring about the closest possible *rapprochement* between philosophy and science?

As a physicist Frank was a creative contributor, working on fundamental problems of theoretical physics during an exciting period of its growth. Perhaps his most widely known publication of those years was the two-volume collection, edited with his lifelong friend Richard von Mises, *Die Differential- und Integralgleichungen der Mechanik und Physik.* Frank's own research was concerned with variational calculus, Fourier series, function spaces, Hamiltonian geometrical optics, Schrödinger's wave mechanics, and relativity theory. In an early paper with Hermann Rothe he derived the Lorentz transformation equations without assuming constancy of light velocity from the fact that the equations form a group.

But his first and most lasting love was the philosophy of science. From the beginning Frank was intrigued by Poincaré's neo-Kantian idea that many basic principles of science are purely conventional. In 1907 Frank took the bold step of using that idea to analyze the law of causality. This paper attracted Einstein's attention and started a lasting friendship. In 1912 Einstein recommended Frank as his successor as professor of theoretical physics at the German

University of Prague, a position Frank held until 1938. Frank's original paper on causality—which Lenin criticized in his 1908 book on positivist philosophy and the sciences—was later expanded into his widely influential work *Das Kausalgesetz und seine Grenzen* (1932). In 1947 Frank published an authoritative biography, *Einstein: His Life and Times.*

Frank was a logical positivist, although a less doctrinaire one than many of those with whom he formed the Vienna circle in the 1920's. The breadth of interest which he exhibited in his work and fostered in his students made science a liberal discipline and reflected a style of life as well as of mind. As he once remarked, he sought always to achieve a balanced outlook on man and nature; and for him physics not only provided reliable answers to particular technical problems but also raised and illuminated important questions concerning the nature, scope, and validity of human knowledge. Indeed, Frank believed that a stable perspective on life can best be achieved through the critical, intellectual method of modern natural science.

He therefore saw it as a misfortune that science and philosophy are widely regarded as unrelated and incongruous. But it was also his conviction that this breach between a scientific and a humanist orientation toward life—a breach that he thought to be of relatively recent origin—could be diminished, if not overcome, by an adequate philosophy of science.

Holding that the meaning and validity of theoretical assumptions can be determined only if detailed consideration is given to the verifiable consequences which the assumptions entail, Frank called attention to certain misinterpretations of relativity theory and quantum mechanics and their fallacious use in support of questionable doctrines. The titles of some of his works indicate these concerns—"Das Ende der mechanistischen Physik" (1935), *Interpretations and Misinterpretations of Modern Physics* (1938), and *Philosophy of Science: The Link Between Science and Philosophy* (1957).

Frank was organizer or chief participant in the *International Encyclopedia of Unified Science,* the Philosophy of Science Association, *Synthèse,* the Institute for the Unity of Science, and the Boston Colloquium for the Philosophy of Science.

In 1938 Frank and his wife, Hania, came to the United States. After serving as a visiting lecturer, he remained as lecturer on physics and mathematics at Harvard, where his influential course on philosophy of science, his erudite mastery, and his warm and witty manner were remembered long after his retirement in 1954.

BIBLIOGRAPHY

I. ORIGINAL WORKS. Frank's books include *Die Differential- und Integralgleichungen der Mechanik und Physik,* 2 vols. (Brunswick, 1925; last rev. ed., 1935), trans. into Russian (Moscow, 1937), written with Richard von Mises; *Das Kausalgesetz und seine Grenzen* (Vienna, 1932), also trans. into French (Paris, 1937); the collection of papers in philosophy of science, *Between Physics and Philosophy* (Cambridge, Mass., 1941), later repr. and enl. as *Modern Science and Its Philosophy* (New York, 1949); *Einstein: His Life and Times* (New York, 1947; rev. 1953), published in German (Munich, 1949); *Relativity: A Richer Truth* (Boston, 1950); and *Philosophy of Science: The Link Between Science and Philosophy* (Englewood Cliffs, N.J., 1957).

Frank's papers in theoretical physics include "Das Relativitätsprinzip und die Darstellung der physikalischen Erscheinungen im vierdimensionalen Raum," in Ostwald's *Annalen der Naturphilosophie,* **10** (1911), 129–161; "Die statistische Betrachtungsweise in der Physik," in *Naturwissenschaften,* **7** (1919), 701–740; "Über die Eikonalgleichung in allgemein anisotropen Medien," in *Annalen der Physik,* 4th ser., **84** (1927), 891–898; "Relativitätsmechanik," in *Handbuch für physikalische und technische Mechanik,* II (Leipzig, 1928), 52 ff.; "Die Grundbegriffe der analytischen Mechanik als Grundlage der Quanten- und Wellenmechanik," in *Physikalische Zeitschrift,* **30** (1929), 209–228; "Statistische Mechanik Boltzmanns als Näherung der Wellenmechanik," in *Zeitschrift für Physik,* **61** (1930), 640–643, written with W. Glaser.

His epistemological writings include "Kausalgesetz und Erfahrung," in Ostwald's *Annalen der Naturphilosophie,* **6** (1908), 445–450; "Über die Anschaulichkeit physikalischer Theorien," in *Naturwissenschaften,* **16** (1928), 122–128; "Was bedeuten die gegenwärtigen physikalischen Theorien für die allgemeine Erkenntnislehre?," *ibid.,* **17** (1929), 971–977; "Das Ende der mechanistischen Physik," in *Einheitswissenschaft,* **5** (1935), 23–25; "The Mechanical Versus the Mathematical Conception of Nature," in *Philosophy of Science,* **4** (1937), 41–74; *Interpretations and Misinterpretations of Modern Physics* (Paris, 1938); "Physik und logischer Empirismus," in *Erkenntnis,* **7** (1938), 297–301; *Foundations of Physics,* I, no. 7 of the *International Encyclopedia of Unified Science* (Chicago, 1946); and "Metaphysical Interpretations of Science," in *British Journal for the Philosophy of Science,* **1** (1950), 60–91.

Frank's papers on sociological and cultural aspects of science include "Mechanismus oder Vitalismus? Versuch einer präzisen Formulierung der Fragestellung," in Ostwald's *Annalen der Naturphilosophie,* **7** (1908), 393–409; "Die Bedeutung der physikalischen Erkenntnistheorie Machs für das Geistesleben der Gegenwart," in *Naturwissenschaften,* **5** (1917), 65–72; "The Philosophical Meaning of the Copernican Revolution," in *Proceedings of the American Philosophical Society,* **87** (1944), 381–386; "Science Teaching and the Humanities," in *ETC: A Review of General Semantics,* **4** (1946), 3–24; "The Place of Logic and Metaphysics in the Advancement of Modern Science," in *Philosophy of Science,* **15** (1948), 275–286; "Einstein, Mach, and Logical Positivism," in *Albert Einstein: Philosopher-Scientist,* P. A. Schilpp, ed. (Chicago, 1949), pp. 271–286; "Einstein's Philosophy of Science," in *Review of Modern Physics,* **21** (1949), 349–355; "The Logical and Sociological Aspects of Science," in *Proceedings of the American Academy of Arts and Sciences,* **80** (1951), 16–30; "The Origin of the Separation Between Science and Philosophy," *ibid.* (1952), 115–139; "The Variety of Reasons for the Acceptance of Scientific Theories," in *The Validation of Scientific Theories,* Philipp Frank, ed. (Boston, 1956), pp. 3–17, first pub. in *Scientific Monthly,* **79,** no. 3 (1954), 139–145; and "The Pragmatic Component in Carnap's 'Elimination of Metaphysics,'" in *The Philosophy of Rudolf Carnap,* P. A. Schilpp, ed. (Chicago, 1963), pp. 159–164.

Frank edited a number of works, including *The Validation of Scientific Theories* (Boston, 1956) and *The International Encyclopedia of Unified Science* (Chicago, various dates). He also served on the editorial boards of the journals *Synthèse* (1946–1963) and *Philosophy of Science* (1941–1955).

II. SECONDARY LITERATURE. A *Festschrift* for Philipp Frank was published as vol. II of *Boston Studies in the Philosophy of Science,* R. S. Cohen and M. W. Wartofsky, eds. (Dordrecht–New York, 1965), with tributes by Peter G. Bergmann, Rudolf Carnap, R. Fürth, Gerald Holton, Edwin C. Kemble, Henry Margenau, Hilda von Mises, Ernest Nagel, Raymond J. Seeger, and Kurt Sitte, and essays in the philosophy of science.

A memorial booklet based on talks delivered by some of Frank's colleagues and friends at the memorial meeting of 25 October 1966 at Harvard University was distributed the following year, and an article "In Memory of Philipp Frank" appeared in *Philosophy of Science,* **35** (1968), 1–5.

GERALD HOLTON
ROBERT S. COHEN

FRÉCHET, RENÉ MAURICE (*b.* Maligny, France, 10 September 1878; *d.* Paris, France, 4 June 1973)

Maurice Fréchet (he never used the name René) was the fourth of six children born to Protestant parents of modest means. His father, Jacques Fréchet, was director of a Protestant orphanage. The family moved to Paris while Maurice was still a boy. There his father was a schoolteacher and his mother, Zoé, ran a boardinghouse for foreigners. At the Lycée Buffon in Paris the young Fréchet was taught mathematics by Jacques Hadamard, then in his twenties, who perceived his pupil's precocity and gave him special attention. This tutelage extended to encouragement well beyond the ordinary student-teacher relationship and continued (by correspondence) even after Hadamard's appointment as professor at Bordeaux in 1894. Fréchet entered the École Normale Supérieure in 1900, graduating in 1903. In the winter of 1903–1904 he wrote up the lectures of Émile Borel that were turned into a book, *Leçons sur les fonctions de variables réelles et les développements en séries de polynômes* (1905). This work was part of a long and close relationship between Borel and Fréchet that continued as long as Borel lived.

Fréchet wrote his doctoral thesis (completed in 1906) as a student of Hadamard, by that time a professor in Paris. Under the influence of Hadamard and as a result of reading the work of Vito Volterra, Fréchet had become interested in what was then called the "functional calculus," the study of numerically valued functions (Hadamard called them functionals) defined on a class of ordinary functions (or, perhaps, curves). Fréchet made the bold jump to numerical functions defined on an abstract class. In order to be able to speak about limits and continuity, he introduced several ways of developing a theory of point set topology in an abstract space. The most important of these involved what came to be called a metric space, a concept invented by Fréchet.

In his thesis Fréchet was the first to demonstrate conclusively the feasibility and fruitfulness of developing in abstract spaces an effective generalization of the point set topology that had been developed for Euclidean spaces. Following Georg Cantor, Fréchet took as fundamental the concept of a derived set of a given set. Fréchet introduced the concepts of compactness, separability, and completeness. He established the connection between compactness and what later came to be known as total boundedness. He also established, under certain conditions, the linkage in metric spaces between two properties of a set: that of being closed and compact, and that of having the property concerning open coverings that is expressed in the Borel-Lebesgue (also called Heine-Borel) theorem for closed and bounded sets in Euclidean space.

Hadamard, reporting to the Académie des Sciences in 1934 on the work of Fréchet (in connection with the latter's candidacy for election to the Section de Géométrie of the academy), said that the boldness of Fréchet's effort of abstraction was without precedent since the work of Évariste Galois. (The report by Hadamard, as well as one by Borel, can be found in the archives of the academy in Paris.) Jean Dieudonné, in his *History of Functional Analysis* (1981), wrote that the blend of algebra and topology that has come to be known as functional analysis emerged largely because of a sudden crystallization of ideas that was essentially due to the publication of four fundamental papers, of which one was Fréchet's thesis (1906), the others being works by Ivar Fredholm (1900), Henri Lebesgue (1902), and David Hilbert (1906).

From 1907 to 1910 Fréchet held teaching positions at lycées in Besançon and Nantes and at the University of Rennes. He married Suzanne Carrive in 1908, and they had four children. He held a professorship at Poitiers from 1910 to 1918, but was on leave in military service throughout World War I, mainly as an interpreter with the British army. From 1919 to 1928 he was head of the Institute of Mathematics at the University of Strasbourg.

The most important further accomplishments of Fréchet in his pre-Paris years were: (1) the representation theorem (1907) for continuous linear functionals on the vector space of functions now known as L^2 (a theorem discovered independently at almost exactly the same time by F. Riesz); (2) the formulation of the concept of the differential of a function (1911 and 1925), generalizing the concept from ordinary calculus, in a way suitable for use in the general analysis of functions in abstract normed vector spaces; (3) the formulation in 1915 of an imporant geneıalization of the work of J. Radon, showing how to extend the work of Lebesgue and Radon to the integration of real functions on an abstract set without a topology, using merely a generalized measurelike set function; (4) a theory of an abstract topological space, now known as a T_1-space, which Fréchet called an *H*-class, or, alternatively, an accessible space, which he first defined in 1918 using axioms about derived sets, and in 1921 using axioms about neighborhoods. Such a topological space is more general than the type of topological space introduced in 1914 in a book by Felix Hausdorff.

Fréchet moved to the University of Paris in 1928, where he taught until his retirement in 1949 (he was made honorary professor in 1951). His book *Les espaces abstraits* was published before his move. It is devoted almost exclusively to his work on general topology. Fréchet's early influence as the pioneer of an effective theory of topology in abstract spaces was substantial, but in time his influence was superseded by that of Hausdorff, whose book became an important resource for students and scholars, and in the 1920's by the brilliant work of two young Russians, Paul Aleksandrov and Paul Urysohn, who were notably influenced by both Fréchet and Hausdorff.

Fréchet's career in Paris was mainly devoted to probability theory and its applications. This interest had developed while he was at Strasbourg. Following Borel's wishes, Fréchet wrote expositions of probability theory in two books (1937–1938). Although he published prolifically on probability and statistics, bringing functional analysis to bear, his contributions in these fields did not match in originality and importance his early work on topology and general analysis.

Apart from his standing with Borel and Hadamard and certain other good friends among French mathematicians, Fréchet did not secure as much approbation in France as he did abroad, notably in America and Poland. He lost out repeatedly to more classical analysts in running for election to the Académie des Sciences. He was finally elected in 1956 to the vacancy created by the death of Borel. He was a chevalier of the Légion d'Honneur, was elected to the Polish Academy of Sciences in 1929, and was an honorary member of the Royal Society of Edinburgh and a member of the International Institute of Statistics.

BIBLIOGRAPHY

I. ORIGINAL WORKS. Fréchet's thesis was published as "Sur quelques points du calcul fonctionnel," in *Rendiconti del Circolo matematico di Palermo*, **22** (1906), 1–74. Two works dealing with the representation theorem for functionals on L^2 are "Sur les ensembles de fonctions et les opérations linéaires," in *Comptes rendus de l'Académie des sciences, Paris*, **144** (1907), 1414–1416; and "Sur les opérations linéaires," in *Transactions of the American Mathematical Society*, **8** (1907), 433–446. Other works include "Sur la notion de différentielle," in *Comptes rendus de l'Académie des sciences, Paris*, **152** (1911), 845–847; "Sur l'intégrale d'une fonctionelle étendue à un ensemble abstrait," in *Bulletin société mathématique de France*, **43** (1915), 248–264; "Sur la notion de voisinage dans les ensembles abstraits," in *Bulletin des sciences mathématiques*, **42** (1918), 138–156.

"Sur les ensembles abstraits," in *Annales scientifiques de l'École normal supérieure*, 3rd ser., **38** (1921), 341–388 (includes a characterization of *H*-classes, which are also known as T_1-spaces); "La notion de différentielle dans l'analyse générale," *ibid.*, **42** (1925), 293–323; *Les espaces abstraits et leur théorie considérée comme introduction à l'analyse générale* (Paris, 1928); *Notice sur les travaux scientifiques de Maurice Fréchet* (Paris, 1933); *Recherches théoriques modernes sur le calcul des probabilités*, 2nd ed., I, *Généralités sur les probabilités: Éléments aléatoires*, II, *Méthode des fonctions arbitraires: Theorie des événements en chaîne dans le cas d'un nombre fini d'états possibles* (Paris, 1950–1952).

II. SECONDARY LITERATURE. Obituaries are by Daniel Dugué in *International Statistical Review*, **42** (1974), 113–114; by Szolem Mandelbrojt in *Comptes rendus de l'A-*

cadémie des sciences, Paris, Vie académique, **277** (19 November 1973), 73–76; and by F. Smithies in *Year Book of the Royal Society of Edinburgh, 1975* (1975), 31–33. See also L. C. Arboleda, "Les débuts de l'école topologique soviétique: Notes sur les lettres de Paul S. Alexandroff et Paul S. Unysohn à Maurice Fréchet," in *Archive for History of Exact Sciences*, **20** (1979), 73–89; Jean Dieudonné, *History of Functional Analysis* (Amsterdam, 1981); Angus E. Taylor, "A Study of Maurice Fréchet, I, His Early Work on Point Set Theory and the Theory of Functionals," "II, Mainly About His Work on General Topology, 1909–1928," and "III, Fréchet as Analyst, 1909–1930," in *Archive for History of Exact Sciences*, **27** (1982), 233–295, **34** (1985), 279–380, and **37** (1987), 25–76.

ANGUS E. TAYLOR

FREDHOLM, (ERIK) IVAR (*b.* Stockholm, Sweden, 7 April 1866; *d.* Stockholm, 17 August 1927)

Ivar Fredholm's small but pithy output was concentrated in the area of the equations of mathematical physics. Most significantly, he solved, under quite broad hypotheses, a very general class of integral equations that had been the subject of extensive research for almost a century. His work led indirectly to the development of Hilbert spaces and so to other more general function spaces.

Fredholm was born into an upper-middle-class family; his father was a wealthy merchant and his mother, née Stenberg, was from a cultured family. His early education was the best obtainable, and he soon showed his brilliance. After passing his baccalaureate examination in 1885, he studied for a year at the Polytechnic Institute in Stockholm. During this single year he developed an interest in the technical problems of practical mechanics that was to last all his life and that accounted for his continuing interest in applied mathematics. In 1886 Fredholm enrolled at the University of Uppsala—the only institution in Sweden granting doctorates at that time—from which he received the Bachelor of Science in 1888 and the Doctor of Science in 1898. Because of the superior instruction available at the University of Stockholm, Fredholm also studied there from 1888, becoming a student of the illustrious Mittag-Leffler. He remained at the University of Stockholm the rest of his life, receiving an appointment as lecturer in mathematical physics in 1898 and in 1906 becoming professor of rational mechanics and mathematical physics.

Fredholm's first major work was in partial differential equations. His doctoral thesis, written in 1898 and published in 1900, involved the study of the equation—written in Fredholm's own operator notation—

$$f\left(\frac{\partial}{\partial x_1}, \frac{\partial}{\partial x_2}, \frac{\partial}{\partial x_3}\right) u = 0,$$

where $f(\xi,\eta,\zeta)$ is a definite homogeneous form. This equation is significant because it occurs in the study of deformation of anisotropic media (such as crystals) subjected to interior or exterior forces. Initially, Fredholm solved only the particular equations associated with the physical problem; in 1908 he completed this work by finding the fundamental solution to the general elliptical partial differential equations with constant coefficients.

Fredholm's monument is the general solution to the integral equation that bears his name:

$$(1) \qquad \phi(x) + \int_0^1 f(x,y)\phi(y)\,dy = \psi(x).$$

In this equation the functions f (called the kernel) and ψ are supposed to be known continuous functions, and ϕ is the unknown function to be found. This type of equation has wide application in physics; for example, it can be shown that solving a particular case of (1) is equivalent to solving $\Delta u + \lambda u = 0$ for u, an equation that arises in the study of the vibrating membrane.

Equation (1) had long been under investigation, but only partial results had been obtained. In 1823, Niels Abel had solved a different form of (1) that also had a particular kernel. Carl Neuman had obtained, in 1884, a partial solution for (1) by use of an iteration scheme, but he had to impose certain convexity conditions to ensure convergence of his solution. By 1897 Vito Volterra had found a convergent iteration scheme in the case where f has the property that $f(x,y) = 0$ for $y > x$.

Fredholm began work on equation (1) during a trip to Paris in 1899, published a preliminary report in 1900, and presented the complete solution in 1903. His approach to this equation was ingenious and unique. Fredholm recognized the analogy between equation (1) and the linear matrix-vector equation of the form $(I + F)U = V$. He defined

$$D_f = 1 + \sum_{n=1}^{\infty} \frac{1}{n!} \int_0^1 \int_0^1 \cdots \int_0^1 [f(x_i,x_j)]dx_1\,dx_2 \cdots dx_n,$$

where $[f(x_i,y_j)]$ is the determinant of the $n \times n$ matrix whose ij^{th} component is $f(x_i,x_j)$. The quantity D_f, Fredholm showed, plays the same role in equation (1) that the determinant of $I + F$ plays in the matrix equation; that is, there is a unique solution ϕ of equation (1) for every continuous function ψ whenever D_f is not zero. Furthermore, he proved that the homogeneous equation associated with equation (1),

$$\phi(x) + \int_0^1 f(x,y)\phi(x)\,dy = 0, \tag{2}$$

has a nontrivial solution (that is, one not identically zero) if and only if $D_f = 0$.

The analogy between the matrix and integral equations was further pointed up by Fredholm when he defined the nth order minor of f—denoted by $D_f\begin{pmatrix}\xi_1, \xi_2, \cdots, \xi_n \\ \eta_1, \eta_2, \cdots, \eta_n\end{pmatrix}$—by an expression similar to that for D_f. Then he showed that if D_f is not zero, an explicit representation for the solution of equation (1) similar to Cramer's rule was given by

$$\phi(x) = \psi(x) - \int_0^1 \frac{D_f\begin{pmatrix}x \\ y\end{pmatrix}}{D_f}\,\psi(y)\,dy.$$

Fredholm then went on to show that if D_f is equal to zero, the dimension of the null space (the vector space of the set of solutions) of equation (2) is finite dimensional. He did this by setting

$$\Phi_i(x) = \frac{D_f\begin{pmatrix}\xi_1, \xi_2, \cdots, \xi_i, \cdots, \xi_n \\ \eta_1, \eta_2, \quad \cdots, \quad \eta_n\end{pmatrix}}{D_f\begin{pmatrix}\xi_1, \xi_2, \cdots, \xi_n \\ \eta_1, \eta_2, \cdots, \eta_n\end{pmatrix}}, \; i = 1, 2, \cdots n,$$

where the denominator is a nonvanishing minor of least nth (finite) order (which he showed always exists) and where the same minor is denoted in the numerator, but with ξ_i replaced by the variable x. Then he proved the set $\{\Phi_i : i = 1,2,\cdots,n\}$ to be a basis for the null space of equation (2). Finally, to solve equation (1) in the case $D_f = 0$, Fredholm first showed that a solution will exist when and only when $\psi(x)$ is orthogonal to the null space of the transposed homogeneous equation—or, equivalently, when

$$\int_0^1 \psi(x)\Psi_i(x)\,dx = 0 \; (i = 1,2, \cdots, n),$$

where $\{\Psi_i : i = 1,2, \cdots, n\}$ is a basis for the null space of the equation

$$\phi(x) + \int_0^1 f(y,x)\phi(y)\,dy = 0.$$

In this case, the solutions are not unique but can be represented by

$$\phi(x) = \psi(x) + \int_0^1 g(x,y)\psi(y)\,dy + \sum_{i=1}^{n} a_i\Phi_i,$$

where

$$g(x,y) = \frac{-D_f\begin{pmatrix}x \; \xi_1, \xi_2, \cdots, \xi_n \\ y \; \eta_1, \eta_2, \cdots, \eta_n\end{pmatrix}}{D_f\begin{pmatrix}\xi_1, \xi_2, \cdots, \xi_n \\ \eta_1, \eta_2, \cdots, \eta_n\end{pmatrix}}$$

and $\{a_i : i = 1,2, \cdots, n\}$ is a set of arbitrary constants.

Thus, Fredholm proved that the analogy between the matrix equation $(I + F)U = V$ and equation (1) was complete and even included an alternative theorem for the integral equation. Yet he showed more. His result meant that the solution $\phi(x)$ for equation (1) could be developed in a power series in the complex variable λ

$$\phi(x) = \psi(x) + \sum_{p=1}^{\infty} \psi_p(x)\lambda^p$$

which is a meromorphic function of λ for every λ satisfying $D_{\lambda f} \neq 0$. (To see this, replace $f(x,y)$ with $\lambda f(x,y)$ in equation [1].) This result was so important that, unable to prove it, Henri Poincaré was forced to assume it in 1895–1896 in connection with his studies of the partial differential equation $\Delta u + \lambda u = h(x,y)$.

Fredholm's work did not represent a dead end. His colleague Erik Holmgren carried Fredholm's discovery to Göttingen in 1901. There David Hilbert was inspired to take up the study; he extended Fredholm's results to include a complete eigenvalue theory for equation (1). In the process he used techniques that led to the discovery of Hilbert spaces.

BIBLIOGRAPHY

The *Oeuvres complètes de Ivar Fredholm* (Malmö, 1955) includes an excellent obituary by Nils Zeilon.

Ernst Hellinger and Otto Toeplitz, "Integralgleichungen und Gleichungen mit unendlichvielen Unbekannten," in *Encyklopädie der mathematische Wissenschaften,* (Leipzig, 1923–1927), pt. 2, vol. III, art. 13, 1335–1602, was also published separately (Leipzig-Berlin, 1928). It presents an excellent historical perspective of Fredholm's work and the details of his technique; it also contains an excellent bibliography.

M. BERNKOPF

FREGE, FRIEDRICH LUDWIG GOTTLOB (*b.* Wismar, Germany, 8 November 1848; *d.* Bad Kleinen, Germany, 26 July 1925)

Gottlob Frege was a son of Alexander Frege, principal of a girl's high school, and of Auguste Bialloblotzky. He attended the Gymnasium in Wismar, and from 1869 to 1871 he was a student at Jena. He then went to Göttingen and took courses in mathematics, physics, chemistry, and philosophy for five semesters. In 1873 Frege received his doctorate in philosophy at Göttingen with the thesis, *Ueber eine geometrische Darstellung der imäginaren Gebilde in der Ebene.* The following year at Jena he obtained the *venia docendi* in the Faculty of Philosophy with a dissertation entitled "Rechungsmethoden, die sich auf eine Erweitung des Grössenbegriffes gründen," which concerns one-parameter groups of functions and was motivated by his intention to give such a definition of quantity as gives maximal extension to the applicability of the arithmetic based upon it. The idea presented in the dissertation of viewing the system of an operation *f* and its iterates as a system of quantities, which in the introduction to his *Grundlagen der Arithmetik* (1884) Frege essentially ascribes to Herbart, hints at the notion of *f*-sequence expounded in his *Begriffsschrift* (1879).

After the publication of the *Begriffsschrift,* Frege was appointed extraordinary professor at Jena in 1879 and honorary professor in 1896. His stubborn work toward his goal—the logical foundation of arithmetic—resulted in his two-volume *Grundgesetze der Arithmetik* (1893–1903). Shortly before publication of the second volume Bertrand Russell pointed out in 1902, in a letter to Frege, that his system involved a contradiction. This observation by Russell destroyed Frege's theory of arithmetic, and he saw no way out. Frege's scientific activity in the period after 1903 cannot be compared with that before 1903 and was mainly in reaction to the new developments in mathematics and its foundations, especially to Hilbert's axiomatics. In 1917 he retired. His *Logische Untersuchungen,* written in the period 1918–1923, is an extension of his earlier work.

In his attempt to give a satisfactory definition of number and a rigorous foundation to arithmetic, Frege found ordinary language insufficient. To overcome the difficulties involved, he devised his *Begriffsschrift* as a tool for analyzing and representing mathematical proofs completely and adequately. This tool has gradually developed into modern mathematical logic, of which Frege may justly be considered the creator.

The *Begriffsschrift* was intended to be a formula language for pure thought, written with specific symbols and modeled upon that of arithmetic (i.e., it develops according to definite rules). This is an essential difference between Frege's calculus and, for example, Boole's or Peano's, which do not formalize mathematical proofs but are more flexible in expressing the logical structure of concepts.

One of Frege's special symbols is the assertion sign $\vdash$ (properly only the vertical stroke), which is interpreted if followed by a symbol with judgeable content. The interpretation of $\vdash A$ is "*A* is a fact." Another symbol is the conditional $\sqsubset$, and $\sqsubset\, {}^{A}_{B}$ is to be read as "*B* implies *A*." The assertion $\vdash {}^{A}_{B}$ is justified in the following cases: (1) *A* and *B* are true; (2) *A* is true and *B* is false; (3) *A* and *B* are false.

Frege uses only one deduction rule, which consists in passing from $\vdash B$ and $\vdash {}^{A}_{B}$ to $\vdash A$. The assertion that *A* is not a fact is expressed by $\vdash\!\neg A$, i.e., the small vertical stroke is used for negation. Frege showed that the other propositional connectives, "and" and "or," are expressible by means of negation and implication, and in fact developed propositional logic on the basis of a few axioms, some of which have been preserved in modern presentations of logic. Yet he did not stop at propositional logic but also developed quantification theory, which was possible because of his general notion of function. If in an expression a symbol was considered to be replaceable, in all or in some of its occurrences, then Frege calls the invariant part of the expression a function and the replaceable part its argument. He chose the expression $\Phi(A)$ for a function and, for functions of more than one argument, $\Psi(A,B)$. Since the Φ in $\Phi(A)$ also may be considered to be the replaceable part, $\Phi(A)$ may be viewed as a function of the argument Φ. This stipulation proved to be the weak point in Frege's system, as Russell showed in 1902.

Generality was expressed by

$$\vdash\!\smile^{\mathfrak{a}}\!\!-\; \Phi(\mathfrak{a})$$

which means that $\Phi(a)$ is a fact, whatever may be chosen for the argument. Frege explains the notion of the scope of a quantifier and notes the allowable transition from $\vdash X(a)$ to $\vdash\!\smile^{\mathfrak{a}}\!\!-\; X(\mathfrak{a})$, where *a* occurs only as argument of $X(a)$, and from $\vdash {}^{\Phi(a)}_{A}$ to $\vdash\!\smile^{\mathfrak{a}}\!\!-\; {}^{\Phi(\mathfrak{a})}_{A}$, where *a* does not occur in *A* and in $\Phi(a)$ occurs only in the argument places.

Existence was expressed by $\vdash\!\neg\!\smile^{\mathfrak{a}}\!\!\neg\; \Lambda(\mathfrak{a})$. There was no explicitly stated rule of substitution.

It should be observed that Frege did not construct his system for expressing pure thought as a formal system and therefore did not raise questions of completeness or consistency. Frege applied his *Begriffsschrift* to a general theory of sequences, and in part III he defines the ancestral relation on which he

FREGE

founded mathematical induction. This relation was afterward introduced informally by Dedekind and formally by Whitehead and Russell in *Principia mathematica.*

The *Begriffsschrift* essentially underlies Frege's definition of number in *Grundlagen der Arithmetik* (1884), although it was not used explicitly. The greater part of this work is devoted to a severe and effective criticism of existing theories of number. Frege argues that number is something connected with an assertion concerning a concept; and essential for the notion of number is that of equality of number (i.e., he has to explain the sentence "The number which belongs to the concept F is the same as that which belongs to G."). He settled on the definition "The number which belongs to the concept F is the extension of the concept of being equal to the concept F," where equality of concepts is understood as the existence of a one-to-one correspondence between their extensions. The number zero is that belonging to a concept with void extension, and the number one is that which belongs to the concept equal to zero. Using the notion of f-sequence, natural numbers are defined, with ∞ the number belonging to the notion of being a natural number.[1]

Frege's theories, as well as his criticisms in the *Begriffsschrift* and the *Grundlagen,* were extended and refined in his *Grundgesetze,* in which he incorporated the essential improvements on his *Begriffsschrift* that had been expounded in the three important papers "Funktion und Begriff" (1891), "Über Sinn und Bedeutung" (1892), and "Über Begriff und Gegenstand" (1892). In particular, "Über Sinn und Bedeutung" is an essential complement to his *Begriffsschrift.* In addition, it has had a great influence on philosophical discussion, specifically on the development of Wittgenstein's philosophy. Nevertheless, the philosophical implications of the acceptance of Frege's doctrine have proved troublesome.

An analysis of the identity relation led Frege to the distinction between the sense of an expression and its denotation. If a and b are different names of the same object (refer to or denote the same object), we can legitimately express this by $a = b$, but $=$ cannot be considered to be a relation between the objects themselves.

Frege therefore distinguishes two aspects of an expression: its denotation, which is the object to which it refers, and its sense, which is roughly the thought expressed by it. Every expression expresses its sense. An unsaturated expression (a function) has no denotation.

These considerations led Frege to the conviction that a sentence denotes its truth-value; all true sentences denote the True and all false sentences denote the False—in other words, are names of the True and the False, respectively. The True and the False are to be treated as objects. The consequences of this distinction are further investigated in "Über Begriff und Gegenstand." There Frege admits that he has not given a definition of concept and doubts whether this can be done, but he emphasizes that concept has to be kept carefully apart from object. More interesting developments are contained in his "Funktion und Begriff." First, there is the general notion of function already briefly mentioned in the *Grundlagen,* and second, with every function there is associated an object, the so-called *Wertverlauf,* which he used essentially in his *Grundgesetze der Arithmetik.*

Since a function is expressed by an unsaturated expression $f(x)$, which denotes an object if x in it is replaced by an object, there arises the possibility of extending the notion of function because sentences denote objects (the True [T] and the False [F]), and one arrives at the conclusion that, e.g., $(x^2 = 4) = (x > 1)$ is a function. If one replaces x by 1, then, because $1^2 = 4$ denotes F, as does $1 > 1$, it follows that $(1^2 = 4) = (1 > 1)$ denotes T.

Frege distinguishes between first-level functions, with objects as argument, and second-level functions, with first-level functions as arguments, and notes that there are more possibilities. For Frege an object is anything which is not a function, but he admits that the notion of object cannot be logically defined. It is characteristic of Frege that he could not take the step of simply postulating a class of objects without entering into the question of their nature. This would have taken him in the direction of a formalistic attitude, to which he was fiercely opposed. In fact, at that time formalism was in a bad state and rather incoherently maintained. Besides, Frege was not creating objects but was concerned mainly with logical characterizations. This in a certain sense also holds true for Frege's introduction of the *Wertverlauf,* which he believed to be something already there and which had to be characterized logically.

In considering two functions, e.g., $x^2 - 4x$ and $x(x - 4)$, one may observe that they have the same value for the same argument. Therefore their graphs are the same. This situation is expressed by Frege true for Frege's introduction of the *Wertverlauf,* as $x^2 - 4x$." Without any further ado he goes on to speak of the *Wertverlauf* of a function as being something already there, and introduced a name for it. The *Wertverläufe* of the above mentioned functions $x(x - 4)$ and $x^2 - 4x$ are denoted by $\dot{\alpha}(\alpha - 4)$ and $\dot{\epsilon}(\epsilon^2 - 4\epsilon)$ respectively, and in general $\dot{\epsilon}f(\epsilon)$ is used to denote the *Wertverlauf* of function $f(\xi)$. This *Wert-*

verlauf is taken to be an object, and Frege assumes the basic logical law characterizing equality of *Wertverläufe:*

$$(\grave{\epsilon}f(\epsilon) = \grave{\alpha}\, g(\alpha)) = (\overset{\mathfrak{a}}{\smile} f(\mathfrak{a}) = g(\mathfrak{a})).$$

Frege extends this to logical functions (i.e., concepts), which are conceived of as functions whose values are truth-values, and thus extension of a concept may be identified with the *Wertverlauf* of a function assuming only truth-values. Therefore, e.g., $\grave{\epsilon}(\epsilon^2 = 1) = \grave{\alpha}(\alpha + 1)^2 = 2(\alpha + 1)$.

In the appendix to volume II of his *Grundgesetze,* Frege derives Russell's paradox in his system with the help of the above basic logical law. Russell later succeeded in eliminating his paradox by assuming the theory of types.

It is curious that the man who laid the most suitable foundation for formal logic was so strongly opposed to formalism. In volume II of the *Grundgesetze,* where he discusses formal arithmetic at length, Frege proves to have a far better insight than its exponents and justly emphasizes the necessity of a consistency proof to justify creative definitions. He is aware that because of the introduction of the *Wertverläufe* he may be accused of doing what he is criticizing. Nevertheless, he argues that he is not, because of his logical law concerning *Wertverläufe* (which proved untenable).

When Hilbert took the axiomatic method a decisive step further, Frege failed to grasp his point and attacked him for his imprecise terminology. Frege insisted on definitions in the classic sense and rejected Hilbert's "definition" of a betweenness relation and his use of the term "point." For Frege geometry was still the theory of space. But even before 1814 Bolzano had already reached the conclusion that for an abstract theory of space, one may be obliged to assume the term point as a primitive notion capable of various interpretations. Hilbert's answer to Frege's objections was quite satisfactory, although it did not convince Frege.

BIBLIOGRAPHY

I. ORIGINAL WORKS. Frege's writing includes *Ueber eine geometrische Darstellung der imaginären Gebilde in der Ebene,* his inaugural diss. to the Faculty of Philosophy at Göttingen (Jena, 1873); *Begriffsschrift, eine der arithmetischen nachgebildete Formelsprache des reinen Denkens* (Halle, 1879), 2nd ed., I. Angelelli, ed. (Hildesheim, 1964), English trans. in J. van Heijenoort, *From Frege to Godel* (Cambridge, 1967), pp. 1–82; *Die Grundlagen der Arithmetik* (Breslau, 1884), trans. with German text by J. L. Austin (Oxford, 1950; 2nd rev. ed. 1953), repr. as *The Foundations of Arithmetic* (Oxford, 1959); *Function und Begriff* (Jena, 1891), English trans. in P. Geach and M. Black, pp. 21–41 (see below); "Über Sinn und Bedeutung," in *Zeitschrift für Philosophie und philosophische Kritik,* n.s. **100** (1892), 25–50, English trans. in P. Geach and M. Black, pp. 56–78 (see below); "Über Begriff und Gegenstand," in *Vierteljahrschrift für wissenschaftliche Philosophie,* **16** (1892), 192–205, English trans. in P. Geach and M. Black, pp. 42–55 (see below); *Grundgesetze der Arithmetik,* 2 vols. (Jena, 1893–1903), repr. in 1 vol. (Hildesheim, 1962); and "Über die Grundlagen der Geometrie," in *Jahresbericht der Deutschen Mathematikervereinigung,* **12** (1903), 319–324, 368–375; **15** (1906), 293–309, 377–403, 423–430.

II. SECONDARY LITERATURE. On Frege and his work, see I. Angelelli, *Studies on Gottlob Frege and Traditional Philosophy* (Dordrecht, 1967); P. Geach and M. Black, *Translation of the Philosophical Writings of Gottlob Frege,* 2nd ed. (Oxford, 1960); H. Hermes, *et al., Gottlob Frege, Nachgelassene Schriften* (Hamburg, 1969); J. van Heijenoort, *From Frege to Godel* (Cambridge, 1967); P. E. B. Jourdain, "The Development of the Theories of Mathematical Logic and the Principles of Mathematics. Gottlob Frege," in *Quarterly Journal of Pure and Applied Mathematics,* **43** (1912), 237–269; W. Kneale and Martha Kneale, *The Development of Logic* (Oxford, 1962) pp. 435–512; J. Largeault, *Logique et philosophie chez Frege* (Paris–Louvain, 1970); C. Parsons, "Frege's Theory of Number," in M. Black, ed., *Philosophy in America* (London, 1965), pp. 180–203; G. Patzig, *Gottlob Frege, Funktion, Begriff, Bedeutung* (Göttingen, 1966); and *Gottlob Frege, Logische Untersuchungen* (Göttingen, 1966); B. Russell, *The Principles of Mathematics* (Cambridge, 1903), Appendix A, "The Logical and Arithmetical Doctrines of Frege"; M. Steck, "Ein unbekannter Brief von Gottlob Frege über Hilberts erste Vorlesung über die Grundlagen der Geometrie," in *Sitzungsberichte der Heidelberger Akademie der Wissenschaften,* Abhandlung 6 (1940); and "Unbekannte Briefe Frege's über die Grundlagen der Geometrie und Antwortbrief Hilbert's an Frege," *ibid.,* Abhandlung 2 (1941); H. G. Steiner, "Frege und die Grundlagen der Geometrie I, II," in *Mathematische-physikalische Semesterberichte,* n.s. **10** (1963), 175–186, and **11** (1964), 35–47; and J. D. B. Walker, *A Study of Frege* (Oxford, 1965).

B. VAN ROOTSELAAR

FRENET, JEAN-FRÉDÉRIC (*b.* Périgueux, France, 7 February 1816; *d.* Périgueux, 12 June 1900)

Frenet was the son of Pierre Frenet, a *perruquier.* In 1840 he entered the École Normale Supérieure and later studied at the University of Toulouse, where he received the doctorate for the thesis *Sur les fonctions qui servent à déterminer l'attraction des sphéroïdes quelconques. Programme d'une thèse sur quelques propriétés des courbes à double courbure* (1847). The latter part of the thesis was subsequently published in the *Journal de mathématiques pures et appliquées* (1852) and contains what are known in the theory of space curves as the Frenet-Serret formulas. Frenet, however, presents only six formulas explicitly, whereas Serret presents all nine. Frenet subsequently explained the use of his formulas in "Théorèmes sur les courbes gauches" (1853).

After a period as a professor in Toulouse, Frenet went to Lyons, where in 1848 he became professor of mathematics at the university. He was also director of the astronomical observatory, where he conducted meteorological observations. He retired in 1868 with the title of honorary professor and settled at Bayot, a family estate in his native Périgueux. Unmarried, he lived quietly with a sister until his death.

Frenet's constantly revised and augmented *Recueil d'exercises sur le calcul infinitésimal* (1856) was popular for more than half a century. It contains problems with full solutions and often with historical remarks.

Frenet was a man of wide erudition and a classical scholar who was respected in this community, but his mathematical production was limited.

BIBLIOGRAPHY

Frenet's best-known works are *Sur les fonctions qui servent à déterminer l'attraction des sphéroïdes quelconques. Programme d'une thèse sur quelques propriétés des courbes à double courbure* (Toulouse, 1847); "Sur quelques propriétés des courbes à double courbure," in *Journal de mathématiques pures et appliquées,* **17** (1852), 437–447; "Théorèmes sur les courbes gauches," in *Nouvelles annales de mathématiques,* **12** (1853), 365–372; and *Recueil d'exercises sur le calcul infinitésimal* (Paris, 1856; 7th ed., 1917).

Minor mathematical papers are "Note sur un théorème de Descartes," in *Nouvelles annales de mathématiques,* **13** (1854), 299–301; "Sur une formule de Gauss," in *Mémoires de la Société des sciences physiques et naturelles de Bordeaux,* **6** (1868), 385–392. Meteorological observations are in *Mémoires de l'Académie impériale de Lyon, Classe des sciences,* **3** (1853), 177–225; **6** (1856), 263–326; and **8** (1858), 73–121, continued afterward by A. Drian.

An obituary of Frenet is in *L'avenir de Dordogne* (17 June 1900).

D. J. STRUIK

FRENICLE DE BESSY, BERNARD (*b.* Paris, France, *ca.* 1605; *d.* Paris, 17 January 1675)

Frenicle was an accomplished amateur mathematician and held an official position as counselor at the Cour des Monnaies in Paris. In 1666 he was appointed member of the Academy of Sciences by Louis XIV. He maintained correspondence with the most important mathematicians of his time—we find his letters in the correspondence of Descartes, Fermat, Huygens, and Mersenne. In these letters he dealt mainly with questions concerning the theory of numbers, but he was also interested in other topics. In a letter to Mersenne, written at Dover on 7 June 1634, Frenicle described an experiment determining the trajectory of bodies falling from the mast of a moving ship. By calculating the value of g from Frenicle's data we obtain a value of 22.5 ft./sec.^{2}, which is not far from Mersenne's 25.6 ft./sec.^{2}. In addition, Frenicle seems to have been the author, or one of the authors, of a series of remarks on Galileo's *Dialogue.*

On 3 January 1657 Fermat proposed to mathematicians of Europe and England two problems:

(1) Find a cube which, when increased by the sum of its aliquot parts, becomes a square; for example, $7^3 + (1 + 7 + 7^2) = 20^2$.

(2) Find a square which, when increased by the sum of its aliquot parts, becomes a cube.

In his letter of 1 August 1657 to Wallis, Digby says that Frenicle had immediately given to the conveyer of Fermat's problems four different solutions of the first problem and, the next day, six more. Frenicle gave solutions of both problems in his most important mathematical work, *Solutio duorum problematum circa numeros cubos et quadratos, quae tanquam insolubilia universis Europae mathematicis a clarissimo viro D. Fermat sunt proposita* (Paris, 1657), dedicated to Digby. Although it was assumed for a long time that the work was lost, four copies exist. In it Frenicle proposed four more problems: (3) Find a multiply perfect number x of multiplicity 5, provided that the sum of the aliquot parts (proper divisors) of $5x$ is $25x$. A multiply perfect number x of multiplicity 5 is one the sum of whose divisors, including x and 1, is $5x$. (4) Find a multiply perfect number x of multiplicity 7, provided that the sum of the aliquot divisors of $7x$ is $49x$. (5) Find a central hexagon equal to a cube. (6) Find r central hexagons, with consecutive sides, whose sum is a cube. By a central hexagon of n sides Frenicle meant the number

$$H_n = 1 + 6 + 2\cdot 6 + 3\cdot 6 + \cdots + (n-1)\cdot 6 = n^3 - (n-1)^3.$$

Probably in the middle of February 1657 Fermat proposed a new problem to Frenicle: Find a number x which will make $(ax^2 + 1)$ a square, where a is a (nonsquare) integer. We find equations of this kind for the first time in Greek mathematics, where the Pythagoreans were led to solutions of the equations $y^2 - 2x^2 = \pm 1$ in obtaining approximations to $\sqrt{2}$. Next the Hindus Brahmagupta and Bhaskara II gave the method for finding particular solutions of the equation $y^2 - ax^2 = 1$ for $a = 8$, 61, 67, and 92. Within a very short time Frenicle found solutions of the problem. In the second part of the *Solutio* (pp. 18–30) he cited his table of solutions for all values of a up to 150 and explained his method of solution. Fermat stated in his letter to Carcavi of August 1659 that he had proved the existence of an infinitude of solutions of the equation by the method of descent. He admitted that Frenicle and Wallis had given various special solutions, although not a proof and general construction. After noting in the first part of the *Solutio* (pp. 1–17) that he had made a fruitless attempt to prove that problem (1) is unsolvable for a prime x greater than 7, Frenicle investigated solutions of the problem for values of x that are either primes or powers of primes. At the end of this part he made some remarks about solutions of the equations $\sigma(x^3) = ky^2$ and $\sigma(x^2) = ky^3$, where $\sigma(x)$ is the sum of the divisors (including 1 and x) of x.

Also in 1657 Fermat proposed to Brouncker, Wallis, and Frenicle the problem: Given a number composed of two cubes, to divide it into two other cubes. For finding solutions of this problem Frenicle used the so-called secant transformation, which can be represented as

$$x_3 = x_1 + t(x_2 - x_1); \qquad y_3 = y_1 + t(y_2 - y_1).$$

Although Lagrange is usually considered the inventor of this transformation, it seems that Frenicle was first. Other works by Frenicle were published in the *Mémoires de l'Académie royale des sciences.* In the first of these, "Méthode pour trouver la solution des problèmes par les exclusions," Frenicle says that in his opinion, arithmetic has as its object the finding of solutions in integers of indeterminate problems. He applied his method of exclusion to problems concerning rational right triangles, e.g., he discussed right triangles, the difference or sum of whose legs is given. He proceeded to study these figures in his *Traité des triangles rectangles en nombres,* in which he established some important properties. He proved, e.g., the theorem proposed by Fermat to André Jumeau, prior of Sainte-Croix, in September 1636, to Frenicle in May (?) 1640, and to Wallis on 7 April 1658: If the integers a, b, c represent the sides of a right triangle, then its area, $bc/2$, cannot be a square number. He also proved that no right triangle has each leg a square, and hence the area of a right triangle is never the double of a square. Frenicle's "Abrégé des combinaisons" contained essentially no new things either as to the theoretical part or in the applications. The most important of these works by Frenicle is the treatise "Des quarrez ou tables magiques." These squares, which are of Chinese origin and to which the Arabs were so partial, reached the Occident not later than the fifteenth century. Frenicle pointed out that the number of magic squares increased enormously with the order by writing down 880 magic squares of the fourth order, and gave a process for writing down magic squares of even order. In his *Problèmes plaisants et délectables* (1612), Bachet de Méziriac had given a rule "des terrasses" for those of odd order.

BIBLIOGRAPHY

I. Original Works. Copies of the *Solutio* are in the Bibliothèque Nationale, Paris: V 12134 and Vz 1136; in the library of Clermont-Ferrand: B.5568.R; and in the Preussische Staatsbibliothek, Berlin: Ob 4569. Pt. 1 of the *Traité des triangles rectangles en nombres* was printed at Paris in 1676 and reprinted with pt. 2 in 1677. Both pts. are in *Mémoires de l'Académie royale des sciences,* **5** (1729), 127–208; this vol. also contains "Méthode pour trouver la solution des problèmes par les exclusions," pp. 1–86; "Abrégé des combinaisons," pp. 87–126; "Des quarrez ou tables magiques," pp. 209–302; and "Table générale des quarrez magiques de quatres côtez," pp. 303–374, which were published by the Academy of Sciences in *Divers ouvrages de mathématique et de physique* (Paris, 1693).

II. Secondary Literature. There is no biography of Frenicle. Some information on his work may be found in A. G. Debus, "Pierre Gassendi and His 'Scientific Expedition' of 1640," in *Archives internationales d'histoire des sciences,* **63** (1963), 133–134; L. E. Dickson, *History of the Theory of Numbers* (Washington, D.C., 1919–1927), II, *passim;* C. Henry, "Recherches sur les manuscrits de Pierre de Fermat suivies de fragments inédits de Bachet et de Malebranche," in *Bullettino di bibliografia e di storia delle scienze matematiche e fisiche,* **12** (1870), 691–692; and J. E. Hofmann, "Neues über Fermats zahlentheoretische Herausforderungen von 1657," in *Abhandlungen der Preussischen Akademie der Wissenschaften,* Math.-naturwiss. Klasse, Jahrgang 1943, no. 9 (1944); and "Zur Frühgeschichte des Vierkubenproblems," in *Archives internationales d'histoire des sciences,* **54–55** (1961), 36–63.

H. L. L. Busard

FRIEDMANN, ALEKSANDR ALEKSANDROVICH (*b.* St. Petersburg, Russia, 29 June 1888; *d.* Leningrad, U. S. S. R., 16 September 1925)

Friedmann was born into a musical family—his father, Aleksandr Friedmann, being a composer and his mother, Ludmila Vojáčka, the daughter of the Czech composer Hynek Vojáček.

In 1906 Friedmann graduated from the Gymnasium with the gold medal and immediately enrolled in the mathematics section of the department of physics and mathematics of St. Petersburg University.

While still a student, he wrote a number of unpublished scientific papers, one of which, "Issledovanie neopredelennykh uravneny vtoroy stepeni" ("An Investigation of Second-degree Indeterminate Equations," 1909), was awarded a gold medal by the department. After graduation from the university in 1910, Friedmann was retained in the department to prepare for the teaching profession.

At the beginning of 1913, Friedmann began work at the aerological observatory located in Pavlovsk, near St. Petersburg. There he immersed himself in a study of the means of observing the atmosphere. In addition to synoptic and dynamic meteorology, he familiarized himself with the theory of the earth's magnetism and quickly became a prominent specialist in meteorology and related fields.

The year 1914 was marked for Friedmann by two important events: he passed the examinations for the degree of master of pure and applied mathematics at St. Petersburg University and he published in the *Geofizichesky sbornik* an important paper, "O raspredelenii temperatury vozdukha s vysotoyu" ("On the Relationship of Air Temperature to Altitude"). In this paper he examined theoretically the question of the existence of an upper temperature inversion point in the stratosphere.

In the fall of 1914, Friedmann volunteered for service in an aviation detachment, in which he worked, first on the northern front and later on other fronts, to organize aerologic and aeronavigational services. While at the front, Friedmann often participated in military flights as an aircraft observer. In the summer of 1917 he was appointed a section chief in Russia's first factory for the manufacture of measuring instruments used in aviation; he later became director of the factory. Friedmann had to relinquish this post because of the onset of heart disease. From 1918 until 1920, he was professor in the department of theoretical mechanics of Perm University.

In 1920 he returned to Petrograd and worked at the main physics observatory of the Academy of Sciences, first as head of the mathematical department and later, shortly before his death, as director of the observatory.

Friedmann's creative thought penetrated into every area of his knowledge and illuminated it with the brilliance of his disciplined mind and creative imagination. His scientific activity was concentrated in the areas of theoretical meteorology and hydromechanics. Here were manifested his mathematical talent and his unwavering striving for, and ability to attain, the concrete, practical application of solutions to theoretical problems.

Friedmann was one of the founders of dynamic meteorology. To him belong fundamental works in such areas as the theory of atmospheric vortices and vertical air fluxes. He also studied the problems of applying to aeronautics the theory of physical processes that occur in the atmosphere.

Friedmann's most important work in hydromechanics is *Opyt gidromekhaniki szhimaemoy zhidkosti* (1922). In this work he gave the fullest theory of vortical motion in a fluid and examined—and in a number of cases solved—the important problem of the possible motions of a compressible fluid under the influence of given forces.

Friedmann made a valuable contribution to Einstein's general theory of relativity. As always, his interest was not limited simply to familiarizing himself with this new field of science but led to his own remarkable investigations. Friedmann's work on the theory of relativity dealt with one of its most difficult questions, the cosmological problem. In his paper "Über die Krümmung des Raumes" (1922), he outlined the fundamental ideas of his cosmology: the supposition concerning the homogeneity of the distribution of matter in space and the consequent homogeneity and isotropy of space-time; that is, the existence of "world" time, for which, at any moment in time, the metrics of space will be identical at all points and in all directions. This theory is especially important because it leads to a sufficiently correct explanation of the fundamental phenomenon known as the "red shift." This solution of the Einstein field equations, obtained from the above propositions, is the model for any homogeneous and isotropic cosmological theory. It is interesting to note that Einstein thought that the cosmological solution to the equations of a field had to be static and had to lead to a closed model of the universe. Friedmann discarded both conditions and arrived at an independent solution. Einstein welcomed Friedmann's results because they showed the dispensability of the ad hoc cosmological term Einstein had been forced to introduce into the basic field equation of general relativity. Friedmann's interest in the theory of relativity was by no means a passing fancy. In the last years of his life, together with V. K. Frederiks, he began work on a multivolume text on modern physics. The first book, *The World as Space and Time,* is devoted to the theory of relativity, knowledge of which Friedmann considered one of the cornerstones of an education in physics.

In addition to his scientific work, Friedmann for several years taught courses in higher mathematics and theoretical mechanics at various colleges in Petrograd (the Polytechnical Institute, the Institute of Ways and Means of Communication, and the Military

Naval Academy). He found time to create new and original courses, brilliant in their form and exceedingly varied in their content, which covered approximation and solution of numerical equations, differential geometry and tensor analysis, hydromechanics, applied aerodynamics, and theoretical mechanics. Friedmann's unique course in theoretical mechanics combined mathematical precision and logical continuity with original procedural and physical trends. He is rightfully considered a distinguished representative of a renowned pleiad of Russian students of mechanics to which also belonged such leading figures as Zhukovsky, Chaplygin, Krylov, and Kochin.

Friedmann died of typhoid fever at the age of thirty-seven. In 1931, he was posthumously awarded the Lenin Prize for his outstanding scientific work.

BIBLIOGRAPHY

I. ORIGINAL WORKS. Friedmann's most important works include "Zur Theorie der Vertikaltemperaturverteilung," in *Meteorologische Zeitschrift,* **31,** no. 3 (1914), 154–156; "O raspredelenii temperatury vozdukha s vysotoyu" ("On the Relationship of Air Temperature to Altitude"), in *Geofizichesky sbornik,* **1,** pt. 1 (1914), 35–55; "Sur les tourbillons dans un liquide à température variable," in *Comptes rendus hebdomadaires des séances de l'Académie des sciences,* **163,** no. 9 (1916), 219–222; "O vikhryakh v zhidkosti s menyayushcheysya temperaturoy" ("On Whirlpools in a Liquid With Changing Temperature"), in *Soobshcheniya i protokoly Kharkovskago matematicheskago obshchestva,* 2nd ser., **15,** no. 4 (1917), 173–176; "Die Grössenordnung der meteorologischen Elemente und ihrer räumlichen und zeitlichen Abteilungen," in *Veröffentlichungen des Geophysikalischen Instituts der Universität Leipzig,* 2nd ser., no. 10 (1914), written with K. G. Hesselberg; "O vertikalnykh techeniakh v atmosfere" ("On Vertical Fluxes in the Atmosphere"), in *Zhurnal fiziko-matematicheskogo obshchestva pri Permskom gosudarstvennom universitete,* pt. 2 (1919), pp. 67–104; "O raspredelenii temperatury s vysotoy pri nalichnosti luchistogo teploobmena Zemli i Solntsa" ("On the Relation of Temperature to Altitude in the Presence of Radiation Heat Exchange Between the Earth and Sun"), in *Izvestiya Glavnoi geofizicheskoi observatorii,* no. 2 (1920), pp. 42–44; "O vertikalnykh i gorizontalnykh atmosfernykh vikhrvakh" ("On Vertical and Horizontal Atmospheric Whirlwinds"), *ibid.,* no. 3 (1921), pp. 3–4; *Opyt gidromekhaniki szhimaemoy zhidkosti* (Petrograd, 1922); "Über die Krümmung des Raumes," in *Zeitschrift für Physik,* **10,** no. 6 (1922), 377–386; *Mir kak prostranstvo i vremya* ("The World as Space and Time," Petrograd, 1923; 2nd ed., Moscow, 1965), written with V. K. Frederiks; "O dvizhenii szhimaemoy zhidkosti" ("On the Motion of a Compressible Liquid"), in *Izvestiya gidrologicheskogo instituta,* no. 7 (1923), pp. 21–28; "Über die Möglichkeit einer Welt mit konstanter negativer Krümmung des Raumes," in *Zeitschrift für Physik,* **21** (1924), 326–332; "O rasprostranenii preryvistosti v szhimaemoy zhidkosti" ("On the Extent of Discontinuity in a Compressible Liquid"), in *Zhurnal Russkago fiziko-khimicheskago obshchestva,* **56,** no. 1 (1924), 40–58; "O krivizne prostranstva" ("On the Curvature of Space"), *ibid.* (1924), 59–68; and "Théorie du mouvement d'un fluide compressible," in *Geographische Zeitschrift* (1924).

II. SECONDARY LITERATURE. On Friedmann and his work, see (in chronological order), A. F. Vangengeim, "A. A. Friedman," in *Klimat i pogoda,* nos. 2–3 (1925), pp. 5–7, an obituary; N. M. Gyunter, "Nauchnie trudy A. A. Freidmana" ("The Scientific Works of A. A. Friedmann"), in *Zhurnal Leningradskogo fiziko-matematicheskogo obshchestva,* **1,** no. 1 (1926), 5–11; and A. F. Gavrilov, "Pamyati A. A. Friedmanna" ("In Memory of A. S. Friedmann"), in *Uspekhi fizicheskikh nauk,* **6,** no. 1 (1926), 73–75.

See also *Geofizichesky sbornik* (Leningrad, 1927), V, pt. 1, which contains, in addition to an obituary by V. A. Steklov, E. P. Friedmann, "Pamyati A. A. Friedmanna" ("In Memory of A. A. Friedmann"), pp. 9–10; I. V. Meshchersky, "Trudy A. A. Friedmanna po gidromekhanike" ("A. A. Friedmann's Works on Hydromechanics"), pp. 57–60; and M. A. Loris-Melikov, "Raboty Friedmanna po teorii otnositelnosti" ("Friedmann's Works on the Theory of Relativity"), pp. 61–63.

Also useful is L. G. Loytsyansky and A. I. Lurie, "A. A. Friedmann," in *Trudy Leningradskogo politekhnicheskogo instituta imeni M. I. Kalinina,* no. 1 (1949), pp. 83–86.

A. T. GRIGORIAN

FRIES, JAKOB FRIEDRICH (*b.* Barby, Germany, 23 August 1773; *d.* Jena, Germany, 10 August 1843)

Fries was educated in Niesky at the Moravian Academy of the United Brethren of Herrenhut. This upbringing had a lasting influence upon him, even though he early freed himself from the religious dogmas learned in his theological studies there. In 1795 Fries went to Leipzig to study philosophy and in 1797 he transferred to Jena to study with Fichte. By 1798 he had published five essays on the relation of metaphysics to psychology. Having completed his course at Jena, he spent a year as a private tutor in Switzerland. At the same time he worked to finish his thesis, "De intuitu intellectuali," with which he qualified as docent at Jena in 1801.

In 1805 Fries was called to become an assistant professor of philosophy and elementary mathematics at Heidelberg. In 1816 he returned to Jena as full professor of theoretical philosophy. He was suspended because of political pressures following his participation in the Wartburgfest, a demonstration by liberal students in October 1817. Fries did not obtain permission to teach again at Jena until 1824, when he received a professorship of physics and mathematics. In 1825 he became professor of philosophy, a post he held for the rest of his life.

Fries considered himself Kant's most loyal disciple. He believed that Kant had finished the philosopher's task for all time and that only individual elements of his doctrine were susceptible to correction. Despite this belief Fries himself decisively altered the Kantian formulation by psychologizing Kant's transcendental idealism in his major book, *Neue oder anthropologische Kritik der Vernunft* (Heidelberg, 1807). He was opposed to all contemporary speculative systems and considered the Romantic interpretation of nature good only for aesthetics. In opposition to Schelling and his school, he went back to the attitude of critical Kantianism that held *Naturphilosophie* to be the philosophy of exact sciences (see, for example, his *Die mathematische Naturphilosophie* [Heidelberg, 1822]).

Fries also spoke for contemporary positive scientific research, for which he gained authority from his works on physiological optics and the theory of probabilities, as well as from his textbook on experimental physics. With Kant he asserted the possibility of an a priori natural science, designed to show how the categories are applicable to experience as determinations of time through universal mathematical schema and how a system of universal laws of nature arises from this union. This system encompasses the theory of pure motion, which unites Newton's mathematical approach with Kantian philosophy. (Fries's interpretation of Newton was strongly influenced by the commentary of Le Seur and Jacquier to their four-volume 1739 edition of the *Principia,* which contains the development of those mathematical propositions that Fries presented in detail in his own *Die mathematische Naturphilosophie.*)

Fries's system almost yields the philosophy of applied mathematics, although there remains the field of derivable statements a priori. Among them Fries considers the Newtonian axioms to be foremost. On the other hand, attraction and its lawfulness cannot be deduced a priori. While Fries took over Kant's classification of natural knowledge into the four disciplines of phoronomy, dynamics, mechanics, and phenomenology, he added two new ones that he designated stochiology and morphology. Stochiology treats dynamics from a comprehensive viewpoint and attempts to establish a dynamic explanation of heat and light, as well as electrical and chemical phenomena.

Whereas Fries, like Kant, explained matter dynamically—and indeed he was much more sharply opposed to the atomists than was Kant—he deviated from him considerably with regard to dynamics itself. This is illustrated particularly by his rejection of apriorism in the concrete determination of the degree of force with which masses act upon each other. In further opposition to Kant, Fries posited four types of fundamental force in the constitution of matter: attractive and repulsive forces acting at a distance as well as attractive and repulsive contact forces. For the first two types of force the simplest mode of action is given by their proportionality to $1/v^2$, for the latter two, by the proportionality

$$k = \frac{\text{density}}{mv}.$$

Fries took a final important step beyond Kant in the introduction of the organic into his system of nature through the supposition of natural instincts. This doctrine of the instincts stated that along with the determination of the forms of interaction, the law of the counteraction of the fundamental forces (that is, the behavior of the moved mass in space) must also be considered. According to Fries, the succession of appearances is caused by such instincts, which display complete forms of reciprocal action. They alone, rather than particular materials and forces, provide the explanation of physical phenomena and processes.

Physical processes may be divided into four types: gravitational (heavy masses acting at a distance); chemical (heavy masses in admixtures and dissociations with contact action); phlogistic (in which the counteraction is determined by caloric); and morphotic (in which the counteraction is determined primarily by the rigidity of the moving forces). The instincts on which these processes are based may be further divided into two classes—instincts of mechanisms and instincts of organisms. In Fries's view, all processes that are freely determined by uniformly accelerating attractive forces must be attributed to organic instincts; and all processes that are determined by attraction of bodies in contact without acceleration, and are thus reaching a state of rest in reestablished equilibrium, must be attributed to mechanical instincts.

Planetary orbits and pendulum motion may, if air resistance and friction are ignored, serve as examples of the action of organic instincts. Organizing instincts here predominate over mechanical ones, since otherwise the world, beginning in chaos, would attain motionless equilibrium in finite time. The prevalence of organizing instincts is necessary to the closed system of periodic recurrence of events required for a

 FRIES

world without beginning and without end. Lesser cycles of events are the only ones that can be altered from the outside alone. If one supposes these comprised in greater cycles of events in which, again, the organic force predominates, and then supposes these greater cycles included in still greater ones, and so on, a lack of exact periodicity in the whole is understandable.

The distinction between organic and mechanical instincts makes it possible to distinguish between organic and inorganic nature. An inorganic (dead) body, or mechanical formation, is any that is formed according to the law of equilibrium; a living body obeys the law of self-preservation of its motion—this principle of self-preservation is the corporeal soul. The corporeal soul itself exhibits only the form of the interaction of the corporeal parts. This definition reflects Kant's determination of the organism as the *causalitas mutua* of its parts.

According to Fries's speculative natural history, the cosmos is constructed out of three elements—earth, water, and air—according to weight. In the solid core of the earth the forces have long maintained themselves in equilibrium. Above the earth, in the water and air, the equilibrium is preserved by the action of sunlight, the daily and yearly motion of the earth, and the electrical reaction of the atmosphere to daily and annual heating and cooling cycles. In addition, the vigor of the life-movements and the circulation of life as the basic vital principle also depend upon thermal-electrical relationships. "All morphotic processes are dominated by the formative instincts [*Bildungstrieben*], and specifically the mineral and the two organic instincts," Fries wrote.

The laws of crystallization display the true morphotic principle. Without denying the differences between crystal and organism (including the difference in mode of growth, namely apposition as opposed to intussusception), Fries maintained that these laws are crucial to an understanding of organic form. Indeed, organic formation to the extent that it represents a higher, correspondingly altered process, is to be understood only on the basis of crystallization. Fries called for a theory of free crystallization to expedite a theory of organic formation; he thereby thought to explain a self-maintaining organic process by means of the circuit law of the voltaic cell. It is necessary to this hypothesis, however, that the electrical currents that arise in the play of chemical combinations and dissociations flow in such a way as to transform the oxides emerging from contact with the conductor of the second class, so that the material of this conductor be replaced. Fries could thus ask if a plant might be a self-maintaining open voltaic chain whose root acts as a negative conductor while the opposite pole puts forth leaves and flowers, or if an animal might be a self-maintaining closed voltaic chain that therefore also possesses its own inherent magnetism.

Fries devised a diagram

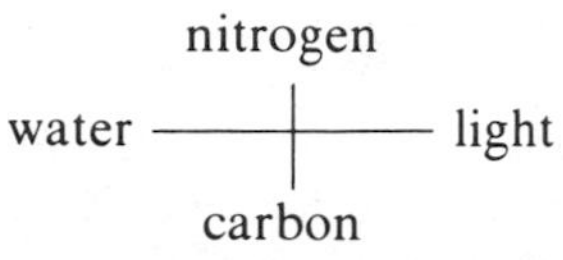

to represent the bases of all empirical theories of formation and dissolution in the three natural kingdoms. His representation combined the two polar principles of electrical and material opposition. In this system electrical opposition emerged as the principle of all animation through the activity of sunlight on water, while the differences between chemical materials, represented by the original opposition of carbon and nitrogen, is the principle of all production of form. The effect of these two original polarities on each other allowed the reconciliation of the three natural instincts posited by Fries. Specifically, the water-light polarity reconciled the mechanical-mineral instinct; the open circuit between water, carbon, and nitrogen, the vegetative one; and the closed circuit between nitrogen, light, carbon, and water (which encompasses the whole of nature), the animal instinct.

Fries's doctrine of nature thus can be understood only in connection with romantic *Naturphilosophie,* in which the idea of polarity and the importance of magnetism and galvanism were employed to account for far more than just physical events. Fries's doctrine of nature, however, employed the natural science available at the time in a serious attempt to overcome Kant's vitalism, which even a Newton of the grassblades would not accept. Indeed, his speculations in natural philosophy were actually fruitful for the development of modern biology through the work of his student Matthias Schleiden, who sought to put into practice the idea of the reduction of the organic to crystallization processes and thereby became the founder of modern cytology.

BIBLIOGRAPHY

I. Original Works. Fries's principal work is *Neue oder anthropologische Kritik der Vernunft,* 3 vols. (Heidelberg, 1807; 2nd ed. 1828–1831). His other scientific works include *Entwurf eines Systems der theoretischen Physik* (1813); *Die mathematische Naturphilosophie nach philosophischer Methode bearbeitet* (Heidelberg, 1822); and *Versuch einer Kritik der Prinzipien der Wahrscheinlichkeitsrechnung*

(Brunswick, 1842). A detailed bibliography of his books and essays is contained in the biography written by his son-in-law Henke, pp. 379 ff.

A 26-vol. ed. of Fries's collected works, ed. and with intro. and index by Gert Koenig and Lutz Geldsetzer, is in publication (Aalen, 1969–).

II. SECONDARY LITERATURE. Works about Fries include T. Elsenhaus, *Fries und Kant. Ein Beitrag zur systematischen Grundlegung der Erkenntnistheorie,* 2 vols. (Giessen, 1906); Kuno Fischer, *Die beiden Kantischen Schulen in Jena,* Akademische Reden no. 2 (Stuttgart, 1862); M. Hasselblatt, *J. Fr. Fries, Seine Philosophie und seine Persoenlichkeit* (Munich, 1922); E. L. T. Henke, *J. Fr. Fries; Aus seinem handschriftlichen Nachlass dargestellt* (Leipzig, 1867); J. G. Meusel, in *Das gelehrte Teuschland oder Lexicon der jetzt lebenden teuschen Schriftsteller,* vol. II, and also in *Neuer Nekrolog der Deutschen Jgg.* (1823–1853), *Conversations-lexicon,* vol. X–A (Leipzig, 1851–1855); and C. Siegel, "Fries, Fortbildung der Kantischen Naturphilosophie," in *Geschichte der deutschen Naturphilosophie* (Leipzig, 1913), pp. 119–130.

H. M. NOBIS

FRISI, PAOLO (*b.* Milan, Italy, 13 April 1728; *d.* Milan, 22 November 1784)

Frisi was a member of the Barnabite order. In physics his research must be evaluated in relation to the concepts dominant in his time, which led him to justify and interpret certain phenomena of light and aspects of electricity, referring to the vibratory motion of ether and other properties attributed to it.

As an astronomer he concerned himself with the daily movement of the earth (in *De motu diurno terrae,* awarded a prize by the Berlin Academy), the obliquity of the ecliptic, the movement of the moon, the determination of the meridian circle, and matters concerning gravity in relation to Newton's general theories.

His mathematical activity included studies on kinematics (composition of rotatory movements, etc.) and, notably, on isoperimetry. He also did work in hydraulics and was called upon to plan works for the regulation of rivers and canals in various parts of northern Italy. He was responsible for laying out the canal built in 1819 between Milan and Pavia.

Frisi wrote critical notes in honor of Galileo, Cavalieri, Newton, and d'Alembert, illustrating the contributions each had made to science and the influence each had exerted. In Italy during his lifetime he was considered a scientific authority and was also well known abroad, so much so that his major works (which he wrote in Latin) were translated into French and English. *Algebra e geometria analitica* (1782), *Meccanica* (1783), and *Cosmografia* (1785), in which he brought together the best of his work, were, for that era, very up-to-date. Frisi was an editor of *Il caffè,* a newspaper that was influenced by the thought of the French Illuminati and that exerted a notable influence on the cultural, social, and political life of Milan in the second half of the eighteenth century.

BIBLIOGRAPHY

I. ORIGINAL WORKS. Among Frisi's works are *Disquisitio mathematica in causam physicam figurae* (Milan, 1751); *De methodo fluxionum geometricarum* (Milan, 1753); *Nova electricitas theoria* (Milan, 1755); *De motu diurno terrae dissertatio* (Pisa, 1756); *Piano de' lavori da farsi per liberare* (Lucca, 1761); *Del modo di regolare i fiumi, e i torrenti* (Lucca, 1762); *De gravitate universali corporum* (Milan, 1768); *Danielis Melandri et Paulli Frisii alterius ad alterum de theoria lunae commentaria* (Parma, 1769); *Opuscoli filosofici* (Milan, 1781); *Opera,* 3 vols. (Milan, 1782–1785); and *Operette scelte* (Milan, 1825).

His many papers include "Dell'equilibrio delle cupole e delle volte," in *Atti della Società patriotica di Milano,* **1** (1773), 222 ff.; and "Dissertatio de quantitatibus maximis et minimis isoperimetricis," in *Atti dell'Accademia dei fisiocritici di Siena,* **6** (1781), 121 ff.

II. SECONDARY LITERATURE. On Frisi and his work, see Girolamo Boccardo, in *Nuova enciclopedia italiana* (Turin, 1875–1888), IX, 1005–1006; Francesco Jacquier, *Elogio accademico* (Venice, 1786); Pietro Riccardi, *Biblioteca matematica italiana dall'origine della stampe . . .* (Modena, 1870; 7th ed., 1928); and Pietro Verri, *Memorie appartenenti alla vita ed agli studi del sig. D. Paolo Frisi* (Milan, 1784), which is reprinted in *Operette scelte.*

LUIGI CAMPEDELLI

FROBENIUS, GEORG FERDINAND (*b.* Berlin, Germany, 26 October 1849; *d.* Charlottenburg, Berlin, Germany, 3 August 1917)

Frobenius was the son of Christian Ferdinand Frobenius, a parson, and Christiane Elisabeth Friedrich. He attended the Joachimthal Gymnasium in Berlin and then began his mathematical studies at Göttingen in 1867, completing them with a doctorate at Berlin in 1870. In the latter year he taught at the Joachimthal Gymnasium and moved to the Sophienrealschule the following year. In 1874, on the basis of his mathematical papers, Frobenius was appointed assistant professor at the University of Berlin. The next year he was made a full professor at the Eidgenössische Polytechnikum in Zurich. In 1876 he married Auguste Lehmann. Frobenius returned permanently to the University of Berlin in 1892, as professor of mathematics. Important publications led to his election to membership in the Prussian Academy of Sciences at Berlin in 1893.

Frobenius wrote many papers, a number of them of decisive importance. Several were done with other prominent researchers, particularly with Ludwig Stickelberger and Issai Schur.

Frobenius' major achievements were in group theory, which in the 1870's and 1880's, through the joining of its three historical roots—the theory of solutions of algebraic equations (Galois theory, permutation groups), geometry (finite and infinite transformation groups, Lie theory), and number theory (composition of quadratic forms, modules)—produced the concept of the abstract group, the first abstract mathematical structure in the modern sense.

Frobenius, who had become acquainted with the idea of abstract algebra in Berlin, through Leopold Kronecker and Ernst Kummer, made fundamental contributions to the concept of the abstract group in "Ueber Gruppen von vertauschbaren Elementen" (1879), written with Stickelberger, and in "Über endliche Gruppen" (1895). He exerted even greater influence on the development of group theory by means of the theory of finite groups of linear substitutions of *n* variables. This theory, which he and Schur completed in all its essential aspects, was conceived from the beginning as a representation theory of abstract groups. Its nucleus is the theory of group characters. Among the relevant works on this topic are "Über die Gruppencharaktere" (1896), "Über die Darstellung der endlichen Gruppen durch lineare Substitutionen" (1897, 1899), "Über die Komposition der Charaktere einer Gruppe" (1899), and "Über die reellen Darstellungen der endlichen Gruppen" (1906), written with Schur.

The representation theory of finite groups through linear substitutions was later to offer the possibility of surprising and important applications to difficult questions in the theory of finite groups, properly speaking, and, in the 1920's and 1930's, to group-theory questions in quantum mechanics.

BIBLIOGRAPHY

I. Original Works. Frobenius' writings were brought together in *Gesammelte Abhandlungen*, J. P. Serre, ed., 3 vols. (Berlin-Heidelberg-New York, 1968). Among his works are "Ueber Gruppen von vertauschbaren Elementen," in *Journal für die reine und angewandte Mathematik*, **86** (1879), 217-262, written with L. Stickelberger; "Über endliche Gruppen," in *Sitzungsberichte der Preussischen Akademie der Wissenschaften zu Berlin* (1895), 81-112; "Über die Darstellung der endlichen Gruppen durch lineare Substitutionen," in *Monatsberichte der Preussischen Akademie der Wissenschaften zu Berlin* (1897), 994-1015, (1899), 482-500; and "Über die reellen Darstellungen der endlichen Gruppen," *ibid.* (1906), 186-208, written with I. Schur.

II. Secondary Literature. Frobenius' work is discussed in H. Wussing, *Die Genesis des abstrakten Gruppenbegriffes* (Berlin, 1969), pp. 182-184. A short biography is N. Stuloff, "G. F. Frobenius," in *Neue Deutsche Biographie*, V (1961), 641. There are also biographies and information on works in *Deutsches biographisches Jahrbuch* (1917-1920; 2nd ed., Berlin-Leipzig, 1928), p. 654; Poggendorff, III, 481; IV, 463-464; V, 399, and VI, pt. 2, 824; and *Vierteljahrsschrift der Naturforschenden Gesellschaft in Zürich*, **62** (1917), 719.

H. Wussing

FUBINI, GUIDO (*b.* Venice, Italy, 19 January 1879; *d.* New York, N.Y., 6 June 1943)

Fubini was the son of Lazzaro Fubini, who taught mathematics at the Scuola Macchinisti in Venice, and Zoraide Torre. At the age of seventeen, after brilliantly completing secondary studies in his native city, he entered the Scuola Normale Superiore di Pisa, where Dini and Bianchi were among his teachers. In 1900 he defended a thesis on Clifford's parallelism in elliptical spaces, the results of which rapidly became classic because of their inclusion in the 1902 edition of Luigi Bianchi's treatise on differential geometry. Fubini remained in Pisa for another year to complete work on the diploma allowing him to teach at the university level. The important memoir that he wrote in this connection deals with the fundamental principles of the theory of harmonic functions in spaces of constant curvature, a subject quite different from that of his doctoral thesis.

Placed in charge of a course at the University of Catania toward the end of 1901, Fubini soon won the competition for nomination as full professor. From Catania he went to the University of Genoa and then, in 1908, to the Politecnico in Turin. There he taught mathematical analysis, and at the same time, at the University of Turin, higher analysis. In 1938 Fubini was forced to retire under the racial laws promulgated by the Fascist government. The following year, at the invitation of the Institute for Advanced Study at Princeton, he immigrated to the United States and was welcomed among the institute's members. His prudent decision to seek voluntary exile was in part dictated by his concern for the future of his two sons, both engineers. Already in poor health, he continued to teach at New York University until he died of a heart ailment at the age of sixty-four.

A man of great cultivation, fundamentally honorable and kind, Fubini possessed unequaled pedagogic talents. His witty banter and social charm made him delightful company; he was small in stature, and his voice was vigorous and pleasant. Deeply imbued with a sense of family, he wished toward the end of his life legally to add Ghiron—the maiden name of his wife, whom he had married in 1910—to his own. Those works on mathematical subjects designed to be of use to engineers resulted from his own interest in watching over his sons' studies. With regard to Luigi Bianchi, Fubini's gratitude was the equal of his respect and admiration for Bianchi as a model for both his life and his work. Upon Bianchi's death in 1928, Fubini succeeded him as coeditor of the *Annali di matematica pura ed applicata,* a position that he held until 1938. A member of several Italian scientific academies, Fubini received the royal prize of the Lincei in 1919.

Fubini was one of Italy's most fecund and eclectic mathematicians. His contributions opened new paths for research in several areas of analysis, geometry, and mathematical physics. Guided by an ever-alert geometric intuition and possessed of an absolute mastery of all the techniques of calculation, he was able to follow leads that had barely been glimpsed. His technical mastery often permitted him to discover simpler demonstrations of such theorems as those of Bernstein and Pringsheim on the development of Taylor series.

In analysis Fubini did work on linear differential equations, partial differential equations, analytic functions of several complex variables, and monotonic functions. He also studied, in the calculus of variations, the reduction of Weierstrass' integral to a Lebesgue integral; the possibility of expressing every surface integral by two simple integrations, and the converse; and the manner of deducing from the existence of $\delta^n f/\delta x^n$ and $\delta^n f/\delta y^n$ the existence of lower-order derivatives of the function $f(x,y)$. In addition, Fubini determined, with regard to the minimum-value principle, the limit of a series of functions that take on given values on the contour of a domain, by supposing that the corresponding Dirichlet integrals tend toward their lower limit; he also indicated how his procedure could be applied to the calculus of variations. Finally, he investigated nonlinear integral equations and those with asymmetric kernels.

In the field of discontinuous groups, Fubini studied linear groups and groups of movement on a Riemannian variety in order to establish their criteria of discontinuity, as well as to prove the existence of fundamental domains and to indicate the method of constructing them. He examined functions admitting of such groups, as well as the automorphic harmonic functions in a space of n dimensions, in this way generalizing certain theorems of Weierstrass. For continuous groups, he established the conditions required in order to be able to attribute a metric to them.

In the field of non-Euclidean spaces Fubini, in his thesis on Clifford's notion of parallelism, introduced sliding parameters, which made possible the transposition to elliptical geometry of certain results of ordinary differential geometry, such as Frenet's formulas and the determination of couples of applicable surfaces. His work on the theory of harmonic functions in spaces of constant curvature contains an extension of the Neumann method and of the Appell and Mittag-Leffler theorems.

The most extensive field that Fubini cultivated was that of differential projective geometry, for which he elaborated general procedures of systematic study that still bear his name. The difficulties to be surmounted in order to pass from classical to projective differential geometry arise mainly from mathematical techniques and their use. To succeed in this endeavor, Fubini utilized absolute differential calculus and certain contravariant differentials. First he defined the local application of two varieties with respect to a Lie group; then he introduced the "projective linear element" as the quotient of two covariant differential forms and demonstrated that the necessary and sufficient condition for a projective application is the equality of these elements. He envisaged homogeneous coordinates normalized from a variable point on the surface or hypersurface, and he defined the "projective normals," the "projective geodesics," and the more general geodesics. In a Euclidean space the transformation by affinity of a surface of constant curvature is characterized by its second projective normal's being extended to infinity. These fundamental investigations of metric, or affine, geometry, which were pursued by other researchers, are collected in *Geometria proiettiva differenziale* and *Introduction à la géométrie projective différentielle des surfaces,* both written in collaboration with Eduard Čech.

Fubini's contributions to mathematical physics are varied. They began during World War I with theoretical studies on the accuracy of artillery fire and then turned to such problems in acoustics and electricity as anomalies in the propagation of acoustic waves of large amplitude, the pressure of acoustic radiation, and electric circuits containing rectifiers. Fubini was also interested in the equations of membranes and vibrating diaphragms. The mathematical aspects of the engineering sciences likewise occupied his attention. A work on engineering mathematics and its applications appeared posthumously in 1954. Finally, one must note his textbooks—courses in analysis and collections of problems which have been used by many generations of students—to appreciate fully the many-faceted work of Fubini, one of the most luminous and original minds in mathematics during the first half of the twentieth century.

BIBLIOGRAPHY

I. ORIGINAL WORKS. Fubini's writings were brought together in *Opere scelte,* 3 vols. (Rome, 1957–1962).

Among his articles are "Di un metodo per l'integrazione e lo studio delle equazioni alle derivate parziali," in *Rendiconti del Circolo matematico di Palermo,* **17** (1903), 222–235; "Nuove ricerche intorno ad alcune classi di gruppi discontinui," *ibid.*, **21** (1906), 177–187, in which, in a note, Fubini mentions seven of his articles on the same subject; "Sul principio di Dirichlet," *ibid.,* **22** (1906), 383–386; "Il principio di minimo e i teoremi di esistenza per i problemi al contorno relativi alle equazioni alle derivate parziali di ordine pari," *ibid.,* **23** (1907), 58–84, 300–301; "Applicabilità proiettiva di due superficie," *ibid.,* **41** (1916), 135–162; "Su una classe di congruenze W di carattere proiettivo," in *Atti della R. Accademia nazionale dei Lincei. Rendiconti,* **25** (1916), 144–148; "Invarianti proiettivo-differenziali delle curve tracciate su una superficie e definizione proiettivo-differenziale di una superficie," in *Annali di matematica pura ed applicata,* **25** (1916), 229–252; "Fondamenti di geometria proiettivo-differenziale," in *Rendiconti del Circolo matematico di Palermo,* **43** (1918–1919), 1–46; "Su alcune classi di congruenze di rette e sulle trasformazioni delle superficie R," in *Annali di matematica pura ed applicata,* **58** (1924), 241–257; and "Luigi Bianchi e la sua opera scientifica," *ibid.,* **62** (1929), 45–81.

Fubini's books are *Introduzione alla teoria dei gruppi discontinui e delle funzioni automorfe* (Pisa, 1908); *Lezioni di analisi matematica* (Turin, 1913; 2nd ed., 1915); *Esercizi di analisi matematica (calcolo infinitesimale) con speciale riguardo alle applicazioni* (Turin, 1920), written with G. Vivanti; *Geometria proiettiva differenziale,* 2 vols. (Bologna, 1926–1927), written with E. Čech; *Introduction à la géométrie différentielle des surfaces* (Paris, 1931), written with E. Čech; *Anomalie nella propagazione di onde acustiche di grande ampiezza* (Milan, 1935); *Circuiti elettrici contenenti raddrizzatori* (Turin, 1936); *Acustica non lineare delle onde di ampiezza* (Milan, 1938); and *La matematica dell'ingegnere e le sue applicazioni* (Bologna, 1954), written with G. Albenga.

II. SECONDARY LITERATURE. See the unsigned "Guido Fubini Ghiron," in *Annali di matematica pura ed applicata,* 4th ser., **25** (1946), ix–xii; and M. Picone, in *Bollettino dell'Unione matematica italiana,* 2nd ser., **1**, no. 1 (Dec., 1946), 56–58.

PIERRE SPEZIALI

FUCHS, IMMANUEL LAZARUS (*b.* Moschin, near Posen, Germany [now Poznan, Poland], 5 May 1833; *d.* Berlin, Germany, 26 April 1902)

Fuchs was a gifted analyst whose works form a bridge between the fundamental researches of Cauchy, Riemann, Abel, and Gauss and the modern theory of differential equations discovered by Poincaré, Painlevé, and Picard.

By the time Fuchs was a student at the Friedrich Wilhelm Gymnasium, his unusual aptitude in mathematics had awakened a corresponding interest in the discipline. At the University of Berlin he studied with Ernst Eduard Kummer and Karl Weierstrass, and it was the latter who introduced him to function theory, an area that was to play an important role in his own researches. Fuchs received the doctorate from Berlin in 1858, then taught first at a Gymnasium and later at the Friedrich Werderschen Trade School. In 1865 he went to the University of Berlin as a *Privatdozent,* and there he began the study of regular singular points. In 1866 he became an extraordinary professor at the university. From 1867 to 1869 Fuchs was professor of mathematics at the Artillery and Engineering School and then went as ordinary professor to Greifswald. He remained there five years, spent one year at Göttingen and then, in 1875, went to Heidelberg. In 1882 Fuchs returned to Berlin, where he became professor of mathematics, associate director of the mathematics seminars, and a member of the Academy of Sciences. He remained at Berlin until his death. For the last ten years of his life he was editor of the *Journal für die reine und angewandte Mathematik.*

Except for a few early papers in higher geometry and number theory, all of Fuchs's efforts were devoted to differential equations.

In his monumental 1812 work, *Disquisitiones generales circa seriem infinitam,* Gauss investigated the hypergeometric series and noted that, for appropriately chosen parameters, most known functions could find representation through this series. In 1857 Riemann conjectured that functions so expressed, which satisfy a homogeneous linear differential equation of the second order with rational coefficients, might be employed in the solution of any linear differential equation. This provided an alternate approach to the power series development which had been presented by Cauchy and extended by Briot and Bouquet. With Riemann's work as inspiration these methods were synthesized and extended by Fuchs in a series of papers that began to appear in 1865.

In the real domain the method of successive approximations was first applied by Liouville (1838) to homogeneous linear differential equations of the second order and later (1864) by M. J. Caqué to the nth-order case. A second method of proving the existence of solutions derives from a method suggested by Euler (1768), developed by Cauchy (1820–1830), and refined by Lipschitz in 1876.

For a first-order equation, $dw/dz = f(z,w)$, the Cauchy-Lipschitz method can be extended to the complex domain, as can the method of limits. It was Fuchs, however, who provided the proof of the existence of solutions, satisfying initial conditions for $z = z_0$, for the linear differential equation of order n. The general homogeneous linear differential equation of order n has the form

$$(1) \qquad \frac{d^n w}{dz^n} + p_1(z)\frac{d^{n-1}w}{dz^{n-1}} + \cdots + p_n(z)w = 0,$$

and it is assumed that the $p_i(z)$ are analytic throughout a domain D in the Z plane. With z_0 and z in D, c_r are chosen so that the Taylor series,

$$w(z) = \Sigma\, c_r(z - z_0)^r,$$

formally satisfies the differential equation. The c_r are shown to be finite as long as the initial values are finite. Furthermore, if M_ν is the upper bound of $|p_\nu(z)|$ on $|z - z_0| = a$, then $p_\nu^{(r)} \leqslant M_\nu/a^r$, so that if

$$P_\nu(z) = \frac{M_\nu}{1 - \dfrac{z - z_0}{a}},$$

then

$$|p_\nu(z)| \leq |P_\nu(z)|$$

within $|z - z_0| = a$ and on the circumference.

If now w is replaced by W in equation (1), where, as above,

$$W(z) = \Sigma C_r(z - z_0)^r$$

where $C_i = |c_i|$, then

$$|w^{(r)}(z_0)| \leq W^{(r)}(z_0)$$

and, hence,

$$\Sigma|c_r(z - z_0)^r| \leq \Sigma C_r(z - z_0)^r.$$

But the circle of convergence of the dominant series can, as Fuchs showed, be readily found to be $|z - z_0| = a$. Consequently there is a solution to the differential equation, satisfying the given initial conditions, when $z = z_0$, which is expressible by a Taylor series that is absolutely and uniformly convergent within any circle, that has its center at z_0, in which the $p_i(z)$ are analytic.

The singularities of the solution are precisely the singularities of equation (1), so that, because of the linearity of this equation, there are neither movable singularities nor movable poles. To determine whether the point at infinity is a singular point, it is necessary only to effect the substitution $z = 1/Z$ and reduce the equation to the form given by (1). If the equation in Z has singularities at the origin, then the equation in z has a singular point at infinity. Thus, in all cases the singular points can be found simply by inspecting the equation itself.

Fuchs introduced the term "fundamental system" to describe n linearly independent solutions of the linear differential equation $L(u) = 0$. It is clear that for any nonsingular point such a fundamental set of solutions exists. The so-called Fuchsian theory is concerned with the same existence question in relation to an arbitrarily given singular point and, once the existence problem is solved, an investigation of the behavior of the solutions in the neighborhood of the singular point.

BIBLIOGRAPHY

Fuchs's works were published as *Gesammelte mathematische Werke*, Richard Fuchs and Ludwig Schlesinger, eds., 3 vols. (Berlin, 1904–1909). His speech as rector, given 3 Aug. 1900, is *Rede zur Gedächtnissfeier des Stifters der Berliner Universität* (Berlin, 1900).

Obituaries include E. J. Wilczynski, in *Bulletin of the American Mathematical Society*, **9** (1902), 46–49; *Atti dell'Accademia nazionale dei Lincei. Rendiconti*, 5th ser., **11** (1902), 397–398; *Bibliotheca mathematica*, 3rd ser., **3** (1902), 334; and *Enseignement mathématique*, **4** (1902), 293–294.

See also Otto Biermann, *Zur Theorie Fuchs'schen Functionen* (Vienna, 1885), reprinted from *Sitzungsberichte der Wien Akademie der Wissenschaften*, **92** (1885).

JEROME H. MANHEIM

FUETER, KARL RUDOLF (*b.* Basel, Switzerland, 30 June 1880; *d.* Brunnen, Switzerland, 9 August 1950)

Fueter was the son of Eduard Rudolf Fueter, an architect, and Adèle Gelzer. In 1908 he married Amélie von Heusinger.

After receiving his early education in Basel, Fueter began to study mathematics at Göttingen in 1899 and graduated in 1903. Under the supervision of David Hilbert he presented a work dealing with the theory of quadratic number fields. After further study in Paris, Vienna, and London and teaching in Marburg and

Clausthal (now Clausthal-Zellerfeld), Fueter became a professor of mathematics in Basel in 1908; he accepted the same post at the Technische Hochschule in Karlsruhe in 1913 and at the University of Zurich in 1916. His field of interest was the theory of numbers as presented in Hilbert's work. He derived the class formula for the entire group of Abelian number fields over an imaginary quadratic base field. He gave a summary of these in his *Vorlesungen über die singulären Moduln und die komplexe Multiplikation der elliptischen Funktionen* (1924–1927). Later he founded his own school of thought on the theory of functions of a quaternion variable.

Fueter was cofounder and president of the Swiss Mathematical Society, rector of the University of Zurich, and president of the Euler Commission of the Swiss Society of Sciences (editors of the *Opera Omnia Leonhardi Euleri*). He held the rank of colonel in the artillery of the Swiss militia, and at the outbreak of World War II he served in the Department of Press and Radio. In *Spying for Peace* (London, 1961), Jon Kimche states, "Fueter restated the democratic rights of the press in almost classical form. . . . In his report of April 10, 1940 . . . Fueter developed his argument more fully. 'It is the duty of our press to reject the domestic and foreign policies of the National Socialists both clearly and forcefully.' " Fueter was, therefore, particularly noted for his opposition to Nazism and to the spread of its policies within Switzerland.

BIBLIOGRAPHY

Fueter's major works are *Synthetische Zahlentheorie* (Berlin, 1917; 3rd ed., 1950); *Vorlesungen über die singulären Moduln und die komplexe Multiplikation der elliptischen Funktionen*, 2 vols. (Leipzig-Berlin, 1924–1927); and *Das mathematische Werkzeug des Chemikers, Biologen und Statistikers* (Zurich, 1926; 3rd ed., 1947).

A biography is A. Speiser, in *Elemente der Mathematik*, **5** (1950), published with Fueter's autobiographical notes.

J. J. BURCKHARDT

FUSS, NICOLAUS (or **Nikolai Ivanovich Fus**), (*b.* Basel, Switzerland, 30 January 1755; *d.* St. Petersburg, Russia, 4 January 1826)

Fuss was born into a Swiss family of modest means. His mathematical abilities, which manifested themselves quite early, attracted the attention of a number of prominent scholars, including Daniel Bernoulli, who in 1772 recommended him to Euler, then living in Russia, as a secretary. Fuss arrived in St. Petersburg at the age of seventeen and spent the rest of his life in Russia.

Fuss wrote his first papers, which had purely practical goals, under Euler's direct guidance. These were *Instruction détaillée pour porter les lunettes* . . . (1774) and *Éclaircissemens sur les établissemens publics en faveur tant des veuves* . . . (1776). The latter concerns problems of the insurance business.

In January 1776, Fuss was selected as a junior scientific assistant of the St. Petersburg Academy of Sciences; in February 1783, he became an academician in higher mathematics; and from September 1800 until his death he was the academy's permanent secretary.

The majority of Fuss's writings contain solutions to problems raised in Euler's works. They deal with several branches of mathematics (spherical geometry, trigonometry, the theory of series, the geometry of curves, the integration of differential equations) and with mechanics, astronomy, and geodesy. From 1774—the year of his first published paper—more than 100 of his articles appeared in the publications of the St. Petersburg Academy of Sciences.

Fuss's best papers deal with spherical geometry, the problems of which he worked out with the St. Petersburg academicians A. J. Lexell and F. T. Schubert. In his first paper on spherical geometry, which was published in *Nova acta Academiae scientiarum imperialis Petropolitanae* (1788), he gave solutions to three new problems concerning spherical triangles which are constructed on a given base, between two given great circles, and satisfy certain extremal conditions. In another article (1788) the characteristics of a spherical ellipse, i.e., of the geometrical locus of the vertexes of spherical triangles with a given base and a sum of two other sides, are studied in detail.

Fuss was also responsible for new solutions to a number of difficult problems in elementary geometry. These included Apollonius' problem of constructing a circle tangent to three given circles (1790) and Cramer's problem—which generalizes Pappus' problem—of inscribing a triangle inside a given circle, such that the sides of the triangle, or their extensions, pass through three given points (1783).

In differential geometry Fuss solved a number of problems concerning the determination of the properties of curves which are defined by certain relationships between the radius of curvature, the radius vector, and the length of an arc (1789). These papers partially bordered on so-called intrinsic geometry, which was developed into an independent mathematical discipline by Ernesto Cesàro and others at the end of the nineteenth century.

Fuss was an honorary member of the Berlin, Swedish, and Danish academies. In 1778 the Paris Academy of Sciences awarded him a prize for his astronomical paper "Recherche sur le dérangement d'une comète qui passe près d'une planète" (*Mémoires des savants étrangers,* **10** [1785]). In 1798 a prize was awarded to him by the Danish Society of Sciences for his paper *Versuch einer Theorie des Widerstandes zwei-und vierrädiger Wagen usw.* (Copenhagen, 1798).

Fuss also did much in the field of education. He taught for many years at the military and naval cadet academies. At the beginning of the nineteenth century he was active in the reform of the Russian national education system. He compiled a number of textbooks, including *Leçons de géométrie à l'usage du Corps impérial des cadets . . .* (St. Petersburg, 1798), *Nachalnye osnovania ploskoy trigonometrii, vysshey geometrii i differentsialnogo ischislenia* ("Foundations of Plane Trigonometry, Higher Geometry, and Differential and Integral Calculus," 3 vols., St. Petersburg, 1804), and *Nachalnye osnovania chistoy matematiki* ("Fundamentals of Pure Mathematics," 3 vols., St. Petersburg, 1810–1812). These textbooks show the influence of all of Euler's work, especially his *Vollständige Anleitung zur Algebra* (2 vols., St. Petersburg, 1770), which Fuss used as a model in compiling a handbook for the cadet corps and the first algebra textbook for Russian Gymnasiums.

BIBLIOGRAPHY

I. Original Works. Fuss's writings include *Instruction détaillée pour porter les lunettes de toutes les différentes espèces au plus haut degré de perfection . . . tirée de la théorie dioptrique de M. Euler . . .* (St. Petersburg, 1774); *Éclaircissemens sur les établissemens publics en faveur tant des veuves que des morts, avec la déscription d'une nouvelle espece de tontine. . . . Calculés sous la direction de Mr. Léonard Euler par Mr. N[icolaus] F[uss]* (St. Petersburg, 1776); "Solutio problematis geometrici Pappi Alexandrini," in *Acta Academiae Scientiarum imperialis Petropolitanae,* **4,** pt. 1 (1783), 97–104; "Problematum quorundam sphaericorum solutio," in *Nova Acta Academiae Scientiarum imperialis Petropolitanae,* **2** (1788), 67–80; "De proprietatibus quibusdam ellipseos in superficie sphaerica descriptae," *ibid.,* **3** (1788), 90–99; "Solutio problematis ex methodo tangentium inversa," *ibid.,* **4** (1789), 104–128; "Recherches sur un problème de mécanique," *ibid.,* **6** (1790), 172–184.

A full bibliography of Fuss's mathematical works can be found in the following publications: *Matematika v izdaniakh Akademii Nauk (1728–1935). Bibliografichesky Ukazatel* ("Mathematics in the Publications of the Academy of Sciences [1728–1935]. Bibliographic Index"), compiled by O. V. Dinze and K. I. Shafranovsky (Moscow–Leningrad, 1936), see index; F. A. Brokgauz and I. A. Efron, eds., *Entsiklopedichesky slovar* ("Encyclopedic Dictionary"), XXXVI A (St. Petersburg, 1902), 913–914; Poggendorff, I, 822–823; and M. Cantor, *Vorlesungen über die Geschichte der Mathematik,* 3rd ed., IV (Leipzig, 1913), see index.

II. Secondary Literature. On Fuss or his work, see V. V. Bobynin, "Fuss, Nikolai," in F. A. Brokgauz and I. A. Efron, eds., *Entsiklopedichesky slovar,* XXXVI A (St. Petersburg, 1902), 913–914; V. I. Lysenko, "O rabotakh peterburgskikh akademikov A. I. Lekselya, N. I. Fussa i F. I. Shuberta po sfericheskoy geometrii i sfericheskoy trigonometrii" ("On the Works of the Petersburg Academicians A. J. Lexell, N. I. Fuss, and F. T. Schubert in Spherical Geometry and Spherical Trigonometry"), in *Trudy Instituta istorii estestvoznaniya i tekhniki. Akademiya nauk SSSR,* **34** (1960), 384–414, which examines several of Fuss's unpublished compositions, which are preserved in the archives of the Soviet Academy of Sciences; and "Iz istorii pervoy peterburgskoy matematicheskoy shkoly" ("From the History of the First Petersburg School of Mathematics"), *ibid.,* **43** (1961), 182–205.

See also A. P. Youschkevitch, "Matematika" ("Mathematics"), in *Istoria estestvoznania v Rossii* ("History of Natural Science in Russia"), I, pt. 1 (Moscow, 1957), 215–272; and "Matematika i mekhanika" ("Mathematics and Mechanics"), in *Istoria Akademii nauk SSSR* ("History of the USSR Academy of Sciences"), I (Moscow–Leningrad, 1958), 350–352.

A. I. Volodarsky

FYODOROV (or **FEDOROV**), **EVGRAF STEPANOVICH** (*b.* Orenburg, Russia [now Chkalov, U.S.S.R.], 22 December 1853; *d.* Petrograd [now Leningrad], U.S.S.R., 21 May 1919)

His father, Stepan Ivanovich Fyodorov, came from a peasant family and was a major-general in the Engineer Corps. He was noted for the sharpness of his disposition, which he evidently passed on to his son.

Fyodorov's mother, Yulia Gerasimovna Botvinko, the daughter of a procurator in Vilna, was a progressive and cultured woman. She gave her son the elements of a musical education and, in particular, imparted a love of reading and accustomed him to steady work and discipline. Fyodorov later said that he was wholly indebted to his mother for his exceptional capacity for work. She made him knit large tablecloths with intricate figures, which probably developed his feeling for symmetry.

Fyodorov's mathematical abilities appeared very early; when he was five, he had already mastered the rules of arithmetic. At the age of seven he studied with fascination and finished in two days a textbook of elementary geometry. In his own words, the content of the first pages of the text evoked "a resonance in my psyche, so that I was literally carried away." At the age of ten Fyodorov entered the second class of Annensky College. After the death of his father in 1866, the straitened circumstances of his family forced him to transfer to the military Gymnasium, which he could attend at state expense. Here he joined a small group of friends who were studying natural science and philosophy intensively. At the same time Fyodorov independently immersed himself in the mathematical disciplines, which for him were always invested with an aura of special beauty. In 1869 he transferred to the Petersburg Military Engineering School. There he became an active member of an illegal group devoted to self-education, in which, under the influence of the literary critic, Dmitry Pisarev, the works of the materialist natural scientists were studied.

In 1872 Fyodorov graduated and went to Kiev with the rank of second lieutenant in a combat engineering battalion; the following year he returned to St. Petersburg, and in 1874 he retired completely from military service. As a result of his enthusiasm for natural sciences he became a free auditor at the Military Medical and Surgical Academy. Having passed the necessary examinations, Fyodorov entered the second-year course of the Technological Institute, where he concentrated on physics and chemistry. All his thoughts and interests were already directed toward theoretical mathematics, particularly geometry; this made possible the completion of his important monograph, *Nachala uchenia o figurakh,* which he had begun at the age of sixteen. In it he touched on symmetry and the theory of crystal structure and set forth the principles of contemporary theoretical crystallography. His work on the theory of mathematical polyhedrons brought Fyodorov to questions relating to natural polyhedrons—the crystals of minerals—and to geometric mineralogy.

Because of his enthusiasm for crystallography Fyodorov chose the specialty closest to this science and in 1880, at the age of twenty-seven, he entered the third-year course at the Mining Institute, where a general course in crystallography and related mineralogy was taught. After graduating from the Mining Institute in 1883 (his name was placed at the top of the list carved in marble), Fyodorov joined a Mining Department expedition to investigate the northern Urals.

Fyodorov married Ludmila Vasilievna Panyutina, a vivacious and purposeful girl who had come from Kungur in the Urals to study medicine in St. Petersburg. She selflessly helped him in his scientific and revolutionary work. Fyodorov's son, Evgraf Evgrafovich, was a specialist in climatology and later a corresponding member of the Soviet Academy of Sciences.

In childhood Fyodorov had been sickly; in his middle years he was extremely robust. He always worked a great deal and was extraordinarily precise in carrying out the life plan he had set for himself. He went on expeditions to the Urals and other regions, distinguishing himself on them because of his great endurance. Fyodorov traveled under conditions of great privation and worked to the point of exhaustion; on expeditions he was sunburned and thin but cheerful and energetic. In his old age he was often ill.

In 1896 Fyodorov was elected a member of the Bavarian Academy of Sciences and in 1901 an adjunct of the Petersburg Academy of Sciences; but, not having received support for his demands for the creation of a mineralogical institute, he withdrew from the Petersburg academy in 1905. He was elected a member of the Soviet Academy of Sciences in 1919, when an institute in which mineralogy occupied an important place was organized.

Revolutionary activity gave meaning to Fyodorov's life. In 1876 he became a member of the populist Land and Freedom party; the following year he was commissioned to set up connections with revolutionary organizations in France, Belgium, and Germany, a task which he handled well. His apartment in Petersburg contained an underground revolutionary press.

Fyodorov's scientific and literary work is distinguished for its richness and extraordinary variety. Most numerous among his more than 500 scientific published works are those on crystallography, followed by geometry, mineralogy, petrography, geology, history of science, and philosophy.

Fyodorov devoted forty-three publications to mineralogy, but the only one to deal with the field as a whole is *Kritichesky peresmotr form mineralnogo tsarstva* (1903), in which the morphology of minerals is examined relative to crystal structure theory. Fyodorov exerted a very strong influence on the development of mineralogy and opened a new stage in it. He also contributed to the accumulation of significant new factual material and helped to change the methodological approach to the study of minerals. He used the analytical approach and attempted to understand natural processes and phenomena by starting from more general mathematical and physical-chemical principles. Through his work Fyodorov laid the foundations for the analytical period in the development of mineralogy.

The foundation of all of Fyodorov's scientific work was geometry. Among his first works was the monograph *Nachala uchenia o figurakh,* and his last article treated questions of the new geometry. Geometrical research led Fyodorov to the brilliant derivation of the 230 space groups—the symmetry groups governing the periodic distribution within crystalline matter.

The derivation is the foundation of contemporary mineralogy and the basis of the atomic structure of minerals. His first work was an exposition of all those parts of the theory of figures which constitute the basis of contemporary crystallography.

The period of the first geometrical investigations and publications was crowned by the classic work *Simmetria pravilnykh sistem figur* (1890), which contained the first deduction of the 230 space groups. The publication in 1891 of Schoenflies' book with his derivation of the 230 space groups prompted Fyodorov to publish several articles in the *Zeitschrift für Kristallographie.* He compared his results with those of Schoenflies and made a series of essential corrections and notations. In these articles he gave a strict mathematical definition of thirty-two point groups for six crystallographic systems, which still retain their significance. At the basis of this classification he placed a number of single and symmetrically equivalent axes in crystals. This classification led to the working out of a new nomenclature of systems and point group symmetries, accepted throughout the world and known as Fyodorov-Groth nomenclature. For these accomplishments, and at the insistence of such eminent crystallographers as Groth and L. Sohncke, Fyodorov was elected a member of the Bavarian Academy of Sciences in 1896. Fyodorov himself considered these works as belonging to the theory of crystallography, specifically to geometric mineralogy. Fyodorov's group classifications are, with the aid of X-ray diffraction, at the base of modern mineralogical determinations of the atomic structure of minerals.

In the category of physical crystallography are Fyodorov's works that explain a universal method of optical research, which played an important role in mineralogy and petrography. In 1889, at a session of the Mineralogical Society, Fyodorov reported on his projected two-circle optical goniometer for the measurement of all angles in crystals with a single setting of the specimen. It differed from previous goniometers, which had only a single axis of rotation. (A two-circle goniometer had been proposed earlier by W. H. Miller.) This produced a revolution in the method of investigating minerals. Following Fyodorov and using his idea, Victor Goldschmidt, S. Czapski, Y. Flint, and others designed two-circle goniometers. Crystallographers and mineralogists throughout the world began to work exclusively with these instruments.

In 1891 Fyodorov proposed to the Geological Committee the construction of a universal stage for the petrographic microscope that would locate the specimen at the center of two glass hemispheres. In essence this method is crystallographic, but its application is to mineralogy and petrography. With what became known as the Fyodorov method the optical constants of minerals could be established and, without resorting to chemical analysis, the composition of the isomorphic lime-soda feldspars (plagioclases) was determined, as were those of other minerals.

Of all the instruments constructed and developed by Fyodorov, the universal stage (also called U-stage or Fyodorov table) has enjoyed the greatest popularity. Special courses in its use are given to students of mineralogy and petrography. Handbooks and special studies on the Fyodorov method have been published by Russian and foreign authors: S. N. Nikitin, M. A. Usov, V. S. Sobolev, L. Duparc, M. Reinhard, M. Berek, and others. The Fyodorov method has allowed researchers to carry out quickly the optical study of plagioclases, pyroxenes, and other minerals, using thin sections of rock. The present Fyodorov table is a refined instrument with five axes of rotation, convenient for the study of minerals in any cross section.

In describing Fyodorov's activity in petrography and mineralogy, it must be noted that he himself never drew a sharp boundary between these sciences. He considered that all the physical, mathematical, and natural sciences were used in them. He also believed that in the cycle of mineralogical and geological sciences one used the totality of knowledge of the earth—which, in his view, is located in infinite, starry space and interacts with it. These ideas are only now being worked out in detail by his followers in the fields of astrogeology and planetology.

Fyodorov gave much attention to the chemical composition of rocks and their graphic representation, and he introduced symbols of chemical composition, petrographic nomenclature, and rock classification. He conducted important research on the northern Urals, the Bogoslovsky (now Sverdlovsk) district, the coast of the White Sea, the Caucasus, and Kazakhstan. He was one of the first to show the great importance of the apatite resources lying in the depths of the Soviet north (1909).

In one of his first scientific works, the tract "Perfektsionizm" (1906), Fyodorov showed that he was a convinced materialist. Starting from the materialistic principle that natural conditions are in essence conditions of eternal change, he attacked authors who teach the theory of stability and equilibrium in nature. The essence of evolution, in his opinion, is not in the tendency toward a higher order, stability, and equilibrium of organisms but in their life movement. Criticizing the outlook of Herbert Spencer and other partisans of equilibrium in nature, Fyodorov showed that the main effect of such points of view when applied to the evolution of natural history was to give attention to the least changeable. But the creators of these systems of philosophy systematically failed to take into account the fact that equilibrium is attained only at the moment of death. As long as life is active, changing forms are developing. For this reason Fyodorov considered deeply erroneous the introduction into natural philosophy of the concept of the constant and the stable as the supreme mission of life. He asserted that life never finally achieves anything but eternally strives to achieve. It was in this that the true philosophy of nature lay for him.

Later, in published statements, Fyodorov defended science against positivism, which, in his view, reduces the significance of mind to simply a mold for the more convenient organization of material gathered by experimentation. Attacking the attempts of positivists and followers of Ernst Mach to disregard the atomic theory, Fyodorov wished to remove all metaphysical errors from contemporary science and to be led by the clear guide of atomic theory, which has produced so many valuable and stunning developments in contemporary theory.

Fyodorov's work harmoniously combined the achievements of varied fields of science. Mathematics was the basis of Fyodorov's theory of structure and symmetry of crystals. He was able to combine the methods drawn from mathematical analysis with the older empirical laws of crystallography and the methods of crystallographic research with descriptive mineralogy; he introduced principles of geometry into petrography; he combined chemistry with crystallography, thus creating crystal chemistry; and he introduced the principles of the new geometry into mine surveying. Fyodorov knew how to make generalizations and find simple solutions in the analysis of natural phenomena. His "simple" theodolite method in crystallography and petrography played a role in the history of these sciences no less than the most profound generalizations and theoretical achievements. Fyodorov presented all his scientific conclusions in mathematical form. He asserted that the crown of man's conscious activity, of man's intelligence, was the solution of the questions facing him by means of mathematical analysis.

The enormous *Tsarstvo kristallov* ("The Crystal Kingdom," 1920) was the fruit of forty years of work by Fyodorov and his colleagues. In it he noted that strongly developed sciences satisfy the spiritual needs of part of mankind and at the same time provide great power to direct the active forces of nature for man's use, thus forcing nature to serve man to a great degree. Lately it has become clear that special sciences can master nature in some respects and in certain areas of natural phenomena, directing them according to the wishes of man.

BIBLIOGRAPHY

I. ORIGINAL WORKS. Fyodorov's writings include "Teodolitny metod v mineralogii i petrografii" ("The Theodolitic Method in Mineralogy and Petrography"), in *Trudy Geologicheskogo komiteta*, **10**, no. 2 (1893), 1-191; "Iz itogov tridtsatipyatiletia" ("From the Results of Thirty-five Years"), in *Rech i otchet, chitannye v godichnom sobranii Moskovskogo selskokhozyaistvennago instituta, 26 sentyabrya 1904 g.* ("Speech and Report Given at the Annual Meeting of the Moscow Agricultural Institute, 26 September 1904," Moscow, 1904), pp. 1-15; "Perfektsionizm" ("Perfectionism"), in *Izvestiya S. Peterburgskoi biologicheskoi laboratorii*, **8**, pt. 1 (1906), 25-65; *ibid.*, pt. 2, 9-67; "Beloe more kak istochnik materiala dlya selskokhozyaystvennoy kultury" ("The White Sea as a Source of Material for Agriculture"), in *Izvestiya Moskovskago selskokhozyaistvennago instituta*, **1** (1908), 94-97; "Iz rezultatov poezdki v Bogoslovsky okrug letom 1911 g." ("From the Results of a Trip to the Bogoslov District in the Summer of 1911"), in *Zapiski Gornago instituta Imperatritsy Ekateriny II*, **3** (1912), 340-348; "Tsarstvo kristallov" ("The Crystal Kingdom"), in *Zapiski Rossiiskoi akademii nauk*, **36** (1920); and *Nachala uchenia o figurakh* ("Principles of the Theory of Figures," Leningrad, 1953).

II. SECONDARY LITERATURE. On Fyodorov or his work, see O. M. Ansheles, "100-letie so dnya rozhdenia velikogo russkogo uchenogo E. S. Fyodorova" ("Centenary of the Birth of the Great Russian Scientist E. S. Fyodorov"), in *Vestnik Leningradskogo gosudarstvennogo universiteta*, no. 1 (1954), 223-226; N. V. Belov, *Chetyrnadtsat reshetok Brave i 230 prostranstvennykh grupp simmetrii* ("The Fourteen Bravais Lattices and the 230 Three-Dimensional Groups of Symmetries," Moscow-Leningrad, 1962); N. V. Belov and I. I. Shafranovsky, "Rol E. S. Fyodorov v predistorii rentgenostrukturnoy kristallografii . . ." ("E. S. Fyodorov's Role in the Early Development of X-ray Structural Crystallography . . ."), in *Zapiski Vsesoyuznogo mineralogicheskogo obshchestva*, pt. 91, no. 4 (1962), 465-471; G. B. Boky, "O zakone raspolozhenia atomov v kristallakh" ("On the Law of Arrangement of Atoms in Crystals"), no. 5 in the collection *Kristallografiya* (Leningrad, 1956), pp. 25-36; F. Y. Levinson-Lessing, "Neskolko yubileynykh dat v petrografii (v tom chisle 'Sorokopyatiletie tak nazyvaemogo universalnogo, ili fyodorovskogo metoda v petrografii')" ("Several Jubilee Dates in Petrography [Including the 'Fortieth Anniversary of the So-called Universal or Fyodorov Method in Petrography']"), in *Priroda* (1938), no. 6, 137-144; I. I. Shafranovsky, *Evgraf Stepanovich Fyodorov* (Moscow-Leningrad, 1963); and N. M. Sokolov, "O mirovozzrenii E. S. Fyodorov" ("On the World View of E. S. Fyodorov"), in *Kristallografiya*, no. 5 (Leningrad, 1956), pp. 5-23.

A. MENIAILOV

GALERKIN, BORIS GRIGORIEVICH (*b.* Polotsk, Russia, 4 March 1871; *d.* Moscow, U.S.S.R., 12 June 1945)

Galerkin was born into a poor family. He received his secondary education at Minsk, and in 1893 he entered the Petersburg Technological Institute. During his studies there Galerkin had to support himself first by giving private lessons and then, from the year 1896, by working as a designer.

In 1899, after graduating from the Technological Institute, Galerkin entered the Kharkov Locomotive Building Mechanical Plant. In 1903 he moved to St. Petersburg and started work in the Northern Mechanical and Boiler Plant as manager of the technical section. He quickly became known in engineering circles.

From 1909 to 1914 Galerkin studied Russian and foreign factories and engineering installations. He visited Germany, Sweden, Switzerland, Belgium, and Austria, becoming acquainted with the outstanding examples of foreign technology. In 1909 Galerkin was invited to teach at the Petersburg Polytechnical Institute. He was chosen head of the department of structural mechanics there in 1920. From 1923 to 1929 he was dean of the structural engineering department. During this period Galerkin was professor of the theory of elasticity at the Leningrad Institute of Communications Engineers and professor of structural mechanics at Leningrad University. From 1940 to 1945 he headed the Institute of Mechanics of the Soviet Academy of Sciences.

In 1928 Galerkin was elected a corresponding member of the Soviet Academy of Sciences, and in 1935 an active member. In 1934 he was awarded the title of honored scientist and technologist. In 1942 he received the title of state prize laureate.

Galerkin's scientific work was devoted to difficult problems in the theory of elasticity and structural mechanics. His first scientific work, *Teoria prodolnogo izgiba . . .* ("Theory of Longitudinal Curvature . . ."), appeared in 1909. Galerkin extended the theory of longitudinal curvature, created by Leonhard Euler, to multistage uprights formed by the joining of a series of vertical and horizontal rods.

In his second work, *Izgib i szhatie* ("Curvature and Compression," 1910), Galerkin investigated the curvature of a rod strengthened at one end by the action of force applied, parallel to the axis, to the free end with eccentricity (or force applied at any angle to the axis). Galerkin's early works in the area of longitudinal curvature opened broad possibilities for the application of the theory of longitudinal curvature to the calculation of the stability of bridges, the frames of buildings, and similar systems.

From 1915 to 1917, in connection with the beginning of the use of beamless floors in industrial and civil construction, Galerkin made his first profound research in the theory of the curvature of thin plates. He devoted many years of his life to its development. Galerkin's many works in this field were generalized in the monograph *Uprugie tonkie plity* ("Elastic Thin Plates"), published in 1933. In 1915 Galerkin proposed a method for the approximate integration of differential equations that was widely used for the solution of problems in mathematical physics and technology. It became known as Galerkin's method.

A series of works by Galerkin on the theory of torsion and the curve of prismatic rods, published in 1919–1927, developed an interesting problem in the theory of elasticity. In 1930–1931 his fundamental works on the theory of elasticity, which contain a general solution of three-dimensional problems, appeared.

Galerkin's scientific research in the theory of casing (1934–1945) revealed its broad application in industrial construction. His works in the field constitute a new direction in this important area.

Galerkin was a consultant in the planning and building of many of the Soviet Union's largest hydrostations. In 1929, in connection with the building of the Dnepr dam and hydroelectric station, Galerkin investigated stress in dams and breast walls with trapezoidal profile. His results were used in planning the dam. For many years Galerkin was head of the All-Union Scientific Engineering-Technical Society of Builders.

The Soviet government established prizes in Galerkin's name for distinguished work in the theory of elasticity, structural mechanics, and the theory of plasticity, as well as stipends for graduate students.

BIBLIOGRAPHY

I. ORIGINAL WORKS. Galerkin's writings were brought together in *Sobranie sochineny* ("Collected Works"), 2 vols.: I, *Issledovania po stroitelnoy mekhanike teorii uprugosti, teorii obolochek* ("Research in Structural Mechanics, the Theory of Elasticity, and the Theory of Casing," Moscow, 1952); II, *Raboty po teorii uprugikh plit* ("Works in the Theory of Elastic Plates," Moscow, 1953).

II. SECONDARY LITERATURE. On Galerkin or his work see "Akademik Boris Grigorievich Galerkin. K

70-letiyu so dnya rozhdenia i 45-letiyu nauchnoy deyatelnosti" ("Academician Boris Grigorievich Galerkin. On the Seventieth Anniversary of His Birth and the Forty-Fifth Anniversary of the Beginning of His Scientific Career"), in *Izvestiya Akademii nauk SSSR, Otdelenie tekhnicheskikh nauk*, no. 4 (1941), pp. 115–120; *Boris Grigorievich Galerkin. K 70-letiyu so dnya rozhdenia i 45-letiyu inzhenernonauchnoy, pedagogicheskoy i obshchestvennoy deyatelnosti* ("Boris Grigorievich Galerkin. On the Seventieth Anniversary of His Birth and the Forty-Fifth Anniversary of the Beginning of His Engineering, Teaching and Public Career," Leningrad–Moscow, 1941); A. Joffe, A. Krylov, and P. Lazarev, "Zapiska ob uchenykh trudakh professora B. G. Galerkina" ("A Note on the Scientific Works of Professor B. G. Galerkin"), *ibid., Otdelenie fiziko-matematicheskikh nauk*, nos. 8–10 (1928), pp. 616–618; A. N. Krylov *et al.*, "Akademik B. G. Galerkin. (K 70-letiyu so dnya rozhdenia)" ("Academician B. G. Galerkin. [On the Seventieth Anniversary of His Birth]"), in *Vestnik Akademii nauk SSSR*, no. 4 (1941), pp. 91–94; V. V. Sokolovsky, "O zhizni i nauchnoy deyatelnosti akademika B. G. Galerkina" (" On the Life and Scientific Career of Academician B. G. Galerkin"), in *Izvestiya Akademii nauk SSSR, Otdelenie tekhnicheskikh nauk*, no. 8 (1951), pp. 1159–1164; and V. V. Sokolovsky and G. S. Shapiro, "Metody B. G. Galerkina v teorii uprugosti" ("B. G. Galerkin's Methods in the Theory of Elasticity"), in *Yubileyny sbornik, posvyashchenny tridtsatiletiyu velikoy oktyabrskoy sotsialisticheskoy revolyutsii* ("Jubilee Collection, Dedicated to the Thirtieth Anniversary of the Great October Socialist Revolution"), pt. 2 (Moscow–Leningrad, 1947); and "Boris Grigorievich Galerkin (1871–1945)," in *Materialy i konstruktsii v sovremennoy arkhitekture* ("Materials and Construction in Contemporary Architecture"), pt. 2 (Moscow, 1948).

A. T. GRIGORIAN

GALOIS, EVARISTE (*b.* Bourg-la-Reine, near Paris, France, 25 October 1811; *d.* Paris, 31 May 1832)

There have been few mathematicians with personalities as engaging as that of Galois, who died at the age of twenty years and seven months from wounds received in a mysterious duel. He left a body of work—for the most part published posthumously—of less than 100 pages, the astonishing richness of which was revealed in the second half of the nineteenth century. Far from being a cloistered scholar, this extraordinarily precocious and exceptionally profound genius had an extremely tormented life. A militant republican, driven to revolt by the adversity that overwhelmed him and by the incomprehension and disdain with which the scientific world received his works, to most of his contemporaries he was only a political agitator. Yet in fact, continuing the work of Abel, he produced with the aid of group theory a definitive answer to the problem of the solvability of algebraic equations, a problem that had absorbed the attention of mathematicians since the eighteenth century; he thereby laid one of the foundations of modern algebra. The few sketches remaining of other works that he devoted to the theory of elliptic functions and that of Abelian integrals and his reflections on the philosophy and methodology of mathematics display an uncanny foreknowledge of modern mathematics.

Galois's father, Nicolas-Gabriel Galois, an amiable and witty liberal thinker, directed a school accommodating about sixty boarders. Elected mayor of Bourg-la-Reine during the Hundred Days, he retained this position under the second Restoration. Galois's mother, Adelaïde-Marie Demante, was from a family of jurists and had received a more traditional education. She had a headstrong personality and was eccentric, even somewhat odd. Having taken charge of her son's early education, she sought to inculcate in him, along with the elements of classical culture, the principles of an austere religion and respect for a Stoic morality. Affected by his father's imagination and liberalism, the varying severity of his mother's eccentricity, and the affection of his elder sister Nathalie-Théodore, Galois seems to have had an early youth that was both happy and studious.

Galois continued his studies at the Collège Louis-le-Grand in Paris, entering as a fourth-form boarder in October 1823. He found it difficult to submit to the harsh discipline imposed by the school during the Restoration at the orders of the political authorities and the Church, and although a brilliant student, he presented problems. In the early months of 1827 he attended the first-year preparatory mathematics courses given by H. J. Vernier, and this first contact with mathematics was a revelation for him. But he rapidly tired of the elementary character of this instruction and of the inadequacies of certain of the textbooks and soon turned to reading the original works themselves. After appreciating the rigor of Legendre's *Géométrie,* Galois acquired a solid grounding from the major works of Lagrange. During the next two years he followed the second-year preparatory mathematics courses taught by Vernier, then the more advanced ones of L.-P.-E. Richard, who was the first to recognize his indisputable superiority in mathematics. With this perceptive teacher Galois was an excellent student, even though he was already devoting much more of his time to his personal work than to his classwork. In 1828 he began to study certain recent works on the theory of equations, number theory, and the theory of elliptic functions.

This was the period of his first memorandum, published in March 1829 in Gergonne's *Annales de mathématiques pures et appliquées;* making more explicit and demonstrating a result of Lagrange's concerning continuous fractions, it reveals a certain ingenuity but does not herald an exceptional talent.

By his own account, in the course of 1828 Galois wrongly believed—as Abel had eight years earlier—that he had solved the general fifth-degree equation. Rapidly undeceived, he resumed on a new basis the study of the theory of equations, which he pursued until he achieved the elucidation of the general problem with the help of group theory. The results he obtained in May 1829 were communicated to the Académie des Sciences by a particularly competent judge, Cauchy. But events were to frustrate these brilliant beginnings and to leave a deep mark on the personality of the young mathematician. First, at the beginning of July came the suicide of his father, who had been persecuted for his liberal opinions. Second, a month later he failed the entrance examination for the École Polytechnique, owing to his refusal to follow the method of exposition suggested by the examiner. Seeing his hopes vanish for entering the school which attracted him because of its scientific prestige and liberal tradition, he took the entrance examination for the École Normale Supérieure (then called the École Préparatoire), which trained future secondary school teachers. Admitted as the result of an excellent grade in mathematics, he entered this institution in November 1829; it was then housed in an annex of the Collège Louis-le-Grand, where he had spent the previous six years. At this time, through reading Férussac's *Bulletin des sciences mathématiques,* he learned of Abel's recent death and, at the same time, that Abel's last published memoir contained a good number of the results he himself had presented as original in his memoir to the Academy.

Cauchy, assigned to report on Galois's work, had to counsel him to revise his memoir, taking into account Abel's researches and the new results he had obtained. (It was for this reason that Cauchy did not present a report on his memoir.) Galois actually composed a new text that he submitted to the Academy at the end of February 1830, hoping to win the *grand prix* in mathematics. Unfortunately this memoir was lost upon the death of Fourier, who had been appointed to examine it. Brusquely eliminated from the competition, Galois believed himself to be the object of a new persecution by the representatives of official science and of society in general. His manuscripts have preserved a partial record of the elaboration of this memoir of February 1830, a brief analysis of which was published in Férussac's *Bulletin des sciences mathématiques* of April 1830. In June 1830 Galois published in the same journal a short note on the resolution of numerical equations and a much more important article, "Sur la théorie des nombres," in which he introduced the remarkable theory of "Galois imaginaries." That this same issue contains original works by Cauchy and Poisson is sufficient testimony to the reputation Galois had already acquired, despite the misfortune that plagued him. The July Revolution of 1830, however, was to mark a severe change in his career.

After several weeks of apparent calm the revolution provoked a renewal of political agitation in France and an intensification in republican propaganda, especially among intellectuals and students. It was then Galois became politicized. Before returning for a second year to the École Normale Supérieure in November 1830, he already had formed friendships with several republican leaders, particularly Blanqui and Raspail. He became less and less able to bear the strict discipline in his school, and he published a violent article against its director in an opposition journal, the *Gazette des écoles.* For this he was expelled on 8 December 1830, a measure approved by the Royal Council on 4 January 1831.

Left to himself, Galois devoted most of his time to political propaganda and participated in the demonstrations and riots then agitating Paris. He was arrested for the first time following a regicide toast that he had given at a republican banquet on 9 May 1831, but he was acquitted on 15 June by the assize court of the Seine. Meanwhile, to a certain extent he continued his mathematical research. His last two publications were a short note on analysis in Férussac's *Bulletin des sciences mathématiques* of December 1830 and "Lettre sur l'enseignement des sciences," which appeared on 2 January 1831 in the *Gazette des écoles.* On 13 January he began a public course on advanced algebra in which he planned to present his own discoveries; but this project seems not to have had much success. On 17 January 1831 Galois presented to the Academy a new version of his "Mémoire sur la résolution des équations algébriques," hastily written up at the request of Poisson. Unfortunately, in his report of 4 July 1831 on this, Galois's most important piece of work, Poisson hinted that a portion of the results could be found in several posthumous writings of Abel recently published and that the remainder was incomprehensible. Such a judgment, the profound injustice of which would become apparent in the future, could only stiffen Galois's rebellion.

Galois was arrested again during a republican demonstration on 14 July 1831 and placed in detention at the prison of Sainte-Pélagie, where in a troubled and often painful situation he pursued his mathematical investigations, revised his memoir on equations, and worked on the applications of his theory and on elliptic functions. On 16 March 1832, upon the announcement of a cholera epidemic, he was transferred to a nursing home, where he resumed his research, wrote several essays on the philosophy of science, and became involved in a love affair, of which the unhappy ending grieved him deeply.

Provoked to a duel in unclear circumstances following this breakup, Galois felt his death was near. On 29 May he wrote desperate letters to his republican friends, hastily sorted his papers, and addressed to his friend Auguste Chevalier—but really intended for Gauss and Jacobi—a testamentary letter, a tragic document in which he attempted to sketch the principal results he had achieved. On 30 May, mortally wounded by an unknown adversary, he was hospitalized; he died the following day. His funeral, on 2 June, was the occasion for a republican demonstration heralding the tragic riots that bloodied Paris in the days that followed.

Galois's work seems not to have been fully appreciated by any of his contemporaries. Cauchy, who would have been capable of grasping its importance, had left France in September 1830, having seen only its first outlines. Moreover, the few fragments published during Galois's lifetime did not give an overall view of his achievement and, in particular, did not afford a means of judging the exceptional interest of the results obtained in the theory of equations and rejected by Poisson. The publication in September 1832 of the famous testamentary letter does not appear to have attracted the attention it deserved. It was not until September 1843 that Liouville, who prepared Galois's manuscripts for publication, announced officially to the Academy that the young mathematician had effectively solved the problem, already considered by Abel, of deciding whether an irreducible first-degree equation is or is not "solvable with the aid of radicals." Although announced and prepared for the end of 1843, the publication of the celebrated 1831 memoir and of a fragment on the "primitive equations solvable by radicals" did not occur until the October–November 1846 issue of the *Journal de mathématiques pures et appliquées.*

It was, therefore, not until over fourteen years after Galois's death that the essential elements of his work became available to mathematicians. By this time the evolution of mathematical research had created a climate much more favorable to its reception: the dominance of mathematical physics in the French school had lessened, and pure research was receiving a new impetus. Furthermore, the recent publication of the two-volume *Oeuvres complètes de Niels-Henrik Abel* (1839), which contained fundamental work on the algebraic theory of elliptic functions and an important, unfinished memoir, "Sur la résolution algébrique des équations," had awakened interest in certain of the fields in which Galois has become famous. Lastly, in a series of publications appearing in 1844–1846, Cauchy, pursuing studies begun in 1815 but soon abandoned, had—implicitly—given group theory a new scope by the systematic construction of his famous theory of permutations.

Beginning with Liouville's edition, which was reproduced in book form in 1897 by J. Picard, Galois's work became progressively known to mathematicians and exerted a profound influence on the development of modern mathematics. Also important, although they came to light too late to contribute to the advance of mathematics, are the previously unpublished texts that appeared later. In 1906–1907 various manuscript fragments edited by J. Tannery revealed the great originality of the young mathematician's epistemological writings and provided new information about his research. Finally, in 1961 the exemplary critical edition of R. Bourgne and J. P. Azra united all of Galois's previously published writings and most of the remaining mathematical outlines and rough drafts. While this new documentary material provides no assistance to present-day mathematicians with their own problems, it does permit us to understand better certain aspects of Galois's research, and it will perhaps help in resolving a few remaining enigmas concerning the basic sources of his thought.

To comprehend Galois's work, it is important to consider the earlier writings that influenced its initial orientation and the contemporary investigations that contributed to guiding and diversifying it. It is equally necessary to insist on Galois's great originality: while assimilating the most vital currents of contemporary mathematical thought, he was able to transcend them thanks to a kind of prescience about the conceptual character of modern mathematics. The epistemological texts extracted from his rough drafts sketch, in a few sentences, the principal directions of present-day research; and the clarity, conciseness, and precision of the style add to the novelty and impact of the ideas. Galois was undoubtedly the beneficiary of his predecessors and of his rivals, but his multifaceted personality and his brilliant sense of the indispensable renewal of mathematical thinking made him an exceptional innovator whose influence was long felt in vast areas of mathematics.

Galois's first investigations, like Abel's, were inspired by the works of Lagrange and of Gauss on the conditions of solvability of certain types of algebraic equations and by Cauchy's memoirs on the theory of substitutions. Consequently their similarity is not surprising, nor is the particular fact that the principal results announced by Galois in May–June 1829 had previously been obtained by Abel. In the second half of 1829 Galois learned that Abel had published his findings in Crelle's *Journal für die reine und angewandte Mathematik* a few days before he himself died young. The interest that Galois took from that time in the work of Abel and of his other youthful rival, Jacobi, is evident from numerous reading notes. If, as a result of the progressive elaboration of group theory, Galois pursued the elucidation of the theory of algebraic equations far beyond the results published by Abel, beginning with the first months of 1830 he directed a large proportion of his research toward other new directions opened by both Abel and Jacobi, notably toward the theory of elliptic functions and of certain types of integrals.

The advances that Galois made in his first area of research, that of the theory of algebraic equations, are marked by two great synthetic studies. The first was written in February 1830 for the Academy's grand prize; the summary of it that Galois published in April 1830 in Férussac's *Bulletin des sciences mathématiques* establishes that he had made significant progress beyond Abel's recent memoir but that certain obstacles still stood in the way of an overall solution. The publication in Crelle's *Journal für die reine und angewandte Mathematik* of some posthumous fragments of Abel's work containing more advanced results (the unfinished posthumous memoir on this subject was not published until 1839) encouraged Galois to persevere in his efforts to overcome the remaining difficulties and to write a restatement of his studies. This was the purpose of the new version of the "Mémoire sur la résolution des équations algébriques" that he presented before the Academy.

Despite Poisson's criticisms Galois rightly persisted in thinking that he had furnished a definitive solution to the problem of the solvability of algebraic equations and, after having made a few corrections in it, he gave this memoir the first place in the list of his writings in his testamentary letter of 29 May 1837. This was the "definitive" version of his fundamental memoir, and in it Galois continued the studies of his predecessors but at the same time produced a thoroughly original work. True, he formulated in a more precise manner essential ideas that were already in the air, but he also introduced others that, once stated, played an important role in the genesis of modern algebra. Moreover, he daringly generalized certain classic methods in other fields and succeeded in providing a complete solution—and indeed a generalization—of the problem in question by systematically drawing upon group theory, a subject he had founded concurrently with his work on equations.

Lagrange had shown that the solvability of an algebraic equation depends on the possibility of finding a chain of intermediate equations of binomial type, known as resolvent equations. He had thus succeeded in finding the classic resolution formulas of the "general" equations of second, third, and fourth degree but had not been able to reach any definitive conclusion regarding the general fifth-degree equation. The impossibility of solving this last type of equation through the use of radicals was demonstrated by Paolo Ruffini and in a more satisfactory manner by Abel in 1824. Meanwhile, in 1801, Gauss had published an important study of binomial equations and the primitive roots of unity; and Cauchy in 1815 had made important contributions to the theory of permutations, a particular form of the future group theory.

In his study of the solvability of algebraic equations, Galois, developing an idea of Abel's, considered that with each intermediate resolvent equation there is associated a field of algebraic numbers that is intermediate between the field generated by the roots of the equation under study and the field determined by the coefficients of this equation. His leading idea, however, was to have successfully associated with the given equation, and with the different intermediate fields involved, a sequence of groups such that the group corresponding to a certain field of the sequence associated with the equation is a subgroup distinct from the one associated with the antecedent field. Such a method obviously presupposes the clarification of the concept of field already suspected (without use of the term) by Gauss and Abel, as well as a searching study of group theory, of which Galois can be considered the creator.

Galois thus showed that for an irreducible algebraic equation to be solvable by radicals, it is necessary and sufficient that its group be solvable, i.e., possess a series of composition formed of proper subgroups having certain precisely defined properties. Although this general rule did not in fact make the actual resolution of a determinate equation any simpler, it did provide the means for finding, as particular cases, all the known results concerning the solvability of the general equations of less than fifth degree as well as binomial equations and certain other particular types of equations; it also permitted almost immediate demonstration that the general equation of higher than fourth degree is not solvable by radicals, the associated group (permutation group of n objects) not being solvable. Galois was aware that his study went beyond the limited problem of the solvability of algebraic equations by means of radicals and that it allowed one to take up the much more general problem of the classification of the irrationals.

In his testamentary letter, Galois summarized a second memoir (of which several fragments are extant) that dealt with certain developments and applications of the theory of equations and of group theory. The article "Sur la théorie des nombres" is linked with it; it contained, notably, a daring generalization of the theory of congruences by means of new numbers that are today called Galois imaginaries and its application to research in those cases where a primitive equation is solvable by radicals. Beyond the precise definition of the decomposition of a group, this second memoir included applications of Galois's theory to elliptic functions; in treating the algebraic equations obtained through the division and transformation of these functions, it presents, without demonstration, the results concerning the modular equations upon which the division of the periods depends.

The third memoir that Galois mentions in his testamentary letter is known only through the information contained in this poignant document. This information very clearly demonstrates that, like Abel and Jacobi, Galois passed from the study of elliptic functions to consideration of the integrals of the most general algebraic differentials, today called Abelian integrals. It seems that his research in this area was already quite advanced, since the letter summarizes the results he had achieved, particularly the classification of these integrals into three categories, a result obtained by Riemann in 1857. This same letter alludes to recent meditations entitled "Sur l'application à l'analyse transcendante de la théorie de l'ambiguïté," but the allusion is too vague to be interpreted conclusively.

Galois often expressed prophetic reflections on the spirit of modern mathematics: "Jump with both feet on the calculus and group the operations, classifying them according to their difficulties and not according to their forms; such, in my view, is the task of future mathematicians" (*Écrits et mémoires,* p. 9).

He also reflected on the conditions of scientific creativity: "A mind that had the power to perceive at once the totality of mathematical truths—not just those known to us, but all the truths possible—would be able to deduce them regularly and, as it were, mechanically . . . but it does not happen like that" (*ibid.,* pp. 13–14). Or, again, "Science progresses by a series of combinations in which chance does not play the smallest role; its life is unreasoning and planless [*brute*] and resembles that of minerals that grow by juxtaposition" (*ibid.,* p. 15).

Yet we must also recall the ironic, mordant, and provocative tone of Galois's allusions to established scientists: "I do not say to anyone that I owe to his counsel or to his encouragement everything that is good in this work. I do not say it, for that would be to lie" (*ibid.,* p. 3). The contempt that he felt for these scientists was such that he hoped the extreme conciseness of his arguments would make them accessible only to the best among them.

Galois's terse style, combined with the great originality of his thought and the modernity of his conceptions, contributed as much as the delay in publication to the length of time that passed before Galois's work was understood, recognized at its true worth, and fully developed. Indeed, very few mathematicians of the mid-nineteenth century were ready to assimilate such a revolutionary work directly. Consequently the first publications that dealt with it, those of Enrico Betti (beginning in 1851), T. Schönemann, Leopold Kronecker, and Charles Hermite, are simply commentaries, explanations, or immediate and limited applications. It was only with the publication in 1866 of the third edition of Alfred Serret's *Cours d'algèbre supérieure* and, in 1870, of Camille Jordan's *Traité des substitutions* that group theory and the whole of Galois's *oeuvre* were truly integrated into the body of mathematics. From that time on, its development was very rapid and the field of application was extended to the most varied branches of the science; in fact, group theory and other more subtle elements included in Galois's writings played an important role in the birth of modern algebra.

BIBLIOGRAPHY

I. ORIGINAL WORKS. Galois's scientific writings have appeared in the following versions: "Oeuvres mathématiques d'Evariste Galois," J. Liouville, ed., in *Journal de mathématiques pures et appliquées,* **11** (Oct.-Nov. 1846), 381–448; *Oeuvres mathématiques d'Evariste Galois,* J. Picard, ed. (Paris, 1897), also in facs. repro. (Paris, 1951) with a study by G. Verriest; "Manuscrits et papiers inédits de Galois," J. Tannery, ed., in *Bulletin des sciences mathématiques,* 2nd ser., **30** (Aug.-Sept. 1906), 246–248, 255–263; **31** (Nov. 1907), 275–308; *Manuscrits d'Evariste Galois,* J. Tannery, ed. (Paris, 1908); and *Écrits et mémoires mathématiques d'Evariste Galois,* R. Bourgne and J.-P. Azra, eds. (Paris, 1962), with pref. by J. Dieudonné. These eds. will be designated, respectively, as "Oeuvres," *Oeuvres,* "Manuscrits," *Manuscrits,* and *Écrits et mémoires.* Since the *Oeuvres* and *Manuscrits* are simply reeditions in book form of the "Oeuvres" and of the "Manuscrits," they are not analyzed below; the contents of the other three are specified according to date in the following list.

1. Scientific texts published during his lifetime.

Apr. 1829: "Démonstration d'un théorème sur les fractions continues périodiques," in Gergonne's *Annales de mathématiques pures et appliquées,* **19,** 294–301.

Apr. 1830: "Analyse d'un mémoire sur la résolution algébrique des équations," in Férussac's *Bulletin des sciences mathématiques,* **13,** 271–272.

June 1830: "Note sur la résolution des équations numériques," *ibid.,* 413–414.

June 1830: "Sur la théorie des nombres," *ibid.,* 428–436.

Dec. 1830: "Notes sur quelques points d'analyse," in Gergonne's *Annales de mathématiques pures et appliquées,* **21,** 182–184.

Jan. 1831: "Lettre sur l'enseignement des sciences," in *Gazette des écoles,* no. 110 (2 Jan. 1831).

2. Posthumous publications.

Sept. 1832: "Lettre à Auguste Chevalier," in *Revue encyclopédique,* **55,** 568–576.

Oct.–Nov. 1846: "Oeuvres," considered definitive until 1906; in addition to the memoirs published in Galois's lifetime (except for the last) and the letter to Auguste Chevalier, this ed. contains the following previously unpublished memoirs: "Mémoire sur les conditions de résolubilité des équations par radicaux," pp. 417–433; and "Des équations primitives qui sont solubles par radicaux," pp. 434–444.

Aug.–Sept. 1906: "Manuscrits," pt. 1, which contains, besides a description of Galois's MSS, the text of the following previously unpublished fragments (titles given are those in *Écrits et mémoires*): "Discours préliminaire"; "Projet de publication"; "Note sur Abel"; "Préface" (partial); "Discussions sur les progrès de l'analyse pure"; "Fragments"; "Science, hiérarchie, écoles"; and "Catalogue, note sur la théorie des équations."

Nov. 1907: "Manuscrits," pt. 2, containing "Recherches sur la théorie des permutations et des équations algébriques"; "Comment la théorie des équations dépend de celle des permutations"; "Note manuscrite"; "Addition au second mémoire"; "Mémoire sur la division des fonctions elliptiques de première espèce"; "Note sur l'intégration des équations linéaires"; "Recherches sur les équations du second degré."

Jan.–Mar. 1948; entire text of the "Préface" and of the "Projet de publication," R. Taton, ed., in *Revue d'histoire des sciences,* **1,** 123–128.

1956: "Lettre sur l'enseignement des sciences," repr. in A. Dalmas, *Evariste Galois . . .* (Paris, 1956), pp. 105–108.

1962: *Écrits et mémoires mathématiques d'Evariste Galois,* R. Bourgne and J.-P. Azra, eds. (Paris, 1962). This remarkable ed. contains all of Galois's *oeuvre:* the articles published in his lifetime and a critical ed., with corrections and variants, of all his MSS, including his rough drafts. The majority of the many previously unpublished texts presented here are grouped in two categories: the "Essais," dating from the period when Galois was a student (pp. 403–453, 519–521) and the "Calculs et brouillons inédits" (pp. 187–361, 526–538), classed under five headings—"Intégrales eulériennes," "Calcul intégral," "Fonctions elliptiques," "Groupes de substitutions," and "Annexe." Galois's nine known letters are reproduced and described (pp. 459–471, 523–525). Galois's MSS, preserved at the Bibliothèque de l'Institut de France (MS 2108), are the subject of a detailed description that provides many complementary details (App. I, 478–521; App. II, 526–538).

II. Secondary Literature. At the present time there is no major synthetic study of Galois's life and work. The principal biographical source remains P. Dupuy, "La vie d'Evariste Galois," in *Annales scientifiques de l'École normale supérieure,* 3rd ser., **13** (1896), 197–266, with documents and two portraits; reiss. as *Cahiers de la quinzaine,* 5th ser., no. 2 (Paris, 1903).

Among the few earlier articles the only ones of any documentary value are the two brief obituaries in *Revue encyclopédique,* **55** (Sept. 1832): the first (pp. 566–568), unsigned, is very general; the second ("Nécrologie," pp. 744–754), by Auguste Chevalier, Galois's best friend, is a source of valuable information. See also an anonymous notice, inspired by Evariste's younger brother, Alfred Galois, and by one of his former classmates, P.-P. Flaugergues, in *Magasin pittoresque,* **16** (1848), 227–228; and a note by O. Terquem in *Nouvelles annales de mathématiques,* **8** (1849), 452.

Of the later biographical studies a few present new information: J. Bertrand, "La vie d'Evariste Galois par P. Dupuy," in *Journal des savants* (July 1899), pp. 389–400, reiss. in *Éloges académiques,* n.s. (Paris, 1902), pp. 331–345; R. Taton, "Les relations scientifiques d'Evariste Galois avec les mathématiciens de son temps," in *Revue d'histoire des sciences,* **1** (1947), 114–130; A. Dalmas, *Evariste Galois, révolutionnaire et géomètre* (Paris, 1956); the ed. of *Écrits et mémoires mathématiques* by R. Bourgne and J.-P. Azra cited above; C. A. Infantozzi, "Sur la mort d'Evariste Galois," in *Revue d'histoire des sciences,* **21** (1968), 157–160; art. by J.-P. Azra and R. Bourgne in *Encyclopaedia universalis,* VII (Paris, 1970), 450–451; and R. Taton, "Sur les relations mathématiques d'Augustin Cauchy et d'Evariste Galois," in *Revue d'histoire des sciences,* **24** (1971), 123–148.

G. Sarton, "Evariste Galois," in *Scientific Monthly,* **13** (Oct. 1921), 363–375, repr. in *Osiris,* **3** (1937), 241–254; and E. T. Bell, *Men of Mathematics* (New York, 1937), pp. 362–377, were directly inspired by Dupuy. L. Infeld, *Whom the Gods Love. The Story of Evariste Galois* (New York, 1948); and A. Arnoux, *Algorithme* (Paris, 1948), mix facts with romantic elements.

Galois's scientific work has not yet received the thorough study it merits, although numerous articles attempt to bring out its main features. Among the older ones, beyond the "commentaries" of the first disciples, particularly Betti and Jordan, are the following: J. Liouville, "Avertissement" to the "Oeuvres," in *Journal de mathématiques pures et appliquées,* **11** (1846), 381–384; S. Lie, "Influence de Galois sur le développement des mathématiques," in *Le centenaire de l'École normale* (Paris, 1895), pp. 481–489; E. Picard, "Introduction" to *Oeuvres* (Paris, 1897), pp. v–x; J. Pierpont, "Early History of Galois's Theory of Equations," in

Bulletin of the American Mathematical Society, **4** (Apr. 1898), 332–340; J. Tannery, "Introduction" to "Manuscrits" in *Bulletin des sciences mathématiques,* **30** (1906), 1–19, repr. in *Manuscrits,* pp. 1–19.

The most important recent studies are G. Verriest, *Evariste Galois et la théorie des équations algébriques* (Louvain–Paris, 1934; reiss. Paris, 1951); L. Kollros, *Evariste Galois* (Basel, 1949); J. Dieudonné, "Préface" (pp. v–vii), R. Bourgne, "Avertissement" (pp. ix–xvi), and J.-P. Azra, "Appendice" (pp. 475–538), in *Écrits et mémoires mathématiques* (cited above); N. Bourbaki, *Éléments d'histoire des mathématiques,* 2nd ed. (Paris, 1969), pp. 73-74, 104-109; and K. Wussing, *Die Genesis des abstrakten Gruppenbegriffes* (Berlin, 1969), esp. pp. 73–87, 206–211.

René Taton

GALTON, FRANCIS (*b.* Birmingham, England, 16 February 1822; *d.* Haslemere, Surrey, England, 17 January 1911)

Galton's paternal ancestors were bankers and gunsmiths, of the Quaker faith, and long-lived. His mother was Erasmus Darwin's daughter, and thus he was Charles Darwin's cousin. Galton's intellectual precocity has become a textbook item, and Lewis Terman estimated his IQ to have been of the order of 200. His education, though, was desultory, its formal peaks being a few mathematics courses at Cambridge (he took a pass degree) and some unfinished medical studies in London. He quit the latter at the age of twenty-two when his father died, leaving him a fortune. He then traveled. Journeying through virtually unknown parts of southwestern Africa in 1850–1852, Galton acquired fame as an intrepid explorer. His immediate reward was a gold medal from the Geographical Society, and his later reports led to election as a fellow of the Royal Society in 1860. In 1853 he married, and in 1857 he settled into a quiet London home, where he remained, except for occasional European vacations, until his death over half a century later. Galton was knighted in 1909. He died childless.

Galton was perhaps the last of a now extinct breed—the gentleman scientist. He never held any academic or professional post, and most of his experiments were done at home or while traveling, or were farmed out to friends. He was not a great reader, and his small personal library was said to consist mainly of autographed copies of fellow scientists' books. He composed no *magnum opus,* but he kept up a rich flow of original ideas. An endless curiosity about the phenomena of nature and mankind was nicely coupled with mechanical ingenuity and inventiveness. Secure and contented in the employment of his wide-ranging talents, Galton was an unusually equable person. Anger and polemic were alien to him. In his later years he was fortunate in having the ebullient Karl Pearson as champion and extender of his ideas. Pearson subsequently became the first holder of the chair of eugenics at University College, London, that Galton had endowed in his will.

Galton's earliest notable researches were meteorologic, and it was he who first recognized and named the anticyclone.

Foremost in Galton's life was a belief that virtually anything is quantifiable. Some of his exercises in this direction are now merely amusing—a solemn assessment of womanly beauty on a pocket scale, a study of the body weights of three generations of British peers, and a statistical inquiry into the efficacy of prayer are examples—but there can be little doubt that his general attitude was salutary in its day. Moreover, against the trivia have to be set such good things as his developing Quetelet's observation that certain measurable human characteristics are distributed like the error function. Galton initiated an important reversal of outlook on biological and psychological variation, previously regarded as an uninteresting nuisance. In his own words: "The primary objects of the Gaussian Law of Errors were exactly opposed, in one sense, to those to which I applied them. They were to get rid of, or to provide a just allowance for, errors. But these errors or deviations were the very things I wanted to preserve and know about." In psychology Galton sowed the seeds of mental testing, of measuring sensory acuity, and of scaling and typing. In statistics he originated the concepts of regression and correlation.

Galton's best-known work was on the inheritance of talent—scholarly, artistic, and athletic—the raw data being the records of notable families. He found strong evidence of inheritance. Upholders of the rival nurture-not-nature theory attacked the work, on the ground that the children of gifted and successful parents are environmentally favored; but even when allowance was made for this truth, Galton's contention could not be wholly denied. One outcome of the investigation was a conviction in many people's minds—and particularly deeply in Galton's own mind—that a eugenic program to foster talent and healthiness and to suppress stupidity and sickliness was a *sine qua non* in any society that wished to maintain, let alone promote, its quality and status. (Galton coined the word "eugenics" in 1883.)

Galton's views on genetics are historically curious. Influenced by Darwin's belief that inheritance is conditioned by a blending mechanism, Galton propounded his law of ancestral heredity, which set the average contribution of each parent at 1/4, of each grandparent at 1/16, and so forth (the sum, over all ancestors of both parents, being asymptotic to unity). Karl Pearson and his colleagues pursued the notion in a series of sophisticated researches, but Galton's law received withering criticisms after the rediscovery, in 1900, of Mendel's work on particulate inheritance. Yet Galton had himself toyed with the notion of particulate inheritance, and in a remarkable correspondence with Darwin in 1875 he sketched the essence of the theory and even discussed something very like what we now know as genotypes and phenotypes under the names "latent" and "patent" characteristics. He did not press these views, perhaps because of the strong climate of opinion in favor of blending inheritance at that time.

Galton's establishment of fingerprinting as an easy and almost infallible means of human identification transformed a difficult subject, and his taxonomy of prints is basically that used today. He was disappointed, however, to find no familial, racial, moral, or intellectual subgroupings in the collections he examined.

BIBLIOGRAPHY

I. Original Works. Galton wrote sixteen books and more than 200 papers. Of the books, recent printings are *Hereditary Genius* (London, 1869; 3rd ed., 1950); *Art of Travel* (5th ed., London, 1872; repr. Harrisburg, Pa., 1971); and *Finger Prints* (London, 1893; facs., New York, 1965). An unpublished utopian book, "The Eugenic College of Kantsaywhere," written toward the end of his life, is excerpted in Karl Pearson's biography (see below). His autobiography, *Memories of My Life* (London, 1908), is worth reading. The best listing of Galton's publications is appended to Blacker's book (see below).

II. Secondary Literature. Immediately after Galton's death his friend Karl Pearson started a biography that was to become one of the most elaborate and comprehensive works of its kind in this century: *The Life, Letters and Labours of Francis Galton,* 4 vols. (London, 1914–1930). A treatment emphasizing the interests of his later years is C. P. Blacker, *Eugenics, Galton and After* (London, 1952). A good survey of his psychologic contributions is H. E. Garratt, *Great Experiments in Psychology* (New York, 1951), ch. 13. The 1965 repr. of *Finger Prints* (see above) contains a biographical intro. by Harold Cummins that places Galton's fingerprint work in historic context.

Norman T. Gridgeman

GAUSS, CARL FRIEDRICH (*b.* Brunswick, Germany, 30 April 1777; *d.* Göttingen, Germany, 23 February 1855)

The life of Gauss was very simple in external form. During an austere childhood in a poor and unlettered family he showed extraordinary precocity. Beginning when he was fourteen, a stipend from the duke of Brunswick permitted him to concentrate on intellectual interests for sixteen years. Before the age of twenty-five he was famous as a mathematician and astronomer. At thirty he went to Göttingen as director of the observatory. There he worked for forty-seven years, seldom leaving the city except on scientific business, until his death at almost seventy-eight.

In marked contrast to this external simplicity, Gauss's personal life was complicated and tragic. He suffered from the political turmoil and financial insecurity associated with the French Revolution, the Napoleonic period, and the democratic revolutions in Germany. He found no mathematical collaborators and worked alone most of his life. An unsympathetic father, the early death of his first wife, the poor health of his second wife, and unsatisfactory relations with his sons denied him a family sanctuary until late in life.

In this difficult context Gauss maintained an amazingly rich scientific activity. An early passion for numbers and calculations extended first to the theory of numbers and then to algebra, analysis, geometry, probability, and the theory of errors. Concurrently he carried on intensive empirical and theoretical research in many branches of science, including observational astronomy, celestial mechanics, surveying, geodesy, capillarity, geomagnetism, electromagnetism, mechanics, optics, the design of scientific equipment, and actuarial science. His publications, voluminous correspondence, notes, and manuscripts show him to have been one of the greatest scientific virtuosos of all time.

Early Years. Gauss was born into a family of town workers striving on the hard road from peasant to lower middle-class status. His mother, a highly intelligent but only semiliterate daughter of a peasant stonemason, worked as a maid before becoming the second wife of Gauss's father, a gardener, laborer at various trades, foreman ("master of waterworks"), assistant to a merchant, and treasurer of a small insurance fund. The only relative known to have even modest intellectual gifts was the mother's brother, a master weaver. Gauss described his father as "worthy of esteem" but "domineering, uncouth, and unrefined." His mother kept her cheerful disposition in spite of an unhappy marriage, was always her only son's devoted support, and died at ninety-seven, after living in his house for twenty-two years.

Without the help or knowledge of others, Gauss learned to calculate before he could talk. At the age of three, according to a well-authenticated story, he corrected an error in his father's wage calculations. He taught himself to read and must have continued arithmetical experimentation intensively, because in his first arithmetic class at the age of eight he astonished his teacher by instantly solving a busy-work problem: to find the sum of the first hundred integers. Fortunately, his father did not see the possibility of commercially exploiting the calculating prodigy, and his teacher had the insight to supply the boy with books and to encourage his continued intellectual development.

During his eleventh year, Gauss studied with Martin Bartels, then an assistant in the school and later a teacher of Lobachevsky at Kazan. The father was persuaded to allow Carl Friedrich to enter the Gymnasium in 1788 and to study after school instead of spinning to help support the family. At the Gymnasium, Gauss made very rapid progress in all subjects, especially classics and mathematics, largely on his own. E. A. W. Zimmermann, then professor at the local Collegium Carolinum and later privy councillor to the duke of Brunswick, offered friendship, encouragement, and good offices at court. In 1792 Duke Carl Wilhelm Ferdinand began the stipend that made Gauss independent.

When Gauss entered the Brunswick Collegium Carolinum in 1792, he possessed a scientific and classical education far beyond that usual for his age at the time. He was familiar with elementary geometry, algebra, and analysis (often having discovered important theorems before reaching them in his studies), but in addition he possessed a wealth of arithmetical information and many number-theoretic insights. Extensive calculations and observation of the results, often recorded in tables, had led him to an intimate acquaintance with individual numbers and to generalizations that he used to extend his calculating ability. Already his lifelong heuristic pattern had been set: extensive empirical investigation leading to conjectures and new insights that guided further experiment and observation. By such means he had already independently discovered Bode's law of planetary distances, the binomial theorem for rational exponents, and the arithmetic-geometric mean.

During his three years at the Collegium, Gauss continued his empirical arithmetic, on one occasion finding a square root in two different ways to fifty decimal places by ingenious expansions and interpolations. He formulated the principle of least squares, apparently while adjusting unequal approximations and searching for regularity in the distribution of prime numbers. Before entering the University of Göttingen in 1795 he had rediscovered the law of quadratic reciprocity (conjectured by Lagrange in 1785), related the arithmetic-geometric mean to infinite series expansions, conjectured the prime number theorem (first proved by J. Hadamard in 1896), and found some results that would hold if "Euclidean geometry were not the true one."

In Brunswick, Gauss had read Newton's *Principia* and Bernoulli's *Ars conjectandi,* but most mathematical classics were unavailable. At Göttingen, he devoured masterworks and back files of journals, often finding that his own discoveries were not new. Attracted more by the brilliant classicist G. Heyne than by the mediocre mathematician A. G. Kästner, Gauss planned to be a philologist. But in 1796 came a dramatic discovery that marked him as a mathematician. As a by-product of a systematic investigation of the cyclotomic equation (whose solution has the geometric counterpart of dividing a circle into equal arcs), Gauss obtained conditions for the constructibility by ruler and compass of regular polygons and was able to announce that the regular 17-gon was constructible by ruler and compasses, the first advance in this matter in two millennia.

The logical component of Gauss's method matured at Göttingen. His heroes were Archimedes and Newton. But Gauss adopted the spirit of Greek rigor (insistence on precise definition, explicit assumption, and complete proof) without the classical geometric form. He thought numerically and algebraically, after the manner of Euler, and personified the extension of Euclidean rigor to analysis. By his twentieth year, Gauss was driving ahead with incredible speed according to the pattern he was to continue in many contexts—massive empirical investigations in close interaction with intensive meditation and rigorous theory construction.

During the five years from 1796 to 1800, mathematical ideas came so fast that Gauss could hardly write them down. In reviewing one of his seven proofs of the law of quadratic reciprocity in the *Göttingische gelehrte Anzeigen* for March 1817, he wrote autobiographically:

> It is characteristic of higher arithmetic that many of its most beautiful theorems can be discovered by induction with the greatest of ease but have proofs that lie anywhere but near at hand and are often found only after many fruitless investigations with the aid of deep analysis and lucky combinations. This significant phenomenon arises from the wonderful concatenation of different teachings of this branch of mathematics, and from this it often happens that many theorems, whose proof for years was sought in vain, are later proved in many

> different ways. As soon as a new result is discovered by induction, one must consider as the first requirement the finding of a proof by *any possible* means. But after such good fortune, one must not in higher arithmetic consider the investigation closed or view the search for other proofs as a superfluous luxury. For sometimes one does not at first come upon the most beautiful and simplest proof, and then it is just the insight into the wonderful concatenation of truth in higher arithmetic that is the chief attraction for study and often leads to the discovery of new truths. For these reasons the finding of new proofs for known truths is often at least as important as the discovery itself [*Werke,* II, 159–160].

The Triumphal Decade. In 1798 Gauss returned to Brunswick, where he lived alone and continued his intensive work. The next year, with the first of his four proofs of the fundamental theorem of algebra, he earned the doctorate from the University of Helmstedt under the rather nominal supervision of J. F. Pfaff. In 1801 the creativity of the previous years was reflected in two extraordinary achievements, the *Disquisitiones arithmeticae* and the calculation of the orbit of the newly discovered planet Ceres.

Number theory ("higher arithmetic") is a branch of mathematics that seems least amenable to generalities, although it was cultivated from the earliest times. In the late eighteenth century it consisted of a large collection of isolated results. In his *Disquisitiones* Gauss summarized previous work in a systematic way, solved some of the most difficult outstanding questions, and formulated concepts and questions that set the pattern of research for a century and still have significance today. He introduced congruence of integers with respect to a modulus ($a \equiv b \pmod c$ if c divides a-b), the first significant algebraic example of the now ubiquitous concept of equivalence relation. He proved the law of quadratic reciprocity, developed the theory of composition of quadratic forms, and completely analyzed the cyclotomic equation. The *Disquisitiones* almost instantly won Gauss recognition by mathematicians as their prince, but readership was small and the full understanding required for further development came only through the less austere exposition in Dirichlet's *Vorlesungen über Zahlentheorie* of 1863.

In January 1801 G. Piazzi had briefly observed and lost a new planet. During the rest of that year the astronomers vainly tried to relocate it. In September, as his *Disquisitiones* was coming off the press, Gauss decided to take up the challenge. To it he applied both a more accurate orbit theory (based on the ellipse rather than the usual circular approximation) and improved numerical methods (based on least squares). By December the task was done, and Ceres was soon found in the predicted position. This extraordinary feat of locating a tiny, distant heavenly body from seemingly insufficient information appeared to be almost superhuman, especially since Gauss did not reveal his methods. With the *Disquisitiones* it established his reputation as a mathematical and scientific genius of the first order.

The decade that began so auspiciously with the *Disquisitiones* and Ceres was decisive for Gauss. Scientifically it was mainly a period of exploiting the ideas piled up from the previous decade (see Figure 1). It ended with *Theoria motus corporum coelestium in sectionibus conicis solem ambientium* (1809), in which Gauss systematically developed his methods of orbit calculation, including the theory and use of least squares.

Professionally this was a decade of transition from mathematician to astronomer and physical scientist. Although Gauss continued to enjoy the patronage of the duke, who increased his stipend from time to time (especially when Gauss began to receive attractive offers from elsewhere), subsidized publication of the *Disquisitiones,* promised to build an observatory, and treated him like a tenured and highly valued civil servant, Gauss felt insecure and wanted to settle in a more established post. The most obvious course, to become a teacher of mathematics, repelled him because at this time it meant drilling ill-prepared and unmotivated students in the most elementary manipulations. Moreover, he felt that mathematics itself might not be sufficiently useful. When the duke raised his stipend in 1801, Gauss told Zimmermann: "But I have not earned it. I haven't yet done anything for the nation."

Astronomy offered an attractive alternative. A strong interest in celestial mechanics dated from reading Newton, and Gauss had begun observing while a student at Göttingen. The tour de force on Ceres demonstrated both his ability and the public interest, the latter being far greater than he could expect in mathematical achievements. Moreover, the professional astronomer had light teaching duties and, he hoped, more time for research. Gauss decided on a career in astronomy and began to groom himself for the directorship of the Göttingen observatory. A systematic program of theoretical and observational work, including calculation of the orbits of new planets as they were discovered, soon made him the most obvious candidate. When he accepted the position in 1807, he was already well established professionally, as evidenced by a job offer from St. Petersburg (1802) and by affiliations with the London Royal Society and the Russian and French academies.

During this decisive decade Gauss also established

personal and professional ties that were to last his lifetime. As a student at Göttingen he had enjoyed a romantic friendship with Wolfgang Bolyai, and the two discussed the foundations of geometry. But Bolyai returned to Hungary to spend his life vainly trying to prove Euclid's parallel postulate. Their correspondence soon practically ceased, to be revived again briefly only when Bolyai sent Gauss his son's work on non-Euclidean geometry. Pfaff was the only German mathematician with whom Gauss could converse, and even then hardly on an equal basis. From 1804 to 1807 Gauss exchanged a few letters on a high mathematical level with Sophie Germain in Paris, and a handful of letters passed between him and the mathematical giants in Paris, but he never visited France or collaborated with them. Gauss remained as isolated in mathematics as he had been since boyhood. By the time mathematicians of stature appeared in Germany (e.g., Jacobi, Plücker, Dirichlet), the uncommunicative habit was too ingrained to change. Gauss inspired Dirichlet, Riemann, and others, but he never had a collaborator, correspondent, or student working closely with him in mathematics.

In other scientific and technical fields things were quite different. There he had students, collaborators, and friends. Over 7,000 letters to and from Gauss are known to be extant, and they undoubtedly represent only a fraction of the total. His most important astronomical collaborators, friends, and correspondents were F. W. Bessel, C. L. Gerling, M. Olbers, J. G. Repsold, H. C. Schumacher. His friendship and correspondence with A. von Humboldt and B. von Lindenau played an important part in his

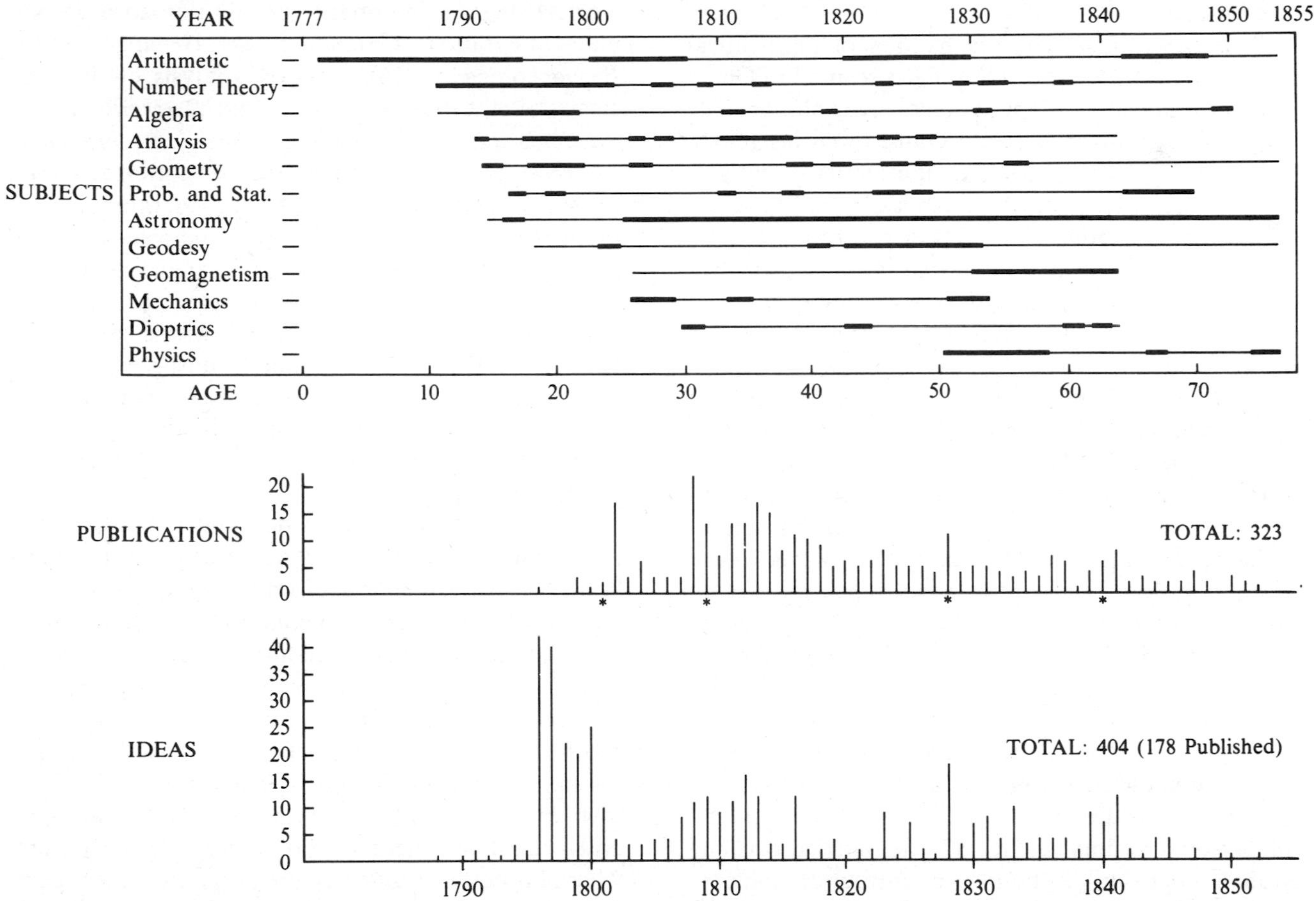

FIGURE 1. Interests, ideas, and publications. The horizontal lines show time spans of Gauss's interests in different subjects. Heavy lines indicate periods of intensive activity. The annual counts of recorded ideas include published and unpublished "results" (conjectures, theorems, proofs, concepts, hypotheses, theories), significant observations, experimental findings, and inventions. They are based on an examination of published materials, including correspondence and notebooks published after his death. Because of intrinsic ambiguities in dating, identification, and evaluation, this chart gives only an approximate picture of creative flux. The graph of publications shows the number of titles published in each year, including reviews. A count of pages would be similar except for surges (marked by *): 1801 (*Disquisitiones*), 1809 (*Theoria motus*), 1828 (least squares, surfaces, astronomy, biquadratic residues), and 1840 (geomagnetism).

professional life and in the development of science in Germany. These relations were established during the period 1801–1810 and lasted until death. Always Gauss wrote fewer letters, gave more information, and was less cordial than his colleagues, although he often gave practical assistance to his friends and to deserving young scientists.

Also in this decade was established the pattern of working simultaneously on many problems in different fields. Although he never had a second burst of ideas equal to his first, Gauss always had more ideas than he had time to develop. His hopes for leisure were soon dashed by his responsibilities, and he acquired the habit of doing mathematics and other theoretical investigations in the odd hours (sometimes, happily, days) that could be spared. Hence his ideas matured rather slowly, in some cases merely later than they might have with increased leisure, in others more felicitously with increased knowledge and meditation.

This period also saw the fixation of his political and philosophical views. Napoleon seemed to Gauss the personification of the dangers of revolution. The duke of Brunswick, to whom Gauss owed his golden years of freedom, personified the merits of enlightened monarchy. When the duke was humiliated and killed while leading the Prussian armies against Napoleon in 1806, Gauss's conservative tendencies were reinforced. In the struggles for democracy and national unity in Germany, which continued throughout his lifetime, Gauss remained a staunch nationalist and royalist. (He published in Latin not from internationalist sentiments but at the demands of his publishers. He knew French but refused to publish in it and pretended ignorance when speaking to Frenchmen he did not know.) In seeming contradiction, his religious and philosophical views leaned toward those of his political opponents. He was an uncompromising believer in the priority of empiricism in science. He did not adhere to the views of Kant, Hegel, and other idealist philosophers of the day. He was not a churchman and kept his religious views to himself. Moral rectitude and the advancement of scientific knowledge were his avowed principles.

Finally, this decade provided Gauss his one period of personal happiness. In 1805 he married a young woman of similar family background, Johanna Osthoff, who bore him a son and daughter and created around him a cheerful family life. But in 1809 she died soon after bearing a third child, which did not long survive her. Gauss "closed the angel eyes in which for five years I have found a heaven" and was plunged into a loneliness from which he never fully recovered. Less than a year later he married Minna Waldeck, his deceased wife's best friend. She bore him two sons and a daughter, but she was seldom well or happy. Gauss dominated his daughters and quarreled with his younger sons, who immigrated to the United States. He did not achieve a peaceful home life until the younger daughter, Therese, took over the household after her mother's death (1831) and became the intimate companion of his last twenty-four years.

Early Göttingen Years. In his first years at Göttingen, Gauss experienced a second upsurge of ideas and publications in various fields of mathematics. Among the latter were several notable papers inspired by his work on the tiny planet Pallas, perturbed by Jupiter: *Disquisitiones generales circa seriem infinitam* (1813), an early rigorous treatment of series and the introduction of the hypergeometric functions, ancestors of the "special functions" of physics; *Methodus nova integralium valores per approximationem inveniendi* (1816), an important contribution to approximate integration; *Bestimmung der Genauigkeit der Beobachtungen* (1816), an early analysis of the efficiency of statistical estimators; and *Determinatio attractionis quam in punctum quodvis positionis datae exerceret planeta si eius massa per totam orbitam ratione temporis quo singulae partes describuntur uniformiter esset dispertita* (1818), which showed that the perturbation caused by a planet is the same as that of an equal mass distributed along its orbit in proportion to the time spent on an arc. At the same time Gauss continued thinking about unsolved mathematical problems. In 1813 on a single sheet appear notes relating to parallel lines, declinations of stars, number theory, imaginaries, the theory of colors, and prisms (*Werke,* VIII, 166).

Astronomical chores soon dominated Gauss's life. He began with the makeshift observatory in an abandoned tower of the old city walls. A vast amount of time and energy went into equipping the new observatory, which was completed in 1816 and not properly furnished until 1821. In 1816 Gauss, accompanied by his ten-year-old son and one of his students, took a five-week trip to Bavaria, where he met the optical instrument makers G. von Reichenbach, T. L. Ertel (owner of Reichenbach's firm), J. von Fraunhofer, and J. von Utzschneider (Fraunhofer's partner), from whom his best instruments were purchased. As Figure 1 shows, astronomy was the only field in which Gauss worked steadily for the rest of his life. He ended his theoretical astronomical work in 1817 but continued positional observing, calculating, and reporting his results until his final illness. Although assisted by students and colleagues, he observed regularly and was involved in every detail of instrumentation.

It was during these early Göttingen years that Gauss matured his conception of non-Euclidean geometry. He had experimented with the consequences of denying the parallel postulate more than twenty years before, and during his student days he saw the fallaciousness of the proofs of the parallel postulate that were the rage at Göttingen; but he came only very slowly and reluctantly to the idea of a different geometric theory that might be "true." He seems to have been pushed forward by his clear understanding of the weaknesses of previous efforts to prove the parallel postulate and by his successes in finding non-Euclidean results. He was slowed by his deep conservatism, the identification of Euclidean geometry with his beloved old order, and by his fully justified fear of the ridicule of the philistines. Over the years in his correspondence we find him cautiously, but more and more clearly, stating his growing belief that the fifth postulate was unprovable. He privately encouraged others thinking along similar lines but advised secrecy. Only once, in a book review of 1816 (*Werke,* IV, 364–368; VIII, 170–174), did he hint at his views publicly. His ideas were "besmirched with mud" by critics (as he wrote to Schumacher on 15 January 1827), and his caution was confirmed.

But Gauss continued to find results in the new geometry and was again considering writing them up, possibly to be published after his death, when in 1831 came news of the work of János Bolyai. Gauss wrote to Wolfgang Bolyai endorsing the discovery, but he also asserted his own priority, thereby causing the volatile János to suspect a conspiracy to steal his ideas. When Gauss became familiar with Lobachevsky's work a decade later, he acted more positively with a letter of praise and by arranging a corresponding membership in the Göttingen Academy. But he stubbornly refused the public support that would have made the new ideas mathematically respectable. Although the friendships of Gauss with Bartels and W. Bolyai suggest the contrary, careful study of the plentiful documentary evidence has established that Gauss did not inspire the two founders of non-Euclidean geometry. Indeed, he played at best a neutral, and on balance a negative, role, since his silence was considered as agreement with the public ridicule and neglect that continued for several decades and were only gradually overcome, partly by the revelation, beginning in the 1860's, that the prince of mathematicians had been an underground non-Euclidean.

Geodesist. By 1817 Gauss was ready to move toward geodesy, which was to be his preoccupation for the next eight years and a burden for the next thirty. His interest was of long standing. As early as 1796 he worked on a surveying problem, and in 1799–1800 he advised Lt. K. L. E. von Lecoq, who was engaged in military mapping in Westphalia. Gauss's first publication was a letter on surveying in the *Allgemeine geographische Ephemeriden* of October 1799. In 1802 he participated in surveying with F. X. G. von Zach. From his arrival in Göttingen he was concerned with accurately locating the observatory, and in 1812 his interest in more general problems was stimulated by a discussion of sea levels during a visit to the Seeberg observatory. He began discussing with Schumacher the possibility of extending into Hannover the latter's survey of Denmark. Gauss had many motives for this project. It involved interesting mathematical problems, gave a new field for his calculating abilities, complemented his positional astronomy, competed with the French efforts to calculate the arc length of one degree on the meridian, offered an opportunity to do something useful for the kingdom, provided escape from petty annoyances of his job and family problems, and promised additional income. The last was a nontrivial matter, since Gauss had increasing family responsibilities to meet on a salary that remained fixed from 1807 to 1824.

The triangulation of Hannover was not officially approved until 1820, but already in 1818 Gauss began an arduous program of summer surveying in the field followed by data reduction during the winter. Plagued by poor transportation, uncomfortable living conditions, bad weather, uncooperative officials, accidents, poor health, and inadequate assistance and financial support, Gauss did the fieldwork himself with only minimal help for eight years. After 1825 he confined himself to supervision and calculation, which continued to completion of the triangulation of Hannover in 1847. By then he had handled more than a million numbers without assistance.

An early by-product of fieldwork was the invention of the heliotrope, an instrument for reflecting the sun's rays in a measured direction. It was motivated by dissatisfaction with the existing unsatisfactory methods of observing distant points by using lamps or powder flares at night. Meditating on the need for a beacon bright enough to be observed by day, Gauss hit on the idea of using reflected sunlight. After working out the optical theory, he designed the instrument and had the first model built in 1821. It proved to be very successful in practical work, having the brightness of a first-magnitude star at a distance of fifteen miles. Although heliostats had been described in the literature as early as 1742 (apparently unknown to Gauss), the heliotrope added greater precision by coupling mirrors with a small telescope.

It became standard equipment for large-scale triangulation until superseded by improved models from 1840 and by aerial surveying in the twentieth century. Gauss remarked that for the first time there existed a practical method of communicating with the moon.

Almost from the beginning of his surveying work Gauss had misgivings, which proved to be well founded. A variety of practical difficulties made it impossible to achieve the accuracy he had expected, even with his improvements in instrumentation and the skillful use of least squares in data reduction. The hoped-for measurement of an arc of the meridian required linking his work with other surveys that were never made. Too hasty planning resulted in badly laid out base lines and an unsatisfactory network of triangles. He never ceased trying to overcome these faults, but his virtuosity as a mathematician and surveyor could not balance the factors beyond his control. His results were used in making rough geographic and military maps, but they were unsuitable for precise land surveys and for measurement of the earth. Within a generation, the markers were difficult to locate precisely or had disappeared altogether. As he was finishing his fieldwork in July 1825, Gauss wrote to Olbers that he wondered whether other activities might have been more fruitful. Not only did the results seem questionable but he felt during these years, even more than usual, that he was prevented from working out many ideas that still crowded his mind. As he wrote to Bessel on 28 June 1820, "I feel the difficulty of the life of a practical astronomer, without help; and the worst of it is that I can hardly do any connected significant theoretical work."

In spite of these failures and dissatisfactions, the period of preoccupation with geodesy was in fact one of the most scientifically creative of Gauss's long career. Already in 1813 geodesic problems had inspired his *Theoria attractionis corporum sphaeroidicorum ellipticorum homogeneorum methodus nova tractata,* a significant early work on potential theory. The difficulties of mapping the terrestrial ellipsoid on a sphere and plane led him in 1816 to formulate and solve in outline the general problem of mapping one surface on another so that the two are "similar in their smallest parts." In 1822 a prize offered by the Copenhagen Academy stimulated him to write up these ideas in a paper that won first place and was published in 1825 as the *Allgemeine Auflösung der Aufgabe die Theile einer gegebenen Fläche auf einer anderen gegebenen Fläche so auszubilden dass die Abbildung dem Abgebildeten in den kleinsten Theilen ähnlich wird.* This paper, his more detailed *Untersuchungen über Gegenstände der höhern Geodäsie* (1844–1847), and geodesic manuscripts later published in the *Werke* were further developed by German geodesists and led to the Gauss-Krueger projection (1912), a generalization of the transverse Mercator projection, which attained a secure position as a basis for topographic grids taking into account the spheroidal shape of the earth.

Surveying problems also motivated Gauss to develop his ideas on least squares and more general problems of what is now called mathematical statistics. The result was the definitive exposition of his mature ideas in the *Theoria combinationis observationum erroribus minimis obnoxiae* (1823, with supplement in 1828). In the *Bestimmung des Breitenunterschiedes zwischen den Sternwarten von Göttingen und Altona durch Beobachtungen am Ramsdenschen Zenithsector* of 1828 he summed up his ideas on the figure of the earth, instrumental errors, and the calculus of observations. However, the crowning contribution of the period, and his last breakthrough in a major new direction of mathematical research, was *Disquisitiones generales circa superficies curvas* (1828), which grew out of his geodesic meditations of three decades and was the seed of more than a century of work on differential geometry. Of course, in these years as always, Gauss produced a stream of reviews, reports on observations, and solutions of old and new mathematical problems of varying importance that brought the number of his publications during the decade 1818–1828 to sixty-nine. (See Figure 1.)

Physicist. After the mid-1820's, there were increasing signs that Gauss wished to strike out in a new direction. Financial pressures had been eased by a substantial salary increase in 1824 and by a bonus for the surveying work in 1825. His other motivations for geodesic work were also weakened, and a new negative factor emerged—heart trouble. A fundamentally strong constitution and unbounded energy were essential to the unrelenting pace of work that Gauss maintained in his early years, but in the 1820's the strain began to show. In 1821, family letters show Gauss constantly worried, often very tired, and seriously considering a move to the leisure and financial security promised by Berlin. The hard physical work of surveying in the humid summers brought on symptoms that would now be diagnosed as asthma and heart disease. In the fall of 1825, Gauss took his ailing wife on a health trip to spas in southern Germany; but the travel and the hot weather had a very bad effect on his own health, and he was sick most of the winter. Distrusting doctors and never consulting one until the last few months of his life, he treated himself very sensibly by a very simple life, regular habits, and the avoidance of travel, for which he had never cared anyway. He resolved to drop direct participation in summer surveying and to spend the rest of his life "undisturbed in my study," as he had written Pfaff on 21 March 1825.

Apparently Gauss thought first of returning to a concentration on mathematics. He completed his work on least squares, geodesy, and curved surfaces as mentioned above, found new results on biquadratic reciprocity (1825), and began to pull together his long-standing ideas on elliptic functions and non-Euclidean geometry. But at forty-eight he found that satisfactory results came harder than before. In a letter to Olbers of 19 February 1826, he spoke of never having worked so hard with so little success and of being almost convinced that he should go into another field. Moreover, his most original ideas were being developed independently by men of a new generation. Gauss did not respond when Abel sent him his proof of the impossibility of solving the quintic equation in 1825, and the two never met, although Gauss praised him in private letters. When Dirichlet wrote Gauss in May 1826, enclosing his first work on number theory and asking for guidance, Gauss did not reply until 13 September and then only with general encouragement and advice to find a job that left time for research. As indicated in a letter to Encke of 8 July, Gauss was much impressed by Dirichlet's "eminent talent," but he did not seem inclined to become mathematically involved with him. When Crelle in 1828 asked Gauss for a paper on elliptic functions, he replied that Jacobi had covered his work "with so much sagacity, penetration and elegance, that I believe that I am relieved of publishing my own research." Harassed, overworked, distracted, and frustrated during these years, Gauss undoubtedly underestimated the value of his achievements, something he had never done before. But he was correct in sensing the need of a new source of inspiration. In turning toward intensive investigations in physics, he was following a pattern that had proved richly productive in the past.

In 1828 Alexander von Humboldt persuaded Gauss to attend the only scientific convention of his career, the Naturforscherversammlung in Berlin. Since first hearing of Gauss from the leading mathematicians in Paris in 1802, Humboldt had been trying to bring him to Berlin as the leading figure of a great academy he hoped to build there. At times negotiations had seemed near success, but bureaucratic inflexibilities in Berlin or personal factors in Göttingen always intervened. Humboldt still had not abandoned these hopes, but he had other motives as well. He wished to draw Gauss into the German scientific upsurge whose beginnings were reflected in the meeting; and especially he wished to involve Gauss in his own efforts, already extending over two decades, to organize worldwide geomagnetic observations. Humboldt had no success in luring Gauss from his Göttingen hermitage. He was repelled by the Berlin convention, which included a "little celebration" to which Humboldt invited 600 guests. Nevertheless, the visit was a turning point. Living quietly for three weeks in Humboldt's house with a private garden and his host's scientific equipment, Gauss had both leisure and stimulation for making a choice. When Humboldt later wrote of his satisfaction at having interested him in magnetism, Gauss replied tactlessly that he had been interested in it for nearly thirty years. Correspondence and manuscripts show this to be true; they indicate that Gauss delayed serious work on the subject partly because means of measurement were not available. Nevertheless, the Berlin visit was the occasion for the decision and also provided the means for implementing it, since in Berlin Gauss met Wilhelm Weber, a young and brilliant experimental physicist whose collaboration was essential.

In September 1829 Quetelet visited Göttingen and found Gauss very interested in terrestrial magnetism but with little experience in measuring it. The new field had evidently been selected, but systematic work awaited Weber's arrival in 1831. Meanwhile, Gauss extended his long-standing knowledge of the physical literature and began to work on problems in theoretical physics, and especially in mechanics, capillarity, acoustics, optics, and crystallography. The first fruit of this research was *Über ein neues allgemeines Grundgesetz der Mechanik* (1829). In it Gauss stated the law of least constraint: the motion of a system departs as little as possible from free motion, where departure, or constraint, is measured by the sum of products of the masses times the squares of their deviations from the path of free motion. He presented it merely as a new formulation equivalent to the well-known principle of d'Alembert. This work seems obviously related to the old meditations on least squares, but Gauss wrote to Olbers on 31 January 1829 that it was inspired by studies of capillarity and other physical problems. In 1830 appeared *Principia generalia theoriae figurae fluidorum in statu aequilibrii,* his one contribution to capillarity and an important paper in the calculus of variations, since it was the first solution of a variational problem involving double integrals, boundary conditions, and variable limits.

The years 1830–1831 were the most trying of Gauss's life. His wife was very ill, having suffered since 1818 from gradually worsening tuberculosis and hysterical neurosis. Her older son left in a huff and immigrated to the United States after quarreling with his father over youthful profligacies. The country was in a revolutionary turmoil of which Gauss thoroughly disapproved. Amid all these vexations, Gauss continued work on biquadratic residues, arduous geodesic calculations, and many other tasks. On 13 September 1831 his wife died. Two days later Weber arrived.

As Gauss and Weber began their close collaboration and intimate friendship, the younger man was just half the age of the older. Gauss took a fatherly attitude. Though he shared fully in experimental work, and though Weber showed high theoretical competence and originality during the collaboration and later, the older man led on the theoretical and the younger on the experimental side. Their joint efforts soon produced results. In 1832 Gauss presented to the Academy the *Intensitas vis magneticae terrestris ad mensuram absolutam revocata* (1833), in which appeared the first systematic use of absolute units (distance, mass, time) to measure a nonmechanical quantity. Here Gauss typically acknowledged the help of Weber but did not include him as joint author. Stimulated by Faraday's discovery of induced current in 1831, the pair energetically investigated electrical phenomena. They arrived at Kirchhoff's laws in 1833 and anticipated various discoveries in static, thermal, and frictional electricity but did not publish, presumably because their interest centered on terrestrial magnetism.

The thought that a magnetometer might also serve as a galvanometer almost immediately suggested its use to induce a current that might send a message. Working alone, Weber connected the astronomical observatory and the physics laboratory with a mile-long double wire that broke "uncountable" times as he strung it over houses and two towers. Early in 1833 the first words were sent, then whole sentences. This first operating electric telegraph was mentioned briefly by Gauss in a notice in the *Göttingische gelehrte Anzeigen* (9 August 1834; *Werke,* V, 424–425), but it seems to have been unknown to other inventors. Gauss soon realized the military and economic importance of the invention and tried unsuccessfully to promote its use by government and industry on a large scale. Over the years, the wire was replaced twice by one of better quality, and various improvements were made in the terminals. In 1845 a bolt of lightning fragmented the wire, but by this time it was no longer in use. Other inventors (Steinheil in Munich in 1837, Morse in the United States in 1838) had independently developed more efficient and exploitable methods, and the Gauss–Weber priority was forgotten.

The new magnetic observatory, free of all metal that might affect magnetic forces, was part of a network that Humboldt hoped would make coordinated measurements of geographical and temporal variations. In 1834 there were already twenty-three magnetic observatories in Europe, and the comparison of data from them showed the existence of magnetic storms. Gauss and Weber organized the Magnetische Verein, which united a worldwide network of observatories. Its *Resultate aus den Beobachtungen des magnetischen Vereins* appeared in six volumes (1836–1841) and included fifteen papers by Gauss, twenty-three by Weber, and the joint *Atlas des Erdmagnetismus* (1840). These and other publications elsewhere dealt with problems of instrumentation (including one of several inventions of the bifilar magnetometer), reported observations of the horizontal and vertical components of magnetic force, and attempted to explain the observations in mathematical terms.

The most important publication in the last category was the *Allgemeine Theorie des Erdmagnetismus* (1839). Here Gauss broke the tradition of armchair theorizing about the earth as a fairly neutral carrier of one or more magnets and based his mathematics on data. Using ideas first considered by him in 1806, well formulated by 1822, but lacking empirical foundation until 1838, Gauss expressed the magnetic potential at any point on the earth's surface by an infinite series of spherical functions and used the data collected by the world network to evaluate the first twenty-four coefficients. This was a superb interpolation, but Gauss hoped later to explain the results by a physical theory about the magnetic composition of the earth. Felix Klein has pointed out that this can indeed be done (*Vorlesungen über die Entwicklung der Mathematik im 19. Jahrhundert* [Berlin, 1926], pt. 1, p. 22), but that little is thereby added to the effective explanation offered by the Gaussian formulas. During these years Gauss found time to continue his geodesic data reduction, assist in revising the weights and measures of Hannover, make a number of electric discoveries jointly with Weber, and take an increasing part in university affairs.

This happy and productive collaboration was suddenly upset in 1837 by a disaster that soon effectively terminated Gauss's experimental work. In September, at the celebration of the 100th anniversary of the university (at which Gauss presented Humboldt with plans for his bifilar magnetometer), it was rumored that the new King Ernst August of Hannover might abrogate the hard-won constitution of 1833 and demand that all public servants swear a personal oath of allegiance to himself. When he did so in November, seven Göttingen professors, including Weber and the orientalist G. H. A. von Ewald, the husband of Gauss's older daughter, Minna, sent a private protest to the cabinet, asserting that they were bound by their previous oath to the constitution of 1833. The "Göttingen Seven" were unceremoniously fired, three to be banished and the rest (including Weber and Ewald) permitted to remain in the town. Some thought that Gauss might resign, but he took no public action; and his private efforts, like the public protest of six additional professors, were ignored. Why did Gauss not act more energetically? At age sixty he was too set in his ways, his mother was too old to move, and he hated anything politically radical and disapproved of the protest. The seven eventually found jobs elsewhere. Ewald moved to Tübingen, and Gauss was deprived of the company of his most beloved daughter, who had been ill for some years and died of consumption in 1840. Weber was supported by colleagues for a time, then drifted away and accepted a job at Leipzig. The collaboration petered out, and Gauss abandoned further physical research. In 1848, when Weber recovered his position at Göttingen, it was too late to renew collaboration and Weber continued his brilliant career alone.

As Gauss was ending his physical research, he published *Allgemeine Lehrsätze in Beziehung auf die im verkehrten Verhältnisse des Quadrats der Entfernung wirkenden Anziehungs- und Abstossungskräfte* (1840). Growing directly out of his magnetic work but linked also to his *Theoria attractionis* of 1813, it was the first systematic treatment of potential theory as a mathematical topic, recognized the necessity of existence theorems in that field, and reached a standard of rigor that remained unsurpassed for more than a century, even though the main theorem of the paper was false, according to C. J. de la Vallée Poussin (see *Revue des questions scientifiques,* **133** [1962], 314–330, esp. 324). In the same year he finished *Dioptrische Untersuchungen* (1841), in which he analyzed the path of light through a system of lenses and showed, among other things, that any system is equivalent to a properly chosen single lens. Although Gauss said that he had possessed the theory forty years before and considered it too elementary to publish, it has been labeled his greatest work by one of his scientific biographers (Clemens Schäfer, in *Werke,* XI, pt. 2, sec. 2, 189 ff.). In any case, it was his last significant scientific contribution.

Later Years. From the early 1840's the intensity of Gauss's activity gradually decreased. Further publications were either variations on old themes, reviews, reports, or solutions of minor problems. His reclusion is illustrated by his lack of response in 1845 to Kummer's invention of ideals (to restore unique factorization) and in 1846 to the discovery of Neptune by Adams, Le Verrier, and Galle. But the end of magnetic research and the decreased rate of publication did not mean that Gauss was inactive. He continued astronomical observing. He served several times as dean of the Göttingen faculty. He was busy during the 1840's in finishing many old projects, such as the last calculations on the Hannover survey. In 1847 he eloquently praised number theory and G. Eisenstein in the preface to the collected works of this ill-fated young man who had been one of the few to tell Gauss anything he did not already know. He spent several years putting the university widows' fund on a sound actuarial basis, calculating the necessary tables. He learned to read and speak Russian fluently, apparently first attracted by Lobachevsky but soon extending his reading as widely as permitted by the limited material available. His notebooks and correspondence show that he continued to work on a variety of mathematical problems. Teaching became less distasteful, perhaps because his students were better prepared and included some, such as Dedekind and Riemann, who were worthy of his efforts.

During the Revolution of 1848 Gauss stood guard with the royalists (whose defeat permitted the return of his son-in-law and Weber). He joined the Literary Museum, an organization whose library provided conservative literature for students and faculty, and made a daily visit there. He carefully followed political, economic, and technological events as reported in the press. The fiftieth anniversary celebration of his doctorate in 1849 brought him many messages and formal honors, but the world of mathematics was represented only by Jacobi and Dirichlet. The paper that Gauss delivered was his fourth proof of the fundamental theorem of algebra, appropriately a variation of the first in his thesis of 1799. After this celebration, Gauss continued his interests at a slower pace and became more than ever a legendary figure unapproachable by those outside his personal circle. Perhaps stimulated by his actuarial work, he fell into the habit of collecting all sorts of statistics from the newspapers, books, and daily observations. Undoubtedly some of these data helped him with financial speculations shrewd enough to create an estate equal to nearly 200 times his annual salary. The "star gazer," as his father called him, had, as an afterthought, achieved the financial status denied his more "practical" relatives.

Due to his careful regimen, no serious illnesses had troubled Gauss since his surveying days. Over the years he treated himself for insomnia, stomach discomfort, congestion, bronchitis, painful corns, shortness of breath, heart flutter, and the usual signs of aging without suffering any acute attacks. He had been less successful in resisting chronic hypochondria and melancholia which increasingly plagued him after the death of his first wife. In the midst of some undated scientific notes from his later years there suddenly appears the sentence "Death would be preferable to such a life," and at fifty-six he wrote Gerling (8 February 1834) that he felt like a stranger in the world.

After 1850, troubled by developing heart disease, Gauss gradually limited his activity further. He made his last astronomical observation in 1851, at the age of seventy-four, and later the same year approved Riemann's doctoral thesis on the foundations of complex analysis. The following year he was still working on minor mathematical problems and on an improved Foucault pendulum. During 1853–1854 Riemann wrote his great *Habilitationsschrift* on the foundations of geometry, a topic chosen by Gauss. In June 1854 Gauss, who had been under a doctor's care for several months, had the pleasure of hearing Riemann's probationary lecture, symbolic of the presence in Germany at last of talents capable of continuing his work. A few days later he left Göttingen for the last time to observe construction of the railway from Kassel. By autumn his illness was much worse. Although gradually more bedridden, he kept up his reading, correspondence, and trading in securities until he died in his sleep late in February 1855.

Mathematical Scientist. Gauss the man of genius stands in the way of evaluating the role of Gauss as a scientist. His mathematical abilities and exploits caused his contemporaries to dub him *princeps,* and biographers customarily place him on a par with Archimedes and Newton. This traditional judgment is as reasonable as any outcome of the ranking game, but an assessment of his impact is more problematic because of the wide gap between the quality of his personal accomplishments and their effectiveness as contributions to the scientific enterprise. Gauss published only about half his recorded innovative ideas (see Figure 1) and in a style so austere that his readers were few. The unpublished results appear in notes, correspondence, and reports to official bodies, which became accessible only many years later. Still other methods and discoveries are only hinted at in letters or incomplete notes. It is therefore necessary to reexamine Gauss as a participant in the scientific community and to look at his achievements in terms of their scientific consequences.

The personality traits that most markedly inhibited the effectiveness of Gauss as a participant in scientific activity were his intellectual isolation, personal ambition, deep conservatism and nationalism, and rather narrow cultural outlook. It is hard to appreciate fully the isolation to which Gauss was condemned in childhood by thoughts that he could share with no one. He must soon have learned that attempts to communicate led, at best, to no response; at worst, to the ridicule and estrangement that children find so hard to bear. But unlike most precocious children, who eventually find intellectual comrades, Gauss during his whole life found no one with whom to share his most valued thoughts. Kästner was not interested when Gauss told him of his first great discovery, the constructibility of the regular 17-gon. Bolyai, his most promising friend at Göttingen, could not appreciate his thinking. These and many other experiences must have convinced Gauss that there was little to be gained from trying to interchange theoretical ideas. He drew on the great mathematicians of the past and on contemporaries in France (whom he treated as from another world); but he remained outside the mathematical activity of his day, almost as if he were actually no longer living and his publications were being discovered in the archives. He found it easier and more useful to communicate with empirical scientists and technicians, because in those areas he was among peers; but even there he remained a solitary worker, with the exception of the collaboration with Weber.

Those who admired Gauss most and knew him best found him cold and uncommunicative. After the Berlin visit, Humboldt wrote Schumacher (18 October 1828) that Gauss was "glacially cold" to unknowns and unconcerned with things outside his immediate circle. To Bessel, Humboldt wrote (12 October 1837) of Gauss's "intentional isolation," his habit of suddenly taking possession of a small area of work, considering all previous results as part of it, and refusing to consider anything else. C. G. J. Jacobi complained in a letter to his brother (21 September 1849) that in twenty years Gauss had not cited any publication by him or by Dirichlet. Schumacher, the closest of Gauss's friends and one who gave him much personal counsel and support, wrote to Bessel (21 December 1842) that Gauss was "a queer sort of fellow" with whom it is better to stay "in the limits of conventional politeness, without trying to do anything uncalled for."

Like Newton, Gauss had an intense dislike of controversy. There is no record of a traumatic experience that might account for this, but none is required to explain a desire to avoid emotional involvements that interfered with contemplation. With equal rationality, Gauss avoided all noncompulsory ceremonies and formalities, making an exception only when royalty was to be present. In these matters, as in his defensive attitude toward possible wasters of his time, Gauss was acting rationally to maximize his scientific output; but the result was to prevent some interchanges that might have been as beneficial to him as to others.

Insatiable drive, a characteristic of persistent high achievers, could hardly in itself inhibit participation; but conditioned by other motivations it did so for Gauss. Having experienced bitter poverty, he worked toward a security that was for a long time denied him. But he had absorbed the habitual frugality of the striving poor and did not want or ever adopt luxuries of the parvenu. He had no confidence in the democratic state and looked to the ruling aristocracy for security. The drive for financial security was accompanied by a stronger ambition, toward great achievement and lasting fame in science. While still an adolescent Gauss realized that he might join the tiny superaristocracy of science that seldom has more than one member in a generation. He wished to be worthy of his heroes and to deserve the esteem of future peers. His sons reported that he discouraged them from going into science on the ground that he did not want any second-rate work associated with his name. He had little hope of being understood by his contemporaries; it was sufficient to impress and to avoid offending them. In the light of his ambitions for security and lasting fame, with success in each seemingly required for the other, his choice of career and his purposeful isolation were rational. He did achieve his twin ambitions. More effective communication and participation might have speeded the development of mathematics by several decades, but it would not have added to Gauss's reputation then or now. Gauss probably understood this well enough. He demonstrated in some of his writings, correspondence, lectures, and organizational activities that he could be an effective teacher, expositor, popularizer, diplomat, and promoter when he wished. He simply did not wish.

Gauss's conservatism has been described above, but it should be added here that it extended to all his thinking. He looked nostalgically back to the eighteenth century with its enlightened monarchs supporting scientific aristocrats in academies where they were relieved of teaching. He was anxious to find "new truths" that did not disturb established ideas. Nationalism was important for Gauss. As we have seen, it impelled him toward geodesy and other work that he considered useful to the state. But its most important effect was to deny him easy communication with the French. Only in Paris, during his most productive years, were men with whom he could have enjoyed a mutually stimulating mathematical collaboration.

It seems strange to call culturally narrow a man with a solid classical education, wide knowledge, and voracious reading habits. Yet outside of science Gauss did not rise above petit bourgeois banality. Sir Walter Scott was his favorite British author, but he did not care for Byron or Shakespeare. Among German writers he liked Jean Paul, the best-selling humorist of the day, but disliked Goethe and disapproved of Schiller. In music he preferred light songs and in drama, comedies. In short, his genius stopped short at the boundaries of science and technology, outside of which he had little more taste or insight than his neighbors.

The contrast between knowledge and impact is now understandable. Gauss arrived at the two most revolutionary mathematical ideas of the nineteenth century: non-Euclidean geometry and noncommutative algebra. The first he disliked and suppressed. The second appears as quaternion calculations in a notebook of about 1819 (*Werke,* VIII, 357–362) without having stimulated any further activity. Neither the barycentric calculus of his own student Moebius (1827), nor Grassmann's *Ausdenunglehre* (1844), nor Hamilton's work on quaternions (beginning in 1843) interested him, although they sparked a fundamental shift in mathematical thought. He seemed unaware of the outburst of analytic and synthetic projective geometry, in which C. von Staudt, one of his former students, was a leading participant. Apparently Gauss was as hostile or indifferent to radical ideas in mathematics as in politics.

Hostility to new ideas, however, does not explain Gauss's failure to communicate many significant mathematical results that he did approve. Felix Klein (*Vorlesungen über die Entwicklung der Mathematik im 19. Jahrhundert,* pt. 1, 11–12) points to a combination of factors—personal worries, distractions, lack of encouragement, and overproduction of ideas. The last might alone have been decisive. Ideas came so quickly that each one inhibited the development of the preceding. Still another factor was the advantage that Gauss gained from withholding information, although he hotly denied this motive when Bessel suggested it. In fact, the Ceres calculation that won Gauss fame was based on methods unknown to others. By delaying publication of least squares and by never publishing his calculating methods, he maintained an advantage that materially contributed to his reputation. The same applies to the careful and conscious removal from his writings of all trace of his heuristic methods. The failure to publish was certainly not based on disdain for priority. Gauss cared a great deal for priority and frequently asserted it publicly and privately with scrupulous honesty. But to him this meant being first to discover, not first to publish; and he was satisfied to establish his dates by private records, correspondence, cryptic remarks in publications, and in one case by publishing a cipher. (See bibliography under "Miscellaneous.") Whether he intended it so or not, in this way he maintained the advantage of secrecy without losing his priority in the eyes of later generations. The common claim that Gauss failed to publish because of his high standards is not convincing. He did have high standards, but he had no trouble achieving excellence once the mathematical results were in hand; and he did publish all that was ready for publication by normal standards.

In the light of the above discussion one might expect the Gaussian impact to be far smaller than his reputation—and indeed this is the case. His inventions, including several not listed here for lack of space, redound to his fame but were minor improvements of temporary importance or, like the telegraph, uninfluential anticipations. In theoretical astronomy he perfected classical methods in orbit calculation but otherwise did only fairly routine observations. His personal involvement in calculating orbits saved others trouble and served to increase his fame but were of little long-run scientific importance. His work in geodesy was influential only in its mathematical by-products. From his collaboration with Weber arose only two achievements of significant impact. The use of absolute units set a pattern that became standard, and the Magnetische Verein established a precedent for international scientific cooperation. His work in dioptrics may have been of the highest quality, but it seems to have had little influence; and the same may be said of his other works in physics.

When we come to mathematics proper, the picture is different. Isolated as Gauss was, seemingly hardly aware of the work of other mathematicians and not caring to communicate with them, nevertheless his influence was powerful. His prestige was such that young mathematicians especially studied him. Jacobi and Abel testified that their work on elliptic functions was triggered by a hint in the *Disquisitiones arithmeticae.* Galois, on the eve of his death, asked that his rough notes be sent to Gauss. Thus, in mathematics, in spite of delays, Gauss did reach and inspire mathematicians. Although he was more of a systematizer and solver of old problems than an opener of new paths, the very completeness of his results laid the basis for new departures—especially in number theory, differential geometry, and statistics. Although his mathematical thinking was always concrete in the sense that he was dealing with structures based on the real numbers, his work contained the seeds of many highly abstract ideas that came later. Gauss, like Archimedes, pushed the methods of his time to the limit of their possibilities. But unlike his other ability peer, Newton, he did not initiate a profound new development, nor did he have the revolutionary impact of a number of his contemporaries of perhaps lesser ability but greater imagination and daring.

Gauss is best described as a mathematical scientist, or, in the terms common in his day, as a pure and applied mathematician. Ranging easily, competently, and productively over the whole of science and technology, he always did so as a mathematician, motivated by mathematics, utilizing every experience for mathematical inspiration. (Figure 2 shows some of the interrelations of his interests.) Clemens Schäfer, one of his scientific biographers, wrote in *Nature* (**128** [1931], 341): "He was not really a physicist in the sense of searching for new phenomena, but rather

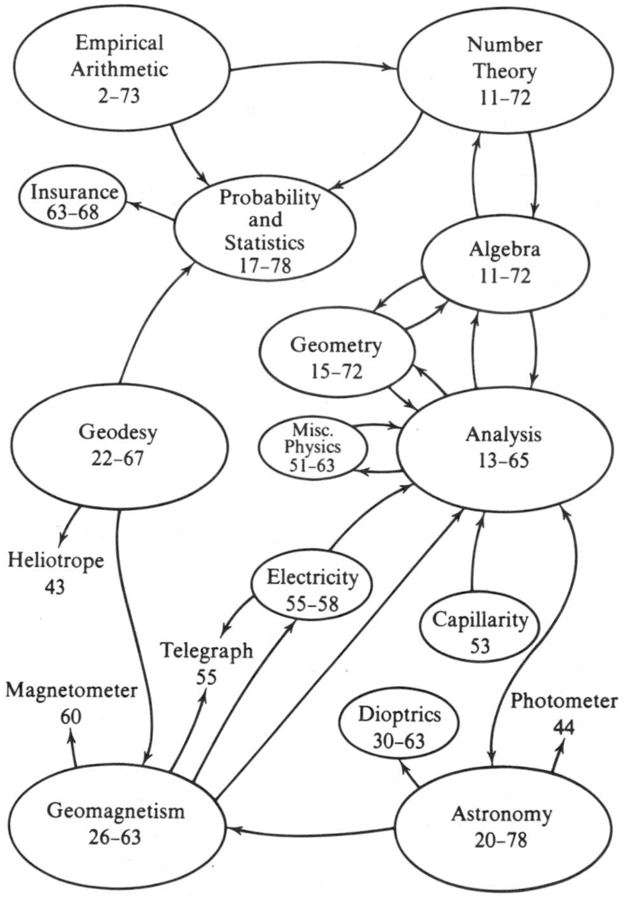

FIGURE 2. Main lines of development of Gauss's scientific ideas. Arrows suggest the most important directions of motivation and inspiration. Numerals indicate ages. His four most important inventions are given outside of any enclosing curves. The sizes of the ellipses suggest the weight of each field in his total effort, and the year span is indicative also of the number and variety of activities in each field. This figure should be compared with Figure 1.

always a mathematician who attempted to formulate in exact mathematical terms the experimental results obtained by others." Leaving aside his personal failures, whose scientific importance was transitory, Gauss appears as the ideal mathematician, displaying in heroic proportions in one person the capabilities attributed collectively to the community of professional mathematicians.

BIBLIOGRAPHY

A complete Gauss bibliography would be far too large to include here, and the following is highly selective. Abbreviations used throughout are the following: *AMM: American Mathematical Monthly. AN: Astronomische Nachrichten. BA: Abhandlungen der (Königlichen) Bayerischen Akademie der Wissenschaften,* Mathematisch-naturwissenschaftliche Abteilung, II Klasse. *BAMS: Bulletin of the American Mathematical Society. BB: Bullettino (Bollettino) di bibliografia e di storia delle scienze matematiche (e fisiche)* (Boncompagni). *BSM: Bulletin des sciences mathématiques et astronomiques* (Darboux). *Crelle: Journal für die reine und angewandte Mathematik. DMV: Jahresbericht der Deutschen Mathematiker-vereinigung. FF: Forschungen und Fortschritte. GA: Abhandlungen der Akademie (K. Gesellschaft) der Wissenschaften zu Göttingen,* Mathematisch-naturwissenschaftliche Klasse. *GGM: Gauss-Gesellschaft Mitteilungen. GN: Nachrichten (Jahrbuch, Jahresbericht) der Gesellschaft der Wissenschaften zu Göttingen. HUB: Wissenschaftliche Zeitschrift der Humboldt-Universität Berlin,* Mathematisch-naturwissenschaftliche Reihe. *IINT: Trudy (Arkhiv) Instituta istorii nauki i tekhniki. IMI: Istoriko-matematicheskie issledovaniya. JMPA: Journal de mathématiques pures et appliquées* (Liouville). *LB: Berichte über die Verhandlungen der (Königlichen) Sächsischen Gesellschaft der Wissenschaften zu Leipzig. MA: Mathematische Annalen. MDA: Monatsberichte der Deutschen Akademie der Wissenschaften zu Berlin. NA: Nouvelles annales de mathématiques. NMM: National Mathematics Magazine.* OK: Ostwalds Klassiker der exacten Wissenschaften (Leipzig). *SM: Scripta mathematica. TSM: Scientific Memoirs, Selected from the Transactions of Foreign Academies and Learned Societies and From Foreign Journals* by Richard Taylor. *VIET: Voprosy istorii estestvoznaniya i tekhniki. Zach: Monatliche Correspondenz zur Beförderung der Erd- und Himmelskunde* (Zach). *ZV: Zeitschrift für Vermessungswesen.*

I. ORIGINAL WORKS. All of Gauss's publications (including his fine reviews of his own papers) are reprinted in the *Werke,* published in 12 vols. by the Königliche Gesellschaft der Wissenschaften zu Göttingen (Leipzig-Berlin, 1863-1933). The *Werke* contains also a generous selection of his unpublished notes and papers, related correspondence, commentaries, and extensive analyses of his work in each field. The first 7 vols., edited by Ernst C. J. Schering, who came to Göttingen as a student in 1852 and taught mathematics there from 1858 until his death in 1897, contain Gauss's publications arranged by subject, as follows: I. *Disquisitiones arithmeticae* (1863; 2nd ed., with commentary, 1870). II. Number Theory (1863; 2nd ed., with the unpublished sec. 8 of the *Disquisitiones,* minor additions, and revisions, 1876). III. Analysis (1866; 2nd ed., with minor changes, 1876). IV. Probability, Geometry, and Geodesy (1873; 2nd ed., almost unchanged, 1880). V. Mathematical Physics (1867; unchanged 2nd ed., 1877). VI. Astronomy (1873). VII. *Theoria motus* (1871; 2nd ed., with new commentary by Martin Brendel and previously unpublished Gauss MSS, 1906).

After the death of Schering, work was continued under the aggressive leadership of Felix Klein, who organized a campaign to collect materials and enlisted experts in special fields to study them. From 1898 until 1922 he rallied support with fourteen reports, published under the title "Bericht über den Stand der Herausgabe von Gauss' Werken," in the *Nachrichten* of the Göttingen Academy and reprinted in *MA* and *BSM.* The fruits of this effort were a much enlarged Gauss Archive at Göttingen, many individual publications, and vols. VIII-XII of the *Werke,* as follows: VIII. Supp. to vols. I-IV (1900), papers and correspondence on mathematics (the paper on pp. 36-64 is spurious. See *Werke,* X, pt. 1, 137). IX. Geodesy (1903). Supp. to vol. IV, including some overlooked Gauss publications. X, pt. 1. Supp. on pure mathematics (1917), including the famous *Tagebuch* in which Gauss from 1796 to 1814 recorded mathematical results. Found in 1898 by P. Stäckel and first published by F. Klein in the *Festschrift zur Feier des hundertfünfzigjährigen Bestehens der Königlichen Gesellschaft der Wissenschaften zu Göttingen* (Berlin, 1901) and in *MA,* **57** (1903), 1-34, it was here reprinted with very extensive commentary and also in facsimile. A French trans. with commentary by P. Eymard and J. P. Lafon appeared in *Revue d'histoire des sciences et de leurs applications,* **9** (1956), 21-51. See also G. Herglotz, in *LB,* **73** (1921), 271-277. X, pt. 2. Biographical essays described below (1922-1933). XI, pt. 1. Supp. on Physics, Chronology, and Astronomy (1927). XI, pt. 2. Biographical essays described below (1924-1929). XII. Varia. *Atlas des Erdmagnetismus* (1929). A final volume, XIII, planned to contain further biographical material (especially on Gauss as professor), bibliography, and index, was nearly completed by H. Geppert and E. Bessel-Hagen but not published.

A. *Translations and Reprints.* The *Demonstratio nova* of 1799 together with the three subsequent proofs of the fundamental theorem (1815, 1816, 1849) were published in German with commentary by E. Netto under the title *Die vier Gauss'schen Beweise* . . . in OK, no. 14 (1890). The *Disquisitiones* (1801) is available in French (1807), German, with other works on number theory (1889; repr. New York, 1965), Russian (1959), and English (1966). Gauss's third published proof of the law of quadratic reciprocity (1808) is translated in D. E. Smith, *Source Book in Mathematics,* I (New York, 1929), 112-118. All his published proofs of this theorem are collected in *Sechs Beweise des Fundamentaltheorems über quadratische Reste,* E. Netto, ed., in OK, no. 122 (1901).

The *Theoria motus* (1809) was translated into English (1857), Russian (1861), French (1864), and German (1865). *Disquisitiones generales circa seriem* (1813) appeared in a German translation by H. Simon in 1888, and *Theoria attractionis* (1813) was translated in *Zach,* **28** (1813), 37–57, 125–234, and reprinted in OK, 19 (1890). The *Determinatio attractionis* (1818) was translated in OK, 225 (1927). The *Allgemeine Auflösung* (1825) was reprinted with related works of Lagrange in OK, 55 (1894). *Theoria combinationis* and supps. of 1823 appeared in French (by J. Bertrand, 1855), German (1887), and with other related work in *Abhandlungen zur Methode der kleinsten Quadrate,* translated by A. Börsch and P. Simon (Berlin, 1887), and in *Gauss's Work (1803–1826) on the Theory of Least Squares,* translated from French by H. F. Trotter (Princeton, N.J., 1957). The *Allgemeine Auflösung* of 1825 appeared in *Philosophical Magazine,* **4** (1828), 104–113, 206–215. *Disquisitiones generales circa superficies curvas* (1828) was translated into French in *NA,* **11** (1852), 195–252, and with notes by E. Roger (Grenoble, 1855); into German by O. Böklen in his *Analytische Geometrie des Raumes* (1884), and by Wangerin in OK, 5 (1889); into Russian (1895), Hungarian (1897); and English (1902). *Über ein neues allgemeines Grundgesetz* (1829) was translated in *NA,* **4** (1845), 477–479.

The *Intensitas vis magneticae* (1833) appears in the *Effemeridi astronomiche di Milano, 1839* (Milan, 1838); in OK, 53 (1894); and in W. F. Magie, *Source Book in Physics* (New York–London, 1935; repr., Cambridge, Mass., 1963), pp. 519–524. The *Allgemeine Theorie des Erdmagnetismus* of 1839 was promptly published in English in *TSM,* **2** (1841), 184–251, 313–316. The *Allgemeine Lehrsätze* (1840) was translated in *JMPA,* **7** (1842), 273–324, and reprinted in OK, 2 (1889). *Dioptrische Untersuchungen* (1841) appeared in English in *TSM,* **3** (1843), 490–498 (see also *Ferrari's Dioptric Instruments* [London, 1919]); and in French in *Annales de chimie,* **33** (1851), 259–294, and in *JMPA,* **1** (1856), 9–43. The *Untersuchungen über Gegenstände der höheren Geodäsie* (1844, 1847) was reprinted as OK, 177 (Leipzig, 1910).

Very little material from the *Nachlass* first printed in the *Werke* has been reprinted or translated. Parts of *Werke,* XI, pt. 1, on the arithmetic-geometric mean and modular functions appear in the OK, 255 (1927), translation of the *Determinatio attractionis* (1818). Some Gauss MSS and editor's commentary are translated from *Werke,* XII, by Dunnington in *Carl Friedrich Gauss, Inaugural Lecture on Astronomy and Papers on the Foundations of Mathematics* (Baton Rouge, La., 1937). Notes on Gauss's astronomy lectures by A. T. Kupffer are printed in A. N. Krylov, *Sobranie trudy* (Moscow–Leningrad, 1936), VI. The following selecta have appeared in Russian: *Geodezicheskie issledovania Gaussa . . .* (St. Petersburg, 1866); *Izbrannye trudy po zemnomu magnetizmu* (Leningrad, 1952); *Izbrannye geodezicheskie sochinenia* (Moscow, 1957).

B. *Correspondence.* Only the major collections are listed here. Many other letters have been published in journal articles and in bibliographies. G. F. J. A. von Auwers, *Briefwechsel zwischen Gauss und Bessel* (Leipzig, 1880). E. Schönberg and T. Gerardy, "Die Briefe des Herrn P. H. L. von Bogulawski . . .," in *BA,* **110** (1963), 3–44. F. Schmidt and P. Stäckel, *Briefwechsel zwischen C. F. Gauss and W. Bolyai* (Leipzig, 1899). P. G. L. Dirichlet, *Werke,* II (Berlin, 1897), 373–387. C. Schäfer, *Briefwechsel zwischen Carl Friedrich Gauss und Christian Ludwig Gerling* (Berlin, 1927). T. Gerardy, *Christian Ludwig Gerling und Carl Friedrich Gauss. Sechzig bisher unveröffentlichte Briefe* (Göttingen, 1964). H. Stupuy, ed., *Oeuvres philosophiques de Sophie Germain* (Paris, 1879), pp. 298 ff.; and 2nd ed., pp. 254 ff. K. Bruhns, *Briefe zwischen A. v. Humboldt und Gauss* (Leipzig, 1877) (see also K.-R. Bierman, in *FF,* **36** [1962], 41–44, also in *GGM,* **4** [1967], 5–18). T. Gerardy, "Der Briefwechsel zwischen C. F. Gauss und C. L. Lecoq," in *GN* (1959), 37–63. W. Gresky, "Aus Bernard von Lindenaus Briefen an C. F. Gauss," in *GGM,* **5** (1968), 12–46. W. Valentiner, *Briefe von C. F. Gauss an B. Nicolai* (Karlsruhe, 1877). C. Schilling and I. Kramer, *Briefwechsel zwischen Olbers und Gauss,* 2 vols. (Berlin, 1900–1909). C. Pfaff, *Sammlung von Briefen, gewechselt zwischen Johann Friedrich Pfaff und . . . anderen* (Leipzig, 1853). P. Riebesell, "Briefwechsel zwischen C. F. Gauss und J. C. Repsold," in *Mitteilungen der mathematischen Gesellschaft in Hamburg,* **6** (1928), 398–431. C. A. Peters, *Briefwechsel zwischen C. F. Gauss und H. C. Schumacher,* 6 vols. (Altona, 1860–1865). T. Gerardy, *Nachtrage zum Briefwechsel zwischen Carl Friedrich Gauss und Heinrich Christian Schumacher* (Göttingen, 1969).

C. *Archives.* The MSS, letters, notebooks, and library of Gauss have been well preserved. The bulk of the scientific *Nachlass* is collected in the Gauss Archiv of the Handschriftenabteilung of the Niedersächsischen Staats- und Universitätsbibliothek, Göttingen, and fills 200 boxes. (See W. Meyer, *Die Handschriften in Göttingen* [Berlin, 1894], III, 101–113.) Theo Gerardy has for many years been working to arrange and catalog these materials. (See T. Gerardy, "Der Stand der Gaussforschung," in *GGM,* **1** [1964], 5–11.) Personal materials are concentrated in the municipal library of Brunswick. These include the contents of the Gauss Museum, removed from Gauss's birthplace before its destruction during World War II. (See H. Mack, "Das Gaussmuseum in Braunschweig," in *Museumskunde,* n.s. **1** [1930], 122–125.) Gauss's personal library forms a special collection in the Göttingen University Library. His scientific library was merged with the observatory library. There are also minor deposits of MSS, letters, and mementos scattered in the libraries of universities, observatories, and private collectors throughout the world. The best published sources on the Gauss archival material are Felix Klein's reports on the progress of the *Werke* mentioned above and in the yearly *Mitteilungen* of the Gauss-Gesellschaft (GGM), founded in Göttingen in 1962.

II. Secondary Literature. There is no full-scale biography of the man and his work as a whole, although there are many personal biographies and excellent studies of his work in particular fields.

A. *Bibliography.* No complete Gauss bibliography has been published. The best ones are in Poggendorff, VII A, supp., Lieferung 2 (1970), 223–238; and in Dunnington's biography (see below).

B. *Biography.* The year after Gauss's death, Sartorius von Waltershausen, a close friend of his last years, published *Gauss zum Gedächtniss* (Leipzig, 1856). An English trans. by his great-granddaughter, Helen W. Gauss, was published as *Gauss, a Memorial* (Colorado Springs, Colo., 1966).

Other sources based on personal acquaintance and/or more or less reliable contemporary evidence are the following: L. Hänselmann, *K. F. Gauss. Zwölf Capital aus seinem Leben* (Leipzig, 1878); I. M. Simonov, *Zapiski i vospominaniya o puteshestvii po Anglii, Frantsii, Belgii i Germanii v 1842 godu* (Kazan, 1844); A. Quetelet, in *Correspondance mathématique et physique,* **6** (1830), 126–148, 161–178, 225–239, repr. in A. Quetelet, *Sciences mathématiques et physiques chez les Belges* (Brussels, 1866); Ernst C. J. Schering, *Carl Friedrich Gauss' Geburtstag nach hundertjähriger Wiederkehr, Festrede* (Göttingen, 1877); M. A. Stern, *Denkrede . . . zur Feier seines hundertjährigen Geburtstages* (Göttingen, 1877); F. A. T. Winnecke, *Gauss. Ein Umriss seines Lebens und Wirkens* (Brunswick, 1877); Theodor Wittstein, *Gedächtnissrede auf C. F. Gauss zur Feier des 30 April 1877* (Hannover, 1877); R. Dedekind, *Gauss in seiner Vorlesungen über die Methode der kleinsten Quadrate. Festschrift . . . Göttingen* (Berlin, 1901), repr. in Dedekind, *Gesammelte mathematische Werke,* II (1931), 293–306; Moritz Cantor lecture of 14 November 1899, in *Neue Heidelberger Jahrbucher,* **9** (1899), 234–255; and Rudolf Borch, "Ahnentafel des . . . Gauss," in *Ahnentafeln berühmter Deutscher,* I (Leipzig, 1929), 63–65.

Most of the personal biographical literature is derivative from the above sources and is of the "beatification forever" type, in which fact and tradition are freely mixed. Only a few works of special interest are mentioned here. Heinrich Mack, *Carl Friedrich Gauss und die Seinen* (Brunswick, 1927), contains substantial excerpts from family correspondence and a table of ancestors and descendants. F. Cajori published family letters in *Science,* n.s. **9** (19 May 1899), 697–704, and in *Popular Science Monthly,* **81** (1912), 105–114. Other studies based on documents are T. Gerardy, "C. F. Gauss und seine Söhne," in *GGM,* **3** (1966), 25–35; W. Lorey, in *Mathematisch-physikalische Semesterberichte* (Göttingen), **3** (1953), 179–192; and Hans Salié, in the collection edited by Reichardt described below. The most complete biography to date is G. W. Dunnington, *Carl Friedrich Gauss, Titan of Science* (New York, 1955), a useful derivative compendium of personal information and tradition, including translations from Sartorius, Hänselmann, and Mack, the largest bibliography yet published, and much useful data on genealogy, friends, students, honors, books borrowed at college, courses taught, etc.

During the Third Reich two rather feeble efforts—L. Bieberbach, *C. F. Gauss, ein deutsches Gelehrtenleben* (Berlin, 1938); and E. A. Roloff, *Carl Friedrich Gauss* (Osnabrück, 1942)—were made to claim Gauss as a hero, but it is clear that Gauss would have loathed the fascists as the final realization of his worst fears about bourgeois politics. Neither author mentions that Gauss's favorite mathematician, whom he praised extravagantly, was Gotthold Eisenstein.

Erich Worbs, *Carl Friedrich Gauss, Ein Lebensbild* (Leipzig, 1955), makes an effort to relate Gauss realistically to his times. W. L. Schaaf, *Carl Friedrich Gauss, Prince of Mathematicians* (New York, 1964), is a popularization addressed to juveniles.

C. *Scientific Work.* The literature analyzing Gauss's scientific work is expert and comprehensive, although its fragmentation by subject matter gives the impression of dealing with several different men. Beginning in 1911, F. Klein, M. Brendel, and L. Schlesinger edited a series of eight studies under the title *Materialien für eine wissenschaftliche Biographie von Gauss* (Leipzig, 1911–1920), most of which were later incorporated in the *Werke.* On the occasion of the hundredth anniversary of Gauss's death, there appeared *C. G. Gauss Gedenkband,* Hans Reichardt, ed. (Leipzig, 1957), republished as *C. F. Gauss, Leben und Werk* (Berlin, 1960); and I. M. Vinogradov, ed., *Karl Friedrich Gauss, 100 let so dnya smerti, sbornik statei* (Moscow, 1956). These collections will be abbreviated as Klein, Reichardt, and Vinogradov, respectively, when individual articles are listed below.

Brief anniversary evaluations by mathematicians are the following: R. Courant and R. W. Pohl, *Carl Friedrich Gauss, Zwei Vorträge* (Göttingen, 1955)—Courant's lecture also appeared in *Carl Friedrich Gauss . . . Gedenkfeier der Akademie der Wissenschaften . . . Göttingen anlässlich seines 100ten Todestages* (Göttingen, 1955) and was translated in T. L. Saaty and J. F. Weyl, eds., *The Spirit and the Uses of the Mathematical Sciences* (New York, 1969), pp. 141–155; J. Dieudonné, *L'oeuvre mathématique de C. F. Gauss* (Paris, 1962), a talk at the Palais de la Découverte, 2 December 1961; R. Oblath, "Megemlékezés halálának 100-ik évfordulóján," in *Matematikai lapok,* **6** (1955), 221–240; and K. A. Rybnikov, in *VIET,* **1** (1956), 44–53.

The following selected titles are arranged by topic.

Algebra. A. Fraenkel, "Zahlbegriff und Algebra bei Gauss," (Klein, VIII), in *GN,* supp. (1920); "Der Zusammenhang zwischen dem ersten und dem dritten Gauss'schen Beweis des Fundamentalsatzes der Algebra," in *DMV,* **31** (1922), 234–238; A. Ostrowski, "Über den ersten und vierten Gauss'schen Beweis des Fundamentalsatzes der Algebra," in *Werke,* X, pt. 2, sec. 3 (1933), 3–18 (an enlarged revision of Klein, VIII [1920], 50–58); R. Kochendörfer, in Reichardt, pp. 80–91; and M. Bocher, "Gauss's Third Proof of the Fundamental Theorem of Algebra," in *BAMS,* **1** (1895), 205–209.

Analysis. A. I. Markushevich, "Raboty Gaussa po matematicheskomu analizu," in Vinogradov, pp. 145–216, German trans. in Reichardt, pp. 151–182; K. Schröder, "C. F. Gauss und die reelle Analysis," in Reichardt, pp. 184–191; O. Bolza, "Gauss und die Variationsrechnung," in *Werke,* X, pt. 2, sec. 5 (1922), 3–93; L. Schlesinger, "Fragment zur Theorie des arithmetisch-geometrischen Mittels" (Klein, II), in *GN* (1912), 513–543; *Über Gauss' Arbeiten zur Funktionentheorie* (Berlin, 1933), also in *Werke,* X, pt. 2, sec. 2 (1933), 3–210—an enlarged revision of Klein II which appeared in *GN* (1912), 1–140; H. Geppert, "Wie Gauss zur elliptischen Modul-funktion kam," in *Deutsche*

Mathematik, **5** (1940), 158-175; E. Göllnitz, "Über die Gauss'sche Darstellung der Funktionen sinlemn *x* und coslemn *x* als Quotienten unendlicher Produkte," in *Deutsche Mathematik,* **2** (1937), 417-420; P. Gunther, "Die Untersuchungen von Gauss in der Theorie der elliptischen Funktionen," in *GN* (1894), 92-105, and in trans. in *JMPA,* 5th ser., **3** (1897), 95-111; H. Hattendorff, *Die elliptischen Funktionen in dem Nachlasse von Gauss* (Berlin, 1869); A. Pringsheim, "Kritisch-historische Bemerkungen zur Funktionentheorie," in *BA* (1932), 193-200; (1933), 61-70; L. Schlesinger, "Über die Gauss'sche Theorie des arithmetisch-geometrischen Mittels . . .," in *Sitzungsberichte der Preussischen Akademie der Wissenschaften zu Berlin,* **28** (1898), 346-360; and "Über Gauss Jugendarbeiten zum arithmetisch-geometrischen Mittel," in *DMV,* **20** (1911), 396-403.

Astronomy. M. Brendel, "Über die astronomischen Arbeiten von Gauss," in *Werke,* XI, pt. 2, sec. 3 (1929), 3-254, enlarged revision of Klein, vol. VII, pt. 1 (Leipzig, 1919); M. F. Subbotin, "Astronomicheskie i geodesicheskie raboty Gaussa," in Vinogradov, pp. 241-310; and O. Volk, "Astronomie und Geodäsie bei C. F. Gauss," in Reichardt, pp. 206-229.

Geodesy and Surveying. A. Galle, "Über die geodätischen Arbeiten von Gauss," in *Werke,* XI, pt. 2, sec. 1 (1924), 3-161; W. Gronwald *et al., C. F. Gauss und die Landesvermessung in Niedersachsen* (Hannover, 1955); T. Gerardy, *Die Gauss'sche Triangulation des Königreichs Hannover* (*1821 bis 1844*) *und die Preussischen Grundsteuermessungen* (*1868 bis 1873*) (Hannover, 1952); G. V. Bagratuni, *K. F. Gauss, kratky ocherk geodezicheskikh issledovanii* (Moscow, 1955); M. F. Subbotin, in Vinogradov (see under Astronomy); W. Gäde, "Beiträge zur Kenntniss von Gauss' praktisch-geodätischen Arbeiten," in *ZV,* **14** (1885), 53-113; T. Gerardy, "Episoden aus der Gauss'schen Triangulation des Königreichs Hannover," in *ZV,* **80** (1955), 54-62; H. Michling, *Erläuterungsbericht zur Neuberechnung der Gauss-Kruegerischen Koordinaten der Dreiecks- und Polygonpunkte der Katasterurmessung* (Hannover, 1947); "Der Gauss'sche Vizeheliotrop," in *GGM,* **4** (1967), 27-30; K. Nickul, "Über die Herleitung der Abbildungsgleichung der Gauss'schen Konformen Abbildung des Erdellipsoids in der Ebene," in *ZV,* **55** (1926), 493-496; and O. Volk, in Reichardt (see under Astronomy).

Geomagnetism. Ernst Schering, "Carl Friedrich Gauss und die Erforschung des Erdmagnetismus," in *GA,* **34** (1887), 1-79; T. N. Roze and I. M. Simonov, in *K. F. Gauss, Izbrannye trudy po zemnomu magnitizmu* (Leningrad, 1952), pp. 237-336; H.-G. Körber, "Alexander von Humboldts und Carl Friedrich Gauss' organisatorisches Wirken auf geomagnetischen Gebiet," in *FF,* **32** (1958), 1-8; and K.-R. Biermann, "Aus der Vorgeschichte der Aufforderung A. v. Humboldts an der Präsidenten der Royal Society . . .," in *HUB,* **12** (1963), 209-227.

Geometry. P. Stäckel, "C. F. Gauss als Geometer," in *Werke,* X, pt. 2, sec. 4 (1923), 3-121, repr. with note by L. Schlesinger from Klein, V (1917), which appeared also in *GN,* **4** (1917), 25-140; A. P. Norden, "Geometricheskie raboty Gaussa," in Vinogradov, pp. 113-144; R. C. Archibald, "Gauss and the Regular Polygon of Seventeen Sides," in *AMM,* **27** (1920), 323-326; H. Carslaw, "Gauss and Non-Euclidean Geometry," in *Nature,* **84,** no. 2134 (1910), 362; G. B. Halsted, "Gauss and non-Euclidean Geometry," in *AMM,* **7** (1900), 247, and on the same subject, in *AMM,* **11** (1904), 85-86, and in *Science,* **9,** no. 232 (1904), 813-817; and E. Hoppe, "C. F. Gauss und der Euklidische Raum," in *Naturwissenschaften,* **13** (1925), 743-744, and in trans. by Dunnington in *Scripta mathematica,* **20** (1954), 108-109 (Hoppe objects to the story that Gauss measured a large geodesic triangle in order to test whether Euclidean geometry was the "true" one, apparently under the impression that this would have been contrary to Gauss's ideas. Actually, Gauss considered geometry to have an empirical base and to be testable by experience.); V. F. Kagan, "Stroenie neevklidovoi geometrii u Lobachevskogo, Gaussa i Boliai," in *Trudy Instituta istorii estestvoznaniya,* **2** (1948), 323-389, repr. in his *Lobachevskii i ego geometriya* (Moscow, 1955), pp. 193-294; N. D. Kazarinoff, "On Who First Proved the Impossibility of Constructing Certain Regular Polygons . . .," in *AMM,* **75** (1968), 647; P. Mansion, "Über eine Stelle bei Gauss, welche sich auf nichteuklidische Metrik bezieht," in *DMV,* **7** (1899), 156; A. P. Norden, "Gauss i Lobachevskii," in *IMI,* **9** (1956), 145-168; A. V. Pogorelov, "Raboty K. F. Gaussa po geometrii poverkhnostei," in *VIET,* **1** (1956), 61-63; and P. Stäckel and F. Engel, *Die Theorie der Parallelinien* (Leipzig, 1895); "Gauss, die beiden Bolyai und die nichteuklidische Geometrie," in *MA,* **49** (1897), 149-206, translated in *BSM,* 2nd ser., **21** (1897), 206-228.

Miscellaneous. K.-R. Biermann, "Einige Episoden aus den russischen Sprachstudien des Mathematikers C. F. Gauss," in *FF,* **38** (1964), 44-46; E. Göllnitz, "Einige Rechenfehler in Gauss' Werken," in *DMV,* **46** (1936), 19-21; and S. C. Van Veen, "Een conflict tusschen Gauss en een Hollandsch mathematicus," in *Wiskunstig Tijdschrift,* **15** (1918), 140-146. The following four papers deal with the ciphers in which Gauss recorded some discoveries: K.-R. Biermann, in *MDA,* **5** (1963), 241-244; **11** (1969), 526-530; T. L. MacDonald, in *AN,* **241** (1931), 31; P. Männchen, in *Unterrichtsblätter für Mathematik und Naturwissenschaften,* **40** (1934), 104-106; and A. Wietzke, in *AN,* **240** (1930), 403-406.

Number Theory. P. Bachmann, "Über Gauss' Zahlentheoretische Arbeiten" (Klein, I), in *GN* (1911), pp. 455-508, and in *Werke,* X, pt. 2, sec. 1 (1922), 3-69; B. N. Delone, "Raboty Gaussa po teorii chisel," in Vinogradov, pp. 11-112; G. J. Rieger, "Die Zahlentheorie bei C. F. Gauss," in Reichardt, pp. 37-77; E. T. Bell, "The Class Number Relations Implicit in the *Disquisitiones arithmeticae,*" in *BAMS,* **30** (1924), 236-238; "Certain Class Number Relations Implied in the *Nachlass* of Gauss," *ibid.,* **34** (1928), 490-494; "Gauss and the Early Development of Algebraic Numbers," in *NMM,* **18** (1944), 188-204, 219-223; L. E. Dickson, *History of the Theory of Numbers,* 3 vols. (Washington, D.C., 1919)—the indexes are a fairly complete guide to Gauss's extraordinary achievements in this field; J. Ginsburg, "Gauss' Arithmetization of the Problem of 8 Queens," in *SM,* **5** (1938), 63-66; F.

Van der Blij, "Sommen van Gauss," in *Euclides* (Groningen), **30** (1954), 293-298; and B. A. Venkov, "Trudy K. F. Gaussa po teorii chisel i algebra," in *VIET,* **1** (1956), 54-60. The following papers concern an erroneous story, apparently started by W. W. R. Ball, that the Paris mathematicians rejected the *Disquisitiones arithmeticae:* R. C. Archibald, "Gauss's *Disquisitiones arithmeticae* and the French Academy of Sciences," in *SM,* **3** (1935), 193-196; H. Geppert and R. C. Archibald, "Gauss's *Disquisitiones Arithmeticae* and the French Academy of Sciences," *ibid.,* 285-286; G. W. Dunnington, "Gauss, His Disquisitiones Arithmeticae and His Contemporaries in the Institut de France," in *NMM,* **9** (1935), 187-192; A. Emch, "Gauss and the French Academy of Science," in *AMM,* **42** (1935), 382-383. See also G. Heglotz, "Zur letzten Eintragung im Gauss'schen Tagebuch," in *LB,* **73** (1921), 271-277.

Numerical Calculations. P. Männchen, "Die Wechselwirkung zwischen Zahlenrechnung und Zahlentheorie bei C. F. Gauss" (Klein, VI), in *GN,* supp. **7** (1918), 1-47, and in *Werke,* X, pt. 2, sec. 6 (1930), 3-75; and A. Galle, "C. F. Gauss als Zahlenrechner" (Klein, IV), in *GN,* supp. **4** (1917), 1-24.

Philosophy. A. Galle, "Gauss und Kant," in *Weltall,* **24** (1925), 194-200, 230, repr. in *GGM,* **6** (1969), 8-15; P. Mansion, "Gauss contre Kant sur la géométrie non-Euclidienne," in *Mathesis,* 3rd ser., **8,** supp. (Dec. 1908), 1-16, in *Revue néoscolastique,* **15** (1908), 441-453, and in *Proceedings of the Third (1908) International Congress of Philosophy in Heidelberg* (Leipzig, 1910), pp. 438-447; and H. E. Timerding, "Kant und Gauss," in *Kant-Studien,* **28** (1923), 16-40.

Physics. H. Falkenhagen, "Die wesentlichsten Beiträge von C. F. Gauss aus der Physik," in Reichardt, pp. 232-251; H. Geppert, "Über Gauss' Arbeiten zur Mechanik und Potentialtheorie," in *Werke,* X, pt. 2, sec. 7 (1933), 3-60; and C. Schäfer, "Gauss physikalische Arbeiten (Magnetismus, Elektrodynamik, Optik)," in *Werke,* XI, pt. 2, sec. 2 (1929), 2-211; "Gauss's Investigations on Electrodynamics," in *Nature,* **128** (1931), 339-341.

Probability and Statistics (Including Least Squares). B. V. Gnedenko, "O raboty Gaussa po teorii veroyatnostei," in Vinogradov, pp. 217-240; A. Galle, "Über die geodätischen Arbeiten von Gauss," in *Werke,* XI, pt. 2, sec. 6 (1924), 3-161; C. Eisenhart, "Gauss," in *International Encyclopedia of the Social Sciences,* VI (New York, 1968), 74-81; P. Männchen, "Über ein Interpolationsverfahren des jugendlichen Gauss," in *DMV,* **28** (1919), 80-84; H. L. Seal, "The Historical Development of the Gauss Linear Model," in *Biometrika,* **54** (1967), 1-24; T. Sofonea, "Gauss und die Versicherung," in *Verzekerings-Archive,* **32** (Aktuar Bijv, 1955), 57-69; and Helen M. Walker, *Studies in the History of Statistical Method* (Baltimore, 1931).

Telegraph. Ernst Feyerabend, *Der Telegraph von Gauss und Weber im Werden der elektrischen Telegraphie* (Berlin, 1933); and R. W. Pohl, "Jahrhundertfeier des elektromagnetischen Telegraphen von Gauss und Weber," in *GN* (1934), pp. 48-56, repr. in *Carl Friedrich Gauss, Zwei Vorträge* (Göttingen, 1955), pp. 5-12.

The author gratefully acknowledges many helpful suggestions and comments from Kurt-R. Biermann. Thanks are due also to the library staff at the University of Toronto for many services. The author claims undivided credit only for errors of fact and judgment.

KENNETH O. MAY

GEISER, KARL FRIEDRICH (*b.* Langenthal, Bern, Switzerland, 26 February 1843; *d.* Küsnacht, Zurich, Switzerland, 7 May 1934)

Geiser was the son of Friedrich Geiser, a butcher, and Elisabeth Geiser-Begert. Following graduation from the Polytechnikum in Zurich and the University of Berlin, where the influence of his great-uncle, Jakob Steiner, was of help to him, Geiser became *Dozent* in 1863. In 1873 he became professor at the Zurich Polytechnikum (later renamed the Eidgenössische Technische Hochschule), where he remained until his retirement.

Geiser made an outstanding contribution to the development of the Swiss system of higher education. Acquainted with many persons in the fields of politics and economics as well as with important mathematicians in the neighboring countries, and a close adviser of the chairman of school supervisors, Geiser worked effectively within the professoriate to attract first-rate teachers. There devolved upon him, above all, the instruction of candidates for the teaching of algebraic geometry, differential geometry, and invariant theory.

Geiser's scientific works are concerned especially with algebraic geometry. He explained the relation of the twenty-eight double tangents of the plane quadric to the twenty-seven straight lines of the cubic surface. An involution that he discovered bears his name. Minimal surfaces also engaged his attention: he investigated the intersection of an algebraic minimal surface with an infinite plane and determined all the algebraic minimal surfaces. In addition, Geiser edited Jakob Steiner's unpublished lectures and treatises. He was organizer and president of the first International Congress of Mathematicians, held at Zurich in 1897.

BIBLIOGRAPHY

I. ORIGINAL WORKS. Geiser's major works are *Einleitung in die synthetische Geometrie* (Leipzig, 1869); and *Zur Erinnerung an Jakob Steiner* (Schaffhausen, 1874). His papers are listed in the articles by Kollros and by Meissner and Scherrer (see below).

Die Theorie der Kegelschnitte, pt. 1 of Jakob Steiner's

Vorlesungen über Geometrie, was compiled and edited by Geiser (Leipzig, 1867).

II. SECONDARY LITERATURE. See the following obituary notices: A. Emch, in *National Mathematics Magazine,* **12,** no. 6 (1938), 287–289, with portrait; L. Kollros, in *Verhandlungen der Schweizerischen naturforschenden Gesellschaft,* **115** (1934), 522–528, with list of publications and portrait; and E. Meissner and F. R. Scherrer, in *Vierteljahrsschrift der Naturforschenden Gesellschaft in Zürich,* **79** (1934), 371–376, with list of publications.

J. J. BURCKHARDT

GELFOND, ALEXANDR OSIPOVICH (*b.* St. Petersburg [now Leningrad], Russia, 24 October 1906; *d.* Moscow, U.S.S.R., 7 November 1968)

Gelfond was the son of Osip Isaacovich Gelfond, a physician who also did work in philosophy. From 1924 to 1927 he studied in the division of mathematics of the department of physics and mathematics at Moscow University; later he took a postgraduate course (1927–1930) under A. J. Khintchine and V. V. Stepanov. In 1929–1930 Gelfond taught mathematics at Moscow Technological College, and from 1931 until his death he was at Moscow University, where for a number of years he held the chair of analysis. He later held the chair of the theory of numbers, to which was subsequently added the history of mathematics. From 1933 he also worked in the Soviet Academy of Sciences Mathematical Institute. He became professor of mathematics in 1931 and doctor of mathematics and physics in 1935; he was elected corresponding member of the Academy of Sciences of the U.S.S.R. in 1939 and corresponding member of the International Academy of the History of Science in 1968.

Most important in Gelfond's scientific work were the analytical theory of numbers and the theory of interpolation and approximation of functions of a complex variable. Studies in both fields were closely related; he used and improved methods of the theory of functions in working on the problems of the theory of transcendental numbers.

In 1748 Euler had expressed the idea that logarithms of rational numbers with rational bases are either rational or transcendental. Generalizing that statement, among the famous twenty-three problems that Hilbert posed in 1900, was the hypothesis of the rationality or transcendence of logarithms of algebraic numbers with algebraic bases; i.e., he presumed the transcendence of a^b, where a is any algebraic number not 0 or 1 and b is any irrational algebraic number. For thirty years no approach to a solution of this, the seventh of Hilbert's problems, could be found. In 1929 Gelfond established profound connections between the growth and other properties of an entire analytic function and the arithmetic nature of its values when the values of argument belonged to a given algebraic field. This enabled him to find, proceeding from the expansion of the exponential function a^z, a being an algebraic number not 0 or 1, into the interpolating series of Newton,

$$a^z = \sum_{n=0}^{\infty} A_n (z - x_0)(z - x_1) \cdots (z - x_n),$$

where $x_0, x_1, x_2, \cdots$ are integers of an algebraic field $K(\sqrt{-D})$, $D > 0$, a solution of the problem in a particular case: the number a^b, where $b = i\sqrt{D}$ and D is a positive integer that is not a perfect square, is transcendental.

In 1930 R. O. Kuzmin extended Gelfond's method to real $b = \sqrt{D}$, and in 1932 C. L. Siegel applied it to the study of the transcendence of the periods of elliptic functions. Soon after, Gelfond consolidated his method with new ingenious ideas and, introducing linear forms of exponential function into consideration, confirmed in 1934 Hilbert's hypothesis in its entirety. His methods and results led to the most important contributions to the theory of transcendental numbers since Hermite's demonstration of the transcendence of e (1873) and K. L. F. Lindemann's of π (1882).

Applying his method to functions of p-adic variables, Gelfond made a number of new discoveries. Among them is the theorem that if α, β, γ are real algebraic numbers and at least one of them is not an algebraic unit, with γ being not equal to 2^n (n is a rational integer), the equation $\alpha^x + \beta^y = \gamma^z$ can possess only a finite number of solutions in rational integers x, y, z (1940). The further development of the method enabled Gelfond to solve a number of problems of mutual algebraic independence of numbers and to construct new classes of transcendental numbers. A considerable part of his discoveries in the theory of transcendental numbers is described in his monograph *Transtsendentnye i algebraicheskie chisla* (1952). Gelfond also wrote on other problems of the theory of numbers, including the diophantine approximations, the distribution of fractional parts of functions, and elementary methods of analytic theory.

In the theory of functions of a complex variable, Gelfond conducted numerous studies on problems of convergence of interpolation processes depending upon the density of a set of basic points of interpolation and upon the properties of the function to be approximated; on necessary and sufficient conditions for the determination of an entire analytical function on its given values or some other element; and on corresponding methods for the construction of functions. These studies were to a great extent summed up in *Ischislenie konechnykh raznostey* (1952).

Gelfond also promoted the history of mathematics, brilliantly characterizing Euler's work and his investigations in the theory of numbers. For many years he was the chairman of the scientific council that refereed theses on the history of physics and mathematics for the Soviet Academy of Sciences Institute of the History of Science and Technology.

Gelfond, creator of a large scientific school in the Soviet Union, profoundly influenced the advance of the theory of transcendentals and the theory of interpolation and approximation of functions of a complex variable.

BIBLIOGRAPHY

I. ORIGINAL WORKS. Gelfond's writings include "Sur les nombres transcendants," in *Comptes rendus hebdomadaires des séances de l'Académie des sciences,* **189** (1929), 1224–1228; "Sur le septième problème de Hilbert," in *Izvestiya Akademii nauk SSSR,* **7** (1934), 623–630; "Sur la divisibilité de la différence des puissances de deux nombres entiers par une puissance d'un idéal premier," in *Matematicheskii sbornik,* **7 (49)** (1940), 7–26; *Ischislenie konechnykh raznostey* ("Calculus of Finite Differences"; Moscow–Leningrad, 1952; 3rd ed., 1967), translated into German as *Differenzenrechnung* (Berlin, 1958); *Transtsendentnye i algebraicheskie chisla* (Moscow, 1952), translated into English as *Transcendental and Algebraic Numbers* (New York, 1960); and *Elementarnye metody v teorii chisel* (Moscow, 1962), written with Y. V. Linnik.

Complete bibliographies of Gelfond's works are in Linnik and Marcushevich and Pjatetsky-Shapiro and Shidlovsky (see below).

II. SECONDARY LITERATURE. On Gelfond or his work, see Y. V. Linnik and A. I. Marcushevich, "Alexandr Osipovich Gelfond," in *Uspekhi matematicheskikh nauk,* **11,** no. 5 (1956), 239–248; *Matematica v SSSR za sorok let* ("Forty Years of Mathematics in the U.S.S.R."), 2 vols. (Moscow, 1959), index; *Matematica v SSSR za tridtsat let* ("Thirty Years of Mathematics in the U.S.S.R."; Moscow–Leningrad, 1948), index; I. I. Pjatetsky-Shapiro and A. B. Shidlovsky, "Alexandr Osipovich Gelfond," in *Uspekhi matematicheskikh nauk,* **22,** no. 3 (1967), 247–256; and I. Z. Shtokalo, ed., *Istoria otechestvennoy matematiki* ("History of Native Mathematics"), III (Kiev, 1968), index.

A. P. YOUSCHKEVITCH

GELLIBRAND, HENRY (*b.* London, England, 17 November 1597; *d.* London, 16 February 1636)

Gellibrand was the son of a graduate of All Souls College, Oxford. He became a commoner of Trinity College, Oxford, in 1615, a few weeks after his father's death. After graduating in arts (B.A., 1619, M.A., 1623) he took holy orders, and before 1623 he held a curacy at Chiddingstone, Kent. Gellibrand was introduced to mathematics by one of Sir Henry Savile's lectures, and he had at least enough geometry to set up a sundial on the east side of his college quadrangle. When the professorship of astronomy at Gresham College, London, was vacated following the death of Edmund Gunter, Gellibrand was elected to the chair on 2 January 1627. He completed the second volume of his sponsor Henry Briggs's *Trigonometria Britannica* (left unfinished at his death in 1630) and saw it through the press in 1633.

By this time Gellibrand's Puritanism had brought him into conflict with William Laud, then bishop of London. Gellibrand and his servant were cited by Laud before the Court of High Commission in 1631 for the publication of an almanac in which the saints and martyrs from John Foxe's *Book of Martyrs* replaced those permitted by the Church of England. They were acquitted on the grounds that this was not the first almanac of its kind, and the case was later cited against Laud at his own trial in 1643.

Gellibrand's most widely appreciated scientific discovery, which he should share with John Marr, was that of the secular change in the magnetic variation (declination). It was announced, without much comment, in *A Discourse Mathematicall on the Variation of the Magneticall Needle, Together With Its Admirable Diminution Lately Discovered* (1635). His predecessor, Gunter, had noticed that the variation at Limehouse in 1622 differed from the value found by William Borough in 1580, but he ascribed the difference to an error on Borough's part. In 1633 some rough observations of his own and John Marr's convinced Gellibrand that the value was now even less, but not until 1634 was he sufficiently confident to make a categorical assertion of its secular change. As his main evidence he referred to an appendix to Edward Wright's *Certaine Errors in Navigation . . .* (1599, 1610). This contains a compendium of recorded values of variation at various places made by a number of physicists and navigators the world over. (Henry Bond, editor of *Tapp's Seaman's Kalendar,* spent many years elaborating upon Gellibrand's findings and argued that despite its change, variation could even now be used by sailors to determine terrestrial longitudes. This would have been easier, of course, granted constant variation.)

Gellibrand's position at Gresham College drew him into matters of mathematical navigation, and an example of his attempts at solving the problem of longitude is a three-page appendix to *The Strange and*

Dangerous Voyage of Captain Thomas James (1633). James, a gentleman mariner who voyaged in 1631 to seek the Northwest Passage, had by prior arrangement observed at Charlton Island, James Bay, a lunar eclipse also observed by Gellibrand at Gresham. James's position in longitude was thus calculated (79°30′ west of Gresham, being 15′ too low).

The essentially practical quality of Gellibrand's work, which is of very slight mathematical interest, may also be judged from four works: his "Treatise of Building of Ships," a manuscript mentioned by Anthony à Wood as belonging to Edward, Lord Conway; his textbook *An Institution Trigonometrical;* a longer Latin work translated by John Newton, *An Institution Trigonometrical . . . With the Application . . . to Questions of Astronomy and Navigation* (1652); and *An Epitome of Navigation . . .* (1674). This last and posthumous book (written after 1631 and before 1634) contains a number of logarithmic tables, including trigonometrical ones, and has an appendix on the use of the cross-staff, quadrant, and nocturnal in navigation. That it was found valuable is suggested by the appearance of later editions, in 1698 (by Euclid Speidell), 1706 and subsequently (by J. Atkinson), and 1759 (by William Mountaine under the title *A Short and Methodical Way to Become a Complete Navigator*).

Gellibrand's work was mainly derivative, leading influences on it having been Wright's *Certaine Errors* and Richard Norwood's *Trigonometrica* (1631). It can be said that he was a reasonably good calculator and a competent writer of textbooks which helped to raise English standards of navigation to new heights.

BIBLIOGRAPHY

I. ORIGINAL WORKS. Besides works mentioned in the text, Gellibrand wrote "Astronomia lunaris . . .," composed between 20 December 1634 and 22 January 1635. This belonged to Sir Hans Sloane but is not indexed in the catalog of the Sloane Collection in the British Museum. He also added a preface to and published *Sciographia, or the Art of Shadows* (London, 1635), written by J(ohn) W(ells), a Roman Catholic of Hampshire. A Latin oration, "In laudem Gassendi astronomiae," delivered in Christ Church Hall, Oxford, is now Brit. Mus. Add. MS 6193, f. 96.

II. SECONDARY LITERATURE. The two main sources for Gellibrand's life are Anthony à Wood, *Athenae Oxonienses,* rev. and enl. ed. (Oxford, 1721); and John Ward, *The Lives of the Professors of Gresham College* (London, 1740), pp. 81–85, 336. Gellibrand's work on navigation has received little attention from historians, but for some discussion of navigation in his time see D. W. Waters, *The Art of Navigation in England in Elizabethan and Early Stuart Times* (London, 1958), *passim;* and E. G. R. Taylor, *The Mathematical Practitioners of Tudor and Stuart England* (Cambridge, 1954), pp. 138, 164, 165, 175.

J. D. NORTH

GEMINUS (*fl.* Rhodes [?], *ca.* 70 B.C.)

Geminus' name is Latin, but his works and manner are patently Greek—the forms Γεμῖνος and Γεμεῖνος, also found in the manuscripts, are probably false analogies based on true Greek forms such as Ἀλεξῖνος and Ἐργῖνος. He was author of an *Introduction (Isagoge) to Astronomy* (still extant) and of a work on mathematics (lost, except for quoted extracts from it). Nothing is known of the circumstances of his life, but his date and place of work may be inferred from internal evidence in the *Isagoge.* In chapter 8, sections 20–24 of the Manitius edition, Geminus corrects a widespread Greek view that the Egyptian festival of Isis coincided with the winter solstice; he explains that although this was so 120 years ago, in his own time there was a whole month's difference between the two dates, since every four years the Egyptian calendar (based on a "year" of twelve months of thirty days each plus five additional days)[1] became out of step with the solar year by one day. The festival of Isis took place from the seventeenth to the twentieth day of the Egyptian month Athyr, and a papyrus fragment tells us that in the calendar of Eudoxus of Cnidus the winter solstice occurred on 20 or 19 Athyr. By Julian reckoning the winter solstice in Eudoxus' time (*ca.* 350 B.C.) occurred on 25 December or 28 December, and the first years in which these Julian dates can coincide with 19 Athyr are 185 B.C. and 197 B.C.[2] Hence, the papyrus presumably was written at this time; and subtracting the 120 years mentioned by Geminus, we obtain a date for the *Isagoge* of 65 or 77 B.C., which agrees with other evidence indicating a date about 70 B.C.[3]

We have no definite evidence about where Geminus was born or worked, but the commonly held opinion that his place of work was Rhodes may be correct. It is the "clima" of Rhodes that he uses to illustrate his account of various astronomical phenomena (e.g., I, 10; I, 12; III, 15; V, 25); in XVII, 4, he refers to Mt. Atabyrius,[4] i.e., the modern Mt. Attaviros, in the center of Rhodes, without feeling it necessary to specify its location, whereas in the same passage he is careful to explain that Mt. Cyllene is in the Peloponnesus; and Rhodes had a reputation in the last two centuries B.C. as a center for those subjects (philosophy, astronomy, and mathematics) with which Geminus was concerned, Panaetius, Posidonius, and Hipparchus all having worked there.

On the other hand, the choice of Rhodes as a typical example may simply have been dictated by its position on the best-known and most central parallel of latitude, 36°N. (Geminus himself says [XVI, 12] that all globes were constructed for this "clima," which for practical purposes was regarded as the latitude of Greece as well),[5] or Geminus may merely have used the examples he found in his sources, in this case almost certainly Hipparchus (see below), just as Ptolemy in the *Almagest* (II, 3 and 4), some 200 years later, was to use the same example from the same source. Similarly, Geminus may have taken the examples of Mt. Cyllene and Mt. Atabyrius straight from Dicaearchus (who is cited for their heights in XVII, 5); and even though two of his chief authorities, Hipparchus and Posidonius, worked in Rhodes, it does not necessarily follow that Geminus did.

The *Isagoge* is an early example of an elementary astronomical handbook written to popularize the main ideas in the technical treatises of the scientists; it belongs to the same tradition as the *De motu circulari corporum caelestium* of Cleomedes, and there are many similarities in style and arrangement between the two works, although, as might be expected from its later date, Cleomedes' work is fuller and less elementary than its precursor. One interesting difference is that Geminus includes a chapter (*Isagoge,* II) on the astrological "aspects" of the zodiacal signs, i.e., their arrangement in pairs, triplets, quadruplets, etc., according to which the astrologers calculated the signs' influence on human affairs; Cleomedes has no such chapter and, in fact, does not mention astrological doctrines at all. Geminus gives a simplified description of basic astronomy as known in the time of Hipparchus, omitting most of the mathematics and giving (I, 23 f.) little information about the planets apart from their zodiacal periods (thirty years for Saturn, twelve for Jupiter, two and a half for Mars, one year each for Mercury, Venus, and the sun,[6] and $27\frac{1}{3}$ days for the moon); there is no mention of epicycles, but the eccentricity of the sun's path relative to the earth is carefully described (I, 31 ff.) and the Hipparchian values for the four astronomical seasons are given (I, 13 f.)—$94\frac{1}{2}$, $92\frac{1}{2}$, $88\frac{1}{8}$, and $90\frac{1}{8}$ days, respectively, starting from the vernal equinox.[7]

Chapter III describes the main constellations; chapters IV and V describe the chief circles of the celestial sphere; and chapter VI explains the variations in the lengths of day and night at different latitudes. Chapter VII (which is based largely on Aratus and, almost certainly, on Hipparchus' commentary on Aratus' astronomical poem entitled *Phaenomena*) deals with the rising of the zodiacal signs, and chapter VIII with the length of the lunar month, for which a figure of $29\frac{1}{2} + 1/33$ days is given (rounded off from the accurate Hipparchian value of 29 days, 12 hours, 44 minutes, 3 seconds);[8] this last chapter is especially valuable for its account of how the Greeks developed an astronomically based calendar with a scientific system of intercalation.[9] Chapter IX explains the phases of the moon, chapters X and XI solar and lunar eclipses, and chapter XII the general motions of the planets. Chapters XIII and XIV deal with the risings and settings and courses of the fixed stars, and chapters XV and XVI with the zones of the terrestrial globe, delineated according to the estimates of Eratosthenes, which Hipparchus also accepted.[10]

Chapter XVII discusses sensibly the principles on which the "parapegmata" (astronomical calendars containing weather prognostications connected with the risings and settings of certain stars and constellations)[11] were based. Chapter XVIII deals with the "exeligmus" (ἐξελιγμός), or shortest period containing a whole number of synodic months, of anomalistic months, and of days (cf. *Almagest,* IV, 2); this chapter, far more technical than the others and out of keeping with the elementary character of the rest of the book, may well be an unrelated fragment.[12] Finally, there is an astronomical calendar, or "parapegma," which begins with Cancer and is evidently based on figures for the astronomical seasons which are not Hipparchian;[13] it seems probable that this was not part of the original treatise but represents older material.

Geminus' exposition is usually sound and clear and includes some intelligent criticism, e.g., of the notion held "by many philosophers" that the planetary bodies do not in fact exhibit two opposite motions (the diurnal and the zodiacal) but only seem to do so because they revolve at different speeds (*Isagoge,* XII, 14 ff.); this idea, says Geminus, "is not in accordance with observed phenomena" (XII, 19, ἀσύμφωνός ἐστι τοῖς φαινομένοις). He also gives a shrewd appreciation of the limitations of parapegmata, points out that weather forecasting based on observation of the rising and setting of various stars is by no means an exact science but a rough codification of general trends, and asserts firmly that stellar risings do not cause changes in the weather but merely indicate them (οὐκ αὐταὶ παραίτιοί εἰσι τῶν περὶ τὸν ἀέρα μεταβολῶν, ἀλλὰ σημεῖα ἐκκειντται, XVII, 11; see the whole of this chapter, especially 6–41); this last assertion contrasts strangely with the belief underlying chapter II.

There are, of course, some errors and infelicities. The chapter which gives a rational discussion of parapegmata (XVII) also contains an absurdly exaggerated view of the restricted range of atmospheric phenomena, according to which no wind or rain is experienced at the top of a mountain under 10,000 feet high (XVII, 3–5). In chapters X and XI no mention is made that, for an eclipse to take place, the moon must be at a node; and in XVI, 13, it is wrongly stated that the magnitudes of eclipses are the same for people living on the same parallel of latitude. There are also minor errors in the description of a star's evening rising (XIII, 13) and morning setting (XIII, 16), which may be the result of scribal errors in the transmission of the text (cf. Manitius, Anmerkung 25, 26); but Manitius' theory (pp. 246–248) that our present text represents a Byzantine compilation from an epitome of Geminus' original work, although it cannot be disproved, rests on very slender evidence.[14]

A work on mathematics (known only from extracts quoted by later writers) is also attributed to Geminus; and although it has been thought that this is not the same man as the author of the *Isagoge,* there can, in fact, be little doubt of the identity of the two.[15] The title of the work was probably *Theory of Mathematics* (Θεωρία τῶν μαθημάτων),[16] and it must have extended to at least six books, since Eutocius quotes from the sixth. Our chief source for its contents is Proclus,[17] who quotes extensive extracts from it; parallel quotations appear in the scholia to book I of Euclid's *Elements*[18] and in the collection of writings attributed to Hero of Alexandria;[19] and there are isolated quotations elsewhere.[20] There is also an Arabic commentary on Euclid by al-Nayrīzī[21] which contains extracts from a commentary on the *Elements* by Simplicius, who quotes a certain "Aghanis" on the definition of parallels; from similarities with what we know from Proclus of Geminus' views on this subject, it has been suggested that Aghanis is actually Geminus, but there are grave objections to such an identification, which must therefore remain doubtful.[22] A Latin translation of this Arabic text by Gerard of Cremona is extant.[23]

The *Theory of Mathematics* apparently dealt with the logical subdivisions of the mathematical sciences, discussing the philosophical principles of their classification, distinguishing carefully between such terms as "hypothesis" and "theorem," "postulate" and "axiom," and paying particular attention to accurate definitions not only of the various branches of mathematics but also of concepts such as "line," "surface," "figure," and "angle." It seems to have been a more substantial work than the *Isagoge* and to have contained some very pertinent criticism of Euclid's postulates, particularly the fifth, the so-called parallel postulate, for which Geminus believed he had found a proof.[24]

We learn from Simplicius that Geminus wrote an exegesis on the *Meteorologica* of Posidonius;[25] Simplicius cites Alexander of Aphrodisias as transcribing a long extract from an "epitome" of Geminus' work (ἐκ τῆς ἐπιτομῆς τῶν Ποσειδωνίου Μετεωρολογικῶν ἐξηγήσεως), but an epitome of an exegesis sounds unlikely and it is tempting to excise the word ἐπιτομῆς as an otiose gloss that has crept into the text. The extract discusses the different aims of physics and astronomy and has obvious relevance to a work on meteorology, which has affinities with both these sciences. Simplicius ends his citation with the following: "In this manner, then, Geminus also, or rather Posidonius in Geminus, expounds the difference . . . ." (οὕτω μὲν οὖν καὶ ὁ Γεμῖνος ἤτοι ὁ παρὰ τῷ Γεμίνῳ Ποσειδώνιος τὴν διαφορὰν . . . παραδίδωσιν). From this it has been implied that Geminus did little else but reproduce the opinions of Posidonius.

Such an implication certainly overestimates Geminus' debt to Posidonius. There is no doubt that both writers subscribed to Stoic views of the universe, and both were concerned to combat the attacks on the validity of the mathematical sciences, which, as we learn from Proclus and Sextus Empiricus, were mounted by both Skeptic and Epicurean philosophers;[26] but Geminus shows his independence of Posidonius in several respects. In *Isagoge* XVI, it is Eratosthenes' estimate of 252,000 stades that is taken as the basis of the division of the earth into zones and not Posidonius' figure of 240,000 (Cleomedes, *De motu circulari,* I, 10) or 180,000 (Strabo, *Geography,* 95),[27] neither of which is mentioned (nor, in fact, is Posidonius named in the entire treatise). Chapters VIII and XVIII, on the calendar and the length of the lunar month, almost certainly owe nothing to Posidonius, as there is no evidence that he did any work on calendrical problems; and there are other indications that Geminus, although he must have been well acquainted with Posidonius' opinions and was probably Proclus' chief authority for the latter,[28] did not hesitate to differ from the latter in following other sources (particularly Eratosthenes and Hipparchus for geography and astronomy) or putting forward his own views, as in his criticism of Euclid's postulates.

NOTES

1. On this, see O. Neugebauer, *The Exact Sciences in Antiquity,* 2nd ed. (Providence, R.I., 1957), pp. 81, 94.
2. 25 December according to W. Kubitschek, *Grundriss der antiken Zeitrechnung* (Munich, 1928), p. 109; 28 December according to Böckh, cited by Manitius in his ed. of *Elementa,* p. 264. See also "Synchronistic Table," in E. J. Bickerman,

Chronology of the Ancient World (London–Ithaca, N.Y., 1968), p. 150.
3. For details, see Manitius ed. of *Elementa,* Anmerkung 16, pp. 263–266.
4. The Σαταβύριον of the MSS must be corrected to Ἀταβύριον; see D. R. Dicks, *Geographical Fragments of Hipparchus* (London, 1960), p. 30.
5. See V, 48; Dicks, *op. cit.,* pp. 123, 130, 176.
6. See D. R. Dicks, *Early Greek Astronomy to Aristotle* (London, 1970), notes 174, 345.
7. See Ptolemy, *Almagest,* III, 4.
8. *Ibid.,* IV, 2.
9. See Dicks, *Early Greek Astronomy,* pp. 86 f.
10. See Dicks, *Geographical Fragments,* p. 148.
11. See Dicks, *Early Greek Astronomy,* pp. 84 f.
12. See Manitius ed. of *Elementa,* p. 278.
13. *Ibid.,* Anmerkung 34.
14. See Tittel, "Geminos I," cols. 1031–1032.
15. *Ibid.,* cols. 1029–1030.
16. See Eutocius, *Commentaria in Conica I,* in *Apollonii Pergaei quae graece exstant,* J. L. Heiberg, ed., II (1893), 170, 25.
17. *Commentarii in primum Euclidis elementorum librum,* G. Friedlein, ed. (Leipzig, 1873).
18. *Euclidis opera omnia,* J. L. Heiberg and H. Menge, eds., V (Leipzig, 1888), 81, 4; 82, 28; 107, 20.
19. *Heronis Alexandri reliquiae,* F. Hultsch, ed. (Berlin, 1864), nos. 5–14, 80–86.
20. See Tittel, *op. cit.,* cols. 1039–1040.
21. *Codex Leidensis 399,1,* R. O. Besthorn, J. L. Heiberg, G. Junge, J. Raeder, and W. Thomson, eds., 3 pts. (Copenhagen, 1893–1932).
22. T. L. Heath, *History of Greek Mathematics,* II, 224, accepts it; but the same scholar, in *The Thirteen Books of Euclid's Elements,* 2nd ed. (Cambridge, 1925), pp. 27–28, rejects it. Compare A. I. Sabra, "Thabit Ibn Qurra on Euclid's Parallels Postulate," in *Journal of the Warburg and Courtauld Institutes,* **31** (1968), 13.
23. *Euclidis opera omnia. Supplementum: Anaritii in decem libros priores Elementorum Euclidis commentarii,* M. Curtze, ed. (Leipzig, 1899).
24. For details see Heath, *History of Greek Mathematics,* II, 223–231.
25. *Simplicii in Aristotelis Physicorum libros IV priores commentaria,* H. Diels, ed. (Berlin, 1882), pp. 291–292; this passage is also printed by Manitius in his ed. of the *Isagoge* as Fragmentum I, pp. 283–285.
26. Proclus, G. Friedlein, ed., pp. 199 f., 214 ff.; Sextus Empiricus, *Adversus mathematicos,* H. Mutschmann-J. Mau, eds., I, 1 ff.; compare the whole of III.
27. See E. H. Bunbury, *History of Ancient Geography,* II (London, 1879), 95–96; Dicks, *Geographical Fragments,* p. 150.
28. See Tittel, *op. cit.,* col. 1042.

BIBLIOGRAPHY

K. Manitius edited the *Gemini Elementa astronomiae* (Leipzig, 1898); chs. I, III–VI, VIII–XVI have been published by E. J. Dijksterhuis as *Gemini Elementorum astronomiae,* no. 22 in the series Textus Minores (Leiden, 1957).

See T. L. Heath, *History of Greek Mathematics,* II (Oxford, 1921; repr. 1960), 222–234; and Tittel, "Geminos I," in *Real-Encyclopädie,* Halbband XIII (1910), cols. 1026–1050.

D. R. DICKS

GEMMA FRISIUS, REINER (*b.* Dokkum, Netherlands, 1508; *d.* Louvain, Belgium, 1555)

Gemma Frisius was a native of Friesland; hence his nickname Frisius. He received his medical degree at Louvain, practiced medicine there, and taught later at its medical faculty. Although he was a practicing physician, he is remembered for his contributions to geography and mathematics, his avocations.

At the age of twenty-one Gemma Frisius published *Cosmographicus liber Petri Apiani mathematici . . .* (Antwerp, 1529), an edition of Peter Apian's *Cosmography,* "carefully corrected and with all errors set to right." In 1530 he published at Antwerp his first original work, *Gemma Phrysius de principiis astronomiae & cosmographiae . . .*, which was translated into several languages and reprinted numerous times. The Spanish Netherlands was in close contact with court and business circles in Spain, and Brussels was an ideal place to gather current information on the discoveries. Gemma Frisius designed globes and astronomical instruments that were well known and much sought after throughout Europe. Several of them still survive and are of key importance in tracing the growth of knowledge of the newly discovered lands. Some of Gemma Frisius' globes were completed by Gerard Mercator, who had attended mathematical lectures that Gemma Frisius gave at his home.

Gemma Frisius made two significant contributions to the earth sciences. In a chapter added to the 1533 Antwerp edition of the *Cosmographicus,* entitled "Libellus de locorum describendorum ratione," he was first to propose—and illustrate—the principle of triangulation as a means of carefully locating places and accurately mapping areas. Twenty years later, in the 1553 Antwerp edition of *De principiis astronomiae,* he added a chapter entitled "De novo modo investigandi latitudinem regionis absq. meridiani vel loci solis cognitione," in which he was the first to suggest in explicit terms the use of portable timepieces to measure longitude by lapsed time. Although this important idea could not be put into practice until after the invention of optical instruments and accurate portable timepieces, the credit for first suggesting it rests with Gemma Frisius.

BIBLIOGRAPHY

The basic reference work, which includes the text of the few items of Gemma Frisius' surviving correspondence, is Fernand van Ostroy, "Biobibliographie de Gemma Frisius, fondateur de l'école belge de géographie . . .," in *Mémoires de l'Académie royale des sciences . . . de Belgique,* Classe des Lettres, 2nd ser., **11** (1920). The original text of the method of measuring longitude is reproduced in

A. Pogo, "Gemma Frisius, His Method of Determining Longitude . . .," in *Isis,* **22** (1935), i-xix, 469-485. A brief biographical sketch and an appraisal of Gemma Frisius' work is George Kish, "Medicine · Mensura · Mathematica; The Life and Works of Gemma Frisius, 1508-1555," James Ford Bell lecture no. 4 (1967), published by the Associates of the James Ford Bell Collection, University of Minnesota Library.

GEORGE KISH

GENTZEN, GERHARD (*b.* Greifswald, Germany, 24 November 1909; *d.* Prague, Czechoslovakia, 4 August 1945)

Gentzen was a born mathematician. As a boy he declared his dedication to mathematics, and his short life constituted a realization of that promise. He benefited from the teaching of such renowned scholars as P. Bernays, C. Carathéodory, R. Courant, D. Hilbert, A. Kneser, E. Landau, and H. Weyl and, at the age of twenty-three, received his doctorate in mathematics. In 1934 he became one of Hilbert's assistants and held that position until 1943, with the exception of a two-year period of compulsory military service from 1939 to 1941, when he was requested to take up a teaching post at the University of Prague. He died at Prague of malnutrition three months after his internment by the liberating authorities in May 1945.

Gentzen combined in rare measure an exceptional inventiveness and the talent for coordinating diverse existing knowledge into a systematic conceptual framework. He invented "natural deduction" in order to create a predicate logic more akin to actual mathematical reasoning than the Frege-Russell-Hilbert systems, then used P. Hertz's "sentences" to transform his natural calculus into a "calculus of sequents." Thus he succeeded in making classical logic appear as a simple extension of intuitionist logic and in enunciating his *Hauptsatz* (chief theory), which he had discovered while studying more closely the specific properties of natural deduction. A formalization of elementary number theory based on sequents and his ingenious idea of using restricted transfinite induction as a metamathematical technique enabled Gentzen to carry out the first convincing consistency proof for elementary number theory, in spite of the limitations imposed on such proofs by Gödel's theorem. He eventually proved directly the nonderivability in elementary number theory of the required transfinite induction up to ϵ_0. In view of subsequent developments, Gentzen's consistency proof must be considered as the most outstanding single contribution to Hilbert's program.

The *Hauptsatz* says that in both intuitionist and classical predicate logic, a purely logical sequent can be proved without "cut" (*modus ponens,* in Hilbert-type systems). A corollary is the subformula property, to the effect that the derivation formulas in a cut-free proof are compounded in the sequent proved. This entails, for example, the consistency of classical and intuitionist predicate logic, the decidability of intuitionist propositional logic, and the nonderivability of the law of the excluded middle in intuitionist predicate logic. Gentzen succeeded in sharpening the *Hauptsatz* for classical logic to the midsequent theorem (Herbrand-Gentzen theorem) for sequents whose formulas are prenex, by proving that any such sequent has a cut-free proof consisting of two parts, the first part quantifier-free and the second consisting essentially of instances of quantification. The last quantifier-free sequent in the proof is the "midsequent" and corresponds closely to a "Herbrand tautology."

Among the consequences of the midsequent theorem are the consistency of arithmetic without induction, Craig's interpolation lemma, and Beth's definability theorem. Recent extensions of the *Hauptsatz* to stronger deductive systems, including infinitary logic, have yielded partial results at the second stage of Hilbert's program in the form of consistency proofs for subsystems of classical analysis. Only a few days before his death, Gentzen had in fact announced the feasibility of a consistency proof for classical analysis as a whole.

BIBLIOGRAPHY

Gentzen's writings include "Über die Existenz unabhängiger Axiomensysteme zu unendlichen Satzsystemen," in *Mathematische Annalen,* **107** (1932), 329-350; "Untersuchungen über das logische Schliessen," in *Mathematische Zeitschrift,* **39** (1935), 176-210, 405-431, his inaugural dissertation, submitted to the Faculty of Mathematics and Natural Science of the University of Göttingen in the summer of 1933; "Die Widerspruchsfreiheit der reinen Zahlentheorie," in *Mathematische Annalen,* **112** (1936), 493-565; "Die Widerspruchsfreiheit der Stufenlogik," in *Mathematische Zeitschrift,* **41,** no. 3 (1936), 357-366; "Der Unendlichkeitsbegriff in der Mathematik," in *Semester-Berichte, Münster in Westphalen,* 9th semester (Winter 1936/1937), pp. 65-80; "Unendlichkeitsbegriff und Widerspruchsfreiheit der Mathematik," in *Travaux du IXe Congrès International de Philosophie,* VI (Paris, 1937), 201-205; "Die gegenwärtige Lage in der mathematischen Grundlagenforschung," in *Forschungen zur Logik und zur Grundlegung der exakten Wissenschaften,* n.s. **4** (1938), 5-18, also in *Deutsche Mathematik,* **3** (1939), 255-268; "Neue Fassung des Widerspruchsfreiheitsbeweises

GERARD OF BRUSSELS

für die reine Zahlentheorie," in *Forschungen zur Logik und zur Grundlegung der exakten Wissenschaften,* n.s. **4** (1938), 19–44; "Beweisbarkeit und Unbeweisbarkeit von Anfangsfällen der transfiniten Induktion in der reinen Zahlentheorie," in *Mathematische Annalen,* **119,** no. 1 (1943), 140–161, his Ph.D. *Habilitation* thesis, submitted to the Faculty of Mathematics and Natural Science of the University of Göttingen in the summer of 1942; and "Zusammenfassung von mehreren vollständigen Induktionen zu einer einzigen," in *Archiv für mathematische Logik und Grundlagenforschung,* **2,** no. 1 (1954), 1–3.

For a detailed account of Gentzen's life, extensive cross-references to his papers, and a critical appraisal of germane subsequent developments, see M. E. Szabo, *Collected Papers of Gerhard Gentzen,* in the series Studies in Logic (Amsterdam, 1969); of particular interest are the trans. of two articles Gentzen submitted to *Mathematische Annalen* but withdrew before publication (of which galley proofs are privately owned), "Über das Verhältnis zwischen intuitionistischer und klassischer Arithmetik" (1933) and sections 4 and 5 of "Die Widerspruchsfreiheit der reinen Zahlentheorie" (1935).

MANFRED E. SZABO

GERARD OF BRUSSELS (*fl.* first half of the thirteenth century)

Gerard played a minor but not unimportant role in the development of kinematics and the measure of geometrical figures. His career remains obscure except for his having written a treatise entitled *Liber de motu,* which remains in six manuscripts. Four of these date from the thirteenth century. Written sometime between 1187 and 1260, the *Liber de motu* quotes the translation of Archimedes' *De quadratura circuli* ("On the Measurement of the Circle") by Gerard of Cremona; the translation was completed before the translator died in 1187. On the other hand, the *Liber de motu* is mentioned in the *Biblionomia* of Richard of Fournival, who died in 1260.

Gerard seems to have known the *Liber philotegni de triangulis* of Jordanus de Nemore, whose exact dating is as difficult to determine as that of Gerard but who can be placed, with some confidence, in the early decades of the thirteenth century. The similarity in their names suggests that Gerard may be identified with the unknown mathematician Gernardus who wrote an arithmetical tract *Algorithmus demonstratus.* That Gerard is referred to as *magister* in the title of *Liber de motu* and his apparent knowledge of Jordanus suggest a university milieu for this work—perhaps the University of Paris.

The *Liber de motu* contains thirteen propositions, in three books. In these propositions the varying curvilinear velocities of the points and parts of geometrical figures in rotation are reduced to uniform rectilinear velocities of translation. The four propositions of the first book relate to lines in rotation, the five of the second to areas in rotation, and the four of the third to solids in rotation. Gerard's proofs are particularly noteworthy for their ingenious use of an Archimedean-type *reductio* demonstration, in which the comparison of figures is accomplished by the comparison of their line elements. In this latter technique Gerard assumed that if the ratio of the elements of two figures taken in pairs is the same, then the ratio of the totalities of the elements of the figures is the same. Such a technique resembles the procedure followed in Archimedes' *Method,* which Gerard could not have read. The proposition most influential on later authors was the first: "Any part as large as you wish of a radius describing a circle . . . is moved equally as its middle point. Hence the radius is moved equally as its middle point."[1] This is similar in a formal way to the rule for uniform acceleration, which appears to have originated with William of Heytesbury at Merton College, Oxford, in the 1330's.[2] This rule asserted that a body which is uniformly accelerated traverses the same space in the same time as a body which moves with a uniform velocity equal to the velocity that is the mean between the initial and final velocities of the accelerating body. Gerard's proposition concerns itself with movements that uniformly vary over some part or all of the linear magnitude rotating, while Heytesbury's rule concerns instantaneous velocities that uniformly vary through some period of time. The "middle velocity" is used in both rules to convert the movements to uniformity.

Gerard's influence on Thomas Bradwardine, the founder of the Merton school of kinematics, is evident, for Bradwardine knew and quoted Gerard's tract. Furthermore, Nicole Oresme's *De configurationibus qualitatum,* written in the 1350's, shows some possible dependency on the *De motu.*[3]

NOTES

1. *Liber de motu,* M. Clagett, ed., p. 112.
2. For a discussion of the Merton rule, see M. Clagett, *Science of Mechanics,* ch. 5.
3. M. Clagett, *Nicole Oresme and the Medieval Geometry of Qualities and Motions* (Madison, Wis., 1968), p. 466.

BIBLIOGRAPHY

The *Liber de motu* has been edited by M. Clagett, "The *Liber de motu* of Gerard of Brussels," in *Osiris,* **12** (1956), 73–175. See M. Clagett, *Science of Mechanics in the Middle*

Ages (Madison, Wis., 1959; repr. 1961), ch. 3; G. Sarton, *Introduction to the History of Science,* II (Baltimore, 1931), 629; and V. Zubov, "Ob 'Arkhimedovsky traditsii' v srednie veka (Traktat Gerarda Bryusselskogo 'Odvizhenii')" ("The Archimedean Tradition in the Middle Ages [Gerhard of Brussels' Treatise on Motion]"), in *Istoriko-matematicheskie issledovaniya,* **16** (1965), 235–272.

MARSHALL CLAGETT

GERBERT, also known as **Gerbert d'Aurillac,** later **Pope Sylvester II** (*b.* Aquitaine, France, *ca.* 945; *d.* Rome, 12 May 1003)

Gerbert received his early education at the Benedictine convent of Saint Géraud in Aurillac. He left it in 967 in the company of Borel, count of Barcelona. In Catalonia he continued his studies under Atto, bishop of Vich; he concentrated on mathematics, probably on the works of such authors as Boethius, Cassiodorus, and Martianus Capella. How much Moorish science Gerbert was able to study as far north as Vich is uncertain. In 970 he accompanied Borel and Atto to Rome, where he attracted the attention of Pope John XIII and, through him, of Otto I, Holy Roman Emperor, who was then residing in Rome.

This was the beginning of Gerbert's career, which was based not only on his intellectual gifts but also on his allegiance to the Saxon imperial house and its political dream—the restoration of the empire of Charlemagne, ruled in harmony by emperor and pope. Gerbert was assigned to Adalbero, the energetic and learned archbishop of Rheims; there he reorganized the cathedral school with such success that pupils began to flock to it from many parts of the empire. Equal attention was paid to Christian authors and to such pagan writers as Cicero and Horace; great pains were taken to enrich the library.

For many years experts have tried, without reaching full agreement, to date the many existing mathematical manuscripts dating from the tenth to the thirteenth centuries and ascribed to Boethius or Gerbert or their pupils. From what most authorities believe are transcripts of Boethius and Gerbert themselves, it seems that in arithmetic some Pythagorean number theory was taught in the spirit of Nicomachus, and in geometry, some statements (without proofs) of Euclid together with the mensuration rules of ancient Roman surveyors; the art of computing was taught with the aid of a special type of abacus. For his lessons in astronomy Gerbert constructed some armillary spheres.

Among Gerbert's pupils were Robert, son of Hugh Capet (later Robert II of France); Adalbold, later bishop of Utrecht; Richer of Saint-Remy, who wrote Gerbert's biography; and probably also a certain Bernelinus, the Paris author of a *Liber abaci* that mentions Gerbert as pope and may well represent his teachings. Gerbert's influence probably extended to other cathedral or monastic schools, especially in Lorraine. This school of training in the quadrivium (music, geometry, arithmetic, astronomy), which is also represented by the *Quadratura circuli* of Franco of Liège (*ca.* 1050), indicates the vivid interest in mathematics that was beginning to appear in western Europe. The only works available, however, were poor remains of Greek knowledge transmitted in the later Roman period. These prepared the way for Arabic science; a work entitled *De astrolabia,* which shows Arabic influence and of which the earliest manuscript is from the eleventh century, has occasionally been ascribed to Gerbert.

In 983 Otto II, a great admirer of Gerbert, appointed him abbot of Bobbio in the Apennines, but by 984 he was back in Rheims. From then on, he took an active part in the political schemes among the Saxons, Carolingians, and Capets; he and Adalbero were deeply involved on the side of the emperor. The Carolingian dynasty came to an end, and in 987 Gerbert assisted in the coronation of Hugh Capet as king of France. In 991 he became archbishop of Rheims, but in 997 he left his see amid controversy and intrigue. He followed the court of young Otto III through Germany to Italy. At Magdeburg between 994 and 995 he constructed an *oralogium,* either a sundial or an astrolabe, for which he took the altitude of the pole star. In 998 Gerbert became archbishop of Ravenna; and in 999, through Otto's influence, he was the first Frenchman to be elected pope. A lover of arts and sciences, Otto hoped that emperor and pope would revive the Carolingian Renaissance. Significantly, Gerbert assumed the name Sylvester II, Sylvester I having been pope at the time of Constantine and, thus, a participant in the first holy alliance of pope and emperor.

The great scheme, however, came to naught with the death of Otto in 1002 and of Gerbert the following year. Legendary ascriptions to Gerbert of supernatural and demonic powers (which even found their way into Victor Hugo's *Welf, castellan d'Osbor*) testify to the impression that his learning made on posterity.

Information about Gerbert's life is in the "Historiae" written from 996 to 998 by his pupil Richer, in 224 published letters, and in contemporary chronicles. Many theological and scientific writings testify to his work and influence. Among those that seem to be authentic are *Regulae de numerorum abaci rationibus* (also called *Libellus de numerorum divisione*), *De sphaera,* sections of a *Geometria,* a letter to Adalbold on the area of an isosceles triangle, and a *Libellus de rationali et ratione uti* (997 or 998) with considerations on the rational and the use of reason. A text that Olleris entitled *Regula de abaco computi* and ascribed to Gerbert is ascribed to Heriger by Bubnov. The authenticity of the *Geometria* has been the subject of much controversy, often in connection with that of Boethius' work of the same title.

The abacus connected with Gerbert was a board with as many as twenty-seven columns, combined in groups of three. From left to right they were headed by the letters *C* (*centum,* hundred), *D* (*decem,* ten), and *S* or *M* (*singularis* or *monad,* one); other columns (and other letters) were for higher decimal units. Numbers were expressed by counters (apices) which carried symbols equivalent to our 1, 2, $\cdots$ 9 (which may indicate some Arabic influence), so that 604, for instance, was expressed by an apex with 6 in the *C* column and an apex with 4 in the *S* column. There was no apex for zero. With such an apparatus Gerbert and his school were able to perform addition, subtraction, multiplication, and even division, something considered complicated. This art of computation probably remained confined to ecclesiastical schools, never replacing older forms of reckoning, and went out of fashion with the gradual introduction of Hindu-Arabic numerals. A letter from Adalbold to Gerbert "de ratione inveniendi crassitudinem sperae" mentions the equivalent of $\pi = 22/7$, which was probably considered as exact. For $\sqrt{3}$ Gerbert accepted 26/15 (at another place 12/7), and for $\sqrt{2}$, 17/12.

Low as the level of Gerbert's mathematical knowledge was, it surpassed that of his monastic contemporaries and their pupils. This is shown in eight letters exchanged between two monastic friends of Adalbold, edited by P. Tannery and Abbé Clerval (see *Mémoires scientifiques,* volume 5).

BIBLIOGRAPHY

I. ORIGINAL WORKS. Gerbert's extant work can be found in *Oeuvres de Gerbert,* A. Olleris, ed. (Paris–Clermont-Ferrand, 1867); *Lettres de Gerbert,* J. Havet, ed. (Paris, 1889); and *Gerberti Opera mathematica,* N. Bubnov, ed. (Berlin, 1899). An added document is found in H. Omont, "Opuscules mathématiques de Gerbert et de Hériger de Lobbes," in *Notices et extraits des manuscrits de la Bibliothèque nationale et autres bibliothèques,* **39** (1909), 4–15.

II. SECONDARY LITERATURE. Works on Gerbert include Moritz Cantor, *Vorlesungen über Geschichte der Mathematik,* 3rd ed., I (Leipzig, 1907), 848–878; O. G. Darlington, "Gerbert the Teacher," in *American Historical Review,* **52** (1947), 456–476, with titles of the articles published at the time of Gerbert's millennary commemoration in 1938; J. Leflon, *Gerbert, humanisme et chrétienté au Xe siècle* (Abbaye Saint Wandrille, 1946); F. Picavet, *Gerbert, un pape philosophe* (Paris, 1917); P. Tannery, ed., *Mémoires scientifiques,* V (Toulouse–Paris, 1922), arts. 5, 6, and 10; M. Uhlirz, *Untersuchungen über Inhalt und Datierung der Briefe Gerberts von Aurillac, Papst Sylvester II* (Göttingen, 1957); and J. M. Millás Vallicrosa, *Nueve estudios sobre historia de la ciencia española* (Barcelona, 1960).

Richer's "Historiae" were published in R. Latouche, *Richer, Histoire de France (888–995)* (Paris, 1937), with French trans., and in *Monumenta Germaniae historica, Scriptorum,* III, G. H. Pertz, ed. (Hannover, 1839). See also A. J. E. M. Smeur, "De verhandeling over de cirkelkwadratuur van Franco van Luik van omstreeks 1050," in *Mededelingen van de K. Vlaamsche academie voor wetenschappen, letteren en schoone kunsten van België,* Klasse der wetenschappen, **30,** no. 11 (1960).

D. J. STRUIK

GERGONNE, JOSEPH DIAZ (*b.* Nancy, France, 19 June 1771; *d.* Montpellier, France, 4 May 1859)

Gergonne's father, a painter and architect, died when Joseph was twelve years old. Joseph studied at the religious *collège* of Nancy, did some private tutoring, and in 1791 became a captain in the National Guard. In 1792 he joined the volunteers to fight the Prussians. He saw action at Valmy, and later that year went to Paris as secretary to his uncle. After a year he was in the army again, this time as secretary to the general staff of the Moselle army. In 1794, after a month at the Châlons artillery school, Gergonne received a commission as lieutenant. Sent to the army in the east Pyrenees, he participated in the siege of Figueras in Catalonia. After the Treaty of Basel in 1795, Gergonne was sent with his regiment to Nîmes, where he obtained the chair of transcendental mathematics at the newly organized École Centrale. He then married, settled down, and began his mathematical career under the influence of Gaspard Monge, the guiding spirit of the École Polytechnique in Paris.

Not finding a regular outlet for mathematical papers in the existing journals, such as the *Mémoires* of the Academy of Sciences or the *Journal de l'École polytechnique,* Gergonne began to publish (1810) the *Annales de mathématiques pures et appliquées,* the first purely mathematical journal. It appeared regularly every month until 1832 and was known as the *Annales de Gergonne.* His colleague J. E. Thomas-Lavernède was coeditor of the first two volumes. Gergonne continued editing the journal after he had accepted, in 1816, the chair of astronomy at the University of Montpellier. In 1830 he became rector at Montpellier and discontinued publishing his *Annales* after twenty-one volumes and a section of the twenty-second had appeared. In these volumes alone he had published more than 200 papers and questions, dealing mainly with geometry but also with analysis, statics, astronomy, and optics.

By 1831 the *Annales* had ceased to be the only wholly mathematical journal. In 1825 there appeared at Brussels A. Quetelet's *Correspondance mathématique et physique* (1825–1839), and in 1826 at Berlin A. L. Crelle's *Journal für die reine und angewandte Mathematik.* In 1836 J. Liouville continued Gergonne's work in France through his *Journal de mathématiques pures et appliquées.* The latter two journals are still being published.

Although Gergonne had given up his journal, he continued to teach after 1830. It is said that during the July Revolution of that year, when rebellious students began to whistle in his class, he regained their sympathy by beginning to lecture on the acoustics of the whistle. He retired in 1844, and during the last years of his life suffered from the infirmities of advanced age.

Gergonne's *Annales* played an essential role in the creation of modern projective and algebraic geometry. It offered space for many contributors on these and other subjects. The journal contains papers by J. V. Poncelet, F. Servois, E. Bobillier, J. Steiner, J. Plücker, M. Chasles, C. J. Brianchon, C. Dupin, and G. Lamé; in volume **19** (1828–1829) there is an article by E. Galois. The geometry papers stressed polarity and duality, first mainly in connection with conics, then also with structures of higher order. Here the terms "pole," "polar," "reciprocal polars," "duality," and "class" (of a curve) were first introduced. After Poncelet, in his monumental *Traité des propriétés projectives des figures* (1822), had given the first presentation of this new geometry in book form, a priority struggle developed between Gergonne and Poncelet. The result was that Poncelet switched to other journals, including Crelle's.

The discovery of the principle of duality in geometry can be said to have started with C. J. Brianchon, a pupil of Monge, who in 1806 derived by polar reciprocity, from Pascal's theorem, the theorem now named for him. This method of derivation was used by several contributors to the *Annales,* together with the polarity method typical of spherical trigonometry. In his *Traité*, Poncelet stressed polar reciprocity. Then, in three articles in the *Annales* (**15–17** [1824–1827]), Gergonne generalized this method into the general principle that every theorem in the plane, connecting points and lines, corresponds to another theorem in which points and lines are interchanged, provided no metrical relations are involved (*géométrie de la règle*).

In his "Considérations philosophiques sur les élémens de la science de l'étendue" (*Annales,* **16** [1825–1826], 209–232) Gergonne used the term "duality" for this principle and indicated the dual theorems by the now familiar device of double columns. He applied his principle first to polygons and polyhedrons, then to curves and surfaces; it is here that he made the now accepted distinction between curves of degree m and of class m (instead of "order" for both). These papers led to the controversy between him and Poncelet, which was partly based on the way Gergonne edited the papers for the *Annales.* In the meantime, however, A. F. Moebius had introduced duality for the plane in full generality in *Der barycentrische Calcul* (Leipzig, 1827).

One subject of contention between Gergonne and Poncelet was that Poncelet was the foremost representative of the synthetic (i.e., the purely geometric) method, while Gergonne believed in analytic methods. True, Gergonne said, the methods of analytic geometry were often clumsy, but this was only due to lack of *adresse.* He illustrated this point in "Recherche du cercle qui en touche trois autres sur un plan" (*Annales,* **7** [1816–1817], 289–303), in which he gave an elegant analytic solution of this, the "Apollonian," tangent problem. Then, in his third article on duality (*Annales,* **17** [1826–1827], 214–252), following ideas developed by Gabriel Lamé in a study published in 1818 (*Examen des différentes méthodes employées pour résoudre les problèmes de la géométrie*) of which Lamé already had had an abstract published in the *Annales* (**7** [1816–1817], 229–240), Gergonne showed the power of what we now call the "abbreviated" notation, in which, for instance, the pencil of circles in the plane is represented by $C_1 + \lambda C_2 = 0$. This method was fully developed by J. Plücker in his *Analytisch-geometrische Entwicklungen* (1828–1831).

In 1834 Plücker solved a problem which to both Gergonne and Poncelet had seemed something of a paradox. Poncelet (*Annales,* **8** [1817–1818], 215–217) had found that from a point outside a curve of degree m there can be drawn $m(m - 1)$ tangents to the curve. Gergonne missed this fact until (*Annales,* **18** [1827–1828], 151) he corrected himself on several points and introduced for the polar reciprocal of a curve of order m the term "curve of class m," which is therefore of order $m(m - 1)$. But the reciprocal of this curve is the original one, and this seems therefore of order $m(m - 1)\{m(m - 1) - 1\}$, which is greater than m except when $m = 2$. Poncelet had already stated that the answer was to be found in the fact that the polar curve was not fully general. Plücker gave the precise answer by means of his formulas on the number of singularities of a plane curve (*Journal für die reine und angewandte Mathematik,* **12** [1834], 105 ff.).

Among the many other theorems discovered by Gergonne is the following (*Annales,* **16** [1825–1826], 209–232): If two plane curves C_m of degree m intersect in such a way that mp points of intersection are on a C_p, then the $m(m-p)$ other points of intersection are on a C_{m-p}. This leads to a simple proof of Pascal's theorem by considering the six sides of the hexagon inscribed in a conic alternately as two C_3.

Gergonne liked to season his papers with "philosophic" remarks. In one such remark he said, "It is not possible to feel satisfied at having said the last word about some theory as long as it cannot be explained in a few words to any passerby encountered in the street" (M. Chasles, *Aperçu historique . . .* [Paris, 1889], p. 115).

BIBLIOGRAPHY

I. ORIGINAL WORKS. Almost all of Gergonne's papers are in the *Annales,* and a bibliography is in Lafon (see below). The more important ones are mentioned in the text. Those on differential geometry include "Demonstration des principaux théorèmes de M. Dupin sur la courbure des surfaces," in *Annales,* **4** (1813–1814), 368–378; and "Théorie élémentaire de la courbure des lignes et des surfaces courbes," *ibid.,* **9** (1818–1819), 127–196. On statics, see "Démonstrations des deux théorèmes de géométrie," *ibid.,* **11** (1820–1821), 326–336. He returned to one of his old loves in an address at Lille: "Notes sur le principe de dualité en géométrie," in *Mémoires de l'Académie des sciences et lettres de Montpellier pour 1847,* Section des Sciences.

II. SECONDARY LITERATURE. A. Lafon, "Gergonne, ses travaux," in *Mémoires de l'Académie de Stanislas,* **1** (1860), xxv–lxxiv, includes a bibliography of Gergonne's works. For further information, see E. Kötter, "Die Entwicklung der synthetischen Geometrie von Monge bis auf Staudt (1847)," in *Jahresbericht der Deutschen Mathematiker-vereinigung,* **5**, no. 2 (1901), with details on the controversy between Poncelet and Gergonne (pp. 160–167). The documents in this case were reprinted by Poncelet in his *Traité des propriétés projectives des figures,* II (Paris, 1866), 351–396.

See also C. B. Boyer, *History of Analytic Geometry* (New York, 1956), ch. 9; and *A History of Mathematics* (New York, 1968), ch. 24; M. Chasles, *Aperçu historique sur l'origine et le développement des méthodes en géométrie* (Paris, 1837; 3rd ed., 1889); and *Rapport sur le progrès de la géométrie* (Paris, 1870), pp. 54–60; and H. de Vries, *Historische Studien,* II (Groningen, 1934), 114–142.

D. J. STRUIK

GERMAIN, SOPHIE (*b.* Paris, France, 1 April 1776; *d.* Paris, 27 June 1831)

Sophie Germain, France's greatest female mathematician prior to the present era, was the daughter of Ambroise-François Germain and Marie-Madeleine Gruguelu. Her father was for a time deputy to the States-General (later the Constituent Assembly). In his speeches he referred to himself as a merchant and ardently defended the rights of the Third Estate, which he represented. Somewhat later he became one of the directors of the Bank of France. His extensive library enabled his daughter to educate herself at home. Thus it was that, at age thirteen, Sophie read an account of the death of Archimedes at the hands of a Roman soldier. The great scientist of antiquity became her hero, and she conceived the idea that she too must become a mathematician. After teaching herself Latin and Greek, she read Newton and Euler despite her parents' opposition to a career in mathematics.

The Germain library sufficed until Sophie was eighteen. At that time she was able to obtain the lecture notes of courses at the recently organized École Polytechnique, in particular the *cahiers* of Lagrange's lectures on analysis. Students at the school were expected to prepare end-of-term reports. Pretending to be a student there and using the pseudonym Le Blanc, Sophie Germain wrote a paper on analysis and sent it to Lagrange. He was astounded at its originality, praised it publicly, sought out its author, and thus discovered that M. Le Blanc was Mlle. Germain. From then on, he became her sponsor and mathematical counselor.

Correspondence with great scholars became the means by which she obtained her higher education in mathematics, literature, biology, and philosophy. She wrote to Legendre about problems suggested by his 1798 *Théorie des nombres.* The subsequent Legendre-Germain correspondence was so voluminous that it was virtually a collaboration, and Legendre included some of her discoveries in a supplement to the second edition of the *Théorie.* In the interim she had read Gauss's *Disquisitiones arithmeticae* and, under the pseudonym of Le Blanc, engaged in correspondence with its author.

That Sophie Germain was no ivory-tower mathematician became evident in 1807, when French troops were occupying Hannover. Recalling Archimedes' fate and fearing for Gauss's safety, she addressed an inquiry to the French commander, General Pernety, who was a friend of the Germain family. As a result of this incident, Gauss learned her true identity and accorded even more praise to her number-theoretic proofs.

One of Sophie Germain's theorems is related to the baffling and still unsolved problem of obtaining a general proof for "Fermat's last theorem," which is the conjecture that $x^n + y^n = z^n$ has no positive integral solutions if n is an integer greater than 2. To prove the theorem, one need only establish its truth for $n = 4$ (accomplished by Fermat himself) and for all values of n that are odd primes. Euler proved it for $n = 3$ and Legendre for $n = 5$. Sophie Germain's contribution was to show the impossibility of positive integral solutions if x, y, z are prime to one another and to n, where n is any prime less than 100. In 1908 the American algebraist L. E. Dickson generalized her theorem to all primes less than 1,700, and more recently Barkley Rosser extended the upper limit to 41,000,000. In his history of the theory of numbers, Dickson describes her other discoveries in the higher arithmetic.

Parallel with and subsequent to her pure mathematical research, she also made contributions to the applied mathematics of acoustics and elasticity. This came about in the following manner. In 1808 the German physicist E. F. F. Chladni visited Paris, where he conducted experiments on vibrating plates. He exhibited the so-called Chladni figures, which can be produced when a metal or glass plate of any regular shape, the most common being the square or the circle, is placed in a horizontal position and fastened at its center to a supporting stand. Sand is scattered lightly over the plate, which is then set in vibration by drawing a violin bow rapidly up and down along the edge of the plate. The sand is thrown from the moving points to those which remain at rest (the nodes), forming the nodal lines or curves constituting the Chladni figures.

Chladni's results were picturesque, but their chief effect on French mathematicians was to emphasize that there was no pure mathematical model for such phenomena. Hence, in 1811 the Académie des Sciences offered a prize for the best answer to the following challenge: Formulate a mathematical theory of elastic surfaces and indicate just how it agrees with empirical evidence.

Most mathematicians did not attempt to solve the problem because Lagrange assured them that the mathematical methods available were inadequate for the task. Nevertheless, Sophie Germain submitted an anonymous memoir. No prize was awarded to anyone; but Lagrange, using her fundamental hypotheses, was able to deduce the correct partial differential equation for the vibrations of elastic plates. In 1813 the Academy reopened the contest, and Sophie Germain offered a revised paper which included the question of experimental verification. That memoir received an honorable mention. When, in 1816, the third and final contest was held, a paper bearing her own name and treating vibrations of general curved as well as plane elastic surfaces was awarded the grand prize—the high point in her scientific career.

After further enlargement and improvement of the prize memoir, it was published in 1821 under the title *Remarques sur la nature, les bornes et l'étendue de la question des surfaces élastiques et équation générale de ces surfaces.* In that work Sophie Germain stated that the law for the general vibrating elastic surface is given by the fourth-order partial differential equation

$$N^2\left[\frac{\partial^4 \rho}{\partial {s_1}^4} + 2\frac{\partial^4 \rho}{\partial {s_1}^2 \partial {s_2}^2} + \frac{\partial^4 \rho}{\partial {s_2}^4} - \frac{4}{S^2}\left(\frac{\partial^2 \rho}{\partial {s_1}^2} + \frac{\partial^2 \rho}{\partial {s_2}^2}\right)\right] + \frac{\partial^2 \rho}{\partial t^2} = 0.$$

Here N is a physical constant if the "surface" is an elastic membrane of uniform thickness. The generality is achieved because S, the radius of mean curvature, varies from point to point of a general curved surface. The very concept of mean curvature ($1/S$) was created by Sophie Germain.

The notion of the curvature of a surface generalizes the corresponding concept for a plane curve by considering the curvatures of all plane sections of the surface through the normal at a given point of the surface and then using only the largest and smallest of those curvatures. The extremes, called the principal curvatures, are multiplied to give the Gaussian total curvature at a point and are added to give the mean curvature. Sophie Germain, however, defined the mean curvature as half the sum, that is, the arithmetic mean, of the principal curvatures. Her definition seems more in accordance with the term "mean." Moreover, she indicated that her measure is a representative one, an average in the statistical sense, by demonstrating that if one passes planes through the normal at a point of a surface such that the angle between successive planes is $2\pi/n$ where n is very large (thus yielding sample sections in many different directions), the arithmetic mean of the curvatures of all the sections is the same as the mean of the two principal curvatures, a fact that remains true in the limit as n gets larger and larger. Also, while the Gaussian curvature completely characterizes the local metric geometry of a surface, the mean curvature is more suitable for applications in elasticity theory. A plane has zero mean curvature at all points. Hence $4/S^2 = 0$ in Germain's differential equation, and it reduces to the equation which she and Lagrange had derived for the vibration of flat plates. The same simplification holds for all surfaces of zero mean curvature, the so-called minimal surfaces (such as those formed by a soap film stretched from wire contours).

In later papers Sophie Germain enlarged on the physics of vibrating curved elastic surfaces and considered the effect of variable thickness (which emphasizes that one is, in fact, dealing with elastic solids).

She also wrote two philosophic works entitled *Pensées diverses* and *Considérations générales sur l'état des sciences et des lettres,* which were published posthumously in the *Oeuvres philosophiques.* The first of these, probably written in her youth, contains capsule summaries of scientific subjects, brief comments on the contributions of leading mathematicians and physicists throughout the ages, and personal opinions. The *État des sciences et des lettres,* which was praised by Auguste Comte, is an extremely scholarly development of the theme of the unity of thought, that is, the idea that there always has been and always will be no basic difference between the sciences and the humanities with respect to their motivation, their methodology, and their cultural importance.

BIBLIOGRAPHY

I. ORIGINAL WORKS. Among Sophie Germain's scientific writings are *Remarques sur la nature, les bornes et l'étendue de la question des surfaces élastiques et équation générale de ces surfaces* (Paris, 1826); *Mémoire sur la courbure des surfaces* (Paris, 1830); *Oeuvres philosophiques de Sophie Germain* (Paris, 1879); and *Mémoire sur l'emploi de l'épaisseur dans la théorie des surfaces élastiques* (Paris, 1880).

II. SECONDARY LITERATURE. On Sophie Germain or her work, see L. E. Dickson, *History of the Theory of Numbers* (New York, 1950), I, 382; II, 732–735, 757, 763, 769; M. L. Dubreil-Jacotin, "Figures de mathématiciennes," in F. Le Lionnais, *Les grands courants de la pensée mathématique* (Paris, 1962), pp. 258–268; and H. Stupuy, "Notice sur la vie et les oeuvres de Sophie Germain," in *Oeuvres philosophiques de Sophie Germain* (see above), pp. 1–92.

EDNA E. KRAMER

GHETALDI (GHETTALDI), MARINO (*b.* Ragusa, Dalmatia [now Dubrovnik, Yugoslavia], 1566 [1568?]; *d.* Ragusa, 11 April 1626)

Ghetaldi was born to a patrician family originally from Taranto, Italy. Ragusa was then an independent republic and very jealous of its Latinism. Ghetaldi spent only the latter part of his life (from 1603) there, holding various public and legal positions. As a young man, after his education in Ragusa, he had moved to Rome and then traveled extensively through Europe, returning to Rome briefly in 1603.

Ghetaldi lived the peripatetic life of a scholar participating in the intense scientific awareness of early seventeenth-century Italian culture, a last flowering of the Renaissance spirit. Galileo was its most notable example. Archimedes and Apollonius were its inspiration. In Rome Ghetaldi came under the influence of Christoph Clavius, famous as teacher and editor of Euclid. He then went to Antwerp to study with Michel Coignet. Thence he moved to Paris, where he associated with Viète, who entrusted him with an unpublished manuscript to revise and edit, although Ghetaldi had as yet published nothing of his own.

Ghetaldi's first publications appeared at Rome in 1603 and were part of the beginning of research on Archimedes. The first, *Promotus Archimedis,* dealt with the famous problem of the crown; it also included tables that Ghetaldi calculated from experiments on the specific weights of certain substances, with results that were, for the time, remarkably accurate. For this, and for research on burning glasses, a topic then of great interest, he also became known as a physicist. In his second work, *Nonnullae propositiones de parabola,* Ghetaldi treated parabolas which he had obtained as sections of a right circular cone of any proportions.

From the analysis of Apollonius' known work, Ghetaldi turned to the task of reconstructing the content of his lost works. He followed the example of his master Viète, who had attempted such reconstruction in his two books of 1600, *Tactionum* (Περὶ ἐπαφῶν), and was consequently nicknamed Apollonius Gallus. Ghetaldi took over and completed that work, although on less restricted problems, as *Supplementum Apollonii Galli* (1607). Ghetaldi later concentrated his attention on the last of Apollonius' books mentioned by Pappus, Περὶ νεύσεων (*Inclinationum libri duo*) and solved the four problems that were supposed to form the first book. The problems of insertion, as they were called, consisted of constructing certain segments with their extremes touching arcs of a circle or other given figure; the book was entitled *Apollonius redivivus seu restituta Apollonii Pergaei inclinationum geometria* (1607). Later, Ghetaldi reexamined the problem which, according to Pappus, made up the second book of *Inclinationum;* although it was rather complex, involving insertions between two semicircles, Ghetaldi declared he had needed only a few days to complete it. Published in 1613, it was entitled *Apollonius redivivus seu restitutae Apollonii Pergaei de inclinationibus geometriae, liber secundus.*

Meanwhile, Ghetaldi had produced a pamphlet with the solutions of forty-two geometrical problems, *Variorum problematum collectio* (1607). The method used in some of the solutions suggests that he was already applying methods of algebra to geometry, such as first-degree and second-degree problems, determinate or not, which he later treated specifically in a volume that appeared after his death, *De resolutione et de compositione mathematica, libri quinque* (1630). Because of this work, possibly his most significant, Ghetaldi has been considered the precursor of analytic geometry—a hypothesis difficult to support, especially in the light of the methods used by Descartes and Fermat.

Ghetaldi wrote in Latin, and his works were well and widely known—some for a long time. Pierre Herigone, for instance, included in the first volume of his *Cursus mathematicus* (1634) the first of Ghetaldi's two works devoted to the problems of insertion, translating it in a notation anticipating modern mathematical logic.

Ghetaldi was held in great esteem not only as a scientist, but also as a man. While still young he had been offered a chair at the University of Louvain, which he did not accept; and in 1621 his name was included in a list of scientists proposed for membership in the flourishing new Accademia dei Lincei. He was not nominated, however, because he returned to Ragusa without notice and the Academy did not know his whereabouts.

In letters of that time Ghetaldi was described as having "the morals of an angel" and Paolo Sarpi, his close friend, called him "a Ragusan gentleman of discernment." For his exceptional skill and intelligence Ghetaldi was good-naturedly called "a mathematical demon." Later, in Ragusa, he was even called a magician and gained the reputation of being a sorcerer because he made frequent astronomical observations and experimented with burning glasses; another explanation attributes the sobriquet to his using a nearby cave popularly called "the magician's den" for his research.

Ghetaldi had met Sarpi in Venice before 1600, during his frequent peregrinations between Rome, Padua, and Venice. In Rome his teacher Clavius had introduced him to another Jesuit scholar, Christopher Grinberg, author of a treatise on trigonometry and, later, famous as one of the four Jesuits whom Robert Cardinal Bellarmine consulted in April 1611 on the value of Galileo's *Sidereus nuncius.* Ghetaldi must certainly have met Grinberg again in Padua, where Grinberg lived from 1592 to 1610, and later the two maintained a correspondence, as shown by a letter of 1608 and another of 1614, which accompanied the second part of Ghetaldi's *Apollonius redivivus . . . liber secundus* and in which Ghetaldi declared he was sending the volume "as a sign of reverence and in memory of our old friendship."

In June 1606 the government of Ragusa charged Ghetaldi with a mission to the sultan of Constantinople. The task absorbed him considerably, and to it must be attributed the break in his scientific work that coincides with this period. The mission must have had its dangers, since rumors of his death began to circulate. So persistent were these rumors that even J. E. Montucla, in his *Histoire des mathématiques,* gave Ghetaldi's date of death as about 1609, "in the course of his mission to the [Sublime] Porte."

BIBLIOGRAPHY

Ghetaldi's writings were collected as *Opera omnia,* Žarko Dadić, ed. (Zagreb, 1968). Among his works are *Promotus Archimedes seu de variis corporum generibus gravitate et magnitudine comparatis* (Rome, 1603); *Nonnullae propositiones de parabola* (Rome, 1603); *Apollonius redivivus seu restituta Apollonii Pergaei inclinationum geometria* (Venice, 1607); *Supplementum Apollonii Galli seu exsuscitata Apollonii Pergaei tactionum geometriae pars reliqua* (Venice, 1607); *Variorum problematum collectio* (Venice, 1607); *Apollonius redivivus seu restitutae Apollonii Pergaei de inclinationibus geometriae, liber secundus* (Venice, 1613); and *De resolutione et compositione mathematica, libri quinque* (Rome, 1630).

See also A. Favaro, "Amici e corrispondenti de Galileo Galilei," in *Atti del Istituto veneto di scienze, lettere ed arti,* **69,** 303–324; E. Gelcich, in *Abhandlungen zur Geschichte der Mathematik,* **4,** 191–231; and H. Wieleitner, "Marino Ghetaldi," in *Bibliotheca mathematica,* **13,** 242–247.

LUIGI CAMPEDELLI

GIORGI, GIOVANNI (*b.* Lucca, Italy, 27 November 1871; *d.* Castiglioncello, Italy, 19 August 1950)

Giorgi's father was an eminent jurist, who served as president of the Council of State and senator of the kingdom. From him Giorgi inherited a respect for scholarship and an austere way of life. Giorgi's dedication to the doctrines of physics and their applications began early and lasted throughout his life; his more than 350 publications include works on engineering, pure physics, mathematical physics, electricity, magnetism, natural sciences, chemistry, and philosophy.

Giorgi took the degree in civil engineering from the Institute of Technology in Rome when he was twenty-two; his most important technological achievements include projects in steam-generated electrical traction, innovations in urban trolley systems, and pioneering concepts in hydroelectric installations (integral utilization of rivers) and distribution networks (as, for example, the secondary three-phase network with the fourth wire, used by him for the first time in Rome's municipal installation). The work in large part coincided with his tenure as director of the Technology Office of the city of Rome from 1906 to 1923.

Giorgi's teaching activities further reflect the scope of his interests. From 1913 to 1927 he taught courses in the Physics and Mathematics Faculty of the University of Rome, at the School of Aeronautics, and in the School of Engineering; he was later titular professor of mathematical physics and, by annual contract, head of the department of rational mechanics at the universities of Cagliari and Palermo. From 1934 he was professor of electrical communications at the University of Rome and in 1939 he became associate professor at the Royal Institute of Higher Mathematics. In addition to teaching and practical engineering, he did original scientific work (particularly in mathematics) and wrote popular treatments of scientific and technological subjects.

Giorgi's chief fame, however, arises from his concept of a new absolute system of measurement to be simultaneously applicable to all electrical, magnetic, and mechanical units. In a letter to the English periodical *Electrician,* dated 28 March 1895 and published in April 1896, Giorgi took issue with the French physicist Alfred Cornu about the rationality of retaining the c.g.s. system of Wilhelm Weber and the English physicists, standardized in 1898. Giorgi held that the system, whose basic energy unit was the erg—one gram cm./sec.^{2}, or one centimeterdyne—was ill-adapted to current physics, given the connection between electrical and magnetic phenomena long since revealed by the researches of Oersted and Ampère.

Giorgi then devoted considerable time to the systematization of electrical units, and on 13 October 1901 presented to a meeting of the Italian Electrical Engineering Association a report entitled "Unità razionali di elettromagnetismo"—the cornerstone of his subsequent work. In this paper he proposed a consistent measurement system based on the meter, the kilogram, and the mean solar second (and hence called the M.K.S. system, as well as the Giorgi International System). The Giorgi system, of which the basic energy unit is the joule (one kg. meter^2/sec.^{2}, or one meternewton), is adaptable to electrical, magnetic, and mechanical units; is entirely composed of the standard units of mechanics; and requires no conversion factors since it is applicable to both electrostatic and electromagnetic systems. It therefore offers fewer irrationalities and greater convenience than the c.g.s. system because of its establishment of a single basic unit of appropriate size for each application.

Giorgi's proposals were supported by Silvanus Thompson in England, Fritz Emde in Germany, and the U.S. Bureau of Standards, among others, but it was not until June 1935 that the plenary session of the International Electrical Engineering Commission, meeting in Scheveningen, Netherlands, and in Brussels, unanimously recommended the adoption of the new system of units to supersede the c.g.s. system. In October 1960 the General Conference of Weights and Measures confirmed the International System, based on the meter, the kilogram, and the second, as well as the ampere, kelvin, and candle. It is interesting to note that Giorgi himself had proposed the ohm or some other such unit as a fourth standard.

A half century thus elapsed between Giorgi's letter to *Electrician* and the final adoption of a system based upon his principles. The Giorgi system is the clear manifestation of his versatility and of his abilities as a synthesizer.

BIBLIOGRAPHY

I. ORIGINAL WORKS. Giorgi reprinted several of his works that are most important to reforms in the study of electrical engineering and the system of units—together with biographical data and a bibliography to December 1948 that lists more than 300 publications—in *Verso l'elettrotecnica moderna* (Milan, 1949).

His textbooks include *Lezioni di costruzioni elettromeccaniche* (Rome, 1905); *Lezioni di meccanica generale (superiore)* (Rome, 1914); *Lezioni di fisica matematica (elettricità e magnetismo)* (Cagliari, 1926); *Lezioni di fisica matematica* (Rome, 1927); *Compendio delle lezioni di meccanica razionale* (Rome, 1928); *Lezioni di meccanica razionale,* 2 vols. (Rome, 1931-1934); *Lezioni del corso di communicazioni elettriche* (Rome, 1934-1939); *Meccanica razionale* (Rome, 1946); *Compendio di storia delle matematiche* (Turin, 1948); *Aritmetica per scuole medie* (Rome, 1948); and *Verso l'elettrotecnica moderna* (Milan, 1949).

His scientific popularizations include *Le ferrovie a trazione elettrica* (Bologna, 1905); *Che cos'è l'elettricità?,* no. 8 in Collezione Omnia (Rome, 1928); *Metrologia elettrotecnica antica e nuova* (Milan, 1937), a repr. of three arts. published in *Energia elettrica,* **14,** nos. 3-5 (Mar.-May, 1937); *L'etere e la luce (dall'etere cosmico alle moderne teorie della luce*), no. 32 in Collezione Omnia (Rome, 1939); and *La frantumazione dell'atomo* (Rome, 1946).

In addition, Giorgi wrote 37 papers on the new system of measurement, 32 on machinery and electrical installations, 14 on electrical traction, 45 on general electrical engineering, 93 on theories in mathematics and mathematical physics, 19 on the history of science, and 27 articles for the *Enciclopedia italiana Treccani.*

II. SECONDARY LITERATURE. A very good summary of Giorgi's life and work was given by Basilio Focaccia at the commemoration ceremony in Rome on 26 April 1951 and was published in *Elettrotecnica,* **38** (1951).

MARIO LORIA

GIRARD, ALBERT (*b.* St. Mihiel, France, 1595; *d.* Leiden, Netherlands, 8 December 1632)

Girard's birthplace is fixed only by the adjective *Samielois* that he often added to his name, an adjective the printers of St. Mihiel often applied to themselves in the seventeenth century. The city belonged at that time to the duchy of Lorraine. The exact date of Girard's birth is subject to dispute. That of his death is known from a note in the *Journal* of Constantijn Huygens for 9 December 1632. The place of death is only conjectured.

Girard was undoubtedly a member of the Reformed church, for in a polemic against Honorat du Meynier he accused the latter of injuring "those of the Reformed religion by calling them heretics." This explains why he settled—at an unknown date—in the Netherlands, the situation of Protestants being very precarious in Lorraine.

The respectful and laudatory tone in which he speaks of Willebrord Snell in his *Trigonometry* leads one to suppose that Girard studied at Leiden. According to Johann Friedrich Gronovius, in his *éloge* of Jacob Golius, in 1616 Girard engaged in scientific correspondence with Golius, then twenty years old.

When Golius succeeded Snell at Leiden in 1629, Constantijn Huygens wrote to him to praise the knowledge of Girard (*vir stupendus*), particularly in the study of refraction. On 21 July of the same year Pierre Gassendi wrote from Brussels to Nicholas de Peiresc that he had dined at the camp before Bois-le-Roi with ". . . Albert Girard, an engineer now at the camp." We thus know definitely that Girard was an engineer in the army of Frederick Henry of Nassau, prince of Orange; yet the only title that he gives himself in his works is that of mathematician.

The end of Girard's life was difficult. He complains, in his posthumously published edition of the works of Stevin, of living in a foreign country, without a patron, ruined, and burdened with a large family. His widow, in the dedication of this work, is more precise. She is poor, with eleven orphans to whom their father has left only his reputation of having faithfully served and having spent all his time on research on the most noble secrets of mathematics.

Girard's works include a translation from Flemish into French of Henry Hondius' treatise on fortifications (1625) and editions of the mathematical works of Samuel Marolois (1627–1630), of the *Arithmetic* of Simon Stevin (1625), and of Stevin's works (1634). He also prepared sine tables and a succinct treatise on trigonometry (1626; 1627; 2nd ed., 1629) and published a theoretical work, *Invention nouvelle en l'algèbre* (1629). Although in the preface to the trigonometric tables (1626) he promised that he would very soon present studies inspired by Pappus of Alexandria (plane and solid loci, inclinations, and determinations), no such work on these matters appeared. Likewise, his restoration of Euclid's porisms, which he stated he "hopes to present, having reinvented them," never appeared.

Contributions to the mathematical sciences are scattered throughout Girard's writings. It should be said at the outset that, always pressed for time and generally lacking space, he was very stingy with words and still more so with demonstrations; thus, he very often suggested more than he demonstrated. His notations were, in general, those of Stevin and François Viète, "who surpasses all his predecessors in algebra." He improved Stevin's writing of the radicals by proposing that the cube root be written not as $\sqrt{③}$ but as $\sqrt[3]{\ }$ (*Invention nouvelle,* 1629) but, like Stevin, favored fractional exponents. He had his own symbols for $>$ and $<$, and in trigonometry he was one of the first to utilize incidentally—in several very clear tables—the abbreviations sin, tan, and sec for sine, tangent, and secant.

In spherical trigonometry, following Viète and like Willebrord Snell, but less clearly than Snell, Girard made use of the supplementary triangle. In geometry he generalized the concept of the plane polygon, distinguishing three types of quadrilaterals, eleven types of pentagons, and sixty-nine (there are seventy) types of hexagons (*Trigonométrie,* 1626). With the sides of a convex quadrilateral inscribed in a circle one can construct two other quadrilaterals inscribed in the same circle. Their six diagonals are equal in pairs. Girard declared that these quadrilaterals have an area equal to the product of the three distinct diagonals divided by twice the diameter of the circle.

Girard was the first to state publicly that the area of a spherical triangle is proportional to its spherical excess (*Invention nouvelle*). This theorem, stemming from the optical tradition of Witelo, was probably known by Regiomontanus and definitely known by Thomas Harriot—who, however, did not divulge it. Girard gave a proof of it that did not fully satisfy him and that he termed "a probable conclusion." It was Bonaventura Cavalieri who furnished, independently, a better-founded demonstration (1632).

In arithmetic Girard took up Nicolas Chuquet's expressions "million," "billion," "trillion," and so on. He "explains radicals extremely close to certain numbers, such that if one attempted the same things with other numbers, it would not be without greatly increasing the number of characters" (*Arithmétique de . . . Stevin,* 1625). He gave, among various examples, Fibonacci's series, the values 577/408 and 1393/985 for $\sqrt{2}$, and an approximation of $\sqrt{10}$. One should see in these an anticipation of continuous fractions. They are also similar to the approximation 355/113 obtained for π by Valentin Otho (1573) and by Adriaan Anthoniszoon (1586) and to the contemporary writings of Daniel Schwenter.

In the theory of numbers Girard translated books V and VI of Diophantus from Latin into French (*Arithmétique de . . . Stevin*). For this work he knew and utilized not only Guilielmus Xylander's edition, as Stevin had for the first four books, but also that of Claude Gaspar Bachet de Méziriac (1621), which he cited several times. He gave fourteen right triangles in whole numbers whose sides differ from unity. For the largest the sides are on the order of 3×10^{10} (*ibid.,* p. 629).

Girard stated the whole numbers that are sums of two squares and declared that certain numbers, such as seven, fifteen, and thirty-nine, are not decomposable into three squares; but he affirmed, as did Bachet, that all of them are decomposable into four squares (*ibid.,* p. 662). The first demonstration of this theorem was provided by Joseph Lagrange (1772). Girard also contributed to problems concerning sums of cubes by improving one of Viète's techniques (*ibid.,* p. 676).

In algebra, as in the theory of numbers, Girard showed himself to be a brilliant disciple of Viète, whose "specious logistic" he often employed but called "literal algebra." In his study of incommensurables Girard generally followed Stevin and the tradition of book X of Euclid, but he gave a very clear rule for the extraction of the cube root of binomials. It was an improvement on the method of Rafael Bombelli and was, in turn, surpassed by that which Descartes formulated in 1640 (*Invention nouvelle*).

Unlike Harriot and Descartes, Girard never wrote an equation in which the second member was zero. He particularly favored the "alternating order," in which the monomials, in order of decreasing degree, are alternately in the first member and the second member. That permitted him to express, without any difficulty with signs, the relations between the coefficients and the roots. In this regard he stated, after Peter Roth (1608) and before Descartes (1637), the fundamental algebraic theorem: "Every equation in algebra has as many solutions as the denominator of its largest quantity" (1629).

A restriction immediately follows this statement, but it is annulled soon after by the introduction of solutions which are "enveloped like those which have $\sqrt{-}$." From this point of view, Girard hardly surpassed Bombelli, his rare examples treating only equations of the third and fourth degrees. For him the introduction of imaginary roots was essentially for the generality and elegance of the formulas. In addition, Girard gave the expression for the sums of squares, cubes, and fourth powers of roots as a function of the coefficients (Newton's formulas).

Above all, Girard thoroughly studied cubic and biquadratic equations. He knew how to form the discriminant of the equations $x^3 = px + q$, $x^3 = px^2 + q$, and $x^4 = px^3 + q$. These are examples of the "determinations" that he had promised in 1626. The first equation is of the type solved by Niccolò Tartaglia and Girolamo Cardano, the second relates to book II of the *Sphere* of Archimedes, and the third to Plato's problem in the *Meno.* With the aid of trigonometric tables Girard solved equations of the third degree having three real roots. For those having only one root he indicated, beside Cardano's rules, an elegant method of numerical solution by means of trigonometric tables and iteration. He constructed equations of the first type geometrically by reducing them, as Viète did, to the trisection of an arc of a circle. This trisection was carried out by using a hyperbola, as Pappus had done. The figure then made evident the three roots of the equation.

Girard was the first to point out the geometric significance of the negative numbers: "The negative solution is explained in geometry by moving backward, and the minus sign moves back when the + advances." To illustrate this affirmation he took from Pappus a problem of intercalation that Descartes later treated in an entirely different spirit (1637). This problem led him to an equation of the fourth degree. The numerical case that he had chosen admitted two positive roots and two negative roots; he made the latter explicit and showed their significance.

BIBLIOGRAPHY

I. ORIGINAL WORKS. Girard's two books are *Tables des sinus, tangentes et sécantes selon le raid de 100,000 parties . . .* (The Hague, 1626; 1627; 2nd ed., 1629), which also appeared in Flemish but had the Latin title *Tabulae sinuum tangentium et secantium ad radium 100,000* (The

Hague, 1626; 1629); and *Invention nouvelle en l'algèbre* (Amsterdam, 1629; repr. Leiden, 1884). The repr. of the latter, by D. Bierens de Haan, is a faithful facs., except for the notation of the exponents, in which parentheses are substituted for the circles used by Girard and Stevin. However, the parentheses had been used by Girard in the *Tables.*

Girard was also responsible for trans. and eds. of works by others: *Oeuvres de Henry Hondius* (The Hague, 1625), which he translated from the Flemish; Samuel Marolois's *Fortification ou architecture militaire* (Amsterdam, 1627), which he enlarged and revised, and also issued in Flemish as *Samuel Maroloys, Fortification* . . . (Amsterdam, 1627), and *Géométrie contenant la théorie et practique d'icelle, necessaire à la fortification* . . ., 2 vols. (Amsterdam, 1627–1628; 1629), which he revised and also issued in Flemish as *Opera mathematica ofte wis-konstige, Wercken . . . beschreven door Sam. Marolois* . . . (Amsterdam, 1630); and Simon Stevin's *L'arithmétique* (Leiden, 1625), which he revised and enlarged, and *Les oeuvres mathématiques de Simon Stevin* (Leiden, 1634), also revised and enlarged.

II. SECONDARY LITERATURE. On Girard or his work, see several articles by Henri Bosmans in *Mathesis,* **40** and **41** (1926); Antonio Favaro, "Notizie storiche sulle frazioni continue," in *Bullettino di bibliografia e di storia delle scienze matematiche e fisiche,* **7** (1874), 533–596, see 559–565; Gino Loria, *Storia delle matematiche,* 2nd ed. (Milan, 1950), pp. 439–444; Georges Maupin, "Étude sur les annotations jointes par Albert Girard Samielois aux oeuvres mathématiques de Simon Stevin de Bruges," in *Opinions et curiosités touchant le mathématique,* II (Paris, 1902), 159–325; Paul Tannery, "Albert Girard de Saint-Mihiel," in *Bulletin des sciences mathématiques et astronomiques,* 2nd ser., **7** (1883), 358–360, also in Tannery's *Mémoires scientifiques,* VI (Paris, 1926), 19–22; and G. A. Vosterman van Oijen, "Quelques arpenteurs hollandais de la fin du XVIème et du commencement du XVIIème siècle," in *Bullettino di bibliografia e di storia delle scienze matematiche e fisiche,* **3** (1870), 323–376, see 359–362.

See also *Nieuw Nederlandsch Woordenboek,* II (1912), cols. 477–481.

JEAN ITARD

GLAISHER, JAMES WHITBREAD LEE (*b.* Lewisham, Kent, England, 5 November 1848; *d.* Cambridge, England, 7 December 1928)

Glaisher was the eldest son of James Glaisher, an astronomer who was also interested in the calculation of numerical tables. His given names were derived from those of his father and his father's colleagues in the founding of the British Meteorological Society, S. C. Whitbread and John Lee.

Glaisher attended St. Paul's School, London (1858–1867), and Trinity College, Cambridge, where he graduated as second wrangler in 1871. Elected to a fellowship and appointed an assistant tutor at Trinity, he remained there the rest of his life. He never married.

A tall, slim, upright man who retained good health until his last few years, Glaisher enjoyed walking, bicycling, collecting, travel (often in the United States), and teaching as well as mathematical research and participation in the meetings of scientific societies. He became an authority on English pottery, writing parts of several books on the subject and leaving his fine collection to the Fitzwilliam Museum, Cambridge. Glaisher was active in the British Association for the Advancement of Science, as president in 1900 and as a member of several committees. He was the "reporter," as well as a member—along with A. Cayley, G. G. Stokes, W. Thomson, and H. J. S. Smith—of the Committee on Mathematical Tables. Its 175-page *Report,* containing much historical and bibliographical data, appeared in 1873.

Glaisher's honors included memberships in the councils of the Royal Society (for three different periods), the London Mathematical Society, and the Royal Astronomical Society (from 1874 until his death), as well as the presidency of the last two societies. Cambridge University awarded him the new D.Sc. degree in 1887, and Trinity College of Dublin and Victoria University of Manchester awarded him honorary D.Sc. degrees. Glaisher was an honorary fellow of the Royal Society of Edinburgh, of the Manchester Literary and Philosophical Society, and of the National Academy of Sciences, Washington. He was awarded the De Morgan Medal of the London Mathematical Society in 1908 and the Sylvester Medal of the Royal Society in 1913.

Glaisher's first paper typified three of his continuing interests: special functions, tables, and the history of mathematics. It was written while he was an undergraduate and was communicated to the Royal Society by Arthur Cayley in 1870. It dealt with the integral sine, cosine, and exponential functions and included both tables which he had calculated and much historical matter. Glaisher's first astronomical paper also typified his interest: "The Law of the Facility of Errors of Observations and on the Method of Least Squares," published in the *Memoirs of the Royal Astronomical Society* for 1872. This paper was inspired by a historical note in an American journal giving Robert Adrain credit for the independent discovery of Gauss's law of errors. A. R. Forsyth labels it, along with a paper on Jacopo Riccati's differential equation and one on the history of plus and minus signs, as "classical."

Glaisher published nearly 400 articles and notes

but never a book of his own. The nearest he came was the *Report* noted above, the *Collected Mathematical Papers of Henry John Stephen Smith,* which he edited, and volumes VIII and IX of the *Mathematical Tables* of the British Association for the Advancement of Science, published in 1940. The latter were revisions and extensions of number theoretical tables (divisors, Euler's ϕ function and its inverse, and others) which he had completed in 1884.

Glaisher served as editor of two journals, *Messenger of Mathematics* (1871–1928) and *Quarterly Journal of Mathematics* (from 1878 until his death). G. H. Hardy wrote, "A generation of well known English mathematicians began their careers as authors in the *Messenger,*" and stated that Glaisher was ". . . underestimated as a mathematician. He wrote a great deal of very uneven quality, and he was old-fashioned, but the best of his work is really good." He applied to number theory, especially to representations by sums of squares, the properties of special functions, especially elliptic modular functions.

Glaisher's interest in students and publications affected American mathematics. He befriended an American student at Cambridge, Thomas S. Fiske, and took him to meetings of the London Mathematical Society. When he returned to Columbia University, Fiske organized the New York Mathematical Society (later the American Mathematical Society) in 1888 and copied the format of the *Messenger* when the *Bulletin of the New York Mathematical Society* was initiated.

Forsyth's characterization of Glaisher as "a mathematical stimulus to others rather than a pioneer" seems sound.

BIBLIOGRAPHY

I. Original Works. For lists of papers see Poggendorff, III, 524–525; IV, 502; V, 427–428; VI, 900.

For Glaisher's contributions to number theory, see the author index in Leonard Eugene Dickson, *History of the Theory of Numbers* (New York, 1934). "On Riccati's Equation and its Transformations and on Some Definite Integrals Which Satisfy Them," is in *Philosophical Transactions of the Royal Society of London,* **172,** pt. 3 (1882), 759–828. His article on the history of plus and minus signs appeared in *Messenger of Mathematics,* vol. **51** (1922).

II. Secondary Literature. A. R. Forsyth published a biography in *Journal of the London Mathematical Society,* **4,** pt. 2, no. 14 (Apr. 1929), 101–112, repr. in *Proceedings of the Royal Society,* **126A,** no. A802 (22 Jan. 1929), i–xi, with a portrait facing p. i. Forsyth also wrote the biography in *Dictionary of National Biography. 1922–1930* (London, 1937), pp. 339–340, which records that there is a pencil drawing of Glaisher by Francis Dodd in Trinity College, Cambridge.

See also H. H. Turner, "James Whitbread Lee Glaisher," in *Monthly Notices of the Royal Astronomical Society,* **89** (Feb. 1929), 300–308; and G. H. Hardy, "Dr. Glaisher and the Messenger of Mathematics," in *Messenger of Mathematics,* **58** (1929), 159–160.

Phillip S. Jones

GÖDEL, KURT FRIEDRICH (*b.* Brünn, Moravia [now Brno, Czechoslovakia], 28 April 1906; *d.* Princeton, New Jersey, 14 January 1978)

The character and achievement of Gödel, the most important logician since Aristotle, bear comparison with those of the most eminent mathematicians. His aversion to controversy is reminiscent of Newton's, while his relatively small number of publications—each quite precise and almost all making a major contribution—echo Gauss's motto of "few but ripe." Like Newton, he revolutionized a branch of mathematics—in this case, mathematical logic—giving it a structure and a Kuhnian paradigm for research. His notebooks, like those of Gauss, show him to be well in advance of his contemporaries. While Newton made substantial efforts in theology as well as in mathematical physics, Gödel contributed to philosophy as well as to mathematical logic. But during the formative period of his career, unlike either Gauss or Newton, he was torn between two cultures, the Austrian and the American, and he spent most of his life on foreign soil.

Life. Gödel's family belonged to the German-speaking minority in Brünn, a textile-producing city in the Austro-Hungarian province of Moravia, where they had lived for several generations. His grandfather, Josef Gödel, after marrying a Viennese wife, Aloisia Keimel, moved from Brünn to Vienna, where he worked in the leather industry. He allegedly committed suicide in the 1890's. Subsequently his wife left their son, Rudolf, with a sister-in-law, "Aunt Anna," who raised him in Brünn and later lived with Kurt's family until her death. Rudolf was first sent to a gymnasium, where the classical education bored him, and then to a weavers' school, from which he graduated with honors. An energetic and practical man intrigued by weaving machinery, he worked until his death for the Friedrich Redlich textile factory in Brünn, eventually becoming manager and part owner of it—a man of property who belonged to the upper middle class. He married Marianne Handschuh, the daughter of a weaver originally from the Rhineland. She had been educated at a French institute in Brünn and had broad cultural interests. They had two children; the elder, Rudolf, became a radiologist in Vienna; the younger was Kurt Gödel.

According to his brother, Kurt had a happy childhood, though he was shy and easily upset. His family dubbed him Herr Warum (Mr. Why) because of his continual questions. When two weeks old, he was baptized a Lutheran, his mother's religion, with Friedrich Redlich as his godfather and as the source of his middle name, Friedrich; his father remained nominally Old Catholic. At the age of five, according to his brother, he experienced a mild anxiety neurosis, from which he recovered completely. Three or four years later he contracted rheumatic fever, which, despite his recovery, left him convinced that his heart had been permanently damaged. World War I did not directly affect him, since Brünn was far from the fighting, but the establishment of Czechoslovakia as a nation in 1918 tended to isolate the German-speaking minority there. In 1929 he was to renounce his Czechoslovakian citizenship and officially become an Austrian.

Gödel's education began in September 1912, when he enrolled in the Evangelische Privat-Volks- und Bürgerschule, a Lutheran school in Brünn, from which he graduated in 1916. That fall he entered the Staats-Realgymnasium, a German-language high school in Brünn, where he excelled in mathematics, languages, and religion. (He took religious questions more seriously than the rest of his family, later describing his belief as "theistic.") As an adolescent he became interested first in foreign languages, then in history, and finally, around 1920, in mathematics; about a year later he was attracted to philosophy as well, and in 1922 he read Kant. According to his brother, he had mastered a good deal of university mathematics before graduating from the gymnasium in 1924.

That year Gödel matriculated at the University of Vienna, intending to study mathematics, physics, and philosophy, and to take a degree in physics. He had become interested in science by reading Goethe's theory of colors. At the university he attended lectures on theoretical physics by Hans Thirring, who had just published a book on the theory of relativity, and his interests focused on the foundations of physics. But about 1926, influenced by the number theorist Philipp Furtwängler, he changed to mathematics. During 1927 he attended Karl Menger's course in dimension theory. About this time his philosophical interests were greatly stimulated through a course in the history of philosophy given by Heinrich Gomperz.

Soon Hans Hahn, an analyst intrigued by general topology and logic, became his principal teacher and introduced him to the group of philosophers around Moritz Schlick, the logical positivists later known abroad as the Vienna Circle. He wrote in the curriculum vitae submitted with his *Habilitationsschrift*: "At that time [1926–1928], stimulated by Prof. Schlick, whose philosophical circle I frequently attended, I was also occupied with modern works in epistemology." In 1928 he grew less involved with the Vienna Circle and attended its meetings sporadically until 1933, when he stopped going altogether. This occurred, despite their common interest in logic, because Gödel's Platonism conflicted with their positivism. "I only agreed with some of their tenets," he later noted; "I never believed that mathematics is syntax of language." All the same, he remained in contact with one member of the Vienna Circle, Rudolf Carnap, whose 1928 lectures on mathematical logic and the philosophical foundations of arithmetic strongly influenced the future direction of his research.

In February 1929, Gödel's father died from an abscess of the prostate, a medical condition that Kurt later experienced. Soon his mother moved with her two sons to Vienna. The three of them often went to the theater together, since Kurt was greatly interested in it at that time; his taste in music ran to light opera and Viennese operettas. In 1937 his mother returned to the family villa in Brünn; she died three decades later, in Vienna.

After Gödel completed his dissertation in the summer of 1929, it was approved by his supervisor Hahn and by Furtwängler. He received a doctorate in mathematics from the University of Vienna in February 1930. During the academic year 1931–1932 he was assistant in Hahn's seminar in mathematical logic, selecting much of the material discussed.

By invitation, in October 1929 Gödel began attending Menger's mathematics colloquium, which was modeled on the Vienna Circle. There in May 1930 he presented his dissertation results, which he had discussed with Alfred Tarski three months earlier, during the latter's visit to Vienna. From 1932 to 1936 he published numerous short articles in the proceedings of that colloquium (including his only collaborative work) and was coeditor of seven of its volumes. Gödel attended the colloquium quite regularly and participated actively in many discussions, confining his comments to brief remarks that were always stated with the greatest precision.

At a conference in September 1930, Gödel announced his startling first incompleteness theorem: there are formally undecidable propositions in number theory. He sent a paper on his incompleteness results to *Monatshefte für Mathematik und Physik* in November 1930; it was published two months later. The theorem constituted his *Habilitationsschrift*, which he submitted to the University of Vienna in June 1932 and for which Hahn served as referee. In December 1932 Hahn wrote an evaluation of it for the university, praising Gödel's submission as

> a scientific achievement of the first rank which . . . will find its place in the history of mathematics. . . . The work submitted by Dr. Gödel surpasses by far the standard usually required for *Habilitation*. Today Dr. Gödel is already the principal authority in the field of symbolic logic and research on the foundations of mathematics.

The following March, Gödel was made *Privatdozent*, and during the summer he gave his first course, on the foundations of arithmetic. Extremely shy as a teacher, he always lectured to the blackboard; he had few students. During the next seven years he gave only two more courses at the University of Vienna.

The most obvious reason for this situation was Gödel's increasing association with the Institute for Advanced Study at Princeton, of which he was a member for three years during the 1930's; a less obvious reason was the state of his mental health. When the institute first began operation in the fall of 1933, he was a visiting member for the academic year, thanks to the efforts of Oswald Veblen, and from February to May 1934, he lectured on the incompleteness results. There he made Einstein's acquaintance, but came to know him well only a decade later. Lonely and depressed while at Princeton, he had a nervous breakdown after returning to Europe in June 1934, and was treated for this condition by the eminent psychiatrist Julius von Wagner-Jauregg. That fall he again stayed briefly in a sanatorium (the first stay had been in 1931, for suicidal depression), postponing an invitation to return to the Institute for Advanced Study for the spring term of 1935 and informing Veblen that the delay was due to an inflammation of the jawbone. At Vienna, during the summer semester of 1935, he gave a course on topics in mathematical logic, then traveled to Princeton in September. Suffering from depression and overwork, he resigned suddenly from the institute in mid-November, returned to Europe in early December, and spent the winter and spring of 1936 in a sanatorium. Veblen who had seen him to the boat, wrote to Paul Heegaard (who was on the organizing committee for the 1936 International Congress of Mathematicians), urging that Gödel "be invited to give one of the principal addresses. There is no doubt that his work on the foundations of mathematics is the most important which has been done in this field in our time."

In 1935 Gödel had made the first breakthrough in his new area of research: set theory. During May and June 1937 he lectured at Vienna on his striking result that the axiom of choice is relatively consistent. That summer he obtained the much stronger result that the generalized continuum hypothesis is relatively consistent; and in September 1937 John von Neumann, an editor of the Princeton journal *Annals of Mathematics*, urged him to publish his new discoveries there. Yet Gödel did not announce them until November 1938, and then not in the *Annals* but in a brief summary communicated to the *Proceedings of the National Academy of Sciences*.

Two weeks after marrying Adele Porkert Nimbursky, a nightclub dancer, on 20 September 1938, Gödel left Austria to work for a term at the Institute for Advanced Study. At Menger's invitation he spent the first half of 1939 as visiting professor at Notre Dame. Both at the institute and at Notre Dame, he gave a lecture course on his relative consistency results in set theory; he also presented them in December 1938 at the annual meeting of the American Mathematical Society. In February 1939, Gödel wrote to Veblen, asking him to submit the manuscript containing the proof to the *Proceedings of the National Academy of Sciences*, and promising a lengthy article with a detailed proof for the *Annals of Mathematics*. No such article ever appeared in the *Annals*, and the standard source for his proof remained notes of his lectures taken by George W. Brown in the fall/winter of 1938–1939 and published in 1940.

When he returned to Vienna in June 1939, both Gödel's personal situation and the global one were darkening. After the *Anschluss* of March 1938, when Nazi Germany forcibly annexed Austria, the position of *Privatdozent* had been abolished and replaced by that of *Dozent neuer Ordnung*. Most lecturers at the University of Vienna were quickly transferred to the new position, but Gödel was not. He formally applied for it in September 1939. Within a week he received a letter responding to his application and noting that he moved in Jewish-liberal circles, although he was not known to have spoken for or against the Nazis. Finally, in June 1940, he was granted the position of *Dozent neuer Ordnung*, when it was no longer of any use to him. Ironically, from 1941 to 1945 he was listed at the University of Vienna as *Dozent für Grundlagen der Mathematik und Logik*.

During the summer of 1939 Austria, as a part of

Germany, was preparing for war. Gödel, ordered by the military authorities to report for a physical examination, was declared "fit for garrison duty" in September and feared that he would soon be called into service. In late November he wrote to Veblen, urgently seeking an American nonquota immigrant visa. During the summer, in Vienna, ultrarightist students had physically assaulted him. While attempting to obtain German exit permits for himself and his wife, he lectured at Göttingen in December on the continuum problem. By early January 1940, thanks to the vigorous efforts of Veblen and of Abraham Flexner, those permits had arrived, as had the U.S. visas and the Soviet transit visas. Since the war made it dangerous to cross the Atlantic, he took the Trans-Siberian Railway, then a ship from Yokohama to San Francisco, finally reaching Princeton, where he was appointed an ordinary member of the Institute. He never returned to Europe.

In Princeton, Gödel had a quiet social life, his closest friends being Albert Einstein and, later, Oskar Morgenstern, who was also from Vienna. Both of them served as witnesses when he became an American citizen in 1948. The gregarious Einstein and the reclusive Gödel often walked home together from the institute. During 1942 Gödel had begun to be close to Einstein, and their conversations generally concerned philosophy, physics, or politics. Einstein regularly informed him of advances in unified field theory, but Gödel did not collaborate with Einstein because he remained skeptical of this theory.

Gödel had no formal duties at the Institute for Advanced Studies, and thus was free to pursue his research. Several of his working notebooks from that time (in the now archaic Gabelsberger shorthand) record the development of his ideas. In particular, they chronicle his attempts around 1942 to prove the independence of the continuum hypothesis and of the axiom of choice. Slightly earlier, he found some essential errors in Jacques Herbrand's proof that there is a quantifier-free interpretation of first-order logic; these errors were independently rediscovered two decades later by Peter Andrews and others.

In 1943, however, Gödel began to turn his research from mathematics to philosophy—at first, philosophy of mathematics, and later, philosophy in general. He expressed his Platonist views publicly in two well-known articles, one on Russell's mathematical logic in 1944 and the other on Cantor's continuum problem in 1947. Later he wrote that "the greatest philosophical influence on me came from Leibniz, whom I studied about 1943–1946," adding that Kant influenced him to some degree. According to Gödel, his Platonism had earlier led him to give a philosophical analysis that culminated in the discovery of both his completeness theorem and his incompleteness results.

Moreover, it was Kant who stimulated Gödel, during the period 1947–1951, to consider new cosmological models, in some of which "time travel" into the past was theoretically possible. These models, so far removed from mathematical logic, echoed his work on differential geometry in Menger's colloquium in the early 1930's.

Late in his career, honors were showered upon Gödel in abundance. In 1946 he was finally made a permanent member of the Institute for Advanced Study. In 1950 he gave an invited address on relativity theory to the International Congress of Mathematicians, and the following year he was one of two recipients of the first Einstein Award. He was also asked to deliver the annual Gibbs Lecture to the American Mathematical Society, and did so in December 1951, arguing against mechanism in the philosophy of mind. That same year Yale University granted him an honorary D.Litt., and Harvard followed with an honorary Sc.D. in 1952. (Later there were two more honorary doctorates, one from Amherst College in 1967 and the other from Rockefeller University in 1972.) In 1955 Gödel was elected a member of the National Academy of Sciences. In 1957 he was elected a fellow of the American Academy of Arts and Sciences and, in 1967, an honorary member of the London Mathematical Society. He was made a foreign member of the Royal Society a year later, and a corresponding member of the Institut de France in 1972. The United States honored him in 1975 with a National Medal of Science.

Gödel repeatedly refused honors from Austrian academic institutions (for instance, in 1966, honorary membership in the Vienna Academy of Sciences), apparently because he was still perturbed by his treatment after the *Anschluss*. He could not, however, refuse the honorary doctorate that the University of Vienna awarded him posthumously.

After his promotion to professor of mathematics in 1953, Gödel spent a great deal of his time on institute business, particularly to ensure that aspiring young logicians were made visiting members. His promotion had been considerably delayed for fear of burdening him with administrative duties (and for fear that he would be overzealous in carrying them out).

Gödel's personality was idiosyncratic. Shy and solemn, short and slight of build, he was very courteous but lacked warmth and sensitivity. Since he was very much an introvert, he and his wife had guests infrequently; he found the excitement tiring. A hypochondriac whose health actually was relatively poor, he often complained of stomach trouble but remained distrustful of doctors, believing throughout his life that his medical judgment was better than theirs. (In the 1940's he delayed treatment of a bleeding duodenal ulcer for so long that blood transfusions were required to save his life.) Keenly sensitive to the cold, he was often seen in Princeton wearing a large overcoat, even on warm summer days.

In 1976 Gödel retired from the Institute for Advanced Study as professor emeritus. Soon illness and death visited those near to him. In 1977 his wife underwent major surgery, and Oskar Morgenstern, to whom he had become especially close since Einstein's death, died. His own health, uncertain throughout his life, had turned worse near the end of the 1960's. At that time he experienced a severe prostate condition, but he refused to have surgery performed, despite the urgings of his doctor and friends. During the last year of his life, he suffered from depression and paranoia. Late in December 1977, at his wife's insistence, he was hospitalized; two weeks later he died. According to the death certificate, this was due to "malnutrition and inanition" caused by a "personality disturbance." Fearing that his food would be poisoned, he refused to eat, and thus starved himself to death. His wife died three years later. They had no children.

Work. When, in 1928, Gödel began to do research in mathematical logic, it was not a well-defined field. It was still a part of the "foundations of mathematics"—a subject that belonged more to philosophy than to mathematics. As Ernst Zermelo described the situation in logic about that time, apropos of his axiomatization of set theory two decades earlier, "A generally accepted 'mathematical logic' . . . did not exist then, any more than it does today, when every foundational researcher has his own logistical system." The state of foundations was epitomized by the 1930 conference at Königsberg at which Gödel announced his incompleteness result. The conference was primarily devoted to a discussion of the three competing foundational schools—formalism, intuitionism, and logicism—that had dominated the subject for more than a decade.

Formalism, developed by David Hilbert, treated mathematics as a purely formal and syntactical subject in which meaning was introduced only at the metamathematical level. "Hilbert's program," as it was called, was concerned primarily with proving the consistency of classical mathematics and the existence of a decision procedure for it. Intuitionism, developed by L. E. J. Brouwer, stressed the role of intuition as opposed to the formal aspect, and rejected much of both classical logic and classical mathematics. Logicism, developed by Bertrand Russell and embodied in his *Principia Mathematica*, asserted that mathematics was a part of logic and could be developed as a logical system without any further recourse to intuition. All three schools were to influence Gödel, who followed none of them but established a new paradigm: mathematical logic as a part of classical mathematics, answering questions of genuine mathematical interest and only indirectly of philosophical import.

Gödel's dissertation, completed in 1929 and published the following year, grew out of a problem that Hilbert and Wilhelm Ackermann had posed in their book *Grundzüge der theoretische Logik*. (He became interested in this problem in 1928, a year before he first read *Principia Mathematica*.) Hilbert and Ackermann remarked that it was not known whether every valid formula of first-order logic is provable and, moreover, whether each axiom of first-order logic is independent. In his dissertation Gödel solved both problems, considering only a countable set of symbols, since uncountable languages had not yet been introduced. His solution to the first problem is now known as the completeness theorem for first-order logic. In addition to showing that every valid first-order formula is provable, and then extending this result to countably infinite sets of first-order formulas, he gave a different form of the theorem: A first-order formula (or a countable set of such formulas) is consistent if and only if it has a model. In this form the theorem made rigorous a long-standing fundamental belief of Hilbert's.

In 1930 a revised version of Gödel's dissertation was published, now supplemented by a theorem that became very important two decades later, the compactness theorem for first-order logic: A countably infinite set A of first-order formulas has a model if and only every finite subset of A has a model. The published version omitted the philosophical remarks found at the beginning of his dissertation, where he cast doubt on Hilbert's program (even hinting at possible incompleteness) at the same time that he furthered the program by his proof of the completeness theorem. Apparently his doubts about Hilbert's program had been nurtured by Brouwer's lectures, given at Vienna in March 1928, on the inadequacy of consistency as a criterion for mathematical existence.

Hilbert and Ackermann had made the theory of types their framework for logic, considering first-order logic and second-order logic as subsystems. Hence it is not surprising that Gödel, after publishing his completeness results, soon turned to considering higher-order logic. He began by an attack on Hilbert's problem of finding a finitist consistency proof for analysis (that is, second-order number theory). His attack first divided the problem into two parts: (1) to establish the consistency of number theory by means of finitist number theory, and (2) to show the consistency of analysis by means of (the truth of) number theory. But he found that truth in number theory cannot be defined within number theory itself, and so his plan of attack failed. Thereby he was led to his first incompleteness theorem, which he announced privately to Carnap on 26 August 1930.

On 7 September, Gödel made his first public announcement at the Königsberg conference. By 23 October, when he submitted an abstract of the result to the Vienna Academy of Sciences, he had obtained the second incompleteness theorem: The consistency of a formal system S cannot be proved in S if S contains elementary number theory, unless S is inconsistent. (Von Neumann, who had heard him discuss the first incompleteness theorem at Königsberg and was keenly interested in it, wrote to him on 20 November with an independent discovery of the second theorem.) Although Gödel proved his incompleteness results for higher-order logic—in particular, for the theory of types—he pointed out that they applied equally to axiomatic set theory. Adding finitely many new axioms would not change the situation, nor would adding infinitely many new axioms, as long as the resulting system was omega-consistent.

Although Gödel's incompleteness theorems were eventually recognized as the most important theorems of mathematical logic, at first they had a mixed reception. At Princeton, where von Neumann soon lectured on them, Stephen Kleene was enthusiastic about them but Alonzo Church believed, mistakenly, that his new formal system (which included the lambda calculus) could escape incompleteness. In Europe, Paul Bernays corresponded with Gödel about the results and, after some initial reservations, came to accept them. By contrast, Zermelo was skeptical both in correspondence and in person. As late as 1934, Hilbert denied in print that the incompleteness results refuted his program. During the correspondence with Bernays and Zermelo, Gödel showed that for a language truth cannot be defined in the same language, a theorem that was found independently by Tarski in 1933.

In 1932 Gödel published his formulation of the incompleteness results from the standpoint of first-order logic. If number theory is regarded as a formal system in first-order logic, then the above results about incompleteness and unprovability of consistency apply to S. If, however, S is extended by variables for sets of numbers, for sets of sets of numbers, and so on (together with the corresponding comprehension axioms), then we obtain a sequence of systems S_n; the consistency of each system is provable in all subsequent systems. But in each subsequent system there are undecidable propositions. Going up in type in this way, he noted, corresponds in a type-free system of set theory to adding axioms that postulate the existence of larger and larger infinite cardinalities. This was the beginning of Gödel's interest in large cardinal axioms, an interest that he elaborated in 1947 in regard to the continuum problem.

One consequence of Gödel's research was that in 1931 the editors of *Zentralblatt für Mathematik* invited him and Arend Heyting to prepare a joint report on the foundations of mathematics. Although Gödel labored for some time at this report, he eventually withdrew from the venture, and Heyting published his version alone in 1934. Gödel's fragmentary draft survives in his *Nachlass*.

From 1932 to 1936 Gödel published a variety of brief but substantial papers on logic as well as on differential and projective geometry, primarily for Menger's colloquium. The articles on geometry, all published in 1933, dealt with curvature in convex metric spaces, projective mappings, and coordinate-free differential geometry.

Articles on logic were more numerous and diverse, treating certain cases of Hilbert's decision problem (*Entscheidungsproblem*), the propositional calculus, intuitionistic logic and arithmetic, and speed-up theorems. In 1933 Gödel's results on the decision problem extended work by Ackermann and by Thoralf Skolem to obtain a sharp boundary between decidable and undecidable first-order formulas. In the propositional calculus he solved a problem of Hahn's by showing that some independence results in this calculus require infinite truth tables, and he answered a question of Menger's by formulating the propositional calculus so as to have uncountably many symbols. He did not, however, introduce a first-order language with uncountably many symbols, as Anatolii Ivanovich Maltsev was to do in 1936.

As for intuitionism, Gödel established that if only finitely many truth-values are permitted, then there is no completeness theorem for the intuitionistic propositional calculus; moreover, there are infinitely many systems of logic between the intuitionistic and the classical propositional calculi, each stronger than the previous system. In another paper he proved the philosophically important result that if intuitionistic number theory is consistent, then so is classical number theory; this was done by interpreting the latter theory within the former. Then Gödel reversed direction, showing that the intuitionistic propositional calculus can be given a "provability" interpretation within the classical propositional calculus—an interpretation that, by his second incompleteness theorem, cannot represent provability in a formal system.

What turned out to be an important contribution occurred in Gödel's 1934 lectures on incompleteness. There, refining a suggestion made by Herbrand three years earlier, he introduced the notion of a general recursive function. But he did not believe at the time that this notion captured the general informal concept of computability, and was convinced that it did so ("Church's thesis") only by Alan Turing's work in 1936.

In 1936 Gödel published the first example of a speed-up theorem—pointing out that if one goes from a logic S_n of order n to a logic S_{n+1} of next higher order, there are infinitely many theorems of S_n, each of whose shortest proof in S_{n+1} is vastly shorter than its shortest proof in S_n. Such speed-up theorems later were studied extensively in computer science.

Gödel's next major accomplishment occurred in set theory. Around 1930 he began to think about the continuum hypothesis and learned of Hilbert's attempt, during the period 1925–1928, to prove it. In contrast with Hilbert, he felt that one should not build up the sets involved in a strictly constructive way. Then he reconsidered the question from the standpoint of relative consistency and of models of set theory, in which his discoveries in time became just as famous as his incompleteness theorems. The first breakthrough came in 1935. In October, while at the Institute for Advanced Study, he informed von Neumann of his new result, obtained by means of his "constructible" sets, that the axiom of choice is consistent relative to the other axioms of set theory. When he gave a course on axiomatic set theory at Vienna in 1937, he used what was later called Bernays-Gödel set theory; this is a slight variant of Bernays' system (about which Bernays had informed him in a 1931 letter) used to identify a set with the corresponding class. One of those attending the course was Andrzej Mostowski, who later recalled that Gödel "constructed a model in which the axiom of choice was valid; at that time, I am sure that he did not have the consistency proof for the continuum hypothesis."

During this period Gödel was trying to prove that the generalized continuum hypothesis is true in the model of constructible sets. On 14 June 1937 he found the crucial step in establishing this fact. By September he had communicated his new result to von Neumann, but refrained from publishing it for over a year. When it appeared, late in 1938, it was clear that he had taken Zermelo's cumulative type hierarchy in set theory and had treated it from the standpoint of Russell's ramified theory of types, extending the latter theory to transfinite orders. In particular, Gödel stated that the generalized continuum hypothesis can be proved consistent relative to von Neumann's system of set theory, Zermelo-Fraenkel set theory, or the system of *Principia Mathematica*. At that time he did not mention first-order logic as the basis of his notion of "constructible set" but merely regarded it as excluding impredicative definitions.

When he communicated his second brief paper on the subject, in February 1939, Gödel spelled out in detail how to prove that the generalized continuum hypothesis holds in the model. The hierarchy of constructible sets was introduced by transfinite recursion in such a way that its definition differed from Zermelo's cumulative hierarchy only at successor ordinals, where $M_{\alpha+1}$, the next level after M_α, was defined as the set of all subsets of M_α that are first-order definable from parameters in M_α. The critical step, later called the condensation lemma, used a form of the Löwenheim-Skolem theorem to show that each constructible subset of $M\omega_\alpha$ is $\aleph_\alpha$. Then the generalized continuum hypothesis holds in the model, since the cardinality of $M\omega_\alpha$ is $\aleph_\alpha$. Finally, Gödel gave two set models, $M\omega_\omega$ and M_Ω, where Ω was the first inaccessible cardinal. The first of these was a model of Zermelo set theory, while the second was a model of Zermelo-Fraenkel set theory.

In the 1938 paper Gödel introduced the axiom of constructibility, which stated that every set is a constructible set. He asserted that this proposition, "added as a new axiom, seems to give a natural completion of the axioms of set theory, in so far as it determines the vague notion of an arbitrary infinite set in a definite way." The axiom of constructibility, as he showed in the 1939 paper and in the 1940 monograph, implies both the axiom of choice and the generalized continuum hypothesis. The last step was to establish that the axiom of constructibility holds in the model. To do so, he introduced and developed the critical notion of being "absolute." That is, a formula is absolute for a model if it holds in the model precisely when it is true.

Gödel's 1938 paper also asserted that the axiom of constructibility implies that there is a nonmeasurable set of real numbers (as well as an uncountable set of real numbers having no perfect subset) that occurs low in the projective hierarchy. These results followed from an observation of Stanislaw Ulam, who noticed that in the model there is a projective well-ordering of the real numbers.

Gödel's results on constructible sets became known largely through his 1940 monograph, based on lectures delivered at the Institute for Advanced Study during October–December 1938. There he did not use the hierarchy M_α but presented the constructible sets as built up by transfinite recursion from eight fundamental operations on sets, formulated within Bernays-Gödel set theory. Later set theorists tended to find this second approach less intuitive than the first.

It is uncertain why Gödel refrained from submitting for publication his results on the relative consistency of the axiom of choice and the generalized continuum hypothesis, known by the summer of 1937, until November 1938. But a clue can be found in a letter he wrote to Menger in December 1937:

> I have continued my work on the continuum problem last summer and I finally succeeded in proving the consistency of the continuum hypothesis (even the generalized form) with respect to general set theory. But for the time being please do not tell anyone of this. So far, I have communicated this, besides to yourself, only to von Neumann. . . . Right now I am trying to prove also the independence of the continuum hypothesis, but do not yet know whether I will succeed with it. (Wang, *Reflections*, p. 99)

Gödel persisted in his attempts to prove that the continuum hypothesis is independent. During the summer of 1942, while on vacation in Maine, he obtained a proof of a related result, the independence of the axiom of choice relative to the theory of types as well as the independence of the axiom of constructibility. But he did not succeed in showing the independence of the continuum hypothesis.

Gödel never published his result on the independence of the axiom of choice. According to comments he made later to John Addison and others, he feared that such independence results would lead research in set theory "in the wrong direction." What he considered to be the right direction became apparent in his expository paper of 1947 on the continuum problem.

It was very likely, he observed in that paper, that the continuum hypothesis would eventually be proved independent of the axioms of set theory; to seek such a proof was the best way to attack the continuum problem. But, he insisted, even such a proof of independence would not solve the continuum problem because, he argued Platonistically, the cumulative hierarchy of sets forms a well-determined reality, and thus it should be possible to establish the truth or falsity of the continuum hypothesis. The way to proceed was to search for new true axioms (especially large cardinal axioms) that would settle its truth or falsity. It was very likely, he believed, that the continuum hypothesis was false.

In 1946 Gödel had delivered a paper on set theory at the Princeton Bicentennial Conference on Problems of Mathematics. There he introduced the notion of ordinal-definable set (which was related to, but distinct from, his notion of constructible set), and conjectured that the ordinal-definable sets would provide a model of set theory in which the axiom of choice held, thereby providing a new proof for its relative consistency. Moreover, Gödel asserted, it would be impossible to prove that the continuum hypothesis held in that model. Because this paper circulated only in manuscript at the time, the ordinal-definable sets were rediscovered independently in 1962 by John Myhill and Dana Scott, who used them in the way proposed by Gödel.

During the 1940's Gödel turned increasingly to philosophy. The first fruits were found in his 1944 article on Russell's mathematical logic. Like almost all of his publications from this date on, it was requested by an editor—in this case by Paul Schilpp for the volume *The Philosophy of Bertrand Russell*. The article, solicited in November 1942, was sent to Schilpp six months later. In September 1943 Gödel wrote to Russell, urging him to reply in detail to the criticisms contained in the article. But Russell, who had not worked in logic for three decades, declined to answer the criticisms and merely granted that they had some merit.

This article was Gödel's first public defense of his Platonism, which was unfashionable in philosophy of mathematics at the time. He put forward suggestions for further research in foundations, especially in regard to the theory of types, and considered (though he was somewhat dubious) the possibility of infinitely long logical formulas. Such infinitary logics were fully developed only a decade later by Alfred Tarski and others.

In July 1946, Schilpp asked Gödel to write an article (completed three years later) for the volume *Albert Einstein: Philosopher-Scientist*. This request prompted Gödel to return to his early interest in the foundations of physics, and thereby led him to publish two technical papers on the general theory of relativity (1949). Highly original and eventually quite influential, these papers gave the first rotating solutions to Einstein's cosmological equations. The original solution put forward by Gödel permitted an observer, in principle, to travel into the past, while his later solutions (for an expanding universe) did not allow this. The article for Schilpp's volume dealt with the relationship between relativity theory and Kantian philosophy. Gödel elaborated on this subject in a still unpublished paper, in which he argued that relativity justified certain aspects of Kant's view of time. "Einstein told me," Oskar Morgenstern wrote in May 1972, "that Gödel's papers were the most important ones on relativity theory since his own [Einstein's] original paper appeared. On the other hand, other cosmologists such as Robertson did not like Gödel's work at all."

In December 1951, Gödel delivered to the American Mathematical Society the Gibbs Lecture, "Some Basic Theorems on the Foundations of Mathematics and Their Implications," which remains unpublished. In it he discussed the implications of his incompleteness theorems for mathematics and philosophy. His chief result was that "either mathematics is incompletable in the sense that its evident axioms can never be comprised in a finite rule, i.e. the human mind (even within the realm of pure mathematics) infinitely surpasses the powers of any finite machine, or else there exist absolutely unsolvable Diophantine problems." From this time on Gödel made it a policy to refuse any invitation to lecture, turning down many important ones.

In May 1953 Schilpp requested a third article from Gödel, this time for the volume *The Philosophy of Rudolf Carnap*. Gödel worked for an extended period on this article, "Is Mathematics Syntax of Language?" which was devoted to showing why the answer was no. He was, however, not satisfied with any of his six versions of the article, and it remains unpublished. Indeed, because he published so little after the 1940's, Gödel appeared rather unproductive to many of the mathematicians interested in his work.

In 1958 there appeared the last of Gödel's published papers, solicited two years earlier for a volume honoring Bernays' seventieth birthday. Known as the "Dialectica Interpretation" (after the journal *Dialectica*, in which it was published), the paper supplied a new quantifier-free interpretation for intuitionistic logic by using primitive recursive functionals of any finite type. The paper extended Hilbert's program by not confining the notion of "finitary," as Hilbert had, to concrete objects, but permitting abstract objects as well. This was an instance, however, of a result that was first published decades after Gödel found it. For he discovered it in 1941 and lectured on it that year at both Princeton and Yale. Late in the 1960's he wrote an expanded version of this paper, but never published it—despite Bernays' repeated pleas.

In 1963, when Paul Cohen discovered the method of forcing and used it to prove the independence of the axiom of choice as well as that of the continuum hypothesis, he went to Princeton to seek Gödel's *imprimatur*. At Cohen's request, Gödel submitted Cohen's article containing these results to the *Proceedings of the National Academy of Sciences*, in which Gödel's relative consistency results had appeared a quarter-century earlier. Their correspondence makes it clear that Gödel made many revisions in Cohen's paper.

That correspondence also reveals Gödel's concern with showing the existence of a "scale" of length $\aleph_1$ majorizing the real numbers (treated as the set of all sequences of natural numbers). He regarded this question as, "once the continuum hypothesis is dropped, the key problem concerning the structure of the continuum." In 1970 Gödel drafted a paper, intended for the *Proceedings*, on this problem and gave in it some axioms on scales (the square axioms) that, he claimed, imply that the continuum hypothesis is false and that the power of the real numbers is $\aleph_2$. Gödel submitted this paper to Tarski for his judgment and, when D. A. Martin found an error in it, withdrew it. Thus his final contribution to Cantor's continuum problem ended inconclusively.

During the 1970's, and perhaps earlier, in his philosophical research Gödel pursued the ideal of establishing metaphysics as an exact axiomatic theory, but he never achieved what he regarded as a satisfactory treatment. His work in this area was stimulated by Leibniz's *Monadology*. Leibniz also influenced his version, which began to circulate about 1970, of the ontological argument for the existence of God.

Since much on Gödel's philosophical work remains unpublished, his philosophical influence will likely increase as more of his work becomes available. By contrast, his mathematical work (essentially complete three decades before his death) was, and is, in the words of von Neumann, "a landmark which will remain visible far in space and time."

BIBLIOGRAPHY

I. Original Works. Gödel's *Collected Works* are being prepared by Solomon Feferman (editor in chief), John W. Dawson, Jr., Stephen C. Kleene, Gregory H. Moore,

Robert M. Solovay, and Jean van Heijenoort. Vol. I, containing publications from 1929 to 1936, was published in 1986; the second volume, containing his publications after 1937, appeared in 1988. A third volume, consisting of correspondence and previously unpublished manuscripts, is in preparation.

Gödel's scientific *Nachlass* is in the Firestone Library at Princeton University. Part of his personal *Nachlass*, including about 1,000 letters (mainly to his mother), is in Vienna at the Nueu Stadtbibliothek.

II. SECONDARY LITERATURE. An excellent account of Gödel's life and work is in the biography by Solomon Feferman in vol. I of Godel's *Collected Works* (1986), 1–36. For more personal accounts, see G. Kreisel, "Kurt Gödel," in *Biographical Memoirs of Fellows of the Royal Society*, **26** (1980), 149–224 (corrections *ibid.*, **27**, p. 697, and **28**, p. 718); and Hao Wang, *Reflections on Kurt Gödel* (Cambridge, Mass., 1987). On Gödel's life, see also Curt Christian, "Leben und Wirken Kurt Gödels," in *Monatshefte für Mathematik*, **89** (1980), 261–273; John W. Dawson, Jr., "Kurt Gödel in Sharper Focus," in *Mathematical Intelligencer*, **6**, no. 4 (1984), 9–17; Stephen C. Kleene, "Kurt Gödel," in *Biographical Memoirs. National Academy of Sciences*, **56** (1987), 135–178; Willard V. Quine, "Kurt Gödel," in *Year Book of the American Philosophical Society 1978* (1979), 81–84; and Hao Wang, "Kurt Gödel's Intellectual Development," in *Mathematical Intelligencer*, **1** 1978), 182–184, and "Some Facts About Kurt Gödel," in *Journal of Symbolic Logic*, **46** (1981), 653–659. Studies of his work are in the "Introductory Notes" in the *Collected Works*, as well as in Martin Davis, "Why Gödel Didn't Have Church's Thesis," in *Information and Control*, **54** (1982), 3–24; John W. Dawson, Jr., in *PSA 1984: Proceedings of the 1984 Biennial Meeting of the Philosophy of Science Association*, **2** (1985), 253–271; Stephen C. Kleene, "The Work of Kurt Gödel," in *Journal of Symbolic Logic*, **41** (1976), 761–778 (addendum, *ibid.*, **43**, 613) and in articles by Stephen C. Kleene, G. Kreisel, and O. Taussky-Todd in *Gödel Remembered* (1987), edited by P. Weingartner and L. Schmetterer. On Gödel's contributions to philosophy, see Hao Wang, *From Mathematics to Philosophy* (1974). Finally, there is a biographical video, 'Dr. Kurt Gödel: Ein mathematischer Mythos," by P. Weibel and W. Schimanovich.

GREGORY H. MOORE

GOLDBACH, CHRISTIAN (*b.* Königsberg, Prussia [now Kaliningrad, R.S.F.S.R.], 18 March 1690; *d.* Moscow, Russia, 20 November 1764)

The son of a minister, Goldbach studied medicine and mathematics at the University of Königsberg before embarking, sometime around 1710, on a series of travels across Europe. Everywhere he went, he formed acquaintances with the leading scientists of his day, laying the basis for his later success as first corresponding secretary of the Imperial Academy of Sciences in St. Petersburg. Among others, he met Leibniz in Leipzig in 1711, Nikolaus I Bernoulli and Abraham de Moivre in London in 1712, and Nikolaus II Bernoulli in Venice in 1721. At Nikolaus II's suggestion, in 1723 Goldbach initiated a correspondence with Daniel Bernoulli which continued until 1730. Back in Königsberg in 1724, Goldbach met Jakob Hermann and Georg Bilfinger on their way to participate in the formation of the Imperial Academy and decided to follow them. Writing from Riga in July 1725, he petitioned the president-designate of the new academy, L. L. Blumentrost, for a post in that body. Among his references he named General James Bruce, commander of the imperial forces, with whom he had exchanged ideas on a problem in ballistics around 1718. Although at first informed that no places were open, Goldbach soon received the position of professor of mathematics and historian of the academy at a yearly salary of 600 rubles. In the latter capacity he acted as recording secretary from the first meeting until January 1728, when he moved to Moscow.

That move resulted from Goldbach's new post as tutor to Tsarevich Peter II and his distant cousin Anna of Courland. Introduced into court circles by Blumentrost as early as 1726, Goldbach was in a position to benefit from the split between Peter II and Prince Menshikov by replacing the tutors appointed by the prince. Peter's sudden death in 1730 ended Goldbach's teaching career but not his connections with the imperial court. He continued to serve Peter's successor Anna and returned to St. Petersburg and the Imperial Academy only when she moved the court there in 1732. While in Moscow in 1729, Goldbach began the exchange of letters with Leonhard Euler that would continue regularly until 1763.

Returning to the Imperial Academy in 1732, Goldbach quickly rose to a commanding position. Under the presidency of Baron Johann-Albrecht Korf, he was first designated corresponding secretary (1732) and later named a *Kollegialrat* and, together with J. D. Schuhmacher, was charged with the administration of the Academy (1737). At the same time he rose steadily in court and government circles. The two roles began to conflict seriously in 1740, when Goldbach requested release from administrative duties at the Academy; and his promotion to *Staatsrat* in the Ministry of Foreign Affairs in 1742 ended his ties to the Imperial Academy. In 1744 his new position was confirmed with a raise in salary and (in 1746) a grant of land; in 1760 he attained the high rank of privy councilor at 3,000 rubles annually. That same year he set down guidelines for the education of the royal children that served as a model during the next century.

Coupled with a vast erudition that equally well addressed mathematics and science or philology and archaeology, and with a superb command of Latin style and equal fluency in German and French, Goldbach's polished manners and cosmopolitan circle of friends and acquaintances assured his success in an elite society struggling to emulate its western neighbors. But this very erudition and political success prevented Goldbach's obvious talent in mathematics from attaining its full promise. Unable or unwilling to concentrate his efforts, he dabbled in mathematics, achieving nothing of lasting value but stimulating others through his flashes of insight.

Goldbach's mathematical education set the pattern for his episodic career. Rather than engaging in systematic reading and study, he apparently learned his mathematics in bits and pieces from the various people he met, with the result that later he frequently repeated results already achieved or was unable to take full advantage of his insights. As he himself related in a letter to Daniel Bernoulli, he first encountered the subject of infinite series while talking to Nikolaus I Bernoulli at Oxford in 1712. Unable to understand a treatise by Jakob I Bernoulli on the subject, loaned to him by Nikolaus, he dropped the matter until 1717, when he read Leibniz's article on the quadrature of the circle in the *Acta eruditorum.* His reawakened interest led to his own article "Specimen methodi ad summas serierum," which appeared in the *Acta* in 1720. Only afterward did Goldbach discover that the substance of his article formed part of Jakob I's *Ars conjectandi,* published in 1713. In his article "De divisione curvarum . . ." Goldbach frankly admitted that Johann I Bernoulli had already solved the problem in question but that he could not remember the solution and so was deriving it again. Often Goldbach's mathematical knowledge showed surprising bare spots. Impressed by his solution of several cases of the Riccati equation (in "De casibus quibus integrari potest aequatio differentialis . . ." and "Methodus integrandi aequationis differentialis . . ." and in correspondence),[1] Daniel Bernoulli encouraged him to extend his results to exponential functions. Goldbach replied that he knew nothing about exponential functions and did not want to give the impression that he did.

Of Goldbach's other published articles, the two on infinite series—"De transformatione serierum" and "De terminis generalibus serierum"—and the one on the theory of equations, "Criteria quaedam aequationum . . .," show the greatest originality. "De transformatione serierum," read to the Imperial Academy in 1725, contains a technique for transforming one series, *A,* into another series, *B,* having the same sum, through term-by-term addition of *A* to, or subtraction of *A* from, a series, *C,* of which the sum is zero. Adjustment of the technique leads to a similar transformation through multiplication of the given series by a series of which the sum is one. In reply to objections that the multiplicative method may involve a divergent series as unit multiplier,[2] Goldbach defended the use of such a series provided that it leads to a convergent result. "De terminis generalibus serierum," read in 1728, continues the work begun in "Specimen methodi ad summas serierum" (1720) by addressing the problem of determining the "general term" of any sequence;[3] that is, it seeks a function (either explicit or finitely recursive) that yields the *n*th term of the sequence for a given *n*. Goldbach shows that the general term can always be expressed as an infinite series and that the problem therefore reduces to one of finding a general formula for the sum of that series. The general term of an infinite sequence proves useful, he argues, both for interpolation of missing terms and for the determination of terms for noninteger indices. Although Goldbach and Daniel Bernoulli corresponded on the specific problem of determining the general term of the sequence $\{n!\}$, neither could offer a solution (Euler later provided one).

In the article "Criteria quaedam aequationum quarum nulla radix rationalis est" Goldbach begins from results contained in "Excerpta a litteris C. G. ad * * * Regiomonte datis" and applies further some of the number-theoretical results worked out in correspondence with Euler to obtain a technique for testing quickly whether an algebraic equation has a rational root. For equations of the form $x^n = P(x)$, where P is an algebraic polynomial of degree $n - 1$ or less, the technique rests basically on determining all integers m for which P can be expressed in the form $mxR(x) + r$ and then ascertaining whether r is an nth-degree residue *modulo m.* If no such residue exists, the equation in question has no rational root.

If, in the realm of analysis, Goldbach's native talent could not substitute for thorough training in the subject, that talent did come into full play in his correspondence with Euler on number theory, a field then still at a rudimentary stage of development. Here Goldbach could be provocative on a fundamental level, as "Demonstratio theorematis Fermatiani . . ." and "Criteria quaedam aequationum quarum nulla radix rationalis est" show. Calling attention in his correspondence to Pierre de Fermat's assertion that all numbers of the form $2^{2^n} + 1$ are prime, he stimulated Euler's disproof for the case $n = 5$ (Euler's memoir in fact immediately follows Goldbach's "Criteria . . ."). Not all of his suggestions led to such positive results. In 1742 Goldbach conjectured that all even numbers may be expressed as the sum of two primes (taking 1 as a prime where necessary). Euler agreed with the assertion but could offer no proof, nor has any proof of "Goldbach's conjecture" yet been found. Goldbach also stated that every odd number may be expressed as the sum of three primes; in the form given it by Edward Waring (which excludes 1 as a prime) this assertion also remains an unproved conjecture. The above are only the outstanding results of the prolix correspondence with Euler on number theory.[4] That correspondence as a whole marks Goldbach as one of the few men of his day who understood the implications of Fermat's new approach to the subject.

NOTES

1. The solution includes the full conditions for the integrability of binomial differentials usually credited to Euler. See Youschkevich, *Istoria matematiki v Rossii,* p. 96.
2. I.e., the unit multiplier may not share the same domain of convergence as the resultant series.
3. Goldbach uses the same Latin term, *series,* to denote both series and sequences.
4. For details, consult Leonard E. Dickson, *History of the Theory of Numbers,* 2nd ed. (New York, 1952), I and II, *passim.*

BIBLIOGRAPHY

I. Original Works. Goldbach's writings include "Temperamentum musicum universale," in *Acta eruditorum,* **36** (1717), 114–115; "Excerpta a litteris C[hristiani]. G[oldbachi]. ad * * * Regiomonte datis," in *Actorum eruditorum supplementum,* **6** (1718), 471–472; "Specimen methodi ad summas serierum," in *Acta eruditorum,* **39** (1720), 27–31; "Demonstratio theorematis Fermatiani, nullum numerum triangularem praeter 1 esse quadrato-quadratum," in *Actorum eruditorum supplementum,* **8** (1724), 483–484; "De casibus quibus integrari potest aequatio differentialis $ax^m dx + byx^p dx + cy^2 dx = dy$ observationes quaedam," in *Commentarii Academiae scientiarum imperialis Petropolitanae,* **1** (1728), 185–197; "Methodus integrandi aequationis differentialis $aydx + bx^n dx + cx^{n-1}dx + ex^{n-2}dx = dy$ ubi *n* sit numerus integer positivus," *ibid.,* 207–209; "De transformatione serierum," *ibid.,* **2** (1729), 30–34; "De divisione curvarum in partes quotcunque quarum subtensae sint in data progressione," *ibid.,* 174–179; "De terminis generalibus serierum," *ibid.,* **3** (1732), 164–173; and "Criteria quaedam aequationum quarum nulla radix rationalis est," *ibid,* **6** (1738), 98–102.

For Goldbach's correspondence with Nikolaus II and Daniel Bernoulli and Leonhard Euler, see Paul-Henri Fuss, *Correspondance mathématique et physique de quelques célèbres géomètres du XVIIIème siècle,* 2 vols. (St. Petersburg, 1843); for a more recent ed. of part of that correspondence, see *Leonhard Euler und Christian Goldbach, Briefwechsel, 1729–1764,* edited with introduction by A. P. Juškevič [Youschkevich] and E. Winter (Berlin, 1965).

II. Secondary Literature. Piotr P. Pekarskii, *Istoria imperatorskoi akademii nauk v Peterburge,* I (St. Petersburg, 1870), 155–172, contains the most complete biography of Goldbach and quotes heavily from his nonmathematical correspondence and papers now in the State Archives, Moscow. A. P. Youschkevich includes a fairly complete account of Goldbach's mathematical work in his *Istoria matematiki v Rossii* (Moscow, 1968), pp. 92–97. See also the eds. cited above and the works cited in the notes.

Michael S. Mahoney

GOMPERTZ, BENJAMIN (*b.* London, England, 5 March 1779; *d.* London, 14 July 1865)

One of three prominent sons of a distinguished mercantile family that emigrated from Holland in the eighteenth century, Gompertz appeared destined for a financial career. Denied matriculation at the universities because he was Jewish, he joined the Society of Mathematicians of Spitalfields in 1797 and educated himself by reading the masters, especially Newton, Colin Maclaurin, and William Emerson. He found in various learned societies the intellectual stimulation that led to many publications and a wide spectrum of accomplishments. Papers to the Royal Astronomical Society on the differential sextant and the aberration of light belie Gompertz's own statement that he was not a practicing astronomer. The Royal Society, of which he was elected a fellow in 1819; the London Mathematical Society, of which he was a charter member; the Society of Actuaries; and the Royal Statistical Society were only a few of the learned and philanthropic organizations to which he gave of his talent and energy.

In 1810 Gompertz married Sir Moses Montefiore's daughter Abigail and joined the stock exchange. In 1820, in a paper to the Royal Society, he applied the method of fluxions to the investigation of various life contingencies. In 1824 he was appointed actuary and head clerk of the newly founded Alliance Assurance Company. A year later he published what is now called Gompertz's law of mortality, which states " . . . the average exhaustion of man's power to avoid death to be such that at the end of equal infinitely small intervals of time he lost equal portions of his remaining power to oppose destruction which he had at the commencement of these intervals." His rigid adherence to Newton's fluxional notation prevented wide recognition of this accomplishment, but he must be rated as a pioneer in actuarial science and one of the great amateur scholars of his day. Augustus De Morgan called Gompertz "the link between the old and new" when he mourned "the passing of the last of the learned Newtonians."

BIBLIOGRAPHY

I. ORIGINAL WORKS. Gompertz's work on life contingencies appeared in the *Philosophical Transactions of the Royal Society:* "A Sketch of the Analysis and Notation Applicable to the Value of Life Contingencies," **110** (1820), 214–294; "On the Nature of the Function Expressive of the Law of Human Mortality, and on a New Mode of Determining the Value of Life Contingencies," **115** (1825), 513–585; and "A Supplement to the Two Papers of 1820 and 1825," **152** (1862), 511–559.

"The Application of a Method of Differences to the Species of Series Whose Sums Are Obtained by Mr. Landen by the Help of Impossible Quantities," *ibid.,* **96** (1806), 174–194, led to *The Principles and Applications of Imaginary Quantities,* 2 vols. (London, 1817–1818). The sequel to these two tracts is *Hints on Porisms* . . . (London, 1850).

A regular contributor to the *Gentleman's Mathematical Companion* from 1796, Gompertz was awarded their annual problem-solution prize every year from 1812 to 1822.

II. SECONDARY LITERATURE. P. F. Hooker, "Benjamin Gompertz," in *Journal of the Institute of Actuaries,* **91,** pt. 2, no. 389 (1965), 203–212, is a competent biography with a complete bibliography of Gompertz's works (twenty-two titles) and works about him (twenty-four titles). Augustus De Morgan, "The Old Mathematical Society," repr. in J. R. Newman, *The World of Mathematics,* IV, 2372–2376, contains a view by a close friend. Also worth reading is De Morgan's obituary in *The Atheneum* (22 July 1865), p. 117. Other informative obituaries are *Monthly Notices of the Royal Astronomical Society,* **26** (1865), 104–109; and M. N. Adler, "Memoirs of the Late Benjamin Gompertz," in *Journal of the Institute of Actuaries,* **13** (Apr. 1866), 1–20.

HENRY S. TROPP

GÖPEL, ADOLPH (*b.* Rostock, Germany, 29 September 1812; *d.* Berlin, Germany, 7 June 1847)

The son of a music teacher, Göpel was able, thanks to an uncle, the British consul in Corsica, to spend several years of his childhood in Italy, where in 1825–1826 he attended lectures on mathematics and physics in Pisa. His real studies did not begin until 1829, at the University of Berlin. After earning his doctorate there in 1835, he taught at the Werder Gymnasium and at the Royal Realschule before becoming an official at the royal library in Berlin. Since he had little contact with his mathematical colleagues, all we know about him is what C. G. J. Jacobi and A. L. Crelle wrote in the brief accounts they contributed to Crelle's *Journal für die reine und angewandte Mathematik* shortly after his death. Of the two, only Crelle knew him personally, and for but a short time.

In his doctoral dissertation Göpel sought to derive from the periodic continued fractions of the roots of whole numbers the representation of those numbers by certain quadratic forms. Following an eight-year pause after his dissertation, he wrote several works for Grunert's *Archiv der Mathematik und Physik,* for which he was then working. In them he showed thorough familiarity with Jacob Steiner's style of synthetic geometry.

Göpel owes his fame to "Theoriae transcendentium Abelianarum primi ordinis adumbratio levis," published after his death in *Journal für die reine und angewandte Mathematik.* The investigations contained in this paper can be viewed as a continuation of the ideas of C. G. J. Jacobi. The latter had taught that elliptic functions of one variable should be considered as inverse functions of elliptic integrals, but later he also explained them in his lectures as quotients of theta functions of one variable. Moreover, Jacobi had formulated the inverse problem, named for him, for Abelian integrals of arbitrary genus p. From this arose the next task: to solve the problem for $p = 2$. This was done by Göpel and Johann Rosenhain in works published almost simultaneously. In "Theoriae transcendentium . . . ," Göpel started from sixteen theta functions in two variables (analogous to the four Jacobian theta functions in one variable) and showed that their quotients are quadruply periodic. Of the squares of these sixteen functions, four proved to be linearly independent. Göpel linked four more of these quadratics through a homogeneous fourth-degree relation, later named the "Göpel relation," which coincides with the equation of the Kummer surface. Göpel then presented differential equations satisfied by the sixteen theta functions and finally, after ingenious calculations, obtained the result that the quotients of two theta functions are solutions of the Jacobian inverse problem for $p = 2$.

BIBLIOGRAPHY

Göpel's major work is "Theoriae transcendentium Abelianarum primi ordinis adumbratio levis," in *Journal für die reine und angewandte Mathematik,* **35** (1847), 277–312, trans. into German as *Entwurf einer Theorie der Abelschen Transcendenten l. Ordnung,* Ostwalds Klassiker der Exacten Wissenschaften, no. 67 (Leipzig, 1895).

C. G. J. Jacobi and A. Crelle, "Notiz über A. Göpel," in *Journal für die reine und angewandte Mathematik,* **35** (1847), 313–318, was reprinted in the German version of "Theoriae. . . ."

WERNER BURAU

GORDAN, PAUL ALBERT (*b.* Breslau, Germany, 27 April 1837; *d.* Erlangen, Germany, 21 December 1912)

The son of David Gordan, a merchant, Paul Albert attended Gymnasium and business school, then worked for several years in banks. His early interest in mathematics was encouraged by the private tutoring he received from N. H. Schellbach, a professor at the Friedrich Wilhelm Gymnasium. He attended Ernst Kummer's lectures in number theory at the University of Berlin in 1855, then studied at the universities of Breslau, Königsberg, and Berlin. At Königsberg he came under the influence of Karl Jacobi's school, and at Berlin his interest in algebraic equations was aroused. His dissertation (1862), which concerned geodesics on spheroids, received a prize offered by the philosophy faculty of the University of Breslau. The techniques that Gordan employed in it were those of Lagrange and Jacobi.

Gordan's interest in function theory led him to visit F. B. Riemann in Göttingen in 1862, but Riemann was ailing and their association was brief. The following year, Gordan was invited to Giessen by A. Clebsch, with whom he worked on the theory of Abelian functions. Together they wrote an exposition of the theory. In 1874 Gordan became a professor at Erlangen, where he remained until his retirement in 1910. He married Sophie Deuer, the daughter of a Giessen professor of Roman law, in 1869.

In 1868 Clebsch introduced Gordan to the theory of invariants, which originated in an observation of George Boole's in 1841 and was further developed by Arthur Cayley in 1846. Following the work of these two Englishmen, a German branch of the theory was developed by S. H. Aronhold and Clebsch, the latter elaborating the former's symbolic methods of characterizing algebraic forms and their invariants. Invariant theory was Gordan's main interest for the rest of his mathematical career; he became known as the greatest expert in the field, developing many techniques for representing and generating forms and their invariants. Correcting an error made by Cayley in 1856, Gordan in 1868 proved by constructive methods that the invariants of systems of binary forms possess a finite base. Known as the Gordan finite basis theorem, this instigated a twenty-year search for a proof in case of higher-order systems of forms. Making use of the Aronhold-Clebsch symbolic calculus and other elaborate computational techniques, Gordan spent much of his time seeking a general proof of finiteness. The solution to the problem came in 1888, when David Hilbert proved the existence of finite bases for the invariants of systems of forms of arbitrary order. Hilbert's proof, however, provided no method for actually finding the basis in a given case. Although Gordan was said to have objected to Hilbert's existential procedures, in 1892 he wrote a paper simplifying them. His version of Hilbert's theorem is the one presented in many textbooks.

Apparently unaware of James J. Sylvester's attempts in 1878, Gordan and a student, G. Alexejeff, applied the theory of invariants to the problems of chemical valences in 1900. Alexejeff went so far as to write a textbook on invariant theory that was intended for chemists. After some very hostile criticism from the mathematician Eduard Study and an indifferent reception by chemists, the project of introducing invariants into chemistry was dropped. Gordan made a few more contributions to invariant theory, but in the thirty years following Hilbert's work, interest in the subject declined among mathematicians.

The second major area of Gordan's contributions to mathematics is in solutions of algebraic equations and their associated groups of substitutions. Working jointly with Felix Klein in 1874–1875 on the relationship of icosahedral groups to fifth-degree equations, Gordan went on to consider seventh-degree equations with the group of order 168; and toward the end of his career, equations of the sixth degree with the group of order 360. His work was algebraic and computational, and utilized the techniques of invariant theory. Typical of Gordan's many contributions to these subjects are papers in 1882 and 1885 in which, following Klein's exposition of the general problem, he carries out the explicit reduction of the seventh-degree equation to the setting of the substitution group of order 168.

Gordan made other contributions to algebra and gave simplified proofs of the transcendence of e and π. The overall style of Gordan's mathematical work was algorithmic. He shied away from presenting his ideas in informal literary forms. He derived his results computationally, working directly toward the desired goal without offering explanations of the concepts that motivated his work.

Gordan's only doctoral student, Emmy Noether, was one of the first women to receive a doctorate in Germany. She carried on his work in invariant theory for a while, but under the stimulus of Hilbert's school at Göttingen her interests shifted and she became one of the primary contributors to modern algebra.

BIBLIOGRAPHY

Further information on Gordan and his work may be found in Charles Fisher, "The Death of a Mathematical Theory," in *Archive for History of Exact Sciences,* **3,** no. 2 (1966), 137–159; and "The Last Invariant Theorists," in *European Journal of Sociology,* **8** (1967), 216–244. See also Felix Klein, *Lectures on the Icosahedron* (London, 1888), and *Lectures on Mathematics* (New York, 1911), lecture 9; Max Noether, "Paul Gordan," in *Mathematische Annalen,* **75** (1914), 1–41, which contains a complete bibliography of Gordan's works; and Hermann Weyl, "Emmy Noether," in *Scripta mathematica,* **3** (1935), 201–220.

C. S. FISHER

GOSSET, WILLIAM SEALY (also **"Student"**) (*b.* Canterbury, England, 13 June 1876; *d.* Beaconsfield, England, 16 October 1937)

The eldest son of Col. Frederic Gosset and Agnes Sealy, Gosset studied at Winchester College and New College, Oxford. He read mathematics and chemistry and took a first-class degree in natural sciences in 1899. In that year he joined Arthur Guinness and Sons, the brewers, in Dublin. Perceiving the need for more accurate statistical analysis of a variety of processes, from barley production to yeast fermentation, he urged the firm to seek mathematical advice. In 1906 he was therefore sent to work under Karl Pearson at University College, London. In the next few years Gosset made his most notable contributions to statistical theory, publishing under the pseudonym "Student." He remained with Guinness throughout his life, working mostly in Dublin, although he moved to London to take charge of a new brewery in 1935. He married Marjory Surtees in 1906; they had two children.

All of Gosset's theoretical work was prompted by practical problems arising at the brewery. The most famous example is his 1908 paper, "The Probable Error of a Mean." He had to estimate the mean value of some characteristic in a population on the basis of very small samples. The theory for large samples had been worked out from the time of Gauss a century earlier, but when in practice large samples could not be obtained economically, there was no accurate theory of estimation. If an *n*fold sample gives values $x_1, x_2, \cdots x_n$, the sample mean

$$m = \frac{1}{n}\sum x_i$$

is used to estimate the true mean. How reliable is the estimate? Let it be supposed that the characteristic of interest is normally distributed with unknown mean μ and variance σ^2. The sample variance is

$$s^2 = \frac{1}{n}\sum (x_i - m)^2.$$

It was usual to take s as an estimate of σ; if it is assumed that $\sigma = s$, then for any error e, the probability that $|m - \mu| \leqslant e$ can be computed; and thus the reliability of the estimate of the mean can be assessed. But if n is small, s is an erratic estimator of σ; and hence the customary measure of accuracy is invalid for small samples.

Gosset analyzed the distribution of the statistic $z = (m - \mu)/s$. This is asymptotically normal as n increases but differs substantially from the normal for small samples. Experimental results m and s map possible values of z onto possible values of μ. Through this mapping a probability that $|x - \mu| \leqslant e$ is obtained. In particular, for any large probability, say 95 percent, Gosset could compute an error e such that it is 95 percent probable that $|x - \mu| \leqslant e$.

R. A. Fisher observed that the derived statistic $t = (n - 1)^{1/2}z$ can be computed for all n more readily than z can be. What came to be called Student's t-test of statistical hypotheses consists in rejecting a hypothesis if and only if the probability, derived from t, of erroneous rejection is small. In the theory of testing later advanced by Jerzy Neyman and Egon S. Pearson, Student's t-test is shown to be optimum. In the competing theory of fiducial probability advanced by R. A. Fisher, t is equally central.

Gosset was perhaps lucky that he hit on the statistic which has proved basic for the statistical analysis of the normal distribution. His real insight lies in his observation that the sampling distribution of such statistics is fundamental for inference. In particular, it paved the way for the analysis of variance, which was to occupy such an important place in the next generation of statistical workers.

BIBLIOGRAPHY

Gosset's *"Student's" Collected Papers* were edited by E. S. Pearson and John Wishart (Cambridge-London, 1942; 2nd ed., 1947).

For further biogrəphy, consult E. S. Pearson, "Student as Statistician," in *Biometrika,* **30** (1938), 210–250; and "Studies in the History of Probability and Statistics, XVII," *ibid.,* **54** (1967), 350–353; and ". . . XX," *ibid.,* **55** (1968), 445–457.

IAN HACKING

GOURSAT, ÉDOUARD JEAN-BAPTISTE (*b.* Lanzac, Lot, France, 21 May 1858; *d.* Paris, France, 25 November 1936)

Goursat completed his elementary and secondary studies at the *collège* of Brive-la-Gaillarde and after only one preparatory year at the Lycée Henri IV in Paris was admitted in 1876 to the École Normale Supérieure. There he began a lifelong association with Émile Picard, whom he credited with being instrumental in his choice of a career. Claude Bouquet, Charles Briot, Jean Darboux, and Charles Hermite were among the faculty who provided inspiration and style to Goursat, who received his D.Sc. in 1881. "Hermite," Goursat said in 1935, "is the first who revealed to me the artistic side of mathematics."

Goursat was devoted throughout his academic career to research, teaching, and the training of future mathematics teachers. In 1879 he was appointed lecturer at the University of Paris, a post he held until 1881, when he was appointed to the Faculty of Sciences of Toulouse. He returned to the École Normale Supérieure in 1885 and remained there until 1897, when he was appointed professor of analysis at the University of Paris. He held this post until he reached the age of mandatory retirement, at which time he became an honorary professor. Simultaneously he was tutor in analysis at the École Polytechnique (1896–1930) and at the École Normale Supérieure, St.-Cloud (1900–1929).

Goursat received numerous honors, including the Grand Prix des Sciences Mathématiques (1886) for "Études des surfaces qui admettent tous les plans de symétrie d'un polyèdre régulier." He was awarded the Prix Poncelet in 1889 and the Prix Petit d'Ormoy in 1891. In 1919 he was elected to the Academy of Sciences. Goursat was also a chevalier of the Legion of Honor and president of the Mathematical Society of France. In 1936 an issue of the *Journal de mathématiques pures et appliquées* was dedicated to him on the occasion of the fiftieth anniversary of his becoming a teacher.

Goursat was a leading analyst of his day. At the University of Paris the "Goursat course" and "Goursat certificate" became synonyms for his course in analysis and its successful completion. One of his earliest works removed the redundant requirement of the continuity of the derivative in Augustin Cauchy's integral theorem. The theorem, now known as the Cauchy-Goursat theorem, states that if a function $f(z)$ is analytic inside and on a simple closed contour C, then

$$\int_c f(z)dz = 0.$$

Goursat's papers on the theory of linear differential equations and their rational transformations, as well as his studies on hypergeometric series, Kummer's equation, and the reduction of Abelian integrals, form, in the words of Picard, "a remarkable ensemble of works evolving naturally one from the other." Goursat introduced the notion of orthogonal kernels and semiorthogonals in connection with Erik Fredholm's work on integral equations. He made original contributions to almost every important area of analysis of his time. His *Cours d'analyse mathématique,* long a classic text in France, contained much material that was original at the time of publication.

Goursat brought warmth to his teaching and the same dedication that he applied to his research. He more than fulfilled the prediction of Darboux, who wrote in 1879: "Student [Goursat] whose development was extremely rapid, excellent mathematician, sure to become as superior a teacher as Appell and Picard." Former students and colleagues alike praised his clarity, precision, orderly teaching, and devotion to his students. His personal warmth and effectiveness are perhaps best summed up in the encomium of a former student and later collaborator, Gaston Julia: ". . . in the name of all those who received . . . not only the treasures of your science, but also the treasures of your heart, let me express . . . our faithful gratitude, . . . having received from you the nourishment of the soul, the bread of science and the example of virtue."

BIBLIOGRAPHY

I. ORIGINAL WORKS. Goursat's doctoral thesis was "Sur l'équation différentielle linéaire qui admet pour intégrale la série hypergéometrique," in *Annales scientifiques de l'École normale superieure,* **10,** supp. (1881), 3–142. The Cauchy-Goursat theorem first appeared under the title "Démonstration du théorème de Cauchy," in *Acta mathematica,* **4** (1884), 197–200. This article is reproduced under the same title in *Bihang till K. Svenska vetenskapsakademiens handlingar,* **9,** no. 5 (1884), and essentially the same material appeared under the title "Sur la définition générale des fonctions analytiques, d'après Cauchy," in *Transactions of the American Mathematical Society,* **1** (1900), 14–16. "Études des surfaces qui admettent tous les plans de symétrie d'un polyèdre régulier" was published in *Annales scientifiques de l'École normale supérieure,* **4** (1887), 161–200, 241–312, 317–340.

Goursat's best-known work is *Cours d'analyse mathématique,* 2 vols. (Paris, 1902–1905; 2nd ed., 3 vols., 1910–1913); Earle Raymond Hedrick provided the English trans. of vol. I: *A Course in Mathematical Analysis* (Boston, 1904) and, with Otto Dunkel, of vol. II (Boston, 1917).

Other major works include *Leçons sur l'intégration des équations aux dérivées partielles du premier ordre,* Carlo Bourlet, ed. (Paris, 1891), trans. into German with a preface by Sophus Lie (1893), and a 2nd ed., rev. and enl. by J. Hermann (Paris, 1921); *Le problème de Backlund* (Paris, 1925); and *Leçons sur les séries hypergéométriques et sur quelques fonctions qui s'y rattachent* (Paris, 1936).

Notice sur les travaux scientifiques de M. Édouard Goursat (Paris, 1900), the best single source on Goursat's work up to that year, contains discussions by Goursat of his work in various branches of analysis, listed by topic. The bibliography (104 titles) is listed by journal of publication. The variety of topics and the level of their discussion clearly demonstrate Goursat's breadth and depth of accomplishments.

II. SECONDARY LITERATURE. The notice on Goursat, in *Larousse mensuel,* no. 151 (Sept. 1919), p. 894, in honor of his election to the Academy of Sciences, is a good survey of Goursat's research contributions to that year.

Jubilé scientifique de M. Édouard Goursat (Paris, 1936) is a collection of speeches delivered to Goursat on 20 Nov. 1935 by former students, colleagues, and associates on the occasion of his fiftieth teaching anniversary. His responses to each address are included. This small vol. consists of encomiums relating to his mathematical and teaching accomplishments. The address of Gaston Julia, with its allusions to Kipling's *Jungle Book,* is particularly delightful. All of the quotations used in the body of this notice were translated from this source.

HENRY S. TROPP

GRÄFFE, KARL HEINRICH (*b.* Brunswick, Germany, 7 November 1799; *d.* Zurich, Switzerland, 2 December 1873)

Gräffe was the son of Dietrich Heinrich Gräffe, a jeweler, and Johanna Frederike Gräffe-Moritz. Born in simple circumstances, he studied from 1813 until 1816 with a jeweler in Hannover. Then, almost ready to begin a career as a goldsmith, through unflagging industry he made up his educational deficiencies and in 1821 was accepted as a scholarship student at the Carolineum in Brunswick. In 1824 he entered the University of Göttingen, attended the classes of Bernhard Thibaut and C. F. Gauss, and concluded his studies with the prize-winning dissertation "Die Geschichte der Variationsrechnung vom Ursprung der Differential- und Integralrechnung bis auf die heutige Zeit" (1825).

In 1828 Gräffe became a teacher at the Technische Institut in Zurich, and in 1833 a professor at the Oberen Industrieschule there, working also as a *Privatdozent.* He was appointed extraordinary professor of mathematics at the University of Zurich in 1860. His name remains attached to a method for the numerical solution of algebraic equations, which he invented in response to a prize question posed by the Berlin Academy of Sciences. Let (1) $f(x) = x^n + ax^{n-1} + \cdots a_n = 0$, and let it then be supposed that all roots $\alpha_1, \cdots, \alpha_n$ are real and different from each other: (2) $|\alpha_1| > |\alpha_2| > \cdots > |\alpha_m|$. Let it further be possible to find an equation (3) $F(x) = x^n + A_1x^{n-1} + \cdots A_n = 0$, whose roots are the mth powers $\alpha_1^m, \cdots \alpha_n^m$ of (1). It follows from (2) that (4) $|\alpha_1^m| > \cdots > |\alpha_n^m|$. Since $\alpha_1^m + \cdots + \alpha_n^m = -A_1$, it follows from (4) that $|\alpha_1^m|$, for large m, is approximately equal to A_1, $|\alpha_1^m| \sim A_1$. Correspondingly, $|\alpha_2^m| \sim \left(\frac{A_2}{A_1}\right)$, and so on. One can find an equation (3) with $m = 2$ by constructing $g(x) = (-1)^n f(-x)f(x)$; proceeding in this manner one obtains, with $m = 2^k$, the equation $F(x) = 0$.

The method may be extended to equations with equal roots and to equations with complex roots. The method has found application in modern numerical mathematics.

BIBLIOGRAPHY

A bibliography of Gräffe's works may be found in *Historisch biographische Lexikon der Schweiz,* III (Neuenburg, 1926), 621 ff. His most important work is *Die Auflösung der höheren numerischen Gleichungen* (Zurich, 1837; with additions, 1839).

A biography is Rudolph Wolf, "Carl Heinrich Gräffe; Ein Lebensbild," in *Neue Zürcherzeitung,* nos. 30 and 31 (1874), also pub. separately (Zurich, 1874).

J. J. BURCKHARDT

GRANDI, GUIDO (*b.* Cremona, Italy, 1 October 1671; *d.* Pisa, Italy, 4 July 1742)

At the age of sixteen, Grandi entered the religious order of the Camaldolese and changed his baptismal name of Francesco Lodovico to Guido. His appointment in 1694 as teacher of mathematics in his order's monastery in Florence led him to study Newton's *Principia.* In order to understand it, he was obliged to increase his knowledge of geometry, and made such rapid progress that he was soon able to discover new properties of the cissoid and the conchoid and to determine the points of inflection of the latter curve. When in 1700 Grandi was called to Rome, Cosimo de' Medici encouraged him to stay in Tuscany, by making him professor of philosophy at Pisa. In 1707 he received the honorary post of mathematician to the grand duke, in 1709 he was made a member of the Royal Society of London, and in 1714 he became professor of mathematics at Pisa. Grandi's voluminous scientific correspondence preserved in the library of the University of Pisa testifies to the esteem he enjoyed among the mathematicians of his time.

Grandi also did successful work in theoretical and practical mechanics; his studies in hydraulics evoked considerable interest from the governments of central Italy (for example, the drainage of the Chiana Valley and the Pontine Marshes).

As a collaborator in the publication of the first Florentine edition of the works of Galileo, Grandi contributed to it a "Note on the Treatise of Galileo Concerning Natural Motion," in which he gave the first definition of a curve he called the *versiera* (from the Latin *sinus versus*): Given a circle with diameter AC, let BDM be a moving straight line perpendicular

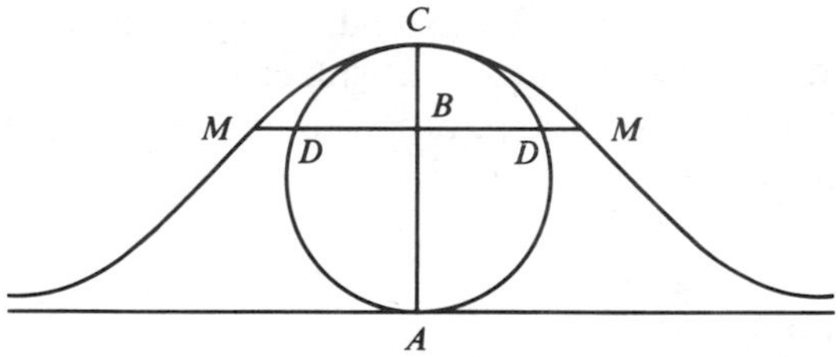

FIGURE 1

to AC at B, and intersecting the circumference of the circle at D. Let point M be determined by length BM satisfying the proportion $AB:BD = AC:BM$. The locus of all such points M is the *versiera*;[1] for a circle of diameter a, tangent to the x-axis at the origin, its Cartesian equation is $x^2y = a^2(a - y)$. The curve is more commonly known as the "witch of Agnesi" as the result of a mistranslation and a false attribution to Maria Gaetana Agnesi, who referred to it in her treatise *Istituzioni analitiche ad uso della gioventù italiana* (1748). Although Fermat had already investigated this particular equation,[2] Grandi's study extended to the more general family of curves of the form

$$y = \frac{a^{(m/n)+1}}{(a^2 + x^2)^{m/2n}},$$

where m and n are positive integers (1710). In an unpublished treatise Grandi also studied a curve known as the strophoid.

Grandi's reputation rests especially on the curves that he named "rodonea" and "clelia," after the Greek word for "rose" and the Countess Clelia Borromeo, respectively. He arrived at these curves in attempting to define geometrically the curves that have the shape of flowers, in particular the multileaved roses. They are represented in polar coordinates by equations of the form

$$\rho = R \sin a\vartheta,$$

in which R is a given line segment and a a positive integer. Grandi communicated the most significant properties of these curves to Leibniz in two letters dated December 1713 but did not make them generally known until ten years later in a memoir presented to the Royal Society of London. He later explained his complete theory in a special pamphlet (1728). Whereas analytic geometry now teaches the study of curves with given equations, Grandi here solved the inverse problem of determining the equations of curves having a preestablished form. The clelias are curves inscribed in a spherical zone, and their projection on a base plane of the zone yields the rodonea.

The *Acta eruditorum* of 4 April 1692 contained, under a pseudonym, the problem of constructing in a hemispheric cupola four equal-sized windows such that the remaining area of the cupola is quadrable. This is known as Viviani's problem, after Vincenzo Viviani who suggested it. It is an indeterminate problem and was solved shortly afterward by Leibniz and by Viviani himself;[3] Grandi also devoted a memoir to it (1699).

The curve

$$y = b \ln(x/a)$$

or

$$x = ae^{y/b},$$

called the logarithmic or logistic curve, was studied by Evangelista Torricelli as early as 1647; Huygens revealed its most important properties in a communication read before the Paris Academy in 1669. In 1701 Grandi demonstrated the theorems enunciated by Huygens.

On a more general level, Grandi's treatise on quadrature of 1703, in which he abandoned the Galilean methods of Cavalieri and Viviani in favor of those of Leibniz, marks the introduction of the Leibnizian calculus into Italy. Grandi was also the author of several noteworthy and popular textbooks.

NOTES

1. Cf. also Grandi's *Quadratura circuli et hyperbolae.*
2. Cf. *Oeuvres de Fermat,* Charles Henry and Paul Tannery, eds. (Paris, 1891–1922), I, 279–280.
3. Vincenzo Viviani, *Formatione e misura di tutti i cieli* (Florence, 1692).

BIBLIOGRAPHY

I. ORIGINAL WORKS. Grandi's writings include *Geometrica divinatio Vivianeorum problematum* (Florence,

1699); *Geometrica demonstratio theorematum Hugenianorum circa logisticam seu logarithmicam* (Florence, 1701); *Quadratura circuli et hyperbolae* (Pisa, 1703, 1710); *De infinitis infinitorum et infinite parvorum* . . . (Pisa, 1710); "Florum geometricarum manipulus," in *Philosophical Transactions of the Royal Society* (1723); *Flores geometrici ex rhodonearum et cloeliarum curvarum descriptione resultantes* . . . (Florence, 1728); *Elementi geometrici piani e solidi di Euclide, posti brevemente in volgare* (Florence, 1731); *Istituzioni di aritmetica pratica* (Florence, 1740); and *Istituzioni geometriche* (Florence, 1741).

II. SECONDARY LITERATURE. Grandi's letters to Leibniz are in *Leibnizens mathematische Schriften, herausgegeben von C. J. Gerhardt,* 7 vols. and supp. (Berlin and Halle, 1848–1863), IV, 221, 224. There are three works of value by Gino Loria: *Curve sghembe speciali algebriche e trascendenti,* 2 vols. (Bologna, 1925), esp. II, 57; *Curve piane speciali algebriche e trascendenti,* 2 vols. (Milan, 1930), I, 94, 419 ff.; and *Storia delle matematiche,* 2nd ed. (Milan, 1950).

A. NATUCCI

GRASSMANN, HERMANN GÜNTHER (*b.* Stettin, Pomerania [now Szczecin, Poland], 15 April 1809; *d.* Stettin, 26 September 1877)

Life and Works. Grassmann came from a family of scholars. His father, Justus Günther Grassmann, studied theology, mathematics, and physics. He was a minister for a short time, then became a teacher of mathematics and physics at the Gymnasium in Stettin, where he did much to raise the level of education. He also wrote elementary mathematics textbooks and did research on problems in physics and crystallography. Grassmann's mother was Johanne Medenwald, a minister's daughter, from Klein-Schönfeld.

The third of twelve children, Grassmann received his earliest instruction from his mother and at a private school before attending the Stettin Gymnasium. He also learned to play the piano. At the age of eighteen he passed the final secondary school examination, ranking second. With his eldest brother, Gustav, Hermann studied theology for six semesters at the University of Berlin, where his teachers included August Neander and Friedrich Schleiermacher. At the same time he studied classical languages and literature and attended the lectures of August Böckh.

Grassmann returned to Stettin in the fall of 1830 and began intensive independent study of mathematics and physics. In December 1831, at Berlin, he took the examination for teaching at the Gymnasium level; the examiners stated, however, that Grassmann had to display greater knowledge of his subjects before he could be considered qualified to teach the higher grades. At Easter 1832 he obtained a post as assistant teacher at the Stettin Gymnasium, and two years later he passed the first-level theology examination given by the Lutheran church council of Stettin.

Grassmann did not become a minister, however. In the autumn of 1834 he was hired as senior master at the Gewerbeschule in Berlin, succeeding Jakob Steiner, who had been called to the University of Berlin. A year later Grassmann was appointed to the faculty of the newly founded Otto Schule in Stettin, where he taught mathematics, physics, German, Latin, and religion. Meanwhile he pursued his studies in theology, mathematics, and natural science. In 1839 he passed the second-level theology examination in Stettin and, the following year at Berlin, an examination in mathematics, physics, chemistry, and mineralogy that fully qualified him to teach all grades of secondary school.

The latter examination included a written portion to be done at home, the subject of which was the theory of the tides. This assignment proved decisive for Grassmann's career. In 1832 he had begun to work on a new geometric calculus. With its aid he was now able to give a simplified exposition of the mathematical developments in Lagrange's *Mécanique analytique* and to derive, in an original manner different from that of Laplace, the portions of the latter's *Mécanique céleste* relevant to the theory of the tides. Although Grassmann used the new methods only to the extent necessary to solve the problem at hand, he was undoubtedly aware of the far-reaching significance of his creation; and by 1840 he had decided to concentrate entirely on mathematical research.

At first, however, Grassmann devoted considerable effort to teaching. He wrote several brief textbooks for use in secondary school, some of which were frequently reprinted. They included *Grundriss der deutschen Sprachlehre* (1842) and *Leitfaden für den ersten Unterricht in der lateinischen Sprache* (1842). In collaboration with W. Langbein he published *Deutsches Lesebuch für Schüler von acht bis zwölf Jahren* (1846). Reorganizations of the Stettin school system led to his being transferred on several occasions (the Otto Schule, the Gymnasium, the Friedrich Wilhelm Schule; at the last he received the title *Oberlehrer* in May 1847). In 1852 Grassmann succeeded his father (who had died in March of that year) as fourth-ranking teacher at the Stettin Gymnasium, a post that brought with it the title of professor.

Meanwhile, in the fall of 1843, Grassmann had completed the manuscript of the first volume of his chief work, *Die lineale Ausdehnungslehre*, which appeared the following year as *Die Wissenschaft der extensiven Grösse oder die Ausdehnungslehre*. Its fundamental significance was not grasped by contemporaries; and even a mathematician of the caliber of A. F. Möbius—whose own geometric research was to some extent related to Grassmann's—did not fully understand the author's intentions. Disapproving of the many new concepts and certain philosophical formulations, he declined to write a review of the book, and thus it was totally disregarded by the experts.

As an application of the *Ausdehnungslehre*, which is based on the general concept of connectivity, Grassmann published *Neue Theorie der Elektrodynamik* (1845), in which he replaced Ampère's fundamental law for the reciprocal effect of two infinitely small current elements with a law requiring less arbitrary assumptions. Thirty years later Clausius independently rediscovered Grassmann's law but acknowledged his priority as soon as he was apprised of it. In a series of articles published between 1846 and 1856 Grassmann applied his theory to the generation of algebraic curves and surfaces, in the hope that these papers, which were much less abstract than his book, would inspire mathematicians to read the *Ausdehnungslehre*. His hopes were not fulfilled.

On the other hand, Grassmann received rapid public recognition for a work submitted in 1846, at Möbius' suggestion, to the Fürstlich Jablonowsky'sche Gesellschaft der Wissenschaften in Leipzig. In it he solved the problem posed by the society of establishing the geometric characteristic, first outlined by Leibniz, for designating topological relations, without recourse to metric properties. His entry, *Geometrische Analyse*, was awarded the full prize and was published by the society in 1847. Möbius, who was one of the judges, justly criticized both the abstract manner in which Grassmann introduced his new concepts and his neglect of intuitive aids, defects that made the last part of the text particularly difficult to read. Accordingly, Möbius incorporated into the book his own essay, "Die Grassmann'sche Lehre von den Punktgrössen und den davon abhängigen Grössenformen," in which he explained Grassmann's *Scheingrössen* as abbreviated expressions of intuitively interpretable quantities.

In May 1847 Grassmann wrote to the Prussian ministry of education, requesting that he be considered for a post as university professor, in the event that one became available. The ministry thereupon requested an opinion of Grassmann's prize essay from E. E. Kummer, a mathematician at Breslau. Kummer's severe judgment that the work contained "commendably good material expressed in a deficient form" led to the rejection of Grassmann's application.

A man of broad interests and a strong sense of political responsibility, Grassmann participated in the political events leading to the Revolution of 1848. With his brother Robert, his scientific collaborator for many years, he founded the *Deutsche Wochenschrift für Staat, Kirche und Volksleben*, which was soon replaced by the daily *Norddeutsche Zeitung*. Advocates of a Germany united under Prussian leadership, the brothers hoped for the establishment of a constitutional monarchy, ruled by the king in cooperation with the Reichstag. Revolution and civil war, they contended, were not the proper means of winning greater freedom. In articles published in 1848 and 1849 Grassmann considered chiefly problems of constitutional law; but with the restoration he became increasingly dissatisfied and withdrew from the paper.

On 12 April 1849 Grassmann married Marie Therese Knappe, the daughter of a Pomeranian landowner. Of their eleven children, two died in early childhood and two others somewhat later. His sons Justus and Max became mathematics teachers at the Stettin Gymnasium; Ludolf, a physician; Hermann, professor of mathematics at the University of Giessen; and Richard, professor of mechanical engineering at the Technische Hochschule in Karlsruhe.

As a student Grassmann had been admitted to the Freemason lodge in Stettin, and from 1856 he held the post of treasurer. In 1857 he became a member of the board of directors of the Pommersche Hauptverein für die Evangelisierung Chinas. Founded in 1850, this society published a journal and occasionally sent missionaries to China. Under Grassmann's chairmanship it was unified with the Rheinische Missions-Gesellschaft in Barmen in 1873.

Soon after the political unrest of 1848–1849 had subsided, Grassmann began to study Sanskrit and then Gothic, Lithuanian, Old Prussian, Old Persian, Russian, and Church Slavonic—investigations that laid the foundations for his studies in comparative linguistics. Profiting from his acute sense of hearing and his capacity for making careful observations, Grassmann developed a theory of the physical nature of speech sounds (1854). He had recognized that each vowel sound arises through definite overtones that are specifically characteristic of it and planned to substantiate his theory experimentally, using a tone generator instead of the human voice. The device he intended to use, however, did not furnish sufficiently pure vibrations—that is, it was not sufficiently free of overtones.

In "Zur Theorie der Farbenmischung" (1853) Grassmann opposed certain conclusions that Helmholtz had drawn from experiments on the mixing of colors. According to Grassmann's theory, each color can be represented by a weighted point plotted on a circular surface; the position of the point indicates its hue and saturation, and the weight, its intensity. If the colors to be mixed are thus represented, then the center of gravity, in which the entire mass is seen as being concentrated, gives the intensity of the visual impression of the mixture. Helmholtz later acknowledged the correctness of the center-of-gravity construction but retained reservations concerning the circular form of the overall field.

Around the middle of 1854 Grassmann resumed work on the *Ausdehnungslehre.* He may have been stimulated in this effort by a remark made by Möbius, who informed him of two papers in which equations with several unknowns were solved by means of an approach incorporating *clefs algébriques* that corresponded to the one that Grassmann had developed in sections 45, 46, and 93 of his book. Indeed, Möbius insisted that Grassmann assert his priority against the authors of these papers, A. B. de Saint-Venant (in *Comptes rendus . . . de l'Académie des sciences,* **21** [1845], 620–625) and Cauchy (*ibid.,* **36** [1853], 70–76, 129–136). Grassmann subsequently addressed himself to the Paris Academy as well as to both authors, without charging plagiarism. Whether Cauchy, in particular, knew of the *Ausdehnungslehre* when he wrote his paper cannot be established.

Rather than writing a second volume of the *Ausdehnungslehre,* as he had originally intended, Grassmann decided to rework the text; and *Die Ausdehnungslehre. Vollständig und in strenger Form bearbeitet* was published at Berlin in 1862. The new version, unfortunately, fared no better than the first; Grassmann, in presenting a systematic foundation of his theory, had failed to see that a different approach was necessary for mathematicians to acquaint themselves with the new concepts. Given the failure of the first edition, it is all the more astonishing that Grassmann did not attempt to emphasize the advantages of his ideas by demonstrating them through specific examples. Again, no serious attempts were made by mathematicians to work through the peculiar terminology of this strange theory, and the revised edition was long ignored. Although the Leopoldina elected Grassmann to membership in 1864, it was in recognition of his achievements in physics—not in mathematics.

Disappointed by his continued lack of success, Grassmann gradually turned away from mathematical research. Besides a few minor articles, in 1865 he published a supplement to his *Lehrbuch der Arithmetik* (1860) entitled *Lehrbuch der Trigonometrie für höhere Lehranstalten* (a planned third part on geometry never appeared) and "Grundriss der Mechanik," in the *Stettiner Gymnasialprogramm* of 1867.

Grassmann also concentrated increasingly on linguistic research. Works on phonetics that were based on the historical study of language (1860, 1862) were followed by the important "Über die Aspiranten und ihr gleichzeitiges Vorhandensein im An- und Auslaute der Wurzeln" (1863), in which he formulated the law of aspirates that is named for him. A crucial contribution to the study of the Germanic sound shift, this law has become part of the science of comparative linguistics.

Linguistic research of a different kind forms the basis of *Deutsche Pflanzennamen* (1870), which Grassmann wrote with his brother Robert and his brother-in-law Christian Hess. The goal of the work was to introduce German names for all plants grown in the German-language area, terms as precise as the Latin and Greek forms that would be derived etymologically from the various Germanic languages. Grassmann hoped that the effort of collecting and explicating involved in the project would prove useful to both botanists (especially biology teachers) and linguists.

An achievement of a much higher order is represented by Grassmann's work on the Sanskrit language. Realizing that research in comparative linguistics must take the oldest Indic languages as a starting point, Grassmann began an intensive study of the hymns of the *Rig-Veda* about 1860. Unlike his mathematical work, which was greatly ahead of its time, these studies benefited from opportune timing. Theodor Aufrecht's authoritative text of the *Rig-Veda* and the St. Petersburg Sanskrit dictionary compiled by Otto von Böthlingk and W. R. von Roth were also published at this time. Grassmann's complete glossary of the *Rig-Veda* was modeled on the Biblical concordances, and the entry for each word indicates the grammatical form in which it appears. Although criticized on points of detail, the six-part *Wörterbuch zum Rigveda* (1873–1875) was generally praised by specialists and remained the standard work for many years.

Although Grassmann had originally planned to follow the glossary with a grammar, he came to consider it more important to publish a translation of the hymns, believing it essential to their interpretation; it appeared in two parts as *Rig-Veda. Übersetzt und mit kritischen Anmerkungen versehen* (1876–1877). Alfred Ludwig's simultaneously published complete translation of the texts (1876), although far superior philologically to Grassmann's work, was presented in a German that was difficult to understand. Grassmann, in contrast, seeking to reproduce not only the meanings of the words but also the overall feeling of the original, retained a metrical form—at the sacrifice of a faithful rendering in certain passages.

Unlike his mathematical works, Grassmann's linguistic research was immediately well received by scholars. A year before his death he became a member of the American Oriental Society, and the Faculty of Philosophy of the University of Tübingen awarded him an honorary doctorate.

In the meantime, a few mathematicians had become aware of Grassmann's work. His election on 2 December 1871 as a corresponding member of the Göttingen Academy of Sciences encouraged him to publish some short mathematical papers during the last years of his life. In 1877 he prepared another edition of the *Ausdehnungslehre* of 1844 for publication; it appeared posthumously in 1878. Despite steadily increasing infirmity, he continued to work until succumbing to cardiac insufficiency.

Influence. Toward the end of his life, and even more after his death, a growing recognition of Grassmann's accomplishments was observed among specialists. Alfred Clebsch, the leading German mathematician of the time, for example, made a special effort to call attention to Grassmann during a memorial address that he delivered in honor of Julius Plücker in 1871. H. Hankel was the first to discuss the *Ausdehnungslehre* in a book: *Theorie der komplexen Zahlensysteme* (1867). The obituary of Grassmann by Sturm, Schröder, and Sohncke displays considerable appreciation for his work. At about the same time there appeared a short biography of him by V. Schlegel, who had previously used Grassmann's ideas in his *System der Raumlehre* (1872–1875).

The geometry that Grassmann established on the basis of the *Ausdehnungslehre* was later elaborated as *Punktrechnung*, first in Peano's *Calcolo geometrico* (1888). Grassmann's most gifted son, Hermann, wrote three textbooks on analytic geometry based on the approach of the *Ausdehnungslehre*; and in 1909 he applied the latter to the theory of gyroscopic motion. The other most important German advocates of the book were R. Mehmke and his student A. Lotze. French mathematicians were introduced to Grassmann's concepts by F. Caspary, who used them in his research on the generation of algebraic curves. The spread of Grassmann's ideas was further aided by the publication of a collected edition of his works and of papers written on the centenary of his birth. An early advocate of Grassmann's *Ausdehnungslehre* was the American physicist J. W. Gibbs (1839–1903). Well-known, among many other achievements, for his popularization of a vector algebra as it may be derived from Grassmann's and W. R. Hamilton's ideas, he emphatically preferred—in contrast to Tait's rival claims for Hamilton's quaternions—Grassmann's less limited concepts. Gibbs created what he called "dyadics," an operational approach that found favor with theoretical physicists until it was replaced by modern vector and tensor analysis. In this dyadics, a matrix in its operational application is understood as a sum of more simple operators, the so-called simple dyads. As Gibbs himself explained, the germ of these ideas must be seen in certain indeterminate products (*Lückenausdrücke*), which Grassmann introduced in a note at the end of the first edition of his *Ausdehnungslehre* of 1844. Thus the birth of linear matrix algebra, often associated with the publication of Cayley's classic "Memoir on the Theory of Matrices" in 1858, may be said to have occurred already in 1844. A century later H. G. Forder's *Calculus of Extension* (1941) testified to the continuing appeal of the *Ausdehnungslehre* among mathematicians in the English-speaking world.

The Ausdehnungslehre. The *Ausdehnungslehre* concerns geometric analysis, a border region between analytic geometry, which uses only the algebra of coordinates and equations, and synthetic geometry, which dispenses with all algebraic aids. The first to conceive of this kind of geometric analysis was Leibniz. In a letter of 1679 to Huygens (see Grassmann, *Werke*, I, 417) he wrote that in order to develop such an analysis, one should work directly with the symbols of geometric concepts—such as points, straight lines, and planes—that is, without the intermediary of coordinates; further, loci and other properties should always be expressed through algebraic expressions written in the symbols of these basic concepts. Leibniz did not fully elaborate his idea, and systems of geometric analysis did not appear until the nineteenth century, after analytic and synthetic geometry had undergone considerable development. On this question one may consult three articles by H. Rothe, A. Lotze, and C. Betsch in the *Encyklopädie der mathematischen Wissenschaften* (1916–1923); the article by Lotze deals especially with the *Ausdehnungslehre.*

All systems of geometric analysis share the characteristic that one of their fundamental elements is the geometric addition of directed line segments, an operation borrowed from mechanics. Accordingly, one may place among these systems the description of Euclidean plane geometry by means of complex numbers that was formulated around 1800. Although known as the theory of the Gaussian plane, it was also elaborated independently of Gauss by Wessel and Argand. A purely geometric computation of line segments in the plane, in which even the complex numbers do not appear explicitly, had to await the appearance of the method of equipollences elaborated by Bellavitis in the 1830's. Another example of geometric analysis is Möbius' barycentric calculus (1827). The barycentric coordinates of Euclidean space are special systems of projective coordinates obtained with the aid of concepts drawn from point mechanics. More important in the present context, however, is the fact that in 1844, in a work devoted to establishing the barycentric calculus on a firmer basis, Möbius conceived of the line segment as the difference between two points, a notion that played an important role in the calculus of points based on the *Ausdehnungslehre.*

The theory of quaternions developed by W. R. Hamilton between 1843 and 1853 originated in an attempt to generalize the complex numbers in a manner that would preserve, if possible, all the laws of arithmetic. This generalization could be effected, however, only by giving up the commutative law of multiplication. Doing so gave rise to the system of quaternions named for Hamilton. In current terminology, this system is a skew field of a fourth-rank algebra over the field R of the real numbers.

During this same period, Grassmann developed his *Ausdehnungslehre.* Its algebraic entities are the extensive quantities. These consist, in the first instance, of quantities of the first rank of the base domain S_n^1; this, in modern terms, is an n-dimensional vector space over R, which is expressed here for the first time in such generality. Its base vectors are $e_1, \cdots, e_n$. In his attempt to find a suitable multiplication of two quantities of S_n^1, Grassmann proceeded differently from Hamilton. He did not seek to make S_n^1 into a ring but, instead, added to S_n^1 a domain $S^2{}_{\binom{n}{2}}$ of quantities of the second rank—that is, a vector space of dimension $\binom{n}{2}$ with base quantities e_{ij} $(1 \leq i < j \leq n)$. The product of two quantities of S_n^1—which he called the outer product—is so constructed that it lies in $S^2{}_{\binom{n}{2}}$. This outer multiplication is to be distributive, so it need be defined only for the e_i. If the multiplication is designated by brackets, then

$$[e_i e_j] = -[e_j e_i] = e_{ij} \qquad (1 \leq i < j \leq n)$$

and

$$[e_i e_i] = 0 \qquad (1 \leq i \leq n).$$

Then, for arbitrary r where $1 \leq r \leq n$, Grassmann established the domain $S^r{}_{\binom{n}{r}}$ of the quantities of the r-th rank with base $e_{i_1 \cdots i_r}$ $(1 \leq i_1 < \cdots < i_r \leq n)$. By using the formulation $[e_{j_1} \cdots e_{j_r}] = +e_{i_1 \cdots i_r}$, *or* $= -e_{i_1 \cdots i_r}$, or $= 0$—according as $(j_1 \cdots j_r)$ is an even permutation of $(i_1 \cdots i_r)$ or an odd permutation of it, or whether the j_ν are not all different—the outer product of r base quantities of S_n^1 can be expressed as a quantity of $S^r{}_{\binom{n}{r}}$. At this stage one can immediately calculate the outer product of r arbitrary quantities of S_n^1. Grassmann called "simple" the special quantities of $S^r{}_{\binom{n}{r}}$ that arise in this manner. Since he set $e_{1 \cdots n} = 1$, he was again able to conceive S_n^1 as the scalar domain R.

Through reduction to the basic unities and use of the associative law, it can be shown that for arbitrary unities of S^r and S^s $[e_{i_1 \cdots i_r} e_{j_1 \cdots j_s}] = 0$, if i and j are not all different; that this expression equals $+1$ or -1 in the cases, respectively, that $(i_1 \cdots i_r j_1 \cdots j_s)$ is an even or an odd permutation of a combination $(n_1 \cdots n_r \cdots n_{r+s})$, where $1 \leq n_1 < \cdots < n_{r+s} \leq n$. From this result one may easily obtain, through distributive multiplication, the progressive product of the quantities $A^r \in S^r$ and $B^s \in S^s$. If one takes $e_{1 \cdots n}$ as an independent unity and adds quantities of arbitrary rank, which Grassmann avoided doing, one obtains, in modern terms, the Grassmann algebra of rank 2^n over S_n^1. In this algebra $[A^r, B^s]$ vanishes for $r + s > n$. Grassmann therefore constructed a "regressive" product of A^r and B^s. To this end he associated to each unity $e_{i_1 \cdots i_r}$ its supplement $| e_{i_1 \cdots i_r} = \pm e_{i_{r+1} \cdots i_n}$.

Here $(i_1 \cdots i_n)$ is a permutation of $(1 \cdots n)$, and equals $+1$ or -1 according as the latter is even or odd. From this it can be shown that the extension $|A^r$ for every $A^r \in S^r$ is a quantity of S^{n-r}.

The inner product of two quantities A^r, B^r of S^r is given by $P = [A \cdot |B]$, which Grassmann considered a scalar, since it is a quantity in S^n. At this point he could explain the notation of orthogonality and absolute value in S^r. He interpreted the regressive product of the quantities $A^r \in S^r$ and $B^s \in S^s$ (where $r + s > n$), for the unities ϵ^r, η^s, as that unity of rank $2n - (r + s)$ the supplement of which is the progressive product of the supplement of ϵ^r and η^s. This makes it easy to define the regressive product of arbitrary $A^r \in S^r$ and $B^s \in S^s$, where $r + s > n$.

On the basis of the preceding steps, Grassmann could obtain the outer products of arbitrarily many extensive quantities. These are "pure" if the multiplications to be performed are either all progressive or all regressive, and "mixed" if this is not the case. In general, a mixed product is neither commutative nor associative, although it does fulfill certain computational rules that Grassmann established. In addition to the outer products, Grassmann developed a multiplication that he termed "algebraic," which obeys the law $e_ie_j = e_je_i$ for $i = 1 \cdots n$ and leads to what is today known as the polynomial ring.

Grassmann derived the ideas of his *Ausdehnungslehre,* as well as his new way of forming products, essentially from geometry, particularly from the geometry of n dimensions, which was then still in its infancy. In his calculus of points, the points of R_n, which are provided with weights (that is, numbers different from zero), are conceived as the fundamental domain S^1_{n+1} of a totality of extensive quantities. The points that are assigned weight 1 are also called "simple." $\lambda a + \mu b$ then yields all points of the straight line A spanned by the simple points a, b, those points having the weight $\lambda + \mu$. This is identical to the scheme developed by Möbius, where (λ, μ) are the barycentric coordinates of the relevant point of A. The only difference is that no weighted point of A corresponds to a-b but, rather, to the vector leading from b to a. In Grassmann's calculus, therefore, the vector space V_n over R appears as a subset of the domain S^1_{n+1} of the point range. If $a_0 \cdots a_k$ and $b_0 \cdots b_k$ are each linearly independent simple points that span the same $R_k \subset R_n$, then the outer products $[a_0 \cdots a_k]$ and $[b_0 \cdots b_k]$ do not vanish; and they differ by, at most, a scalar factor $\lambda \neq 0$. They are therefore associated with this R_k. Their components, related to a base $e_{i_0 \cdots i_k}$, are now called the Grassmann coordinates of R_k. They fulfill a system of quadratic relations that Grassmann gave for $k = 1$; and if they are interpreted as points of a projective space, they describe the manifold $G_{n,k}$ that is named for Grassmann.

If the simple quantities $[a_0 \cdots a_r]$ and $[b_0 \cdots b_s]$ are associated with the spaces R^a_r and R^b_s of R_n, and if these have no finite or infinite point in common, then the progressive outer product $[a_0 \cdots a_rb_0 \cdots b_s]$ corresponds to the connection space R_{r+s+1} of R^a_r and R^b_s. If R^a_r and R^b_s span the entire R_n, then the regressive product of $[a_0 \cdots a_r]$ and $[b_0 \cdots b_s]$ is associated with the intersection space $R^a_r \cap R^b_s$. In works directly inspired by Grassmann the perceptual spaces R_2, R_3 are treated in detail with these methods, as are the projective spaces P_2, P_3 over R. For example, in them the line vector (also known as the rod), which is bound to the connecting line A of a,b, is described by means of the outer product $[a,b]$ of the points a,b. Then $[abc]$ defines an oriented surface element bound to the plane containing a,b,c; its content can be either positive or negative, or zero when a, b, and c are collinear. The outer product of two free vectors yields a bivector.

Apart from details, the *Ausdehnungslehre* appears in retrospect as a very general and comprehensive treatise, the implications of which reached far beyond the "state of the art" in 1844 or even in 1862. In geometry, mathematicians were still thinking in terms of a "real" three-dimensional space and saw no need to occupy themselves with such a theory of "extended magnitudes" in a fictional n-dimensional space. Hamilton's goal had been to find a consistent algebra of rotations and vectors in three-dimensional space; when he reached it in his system of quaternions he was forced to sacrifice the traditional principle of commutativity for multiplication. Grassmann, on the other hand, had not only immediately considered manifolds of an arbitrary number of dimensions, but also had introduced new, seemingly artificial kinds of multiplication for its various types of elements. Nobody in his day could foresee that, in its general algebraic aspects, the *Ausdehnungslehre* did much more than merely accomplish for any finite number of dimensions what Hamilton's quaternions were designed to do for Euclidean space of three dimensions. Beyond that it anticipated (or even included) wide areas of modern linear algebra and of matrix, vector, and tensor analysis. Thus, three lines of later development may be distinguished in connection with Grassmann's principal work: first, the generalization of the geometrical concept of space (also anticipated at much the same time by Cayley and by Riemann); second, the influence on Gibbs and thus on the creation of vector analysis; and third, the important anticipation of fundamental parts of modern algebra, though this was not immediately noticed by the mathematical public.

Other Mathematical Works. Despite the long neglect of his ideas, Grassmann was always convinced of their importance. In several works he attempted to show how the theory of quaternions and invariant theory (then called modern algebra) can be understood on the basis of the *Ausdehnungslehre*. Still more important, however, are his writings on the "lineal" generation of algebraic entities, in which he also draws on his theory. This group of publications deals, for example, with the theory of constructing points of algebraic curves and surfaces by simply drawing straight lines and planes through given points, as well as with the determination of intersection points of known straight lines.

As early as 1721 Maclaurin had demonstrated that given the three points a, b, c and the two straight lines A, B of general position in the plane, the locus of the third vertices of all triangles the first two vertices of which lie, respectively, on A and B and the sides of which pass, correspondingly, through a, b, c is a conic section. In terms of the calculus of points, this statement means that the mixed outer product $(a \times AbB \times c)$ vanishes. Grassmann made the important discovery that in this way every plane algebraic curve C can be generated lineally. As a result, if C is of order n, it can be described by setting equal to zero an outer product in which, in addition to symbols for certain fixed points and straight lines, the expression for the variable point x of C appears n times. A cubic can be expressed, accordingly, as $(xaA) \cdot (xbB) \cdot (xcC) = 0$. This signifies that the locus of the point x of the plane is a cubic, if the line connecting x with three fixed points a, b, c cuts the three fixed straight lines A, B, C in three collinear points. Moreover, one can obtain every plane cubic in this manner. Grassmann was thus able to refute Plücker's assertion that curves higher than the second degree could be conceived only in terms of coordinate geometry. In writings collected in volume II, part 1, of the *Werke*, Grassmann considered, in particular, the lineal generations of plane cubics and quartics, as well as of third-degree spatial surfaces. (One of these generations bears his name.) He demonstrated that by setting equal to zero the products he designated as planimetric or stereometric, all these generations could be obtained from the *Ausdehnungslehre*.

A large portion of the *Ausdehnungslehre* is devoted to analysis. Grassmann treats functions of n real variables as functions of extensive quantities of a base domain S_n^1. Since he introduced a metric into S_n^1 in the form of the inner product, he was able to derive Taylor expansions, remainder formulas, and other items. His most important studies in analysis concern Pfaff's problem—that is, the theory of the integration of a Pfaffian equation

$$\omega = A_1(x_1 \cdots x_n)dx_1 + \cdots + A_n(x_1 \cdots x_n)dx_n = 0.$$

This question had interested leading nineteenth-century mathematicians both before and after Grassmann, especially Pfaff and Jacobi. Grassmann contributed the following important theorem: If one calls k the class of ω—that is, the minimum number of variables into which ω can be transformed—then, when $k = 2h$, ω can be transformed into the normal form

$$z_{h+1}\,dz_1 + \cdots + z_{2h}\,dz_h^1$$

and, when $k = 2h - 1$, into

$$p \cdot (dz_h + z_{h+1}\,dz_1 + \cdots + z_{2h-1}\,dz_{h-1}),$$

where p is a function of $z_1 \cdots z_{2h-1}$. Even these results, however, which appeared in the 1862 edition of the *Ausdehnungslehre* and surpassed Jacobi's achievements, obviously did not attract much attention. Recognition had to await their translation into the more customary language of analysis by F. Engel in his commentary on Grassmann's works.

The calculus of differential forms, which is based on Grassmann's outer multiplication, occupies a firm position in modern analysis. This calculus has enabled mathematicians to develop differential geometry in an elegant manner, as is particularly evident in the work of E. Cartan.

BIBLIOGRAPHY

Grassmann's writings were collected as *Mathematische und physikalische Werke*, F. Engel, ed., 3 vols. in 6 pts. (Leipzig, 1894–1911).

Biographical and historical works are E. T. Bell, *The Development of Mathematics* (New York–London, 1945), 198–206; M. J. Crowe, *A History of Vector Analysis* (Notre Dame, Ind.–London, 1967), ch. 3; A. E. Heath, "Hermann Grassmann. The Neglect of His Work. The Geometric Analysis and Its Connection with Leibniz' Characteristic," in *Monist*, **27** (1917),

1–56; F. Engel, "H. Grassmann," in *Jahresberichte der Deutschen Mathematikervereinigung*, **18** (1909), 344–356; and "Grassmanns Leben," which is Grassmann's *Werke*, III, pt. 2 (1911); G. Sarton, "Grassmann—1844," in *Isis*, **35** (1944), 326–330; V. Schlegel, *Hermann Grassmann, sein Leben und seine Werke* (Leipzig, 1878); and *Die Grassmannsche Ausdehnungslehre. Ein Beitrag zur Geschichte der Mathematik in den letzten 50 Jahren* (Leipzig, 1896); and R. Sturm, E. Schröder, and L. Sohncke, "H. Grassmann. Sein Leben und seine mathematisch-physikalischen Arbeiten," in *Mathematische Annalen*, **14** (1879), 1–45, with bibliography of his works.

Works on geometrical analysis in general include H. Hankel, *Theorie der komplexen Zahlensysteme* (Leipzig, 1867); A. F. Möbius, *Der baryzentrische Kalkül* (Leipzig, 1827), also in his *Gesammelte Werke*, I (1885), 1–388; and "Über die Zusammensetzung gerader Linien und eine daraus entspringende neue Begründung des baryzentrischen Calculs," in *Journal für die reine und angewandte Mathematik*, **28** (1844), 1–9; and three articles collectively entitled "Systeme geometrischer Analyse," in *Encyklopädie der mathematischen Wissenschaften*, III, pt. 1 (1916–1923): by H. Rothe, 1277–1423; A. Lotze, 1425–1550; and C. Betsch, 1550–1595.

Works based on Grassmann's *Ausdehnungslehre* include F. Caspary, "Über die Erzeugung algebraischer Raumkurven durch veränderliche Figuren," in *Journal für die reine und angewandte Mathematik*, **100** (1887), 405–412; and "Sur une méthode générale de la géométrie, qui forme le lieu entre la géométrie synthétique et la géométrie analytique," in *Bulletin des sciences mathématiques et astronomiques*, 2nd ser., **13** (1889), 202–240; H. G. Forder, *Calculus of Extension* (Cambridge, 1941); H. Grassmann, Jr., "Über die Verwertung der Streckenrechnung in der Kreiseltheorie," in *Sitzungsberichte der Berliner mathematischen Gesellschaft*, **8** (1909), 100–114; and *Projektive Geometrie der Ebene, unter Verwendung der Punktrechnung dargestellt*, 2 vols. in 3 pts. (Leipzig, 1909–1923); F. Kraft, *Abriss des geometrischen Calculs nach H. G. Grassmann* (Leipzig, 1893); A. Lotze, *Die Grundgleichungen der Mechanik, neu entwickelt mit Grassmanns Punktrechnung* (Leipzig, 1922); and *Punkt- und Vektorenrechnung* (Berlin–Leipzig, 1929); R. Mehmke, *Vorlesungen über Punkt- und Vektorenrechnung*, I (Leipzig–Berlin, 1913); G. Peano, *Calcolo geometrico* (Turin, 1888); and V. Schlegel, *System der Raumlehre nach den Prinzipien der Grassmann'schen Ausdehnungslehre*, 2 vols. (Leipzig, 1872–1875). A bibliography was compiled by G. Peano: "Elenco bibliografico sull' 'Ausdehnungslehre' di H. Grassmann," in *Rivista di matematica*, **5** (1895), 179–182.

W. Burau
C. J. Scriba

GRAUNT, JOHN (*b.* London, England, 24 April 1620; *d.* London, 18 April 1674)

Graunt, apparently the eldest of seven or eight children born to Henry and Mary Graunt, received some formal "English learning" and, after he was sixteen, was apprenticed in his father's profession of draper. He held various offices in the Freedom of the Drapers' Company and in the city government, and he prospered in his business. In February 1641 he married Mary Scott, who evidently bore him one son and three daughters. Graunt came to know prominent people in London, and before 1650 he had become a friend of William Petty.

After the publication of his only book in January 1662, Graunt was elected, at the request of Charles II, to membership in the Royal Society. He suffered serious losses from the great fire of 1666, and this crisis was worsened by legal harassments occurring after his conversion around that time to Catholicism (earlier he had converted from Puritanism to anti-Trinitarianism). In spite of assistance from Petty, Graunt remained in straitened circumstances until his death.

Graunt's *Natural and Political Observations . . . Upon the Bills of Mortality* was the foundation of both statistics and demography. He had never formally studied mathematics, and the computations in his book were not more complex than what a successful businessman of that time could be expected to know. There has been much speculation over how much assistance Graunt received from Petty in writing the book. Undoubtedly Petty encouraged the undertaking and most likely made some contributions to it, but Graunt seems to deserve the lion's share of credit. He got the idea for his investigation from "having (I know not by what accident) engaged my thoughts upon the *Bills of Mortality*," which had been published for London since the end of the sixteenth century. These statistics were the primary basis for his study, although he supplemented them with parish christening records and data from a rural area, Romsey in Hampshire (Petty's birthplace).

Since Graunt's treatise was the starting point for two sciences, both his discoveries and the form of his presentation were important. He began by listing the kinds of knowledge that could be gained from analyzing vital statistics. Next, he discussed with impressive sophistication the various kinds of defects in his data—geographical inconsistencies, irregular intervals between recordings, lack of thoroughness, inaccurate age approximations, an ambiguous disease nomenclature, and a bias against honest reporting of certain causes of death, such as syphilis. He published tables of some of the data and some important statistical regularities which he discovered were evident from inspecting the data: a few more boys were born than girls; women tended to live longer than men; the sex ratio was about equal and was stable; the numbers of people dying from most causes except epidemic diseases were about the same from year to year; the mortality rate was high among infants; the frequency of death was higher in urban than in rural areas.

Graunt carried his analysis further by deducing various characteristics of populations from his data. These ingenious attempts indicate a good understanding of the kinds of questions that are significant for demography. Usually he explained his steps in solving problems, but he seldom included the actual calculations; and sometimes he omitted important information. Furthermore, his indirect approach sometimes went beyond the reliable use of his data, and the accuracy of some of his answers was difficult to evaluate. His calculations of the populations of England and Wales and of London are two examples.

Since he did realize the shortcomings of his data, on several occasions Graunt set an excellent example by seeking verification of his estimates by different indirect methods. He introduced the use of statistical samples but did not pursue this subject far enough to determine the sizes of samples or means of selection needed for insuring accuracy. He gave information on infant and old-age mortality which modern demographers have shown contained an implicit life table, but Graunt's method of computing it remains uncertain. He also realized that demographic procedures could be used to make projections concerning both past and future populations. In 1663 he furnished the Royal Society with a brief note on the rate of growth of salmon and the rate of increase of carp in a pond, which indicates that he also saw the value of studying animal populations.

BIBLIOGRAPHY

I. Original Works. Graunt's only book is *Natural and Political Observations Mentioned in a Following Index, and Made Upon the Bills of Mortality* (London, 1662; 2nd ed., 1662; 3rd ed., 1665; 4th ed., Oxford, 1665; 5th ed., London, 1676). The 5th ed. was reprinted in *A Collection of the Yearly Bills of Mortality, From 1657 to 1758 Inclusive. Together With Several Other Bills of an Earlier Date . . .*, presumably edited by Thomas Birch (London, 1759). There is a German trans. by Gottfried Schultz (Leipzig, 1702). There is also a reprint of the 5th ed. in *The Economic Writings of Sir William Petty, Together With the Observations Upon the Bills of Mortality More Probably by Captain John Graunt*, Charles Henry Hull, ed., 2 vols. (Cambridge, 1899; repr. New York, 1963), II, 319–431. Hull also gives a full bibliography of earlier eds. in II, 658–660, 641. There are two reprs. of the 1st ed.: Walter F. Willcox, ed. (Baltimore, 1939), and B. Benjamin, ed., in *Journal of the Institute of Actuaries*, **90** (1964), 1–61.

Graunt's notes on fish were first published by Thomas Birch in *The History of the Royal Society of London for Improving of Natural Knowledge, From Its First Rise*, 4 vols. (London, 1756–1757), I, 267, 294. Hull quoted the notes from p. 294 following his repr. of Graunt's book, II, 432.

II. Secondary Literature. The most important contemporary accounts of Graunt are by John Aubrey and Anthony à Wood: *Aubrey's Brief Lives*, Oliver Lawson Dick, ed. (Ann Arbor, Mich., 1957), pp. 114–115; and Anthony à Wood, *Athenae Oxonienses*, 2nd ed., 2 vols. (London, 1721), I, col. 311. Wood's account has been quoted in full in James Bonar, *Theories of Population From Raleigh to Arthur Young* (London, 1931; facs. repr., 1966), pp. 69–71. There are two modern investigations of his life: C. H. Hull, in *Economic Writings of . . . Petty*, I, xxxiv–xxxviii; and D. V. Glass, "John Graunt and His *Natural and Political Observations*," in *Notes and Records. Royal Society of London*, **19** (1964), 63–100, see 63–68, notes on 89–94.

The question of Petty's contribution to Graunt's book has been discussed in Glass, *op.cit.*, pp. 78–89, notes on pp. 97–100; Hull, *op. cit.*, I, xxxix–liv; Major Greenwood, *Medical Statistics From Graunt to Farr* (Cambridge, 1948), pp. 36–39; Walter F. Willcox, introduction to Graunt's *Natural and Political Observations* (Baltimore, 1939), pp. iii–xiii; and P. D. Groenewegen, "Authorship of the *Natural and Political Observations Upon the Bills of Mortality*," in *Journal of the History of Ideas*, **28** (1967), 601–602.

Graunt's contributions to statistics and demography are surveyed and evaluated in B. Benjamin, "John Graunt," in *International Encyclopedia of the Social Sciences*, VI (1968), 253–255; Glass, *op. cit.*, pp. 69–78, notes on pp. 95–97; Hull, *op. cit.*, I, lxxv–lxxix; Greenwood, *op. cit.*, pp. 30–35; Harald Westergaard, *Contributions to the History of Statistics* (London, 1932), pp. 16–23; Ian Sutherland, "John Graunt: a Tercentenary Tribute," in *Journal of the Royal Statistical Society*, **126A** (1963), 537–556; and A. Wolf, F. Dannemann, A. Armitage, and Douglas McKie, *A History of Science, Technology and Philosophy in the 16th & 17th Centuries*, 2nd ed. (New York, 1950), pp. 588–598.

On the background situation for much of the bills of mortality used by Graunt, see Charles F. Mullett, *The Bubonic Plague and England. An Essay in the History of Preventive Medicine* (Lexington, Ky., 1956). Also relevant, and still useful, is the discussion by William Ogle, "An Inquiry Into the Trustworthiness of the Old Bills of Mortality," in *Journal of the Royal Statistical Society*, **55** (1892), 437–460. Norman G. Brett-James has written a very useful paper on the collection of the London data: "The London Bills of Mortality in the 17th Century," in *Transactions of the London & Middlesex Archaeological Society*, **6** (1933), 284–309.

The early reception of Graunt's book is discussed in

Robert Kargon, "John Graunt, Francis Bacon, and the Royal Society: the Reception of Statistics," in *Journal of the History of Medicine and Allied Sciences,* **18** (1963), 337–348.

FRANK N. EGERTON, III

GRAVE, DMITRY ALEKSANDROVICH (*b.* Kirillov, Novgorod province, Russia, 6 September 1863; *d.* Kiev, U.S.S.R., 19 December 1939)

In 1871, after the death of Grave's father, a petty official, the family moved to St. Petersburg. Grave entered the mathematics department of the Physics and Mathematics Faculty of St. Petersburg University in 1881 and studied under P. L. Chebyshev and his pupils A. N. Korkin, I. I. Zolotarev, and A. A. Markov. He began his research while still a student.

After graduating in 1885, Grave continued at St. Petersburg as a postgraduate, and in 1889 he defended his master's thesis. In the same year he started his teaching career at the university as a *Privatdozent.* In 1896 he defended his doctoral dissertation, and in 1899 he became a professor at the University of Kharkov. In 1902 Grave moved to the University of Kiev, where the rest of his work was done.

Grave's mathematical researches were originally connected with Chebyshev's school and were especially influenced by Korkin. In his master's thesis he developed methods originated by C. G. J. Jacobi and Korkin and, taking up a subject proposed by Korkin, contributed to the three-body problem. His doctoral dissertation, the subject of which also was proposed by Korkin, touched upon map projection researches by Euler, Lagrange, and Chebyshev. In it Grave presented a comprehensive study of equal-area plane projections of a sphere, with meridians and parallels being represented on the plane by straight lines and circumferences respectively.

At the beginning of his Kiev period Grave took up algebra and number theory. A brilliant speaker and organizer, he created a school which later became prominent. Among his pupils were Otto J. Schmidt, N. G. Chebotaryov, B. N. Delone, and A. M. Ostrovsky. In 1908–1914 Grave published several original and comprehensive works in algebra and number theory.

He continued his research and teaching activities well after the October Revolution, being elected to the Ukrainian Academy of Sciences (1920) and the Soviet Academy of Sciences (corresponding member from 1924, honorary member from 1929). In this period Grave's interest shifted to mechanics and applied mathematics, then returned to algebra in his last years. His last work on algebraic calculus was conceived as a comprehensive study, of which he was able to publish only two volumes.

BIBLIOGRAPHY

I. ORIGINAL WORKS. Grave published a total of about 180 works; a comprehensive bibliography is in Dobrovolsky (see below). His main works are *Ob integrirovanii chastnykh differentsialnykh uravneny pervogo poryadka* ("On the Integration of Partial Differential Equations of the First Order"; St. Petersburg, 1889), his master's thesis; *Ob osnovnykh zadachakh matematicheskoy teorii postroenia geographicheskikh kart* ("On the Main Problems of the Mathematical Theory of Construction of Geographical Maps"; St. Petersburg, 1896), his doctoral dissertation; *Teoria konechnykh grupp* ("The Theory of Finite Groups"; Kiev, 1908); *Elementarny kurs teorii chisel* ("A Primer in Number Theory"; Kiev, 1909–1910; 2nd ed. 1913); *Arifmeticheskaya teoria algebraicheskikh velichin* ("Arithmetical Theory of Algebraic Quantities"), 2 vols. (Kiev, 1910–1912); *Entsiklopedia matematiki. Ocherk eyo sovremennogo polozhenia* ("Encyclopedia of Mathematics. An Essay on Its Current State"; Kiev, 1912); *Elementy vysshey algebry* ("Elements of Higher Algebra"; Kiev, 1914); and *Traktat po algebraicheskomu analizu* ("Treatise on Algebraic Calculus"), 2 vols. (Kiev, 1938–1939).

II. SECONDARY LITERATURE. Biographies are N. G. Chebotaryov, "Akademik Dmitry Aleksandrovich Grave," in *Sbornik posvyashchenny pamyati akademika D. A. Grave* ("Collected Articles in Memory of Academician D. A. Grave"; Moscow–Leningrad, 1940), pp. 3–14; and V. A. Dobrovolsky, *Dmitry Aleksandrovich Grave* (Moscow, 1968).

The works of Grave are described in a number of general sources on the history of mathematics, such as *Istoria otechestvennoy matematiki* ("History of National Mathematics"), II (Kiev, 1967), 481–486; and A. P. Youschkevitch, *Istoria matematiki v Rossii do 1917 goda* ("History of Mathematics in Russia Until 1917"; Moscow, 1968), pp. 547–554.

A. I. VOLODARSKY

'sGRAVESANDE, WILLEM JACOB (*b.* 'sHertogenbosch, Netherlands, 26 September 1688; *d.* Leiden, Netherlands, 28 February 1742)

'sGravesande was the earliest influential exponent of the Newtonian philosophy in continental Europe, his major work being widely read not only there but also in Britain. His family (originally known as Storm van 'sGravesande) was once important in Delft; like his brothers, he was educated at home by a tutor named Tourton, who was able to encourage his natural mathematical gifts. At Leiden University (1704–

1707) he studied law, presenting a doctoral dissertation on the crime of suicide. Again like his brothers, 'sGravesande practiced law at The Hague, where he collaborated with Prosper Marchand and others in founding the *Journal littéraire de la Haye* (1713), a periodical of significance for twenty years in the history of science. He contributed several book reviews and some essays that were reprinted by J. N. S. Allamand in his *Oeuvres philosophiques et mathématiques de Mr. G. J. 'sGravesande* (Amsterdam, 1774). The most celebrated of these (in vol. **12** of the *Journal; Oeuvres,* I, 217–252) was his "Essai d'une nouvelle théorie du choc des corps fondée sur l'expérience" (1722), in which, departing from his customary attachment to the English school, 'sGravesande adopted the Huygens-Leibniz concept of *vis viva,* affirming (prop. X) that "La force d'un corps est proportionelle à sa masse multipliée par le quarré de sa vitesse." For this he was attacked by Samuel Clarke (1728), against whom he defended himself ably.

His association with the English Newtonian philosophers sprang from his appointment as secretary to the Dutch embassy (Wassenaer van Duyvenvoorde and Borsele van den Hooge) sent early in 1715 to congratulate George I on his accession to the English throne. This duty kept 'sGravesande in England for a year. His introduction to English learned society was facilitated by his acquaintance with the three sons of Gilbert Burnet, one of whom, William, proposed 'sGravesande as a fellow of the Royal Society in February 1715; he was elected on 9 June. On 24 March 1715 he was present (with other foreigners) at a demonstration of experiments by J. T. Desaguliers. There is no other mention of his name in the *Journal Book* until, on the brink of returning to The Hague in February 1716, 'sGravesande made a particular offer of his services to the Royal Society. Nevertheless, it is certain that he became acquainted with Newton and other fellows of the society, especially Desaguliers and John Keill, with whom he afterwards corresponded occasionally.

In June 1717, on the recommendation of Wassenaer van Duyvenvoorde, 'sGravesande was called to Leiden as professor of mathematics and astronomy. His inaugural lecture was on the usefulness of mathematics to all the sciences, physics above all (*Oeuvres,* II, 311–328). In 1734 he was additionally named professor of philosophy. By this time Hermann Boerhaave and 'sGravesande were established as the twin luminaries of Leiden, attracting hundreds of foreign students each year. From the outset of his teaching in both physics and astronomy 'sGravesande modeled his lectures on the example of Newton in the *Principia* and *Opticks,* although in later years they incorporated other influences, especially that of Boerhaave. Moreover, he adopted from Keill and Desaguliers the notion of demonstrating to his classes the experimental proof of scientific principles, accumulating an ever larger collection of apparatus, as may be seen from successive editions of his *Physices elementa mathematica, experimentis confirmata. Sive, introductio ad philosophiam Newtonianam* (Leiden, 1720, 1721). The scientific reputation of 'sGravesande is enshrined in this book, which he constantly corrected and amplified in later editions. An "official" English translation prepared by Desaguliers (to whom copies of the Latin original were sent in haste) was also issued in 1720 and 1721, and it passed through six editions. (The booksellers Mears and Woodward printed a rival version under the name of John Keill.) French translations appeared only in 1746 and 1747, but a critical review by L. B. Castel was published in the *Mémoires de Trévoux* in May and October 1721. The book was at once welcomed by British and a number of German scholars. 'sGravesande also published an abbreviated account for student use, *Philosophiae Newtonianae institutiones* (Leiden, 1723, 1728; and ed. Allamand 1744).

In 1721 and again in 1722 'sGravesande visited Kassel at the request of the landgrave to examine the secret perpetual-motion machine constructed by Orffyreus; he was unable to detect a fraud or (apparently) to convince himself that such a device is impossible.

In 1727 he published at Leiden, as a text for his mathematical teaching, *Matheseos universalis elementa. Quibus accedunt, specimen commentarii in Arithmeticam universalem Newtonii: ut et de determinanda forma seriei infinitae adsumtae regula nova* (*Oeuvres,* I, 89–214). This work, translated into Dutch (1728) and English (1752), is of didactic rather than original merit, but it was significant for its invitation to mathematicians to elucidate systematically Newton's *Universal Arithmetick,* which 'sGravesande exemplified by his own explanation of two passages from Newton's book. 'sGravesande found the lighthearted treatment of infinitesimals and the infinite in Bernard de Fontenelle's *Élémens de la géométrie de l'infini* (Paris, 1727) unacceptable, and he maintained his objections in the *Journal littéraire* against Fontenelle's rejoinder (1730).

After commencing the teaching of philosophy, 'sGravesande again published a textbook, *Introductio ad philosophiam, metaphysicam et logicam continens* (Leiden, 1736; repr. 1737, 1756, 1765; Venice, 1737, 1748; French ed., Leiden, 1748)—a work creating some odium for its author by its treatment of the question of necessity and free will. It was republished in *Oeuvres*, II, 1–215, together with some previously unprinted essays on metaphysics discovered by Allamand.

Apart from his own writings, 'sGravesande was active in promoting the publication at Leiden of the works of his greater countryman Christian Huygens, in *Opera varia* (1724) and *Opera reliqua* (1728), both of which he edited; in republishing the writings of his friend John Keill in 1725, as well as in editing Newton's *Arithmetica universalis* (1732); and in compiling the Dutch publication of the *Mémoires de l'Académie royale des sciences contenant les ouvrages adoptés* . . . (The Hague, 1731). Voltaire made a special journey to Leiden in 1736 to secure 'sGravesande's appraisal of his *Élémens de la philosophie de Newton* (London, 1738), writing afterward a warm appreciation of 'sGravesande's kindness and learning.

Although 'sGravesande was by no means the first semipopular exponent of Newtonian science and the experimental method (having been preceded in England by David Gregory, William Whiston, John Keill, and Desaguliers, among others), his *Mathematical Elements of Physics* was easily the most influential book of its kind, at least before 1750. It was a larger, better-argued, and more philosophical work than most of its predecessors; moreover, it leaned heavily on *Opticks* (including the queries) as well as on the *Principia.* One should therefore distinguish between 'sGravesande's roles as an exponent of Newtonian concepts (the rules of reasoning, the theory of gravitational attraction and its applications in celestial mechanics, theory of matter, theory of light, and so forth) and as an exponent of an empiricist methodology disdaining postulated hypotheses. Indeed, 'sGravesande contributed nothing to the progress of mathematical physics, for which one must look to the work of other contemporaries such as the Bernoullis, Pierre Varignon, and Alexis Clairaut. The strength of his exposition was in his perfection of the method of justifying scientific truths either by self-evidence or by appeal to experimental verification in the manner already begun by Keill and Desaguliers, perfected by him through the design of many new instruments constructed by the instrument maker Jan van Musschenbroek, brother of Pieter. (The extant instruments are preserved in the Rijksmuseum voor de Geschiedenis der Natuurwetenschappen at Leiden.) Yet, 'sGravesande's teaching and his *Elements* were by no means the sole vehicle for the introduction of British empiricism to the Continent, although probably they were the most important. He had been anticipated by Boerhaave (although Boerhaave did not employ didactic experiments) and was paralleled by Pieter van Musschenbroek at Utrecht (from 1730; he joined 'sGravesande at Leiden in 1739).

Unlike Newton, 'sGravesande commences his *Elements* with a prefatory discussion of metaphysics and epistemology directed against the Cartesians. The task of physics, he writes, is to determine the laws of nature laid down by the Creator and to unfold their regular operation throughout the universe. In thus examining the true works of God, fictitious hypotheses are to be set aside; but philosophers have differed in their methods of determining the laws of nature and the properties of bodies. "I have therefore thought fit," he continues, "to make good the Newtonian Method, which I have followed in this Work." Since the properties of bodies are not to be learned a priori, who can deny that there are in matter properties not known to us nor essential to matter, which flow from "the free Power of God"? How are the laws of nature to be sought and the three Newtonian laws of motion justified? 'sGravesande replies to these questions in a curious argument. First he asserts Newton's first rule of reasoning (Ockham's Razor). Next, distinguishing the truths of pure mathematics, which are verified by internal consistency, from those of physics ("mixed mathematics"), which depend on the senses, he argues that the latter are justified by analogy: "We must look up as true, whatever being denied would destroy civil Society, and deprive us of the means of living." This seemingly means that the consequences of induction must be true, for 'sGravesande goes on specifically to declare: "In Physics we are to discover the Laws of Nature by the Phenomena, then by induction prove them to be general Laws; all the rest is to be handled mathematically." The definitions of the scope of natural philosophy and of a law of nature (". . . the Rule and Law, according to which God resolved that certain Motions should always, that is, in all Cases, be performed") follow in chapter 1, which is concluded without further discussion by a statement of Newton's three rules of reasoning.

In volume I, 'sGravesande traverses the theory of matter (influences of the queries in *Opticks* are apparent but not marked), elementary mechanics, the five simple machines, Newton's laws of motion, gravity, central forces, hydrostatics and hydraulics, and pneumatics (including a treatment of sound and wave motion). His second volume opens with three chapters on fire, modeled on Boerhaave's ideas rather than Newton's, in whose manifestations he includes electrical phenomena. There follow two books on optics, one on the system of the world, and a final book entitled "The Physical Causes of the Celestial Motions," in which 'sGravesande can explain only that the cause of these motions is the operation of universal gravitation, whose cause is hidden "and cannot be deduced from Laws that are known." All this is treated with the aid of only trivial mathematics but is enriched with extremely numerous experimental illustrations and examples. Newton's ether does not appear, nor his "fits" of easy transmission and reflection, nor the extremely subtle physical speculation of the queries. No doubt the *Elements* owed almost as much of its success to its omissions and simplicity as to its clear and positive treatment of what it did contain. It was, obviously, very different from such later expositions as those of Henry Pemberton and Colin Maclaurin, and in many respects both more stimulating and more original.

BIBLIOGRAPHY

I. ORIGINAL WORKS. Besides works mentioned in text, Allamand's *Oeuvres* (vol. I) include 'sGravesande's youthful *Essai de perspective* (Leiden, 1711; English trans., London, 1724) and other minor writings: *Usage de la chambre obscure; Remarques sur la construction des machines pneumatiques; Lettre à Mr. Newton sur une machine inventée par Orffyreus; Remarques touchant le mouvement perpétuel;* and *Lettres sur l'utilité des mathematiques.* The philosophical writings are in vol. II.

II. SECONDARY LITERATURE. All biographies of 'sGravesande are based on the life by his friend Allamand, prefaced to the *Oeuvres.* See also Pierre Brunet, *Les physiciens hollandais et la méthode expérimentale en France au XVIIIe siècle* (Paris, 1926), *passim;* and *L'introduction des théories de Newton en France au XVIIIe siècle: avant 1738* (Paris, 1931), esp. pp. 97-107; I. Bernard Cohen, *Franklin and Newton* (Philadelphia, 1956), esp. pp. 234-243; C. A. Crommelin, *Descriptive Catalogue of the Physical Instruments of the 18th Century, Including the Collection 'sGravesande-Musschenbroek* (Leiden, 1951); P. C. Molhuysen, P. J. Blok, and K. H. Kossman, *Nieuw Nederlandsch biografisch woordenboek,* VI (Leiden, 1924), cols. 623-627; and A. Thackray, *Atoms and Powers* (Cambridge, Mass., 1970), pp. 101-104.

A. RUPERT HALL

GREEN, GEORGE (*b.* Nottingham, England, July 1793 [baptized 14 July]; *d.* Sneinton, near Nottingham, 31 May 1841)

Although Green left school at an early age to work in his father's bakery, he had probably already developed an interest in mathematics that was fostered by Robert Goodacre, the leading private schoolmaster of Nottingham and author of a popular arithmetic textbook. Virtually self-taught, Green acquired his knowledge of mathematics through extensive reading. Many of the works he studied were available in Nottingham at the Bromley House Subscription Library, which he joined in 1823. By that time the family had moved to Sneinton, a suburb, where his father had established a successful milling business; Green used the top story of the mill as a study.

Green's most important work, *An Essay on the Application of Mathematical Analysis to the Theories of Electricity and Magnetism,* was published by subscription in March 1828. Apparently, almost all of the fifty-two subscribers were patrons and friends of Green's; a local baronet, Edward ffrench Bromhead of Thurlby, assisted Green later but was not an early promoter. Until other evidence is available, one can only conjecture that Green's supporters included some of the leading members of the Bromley House Library; the list of subscribers suggests only limited circulation outside Nottingham.

In the preface Green indicated that his "limited sources of information" preventing his giving a proper historical sketch of the mathematical theory of electricity, and indeed, he cites few sources. Among them are Cavendish's single-fluid theoretical study of electricity of 1771, two memoirs by Poisson of 1812 on surface electricity and three on magnetism (1821-1823), and contributions by Arago, Laplace, Fourier, Cauchy, and T. Young. The preface concludes with a request that the work be read with indulgence, in view of the limitations of the author's education.

The *Essay* begins with introductory observations emphasizing the central role of the potential function. Green coined the term "potential" to denote the results obtained by adding the masses of all the particles of a system, each divided by its distance from a given point. The general properties of the potential function are subsequently developed and applied to electricity and magnetism. The formula connecting surface and volume integrals, now known as Green's theorem, was introduced in the work, as was "Green's function," the concept now extensively used in the solution of partial differential equations.

Bromhead correctly surmised that Green's "publication must be a complete failure and dead born," but he was unaware that its significance would be appreciated later. Bromhead persuaded Green to matriculate at Caius College, Cambridge—a decision undoubtedly influenced by the death of Green's father in January 1829, for the subsequent sale of the family business afforded him the necessary financial backing. Before he could be admitted, however, he had to close the gaps in his classical education; but it is not known whether this was done at Nottingham, Cambridge, or both.

Green's second work, "The Laws of the Equilibrium of Fluids Analogous to the Electric Fluid," was read at the Cambridge Philosophical Society on 12 November 1832, so it is possible that he had already moved there. The paper was reportedly communicated by Bromhead, as was Green's next memoir, "Exterior and Interior Attractions of Ellipsoids of Variable Densities," read to the society the following May. Although not as significant as the *Essay*, both papers contain generalizations of his methods to cover an inverse nth power law of force and s dimensions.

Admitted to Caius College in October 1833, Green became scholar on 25 March 1834, after having submitted, again through Bromhead, a paper to the Royal Society of Edinburgh. In "Researches on the Vibration of Pendulums in Fluid Media," read in December 1833, Green obtained formulas, valid for small oscillations, for the effective increase of the mass of the pendulum due to the density of the surrounding fluid. In January 1837 Green received the B.A. as fourth wrangler—"to the disappointment of his friends." His attention may perhaps have been distracted by the demands of his own mathematical research.

"On the Motion of Waves in a Variable Canal of Small Depth and Width," read to the Cambridge Philosophical Society in May 1837, included the formula for determining the height of a wave,

$$\zeta \propto \beta^{-1/2}\gamma^{-1/4},$$

where β and γ represent the variable breadth and depth of the canal. A note to the paper, read in February 1839, commented on J. S. Russell's report (1837) to the British Association for the Advancement of Science.

Two papers followed in December 1837: "On the Reflexion and Refraction of Sound" and "On the Reflexion and Refraction of Light at the Common Surface of Two Non-Crystallized Media"; a supplement to the latter work, in which both papers were related, followed in May 1839. The first memoir simplified—and in one respect corrected—Poisson's memoir (1831); the second followed the work of Cauchy and Airy. In May 1839 Green read his second most important paper, "On the Propagation of Light in Crystallized Media," in which he used the vis viva theorem (conservation of mechanical energy) to simplify Cauchy's treatment.

This succession of works secured Green's election in October 1839 as Perse Fellow of Caius College, although he apparently made no significant contribution to academic life. It is reported that he set the problem papers for two college examinations but never lectured. In May 1840 he was in Nottingham; and it is doubtful that Green ever returned to Cambridge. His will, dated 28 July 1840, was probably written at Nottingham and confirms that he was in poor health, but no details of his illness are given. A codicil, added four months before his death, is his last known action. A locally published obituary, referring to Bromhead's support, concluded that "had his life been prolonged, he might have stood eminently high as a mathematician."

Only a few weeks before Green's death, William Thomson had been admitted to St. Peter's College, Cambridge. In a paper by Robert Murphy published in the *Transactions of the Cambridge Philosophical Society*, Thomson noticed a reference to Green's *Essay*, although Murphy did not mention any of his other works published in that journal. Thomson was unable to find a copy of the *Essay* until, just after receiving his degree in January 1845, his coach, William Hopkins, gave him three copies. Sixty years later Thomson recalled his excitement and that of Liouville and Sturm, to whom he showed the work in Paris in the summer of 1845. After returning to Cambridge, Thomson was responsible for republishing the work, with an introduction (1850–1854). Through Thomson, Maxwell, and others, the general mathematical theory of potential developed by an obscure, self-taught miller's son would lead to the mathematical theories of electricity underlying twentieth-century industry.

BIBLIOGRAPHY

I. ORIGINAL WORKS. *An Essay on the Application of Mathematical Analysis to the Theories of Electricity and Magnetism* (Nottingham, 1828) is extremely rare; the total number of copies is estimated to have been less than 100. There are two facsimile reprints (Berlin, 1889; Göteborg, 1958) and a German trans. in *Ostwalds Klassiker der exakten Wissenschaften*, no. 61 (Leipzig, 1895). Thomson republished the *Essay*, with a brief biography of Green, a list of his writings, and a bibliography of eight "independent investigations on the subject of Green's *Essay*," in *Journal für die reine und angewandte Mathematik*, **39** (1850), 73–89; **44** (1852), 356–374; and **47** (1854), 161–221.

All but one of Green's subsequent writings were published in *Transactions of the Cambridge Philosophical Society*, **5–7** (1835–1842). Together with the *Essay*, they were edited for Caius College by N. M. Ferrers (London–Cambridge, 1871; facs. repr., Paris, 1903). The preface includes a brief biography that is chiefly a sketch of the contents of the papers; a few notes on particular points in them are collected in an appendix.

II. SECONDARY LITERATURE. The above account is based largely on H. G. Green, "A Biography of George Green," in *Studies and Essays . . . Offered in Homage to George Sarton* (New York, 1946), 545–594, which includes a complete bibliography. Adam W. Thomas, *A History of Nottingham High School 1513–1953* (Nottingham, 1958), is useful for Green's educational background; and A. R. Hall, *The Cambridge Philosophical Society: A History, 1819–1969* (Cambridge, 1969), provides details of the Society in whose *Transactions* most of Green's work was published. H. G. Green (see above) reveals the importance of the Bromley House Library in providing facilities for the young mathematician; and John Russell, *A History of the Nottingham Subscription Library* (Nottingham, 1916), ch. 5, indicates its keen interest in science in the 1830's. See also J. E. G. Farina, "The Work and Significance of George Green, the Miller-Mathematician, 1793–1841," in *Bulletin of the Institute of Mathematics and Applications*, **12**, no. 4 (1976), 98–105.

J. S. Russell's report was published as "Report of the Committee on Waves," in *Report of the British Association for the Advancement of Science*, **7** (1837), 417–496—see esp. 425 and 494; Poisson's memoir was "Sur le mouvement de deux fluides élastiques superposés," in *Mémoires de l'Académie des sciences*, 2nd ser., **10** (1831), 317–404.

P. J. WALLIS

GREGORY, DAVID (*b.* Aberdeen, Scotland, 3 June 1659; *d.* Maidenhead, Berkshire, England, 10 October 1708)

The eldest surviving son of the laird (also called David) of Kinnairdie in Banffshire, and nephew of James Gregory, David graduated from Marischal College, Aberdeen, and went on to Edinburgh University, where in October 1683—a month before taking his M.A.—he was elected to the chair of mathematics, vacant since his uncle's death in 1675, delivering an inaugural lecture "De analyseos geometricae progressu et incrementis." Staunchly supported by Archibald Pitcairne, an old friend from undergraduate days, he sought conscientiously in his professorial lectures (on elementary optics, astronomy, and mechanics) to impart to his students basic insights into the "new" science of Descartes, John Wallis and, after 1687 (if we are to believe William Whiston) Isaac Newton. Attempts by Gregory in 1684 and 1687 to start a correspondence with Newton failed, but an indirect link with Cambridge was formed in 1685 after a visit to Newton by a mutual acquaintance, John Craig(e).

Increasingly under attack by his fellow professors at Edinburgh for his radical views, Gregory jeopardized his position in 1690 by refusing to swear the required oath of loyalty to the English throne before a visiting parliamentary commission. The retirement of Edward Bernard from the Savilian professorship of astronomy at Oxford in 1691 offered an outlet. Backed by Newton's recommendation of him as "very well skilled in Analysis & Geometry both new & old. . . . understands Astronomy very well . . . & is respected the greatest Mathematician in Scotland," and with Flamsteed's support, Gregory was elected to the chair in face of strong opposition from Edmond Halley (later, after Wallis' death in 1703, to become his companion professor of geometry). In November 1692 he was elected fellow of the Royal Society, but he never took an active part in its affairs except for submitting several papers to its *Transactions.*

During his early years at Oxford, Gregory traveled widely to keep abreast of current developments in science, visiting Johann Hudde and Christian Huygens in Holland in May–June 1693 and Newton at Cambridge in May 1694 and on numerous later occasions in London. His extant Savilian lectures (from 1692) are for the most part a rehash of his Edinburgh *lectiones,* suitably updated; as he told Samuel Pepys, he was concerned to see that his students "should study some Euclid, trigonometry, mechanics, catoptrics and dioptrics, . . . the theory of planets and navigation." His appointment in 1699 as mathematical tutor to the young duke of Gloucester was thwarted by the latter's sudden death; his relations with Flamsteed, a competitor for the post, thereafter rapidly deteriorated, particularly after he joined Newton's committee set up to publish Flamsteed's *Historia coelestis.* Gregory's election in 1705 to the Royal College of Physicians at Edinburgh was purely honorary, but he took a more active role in the Act of Union between England and Scotland in 1707. He married in 1695 and was en route to London to visit his children, sick with smallpox, when he died.

No definitive assessment of Gregory's scientific achievement is possible until a detailed examination of his extant memoranda is made. Doubtless this will reinforce the impression gained from his printed work that a modicum of talent, effectively lacking originality, was stretched a long way. His earliest publication, *Exercitatio geometrica de dimensione figurarum* (1684), was a presentation of a number of manuscript *adversaria* bequeathed to him by his uncle James, interlarded with worked examples from René-François de Sluse's *Miscellanea,* Nicolaus Mercator's *Logarithmotechnia,* and James Gregory's *Geometriae pars universalis* and *Exercitationes* (all 1668) and a citation of Newton's series for the general circle zone communicated to John Collins in 1670 and passed forthwith to Scotland. Ignorant of the general binomial theorem which had been found independently by Newton and his uncle James, Gregory resorted to a brute-force development of the series expansion of the binomial square root by which he accomplished the "dimension" (quadrature and rectification) of various conics, conchoids, the cissoid, the Slusian pearl, and other algebraic curves, while the subtleties of his uncle's use of a Taylor expansion to invert Kepler's equation as an infinite series (first published here, but without any proof) clearly passed him by.

Gregory's *Treatise of Practical Geometry* and *Catoptricae et dioptricae sphaericae elementa* (1695) are printed versions of elementary lectures given at Edinburgh in the 1680's; the latter is often singled out for its appended remark (p. 98) suggesting, on the analogy of the crystalline and vitreous humours "in the Fabrick of the Eye," that an achromatic compound lens might be formed by combining simple lenses of different media, but this insight he might well have had from Newton. His thick folio text on foundations of astronomy, *Astronomiae . . . elementa* (1702), is a well-documented but unimaginative attempt to graft the gravitational synthesis propounded in the first book and especially the third book of Newton's *Principia* onto the findings of traditional astronomy. While respected as a source book it is now chiefly remembered for the remarks by Newton on the *prisca sapientia* of the ancients and their "knowledge" of the inverse-square law of universal gravitation and for the Latin version of Newton's short paper on lunar theory which it reproduces.

Gregory's first collected edition, following Bernard's wish, of *Euclidis quae supersunt omnia* (1703) is a competent gathering of the mathematical and physical writings attributed to Euclid of Alexandria (*Elements, Data, Introductio harmonica, Sectio canonis, Phaenomena, Optica, Catoptrica, Dioptrica, Divisions of figures, De levi et ponderoso*), but the one exciting passage in the preface (on the *Data,* especially 86) again stems from Newton. Of Gregory's articles in the *Philosophical Transactions of the Royal Society* that (1693) on Vincenzo Viviani's "testudo veliformis quadrabilis" is an elegant solution of a tricky but essentially elementary problem; that on the catenary (1697) erroneously derives the correct differential equation of the freely hanging uniform chain (he failed to see the necessity of compounding the tensions at both ends of the curve) and therefrom draws its logarithmic construction and main properties; that (1704) on the Cassini oval or cassinoid briefly sketches its main forms, determining, since it is not convex when its eccentricity is greater than $1/\sqrt{3}$, its inacceptability as a planetary orbit. The poverty of Gregory's astronomical observations merits Flamsteed's jibe of "closet astronomer."

In retrospect, Gregory's true role in the development of seventeenth-century science is not that of original innovator but that of custodian of certain precious papers and verbal communications passed to him by his uncle James and, as privileged information, by Newton.

BIBLIOGRAPHY

I. ORIGINAL WORKS. The brief "Index Chartarum," now in Edinburgh University Library, made by Gregory's son David after his father's death, outlines the content of some 400 MSS and memoranda on mathematical, physical, and astronomical topics gathered in four "M.S." (A–D), of which D is "plerumque Jacobi Gregorii." Those (the greater part) still extant are now scattered in the libraries of Edinburgh and St. Andrews universities and the Royal Society, London. Further memoranda are interleaved in "M.S." E (now Christ Church, Oxford, MS 346), essentially a journal of Gregory's scientific activities at Oxford between March 1696 and September 1708. No concordance to these papers is published, but I have in my possession a rough list of the location of the mathematical items made *ca.* 1950 by H. W. Turnbull. Selected extracts, only a small fraction of the total, are reproduced in W. G. Hiscock, *David Gregory, Isaac Newton and Their Circle* (Oxford, 1937) and in Turnbull's ed. of *The Correspondence of Isaac Newton,* III–IV (Cambridge, 1961–1967).

The MS (A57, Edinburgh) of Gregory's first published work, *Exercitatio geometrica de dimensione figurarum sive specimen methodi generalis dimetiendi quasvis figuras* (Edinburgh, 1684)—reviewed by Wallis in *Philosophical Transactions of the Royal Society,* **14,** no. 163 (20 Sept. 1684), 730–732—contains few variants. His "Lectiones opticae ad Acad. Edinburg. 1683" (B11, Edinburgh DC.1.75) remain unprinted, as does his "Geometria de motu: par[te]s [1–5] lect. ad Acad. Edinburg. [1684–1687]" (B12, B15, B16, Edinburgh DC.1.75: incomplete autographs are in the Royal Society and Christ Church; a complete contemporary copy is in Aberdeen University [MS 2171]) except for an Englished fragment "never printed till now" inserted by John Eames and John Martyn in their *Philosophical Transactions Abridged,* VI (London, 1734), 275–276.

Gregory's "Institutionum astronomicarum libri 1 et 2 in usum Academicorum Edinburgensium scripti 1685" (B7, Edinburgh) was later absorbed into his *Astronomia;* the parallel "Geometria practica . . . conscripta 1685" (B6, Edinburgh DC.1.75/DC.5.57; contemporary copy in Aberdeen MS 2171) was subsequently rendered into English

(Aberdeen MS 672) by an unknown student and later published by Colin Maclaurin as *A Treatise of Practical Geometry . . . Translated from the Latin With Additions* (Edinburgh, 1745; 9th ed. 1780). His astronomical and medical lectures at Oxford during 1692 to 1697 are preserved in Aberdeen (MS 2206/8). His *Catoptricae et dioptricae sphaericae elementa* (B18) was published by him at Oxford in 1695 (2nd ed., Edinburgh, 1713); with addenda by William Brown it appeared in English as *Dr. Gregory's Elements of Catoptrics and Dioptrics* (London, 1715; enl. ed. by J. T. Desaguliers, London, 1735). The 1694 calculus compendium "Isaaci Newtoni methodus fluxionum ubi calculus differentialis Leibnitij et methodus tangentium Barrovij explicantur et exemplis plurimis omnis generis illustrantur"—variant autographs in St. Andrews (QA33G8D12) and Christ Church; contemporary copies by John Keill in the University Library, Cambridge, Lucasian Papers, and by William Jones, Shirburn 180.H.33—is unprinted.

Gregory's "Notae in Isaaci Newtoni *Principia philosophiae* . . . in anno 1693 conscripta"—original in the Royal Society, amanuensis copy in Christ Church; contemporary transcripts in Edinburgh and Aberdeen (MS GY)—was proposed for publication at Cambridge in 1714, but Nicholas Saunderson could find "nobody that can give me any account of it" (to Jones, February 1714); see S. P. Rigaud, *Correspondence of Scientific Men of the Seventeenth Century*, I (Oxford, 1841),* 264. His weighty *Astronomiae physicae & geometricae elementa* (Oxford, 1702; 2nd ed., Geneva, 1726) was "done into English" as *The Elements of Physical and Geometrical Astronomy* (London, 1715; 2nd ed., 1726); influential reviews appeared in *Philosophical Transactions of the Royal Society*, **23**, no. 283 (Jan.-Feb. 1703), 1312-1320; and *Acta eruditorum* (Oct. 1703), 452-462. Gregory's Latin (pp. 332-336) of Newton's "Theory of the Moon" (Cambridge, Add. 3966.10,82r-83v, published in *Correspondence*, IV [1967], 327-329; Gregory's copy [$C121_2$] is now in the Royal Society) appeared soon after in English as *A New and Most Accurate Theory of the Moon's Motion; Whereby All Her Irregularities May Be Solved* . . . (London, 1702). His supervised edition of ΕΥΚΛΕΙΔΟΥ ΤΑ ΣΩΖΟΜΕΝΑ. *Euclidis quae supersunt omnia. Ex recensione Davidis Gregorii* was published at Oxford in 1703. Gregory's abridgment of Newton's 1671 tract, his "Tractatus de seriebus infinitis et convergentibus" (A56, Edinburgh), is printed in *The Mathematical Papers of Isaac Newton*, III (Cambridge, 1969), 354-372.

In the *Philosophical Transactions of the Royal Society* Gregory published a solution of Viviani's Florentine problem (**18**, no. 207 [Jan. 1694], 25-29); two defenses of his uncle James against Jean Gallois's charges of plagiarism from Roberval (**18**, no. 214 [Nov.-Dec. 1694], 233-236; and **25**, no. 308 [autumn 1706], 2336-2341); a study of the "Catenaria" and a reply to Leibniz's "animadversion" (*Acta eruditorum* [Feb. 1699], 87-91) upon it (**19**, no. 231 [Aug. 1697], 637-652; and **21**, no. 259 [Dec. 1699], 419-426); his observations of the solar eclipse of 13 Sept. 1698 (**21**, no. 256 [Sept. 1699], 320-321); a remark on John Perk's quadrature of a circle lunule (**21**, no. 259 [Dec. 1699], 414-417); and a discourse "De orbita Cassiniana," refuting its claim to be a realistic planetary path (**24**, no. 293 [Sept. 1704], 1704-1706).

II. Secondary Literature. The documented assessment in *Biographia Britannica*, IV (London, 1757), 2365-2372, is still unreplaced. Some biographical complements are given in Agnes M. Stewart, *The Academic Gregories* (Edinburgh, 1901), 52-76. Gregory's Savilian "Oratio inauguralis" on 21 April 1692 is printed, with commentary, by P. D. Lawrence and A. G. Mollond in *Notes and Records. Royal Society of London*, **25** (1970), 143-178; see esp. 159-165; the only modern study in depth of any aspect of Gregory's mathematical and scientific output is C. Truesdell's examination of Gregory's spurious derivation of the catenary's differential equation: "The Rational Mechanics of Flexible or Elastic Bodies, 1638-1788," vol. II of *Euleri opera omnia*, 2nd ser. (Zurich, 1960), pt. 2; see esp. 85-86.

D. T. Whiteside

GREGORY, DUNCAN FARQUHARSON (*b.* Edinburgh, Scotland, 13 April 1813; *d.* Edinburgh, 23 February 1844)

Duncan Gregory came from a family with a long tradition of interest in science. His great-grandfather, his grandfather, and his father, James, were each professor of medicine at the University of Edinburgh. His great-great-grandfather was the mathematician James Gregory. Gregory attended the Edinburgh Academy, studied for a year in Geneva, and attended the University of Edinburgh. He matriculated at Trinity College, Cambridge, in 1833 and ranked as fifth wrangler in 1837. He remained at Cambridge as lecturer and tutor, and in 1840 he became a fellow of Trinity. Gregory received his M.A. in 1841. At that time he was offered a position at the University of Toronto, but as he was in poor health, he declined it. In 1838 Gregory, together with Robert Ellis, founded the *Cambridge Mathematical Journal*. Gregory was the first editor, and in this role considerably aided George Boole, who submitted his earliest papers to that journal.

Gregory published two books, both designed for use at Cambridge: one on the calculus (1841) and one on applications of analysis to geometry (published posthumously in 1845). His major contribution to mathematics, however, was his theory of algebra. His earliest papers were on differential and difference equations, in which he used a method that came to be known as the calculus of operations. This method involved treating the symbols of operation

$$\frac{d}{dx} \quad \text{or} \quad \Delta$$

as if they were symbols of quantity. In his attempt to justify the validity of this method, Gregory examined the laws governing the combination of these symbols with constants and by iteration. As a result of these studies he came to a definition of algebra as the study of the combination of operations defined not by their specific nature but rather by the laws of combination to which they were subject. This is wholly modern in tone, and that Gregory's work is not more widely known is probably due to the fact that he did not live to create a large-scale abstract algebra to illustrate his view.

BIBLIOGRAPHY

I. ORIGINAL WORKS. Gregory's books are *Examples of the Processes of the Differential and Integral Calculus* (Cambridge, 1841) and *A Treatise on the Application of Analysis to Solid Geometry,* William Walton, ed. (Cambridge, 1845). See also *The Mathematical Writings by Duncan Farquharson Gregory,* William Walton, ed. (Cambridge, 1865), which contains almost all of Gregory's published papers. *The Royal Society Catalogue* lists Gregory's works but contains several errors, which are corrected in Clock's thesis (see below).

II. SECONDARY LITERATURE. Biographical material on Gregory includes a memoir by Robert Ellis, found in the *Mathematical Writings,* pp. xi–xxiv, and the article by H. R. Luard, "D. F. Gregory," in *Dictionary of National Biography.* The significance of his work is discussed in Daniel Arwin Clock, "A New British Concept of Algebra: 1825–1850," Ph.D. diss. (Univ. of Wis., 1964); Elaine Koppelman, "Calculus of Operations: French Influence on British Mathematics in the First Half of the Nineteenth Century," Ph.D. diss. (Johns Hopkins Univ., 1969); and Ernest Nagel, "'Impossible Numbers': A Chapter in the History of Logic," in Studies in the History of Ideas, III (New York, 1935), 429–475.

ELAINE KOPPELMAN

GREGORY (more correctly **GREGORIE**), **JAMES** (*b.* Drumoak, near Aberdeen, Scotland, November 1638; *d.* Edinburgh, Scotland, late October 1675)

The youngest son of John Gregory, minister of the manse of Drumoak, James Gregory was descended through his father from the fiery Clan Macgregor and through his mother, Janet, from the more scholarly Anderson family, one of whom, Alexander, had been secretary to Viète. Somewhat sickly as a child, he received his early education (including an introduction to geometry) from his mother, but after his father's death in 1651 his elder brother David sent him to Aberdeen, first to grammar school and later to Marischal College. After graduating there and further encouraged by his brother, himself an enthusiastic amateur mathematician, James devoted himself to studies in mathematical optics and astronomy.

In 1662, aware of the lack of scientific opportunities in Scotland, he traveled to London, there publishing *Optica promota* (1663), in which he gathered his earliest researches, and making several influential friends, notably Robert Moray, interim president of the Royal Society in 1660. In April 1663 Moray sought to arrange Gregory's introduction to Christian Huygens in Paris, but this was thwarted by Huygens' absence. Subsequently, to improve his scientific knowledge Gregory went to Italy, studying geometry, mechanics, and astronomy under Evangelista Torricelli's pupil Stefano degli Angeli at Padua (1664–1667) and publishing *Vera circuli et hyperbolæ quadratura* (1667) and *Geometriæ pars universalis* (1668). About Easter 1668 he returned to London; there, backed by John Collins' glowing reviews of his two Italian treatises and much in demand for his fresh contact with recent developments in Italian science, he was elected to the Royal Society on 11 June. Soon after, he made Huygens' attack upon the originality and validity of his *Vera quadratura* and also the publication of Nicolaus Mercator's *Logarithmotechnia* an opportunity for publishing in riposte certain newly composed *Exercitationes geometricæ* of his own.

In late 1668, probably through Moray's intercession, he was nominated to the new chair of mathematics at St. Andrews in Scotland. In 1669, shortly after taking up the post, he married a young widow, Mary Burnet, who bore him two daughters and a son. Much of his time during the next five years was passed in teaching elementary mathematics and the principles of science to his students: "I am now much taken up," he wrote in May 1671, "& hath been so al this winter bypast, both with my publick lectures, which I have twice a week, & resolving doubts which som gentlemen & scholars proposeth to me, . . . al persons here being ignorant of these things to admiration." His London correspondent Collins, a good listener if incapable of appreciating Gregory's deeper insights, was his sole contact with mathematical and scientific developments in the outside world; through him he received extended transcripts of letters written by Isaac Barrow, René-François de Sluse, Huygens, and Newton on a variety of topics, and in return he made Collins privy to many of his researches into equations, infinite series, and number theory.

Early in 1671, when the Académie des Sciences made tentative plans to invite two "Englishmen" (one of them Mercator) to Paris as *pensionnaires,* Moray campaigned actively on Gregory's behalf, but the proposal was not implemented. In 1672 Gregory joined the St. Andrews University "clerk" William Sanders in drafting a scornful reply to a recently published book on hydrostatics by the Glasgow professor George Sinclair: to Sanders' *Great and New Art of Weighing Vanity,* whose title page named as its author "Patrick Mathers, Arch-Bedal to the University of St. Andrews," Gregory contributed a minute dynamical essay, "Tentamina quædam de motu penduli et projectorum." Backed in turn by Sanders, the next year he implemented a long-cherished desire in the face of considerable resistance from his fellow professors, founding at St. Andrews the first public observatory in Britain. Charged with the university's commission, he traveled to London in June 1673 to purchase telescopes and other instruments and to seek John Flamsteed's advice regarding its equipment. Whether or not he did, as he intended, break his return journey at Cambridge to see Newton is not known. His hopes for the new observatory were soon quashed. During his absence the students at St. Andrews had rebelled against their antiquated curriculum, publicly ridiculing the regents; and Gregory, with his radical ideas on introducing the "new" science, was made the scapegoat: "After this the servants of the Colleges got orders not to wait on me at my observations; my salary was also kept back from me; and scholars of most eminent rank were violently kept from me, . . . the masters persuading them that their brains were not able to endure [mathematics]." In 1674 Gregory was glad to accept the newly endowed professorship of mathematics at Edinburgh, "where my salary is double, and my encouragements much greater"; but within a year of his appointment a paralyzing stroke blinded him one evening as he showed Jupiter's satellites through a telescope to his students. A few days later he was dead.

Written in his twenty-fourth year, Gregory's *Optica promota* is—with the notable exception of its "Epilogus"—interesting more for its revelations of the inadequacies of his early scientific training than for its technical novelties. Deprived in Aberdeen of a comprehensive library and contact with any practicing scientist, Gregory nevertheless made good use of available books on optics (Friedrich Risner's 1572 edition of Ibn al-Haytham [Alhazen] and Witelo ["authores perobscuri et prolixi"], Kepler's *Paralipomena,* Kircher's *Ars magna lucis*) and astronomy (Galileo's *Nuncius sidereus,* Kepler's *Astronomia,* Seth Ward's *Astronomia geometrica*). Ignorant of Descartes's *Dioptrique* (1637) and of the sine law of refraction there first publicly announced, in his opening pages Gregory presents an analogical "proof" that all rays incident on a central conic parallel to its main axis are refracted to its further focus for a suitable value of its eccentricity (in fact, as Descartes had shown, when it is the inverse refractive ratio). Departing from the particular cases of infinite and zero refraction when the conic is a circle and a straight line respectively and the parabolic case of reflection (unit negative refraction) and relying on his intuition that the interface is a conic, he "interpolates" the general *mensura refractionis* and then gives his model—equivalent to the sine law he nowhere cites—an experimental basis by displaying its agreement with the refraction tables of Witelo and Kircher.

The following optical propositions (2–59) extend Gregory's Cartesian theorem to systems of conical lenses and also develop the allied properties of reflection in conical mirrors: a neusis construction of the generalized Ibn al-Haytham problem of finding the point(s) of reflection in a general surface (prop. 34) is attained by roughly determining the tangent members of the family of spheroids whose common foci are the object and image points. In his historically significant epilogue Gregory explains how the deficiencies of the conventional pure reflectors and refractors encouraged him to design a compound "catadioptrical" telescope in which their defects were minimized. As an example he sketches "unum hujus perfectissimi generis telescopium" in which a parabolic mirror reflects parallel incident rays to a primary focus, on whose further side they are reflected back through a hole in the center of the first mirror by a small concave elliptical one to a secondary focus and thence through a plano-convex lens to the eye.

In 1663 the London optician Richard Reive was commissioned by Gregory to construct a six-foot "tube" to this design but failed, according to Newton in 1672, to polish its conical mirrors correctly. Newton's own improved design (1668[?]) used a plane mirror to reflect the rays from a spherical main reflector to the side of the telescope tube, and in 1672 through Collins he and Gregory exchanged letters arguing the relative merits of the two mountings. (The 1672 Cassegrain design, in which rays converging on the primary focus are reflected to the secondary focus before they reach it, was dismissed by Gregory as "no great alteration.") The astronomical appendix to the *Optica* (props. 60–90) is of no importance, but it serves to reveal once again Gregory's limited awareness of current scientific research. Much influenced by Seth Ward's *Astronomia* (1656), he here describes at some length geometrical methods for computing solar, lunar, and (hopefully) stellar parallax. A remark (prop. 87, scholium) that the conjunctions of the sun and Earth with Venus or Mercury would have a "pulcherrimum usum" for this purpose ignores the practical difficulties earlier encountered by Jeremiah Horrocks in his observations of the Venus transit in 1639 (first published in 1672). His schemes of planetary computation embody either the Keplerian "hypothesis Ptolemaica" of motion in an excentric circle with equant at the bissextile point or the slightly better Boulliau-Ward hypothesis of elliptical motion round the sun at a focus with mean motion round the second focus.

A still unpublished addendum to the *Optica* (David Gregory, B29, Edinburgh), composed some time after Gregory's arrival in London in 1663, contains a revised discussion of reflections in mirrors and refractions in thin lenses according to the newly encountered sine law of refraction. One theorem, a "notion" of a "burning-glass" (concave leaded spherical glass mirror) was communicated without proof to Collins in March 1673 and published by William Brown in 1715.

By late 1667 a sheen of confidence gleams through Gregory's work. Having absorbed at Padua all that some of the finest intellects in Italian science (Angeli, Gabriele Manfredi, and others) could teach him, he at length emerges fully aware of his hitherto latent mathematical powers. Of the two treatises stemming from his Italian sojourn, the *Vera circuli et hyperbolae quadratura* is the more original. Generalizing a procedure used by Archimedes in his *Measurement of a Circle,* in the case of a general central conic Gregory recursively defines an unbounded double sequence i_n, I_n of inscribed/circumscribed *mixtilinea.* Given a conic arc bounded by its chord and the intersecting tangents at its end points, i_0, I_0 are the inscribed triangle and circumscribed quadrilateral bounding the central sector cut off by the arc and the lines joining its end points to the conic's center. By dividing the arc at the point where it is parallel to its chord, two half-arcs are formed, yielding i_1, I_1 as the total of the two triangles/quadrilaterals inscribed/circumscribed to the two component conic sectors; a similar bisection of the two half-arcs produces corresponding bounding *mixtilinea* i_2, I_2, and so on. Gregory proves (props. 1–5) that i_{n+1}, I_{n+1} are, respectively, the geometric mean of i_n, I_n and the harmonic mean of i_{n+1}, I_n; that is,

$$i_{n+1} = \sqrt{i_n \cdot I_n} \quad \text{and} \quad I_{n+1} = \frac{2i_{n+1} \cdot I_n}{i_{n+1} + I_n}.$$

In the terms of Gregory's "definitiones" 1–10 the general pair i_{n+1}, I_{n+1} forms a "series convergens" (monotonically increasing/decreasing double sequence) of terms "analyticè compositi" (recursively defined by addition, subtraction, multiplication, division, and root extraction) out of the preceding "termini" i_n, I_n; he also proves that as n increases indefinitely, the difference between i_n and I_n becomes arbitrarily small—whence (p. 19) the "ultimi termini convergentes" can be "imagined" to be equal and their common value ($I = \lim_{n\to\infty} i_n = \lim_{n\to\infty} I_n$) is defined to be the "terminatio" (limit) of the "series." As an example of the power of this new terminology and analytical structure he derives purely algebraically the generalized Snell–Huygens inequalities for the central conic: $\frac{1}{3}(i_0 = 2I_0) > I > \frac{1}{3}(4i_1 - i_0)$.

Most tellingly, Gregory reasons that if a "quantitas" (function) can be "compounded" in the "same way" from i_{n+1}, I_{n+1} as from i_n, I_n—say by $\phi(i_n,I_n) = \phi(i_{n+1},I_{n+1})$—then the "terminatio" I is defined by $\phi(i_0,I_0) = \phi(I,I)$. The function $\phi(i_n,I_n)$, i.e.,

$$I_n \sqrt{\frac{i_n}{I_n - i_n}} \cdot \cos^{-1} \sqrt{\frac{i_n}{I_n}};\ \phi(I,I) = I,$$

appropriate to his particular double sequence he was unable to determine, but by considering the "imbalance" of the parametrization $i_n = a^2(a + b)$, $I_n = b^2(a + b)$, and so $i_{n+1} = ab(a + b)$, $I_{n+1} = 2ab^2$, he sought to "prove" not only that ϕ cannot be a rational function, which this makes plausible, but also that it cannot be algebraic, which does not follow at all; in that case I would not be analytically compounded from i_0, I_0 and hence the "true" (algebraic) quadrature of the general conic sector—and of the whole circle in particular—would be impossible. Gregory's ingenious if ultimately ineffective argument was somewhat impercipiently attacked by Huygens when he received a presentation copy of the *Quadratura*: his rebuff, still commonly allowed, that the limit sector I could conceivably be determined in a different, algebraic way from the initial *mixtilinea* i_0, I_0 is in fact invalid since Gregory's argument concerns the structure of the function ϕ, not the passage of i_n,I_n to the limit I (disposed of in the equality $\phi(I,I) = I$). The latter half of the *Quadratura* is of some computational interest: on setting $i_0 = 2$, $I_0 = 4$, then $I = \pi$; while if $i_0 = 99/20$, $I_0 = 18/11$, then $I = \log \text{nat}\ 10$. These and other circle/hyperbola areas are accurately calculated to fifteen places.

Gregory's second Italian treatise is more eclectic in spirit, being designedly a tool kit of contemporary geometrical analysis of tangent, quadrature, cubature, and rectification problems. In the preface to his *Geometriae pars universalis* he expresses his hope that by "transmuting" the essential defining property of a given curve, it may be changed into one of an already known kind; the "universal part of geometry" presaged in his title is that which comprehends such general methods of geometrical transformation. Under that manifesto Gregory produces a systematic exposition of elementary calculus techniques which he freely admits are largely reworkings and generalizations of approaches pioneered by others. Pierre de Fermat's assignment of linear bounds to a convex arc, itself an improvement of Christopher Wren's 1658 discussion of the cycloid, is developed into a general scheme, demonstrated by an extended Archimedean exhaustion proof, for rectifying an arbitrary "curva simplex et non sinuosa"; Grégoire de St. Vincent's use of a "ductus plani in planum" (the geometrical equivalent of a change of variables under a double integral) is applied to reduce the quadrature of a given plane curve to the "planification" of a "hoof" section of a cylindrical surface and thence to the quadrature of a second curve. Another method of quadrature, that by transform to the subtangential curve, stems from Roberval. A geometrical tangent method is borrowed, again by way of Fermat, from Wren's tract on the cycloid, while an analytical one making use of Jacques de Beaugrand's notation for the vanishing increment "nihil seu serum *o*" of the base variable is a revision of that expounded by Descartes in his 1638 *querelle* with Fermat and published by Claude Clerselier in 1667, illustrated by an example (a Slusian cubic) deriving from Michelangelo Ricci.

Above all, Wren's concept, earlier broached by Roberval and Torricelli in the instance of the Archimedean spiral and Apollonian parabola, of the arc length-preserving "convolution" of a spiral into an equivalent Cartesian curve reappears, much extended and given rigorous exhaustion proof, in Gregory's favorite transform of an "involute" into an "evolute," while vigorous use is made of the Pappus-Guldin theorems relating the quadrature and cubature of solids and surfaces of revolution to their cross-section and its center of gravity. On this basis Gregory was enabled to furnish simple proofs of results in the theory of higher curves and the "infinite" spirals beloved of his tutor Angeli, replacing their previous crude, disparate forms by a logically immaculate, standardized demonstration. But too modern an interpretation of Gregory's book should be avoided: what to us (in prop. 6) may seem a proof of the fundamental theorem of the calculus was for him merely a generalization of William Neil's method for rectifying the semicubical parabola, and its wider significance is not mentioned.

The *Geometria* also affords a glimpse of Gregory's scientific interests at the close of his Italian stay. A proposition on the Fermatian spiral allows him to discourse on its origin (in 1636) as a modified Galilean path of free fall to the earth's center and to comment on the current controversy between Angeli and Giovanni Riccioli on the motion of the earth (one which he reviewed for the Royal Society in June 1668, on his return to London). Again, certain appended nonmathematical passages deal briefly with the optical effect of the apparent twinkling of the stars and with the conjectured composition of cometary tails conceived of as a steamy "exhalation" lit up by the sun and, most important for future physical astronomy, offer the suggestion that the apparent brightnesses of stars of the same magnitude are inversely proportional to the squares of their distances with the corollary that Sirius—taken to be of the same magnitude and brightness as the sun—is 83,190 times its distance.

Mathematics retained its central place in Gregory's affection until his death. Back in London he published a compendium, *Exercitationes geometricæ* , containing primarily an "Appendicula" to his *Vera quadratura* which refuted Huygens' objections to its argument but also appending a number of miscellaneous theorems in geometrical calculus. The "Appendicula" itself is noteworthy for its concluding "theorema" (that if a_n, A_n; b_n, B_n are two convergent Gregorian sequences with respective terminations A, B and if for all r $\phi(a_n,A_n) > \phi(b_n,B_n)$, then $A > B$) and for its twenty-seven narrow upper and lower bounds to the sector of a central conic. Since an "approximatio" to the sector I is said to k-plicate the "true notes" of the *mixtilinea*

$$i_n = 2^{n-1} \sin (I/2^{n-1}), I_n = 2^n \tan (I/2^n)$$

when it compounds i_j, I_j, $j = 0, 1, 2, \ldots, n$ so as to equal $I + O(I^{2k+1})$, Gregory's method clearly made use of the series expansion of one or other of the elementary circle functions. To illustrate the power of the techniques elaborated in his *Geometria,* Gregory also, in ignorance of Harriot's prior resolution, reduced the theory of the plane chart (Mercator map) to "adding secants" (integrating sec x over a given interval, $0 \leq x \leq a$), effecting this elegantly if long-windedly by an involved appeal to a "ductus plani in planum." In addition, he gave analogous quadratures of the tangent, conchoid, and cissoid curves; and, further to expedite the "additio secantium naturalium" near the origin, he elaborated simple rules for integrating $y \approx ax^2 + bx$ and $y \approx ax^3 + bx^2$, x small. The former of these is the first published instance of "Simpson's" rule. His rigorous geometrical deduction of the Mercator series for $\pm \log (1 \pm x)$ is of minor importance.

GREGORY, J.

After his return to Scotland, Gregory made no further published contribution to pure mathematics, but his private papers reveal that the last half dozen years of his life were ones of intensive research. His executor William Sanders tells us, "His Elements of plain Geometry, with some few propositions of the solids; his Practicall Arithmetick, and Practicall Geometry taught at St. Andrews . . . are but of small moment, being contrived only for the use of such scholars as cannot be at pains to study the Elements." The lost *Tractatus trigonometricus*, in which he reduced "All Trigonometry rectilineal and spherical . . . unto five short canons," on the lines of Seth Ward's *Idea* (1654), was no doubt also intended for professorial lectures. But his real energy was reserved for deeper matters. At Collins' instigation Gregory spent much time on the theory of equations and the location of their roots: achieving success in the case of the reduced cubic and quartic by introducing an appropriate multiplying factor and equating all terms in the resolvent except those involving cube/fourth powers of the unknown to zero, he sought to solve the general quintic in a similar way by adjoining a factor of the fifteenth degree but failed to notice that the resulting equations to zero implied—ineluctably—a sextic eliminant. His papers on Fermatian equations, rational Heronian triangles, and other topics in Diophantine analysis are (much like Newton's contemporary studies, likewise inspired by the appearance of the Samuel Fermat-Jacques de Billy *Diophantus* in 1670) more workmanlike than profound: the "skailzy brods" (writing slates) found on his desk after his death contained his abortive calculations for Jacques Ozanam's unsolvable problem of cubes.

Gregory's letters to Collins are filled with a miscellany of calculus problems, among them his quadrature and rectification of the logarithmic spiral and "evolute" logarithmic curve, which had briefly made its introductory bow in the preface to his *Geometria*, and his construction of the tangent to the "spiralis arcuum rectificatrix" introduced by Collins for use in the "Mariners Plain Chart." His grasp of the subtleties of infinite series in particular quickly matured. His independent discovery of the general binomial expansion in November 1670—in disguised form as that of antilog $((a/c)(\log(b + d) - \log b))$—was matched a month later by his use of a "Newton-Gauss" interpolation formula to insert general means in a given sequence of sines. As a climax, in February 1671 Gregory communicated without proof a number of trigonometrical series, notably those for the natural and logarithmic tangent and secant, and in April 1672 a series solution of Kepler's problem (intended for publication in Collins' edition of Horrocks's *Opera posthuma*, but the bookseller took fright) regarding which he observed that "these infinite serieses have the same success in the roots of equations." Two examples—the series extraction of the root e of the conchoid's defining equation

$$L^2e^2 = (L + a)^2(L^2 - a^2)$$

and the inversion of the Kepler equation

$$a = \sqrt{2re - e^2} + (b - r) \sin^{-1} (\sqrt{2re - e^2}/r)$$

were later published by David Gregory, without direct acknowledgment, in his *Exercitatio geometrica* (1684). Until the printing in 1939 of Gregory's notes, jotted down on the back of a letter from the Edinburgh bookseller Gideon Shaw in January 1671, it seemed likely that these expansions were obtained by straightforward elementary methods, but we now know that he employed, twenty years before even Newton came upon the approach, a Taylor development of a function in terms of its nth-order derivatives.

Of Gregory's scientific pursuits during this last period of his life too little is known. His "Theory of the whole Hydrostaticks comprehended in a few definitions and five or sixe Theorems" (David Gregory, D18) is seemingly lost, although a short 1672 paper in which he proved Huygens' theorem relating atmospheric height logarithmically to barometric pressure still exists in several versions. In our present state of knowledge it seems impossible to determine how far William Sanders drew upon Gregory's hydrostatical ideas in his largely scurrilous *Great and New Art of Weighing Vanity*, but extant preliminary computations in Gregory's hand confirm contemporary report that the appended "Tentamina quædam de motu penduli et projectorum" is uniquely his. Of considerable historical importance as a bridging text between Galileo's *Discorsi* and Newton's *Principia*, these nine small duodecimo pages are a highly original contribution to dynamics. Independently deriving Huygens' Galilean generalization that the square of the instantaneous speed of a body falling freely under simple gravity in a smooth curve is proportional to the vertical distance fallen (and indeed anticipating an objection to Huygens' definition of the fall curve as the limit of a chain of line segments, which Newton put to Huygens in 1673), Gregory deduced the elliptical integral expressing the time of vibration in a circular pendulum and gave its infinite-series expansion for a small arc of swing. Subsequently, framing the supposition that the resistance is constant in magnitude and direction (opposite to that of initial motion), he determined that the resisted path of a pro-

GREGORY, J.

jectile under simple gravity is a tilted parabola with main axis parallel to the resultant instantaneous force—a theorem, we now know, which had been found seventy years before by Harriot.

The "Fourty or thereabout of excellent Astronomical propositions invented . . . for the compleeting that art" found after his death doubtless originated in his correspondence with Colin Campbell during 1673–1674 on theoretical astronomy, during the course of which he solved—yet again in ignorance of a prior solution by Harriot—the Keplerian problem of constructing a planetary ellipse, given three focal radii in magnitude and position. Apart from his keen discussion with Newton in 1672 on the respective merits of their "catadioptrical" reflecting telescopes, little evidence has survived of Gregory's continuing interest in optics.

For all his talent and promise of future achievement, Gregory did not live long enough to make the major discovery which would have gained him popular fame. For his reluctance to publish his "several universal methods in Geometrie and analyticks" when he heard through Collins of Newton's own advances in calculus and infinite series, he posthumously paid a heavy price: the "Extracts from Mr Gregories Letters" drawn up by Collins in 1676 for Leibniz' enlightenment were used by Newton in 1712 solely to further his claim to calculus priority and were thereafter forgotten. Gregory's published works had little contemporary impact; his *Vera quadratura* was successfully sabotaged by Huygens, his *Geometria* quickly overshadowed by Barrow's *Lectiones geometricæ.* We are only now beginning to realize the extent and depth of his influence, mathematically and scientifically, on Newton. A comprehensive edition of his work is sorely needed.

BIBLIOGRAPHY

I. ORIGINAL WORKS. Gregory's first published work, *Optica promota, seu abdita radiorum reflexorum & refractorum mysteria, geometricè enucleata; cui subnectitur appendix, subtilissimorum astronomiæ problematôn resolutionem exhibens* (London, 1663), is reprinted in C. Babbage and F. Maseres, *Scriptores optici* (London, 1823), 1–104. His *Vera circuli et hyperbolæ quadratura, in propria sua proportionis specie, inventa & demonstrata* (Padua, 1667; reviewed by John Collins in *Philosophical Transactions of the Royal Society*, **3**, no. 33 [16 Mar. 1668], 640–644) was reprinted by W. J. 'sGravesande in his ed. of *Christiani Hugenii opera varia,* I (Leiden, 1724), 405–482; it was reissued at Padua in 1668 together with Gregory's *Geometriæ pars universalis, inserviens quantitatum curvarum transmutationi & mensuræ* (reviewed by Collins in *Philosophical Transactions of the Royal Society,* **3**, no. 35 [18 May 1668], 685–688), which also contains (pp. 132–151) his discussion of "difficultates quædam physicomathematicæ ex principiis opticis geometricè enodatæ." The same year he published his *Exercitationes geometricæ* (London, 1668), comprising "Appendicula ad veram circuli & hyperbolæ quadraturam" (repr. in *Oeuvres complètes de Christiaan Huygens,* VI [The Hague, 1895], 313–321), sig. A2r–A4r/pp. 1–8; "N. Mercatoris quadratura hyperbolæ geometricè demonstrata/Analogia inter lineam meridianam planispherii nautici & tangentes artificiales geometricè demonstrata; seu, quod secantium naturalium additio efficiat tangentes artificiales. . . ." (repr. in F. Maseres, *Scriptores logarithmici,* II (London, 1791), 2–15), pp. 9–24; and "Methodus facilis & accurata componendi secantes & tangentes artificiales," pp. 25–27.

Gregory's "Tentamina quædam geometrica de motu penduli et projectorum" (repr. in Babbage and Maseres, *Scriptores optici,* pp. 372–376) first appeared as an anonymous appendix (pp. $_2$1–9) to "Patrick Mathers" [William Sanders], *The Great and New Art of Weighing Vanity* (Glasgow, 1672). His report on the moving earth dispute in Italy was published by Henry Oldenburg as "An Account of a Controversy betwixt Stephano de Angelis and John Baptista Riccioli," in *Philosophical Transactions of the Royal Society,* **3**, no. 36 (15 June 1668), 693–698 (repr. with commentary by A. Koyré in "A Documentary History of the Problem of Fall from Kepler to Newton," in *Transactions of the American Philosophical Society,* **45**, [1955], 329–395, esp. 354–358). His two "Answers" to the "Animadversions" of Huygens upon his *Quadratura* (*Journal des sçavans* [2 July and 12 Nov. 1668], repr. in Huygens' *Oeuvres,* VI, 228–230 and 272–276, and in Latin in *Opera varia,* I, 463–466 and 472–476) appeared in *Philosophical Transactions of the Royal Society,* **3**, no. 37 (13 July 1668), 732–735 and no. 44 (15 Feb. 1669), 882–886 (repr. in *Opera varia,* I, 466–471 and 476–481; also Huygens' *Oeuvres,* VI, 240–244 and 306–311).

A number of Gregory's minor mathematical and scientific papers are extant in the Royal Society, London, the University Library, Edinburgh, and also in private possession: these derive from John Collins and Gregory's nephew, David. An incomplete listing of those accessible to the public is given by H. W. Turnbull in *James Gregory Tercentenary Memorial Volume* (London, 1939), pp. 36–43. Extracts from Gregory's correspondence with Collins were published by Newton in *Commercium epistolicum D. Johannis Collins* (London, 1712), pp. 22–26, and by Jean Desaguliers in an appendix to *Dr.* [David] *Gregory's Elements of Catoptrics and Dioptrics,* 2nd ed. (London, 1735). His letters to Robert Bruce were printed by Leslie in *Scots Magazine,* **72** (Aug. 1810), 584–586; those to Colin Campbell by John Gregorson and Wallace in *Archaeologia Scotica,* **3**, Artic. 25 (Jan. 1831), 275–284; those to Collins (with Collins' draft replies) by S. P. Rigaud in his *Correspondence of Scientific Men of the Seventeenth Century,* II (Oxford, 1841), 174–281; the originals of Collins' replies, invaluable for Gregory's mathematical notes upon them, were published by H. W. Turnbull in the *Gregory Volume,* pp. 45–343 (the notes themselves, with lavish commentary, follow on pp. 347–447). Gregory's earliest known letter (to Huygens, in Oct. 1667, accompanying a presentation copy of his *Vera quadratura*) is given in Huygens' *Oeuvres,* VI, 154.

II. SECONDARY LITERATURE. Thomas Birch's article on Gregory in the *Biographia Britannica,* IV (London, 1757), 2355–2365 remains unsuperseded, although it is now partially obsolete. For complements see Agnes M. Stewart, *The Academic Gregories* (Edinburgh, 1901), pp. 27–51; and *University of St Andrews James Gregory Tercentenary: Record of the Celebrations Held . . . July Fifth MCMXXXVIII* (St. Andrews, 1939), pp. 5–11 (H. W. Turnbull's commemoration address, repeated in expanded form in the *Gregory Volume,* pp. 1–15) and pp. 12–16 (G. H. Bushnell's notes on the St. Andrews' observatory). Section VII of the *Gregory Volume* contains summaries of Gregory's *Optica promota* and *Exercitationes* (by H. W. Turnbull, pp. 454–459 and 459–465), his *Quadratura* (by M. Dehn and E. Hellinger, pp. 468–478) and *Geometria* (by A. Prag, pp. 487–509), together with an account by E. J. Dijksterhuis of the Gregory–Huygens squabble (pp. 478–486). A short general survey of Gregory's researches in calculus is given by C. J. Scriba in *James Gregorys frühe Schriften zur Infinitesimalrechnung, Mitteilungen aus dem Mathem. Seminar Giessen,* no. 55 (Giessen, 1957). More specialist mathematical topics are explored by H. W. Turnbull in "James Gregory: A Study in the Early History of Interpolation," in *Proceedings of the Edinburgh Mathematical Society,* 2nd ser., **3** (1933), 151–172; and by J. E. Hofmann, in "Über Gregorys systematische Näherungen für den Sektor eines Mittelpunktkegelschnittes," in *Centaurus,* **1** (1950), 24–37. No study of any aspect of Gregory's scientific achievement exists.

D. T. WHITESIDE

GREGORY, OLINTHUS GILBERT (*b.* Yaxley, England, 29 January 1774; *d.* Woolwich, England, 2 February 1841)

Gregory was one of the band of self-taught or privately tutored mathematicians who swelled the ranks of British mathematics during the eighteenth and early nineteenth centuries. Despite his limited schooling he established a reputation as a writer on scientific subjects, and in 1803, through the patronage of Charles Hutton, he was appointed instructor of mathematics at the Royal Military Academy at Woolwich. In 1821 he succeeded to the professorship and held the post until his retirement in 1838.

Gregory's most important scientific publication, *A Treatise of Mechanics,* appeared in 1806 and went through at least four editions. Although it was a didactic compilation rather than a publication of original research, it was one of the most complete works on pure and applied mechanics that had appeared in English. In purpose and presentation it was an early example of what would now be described as "engineering mechanics." Its theoretical sections covered such topics as the analysis of the flexed beam and the theory of the loaded arch, while its descriptive sections dealt extensively with machine design. The book constituted a contribution to the tradition of applied mathematics and applied mechanics which was then being fostered by the Woolwich mathematicians.

In 1825 Gregory produced another book, *Mathematics for Practical Men,* devoted to "the principles and applications of the mechanical sciences for the use of the younger members of the Institution of Civil Engineers" (which had been founded in 1818 and of which Gregory later became an honorary member). Around this time he also did experimental research on the velocity of sound. From 1802 to 1819 he edited the *Gentleman's Diary* and from 1819 to 1840 the *Ladies' Diary.* On the strength of both his reputation in science and his status as a prominent Dissenter in religion he was included among the group that founded London University, the first nonsectarian university in England.

BIBLIOGRAPHY

Gregory's scientific publications include *A Treatise of Mechanics,* 3 vols. (London, 1806); the first volume of the *Treatise* was translated into German as *Darstellung der mechanischen Wissenschaften,* J. F. W. Dietlein, trans. (Halle, 1824); *Mathematics for Practical Men* (London, 1825); "An Account of Some Experiments Made in Order to Determine the Velocity With Which Sound Is Transmitted in the Atmosphere," in *Philosophical Magazine,* **63** (1824), 401–15.

Gregory also translated one of René Just Haüy's works, *An Elementary Treatise on Natural Philosophy,* 2 vols. (London, 1807).

For additional bibliography see *Dictionary of National Biography* and *British Museum Catalogue of Printed Books.*

HAROLD DORN

GROSSMANN, MARCEL (*b.* Budapest, Hungary, 9 April 1878; *d.* Zurich, Switzerland, 7 September 1936)

Grossmann was the son of Jules Grossmann, a businessman, and Henriette Lichtenhahn. He took his final secondary school examination in 1896 in Basel, where his family had moved. He then studied mathematics at the Zurich Polytechnikum (later named the Eidgenössische Technische Hochschule) and in 1900 became an assistant to the geometer W. Fiedler. He earned his doctorate from the University of Zurich in 1912 with a work entitled *Über metrische Eigenschaften Kollinearer Gebilde* (Frauenfeld, 1902). He became a teacher at the cantonal school in Frauenfeld in 1901 and at the Oberrealschule in Basel in 1905. He was appointed professor of descriptive geometry at the Eidgenössische Technische Hochschule in 1907. In 1903 he married Anna Keller.

Grossmann was a classmate of Albert Einstein. When Einstein sought to formulate mathematically his ideas on general relativity theory, he turned to Grossmann for assistance. Grossmann discovered that the law of gravitation could be stated in terms of the absolute differential geometry first developed by E. Christoffel (1864), and later by M. M. G. Ricci together with T. Levi-Civita (1901). Grossmann and Einstein set forth their fundamental discoveries in the joint works cited in the bibliography.

Grossmann was a teacher of outstanding ability and he gave many mathematicians and engineers their training in geometry. His lectures were published in textbooks that enjoyed a large success.

BIBLIOGRAPHY

I. ORIGINAL WORKS. Grossmann's works include *Der mathematische Unterricht an der Eidgenössischen Technischen Hochschule,* Commission Internationale de l'Enseignement-mathématique, no. 7 (Basel-Geneva, 1911); "Mathematische Begriffsbildungen zur Gravitationstheorie," in *Vierteljahrsschrift der Naturforschenden Gesellschaft in Zurich,* **58** (1913), 291–297; and *Darstellende Geometrie* (Leipzig, 1915), with many other eds.

He collaborated with Einstein on "Entwurf einer verallgemeinerten Relativitätstheorie und einer Theorie der Gravitation," in *Zeitschrift für Mathematik und Physik,* **62** (1913), 1–38; the work is in 2 parts: I, "Physikalischer Teil" (pp. 1–22), is by Einstein, and II, "Mathematischer Teil" (pp. 23–38), is by Grossmann. The other collaboration is "Kovarianzeigenschaften der Feldgleichungen," *ibid.,* **63** (1914), 215–225.

II. SECONDARY LITERATURE. For information on Grossmann, see F. Bäschlin, "Marcel Grossmann," in *Schweizerische Zeitschrift für Vermessungswesen, Kulturtechnik und Photogrammetrie,* **34** (1936), 243 ff.; L. Kollros, "Prof. Dr. Marcel Grossmann," in *Verhandlungen der Schweizerischen naturforschenden Gesellschaft,* **118** (1937), 325–329, with portrait and bibliography; and W. Saxer, "Marcel Grossmann," in *Vierteljahrsschrift der Naturforschenden Gesellschaft in Zurich,* **81** (1936), 322–326, with bibliography.

JOHANN JAKOB BURCKHARDT

GUA DE MALVES, JEAN PAUL DE (*b.* near Carcassonne, France, *ca.* 1712; *d.* Paris, France, 2 June 1786)

Very little is known of de Gua's life, and even the precise date and place of his birth are not established. According to Condorcet, he was struck by the contrast between the opulence of his first years and the privation that followed the ruin of his parents, Jean de Gua, baron of Malves, and Jeanne de Harrugue, in the wake of the bankruptcy of John Law in 1720. He planned an ecclesiastical career; while it seems that he never became a priest, this training nevertheless permitted him to obtain several benefices and pensions. After a stay in Italy he appears to have participated for a few years in the activities of the short-lived Société des Arts, a sort of scientific and technical academy founded in 1729 by Louis de Bourbon-Condé, prince of Clermont. In any case, he gradually acquired a thorough grounding in science.

De Gua's first publication (1740) was a work on analytic geometry inspired by both Descartes's *Géométrie* (1637) and Newton's *Enumeratio linearum tertii ordinis* (1704). Its principal aim was to develop a theory of algebraic plane curves of any degree (Descartes's "lignes géométriques") based essentially on algebra. Nevertheless, he drew on infinitesimal methods in order to simplify various calculations and recognized that their use is indispensable, particularly for everything involving the transcendental curves ("mécaniques"). De Gua was especially interested in tangents, asymptotes, and singularities: multiples, points, cusps, and points of inflection. In this area he skillfully used coordinate transformations and systematically made use of an "algebraic" or "analytic" triangle, obtained by a 45° rotation of Newton's parallelogram. The use of the latter had been popularized by the *Enumeratio* and by the commentaries of several of Newton's disciples, among them Brook Taylor, James Stirling, and s'Gravesande. The use of perspective allowed de Gua to associate the different types of points at a finite distance with various infinite branches of curves. Among his other contributions, he explicitly asserted that if a cubic admits three points of inflection, the latter are aligned. He also introduced two new types of cubics into the enumeration undertaken by Newton and Stirling, among others.

De Gua's treatise contributed to the rise of the theory of curves in the eighteenth century and partially inspired the subsequent works of Euler (1748), Gabriel Cramer (1750), A. P. Dionis du Séjour, and M. B. Goudin (1756). The fame of this work led to de Gua's election to the Royal Academy of Sciences as adjoint geometer on 18 March 1741, replacing

P. C. Le Monnier. He presented several mathematical memoirs, two of which, published at the time, deal with the number of roots of an algebraic equation according to their nature and sign and with the famous rule of Descartes. However, on 3 June 1745, following a dispute de Gua renounced the pursuit of a normal academic career and requested that his modest position of associate be made honorary. Although he continued his scientific research, he seems to have moved away from the study of mathematics during this period. Not until the time of the reorganization of 23 April 1785 did he resume his place at the Academy, this time as a pensioner in the new class of natural history and mineralogy, which was closer to his new interests. Moreover, it seems that the contents of the several mathematical memoirs on spherical trigonometry and the geometry of polyhedra that he subsequently published in the *Histoire* of the Academy for 1783 date for the most part from the 1740's.

The career of de Gua was marked by several incidents which certainly resulted, at least in part, from difficulties inherent in his personality. His stay at the Collège Royal (Collège de France) was abnormally brief. Appointed on 30 June 1742 to the chair of Greek and Latin philosophy, which was vacant following the death of Joseph Privat de Molières, de Gua actually filled this post until 26 July 1748, when he resigned; he was replaced by P. C. Le Monnier. Like his predecessors and his successor, de Gua gave to his instruction an orientation having no connection with the official title of the chair; he dealt successively with Newtonian epistemology, differential and integral calculus, the principles of mathematics, arithmetic, and the philosophy of Locke—without, however, publishing anything based on his teaching.

Another incident took place during the same period. In 1745 the publisher A. F. Le Breton had joined with the Paris booksellers A. C. Briasson, M. A. David, and L. Durand for the purpose of publishing a much enlarged French version of the famous *Cyclopaedia* of Ephraim Chambers. Apparently appreciating de Gua's wide-ranging abilities, they made him responsible for the scientific material in the edition in a contract signed on 27 June 1746 in the presence of Diderot and d'Alembert, who acted both as witnesses and as consultants. The agreement was annulled on 3 August 1747. On 16 October 1747 de Gua, who had meanwhile mortgaged his other income to repay a portion of the advances he had received from the booksellers, was replaced by d'Alembert and Diderot as director of this project, which was to become the celebrated *Encyclopédie.*

De Gua next turned his attention to philosophy and political economy, translating works by George Berkeley and Matthew Decker, as well as a debate in the House of Commons that he introduced with a long "Avant-propos" on the problem of the interest rate on loans. At the same time he was actively interested in prospecting for gold in Languedoc and addressed several memoirs on this subject to the government. Having obtained, in 1764, an exploitation permit valid for twenty years, he undertook an unsuccessful venture that partially ruined him. In 1764 he published a work on mineral prospecting and composed the first six volumes of a series of *mémoires périodiques* on subjects in philosophy, science, economics, and so on; the series was never published—for lack, it seems, of official authorization. De Gua also was interested in lotteries, but beginning in the 1760's he specialized in mineralogy and conchology, which explains his change of sections at the Academy in 1785.

This disordered scientific activity and a taste for the unusual give to de Gua's work a special character. The interest of his first mathematical writings evokes regrets that he did not persevere in this direction.

BIBLIOGRAPHY

I. Original Works. Among de Gua's writings are *Usages de l'analyse de Descartes pour découvrir, sans le secours du calcul différentiel, les propriétés, ou affections principales des lignes géométriques de tous les ordres* (Paris, 1740); five mathematical memoirs in *Histoire de l'Académie royale des sciences:* "Démonstration de la règle de Descartes . . .," 72–96, and "Recherches des nombres des racines réelles ou imaginaires . . .," 435–494, in the volume for 1741 (Paris, 1744) and "Trigonométrique sphérique, déduite très brièvement . . .," 291–343, "Diverses mesures, en partie neuves, des aires sphériques et des angles solides . . .," 344–362, and "Propositions neuves . . . sur le tétraèdre . . .," 363–402, in the volume for 1783 (Paris, 1786); and *Projet d'ouverture et d'exploitation de minières et mines d'or et d'autres métaux aux environs du Cézé, du Gardon, de l'Eraut* [*sic*] *et d'autres rivières du Languedoc, du Comté de Foix, du Rouergue etc.* (Paris, 1764). He translated several works from English into French: George Berkeley, *Dialogues entre Hylas et Philonaüs contre les sceptiques et les athées* (Amsterdam, 1750); Matthew Decker, *Essai sur les causes du déclin du commerce étranger de la Grande Bretagne,* 2 vols. (n.p., 1757); and *Discours pour et contre la réduction de l'intérest naturel de l'argent, qui ayant été prononcés en 1737, dans la Chambre des communes du parlement de la Grande Bretagne, occasionnèrent en ce pays la réduction de 4 à 3% . . .* (Wesel-Paris, 1757)—"Avant-propos du traducteur," pp. i–clxviii, is by de Gua. With J. B. Romé de l'Isle he edited *Catalogue systématique et raisonné des curiosités de la nature et de l'art, qui composent le cabinet de M. Davila* . . . (Paris, 1767), for which he wrote I, pt. 2, 71–126: "Coquilles marines."

II. SECONDARY LITERATURE. On de Gua or his work, see the following (listed chronologically): the *éloge* of M. J. A. N. Condorcet, read 15 Nov. 1786, in *Histoire de l'Académie royale des sciences pour l'année 1786* (Paris, 1788), pt. 1, 63–76; X. de Feller, ed., *Dictionnaire historique,* IV (Paris, 1808), 238; J. J. Weiss, in Michaud, ed., *Biographie universelle,* XVIII (Paris, 1817), 575–576, also in new ed., XVIII (Paris, 1857), 1–2; J. M. Quérard, *La France littéraire,* III (Paris, 1829), 494–495; Guyot de Fère, in F. Hoefer, ed., *Nouvelle biographie générale,* XXII (Paris, 1859), col. 278; Poggendorff, I, 967–968; *Intermédiare des mathématiciens,* VIII (1901), 158, and XI (1904), 148–149; P. Sauerbeck, "Einleitung in die analytische Geometrie der höheren algebraïschen Kurven nach der Methoden von Jean-Paul de Gua de Malves. Ein Beitrag zur Kurvendiskussion," in *Abhandlungen zur Geschichte der mathematischen Wissenschaften,* **15** (1902), 1–166; G. Loria, "Da Descartes e Fermat a Monge e Lagrange. Contributo alla storia della geometria analitica," in *Atti dell'Accademia nazionale dei Lincei. Memorie,* classe di scienze fisiche, matematiche e naturale, 5th ser., **14** (1923), 777–845; N. Nielsen, *Géomètres français du XVIIIe siècle* (Copenhagen–Paris, 1935), pp. 195–200; L. P. May, "Documents nouveaux sur l'*Encyclopédie,*" in *Revue de synthèse,* **15** (1938), 5–30; G. Loria, *Storia delle matematiche* (Milan, 1950), pp. 668–689, 739–740, 758, 851; and C. B. Boyer, *History of Analytic Geometry* (New York, 1956), pp. 174–175, 184, 194.

RENÉ TATON

GUCCIA, GIOVANNI BATTISTA (*b.* Palermo, Italy, 21 October 1855; *d.* Palermo, 29 October 1914)

The son of Giuseppe Maria Guccia and Chiara Guccia-Cipponeri, Guccia belonged, through his father, to the noble Sicilian family of the marquis of Ganzaria. As a young man he was an ardent sportsman and was particularly interested in horsemanship. He studied first at Palermo, then at the University of Rome, where he was one of Luigi Cremona's best students. In 1880 he defended a thesis dealing with a class of surfaces representable, point by point, on a plane. Shortly before, he had presented a communication on certain rational surfaces dealt with in this work to the congress of the French Association for the Advancement of Science at Rheims and had been publicly congratulated by J. J. Sylvester. After returning to Palermo, Guccia pondered some grand schemes of theoretical research. In 1889 he was appointed to the newly created chair of higher geometry at the University of Palermo, a post he held for the rest of his life.

The path that Guccia followed throughout his career was that of the great Italian geometers of the nineteenth century. For them the synthetic method, aided by intuition, was the ideal instrument of discovery, more efficacious than the calculus, of which the artifices often conceal the logical structures and the relationships among the elements of a figure. To be sure, the role of algebra is not negligible, but it should be limited to what is linear, for the establishment of certain principles, and then give way to the intuitive method. Guccia's works concern primarily Cremona's plane transformations, the classification of linear systems of plane curves, the singularities of curves and of algebraic surfaces, and certain geometric loci which permit the projective properties of curves and surfaces to be deduced.

In studying the classification of linear systems of types 0 and 1, Guccia was inspired by the method used by Max Nöther to demonstrate that every Cremona transformation is the product of a finite number of quadratic transformations. Guccia's results were completed in 1888 by Corrado Segre, and the question was taken up in 1897 by Guido Castelnuovo in his memoir on linear systems of curves traced on an algebraic surface. In studying the singular points and singular curves of a surface, Guccia discovered theorems analogous to those for linear systems of curves. Although the majority of Guccia's publications are very short, they all contain original ideas and new relations profitably used by other geometers. This is particularly true of his researches on projective involutions, which laid the foundation for the generalizations of Federico Enriques and Francesco Severi. Occasionally, Guccia himself generalized from partial results, as in the case of the projective characteristics of plane algebraic curves and of their linear systems (where he introduced a projective definition of polars), which he extended to surfaces and to gauche curves.

In a period when knowledge of the geometry of algebraic surfaces was extremely limited, Guccia made a useful contribution. It was immediately exploited and absorbed by other mathematicians who, more attracted than he by analytical procedures, achieved greater fame. Compared with the work of his teacher Cremona, Guccia's is on a lower plane, if not in subtlety at least in extent and significance. Yet Guccia's chief merit lies elsewhere: his name remains associated with the foundation of the Circolo Matematico di Palermo.

In 1884, five years before his appointment to the university, Guccia had the idea of establishing a mathematical society in Palermo, for which he would furnish the meeting place, a library, and all necessary funds. His generous offer was favorably received, and on 2 March 1884 the society's provisional statutes were signed by twenty-seven members. The goal was to stimulate the study of higher mathematics by means of original communications presented by the members of the society on the different branches of analysis and geometry, as well as on rational mechanics, mathematical physics, geodesy, and astronomy. The group's activity was soon known abroad through the *Rendiconti del Circolo matematico di Palermo,* the first volume of which consisted of four sections appearing in July 1885, September 1886, December 1886, and September 1887. On 7 November 1887 Joseph Bertrand presented this volume to the Académie des Sciences of Paris, emphasizing its high scientific standard. On 26 February 1888 new statutes for the society authorized the election of foreign corresponding members, and the *Rendiconti* thereby became an international review. Guccia, who had placed his personal fortune at the disposal of the Circolo, established a mathematical publishing house in Palermo in 1893. To the *Rendiconti* he added *Supplemento ai Rendiconti del Circolo matematico di Palermo, Indici delle pubblicazioni del Circolo matematico di Palermo,* and *Annuario biografico del Circolo matematico di Palermo.* He also took personal charge of the editing of all these publications.

BIBLIOGRAPHY

I. Original Works. The list of mathematical works drawn up by de Franchis (see below) contains forty-four titles. Lectures given at the University of Palermo in 1889–1890 appeared as *Teoria generale delle curve e delle superficie algebriche* (Palermo, 1890). His longer arts. include "Teoremi sulle trasformazioni Cremoniane nel piano. Estensione di alcuni teoremi di Hirst sulle trasformazioni quadratiche," in *Rendiconti del Circolo matematico di Palermo,* **1** (1884–1887), 27, 56–57, 66, 119–132; "Generalizzazione di un teorema di Noether," *ibid.,* 139–156; "Sulla riduzione dei sistemi lineari di curve ellittiche e sopra un teorema generale delle curve algebriche di genere *p,*" *ibid.,* 169–189; "Sui sistemi lineari di superficie algebriche dotati di singolarità base qualunque," *ibid.,* 338–349; "Sulle singolarità composte delle curve algebriche piane," *ibid.,* **3** (1889), 241–259; "Ricerche sui sistemi lineari di curve algebriche piane, dotati di singolarità ordinarie," *ibid.,* **7** (1893), 193–255, and **9** (1895), 1–64; and "Un théorème sur les courbes algébriques planes d'ordre *n,*" in *Comptes rendus hebdomadaires des séances de l'Académie des sciences,* **142** (1906), 1256–1259.

II. Secondary Literature. See Michele de Franchis, "XXX anniversario della fondazione del Circolo matematico di Palermo . . .," in *Supplemento ai Rendiconti del Circolo matematico di Palermo,* **9** (1914), 1–68; and "G. B. Guccia, cenni biografici . . .," in *Rendiconti del Circolo matematico di Palermo,* **39** (1915), 1–14.

Pierre Speziali

GUDERMANN, CHRISTOPH (*b.* Vienenburg, near Hildesheim, Germany, 25 March 1798; *d.* Münster, Germany, 25 September 1852)

Gudermann's father was a teacher. After graduating from secondary school Gudermann was to have studied to become a priest, but in Göttingen he studied, among other things, mathematics. From 1823 he was a teacher at the secondary school in Kleve; and from 1832 until his death he taught at the Theological and Philosophical Academy in Münster, first as associate professor, and from 1839 as full professor, of mathematics.

Gudermann's scientific work forms part of German mathematics in the second quarter of the nineteenth century. The characteristic feature of this period is that the ideas of transforming mathematics had been expressed or indicated, but understanding and realizing them in results or comprehensive theories was still beyond the capabilities of the mathematicians; this was achieved only in the second half of the century. Much preparatory work had to be carried out for this transformation. As soon as comprehensive, sufficiently accurate and general theories had been established, the preparatory work was forgotten. This was also the fate of Gudermann's work; he is known as the teacher of Karl Weierstrass rather than as an original thinker.

The depth of Gudermann's understanding of the contemporary trends in mathematics is substantiated by the topic which he discussed in his own work. C. F. Gauss's influence on Gudermann is still unclear, but the topic he chose is close to the intellectual environment of Gauss and his followers. Basically, Gudermann considered only two groups of problems: spherical geometry and the theory of special functions.

His book *Grundriss der analytischen Sphärik* (1830) deals with the former. He considered the study of spherical geometry important for several reasons. In the introduction he pointed out that a plane was a special case of a spherical surface, that is, a sphere with an infinite radius. For this reason and because of its constant curvature there exist many similarities between spherical geometry and plane geometry; yet at the same time Gudermann considered scientifically more interesting the study of cases in which this similarity no longer holds. As part of this program he sought to establish an analytical system for spherical surfaces akin to that formed by the coordinate system in planimetry. But he had to admit the existence of insurmountable difficulties if the required simplicity of the analytical means was to be preserved. At some points in the book Gudermann came close to problems which were important for non-Euclidean geometry but did not stress them, nor did he explicitly mention this aspect.

Gudermann devoted much more attention to the theory of special functions. After the earlier works of Leonhard Euler, John Landen, and A. M. Legendre (Gauss's results were still in manuscript), Niels Abel's studies on elliptical functions, published mostly in A. L. Crelle's *Journal für die reine und angewandte Mathematik,* represented an important divide in treating this area. In 1829 Carl Jacobi's book *Fundamenta nova theoriae functionum ellipticarum* was published. At the time Gudermann was one of the first mathematicians to expand on these results. Beginning with volume **6** (1830) of Crelle's *Journal,* he published a series of papers which he later summarized in two books: *Theorie der Potenzial- oder cyklisch-hyperbolischen Functionen* (1833) and *Theorie der Modular-Functionen und der Modular-Integrale* (1844), which were to have had a sequel which was never written.

In these books Gudermann went back to the origin of the theory of special functions—the problems of integral calculus—and stressed the genetic connection between simply periodic functions and elliptical functions. Since he did not neglect the requirements of integral calculus, he saw the necessity of arranging the theory to allow for numerical calculations. The key appeared to be in the development of the functions into infinite series and infinite products and in the use of suitable transformations. This made it possible to present extensive numerical tables in his first book and to work through to the nucleus of the theory of special functions in his second book, indicating the way which subsequently proved to be exceptionally fruitful. Thus he also came close to Gauss's intentions. Gudermann also introduced a notation for elliptical functions—*sn, cn,* and *dn*—which was adopted. He himself called elliptical functions "Modularfunctionen." It was pointed out later that Gudermann's work had an excess of special cases which in time lost interest.

Gudermann's work drew deserved attention in Germany in the 1830's. Since he was one of the few university professors to treat the problems of elliptical functions systematically, Karl Weierstrass came from the University of Bonn in 1839–1840 to attend Gudermann's lectures and presented "Über die Entwicklung der Modularfunctionen" as a *Habilitationsschrift* in 1841.

Gudermann was one of the first to realize Weierstrass' mathematical talent and scientific ability. Weierstrass, using Gudermann's idea of the development of functions into series and products, formed the principal, mighty, and accurate tool of the theory of functions.

BIBLIOGRAPHY

I. Original Works. Gudermann's books include *Grundriss der analytischen Sphärik* (Cologne, 1830); *Theorie der Potenzial- oder cyklisch-hyperbolischen Functionen* (Berlin, 1833); *Theorie der Modular-Functionen und der Modular-Integrale* (Berlin, 1844); and *Über die wissenschaftliche Anwedung der Belagerungs-Geschütze* (Münster, 1850).

II. Secondary Literature. See *Neue deutsche Biographie,* VII, 252–253; F. Klein, *Vorlesungen über die Entwicklung der Mathematik im 19. Jahrhundert,* I (Berlin, 1926), 278 f.; *Encyklopädie der mathematischen Wissenschaften,* II (Leipzig, 1913); and R. Sturm, "Gudermanns Urteil über die Prüfungsarbiet von Weierstrass (1841)," in *Jahresbericht der Deutschen Mathematiker-Vereinigung,* **19** (1910), 160.

Luboš Nový

GUENTHER, ADAM WILHELM SIEGMUND (*b.* Nuremberg, Germany, 6 February 1848; *d.* Munich, Germany, 3 February 1923)

Guenther was the son of a Nuremberg businessman, Ludwig Leonhard Guenther, and Johanna Weiser. In 1872 he married Maria Weiser; they had one daughter and three sons, one of whom was the political economist and sociologist Gustav Adolf Guenther.

Guenther studied mathematics and physics from 1865 at Erlangen, Heidelberg, Leipzig, Berlin, and Göttingen. He received his doctorate from Erlangen with *Studien zur theoretischen Photometrie* (1872). He participated in the Franco-Prussian War and then took the teaching examination for mathematics and physics. In 1872 he became a teacher at Weissenburg, Bavaria, and immediately qualified for university lecturing at Erlangen with *Darstellung der Näherungswerte der Kettenbrüche in independenter Form* (Erlangen, 1872–1873). Guenther went to the Munich Polytechnicum as a *Privatdozent* in mathematics in 1874 and to Ansbach in 1876 as professor of mathematics and physics at the Gymnasium. From 1886 to 1920 he was professor of geography at the Munich Technische Hochschule, and from 1911 to 1914 he was rector of this school. A member of the Liberal party, he served in the German Reichstag from 1878 to 1884 and in the Bavarian Landtag from 1884 to 1899 and from 1907 to 1918. During World War I he headed the Bavarian flying weather service, beginning in 1917.

Guenther's numerous books and journal articles encompass both pure mathematics and its history and physics, geophysics, meteorology, geography, and astronomy. The individual works on the history of science, worth reading even today, bear witness to a thorough study of the sources, a remarkable knowledge of the relevant secondary literature, and a superior descriptive ability. Although it is true that his compendia contain a great many names and references, only hint at particulars, and are outdated today, they are nevertheless characteristic of their time.

BIBLIOGRAPHY

I. ORIGINAL WORKS. Guenther's principal writings are *Zur reinen Mathematik: Lehrbuch der Determinantentheorie* (Erlangen, 1875; 2nd ed., 1877); *Die Lehre von den gewöhnlichen verallgemeinerten Hyperbelfunktionen* (Halle, 1881); and *Parabolische Logarithmen und parabolische Trigonometrie* (Leipzig, 1882).

On physics, geography, and related fields, see *Einfluss der Himmelskörper auf Witterungsverhältnisse,* 2 vols. (Halle, 1877–1879); *Lehrbuch der Geophysik und physikalischen Geographie,* 2 vols. (Stuttgart, 1884–1885), 2nd ed. entitled *Handbuch der Geophysik* (1897–1899); *Handbuch der mathematischen Geographie* (Stuttgart, 1891); and *Didaktik und Methodik des Geographie-Unterrichtes* (Munich, 1895).

Works on the history of science include *Vermischte Untersuchungen zur Geschichte der mathematischen Wissenschaften* (Leipzig, 1876); *Ziele und Resultäte der neueren mathematisch-historischen Forschung* (Erlangen, 1876); *Antike Näherungsmethoden im Lichte moderner Mathematik* (Prague, 1878); "Geschichte des mathematischen Unterrichtes im deutschen Mittelalter bis zum Jahre 1525," in *Monumenta Germaniae paedagogica,* III (Berlin, 1887); "Abriss der Geschichte der Mathematik und Naturwissenschaften im Altertum," in *Handbuch der klassischen Altertumswissenschaften,* 2nd ed., V. supp. 1 (1894): *Geschichte der anorganischen Naturwissenschaften im 19. Jahrhundert* (Berlin, 1901); *Entdeckungsgeschichte und Fortschritte der Geographie im 19. Jahrhundert* (Berlin, 1902); *Geschichte der Erdkunde* (Vienna, 1904); and *Geschichte der Mathematik,* I, *Von den aeltesten Zeiten bis Cartesius* (Leipzig, 1908; repr., 1927).

Guenther was coeditor of *Zeitschrift für mathematischen und naturwissenschaftlichen Unterricht* (1876–1886); *Zeitschrift für das Ausland* (1892–1893); *Münchener geographische Studien* (from 1896); *Mitteilungen zur Geschichte der Medizin und der Naturwissenschaften* (from 1901); and *Forschungen zur bayerischen Landeskunde* (1920–1921).

II. SECONDARY LITERATURE. Obituaries include E. von Drygalski, in *Jahrbuch der bayerischen Akademie der Wissenschaften* (1920–1923), pp. 79–83; *Geographische Zeitschrift,* **29** (1923), 161–164; L. Günther, in *Lebensläufe aus Franken,* IV (1930), 204–219; W. Schüller, in *Zeitschrift für mathematischen und naturwissenschaftlichen Unterricht,* **56** (1925), 109–113; H. Wieleitner, in *Mitteilungen zur Geschichte der Medizin und der Naturwissenschaften,* **22** (1923), 1-2; and August Wilhelm, in *Neue deutsche Biographie,* VI (1966), 266-267.

J. E. HOFMANN

GULDIN, PAUL (*b.* St. Gall, Switzerland, 12 June 1577; *d.* Graz, Austria, 3 November 1643)

Guldin was of Jewish descent but was brought up as a Protestant. He began work as a goldsmith and as such was employed in several German towns. At the age of twenty he was converted to Catholicism and entered the Jesuit order, changing his first name, Habakkuk, to Paul. In 1609 he was sent to Rome for further education. Guldin taught mathematics at the Jesuit colleges in Rome and Graz. When a severe illness obliged him to suspend his lecturing, he was sent to Vienna, where he became professor of mathematics at the university. In 1637 he returned to Graz, where he died in 1643.

In 1582 the Gregorian calendar was introduced in western Europe, and it met with a great deal of opposition among both scientists and Protestants; one of the opponents was the famous chronologist Sethus Calvisius. To refute him and to defend Pope Gregory XIII and his fellow Jesuit Christoph Clavius, Guldin published his first work, *Refutatio elenchi calendarii Gregoriani a Setho Calvisio conscripti* (Mainz, 1618).

In 1622 Guldin published a physicomathematical dissertation on the motion of the earth caused by alteration of the center of gravity. In it he made the assumption that every unimpeded large body whose center of gravity does not coincide with the center of the universe is moved in such a way that it will coincide with the latter. In the fourteenth century the doctrine of centers of gravity had begun to play a role in the mechanics of large bodies. In his *Quaestiones super libros quattuor de caelo et mundo Aristotelis,* Jean Buridan argued that geological processes are always causing a redistribution of the earth's matter and therefore are continually changing its center of gravity. But the center of gravity always strives to be at the center of the universe, so the earth is constantly shifting about near the latter. Guldin accepted Buridan's hypothesis but was also well-informed about the objection which Nicole Oresme had formulated in his *Le livre du ciel et du monde.*

In 1627 a correspondence on religious subjects developed between Guldin and Johannes Kepler. On the occasion of his journey from Ulm to Prague, which he undertook to solicit funds from Emperor Rudolph II for the publication of the Rudolphine Tables (Ulm, 1627), Kepler wrote on his objections to the Catholic religion to Guldin. In his answer Guldin tried to refute them with theological arguments drawn up for him by a fellow Jesuit. Kepler's reply ended the correspondence.

Guldin's main work was *Centrobaryca seu de centro gravitatis trium specierum quantitatis continuae,* in four volumes (Vienna, 1635–1641). In the first volume

Guldin determined the centers of gravity of plane rectilinear and curvilinear figures and of solids in the Archimedean manner. Against Niccolò Cabeo's attacks in *Philosophia magnetica* (1629) directed toward his theory concerning the motion of the earth, Guldin reproduced in volume I his dissertation of 1622 and a note in which he discussed Cabeo's arguments. The appendix to volume I contains tables of quadratic and cubic numbers and an exposition of the use of logarithms referring to Adriaan Vlacq's *Arithmetica logarithmica* (1628).

Volume II contains what is known as Guldin's theorem: "If any plane figure revolve about an external axis in its plane, the volume of the solid so generated is equal to the product of the area of the figure and the distance traveled by the center of gravity of the figure" (ch. 7, prop. 3, p. 147). This theorem has been much discussed in terms of possible plagiarism from the early part of book VII of Pappus' *Collectio* (*ca.* A.D. 300). However, the theorem cannot have been taken from the first published edition of the *Collectio,* the Latin translation of Federico Commandino (Venice, 1588), because that text shows obvious lacunae. Guldin attempted to prove his theorem by metaphysical reasoning, but Bonaventura Cavalieri pointed out the weakness of his demonstration and proved the theorem by the method of indivisibles. Volume II treats the properties of the Archimedean spiral and the conic sections, their lengths and surfaces, the determination of the center of gravity of a sector of a circle and of a segment of a circle and a parabola, the rise of solids of revolution, and the application of the Guldin theorem to them.

In volume III Guldin determined the surface and the volume of a cone, a cylinder, a sphere, and other solids of revolution and their mutual proportions. In his *Stereometria doliorum* (1615) Kepler determined the volumes of certain vessels and the areas of certain surfaces by means of infinitesimals, instead of the long and tedious method of exhaustions. In volume IV Guldin severely attacked Kepler for the lack of rigor in his use of infinitesimals. He also criticized Cavalieri's use of indivisibles in his *Geometria indivisibilibus* (1635), asserting not only that the method had been taken from Kepler but also that since the number of indivisibles was infinite, they could not be compared with one another. Furthermore, he pointed out a number of fallacies to which the method of indivisibles appeared to lead.

In 1647, after the death of Guldin, Cavalieri published *Exercitationes geometricae sex,* in which he defended himself against the first charge by pointing out that his method differed from that of Kepler in that it made use only of indivisibles, and against the second by observing that the two infinities of elements to be compared are of the same kind.

BIBLIOGRAPHY

Guldin's writings are listed in the text. A very good account of his works may be found in C. Sommervogel, *Bibliothèque de la Compagnie de Jésus,* II (Brussels-Paris, 1891), 1946–1947.

On Guldin or his work, see the following (listed chronologically): C. J. Gerhardt, *Geschichte der Mathematik in Deutschland* (Munich, 1877), pp. 129–130; L. Schuster, *Johann Kepler und die grossen kirchlichen Streitfragen seiner Zeit* (Graz, 1888), pp. 217–228, 233–243; M. Cantor, *Vorlesungen über Geschichte der Mathematik,* II (Leipzig, 1900), 840–844; H. G. Zeuthen, *Geschichte der Mathematik im 16. und 17. Jahrhundert* (Leipzig, 1903), pp. 240, 241, 293; G. A. Miller, "Was Paul Guldin a Plagiarist?," in *Science,* **64** (1926), 204–206; P. Ver Eecke, "Le théorème dit de Guldin considéré au point de vue historique," in *Mathésis,* **46** (1932), 395–397; R. C. Archibald, "Notes and Queries," in *Scripta mathematica,* **1** (1932), 267; P. Duhem, *Le système du monde,* IX (Paris, 1958), 318–321; C. B. Boyer, *The History of the Calculus and Its Conceptual Development* (New York, 1959), pp. 121, 122, 138, 139; and J. E. Hofmann, "Ueber die *Exercitatio geometrica* des M. A. Ricci," in *Centaurus,* **9** (1963), 151, 152.

H. L. L. BUSARD

GUNTER, EDMUND (*b.* Hertfordshire, England, 1581; *d.* London, England, 10 December 1626)

Little is known of Gunter's origins or the details of his life. Of Welsh descent, he was educated at Westminster School and Christ Church, Oxford, graduating B.A. in 1603 and M.A. in 1605. He subsequently entered holy orders, became rector of St. George's, Southwark, in 1615, and received the B.D. degree later that year. In March 1619 he became professor of astronomy at Gresham College, London, retaining this post and his rectorship until his sudden death at the age of forty-five.

Gunter's contributions to science were essentially of a practical nature. A competent but unoriginal mathematician, he had a gift for devising instruments which simplified calculations in astronomy, navigation, and surveying; and he played an important part in the English tradition—begun in 1561 by Richard Eden's translation of Martín Cortes' *Arte de navegar* and furthered by William Borough, John Dee, Thomas Harriot, Thomas Hood, Robert Hues, Robert Norman, Edward Wright, and others—which put the theory of navigation into a form suitable for easy use at sea. Gunter's works, written in English, reflected the practical nature of his teaching and linked the more scholarly work of his time with everyday needs; the tools he provided were of immense value long afterward.

Gunter's first published mathematical work was the *Canon triangulorum* of 1620, a short table, the first of its kind, of common logarithms of sines and tangents. His account of his sector, in the *De sectore et radio* of 1623, had circulated in manuscript for sixteen years before its publication. The sector, a development from Hood's, included sine, tangent, logarithm, and meridional part scales; its uses included the solution of plane, spherical, and nautical triangles (the last formed from rhumb, meridian, and latitude lines). With improvements, the British navy used it for two centuries, and it was also a precursor of the slide rule. Gunter solved such problems as finding the sun's amplitude from its declination and the latitude of the observer by adding similar scales to the seaman's cross-staff. Comparison of the amplitude with the sun's direction, measured by a magnetic compass, was known to give the compass variation; but although Gunter's own observations in 1622 at Limehouse were about five degrees less than Borough's 1580 results there, a statement of the secular change of variation awaited the further decrease observed by Gunter's Gresham successor, Henry Gellibrand.

Gunter's other inventions may have included the so-called Dutchman's log for measuring a ship's way. Henry Briggs acknowledged his suggested use of arithmetical complements in logarithmic work and the terms cosine, contangent, and such are probably Gunter's own; his use of the decimal point and his decimal notation for degrees are to be noted. Gunter's chain, used in surveying, is sixty-six feet long and divided into 100 equal links, thus allowing decimal measurement of acreage. Largely following Willebrord Snell, Gunter took a degree of the meridian to be 352,000 feet; this decision gave English seamen a much improved result.

BIBLIOGRAPHY

I. Original Works. Gunter's chief works went through six eds. by 1680 and were successively augmented by their editors. They are *Canon triangulorum, sive tabulae sinuum et tangentium artificialium ad radium 10000.0000. & ad scrupula prima quadrantis* (London, 1620)—the British Museum copy (C.54.e.10) is bound with Henry Briggs's rare *Logarithmorum chilias prima* (London, n.d. [probably 1617]) and contains copious MS additions; *De sectore et radio. The Description and Use of the Sector in Three Bookes. The Description and Use of the Crosse-Staffe in Other Three Bookes. . . .* (London, 1623), a work of great practical importance; and *The Description and Use of His Majesties Dials in White-Hall Garden* (London, 1624)—the British Museum copy (C.60.f.7) gives evidence of Gunter's friendship with Ben Jonson—describes the large complex of dials, which stood until about 1697. A copy of the enl. 2nd ed. of his works, entitled *The Description and Use of the Sector, Crosse-staffe, and Other Instruments: With a Canon of Artificiall Lines and Tangents, to a Radius of 100,000,000 Parts, and the Use Thereof in Astronomie, Navigation, Dialling and Fortification, etc. . . .* (London, 1636), was bought by Newton for five shillings in 1667 and may be seen, much thumbed, in the library of Trinity College, Cambridge (NQ.9.160); it includes the vexed method of "middle latitude," probably first put forth by Ralph Handson in his 1614 version of Bartolomäus Pitiscus' *Trigonometria* but not used by Gunter himself. The 1653 ed. of the works, amended by Samuel Foster and Henry Bond, contains an early printed statement of the logarithmic result for the integral of the secant function or meridional parts—Gunter's meridian scale, like Wright's earlier one, came from the simple addition of secants; and he was doubtless unaware of Harriot's unpublished calculation of them as (in effect) logarithmic tangents, completed in 1614: he was not, anyway, interested in such theoretical niceties.

II. Secondary Literature. There is little need to refer to the brief early biographical sketches by John Aubrey, Charles Hutton, and John Ward. Accounts of aspects of Gunter's scientific contributions and their contexts are given in James Henderson, *Bibliotheca tabularum mathematicarum Being a Descriptive Catalogue of Mathematical Tables. Part 1. Logarithmic Tables (A. Logarithms of Numbers)* (Cambridge, 1926); and, extensively, in David W. Waters, *The Art of Navigation in England in Elizabethan and Early Stuart Times* (London, 1958), which gives detailed references to the relevant work of his contemporaries, of whom Briggs, Harriot, and Wright are the most important in this context. Christopher Hill, *Intellectual Origins of the English Revolution* (Oxford, 1965), covers the wider background, with much detail on the Gresham College circles. E. G. R. Taylor, *The Mathematical Practitioners of Tudor and Stuart England* (London, 1954), is useful but often infuriating on documentation. A more recent survey of the mathematical and navigational references is in J. V. Pepper, "Harriot's Unpublished Papers," in *History of Science*, **6** (1968), 17–40. The scientific correspondence of the later seventeenth century contains references to Gunter but does not add much of substance.

Jon V. Pepper

HAAR, ALFRÉD (*b.* Budapest, Hungary, 11 October 1885; *d.* Szeged, Hungary, 16 March 1933)

Alfréd was the son of Ignatz Haar and Emma Fuchs. While a student at the Gymnasium in Budapest, he was a collaborator on a mathematical journal for high schools and in 1903, his last year at the Gymnasium, he won first prize in the Eötvös contest in mathematics. He had started studying chemistry, but his success in the contest induced him to switch to mathematics. From 1904 he studied in Göttingen; in 1909 he took his Ph.D. degree as a student of D. Hilbert and that year became a *Privatdozent* at the University of Göttingen.

In 1912, after a short time at the Technical University of Zurich, he returned to Hungary and succeeded L. Fejér at Klausenburg University, first as extraordinary professor and then, from 1917, as ordinary professor. When Klausenburg became Rumanian he went to Budapest with his colleague F. Riesz. Together they continued their activity at Szeged University, where in 1920 they founded *Acta scientiarum mathematicarum,* a journal of great reputation. In 1931 Haar became a corresponding member of the Hungarian Academy of Sciences.

Haar did work in analysis. Although not formally abstract, it is so close to the abstract method that it still looks modern. His doctoral thesis had dealt with orthogonal systems of functions. Twenty years later he returned to the same subject. Haar first extended what was known on divergence, summation, and oscillation for the Fourier system to other orthogonal systems, in particular to solutions of Sturm-Liouville problems. He discovered a curious orthogonal system according to which every continuous function can be developed into an everywhere converging series; its elements are discontinuous functions admitting, at most, three values. Later he became interested in multiplicative relations of orthogonal systems and characterized their multiplication tables. This research led him to the character theory of commutative groups as a precursor of Pontryagin on duality.

In complex functions Haar did work on splitting lines of singularities and on asymptotics. As one of the first applications of Hilbert's integral methods in equations and of Dirichlet's principle, Haar in 1907 studied the partial differential equation $\Delta\Delta u = 0$; with T. von Kármán he put this method to use in elasticity theory. Haar also wrote a number of papers on Chebyshev approximations and linear inequalities.

Two of Haar's shorter papers (1927–1928) that greatly influenced problems and methods in partial differential equations in the 1930's concern the equation

$$F(x,y,z,p,q) = 0,$$

which is usually dealt with by the method of characteristics. Since this method presupposes the existence of the second instead of the first derivative of the solutions, one may ask whether there exist solutions which escape the methods of characteristics. Under rather broad conditions, Haar answered this question in the negative.

Haar's most important contribution to variational calculus (1917–1919) features an analogous principle, Haar's lemma, an extension of Paul du Bois-Reymond's to double integrals: If

$$\iint_B \left(u\frac{\partial f}{\partial x} + v\frac{\partial f}{\partial y}\right) dxdy = 0$$

for all continuously differentiable f which vanish on the boundary of B, then there is a w such that

$$\frac{\partial w}{\partial x} = -v, \frac{\partial w}{\partial y} = u.$$

Haar's lemma allows one to deal with variational problems like

$$\iint_B f(p,q,x,y,z)\, dxdy = \text{minimum},$$

without supplementary assumptions on the second derivative of the unknown function z. He applied his lemma to variational problems like Plateau's. A multitude of papers by others show the influence this lemma exerted on the whole area of variational calculus.

The notion to which Haar's name is most firmly attached is Haar's measure on groups. In 1932 Haar showed, by a bold direct approach, that every locally compact group possesses an invariant measure which assigns positive numbers to all open sets. An immediate consequence of this theorem was the analytic character of compact groups (J. Von Neumann). It was somewhat later applied to locally compact Abelian groups by Pontryagin. The theorem is now one of the cornerstones of those areas of mathematics where algebra and topology meet.

BIBLIOGRAPHY

See *Alfréd Haar: Gesammelte Arbeiten* (Budapest, 1959), B.S.-Nagy, ed.

H. FREUDENTHAL

ḤABASH AL-ḤĀSIB, AḤMAD IBN ʿABDALLĀH AL-MARWAZĪ (*b.* Marw, Turkestan [now Mary, Turkmen S.S.R.]; *d.* 864–874)

Little is known of Ḥabash's life and family. He worked at Baghdad as astronomer under the ʿAbbāsid caliphs al-Maʾmūn and al-Muʿtaṣim, but he may not have belonged to the small group that collaborated in the Mumtaḥan observations. He made observations from 825 to 835 in Baghdad. Abū Jaʿfar ibn Ḥabash, the son of Ḥabash, was also a distinguished astronomer and an instrument maker.

Works. The biographers Ibn al-Nadīm, Ibn al-Qifṭī, and Ḥājjī Khalīfa ascribe the following works to Ḥabash:

1. A reworking of the *Sindhind.*
2. The *Mumtaḥan Zīj,* the best known of his works, which relies on Ptolemy and is based on his own observations. Ibn Yūnus called it *al-Qānūn* ("The Canon").
3. The *Shāh Zīj,* the shortest of his *ziyajāt.*
4. The *Damascene Zīj.*
5. The *Maʾmūnī Zīj* (or *Arabic Zīj*). This and the *Damascene Zīj* are based on the Hijra calendar rather than on the Yazdigird or Seleucid eras.
6. On the *Rukhāmāt* and Measurements.
7. On the Celestial Spheres.
8. On Astrolabes.
9. On the Oblique and Perpendicular Planes.
10. On the Distances of the Stars.

Since not all of these works are extant, it is almost impossible to determine how many *ziyajāt* Ḥabash wrote and their titles. Two manuscripts on the tables of Ḥabash are preserved, one in Istanbul (Yeni Cami, no. 784) and the other in Berlin (no. 5750). These are not copies of his original works. There has been criticism of the Yeni Cami copy, suggesting that it is a revision of Ḥabash's *zīj* by Kūshyār ibn Labbān. In one way or another the introduction and the passages have come to us in their original forms and can be used, as can the Berlin manuscript, as the sources on Ḥabash.

Trigonometry. Ḥabash's trigonometric contributions are very important.

Sines. In the *Sūrya-Siddhānta* (A.D. 400) a table of half chords is given. A special name for the function which we call the sine is first found in the works of Āryabhaṭa I (A.D. 500). Besides half chord he also uses the term *jya* or *jiva.* In the Islamic world this word was transcribed as *jayb.* Al-Khwārizmī (*ca.* 825) was the first to prepare a table of sines. Ḥabash followed him by constructing such a table for

$$\theta = 0;0°, 0;15°, 0;30°, 0;45°, 1;0° \cdots 90;0°.$$

Versed sine. Among the trigonometric functions the versed sine (versine) also attracted attention. We know that it was mentioned in the *Sūrya-Siddhānta,* and a table for the versed sine is given in Āryabhaṭa. In Islam astronomers used special names to distinguish the versed sine, such as *jayb maʿkūs* (used by Ḥabash), *jayb mankūs* (used by al-Khwārizmī), and *sahm.* Ḥabash may be the first who clearly defined the sine and the versed sine as follows: "A perpendicular from the circumference to the diameter is the sine (*jayb mabsūṭ*) of the arc between the diameter and the perpendicular; the distance between the circumference and the perpendicular upon the diameter is the versed sine (*jayb maʿkūs*) of the above-mentioned arc." He showed that if $A < 90°$, the versed sine $= 60^P - \cos A = 1 - \cos A$; and if $A > 90°$, the versed sine$=60^P + \cos A = 1 + \cos A$. Also, if $A < 90°$, the versed sine $<$ sine; if $A > 90°$, the versed sine $>$ sine; and if $A = 90°$, the versed sine $=$ sine.

Tangent. The *Sūrya-Siddhānta* and other Hindu works mention the shadows, particularly in connection with astronomy. Ḥabash seems to have been the first to compile a table of tangents for

$$\theta = 0;0°, 0;30°, 1;0° \cdots 90;0°.$$

The function of *umbra extensa* (the length of shadow) is defined as

$$h = P\frac{\cos h}{\sin h},$$

$P =$ the length of gnomon. For the computation of the *umbra extensa* from the altitude of the sun, he gives the following steps (see Figure 1):

$$\frac{KR}{P} = \frac{RO}{S}$$

$$KR = \sin h$$
$$RO = \cos h$$
$$P = 12$$
$$S = \textit{umbra extensa}$$

$$\frac{\sin h}{12} = \frac{\cos h}{S}$$

$$S = \frac{\cos h}{\sin h}\,12.$$

In addition to finding the *umbra extensa* from the altitude of the sun, Ḥabash presents the following equations:

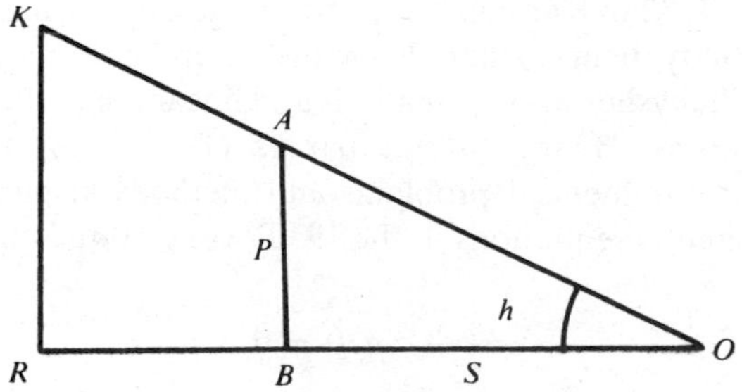

FIGURE 1

$$\text{hypotenuse} = \sqrt{S^2 + P^2}.$$

$$\sin h = \frac{P}{\sqrt{S^2 + P^2}} \cong.$$

Spherical Astronomy. For the solution of problems in spherical astronomy, transformations of coordinates, time measurements, and many other problems, Ḥabash gives astronomical tables of functions which are standard for all *ziyajāt*.

He gives the general rule for calculating the declination of the sun (the first declination, *al-mayl al-awwal*) (see Figure 2):

$$\sin \delta\odot = \sin \varepsilon \cdot \sin \lambda$$
$$\text{obliquity of ecliptic } \varepsilon = 23;35°.$$

The declination depends not only on λ but also on the value of the obliquity of the ecliptic.

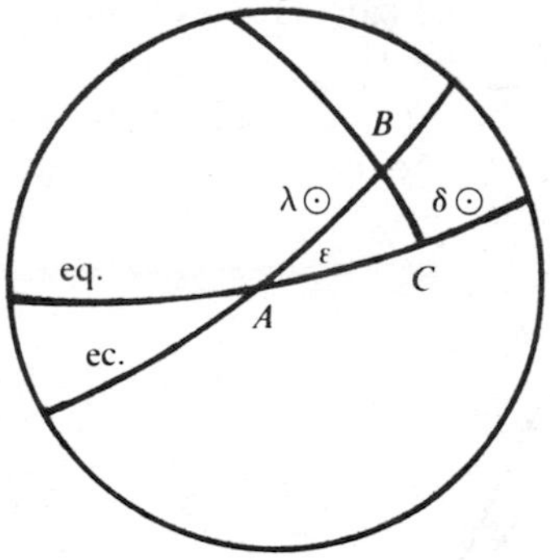

FIGURE 2

The culmination of the sun is defined. (See Figure 3.) If the declination of the sun is northern, $h = (90 - \phi) + \delta\odot$. If the declination of the sun is southern, $h = (90 - \phi) - \delta\odot$.

The time of day, measured from sunrise, is proportional to the altitude of the sun, i.e., the "arc of revolution" (*al-dāʾir min al-falak*). Islamic astronomers gave many trigonometric functions showing the relations between the time and the altitude of the sun. The first exact solution was given by Ḥabash and proved by Abuʾl-Wafāʾ and al-Bīrūnī. This function

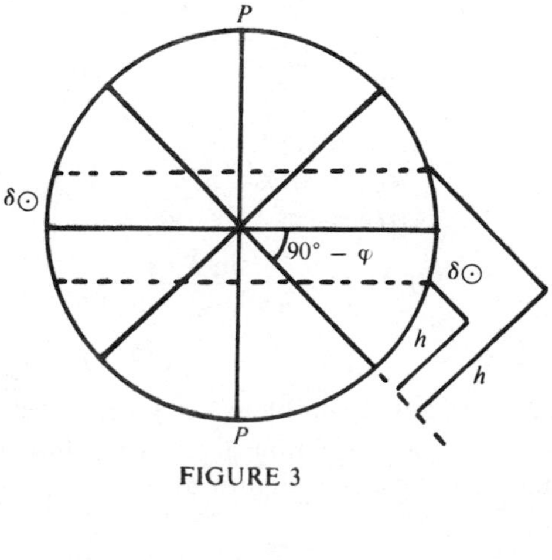

FIGURE 3

is equivalent to the function given by Brahmagupta in his *Khaṇḍakhādyaka:*

$$\text{vers } t = \text{vers } P - \frac{\sin h \cdot \text{vers } P}{\sin \text{alt} \cdot \text{merid}},$$

where P = half of the length of daylight
h = altitude of the sun
t = time
vers P = day sine (*jayb al-nahār;* Sanskrit, *antyā*).

Then he computes the altitude of the sun from the time:

$$\sin h = \frac{(\text{vers } P - \text{vers } t) \sin \text{alt} \cdot \text{merid.}}{\text{vers } P}.$$

Ḥabash calculates the length of daylight, i.e., equation of daylight (*taʿdīl al-nahār*), which al-Khwārizmī calls the ascensional difference. (See Figure 4.)

$$\frac{KD}{DG} = \frac{KL}{LM} \cdot \frac{ME}{EG}$$

$$\frac{\sin \phi}{\cos \phi} = \frac{\cos \delta\odot}{\sin \delta\odot} \cdot \frac{\sin ME}{R}$$

$$\sin ME = R \frac{\sin \phi \cdot \sin \delta\odot}{\cos \phi \cdot \cos \delta\odot}$$

$$\sin ME = R\, tg\, \phi \cdot tg\, \delta\odot.$$

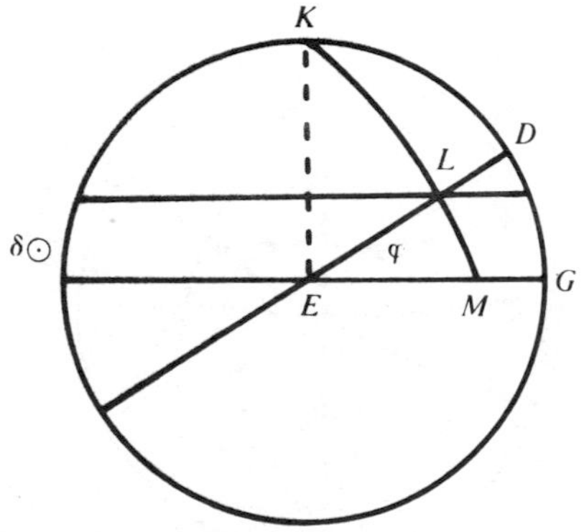

FIGURE 4

He shows that if the declination of the sun is northern, the length of daylight = the equation of daylight + 90°; and if the declination of the sun is southern, the length of daylight = 90° − the equation of daylight. The equation of daylight is tabulated for the planets, the sun, and the moon. With the aid of this table one can easily find the arc of daylight.

The ascensions (*maṭāliʿ al-burūj*) or rising times in the right sphere (*al-falak al-mustaqīm*), i.e., right ascension, is defined (see Figure 5) as

$$\frac{\sin \lambda \cdot \cos \varepsilon}{\cos \delta}.$$

ḤABASH AL-ḤĀSIB

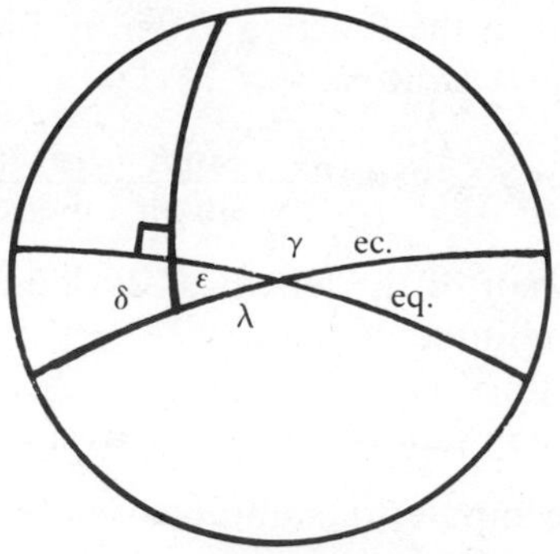

FIGURE 5

Ḥabash prepared such tables because of the right ascension's astrological importance.

The ascension for a particular latitude is called the oblique ascension. Ḥabash showed that if the arbitrary point P on the ecliptic is between the vernal and autumnal equinoxes, the right ascension $-$ 1/2 equation of daylight $=$ oblique ascension; and if it is between the autumnal and vernal equinoxes, the right ascension $+$ 1/2 equation of daylight $=$ oblique ascension.

Ḥabash prepared tables for the seven climates. According to him the first climate (*iqlīm*) was that portion of the northern hemisphere in which

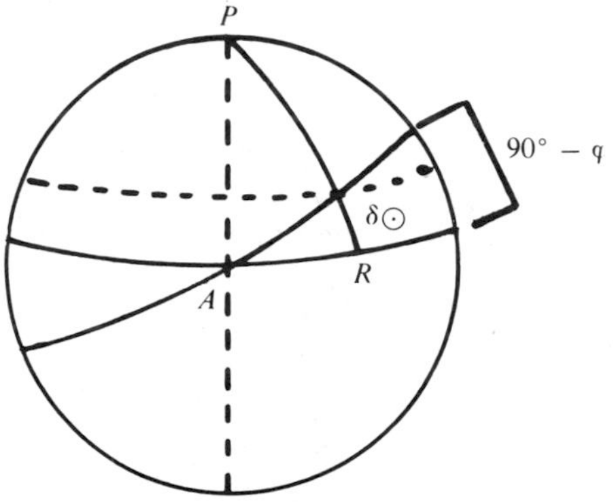

FIGURE 6

$13 \leq$ max. $D \leq 13 - 0.50$, i.e., a band of a half-hour advance in length of daylight.

For finding the ortive amplitude (*jayb al-mashriq*) Ḥabash gives the following function (see Figure 6):

$$\text{Ortive amplitude } AR = \frac{\sin \delta\odot}{\cos \phi}$$

$$\delta\odot = \text{declination of the sun.}$$

Astronomy. Ḥabash generally follows Ptolemy, but some sections of his work are distinctly non-Ptolemaic.

Theory of the Sun. Ḥabash compiled tables of mean motion of the sun for 1, 31, 61, 91, $\cdots$ 691 and 1, 2, 3, 4, 5, $\cdots$ 30 Hijra years; for 1, 2, 3, 4, $\cdots$ 29 days; for 1, 2, 3, 4, $\cdots$ 24 hours; and for 10, 20, 30, $\cdots$ 60 minutes. The mean motion of the sun is 384;55,14° per Hijra year and 0;59,8° per day (the value given in the *Almagest*). He computed the eccentricity of the sun $2^{P}5^{1}$ (2; 1°).

Ḥabash divided half of the ecliptic into eighteen parts, each part called *kardaja.* The Arabic-Persian term *kardaja* (pl., *kardajāt*) is usually derived from the Sanskrit *kramajya.* It seems to have stood for a unit length of arc. He also prepared equation tables of the sun (*taʿdīl al-shams*) for each degree of anomaly.

Methods for the calculation of the equation of the sun were given by Ḥabash. This classical procedure was given in the *Almagest* and followed by the Islamic astronomers. If the mean motion $\bar{\lambda}$ or anomaly is given, to find λe, i.e., the true motion of the sun (see Figure 7):

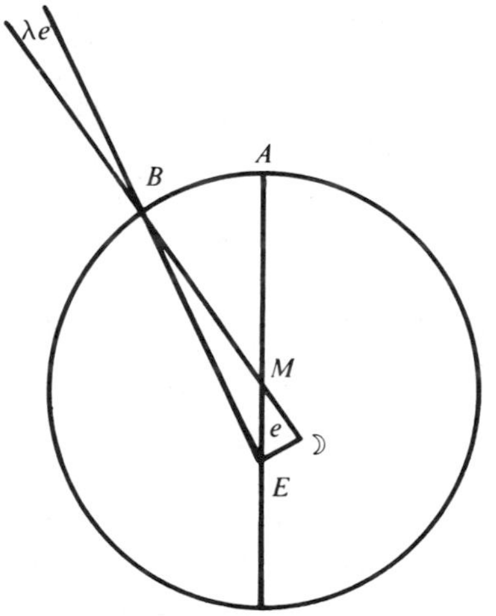

FIGURE 7

$$\text{If } \bar{\lambda} < 90°$$

$$e = \text{eccentricity}$$

$$\text{tg}\,\lambda e = \frac{ED}{BD}$$

$$ED = \sin\bar{\lambda}\cdot e$$

$$BD = MD + MB$$

$$MD = \cos\bar{\lambda}\cdot e$$

$$\text{tg}\,\lambda e = \frac{\sin\bar{\lambda}\cdot e}{\cos\bar{\lambda}\cdot e + 60^{P}}.$$

The converse of the problem, i.e., given λ, determine $\bar{\lambda}$, is set out. This equation gives the following approximate solution (see Figure 8):

$$\text{If } \lambda < 90^\circ$$

$$\operatorname{tg} \lambda e = \frac{ED}{BD}$$

$$ED = \sin \lambda \cdot e.$$

Since the angle λe is small, Ḥabash supposed $BD = BC$, i.e., 60^P:

$$BE = 60^P - EC$$
$$EC = \cos \lambda \cdot e$$
$$BE = 60^P - \cos \lambda \cdot e$$

$$\operatorname{tg} \lambda e = \frac{e \sin \lambda}{60^P - (e \cdot \cos \lambda)}.$$

Ḥabash gave another rule to solve the above problem:

$$\sin \lambda e = \frac{ED}{60^P}$$

$$ED = \sin \lambda \cdot e$$

$$\sin \lambda e = \frac{\sin \lambda \cdot e}{60^P}.$$

This function is correct, but the independent variable is λ rather than $\bar{\lambda}$. If $\bar{\lambda}$ replaces λ, this will lead to the equation $\lambda = \lambda - e \sin \lambda$, which is known as Kepler's equation. The equivalent of this equation is found in Tamil astronomy in south India.

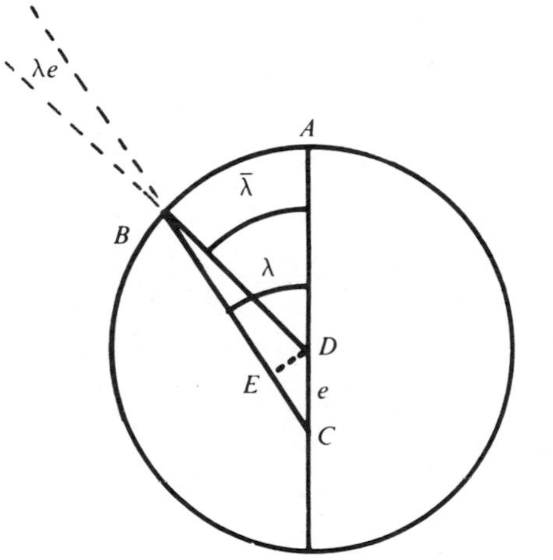

FIGURE 8

From the mean position Ḥabash found the true position of the sun (see Figure 9):

If $\bar{\lambda}\odot > \lambda A$

and $\bar{\lambda}\odot - \lambda A < 90^\circ$,

anomaly $\bar{a} = \bar{\lambda}\odot - \lambda A$,

where $\bar{\lambda}\odot$ = mean longitude of the sun

and λA = longitude of the apogee.

Thus, $$\operatorname{tg} \lambda e = \frac{\sin \bar{a} \cdot e}{\cos \bar{a} \cdot e + 60^P}$$

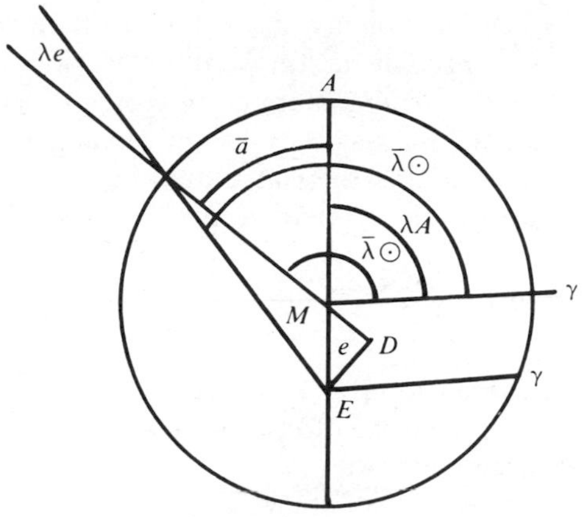

FIGURE 9

and $\bar{\lambda}\odot = \lambda e =$ true position of the sun.

He also computed from the truc position the mean position of the sun (see Figure 10). The true position B, i.e., λB, is given:

$$\lambda B - \lambda A = \angle AEB = a$$

$$\sin \lambda e = \frac{\sin a \cdot e}{60^P}$$

$$\bar{\lambda} B = \lambda B + \lambda e.$$

By applying these methods Ḥabash calculated the

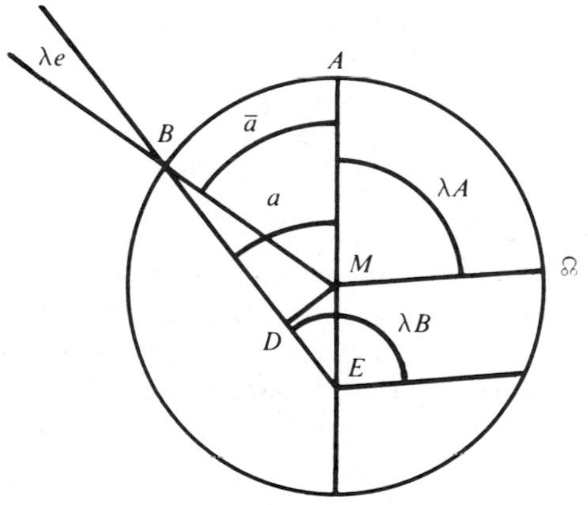

FIGURE 10

entrance of the sun into the zodiacal signs and compiled tables for them.

Lunar Theory. Ḥabash constructed several tables for the longitudinal and latitudinal motions of the moon for periods of thirty lunar years, for years, for months, for days (13;10,35°, the value given in the *Almagest*), for hours (0;32,27°), and for fractions of hours. He also drew up tables for general lunar anomaly and for the equation of the moon (*taʿdīl al-qamar*) in four columns.

Ḥabash's technique for computing the true longitude of the moon was based on the model of the lunar

ḤABASH AL-ḤĀSIB

motion given by Ptolemy in book V of the *Almagest*. The most essential deviation from the previous tables consisted in the arrangement of all corrections of the mean positions so that they are never negative. As Neugebauer remarks, this constituted a great practical advantage over the Ptolemaic method. (See Figure 11.)

The true place of the moon is determined as follows:

M = movable center of eccenter
δ_0 = apparent radius of epicyle when in apogee of eccenter
G = "true apogee" of epicycle
F = "mean apogee" of epicycle
W_0 = maximum angular distance possible between F and G
F_0 = point on the epicycle such that $F = W_0$
$\bar{a}$ = "mean anomaly" of moon counted from F_0
W = angular distance between G and F_0
$a = \bar{a} + w_1$, "true anomaly" counted from G
λ = "true longitude" of the moon counted from γ_0.

The "first correction," W_1:

$$\bar{\lambda}\odot - \bar{\lambda}☾ = K$$

The function of K is tabulated in the first column of the table, called "equation of the moon (*taʿdīl al-qamar*)." It gives the distance from G to F_0, the value given in *Almagest* V, except that Ḥabash had added W_0, which makes W nonnegative.

$$\bar{a} + \text{the first equation} = a.$$

The "second correction," W_2, is a function of a, tabulated in the third column. It corresponds in value to *Almagest* V, 8, col. 4, but the maximum equation δ_0 is added to it. It is assumed that the epicycle is located at the apogee of the eccenter. When it is in the perigee of the eccenter, the amount of the excess of the epicyclic equation is tabulated in the fourth column of the table. This is the function of K (corresponding to *Almagest* V, 8, col. 5); the result will be obtained by multiplying the value of the fourth column by the second: $\delta = W_2 + \mu\gamma$.

If $a < 180°$, the result will be subtracted from or added to the true center. Finally Ḥabash obtains

$$\lambda = \bar{\lambda} - \delta.$$

Latitude of the Moon. The latitude of the moon for a given moment is determined by means of a table prepared for one degree. The true place of the moon (λ☾) is added to the mean position of the ascending node ($-\lambda$☊). Because of the longitude of the ascending node, the distance of the node from γ_0 is counted in a negative direction. This total, A, is the argument with which the table of the latitude of the moon is entered.

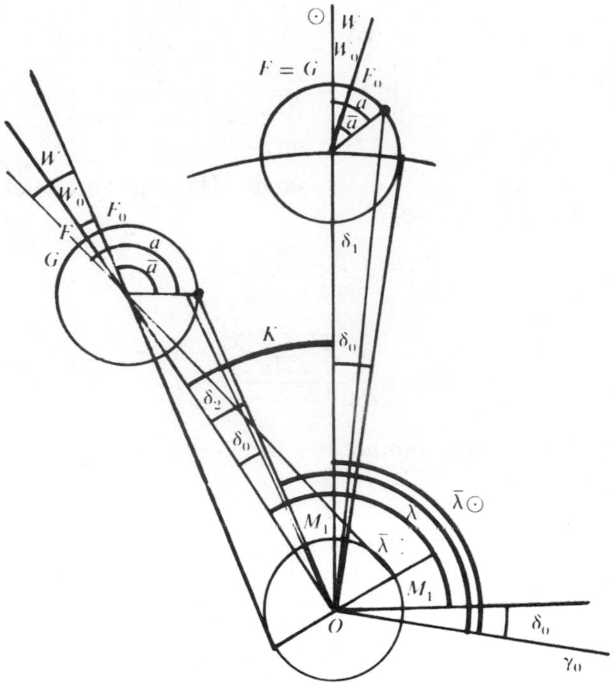

FIGURE 11

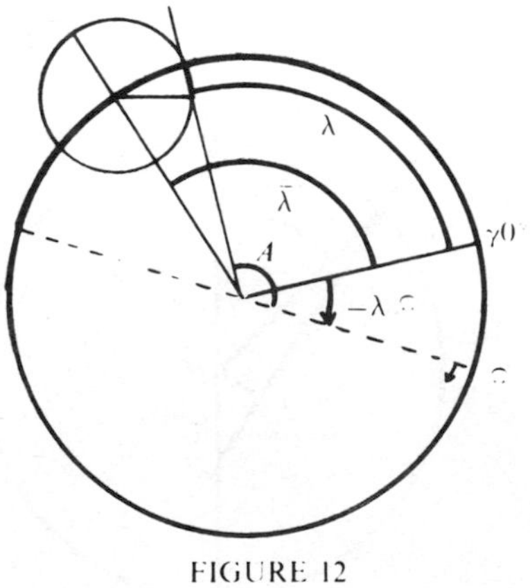

FIGURE 12

Theory of the Planets. For finding the longitudes of the planets Ḥabash prepared several tables for mean motions, in longitude and latitude, and the equations. His procedure for finding the true longitude of a planet for a given moment t is based on the Ptolemaic method (*Almagest* XI).

For outer planets (see Figure 13):

$$\bar{a} = \bar{\lambda}\odot - \bar{\lambda},$$

where $\lambda\odot$ = mean longitude of the sun
λ = mean longitude of the planet
$\bar{a}$ = anomaly or argumentum.

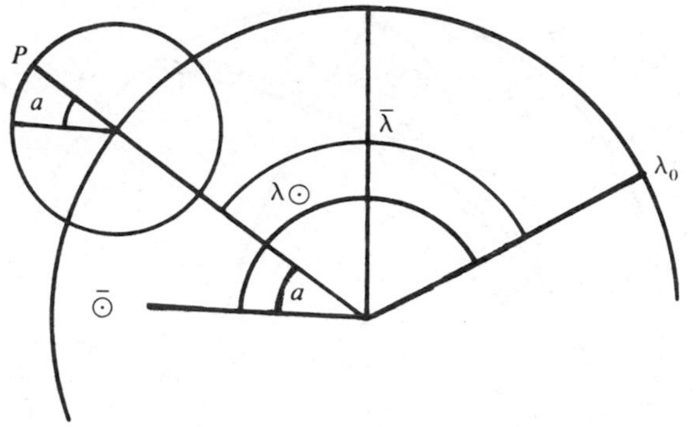

FIGURE 13

It implies that the radius of the planet on the epicycle is always parallel to the direction from 0 to the mean sun.

Inner Planets. For inner planets $\bar{\lambda} = \bar{\lambda}\odot$, and the anomaly can be found from the tables. (See Figure 14.)

For the outer planets he first found the mean longitude $\bar{\lambda}$, mean anomaly *a*, and the longitude of the apogee λA of the planet (see Figure 15): $\bar{\lambda} - \lambda A = \bar{K}$.

He found the distance of the center *C* of the epicycle from the apogee for the given moment. According to the Ptolemaic planetary theory, the planet makes its regular motion not around the point *O* but around *E*, i.e., the "equant." The center of the defer-

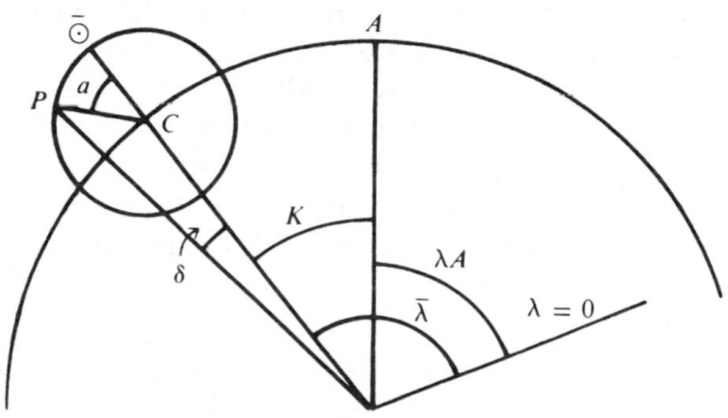

FIGURE 14

ent falls between *O* and *E*. Then he found the epicyclic equation as seen from *O*. Thus the true anomaly, *a*, counted from true apogee, is found. Ḥabash tabulated this difference, $W_1 = a - \bar{a}$, as function $\bar{K}$, in the first column. This is called the "first correction": $a = W_1 + \bar{a}$.

Then he computed the distance of *C* from *A*, i.e., *K*, as seen from *A*. This difference is also equal to the angle W_1:

$$K = \bar{K} - W_1.$$

If $$\bar{K} < 180°$$

$$K = \bar{K} - W_1$$
$$a = \bar{a} + W_1.$$

ḤABASH AL-ḤĀSIB

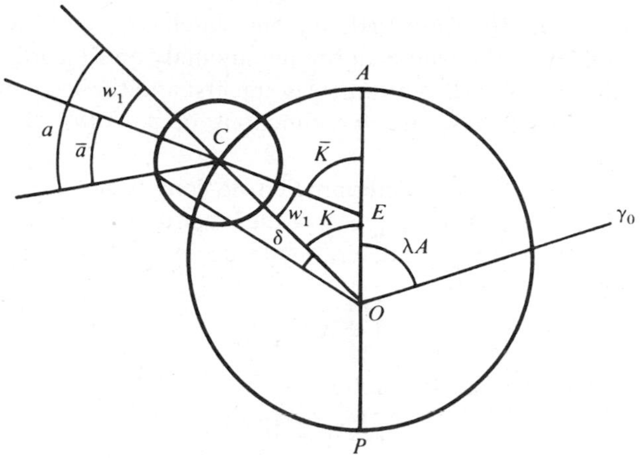

FIGURE 15

Then comes the "second correction," W_2. This depends not only on the true anomaly *a* but also on the position of the epicycle. If it is exactly in the apogee, this amount of correction will be less than W_2 by the amount μA tabulated in column 4 as the function *a*:

$$\delta = W_2 - \mu A \cdot \gamma.$$

γ is found as a function of *K* in the second column.

All these procedures are correct only if the value found in the second column is negative. If it is positive, the second column is multiplied by the value found in the fifth column, then subtracted from the fourth. The true longitude of the planet is

$$\lambda = \lambda A + K + \delta.$$

Latitude of the Planets. The procedure for calculating the latitude of the superior planets is based on Ptolemaic method (*Almagest* XIII, 6). The table of latitudes was prepared in three columns. Ḥabash used the same numeric values as Ptolemy (*Almagest* XIII, table 5). According to him, the latitudes can be found by the addition of two components: the inclination of the epicycle about its second diameter (β_1) and the angle at the line of nodes between the deferent and ecliptic planes (β_2).

The first and second columns are functions of anomaly $a{:}b_1(a)$ and $b_2(a)$. The third column is the function θ.

$$\text{Mars} = \theta = \lambda$$
$$\text{Jupiter} = \theta = \lambda - 20°$$
$$\text{Saturn} = \theta = \lambda + 50°$$
$$c(\theta)$$
$$\beta_1 = b_1 \cdot c$$
$$\beta_2 = b_2 \cdot c$$

The latitude of the planet $\beta = \beta_1 + \beta_2$.

For the inferior planets (based on Ptolemaic

ḤABASH AL-ḤĀSIB

method, *Almagest* XIII, 6), one enters the latitude table with the truly determined anomaly and records the corresponding numbers in the first and the second columns. These are the functions of a: $b_1(a)$ and $b_2(a)$.

One finds the determined true longitude of the planets. For Venus, $A = \lambda -$ the longitude of apogee. For Mercury, if the determined true anomaly is in the first fifteen rows,

$$A = \lambda - 10°;$$

if it is in those that follow,

$$A = \lambda + 10°.$$

Next,
$$A + 90° = \theta \text{ for Venus}$$
$$A + 270° = \theta \text{ for Mercury.}$$

One enters the table with that value and finds the corresponding number in the third column. This is the function $c(\theta)$.

Then, $b_1 \cdot c =$ the first latitude $= \beta_1$.

If θ is in the first fifteen rows, the planet is northern. If it is in those that follow, it is southern. If θ is after the first fifteen rows at the same time that a is in the first fifteen rows, the planet is northern.

Next, one enters the latitude table with

$$\theta \text{ for Venus}$$
$$\theta + 180° \text{ for Mercury}$$

and finds the corresponding value in the third column. This is the function of θ or $\theta + 180°$: $c(\theta)$ or $c(\theta + 180°)$. Then $b_1c =$ the second latitude $= \beta_2$. If (θ) or $(\theta + 180°)$ is in the first fifteen rows and $a < 180°$, the planet has a northern latitude. If $a > 180°$, it has a southern latitude. If (θ) or $(\theta + 180°)$ is below the first fifteen rows and $a < 180°$, the planet has a southern latitude; and if $a > 180°$, the planet has a northern latitude. Then $c^2 + C^2/6 = \beta_3$ for Venus. If the planet has northern latitude, $\beta = \beta_2 + \beta_3$ and $C^2 = 3C^2/4 = \beta_3$ for Mercury. If the planet has southern latitude, $\beta = \beta_2 + \beta_3$.

Parallax (*Ikhtilāf al-Manẓar*) *Theory.* Ḥabash had two entirely different methods for determining the parallax, i.e., parallax in longitude P_λ and parallax in latitude P_β. One of them may seem a transition between that of Ptolemy and the later Islamic astronomers. This solution depends on the first sine (*al-jayb al-awwal*) that can be formulated (see Figure 16):

$$\frac{\sin BV}{\sin FB} \qquad \frac{\sin DB}{\cos DB}$$

equal cos B and the second sine, which is equal to sin B. Without proof he states that

$$\sin P_\lambda = (\text{first sine})\,(\sin P_{am}).$$

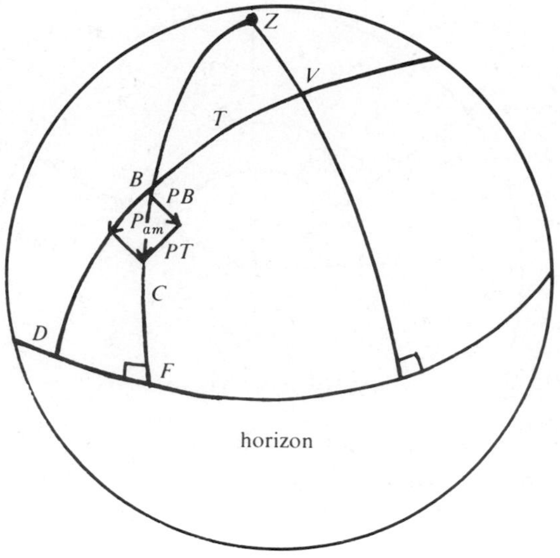

FIGURE 16

P_{am} is measured according to Ptolemy (see Figure 17):

$$\sin P_\beta = \frac{(\sin P_{am})\,(\text{first sine})}{\cos P_\beta}.$$

The other method seems to derive from the *Sūrya-Siddhanta*.

The technique for determining the longitude component is of great interest. Ḥabash first determined t (see Figure 18), then used it as argument in the parallax table. The result was called the first parallax. He added this to t and with that value entered the parallax table. The result was the second parallax. These operations were repeated until the fifth parallax—a quarter of the parallax in longitude, expressed in hours.

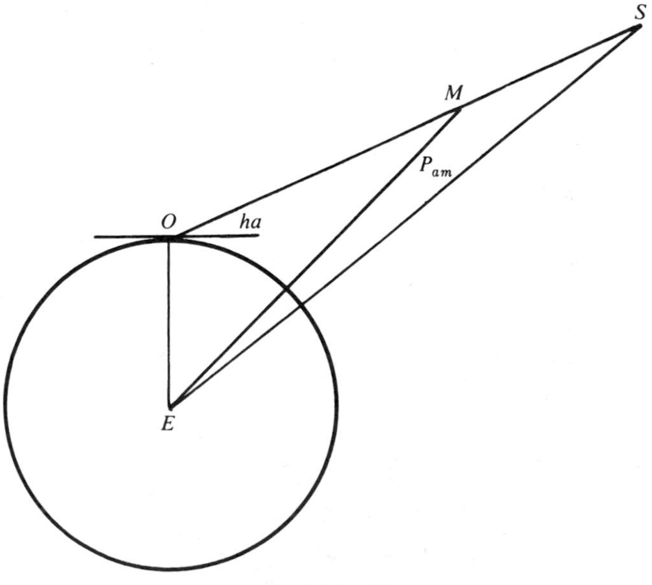

FIGURE 17

For finding the lunar parallax in latitude Ḥabash used A as an argument, and the corresponding value of the function was to be doubled (see Figure 18). This would be the lunar parallax in latitude.

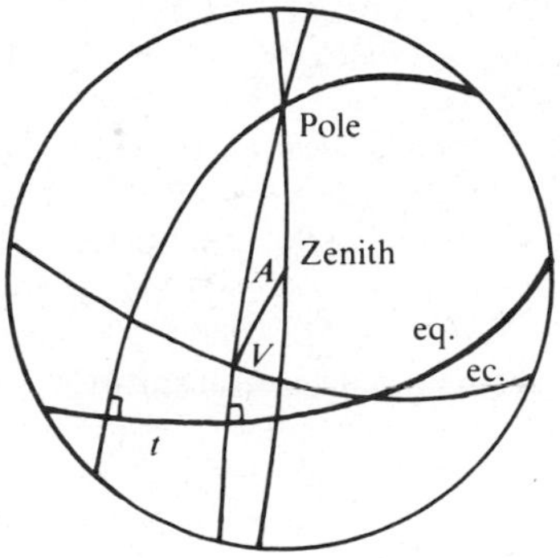

FIGURE 18

Visibility Theory (*Ru'yat al-Hilāl*). Habash may have been the first astronomer to engage in the computation of the new crescent. Like the ancient Babylonians and the Jews, the Muslims depended on visual observation of the new crescent for their religious and secular calendars. This led the Muslim astronomers to realize that the knowledge of the visibility of the new crescent is an essential task of astronomy. Ḥabash used the following method for the determination of the visibility of the new crescent. He added twenty or thirty minutes to the time of sunset, thus obtaining the mean position of the moon at the time when the new crescent becomes visible. Then the true position of the sun, the moon, and the head were needed for the above-mentioned time (see Figure 19). Thus, $\lambda - \lambda\odot = \lambda_1$, which Maimonides called the first elongation.

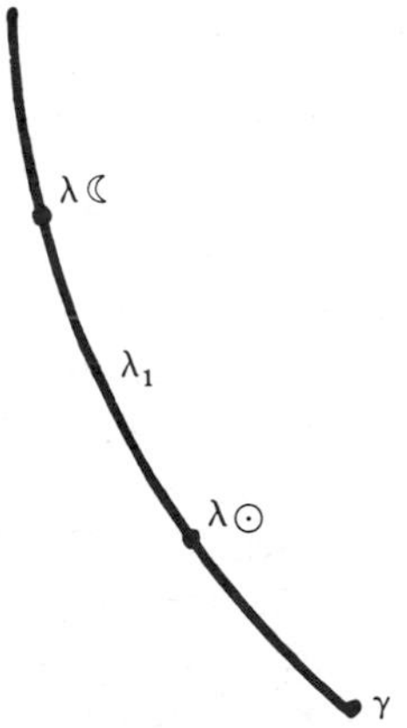

FIGURE 19

For an observer on the surface of the earth, the moon M would appear in a lower position M_1 because of the parallax.

ḤABASH AL-ḤĀSIB

$$\frac{\text{Diameter of the earth}}{\text{The distance of the moon to the center of the earth}} = \text{parallax of the moon } P_{am}.$$

Then the parallax in latitude P_β and longitude P_λ can be obtained (see Figure 20). Thus, $\lambda_1 - P\lambda = \lambda_2$, which Maimonides called the second elongation. The

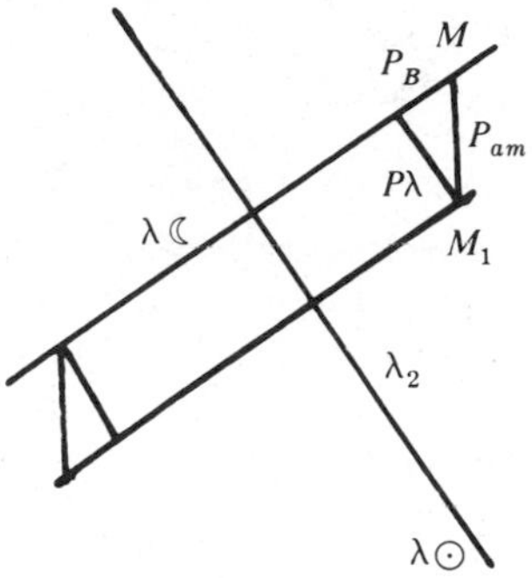

FIGURE 20

true latitude of the moon (Maimonides called it the first latitude) was subtracted from or added to the parallax in latitude, depending on the variable position of the moon:

$$M_\beta - P_\beta = M_{1\beta} \text{ (second latitude).}$$

From this second latitude one can derive half of the day arc of the moon, and from that the equation of the day of the moon is obtained. This equation of the moon is added to or subtracted from the longitude of the moon. Thus the point of the ecliptic O (see Figure 21), which sets simultaneously with the moon, is obtained: $\lambda_2 - C = \lambda_3 O$.

Then the arc of the equator QA, which sets simultaneously with the arc of the ecliptic, λ_3, is calculated

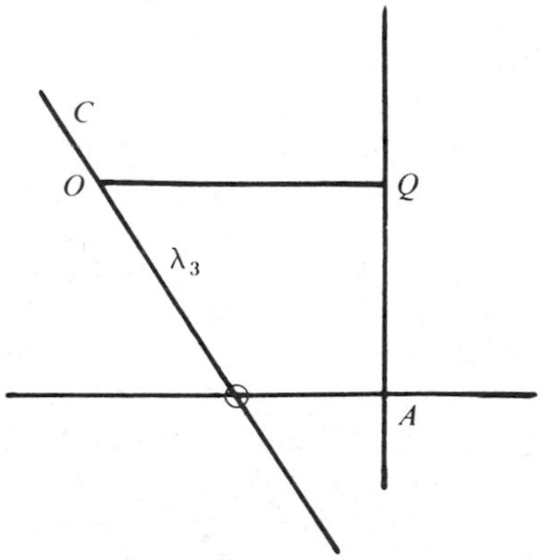

FIGURE 21

(see Figure 22). This is the difference between the rising times of the moon and the sun. This time difference is multiplied by the surplus of the moon in one hour and divided by fifteen. The result K is

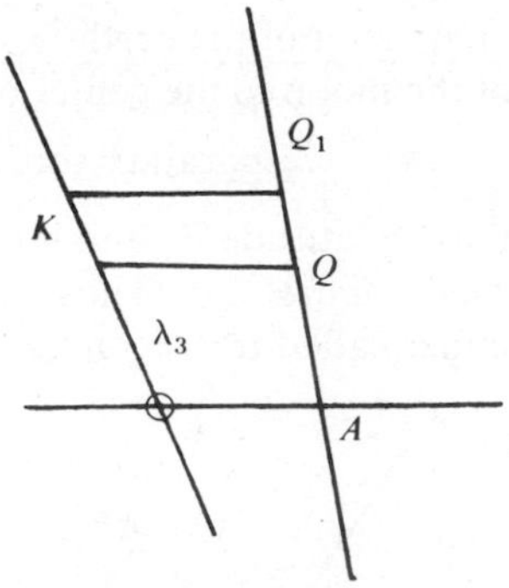

FIGURE 22

added to the true longitude of the moon, i.e., the distance cut by the moon during that time is added to get the distance between the moon and the sun at sunset. Then (see Figure 23)

$$\angle Q_1AR = 90° - \Phi$$
$$\sin Q_1R = \cos \Phi \cdot \sin QA.$$

If $QR > 10°$, the moon will be visible on that day. If $QR < 10°$, the moon will not be visible.

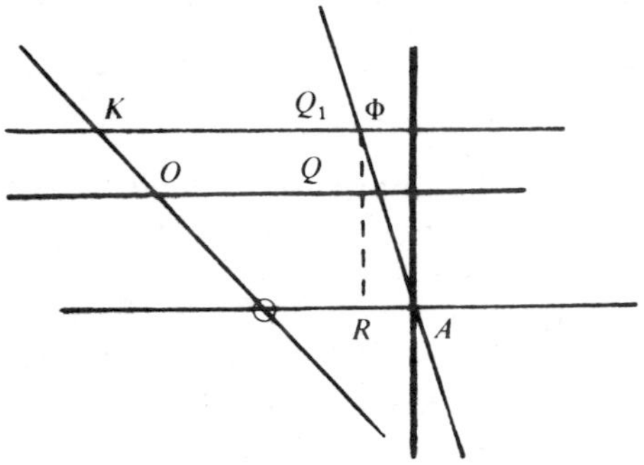

FIGURE 23

BIBLIOGRAPHY

The following works may be consulted for further information: A. Braunmühl, *Vorlesungen über Geschichte der Trigonometrie* (Leipzig, 1900); G. Caussin, *Le livre de la grande Hakémite,* vol. VII of Notices et Extraits des MSS (Paris, 1804); S. Gandz, J. Obemann, and O. Neugebauer, *The Code of Maimonides. Book Three. Treatise Eight; Sanctification of the New Moon* (New Haven, 1956); J. Hamadanizadeh, "A Medieval Interpolation Scheme for Oblique Ascensions," in *Centaurus,* **9** (1963), 257-265; E. S. Kennedy, "An Islamic Computer for Planetary Latitudes," in *Journal of the American Oriental Society,* **71** (1951), 12-21; and "Parallax Theory in Islamic Astronomy," in *Isis,* **47** (1956), 33-53; E. S. Kennedy and M. Agna, "Planetary Visibility Tables in Islamic Astronomy," in *Centaurus,* **7** (1960), 134-140; E. S. Kennedy and Janjanian, "The Crescent Visibility Table in Al-Khwārizmī's Zij," *ibid.,* **11** (1965), 73-78; E. S. Kennedy and Ahmad Muruwwa, "Bīrūnī on the Solar Equation," in *Journal of Near Eastern Studies,* **17** (1958), 112-121; E. S. Kennedy and Sharkas, "Two Medieval Methods for Determining the Obliquity of the Ecliptic," in *Mathematics Teacher,* **55** (1962), 286-290; E. S. Kennedy and W. R. Transue, "A Medieval Iterative Algorism," in *American Mathematical Monthly,* **63,** no. 2 (1956), 80-83; Ḥājjī Khalīfa, *Kashf al-Ẓunūn,* S. Yaltkaya, ed., 2 vols. (Istanbul, 1941-1943); E. Kramer, *The Main Stream of Mathematics* (New York, 1951); Ibn al-Nadīm, *Fihrist,* Flügel, ed., I (1871); N. Nadir, "Abūl-Wāfā' on the Solar Altitude," in *Mathematics Teacher,* **53** (1960), 460-463; C. A. Nallino, *Al-Battānī Opus astronomicum,* 3 vols. (Brera, 1899-1907), see vols. I and III; O. Neugebauer, "The Transmission of Planetary Theories in Ancient and Medieval Astronomy," in *Scripta mathematica,* **22** (1956); "Studies in Byzantine Astronomical Terminology," in *Transactions of the American Philosophical Society,* **50** (1960); "The Astronomical Tables of Al-Khwārizmī," in *Hist. Filos. Skrifter. Danske Videnskabernes Selskab,* **4,** no. 2 (1962); and "Thâbit ben Qurra 'On the Solar Year' and 'On the Motion of the Eighth Sphere,'" in *Transactions of the American Philosophical Society,* **106** (1962), 264-299; Ibn al-Qifṭī, *Ta'rīkh al ḥukamā',* Lippert, ed. (Berlin, 1903); G. Sarton, *Introduction to the History of Science,* I (Baltimore, 1927), 545, 550, 565, 667; A. Sayili, "Habeş el Hasib'in 'El Dimişki' adiyla Maruf Zîci'nin Mukaddemesi," in *Ankara üniversitesi dil ve tarih-coğrafya fakültesi dergisi,* **13** (1955), 133-151; C. Schoy, "Beiträge zur arabischen Trigonometrie," in *Isis,* **5** (1923), 364-399; D. E. Smith, *History of Mathematics,* II (London, 1925); and H. Suter, *Die Mathematiker und Astronomen der Araber und ihre Werke* (Leipzig, 1900).

S. TEKELI

HACHETTE, JEAN NICOLAS PIERRE (*b.* Mézières, Ardennes, France, 6 May 1769; *d.* Paris, France, 16 January 1834)

The son of Jean Pierre Hachette, a bookseller, and Marie Adrienne Gilson, Hachette studied first at the *collège* of Charleville. He also attended the elementary technical courses organized at the École Royale du Génie of Mézières, where he favorably impressed Monge, Clouet, and C. Ferry. Beginning in 1788, after having completed his education at the University of Rheims (1785-1787), he was draftsman and technician at the École Royale du Génie of Mézières and assisted Ferry in teaching descriptive geometry, which Monge had introduced in this school. Following a competitive examination he was appointed professor of hydrography at Collioure and Port Vendres in 1792. The following year he returned to Mézières to teach mathematics, replacing Ferry, who had been elected a deputy to the Convention. A fervent revolutionary, Hachette was active in the political life of his native city, and at the École du Génie he sought rapid training of officers qualified for the revolutionary army and to remove teachers and students whose patriotism seemed doubtful to him.

Summoned to Paris by the Committee of Public Safety in 1794, Hachette carried out various technological and industrial assignments (military applications of balloons, manufacture of weapons, and so on) with Guyton de Morveau and Monge. He participated at the same time in the discussions concerning the reorganization of higher scientific and technical education. At the time of the creation of the École Polytechnique in November 1794—under the name École Centrale des Travaux Publics—Hachette took an active part in preparing the future instructors and then in the teaching of descriptive geometry, as assistant professor (1794) and later as full professor (1799) until April 1816.

Besides this course at the École Polytechnique, Hachette taught descriptive geometry at the short-lived École Normale de l'An III (from January to May 1795, as Monge's assistant) and then, from 1810, as assistant professor, at the Paris Faculty of Sciences and at the newly reestablished École Normale. In addition he taught at various schools that prepared students for the École Polytechnique and at the École des Pages, created by Napoleon in 1805. Through these various posts Hachette became one of the chief popularizers of the new methods that Monge had introduced in the various branches of geometry. An intimate friend and devoted collaborator of Monge—and editor of several of his works—Hachette shared his faith in the great value of science and technology as an element of social progress and in the importance of the École Polytechnique's role in this regard.

Having dedicated himself to the organization and launching of the École Polytechnique in 1794 and 1795, Hachette continued for more than twenty years to take an active interest both in its general orientation—he was several times a member of its Conseil de Perfectionnement—and in the life, work, and future of its students. Many of them were grateful to him for having guided their first research projects and for having kept in touch with them after graduation. Through his influence and contact with former students Hachette helped to raise the prestige of the École Polytechnique, inculcating in its best students a passion for scientific research, both pure and applied. In order to join this effort to the diffusion of his views, he was an editor of the *Journal de l'École polytechnique* and, in addition, created and directed an extremely valuable organ for the presentation of information and for the exchange of ideas, *Correspondance sur l'École polytechnique* (1804–1816), which contained the first works of some of the leading French scientists of the first half of the nineteenth century: Poisson, Fresnel, Cauchy, Malus, Brianchon, Chasles, and Lamé, among others.

In view of this great activity, Hachette was extremely pained when, in September 1816, the Restoration government excluded him from the École Polytechnique at the time of its reorganization. This political rancor manifested itself again in December 1823, when Louis XVIII refused to confirm his election to the mechanics section of the Académie des Sciences. (He was not elected to that body until October 1831, under the reign of Louis Philippe.) Yet, except at Mézières in 1793, Hachette does not seem to have played a notable role in politics, although he did remain faithful to the great ideas of the Revolution.

His exclusion from the École Polytechnique did not prevent Hachette from completing a series of pedagogical works for its students. In fact, it permitted him to concern himself more actively with the rise of new industrial and agricultural techniques. He was a member of the Société d'Encouragement à l'Industrie Nationale, of the Société Royale et Centrale d'Agriculture, and of the Comité Consultatif des Arts et Manufactures. This activity made concrete earlier preoccupations: his posts at the École Royale du Génie of Mézières and at the École Polytechnique, his work during 1794, and the influence of Monge had made him familiar with the problem of the relationships between technology and the mathematical and physical sciences.

By his marriage in 1810 to Jeanne Maugras, the daughter of a surgeon, Hachette had a son, Amédée Barthélémy, who became chief engineer of the Ministère des Ponts et Chaussées, and a daughter, who married the chemist J. J. Ebelmen, later director of the Sèvres porcelain factory.

Despite the internal unity of Hachette's scientific and technical work, the latter can be divided into three major parts: geometry, pure and applied mechanics (including the theory of machines), and physics (electricity, magnetism, optics, and the study of instruments).

Hachette collaborated with Monge in the writing of an exposition of three-dimensional analytic geometry that dealt especially with changes of coordinates and with the theory of second-degree surfaces (*Journal de l'École polytechnique,* **11** [1802], 143–169), a more complete version of which appeared in book form several years later as *Application de l'algèbre à la géométrie* (Paris, 1805). Hachette later drew from this work an analytic theory of second-degree surfaces (1813, 1817) enriched by the progress made in the meantime.

In pure and descriptive geometry Hachette disseminated and continued Monge's work, developing effective procedures for solving various problems and studying diverse properties of space curves and surfaces (tangents and tangent planes, elements of curvature, and so on) by the methods of synthetic geometry joined to perspective and projective geometry. The results he obtained heralded the development of projective geometry and modern geometry in the nineteenth century.

In physics Hachette was especially interested in optics, electricity, magnetism, and the theory of optical instruments. Several of his articles and his *Programme* of 1809 show the influence of Monge, Guyton de Morveau, and Oersted.

In the courses on the theory of machines that he gave at the École Polytechnique beginning in 1806, in the *Programme,* and in the *Traité* that he published in 1808 and 1811, Hachette developed Monge's ideas on the distinction between the motor, the mechanisms of transmission and their movements, and the classification of transmission mechanisms (or elementary machines) according to the nature of the transformations of movements that they produce. The *Traité,* which includes important advances in applied mechanics and detailed studies of many types of machines, exerted a great influence on the beginnings of the theory of machines. Hachette was also interested in applied hydrodynamics and in steam engines and their history.

Although not a scientist of the first rank, Hachette nevertheless contributed to the progress of French science at the beginning of the nineteenth century by his efforts to increase the prestige of the École Polytechnique and by making Monge's work widely known, especially in descriptive and analytic geometry and in the theory of machines.

BIBLIOGRAPHY

I. ORIGINAL WORKS. Besides about 100 memoirs, articles, and notes—a list of which is given in *Correspondance sur l'École polytechnique,* III, 421, and in Royal Society, *Catalogue of Scientific Papers,* III, 106–109—Hachette edited the three vols. of the *Correspondance sur l'École polytechnique* (Paris, 1804–1816) and published the following works: (1) *Application de l'algèbre à la géométrie* (Paris, 1805; reiss. 1807), written with Gaspard Monge, reiss. as *Traité des surfaces du second degré* (1813) and as *Éléments de géométrie à trois dimensions. Partie algébrique* (1817).

(2) *Programme d'un cours élémentaire sur les machines* (Paris, 1808), pub. with P. L. Lanz and A. de Bétancourt, *Essai sur la composition des machines,* and developed in *Traité élémentaire des machines* . . . (Paris, 1811; 4th ed., 1828).

(3) *Programme d'un cours de physique* . . . (Paris, 1809).

(4) *Supplément à la Géométrie descriptive* (Paris, 1811), *Cours de géométrie descriptive* (Paris, 1817), a collection of diagrams, and *Second supplément à la Géométrie descriptive* (Paris, 1818); the various elements of these works reappeared either in *Éléments de géométrie à trois dimensions, Partie synthétique* (Paris, 1817) or in *Traité de géométrie descriptive* (Paris, 1822; 2nd ed., 1828).

(5) *Histoire des machines à vapeur* . . . (Paris, 1830).

In addition, Hachette edited the first separately printed ed. of Monge's *Géométrie descriptive* (Paris, 1799), the reissues of that work, and the new ed. of 1811, as well as the fifth and succeeding eds. of Monge's *Traité élémentaire de statique* (Paris, 1809 ff.), and the third and fourth eds. of his *Application de l'analyse à la géométrie* (1807, 1809). In addition Hachette edited Auguste Comte's French trans. of John Leslie, *Elements of Geometry, Geometrical Analysis, and Trigonometry,* 2nd ed. (London, 1811), as *Analyse géométrique* (Paris, 1818) and published the French trans. of Thomas Young, *A Course of Lectures on Natural Philosophy and the Mechanical Arts,* 2 vols. (London, 1807), as *Précis de mécanique et de la science des machines* (Paris, 1829).

II. SECONDARY LITERATURE. Hachette's life and works were the subject of the following accounts (in chronological order), some of which contain quite serious errors (e.g., date of birth, participation in the Egyptian expedition): F. Arago and S.-D. Poisson, *Funérailles de M. Hachette* (Paris, 1834); A. F. Silvestre, *Discours prononcé sur la tombe de M. Hachette* (Paris, 1834); C. Dupin and A. Quételet, in *Annuaire de l'Académie royale de Bruxelles* for 1836 (1836), 71–77; V. Parisot, in Michaud, ed., *Biographie universelle,* LXVI (supp.), 339–341, also in new ed., XVIII (Paris, 1857), 314–315; L. Louvet, in F. Hoefer, ed., *Nouvelle biographie générale,* XXIII (Paris, 1861), cols. 26–29; Poggendorff, I, cols. 985–986; A. Hannedouche, *Les illustrations ardennaises* . . . (Sedan, 1880), pp. 81–82; L. Sagnet, in *Grande encyclopédie,* XIX (Paris, n.d.), 698–699; and N. Nielsen, *Géomètres français sous la Révolution* (Copenhagen, 1929), pp. 121–125.

RENÉ TATON

HADAMARD, JACQUES (*b.* Versailles, France, 8 December 1865; *d.* Paris, France, 17 October 1963)

Hadamard was the son of Amédée Hadamard, a Latin teacher in a noted Paris lycée; his mother, Claude-Marie Picard, was a distinguished piano teacher. After studying at the École Normale Supérieure from 1884 to 1888, he taught at the Lycée Buffon in Pàris from 1890 to 1893 and received his *docteur ès sciences* degree in 1892. Hadamard was a lecturer at the Faculté des Sciences of Bordeaux from 1893 to 1897, lecturer at the Sorbonne from 1897 to 1909, then professor at the Collège de France from 1909 to 1937, at the École Polytechnique from 1912 to 1937, and at the École Centrale des Arts et Manufactures from 1920 to 1937.

Elected a member of the Académie des Sciences in 1912, Hadamard was also an associate member of several foreign academies, including the National Academy of Sciences of the United States, the Royal Society of London, the Accademia dei Lincei, and the Soviet Academy of Sciences. In addition he held honorary doctorates from many foreign universities.

Hadamard's interest in pedagogy led him to write articles about concepts in elementary mathematics that are introduced in the upper classes of the lycée. His *Leçons de géométrie élémentaire* (1898, 1901) still delight secondary school instructors and gifted pupils. The extent of his grasp on all domains of advanced research in France and abroad was evident in his famous seminar at the Collège de France; no branch of mathematics was neglected. The world's most famous mathematicians came there to present their own findings or those related to their specialty. But it was always Hadamard who had the last word and the surest judgment concerning the significance or the potential of the research presented.

Hadamard's first important works were concerned with analytic functions, notably with the analytic continuation of a Taylor series. Although Karl Weierstrass and Charles Méray were the first to define the meaning that must be attributed to the domain of existence of the analytic continuation of a Taylor series, their reflections amounted to a theorem of existence and uniqueness. Before Hadamard, little was known about the nature and distribution of the singularities of the series in terms of the nature of its coefficients, which define the function a priori. His thesis (1892), preceded by several notes in the *Comptes rendus* of the Academy, is one of his most beautiful works. For the first time an ensemble concept was introduced into function theory. In fact the upper limit—made more precise, explained, and applied to the ensemble composed of the coefficients—permits the determination of the radius of convergence (or, rather, its inverse) of the Taylor series. Conditions affecting the coefficients enable one to characterize the singular points on the circle of convergence. Hadamard's famous theorem on lacunary series (*"lacunes à la Hadamard"*) admitting the circle of convergence as a cut, the theorems on polar singularities, the introduction of the concept of *"écart fini"* and of the "order" of a singular point, and the theorem on the composition of singularities (1898), have remained fundamental in function theory. The results have inspired generations of highly talented mathematicians, especially those working at the beginning of the twentieth century and in the years between the two world wars. His *La série de Taylor et son prolongement analytique* (1901) was the "Bible" of all who were fascinated by the subject.

The year 1892 was one of the most fertile in the history of the theory of functions of a complex variable; it also marked the publication of a work by Hadamard that established the connection between the decrease of the modulus of the coefficients of the Taylor series of an integral function and the genus of the function. This work (which received the Grand Prix of the Académie des Sciences) and the results of his thesis (especially those pertaining to polar singularities), applied to Riemann's ζ function, enabled Hadamard in 1896 to solve the ancient and famous problem concerning the distribution of the prime numbers. He demonstrated (in a less explicit form than is shown here but one easily reducible to it) that the function $\pi(x)$ designating the number of prime numbers less than x is asymptotically equal to $x/\log x$. This is certainly the most important result ever obtained in number theory. Charles de La Vallée-Poussin proved the theorem at the same time, but his demonstration is much less simple than Hadamard's. The total result seems to indicate—without, we believe, its ever having been mentioned in writing by Hadamard—that the research in his thesis and in his work on integral functions was implicitly directed toward the ultimate goal of indicating the properties of the function ζ, in order to derive from it the theorem on the prime numbers.

Returning to analytic functions, one should mention the 1896 theorem on the maximum modulus of an integral function (or of a holomorphic function in a disk). And, while remaining close to the essential principles of analytic functions but leaving aside those with a complex variable, one must emphasize Hadamard's introduction (1912, 1925) of the idea and of the problem of quasi analyticity, which consists in finding a relationship between the growth of the maxima of the moduli of the derivatives of a function on a segment and the fact of being determined in a unique way by the values that the function and its derivatives take at a point. It should be noted that it was Albert Holmgren's considerations relating to Augustin Cauchy's problem for the equation of heat that had led Hadamard to consider classes of infinitely differentiable functions, not necessarily analytic on a segment but nevertheless possessing the characteristic property of uniqueness on the segment. The idea of quasi analyticity plays a significant role in modern analysis.

It is important to emphasize a subject treated by Hadamard in which, avoiding analysis (under the circumstances, differential geometry) and replacing it with consideration of analysis situs or topology, he was able to display, in one of his most beautiful memoirs (1898), the philosophic character—referring to astronomical ideas—of the fundamental concept of "the problem correctly posed," although no concrete allusion to this term figured in it. This idea of the correctly posed problem played an essential part in Hadamard's later researches on equations with partial derivatives. The importance of analysis situs in the theory of differential equations was shown by Henri Poincaré, whom Hadamard admired greatly and to whose work he devoted several memoirs and monographs (1922, 1923, 1954).

The memoirs in question (1898) treat surfaces of negative curvature having a finite number of nappes extending to infinity. All analytic description is abandoned. On these surfaces the geodesics behave in three different ways: (1) they are closed or asymptotic to other such geodesics; (2) they extend to infinity on one of the nappes; (3) entire segments of these geodesics approach successively a series of closed geodesics, the length of these segments growing toward infinity. The striking thing is that the ensemble E of tangents to the geodesics passing through a point and remaining at a finite distance is perfect and never dense; and in each neighborhood of every geodesic whose tangent belongs to E (neighborhood of directions) there exists a geodesic which extends to infinity in an arbitrarily chosen nappe. In each of these neighborhoods there also exist geodesics of the third category. Hadamard states: "*Any change, however small, carried in the initial direction of a geodesic which remains at a finite distance is sufficient to produce any variation whatsoever in the final aspect of the curve,* the disturbed geodesic being able to take on any one of the forms enumerated above" (*Oeuvres,* p. 772).

But in a physics problem a slight modification in the circumstances at a certain moment ought to have little influence on the solution, since one never possesses conditions which are more than approximate. Hadamard concluded from this that the behavior of a trajectory might well depend on the arithmetic character of the constants of integration. One already sees here the genesis of the idea of the "problem correctly posed" which guided Hadamard in his researches on equations with partial derivatives. The problem of geodesics on the surfaces studied by Hadamard is not a correctly posed mechanics problem.

Hadamard fully set out the idea of the correctly posed problem for equations with partial derivatives in his excellent *Lectures on Cauchy's Problem in Linear Differential Equations* (1922; French ed., 1932). Thus, for Laplace's equation, Dirichlet's problem is a correctly posed problem; on the other hand, for an equation of the hyperbolic type, Cauchy's problem is the one which meets this criterion. These ideas have had a great influence on modern research because they have shown the necessity of introducing different types of neighborhoods and, in consequence, different species of continuity; these conceptions led to general topology and functional analysis. Also in the *Lectures* is the notion of the "elementary solution" which has so much in common with that of "distribution" (or "generalized function"). Also in connection with equations with partial derivatives, one should mention the concept of the "finite portion" of a divergent integral, which plays an essential role in the solution of Cauchy's problem.

Hadamard took a lively interest in Vito Volterra's functional calculus and suggested the term "functional" to replace Volterra's term "line function." Above all, in 1903 Hadamard was able to give a general expression for linear functionals defined for continuous functions on a segment. This was the ancestor of Friedrich Riesz's fundamental formula.

Few branches of mathematics were uninfluenced by the creative genius of Hadamard. He especially influenced hydrodynamics, mechanics, probability theory, and even logic.

BIBLIOGRAPHY

Hadamard's writings were collected as *Oeuvres de Jacques Hadamard,* 4 vols. (Paris, 1968). The years within parentheses in the text will enable the reader to find, in the bibliography of the *Oeuvres,* any *mémoire* that interests him.

On Hadamard or his work, see Mary L. Cartwright, "Jacques Hadamard," in *Biographical Memoirs of Fellows of the Royal Society,* **2** (Nov. 1965); P. Lévy, S. Mandelbrojt, B. Malgrange, and P. Malliavin, *La vie et l'oeuvre de Jacques Hadamard,* no. 16 in the series L'Enseignement Mathématique (Geneva, 1967); and S. Mandelbrojt and L. Schwartz, "Jacques Hadamard," in *Bulletin of the American Mathematical* Society, **71** (1965).

S. MANDELBROJT

HALLEY, EDMOND (*b.* London, England, 29 October 1656[?]; *d.* Greenwich, England, 14 January 1743)

Halley was the eldest son of Edmond Halley, a prosperous landowner, salter, and soapmaker of the City of London. There is doubt about when he was born, and the date given is that accepted by Halley himself. Although his father suffered some loss of property in the Great Fire of London in 1666, he remained a rich man and spent liberally on his son's education, arranging for him to be tutored at home before sending him to St. Paul's School and then, at the age of seventeen, to Queen's College, Oxford. Young Halley showed an early interest in astronomy and took to Oxford a valuable collection of astronomical instruments purchased by his father. Halley's mother died in 1672, the year before he went to Oxford; and after his father's disastrous second marriage ten years later, financial support became rather more restricted. Nevertheless, everything points to Halley's having private means, for although he married Mary Tooke, daughter of an auditor of the Exchequer, in 1682 and thus accepted wider financial liabilities, he was able to pay for the publication of Newton's *Principia* four years later. Halley and his wife had three children: Katherine and Margaret, born probably in 1688, and a son, Edmond, born in 1698. The daughters survived their father but young Edmond, a naval surgeon, predeceased his father by one year; Halley's wife died five years earlier, in 1736. Halley seems to have enjoyed life and to have possessed a lively sense of humor; religiously he was a freethinker and did not consider that the Bible should be taken literally throughout. Indeed, when he was thirty-five, he was considered for the Savilian professorship of astronomy at Oxford, but the appointment went to David Gregory.

A man of great natural diplomacy, at twenty-two Halley dedicated a planisphere of the southern hemisphere stars to Charles II and obtained a royal mandamus for his M.A. degree at Oxford, although he had not resided there for the statutory period. A year later, with the blessing of the Royal Society, of which he had been elected a fellow in 1678, Halley visited Johannes Hevelius at Danzig and, in spite of a forty-five-year difference in age, was able to pacify the older astronomer, who had received severe criticisms about his use of open instead of telescopic sights for the measurement of celestial positions. Again, when Newton was writing the *Principia,* it was Halley who contributed important editorial aid and persuaded him to continue, despite an argument with Robert Hooke about priority. In 1698, when Peter the Great visited Deptford to study British shipbuilding, Halley was his frequent guest, discussing with him all manner of scientific questions; perhaps it was this kind of success that led Queen Anne, in 1702 and 1703, to send him on diplomatic missions to Europe to advise on the fortification of seaports, a subject on which he had already shown himself adept by providing intelligence reports on French port fortifications while surveying the English channel in 1701.

Halley's interests were wide, even for a seventeenth-century savant. He showed a lively concern with archaeology, publishing in 1691 a paper on the date and place of Julius Caesar's first landing in Britain, using evidence from an eclipse of the moon and critically analyzing other accounts; in 1695 he published one on the ancient Syrian city of Palmyra, the ruins of which had been described by English merchants a few years previously. The latter paper aroused considerable interest and stimulated British antiquaries in the eighteenth century to make an exhaustive study. When he was elected to assist the honorary secretaries of the Royal Society in 1685—a paid post that obliged him to resign his fellowship—he was able to broaden his interests further by an extensive correspondence. Halley held this post for fourteen years, during which time he discussed microscope observations by letter with Anton van Leeuwenhoek and, with others, matters that ranged from medical abnormalities and general biology to questions of geology, geography, physics, and engineering, as well as his own more familiar subjects of astronomy and mathematics.

When he became deputy controller of the mint at Chester in 1696, during the country's recoinage, Halley retained his Royal Society office and reported everything of archaeological and scientific interest in the area. From 1685 to 1693 he also edited the *Philosophical Transactions of the Royal Society* with outstanding competence at a formative time in the journal's development. Halley was also fortunate in possessing great practical sense as well as intellectual ability, and he carried out many experiments in diving, designing a diving bell and a diver's helmet that were much in advance of anything available. Reports on the colors of sunlight that he observed at various depths were sent to Newton, who incorporated them in his *Opticks.* Halley also formed a public company for exploiting the bell and helmet by using them for salvaging wrecks; its shares were quoted between 1692 and 1696.

Halley's best-known scientific achievement was a scheme for computing the motion of comets and establishing their periodicity in elliptical orbits. Although he took a particular interest in the bright naked-eye comet of 1680, it was only in 1695, after the publication of Newton's *Principia,* that he was able to begin an intensive study of the movements of comets. The difficulty in determining cometary paths arose because a comet could be seen for only a short time and, in consequence, it was possible to fit a series of curves through the observed positions. A straight line had been favored for a long time, but by the mid-seventeenth century it was generally accepted that the path must be an ellipse, a parabola, or a hyperbola. Newton preferred the parabola, but Halley decided to consider in detail the possibility of an ellipse.

Utilizing this hypothesis that cometary paths are nearly parabolic, he made a host of computations that led him to consider that the bright comets of 1531, 1607, and 1682 were the same object, making a periodic appearance approximately every seventy-five years. Later he also identified this object with the bright comets of 1305, 1380, and 1456. Halley next set about calculating its return and, allowing for perturbations by the planet Jupiter, announced that it should reappear in December 1758. The comet was in fact observed on 25 December 1758, arriving some days later than Halley's calculations had indicated, but in that part of the sky he had predicted. He also believed that the bright comet of 1680 was periodic, taking 575 years to complete an orbit, but in this he was mistaken. Halley's cometary views were published in 1705 in the *Philosophical Transactions,* and separately at Oxford in the same year in Latin and at London in English with the title *A Synopsis of the Astronomy of Comets.* Although this work aroused the interest of astronomers, it was not until the 1682 comet reappeared as predicted in 1758 that the whole intellectual world of western Europe took notice. By then Halley had been dead fifteen years; but his hope that posterity would acknowledge that this return "was first discovered by an Englishman" was not misplaced, and the object was named "Halley's comet." This successful prediction acted as a strong independent confirmation of Newtonian gravitation, and it is often said, but without direct evidence, to have helped dissipate the superstitious dread attached to cometary appearances.

Halley's astronomical contributions were not confined to comets, and he made notable advances in the determination of the distance of the sun, in positional and navigational astronomy, and in general stellar astronomy. Determination of the distance of the sun from the earth was crucial, since a correct evaluation was necessary before the size of the planetary system or the distances of the stars could be determined as direct values. Halley proposed evaluating the distance by observing the transit of Venus across the sun, an idea first sketched by James Gregory in 1663. Halley first assessed the practicability of the idea when he observed and timed a transit of Mercury in 1677. By recording the local time at which Mercury appeared to enter the sun's disk and the time at which it left, and then comparing his results with those made at an observing station in a different latitude, the distance of Mercury was obtained. Using Johann Kepler's third law of planetary motion, the distance from the earth to the sun could be found.

Halley appreciated that greater precision could be obtained by observing a transit of Venus, since it lies nearly twice as close to the earth as Mercury and thus the same percentage of error in timing would result in smaller errors in distance determination. Transits of Venus are rare, and the next were to occur in 1761 and 1769, by which time he would doubtless be dead. Nevertheless, Halley worked out methods of observation and subsequent calculation in considerable detail, publishing his results in the *Philosophical Transactions* for 1691, 1694, and, most fully, 1716. Joseph Delisle, who planned to organize expeditions to observe the 1761 transit, came to London in 1724 and discussed the subject with him; and it was Delisle's arrangements for European observations that at last stimulated British astronomers to take action in June 1760, twelve months before the transit. Delisle had devised a method that was a slight modification of what Halley had proposed and, in June 1761, a total of sixty-two observing stations were in operation. For the 1769 transit a total of sixty-three stations sent in observations and a value of 95 million miles was obtained for the sun's distance, a figure that further analysis subsequently reduced to 93 million. This compares favorably with the present figure of 92.87 million miles, but even 95 million represented a great achievement in the mid-eighteenth century.

Halley began positional astronomy assisting Flamsteed in 1675. He broke this connection when he continued on his own, leaving Oxford in 1676 for the island of St. Helena, off the west coast of Africa at a latitude of sixteen degrees south. Here he cataloged the stars of the southern hemisphere and, incidentally, discovered a star cluster in Centaurus (ω Centauri). He compiled his results in *Catalogus stellarum Australium . . .*, which was published late in 1678 at London; a French translation by Augustin Royer appeared at Paris early in 1679. In addition Halley drew up a planisphere, a copy of which was presented in 1678 to the king. The Royal Society received both catalog and planisphere, and it was primarily on the strength of these that he was elected a fellow.

Halley's other positional work was carried out at Greenwich after he was appointed astronomer royal in 1720, succeeding John Flamsteed. Here he found no instruments, since those used by Flamsteed had been removed, but he immediately obtained financial aid from the government. He established the first transit instrument to be put to regular use and ordered a large mural quadrant that was set up in 1724. He then observed the planets and, in particular, studied the motion of the moon. Halley's observing program for the latter was as bold as it was ambitious, for although he was aged sixty-four when appointed astronomer royal, he set about planning observations to cover a complete saros of eighteen years, after which the relative positions of the sun and moon would be repeated with respect to the nodes of the lunar orbit. He adopted this program because he was convinced, correctly, that once the moon's orbit was really known precisely, the problem of determining longitude at sea would be solved.

Flamsteed had made excellent measurements of star positions and some of the moon, so Halley concentrated on completing a set of lunar observations and, surprisingly enough, was able to finish his self-imposed task. By 1731 he was already in a position to publish a method of using lunar observations for determining longitude at sea that gave an error of no more than sixty-nine miles at the equator, a result that showed a real improvement over previous methods and augured well for even greater precision. Halley's observations were later criticized for their lack of precision; but even if they were not all they might have been, he certainly established the viability of the "method of lunars" as a solution of the longitude problem. It is worth noting, too, that while Halley was astronomer royal he was visited by John Harrison, who explained his ideas for an accurate timepiece. On Halley's personal recommendation, the instrument maker George Graham lent Harrison money to enable him to make a clock for submission to the Board of Longitude and thus develop what ultimately was to prove another successful solution.

Halley's achievements in stellar astronomy were of considerable significance, although they were not as fully appreciated in his day as might have been expected. In 1715 he published a paper on novae, listing those previously observed, making comments, and drawing parallels with long-period variables such as *o* Ceti (Mira), which is sometimes visible to the naked eye and sometimes invisible. In the same year Halley also made known his thoughts on nebulae. A few had been detected with the naked eye but the number had increased after the telescope came into use astronomically. Without a telescope they often looked like stars; with a telescope they were clearly seen to be something different. Halley boldly suggested that they were composed of material spread over vast expanses of space, "perhaps not less than our whole Solar System," and were visible because each shone with its own light, which was due not to any central star but to the "lucid Medium's" behavior. In this explanation Halley anticipated some aspects of the later work of William Herschel and William Huggins.

Halley also studied the question of the size of the universe and the number of stars it contained. The problem was much discussed just then, even by Newton, although he had also stated that the universe was infinite—otherwise gravity would attract all matter to the center. Halley's approach was an observational one, and in 1720 he concluded that since every increase in telescopic power had shown the existence of stars fainter than any hitherto observed, it seemed likely that the universe was to be taken as "actually infinite." There was a physical argument, too, for Halley considered the effects of gravitation on material spread out in a finite part of an infinite space and came to a conclusion similar to Newton's.

One contemporary criticism (revived a few years later by Jean de Chésaux and again in 1823 by H. W. M. Olbers) stated that if the number of stars were infinite, the sky should be bright, not dark, at night: Halley believed that he had resolved this paradox. He calculated that if all the stars were as distant from each other as the nearest (to earth) was from the sun, then, in spite of an increase in numbers, they would occupy ever smaller areas of the sky, so that, at very large distances, their diminished brightness would render them too dim to observe. As a corollary, he pointed out that even when observed with the largest telescopes some stars were so dim that it was to be expected that there were others whose light did not reach us.

There was a fallacy in Halley's argument, for he seems to have confused linear and angular dimensions: star disks do become smaller with greater distance, but the solid angle subtended by the heavens does not. Nevertheless, it was a carefully reasoned attempt to analyze an important problem that was to exercise astronomers for many generations. In a subsequent paper Halley discussed the number of stars to be expected in a given volume of space, assuming a given separation between them, and the way in which their brightness would diminish with distance. In this he anticipated what John Herschel was to discover and express precisely a century later: that stars of magnitude six were 100 times dimmer than those of magnitude one. Again Halley worked out figures that led him to conclude that the most distant stars would still be too dim to be detectable; but whatever the faults in all this work, his methods of attack were new and paved the way for later investigators.

Halley's most notable achievement in stellar astronomy was his discovery of stellar motion. From earliest times the stars had been regarded as fixed, and there seemed no reason to question this assumption. In 1710 Halley, who took a great interest in early astronomy, settled down to examine Ptolemy's writings and paid particular attention to his star catalog. It soon became evident that there were discrepancies, even allowing for precession and observational errors; and Halley rightly decided that the differences between Ptolemy's catalog and those compiled some 1,500 years later were so gross that the only rational explanation was to assume that the stars possessed individual motions. Halley was able to detect such proper motion only in the case of three bright stars—Arcturus, Procyon, and Sirius—but he correctly deduced that others which were dimmer, and could therefore be expected to be further away, possessed motions too small to be detected. It was not until a century and a half later that the study of proper motions could really be extended, but this was due to insufficient instrumental accuracy and not to disregard of Halley's opinion. The limitations of precise measurement in Halley's time also prevented the successful determination of even one stellar distance. Claims to have achieved this were made nonetheless, notably in 1714 by Jacques Cassini, who believed he had obtained an annual parallax for Sirius. In 1720 Halley analyzed this claim, showed that it could not be upheld, and made suggestions for observations which he thought might be successful.

Halley's interest in early astronomy was coupled with an equally great interest in early mathematics; and when he was appointed Savilian professor of geometry at Oxford in 1704, Henry Aldrich, dean of Christ Church, suggested to him that he prepare a translation of the *Conics* of Apollonius. Aldrich made a similar proposal to David Gregory, who held the Savilian chair of astronomy; Halley and Gregory worked on the subject together until the latter's death in 1708, after which Halley carried on alone. Two Latin editions of books V-VII (from Arabic) existed, but since these lacked book VIII Halley used Greek lemmas by Pappus to aid him in his reconstruction of the whole work. The *Conics* had attracted other mathematicians, but Halley aimed at and prepared a definitive edition. He also translated Apollonius' *Sectio rationis* (and restored his *Sectio spatii*) and tracts by Serenus of Antinoeia, publishing these in 1706 and 1710. Oxford University recognized the scholarly achievement by conferring a Doctor of Civil Laws degree, and it is worth noting that his *Conics,* although partially supplanted by J. L. Heiberg's translation of books I-IV (Leipzig, 1891–1893), is still used for the remaining books (V-VII). Halley followed up this work on early mathematics by translating the *Sphaerica* of Menelaus of Alexandria, an elegant translation that has won praise even today; it was published posthumously in 1758.

Halley's mathematical interests were not purely historical: between 1687 and 1720 he published seven papers on pure mathematics, ranging from higher geometry and construction and delimitation of the roots of equations to the computation of logarithms and trigonometric functions. He also published papers in which he applied mathematics to the calculation of trajectories in gunnery and the computation of the focal length of thick lenses. Halley was also one of the pioneers of social statistics, demonstrating in 1693 how mortality tables could be used as a basis for the calculation of annuities, a suggestion that was later pursued by Abraham de Moivre.

Halley was not only an astronomer and mathematician; he was also the founder of scientific geophysics. His first major essay in this field was an important paper on trade winds and monsoons (1686) in which he specified solar heating as their cause, although he was aware that this was not a complete explanation and urged others to pursue the matter. To aid them he produced a meteorological chart of the winds, the first provision of data in such a form, in which he depicted the winds by short broken lines, each dash having a thick front and a pointed tail to indicate direction. He also studied tidal phenomena, in 1684 analyzing information received at the Royal Society about tides at Tonkin; his work on tides culminated in his survey of the English Channel in 1701.

Halley's most significant geophysical contribution was his theory of terrestrial magnetism, on which he published two important papers (1683, 1692); in both he developed his own theory, the second paper providing a physical basis for the proposals made in the first. Halley's suggestion was that the earth possessed four magnetic poles, one pair situated at the ends of the axis of an outer magnetic shell and the other at the extremities of the axis of an inner magnetic core. The shell and core had slightly different periods of diurnal rotation to account for observed variations. He also postulated that the space between core and shell was filled with an effluvium—a favorite theoretical device of the seventeenth century—and in 1716 used it as a basis for his suggestion that the aurora was a luminous effluvium that escaped from the earth and that its motion was governed by the terrestrial magnetic field.

Between 1698 and 1700 Halley was commissioned as a naval captain and, in spite of a mutiny on board, took the small ship *Paramore* across the Atlantic, reaching as far as fifty-two degrees south latitude and the same latitude north. He charted magnetic variation in the hope of using it as a means of determining longitude at sea; but although it proved unsatisfactory for this purpose, his chart, published in different editions in 1701, 1702, and 1703, was significant because it was the first to adopt isogonic lines (called "Halleyan lines" by contemporaries) to connect points of equal magnetic variation.

Halley's scientific attitude toward terrestrial physics led him to take an independent and novel approach to the question of the age of the earth. From investigations he made in 1693 on the rate of evaporation of water, he concluded that the salinity of lakes and oceans must gradually be increasing and suggested that if the rate of increase could be determined, it should be possible to obtain factual evidence about the earth's age. From approximate results Halley suggested that the figure derived from biblical genealogies was too low and that an alternative view, that the earth was eternal, was also incorrect. He further suggested a physical explanation for the Flood, postulating a very close approach of a comet to the earth. Although not now accepted, this was an interesting scientific explanation for a biblical event. These views did not commend him to some powerful ecclesiastics of his day.

Throughout much of his life Halley had to suffer the active disapproval of John Flamsteed, the first astronomer royal, who first encouraged and then turned against him. In 1712, at Newton's request, Halley prepared an edition of Flamsteed's observations using materials deposited at the Royal Society. Their publication as *Historia coelestis* . . . infuriated Flamsteed.

Halley was also involved in the Newton-Leibniz controversy to the extent of lending his name to the report of the supposed committee of the Royal Society which in effect sanctioned Newton's own version of the affair.

Recognition came to Halley early in life, with his M.A. and election to the Royal Society; but after that there was a long pause due, to a great extent, to Flamsteed. Nevertheless, he obtained the Savilian chair of geometry at Oxford in 1704, was appointed astronomer royal in 1720, and was elected a foreign member of the Académie des Sciences at Paris in 1729. At his death in 1743 Halley seems to have been widely mourned, for he was a friendly as well as a famous man and always ready to offer support to young astronomers.

BIBLIOGRAPHY

I. Original Works. For a complete list of Halley's publications, see E. F. MacPike, *Correspondence and Papers of Edmond Halley* (Oxford, 1932), pp. 272–278 (but note that the second item under the year 1700 should be dated 1710). Halley's most important publications in astronomy were "A Direct and Geometrical Method of Finding the Aphelia and Eccentricities of the Planets," in *Philosophical Transactions,* **11** (1676), 683–686; *Catalogus stellarum Australium* . . . (London, 1678); *Astronomiae cometicae synopsis* (Oxford, 1705), also in *Philosophical Transactions of the Royal Society,* **24** (1704–1705), 1882–1889; "An Account of Several Nebulae . . .," *ibid.,* **29** (1714–1716), 354–356; "Considerations of the Change of the Latitudes of Some of the Principal Fixt Stars," *ibid.,* 454–464; "Methodus singularis qua Solis Parallaxis . . . Veneris intra Solem conspiciendæ . . .," *ibid.,* **30** (1717–1719), 736–738; "Of the Infinity of the Sphere of Fix'd Stars," *ibid.,* **31** (1720–1721), 22–24; "Of the Number, Order and Light of the Fix'd Stars," *ibid.,* 24–26; "A Proposal . . . for Finding the Longitude at Sea Within a Degree . . .," *ibid.,* **37** (1731–1732), 185–195; and *Edmundi Halleii astronomi dum viveret regii tabulae astronomicae* . . ., John Bevis, ed. (London, 1749).

His main geophysical writings were "A Theory of the Variation of the Magnetical Compass," in *Philosophical Transactions of the Royal Society,* **13** (1683), 208–221; "An Historical Account of the Trade Winds, and Monsoons . . .," *ibid.,* **16** (1686–1687), 153–168; "An Account of the Cause of the Change in the Variation of the Magnetical Needle; With an Hypothesis of the Structure of the Internal Parts of the Earth," *ibid.,* **17** (1691–1693), 563–578; and "A Short Account of the . . . Saltness of the Ocean . . . With a Proposal . . . to Discover the Age of the World," *ibid.,* **29** (1714–1716), 296–300.

On mathematics and vital statistics they are "An Estimate of the Degrees of the Mortality of Mankind . . .," in *Philosophical Transactions of the Royal Society,* **17** (1693), 596–610, 654–656; "Methodus . . . inveniendi radices aequationum . . .," *ibid.,* **18** (1694), 136–148; *Apollonii Pergaei de sectione rationis* . . . (Oxford, 1706); *Apollonii conicorum libri III, posteriores* . . . (Oxford, 1710); *Apollonii Pergaei conicorum libri octo et Sereni Antissensis de sectione cylindri & coni* . . . (Oxford, 1710); and *Menelai sphaericorum* . . . (Oxford, 1758). Other important papers on mathematics which appeared in the *Philosophical Transactions* are in **16,** 335–343, 387–402, 556–558; and **19,** 58–67, 125–128, 202–214.

His main physics writing is "An Instance of . . . Modern Algebra, in . . . Finding the Foci of Optick Glasses Universally," in *Philosophical Transactions of the Royal Society,* **17** (1691–1693), 960–969. His archaeological paper on Palmyra is in *Philosophical Transactions,* **19** (1695–1697), 160–175.

II. Secondary Literature. Besides MacPike's book mentioned above, there are two biographies: A. Armitage, *Edmond Halley* (London, 1966); and C. A. Ronan, *Edmond Halley—Genius in Eclipse* (New York, 1969; London, 1970).

See also the following articles: E. Bullard, "Edmond Halley (1656–1741)," in *Endeavour* (Oct. 1956), pp. 189–199; and G. L. Huxley, "The Mathematical Work of Edmond Halley," in *Scripta Mathematica,* **24** (1959), 265–273.

Colin A. Ronan

HALPHEN, GEORGES-HENRI (*b.* Rouen, France, 30 October 1844; *d.* Versailles [?], France, 23 May 1889)

Halphen's mathematical reputation rests primarily on his work in analytic geometry. Specifically, his principal interests were the study of singular points of algebraic plane curves, the study of characteristics of systems of conics and second-order surfaces, the enumeration and classification of algebraic space curves, the theory of differential invariants and their applications, and the theory of elliptic functions and their applications. His papers are marked by brilliance combined with dogged perseverance.

Halphen was raised in Paris, where his mother moved shortly after she was widowed in 1848. His early schooling was at the Lycée Saint-Louis, and he was admitted to the École Polytechnique in 1862. He served with great distinction in the Franco-Prussian War, and in 1872 he married the daughter of Henri Aron; she eventually bore him four sons and three daughters. Also in 1872 Halphen returned to the École Polytechnique, where he was appointed *répétiteur* and rose to *examinateur* in 1884. His doctorate in mathematics was awarded in 1878 upon the presentation of his thesis, *Sur les invariants différentiels.* In 1880 Halphen won the Ormoy Prize (Grand Prix des Sciences Mathématiques) of the Academy of Sciences in Paris for advances he had made in the theory of linear differential equations, and in 1882 he received the Steiner Prize from the Royal Academy of Sciences in Berlin for his work on algebraic space curves. He was elected to membership in the French Academy in 1886, an honor which he enjoyed for only three years before he died of what was called "overwork."

Halphen first came to the attention of the mathematical community in 1873, when he resolved Michel Chasles's conjecture: Given a family of conics depending on a parameter, how many of them will satisfy a given side condition? Chasles had found a formula for this, but his proof was faulty. Halphen showed that Chasles was essentially correct, but that restrictions on the kinds of singularities were necessary. Halphen's solution was ingenious: he transformed the given system of conics into one algebraic plane curve, and the side condition into another; his results were then obtained from the study of the two curves.

After solving Chasles's problem, Halphen went on to make significant contributions in the theory of algebraic plane curves, especially in the study of their singular points. He was the first to classify singular points and extended earlier work of Bernhard Riemann by giving a general formula for the genus of an algebraic plane curve. Then, considering curves in the same genus, he extended a theorem of Max Noether which proved that in any class there always exist curves with only ordinary singularities.

This work led Halphen to the subject of differential invariants. He had noticed in his earlier work that under projective (i.e., linear and one-to-one) transformations certain differential equations remained unchanged. He was able to characterize all such equations and presented the results in 1878 as his thesis. Henri Poincaré was so impressed that he said: ". . . the theory of differential invariants is to the theory of curvature as projective geometry is to elementary geometry" ("Notice sur Halphen," p. 154; also *Oeuvres,* I, xxxv). Later Halphen applied these results to the integration of linear differential equations, greatly extending the classes of these equations which could be solved. For the latter work he was awarded its prize for 1880 by the French Academy of Sciences.

Halphen's most significant original work was the paper which won the Steiner Prize. In it he made a complete classification of all algebraic space curves up to the twentieth degree. This problem is much more difficult than the corresponding one for algebraic plane curves. A plane curve of degree k can be considered to be a special case of the most general curve of degree k; thus the class and genus of the curve are known if the degree is known, perhaps modified by singularities. But for space curves there is no such thing as a most general curve of degree k (a space curve requires at least two equations) and so, in Halphen's words, ". . . one never knows any geometric entity which includes, as special cases, all space curves of given degree. One cannot, therefore, assert *a priori* for any property of space curves, no matter how general, that it will depend only on the degree" ("Sur quelques propriétés des courbes gauches algébriques," p. 69; also *Oeuvres,* I, 203). For example, the genus has no algebraic relation to the degree but instead satisfies certain inequalities.

Halphen's last work was a monumental treatise on elliptic functions. He intended that it consist of three volumes, but he died before he could finish the last. The aim of the work was to simplify the theory of elliptic functions to the point where they could be put to use by the nonspecialist without losing any of the essential points. In the first volume he realized this aim, proving everything he needed without recourse to more general function theory. In the process Halphen not only simplified the theory but also eliminated much of the very cumbersome notation then in use. The second volume is concerned principally with applications from mechanics, geometry, and differential equations. The problems solved are all difficult and are either new or show new insights. The third volume was to contain material on the theory of transformation and applications to number theory.

The amount and quality of Halphen's work is impressive, especially considering that his mathematically creative life covered only seventeen years. Why, then, is his name so little known? The answer lies partly in the fact that some of his work, the theory of differential invariants, is now only a special case of the more general Lie group theory and thus has lost its identity. But part of the answer is related to a larger question: Why is so much mathematics of even the recent past lost? In Halphen's case, he worked in analytic and differential geometry, a subject so unfashionable today as to be almost extinct. Perhaps with its inevitable revival, analytic geometry will restore Halphen to the eminence he earned.

BIBLIOGRAPHY

Halphen's writings are in *Oeuvres de Georges-Henri Halphen,* 4 vols. (Paris, 1916–1924), compiled for publication by C. Jordan, H. Poincaré, and É. Picard. Among them is "Sur quelques propriétés des courbes gauches algébriques," in *Bulletin de la Société mathématique de France,* **2** (1873–1874), 69–72. See also *Traité des fonctions elliptiques et de leurs applications,* 3 vols. (Paris, 1886–1891); the last vol. consists of fragments only.

Biographical material is in Henri Poincaré, "Notice sur Halphen," in *Journal de l'École polytechnique,* cahier 60 (1890), 137–161, repr. in *Oeuvres,* I, xvii–xliii.

MICHAEL BERNKOPF

HALSTED, GEORGE BRUCE (*b.* Newark, New Jersey, 23 November 1853; *d.* New York, N.Y., 16 March 1922)

Halsted's father, Oliver Spencer Halsted, Jr., was a distinguished lawyer; his mother, Adela Meeker, was the only daughter of a wealthy Charleston, South Carolina, family. Halsted was the fourth generation of his family to attend Princeton, where he received his A.B. in 1875 and his A.M. in 1878. During this period he also attended the Columbia School of Mines.

He received his Ph.D. from Johns Hopkins University in 1879, where he was the first student of J. J. Sylvester. He also studied in Berlin, where he arrived with a flattering letter from Sylvester introducing him to the distinguished Carl Borchardt, then editor of *Crelle's Journal.* From 1879 to 1881 Halsted was tutor at Princeton, and from 1881 to 1894 he was instructor there in postgraduate mathematics. His most productive period occurred from 1894 to 1903, when he held the chair of pure and applied mathematics at the University of Texas. His academic career continued at St. John's College, Annapolis, Maryland (1903); Kenyon College, Gambier, Ohio (1903–1906); and Colorado State College of Education, Greeley (1906–1914). Halsted was married to Margaret Swearingen; they had three sons.

In a period when American mathematics had few distinguished names, the eccentric and sometimes spectacular Halsted established himself as an internationally known scholar, creative teacher, and promoter and popularizer of mathematics. He was a member of and active participant in the major mathematical societies of the United States, England, Italy, Spain, France, Germany, and Russia. His activities penetrated deeply in three main fields: translations and commentaries on the works of Nikolai Lobachevski, János Bolyai, Girolamo Saccheri, and Henri Poincaré; studies in the foundations of geometry; and criticisms of the slipshod presentations of the mathematical textbooks of his day.

Upon his retirement in Greeley, Halsted wrote somewhat bitterly: "I am working as an electrician, as there is nothing [for me] in cultivating vacant lots" ("Princeton University Biographical Questionnaire"). His withdrawal was not complete, however, for his annotated translation of Saccheri's *Euclides vindicatus* was published in 1920; and at the time of his death he was working on a translation of Saccheri's *Logica demonstrativa* from what he believed to be the only extant copy.

BIBLIOGRAPHY

I. ORIGINAL WORKS. No complete bibliography of Halsted's publications has been published. The most extensive appears to be in Poggendorff, III, 578; IV, 573–574; and V, 490. In *American Mathematical Monthly* alone he published over fifty articles, of which twenty were biographical sketches. His main works are the following:

"Bibliography of Hyper-Space and Non-Euclidean Geometry," in *American Journal of Mathematics,* **1** (1878), 261–276, 384–385, and **2** (1879), 65–70; *Basis for a Dual Logic* (Baltimore, 1879), his doctoral diss.; *Mensuration. Metrical Geometry* (Boston, 1881), the unacknowledged source for W. Thomson's article "Mensuration" in the 9th ed. of *Encyclopaedia Britannica* and also the work in which his "prismoidal formula" first appeared (4th ed., 1889, p. 130)—Halsted was unduly proud of this contribution to mensuration; also presented in "Two-Term Prismoidal Formula," in *Scientiae baccalaureus,* **1** (1891), 169–178; and *Rational Geometry* (New York, 1904), an attempt to write an elementary geometry text based on David Hilbert's axioms which, after much criticism, was revised (1907) and later translated into French, German, and Japanese.

Halsted's translations include J. Bolyai, *The Science Absolute of Space,* trans. from Latin (Austin, Texas, 1896); H. Poincaré, *The Foundations of Science,* with a special pref. by Poincaré and an intro. by Josiah Royce (New York, 1913); N. Lobachevski, *The Theory of Parallels* (La Salle, Ill., 1914); and Girolamo Saccheri's *Euclides vindicatus,* also ed. by Halsted (Chicago, 1920), portions of which also appeared in *American Mathematical Monthly,* **1-5** (June 1894-Dec. 1898).

II. Secondary Literature. L. E. Dickson, "Biography. Dr. George Bruce Halsted," in *American Mathematical Monthly,* **1** (1894), 337-340, contains a good deal of the family history and some personal observations. See also A. M. Humphreys, "George Bruce Halsted," in *Science,* **56** (1921), 160-161; F. Cajori, "George Bruce Halsted," in *American Mathematical Monthly,* **29** (1922), 338-340; and H. Y. Benedict, "George Bruce Halsted," in *Alcalde,* **10** (1922), 1357-1359, a notice that is mainly anecdotal. "Princeton University Biographical Questionnaire," which was filled out by Halsted personally, contains details not available elsewhere.

Henry S. Tropp

HAMILTON, WILLIAM (*b.* Glasgow, Scotland, 8 March 1788; *d.* Edinburgh, Scotland, 6 May 1856)

Hamilton's father, William Hamilton, professor of astronomy at the University of Glasgow, died in 1790, leaving William to be raised by his mother, Elizabeth Hamilton. After receiving a degree from the University of Edinburgh in 1807, Hamilton went to Balliol College, Oxford, with a Snell Exhibition. He quickly acquired the reputation of being the most learned authority in Oxford on Aristotle, and the list of books that he submitted for his final examination in 1810 was unprecedented. He did not, however, receive a fellowship, primarily because of the unpopularity of Scots at Oxford. He returned therefore to Edinburgh to study and there became an advocate in 1813. Because he had little interest in his career in the law, he applied in 1821 for the chair of moral philosophy at Edinburgh vacated by the death of Thomas Brown. Hamilton was a Whig, and the Tory town council therefore chose his opponent, John Wilson. When in 1829 Macvey Napier became the editor of the *Edinburgh Review,* he persuaded Hamilton to write a series of articles for that journal. The articles, which appeared between 1829 and 1836, were the basis of his international reputation, a reputation that forced the town council to elect him in 1836 to the chair in logic and metaphysics, which he held until his death.

Hamilton's three most important articles for the *Edinburgh Review* were those on Cousin (1829), on perception (1830), and on logic (1833). In the first two, he revealed his unique philosophical position, a combination of the Kantian view that there is a limitation on all knowledge and the Scottish view that man has, in perception, a direct acquaintance with the external world.

The first paper deals with the possibility of human knowledge of the absolute. In it Hamilton argued against Cousin's view that man has immediate knowledge of the absolute and against Schelling's view that man can know the absolute by becoming identical with it. Hamilton tried to show that neither of these views is coherent and that there is something incoherent about the very notion of thought about the absolute. Hamilton's own position was close to Kant's, but he wanted to go further than Kant and say that the mind cannot use the absolute even as a regulative idea.

The second article is a defense of Reid's view, that the direct object of perception is external, against the attacks of Brown. Hamilton had little trouble in showing that Brown neither understood Reid's position nor could offer arguments that disproved either Reid's position or the position mistakenly attributed to him by Brown. Hamilton did, however, agree with Brown's claim that Reid was mistaken when he identified the direct object of acts of memory with some previously existing external object.

These metaphysical positions were developed further during the twenty years that Hamilton was professor at Edinburgh. Many of his mature opinions, as expressed in the appendixes to his edition of Reid's major works and to his own published lectures, modify what he wrote in these two articles; but he never really gave up these basic positions, which were extremely influential during his lifetime and still have some interest today. They are, however, far less important for the history of thought in general and for the history of science in particular than his work in logic.

Hamilton was one of the first in that series of British logicians—a series that included George Boole, Augustus De Morgan, and John Venn—who radically transformed logic and created the algebra of logic and mathematical logic. To be sure, Hamilton only helped begin this development, and given his dislike of mathematics, he probably would not have been very happy with its conclusion. Nevertheless, his place in it must be recognized.

The traditional, Aristotelian analysis of reasoning allowed for only four types of simple categorical propositions:

(A) All A are B.
(E) No A are B.

(I) Some A are B.
(O) Some A are not B.

Hamilton's first important insight was that logic would be more comprehensive and much simpler if it allowed for additional types of simple categorical propositions. In particular, Hamilton suggested that one treat the signs of quantity ("all," "some," "no") in the traditional propositions as modifiers of the subject term A and that one introduce additional signs of quantity as modifiers of the predicate term B. Hamilton called this innovation the quantification of the predicate. Other logicians before Hamilton had made the same suggestion, but Hamilton was the first to explore the implications of quantifying the predicate, of admitting eight simple categorical propositions:

(1) All A are all B.
(2) All A are some B (traditional A).
(3) Some A are all B.
(4) Some A are some B (traditional I).
(5) Any A is not any B (traditional E).
(6) Any A is not some B.
(7) Some A are not any B (traditional O).
(8) Some A are not some B.

The first important inference that Hamilton drew from this modification had to do with the analysis of simple categorical propositions. There were, according to the traditional, Aristotelian logic, two ways of analyzing a simple categorical proposition such as "All A are B": extensively, that is, as asserting that the extension of the term A is contained within the extension of the term B; or comprehensively, that is, as asserting that the comprehension of the term B is contained within the comprehension of the term A. In either case, the proposition expresses a whole-part relation. But the new Hamiltonian modification, because it distinguished (1) from (2), (3) from (4), (5) from (6), and (7) from (8), enables one to adopt a different analysis of these propositions. According to this new analysis, each of these propositions asserts or denies the existence of an identity-relation between the two classes denoted by the quantified terms. Thus, "All A are all B" asserts that the classes A and B are identical, while "Some A are not some B" asserts that there is a subset of the class A which is not identical with any subset of the class B. One result, therefore, of the quantification of the predicate is that simple categorical propositions become identity claims about classes. This is just the analysis of simple categorical propositions that Boole needed and used in formulating the algebra of logic.

Hamilton's work facilitated a considerably simplified analysis of the validity of reasoning. The traditional, Aristotelian analysis of mediate reasoning, for example, involved many concepts (such as the figure of a syllogism, major and minor terms) that were based on the distinction between the subject of a proposition and its predicate. This subject-predicate distinction had some significance when simple categorical propositions were understood as expressing asymmetrical whole-part relations. But given the new analysis, where these propositions are understood as expressing symmetrical identity relations, there is little point to a distinction between the subject and the predicate of a proposition. Further, if the subject-predicate distinction is dropped, then all of the traditional cumbersome machinery based on it should also be dropped. As a result, the complicated traditional rules for the validity of syllogistic reasoning disappear. One is then left, as Hamilton pointed out in his theory of the unfigured syllogism, with two simple rules for valid syllogisms: If $A = B$ and $B = C$, then $A = C$; and If $A = B$ and $B \neq C$, then $A \neq C$. Similarly, the traditional Aristotelian analysis of immediate reasoning, based upon the complicated distinctions between simple conversion, conversion *per accidens,* and contraposition, is replaceable by the simple rule that all eight propositions are simply convertible. This rule follows directly from the fact that all eight propositions are concerned with symmetrical identity relations.

New advances in a given science, besides simplifying the treatment of previously solved problems, usually enable one to solve problems that one could not previously handle. Hamilton's quantification of the predicate is no exception to this rule. The logician could now explain the validity of many inferences that resisted traditional analysis. The simplest example of this is the inference to the identity of classes A and C from premises asserting that they are both identical with some class B. Traditional analysis did not even recognize the existence of propositions asserting that two classes are identical; it could not, therefore, explain the validity of such an inference. Hamiltonian analysis, however, could do so by referring to the first of the two rules for the validity of all mediate reasoning.

Some of Hamilton's new ideas, such as his class-identity analysis of propositions, were incorporated into Boole's far more sophisticated system. This contribution to mathematical logic would in itself be sufficient to earn for Hamilton an important place in intellectual history, but his claim to recognition is strengthened by the significance of his innovations to the history of logic. As is well known, Kant and most other important eighteenth-century philosophers thought that nothing of importance had been done in formal logic since the time of Aristotle, primarily because of the completeness and perfection of the Aristotelian system. The only people who saw a future for logic were those who wanted to change logic from a formal analysis of the validity of reasoning to an epistemological and psychological analysis of the conditions for, and limits on, human knowledge. Hamilton, by showing that the Aristotelian analysis could be greatly improved and supplemented, changed the minds of many philosophers, logicians, and mathematicians and helped produce the interest in formal logic that was so necessary for the great advances of the nineteenth century.

Despite its great historical significance, Hamilton's quantification of the predicate has had little direct influence in more recent times. This is partly due to the fact that both it and the Boolean algebra of logic, which it so greatly influenced, have been superseded by Frege's far more powerful quantificational analysis—an analysis so different that Hamilton's theory has no relevance to it. It is, however, also due to a certain internal weakness in Hamilton's initial quantification of the predicate, which was pointed out by Hamilton's great adversary, Augustus De Morgan, during their long and acrimonious quarrels.

There really were two quarrels between Hamilton and De Morgan. The first had to do with Hamilton's charge that De Morgan had plagiarized some of Hamilton's basic ideas. In 1846 De Morgan sent a draft of one of his most important papers on logic to William Whewell, who was supposed to transmit it to the Cambridge Philosophical Society. De Morgan then received from Hamilton, in the form of a list of requirements for a prize essay set for Hamilton's students, a brief account of Hamilton's quantification of the predicate. At about this time, De Morgan asked Whewell to return the draft of his paper and then made some changes in it. Hamilton charged that the alterations were based on his communication to De Morgan. In his reply De Morgan claimed that he made the changes before he received the communication from Hamilton. Although it is not clear as to who was right about the date of the changes, it is clear that De Morgan did not plagiarize Hamilton's ideas. Even if De Morgan's ideas were suggested by Hamilton's communication, they are so different from Hamilton's that no one could consider them to be a plagiarism.

The second, far more important, quarrel was about the relative merits of their innovations in logic. This arose out of the first, since De Morgan was not content with pointing out the differences between the two systems. He also argued that Hamilton's innovations, unlike his own, were based on a defective list of basic propositions.

De Morgan first made this claim in an appendix to his book *Formal Logic* (1847). Although he offered several criticisms of Hamilton's list of eight basic categorical propositions, there was only one that was really serious—that Hamilton's first proposition is not a simple categorical proposition because it is equivalent to the joint assertion of the second and third propositions. Thus "All A are some B" and "Some A are all B" can both be true if, and only if, "All A are all B" is also true.

Hamilton was slow in responding to this argument, primarily because he had suffered an attack of paralysis in 1844 that made it very difficult for him to do any work. When, however, in 1852, he published a collection of his articles from the *Edinburgh Review*, he included in the book an appendix in which he argued that De Morgan's criticisms were based on a misunderstanding of the eight propositional forms. De Morgan thought that "some" meant "some, possibly all." If it did, then he would certainly be right in his claim that the first proposition is equivalent to the joint assertion of the second and third propositions. But Hamilton said that he had meant in his forms "some, and not all." Consequently, the conjunction of "All A are some B" and "Some A are all B" is inconsistent, and neither of these propositions can be true if "All A are all B" is true.

The controversy rested at this point until some years after Hamilton's death. Then, De Morgan renewed it in a series of letters in *Athenaeum* (1861–1862) and in his last article on the syllogism, in *Transactions of the Cambridge Philosophical Society* (1863). De Morgan began his new attack by casting doubt on the claim that Hamilton had meant "some, but not all." He did this by showing that much of what Hamilton had to say about the validity of particular inferences made sense only if we suppose that he meant "some, perhaps all." There is little doubt that De Morgan was right about this point. Yet De Morgan now had an even more crushing criticism of Hamilton's list of simple categorical propositions: Even if one grants, he said, that Hamilton meant "some, but not all," there is still something wrong with his list. After all, there are five, and only five, relations of the type discussed in categorical propositions that can hold between two classes: (1) the two classes are coextensive, (2) the first class is a proper subset of the second class, (3) the second class is a proper subset of the first class, (4) the two classes have some members in common but each has members that are not members of the other, and (5) the two classes have no members in common. Thus Hamilton's propositions 6–8 seem to be superfluous.

De Morgan's final critique clearly showed that

Hamilton had not exercised sufficient care in laying the foundations for his new analysis of the validity of reasoning. This was quickly recognized by most logicians; Charles Sanders Peirce, the great American logician, described De Morgan's 1863 paper as unanswerable. While there is no doubt that De Morgan's critique helped lessen the eventual influence of Hamilton's work, it should not prevent the recognition of both the intrinsic merit of Hamilton's work and its role in the development of mathematical logic in Great Britain during the nineteenth century.

BIBLIOGRAPHY

I. Original Works. Hamilton's main writings are important essays supplementary to *The Works of Thomas Reid* (Edinburgh, 1846); *Discussions on Philosophy and Literature and Education and University Reform* (Edinburgh, 1852); *Lectures on Metaphysics*, H. Mansel and J. Veitch, eds. (Edinburgh, 1859); and *Lectures on Logic*, H. Mansel and J. Veitch, eds. (Edinburgh, 1861).

II. Secondary Literature. On Hamilton and his work, see T. S. Baynes, *An Essay on the New Analytic of Logical Forms* (Edinburgh, 1850); S. A. Grave, *The Scottish Philosophy of Common Sense* (Oxford, 1960); L. Liard, *Les logiciens anglais contemporains* (Paris, 1890); J. S. Mill, *An Examination of Sir William Hamilton's Philosophy* (London, 1889); S. V. Radmussen, *The Philosophy of Sir William Hamilton* (Copenhagen, 1925); and J. Veitch, *Sir William Hamilton* (Edinburgh, 1869).

Baruch A. Brody

HAMILTON, WILLIAM ROWAN (*b.* Dublin, Ireland, 4 August 1805; *d.* Dunsink Observatory [near Dublin], 2 September 1865)

His father was Archibald Rowan Hamilton, a Dublin solicitor, whose most important client was the famous Irish patriot Archibald Hamilton Rowan. Both Hamilton and his father took one of their Christian names from Rowan, and the matter is further complicated by the fact that Rowan's real name was Hamilton as well. But there is no evidence of kinship.

The fourth of nine children, Hamilton was raised and educated from the age of three by his uncle James Hamilton, curate of Trim, who quickly recognized his fabulous precocity. By his fifth year he was proficient in Latin, Greek, and Hebrew; and during his ninth year his father boasted of his more recent mastery of Persian, Arabic, Sanskrit, Chaldee, Syriac, Hindustani, Malay, Marathi, Bengali, "and others."

Mathematics also interested Hamilton from an early age, but it was the more dramatic skill of rapid calculation that first attracted attention. In 1818 he competed unsuccessfully against Zerah Colburn, the American "calculating boy"; he met him again in 1820. At about this time he also began to read Newton's *Principia* and developed a strong interest in astronomy, spending much time observing through his own telescope. In 1822 he noticed an error in Laplace's *Mécanique céleste.* His criticism was shown by a friend to the astronomer royal of Ireland, the Reverend John Brinkley, who took an interest in Hamilton's progress and was later instrumental in getting Hamilton appointed as his successor at Dunsink Observatory.

Hamilton's enthusiasm for mathematics caught fire in 1822, and he began studying furiously. The result was a series of researches on properties of curves and surfaces that he sent to Brinkley. Among them was "Systems of Right Lines in a Plane," which contained the earliest hints of ideas that later were developed into his famous "Theory of Systems of Rays." On 31 May 1823 Hamilton announced to his cousin Arthur Hamilton that he had made a "very curious discovery" in optics,[1] and on 13 December 1824 he presented a paper on caustics at a meeting of the Royal Irish Academy with Brinkley presiding. The paper was referred to a committee which reported six months later that it was "of a nature so very abstract, and the formulae so general, as to require that the reasoning by which some of the conclusions have been obtained should be more fully developed. . . ."[2] Anyone who has struggled with Hamilton's papers can sympathize with the committee, but to Hamilton it was a discouraging outcome. He returned to his labors and expanded his paper on caustics into the "Theory of Systems of Rays," which he presented to the Academy on 23 April 1827, while still an undergraduate at Trinity College. Hamilton considered his "Systems of Rays" to be merely an expansion of his paper on caustics. Actually the papers were quite different. The characteristic function appeared only in the "Theory of Systems of Rays," while "On Caustics" investigated the properties of a general rectilinear congruence.

Hamilton had taken the entrance examination for Trinity on 7 July 1823 and, to no one's surprise, came out first in a field of 100 candidates. He continued this auspicious beginning by consistently winning extraordinary honors in classics and science throughout his college career. Trinity College, Dublin, offered an excellent curriculum in mathematics during Hamilton's student years, owing in large part to the work of Bartholomew Lloyd, who became professor at the college in 1812 and instituted a revolution in the teaching of mathematics. He introduced French textbooks and caused others to be written in order to bring the students up to date on Continental methods. These reforms were essentially completed when Hamilton arrived at Trinity.

On 10 June 1827 Hamilton was appointed astronomer royal at Dunsink Observatory and Andrews professor of astronomy at Trinity College. He still had not taken a degree, but he was chosen over several well-qualified competitors, including George Biddell Airy.

As a practical astronomer Hamilton was a failure. He and his assistant Thompson maintained the instruments and kept the observations with the somewhat reluctant help of three of Hamilton's sisters who lived at the observatory. After his first few years Hamilton did little observing and devoted himself entirely to theoretical studies. On one occasion in 1843 he was called to task for not having maintained a satisfactory program of observations, but this protest did not seriously disturb his more congenial mathematical researches.

Life at the observatory gave Hamilton time for his mathematical and literary pursuits, but it kept him somewhat isolated. His reputation in the nineteenth century was enormous; yet no school of mathematicians grew up around him, as might have been expected if he had resided at Trinity College. In the scientific academies Hamilton was more active. He joined the Royal Irish Academy in 1832 and served as its president from 1837 to 1845. A prominent early member of the British Association for the Advancement of Science, he was responsible for bringing the annual meeting of the association to Dublin in 1835. On that occasion he was knighted by the lord lieutenant. In 1836 the Royal Society awarded him the Royal Medal for his work in optics at the same time that Faraday received the medal for chemistry. A more signal honor was conferred in 1863, when he was placed at the head of fourteen foreign associates of the new American National Academy of Sciences.

In 1825 Hamilton fell in love with Catherine Disney, the sister of one of his college friends. When she refused him, he became ill and despondent and was close to suicide. The pain of this disappointment stayed with Hamilton throughout his life and was almost obsessive. In 1831 he was rejected by Ellen De Vere, sister of his good friend the poet Aubrey De Vere, and in 1833 he married Helen Bayly. It was an unfortunate choice. Helen suffered from continual ill health and an almost morbid timidity. She was unable to run the household, which eventually consisted of two sons and a daughter, and absented herself for long periods of time.

When Catherine Disney was dying in 1853, Hamilton visited her twice. He was desperate to get mementos from her brother—locks of hair, poetry, a miniature that he secretly had copied in Dublin—and relieved his distress by writing his confessions to close friends, often daily, sometimes twice a day. Harassed by guilt over his improper feelings and the fear that his secret would become known, Hamilton sought further release in alcohol, and for the rest of his life he struggled against alcoholism.

It would be a mistake to picture Hamilton's life as constant tragedy, however. He was robust and energetic, with a good sense of humor. He possessed considerable eloquence; but his poetry, which he greatly prized, was surprisingly bad. Hamilton had many acquaintances in the Anglo-Irish literary community. He was a frequent visitor at the home of the novelist Maria Edgeworth, and in 1831 he began his long correspondence with De Vere, with whom he shared his metaphysical and poetical ideas and impressions. But his most important literary connection was with William Wordsworth, who took to Hamilton and seemed to feel an obligation to turn him from his poetic ambitions to his natural calling as a mathematician. Hamilton insisted, however, that the "spirit of poetry" would always be essential to his intellectual perfection.

A more important philosophical influence was Samuel Taylor Coleridge. Hamilton was greatly impressed by *The Friend* and *Aids to Reflection,* and it was through Coleridge that he became interested in the philosophy of Immanuel Kant. Hamilton's first serious venture into idealism came in 1830, when he began a careful reading of the collected works of George Berkeley, borrowed from Hamilton's friend and pupil Lord Adare. A letter written in July of the same year mentions Berkeley together with Rudjer Bošković. By 1831 he was struggling with Coleridge's distinction between Reason and Understanding as it appeared in the *Aids to Reflection.* A draft of a letter to Coleridge in 1832, which remained unsent, proclaims his adherence to Bošković's theory of point atoms in space. Coleridge had been very critical of atomism in the *Aids to Reflection,* and Hamilton inquired whether the mathematical atomism, which he believed was required for the undulatory theory of light, was acceptable to Coleridge. He had obtained a copy of Kant's *Critique of Pure Reason* in October 1831 and set about reading it with enthusiasm.

By 1834 Hamilton's idealism was complete. In the introduction to his famous paper "On a General Method in Dynamics" (1834), he declared his support for Bošković and argued for a more abstract and general understanding of "force or of power acting by law in space and time" than that provided by the atomic theory. In a letter also of the same year he wrote: "Power, acting by law in Space and Time, is the ideal base of an ideal world, into which it is the problem of physical science to refine the phenomenal world, that so we may behold as one, and under the forms of our own understanding, what had seemed to be manifold and foreign."[3]

While Hamilton was strongly attracted to the ideas of Kant and Bošković, it is difficult to see how they had any direct effect on his system of dynamics. The "General Method in Dynamics" of 1834 was based directly on the characteristic function in optics, which he had worked out well before he studied Kant or Bošković. The most significant contribution of his philosophical studies was to confirm him in his search for the most general application of mathematics to the physical world. It was this high degree of generality and abstraction that permitted him to include wave optics, particle optics, and dynamics in the same mathematical theory. In reading Kant, Hamilton claimed that his greatest pleasure was in finding his own opinions confirmed in Kant's works. It was more "recognizing" than "discovering."[4] He had the same reaction in talking to Faraday. Faraday, the eminently experimental chemist, had arrived at a view as antimaterialistic as his own, although his own view came completely from theoretical studies.[5]

Scientific Work. Hamilton's major contributions were in the algebra of quaternions, optics, and dynamics. He spent more time on quaternions than on any other subject. Next in importance was optics. His dynamics, for which he is best known, was a distant third. His manuscript notebooks and papers contain many optical studies and drafts of published papers, while there is relatively little on his dynamical theories. One is forced to conclude that the papers on dynamics were merely extensions of fundamental ideas developed in his optics.

The published papers are very difficult to read. Hamilton gave few examples to illustrate his methods, and his exposition is completely analytical with no diagrams. His unpublished papers are quite different. In working out his ideas he tested them on practical problems, often working through lengthy computations. A good example is his application of the theory of systems of rays to the symmetrical optical system—a very valuable investigation that remained in manuscript until his optical papers were collected and published in 1931.

In the "Theory of Systems of Rays" (1827) Hamilton continued the work of his paper "On Caustics" (1824), but he applied the analysis explicitly to geometrical optics and introduced the characteristic function. Only the first of three parts planned for the essay was actually published, but Hamilton continued his analysis in three published supplements between 1830 and 1832. In the "Theory of Systems of Rays," Hamilton considered the rays of light emanating from a point source and being reflected by a curved mirror. In this first study the medium is homogeneous and isotropic, that is, the velocity of light is the same at every point and for every direction in the medium. Under these conditions the rays filling space are such that they can be cut orthogonally by a family of surfaces, and Hamilton proved that this condition continues to hold after any number of reflections and refractions.

Malus had proved the case only for a single reflection or refraction. There had been more general proofs given subsequently by Dupin, Quetelet, and Gergonne, but Hamilton was apparently unaware of their work.[6] He proved the theorem by a modification of the principle of least action which he later called the principle of varying action. The principle of least or stationary action (which was identical to Fermat's principle in the optical case) determined the path of the ray between any fixed end points. By varying the initial point on a surface perpendicular to the ray, Hamilton was able to demonstrate that the final points of the original and varied rays fall on a surface perpendicular to both of them. Therefore, at any time after several reflections the end points of the rays determine a surface perpendicular to the rays.

Hamilton called these surfaces "surfaces of constant action," a term that made sense if light was considered as particles, since all the particles emanating together from the source reached the surface at the same time. But Hamilton continually insisted that this "remarkable analogy" between the principle of least action and geometrical optics did not require the assumption of any hypothesis about the nature of light, because the stationary integral to be found by the calculus of variations was of the same form whether light was considered as particles (in which case the integral is the action $\int v\, ds$) or as waves (in which case the integral is the optical length $\int \mu\, ds$).

From the property that all rays are cut perpendicularly by a family of surfaces, Hamilton showed that the differential form

$$\alpha\, dx + \beta\, dy + \gamma\, dz$$

has to be derived, where α, β, γ are direction cosines of the ray and are taken as functions of the coordinates (x,y,z). The direction cosines must then equal the partial differential coefficients of a function V of x, y, z, so that

$$\alpha = \frac{\partial V}{\partial x},\ \beta = \frac{\partial V}{\partial y},\ \gamma = \frac{\partial V}{\partial z}.$$

From the relation between the direction cosines $\alpha^2 + \beta^2 + \gamma^2 = 1$ Hamilton obtained the expression

$$\left(\frac{\partial V}{\partial x}\right)^2 + \left(\frac{\partial V}{\partial y}\right)^2 + \left(\frac{\partial V}{\partial z}\right)^2 = 1$$

by substitution. He noticed that a solution of this equation is obtained by making V the length of the ray. It is the function V that Hamilton called the "characteristic function," and he declared that it was "the most complete and simple definition that could be given of the application of analysis to optics." The characteristic function contains "the whole of mathematical optics."[7]

The long third supplement of 1832 was Hamilton's most general treatment of the characteristic function in optics and was essentially a separate treatise. Where the initial point was previously fixed so that V was a function only of the coordinates of the final point, the initial coordinates were now added as variables so that V became a function of both initial and final coordinates. The characteristic function now completely described the optical system, since it held for any set of incident rays rather than only for those from a given initial point. Hamilton further generalized his investigation by allowing for heterogeneous and anisotropic media, and this greater generality allowed him to introduce an auxiliary function T, which, in the case of homogeneous initial and final media, is a function of the directions of the initial and final rays.

The importance of the characteristic function came from the fact that it described the system as a function of variables describing the initial and final rays. The principle of least action determined the optical path between fixed points. The characteristic function made the optical length a function of variable initial and final points.

At the end of the third supplement, Hamilton applied his characteristic function to the study of Fresnel's wave surface and discovered that for the case of biaxial crystals there exist four conoidal cusps on the wave surface. From this discovery he predicted that a single ray incident in the correct direction on a biaxial crystal should be refracted into a cone in the crystal and emerge as a hollow cylinder. He also predicted that if light were focused into a cone incident on the crystal, it would pass through the crystal as a single ray and emerge as a hollow cone. Hamilton described his discovery to the Royal Irish Academy on 22 October 1832 and asked Humphrey Lloyd, professor of natural philosophy at Trinity College, to attempt an experimental verification. Lloyd had some difficulty obtaining a satisfactory crystal, but two months later he wrote to Hamilton that he had found the cone.

Hamilton's theoretical prediction of conical refraction and Lloyd's verification caused a sensation. It was one of those rare events where theory predicted a completely unexpected physical phenomenon. Unfortunately it also involved Hamilton in an unpleasant controversy over priority with his colleague James MacCullagh, who had come very close to the discovery in 1830. MacCullagh was persuaded not to push his claim, but after this incident Hamilton was very sensitive about questions of priority.

Hamilton's theory of the characteristic function had little impact on the matter of greatest moment in optics at the time—the controversy between the wave and particle theories of light. Since his theory applied equally well to both explanations of light, his work in a sense stood above the controversy. He chose, however, to support the wave theory; and his prediction of conical refraction from Fresnel's wave surface was taken as another bit of evidence for waves. He entered into the debates at the meetings of the British Association and took part in an especially sharp exchange at the Manchester meeting of 1842, where he defended the wave theory against attacks by Sir David Brewster.

Shortly after completion of his third supplement to the "Theory of Systems of Rays," Hamilton undertook to apply his characteristic function to mechanics as well as to light. The analogy was obvious from his first use of the principle of least action. As astronomer royal of Ireland he appropriately applied his theory first to celestial mechanics in a paper entitled "On a General Method of Expressing the Paths of Light and of the Planets by the Coefficients of a Characteristic Function" (1833). He subsequently bolstered this rather general account with a more detailed study of the problem of three bodies using the characteristic function. The latter treatise was not published, however, and Hamilton's first general statement of the characteristic function applied to dynamics was his famous paper "On a General Method in Dynamics" (1834), which was followed the next year by a second essay on the same subject.

These papers are difficult to read. Hamilton presented his arguments with great economy, as usual, and his approach was entirely different from that now commonly presented in textbooks describing the method. In the two essays on dynamics Hamilton first applied the characteristic function V to dynamics just as he had in optics, the characteristic function being the action of the system in moving from its initial to its final point in configuration space. By his law of varying action he made the initial and final coordinates the independent variables of the characteristic function. For conservative systems, the total energy H was constant along any real path but varied if the initial and final points were varied, and so the characteristic function in dynamics became a function of the $6n$ coordinates of initial and final position (for n particles) and the Hamiltonian H.

The function V could be found only by integrating the equations of motion—a formidable task, as Hamilton realized. His great achievement, as he saw it, was to have reduced the problem of solving $3n$ ordinary differential equations of the second order (as given by Lagrange) to that of solving two partial differential equations of the first order and second degree. It was not clear that the problem was made any easier, but as Hamilton said: "Even if it should be thought that no practical facility is gained, yet an intellectual pleasure may result from the reduction of the most complex . . . of all researches respecting the forces and motions of body, to the study of one characteristic function, the unfolding of one central relation."[8]

The major part of the first essay was devoted to methods of approximating the characteristic function in order to apply it to the perturbations of planets and comets. It was only in the last section that he introduced a new auxiliary function called the principal function (S) by the transformation $V = tH + S$, thereby adding the time t as a variable in place of the Hamiltonian H.

The principal function could be found in a way analogous to the characteristic function; that is, it had to satisfy the following two partial differential equations of the first order and second degree:

$$\frac{\partial S}{\partial t} + \sum \frac{1}{2m}\left[\left(\frac{\partial S}{\partial x}\right)^2 + \left(\frac{\partial S}{\partial y}\right)^2 + \left(\frac{\partial S}{\partial z}\right)^2\right] = U$$

$$\frac{\partial S}{\partial t} + \sum \frac{1}{2m}\left[\left(\frac{\partial S}{\partial a}\right)^2 + \left(\frac{\partial S}{\partial b}\right)^2 + \left(\frac{\partial S}{\partial c}\right)^2\right] = U_0.$$

The variables x, y, z of the first equation represent the position of the particles at some time t; and the variables a, b, c of the second equation are the initial coordinates. U is the negative of the potential energy.

In the second essay, Hamilton deduced from the principal function the now familiar canonical equations of motion and immediately below showed that the same function S was equal to the time integral of the Lagrangian between fixed points

$$S = \int_0^t (T + U)\,dt = \int_0^t L\,dt.$$

The statement that the variation of this integral must be equal to zero is now referred to as Hamilton's principle.

A solution to Hamilton's principal function was very difficult to obtain in most actual cases, and it was K. G. J. Jacobi who found a much more useful form of the same equation.[9] In Jacobi's theory the S function is a generating function which completely characterizes a canonical transformation even when the Hamiltonian depends explicitly on the time. Since the canonical transformation depends on a single function, Jacobi was able to drop the second of Hamilton's two equations and the problem was reduced to the solution of the single partial differential equation

$$\frac{\partial S}{\partial t} + H\left(q_1, \cdots, q_n; \frac{\partial S}{\partial q_1}, \cdots, \frac{\partial S}{\partial q_n}; t\right) = 0,$$

which is usually referred to as the Hamilton-Jacobi equation. Hamilton had shown that the principal function S, defined as the time integral of the Lagrangian L, was a special solution of a partial differential equation; but it was Jacobi who demonstrated the converse, that by the theory of canonical transformations any complete solution of the Hamilton-Jacobi equation could be used to describe the motion of the mechanical system.[10]

The difficulty of solving the Hamilton-Jacobi equation gave little advantage to the Hamiltonian method over that of Lagrange in the nineteenth century. The method had admirable elegance but little practical advantage. With the rise of quantum mechanics, however, Hamilton's method suddenly regained importance because it was the one form of classical mechanics that carried over directly into the quantum interpretation. A great advantage of the Hamiltonian method was the close analogy between mechanics and optics that it contained; and this analogy was exploited by Louis de Broglie and Schrödinger in their formulations of wave mechanics.

Hamilton's tendency to pursue his studies in their greatest generality led to other important contributions. He extended his general method in dynamics to create a "calculus of principal relations," which permitted the solution of certain total differential equations by the calculus of variations. Another important contribution was the hodograph, the curve defined by the velocity vectors of a point in orbital motion taken as drawn from the origin rather than from the moving point.

Hamilton also attempted to apply his dynamics to the propagation of light in a crystalline medium. Previous authors, said Hamilton, had written much on the preservation of light vibrations in different media, but no one had attempted to investigate the propagation of a wave front into an undisturbed medium; or as he explained it to John Herschel, "Much had been done, perhaps, in the dynamics of *light;* little, I thought, in the dynamics of *darkness.*"[11] This new science of the dynamics of darkness he named "skotodynamics." He was actually hampered by his enthusiasm for Bošković's theory because it led him to study the medium as a series of attracting points rather than as a continuum; but his research, as usual, led to important new ideas. One was the distinction between group velocity and phase velocity. Another was his valuable study of "fluctuating functions," an extension of Fourier's theorem, which in turn led him to give the first complete asymptotic expansion for Bessel functions.

All of Hamilton's work in optics and dynamics depended on a single central idea, that of the characteristic function. It was the first of his two great "discoveries." The second was the quaternions, which he discovered on 16 October 1843 and to which he devoted most of his efforts during the remaining twenty-two years of his life. In October 1828 Hamilton complained to his friend John T. Graves about the shaky foundations of algebra. Such notions as negative and imaginary numbers, which appeared to be essential for algebra, had no real meaning for him; and he argued that a radical rewriting of the logical foundations of algebra was badly needed.[12] In the same year John Warren published *A Treatise on the Geometrical Representation of the Square Roots of Negative Quantities.* Hamilton read it in 1829 at Graves's instigation. Warren's book described the so-called Argand diagram by which the complex number is represented as a point on a plane with one rectangular axis representing the real part of the number and the other axis representing the imaginary part. This geometrical representation of complex numbers raised two new questions in Hamilton's mind: (1) Is there any other algebraic representation of complex numbers that will reveal all valid operations on them? (2) Is it possible to find a hypercomplex number that is related to three-dimensional space just as a regular complex number is related to two-dimensional space? If such a hypercomplex number could be found, it would be a "natural" algebraic representation of space, as opposed to the artificial and somewhat arbitrary representation by coordinates.

On 4 November 1833 Hamilton read a paper on algebraic couples to the Royal Irish Academy in which he presented his answer to the first question. His algebraic couples consisted of all ordered pairs of real numbers, for which Hamilton defined rules of addition and multiplication. He then demonstrated that these couples constituted a commutative associative division algebra, and that they satisfied the rules for operations with complex numbers. For some mathematicians the theory of number couples was a more significant contribution to mathematics than the discovery of quaternions.[13] On 1 June 1835 Hamilton presented a second paper on number couples entitled *Preliminary and Elementary Essay on Algebra as the Science of Pure Time,* in which he identified the number couples with steps in time. He combined this paper with his earlier paper of 1833, added some *General Introductory Remarks,* and published them in the *Proceedings of the Royal Irish Academy* of 1837.

This was a time of intense intellectual activity for Hamilton. He was deeply involved in the study of dynamics as well as the algebra of number couples. This was also the time when he was most involved in the study of Kant and was forming his own idealistic philosophy. Manuscript notes from 1830 and 1831 (before he read Kant) already contained Hamilton's conviction that the foundation for algebra was to be found in the ordinal character of numbers, and that this ordering had an intuitive basis in time. Kant's philosophy must certainly have strengthened this conviction.[14] It was through the concept of time that Hamilton hoped to correct the weaknesses in the logical foundations of algebra. He recognized three different schools of algebra. The first was the practical school, which considered algebra as an instrument for the solution of problems; therefore it sought rules of application. The second, or philological school, considered algebra as a language consisting of formulas composed of symbols which could be arranged only in certain specified ways. The third was the theoretical school, which considered algebra as a group of theorems upon which one might meditate. Hamilton identified himself with the last school and insisted that in algebra it was necessary to go beyond the signs of the formalist to the things signified. Only by relating numbers to some real intuition could algebra be truly called a "science."

In the *Critique of Pure Reason,* Kant argued that the ordering of phenomena in space was an operation of the mind and that this ordering had to be part of the mode of perceiving things. The science that studied this aspect of perception in its purest form was geometry; therefore geometry could well be called the "science of pure space." According to Hamilton the intuition of order in time was even more deep-seated in the human mind than the intuition of order in space. We have an intuitive concept of pure or mathematical time more fundamental than all actual chronology or ordering of particular events. This intuition of mathematical time is the real referent of algebraic symbolism. It is "co-extensive and identical with Algebra, so far as Algebra itself is a Science."[15] Hamilton presented this idea to his fellow mathematicians Graves and De Morgan with some hesitation and received an unenthusiastic response, which he probably anticipated. Although the idea had been with him for some time Hamilton mentioned it casually to Graves for the first time in a letter of 11 July 1835 where he referred to it as this "crochet of mine."[16] But in spite of the adverse reaction Hamilton never wavered in his conviction that the intuition of time was the foundation of algebra.

Hamilton had less success in answering the second question posed above, whether it would be possible to write three-dimensional complex numbers or, as he called them, "triplets." Addition of triplets was obvious, but he could find no operation that would follow the rules of multiplication. Thirteen years after Hamilton's death G. Frobenius proved that there is no such algebra and that the only possible associative division algebras over the real numbers are the real numbers themselves, complex numbers, and real quaternions. In searching for the elusive triplets, Hamilton sought some way of making his triplets satisfy the law of the moduli, since any algebra obeying this law is a division algebra. The modulus of a complex number is that number multiplied by its complex conjugate, and the law of the moduli states that the product of the moduli of two complex numbers equals the modulus of the product. By analogy to complex numbers, Hamilton wrote the triplet as $x + iy + jz$ with $i^2 = j^2 = -1$ and took as its modulus $x^2 + y^2 + z^2$. The product of two such moduli can be expressed as the sum of squares; but it is the sum of four squares not the sum of three squares, as would be the case if it were the modulus of a triplet.

The fact that he obtained the sum of four squares for the modulus of the product must have indicated to Hamilton that possibly ordered sets of four numbers, or "quaternions," might work where the triplets failed. Thus he tested hypercomplex numbers of the form $(a + ib + jc + kd)$ to see if they satisfied the law of the moduli. They worked, but only by sacrificing the commutative law. Hamilton had to make the product $ij = -ji$.[17] Hamilton's great insight came in realizing that he could sacrifice commutativity and still have a meaningful and consistent algebra. The laws for multiplication of quaternions then followed immediately:

$$\begin{aligned} ij &= k = -ji, \\ jk &= i = -kj, \\ ki &= j = -ik, \\ i^2 &= j^2 = k^2 = ijk = -1. \end{aligned}$$

The quaternions came to Hamilton in one of those flashes of understanding that occasionally occur after long deliberation on a problem. He was walking into Dublin on 16 October 1843 along the Royal Canal to preside at a meeting of the Royal Irish Academy, when the discovery came to him. As he described it, "An electric circuit seemed to close."[18] He immediately scratched the formula for quaternion multiplication on the stone of a bridge over the canal. His reaction must have been in part a desire to commemorate a discovery of capital importance, but it was also a reflection of his working habits. Hamilton was an inveterate scribbler. His manuscripts are full of jottings made on walks and in carriages. He carried books, pencils, and paper everywhere he went. According to his son he would scribble on his fingernails and even on his hard-boiled egg at breakfast if there was no paper handy.

Hamilton was convinced that in the quaternions he had found a natural algebra of three-dimensional space. The quaternion seemed to him to be more fundamental than any coordinate representation of space, because operations with quaternions were independent of any given coordinate system. The scalar part of the quaternion caused difficulty in any geometrical representation and Hamilton tried without notable success to interpret it as an extraspatial unit. The geometrical significance of the quaternion became clearer when Hamilton and A. Cayley independently showed that the quaternion operator rotated a vector about a given axis.[19]

The quaternions did not turn out to be the magic key that Hamilton hoped they would be, but they were significant in the later development of vector analysis. Hamilton himself divided the quaternion into a real part and a complex part which he called a vector. The multiplication of two such vectors according to the rules for quaternions gave a product consisting again of a scalar part and a complex part.

$$\begin{aligned} \alpha &= xi + yj + zk \\ \alpha' &= x'i + y'j + z'k \end{aligned}$$

$$\alpha\alpha' = -(xx' + yy' + zz') + i(yz' - zy') + j(zx' - xz') + k(xy' - yx')$$

The scalar part, which he wrote as $S.\ \alpha\alpha'$, is recognizable as the negative of the scalar or dot product of vector analysis, and the vector part, which he wrote as $V.\ \alpha\alpha'$, is recognizable as the vector or cross product. Hamilton frequently used these symbols as well as a new operator which he introduced,

$$\lhd = i\frac{d}{dx} + j\frac{d}{dy} + k\frac{d}{dz}$$

and

$$-\lhd^2 = \left(\frac{d}{dx}\right)^2 + \left(\frac{d}{dy}\right)^2 + \left(\frac{d}{dz}\right)^2,$$

and called attention to the fact that the applications of this new operator in physics "must be extensive to a high degree."[20] Gibbs suggested the name "del" for the same operator in vector analysis and this is the term now generally used.

Hamilton was not the only person working on vectorial systems in the mid-nineteenth century.[21] Hermann Günther Grassmann working independently of Hamilton published his *Ausdehnungslehre* in 1844 in which he treated *n*-dimensional geometry and hypercomplex systems in a much more general way than Hamilton; but Grassmann's book was extremely difficult and radical in its conception and so had very few readers. Hamilton's books on quaternions were also too long and too difficult to attract much of an audience. His *Lectures on Quaternions* (1853) ran to 736 pages with a sixty-four-page preface. Any reader can sympathize with John Herschel's request that Hamilton make his principles "clear and familiar down to the level of ordinary unmetaphysical apprehension" and to "introduce the new phrases as strong meat gradually given to babes."[22] His advice was ignored and the *Lectures* bristles with complicated new terms such as *vector, vehend, vection, vectum, revector, revehend, revection, revectum, provector, transvector,* etc.[23] Herschel replied with a cry of distress, but it did no good and the *Elements of Quaternions,* which began as a simple manual, was published only after Hamilton's death and was even longer than the *Lectures.*

The first readable book on quaternions was P. G. Tait's *Elementary Treatise on Quaternions* (1867). Tait and Hamilton had been in correspondence since 1858, and Tait had held up the publication of his book at Hamilton's request until after the *Elements* appeared. Tait was Hamilton's most prominent disciple, and during the 1890's entered into a heated controversy with Gibbs and Heaviside over the relative advantages of quaternions and vectors. One can sympathize with Tait's commitment to quaternions and his dissatisfaction with vector analysis. It was difficult enough to give up the commutative property in quaternion multiplication, but vector analysis required much greater sacrifices. It accepted *two* kinds of multiplication, the dot product and the cross product. The dot product was not a real product at all, since it did not preserve closure; that is, the product was not of the same nature as the multiplier and the multiplicand. Both products failed to satisfy the law of the moduli, and both failed to give an unambiguous method of division. Moreover the cross product (in which closure was preserved) was neither associative nor commutative.[24] No wonder a devout quaternionist like Tait looked upon vector analysis as a "hermaphrodite monster."[25] Nevertheless vector analysis proved to be the more useful tool, especially in applied mathematics. The controversy did not entirely die, however, and as late as 1940 E. T. Whittaker argued that quaternions "may even yet prove to be the most natural expression of the new physics [quantum mechanics]."[26]

The quaternions were not the only contribution that Hamilton made to mathematics. In 1837 he corrected Abel's proof of the impossibility of solving the general quintic equation and defended the proof against G. B. Jerrard, who claimed to have found such a solution. He also became interested in the study of polyhedra and developed in 1856 what he called the "Icosian Calculus," a study of the properties of the icosahedron and the dodecahedron. This study resulted in an "Icosian Game" to be played on the plane projection of a dodecahedron. He sold the copyright to a Mr. Jacques of Piccadilly for twenty-five pounds. The game fascinated a mathematician like Hamilton, but it is unlikely that Mr. Jacques ever recovered his investment.

In spite of Hamilton's great fame in the nineteenth century one is left with the impression that his discoveries had none of the revolutionary impact on science that he had hoped for. His characteristic function in optics did not hit at the controversy then current over the physical nature of light, and it became important for geometrical optics only sixty years later when Bruns rediscovered the characteristic function and called it the method of the eikonal.[27] His dynamics was saved from oblivion by the important additions of Jacobi, but even then the Hamiltonian method gained a real advantage over other methods only with the advent of quantum mechanics. The quaternions, too, which were supposed to open the doors to so many new fields of science turned out to be a disappointment. Yet quaternions were the seed from which other noncommutative algebras grew. Matrices and even vector analysis have a parent in quaternions. Over the long run the success of Hamilton's work has justified his efforts. The high degree of abstraction and generality that made his papers so difficult to read has also made them stand the test of time, while more specialized researches with greater immediate utility have been superseded.

NOTES

1. Graves, *Life of Sir William Rowan Hamilton,* I, 141.
2. *Ibid.,* 186.
3. Hamilton to H. F. C. Logan, 27 June 1834, Graves, II, 87–88.
4. Hamilton to Lord Adare, 19 July 1834, Graves, II, 96; and to Wordsworth, 20 July 1834, Graves, II, 98.
5. Graves, II, 95–96.
6. *Mathematical Papers,* I, 463, editor's note.
7. *Ibid.,* 17, 168.
8. *Ibid.,* II, 105.

9. *Crelle's Journal,* **17** (1837), 97–162.
10. The differences between Hamilton's and Jacobi's formulations are described in detail in the *Mathematical Papers,* II, 613–621, editor's app. 2; and in Lanczos, *Variational Principles,* 229–230, 254–262.
11. *Mathematical Papers,* II, 599.
12. Graves, I, 303–304.
13. C. C. MacDuffee, "Algebra's Debt to Hamilton," in *Scripta mathematica,* **10** (1944), 25.
14. MS notebook no. 25, fol. 1, and notebook no. 24.5, fol. 49. See also Graves, I, 229, where Hamilton in 1827 referred to "the sciences of Space and Time (to adopt here a view of Algebra which I have elsewhere ventured to propose)."
15. *Mathematical Papers,* III, 5.
16. Graves, II, 143.
17. E. T. Whittaker, "The Sequence of Ideas in the Discovery of Quaternions," in *Proceedings of the Royal Irish Academy,* **50A** (1945), 93–98.
18. Graves, II, 435.
19. *Mathematical Papers,* III, 361–362.
20. *Ibid.,* 262–263.
21. Crowe, *History of Vector Analysis,* pp. 47–101.
22. Graves, II, 633.
23. Crowe, p. 36.
24. *Ibid.,* pp. 28–29.
25. *Ibid.,* p. 185.
26. E. T. Whittaker, "The Hamiltonian Revival," in *Mathematical Gazette,* **24** (1940), 158.
27. J. L. Synge, "Hamilton's Method in Geometrical Optics," in *Journal of the Optical Society of America,* **27** (1937), 75–82.

BIBLIOGRAPHY

I. ORIGINAL WORKS. Hamilton's mathematical papers have been collected in three volumes, *The Mathematical Papers of Sir William Rowan Hamilton* (Cambridge, 1931–1967). These volumes are carefully edited with short introductions and very valuable explanatory appendices and notes. The collection is not complete, but the editors have selected the most important papers, including many that were previously unpublished. A complete bibliography of Hamilton's published works appears at the end of vol. III of Robert P. Graves, *Life of Sir William Rowan Hamilton,* 3 vols. (Dublin, 1882–1889). Graves collected Hamilton's papers and letters for his biography shortly after Hamilton's death. The bulk of these manuscripts is now at the library of Trinity College, Dublin, with a smaller collection at the National Library of Ireland, Dublin. The manuscript collection at Trinity is very large, containing approximately 250 notebooks and a large number of letters and loose papers.

II. SECONDARY LITERATURE. R. P. Graves's biography is composed largely of letters which have been edited to remove much of the mathematical content. Graves also suppressed some correspondence that he considered too personal.

Most of the secondary literature on Hamilton has been written by mathematicians interested in the technical aspects of his work. An exception is Robert Kargon, "William Rowan Hamilton and Boscovichean Atomism," in *Journal of the History of Ideas,* **26** (1965), 137–140. The best introduction to Hamilton's optics is John L. Synge, *Geometrical Optics; an Introduction to Hamilton's Method* (Cambridge, 1937). Also valuable are his "Hamilton's Method in Geometrical Optics," in *Journal of the Optical Society of America,* **27** (1937), 75–82; G. C. Steward, "On the Optical Writings of Sir William Rowan Hamilton," in *Mathematical Gazette,* **16** (1932), 179–191; and George Sarton, "Discovery of Conical Refraction by Sir William Rowan Hamilton and Humphrey Lloyd (1833)," in *Isis,* **17** (1932), 154–170.

Hamilton's work in dynamics is described in René Dugas, "Sur la pensée dynamique d'Hamilton: origines optiques et prolongements modernes," in *Revue scientifique,* **79** (1941), 15–23; and A. Cayley, "Report on the Recent Progress of Theoretical Dynamics," in *British Association Reports* (1857), pp. 1–42. Another valuable exposition of the method is in Cornelius Lanczos, *The Variational Principles of Mechanics,* 3rd ed. (Toronto, 1966).

The centenary of Hamilton's discovery of quaternions was the occasion for two very important collections of articles, in *Proceedings of the Royal Irish Academy,* **50A,** no. 6 (Feb. 1945), 69–121; and in *Scripta mathematica,* **10** (1944), 9–63. These collections cover not only the quaternions, but also contain biographical notices, an article on the mathematical school at Trinity College, Dublin, and articles on Hamilton's dynamics, his optics, and his other contributions to algebra. The relationship between quaternions and vector analysis is described in great detail in Michael Crowe, *A History of Vector Analysis; the Evolution of the Idea of a Vectorial System* (Notre Dame, Ind., 1967); and in Reginald J. Stephenson, "Development of Vector Analysis From Quaternions," in *American Journal of Physics,* **34** (1966), 194–201; and Alfred M. Bork, "'Vectors Versus Quaternions'—the Letters in Nature," in *American Journal of Physics,* **34** (1966), 202–211.

THOMAS L. HANKINS

HANKEL, HERMANN (*b.* Halle, Germany, 14 February 1839; *d.* Schramberg, near Tübingen, Germany, 29 August 1873)

Hankel's father, the physicist Wilhelm Gottlieb Hankel, was associate professor at Halle from 1847 and full professor at Leipzig from 1849. Hankel studied at the Nicolai Gymnasium in Leipzig, where he improved his Greek by reading the ancient mathematicians in the original. Entering Leipzig University in 1857, he studied with Moritz Drobisch, A. F. Moebius, Wilhelm Scheibner, and his father. In 1860 Hankel proceeded to Göttingen, where from Georg Riemann he acquired his special interest in the theory of functions. At this time he published his prize-winning *Zur allgemeinen Theorie der Bewegung der Flüssigkeiten* (Göttingen). The following year he studied in Berlin with Karl Weierstrass and Leopold Kronecker, and in 1862 he received his doctorate at Leipzig for *Ueber eine besondere Classe der symmetrischen Determinanten* (Göttingen, 1861). He qualified for teaching in 1863 and in the spring of 1867 was named associate professor at Leipzig. In the fall of that year he became full professor at Erlangen, where he married Marie Dippe. Called to Tübingen in 1869, he spent the last four years of his life there.

Hankel's contributions to mathematics were concentrated in three areas: the study of complex and higher complex numbers, the theory of functions, and the history of mathematics. His most important contribution in the first area was *Theorie der complexen Zahlensysteme* (Leipzig, 1867), to which he had hoped to add a treatise on the functions of a complex variable. This work constitutes a lengthy presentation of much of what was then known of the real, complex, and hypercomplex number systems. In it Hankel presented algebra as a deductive science treating entities which are intellectual constructs. Beginning with a revised statement of George Peacock's principle of the permanence of formal laws, he developed complex numbers as well as such higher algebraic systems as Moebius' barycentric calculus, some of Hermann Grassmann's algebras, and W. R. Hamilton's quaternions. Hankel was the first to recognize the significance of Grassmann's long-neglected writings and was strongly influenced by them. The high point of the book lies in the section (pp. 106–108) in which he proved that no hypercomplex number system can satisfy all the laws of ordinary arithmetic.

In the theory of functions Hankel's major contributions were *Untersuchungen über die unendlich oft oscillirenden und unstetigen Functionen* (Tübingen, 1870) and his 1871 article "Grenze" for the Ersch-Gruber *Encyklopädie.* In the former, he reformulated Riemann's criterion for integrability, placing the emphasis upon measure-theoretic properties of sets of points. After making explicit that functions do not possess general properties, he attempted a fourfold classification of functions, discussed the integrability of each type, and presented a method, based on his principle of the condensation of singularities, for constructing functions with singularities at every rational point. Although he confounded the notions of sets of zero content and nowhere-dense sets, his work marked an important advance toward modern integration theory. In "Grenze" he pointed out for the first time the importance of Bernard Bolzano's work on infinite series and published an example of a continuous function that was nondifferentiable at an infinite number of points. In a series of papers in *Mathematische Annalen,* Hankel showed the significance of what are now known as "Hankel functions" or "Bessel functions of the third kind."

Among Hankel's historical writings the best-known are his short *Entwicklung der Mathematik in den letzten Jahrhunderten* (Tübingen, 1869) and his long *Zur Geschichte der Mathematik in Alterthum und Mittelalter* (Leipzig, 1875). Although Moritz Cantor pointed out many errors in the latter book he, G. J. Allman, Florian Cajori, T. L. Heath, and J. T. Merz have recognized the brilliance of Hankel's historical insight.

BIBLIOGRAPHY

I. ORIGINAL WORKS. A list of all Hankel's publications through 1875 will be found in *Bullettino di bibliographia e di storia delle scienze matematiche e fisiche,* **9** (1876), 297–308. This is completed by the following additions: *Untersuchungen über die unendlich oft oscillirenden und unstetigen Functionen,* republished in *Mathematische Annalen,* **20** (1882), 63–112, and as Ostwalds Klassiker der Exacten Wissenschaften, no. 153 (Leipzig, 1905), with comments by P. E. B. Jourdain. Also republished were *Entwicklung der Mathematik* (Tübingen, 1884) and, recently, *Zur Geschichte der Mathematik* (Hildesheim, 1965), with a foreword by J. E. Hofmann.

II. SECONDARY LITERATURE. Hankel's life was discussed by W. von Zahn in *Mathematische Annalen,* **7** (1874), 583–590; and by M. Cantor in *Allgemeinen deutsche Biographie,* X (Leipzig, 1879), 516–519. For his work on complex numbers, see M. J. Crowe, *A History of Vector Analysis* (Notre Dame, Ind., 1967). His contributions to analysis are discussed in P. E. B. Jourdain, "The Development of the Theory of Transfinite Numbers," in *Archiv der Mathematik und Physik,* 3rd ser., **10** (1906), 254–281; and in Thomas Hawkins, *Lebesgue's Theory of Integration: Its Origins and Development* (Madison, Wis., 1970). J. E. Hofmann's foreword to his republication of Hankel's *Zur Geschichte der Mathematik in Altertum und Mittelalter* (Hildesheim, 1965) contains a brief discussion of the quality of Hankel's historical writing as well as a portrait.

MICHAEL J. CROWE

HARDY, CLAUDE (*b.* Le Mans, France, *ca.* 1598; *d.* Paris, France, 5 April 1678)

Little is known about Hardy's life. He is said to have been born in 1598 (G. Loria) or in 1605 (Claude Irson). In 1625 he was a lawyer attached to the court of Paris and in 1626 a counselor in the Châtelet. He took part in the weekly meetings of Roberval, Mersenne, and the other French geometricians in the Académie Mersenne, and was a friend of Claude Mydorge, who introduced him to Descartes. Several writers of the seventeenth century suggested methods for the duplication of the cube, including Viète, Descartes, Fermat, and Newton. Among the less well-known persons who also occupied themselves with this problem was Paul Yvon, lord of Laleu, who claimed that he had found the construction of the two mean proportionals, required in solving the problem. In addition to Mydorge and J. de Beaugrand, Hardy exposed the fallacy of Yvon's construction in his *Examen* of 1630 and again in his *Refutation* of 1638. In turn Hardy was attacked by other scholars. Owing to a lack of explicitness in statement, Fermat's method of maxima and minima and of tangents was severely attacked by Descartes. In the ensuing dispute Fermat found two zealous defenders in Roberval and Pascal, while Mydorge, Desargues, and Hardy supported Descartes.

Hardy owed his greatest fame, however, to his knowledge of Arabic and other exotic languages, and in particular, to his edition of Euclid's *Data* (1625), the *editio princeps* of the Greek text, together with a Latin translation. He is said to have translated the *Isagoge* (Tours, 1591) and the *Zetetica* (Tours, 1593) of Viète and to have occupied himself with a project for a universal language.

BIBLIOGRAPHY

I. ORIGINAL WORKS. Hardy's ed. of the *Data* was published as *Euclidis Data. Opus ad veterum geometriae autorum Archimedis, Apollonii, Pappi, Eutocii ceterorumque* . . . (Paris, 1625). He was author of *Examen de la duplication du cube et quadrature du cercle, cy-devant publiée à diverses fois par le Sieur de Laleu* . . . (Paris, 1630); and *Refutation de la manière de trouver un quarré égal au cercle rapportée ès pages 130 et 131 du livre nouvellement imprimé sous le titre de Propositions mathématiques de Monsieur de Laleu demonstrées par I. Pujos, et au prétendu triangle équilatéral mentionné au placard dudit sieur* . . . (Paris, 1638).

II. SECONDARY LITERATURE. On Hardy and his work, see (listed in chronological order) P. Colomiès, *Gallia orientalis* (The Hague, 1665), pp. 165–166, 259–260; C. Irson, *Nouvelle méthode pour apprendre facilement les principes et la pureté de la langue françoise* (Paris, 1667), p. 317; G. Loria, *Storia delle matematiche,* II (Milan, 1931), 309; and C. de Waard, ed., *Correspondance du M. Mersenne,* I (Paris, 1932), 187, 619, 666; II (Paris, 1937), 116, 550, 551; III (Paris, 1946), 230; IV (Paris, 1955), 322, 323; V (Paris, 1959), 136; VII (Paris, 1962), 63, 288–292; VIII (Paris, 1963), 417, 418.

H. L. L. BUSARD

HARDY, GODFREY HAROLD (*b.* Cranleigh, England, 7 February 1877; *d.* Cambridge, England, 1 December 1947)

Hardy was the elder of two children of Isaac Hardy, a master at Cranleigh School, and Sophia Hall. The parents were intelligent and mathematically minded, but lack of money had precluded them from a university education. They provided an enlightened upbringing for Hardy and his sister.

The freedom to ask questions and to probe led Hardy to an early established disbelief in religious doctrine. (As a fellow of New College, Oxford, he refused to enter the chapel to take part in electing a warden.) Neither Hardy nor his sister married, and he owed much to her devoted care throughout his life, particularly in his later years.

As a boy Hardy showed all-around ability with a precocious interest in numbers. At the age of thirteen he moved from Cranleigh School with a scholarship to Winchester College, to this day a famous nursery of mathematicians. He went on to Trinity College, Cambridge, in 1896, was fourth wrangler in the mathematical tripos in 1898, was elected a fellow of Trinity in 1900, and won (with J. H. Jeans) a Smith's Prize in 1901. Success in the tripos depended on efficient drilling in solving problems quickly. Hardy, resenting the routine of the famous "coach" R. R. Webb, had the good fortune to be transferred to A. E. H. Love. No description of Hardy's development into a mathematician can be so vivid as his own:

> My eyes were first opened by Professor Love, who taught me for a few terms and gave me my first serious conception of analysis. But the great debt which I owe to him was his advice to read Jordan's famous *Cours d'analyse;* and I shall never forget the astonishment with which I read that remarkable work, the first inspiration for so many mathematicians of my generation, and learnt for the first time as I read it what mathematics really meant [*A Mathematician's Apology,* sec. 29].

Hardy flung himself eagerly into research and between 1900 and 1911 wrote many papers on the convergence of series and integrals and allied topics. Although this work established his reputation as an analyst, his greatest service to mathematics in this early period was *A Course of Pure Mathematics* (1908). This work was the first rigorous English exposition of number, function, limit, and so on, adapted to the undergraduate, and thus it transformed university teaching.

The quotation from the *Apology* continues, "The real crises of my life came ten or twelve years later, in 1911, when I began my long collaboration with Littlewood, and in 1913, when I discovered Ramanujan."

J. E. Littlewood, eight years younger than Hardy, proved in 1910 the Abel-Tauber theorem that, if na_n is bounded and $\Sigma a_n x^n \to s$ as $x \to 1$, then $\Sigma a_n = s$. The two then entered into a collaboration which was to last thirty-five years. They wrote nearly a hundred joint papers. Among the topics covered were Diophantine approximation (the distribution, modulo 1, of functions $f(n)$ of many types, such as θn^2 for irrational θ), additive and multiplicative theory of numbers and the Riemann zeta function, inequalities, series and integrals in general (for instance, summability and Tauberian theorems), and trigonometric series.

The partnership of Hardy and Littlewood has no parallel, and it is remarkable that, at its greatest intensity (1920–1931), Hardy lived in Oxford and Littlewood in Cambridge. They set up a body of axioms expressing the freedom of their collaboration, for example, "When one received a letter from the other he was under no obligation to read it, let alone to answer it." The final writing of the papers was done by Hardy.

Hardy called his discovery of Srinivasa Ramanujan the one romantic incident of his life. One morning early in 1913, he received a letter from this unknown Indian, containing a number of formulae without any proofs. Established mathematicians are exposed to manuscripts from amateurs, and Hardy could not at a glance assess it. A few hours' work convinced him that the writer was a man of genius. Ramanujan turned out to be a poor, self-taught clerk in Madras, born in 1887. Hardy brought him to England in April 1914 and set about the task of filling the gaps in his formal mathematical education. Ramanujan was ill from May 1917 onward; he returned to India in February 1919 and died in April 1920. In his three years of health and activity, he and Hardy had arrived at spectacular solutions of problems about the partition of numbers which called forth the full power of the Indian's natural insight and the Englishman's mastery of the theory of functions.

Denote by $p(n)$ the number of ways of writing n as the sum of positive integers (repetitions allowed), so that $p(5) = 7$. As n increases, $p(n)$ increases rapidly; for instance, $p(200)$ is a number of thirteen digits, a computation which in 1916 took a month. Hardy and Ramanujan established an asymptotic formula for $p(n)$, of which five terms sufficed to give the value of $p(200)$.

Hardy was a lecturer at Trinity College until 1919, when he became Savilian professor of geometry at Oxford; there he founded a flourishing school of research. For the year 1928–1929 he went to Princeton, exchanging places with Oswald Veblen. He returned to Cambridge in 1931, succeeding E. W. Hobson as Sadleirian professor of pure mathematics; he held this chair until his retirement in 1942.

Besides Littlewood and Ramanujan, Hardy collaborated with many other mathematicians, including E. C. Titchmarsh, A. E. Ingham, E. Landau, G. Pólya, E. M. Wright, W. W. Rogosinski, and M. Riesz. He had an exceptional gift for working with others, as he had for leading young men in their early days of research.

Hardy had one ruling passion—mathematics. Apart from that his main interest was in ball games, particularly cricket, of which he was a stylish player and an expert critic. Some of his interests and antipathies are revealed by this list of six New Year wishes which he sent on a postcard to a friend in the 1920's: (1) prove the Riemann hypothesis; (2) make 211 not out in the fourth innings of the last test match at the Oval; (3) find an argument for the nonexistence of God which shall convince the general public; (4) be the first man at the top of Mt. Everest; (5) be proclaimed the first president of the U.S.S.R. of Great Britain and Germany; (6) murder Mussolini.

Hardy was generally recognized as the leading English pure mathematician of his time. His writings attest both his technical power and his mastery of English prose. The photographs in *Collected Papers* show his finely cut features and something of his physical grace. His liveliness and enthusiasm are vivid in the memory of all who knew him. He received awards from many universities and academies, being elected in 1947 *associé étranger* of the Paris Academy of Sciences—of whom there are only ten from all nations in all subjects.

BIBLIOGRAPHY

I. ORIGINAL WORKS. Hardy published, alone or in collaboration, about 350 papers. A complete list is in *Journal of the London Mathematical Society,* **25** (1950), 89–101. Collected papers are being published in 7 vols. (Oxford, 1966–), edited, with valuable comments, by a committee appointed by the London Mathematical Society.

Hardy wrote four tracts published at Cambridge: *The Integration of Functions of a Single Variable* (1905); *Orders of Infinity* (1910); *The General Theory of Dirichlet's Series* (1915), written with M. Riesz; and *Fourier Series* (1944), written with W. W. Rogosinski. The last, in particular, is a model of concise lucidity.

Hardy underlined the neglect of analysis in England by writing in the preface to the 1st ed. of *A Course of Pure Mathematics* (Cambridge, 1908; 10th ed., 1952): "I have indeed in an examination asked a dozen candidates, including several future senior wranglers, to sum the series $1 + x + x^2 + \cdots$ and not received a single answer that was not practically worthless." His book changed all that. *Inequalities* (Cambridge, 1934), written with J. E. Littlewood and G. Pólya, is a systematic account and includes much material previously accessible only in journals. *The Theory of Numbers* (Oxford, 1938), written with E. M.

Wright, includes chapters on a variety of topics.

Other works include *A Mathematician's Apology* (Cambridge, 1940; repr. 1967 with a foreword by C. P. Snow); *Ramanujan* (Cambridge, 1940), twelve lectures on his life and work; *Bertrand Russell and Trinity* (Cambridge, 1970), an account of a 1914–1918 controversy, showing Hardy's sympathy with Russell's opposition to the war. See especially *Divergent Series* (Cambridge, 1948), completed by Hardy shortly before his death. According to Littlewood in his foreword, "All his books gave him some degree of pleasure, but this one, his last, was his favourite."

II. SECONDARY LITERATURE. Notices on Hardy are in *Nature,* **161** (1948), 797; *Obituary Notices of Fellows of the Royal Society of London,* **6** (1949), 447–470, with portrait; *Journal of the London Mathematical Society,* **25** (1950), 81; and *Dictionary of National Biography 1941–1950* (Oxford, 1959), 358–360.

J. C. BURKILL

HARISH-CHANDRA (*b.* Kanpur, India, 11 October 1923; *d.* Princeton, New Jersey, 16 October 1983)

Harish-Chandra was one of the most profound mathematicians of his time. Although he started his scientific career as a theoretical physicist, he was always preoccupied with the purely mathematical aspects of physical theories, and eventually worked entirely in mathematics. His work, in algebra and analysis, is concerned almost exclusively with the theory of representations of groups and their harmonic analysis. This area of mathematics is at the interface of such varied disciplines as physics, number theory, and geometry; and some of the greatest mathematicians—such as Georg Frobenius, Élie Cartan, Hermann Weyl, I. M. Gel'fand, Atle Selberg, and Robert Langlands—have been attracted to it. Harish-Chandra's work is widely regarded as a brilliant and enduring part of it. That representation theory and harmonic analysis are among the most central and active areas of interest in present-day mathematics is partly due to his lifelong efforts dating from the 1940's. He had his early scientific training in India but settled in the United States, where almost all of his work was done. No mathematician of comparable stature has arisen from India in the second half of the twentieth century.

Harish-Chandra was born into an upper-middle-class family. His father, Chandra Kishore, was a civil engineer in the government of Uttar Pradesh (then known as the United Provinces); his mother, Satyagati Seth Chandrarani, was the daughter of a lawyer. Harish-Chandra was a brilliant student, and graduated with an M.Sc. from the university of Allahabad in 1943. Although the educational system under the British colonial administration was mostly sterile, there were some exceptions here and there, mainly due to the efforts of a few remarkable but isolated individuals, such as C. V. Raman in Bangalore and P. C. Mahalanobis in Calcutta. Another was K. S. Krishnan, a physicist at the University of Allahabad. Harish-Chandra studied under Krishnan, whose influence stayed with him throughout his life.

From Allahabad, Harish-Chandra went to Bangalore in southern India as a research student with H. J. Bhabha, a leading theoretical physicist who later created the Tata Institute of Fundamental Research and developed it into a world-class research institution in mathematics and physics. In 1945 Harish-Chandra went to England to work with P. A. M. Dirac at Cambridge. His thesis, on the classification of irreducible representations of the Lorentz group, gave clear indications that he was already becoming fascinated with the purely mathematical. In the year 1947–1948 he was at the Institute for Advanced Study at Princeton as an assistant to Dirac, who was a visiting professor there. In 1950 he went to Columbia University, remaining there until 1963. He then returned to the Institute for Advanced Study as a permanent member, a position he held until his death. In 1968 Harish-Chandra was named the I.B.M.–von Neumann professor of mathematics at the institute. He was elected a fellow of the Royal Society in 1973 and a member of the U.S. National Academy of Sciences in 1981. He was awarded honorary doctorates by Delhi University in 1973 and Yale University in 1981.

In 1952 Harish-Chandra married Lalitha Kale; they had two daughters.

Harish-Chandra's health was always fragile, and his health problems were compounded by the relentlessly ascetic and overwhelmingly intense nature of his work patterns. He suffered a heart attack in 1969, but continued to work on the central questions, as he saw them, of representation theory. But the damage to his heart was irreversible and his problems grew worse, resulting in a fatal heart seizure as he was walking in the woods near the institute at Princeton.

The origins of the theory of group representations go back at least to the work of Georg Frobenius in the nineteenth century; its main problem is to represent abstractly given groups by concrete matrices in such a way that the group operation corresponds to multiplication of matrices. Originally only finite groups and matrices of finite size were considered. However, with the rise of quantum mechanics it became increasingly clear that infinite groups and matrices have to be included. Indeed, one of the fundamental techniques for understanding very complex interacting systems of highly energetic elementary particles is to study the groups of symmetries that leave the system unchanged, and to use this study to limit the possibilities.

In order to apply this technique, it is indispensable to have a complete knowledge of the representations of the symmetry groups. The groups that are important in these problems, such as the rotation and Lorentz groups and their variants, are examples of what mathematicians call simple groups. The simple groups were classified by Cartan and Wilhelm Killing in the nineteenth century, and by 1925 all their finite dimensional representations were classified by Cartan and Weyl. What Harish-Chandra did was to construct the most fundamental infinite dimensional representations of all the simple groups and use them to carry out the harmonic analysis of functions and generalized functions in these groups. The technical problems that he had to overcome in completing this project involved entirely novel aspects of the theory of differential equations on group manifolds.

High-energy physics is not the only area where representation theory of simple groups is a crucial ingredient. Modern number theory is another, and current formulations of the problem of understanding the arithmetic of Galois extensions of algebraic number fields make essential use of the language and results of the representation theory. The classical number theoretic investigations, culminating in the work of David Hilbert, Teiji Takagi, Emil Artin, Helmut Hasse, and others, had obtained a marvelous description of the Abelian extensions of number fields. One of the great achievements of modern number theory is the discovery that similar descriptions of *all* extensions (Abelian or not) of number fields ultimately depend on establishing certain natural correspondences between representations of the Galois groups and appropriate representations of certain simple groups associated to the number fields.

Although there had been many attempts to study infinite-dimensional representations of groups before Harish-Chandra, it was he who began the systematic theory of representations of all simple groups. Unlike his predecessors, who worked with special groups and ad hoc methods, Harish-Chandra realized immediately that it was essential to develop an approach that integrated the algebraic, geometric, and analytic aspects of simple groups. For instance, his papers were the first to consider representations of nontrivial infinite-dimensional associative algebras. Quite early in his work he made the major discovery that one can associate to any irreducible representation of a simple group a character that is the trace of the matrices that represent the group elements. Characters are not new, of course; both Frobenius and Weyl had worked with them and obtained beautiful formulas for them, but they worked with matrices of finite size and there was no conceptual difficulty in defining the characters and developing their theory. But the Harish-Chandra character is more subtle and singular, being the trace of an infinite matrix; indeed, it is a nontrivial matter even to define it, and the only tools available for its study are the differential equations satisfied by it.

The cornerstone of Harish-Chandra's work is a profound and astonishingly complete study of the solutions of these differential equations that led him to a complete description of all the fundamental characters. Complicating the development was the fact that the characters are a priori functions only in a very generalized sense, and Harish-Chandra had to prove ex post facto that they are functions in the classical sense. This result, known as the Harish-Chandra regularity theorem, is one of his greatest achievements and its influence pervades the entire subject. In spite of repeated efforts by many people, it has not been possible to deduce this theorem as a consequence of general principles from the theory of differential equations.

In order to carry out the harmonic analysis of functions on the simple groups in terms of the characters, it is necessary to understand how the elementary functions that arise from the characters behave at infinitely distant parts of the group manifold. The second major achievement of Harish-Chandra was his complete solution to this problem and the explicit harmonic analysis that flowed from this asymptotic theory. Roughly speaking, these elementary functions can be expanded in an infinite series at infinity, and the leading terms of these expansions determine in a very simple and explicit manner the weights with which the various characters enter the harmonic analysis of the delta function on the group.

BIBLIOGRAPHY

I. Original Works. Harish-Chandra's works were brought together in his *Collected Papers*, V. S. Varadarajan, ed., 4 vols. (New York and Berlin, 1984).

II. Secondary Literature. Robert P. Langlands, in *Biographical Memoirs of Fellows of the Royal Society*, **31** (1985), 199–225; and V. S. Varadarajan, "Harish-Chandra (1923–1983)," *The Mathematical Intelligencer*, **6**, no. 3 (1984), 9–19.

V. S. Varadarajan

HARRIOT (or **HARIOT), THOMAS** (*b.* Oxford, England, *ca.* 1560; *d.* London, England, 2 July 1621)

Little is known of Harriot's early life. In 1584 he was in the service of Walter Ralegh where he had possibly been since 1580, when he finished his undergraduate studies at Oxford. Ralegh, who needed an expert in cartography and the theory of oceanic navigation, sent a colonizing expedition to Virginia in 1585, with Harriot as its scientist "in dealing with the naturall inhabitants specially imployed." He investigated their life, language, and customs and surveyed the coasts, islands, and rivers.

Harriot left Virginia in 1586, having learned, among other things, how to "drink" tobacco smoke, which he recommended in his *Briefe Report* (1588) as a cure for many complaints. When Ralegh turned his activities to Ireland and sought to colonize Munster, he leased Molana Abbey to Harriot. We do not know much about his life there, for he took care to order that all papers concerning the "Irische Accounts" be burned after his death. Although the *Briefe Report* had stressed Harriot's missionary zeal, some years later he joined a circle (Shakespeare's "School of Night") which included the atheist Christopher Marlowe and theists like Ralegh and the ninth earl of Northumberland. When, in about 1598, Harriot left Ralegh and Durham House, Northumberland gave him a yearly pension and living quarters in Sion House, Isleworth, and later (1608?) he lived in a house of his own, near the main building.

Harriot and his patron were imprisoned after the Gunpowder Plot of 5 November 1605. Although the earl was kept in the Tower of London until 1622, Harriot was released after a short time, a search of his papers having produced nothing incriminating. Subsequently he complained to Johann Kepler of impaired health; he was able nonetheless to proceed with his scientific investigations and even to undertake prolonged telescopic observations (1610–1613) of Jupiter's satellites and of sunspots. In 1613 he began to suffer from an ulcer in his left nostril. It proved to be cancerous and led to his death in 1621. He left more than 10,000 folio pages of scientific papers containing measurements, diagrams, tables, and calculations pertaining to important experimental and theoretical work in different fields.

Harriot was an accomplished mathematician who enriched algebra with a comprehensive theory of equations. By using an extremely convenient system of notation he simplified not only algebra, but also many other areas of mathematics. Among his innovations and discoveries is his proof that stereographic projection is conformal and therefore transforms rhumb lines on a sphere into equiangular helixes (logarithmic spirals) in its equatorial plane. He also made ingenious attempts to rectify and

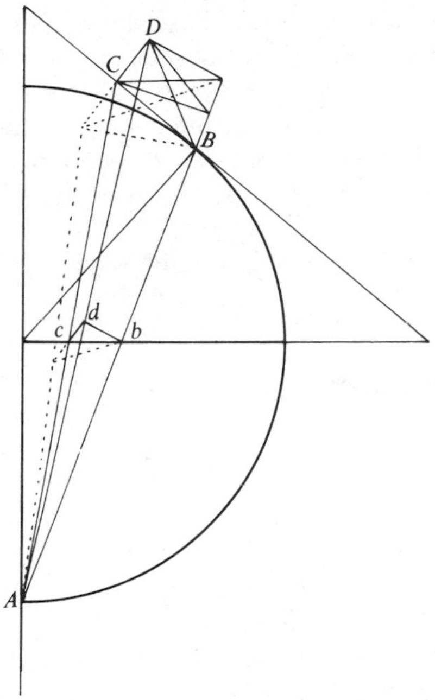

FIGURE 1. Harriot's diagram to his proof that the stereographic projection is conformal, much simplified (Add. 6789, f. 18).

square these spirals. In 1603 he computed the area of a spherical triangle: "Take the sum of all three angles and subtract 180 degrees. Set the remainder as numerator of a fraction with denominator 360 degrees. This fraction tells us how great a portion of the hemisphere is occupied by the triangle."

In about 1614 he resumed his early investigations of rhumb lines and the theory of the Mercator map, and nearly finished a table of meridional parts for this map. These computations were calculated for one-minute intervals, an enormous task that necessitated the use of sophisticated techniques of finite-difference interpolation, on which he wrote a monograph, *De numeris triangularibus.* His notational advances in this treatise are great, but even more interesting, and found only in preliminary drafts, are some symbols, including $\overset{1}{p}, \overset{2}{p}, \overset{3}{p}, \overset{4}{p}, \cdots$, for our figured numbers (or binomial coefficients)

$$\binom{n}{1}, \binom{n+1}{2}, \binom{n+2}{3}, \binom{n+3}{4}, \cdots.$$

Harriot knew that such formulas are valid even when negative integers or fractions are substituted for the number n. Not only are his apt notation and sense of structure admirable, but also the exceptional clarity of his exposition, as is evident in both finished manuscript tracts and his rough work sheets.

Harriot's *Artis analyticae praxis,* published posthumously in 1631 (in a poor edition), contains an interesting attempt at a uniform treatment of all algebraic equations, with worked-out examples of linear, quadratic, cubic, quartic, and quintic equations. Because he composed this "practice of the art of analysis" primarily for amateurs, he did not treat negative roots, but in other manuscripts he even considered "noetical" (that is, imaginary) roots, as, for example,

$$\left.\begin{array}{r} b - a \\ c - a \\ df - aa \end{array}\right| \begin{array}{l} = bcdf - bdfa + dfaa + baaa \\ \quad - dcfa - bcaa + caaa - aaaa = 0000 \end{array}$$

$$\begin{aligned} a &= b \\ a &= c \\ aa &= -df \\ a &= \sqrt{-df}, \end{aligned}$$

a being the unknown quantity of this quartic, whose solutions appear on the right.

At times Harriot developed his mathematical deduction vertically downward, a method which may be advantageous to the mathematician, but posed a problem for the printer, as did his use of many new symbols. His symbolic shorthand and instructive examples often allowed him to dispense with explicit verbal explanation in mathematical writings. This is also apparent where he made trials of binary number systems. Unfortunately, the exact dates of Harriot's mathematical tracts and discoveries are known only in rare cases.

In his optics research it is easier to fix a chronology. No later than the early 1590's, he made a penetrating study of Ibn al-Haytham's (Alhazen's) *Optics* (Friedrich Risner's 1572 edition). To solve Alhazen's mirror problem he considered the locus of the reflection point for a spherical mirror expanding about its center. He thus anticipated Isaac Barrow, who proposed the same curve in 1669. Then Harriot investigated optical phenomena which Alhazen had neglected, or had not fully explored.

In order to establish a firm basis for the theory of burning glasses and of the rainbow, Harriot began in 1597 to measure the refraction of light rays in water and glass. He soon found that the Ptolemaic tables, then attributed to Witelo, were inaccurate. About 1601 he discovered that the *extensa* (essentially our refractive index) is the same for all angles of incidence. This enabled him to compute refraction for one-degree intervals of the angles of incidence. For water his index of refraction was cosec 48°30′ and for glass cosec 40°. In 1606 Harriot sent Kepler refraction angles and specific weights for thirteen substances, but he withheld the sine proportion from him.

Harriot also studied prismatic colors. When he looked through a prism at a white object on a dark background, it seemed to be fringed with a yellow and red border. (Blue is not mentioned.) From the breadth of the colors Harriot computed (1604) refractive indexes of the green, orange, and (extremal) red rays. By pouring liquids into hollow glass prisms, he determined analogous refractive indexes for fresh water, saturated salt water, turpentine, and spirits of alcohol. With his refraction tables Harriot calculated the *refractio caeca* (total refraction) in prisms and the path of solar rays through plano-convex lenses and glass balls. For a ray traversing water drops he found that the *arcus egressionis* (exit arc) $2r - i$ should have a maximum value

$$2 \times 40°5' - 59°17' = 20°53'.$$

Although in 1606 Harriot told Kepler that he planned a book on colors and the rainbow, his preserved manuscripts contain no statement of the exact relationship between maximum exit arc and the angular radius R, of the first rainbow, namely

$$R, = 2 \times 20°53' = 41°46'.$$

Until the early 1590's Harriot's astronomical researches centered on nautical applications. Observing from the roof of Durham House (1591–1592), he measured an angular distance of 2°56′ between the celestial north pole and the North Star. Prominent among his suggestions for improved navigational instruments was an ingenious backstaff for measuring solar altitudes. The comet of 1607 ("Halley's comet") was observed by Harriot in London and by his pupil Sir William Lower in Wales. In a letter of 6 February 1610 Lower mentions that Harriot for some years had mistrusted the "circular astronomy" of Copernicus. Accordingly, as soon as Kepler's newly published *Astronomia Nova* reached England in 1609, they both studied it eagerly. Reworking a number of Kepler's computations, they discovered many minor errors. In the summer of 1609 Harriot turned a 6X telescope on the moon. Soon after, when he heard of Galileo's findings, he began a systematic survey of the sky and to this end his assistant and amanuensis Christopher Tooke constructed better telescopes, the finest having a magnification of thirty. A few detailed moon maps, ninety-nine drawings of Jupiter with satellites, and seventy-four folios of sun disks with spots testify to Harriot's hard work and perseverance as an observing astronomer from 1610 to 1613. Despite increasing ill health he was still able to make some observations of comets in 1618.

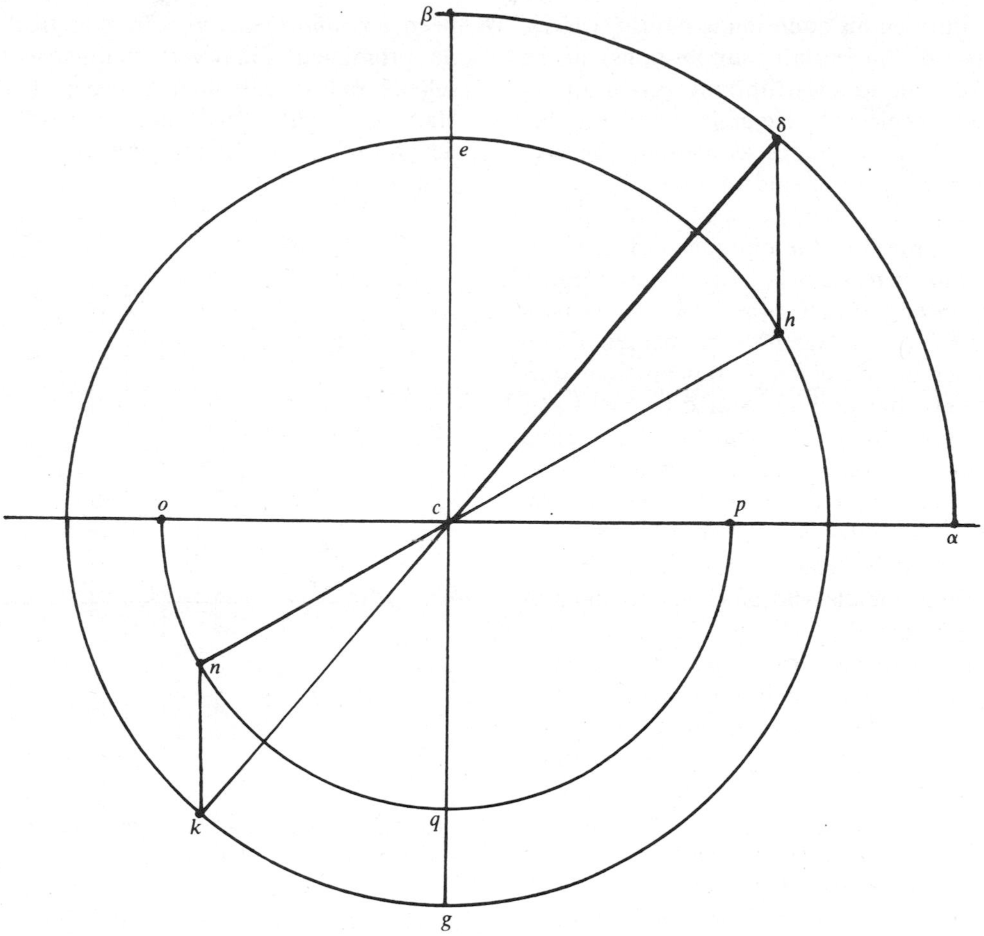

FIGURE 2. Harriot's "Regium" diagram, simplified (Add. 6789, f. 320). If k is the image point and h the eye, cn is Harriot's *linea contracta.* If h is the object point and k the eye, $c\delta$ is the *linea extensa.*

Harriot's manuscripts reveal little about his possibly extensive chemical researches and not much about his meteorological observations. He once measured the rainfall per square foot on the roof of Durham House, and he apparently possessed a scale for wind velocity. About 1600 he may for some time have been one of Cecil's decoding experts. Of great importance are his investigations on free and resisted motion in air. From the roof of Sion House (about forty-three feet) Harriot dropped twenty bullets, releasing each when the preceding one struck the ground. He determined the total fall time by pulse beats. In order to evaluate his results theoretically, he first rejected as negligible any *gradus naturae* (initial velocity). Then, after some hesitation, he decided to take acceleration proportional to time spent and not to space traversed. These assumptions yielded fall spaces equivalent to thirteen feet (in other trials sixteen feet) after one second. On dropping bullets of different specific weights simultaneously, he observed no appreciable difference between bullets of iron and lead, but wax bullets lagged behind.

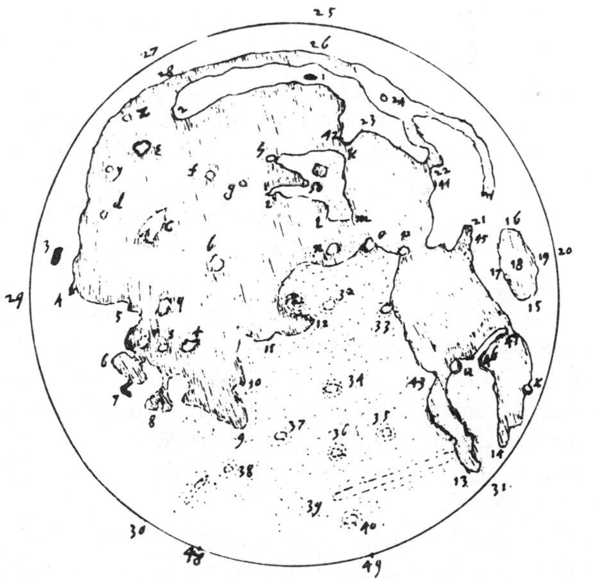

FIGURE 3. The most elaborate of Harriot's moon maps (Petworth 241).

Harriot next turned his attention to ballistic curves, which he proved (on certain suppositions) to be parabolas with oblique axes (upright axes if air resistance could be neglected). He did not expressly say that he regarded air resistance as constant, but applied the kinematic rule of odd numbers 1, 3, 5, 7, . . ., not only for the vertical component of fall, but also "in inverse order" to the oblique component of motion subject to air resistance. Later James Gregory also proposed tilted parabolas in *Tentamina de motu projectorum* (1672), but Harriot's mathematical deduction had been more elegant. It appears from Harriot's manuscripts that he had studied printed tracts of William Heytesbury, Bernhard Tornius, and Aluarus Thomas on problems of uniform and difform change. Some of Harriot's diagrams on uniform difform motion resemble those of Nicole Oresme.

In 1603 and 1604 Harriot measured specific weights. For those metals and chemical compounds which could be obtained nearly pure, his results agree remarkably well with modern values. Near the end of his life he wrote a small treatise entitled *De reflectione corporum rotundorum* (1619) that contains two suggestive diagrams and a small web of equations, which, when unraveled, emerge as relations between the velocities of balls before and after collision. He lacked, however, any concept equivalent to the modern principle that kinetic energy is preserved in perfectly elastic collision. Apparently he considered this last treatise fundamental to understanding how atoms collide with other atoms or light globules. Two or three of his rough diagrams show light globules zigzagging between layers of atoms.

Harriot was acquainted with older mathematicians like John Dee and, according to Anthony à Wood, Thomas Allen had been his teacher at Oxford. Harriot soon surpassed these two and all other English mathematicians of his time. Apart from a few letters exchanged with Kepler, there is no documented knowledge of correspondence or personal contact with scientists of his own rank but scanty references suggest that distinguished contemporaries like William Gilbert, Bacon, and Briggs knew something of Harriot's scientific work. The mathematicians of Harriot's own circle were Nathaniel Torporley, Walter Warner, and Robert Hughes. He was also closely acquainted with such scientifically minded men as William Lower, Thomas Aylesbury, Robert Sidney, and Lord Harington.

George Chapman, the poet, praised Harriot as a universal genius and a connoisseur of poetry. Long after Harriot's death, at the time of John Aubrey, rumors still persisted of Harriot's disputes with theologians. Although his favorite maxim is said to have been *Ex nihilo nihil fit,* such heretical opinions are not prominent in his extant manuscripts, and a bookseller's bill reveals that between 1617 and 1619, Harriot bought many tracts on Christian theology. Several of his minor manuscripts deal with infinity and its paradoxes.

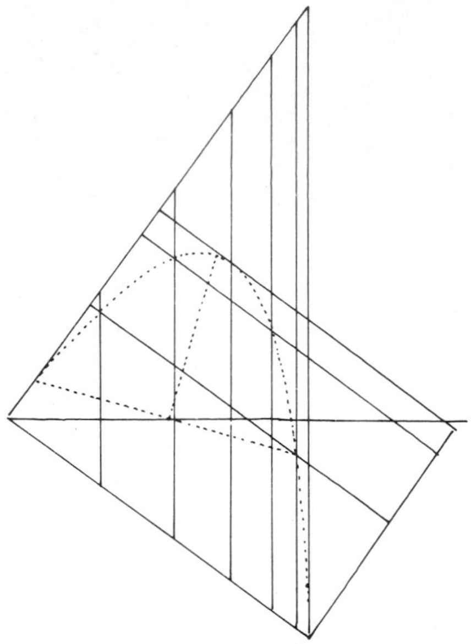

FIGURE 4. One of Harriot's ballistic parabolas with tilted axis, slightly simplified (Add. 6789, f. 64).

Harriot seldom completed his planned scientific treatises and never published any of them. This may largely be explained by adverse external circumstances, procrastination, and his reluctance to publish a tract when he thought that further work might improve it. Unlike Kepler, Harriot did not commit his inner thoughts and personal motives to paper. During the last years of his life, weakened health prevented his preparing any manuscript for the press. His will delegated this task to Torporley. Walter Warner, supervised by Aylesbury, then took over in 1627 and published the *Artis analyticae praxis,* but the planned edition of Harriot's major works came to nothing.

In the summer of 1627 Aylesbury and Warner measured refractions in several glass prisms and then calculated refraction tables modeled on Harriot's. Warner's young friend, John Pell, wrote to Mersenne on 24 January 1640 that Harriot had found the law of refraction. When, however, in 1644 Mersenne published, in *Universae geometriae . . . synopsis* (pp. 549–566), a posthumous tract by Warner on the sine law, Harriot's name was not even mentioned. Pell, who had borrowed some Harriot manuscripts from Aylesbury, later said that if Harriot had "published all he knew in algebra, he would have left little of the chief mysteries of that art unhandled" (S. P. Rigaud, *Correspondence of Scientific Men,* p. 153). After 1649, when Aylesbury was forced to leave England, Harriot's papers disappeared, but in 1784 F. X. von Zach rediscovered them under stable accounts in Petworth House, Sussex. Harriot's reputation has alternately waxed (owing to excessive praise by John Wallis and Zach) and waned (as a result of criticism by J. E. Montucla and Rigaud). More recently, on the basis of comprehensive and penetrating studies of his surviving manuscripts, his name is becoming increasingly important.

BIBLIOGRAPHY

I. Original Works. The chief—and far from fully explored—sources for Harriot's science are fifteen small Harriot MSS in Petworth House archives, Sussex, England, and eight big unordered MSS in the British Museum (Add. 6782–6789). Unless otherwise stated, the following items are British Museum MSS:

Arcticon, a textbook on navigation, and a *Chronicle* on the Virginia expedition, both lost; *A Briefe and True Report of the New Found Land of Virginia* (London, 1588), incorporated in vol. III of Richard Hakluyt's *Principall Navigations,* 3 vols. (London, 1598–1600); also translated into French, German, and Latin; "Doctrine of Nauticall Triangles Compendious," Petworth 241, vol. 6b; a tract "De rumborum ortu, natura et usu," announced in the preface to Robert Hughes, *De Globis* (1594); "Some Instructions for Ralegh's Voyage to Guiana" (1595), Add. 6708; "De numeris triangularibus," Add. 6782, fols. 107–146; "Optics and Caustics" (*ca.* 1604), Add. 6789, fols. 89–400, the most important of his works in optics; "On Ballistics," Add. 6789; numerous tables intended probably for a tract (*ca.* 1604) on specific weights, Add. 6788; drafts of chapters on algebra, not incorporated in Warner's ed. of the *Praxis,* Add. 6783; Harriot's and Lower's observations of the comet of 1607, Petworth 241, vol. 7, published in supp. I to Bradley's *Miscellaneous Works* (Oxford, 1832), pp. 511–522; "De Jovialibus planetis," ninety-nine annotated diagrams (Oct. 1610–Feb. 1612) and "Sun Spots," seventy-four fols. (Dec. 1610–Jan. 1613), Petworth 241, vol. 8; "Canon nauticus" (1614?), tables of meridional parts, Petworth 240, fols. 1–453; and "De reflectione corporum rotundorum" (1619), Petworth 241, vol. 6a, 23–31, transcription in Harley 6002, fols. 17–22r.

For John Protheroe's inventory of Harriot's MSS bundled at his death, see Add. 6789, fols. 449v–451v. Harriot's will was printed by Henry Stevens (see below), pp. 193–203, and R. C. H. Tanner (see below), pp. 244–247.

Harriot's correspondence with Kepler (1606–1609) is preserved in the Nationalbibliothek, Vienna, Codex 10703. See also *Kepler's Gesammelte Werke,* Max Caspar, ed. (Munich, 1951, 1954), vol. XV, 348–352, 365–368; vol. XVI, 31–32, 172–173, 250–251.

II. Secondary Literature. For information on Harriot, see John Aubrey, *Brief Lives,* O. L. Dicks, ed. (1962); Edward Edwards, *The Life of Sir Walter Ralegh,* 2 vols. (1868); Edward B. Fonblanque, *Annals of the House of Percy,* 2 vols. (London, 1887), privately printed (on the earl and the Gunpowder Plot, see pp. 252–329); J. E. Montucla, *Histoire des mathématiques* (Paris, 1758–1759; 2nd ed., 1799–1802); Muriel Rukeyser, *The Traces of Thomas Harriot* (New York, 1971), a nonscientific treatment; Henry Stevens, *Thomas Harriot, the Mathematician, the Philosopher, and the Scholar* (London, 1900), privately printed; John Wallis, *Treatise of Algebra, Both Historical and Practical* (Oxford, 1685), esp. chs. 53–54; and Anthony à Wood, *Athenae Oxonienses,* 3rd ed., vol. IV (1815), 459.

There are several articles by F. X. von Zach. These may be found in Bode's *Astronomisches Jahrbuch für 1788* (Berlin, 1785), 139–155, and in the first supp. to the Jahrbuch (1793); *Monatliche correspondenz zur Beförderung der Erd- und Himmels-Kunde,* **8** (1803), 36–60; and *Correspondance astronomique,* **6** (1822), 105–138. Zach's publications were severely criticized by S. P. Rigaud; see his two supplements to *Dr. Bradley's Miscellaneous Works* (Oxford, 1832–1833).

Recent books with reference to Harriot include *Correspondance du P. Marin Mersenne,* Tannery, de Waard, Rochot, eds. (Paris, 1936–1965); vol. IX, 61–65, contains an interesting letter on Harriot; vols. X and XI contain information on the law of refraction, as presented by Warner, Pell, and Hobbes; G. R. Batho, *The Household Papers of Henry Percy* (London, 1962), with scattered references to Harriot, Warner, and Torporley; R. H. Kargon, *Atomism in England From Harriot to Newton* (Oxford, 1966), 4–42, 144–150; D. B. Quinn, *Ralegh and the British Empire,* 2nd ed. (London, 1962), 67–69, 85, 142; and D. W. Waters, *The Art of Navigation in England in Elizabethan and Early Stuart Times* (London, 1958), 546–547, 582–591.

Among the numerous recent articles on Harriot, see Jean Jacquot, "Thomas Harriot's Reputation for Impiety," in *Notes and Records. Royal Society of London,* **9** (1952), 164–187; J. A. Lohne, "Thomas Harriott," in *Centaurus,* **6** (1959), 113–121; "Zur Geschichte des Brechungsgesetzes," in *Sudhoffs Archiv für Geschichte der Medizin und der Naturwissenschaften,* **47** (1963), 152–172; "Regenbogen und Brechzahl," *ibid.,* **49** (1965), 401–415; "Thomas Harriot als Mathematiker," in *Centaurus,* **11** (1965), 19–45; and "Dokumente zur Revalidierung von Thomas Harriot als Algebraiker," in *Archive for History of Exact Sciences,* **3** (1966), 185–205; J. V. Pepper, "Harriot's Calculation of Meridional Parts as Logarithmic Tangents," *ibid.,* **4** (1968), 359–413; "Harriot's Unpublished Papers," in *History of Science,* **6** (1968), 17–40; D. H. Sadler, "The Doctrine of Nauticall Triangles Compendious. II. Calculating the Meridional Parts," in *Journal of the Institute of Navigation,* **6** (1953), 141–147; J. W. Shirley, "Binary Numeration Before Leibniz," in *American Journal of Physics,* **19** (1951), 452–454; "An Early Experimental Determination of Snell's Law," *ibid.,* 507–508; and R. C. H. Tanner, "Thomas Harriot as Mathematician," in *Physics,* **9** (1967), 235–247, 257–292.

For other sources, see George Chapman, "To My Admired and Souleloved Friend Mayster of All Essential and True Knowledge, M. Harriots," a poetic preface to *Achil-*

HARTMANN, G.

les' Shield (1598); and Nathaniel Torporley, "Corrector Analyticus: or Strictures on . . . Harriot," in J. O. Halliwell, *Collection of Letters Illustrative of the Progress of Science* (London, 1841), pp. 109–110. Letters concerning Harriot are in S. P. Rigaud, *Correspondence of Scientific Men* (Oxford, 1841); E. Edwards (see above), vol. II, 420–422; *Calendar of the Salisbury MSS at Hatfield House,* XVI (1933); XVII, 544; a letter from Torporley (1602?), Add. 6788, f. 117; letters, mostly from Lower, Add. 6789, fols. 424–449. See also Thomas Aylesbury's report to Northumberland on the publication of Harriot's *Praxis,* Birch 4396, f. 87, British Museum; and Henry Briggs's comments in *Kepler's Gesammelte Werke,* XVIII (Munich, 1959), 228–229; and in George Hakewill, *Apologie or Declaration . . .,* 2nd ed. (Oxford, 1630), pp. 301–302.

Sporadic information on Harriot is in the *Calendars of State Papers, Domestic Series* and *Calendars of State Papers Relating to Ireland.* Sloane MS 2086, fols. 54–57, British Museum, contains Theodore de Mayerne's diagnosis of Harriot's cancerous ulcer with prescription for treatment. See also, in British Museum, Walter Warner's MSS bound in 3 vols, Birch 4394–4396; and Charles Cavendish's MS 6002, with transcriptions of important parts of Harriot's papers.

J. A. LOHNE

HARTMANN, GEORG (*b.* Eggolsheim, near Forchheim, Germany, 9 February 1489; *d.* Nuremberg, Germany, 9 April 1564)

Hartmann studied mathematics with Heinrich Glareanus and theology at Cologne in 1510. In Italy during the summer of 1518 he became friendly with Copernicus' brother Andreas, began designing sundials, and discovered the magnetic dip. The (inaccurate) declination of six degrees which he found for Rome, probably the earliest determination on land, was revealed in a letter to Duke Albert of Prussia dated 4 March 1544, but it remained unpublished until 1831. (Robert Norman published his independent discovery in *The Newe Attractive* [1580].) Settling at Nuremberg in 1518, Hartmann designed and produced timepieces, astrolabes, globes, quadrants, armillary spheres, a star altimeter, and the caliber gauge, which he invented in 1540 to determine the weights of cannonballs from the muzzle sizes of cannons.

Hartmann was vicar of St. Sebaldus from 1518 to 1544 and in 1527 became chaplain of St. Moritz. He was friendly with Willibald Pirkheimer and Albrecht Dürer, about whose death he later reported (see E. Zinner, *Astronomische,* p. 357). From Regiomontanus' literary estate Hartmann treasured a fragment of a letter with important information; he was familiar with Regiomontanus' handwriting, his physical appearance from a portrait, and several astrolabes. In 1526, at Hartmann's request, Johann Schöner published Regiomontanus' manuscript on Ptolemy's optics, *Problemata XXIX. Saphaeae* ("Twenty-nine Problems With the Saphea"). Following Werner's death in 1528 and the dispersal of his manuscripts, Hartmann rescued two on spherical triangles and "De meteoroscopiis," which he gave to Joachim Rheticus in 1542, making a more accurate copy for himself; in 1544 Rheticus published the *De revolutionibus* chapter on triangles as *Nic. Copernici De lateribus et angulis triangulorum tum planerum rectilineorum tum sphaericorum libellus* and dedicated it to Hartmann. Hartmann published *Joh. Pisani Perspectiva communis* in 1542 and an astrological work, *Directorium,* in 1554. His unpublished "Fabrica horologium" (1527) included figures from Ptolemy's *Organum* and influenced Sebastian Münster's *Compositio horologiorum* of 1531.

BIBLIOGRAPHY

I. ORIGINAL WORKS. The letter from Hartmann to Albert of Prussia (4 Mar. 1544), containing the report of his discovery of magnetic inclination and of the first determination of the declination on land, is repr. with a facs. in G. Hellmann, ed., *Rara magnetica 1269–1599,* Neudrucke von Schriften und Karten über Meteorologie und Erdmagnetismus, no. 10 (Berlin, 1898). The original remained unnoticed in the Royal Archives at Königsberg until published by J. Voigt, in Raumer's *Historisches Taschenbuch,* II (Leipzig, 1831), 253–366, then by H. W. Dove in *Reportorium der Physik,* II (Berlin, 1838), 129–132, and again by J. Voigt with twelve other Hartmann letters and four by Albert in *Briefwechsel der berühmsten Gelehrten des Zeitalter der Reformation mit Herzog Albrecht von Preussen 1541–1544* (Königsberg, 1841).

This correspondence provides important insight into the relationship between sovereign and scientist; Hartmann not only discusses the instruments he is making for Archduke Albert but also reports on his visits with and commissions from King Ferdinand of Bohemia and Hungary, and the apostolic envoy and Venetian *orarier,* and his correspondence with Duke Ottheinrich, who in August 1544 sent Hartmann a 1417 boxwood sundial and a commission for two ivory sundials, a brass astrolabe, and a brass armillary sphere. Details of this correspondence are described in Ernst Zinner, *Deutsche und niederländische astronomische Instrumente des 11.-18. Jahrhunderts* (Munich, 1956), p. 358. Zinner's extensive listing, pp. 362–368, of Hartmann's scientific instruments and engravings of 1523–1563 seems limited to European museums and libraries; it omits the nine astronomical charts, unaccompanied by text, in the Weaver Collection of the American Institute of Electrical Engineers, New York City.

Although Nuremberg was a printing center and Hartmann's correspondence reveals that for his instruments he engraved copperplates and printed them himself on his own presses, he put only two works into print: *Joh. Pisani Perspectiva communis* (Nuremberg, 1542), which he edited with extensive corrections and restorations (although unlisted by the Library of Congress, Columbia University and the University of Michigan each own a copy), and his astrological work *Directorium* (Nuremberg, 1554). He reproduced his writings of 1518–1528 in pre-Gutenberg style—Zinner, pp. 358–360, describes in detail "Die Wiener Handschrift Vin 12768," containing copies, completed 14 June 1526 and 19 July 1527, which Hartmann presented to Chaplain Geuder and Ulrich Stocker, and illustrations for sun-clocks for the city of Nuremberg (1526); the Weimar Landesbibliothek no. F. max. 29, a *Prachthandschrift* of 1525[?]–1527 devoted primarily to the design of sundials but including a few figures of astrolabes; Weimar Landesbibliothek no. F. 324, a copy by Hartmann with very careful figures, probably by Hartmann, of Werner's works on the spherical triangles and on the meteoroscope, the original of which Hartmann gave Rheticus for publication.

Other items of interest are an astronomical broadside, an engraving of a sundial, dated 1535, in the Houghton Library of Harvard University; a brass skaphe signed "Georgius Hartmann Noremberge Faciebat 1539," listed in the Wray sale at Sotheby's, Nov. 1959, and purchased by Dr. Weil, a dealer; and a gilt-brass dial of Ahaz, dated 1548, in a private collection in America; see Zinner, pp. 357–368. The Adler Planetarium and Astronomical Museum in Chicago has two instruments not mentioned in Zinner: (1) a gilt-brass astrolabe on which appears the inscription "GEORGIUS HARTMANN NOREMBERG FACIEBAT ANNO MDXL," the rete being a later replacement, and (2) a gilt-brass, silver, and ivory astronomical compendium of astrolabe and sundial in a box of finest goldsmith work inscribed "HARTMANN NURNBERG 1558," believed to be a gift from Emperor Charles V to Duke Emmanuel Philibert of Savoy. The catalog numbers are M-22 and A-7, respectively. Some later instruments are signed "H. G."

II. SECONDARY LITERATURE. Zinner's *Astronomische Instrumente* (cited above) is the major work. J. G. Doppelmayr, *Historische Nachricht von den Nürnbergischen Mathematicis und Kunstlern* (Nuremberg, 1730), pp. 56–58; Karl Heger, "Georg Hartmann von Eggolsheim," in *Der frankische Schatzgräber,* **2** (1924), 25–29; and K. Kupfer, "Nachtrag zu Georg Hartmann," *ibid.,* **7** (1929), 37–38, were all used by Zinner. Hellmann discusses Hartmann's discovery of the magnetic dip in the introduction to *Rara magnetica* (cited above), pp. 15–16, and attributes Hartmann's knowledge of other magnetic properties to the "Epistola Petri Peregrini de magnete" of 1269, which was probably the "alte Pergamentbuch" (parchment manuscript) Hartmann obtained in 1525, during the Peasants' War. For details of the Regiomontanus letter fragment owned by Hartmann, see Ernst Zinner, *Leben und Wirken des Johannes Müller von Königsberg* (Munich, 1938), pp. 195, 202–203.

English references to Hartmann are found scattered in Lynn Thorndike, *History of Magic and Experimental Science* (New York, 1941), V, 337, 353, 355, 364–365, 414, and VI, 60; R. J. Forbes, *Man the Maker* (New York, 1950), p. 123; and Abraham Wolf, *A History of Science, Technology and Philosophy in the 16th and 17th Centuries* (New York, 1959), I, 292. The geographer Baron N.A.E. Nordenskjold, in his *Facsimile-Atlas to the Early History of Cartography With Reproductions of the Most Important Maps Printed in the XV and XVI Centuries,* trans. from the Swedish by Johan Adolf Ekelof and Clements R. Markham (Stockholm, 1889), reasons that Hartmann, "a celebrated manufacturer of globes and cosmographical instruments," rather than Schöner probably made the unsigned terrestrial globe portrayed in Hans Holbein's *Ambassadors;* Mary F. S. Hervey, *Holbein's "Ambassadors"* (London, 1900), pp. 210–218, upholds the opposite position. The original woodcut terrestrial globe gores, twelve to a plate, reproduced by Nordenskjold, are in the New York Public Library, catalogued as "[Globe gores with Magellan's route Nuremberg? 153–?] Possibly the work of Georg Hartmann of Nuremberg."

LUCILLE B. RITVO

HARTMANN, JOHANNES (*b.* Amberg, Oberpfalz, Germany, 14 January 1568; *d.* Kassel, Germany, 7 December 1631)

Hartmann, a weaver's son, worked as a bookbinder; scholarship aid enabled him to attend the university. He studied the arts, notably mathematics, at Jena, Wittenberg, and, from 1591, Marburg, from which he received a master's degree. He may also have attended the universities of Altdorf, Helmstedt, and Leipzig. A friend, the Hessian court chronicler Wilhelm Dilich, introduced Hartmann to Landgrave Wilhelm IV of Hesse-Kassel, who was interested in the natural sciences, and to the landgrave's son Moritz, who was interested particularly in alchemical metallurgical processes. In 1592 Hartmann became professor of mathematics at the University of Marburg, which was under the jurisdiction of Wilhelm IV's brother, Landgrave Ludwig. He also studied medicine and received a doctorate in this subject in 1606. In addition, in 1594 he became adviser to Landgrave Moritz in Kassel, where he taught at the court school until 1601.

Thereafter Hartmann combined his interest in mathematics, astronomy, and alchemy with medicine. Starting in 1609 he gave lectures and practical laboratory instruction on materia medica and the chemical and mineralogical preparation of medicines in the "laboratorium chymicum publicum" at Marburg. In the same year he was appointed professor of medical and pharmaceutical chemistry, in effect the first such professorship in Europe. He was several times dean and rector of the University of Marburg and was also very successful in his scientific work. By 1616 ten of his students had earned the doctorate. Following disputes with the university and the landgrave, Hartmann moved in 1621 to Kassel—nominally retaining his professorship—and became court physician, a post he lost as a result of the abdication of Landgrave Moritz in 1627. Until his death in 1631 Hartmann was professor of natural science and medicine at the new University of Kassel, which had offered courses for four years before its official opening in 1633.

Hartmann's importance is in having introduced pharmaceutical and medical chemistry into the university and in having given practical instruction in it. This new field, which had been developed in the works of Paracelsus and his disciples, was then emerging from alchemy. Yet Hartmann did not fall into alchemical speculations; instead, he sought to mediate between the Galenists and the iatrochemists. He left few writings on the practical aspects of the subject, and most of his works appeared posthumously. A glimpse of his activity is given by a laboratory journal for the year 1615.

As a physician Hartmann was not especially successful. His nickname "Theophrastus Cassellanus" derives from his Paracelsian-chemical activity. There is no doubt that his Hermetic philosophical ideas had a considerable influence during 1614–1626, which even his contemporaries called the "Rosicrucian" period; and his views, a union of animistic and vitalistic notions, reached far beyond his native land, carried by friends and students including Oswald Crollius, Johann Daniel Mylius, and Johannes Rhenanus. In addition, he corresponded with English and Polish iatrochemists and with alchemists in Prague. The many editions of his principal work, *Praxis chymiatrica,* testify to the respect that contemporaries accorded to this textbook of pharmaceutical chemistry.

BIBLIOGRAPHY

I. ORIGINAL WORKS. Hartmann's works were collected as *Opera omnia medico-chymica,* Conrad Johrenius, ed. (Frankfurt, 1684; 1690), also translated into German (1698). His individual works include *Disputationes elementorum geometricorum* (Kassel, 1600); 'Επιφυλλιδες *sive miscellae medicae cum* προθηκη *chymico therapeutica doloris colici* (Marburg, 1606); *Philosophus sive naturae consultus medicus, oratio* (Marburg, 1609); *Disputationes chymicomedicae quatuordecim* (Marburg, 1611; 1614), also translated into English as *Choice Collection of Chymical Experiments* (London, 1682) and into German as *Philosophische Geheimnisse und chymische Experimenta* (Hamburg, 1684); *Praxis chymiatrica* (Leipzig, 1633; Frankfurt, 1634; 1671; Geneva, 1635; 1639; 1647; 1649; 1659; 1682; Leiden, 1663; Nuremberg, 1677), also translated into German as *Chymische Arzneiübung* (Nuremberg, 1678); and *Tractatus physico-medicus de opio* (Wittenberg, 1635; 1658). In addition, Hartmann prepared an edition, which was finished by his son, G. E. Hartmann, of Oswald Crollius' *Basilica chymica* (Geneva, 1635) and works of Joseph Duchesne (Quercetanus). Under the pseudonym Christopher Glückradt he commented on the *Tyrocinium chymicum* of J. Beguin (Wittenberg, 1634, 1666).

II. SECONDARY LITERATURE. The following, listed in chronological order, may be consulted: Andreas Libavius, *Examen philosophiae novae* (Frankfurt, 1615), which discusses Hartmann's ideas on vital and Hermetic philosophy; and *Appendix necessaria syntagmatis . . .* (Frankfurt, 1615), with the ch. "Censura philosophiae vitalis Joannis Hartmanni"; Friedrich W. Strieder, *Grundlage zu einer hessischen Gelehrten- und Schriftstellergeschichte,* V (Kassel, 1785), 281–289; John Ferguson, *Bibliotheca chemica,* I (Glasgow, 1906; repr. London, 1954), 365, 366; Wilhelm Ganzenmüller, "Das chemische Laboratorium der Universität Marburg im Jahre 1615," in *Angewandte Chemie,* **54** (1941), also in Ganzenmüller's *Beiträge zur Geschichte der Technologie und der Alchemie* (Weinheim, 1956), pp. 314–322; Lynn Thorndike, *A History of Magic and Experimental Science,* VIII (New York–London, 1958), 116–118; Rudolf Schmitz, "Die Universität Kassel und ihre Beziehung zu Pharmazie und Chemie," in *Pharmazeutische Zeitung,* **104** (1959), 1413–1417; J. R. Partington, *A History of Chemistry,* II (London–New York, 1961), 177–178; Rudolf Schmitz, "Naturwissenschaft an der Universität Marburg," in *Sitzungsberichte der Gesellschaft zur Beförderung der gesamten Naturwissenschaften zu Marburg,* **83–84** (1961–1962), 12–21; and Rudolf Schmitz and Adolf Winkelmann, "Johannes Hartmann (1568–1631) Doctor, Medicus et Chymiatriae Professor Publicus," in *Pharmazeutische Zeitung,* **111** (1966), 1233–1241.

R. SCHMITZ

HARTREE, DOUGLAS RAYNER (*b.* Cambridge, England, 27 March 1897; *d.* Cambridge, 12 February 1958)

Hartree's chief contribution to science was his development of powerful methods of numerical mathematical analysis, which made it possible for him to apply successfully the so-called self-consistent field method to the calculation of atomic wave functions of polyelectronic atoms, that is, those which in the neutral condition have more than one electron surrounding the nucleus. These calculations involved the numerical solution of the partial differential equations of quantum mechanics for many-body systems subject to the usual boundary conditions. From the atomic wave functions it is possible to calculate the average distribution of negative electric charge as a function of distance from the nucleus. If the distribution has been correctly found for all the electrons in the atom under study, the electric field due to this distribution should lead to the original distribution, in which case the field is called self-consistent.

Hartree developed ingenious approximation methods for the rather rapid evaluation of such self-consistent fields. The corresponding wave functions and associated charge distributions are of great importance in the theoretical calculation of macroscopic properties of matter in various states of aggregation. Hartree and his collaborators evaluated wave functions for more than twenty-five different atomic species in various states of ionization. Through his stimulus and encouragement many more atoms were investigated by physicists throughout the world. Hartree's equations as generalized by V. Fock proved to be extremely valuable in theoretical calculations in solid state physics.

Hartree also applied his methods of numerical analysis to problems in ballistics, atmospheric physics, and hydrodynamics. Much of this work was of importance to Britain's war effort from 1939 to 1945. He further turned his attention to industrial control and made valuable contributions to the control of chemical engineering processes. He early became interested in machine calculation and built the first differential analyzer in Britain for the graphical solution of differential equations. He later pioneered in the introduction of digital computers and their use in the United Kingdom. He made numerous visits to the United States and shared his knowledge freely with American colleagues in the same field.

Hartree was the great-grandson on his father's side of the famous Samuel Smiles, whose book *Self Help* is an English classic. His mother, Eva Rayner, was the sister of E. H. Rayner, for many years superintendent of the Electricity Division of the National Physical Laboratory in Teddington. She was active in public service and was for a time mayor of Cambridge. Hartree's father taught engineering at the University of Cambridge and in his later years frequently collaborated with his son in his atomic calculations.

Hartree received his higher education at Cambridge University, where he was a student and later fellow of St. John's College. He did postgraduate work under R. H. Fowler and received the Ph.D. in 1926. He was elected a fellow of the Royal Society in 1932. From 1929 until 1937 he held the chair of applied mathematics at the University of Manchester. In the latter year he was appointed professor of theoretical physics there and held this post formally until 1946, although the latter years of his tenure were spent mainly on war research for the Ministry of Supply. From 1946 until his death Hartree was Plummer professor of mathematical physics at Cambridge, where he was active in promoting and operating the computing laboratory, although he continued his interest in atomic wave functions to the very end.

Hartree was universally admired for the clarity of his lectures and writings. An outstanding trait was his unselfish generosity in giving aid to others working along similar lines of research throughout the world.

Among Hartree's avocational interests was music, in which he was a proficient performer on the piano and the drums and a competent orchestra conductor. He also had a passion for railways, extending to a professional interest in signaling and traffic control. It was a distinct pleasure to take a railway journey with him since he had such an exact knowledge of the whole industry and knew how to discuss it so entertainingly.

BIBLIOGRAPHY

I. Original Works. Hartree's complete bibliography includes five books and 123 articles. A complete list is given by Darwin, below. His books are *Text-book of Anti-aircraft Gunnery* (London, 1925), part only; *The Mechanics of the Atom,* his trans. and rev. of Born's *Atommechanik* (London, 1927); *Calculating Instruments and Machines* (Urbana, Ill., 1949; Cambridge, 1950); *Numerical Analysis* (Oxford, 1952; 2nd ed., 1958); and *The Calculation of Atomic Structures* (New York, 1957).

II. Secondary Literature. On Hartree's life and work see Charles Galton Darwin in *Biographical Memoirs of Fellows of the Royal Society,* **4** (1958), 103–116; and T. S. Kuhn, J. L. Heilbron, P. Forman, and L. Allen, eds., *Sources for the History of Quantum Physics* (Philadelphia, 1960), p. 45.

R. B. Lindsay

HASSE, HELMUT (*b.* Kassel, Germany, 25 August 1898; *d.* Ahrensburg, near Hamburg, Federal Republic of Germany, 26 December 1979)

One of the most important mathematicians of the twentieth century, Helmut Hasse was a man whose accomplishments spanned research, mathematical exposition, teaching, and editorial work. In research his contributions permeate modern number theory; particularly noteworthy are his "local-global principle," which established Kurt Hensel's *p*-adic numbers as indispensable tools of number theory, and his proof of the "Riemann hypothesis" for elliptic curves. In exposition his report on class field theory in the 1920's made the work of Teiji Takagi, Philipp

Furtwängler, Emil Artin, Hasse, and others available to a wide audience (and, like any good exposition, contained a great deal of Hasse's own reworking of the material). Later books and monographs confirmed Hasse's reputation as a writer who could be counted on to present the most difficult subjects with great clarity. In teaching, the long list of his students and their descriptions of his inspiring lectures give ample testimony to his excellence. In his editorial work the continuation of "Crelle's Journal"—*Journal für die reine und angewandte Mathematik*—as one of the world's foremost mathematical periodicals during the fifty years of his editorship was largely a result of his painstaking efforts, high standards, and editorial ability.

Hasse's parents were Paul Reinhard Hasse, a judge, and Margaretha Quentin (born in Milwaukee, Wisconsin, but raised from the age of five by an aunt in Kassel). His secondary education was in gymnasiums in the Kassel area until the family moved to Berlin, where his father had received a high judicial appointment in 1913. After two years in the Fichte-Gymnasium there, he took the exit examination early (a *Notabitur*) in order to volunteer for the navy. Hasse had evidently decided on a career in mathematics while still at gymnasium, because while he was stationed in the Baltic, he studied, on the advice of his gymnasium teacher, the Dirichlet-Dedekind lectures on number theory. During the last year of his naval service he was stationed in Kiel, where he attended classes in mathematics under Otto Toeplitz. Upon leaving the navy in December 1918, Hasse went to Göttingen to begin his mathematical studies in earnest. The teacher at Göttingen who made the greatest impression on him was Erich Hecke, who left Göttingen to go to Hamburg in the spring of 1919. Hasse left the following year. Hasse did not, however, follow Hecke. Greatly impressed by Kurt Hensel's book *Zahlentheorie* (1913), which he had found while browsing in a Göttingen bookstore, he decided to go to Marburg to study with Hensel. What made Hensel's book special was his introduction of p-adic numbers, and it was in order to study this new tool of number theory that Hasse went to Marburg.

In October 1920 Hasse discovered his "local-global principle," which transformed the p-adic numbers from a curiosity that the Göttingen establishment regarded as a fruitless sidetrack into a natural tool of number theory. In 1975, in a *Geleitwort* to the first volume of his mathematical papers, Hasse recounted his discovery of the local-global principle, emphasizing Hensel's role in it. At Hensel's suggestion, Hasse had investigated the necessary and sufficient conditions for a rational number to be representable by a rational quadratic form. He found the key to the answer in a reduction procedure of Lagrange for ternary quadratic forms that he had learned from his reading of Dirichlet-Dedekind. However, to his disappointment, his solution did not appear to call for the use of p-adic numbers. He communicated this to Hensel, whose reply—a postcard that Hasse kept all his life—opened Hasse's eyes, as he later said, to the true significance of what he had proved: a ternary quadratic form that represents 0 nontrivially over the p-adic numbers for all p (including $p = \infty$, which corresponds to the real numbers) represents 0 nontrivially over the rationals. That is, if there is a solution "locally" for all p, then there is a "global" (rational) solution. Hasse soon expanded this principle to a wide range of problems dealing with the equivalence of quadratic forms, work that allowed him to complete his doctoral dissertation in 1921 and his *Habilitationsschrift* in 1922.

Hasse left Marburg in 1922 to accept a paid teaching appointment as *Privatdozent* in Kiel. Hasse married Clara Ohle on 11 April 1923. They had a daughter, Jutta, and a son, Rüdiger.

In 1925 he was appointed professor at Halle, and in 1930 he returned to Marburg to assume the chair made vacant by Hensel's retirement. This succession, which was the realization of Hensel's fondest wish, was of short duration. The strong center of German mathematics, Göttingen, was demolished by the firings and resignations that followed the coming to power of the Nazis in 1933. Hasse, who appeared to be politically acceptable to the Nazis and yet was a mathematician of the highest caliber, was a natural choice as a successor to the deposed director of the Mathematics Institute at Göttingen, Richard Courant. Even Courant, in the interest of the continuation of mathematics in Göttingen, favored Hasse's appointment. (The directorship of the institute was not linked to any one chair. Courant was still "on leave" in 1934, and his chair was not vacant. Hasse was appointed to the more prestigious chair left vacant by Hermann Weyl's resignation, the chair that had formerly been David Hilbert's.) Hasse became the director at Göttingen in 1934 and remained in that post formally—although he was on leave and engaged in naval research in Berlin from 1939 to 1945—until he was dismissed by the British occupation authorities in September 1945.

During the years in Kiel, Hasse explored the subject of norm residue symbols and explicit reciprocity laws by means of p-adic techniques. The proximity of these interests to those of Emil Artin, and Artin's physical proximity in Hamburg, led to friendly collaboration and frequent meetings to exchange ideas. (A joint paper, written in 1925, says the work was drafted by "the younger" of the two authors. Few readers could have known that Hasse was younger—by less than half a year.) During this period Hasse undertook to prepare for the Deutsche Mathematiker Vereinigung a report on recent developments in class field theory, particularly the advances of the Japanese mathematician Teiji Takagi. The report was delivered at Danzig in the summer of 1925, but the published *Klassenkörperbericht*, as it was called, took longer to produce. It was published in two parts, the second part not appearing until 1930; by this time Artin had succeeded in proving his general law of reciprocity (1927), and Hasse included a full account of it in the second part of the *Bericht*.

In the early 1930's Hasse completed a thoroughgoing revision of class field theory—including reciprocity laws and norm residue symbols—in terms of the theory of noncommutative algebras applied to p-adic number fields, an approach that has been called "the high point of the local-global principle."

Soon after this success, Hasse began work in another area that was to become one of the central subjects of modern number theory. Challenged by his English colleague Harold Davenport to bring his algebraic methods to bear on a problem Davenport and Louis Joel Mordell had been studying concerning the number of solutions of a congruence of the form $y^2 = f(x)$ mod p for large primes p when $f(x)$ is a fixed cubic polynomial, Hasse succeeded magnificently. He first perceived that the problem Davenport and Mordell had been considering was in fact equivalent to a problem that Artin had formulated in an altogether different form as an analogue of the Riemann hypothesis, and he then proved this analogue in the case Davenport and Mordell considered, which was the "Riemann hypothesis" in the case of a function field of an elliptic curve over a finite field. To establish connections between such apparently disparate subjects in mathematics and, more than that, to solve a problem using techniques that were developed for altogether different purposes is an achievement of the highest sort in pure mathematics. Great progress has since been made in generalizing Hasse's solution. It is now known that the "Riemann hypothesis" is true in a vast range of cases, provided that algebraic techniques apply; the actual Riemann hypothesis, which is transcendental rather than algebraic, is still an unsolved problem.

Hasse's political views and his relations with the Nazi government are not easily categorized. On the one hand, his relations with his teacher Hensel, who was unambiguously Jewish by Nazi standards, were extremely close, right up to Hensel's death in 1941, and his relations with the Hensel family remained close and warm throughout his life. One of his most important papers was a collaboration with Emmy Noether and Richard Brauer, both Jewish, published in 1932 in honor of Hensel's seventieth birthday (which occurred at the end of 1931). Also in 1932 he dedicated an extremely important paper to Emmy Noether on the occasion of her fiftieth birthday. Hasse did not compromise his mathematics for political reasons. In his years as director of the Mathematics Institute in Göttingen, he brought to Göttingen as difficult a figure as Carl Ludwig Siegel, and he struggled against Nazi functionaries who tried (sometimes successfully) to subvert mathematics to political doctrine. Hasse never published in the journal *Deutsche Mathematik*. On the other hand, he made no secret of his strongly nationalistic views and of his approval of many of Hitler's policies. As an academic administrator and, during the war, as a military officer, he was of course a participant in the regime. He did apply, in 1937, for membership in the National Socialist Party, but the application was refused because he had a remote Jewish ancestor. (However, Siegel reported in a letter to Courant in March 1939 that he had seen Hasse wearing Nazi insignia.) After the war, many emigrant mathematicians condemned Hasse's activities during the Nazi period; invitations to the United States were few, considering his scientific eminence, and what invitations there were aroused controversy.

The occupation authorities revoked Hasse's right to teach in September 1945. He refused to remain in Göttingen in a purely research capacity, on the grounds that his inability to teach would be detrimental to his research. However, after a difficult year, he finally decided to accept an appointment as a research professor at the Berlin Academy, and moved to Berlin in September 1946. During the next two years he gave private lectures to a small group of students, many of whom later had successful careers. In 1948, Hasse's rating in the "denazification" program was improved to the point where he was allowed to give public lectures at Humboldt University in Berlin, and in 1949 he was named to a professorship there. One year later he accepted an appointment as professor at the University of Hamburg. He retired in 1966, but continued to make his home in Ahrensburg, outside Hamburg, for the rest of his life. In the postwar period he remained active as a teacher, as a writer of both research and expository works, and as an editor, although in his last years his work was curtailed by ill health.

Among the many honors Hasse received were the German National Prize, First Class, for Science and Technology (1953), an honorary doctorate from the University of Kiel (1968), and the Cothenius Medal of the Academia Leopoldina in Halle (1968). He was a member of the academies of science of Berlin, Halle, Göttingen, Helsinki, Mainz, and Madrid.

BIBLIOGRAPHY

I. Original Works. *Mathematische Abhandlungen*, Heinrich Wolfgang Leopoldt and Peter Roquette, eds., 3 vols. (Berlin and New York, 1975). A complete list of Hasse's scientific publications is at the end of vol. III.

II. Secondary Literature. G. Frei, "Helmut Hasse (1898–1979)," in *Expositiones Mathematicae*, **3** (1985), 55–69; Heinrich Wolfgang Leopoldt, "Zum wissenschaftlichen Werk von Helmut Hasse," in *Journal für die reine und angewandte Mathematik*, **262/263** (1973), 1–17, and "Helmut Hasse," in *Journal of Number Theory*, **14** (1982), 118–120; and S. L. Segal, "Helmut Hasse in 1934," in *Historia Mathematica*, **7** (1980), 46–56.

Harold M. Edwards

HAUSDORFF, FELIX (*b.* Breslau, Germany [now Wrocław, Poland], 8 November 1868; *d.* Bonn, Germany, 26 January 1942)

Hausdorff's father was a wealthy merchant. After finishing his secondary education in Leipzig, Hausdorff studied mathematics and astronomy at Leipzig, Freiburg, and Berlin. He graduated from Leipzig in 1891 and five years later became a *Dozent* there. Until 1902, when he was appointed professor at Leipzig, he lived independently and devoted himself to a wide range of interests. From 1891 to 1896 he published four papers in astronomy and optics, and in the following years several papers in various branches of mathematics. His main interests, though, were philosophy and literature, and his friends were mainly artists and writers. Under the pen name Dr. Paul Mongré he published two books of poems and aphorisms; a philosophical book, *Das Chaos in kosmischer Auslese* (1898); and a number of philosophical essays and articles on literature. In 1904 he published a farce, *Der Arzt seiner Ehre,* which was produced in 1912 and had considerable success.

In 1902 Hausdorff became associate professor at Leipzig. From that time, mainly after 1904, he seems to have dealt more with set theory, at the same time gradually decreasing his nonscientific writing. In 1910 he went to Bonn as associate professor and there wrote the monograph *Grundzüge der Mengenlehre,* which appeared in 1914. In 1913 Hausdorff became full professor at Greifswald and in 1921 returned to Bonn, where he was active until his forced retirement in 1935. Even then he continued working on set theory and topology, although his work was published only outside Germany. As a Jew he was scheduled to be sent to an internment camp in 1941. It was temporarily avoided; but when internment became imminent, Hausdorff committed suicide with his wife and her sister on 26 January 1942.

Hausdorff's scientific activity contributed greatly to several fields of mathematics. In mathematical analysis he proved important theorems concerning summation methods, properties of moments, and Fourier coefficients (1921). In algebra he derived and investigated the so-called symbolic exponential formula (1906). He introduced and investigated a very important class of measures and, in connection with them, a kind of dimension which may assume arbitrary nonnegative values (1919). Both are now named for Hausdorff and are applied in particular to examination of fine properties of numerical sets.

Hausdorff's main work was in topology and set theory. Various definitions of topological spaces and related concepts had been given, mainly by Maurice Fréchet, before Hausdorff's *Grundzüge der Mengenlehre* appeared. The interrelations of these different approaches had not been completely recognized; and no clear way had been known to effect a gradual transition from very general spaces to those similar to spaces actually occurring in analysis and geometry.

In the *Grundzüge,* Hausdorff took a decisive step in this direction. His broad approach, his aesthetic feeling, and his sense of balance may have played a substantial part. He succeeded in creating a theory of topological and metric spaces into which the previous results fitted well, and he enriched it with many new notions and theorems. From the modern point of view, the *Grundzüge* contained, in addition to other special topics, the beginnings of the theories of topological and metric spaces, which are now included in all textbooks on the subject. In the *Grundzüge,* these theories were laid down in such a way that a strong impetus was provided for their further development. Thus, Hausdorff can rightly be considered the founder of general topology and of the general theory of metric spaces.

The *Grundzüge* is a very rare case in mathematical literature: the foundations of a new discipline are laid without the support of any previously published comprehensive work.

Hausdorff's work in topology and set theory has also brought about a number of separate results of primary importance: in topology, a detailed investigation into the basic properties of general closure spaces (1935); in general set theory, the so-called Hausdorff maximal principle (stated, although not explicitly, in the *Grundzüge*), the introduction of partially ordered sets, and several theorems on ordered sets (1906–1909); in descriptive set theory, the theorem on the cardinality of Borel sets (1916; proved independently by P. S. Alexandrov in the same year) and the introduction of the δs-operations, now often called Hausdorff operations (1927).

Hausdorff's manuscripts have not yet been fully prepared for publication, but they are not likely to provide any new scientific results.

BIBLIOGRAPHY

I. ORIGINAL WORKS. Hausdorff's major work is *Grundzüge der Mengenlehre* (Leipzig, 1914); the 2nd ed., entitled *Mengenlehre* (Leipzig, 1927), is in fact a new book. The Russian trans. (Moscow, 1935) is a revised combination of both. Hausdorff's MSS are being published under the title *Nachgelassene Schriften,* Günter Bergmann, ed.; vols. I and II appeared in Stuttgart in 1969. Numerous papers are in *Fundamenta mathematicae, Mathematische Annalen,* and *Mathematische Zeitschrift.*

II. SECONDARY LITERATURE. A short biography, an analysis of Hausdorff's work, a list of scientific papers, and a survey of his MSS are in M. Dierkesmann *et al.,* "Felix Hausdorff zum Gedächtnis," in *Jahresberichte der Deutschen Mathematikervereinigung,* **69** (1967), 51–76. An article on Hausdorff by W. Krull in "Bonner Gelehrte," in *Beiträge zur Geschichte der Wissenschaften in Bonn,* Mathematik und Naturwissenschaften (1970), pp. 54–69, contains a short biography including an account of Hausdorff's activity outside mathematics, and a detailed analysis of the *Grundzüge.* See also W. Krull, "Felix Hausdorff," in *Neue deutsche Biographie,* VIII (Berlin, 1969), 111–112. The pref. to vol. I of *Nachgelassene Schriften* includes material on Hausdorff as a university teacher and a number of short excerpts from his correspondence.

M. KATĚTOV

IBN AL-HAYTHAM, ABŪ ʿALĪ AL-ḤASAN IBN AL-ḤASAN, called **al-Baṣrī** (of Baṣra, Iraq), **al-Miṣrī** (of Egypt); also known as **Alhazen,** the Latinized form of his first name, **al-Ḥasan** (*b.* 965; *d.* Cairo, *ca.* 1040)

About Ibn al-Haytham's life we have several, not always consistent, reports, most of which come from the thirteenth century. Ibn al-Qifṭī (*d.* 1248) gives a detailed account of how he went from Iraq to Fāṭimid Egypt during the reign of al-Ḥākim (996–1021), the caliph who patronized the great astronomer Ibn Yūnus (*d.* 1009) and who founded in Cairo a library, the Dār al-ʿIlm, whose fame almost equalled that of its precursor at Baghdad (the Bayt al-Ḥikma, which flourished under al-Maʾmūn [813–833]). Impressed by a claim of Ibn al-Haytham that he would be able to build a construction on the Nile which would regulate the flow of its waters, the caliph persuaded the already famous mathematician to come to Egypt and, to show his esteem, went out to meet him on his arrival at a village outside Cairo called al-Khandaq.

Ibn al-Haytham, according to Ibn al-Qifṭī, soon went at the head of an engineering mission to the southern border of Egypt where, he had assumed, the Nile entered the country from a high ground. But even before reaching his destination he began to lose heart about his project. The excellently designed and perfectly constructed ancient buildings which he saw on the banks of the river convinced him that if his plan had been at all possible it would have been already put into effect by the creators of those impressive structures. His misgivings were proved right when he found that the place called *al-Janādil* (the cataracts), south of Aswan, did not accord with what he had expected. Ashamed and dejected he admitted his failure to al-Ḥākim, who then put him in charge of some government office. Ibn al-Haytham at first accepted this post out of fear, but realizing his insecure position under the capricious and murderous al-Ḥākim he pretended to be mentally deranged and, as a result, was confined to his house until the caliph's death. Whereupon Ibn al-Haytham revealed his sanity, took up residence near the Azhar Mosque, and, having been given back his previously sequestered property, spent the rest of his life writing, copying scientific texts, and teaching.

To this account Ibn al-Qifṭī appends a report which he obtained from his friend Yūsuf al-Fāsī (*d.* 1227), a Jewish physician from North Africa who settled in Aleppo after a short stay in Cairo where he worked with Maimonides.[1] Yūsuf al-Fāsī had "heard" that in the latter part of his life Ibn al-Haytham earned his living from the proceeds (amounting to 150 Egyptian dinars) of copying annually the *Elements* of Euclid, the *Almagest,* and the *Mutawassiṭāt,*[2] and that he continued to do so until he died "in [*fī ḥudūd*][3] the year 430 [A.D. 1038–1039] or shortly thereafter [*aw baʿdahā bi-qalīl*]." These words are immediately followed by a statement, of which the author must be presumed to be Ibn al-Qifṭī, to the effect that he possessed a volume on geometry in Ibn al-Haytham's hand, written in 432 (A.D. 1040–1041).

An earlier account of Ibn al-Haytham's visit to Egypt is given by ʿAlī ibn Zayd al-Bayhaqī (*d.* 1169–1170).[4] According to him the mathematician had only a brief and unsuccessful meeting with al-Ḥākim outside an inn in Cairo. The caliph, sitting on a donkey with silver-plated harness, examined a treatise composed by Ibn al-Haytham on his Nile project, while the author, being short of stature, stood on a bench (*dukkān*) in front of him. The caliph condemned the project as impractical and expensive, ordered the bench to be demolished, and rode away. Afraid for his life, Ibn al-Haytham immediately fled the country under cover of darkness, going to Syria, where he later secured the patronage of a well-to-do governor. But this account, vivid though it is, must be discarded as being unsupported by other evidence. For example, we are told by Ṣāʿid al-Andalusī (*d.* 1070) that a contemporary of his, a judge named ʿAbd al-Raḥman ibn ʿĪsā, met Ibn al-Haytham in Egypt in 430 A.H., that is, a short time before the latter died.

Ibn Abī Uṣaybiʿa (*d.* 1270) gives the name of Ibn al-Haytham as Muḥammad (rather than al-Ḥasan) ibn al-Ḥasan; and he joins Ibn al-Qifṭī's story (which he quotes in full with the omission of the last statement about Ibn al-Haytham's autograph of 432) to a report which he heard from ʿAlam al-Dīn Qayṣar ibn Abi 'l-Qāsim ibn Musāfir, an Egyptian mathematician who resided in Syria and died at Damascus in 649 A.H./A.D. 1251.[5] According to this report, Ibn al-Haytham at first occupied the office of minister at Baṣra and its environs, but to satisfy his strong desire to devote himself entirely to science and learning he feigned madness until he was relieved from his duties. Only then did he go to Egypt, where he spent the rest of his life at the Azhar Mosque, living on what he earned from copying Euclid and the *Almagest* once every year. We may add that the title of one of his writings (no. II 13, see below) appears to imply that he was at Baghdad in 1027, six years after al-Ḥākim died.[6]

It is unfortunate that the autobiography of Ibn al-Haytham, which Ibn Abī Uṣaybiʿa quotes from an autograph, throws no light on these different reports. Written at the end of 417 A.H./A.D. 1027, when the author was sixty-three lunar years old, and clearly modeled after Galen's *De libris propriis*,[7] it lists the works written by Ibn al-Haytham up to that date but speaks in only general terms about his intellectual development.

As cited by Ibn Abī Uṣaybiʿa, Ibn al-Haytham, reflecting in his youth on the conflicting but firmly held beliefs of the various religious sects, was led to put them all in doubt and became convinced that truth was one. When in later years he was ready to grasp intellectual matters, he decided to turn his back on the common people and devote himself to seeking knowledge of the truth as the worthiest possession that could be obtained in this world and the surest way to gain favor with God—a decision which, using Galen's expressions in *De methodo medendi*,[8] he attributed to his "good fortune, or a divine inspiration, or a kind of madness." Frustrated in his intensive inquiries into the religious sciences, he finally emerged with the conviction that truth was to be had only in "doctrines whose matter was sensible and whose form was rational." Such doctrines Ibn al-Haytham found exemplified in the writings of Aristotle (of which he here gave a conspectus) and in the philosophical sciences of mathematics, physics, and metaphysics. As evidence of his having stood by his decision, he provided a list of his writings to 10 February 1027, containing twenty-five titles on mathematical subjects (list I*a*) and forty-five titles on questions of physics and metaphysics (list I*b*).

Ibn Abī Uṣaybiʿa gives two more lists of Ibn al-Haytham's work, which we shall designate as II and III. List II, which he found attached to list I and in the author's hand, contains twenty-one titles of works composed between 10 February 1027 and 25 July 1028. Ibn Abī Uṣaybiʿa does not say whether he also copied list III from an autograph but simply describes it as a catalogue (*fihrist*) which he found of Ibn al-Haytham's works to the end of 429 A.H./2 October 1038. Nor does he specify the *terminus a quo* of this catalogue. However that may be, two things are remarkable about this last list: consisting of ninety-two titles, it includes all sixty-nine titles ascribed to Ibn al-Haytham by Ibn al-Qifṭī, with two exceptions; and in it are to be found all of Ibn al-Haytham's extant works (not fewer than fifty-five), again with only a very few exceptions. It may also be noted that the order of works in list III almost always agrees with the chronological order of their composition, whenever the latter can be independently determined from internal cross references. Thus, III 2 was written before III 53; III 3 before III 36, III 49, III 60, III 77, and III 80; III 20 before III 21; III 25 before III 31; III 26 before III 38 and III 68; III 42 before III 74; III 53 before III 54; III 61 before III 63; III 63 before III 64; and III 66 before III 77. Item III 17, however, was written before III 16 (see bibliography).

Among the subjects on which Ibn al-Haytham wrote are logic, ethics, politics, poetry, music, and theology (*kalām*); but neither his writings on these subjects nor the summaries he made of Aristotle and Galen have survived. His extant works belong to the fields in which he was reputed to have made his most important contributions: optics, astronomy, and mathematics.

Optics: Doctrine of Light. Ibn al-Haytham's theory

IBN AL-HAYTHAM

of light and vision is neither identical with nor directly descendant from any one of the theories known to have previously existed in antiquity or in Islam. It is obvious that it combines elements of earlier theories—owing perhaps more to Ptolemy than to any other writer—but in it these elements are reexamined and rearranged in such a way as to produce something new. Ibn al-Haytham's writings on optics included a treatise written "in accordance with the method of Ptolemy" (III 27), whose *Optics* was available to him in an Arabic translation lacking the first book and the end of the fifth and last book, and a summary of Euclid and Ptolemy in which he "supplemented the matters of the first Book, missing from Ptolemy's work" (*Ia* 5). These two works are now lost.

But in his major work, the *Optics* or *Kitāb al-Manāzir* (III 3),[9] in seven books, Ibn al-Haytham deliberately set out to dispel what appeared to him to be a prevailing confusion in the subject by "recommencing the inquiry into its principles and premises, starting the investigation by an induction of the things that exist and a review of the conditions of the objects of vision." Once the results of induction were established he was then to "ascend in the inquiry and reasonings, gradually and in order, criticizing premises and exercising caution in the drawing of conclusions," his aim in all this being "to employ justice, not to follow prejudice, and to take care in all that we judge and criticize that we seek the truth and not to be swayed by opinions" (Fatih MS 3212, fol. 4a r).

The book is in fact an earnest and assiduous exercise in the method outlined. Its arguments are either inductive, experimental, or mathematical, and it cites no authorities. Experiment (*iʿtibār*) in particular emerges in it as an explicit and identifiable methodological tool involving the manipulation of artificially constructed devices. (In the Latin translation of the *Optics* the word *iʿtibār* and its cognates *iʿtabara* and *muʿtabir* became *experimentum, experimentare,* and *experimentator,* respectively.) Perhaps as a result of its derivation from the astronomical procedure of testing past observations by comparing them with new ones, the method of *iʿtibār* often appears aimed at proof rather than discovery. It establishes beyond doubt that which is insecurely suggested by inadequate observations.

The *Optics* is not a philosophical dissertation on the nature of light, but an experimental and mathematical investigation of its properties, particularly insofar as these relate to vision. With regard to the question "What is light?," Ibn al-Haytham readily adopted the view ascribed by him to "the physicists" or natural philosophers (*al-ṭabīʿiyyūn*)—not, however, because that view was by itself sufficient, but because it constituted an element of the truth which had to be combined with other elements derived from "mathematicians" (*taʿlīmiyyūn*) such as Euclid and Ptolemy. In the resulting synthesis (*tarkīb*) the approach of "the mathematicians" dominated the form of inquiry, while their doctrines were altered, indeed reversed, in the light of those of "the physicists." That "the physicists" were the natural philosophers working in the Aristotelian tradition is clear enough from comparing the view attributed to them by Ibn al-Haytham with expressions and doctrines that had been current in the works of peripatetics from Alexander to Avicenna.

Light, says Ibn al-Haytham, is a form (*ṣūra*, εἶδος) essential (*dhātiyya*) in self-luminous bodies, accidental (*ʿaraḍiyya*) in bodies that derive their luminosity from outside sources. Transparency (*al-shafīf*) is an essential form in virtue of which transparent bodies, such as air or water, transmit light. An opaque body, such as a stone, has the power to "receive" or take on and make its own the light shining upon it and thereby to become itself a luminous source. This received light is called accidental because it belongs to the body only as long as the body is irradiated from outside. There are no perfectly transparent bodies. All transparent bodies possess a certain degree of opacity which causes light to be "received" or "fixed" in them as accidental light.

The light which radiates directly from a self-luminous source is called "primary" (*awwal*); that which emanates from accidental light is called "secondary" (*thānī*). Primary and secondary lights are emitted by their respective sources in exactly the same manner, that is, from every point on the source in all directions along straight lines. The only difference between these two kinds of light is one of intensity: accidental light is weaker than its primary source and the secondary light deriving from it is weaker still. All radiating lights become weaker the farther they travel. The distinction is made in transparent bodies between the accidentally fixed and the traversing light, and it is from the former that secondary light is emitted. Thus from every point of the sunlit air, or on the surface of an illuminated opaque object, a secondary light, fainter than the light coming to this point directly from the sun, radiates "in the form of a sphere," rectilinearly in all directions. (The picture is interesting since it later appears in the doctrine of the multiplication of species and it is at the basis of Huygens' principle.)

Two other modes of propagation are the reflection of light from smooth bodies and its refraction when passing from one transparent body into another. Unlike an opaque body, a smooth surface does not behave, when illuminated, like a self-luminous object; rather than "receive" the impinging light it sends

IBN AL-HAYTHAM

it back in a determinate direction. In *Optics,* book I, chapter 3, numerous experiments involving the use of various devices—sighting tubes, strings, dark chambers—are adduced to support all of the above statements, and in particular to establish the property of rectilinear propagation for all four kinds of radiation: primary, secondary, reflected, and refracted.

Colors are asserted to be as real as light and distinct from it; they exist as forms of the colored objects. A self-luminous body either possesses the form of color or something of "the same sort as color." Like light, colors radiate their forms upon surrounding bodies and this radiation originates from every point on the colored object and extends in all directions. It is possible that colors should be capable of extending themselves into the surrounding air in the absence of light; but experiments show that they are always found in the company of light, mingled with it, and they are never visible without it. Whatever rules apply to light also apply to colors.

Some time after writing the *Optics,* Ibn al-Haytham remarked in the *Discourse* (III 60) that natural philosophers, in contrast to mathematicians, had failed to supply a definite concept of ray. In book IV of the *Optics* he had in fact tried to remedy the defect by introducing the concept of a physical ray. The underlying idea is that for a body to be able to carry the form of light it must be of certain minimal magnitude. Imagine, then, that a transparent body through which light travels is made progressively thinner by a process of division. (The operation is essentially the same as that of narrowing an aperture through which the light passes.)

Ibn al-Haytham considered that a limit would be reached after which further division would cause the light to vanish. At this limit there would pass through the thin body a light of finite breadth which he calls the smallest or least light (*aṣghar al-ṣaghīr min al-ḍaw'*), a single ray whose only direction of propagation is the straight line extending through its length. A wider volume of light should not, however, be regarded as an aggregate of such minimal parts (*aḍwā' diqāq mutaḍāmma*), but a continuous and coherent whole in which propagation takes place along all the straight lines, both parallel and intersecting, that can be imagined within its width. It follows that an aperture will either be wide enough to allow only rectilinear propagation, or too small to let any light pass through; there is no room for the diffraction of light. The result of the new concept is thus an uncompromising formulation of the ray theory of light. (Compare Newton's concept of "least Light or part of Light" which accords with his interpretation of diffraction as a kind of refraction.)[10]

Theory of Vision. As employed by Ibn al-Haytham the language of forms serves merely to express the view that light and color are real properties of physical bodies. He sometimes conducted his discussion without even using the term "form" (as in the greater part of book I, chapter 3) and his experimental arguments would lose nothing of their import if that term were to be removed from them. And yet it was the term "form" that had been closely associated with the intromission theory of vision maintained in the Peripatetic tradition, whereas mathematical opticians had formulated their geometrically represented explanations in terms of "visual rays" issuing from the eye. Ibn al-Haytham adopted the intromission hypothesis as the more reasonable one and took over with it the vocabulary of forms. To this he added, as we saw, a new concept of ray that satisfied the mathematical condition of rectilinearity but was consistent with the physics of forms. His theory of vision (to be described presently) may thus be seen as one chief illustration of the program he outlined in the *Optics* (III 3), in the treatise *On the Halo and the Rainbow* (III 8), and in the *Discourse on Light* (III 60): optical inquiry must "combine" the physical and the mathematical sciences.

In chapter 5 of book I of the *Optics* Ibn al-Haytham described the construction of the eye on the basis of what had been generally accepted in the tradition of medical and anatomical writings derived from Galen's works. But he adapted the geometry

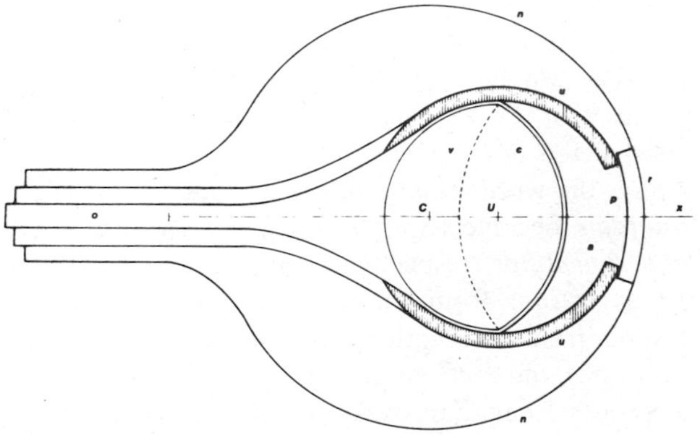

FIGURE 1. A cross section of the eye. Constructed from the text of *Kitāb al-Manāẓir.* After M. Nazīf.

a, albugineous humor, *al-bayḍiyya; C,* center of eyeball; *c,* crystalline humor, *al-jalīdiyya; n,* exterior surface of conjunctiva, *al-multaḥima; o,* optic nerve, *al-ʿaṣab al-baṣarī; p,* uveal opening or pupil, *thaqb al-ʿinabiyya; r,* cornea, *al-qarniyya; U,* center of uvea; *u,* uvea, *al-ʿinabiyya; v,* vitreous humor, *al-zujājiyya; x,* axis of symmetry.

The axis of symmetry, passing through the middle of the pupil, the center of the uvea, and the center of the eye, goes to the middle of the optic nerve where the eyeball bends as a whole in its socket. The uvea is displaced forward toward the surface of the eye.

of this construction to suit his own explanation of vision. In particular he assumed both surfaces of the cornea opposite the pupil to be parallel to the anterior surface of the crystalline humor, all these surfaces being spherical and having the center of the eye as common center. He placed the center of the eye behind the posterior surface of the crystalline humor. The latter surface may be plane or spherical, so that the line passing through the middle of the pupil and the center of the eye would be perpendicular to it. (See Figure 1.[11]) The theory of vision is itself expounded in chapters 2, 4, 6, and 8.

Observations (such as the feeling of pain in the eye when gazing on an intense light, or the lingering impression in the eye of a strongly illuminated object) show that it is a property of light to make an effect on the eye, and a property of sight to be affected by light; visual sensation is therefore appropriately explained solely in terms of light coming to the eye from the object. As maintained by natural philosophers this effect is produced by the forms of the light and color in the visible object. But as an explanation of vision this statement in terms of forms is, by itself, "null and void" (*tantaqiḍ wa-tabṭul, destruitur*).[12]

The problem Ibn al-Haytham posed for himself was to determine what further conditions are needed in order to bring the form of an external object intact into the eye where it makes its visual effect. His solution assumed the crystalline humor to be the organ in which visual sensation first occurs—an assumption which had been current since Galen. The solution also employs the experimentally supported principle which considers the shining object as a collection of points individually radiating their light and color (or the forms of their light and color) rectilinearly in all directions.[13] In consequence of this principle any point on a visible object may be regarded as the origin of a cone of radiation with a base at the portion of the surface of the eye opposite the pupil. Since this holds for all points of the object, there will be spread over the whole of that portion the forms of the light and color of every one of these points.

Further confusion will result after the majority of these forms have been refracted upon their passage through the cornea. Ibn al-Haytham considered that for veridical perception to be possible it must be assumed that vision of any given object point can occur only through a given point on the surface of the eye, and he defined the latter point as that at which the perpendicular from the object point meets the cornea. It follows from the geometry of the eye that forms coming from all points on the object along perpendiculars to the surface of the eye will pass unrefracted through the pupil into the albugineous humor and again strike the anterior surface of the crystalline at right angles. There will then be produced on the crystalline humor a total form whose points will correspond, one-to-one, with all the points on the object, and it is this "distinct" and erect form which the crystalline humor will sense. Because the effective perpendiculars are precisely those that make up the outward extension of the cone having the center of the eye as vertex and the pupil as base (the so-called "radial cone," *makhrūṭ al-shuʿāʿ*), what we have in the end is the geometry of the Euclidean visual-ray theory.

But now the "mathematicians'" rays are strictly mathematical, that is, they are no more than abstract lines along which the light travels toward the eye—which is enough to save the geometrical optics of the ancients. As for the hypothesis that something actually goes out of the eye, it is clearly declared to be "futile and superfluous"—"Exitus ergo radiorum est superfluus et otiosus."[14] It would be absurd, says Ibn al-Haytham, to suppose that a material effluence flowing out of the eye would be capable of filling the visible heavens almost as soon as we lift our eyelids. If such effluence or visual rays are not corporeal, then they would not be capable of sensation and their function would merely be to serve as vehicles for bringing back something else from the object which itself would produce vision in the eye. But since this function is already fulfilled by the transparent medium through which light and color (or their forms) extend, visual rays are no longer of any use. (In the presence of this decisive argument it is curious that the editor of the Latin translation should misinterpret Ibn al-Haytham's remarks about preserving the geometrical property of the mathematicians' rays as an argument in support of the "Platonic" theory of συναύγεια, combining the intromission and extramission hypotheses.)[15]

Ibn al-Haytham managed to introduce the form of the visible object into the eye—an achievement which had apparently defeated his predecessors. But it should be noted that the "distinct form" he succeeded in realizing inside the eye is apparent only to the sensitive faculty; it is not a visibly articulate image such as that produced by a pinhole camera. In one place he ascribed the privileged role of the perpendicular rays to their superior strength. But there is another dominant idea. As a transparent body the crystalline humor allows non-perpendicular rays to be refracted into it from all points on its surface; as a sensitive body, however, it is especially concerned with those rays that go through it without suffering refraction. Veridical vision is thus due in the first place to the selective or directional sensitivity of the crystalline humor.

The vitreous humor, whose transparency differs from that of the crystalline, has still another property, namely that of preserving the integrity of the form handed down to it at its common face with the crystalline, where refraction of the effective rays takes place away from the axis of symmetry. The sensitive body (visual spirit), issuing along independent and parallel lines from the brain into the optic nerve, finally receives the form from the vitreous body and channels it back along the same lines to the front of the brain where the process of vision is completed. In the optic chiasma, where corresponding lines of the optic nerves join together, the form from the one eye coincides with that from the other, and from there the two forms proceed to the brain as one.

In book VII Ibn al-Haytham introduced what may be considered a generalization of the theory of vision already set out in book I. The form of his inquiry is the same as before: the determination of the conditions that must be assumed in order to accommodate the results of certain indubitable experiments. The experiments described here at first appear to speak against the earlier theory. A small object placed in the radial cone close to one eye, while the other is shut, does not hide an object point lying behind it on the common line drawn from the center of the eye. This means that the object point must in this case be seen by means of a ray falling obliquely, and therefore refracted, at the surface of the eye. Again, a small object placed outside the radial cone, as when a needle is held close to the corner of one eye, can be seen while the other eye is shut. Since no perpendicular can be drawn from the object in this position to any point in the area cut off from the eye-surface by the radial cone, the object must be seen by refraction.

Briefly stated (and divorced from its rather problematic, though interesting, arguments), the final doctrine intended to take all of these observations into account is that vision of objects within the radial cone is effected both by direct and refracted rays, whereas objects outside the cone are seen only by refraction. Ibn al-Haytham here maintains that sensation of refracted as well as direct forms or rays takes place in the crystalline humor, although (in accordance with the earlier theory) he states that the "sensitive faculty" apprehends them all along perpendiculars drawn from the center of the eye to the objects seen. It is this general doctrine, that whatever we see is seen by refraction,[16] whether or not it is also seen by direct rays, that, according to Ibn al-Haytham, had not been grasped or explained by any writer on optics, ancient or modern.

The main part of Ibn al-Haytham's general theory of light and vision is contained in book I of the *Optics.* In book II he expounded an elaborate theory of cognition, with visual perception as the basis, which was referred to and made use of by fourteenth-century philosophers including, for example, Ockham,[17] and which has yet to receive sufficient attention from historians of philosophy. Book III deals with binocular vision and with the errors of vision and of recognition. Reflection is the subject of book IV, and here Ibn al-Haytham gave experimental proof of the specular reflection of accidental as well as essential light, a complete formulation of the laws of reflection, and a description of the construction and use of a copper instrument for measuring reflections from plane, spherical, cylindrical, and conical mirrors, whether convex or concave. He gave much attention to the problem of finding the incident ray, given the reflected ray (from any kind of mirror) to a given position of the eye. This is characteristic of the whole of the *Optics*—an eye is always given with respect to which the problems are to be formulated. The investigation of reflection—with special reference to the location of images—is continued in book V where the well-known "problem of Alhazen" is discussed, while book VI deals with the errors of vision due to reflection.

Book VII, which concludes the *Optics,* is devoted to the theory of refraction. Ibn al-Haytham gave considerable space to a detailed description of an improved version of Ptolemy's instrument for measuring refractions, and illustrated its use for the study of air-water, air-glass, and water-glass refractions at plane and spherical surfaces. Rather than report any numerical measurements, as in Ptolemy's tables, he stated the results of his experiments in eight rules which mainly govern the relation between the angle of incidence i (made by the incident ray and the normal to the surface) and the angle of deviation d (*zāwiyat al-inʿiṭāf, angulus refractionis*) contained between the refracted ray and the prolongation of the incident ray into the refracting medium. (This concentration on d rather than the angle of refraction r—which being equal to $i - d$ he called the remaining angle, *al-bāqiya*—was also a feature of Kepler's researches.)

His rules may be expressed as follows. Let d_1, d_2 and r_1, r_2 correspond to i_1, i_2, respectively, and let $i_2 > i_1$. It is asserted that

(1) $d_2 > d_1$;
(2) $d_2 - d_1 < i_2 - i_1$;
(3) $\frac{d_2}{i_2} > \frac{d_1}{i_1}$;
(4) $r_2 > r_1$;

(5) In rare-to-dense refraction, $d < 1/2\ i$;
(6) In dense-to-rare refraction, $d < 1/2\ (i + d)$ $[d < 1/2\ r]$;
(7) A denser refractive medium deflects the light more toward the normal; and
(8) A rarer refractive medium deflects the light more away from the normal.

It is to be noted that (2) holds only for rare-to-dense refraction, and (5) and (6) are true only under certain conditions which, however, were implicit in the experiments, as Naẓīf has shown.[18] Concluding that "these are all the ways in which light is refracted into transparent bodies," Ibn al-Haytham does not give the impression that he was seeking a law which he failed to discover; but his "explanation" of refraction certainly forms part of the history of the formulation of the refraction law. The explanation is based on the idea that light is a movement which admits of variable speed (being less in denser bodies) and of analogy with the mechanical behavior of bodies. The analogy had already been suggested in antiquity, but Ibn al-Haytham's elaborate application of the parallelogram method, regarding the incident and refracted movements as consisting of two perpendicular components which can be considered separately, introduced a new element of sophistication. His approach attracted the attention of such later mathematicians as Witelo, Kepler, and Descartes, all of whom employed it, the last in his successful deduction of the sine law.

Minor Optical Works. The extant writings of Ibn al-Haytham include a number of optical works other than the *Optics,* of which some are important, showing Ibn al-Haytham's mathematical and experimental ability at its best, although in scope they fall far short of the *Optics.* The following is a brief description of these works.

The Light of the Moon (III 6). Ibn al-Haytham showed here that if the moon behaved like a mirror, the light it receives from the sun would be reflected to a given point on the earth from a smaller part of its surface than is actually observed. He accordingly argued that the moon sends out its borrowed light in the same manner as a self-luminous source, that is, from every point on its surface in all directions. This is confirmed through the use of an astronomical diopter having a slit of variable length through which various parts of the moon could be viewed from an opposite hole in a screen parallel to the slit. The treatise is a beautiful combination of mathematical deduction and experimental technique. The experiments do not, however, lead to the discovery of a new property, but only serve to prove that the mode of emission from the moon is of the same kind as the already known mode of emission from self-luminous objects. Here, as in the *Optics,* the role of experiment is in contrast to its role in the work of, say, Grimaldi or Newton.

The Halo and the Rainbow (III 8). The subject is not treated in the *Optics.* In this treatise Ibn al-Haytham's explanation of the bow fails, being conceived of solely in terms of reflection from a concave spherical surface formed by the "thick and moist air" or cloud. The treatise did, however, become one of the starting points of Kamāl al-Dīn's more successful researches.

On Spherical Burning Mirrors (III 18). In contrast to the eye-centered researches of the *Optics* the only elements of the problems posed in this treatise (and in III 19) are the luminous source, the mirror, and the point or points in which the rays are assembled. Ibn al-Haytham showed that rays parallel to the axis of the mirror are reflected to a given point on the axis from only one circle on the mirror; his remarks imply a recognition of spherical aberration along the axis.

On Paraboloidal Burning Mirrors (III 19). This refers to Archimedes and Anthemius "and others" as having adopted a combination of spherical mirrors whose reflected rays meet in one point. Drawing ably on the methods of Apollonius, Ibn al-Haytham set out to provide a proof of a fact which, he said, the ancients had recognized but not demonstrated: that rays are reflected to one point from the whole of the concave surface of a paraboloid of revolution.

The Formation of Shadows (III 36). That there were many writings on shadows available to Ibn al-Haytham is clear from his reference here to *aṣḥāb al-aẓlāl* (the authors on shadows). Indeed, a long treatise on shadows by his contemporary al-Bīrunī is extant. Ibn al-Haytham defines darkness as the total absence of light, and shadow as the absence of some light and the presence of another. He made the distinction between umbra and penumbra—calling them *ẓulma* (darkness) or *ẓill maḥḍ* (pure shadow), and *ẓill* (shadow), respectively.

The Light of the Stars (III 48). This argues that all stars and planets, with the sole exception of the moon, are self-luminous.

Discourse on Light (III 60). Composed after the *Optics,* this treatise outlines the general doctrine of light. Some of its statements have been used in the account given above.

The Burning Sphere (III 77). In this work, written after the *Optics,* Ibn al-Haytham continued his investigations of refraction, but, as in III 18 and III 19, without reference to a seeing eye. He studied the path of parallel rays through a glass sphere, tried to determine the focal length of such a sphere, and pointed

IBN AL-HAYTHAM

out spherical aberration. The treatise was carefully studied by Kamāl al-Dīn, who utilized it in his account of the path of rays from the sun inside individual rain drops.

The Shape of the Eclipse (III 80). This treatise is of special interest because of what it reveals about Ibn al-Haytham's knowledge of the important subject of the *camera obscura.* The exact Arabic equivalent of that Latin phrase, *al-bayt al-muẓlim,* occurs in book I, chapter 3 of the *Optics;*[19] and indeed dark chambers are frequently used in this book for the study of such various properties of light as its rectilinear propagation and the fact that shining bodies radiate their light and color on neighboring objects. But such images as those produced by a pinhole camera are totally absent from the *Optics.* The nearest that Ibn al-Haytham gets to such an image is the passage in which he describes the patches of light cast on the inside wall of a "dark place" by candle flames set up at various points opposite a small aperture that leads into the dark place; the order of the images on the inside wall is the reverse of the order of the candles outside.

The experiment was designed to show that the light from one candle is not mingled with the light from another as a result of their meeting at the aperture, and in general that lights and colors are not affected by crossing one another. Although this passage occurs in book I in the context of the theory of vision,[20] the eye does not in Ibn al-Haytham's explanation act as a pinhole camera and it is expressly denied the role of a lens camera. In the present treatise, however, he approached the question, already posed in the pseudo-Aristotelian *Problemata,* of why the image of a crescent moon, cast through a small circular aperture, appears circular, whereas the same aperture will cast a crescent-shaped image of the partially eclipsed sun. Although his answer is not wholly satisfactory, and although he failed to solve the general problem of the pinhole camera, his attempted explanation of the image of a solar crescent clearly shows that he possessed the principles of the working of the camera. He formulated the condition for obtaining a distinct image of an object through a circular aperture as that when

$$\frac{m_a}{m_s} \leq \frac{d_a}{d_s},$$

where m_a, m_s are the diameters of the aperture and of the object respectively, and d_a, d_s the distances of the screen from the aperture and from the object respectively.

Ibn al-Haytham's construction of the crescent-shaped image of the partially eclipsed sun can be clearly understood by reference to Figure 2. (Because Ibn al-Haytham's own diagram shows the crescents but not the circles, the figure shown is that constructed by Naẓīf.) It represents the special case in which the two ratios just mentioned are equal. It is assumed that the line joining the centers of the two arcs forming the solar crescent is parallel to the planes of the aperture and the screen, and further that the line joining the center of the sun and the center of the circular hole is perpendicular to the plane of the latter and to the plane of the screen.

The crescents *p, q, r,* are inverted images produced by three double conical solids of light whose vertices are three different points on the aperture, and whose bases are, on the one side, the shining solar crescent, and, on the other, the inverted image. These solids are each limited by two conical surfaces of which one is convex and the other concave; and in every double solid the convex surface on one side of the aperture corresponds to the concave surface on the other. The middle crescent image *q* is produced by such a double solid having its vertex at the aperture-center; *p* and *r* have their vertices at the extremities of a diameter of the aperture. The circular images are each produced by a single cone whose vertex is a single point on the shining crescent; as many such circles are produced as there are points on the crescent sun.

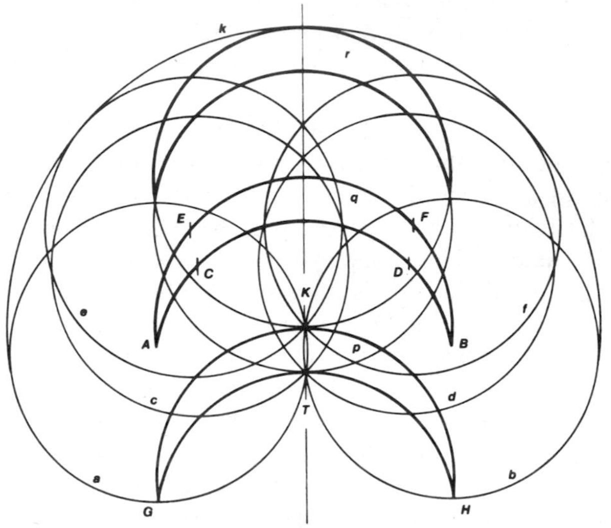

FIGURE 2. Ibn al-Haytham's construction of an inverted image of the partially eclipsed sun.

The center of each circle is therefore the point at which the axis of the cone, passing through the center of the aperture, intersects the screen. It is clear that the centers of all circles will be points on crescent *q,* and that their radii, as well as those of the arcs forming crescents *p, q, r,* will all be equal. The resultant image will therefore be bounded from above by a convex curve of which the upper part is the tangential arc of a circle whose center is the midpoint *K* of the convex arc of crescent *p,* and whose radius is twice the radius of that arc. Although circles of light will occur below arc *GTH,* they will be relatively few.

The sensible overall effect will be, according to Ibn al-Haytham, a crescent-shaped image bordered on the lower side by a sensibly dark cavity. He showed by a numerical example that the cavity will increase or decrease in size according as the ratio $m_a : m_s$ is less or greater than $d_a : d_s$. It is certain that the treatise *On the Shape of the Eclipse* was composed after the *Optics,* to which it refers. It is not impossible that, at the time of writing the *Optics,* Ibn al-Haytham was acquainted with the remarkable explanation revealed in the later work, but of this we have no evidence.

Transmission and Influence of the Optics. Of all the optical treatises of Ibn al-Haytham that have been mentioned, only the *Optics* (III 3) and the treatise *On Paraboloidal Burning Mirrors* (III 9) are known to have been translated into Latin in the Middle Ages, the latter probably by Gerard of Cremona.[21] It is remarkable that in the Islamic world the *Optics* practically disappeared from view soon after its appearance in the eleventh century until, in the beginning of the fourteenth century, the Persian scholar Kamāl al-Dīn composed his great critical commentary on it, the *Tanqīḥ al-Manāẓir,* at the suggestion of his teacher Quṭb al-Dīn al-Shīrāzī.

By this time the *Optics* had embarked on a new career in the West where it was already widely and avidly studied in a Latin translation of the late twelfth or early thirteenth century, entitled *Perspectiva* or *De aspectibus.* Of the manuscript copies that have been located (no fewer than nineteen[22]), the earliest are from the thirteenth century; but where and by whom the *Optics* was translated remains unknown. The Latin text was published by Frederick Risner at Basel in 1572 in a volume entitled *Opticae thesaurus,* which included Witelo's *Perspectiva.* In both Risner's edition and the Latin manuscripts examined by the present writer (see bibliography) the Latin text wants the first three chapters of book I of the Arabic text (133 pages, containing about 130 words per page, in MS Fatih 3212).

The Latin *Perspectiva* shows the drawbacks as well as the advantages of the literal translation which in general it is. Often, however, it only paraphrases the Arabic, sometimes inadequately or even misleadingly, and at times it omits whole passages. But an exhaustive and critical study of the extant manuscripts is needed before a full and accurate evaluation of the translation can be made. In any case there is no doubt that through this Latin medium a good deal of the substance of Ibn al-Haytham's doctrine was successfully conveyed to medieval, Renaissance, and seventeenth-century philosophers in the West. Roger Bacon's *Perspectiva* is full of references to "Alhazen," or *auctor perspectivae,* whose influence on him cannot be overemphasized. Pecham's *Perspectiva communis* was composed as a compendium of the *Optics* of Ibn al-Haytham.[23] That Witelo's *Opticae libri decem* also depends heavily on *Alhazeni libri septem* has been noted repeatedly by scholars; the cross-references provided by Risner in his edition of the two texts have served as a sufficient indication of that. But Witelo's precise debt to Ibn al-Haytham, as distinguished from his own contribution, has yet to be determined.

The influence of Ibn al-Haytham's *Optics* was not channelled exclusively through the works of these thirteenth-century writers. There is clear evidence that the book was directly studied by philosophers of the fourteenth century[24] and an Italian translation made at that time was used by Lorenzo Ghiberti.[25] Risner's Latin edition made it available to such mathematicians as Kepler, Snell, Beeckman, Fermat, Harriot, and Descartes, all of whom except the last directly referred to Alhazen. It was, in fact, in the sixteenth and seventeenth centuries that the mathematical character of the *Optics* was widely and effectively appreciated.

Astronomy. No fewer than twenty of Ibn al-Haytham's extant works are devoted to astronomical questions. The few of these that have been studied by modern scholars do not appear to justify al-Bayhaqī's description of Ibn al-Haytham as "the second Ptolemy." (The description would be apt, however, if al-Bayhaqī had optics in mind.) Many of these works are short tracts that deal with minor or limited, although by no means trivial, theoretical or practical problems (sundials, determination of the direction of prayer, parallax, and height of stars), and none of them seems to have achieved results comparable to those of, say, Ibn Yūnus, al-Ṭūsī, or Ibn al-Shāṭir. Nevertheless, some of Ibn al-Haytham's contributions in this field are both interesting and historically important, as has sometimes been recognized.

As a writer on astronomy Ibn al-Haytham has been mainly known as the author of a treatise *On the Configuration of the World* (III 1 = *Ib* 10). The treatise must have been an early work: it speaks of "the ray that goes out of our eyes" and describes the moon as a "polished body" which "reflects" the light of the sun—two doctrines which are refuted in the *Optics* (III 3) and in *The Light of the Moon* (III 6), respectively. The treatise was widely known in the Islamic world,[26] and it is the only astronomical work of Ibn al-Haytham to have been transmitted to the West in the Middle Ages. A Spanish translation was made by Abraham Hebraeus for Alfonso X of Castile (*d.* 1284), and this translation was turned into Latin (under the title *Liber de mundo et coelo*) by an unknown person.

Jacob ben Maḥir (Prophatius Judaeus, *d. ca.* 1304) translated the Arabic text of the *Configuration* into Hebrew, a task which was suggested to him as a corrective to the *Elements of Astronomy* of al-Farghānī, whose treatment of the subject "did not accord with the nature of existing things," as the unknown person who made the suggestion said.[27] The physician Salomo ibn Pater made another Hebrew translation in 1322. A second Latin version was later made from Jacob's Hebrew by Abraham de Balmes for Cardinal Grimani (both of whom died in 1523). In the fourteenth century Ibn al-Haytham's treatise was cited by Levy ben Gerson. Its influence on early Renaissance astronomers and in particular on Peurbach's *Theoricae novae planetarum* has recently been pointed out.[28]

The declared aim of the *Configuration* was to perform a task which, in Ibn al-Haytham's view, had not been fulfilled either by the popularly descriptive or the technically mathematical works on astronomy. The existing descriptive accounts were only superficially in agreement with the details established by demonstrations and observations. A purely mathematical work like the *Almagest,* on the other hand, explained the laws (*qawānīn*) of celestial motions in terms of imaginary points moving on imaginary circles. It was necessary to provide an account that was faithful to mathematical theory while at the same time showing how the motions were brought about by the physical bodies in which the abstract points and circles must be assumed to exist. Such an account would be "more truly descriptive of the existing state of affairs and more obvious to the understanding."[29]

Ibn al-Haytham's aim here was not therefore to question any part of the theory of the *Almagest* but, following a tradition which goes back to Aristotle and which had been given authority among astronomers by one of Ptolemy's own works, the *Planetary Hypotheses,* to discover the physical reality underlying the abstract theory. The description had to satisfy certain principles already accepted in that tradition: a celestial body can have only circular, uniform, and permanent movement; a natural body cannot by itself have more than one natural movement; the body of the heavens is impassable; the void does not exist. Ibn al-Haytham's procedure was then, for every simple motion assumed in the *Almagest,* to assign a single spherical body to which this motion permanently belongs, and to show how the various bodies may continue to move without in any way impeding one another or creating gaps as they moved.

The heavens were accordingly conceived of as consisting of a series of concentric spherical shells (called spheres) which touched and rotated within one another. Inside the thickness of each shell representing the sphere of a planet other concentric and eccentric shells and whole spheres corresponded to concentric and eccentric circles and epicycles respectively. All shells and spheres rotated in their own places about their own centers, and their movements combined to produce the apparent motion of the planet assumed to be embedded in the epicyclic sphere at its equator. In his careful description of all movements involved Ibn al-Haytham provided, in fact, a full, clear, and untechnical account of Ptolemaic planetary theory—which alone may explain the popularity of his treatise.

A brief look at Ibn al-Haytham's other works will give us an idea of how seriously he took the program he inherited and of its significance for the later history of Islamic astronomy. Perhaps at some time after writing the *Configuration of the World* (III 1 = I*b* 10) Ibn al-Haytham composed a treatise (III 61) on what he called the movement of *iltifāf,* that is the movement or rather change in the obliquities (singular, *mayl*) of epicycles responsible for the latitudinal variations of the five planets (*Almagest,* XIII.2). This treatise is not known to have survived. But we have Ibn al-Haytham's reply to a criticism of it by an unnamed scholar. From this reply, the tract called *Solution of the Difficulties* [*shukūk*] *Concerning the Movement of Iltifāf* (III 63), we learn that in the earlier treatise he proposed a physical arrangement designed to produce the oscillations of epicycles required by the mathematical theory. The same subject is discussed, among other topics, in the work entitled *Al-Shukūk ʿalā Baṭlamyūs* (*Dubitationes in Ptolemaeum*) (III 64). More than any other of Ibn al-Haytham's writings, this work (almost certainly composed after the reply just mentioned) reveals the far-reaching consequences of the physical program to which he was committed.

The *Dubitationes* is a critique of three of Ptolemy's works: the *Almagest,* the *Planetary Hypotheses* and the *Optics.* As far as the first two works are concerned, the criticism is mainly aimed against the purely abstract character of the *Almagest* (this exclusiveness being in Ibn al-Haytham's view a violation of the principles accepted by Ptolemy himself) and against the fact that the *Planetary Hypotheses* had left out many of the motions demanded in the *Almagest* (a proof that Ptolemy had failed to discover the true arrangement of the heavenly bodies).

Ibn al-Haytham's objection to the "fifth motion" of the moon, described in *Almagest* V.5, is particularly instructive, being nothing short of a *reductio ad absurdum* by "showing" that such a motion would be physically impossible. Ptolemy had assumed that as the moon's epicycle moves on its eccentric deferent, the diameter through the epicycle's apogee (when the epicycle-center is at the deferent's apogee) rotates in such a way as to be always directed to a point on the apse-line (called the opposite point, *nuqṭat al-muḥādhāt*), such that the ecliptic-center lies halfway between that point and the deferent-center. The assumption implied that the epicycle's diameter alternately rotates in opposite senses as the epicycle itself completes one revolution on its deferent. But, Ibn al-Haytham argued, such a movement would have to be produced either by a single sphere which would alternately turn in opposite senses, or by two spheres of which one would be idle while the other turned in the appropriate sense. "As it is not possible to assume a body of this description, it is impossible that the diameter of the epicycle should be directed towards the given point."[30] Whatever one thinks of the argument, the problem it raised was later fruitfully explored by Naṣīr al-Dīn al-Ṭūsī in the *Tadhkira*.[31]

Perhaps most important historically was Ibn al-Haytham's objection against the theory of the five planets, and in particular against the device introduced by Ptolemy which later came to be known as the equant. Ptolemy supposed that the point from which the planet's epicycle would appear to move uniformly is neither the center of the eccentric deferent nor that of the ecliptic, but another point (the equant) on the line of apsides as far removed from the deferent-center as the latter is from the ecliptic-center. This entailed, as Ibn al-Haytham pointed out, that the motion of the epicycle-center, as measured on the circumference of its deferent, was not uniform, and consequently that the deferent sphere carrying the epicycle was not moving uniformly—in contradiction to the assumed principle of uniformity.

Although the equant had succeeded in bringing Ptolemy's planetary theory closer to observations, the validity of this criticism remained as long as the principle of uniform circular motion was adhered to. To say that the equant functioned merely as an abstract calculatory device designed for the sake of saving the phenomena was an answer which satisfied none of Ptolemy's critics, down to and including Copernicus. Nor was Ptolemy himself unaware of the objectionable character of such devices. In the *Dubitationes,* Ibn al-Haytham points to a passage in *Almagest* IX. 2 where Ptolemy asks to be excused for having employed procedures which, he admitted, were against the rules (*παρὰ τὸν λόγον*, *khārij ʿan al-qiyās*), as, for example, when for convenience's sake he made use merely of circles described in the planetary spheres, or when he laid down principles whose foundation was not evident. For, Ptolemy said, "when something is laid down without proof and is found to be in accord with the phenomena, then it cannot have been discovered without a method of science [*sabīl min al-ʿilm*], even though the manner in which it has been attained would be difficult to describe."[32]

Ibn al-Haytham agreed that it was indeed appropriate to argue from unproved assumptions, but not when they violated the admitted principles. His final conclusion was that there existed a true configuration of the heavens which Ptolemy had failed to discover.

It has been customary to contrast the "physical" approach of Ibn al-Haytham with the "abstract" approach of mathematical astronomers. The contrast is misleading if it is taken to imply the existence of two groups of researchers with different concerns. The "mathematical" researches of the school of Marāgha (among them al-Ṭūsī and al-Shīrāzī) were motivated by the same kind of considerations as those revealed in Ibn al-Haytham's *Dubitationes.*[33] Al-Ṭūsī, for instance, was as much worried about the moon's "fifth movement" and about the equant as was Ibn al-Haytham, and for the same reasons.[34] His *Tadhkira* states clearly that astronomical science is based on physical as well as mathematical premises. From a reference in it to Ibn al-Haytham,[35] made in the course of expounding alterations based on what is now known as the "Ṭūsī couple," it is clear that al-Ṭūsī recognized the validity of Ibn al-Haytham's physical program, although not the particular solutions offered by his predecessor.

The longest of the astronomical works of Ibn al-Haytham that have come down to us is a commentary on the *Almagest.* The incomplete text in the unique Istanbul manuscript which has recently been discovered occupies 244 pages of about 230 words each (see bibliography, additional works, no. 3). The manuscript, copied in 655 A.H./A.D. 1257, bears no title but twice states the author's name as Muḥammad ibn al-Ḥasan ibn al-Haytham, the name found by Ibn Abī Uṣaybiʿa in Ibn al-Haytham's own bibliographies, that is lists I and II. No title in list III seems to correspond to this work, but there are candidates in the other lists. The first title in Ibn al-Qifṭī's list is *Tahdhīb al-Majisṭī* or *Expurgation of the Almagest.* Number 19 in list II is described as "A book which works out the practical part of the *Almagest.*"

And number 3 in list I*a* begins as follows: "A commentary and summary of the *Almagest,* with demonstrations, in which I worked out only a few of the matters requiring computation. . . ." The last title is highly appropriate to the work that has survived.

Most commentators on the *Almagest,* Ibn al-Haytham says in the introduction, were more interested in proposing alternative techniques of computation than in clarifying obscure points for the beginner. As an example he mentions al-Nayrīzī who "crammed his book with a multiplicity of computational methods, thereby seeking to aggrandize it." Ibn al-Haytham sought rather to explain basic matters relating to the construction of Ptolemy's own tables, and he meant his commentary to be read in conjunction with the *Almagest,* whose terminology and order of topics it followed. The book was therefore to comprise thirteen parts, but, for brevity's sake and also because the *Almagest* was "well known and available," Ibn al-Haytham would not follow the commentators' customary practice of reproducing Ptolemy's own text. Unfortunately the manuscript breaks off before the end of the fifth part, shortly after the discussion of Ptolemy's theories for the sun and the moon. In the course of additions designed to complete, clarify, or improve Ptolemy's arguments, Ibn al-Haytham referred to earlier Islamic writers on astronomy, including Thābit ibn Qurra (on the "secant figure"), Banū Mūsā (on the sphere), and Ibrāhīm ibn Sinān (on gnomon shadows). All diagrams have been provided and are clearly drawn in the manuscript but the copyist has not filled in the tables.

Mathematics. Ibn al-Haytham's fame as a mathematician has rested on his treatment of the problem known since the seventeenth century as "Alhazen's problem." The problem, as viewed by him, can be expressed as follows: from any two points opposite a reflecting surface—which may be plane, spherical, cylindrical, or the surface of a cone, whether convex or concave—to find the point (or points) on the surface at which the light from one of the two points will be reflected to the other. Ptolemy, in his *Optics,* had shown that for convex spherical mirrors there exists a unique point of reflection. He also considered certain cases relating to concave spherical mirrors, including those in which the two given points coincide with the center of the specular sphere; the two points lie on the diameter of the sphere and at equal or unequal distances from its center; and the two points are on a chord of the sphere and at equal distances from the center. He further cited some cases in which reflection is impossible.[36]

In book V of his *Optics,* Ibn al-Haytham set out to solve the problem for all cases of spherical, cylindrical, and conical surfaces, convex and concave. Although he was not successful in every particular, his performance, which showed him to be in full command of the higher mathematics of the Greeks, has rightly won the admiration of later mathematicians and historians. Certain difficulties have faced students of this problem in the work of Ibn al-Haytham. In the Fatih manuscript, and in the Aya Sofya manuscript which is copied from it, the text of book V of the *Optics* suffers from many scribal errors, and in neither of these manuscripts are the lengthy demonstrations supplied with illustrative diagrams.[37] Such diagrams exist in Kamāl al-Dīn's commentary and in Risner's edition of the medieval Latin translation, but neither the diagrams nor the texts of these two editions are free from mistakes. One cannot, therefore, be too grateful to M. Naẓīf for his clear and thorough analysis of this problem, to which he devotes four chapters of his masterly book on Ibn al-Haytham.

Ibn al-Haytham bases his solution of the general problem on six geometrical lemmas (*muqaddamāt*) which he proves separately: (1) from a given point A on a circle ABG, to draw a line that cuts the circumference in H and the diameter BG in a point D whose distance from H equals a given line; (2) from the given point A to draw a line that cuts the diameter BG in a point E and the circumference in a point D such that ED equals the given line; (3) from a given point D on the side BG of a right-angled triangle having the angle B right, to draw a line DTK that cuts AG in T (and the extension of BA in K), such that $KT:TG$ equals a given ratio; (4) from two points E,D outside a given circle AB, to draw two lines EA and DA, where A is a point on the circumference, such that the tangent at A equally divides the angle EAD; (5) from a point E outside a circle having AB as diameter and G as center, to draw a line that cuts the circumference at D and the diameter at Z such that DZ equals ZG; and (6) from a given point D on the side GB of a right-angled triangle having the angle B right, to draw a line that meets the hypotenuse AG at K and the extension of AB on the side of B at T, such that $TK:KG$ equals a given ratio.[38]

Obviously lemmas (1) and (2) are special cases of one and the same problem, and (3) and (6) are similarly related. In his exposition of Ibn al-Haytham's arguments Naẓīf combines each of these two pairs in one construction. It will be useful to reproduce here his construction for (1) and (2) and to follow him in explaining Ibn al-Haytham's procedure by referring to this construction. It happens that (1) and

(2) contain characteristic features of the proposed solution of the geometrical problem involved. In Figure 3, *A* is a given point on the circumference of the small circle with diameter *BG*. It is required to draw a straight line from *A* that cuts the circle at *D* and the diameter, or its extension, at *E*, such that *DE* equals the given segment *z*.

From *G* draw the line *GH* parallel to *AB;* let it cut the circle at *H;* join *BH*. Let the extensions of *AG, AB* respectively represent the coordinate axes *x*, *y* whose origin thus coincides with *A*. Draw the hyperbola passing through *H* with *x, y* as asymptotes. Then, with *H* as center, draw the circle with radius

$$HS = \frac{BG^2}{z}$$

(*HS* being the side of a rectangle whose other side is *z*, and whose area equals BG^2). The circle will, in the general case, cut the two branches of the hyperbola at four points, such as *S, T, U, V.* Join *H* with all four points, and from *A* draw the lines parallel to *HS, HT, HU,* and *HV.* Each of these parallels will cut the circle circumscribing the triangle *ABG* at a point, such as *D,* and the diameter, or its extension, at another point, such as *E.* It is proved that each of these lines satisfies the stated condition.

As distinguished from the above demonstration, Ibn al-Haytham proceeded by considering three cases one after the other: (a) the required line is tangential to the circle, that is, *A* and *D* coincide; (b) *D* is on the arc *AG;* (c) *D* is on the arc *AB.* Despite the generality of the enunciation of lemma (1), he does not consider the case in which the line cuts the extension of *BG* on the side of *B*. Similarly in dealing with lemma (2) he separately examines three possibilities in respect of the relation of the circle *HS* to the "opposite branch" of the hyperbola: (a) the circle cuts that branch at two points; (b) the circle is tangential to it at one point; (c) the circle falls short of it. For finding the shortest line between *H* and the "opposite branch" of the hyperbola he refers to Apollonius' *Conics,* V. 34. Ibn al-Haytham did not, of course, speak of a coordinate system of perpendicular axes whose origin he took to be the same as the given point *A*. He did, however, consider a rectangle similar to *ABHG,* and described the sides of it corresponding to *AB, AG* as asymptotic to the hyperbola he drew through a point corresponding to *H* in Figure 3. For drawing this hyperbola he referred to *Conics,* II. 4.

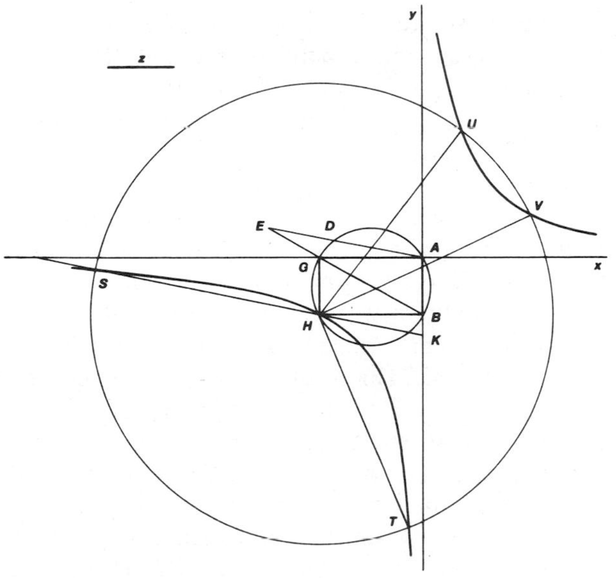

FIGURE 3

Applying the six geometrical lemmas for finding the points of reflection for the various kinds of surface, Ibn al-Haytham again proceeded by examining particular cases in succession. Naẓīf shows that the various cases comprised by lemma 4 constitute a general solution of the problem in respect of spherical surfaces, concave as well as convex. With regard to cylindrical mirrors, Ibn al-Haytham considered the cases in which (a) the two given points are in the plane perpendicular to the axis; and (c) the general case in which the intersection of the plane containing the two points with the cylinder is neither a straight line nor a circle, but an ellipse. He described six different cases in an attempt to show that reflection from convex conical surfaces can take place from only one point, which he determined. For concave conical mirrors, he showed that reflection can be from any number of points up to but not exceeding four. And he argued for the same number of points for concave cylindrical mirrors.

Apart from the mathematical sections of the *Optics,* some twenty of the writings of Ibn al-Haytham which deal exclusively with mathematical topics have come down to us. Most of these writings are short and they vary considerably in importance. About a quarter of them have been printed in the original Arabic and about half of them are available in European translations or paraphrases. Some of the more important among these works fall into groups and will be described as such.

List III includes three works (III 39, III 55, and III 56) which are described as solutions of difficulties arising in three different parts of Euclid's *Elements.* There are no manuscripts exactly answering to these descriptions. There exist, on the other hand, several manuscripts of a large work entitled *Solution of the Difficulties in Euclid's Elements,* which does not appear in list III. It therefore seems likely that III 39,

III 55, and III 56 are parts of the larger work which is listed below in the bibliography as additional work no. 1.

The object of the *Solution* was to put into effect a rather ambitious program. Unlike earlier works by other writers, it proposed to deal with all or most of the difficulties occasioned by Euclid's book, and not with just a few of them; it examined particular cases and offered alternative constructions for many problems; it revealed the "remote mathematical causes" (*al-ʿilal al-taʿlīmiyya al-baʿīda*) of the theoretical propositions (*al-ashkāl al-ʿilmiyya*)—something which "none of the ancients or the moderns had previously mentioned"; and, finally, it replaced Euclid's indirect proofs with direct ones. In this book Ibn al-Haytham referred to an earlier *Commentary on the Premises of Euclid's Elements* (III 2), and said that he meant the two works to form together a complete commentary on the whole of the *Elements.* This earlier work, restricted to the definitions, axioms, and postulates of the *Elements,* is extant both in the Arabic original and in a Hebrew translation made in 1270 by Moses ibn Tibbon. Ibn al-Haytham's interesting treatment of Euclid's theory of parallels well illustrates his approach in these two "commentaries."

In III 2 Ibn al-Haytham ascribed to Euclid the "axiom" that "two straight lines do not enclose a space [*saṭḥ*]" (his own opinion is that the statement should be counted among the "postulates"). Concerning Euclid's definition of parallel lines as nonsecant lines he remarked that the "existence" of such lines should be proved and, for this purpose, introduced the following "more evident" postulate: if a straight line so moves that the one end always touches a second straight line, and throughout this motion remains perpendicular to the second and in the same plane with it, then the other end of the moving line will describe a straight line which is parallel to the second. Ibn al-Haytham thus replaced parallelism in Euclid's sense by the property of equidistance, a procedure which had originated with the Greeks and which had characterized many Islamic attempts to prove Euclid's postulate 5.

Like Thābit ibn Qurra before him Ibn al-Haytham based his proof on the concept of motion—which procedure al-Khayyāmī and, later, al-Ṭūsī found objectionable as being foreign to geometry. The crucial step in the deduction of Euclid's postulate is the demonstration of Saccheri's "hypothesis of the right angle" by reference to a "Saccheri quadrilateral." Let *AG, BD* be drawn at right angles to *AB* (Figure 4): it is to be proved that perpendiculars to *BD* from points on *AG* are equal to *AB,* and, consequently, perpendicular to *AG.* From any point *G* draw *GD* perpendicular to *BD;* produce *GA* to *E* such that *AE* equals *AG;* draw *ET* perpendicular to *DB* produced; and join *BG, BE.* Considering, first, triangles *ABG, ABE,* then triangles *BDG, BTE,* it is seen that *GD* equals *ET.* Let *GD* now move along *DBT,* the angle *GDT* being always right. Then, when *D* coincides with *B, G* will either coincide with *A,* or fall below it on *AB,* or above it (occupying the position of *H* in the figure) on *BA* produced, according as *GD* is assumed equal to, less than, or greater than *AB.* When *D* reaches *T, GD* will exactly coincide with *ET.* During this motion, *G* will have described a straight line which, on the hypothesis that *DG* is not equal to *AB,* would enclose an area, such as *GHEA,* with another straight line, *GAE*—which is impossible. Finally, by considering in turn triangles *BDG, BDA,* and *AKB, GKD,* it is clear that $DGA = BAG =$ a right angle. The Euclidean postulate follows as a necessary consequence.

In the larger commentary, Ibn al-Haytham reformulated postulate 5, stating that two intersecting straight lines cannot both be parallel to a third ("Playfair's axiom"), and referring to the proof set forth in the earlier, and shorter, work. It is to be noted that al-Ṭūsī's criticism (in his own work on the theory of parallels, *Al-Risāla al-Shāfiya*) of Ibn al-Haytham's attempt was based on the remarks in this larger commentary, not on the earlier proof, which al-Ṭūsī said was not available to him.[39]

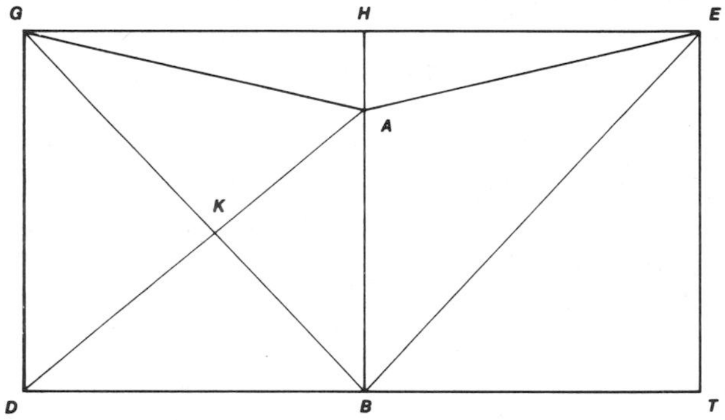

FIGURE 4

Ibn al-Haytham wrote two treatises on the quadrature of crescent-shaped figures (*al-ashkāl al-hilāliyya*) or lunes. (Their titles have sometimes been misunderstood as referring to the moon.) The second, and fuller, treatise (III 21), although extant in several manuscripts, has not been studied. From the introduction we gather that it was composed quite some time after the first (III 20, now lost), although the two works appear consecutively in list III. The treatise comprises twenty-three propositions on lunes, of

IBN AL-HAYTHAM

which some are generalizations of particular cases already proved in the earlier treatise, as the author tells us, while others are said to be entirely new. The subject was connected with that of squaring the circle: if plane figures bounded by two unequal circular arcs could be squared, why not the simpler figure of a circle? Ibn al-Haytham put forward such an argument in a short tract on the *Quadrature of the Circle* (III 30), which has been published. The object of the tract is to prove the "possibility" of squaring the circle without showing how to "find" or construct a square equal in area to a given circle.

To illustrate his point, Ibn al-Haytham proves a generalization of a theorem ascribed to Hippocrates of Chios. The proof is reproduced from his earlier work on lunes. In Figure 5, let *B* be any point on the semicircle with diameter *AG;* describe the smaller semicircles with *AB, BG* as diameters; it is shown that the lunes *AEBH, BZGT* are together equal in area to the right-angled triangle *ABG.* On the basis of Euclid XII.2, which states that circles are to one another as the squares on the diameters, it is easily proved that the semicircles on *AB, BG* are together equal to the semicircle on the hypotenuse *AG.* The equality of the lunes to the triangle *ABG* follows from subtracting the segments *AHB, BTG* from both sides of the equation. Hippocrates had considered the particular case in which the triangle *ABG* is isosceles.[40]

Two more works which are closely related are *On Analysis and Synthesis* (*Maqāla fi 'l-taḥlīl wa 'l-tarkīb,* III 53) and *On the Known Things* (*Maqāla fi 'l-Maʿlūmāt,* III 54). The subject matter of the latter work overlaps with that of Euclid's *Data,* which is called

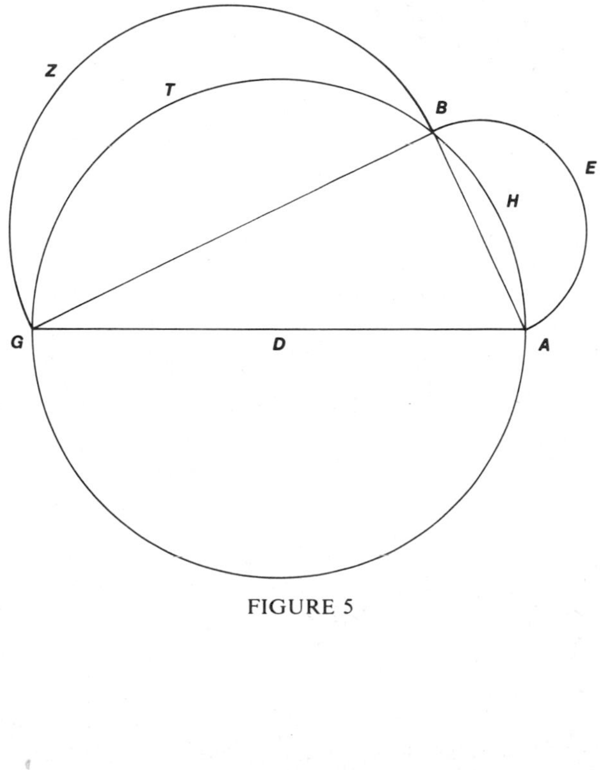

FIGURE 5

in Arabic *Kitāb al-Muʿṭayāt* (Δεδομένα). Ibn al-Haytham's use of *al-maʿlūmāt,* rather than *al-muʿṭayāt,* has a precedent in the Arabic translation of Euclid's book itself, where *al-maʿlūm* (the known) is regularly employed to denote the given. *On Analysis* is a substantial work of about 24,000 words whose object is to explain the methods of analysis and synthesis, necessary for the discovery and proof of theorems and constructions, by illustrating their application to each of the four mathematical disciplines: arithmetic, geometry, astronomy, and music. It lays particular emphasis on the role of "scientific intuition" (*al-ḥads al-ṣināʿī*), when properties other than those expressly stated in the proposition to be proved have to be conjectured before the process of analysis can begin.

In describing the relationship of this treatise to the one on *The Known Things* Ibn al-Haytham made certain claims which should be quoted here. The art of analysis, he says, is not complete without the things that are said to be known.

> Now the known things are of five kinds: the known in number, the known in magnitude, the known in ratio, the known in position, and the known in species [*al-maʿlūm al-ṣūra*]. The book of Euclid called *Al-Muʿṭayāt* includes many of these known things which are the instruments of the art of analysis, and on which the larger part of analysis is based. But that book does not include other known things that are indispensable to the art of analysis . . . nor have we found them in any other book. In the examples of analysis we give in the present treatise we shall prove the known things used, whether or not we have found them in other works. . . . After we have completed this treatise we shall resume the subject in a separate treatise in which we shall show the essence of the known things that are used in mathematics and give an account of all their kinds and of all that relates to them.[41]

The treatise on known things, which is extant, divides in fact into two parts, of which the first (comprising twenty-four propositions) is said to be the invention of Ibn al-Haytham himself. In 1834 L. Sédillot published a paraphrase of the introduction to this work (a discussion of the concept of knowledge) together with a translation of the enunciations of the propositions constituting both parts. There is no study of the work on *Analysis and Synthesis.* The more important of the remaining mathematical works are all available in European translations.

NOTES

1. On al-Fāsī, see Ibn al-Qifṭī, *Taʾrīkh,* pp. 392–394.
2. *Al-Mutawassiṭāt,* or intermediate books, so called because they were studied after the *Elements* of Euclid and before the

Almagest. They included, for instance, Euclid's *Data.* Theodosius' *Spherics,* and the *Spherics* of Menelaus. See the explanation of Abu'l-Ḥasan al-Nasawī in al-Ṭūsī, *Majmū' al-Rasā'il,* II (Hyderabad, 1359 A.H. [1940]), *risāla* no. 3, p. 2. The existence of a copy of Apollonius' *Conics* in Ibn al-Haytham's hand (MS Aya Sofya 2762, 307 fols., dated Ṣafar 415 A.H. [1024]) may be taken to confirm the story that he lived on selling copies of scientific texts, although the *Conics* is not one of the books mentioned in the story.

3. The expression "fī ḥudūd" could also mean "about" or "toward the end of."
4. On Bayhaqī's dates see the article devoted to him in *Encyclopaedia of Islam,* 2nd ed.
5. On Qayṣar see A. I. Sabra, "Simplicius's Proof of Euclid's Parallels Postulate," in *Journal of the Warburg and Courtauld Institutes,* **32** (1969), 8.
6. The title is "[Ibn al-Haytham's] Answer to a Geometrical Question Addressed to Him in Baghdad [*su'ila 'anhā bi-Baghdād*] in the Months of the Year Four Hundred and Eighteen."
7. See Galen's *Opera omnia,* C. G. Kühn, ed., XIX (repr. Hildesheim, 1965), 8–61; and F. Rosenthal, "Die arabische Autobiographie," pp. 7–8. Galen's *De libris propriis* was translated into Arabic by Ḥunayn ibn Isḥāq in the ninth century.
8. See Galen's *Opera omnia, ed. cit.,* X (repr. Hildesheim, 1965), 457, ll. 11–15.
9. In the context of Arabic optics *manāẓir* is the plural, not of *manẓar* (view, appearance) but of *manẓara,* that by means of which vision is effected, an instrument of vision. One evidence for this is Ḥunayn ibn Isḥāq's Arabic translation of Galen's *De usu partium,* where *manẓara* and *manāẓir* correspond to ὄψις and ὄψεις, respectively (see Escorial MS 850, fol. 29v). *Al-Manāẓir* had been used as the Arabic title of Euclid's (and Ptolemy's) Ὀπτικά.
10. Newton, *Opticks,* bk. I, pt. 1, def. 1. See A. I. Sabra, *Theories of Light,* pp. 288–289, 310–311, n. 25.
11. The diagram of the eye in Risner's ed. of the Latin text is taken from Vesalius' *De corporis humani fabrica* (D. Lindberg, "Alhazen's Theory of Vision . . . ." p. 327, n. 30). The diagram in MS Fatih 3212 of *Kitāb al-Manāẓir,* bk. I, does not clearly and correctly represent Ibn al-Haytham's descriptions; it can be seen in S. Polyak, *The Retina* (Chicago, 1957), and in G. Nebbia, "Ibn al-Haytham nel millesimo anniversario della nascita," p. 204.
12. MS Fatih 3212, fol. 83r; *Opticae thesaurus. Alhazeni libri VII,* p. 7, sec. 14, l. 26.
13. The importance of this principle and of its application by Ibn al-Haytham to the problem of vision has been rightly emphasized by Vasco Ronchi in his *Storia della luce,* 2nd ed. (Bologna, 1952), pp. 33–47, trans. into English as *The Nature of Light* (London, 1970), pp. 40–57.
14. *Opticae thesaurus. Alhazeni libri VII,* p. 14, sec. 23, l. 20.
15. *Ibid.,* p. 15, sec. 24: "Visio videtur fieri per συναύγειαν, id est receptos simul et emissos radios."
16. At least some of the Latin MSS have "reflexe." Risner's text, however, correctly reads "refracte" (*bi 'l-in'iṭāf*). See Vescovini, *Studi,* p. 93, n. 10.
17. Vescovini, *Studi,* p. 141.
18. See M. Naẓīf, *Al-Ḥasan ibn al-Haytham,* pp. 709–721. Unlike the Arabic, the Latin text in Risner's ed. expresses rule (5) as $d < i$ (*Alhazeni libri VII,* p. 247, ll. 8–11). Both the Arabic MSS and Risner's ed. omit the words "less than" from rule (6), and consequently express this rule as $d = 1/2\ (i + d)$[!]. The correction has been made by Naẓīf and is supported by Kamāl al-Dīn's formulation of the rule on the basis of Ibn al-Haytham's autograph (see *Tanqīḥ,* I, 7; II, 134, ll. 10–11).
19. The earliest occurrence of "al-bayt al-muẓlim" is in a ninth-century tract on burning mirrors by 'Uṭārid ibn Muḥammad al-Ḥāsib: Istanbul MS Laleli 2759, fols. 1–20. The tract is based on earlier Greek works including at least one by Anthemius of Tralles, and the term may therefore have been derived from them. See M. Schramm, "Ibn al-Haythams Stellung in der Geschichte der Wissenschaften," pp. 15–16.
20. Bk. I, ch. 5, sec. 29, p. 17 in Risner's ed. of the Latin text. The discussion continues in the Arabic for the greater part of two pages to which nothing corresponds in Risner's text.
21. M. Clagett, "A Medieval Latin Translation of a Short Arabic Tract on the Hyperbola," in *Osiris,* **11** (1954), 361.
22. D. Lindberg, *Pecham and the Science of Optics* (Madison, Wis., 1970), p. 29, n. 69. (See bibliography, "Original Works," no. III 3.)
23. *Ibid.,* p. 20.
24. Vescovini, *Studi,* pp. 137 ff.
25. See especially Vescovini, "Contributo per la storia della fortuna di Alhazen in Italia" (in the Bibliography).
26. W. Hartner, "The Mercury Horoscope . . .," esp. pp. 122–124.
27. M. Steinschneider, "Notice . . .," p. 723.
28. Hartner, *op. cit.,* pp. 124, 127 ff.
29. MS India Office, Loth 734, fol. 101r.
30. *Dubitationes* (III 64), *ed. cit.,* p. 19.
31. W. Hartner, "Naṣīr al-Dīn al-Ṭūsī's Lunar Theory," in *Physis,* **11** (1969), 287–304.
32. *Dubitationes* (III 64), *ed. cit.,* p. 39; also p. 33. The English trans. is of Isḥāq's Arabic version quoted by Ibn al-Haytham. The Greek differs only slightly from the Arabic: ". . . οὔτε τὰ ἀναποδείκτως ὑποτιθέμενα, ἐὰν ἅπαξ σύμφωνα τοῖς φαινομένοις καταλαμβάνται, χωρὶς ὁδοῦ τινος καὶ ἐπιστάσεως εὑρῆσθαι δύναται, κἂν δυσέκθετος ᾖ ὁ τρόπος αὐτῶν τῆς καταλήψεως (Ptolemy, *Syntaxis mathematica,* J. L. Heiberg, ed., II [Leipzig, 1903], 212, ll. 11–14).
33. See E. S. Kennedy, "Late Medieval Planetary Theory," in *Isis,* **57** (1966), 365–378, esp. 366–368.
34. I have consulted the British Museum MSS Add. 23, 394; Add. 23, 397; and Add. 7472 Rich, the last two being al-Nīsābūrī's commentary, *Tawḍīḥ,* on the *Tadhkira.*
35. The reference is very probably to the lost tract on the movement of *iltifāf* (III 61).
36. A. Lejeune, *Recherches sur la catoptrique grecque* (Brussels, 1957), pp. 71–74.
37. Diagrams are supplied in MS Köprülü 952 (see bibliography, "Original Works," under III 3). As far as I know, this MS has not been used in studies of the *Optics.*
38. *Opticae thesaurus. Alhazeni libri VII,* pp. 142–150.
39. See al-Ṭūsī, *Rasā'il,* II (cited in note 2 above), *risāla* no. 8, pp. 5–7. See also A. I. Sabra, "Thābit ibn Qurra on Euclid's Parallels Postulate," in *Journal of the Warburg and Courtauld Institutes,* **31** (1968), 12–32; and A. P. Juschkewitsch [Youschkevitch], *Geschichte der Mathematik im Mittelalter* (Leipzig, 1964), pp. 277–288.
40. Sir Thomas Heath, *A History of Greek Mathematics,* I (Oxford, 1921), pp. 183 ff.
41. Chester Beatty MS 3652, fol. 71r–v.

BIBLIOGRAPHY

Ibn Abī Uṣaybi'a's lists I*a,* I*b,* II, and III of Ibn al-Haytham's works, described in the article, have been published, wholly or in part, more than once in European languages. They have recently been reproduced in a convenient form in Italian trans. by G. Nebbia in "Ibn al-Haytham nel millesimo anniversario della nascita," in *Physis,* **9** (1967), 165–214. Since practically all of Ibn al-Haytham's extant works are included in list III, they will be arranged here according to their numbers in that list. The same numbers can be used to refer to Nebbia's article, where the reader will find a useful bibliography, and to M. Schramm's book, *Ibn al-Haythams Weg zur Physik* (Wiesbaden, 1963), where many of the works listed are discussed. (The titles constituting what Nebbia calls list I*c* are in fact chapter headings of the last work in list I*b.*)

IBN AL-HAYTHAM

Arabic MSS of Ibn al-Haytham's works are listed in H. Suter, "Die Mathematiker und Astronomen der Araber und ihre Werke," in *Abhandlungen zur Geschichte der mathematischen Wissenschaften mit Einschluss ihrer Anwendungen,* **10** (Leipzig, 1900), no. 204, 91–95; and "Nachträge und Berichtigungen zur 'Mathematiker . . .,'" *ibid.,* **14** (1902), esp. 169–170; H. P. J. Renaud, "Additions et corrections à Suter 'Die Mathem. u. Astr. der Arab.,'" *Isis,* **18** (1932), esp. 204; C. Brockelmann, *Geschichte der arabischen Literatur,* I (Weimar, 1898), 469–470; 2nd ed. (Leiden, 1943), pp. 617–619; supp. I (Leiden, 1937), 851–854. The Istanbul MSS are more fully described in M. Krause, "Stambuler Handschriften islamischer Mathematiker," in *Quellen und Studien zur Geschichte der Mathematik, Astronomie und Physik,* Abt. B, Studien, **3** (1936), 437–532. P. Sbath, in *Al-Fihris: Catalogue de manuscrits arabes,* 3 pts. plus *Supplément* (Cairo, 1938–1940), pt. I, p. 86, cites MSS, belonging to a private collection in Aleppo, of the following works: III 6, III 8, III 48, III 60, III 65, III 67, III 68, and III 82. (I owe this reference to Robert E. Hall.)

In the list of extant original works that follows, reference will be made to Brockelmann and Krause by means of the abbreviations "Br." and "Kr.," followed by the numbers given to Ibn al-Haytham's treatises in these two authors.

Other abbreviations used are the following:

Rasā'il: Majmū' al-Rasā'il (Hyderabad, 1357 A.H. [1938]). A collection of eight treatises by Ibn al-Haytham to which a ninth, published at Hyderabad, 1366 A.H. (1947), has been added.

Tanqīḥ: Tanqīḥ al-Manāẓir . . ., 2 vols. (Hyderabad, 1347–1348 A.H. [1928–1930]). This is Kamāl al-Dīn al-Fārisī's "commentary" ("*Tanqīḥ*" means revision or correction) on Ibn al-Haytham's *Kitāb al-Manāẓir.* Vol. II has a sequel (*dhayl*) and an appendix (*mulḥaq*) which contain Kamāl al-Dīn's recensions (sing., *taḥrīr*) of a number of Ibn al-Haytham's other optical works.

I. ORIGINAL WORKS.

III 1 (Br. 28). *M(aqāla). f(ī). Hay'at al-'ālam* ("On the Configuration of the World"). A MS that has recently come to light is Kastamonu 2298, 43 fols.; unlike the India Office MS it is incomplete. For Hebrew and Latin MSS see M. Steinschneider, "Notice sur un ouvrage astronomique inédit d'Ibn Haitham," in *Bullettino di bibliografia e di storia delle scienze matematiche e fisiche,* **14** (1881), 721–736, also published as *Extrait . . .* (Rome, 1883); "Supplément," *ibid.,* **16** (1883), 505–513; and *Die hebraeischen Uebersetzungen des Mittelalters und die Juden als Dolmetscher* (Berlin, 1893), II, 559–561; F. Carmody, *Arabic Astronomical and Astrological Sciences in Latin Translation* (Berkeley, Cal., 1955), pp. 141–142; and Lynn Thorndike and Pearl Kibre, *Catalogue of Incipits of Mediaeval Scientific Writings in Latin* (Cambridge, Mass., 1963), cols. 894, 895, 1147 (the last being a Spanish trans. by Abraham Hebraeus).

The Arabic text has not been edited. A Latin version has been published from a MS of the 13th or early 14th century in Millás Vallicrosa, *Las traducciones orientales en los manuscritos de la Biblioteca Catedral de Toledo* (Madrid, 1942), app. II, 285–312; see pp. 206–208. There is a German trans. by K. Kohl, "Über den Aufbau der Welt nach Ibn al Haiṯam," in *Sitzungsberichte der Physikalisch-medizinischen Sozietät in Erlangen,* **54–55** (1922–1923), 140–179.

III 2 (Br. 8, Kr. 14). *M. f. Sharḥ muṣādarāt Kitāb Uqlīdis* ("Commentary on the Premises of Euclid's *Elements*"). Composed before III 53 and before the larger commentary on the *Elements* (see below, "Additional Works," no. 1). MSS of Ibn Tibbon's Hebrew trans. are listed in M. Steinschneider, *Hebraeischen Uebersetzungen* (cited under III 1), II, 509–510. A partial Russian trans. of this work (using a Kazan MS not recorded in Brockelmann) has been published by B. A. Rozenfeld as "Kniga kommentariev k vvedeniyam knigi Evklida 'Nachala,'" in *Istoriko-matematicheskie issledovaniya,* **11** (1958), 743–762.

III 3 (Br. 34, Kr. 15). *Kitāb al-Manāẓir* ("Optics"). All known Arabic MSS of this work are in Istanbul; see Krause. Köprülü MS 952 contains practically the whole of bks. IV, V, VI, and VII. The folios must be rearranged as follows: IV, 108r–133v; V, 2r–v, 74r–81v, 89r–107v, 134r–135v; VI, 3r–47v; VII, 1r–v, 48r–73v, 82r–88v. The reference in Brockelmann to a recension of this work in the Paris MS, ar. 2460 (Br. has 2640) is mistaken; the MS is a recension of Euclid's *Optics* which is attributed on the title page to Ḥasan ibn [Mūsā ibn] Shākir.

I have examined the following Latin MSS: Bruges 512, 113 fols., 13th c.; Cambridge University Library, Peterhouse MS 209 (= 11 · 10 · 63), 111 fols., 14th c.; Cambridge University Library, Trinity College MS 1311 (= 0 · 5 · 30), 165 fols., 13th c.; Edinburgh, Royal Observatory, Crawford Library MS 9 · 11 · 3 (20), 189 fols., dated 1269; Florence, Biblioteca Nazionale, Magliabechi CI.XX.52, 136 fols., incomplete, 15th c.; London, British Museum, Royal 12 G VII, 102 fols., 14th c.; British Museum, Sloane 306, 177 fols., 14th c.; Oxford, Corpus Christi 150, 114 fols., 13th c.; Vienna, Nationalbibliothek 2438, a fragment only from beginning of bk. I, ch. 1 (ch. 4 in Arabic text), fols. 144r–147r, 15th c. Other Latin MSS have been reported in F. Carmody, *Arabic Astronomical and Astrological Sciences,* cited under III 1, p. 140; L. Thorndike and P. Kibre, *Catalogue,* cited under III 1, cols. 774, 803, 1208; and G. F. Vescovini, *Studi sulla prospettiva medievale* (Turin, 1965), pp. 93–94, n. 10.

The only known copy of the fourteenth-century Italian trans. of the *Optics* is MS Vat. Lat. 4595, 182 fols. Like the Latin text it lacks chs. 1–3 of bk. I. It includes an Italian trans. of the *Liber de crepusculis* (see below), fols. 178r–182v.

The Latin text was published in the collective volume bearing the following title: *Opticae thesaurus. Alhazeni Arabis libri septem, nunc primum editi, eiusdem liber de crepusculis et nubium ascensionibus, item Vitellionis Thuringo-Poloni Libri X, omnes instaurati, figuris illustrati et aucti, adjectis etiam in Alhazenum commentariis a Federico Risnero* (Basel, 1572). Concerning the authorship of *De crepusculis,* see below, "Spurious Works."

Kamāl al-Dīn's commentary, the *Tanqīḥ* (cited above), does not reproduce the integral text of the *Optics*, as was at one time supposed. An ed. of the Arabic text of *Kitāb al-Manāẓir* and English trans. are being prepared by the present writer.

III 4 (Br. 51). *M. f. Kayfiyyat al-arṣād* ("On the Method of [Astronomical] Observations").

III 6 (Br. 27). *M. f. Ḍaw' al-qamar* ("On the Light of the Moon"). Composed before 7 Aug. 1031, the date on which a copy was completed by ʿAlī ibn Riḍwān (Ibn al-Qifṭī, *Ta'rīkh*, p. 444). Published as no. 8 in *Rasā'il*. There is a German trans. by Karl Kohl, "Über das Licht des Mondes. Eine Untersuchung von Ibn al-Haitham," in *Sitzungsberichte der Physikalisch-medizinischen Sozietät in Erlangen*, **56-57** (1924-1925), 305-398.

III 7 (Br. 22, Kr. 18). *M.* (or *Qawl*) *f. Samt al-qibla bi 'l-ḥisāb* ("Determination of the Direction of the Qibla by Calculation"). A German trans. is C. Schoy, "Abhandlung des Ḥasan ibn al-Ḥasan ibn al-Haiṯam (Alhazen) über die Bestimmung der Richtung der Qibla," in *Zeitschrift der Deutschen morgenländischen Gesellschaft*, **75** (1921), 242-253.

III 8 (Br. 41, Kr. 19). *M. f. al-Hāla wa-qaws quzaḥ* ("On the Halo and the Rainbow"). Completed in Rajab, 419 A.H. (A.D. 1028); see *Tanqīḥ*, II, p. 279. Recension by Kamāl al-Dīn in *Tanqīḥ*, II, 258-279. A shortened German trans. of this recension is E. Wiedemann, "Theorie des Regenbogens von Ibn al Haiṯam," in *Sitzungsberichte der Physikalisch-medizinischen Sozietät in Erlangen*, **46** (1914), 39-56.

III 9 (Br. 42, Kr. 20). *M. f. Mā yaʿriḍ min al-ikhtilāf fī irtifāʿāt al-kawākib* ("On What Appears of the Differences in the Heights of the Stars").

III 10 = Ia10 (Br. 39, Kr. 16). *M. f. Ḥisāb al-muʿāmalāt* ("On Business Arithmetic").

III 11 (Br. 43, Kr. 21). *M. f. al-Rukhāma al-ufuqiyya* ("On the Horizontal Sundial"). This work refers to a treatise to be written later on "shadow instruments" (*ālāt al-aẓlāl*); the reference may be to III 66.

III 14. *M. f. Marākiz al-athqāl* ("On Centers of Gravity"). This is not extant but has been abstracted by al-Khāzinī in *Mīzān al-ḥikma;* see the Hyderabad ed. (1359 A.H. [1940]), pp. 16-20.

III 15 (Br. 13 a, Kr. 22). *M. f. Uṣūl al-misāḥa* ("On the Principles of Measurement"). A summary of the results of an earlier work or works by Ibn al-Haytham on the subject. Published as no. 7 in *Rasā'il*. German trans. by E. Wiedemann in "Kleinere Arbeiten von Ibn al Haiṯam," in *Sitzungsberichte der Physikalisch-medizinischen Sozietät in Erlangen*, **41** (1909), 16-24.

III 16 (Br. 2, Kr. 23). *M. f. Misāḥat al-kura* ("On the Measurement of the Sphere"). Later in composition than III 17; it may be one of the works referred to in III 15.

III 17 (Br. 14). *M. f. Misāḥat al-mujassam al-mukāfī* ("On the Measurement of the Paraboloidal Solid"). See III 16. Refers to a work on the same subject by Thābit ibn Qurra and another by Wayjan ibn Rustam al-Qūhī. German trans. by H. Suter, "Die Abhandlung über die Ausmessung des Paraboloides von el-Ḥasan b. el-Ḥasan b. el-Haitham," in *Bibliotheca mathematica*, 3rd ser., **12** (1912), 289-332. See also H. Suter, "Die Abhandlungen Thâbit b. Ḳurras und Abû Sahl al-Ḳûhîs über die Ausmessung der Paraboloide," in *Sitzungsberichte der Physikalisch-medizinischen Sozietät in Erlangen*, **48-49** (1916-1917), 186-227.

III 18 (Br. 33, Kr. 10). *M. f. al-Marāya al-muḥriqa bi 'l-dawā'ir* ("On Spherical Burning Mirrors"). Published as no. 4 in *Rasā'il*. German trans. by E. Wiedemann, "Ibn al Haiṯams Schrift über die sphärischen Hohlspiegel," in *Bibliotheca mathematica*, 3rd ser., **10** (1909-1910), 293-307. See also E. Wiedemann, "Zur Geschichte der Brennspiegel," in *Annalen der Physik und Chemie*, n.s. **39** (1890), 110-130, trans. into English by H. J. J. Winter and W. ʿArafāt, "A Discourse on the Concave Spherical Mirror by Ibn al-Haitham," in *Journal of the Royal Asiatic Society of Bengal*, 3rd ser., Science, **16** (1950), 1-16.

III 19 (Br. 33). *M. f. al-Marāya al-muḥriqa bi 'l-quṭūʿ* ("On Paraboloidal Burning Mirrors"). A hitherto unrecorded MS of the Arabic text is Florence, Biblioteca Medicea-Laurenziana, Or. 152, fols. 90v-97v. It was copied in the 13th century and bears no title or author's name. Here Ibn al-Haytham mentions an earlier treatise of his on how to construct all conic sections by mechanical means (*istikhrāj jamīʿ al-quṭūʿ bi-ṭarīq al-āla*); see below, "Additional Works," no. 2. The Arabic text has been published as no. 3 in *Rasā'il*. A medieval Latin trans. as *Liber de speculis comburentibus*, probably made by Gerard of Cremona, has been published together with a German trans. from the Arabic by J. L. Heiberg and E. Wiedemann: "Ibn al Haiṯams Schrift über parabolische Hohlspiegel," in *Bibliotheca mathematica*, 3rd ser., **10** (1909-1910), 201-237. See also E. Wiedemann, "Über geometrische Instrumente bei den muslimischen Völkern," in *Zeitschrift für Vermessungswesen*, nos. 22-23 (1910), 1-8; and "Geschichte der Brennspiegel," cited under III 18. An English trans. is H. J. J. Winter and W. ʿArafāt, "Ibn al-Haitham on the Paraboloidal Focusing Mirror," in *Journal of the Royal Asiatic Society of Bengal*, 3rd ser., Science, **15** (1949), 25-40.

III 20. *Maqāla mukhtaṣara fi 'l-Ashkāl al-hilāliyya* ("A Short Treatise on Crescent-Shaped Figures"). Not extant; see III 21.

III 21 (Br. 1, Kr. 12). *Maqāla mustaqṣāt fi 'l-Ashkāl al-hilāliyya* ("A Longer Treatise on Crescent-Shaped Figures"). Composed after III 20, which it is intended to supersede, and before III 30 (*q.v.*). It may also have been written before the work listed below as "Additional," no. 1 (*q.v.*).

III 22 ([?] Br. 6). *Maqāla mukhtaṣara fī Birkār al-dawā' ir al-ʿiẓām* ("A Short Treatise on the Birkār of Great Circles"). See Wiedemann, "Geometrische Instrumente . . .," cited under III 19. See III 23. *"Birkār"* is Persian for compass. Ibn al-Haytham explains the theory and construction of an instrument suitable for accurately drawing very large circles.

III 23 ([?] Br. 6). *Maqāla mashrūḥa fī Birkār al-dawā'ir al-ʿiẓām* ("An Expanded Treatise on the Birkār of Great Circles"). See III 22.

III 25 (Br. 52). *M. f. al-Tanbīh ʿalā mawāḍiʿ al-ghalaṭ fī kayfiyyat al-raṣd* ("On Errors in the Method of [Astronomical] Observations"). Earlier in composition than III 31.

III 26 (Br. 44, Kr. 24). *M. f. anna 'l-Kura awsaʿ al-ashkāl al-mujassama allatī iḥāṭatuhā muta-sāwiya, wa-anna 'l-dāʾira awsaʿ al-ashkāl al-musaṭṭaḥa allatī iḥaṭatuhā mutasāwiya* ("That the Sphere Is the Largest of the Solid Figures Having Equal Perimeters, and That the Circle is the Largest of the Plane Figures Having Equal Perimeters"). Composed before III 38 and III 68. Refers to Archimedes' *On the Sphere and the Cylinder.*

III 28 (Br. 29). *Kitāb fī Taṣḥīḥ al-aʿmāl al-nujūmiyya, maqālatān* ("A Book on the Corrections of Astrological Operations, Two Treatises").

III 30 (Br. 9, Kr. 2). *M. f. Tarbīʿ al-dāʾira* ("On the Quadrature of the Circle"). Refers to the "book on lunes" (*kitābina fi 'l-hilāliyyāt*), that is either III 20 or III 21. There is an ed. of the Arabic text and German trans. by H. Suter, "Die Kreisquadratur des Ibn el-Haiṯam," in *Zeitschrift für Mathematik und Physik,* Hist.-lit. Abt., **44** (1899), 33–47.

III 31 (Br. 45, Kr. 25). *M. f. Istikhrāj khaṭṭ niṣf al-nahār ʿalā ghāyat al-taḥqīq* ("Determination of the Meridian with the Greatest Precision"). Composed after III 25. Points out the relevance of the subject to astrology.

III 36 (Br. 31, Kr. 7). *M. f. Kayfiyyat al-aẓlāl* ("On the Formation of Shadows"). Composed before the "Commentary on the *Almagest*" (see below, "Additional Works," no. 3) and after III 3. A recension by Kamāl al-Dīn al-Fārisī is in *Tanqīḥ,* II, 358-381. A German trans. by E. Wiedemann is "Über eine Schrift von Ibn al Haiṯam: Über die Beschaffenheit der Schatten," in *Sitzungsberichte der Physikalisch-medizinischen Sozietät in Erlangen,* **39** (1907), 226–248.

III 38 (Br. 30, Kr. 26). *M. f. Ḥall shukūk fi 'l-maqāla l-ūlā min Kitāb al-Majisṭī yushakkiku fīhā baʿḍ ahl al-ʿilm* ("Solution of Difficulties in the First Book of the *Almagest* Which a Scholar Has Raised"). This work is to be distinguished from III 64. It was composed after III 26. The name of "the scholar" appears in MS Fatih 3439, fol. 150v to be Abu 'l-Qāsim ibn [?]Maʿdān, who is otherwise unknown to me. The Title in the Fatih MS (*Ḥall Shukūk fī Kitāb al-Majisṭī yushakkiku fīhā baʿḍ ahl al-ʿilm*) does not limit the discussion to book I of the *Almagest.* The text in fact discusses, among other things, book V of Ptolemy's *Optics.*

III 39 ([?] Kr. 27). *M. f. Ḥall shakk fī mujassamāt Kitāb Uqlīdis* ("Solution of a Difficulty in the Part of Euclid's Book Dealing With Solid Figures"). This may be part of the work listed below as "Additional Works," no. 1. But see Krause, no. 27, where reference is made to a work bearing a partially similar title and of uncertain authorship. (I have not examined MS Yeni Cami T 217, 2^0, 893 A.H., referred to by Krause.)

III 40 (Br. 3). *Qawl fī Qismat al-miqdārayn al-mukhtalifayn al-madhkūrayn fi 'l-shakl al-awwal min al-maqāla 'l-ʿāshira min Kitāb Uqlīdis* ("On the Division of the Two Unequal Magnitudes Mentioned in Proposition I of Book X of Euclid's Book"). The subject is closely connected with the so-called "axiom of Archimedes."

III 41 (Br. 23). *Masʾala fī Ikhtilāf al-naẓar* ("A Question Relating to Parallax"). MS India Office, Loth 734, fols. 120r–120v, specifies that lunar parallax is meant.

III 42 (Br. 17). *Qawl fī Istikhrāj muqaddamat ḍilʿ al-musabbaʿ* ("On the Lemma [Used by Archimedes] for [Constructing] the Side of the Heptagon [in the Book at the End of Which He Mentioned the Heptagon]"). Composed before III 74. German trans. by C. Schoy in *Die trigonometrischen Lehren des persischen Astronomen Abu 'l-Raiḥân Muḥ. ibn Aḥmad al Bîrûnî, dargestellt nach al-Qânûn al-Masʿûdî* (Hannover, 1927), pp. 85-91.

III 43 (Br. 10, Kr. 9). *Qawl fī Qismat al-khaṭṭ alladhī istaʿmalahu Arshimīdis fī Kitāb al-Kura wa 'l-usṭuwāna* ("On the Division of the Line Used by Archimedes in His Book on the Sphere and Cylinder"). Concerned with prop. 4 of bk. II in Archimedes' work. French trans. by F. Woepcke, *L'algèbre d'Omar Alkhayyâmî* (Paris, 1851), pp. 91–93.

III 44 (Br. 46, Kr. 28). *Qawl fī Istikhrāj khaṭṭ niṣf al-nahār bi-ẓill wāḥid* ("Determination of the Meridian by Means of One Shadow").

III 46 (Br. 26). *M. f. al-Majarra* ("On the Milky Way"). German trans. by E. Wiedemann, "Über die Lage der Milchstrasse nach ibn al Haiṯam," in *Sirius,* **39** (1906), 113–115.

III 48 (Br. 24, Kr. 5). *M. f. Aḍwāʾ al-kawākib* ("On the Light of the Stars"). Composed before III 49. Published as no. 1 in *Rasāʾil.* Abridged German trans. by E. Wiedemann, "Über das Licht der Sterne nach Ibn Al Haitham," in *Wochenschrift für Astronomie, Meteorologie und Geographie,* n.s. **33** (1890), 129–133. English trans. by W. ʿArafat and H. J. J. Winter, "The Light of the Stars—a Short Discourse by Ibn al-Haytham," in *British Journal for the History of Science,* **5** (1971), 282–288.

III 49 (BR. 37). *M. f. al-Athar alladhī* [*yurā*] *fī* [*wajh*] *al-qamar* ("On the Marks [Seen] on the [Face of the] Moon"). Composed after III 3, III 6, and III 48, to all of which it refers. German trans. by C. Schoy, as *Abhandlung des Schaichs Ibn ʿAlî al-Ḥasan ibn al-Ḥasan ibn al-Haitham: Über die Natur der Spuren* [*Flecken*], *die man auf der Oberfläche des Mondes sieht* (Hannover, 1925).

III 53 (Br. 35). *M. f. al-Taḥlīl wa 'l-tarkīb* ("On Analysis and Synthesis"). Brockelmann lists a Cairo MS. Another is Dublin, Chester Beatty 3652, fols. 69v-86r, dated 612 A.H. (1215). Composed before III 54 (to which it is closely related) and after III 2.

III 54 (Br. 11). *M. f. al-Maʿlūmāt* ("On the Known Things [Data]"). Trans. of the enunciations of its propositions by L. A. Sédillot, in "Du *Traité* des connues géométriques de Hassan ben Haithem," in *Journal asiatique,* **13** (1834), 435–458.

III 55. *Qawl fī Hall Shakk fi 'l-maqāla 'l-thāniya ʿashar min Kitāb Uqlīdis* ("Solution of a Difficulty in Book XII of Euclid's Book"). Possibly a part of the work listed below as "Additional," no. 1.

III 56. *M. f. Ḥall shukūk al-maqāla 'l-ūlā min Kitāb Uqlīdis* ("Solution of the Difficulties in Book I of Euclid's Book"). Possibly part of the work listed below as "Additional Works," no. 1.

III 60 (Br. 32, Kr. 4). *M.* (or *Qawl*) *f. al-Ḍawʾ* ("A Discourse on Light"). Composed after III 3. Printed as no. 2 in *Rasā'il.* J. Baarmann published an ed. of the Arabic text together with a German trans. as "Abhandlung über das Licht von Ibn al-Haiṯam," in *Zeitschrift der Deutschen morgenländischen Gesellschaft,* **36** (1882), 195–237. (See remarks on this ed. by E. Wiedemann, *ibid.,* **38** (1884), 145–148.) A Cairo ed. by A. H. Mursī correcting Baarmann's text appeared in 1938. There is now a critical French trans. by R. Rashed: "Le 'Discours de la lumière' d'Ibn al-Haytham," in *Revue d'histoire des sciences et de leurs applications,* **21** (1968), 198–224. A recension is in *Tanqīḥ,* II, 401–407. A German trans. of this recension (*taḥrīr*) is E. Wiedemann, "Ueber 'Die Darlegung der Abhandlung über das Licht' von Ibn al Haiṯam," in *Annalen der Physik und Chemie,* n.s. **20** (1883), 337–345.

III 63 (Br. 19, Kr. 29). *M. f. Ḥall shukūk ḥarakat al-iltifāf* ("Solution of Difficulties Relating to the Movement of Iltifāf"). A reply to an unnamed scholar who raised objections against an earlier treatise by Ibn al-Haytham (III 61: "On the Movement of Iltifāf") which is now lost. In the reply Ibn al-Haytham revealed an intention he had entertained to write a critique of Ptolemy's *Almagest, Planetary Hypotheses* (*Kitāb al-Iqtiṣāṣ*), and *Optics* (MS Pet. Ros. 192, fols. 19v–20r)—almost certainly a reference to III 64.

III 64 (Br. 30). *M. f. al-Shukūk ʿalā Baṭlamyūs* ("Dubitationes in Ptolemaeum"). Composed after III 63; see preceding note. There is a critical ed. by A. I. Sabra and N. Shehaby (Cairo, 1971). English trans. of part of this work by A. I. Sabra, "Ibn al-Haytham's Criticism of Ptolemy's *Optics,*" in *Journal of the History of Philosophy,* **4** (1966), 145–149.

III 65. *M. f. al-Juz' alladhī la yatajazza'* ("On Atomic Parts"). A unique copy belonging to a private collection in Aleppo is recorded in P. Sbath, *Al-Fihris* (cited above), I, 86, no. 724.

III 66 (Br. 40, Kr. 17). *M. f. Khuṭūṭ al-sāʿāt* ("On the Lines of the Hours [i.e., on sundials]"). *"Al-sāʿāt"* has sometimes been misread as *"al-shuʿāʿāt"* (rays). The treatise refers to a work by Ibrāhīm ibn Sinān, "On Shadow Instruments." See note for III 11 above.

III 67. *M. f. al-Qarasṭūn* ("On the *Qarasṭūn*"). A unique copy belonging to a private collection in Aleppo is recorded in P. Sbath, *Al-Fihris* (cited above), I, p. 86, no. 726.

III 68 (Br. 12, Kr. 11). *M. f. al-Makān* ("On Place"). Later in composition than III 26. Published as no. 5 in *Rasā'il.* A short account is given by Wiedemann in "Kleinere Arbeiten . . .," cited under III 15 above, pp. 1–7.

III 69 (Br. 18). *Qawl fī Istikhrāj aʿmidat al-jibāl* ("Determination of the Altitudes of Mountains"). A longer title is *Fī Maʿrifat irtifāʿ al-ashkhāṣ al-qā'ima wa-aʿmidat al-jibāl wa irtifāʿ al-ghuyūm* ("Determination of the Height of Erect Objects and of the Altitudes of Mountains and of the Height of Clouds"). A German trans. is H. Suter, "Einige geometrische Aufgaben bei arabischen Mathematiker," in *Bibliotheca mathematica,* 3rd ser., **8** (1907), 27–30. A short account by Wiedemann is in "Kleinere Arbeiten . . .," cited under III 15 above, pp. 27–30.

III 71 (Br. 38). *M. f. Aʿmidat al-muthallathāt* ("On the Altitudes of Triangles"). (An alternate title is *Khawāṣṣ al-muthallath min jihat al-ʿamūd* ("Properties of the Triangle in Respect of Its Altitude"). Published as no. 9 in *Rasā'il.*

III 73. (Br. 13, Kr. 3). *M. f. Shakl Banū Mūsā.* ("On the Proposition of Banū Mūsā [proposed as a lemma for the *Conics* of Apollonius]"). Published as no. 6 in *Rasā'il.* An account of it is in Wiedemann, "Kleinere Arbeiten . . .," cited under III 15 above, pp. 14–16.

III 74 (Br. 48, Kr. 30). *M. f. ʿAmal al-musabbaʿ fi 'l-dā'ira* ("On Inscribing a Heptagon in a Circle"). Composed after III 42, to which it refers. As well as referring to Archimedes it mentions al-Qūhī, whose treatise on the subject has been published and trans. by Y. Dold-Samplonius, "Die Konstruktion des regel-mässigen siebenecks nach Abû Sahl al-Qûhî," in *Janus,* **50** (1963), 227–249.

III 75 (Br. 25, Kr. 1). *M. f. Irtifāʿ al-quṭb ʿalā ghāyat al-taḥqīq* ("Determination of the Height of the Pole With the Greatest Precision"). A German trans. is C. Schoy, "Abhandlung des Ḥasan ben al-Ḥasan ben al-Haiṯam über eine Methode, die Polhöhe mit grösster Genanigkeit zu bestimmen," in *De Zee,* **10** (1920), 586–601.

III 76 (Br. 47, Kr. 31). *M. f. ʿAmal al-binkām* ("On the Construction of the Water Clock").

III 77 (Br. 33b, Kr. 32). *M. f. al-Kura 'l-muḥriqa* ("On the Burning Sphere"). Written after III 3 and III 66. A recension by Kamāl al-Dīn is in *Tanqīḥ,* II, 285–302. A German trans. of this recension is in E. Wiedemann, "Brechung des Lichtes in Kugeln nach Ibn al Haiṯam und Kamâl al Dîn al Fârisî," in *Sitzungsberichte der Physikalisch-medizinischen Sozietät in Erlangen,* **42** (1910), 15–58, esp. 16–35.

III 78 (Br. 15). *M. f. Mas'ala ʿadadiyya mujassama* ("On an Arithmetical Problem in Solid Geometry").

III 79 (Br. 5). *Qawl fī Mas'ala handasiyya* ("On a Geometrical Problem"). A German trans. is in C. Schoy, "Behandlung einiger geometrischen Fragenpunkte durch muslimische Mathematiker," in *Isis,* **8** (1926), 254–263, esp. 254–259.

III 80 (Br. 20, Kr. 8). *M. f. Ṣūrat al-kusūf* ("On the Shape of the Eclipse"). Composed after III 3. A recension by Kamāl al-Dīn is *Tanqīḥ,* II, 381–401. A German trans. of the original text from the India Office MS is in E. Wiedemann, "Über die Camera obscura bei Ibn al Haiṯam," in *Sitzungsberichte der Physikalisch-medizinischen Sozietät in Erlangen,* **46** (1914), 155–169.

III 82 (Br. 21, Kr. 13). *M. f. Ḥarakat al-qamar* ("On the Motion of the Moon"). A vindication of Ptolemy's account of the mean motion of the moon in latitude.

III 83 (Br. 4). *M. f. Masā'il al-talāqī* ("On Problems of Talāqī"). These are problems involving the solution of simultaneous linear equations. There is an account by E. Wiedemann, in "Über eine besondere Art des Gesellschaftsrechnens besondere nach Ibn al Haiṯam," in *Sitzungsberichte der Physikalisch-medizinischen Sozietät in Erlangen,* **58–59** (1926–1927), 191–196.

III 92 (Br. 16). *Qawl fī Istikhrāj mas'ala ʿadadiyya* ("Solution of an Arithmetical Problem"). An account is given by Wiedemann in "Kleinere Arbeiten . . .," cited under

IBN AL-HAYTHAM

III 15 above, pp. 11–13.

ADDITIONAL WORKS. These are extant works whose titles do not appear in list III.

Add. 1 (Br. 7, Kr. 6). *Kitāb fī Ḥall shukūk Kitāb Uqlīdis fi 'l-Uṣūl wa-sharḥ ma'ānīh* ("A Book on the Solution of the Difficulties in Euclid's *Elements* and an Explanation of Its Concepts"). This seems to be a different work from Ia 1: *Sharḥ Uṣūl Uqlīdis fi 'l-handasa wa 'l-'adad wa talkhīṣuhu* ("A Commentary on and Summary of Euclid's *Elements of Geometry and Arithmetic*").

The absence of this comprehensive work from list III may perhaps be explained by supposing III 39, III 55, and III 56 to be parts of it. It refers to III 2 and also to "our treatise on crescent-shaped figures," which is either III 20 or III 21. An Istanbul MS that is not recorded in Brockelmann or in Krause is Üniversite 800, copied before 867 A.H. (1462–1463). The MS has 182 fols. but is not complete.

Add. 2. *Kalām fī tawṭi'at muqaddamāt li-'amal al-quṭū' 'alā saṭḥ mā bi-ṭarīq ṣinā'ī* ("A Passage in Which Lemmas Are Laid Down for the Construction of [Conic] Sections by Mechanical Means"). MS Florence, Biblioteca Medicea-Laurenziana, Or. 152, fols. 97v–100r. No author is named, and the "lemmas" follow immediately after a copy of Ibn al-Haytham's III 19 ("On Paraboloidal Burning Mirrors"), which also does not bear the author's name. Since Ibn al-Haytham refers in III 19 to a treatise of his on the mechanical construction of conic sections, it is very likely that the "passage" we have here is a fragment of that treatise which the copyist found joined to III 19.

Add. 3. "Commentary on the *Almagest,*" Istanbul MS, Ahmet III 3329, copied in Jumādā II 655 (1257), 123 fols. Probably written after III 36, to which it appears to refer (fol. 90r).

SPURIOUS WORKS. Ibn al-Haytham is not the author of the *Liber de crepusculis,* the work on dawn and twilight translated by Gerard of Cremona and included in Risner's *Opticae thesaurus* (see A. I. Sabra, "The Authorship of the *Liber de crepusculis,*" in *Isis,* **58** [1967], 77–85; above, III 3). An astrological work, *De imaginibus celestibus,* Vatican MS Urb. Lat. 1384, fols. 3v–26r, has also been mistakenly ascribed to him (*ibid.,* p. 80, n. 14).

Two more writings are listed in Brockelmann (nos. 49, 50) which may or may not be genuine.

I am grateful to M. Clagett for showing me a microfilm of MS Bruges 512 (III 3) and to M. Schramm for showing me microfilms of the following MSS: Kastamonu 2298 (III 1), Üniversite 800 (Add. 1), and Ahmet III 3329 (Add. 3). For the last three MSS and for other Arabic MSS not hitherto recorded, see the appropriate volume of F. Sezgin, *Geschichte des arabischen Schrifttums* (Leiden, 1967–).

II. SECONDARY LITERATURE. Sources for the biography of Ibn al-Haytham are Ibn al-Qifṭī, *Ta'rīkh al-ḥukamā',* J. Lippert, ed. (Leipzig, 1903), pp. 155–168 (see corrections of this ed. by H. Suter in *Bibliotheca mathematica,* 3rd ser., **4** [1903], esp. 295–296); 'Alī ibn Zayd al-Bayhaqī, *Tatimmat ṣiwān al-ḥikma,* M. Shafī', ed., fasc. I: Arabic text (Lahore, 1935), 77–80 (analysis and partial English trans. of this work by M. Meyerhof in *Osiris,* **8** [1948], 122–216, see esp. 155–156); Ibn Abī Uṣaybi'a, *Ṭabaqāt al-aṭibbā',* A. Müller, ed. (Cairo–Königsberg, 1882–1884), II, 90–98 (German trans. in E. Wiedemann, "Ibn al-Haiṯam, ein arabischer Gelehrter," cited below); Ṣā'id al-Andalusī, *Ṭabaqāt al-umam,* L. Cheikho, ed. (Beirut, 1912), p. 60 (French trans. by R. Blachère [Paris, 1935], p. 116). The account in Abu'l-Faraj ibn al-'Ibrī, *Ta'rīkh mukhtaṣar al-duwal,* A. Ṣālḥānī, ed. (Beirut, 1958), pp. 182–183, derives from Ibn al-Qifṭī. In addition to the works by Suter (*Mathematiker*) and Brockelmann (*Geschichte*) already cited, see M. Steinschneider, "Vite di matematici arabi, tratte da un' opera inedita di Bernardino Baldi, con note di M.S.," in *Bullettino di bibliografia e di storia delle scienze matematiche et fisiche,* **5** (1872), esp. 461–468, also printed separately (Rome, 1874); M. J. de Goeje, "Notice biographique d'Ibn al-Haitham," in *Archives néerlandaises des sciences exactes et naturelles,* 2nd ser., **6** (1901), 668–670; E. Wiedemann, "Ueber das Leben von Ibn al Haiṯam und al Kindî," in *Jahrbuch für Photographie und Reproduktiontechnik,* **25** (1911), 6–11 (not important).

The literary relationship of Ibn al-Haytham's autobiography to Galen's *De libris propriis* is discussed by F. Rosenthal in "Die arabische Autobiographie," in *Studia arabica I,* Analecta Orientalia, no. 14 (Rome, 1937), 3–40, esp. 7–8. There is a discussion of the autobiography in G. Misch, *Geschichte der Autobiographie,* III, pt. 2 (Frankfurt, 1962), 984–991. Lists Ia and III of the works of Ibn al-Haytham are translated from Ibn Abī Uṣaybi'a in F. Woepcke, *L'algèbre d'Omar Alkhayyāmī* (Paris, 1851), pp. 73–76; but see H. Suter's corrections in *Mathematiker,* pp. 92–93. There is a German trans. of Ibn al-Haytham's autobiography and of Lists I–III in E. Wiedemann, "Ibn al Haiṯam, ein arabischer Gelehrter," in *Festschrift [für] J. Rosenthal* (Leipzig, 1906), pp. 169–178. M. Schramm discusses the chronological order of some of Ibn al-Haytham's works in *Ibn al-Haythams Weg zur Physik* (Wiesbaden, 1962), pp. 274–285.

The most complete study of Ibn al-Haytham's optical researches is M. Naẓīf, *Al-Ḥasan ibn al-Haytham, buḥūthuhu wa-kushūfuhu al-baṣariyya* ("Ibn al-Haytham, His Optical Researches and Discoveries"), 2 vols. (Cairo, 1942–1943)—reviewed by G. Sarton in *Isis,* **34** (1942–1943), 217–218. Based on the extant MSS of *Kitāb al-Manāẓir* and on Ibn al-Haytham's other optical works, this voluminous study (more than 850 pages) is distinguished by clarity, objectivity, and thoroughness. It is particularly valuable as a study of the mathematical sections of Ibn al-Haytham's works. M. Schramm, *Ibn al-Haythams Weg zur Physik,* is the most substantial single study of Ibn al-Haytham in a European language, and it has the merit of drawing on MS sources not previously available. In analyzing Ibn al-Haytham's attempt to combine Aristotelian natural philosophy with a mathematical and experimental approach, Schramm illuminates other important treatises of Ibn al-Haytham besides the *Optics.*

The question of mathematizing Aristotelian physics is also discussed in S. Pines, "What Was Original in Arabic Science," in A. C. Crombie, ed., *Scientific Change* (London, 1963), pp. 181–205, esp. 200–202. It is taken up afresh by R. Rashed in "Optique géometrique et doctrine optique chez Ibn al Haytham," in *Archive for History of Exact Sciences,* **6** (1970), 271–298. For further discussions of the concept of experiment in Arabic optics generally and in the work of Ibn al-Haytham in particular, see M. Schramm, "Aristotelianism: Basis and Obstacle to Scientific Progress in the Middle Ages," in *History of Science,* **2** (1963), 91–113, esp. 106, 112; and "Steps Towards the Idea of Function: A Comparison Between Eastern and Western Science of the Middle Ages," *ibid.,* **4** (1965), 70–103, esp. 81, 98; A. I. Sabra, "The Astronomical Origin of Ibn al-Haytham's Concept of Experiment," in *Actes du XIIe Congrès international d'histoire des sciences,* Paris, 1968, III A (Paris, 1971), 133–136.

General accounts mainly based on the *Optics* are J. B. J. Delambre, "Sur l'*Optique* de Ptolémée comparée à celle qui porte le nom d'Euclide et à celle d'Alhazen et de Vitellion," in *Historie de l'astronomie ancienne,* II (Paris, 1817), 411–432; E. Wiedemann, "Zu Ibn al Haiṯams Optik," in *Archiv für Geschichte der Naturwissenschaften und der Technik,* **3** (1910–1911), 1–53, an account of Kamāl al-Dīn's revision (*Tanqīḥ*) of Ibn al-Haytham's *Optics,* based on a Leiden MS; includes an abbreviated trans. of *Optics,* bk. I, chs. 1–3, as reported by Kamāl al-Dīn; L. Schnaasse, *Die Optik Alhazens* (Stargard, 1889); V. Ronchi, "Sul contributo di Ibn al-Haitham alle teorie della visione e della luce," in *Actes du VIIe Congrès international d'histoire des sciences* (Jerusalem, 1953), pp. 516–521; and *The Nature of Light,* a trans. of *Storia della luce* (2nd ed., Bologna, 1952) (London, 1970), pp. 40–57; H. J. J. Winter, "The Optical Researches of Ibn al-Haitham," in *Centaurus,* **3** (1953–1954), 190–210, which includes accounts of treatises other than the *Optics.*

Studies of particular aspects of Ibn al-Haytham's optical work are A. Abel, "La sélénographie d'Ibn al Haitham (965–1039) dans ses rapports avec la science grecque," in *Comptes rendus, IIe Congrès national des sciences* (Brussels, 1935), pp. 76–81 (concerned with III 49); J. Lohne, "Zur Geschichte des Brechungsgesetzes," in *Sudhoffs Archiv für Geschichte der Medizin und der Naturwissenschaften,* **47** (1963), 152–172, esp. 153–157; R. Rashed, "Le modèle de la sphère transparente et l'explication de l'arc-en-ciel: Ibn al-Haytham, al-Fārisī," in *Revue d'histoire des sciences et de leurs applications,* **23** (1970), 109–140; E. Wiedemann, "Ueber den Apparat zur Untersuchung und Brechung des Lichtes von Ibn al Haiṯam," in *Annalen der Physik und Chemie,* n.s. **21** (1884), 541–544; "Über die Erfindung der Camera obscura," in *Verhandlung der Deutschen physikalischen Gesellschaft,* **12** (1910), 177–182; and "Über die erste Erwähnung der Dunkelkammer durch Ibn al Haiṯam," in *Jahrbuch für Photographie und Reproduktiontechnik,* **24** (1910), 12–13; J. Würschmidt, "Zur Theorie der Camera obscura bei Ibn al Haiṯam," in *Sitzungsberichte der Physikalisch-medizinischen Sozietät in Erlangen,* **46** (1914), 151–154; and "Die Theorie des Regenbogens und das Halo bei Ibn al Haiṯam und bei Dietrich von Freiberg," in *Meteorologische Zeitschrift,* **13** (1914), 484–487. Apart from Vescovini's *Studi* (see below) there is one account of Ibn al-Haytham's psychological ideas as expounded in bk. II of the *Optics:* H. Bauer, *Die Psychologie Alhazens auf Grund von Alhazens Optik dargestellt,* in the series Beiträge zur Geschichte der Philosophie des Mittelalters, 10, no. 5 (Münster in Westfalen, 1911). The physiological aspect of vision is discussed in M. Schramm, "Zur Entwicklung der physiologischen Optik in der arabischen Literatur," in *Sudhoffs Archiv für Geschichte der Medizin und der Naturwissenschaften,* **43** (1959), 289–316, esp. 291–299.

The following are concerned with the transmission of Ibn al-Haytham's optical ideas to the West; they include comparisons with Hebrew and Latin medieval, Renaissance, and seventeenth-century writers: M. Steinschneider, "Aven Natan e le teorie sulla origine della luce lunare e delle stelle, presso gli autori ebrei del medio evo," in *Bullettino di bibliografia e di storia delle scienze matematiche e fisiche,* **1** (1868), 33–40; E. Narducci, "Nota intorno ad una traduzione italiana fatta nel secolo decimoquarto, del trattato d'*Ottica* d'Alhazen, matematico del secolo undecimo, e ad altri lavori di questo scienziato," *ibid.,* **4** (1871), 1–48; and "Giunte allo scritto intitolato 'Intorno ad una traduzione italiana, fatta nel secolo decimoquarto, dell' *Ottica* di Alhazen,'" *ibid.,* pp. 137–139; A. I. Sabra, "Explanation of Optical Reflection and Refraction: Ibn al-Haytham, Descartes and Newton," in *Actes du Xe Congrès international d'histoire des sciences,* Ithaca, 1962 (Paris, 1964), I, 551–554; and *Theories of Light From Descartes to Newton* (London, 1967), pp. 72–78, 93–99 (concerned with the theories of reflection and refraction); G. F. Vescovini, *Studi sulla prospettiva medievale* (Turin, 1965), which reveals the influence of Ibn al-Haytham's *Optics* on the development of empiricist theories of cognition in the fourteenth century; and "Contributo per la storia della fortuna di Alhazen in Italia: Il volgarizzamento del MS. Vat. 4595 e il 'Commentario terzo' del Ghiberti," in *Rinascimento,* 2nd ser., **5** (1965), 17–49; D. Lindberg, "Alhazen's Theory of Vision and Its Reception in the West," in *Isis,* **58** (1968), 321–341; and "The Cause of Refraction in Medieval Optics," in *British Journal for the History of Science,* **4** (1968), 23–38. See also G. Sarton, "The Tradition of the *Optics* of Ibn al-Haitham," in *Isis,* **29** (1938), 403–406.

The following are studies relating to Ibn al-Haytham's astronomical works, particularly his treatise on *The Configuration of the World* (III 1): M. Steinschneider, "Notice sur un ouvrage astronomique inédit d'Ibn Haitham," in *Bullettino di bibliografia e di storia delle scienze matematiche e fisiche,* **14** (1881), 721–736; and "Supplément à la 'Notice sur un ouvrage inédit d'Ibn Haitham,'" *ibid.,* **16** (1883), 505–513—*Extrait du Bullettino* . . ., containing the "Notice" and the "Supplément" (Rome, 1884), includes many corrections of the earlier publications; E. Wiedemann, "Ibn al Haiṯam und seine Bedeutung für die Geschichte der Astronomie," in *Deutsche Literaturzeitung,* **44** (1923), 113–118; P. Duhem, *Système du monde,* II (Paris, 1914), 119–129; W. Hartner, "The Mercury Horoscope of Marcantonio Michiel of Venice, a Study in the History of Renaissance Astrology and Astronomy," in A. Beer, ed., *Vistas in Astronomy* (London–New York, 1955), pp. 84–138, esp. 122–127; S. Pines, "Ibn al-Haytham's Critique of Ptolemy," in *Actes du Xe Congrès international d'histoire des sciences,* Ithaca, 1962 (Paris, 1964), I, 547–550 (concerned with Ibn al-Haytham's criticism of the equant in the *Dubitationes in Ptolemaeum,* III 64); M. Schramm, *Ibn al-Haythams Weg zur Physik,* esp. pp. 63–69, 88–146.

For discussions of "Alhazen's problem," see P. Bode, "Die Alhazensche Spiegelaufgabe in ihrer historischen Entwicklung nebst einer analytischen Lösung des verallgemeinerten Problems," in *Jahresbericht des Physikalischen Vereins zu Frankfurt am Main,* for 1891–1892 (1893), pp. 63–107; M. Baker, "Alhazen's Problem. Its Bibliography and an Extension of the Problem," in *American Journal of Mathematics,* **4** (1881), 327–331; M. Naẓīf, *Al-Ḥasan ibn al-Haytham . . .,* pp. 487–589; J. A. Lohne, "Alhazens Spiegelproblem," in *Nordisk matematisk tidskrift,* **18** (1970), 5–35 (with bibliography).

A general survey of Ibn al-Haytham's work in various fields is M. Schramm, "Ibn al-Haythams Stellung in der Geschichte der Wissenschaften," in *Fikrun wa fann,* no. 6 (1965), 2–22. See also M. Naẓīf and P. Ghalioungui, "Ibn at Haitham, an 11th-Century Physicist," in *Actes du Xe Congrès international d'histoire des sciences,* Ithaca, 1962 (Paris, 1964), I, 569–571. No. 2 of the Publications of the Egyptian Society for the History of Science (Cairo, 1958) includes articles in Arabic by M. Naẓīf, M. Madwar, M. ʿAbd al-Rāziq, M. Ghālī, and M. Ḥijāb on various aspects of Ibn al-Haytham's thought. Some of these articles are reprints of previous publications. For a detailed table of contents see *Isis,* **51** (1960), 416.

Many of the European translations of Ibn al-Haytham's works, cited in the first part of the bibliography, include historical and critical notes.

A. I. SABRA

HEATH, THOMAS LITTLE (*b.* Barnetby le Wold, Lincoln, England, 5 October 1861; *d.* Ashtead, Surrey, England, 16 March 1940)

After attending the grammar school at Caistor, he went to Clifton and thence, with a foundation scholarship, to Trinity College, Cambridge, where he became a fellow in 1885 and an honorary fellow in 1920. On leaving Trinity, he entered the civil service in the department of the treasury. He retired from that service in 1926, having been awarded the C.B. (1903); K.C.B. (1909); and K.C.V.O. (1916). His academic distinctions were numerous. The University of Oxford conferred an honorary degree on him; the Royal Society elected him a fellow (1912); and he served on the council of the society. He was a fellow of the British Academy and president of the Mathematical Association from 1922 to 1923.

Heath's main interest lay in the study of Greek mathematics, for which his training in classics and mathematics at Cambridge admirably fitted him; he soon became one of the leading authorities on mathematics in antiquity. The wide range of his interest is reflected in the titles of the works he published. His *History of Greek Mathematics* is usually regarded as his most famous contribution. In *The Thirteen Books of Euclid's Elements* he made available those books of the *Elements* that had hitherto been considered unintelligible; in particular his treatment of book X is a masterpiece.

BIBLIOGRAPHY

I. ORIGINAL WORKS. Heath's works, including his translations, are *Diophantus of Alexandria: A Study in the History of Greek Algebra* (Cambridge, 1885; rev. ed., 1910); *Apollonius of Perga: A Treatise on the Conic Sections* (Cambridge, 1896; repr., 1961); *The Works of Archimedes* (Cambridge, 1897); *The Thirteen Books of Euclid's Elements* (Cambridge, 1908; 2nd ed., 1925); *Aristarchus of Samos: The Ancient Copernicus* (Oxford, 1913); *A History of Greek Mathematics,* 2 vols. (Oxford, 1921); *A Manual of Greek Mathematics* (Oxford, 1931); *Greek Astronomy* (London–Toronto–New York, 1932); and *Mathematics in Aristotle* (Oxford, 1949), on which he was working at the time of his death.

Heath also made numerous contributions to the *Mathematical Gazette* and the *Encyclopaedia Britannica* and assisted in the preparation of the 9th ed. of the Liddell-Scott Greek lexicon.

II. SECONDARY LITERATURE. On his life and work, see the obituaries in the London *Times* (18 Mar. 1940); *Proceedings of the British Academy,* **26** (1940); and *Obituary Notices of the Fellows of the Royal Society,* no. 9 (January 1941).

J. F. SCOTT

HECHT, DANIEL FRIEDRICH (*b.* Sosa, near Eibenstock, Germany, 8 July 1777; *d.* Freiberg, Germany, 13 March 1833)

Virtually nothing is known about Hecht's childhood, youth, or family. It may be supposed that, born in one of the most important German mining districts of the time, he became interested in mining in his early youth and obtained an education in that subject. The course of his life can be followed more exactly from 1803, when, at the age of twenty-six, he enrolled in the Bergakademie at Freiberg, Saxony. After completing his studies he took a position as overseer (mine manager) and then taught at the Freiberger Bergschule.

Hecht's predilection and talent for solving mathematical and mechanical problems resulted in his appointment in 1816 as second professor of mathematics at the Freiberg Bergakademie, where he assumed from F. G. von Busse the lectures on elementary pure mathematics and applied mathematics (mechanics). In the following year he presented a course of lectures on theoretical mining surveying, which with a few interruptions he continued until his death. Following Busse's retirement in 1826, Hecht advanced to first professor of mathematics. He soon ceased lecturing on pure mathematics and devoted his teaching activity solely to mechanics and mining machinery, especially to contemporary mechanical engineering. From this it is evident that, for Hecht, the growing union of engineering with mathematics and physics had become mechanics. It can also be clearly seen in his book *Erste Gründe der mechanischen Wissenschaften* (1819).

Hecht was not a leading figure at the Freiberg Bergakademie, but through his great industry and his strict conscientiousness in carrying out his duties he was of great help to his students. His lectures were designed less for gifted students than for those who needed extra assistance and an external stimulus in their studies. For this and for his friendly, sincere manner Hecht won many friends.

In addition to the *Erste Gründe,* Hecht's scientific activity at the Bergakademie resulted in a number of short essays in journals and widely used high school textbooks on mathematics, geometry, and underground surveying, as well as examples and tables for mathematical calculations.

BIBLIOGRAPHY

I. ORIGINAL WORKS. Hecht's writings include *Lehrbuch der Arithmetik und Geometrie,* 2 vols. (Freiberg, 1812–1814; II, 2nd ed., 1826); *Tafeln zur Berechnung der Seigerteufen und Sohlen für die Länge der schwachen Schnur = 1* (Freiberg, 1814); *Erste Gründe der mechanischen Wissenschaften* (Freiberg, 1819; 2nd ed., 1843); *Tafel zur Berechnung der Längen und Breiten für die Sohle = 1* (Freiberg, 1819); *Von den quadratischen und kubischen Gleichungen, von den Kegelschnitten und von den ersten Gründen der Differential- und Integral-Rechnung* (Leipzig, 1824); *Beispiele und Aufgaben aus der allgemeinen Arithmetik und gemeinen Geometrie* (Freiberg, 1824); *Einfache Construction zur Bestimmung der Kreuzlinie zweier Gänge, nebst einer Anweisung, um mit Hilfe der Kreuzlinie einen verworfenen Gang wieder aufzusuchen* (Leipzig, 1825); *Nachtrag zu den ersten Gründen der Differential- und Integral-Rechnung* (Leipzig, 1827); and *Lehrbuch der Markscheidekunst* (Freiberg, 1829).

II. SECONDARY LITERATURE. See "Daniel Friedrich Hecht," in *Festschrift zum hundertjährigen Jubiläum der Königl. Sächs. Bergakademie zu Freiberg* (Dresden, 1866), pp. 22–23; and "Daniel Friedrich Hecht," in Carl Schiffner, *Aus dem Leben alter Freiberger Bergstudenten,* I (Freiberg, 1935), 244–245.

M. KOCH

HECKE, ERICH (*b.* Buk, Posen, Germany [now Poznan, Poland], 20 September 1887; *d.* Copenhagen, Denmark, 13 February 1947)

Hecke was the son of Heinrich Hecke, an architect. He attended elementary school in Buk and high school in Posen, then studied from 1905 to 1910 at the universities of Breslau, Berlin, and Göttingen. At Berlin he worked mainly with Edmund Landau, and at Göttingen with David Hilbert. In 1910 he obtained his Ph.D. at Göttingen. Subsequently he became Hilbert's and Felix Klein's assistant and was made *Privatdozent* in 1912. In 1915 Hecke became professor at Basel. He went to Göttingen in 1918 and in 1919 to the recently established University of Hamburg, where he was a professor until his death from cancer. He was married and had a son who died young. Hecke was a member of the editorial staff of several mathematical journals and belonged to well-known learned societies.

Most of Hecke's work dealt with analytic number theory, continuing the research of Riemann, Dedekind, and Heinrich Weber. It was Hilbert who influenced him on the subject of his thesis and some additional works on an analogue of complex multiplication, namely, the construction of class fields over real quadratic number fields by adjoining certain values of Hilbert's modular functions. The findings did not meet Hecke's expectations but nevertheless yielded new results, such as an attack on the proof of the functional equation of the Dedekind zeta function. Hecke proved in 1917 that this function can be continued throughout the complex s-plane to a single pole at $s = 1$, where it is "regular" and sufficient for a functional equation of the Riemann zeta-function type.

From this Hecke deduced the decomposition laws of divisors of discriminants for the class fields of complex multiplication. He also defined the generalized Dirichlet L-series for algebraic number fields and derived a functional equation for it. The analogue of the Dirichlet prime number law for number fields followed. Further development of these methods led him to the creation and study of zeta functions $\zeta(s, \lambda)$ with characters λ; that is, Hecke's L-series, which are of fundamental importance to advanced analytic number theory. This research was continued in various directions by Emil Artin, C. L. Siegel, and J. T. Tate.

After these studies and certain related works Hecke turned in 1925 to elliptic modular functions. He systematically applied quadratic number fields to the construction of modular functions. For imaginary quadratic fields he gave an extension of a class of functions known to Klein; for real quadratic fields there arose a new type of function. Hecke was led to these through his functions $\zeta(s, \lambda)$. Hecke then dealt with the Eisenstein series of higher order, especially the partial values of the Weierstrass functions $p(z)$ and $\zeta(z)$. He determined the periods of the Abelian integrals which are received through integration of the p partial values and certain series of the imaginary quadratic number fields. The problem of the periods of the Abelian integral of the first kind concerned him again and again, especially in connection with the representation theory of finite groups.

In 1936 Hecke systematically investigated the connection, restored by the gamma integral and the Mellin integral, of the Dirichlet series with a functional equation of Riemannian type and functions belonging to a certain automorphic group. Through his "operator" T_n Hecke established a theory for the investigation of relations of modular functions to Dirichlet series with Euler's product development. He discovered new connections between prime numbers and analytic functions and new rules for the representation of natural numbers through positive integral quadratic forms of an even number of variables. In 1939 Hans Petersson proved a rule, already anticipated by Hecke, concluding a part of this theory.

Some of Hecke's works are in another field. They are related to his approach to physics, especially the kinetic theory of gases.

BIBLIOGRAPHY

I. Original Works. Hecke's *Mathematische Werke,* 1 vol., Bruno Schoeneberg, ed. (Göttingen, 1959; 2nd ed., 1970), contains his journal articles. See also *Vorlesungen über die Theorie der algebraischen Zahlen* (Leipzig, 1923; 2nd ed., 1958).

II. Secondary Literature. See W. Maak, in "Erich Hecke als Lehrer," in *Abhandlungen aus dem Mathematischen Seminar, Universität Hamburg,* **16** (1949), 1-6; O. Perron, "Erich Hecke," in *Jahrbuch der bayerischen Akademie der Wissenschaften* (1944-1948), 274-276; and H. Petersson, "Das wissenschaftliche Werk von E. Hecke," in *Abhandlungen aus dem Mathematischen Seminar, Universität Hamburg,* **16** (1949), 7-31.

Bruno Schoeneberg

HEILBRONN, HANS ARNOLD (*b.* Berlin, Germany, 8 October 1908; *d.* Toronto, Canada, 28 April 1975)

Heilbronn was born the son of Alfred and Gertrud Heilbronn, middle-class Jews who were cousins. After graduating from the Realgymnasium at Berlin-Schmargenhof in 1926 and studying at the universities of Berlin, Freiburg, and Göttingen, in 1930 he became assistant to Edmund Landau at Göttingen. Heilbronn's work on the distribution of primes rapidly brought him renown. He received the doctorate in 1933.

The advance of Hitler to power forced Heilbronn to emigrate to England in 1933, and until 1935 he was supported at the University of Bristol by refugee organizations. In this period he rose to prominence with his proof of Gauss's conjecture that the class number $h(d)$ of the imaginary quadratic field of discriminant $d < 0$ tends to infinity as d tends to minus infinity. Erich Hecke had already shown in 1918 that this would follow from a generalized Riemann hypothesis. Heilbronn showed that Gauss's conjecture also follows from the falsity of the same hypothesis. By the "law of the excluded middle" Gauss's conjecture holds, but this argument is ineffective in the logical sense: for given h_0 it does not provide a d_0 such that $h(d) > h_0$ for all $d < d_0$. Heilbronn's theorem was strengthened and generalized by C. L. Siegel (1935), Richard Brauer (1950), and others, but the first effective version was obtained only in 1983 by Gross and Zagier, using a conditional result of Goldfeld. In 1934 Heilbronn showed (with E. H. Linfoot) that there are at most ten imaginary quadratic fields with class number $h(d) = 1$. Again the proof was ineffective, and although nine fields with this property were known, the proof gave no means for deciding whether there actually was a tenth. Its existence was claimed to be disproved in 1952 by K. Heegner in a controversial paper (later seen to be basically correct) and by H. M. Stark and A. Baker in 1966–1967.

From 1935 to 1940 Heilbronn was at Cambridge as a fellow of Trinity College. This period saw the beginning of his close collaboration with Harold Davenport, which lasted until the latter's death in 1971. In 1936 Heilbronn published a paper simplifying, strengthening, and making generally accessible the methods by which I. M. Vinogradov had greatly improved the estimates of Godfrey Hardy and John Littlewood for such additive problems as Waring's problem; and in a series of papers (1936–1937) with Davenport he considered specific problems of this type. In another area, Heilbronn showed that there are only finitely many real quadratic fields in which the euclidean algorithm holds. His method was not suited to determining them all, which was done only in the 1950's by Davenport and others, using the geometry of numbers. At that time Heilbronn returned to the problem; he showed that only finitely many cyclic cubic fields have a euclidean algorithm and obtained similar results in other cases to which the methods of the geometry of numbers do not apply.

In 1940, at the outbreak of war, Heilbronn was interned for a period as an "enemy alien" but then served with the British services. He was demobilized in 1945 and, after a brief period at University College, London, returned in 1946 to Bristol as reader and became a British citizen; in 1949 he became professor and head of department. He rapidly built up a strong department, particularly a school of number theory. One of his pupils was A. Fröhlich.

At the beginning of the Bristol period, Heilbronn considered the approximations to an arbitrary real number θ by rational fractions whose denominator is a perfect square. He showed that for every $\eta > 0$ there is a $C(\eta) > 0$ with the property that for every real θ and every integer $N \geq 1$ there are integers n, g such that

$$1 \leq n \leq N : |n^2\theta - g| \leq C(\eta)N^{-1/2+\eta}.$$

A weaker form with ⅖ instead of ½ had been given by Vinogradov (1927). Heilbronn asked whether ½ is the best possible constant, but no further progress has been made; there have, however, been a large number of generalizations. The work on euclidean algorithms in cyclic fields was also done at Bristol, but increasingly Heilbronn's preoccupation with policy problems and administrative irritations left him little time for mathematics.

In 1963, feeling that the university was not supporting his department as it should, Heilbronn resigned his chair at Bristol and in 1964 accepted one in Toronto. He moved to Canada with his wife, Dorothy Greaves, whom he had married that same year. In 1970 he became a Canadian citizen. In Toronto he built up a thriving research school and took an active part in Canadian mathematics. In what was to be his last published paper, he showed that the question of whether there is a real zero s_0 in $\frac{1}{2} < s_0 < 1$ of the zeta-function $\zeta_L(s)$ of an algebraic number field L reduces to the case when L is quadratic. This was subsequently used by Stark to show that the Siegel-Brauer theorem about the class numbers of algebraic number fields (which generalizes Heilbronn's) can be made effective in many cases.

In 1973 Heilbronn had a heart attack and did not recover completely. He died during an operation to implant a pacemaker. During his life Heilbronn was elected to the Royal Society (1951) and to the Royal Society of Canada (1967). He was president of the London Mathematical Society from 1959 to 1961.

BIBLIOGRAPHY

I. ORIGINAL WORKS. Heilbronn's papers are brought together in *The Collected Papers of Hans Arnold Heilbronn*, Ernst J. Kani and Robert A. Smith, eds. (New York, 1988). A complete bibliography of his works is in Cassels and Fröhlich (see below).

II. SECONDARY LITERATURE. A full account of Heilbronn's life and work is J. W. S. Cassels and A. Fröhlich, "Hans Arnold Heilbronn," in *Biographical Memoirs of Fellows of the Royal Society*, **22** (1976), 119–135, reprinted in *Bulletin of the London Mathematical Society*, **9** (1977), 219–232. See also *Proceedings of the Royal Society of Canada*, 4th ser., **13** (1975), 53–56.

For the Gross-Zagier-Goldfeld effective estimate, see D. Zagier, "L-Series of Elliptic Curves, the Birch-Swinnerton-Dyer Conjecture, and the Class Number Problem of Gauss," in *Notices of the American Mathematical Society*, **31** (1984), 739–743. For recent work on the existence of euclidean algorithms in number fields, see H. W. Lenstra, Jr., "Euclidean Number Fields of Large Degree," in *Inventiones Mathematicae*, **38** (1977), 237–254.

J. W. S. CASSELS

HEINE, HEINRICH EDUARD (*b.* Berlin, Germany, 16 March 1821; *d.* Halle, Germany, 21 October 1881)

Eduard Heine, as he is usually called, was the eighth of the nine children of the banker Karl Heinrich Heine and his wife, Henriette Märtens. He was given private instruction at home and then attended the Friedrichswerdersche Gymnasium and finally the Köllnische Gymnasium in Berlin, from which he graduated in the fall of 1838. He studied one semester in Berlin and then went to Göttingen, where he attended the lectures of Gauss and Stern. After three semesters he returned to Berlin; his principal teacher there was Dirichlet, but he also attended courses of Steiner and Encke. After receiving his Ph.D. degree at Berlin University on 30 April 1842, he went to Königsberg, where for two semesters he studied with C. G. J. Jacobi and Franz Neumann. He obtained his *Habilitation* as a *Privatdozent* at Bonn University on 20 July 1844. On 13 May 1848 he was appointed an extraordinary professor at Bonn University and on 6 September 1848 a professor at Halle University, where he finally settled. In the academic year 1864–1865 he held the office of rector of the university. He was a corresponding member of the Prussian Academy of Sciences and a nonresident member of the Göttingen Gesellschaft der Wissenschaften. In 1877 he was awarded the Gauss medal. Two years earlier he turned down the offer of a chair at Göttingen University.

Heine's sister Albertine was married to the banker Paul Mendelssohn-Bartholdy, the brother of the composer. In his brother-in-law's house Heine met his future wife Sophie Wolff, the daughter of a Berlin merchant. They were married in 1850 and had four daughters and a son; one of the daughters was the writer Anselma Heine. Heine's frequent visits to his family in Berlin enabled him to discuss mathematics with Weierstrass, Kummer, Kronecker, and Borchardt. He attracted promising young mathematicians to Halle University, among them Carl Neumann, Gustav Roch, H. A. Schwarz, J. Thomas, and Georg Canton.

Heine published about fifty mathematical papers, most of them in *Zeitschrift für die reine und angewandte Mathematik.* His main fields were spherical functions (Legendre polynomials), Lamé functions, Bessel functions, and related subjects. His greatest work, *Handbuch der Kugelfunctionen,* was first published in 1861. The second edition (1878–1881) of Heine's book was still a standard compendium on spherical functions well into the 1930's if one considers the frequency with which it was quoted; that this edition has never been reprinted, however, belies this impression.

Heine's name is best known for its association with the Heine-Borel covering theorem, the validity of which name has been challenged. Indeed, the covering property had not been formulated and proved before Borel. What Heine did do was to formulate the notion of uniform continuity, which had escaped Cauchy's attention, and to prove the classical theorem on uniform continuity of continuous functions, which could rightfully be called Heine's theorem. One might, however, argue that this was the essential discovery and that Borel's reduction of uniform continuity to the covering property was a relatively minor achievement. Heine's name was connected to this theorem by A. Schoenfliess, although he later omitted Heine's name. Heine wrote a few more papers on fundamental questions. It seems not unlikely that in some way the paper on uniform continuity had its origin in the influence of Cantor, Heine's colleague at Halle.

BIBLIOGRAPHY

I. Original Works. Heine's works include *Handbuch der Kugelfunctionen, Theorie und Anwendungen* (Berlin, 1861; 2nd ed., 1878–1881); and "Die Elemente der Functionenlehre," in *Journal für die reine und angewandte Mathematik,* **74** (1872), 172–188. His papers are listed in Poggendorff, I (1863), 1050, and III (1898), 606.

II. Secondary Literature. On Heine and his work, see A. Wangerin, "Eduard Heine," in *Mitteldeutsche Lebensbilder,* III (Magdeburg, 1928), 429–436. For the theorem with Heine's name, see A. Schoenflies, "Die Entwicklung der Lehre von den Punktmannigfaltigkeiten," in 2 pts., in *Jahresbericht der Deutschen Mathematikervereinigung,* **8** (1900), 51, 109, and supp. 2 (1908), 76; both pts. were reprinted in *Entwicklung der Mengenlehre und ihrer Anwendungen,* 2nd ed., vol. I (Leipzig, 1913), 234.

Hans Freudenthal

HELLINGER, ERNST (*b.* Striegau, Germany, 30 September 1883; *d.* Chicago, Illinois, 28 March 1950)

Hellinger was the son of Emil Hellinger and Julie Hellinger. He grew up in Breslau, where he received the diploma of the Gymnasium in 1902. He studied at the universities of Heidelberg, Breslau, and Göttingen, where in 1907 he received the Ph.D. in mathematics. Like many outstanding mathematicians of his time, Hellinger was a student of David Hilbert. In his dissertation on the orthogonal invariants of quadratic forms of infinitely many variables, Hellinger introduced a new type of integral which is known today as the Hellinger integral. The Hilbert-Hellinger theory of forms profoundly influenced other mathematicians, in particular E. H. Moore of the University of Chicago. From 1907 to 1909, Hellinger was an assistant at the University of Göttingen. There he edited Hilbert's lecture notes and Felix Klein's influential *Elementarmathematik vom höheren Standpunkte aus* (Berlin, 1925) which was translated into English (New York, 1932).

A *Privatdozent* at the University of Marburg from 1909 to 1914, Hellinger became professor of mathematics at the newly founded University of Frankfurt am Main and taught there until 1936, when the Nazi government forced him to retire because he was a Jew. His monumental article "Integralgleichungen und Gleichungen mit unendlichvielen Unbekannten," on integral equations and equations with infinitely many unknowns, which he wrote with Otto Toeplitz over a period of many years for the *Enzyklopädie der mathematischen Wissenschaften,* has attained the status of a classic document. It first appeared in 1927, was separately published in 1928, and was reprinted in 1953.

On 13 November 1938 Hellinger was arrested and held in a concentration camp. He was released after a month and a half, with the stipulation that he leave the country immediately. In March 1939 he found refuge in the United States, where he taught mathematics at Northwestern University in Evanston, Illinois, first as lecturer and later as full professor. He acquired American citizenship in 1944. After retiring at age sixty-five, he took a position at the Illinois Institute of Technology in 1949 but fell ill that November and never recovered.

Although his main field was analysis, Hellinger also worked in the history of mathematics with Max Dehn. Hellinger's lectures were of supreme clarity. Deeply concerned with all aspects of his students' lives, he was an unpretentious, highly effective mentor.

BIBLIOGRAPHY

I. ORIGINAL WORKS. Hellinger's works include "Grundlagen für eine Theorie der unendlichen Matrizen," in *Nachrichten der Gesellschaft der Wissenschaften zu Göttingen* (1906), pp. 351–355, written with O. Toeplitz; *Die Orthogonalinvarianten quadratischer Formen von unendlichvielen Variablen* (Göttingen, 1907), his diss.; "Neue Begründung der Theorie quadratischer Formen von unendlichvielen Veränderlichen," in *Journal für die reine und angewandte Mathematik,* **136** (1909), 210–271; "Grundlagen für eine Theorie der unendlichen Matrizen," in *Mathematische Annalen,* **69** (1910), 289–330, written with O. Toeplitz; "Zur Einordnung der Kettenbruchtheorie in die Theorie der quadratischen Formen von unendlichvielen Veränderlichen," in *Journal für die reine und angewandte Mathematik,* **144** (1914), 213–238, written with O. Toeplitz; and "Die allgemeinen Ansätze der Mechanik der Kontinua," in *Enzyklopädie der mathematischen Wissenschaften,* **4,** no. 30 (1914), 601–694.

See also "Zur Stieltjesschen Kettenbruchtheorie," in *Mathematische Annalen,* **86** (1922), 18–29; "Integralgleichungen und Gleichungen mit unendlichvielen Unbekannten" in *Enzyklopädie der mathematischen Wissenschaften,* **2,** no. 13C (1927), 1335–1648, written with O. Toeplitz, repr. separately (New York, 1953); "Hilberts Arbeiten über Integralgleichungen und unendliche Gleichungssysteme," in *David Hilbert, Gesammelte Abhandlungen,* III (Berlin, 1935), 94–145; "On James Gregory's Vera Quadratura," in H. W. Turnbull, ed., *James Gregory Tercentenary Memorial Volume* (London, 1939), pp. 468–478, written with M. Dehn; *Spectra of Quadratic Forms in Infinitely Many Variables,* no. 1 in Northwestern University Studies in Mathematics and the Physical Sciences, Mathematical Monographs, vol. I (Evanston, Ill., 1941), 133–172; "Certain Mathematical Achievements of James Gregory," in *American Mathematical Monthly,* **50** (1943), 149–163, written with M. Dehn; and "Contributions to the Analytic Theory of Continued Fractions and Infinite Matrices," in *Annals of Mathematics,* **44** (1943), 103–127, written with M. Dehn.

II. SECONDARY LITERATURE. For a biography of Hellinger, see C. L. Siegel, *Zur Geschichte des Frankfurter mathematischen Seminars. Gesammelte Abhandlungen,* III, no. 81 (Berlin–Heidelberg–New York, 1966), 462–474.

WILHELM MAGNUS

HELLY, EDUARD (*b.* Vienna, Austria, 1 June 1884; *d.* Chicago, Illinois, 28 November 1943)

Helly was the only son of Sigmund Helly, a civil servant, and of Sara Necker Helly. He and his sister, Anna, grew up in a sheltered, middle-class home. Helly married Elise Bloch, a mathematician, on 4 July 1921; their only child, Walter Sigmund, became professor of operations research at the Polytechnic Institute of New York in Brooklyn.

Helly entered the Maximilians-Gymnasium in Vienna in 1894, passing his final school examination in 1902; he then took up the study of mathematics, physics, and philosophy at the University of Vienna. Five years later he presented his (handwritten) dissertation, "Beiträge zur Theori der Fredholm'schen Integralgleichung," to the Department of Philosophy, receiving the doctorate on 15 March 1907 (the referees were Wilhelm Wirtinger and Franz Mertens). With the help of a fellowship, Helly then spent two semesters (winter of 1907 to 1908 and summer of 1908) at the University of Göttingen, studying primarily under David Hilbert, Felix Klein, Hermann Minkowski, and Carl Runge.

Upon his return to Vienna, Helly was confronted with the problem of earning a living. He began by giving private lessons in mathematics, and from 1910 on, he also taught at a gymnasium. In 1908 he became a member of the Viennese Mathematical Association (VMA), to which he delivered a total of seventeen lectures at its sessions.

Helly's first paper, "Über lineare Funktionaloperationen," appeared in 1912. His work basically consists of five items: his first work and "Über Systeme linearer Gleichungen . . ." rank as landmarks in the history of functional analysis; "Über Mengen konvexer Körper . . ." and "Über Systeme von abgeschlossenen Mengen . . ." are concerned with his intersection theorem of convex analysis; and his paper "Über Reihenentwicklungen . . ." deals with several convergence criteria for a general class of orthogonal expansions.

Inspired by work of Friedrich Riesz, "Über lineare Funktionaloperationen" is a contribution to the moment problem that played a fundamental role in the development of functional analysis. Using the gliding hump method, Helly gave a first functional analytic proof of a particular case (linear functionals on the space of functions, continuous on a compact interval) of the uniform boundedness principle. Concerning the Hahn-Banach extension theorem, it is his proof, still used in today's courses, by which the matter is extended to one further dimension. This method is to be seen in connection with the particular case $n = 1$ of Helly's intersection theorem: A family of compact, convex sets of the n-dimensional euclidean space possesses a nonempty intersection provided any $n + 1$ of the sets have a common element. Among the many important concepts and assertions developed in Helly's first work is his selection theorem, attributed to the foundations of real analysis and probability theory (see Wintner). Given a set of functions that are bounded and of bounded variation, both uniformly on a compact interval, one may select a subsequence that converges pointwise to a limit function of bounded variation.

In 1913 Helly presented his intersection theorem in a VMA lecture. Further projects he had announced were put aside with the outbreak of World War I. Helly volunteered for the army in 1914, was called up in 1915, and was shot in the chest while serving on the Austrian-Russian front in September 1915. Subsequently taken prisoner, he was deported to eastern Siberia and not released until 1920.

Helly immediately resumed his studies, his goal being the *Habilitation*. Titles of two lectures he delivered at VMA meetings in 1914 ("Über unendliche Gleichungssysteme und lineare Funktionaloperationen"; "Einiges Geometrische über den Raum von unendlich vielen Dimensionen") indicate that he had a concrete conception of his *Habilitationsschrift* even before the war. In fact, he presented his thesis, "Über Systeme linearer Gleichungen," early in 1921 (the referee was Hans Hahn). Emphasizing connections with Minkowski's work, Helly studied general sequence spaces and included an axiomatic introduction of normed linear spaces that parallels the treatments given by Stefan Banach and Norbert Wiener (see Bernkopf, p. 67).

Helly was appointed *Privatdozent* at the University of Vienna in August 1921, remaining in this rank throughout his time in Vienna. Because the position was unpaid, he had to earn a living outside the university. From 1921 to 1929 he was employed in a bank; when it failed in 1929, he became an actuary at the Viennese life insurance company Phönix from 1930 to 1938. This may be the reason why Helly wrote only two further papers: his proof in 1923 of his intersection theorem and a long paper in 1930 in which he showed that the intersection theorem is a particular case of a general, purely topological theorem. (Recent concepts include Helly number, Helly space, and Helly hypergraph [graph theory].) In fact, entry 52A35 in *Subject Classification Scheme 1979* of the American Mathematical Society is devoted to "Helly type theorems."

After the occupation of Austria in 1938, Helly could not teach the course he had announced for the summer semester; he also was dismissed by the insurance company because he was a Jew. In September 1938 the Hellys emigrated to the United States. The first years were difficult ones. Helly was a lecturer at several small colleges in New Jersey, even though he was recommended to more prominent schools by Oswald Veblen, Hermann Weyl, and Albert Einstein. But he was relatively old, had not held a "regular" university position in Europe, and was one of many highly qualified immigrants seeking a position in the United States. His situation seemed to improve in September 1943, when he was appointed a visiting lecturer at the Illinois Institute of Technology in Chicago. He did not long enjoy this first more substantial university position; he died of heart failure two months later.

BIBLIOGRAPHY

I. ORIGINAL WORKS. "Über lineare Funktionaloperationen," in *Österreichische Akademie der Wissenschaften Mathematische-naturwissenschaftliche Klasse*, IIa, **121** (1912), 265–297; "Über Reihenentwicklungen nach Funktionen eines Orthogonalsystems," *ibid.*, 1539–1549; "Über Systeme linearer Gleichungen mit unendlich vielen Unbekannten," in *Monatshefte für Mathematik und Physik*, **31** (1921), 60–91; "Über Mengen konvexer Körper mit gemeinschaftlichen Punkten," in *Jahresbericht der Deutschen Mathematiker-Vereinigung*, **32** (1923), 175–176; and "Über Systeme von abgeschlossenen Mengen mit gemeinschaftlichen Punkten," in *Monatshefte für Mathematik und Physik*, **37** (1930), 281–302.

II. SECONDARY LITERATURE. Michael Bernkopf, "The Development of Function Spaces with Particular Reference to Their Origin in Integral Equation Theory," in *Archive for History of Exact Sciences*, **3** (1966/1967), 1–96; P. L. Butzer, S. Gieseler, F. Kaufmann, R. J. Nessel, and E. L. Stark, "Eduard Helly (1884–1943): Eine nachträgliche Würdigung," in *Jahresbericht der Deutschen Mathematiker-Vereinigung*, **82** (1980), 128–151; P. L. Butzer, R. J. Nessel, and E. L. Stark, "Eduard Helly (1884–1943): In Memoriam," in *Resultate der Mathematik*, **7** (1984), 145–153; Ludwig Danzer, Branko Grünbaum, and Victor Klee, "Helly's Theorem and Its Relatives," in Victor Klee, ed., *Convexity* (Providence, R.I., 1963), 101–180; Jean Dieudonné, *History of Functional Analysis* (Amsterdam and New York, 1981); Eugene Lukacs,

Characteristic Functions, 2nd ed., rev. and enl. (London, 1970); A. F. Monna, *Functional Analysis in Historical Perspective* (New York, 1973); H. M. Mulder and A. Schrijver, "Median Graphs and Helly Hypergraphs," in *Discrete Mathematics*, **25** (1979), 41–50; I. Netuka and J. Veselý, "Eduard Helly: Konvexita a funkcionální analýza," in *Pokroky mathematiky, fyziky astronomie*, **29** (1984), 301–312; Jan van Tiel, *Convex Analysis* (Chichester, West Sussex, and New York, 1984); and Aurel Wintner, *Spektraltheorie der unendlichen Matrizen* (Leipzig, 1929).

PAUL L. BUTZER
ROLF J. NESSEL
EBERHARD L. STARK

HENRION, DENIS or **DIDIER** (*b. ca.* 1580; *d.* Paris [?], France, *ca.* 1632)

Information on Henrion is very scarce and imprecise. The date and place of his birth are unknown. In 1613 he speaks of his youth; and since he had been an engineer in the army of the prince of Orange before settling in Paris in 1607, his birth may be placed around 1580. The date of his death is somewhat delimited by the appearance in 1632 of the French edition of Euclid's *Elements* and *Data,* under his name, sold "en l'Isle du Palais, à l'Image S. Michel, par la veusve [widow] dudit Henrion." His first name is generally indicated as Denis, although he always gave only the initial D.—except in a Latin writing of 1623, where it is given as Desiderius, the Latin form of Désiré or Didier.

Henrion's scientific activity was devoted mainly to private instruction and to the translation into French of Latin mathematical texts. From 1607 it seems to have taken place exclusively in Paris. His first work, published in 1613, is a course in elementary mathematics, in French, for the use of the nobility, that is, for the instruction of officers. Although it displays no great originality, it is a serious work, most particularly the section on geometry, which contains a group of 140 remarkable problems. Yet here, as in all of his work, Henrion drew very freely on his predecessors, especially Clavius.

Henrion's various editions of Euclid's *Elements* were really only translations of the Latin editions done by the Jesuits at Rome. He sometimes embellished them with a summary of the algebra in which this science was presented in a quite antiquated manner, without regard for the advances made by Viète, Albert Girard, and Stevin.

When the *Data* was combined with this translation of Euclid in 1632, Henrion translated the introduction by Marinus of Flavia Neapolis and the text itself from the Latin of Claude Hardy (1625). His French translation of Theodosius of Tripoli's *Spherics* (1615) was drawn from the Latin paraphrase by Clavius (1586).

Henrion's other works are in the same vein. His *Traité des logarithmes* (1626), taken from the work of Briggs, saved his name from oblivion by being the second work on the subject published in France—the first was that of Wingate (1625)—and the first written by a Frenchman.

Henrion was greatly interested in mathematical instruments, especially in the proportional divider, the invention of which he attributed to Jacques Alleaume, who had constructed several copies of it in Paris. He also described the slide rules of Edmund Gunter in the *Logocanon* (1626).

His work was not untouched by polemic. Henrion often bore a grudge against his competitors, the other translators of Euclid and writers of manuals. He was severely taken to task by Claude Mydorge regarding his notes to Jean Leurechon's *Recréations mathématiques.*

In conclusion, the body of Henrion's work, although greatly inferior to that of Hérigone, nevertheless played a not unimportant initiatory role in France.

BIBLIOGRAPHY

Henrion's own writings include *Mémoires mathématiques recueillis et dressez en faveur de la noblesse françoise,* 2 vols. (Paris, 1613–1627; 2nd ed., vol. I, 1623); *Traicté des triangles sphériques* (Paris, 1617); *L'usage du compas de proportion* (Paris, 1618; 2nd ed., Paris, 1624; 4th ed., Paris, 1631; 5th ed., Rouen, 1637, 1664, 1680), further eds. by Deshayes (Paris, 1682, 1685); *Cosmographie ou traicté général des choses tant célestes qu'élémentaires* (Paris, 1620; 2nd ed., Paris, 1626); *Canon manuel des sinus, touchantes et coupantes* (Paris, 1623); *Sommaire de l'algèbre très nécessaire pour faciliter l'interprétation du dixiesme livre d'Euclide* (Paris, 1623), which also appears in Henrion's various eds. of Euclid; *Sinuum, tangentium et secantium canon manualis* (Paris, 1623); *Logocanon, ou Regle proportionelle sur laquelle sont appliquées plusieurs lignes et figures divisées selon diverses proportions et mesures* (Paris, 1626); *Traicté des logarithmes* (Paris, 1626); *L'usage du mecometre, qui est un instrument géometrique avec lequel on peut très facilement mesurer toutes sortes de longueurs* (Paris, 1630); and *Cours mathématique demontré d'une nouvelle méthode* (Paris, 1634).

Henrion edited or translated *Les trois livres des Éléments sphériques de Théodose Tripolitain* (Paris, 1615); *Les quinze livres des Élémens d'Euclide* (Paris, 1614, 1615; 2nd ed., Paris, 1621; 3rd ed., Paris, 1623; 4th ed., Paris, 1631; 5th ed., Rouen, 1649); *Traduction et annotations du Traicté des globes et de leur usage, de Robert Hues* (Paris, 1618); *Edition de la Géométrie et practique générale d'icelle de Jean Errard*

(Paris, 1619); *Les tables des directions et profections de Jean de Montroyal, corrigées, augmentées, et leur usage* . . . (Paris, 1625; annotated new ed., Paris, 1626); *Nottes sur les Récréations mathématiques du Père Jean Leurechon* (Paris, 1627, 1630, 1639, 1659, 1660, 1669); and *Les quinze livres des Élémens géométriques . . . plus le livre des Donnez du mesme Euclide* . . . (Paris, 1632; Rouen, 1676; Paris, 1677, 1683; Rouen, 1683, 1685).

JEAN ITARD

HENSEL, KURT (*b.* Königsberg, Germany [now Kaliningrad, U.S.S.R.], 29 December 1861; *d.* Marburg, Germany, 1 June 1941)

Hensel was descended from a family of artists and scientists; his grandmother, the former Fanny Mendelssohn, was a sister of Felix Mendelssohn-Bartholdy. Until he was nine years old, he was educated at home by his parents; later, in Berlin, he was decisively influenced by the eminent mathematics teacher K. H. Schellbach at the Friedrich-Wilhelm Gymnasium. Hensel studied mathematics at Bonn and Berlin. Among his teachers were Rudolf Lipschitz, Karl Weierstrass, Carl Borchardt, Gustav Kirchhoff, Hermann von Helmholtz, and especially Leopold Kronecker, under whose guidance he took his Ph.D. in 1884 and qualified as *Privatdozent* at the University of Berlin in 1886. In the latter year he married Gertrud Hahn, sister of the renowned educator Kurt Hahn, known for his schools at Salem, Germany, and in Scotland. They had four daughters and a son, Albert.

After Kronecker's death, Hensel devoted many years to preparing the edition of his collected papers. In close cooperation with G. Landsberg, Hensel published his first important book, *Theorie der algebraischen Funktionen* (1902). In 1901 Hensel became full professor at the University of Marburg, where he was an extremely successful teacher and wrote the important books *Theorie der algebraischen Zahlen* (1908) and *Zahlentheorie* (1913). Also in 1901 Hensel became editor of Germany's oldest mathematical periodical, *Journal für die reine und angewandte Mathematik.* He retired in 1930 but continued to teach and advise. The following year he was awarded an honorary Ph.D. by the University of Oslo.

Hensel's scientific work was based on Kronecker's arithmetical theory of algebraic number fields. The Kronecker-Hensel method also yielded a foundation of the arithmetic in algebraic function fields. The latter foundation was developed systematically in *Theorie der algebraischen Funktionen.* The Weierstrass method of power-series development for algebraic functions led Hensel, about 1899, to the conception of an analogue in the theory of algebraic numbers: p-adic numbers. The p-adic numbers must be considered his most important discovery. In evaluating it, one must bear in mind that its conceptual base did not then exist; on the contrary, Hensel's discovery was the decisive stimulus for the development of the abstract algebraic notions required for the base: the theory of valuated fields. In his *Theorie der algebraischen Zahlen* and *Zahlentheorie,* Hensel developed p-adic numbers into a systematic theory; he also gave an application of great interest—to the classical theory of quadratic forms—and a remarkable extension of his p-adic method by the introduction of a p-adic analysis. Further developed by Hensel's pupils, especially Helmut Hasse, the p-adic method proved highly successful in the theory of quadratic forms and in the theory of algebras over number fields and is known today as the local-global principle. Hensel's method led him to many interesting results in the theory of numbers, which were published in a great many papers. At first his p-adic numbers were generally considered of no particular consequence, but he lived to see their recognition as a highly important, widely generalizable mathematical element.

BIBLIOGRAPHY

Hensel's books and contributions to books are *Theorie der algebraischen Funktionen einer Variabeln und ihre Anwendung auf algebraische Kurven und Abelsche Integrale* (Leipzig, 1902), written with G. Landsberg; *Theorie der algebraischen Zahlen* (Leipzig, 1908); *Zahlentheorie* (Berlin–Leipzig, 1913); and "Arithmetische Theorie der algebraischen Funktionen," in *Encyclopädie der mathematischen Wissenschaften,* pt. 2, sec. 5 (1921), 533–650.

Three collections of Leopold Kronecker's work, edited by Hensel, are *Werke,* 5 vols. (Leipzig, 1895–1930); *Vorlesungen über Zahlentheorie* (Leipzig, 1901); and *Vorlesungen über die Theorie der Determinanten* (Leipzig, 1903).

Hensel's most important papers are "Arithmetische Untersuchungen über die Diskriminanten und ihre ausserwesentlichen Teiler" (Berlin, 1884), his diss.; "Über eine neue Begründung der algebraischen Zahlen," in *Jahresbericht der Deutschen Mathematiker-Vereinigung,* **6** (1899), 83–88; "Die multiplikative Darstellung der algebraischen Zahlen für den Bereich eines beliebigen Primteilers," in *Journal für die reine und angewandte Mathematik,* **145** (1915), 92–113; **146** (1916), 189–215; **147** (1917), 1–15; and "Eine neue Theorie der algebraischen Zahlen," in *Mathematische Zeitschrift,* **2** (1918), 433–452.

H. Hasse's commemorative article "Kurt Hensel zum Gedaechtnis," in *Journal für die reine und angewandte Mathematik,* **187** (1950), 1–13, contains a complete bibliography.

HELMUT HASSE

HERACLIDES PONTICUS (*b.* Heraclea Pontica [now Ereğli, Turkey], *ca.* 390 B.C.; *d.* Heraclea Pontica, after 339 B.C.)

Heraclides, son of Euthyphron, came from a noble and wealthy family of Heraclea Pontica, a Greek city on the south coast of the Black Sea. He traced his descent from one of the original founders of Heraclea. His birthdate can be inferred approximately from his relationship to various members of the Academy and from his statement that the destruction of the city of Helice in Achaea by an earthquake (373 B.C.) took place in his lifetime.[1] He came to Plato's Academy in Athens, some time before 360 B.C., if we can believe the story that Plato left the Academy in the charge of Heraclides when he went to Sicily.[2] Although counted as one of Plato's pupils (Heraclides himself said that Plato sent him to Colophon to collect the poems of Antimachus), he was apparently more closely associated with Speusippus, Plato's successor as head of the Academy. He also attended Aristotle's lectures.

Upon the death of Speusippus (339 B.C.), Heraclides was one of the candidates to succeed him, but Xenocrates won by a few votes, whereupon Heraclides returned to his native city, where he died some time later. The attempts to establish a *terminus post quem* for his death from his alleged mention of the cult of Sarapis[3] or of his pupil Dionysius[4] are unconvincing. Two different stories are connected with his death. According to one account, Heraclea was afflicted by a famine and sent envoys to the Delphic oracle to ask what to do. Heraclides bribed the ambassadors and the Pythia to pretend that the god had replied that the city would be relieved if Heraclides were honored with a gold crown while alive and a hero's cult after death. During the ceremony of bestowing the crown in the theater, Heraclides died of a stroke (or fell and hit his head on a step according to another version). The other account is even more implausible: Heraclides raised a tame snake and persuaded a friend to substitute the snake for his body when he died, so that people would think that he had become a god. Both stories may have been invented to match Heraclides' well-attested penchant for tall tales and his pretensions. We are told that he dressed richly, was very fat and stately, and was nicknamed Pompikos by the Athenians ("stately, magnificent") instead of Pontikos.

Heraclides' many books were greatly admired in antiquity both for style and content. Not a single work has survived, and of most we know only the title. Many of them were in the form of dialogues, as was common practice in the Academy. The subjects, which were typical of a fourth-century "philosopher," included ethics, literature, rhetoric, history, politics, and music. Although some of the works were very influential (for example, Heraclides' contribution to the legend of Pythagoras), they do not concern us here. A number of his works belong to a group called φυσικά, which is best translated "on the nature of things." These works too cannot be considered scientific but belong to the kind of prescientific speculation that characterized most early Greek philosophy. The following are some examples: each of the stars is a world of its own; the moon is earth surrounded by mist; and a comet is a high cloud reflecting light.[5] Heraclides' work "On Diseases" was more concerned with thaumaturgy (for example, a woman who lay apparently dead for seven days and was restored to life) than with medicine, to judge from the surviving fragments.[6]

In modern times Heraclides is famous chiefly for an astronomical theory that has been attributed to him, namely that the orbits of Venus and Mercury have the sun as their center, while the sun in turn moves around the earth. Although there is no good reason to believe that Heraclides proposed such a theory, the attribution has become so much the received opinion that the theory commonly goes under the name of "the system of Heraclides Ponticus," and Heraclides is variously considered a precursor of Tycho Brahe, Aristarchus, or Copernicus. It is therefore appropriate to give some account, not only of the ancient evidence on the subject, but also of the numerous modern misunderstandings of that evidence.

The theory was indeed held in antiquity, but the contexts in which it occurs show that it arose at a much later stage of Greek astronomy, for reasons which were not operative at the time of Heraclides. We must start from Ptolemy's discussion of the order of the planets in *Almagest* IX, 1. He says there[7] that while all agree that all the planets lie between the sun and the fixed stars and that Mars, Jupiter, and Saturn lie (in ascending order) beyond the sun, there is disagreement about the position of Venus and Mercury. The "older astronomers" placed them below the sphere of the sun, while some of the later astronomers put them above the sphere of the sun. Ptolemy's account is fully confirmed by our fragmentary sources for pre-Ptolemaic astronomy.[8] It seems likely that the hypothesis that the orbits of Venus and Mercury encircle the sun (and that thus the two planets are sometimes above and sometimes below the sun) was

HERACLIDES PONTICUS

introduced as a third choice. Moreover it seems highly probable that it was introduced after the development of the epicycle theory, according to which the mean motions of the sun, Venus, and Mercury are identical, that is, the centers of their epicycles lie on the same straight line. This is the form in which it is found in our most explicit source, Theon of Smyrna,[9] who says that according to this theory the epicycles of the sun, Venus, and Mercury have a common center. Thus the theory can hardly predate 200 B.C. Of the three sources who mention the theory only one, Macrobius, attributes it to a specific authority, namely "the Egyptians."

The only astronomical doctrine of Heraclides for which there is solid evidence is the rotation of the earth on its axis. This is attested by a number of sources,[10] from which it is abundantly clear that Heraclides proposed that the earth lies in the center of the universe and turns on its axis once a day. This is a simple variation of the common belief, canonized in Ptolemaic astronomy, that the earth is central and stationary, while the whole heavens revolve once a day. In *Almagest* I, 7, Ptolemy argues against the rotation of the earth (on purely physical grounds).[11] Although he mentions no names, it appears that the doctrine was fairly common. Heraclides is the earliest philosopher who is known beyond question to have held this opinion.[12] Unfortunately certain ambiguous expressions in the ancient descriptions of Heraclides' doctrine have misled some modern scholars into thinking that he held that the earth moves in a circular orbit (see below on Schiaparelli and van der Waerden). Examination of all the evidence shows that this is wrong.[13]

The only evidence concerning Heraclides' opinion on Venus is a passage of the commentary on Plato's *Timaeus* by Calcidius (fifth century A.D.), which I translate as follows:

> Finally Heraclides Ponticus, when he drew the circle of Venus, and also [the circle] of the sun, and assigned a single center to both circles, showed that Venus is sometimes above, sometimes below the sun. For he says that the sun and moon and Venus and all the planets, wherever each of them is, are [each] indicated by a single line drawn from the center of the earth through the center of the heavenly body. So there will be one line drawn from the center of the earth indicating the sun, and two other lines drawn to left and right of it, fifty degrees from the sun and a hundred degrees from each other. The eastern line indicates Venus when it is at greatest distance from the sun toward the east, and therefore has the name evening star ("Hesperus") because it appears in the east [sic] in the evening after sunset. The western line [indicates Venus] when it is at greatest distance from the sun toward the west and therefore is called the morning star ("Lucifer"). For it is obvious that it is called evening star when it is seen in the east [sic] following sunset, and morning star when it sets before the sun and rises again before the sun when the night is almost over.[14]

Seizing on the remark that Venus is "sometimes above, sometimes below the sun," modern scholars have concluded that Heraclides believed that the orbit of Venus (and, by analogy, that of Mercury) encircles the sun. The first to draw this conclusion was T. H. Martin in 1849.[15] Schiaparelli not only accepted Martin's conclusion[16] but even conjectured that Heraclides proposed the Tychonic theory, in which the orbits of all the planets encircle the sun, which in turn revolves about the central earth.[17] Since there is not a scrap of evidence that anyone in antiquity proposed the Tychonic theory, discussion of the point is idle. Schiaparelli further suggested that Heraclides anticipated Aristarchus in proposing a heliocentric system as at least a theoretical possibility.[18] The basis for this is the following passage in Simplicius, quoting Geminus (first century A.D.): "So someone comes forward and says [Heraclides Ponticus] that if the earth moves in a certain way and the sun stands still, the apparent anomaly of the sun can be represented."[19] The words "Heraclides Ponticus" are an intrusion into the syntax and sense of the sentence, and are obviously interpolated by a reader who wanted to explain the "someone," as was remarked by Tannery.[20] We can be sure that the interpolator, no doubt misled by the doxographical tradition that Heraclides assumed the axial rotation of the earth, was in error.

Yet another theory was attributed to Heraclides by van der Waerden,[21] according to which the sun, Venus, and the earth (in ascending order) all revolve around a common center. This is based largely on misinterpretation of diagrams in the manuscripts of Calcidius, explaining the maximum elongations of Venus from the sun according to the epicycle theory. In any case, it is flatly contradicted by the unanimous testimony that Heraclides put the earth in the center of the universe.

Although Calcidius was a bungler and certainly did not read Heraclides' work,[22] what he says in the passage translated above makes reasonable sense. It is an explanation of the fact that Venus appears as both a morning and evening star:[23] the sun and Venus both move on circles with the earth as "a

HERACLIDES PONTICUS

single center." If one draws lines from that center to the sun and Venus, one finds that the line earth–Venus is sometimes to the left (to the east) of the line earth–Sun, and sometimes to the right (to the west). The only phrase inconsistent with this is the statement that Venus is "sometimes above, sometimes below the sun." If we interpret "above" and "below" to mean, not "farther from and nearer to the earth," but "to the west" and "to the east" of the sun, the inconsistency is removed. This was suggested by G. Evans[24] and was confirmed by O. Neugebauer, who pointed out that Calcidius' "superior/inferior" is simply a translation of the Greek *ἀνώτερον/κατώτερον*, which are found in works on "spherics" with exactly the meaning required here.[25] Thus the whole basis for attributing to Heraclides the theory that Venus revolves around the sun vanishes, and so does the influence on the development of ancient astronomy, which has often been attributed to him in modern times. Heraclides' only claim to a place in the history of astronomy is his assertion of the axial rotation of the earth, which won him mention as one of the ancient authorities for this in Copernicus' *De revolutionibus*.[26]

NOTES

1. Strabo, *Geography*, VIII, 384 (Wehrli, *Herakleides Pontikos*, fr. 46a).
2. Suidas, s.v. (Wehrli, fr. 2). If true, this must refer to Plato's third Sicilian journey (probably in 360 B.C.). The whole of "Suidas' " account, however, inspires little trust.
3. Plutarch, *Isis and Osiris*, 361e (Wehrli, fr. 139). Even if one emends the MS reading "Heraclitus" to "Heraclides," Plutarch may be referring to another "Heraclides Ponticus," a grammarian of a later period. Furthermore, the date of the foundation of the cult of Sarapis is greatly disputed.
4. Wehrli, fr. 12, with commentary on 62.
5. *Ibid.*, frs. 113a–b, 114a–c, 116.
6. *Ibid.*, frs. 76–89.
7. Heiberg, ed., *Syntaxis mathematica*, II, 206–207.
8. For details, see O. Neugebauer, *A History of Ancient Mathematical Astronomy*, II, 647–650, 690–693.
9. Theon of Smyrna, *Expositio rerum mathematicarum . . .*, Hiller, ed., 186–187. Of the other two sources, Macrobius, *Commentarii in Somnium Scipionis*, I, 19, 5–6, gives the same version in cruder language; while Martianus Capella, VIII, 857, simply says that Venus and Mercury have "the sun" as the center of their circles.
10. Wehrli, frs. 104–108.
11. Heiberg, ed., I, 24–26.
12. It is also ascribed to the obscure figure of "the Pythagorean Ecphantus" (Wehrli, fr. 104). In the 5th century B.C. Philolaus of Crotona had constructed a theory in which the earth not only rotates but moves about "the central fire"; this seems, however, to have been inspired more by mystical speculation than by astronomical considerations (see Kurt von Fritze, *Dictionary of Scientific Biography*, X, 589–591).
13. Best demonstrated by A. Pannekoek, "The Astronomical System of Herakleides," 375–379.
14. Calcidius, *Timaeus a Calcidio . . .*, CX, Waszink, ed., 157. The crucial first sentence is "Denique Heraclides Ponticus, cum circulum Luciferi describeret, item solis, et unum punctum atque unam medietatem duobus daret circulis, demonstrauit ut interdum Lucifer superior, interdum inferior sole fiat."
15. In his edition of Theon of Smyrna, 120, 426–428. Elaborated in *Mémoires de l'Académie des inscriptions et belles-lettres*, **30**, pt. 2 (1883), 21–43.
16. Schiaparelli, "I precursori di Copernico," 401–408.
17. Schiaparelli, "Origine del sistema eliocentrico," esp. 165–166.
18. *Ibid.*, 163–164.
19. Wehrli, fr. 110. On the date of Geminus, which is often wrongly stated to be the first century B.C., see Neugebauer, *History of Ancient Mathematical Astronomy*, II, 579–581.
20. *Mémoires scientifiques*, IX, 255–258. Elaborated by Heath, *Aristarchus*, 275–283.
21. "Die Astronomie des Herakleides von Pontos"; repeated in "Die Astronomie der Pythagoreer," 62–73.
22. Since much of what Calcidius says about astronomy is almost identical to passages in Theon of Smyrna, who is avowedly drawing on a certain Adrastus, it is likely that Adrastus is Calcidius' source here as elsewhere.
23. The discovery that the morning star and evening star are the same body was attributed to Pythagoras, but Heraclides may still have needed to explain it in the 4th century B.C.
24. Evans, "The Astronomy of Heracleides Ponticus," esp. 110–111.
25. Neugebauer, "On the Allegedly Heliocentric Theory of Venus," referring to Theodosius (1st century B.C.).
26. Zeller, ed., IV, 14.

BIBLIOGRAPHY

The chief source for Heraclides' life and works is his biography in Diogenes Laërtius, *Lives of the Philosophers*, V, 86–91 (Leipzig, 1884), 246–248. Like all of Diogenes' biographies, this is a mixture of puerile anecdotes and sound information derived from excellent authorities; it includes a list of the titles of Heraclides' works. The fragments relating to the life and works have been collected in Fritz Wehrli, *Herakleides Pontikos*, 2nd ed. (Basel–Stuttgart, 1969), which is *Die Schule des Aristoteles*, vol. VII. Wehrli also provides a useful commentary (somewhat muddled on astronomical matters), and should be consulted for further bibliography (esp. 57).

The astronomical theory, wrongly attributed to Heraclides, is in Theon of Smyrna, *Expositio rerum mathematicarum ad legendum Platonem utilium*, E. Hiller, ed. (Leipzig, 1878), 186–187; in Macrobius, *Commentarii in Somnium Scipionis*, I, 19, 5–6, J. Willis, ed. (Leipzig, 1973), 74; and in Martianus Capella, *De nuptiis philologiae et Mercurii*, VIII, 857, A. Dick, ed. (Leipzig, 1925), 450–451. Ptolemy's discussion of the order of the planets is in *Syntaxis mathematica*, J. L. Heiberg, ed., 2 vols. (Leipzig, 1898–1903), which is *Claudii Ptolemaei opera quae exstant omnia*, I, IX, 1, Vol. 2, 24–26. An extensive discussion of the ancient evidence on this topic is in O. Neugebauer, *A History of Ancient Mathematical Astronomy*, Studies in the History of Mathematics and the Physical Sciences, no. 1, 3 vols. (New York, 1975), II, 694–696.

The passage of Calcidius referring to Heraclides is *Timaeus a Calcidio translatus commentarioque instructus*, J. H. Waszink, ed., which is *Plato Latinus*, IV (London–Leiden, 1962), Commentarius CX, p. 157. It was first interpreted as making Venus' orbit heliocentric by T. H. Martin, in his edition of part of Theon of Smyrna, *Theonis Smyrnaei liber de astronomia* (Paris, 1849; repr. Groningen, 1971), 120–121, 426–428. See also T. H. Martin, "Mémoire sur l'histoire des hypothèses astronomiques chez les Grecs et les Romains," in *Mémoires de l'Académie des inscriptions et belles-lettres*, **30**, pt. 2 (1883), 1–43; and Giovanni Schiaparelli, "I precursori di Copernico nell'antichità," in his *Scritti sulla storia della astronomia antica*, I (Bologna, 1925), 363–458, originally published in *Memorie dell'Istituto lombardo di scienze e lettere*, **12** (1873). Schiaparelli developed his further hypotheses in "Origine del sistema planetario eliocentrico presso i Greci," in *Scritti . . .*, II (Bologna, 1926), 115–177, originally published in *Memorie dell'Istituto lombardo di scienze e lettere*, Classe di scienze matematiche e naturali, 3rd ser., **18** (1896–1900), 61–100. This was refuted by Paul Tannery, "Sur Héraclide du Pont," in *Revue des études grecques*, **12** (1899), 305–311, repr. in his *Mémoires scientifiques*, IX, J. L. Heiberg, ed. (Toulouse–Paris, 1929), 253–259.

A good account of the ancient evidence and modern discussions is T. L. Heath, *Aristarchus of Samos* (Oxford, 1913; repr., Oxford, 1959), 249–283. B. L. van der Waerden proposed his interpretation in "Die Astronomie des Heraklides von Pontos," in *Sitzungsberichte der Sächsischen Akademie der Wissenschaften zu Leipzig*, Math.-naturwiss. Kl., **96** (1944), 47–56, and repeated it (within a greatly expanded reconstruction of Pythagorean astronomy) in "Die Astronomie der Pythagoreer," *K. Verhandelingen der Nederlandse akademie van wetenschappen*, Afd. Natuurkunde, ser. A, **20**, no. 1 (1951). He was refuted by A. Pannekoek, "The Astronomical System of Herakleides," *ibid.*, ser. B, **55**, no. 4 (1952), 373–381. Godfrey Evans, "The Astronomy of Heracleides Ponticus," in *Classical Quarterly*, n.s. **20** (1970), 102–111, although occasionally confused and ignoring much of the modern literature, was the first to give a correct explanation of the Calcidius passage. A similar explanation, with the crucial terminological evidence, was given independently by O. Neugebauer, "On the Allegedly Heliocentric Theory of Venus by Heraclides Ponticus," in *American Journal of Philology*, **93** (1972), 600–601. See also his *A History of Ancient Mathematical Astronomy*, II (New York, 1975), 694–696.

Copernicus refers to Heraclides in *De revolutionibus orbium caelestium*, F. and C. Zeller, eds. (Munich, 1949), which is *Nikolaus Kopernikus Gesamtausgabe*, vol. II, in the Dedicatory Epistle, p. 5, and IV, p. 14.

G. J. TOOMER

HERBRAND, JACQUES (*b.* Paris, France, 12 February 1908; *d.* La Bérarde, Isère, France, 27 July 1931)

Herbrand gave early signs of his mathematical gifts, entering the École Normale Supérieure at the exceptional age of seventeen and ranking first in the entering class. He completed his doctoral dissertation in April 1929. That October he began a year of service in the French army. He then went to Germany on a Rockefeller fellowship, studying in Berlin (until May 1931) with John von Neumann, then in Hamburg (May–June) with Emil Artin, and in Göttingen (June–July) with Emmy Noether. He left Göttingen for a vacation in the Alps and a few days later was killed in a fall at the age of twenty-three.

Herbrand's contributions to mathematics fall into two domains: mathematical logic and modern algebra. He showed an early interest in mathematical logic, a subject to which French mathematicians were then paying scant attention, and published a note on a question of mathematical logic in the *Comptes rendus* of the Paris Academy of Sciences when he was hardly twenty. Herbrand's main contribution to logic was what is now called the Herbrand theorem, published in his doctoral dissertation: it is the most fundamental result in quantification theory. Consider an arbitrary formula F of quantification theory, then delete all its quantifiers and replace the variables thus made free with constants selected according to a definite procedure. A lexical instance of F is thus obtained. Let F_i be the ith lexical instance of F, the instances being generated in some definite order. The Herbrand theorem states that F is provable in any one of the (equivalent) systems of quantification theory if and only if for some number k the disjunction

$$F_1 \vee F_2 \vee \cdots \vee F_k$$

(now called the kth Herbrand disjunction) is sententially valid. (Herbrand's demonstration of the theorem contains a gap, discovered in 1963 by B. Dreben, P. Andrews, and S. Aanderaa.)

The Herbrand theorem establishes an unexpected bridge between quantification theory and sentential logic. Testing a formula for sentential validity is a purely mechanical operation. Given a formula F of quantification theory, one tests the kth Herbrand disjunction of F successively for $k = 1$, $k = 2$, and so on; if F is provable, one eventually reaches a number k for which the kth Herbrand disjunction is valid. If F is not provable, there is, of course, no such k; and one never learns that there is no such k (in accordance with the fact that there is no decision procedure for quantification theory). Besides yielding a very convenient proof procedure, the Herbrand theorem has many applications (a field explored by Herbrand himself) to decision and reduction problems and to proofs of consistency. Almost all the methods for proving theorems by machine rest upon the Herbrand theorem.

In modern algebra Herbrand's contributions are in class-field theory, the object of which is to gain knowledge about Abelian extensions of a given algebraic number field from properties of the field. Initiated by Leopold Kronecker and developed by Heinrich Weber, David Hilbert, Teiji Takagi, and Emil Artin, the theory received essential contributions from Herbrand in 1930–1931. He wrote ten papers in this field, simplifying previous proofs, generalizing theorems, and discovering important new results.

BIBLIOGRAPHY

Herbrand's logical writings have been reprinted in his *Écrits logiques,* Jean van Heijenoort, ed. (Paris, 1968); the pref. includes reference to the paper by B. Dreben, P. Andrews, and S. Aanderaa, "False Lemmas in Herbrand," in *Bulletin of the American Mathematical Society,* **69** (1963), 699–706, as well as further information about the gap in Herbrand's demonstration of his theorem. Also see *The Logical Writings of Jacques Herbrand,* Warren D. Goldfarb, ed. (Reidel, 1971).

The list of Herbrand's papers on class-field theory can be found in Ernest Vessiot's intro. to Helmut Hasse, *Über gewisse Ideale in einer einfachen Algebra* (Paris, 1934). Herbrand's *Le développement moderne de la théorie des corps algébriques* was published posthumously and edited by his friend Claude Chevalley (Paris, 1936).

JEAN VAN HEIJENOORT

HÉRIGONE, PIERRE (*d.* Paris [?], *ca.* 1643)

Very little is known of Hérigone's life. He was apparently of Basque origin and spent most of his life in Paris as a teacher of mathematics. He also served on a number of official committees dealing with mathematical subjects, notably the one appointed by Richelieu in 1634 to judge the practicality of Morin's proposed scheme for determining longitude from the moon's motion. With the other members of this committee (Étienne Pascal, Mydorge, Beaugrand, J. C. Boulenger, L. de la Porte) he became embroiled in the ensuing controversy with Morin.

Hérigone's only published work of any consequence is the *Cursus mathematicus,* a six-volume compendium of elementary and intermediate mathematics in French and Latin. Although there is little substantive originality in the *Cursus,* it shows an extensive knowledge and understanding of contemporary mathematics. Its striking feature is the introduction of a complete system of mathematical and logical notation, very much in line with the seventeenth-century preoccupation with universal languages. Yet none of Hérigone's notational conventions seem to have become accepted, and his other works are of negligible importance.

It is as a teacher, systematizer, and disseminator of mathematics that Hérigone must be judged. As such he was no doubt a full member of the community of French mathematicians of the first half of the seventeenth century.

BIBLIOGRAPHY

I. ORIGINAL WORKS. Hérigone's only important published work is *Cursus mathematicus nova, brevi et clara methodo demonstratus,* 6 vols. (Paris, 1634–1642). There are three other "editions" of the *Cursus* (1643, 1644), but these consist of nothing but sheets from the original ed. with a few deletions and additions, and new title pages. Hérigone also published a paraphrase of the first six books of Euclid (1639), but it consists of little more than the French portion of vol. I of the *Cursus;* there is also a spurious 2nd ed. (1644).

II. SECONDARY LITERATURE. What little information there is on Hérigone has been collected by B. Boncompagni in *Bullettino di bibliografia e di storia delle scienze matematiche e fisiche,* **2** (1869), 472–476; and P. Tannery in *Mémoires scientifiques,* X (Paris, 1930), 287–289. The controversy with Morin is described by J. E. Montucla in *Histoire des mathématiques,* 2nd ed., IV (Paris, 1802), 543–545. A list of Hérigone's mathematical symbols is given by F. Cajori in *History of Mathematical Notations,* I (Chicago, 1928), 200–204, *passim.*

PER STRØMHOLM

HERMANN (HERMANNUS) THE LAME (also known as **Hermannus Contractus** or **Hermann of Reichenau**) (*b.* Altshausen, Germany, 18 July 1013; *d.* Altshausen, 24 September 1054)

Hermannus was the son of Count Wolferat of Altshausen. He entered the cloister school at Reichenau on 13 September 1020 and became a monk at Reichenau in 1043. Throughout his life he suffered from an extreme physical disability which severely limited his movements and his ability to speak; hence the appellation "contractus," attached to his name since the twelfth century.

Hermannus is one of the key figures in the transmission of Arabic astronomical techniques and in-

HERMANN THE LAME

struments to the Latin West before the period of translation. His familiarity with Islamic materials indicates that this knowledge had reached southern Germany by the early eleventh century. It is unlikely, though, that Hermannus knew Arabic; his devoted pupil Berthold of Reichenau, who has left a biographical sketch of his master (see Manitius, *Geschichte der lateinischen Literatur* . . ., pp. 756–777), would almost surely have mentioned this accomplishment.

Hermannus is one of the earliest Latin authors responsible for the introduction or reintroduction into the West from the Islamic world (undoubtedly Spain) of three astronomical instruments: the astrolabe, the chilinder (a portable sundial), and the quadrant with cursor. Since the thirteenth century a *De mensura astrolabii* has been ascribed to Hermannus. The first section of a second work, often called in its entirety *De utilitatibus astrolabii,* is a treatise on the astrolabe in twenty-one chapters which contains many Arabic expressions; not written by Hermannus, it was attributed to Gerbert as early as the twelfth century. N. Bubnov, the eidtor of Gerbert's mathematical works, has placed the twenty-one-chapter treatise among the doubtful works of Gerbert. The second section of the *De utilitatibus,* containing a description of the chilinder and the quadrant, is generally considered to be by Hermannus. Further evidence for his authorship lies in the subsequent paragraphs of this second section which contain an account of Eratosthenes' measurement of the circumference of the earth as reported by Macrobius, with a calculation of the earth's diameter using the Archimedean value of 22/7 for pi. These paragraphs were the subject of correspondence in 1048 between Hermannus and his former pupil Meinzo of Constance.

The *De mensura astrolabii,* which contains many latinized Arabic words, begins with a description of the fundamental circles of the base plate of the astrolabe, or *walzachora,* followed by a delineation of the rete. The astrolabe is designed for a latitude of forty-eight degrees, the latitude of Reichenau; no mention is made of the number of plates the instrument should have. Designed in the conventional manner for Western astrolabes, the dorsum contains a shadow square. This practice of expressing angles in terms of twelve points of either the inverse or the plane shadow (*umbra versa* or *umbra recta*) stemmed from Hindu sources and was transmitted through Arabic writings. The *De mensura* also contains a star table with the coordinates of twenty-seven stars expressed in right ascension and the stars' meridian altitude.

The chilinder is a portable altitude sundial designed for one latitude—forty-eight degrees in this case. Since the altitude varies symmetrically with the declination throughout the sun's yearly cycle, the surface of the dial with the hour lines is wrapped around a cylindrical column. The dial provides the time in unequal hours, that is, daylight hours derived by dividing the diurnal arc by twelve. Hermannus provides an altitude table expressed in degrees rather than inverse shadow points, as was customary later. His treatise was the first in the Latin West to describe this type of sundial, which had antecedents in Islam. Through Hermannus the chilinder became the inheritor of the *horologium viatorum* (traveler's dial) tradition first mentioned in the West in Vitruvius' *De architectura.*

The quadrant described by Hermannus is a quadrant with cursor, the "Alphonsine" type similar to that appearing in the *Libros del saber de astronomia.* It is the usual one-fourth of a circle with the margin divided into ninety degrees and has two small plates with holes on one edge for sighting and a plumb line. A cursor, inscribed with the months of the year, slides in a groove concentric to the margin. The remainder of the body of the quadrant contains the hour lines. This instrument was used to measure the sun's altitude; with the cursor it could also provide the observer's latitude and the time of day (in unequal hours).

All three instruments were widely used in the Latin West. The popularity of the astrolabe is well attested. The chilinder and quadrant with cursor also are well represented in the Latin manuscript tradition and continued to appear in printed works through the seventeenth century. It is of interest that all of these instruments were used during the Middle Ages to solve problems in mensuration as well as in pure astronomy. Hermannus' astronomical writings include a work on the length of the month (*De mense lunari*) in which he criticizes the Venerable Bede; according to Berthold, Hermannus also wrote a computus.

In mathematics Hermannus composed a treatise teaching multiplication and division with the abacus (*Qualiter multiplicationes fiant in abbaco*); the work uses Roman numerals only. He also wrote the earliest treatise on rithmomachia (*De conflictu rithmimachie*), a very complex game based on Pythagorean number theory derived from Boethius. The game was played with counters on a board; capture of the opponent's pieces was dependent on the determination of arithmetical ratios and arithmetic, geometrical, and harmonic progressions. This game, which enjoyed a considerable vogue during the Middle Ages, has been attributed to Pythagoras, Boethius, and Gerbert.

Hermannus composed an excellent world chronicle

dating from the birth of Christ which was continued by Berthold and was used by later German historians, such as Manegold of Lautenbach and Otto of Freising. He was also the author of a work on music (*Opuscula musica*) containing a system of notation of musical intervals which was his own invention but had no influence, although he did make an original contribution to medieval modal theory. In addition Hermannus wrote poems and hymns.

BIBLIOGRAPHY

I. ORIGINAL WORKS. *De mensura astrolabii* and *De utilitatibus astrolabii* are available in B. Pez, ed., *Thesaurus anecdotorum novissimus,* III, pt. 2 (Augsburg, 1721), cols. 93–106, 94–139; J. P. Migne, ed., *Patrologia latina,* CXLIII (Paris, 1882), cols. 379–412; and *Gerberti, postea Silvestri II papae, opera mathematica,* N. Bubov, ed. (Berlin, 1899), pt. 2, *Gerberti opera dubia,* pp. 109–147; the *De mensura* is also reprinted in R. T. Gunther, *Astrolabes of the World,* II (Oxford, 1932), 404–408. *Regule Herimanni qualiter multiplicationes fiant in abbaco,* P. Treutlein, ed., is in *Bullettino di bibliografia e di storia delle scienze mathematiche e fisiche,* **10** (1877), 643–647. *Opuscula musica* may be found in M. Gerbert, ed., *Scriptores ecclesiastici de musica sacra potissimum,* II (St. Blasius, Belgium, 1784), 124–153; J. P. Migne, ed., *Patrologia latina,* CXLIII (Paris, 1882), cols. 413–414; and *Herimanni Contracti musica,* W. Brambach, ed. (Leipzig, 1884). For *De mense lunari,* see G. Meier, *Die sieben freien Künste im Mittelalter,* II (Einsiedeln, Switzerland, 1887), 34–46. The *De conflictu rithmimachie* is in E. Wappler, "Bemerkungen zur Rhythmomachie," in *Zeitschrift für Mathematik und Physik,* Hist. Abt., **37** (1892), 1–17. His chronicle dating from the birth of Christ is in *Monumenta germaniae historica scriptores,* V (Hannover, 1844), 67–133; see also Aemilius Ussermann, ed., *Chronicon Hermanni Contracti ex inedito hucusque codice Augiensi, una cum eius vita et continuatione a Bertholdo eius disciplo scripta,* 2 vols. (St. Blasius, Belgium, 1790), repr. in J. P. Migne, ed., *Patrologia latina,* CXLIII (Paris, 1882), cols. 55–270. The *Monumenta* text was translated into German by K. Nobbe in *Geschichtsschreiber der deutschen Vorzeit,* XI (Berlin, 1851); a 2nd ed., prepared by W. Wattenbach, appeared in vol. XLII (Leipzig, 1888).

II. SECONDARY LITERATURE. On Hermannus or his work, see M. Cantor, *Vorlesungen über Geschichte der Mathematik,* I (Leipzig, 1880), 758–761; J. Drecker, "Hermannus Contractus über das Astrolab," in *Isis,* **16** (1931), 200–219, which includes the text of *De mensura astrolabii* on pp. 203–212; P. Duhem, *Le système du monde,* III (Paris, 1958), 163–171; E. Dümmler, "Ein Schreiben Meinzos von Constanz an Hermann den Lahmen," in *Neues Archiv der Gesellschaft für ältere deutsche Geschichtskunde,* **5** (1880), 202–206; H. Hansjakob, *Hermann der Lahme* (Mainz, 1885); W. Hartner, "The Principle and Use of the Astrolabe," in A. U. Pope, ed., *A Survey of Persian Art* (London, 1939), p. 2533; C. H. Haskins, *Studies in the History of Mediaeval Science* (Cambridge, Mass., 1927), pp. 52–53; Max Manitius, *Geschichte der lateinischen Literatur des Mittelalters,* II (Munich, 1923), 756–777, 786–787; J. Millás Vallicrosa, "La introducción del cuadrante con cursor en Europa," in *Isis,* **17** (1932), 218–258; R. Peiper, "Fortolfi rythmimachia," in *Abhandlungen zur Geschichte der Mathematik,* **3** (1880), 198–227; G. Reese, *Music in the Middle Ages* (New York, 1940), pp. 137, 155; D. E. Smith, *History of Mathematics,* I (Boston, 1923), 197–200; D. E. Smith and C. C. Eaton, "Rithmomachia, the Great Medieval Number Game," in *Teachers College Record,* **13** (1912), 29–38; L. Thorndike, *A History of Magic and Experimental Science,* I (New York, 1923), ch. 30, pp. 701, 728; W. Wattenbach, *Deutschlands Geschichtsquellen im Mittelalter,* II (Berlin, 1894), 41–47; and E. Zinner, *Geschichte der Sternkunde* (Berlin, 1931), p. 330; and *Deutsche und niederländische astronomische Instrumente des 11.–18. Jahrhunderts* (Munich, 1956), pp. 135–141, 155–156, 373–374.

CLAUDIA KREN

HERMANN, JAKOB (*b.* Basel, Switzerland, 16 July 1678; *d.* Basel, 11 July 1733)

Hermann, the son of Germanus Hermann, a headmaster, devoted much of his time to mathematics while studying theology at Basel (bachelor's degree, 1695; master's degree, 1696; theological examination, 1701). In the last quarter of the seventeenth century mathematics, which he took up under the guidance of Jakob I Bernoulli, was characterized by the creation of the calculus and the stormy development of infinitesimal calculus. Through his exceptional ability and his zeal Hermann was able at a young age to join the small group of the most important mathematicians. In 1696 he defended Bernoulli's third dissertation on the theory of series and in 1701, through the intervention of Leibniz, became a member of the Berlin Academy with a work directed against Bernhard Nieuwentyt, a relentless critic of Leibniz's differential concept and methods. In 1707, again assisted by Leibniz, he was appointed professor of mathematics at Padua—to the same chair that Nikolaus I Bernoulli later held. The following year Hermann was accepted into the Academy at Bologna. Yet, as a Protestant in Italy, he seems not to have been completely happy; and in 1713 he gladly accepted a call—once more arranged by Leibniz—to Frankfurt-an-der-Oder.

While in Italy, Hermann composed the final version of his principal scientific work, the *Phoronomia,* which appeared at Amsterdam in 1716. This textbook—a critical analysis of which is still lacking—concerned advanced mechanics in the modern sense and was considered an important work, very favorably reviewed by Leibniz himself in the *Acta eruditorum.*

From 1724 to 1731 Hermann was connected with the flourishing Academy in St. Petersburg, where he was the predecessor of Leonhard Euler, to whom he was distantly related (he was a second cousin of Euler's mother). In addition to various papers on trajectory problems, algebraically squarable curves, and attraction, Hermann wrote volumes I and III (mathematics and fortification) of the textbook *Abrégé des mathématiques* (St. Petersburg, 1728–1730). He also gave instruction in mathematics to the grandson of Peter the Great, the future Peter II, and to Isaac Bruckner.

Homesick, Hermann repeatedly sought to obtain any reasonably suitable position in Basel (see, for instance, Johann I Bernoulli's letter of 11 November 1724 to J. J. Scheuchzer). In 1722 he received, by lottery, the professorship of ethics and natural law at Basel, but he had a substitute carry out the duties of the office until he finally returned home in 1731. No professorship of mathematics became vacant in his native city before his death—the chair was brilliantly filled by Johann I Bernoulli. Shortly before his death the Paris Academy elected him a member.

Hermann possessed a serious, calm disposition; and through his sympathetic character, objectivity, and learning he won not only the friendship of Leibniz and of Jakob I Bernoulli but also the respect of all the leading mathematicians.

Hermann's scientific importance fully justifies the decision to incorporate his works into the complete edition of Bernoulliana which is now in progress. Of the approximately 600 standard-size pages of his correspondence, about a third has been published by C. J. Gerhardt in Leibniz's *Mathematische Schriften.*

BIBLIOGRAPHY

I. Original Works. Hermann's works include *Responsio ad Clar. Viri Bernh. Nieuwentijt considerationes secundas circa calculi differentialis principia editas* (Basel, 1700); *Phoronomia, sive de viribus et motibus corporum solidorum et fluidorum libri duo* (Amsterdam, 1716); and *Abrégé des mathématiques,* vols. I and III (St. Petersburg, 1728–1730). For his articles, see Poggendorff, I, cols. 1077–1078.

Some of Hermann's letters may be found in C. J. Gerhardt, ed., *G. W. Leibniz' mathematische Schriften,* IV (Halle, 1859), 253–413. Extracts of his correspondence are in *Mitteilungen der Naturforschenden Gesellschaft in Bern* (1850), pp. 118–120. A complete bibliography may be found in the Bernoulli Archives in the university library at Basel.

II. Secondary Literature. On Hermann and his work, see (listed in chronological order) *Mercure suisse* (Oct. 1733), pp. 77–85 and (Feb. 1734) for a eulogy and list of his writings; R. Wolf, "Euler," in *Biographien zur Kulturgeschichte der Schweiz,* IV (Zurich, 1862), pp. 90 ff.; O. Spiess, ed., *Der Briefwechsel von Johann Bernoulli,* I (Basel, 1955), *passim;* J. E. Hofmann, *Ueber Jakob Bernoullis Beiträge zur Infinitesimalmathematik* (Geneva, 1956); and V. I. Lysenko, "Die geometrischen Arbeiten von Jakob Hermann," in *Istoriko-matematicheskie issledovaniya,* **17** (1966), 299–307. On Hermann and mathematics in Russia see the notice by R. Wolf in *Verhandlungen der naturforschenden Gesellschaft in Zürich,* **35** (1890), 98–99; and M. Cantor, *Vorlesungen über Geschichte der Mathematik,* III (Leipzig, 1901), *passim.*

E. A. Fellmann

HERMITE, CHARLES (*b.* Dieuze, Lorraine, France, 24 December 1822; *d.* Paris, France, 14 January 1901)

Hermite was the sixth of the seven children of Ferdinand Hermite and the former Madeleine Lallemand. His father, a man of strong artistic inclinations who had studied engineering, worked for a while in a salt mine near Dieuze but left to assume the draper's trade of his in-laws—a business he subsequently entrusted to his wife in order to give full rein to his artistic bent. Around 1829 Charles's parents transferred their business to Nancy. They were not much interested in the education of their children, but all of them attended the Collège of Nancy and lived there. Charles continued his studies in Paris, first at the Collège Henri IV, where he was greatly influenced by the physics lessons of Despretz, and then, in 1840–1841, at the Collège Louis-le-Grand; his mathematics professor there was the same Richard who fifteen years earlier had taught Evariste Galois. Instead of seriously preparing for his examination Hermite read Euler, Gauss's *Disquisitiones arithmeticae,* and Lagrange's *Traité sur la résolution des équations numériques,* thus prompting Richard to call him *un petit Lagrange.*

Hermite's first two papers, published in the *Nouvelles annales de mathématiques,* date from this period. Still unfamiliar with the work of Ruffini and Abel, he tried to prove in one of these papers the impossibility of solving the fifth-degree equation by radicals. Hermite decided to continue his studies at the École Polytechnique; during the preparation year he was taught by E. C. Catalan. In the 1842 contest of the Paris colleges Hermite failed to win first *prix de mathématiques spéciales* section but received only first "accessit." He was admitted to the École Polytechnique in the fall of 1842 with the poor rank of sixty-eighth. After a year's study at the École Polytechnique, he was refused further study, because of a congenital defect of his right foot, which obliged him to use a cane. Owing to the intervention of influential people the decision was reversed, but under conditions to which Hermite was reluctant to submit. At this time, Hermite—a cheerful youth who, according to some, resembled a Galois resurrected—was introduced into the circle of Alexandre and Joseph Bertrand. Following the example of others, he declined the paramount honor of graduating from the École Polytechnique, contenting himself with the career of *professeur.* He took his examinations for the *baccalauréat* and *licence* in 1847.

At that time Hermite must have become acquainted with the work of Cauchy and Liouville on general function theory as well as with that of C. G. J. Jacobi on elliptic and hyperelliptic functions. Hermite was better able than Liouville, who lacked sufficient familiarity with Jacobi's work, to combine both fields of thought. In 1832 and 1834 Jacobi had formulated his famous inversion problem for hyperelliptic integrals, but the essential properties of the new transcendents were still unknown and the work of A. Göpel and J. G. Rosenhain had not yet appeared. Through his first work in this field, Hermite placed himself, as Darboux says, in the ranks of the first analysts. He generalized Abel's theorem on the division of the argument of elliptic functions to the case of hyperelliptic ones. In January 1843, only twenty years old, he communicated his discovery to Jacobi, who did not conceal his delight. The correspondence continued for at least six letters; the second letter, written in August 1844, was on the transformation of elliptic functions, and four others of unknown dates (although before 1850) were on number theory. Extracts from these letters were inserted by Jacobi in *Crelle's Journal* and in his own *Opuscula,* and are also in the second volume of Dirichlet's edition of Jacobi's work. Throughout his life Hermite exerted a great scientific influence by his correspondence with other prominent mathematicians. It is doubtful that his *Oeuvres* faithfully reflects this enormous activity.

In 1848 Hermite was appointed a *répétiteur* and admissions examiner at the École Polytechnique. The next ten years were his most active period. On 14 July 1856 he was elected a member of the Académie des Sciences, receiving forty out of forty-eight votes.

In 1862, through Pasteur's influence, a position of *maître de conférence* was created for Hermite at the École Polytechnique; in 1863 he became an *examinateur de sortie et de classement* there. He occupied that position until 1869, when he took over J. M. C. Duhamel's chair as professor of analysis at the École Polytechnique and at the Faculté des Sciences, first in algebra and later in analysis as well. His textbooks in analysis became classics, famous even outside France. He resigned his chair at the École Polytechnique in 1876 and at the Faculté in 1897. He was an honorary member of a great many academies and learned societies, and he was awarded many decorations. Hermite's seventieth birthday gave scientific Europe the opportunity to pay homage in a way accorded very few mathematicians.

Hermite married a sister of Joseph Bertrand; one of his two daughters married Émile Picard and the other G. Forestier. He lived in the same building as E. Bournoff at Place de l'Odéon, and it was perhaps his acquaintance with this famous philologist that led him to study Sanskrit and ancient Persian. Hermite was seriously ill with smallpox in 1856, and under Cauchy's influence became a devout Catholic. His scientific work was collected and edited by Picard.

> From 1851–1859 Europe lost four of its foremost mathematicians, Gauss, Cauchy, Jacobi, and Dirichlet. Nobody, except Hermite himself, could guess the profoundness of the work of Weierstrass and Riemann on Abelian functions and of Kronecker and Smith on the mysterious relations between number theory and elliptic functions. Uncontested, the scepter of higher arithmetic and analysis passed from Gauss and Cauchy to Hermite who wielded it until his death, notwithstanding the admirable discoveries of rivals and disciples whose writings have tarnished the splendor of the most brilliant performance other than his [unspecified quotation by P. Mansion].

Throughout his lifetime and for years afterward Hermite was an inspiring figure in mathematics. In today's mathematics he is remembered chiefly in connection with Hermitean forms, a complex generalization of quadratic forms, and with Hermitean polynomials (1873), both minor discoveries. Specialists in number theory may know that some reduction of quadratic forms is owed to him; his solution of the Lamé differential equation (1872, 1877) is even less well known. An interpolation procedure is named after him. His name also occurs in the solution of the fifth-degree equation by elliptic functions (1858). One of the best-known facts about Hermite is that he first proved the transcendence of e (1873). In a sense this last is paradigmatic of all of Hermite's discoveries. By a slight adaptation of Hermite's proof, Felix Lindemann, in 1882, obtained the much more exciting transcendence of π. Thus, Lindemann, a mediocre mathematician, became even more famous than Hermite for a discovery for which Hermite had laid all the groundwork and that he had come within a gnat's eye of making. If Hermite's work were scrutinized more closely, one might find more instances of Hermitean preludes to important discoveries by others, since it was his habit to disseminate his knowledge lavishly in correspondence, in his courses, and in short notes. His correspondence with T. J. Stieltjes, for instance, consisted of at least 432 letters written by both of them between 1882 and 1894. Contrary to Mansion's statement above, Hermite's most important results have been so solidly incorporated into more general structures and so intensely absorbed by more profound thought that they are never attributed to him. Hermite's principle, for example, famous in the nineteenth century, has been forgotten as a special case of the Riemann-Roch theorem. Hermite's work exerted a strong influence in his own time, but in the twentieth century a few historians, at most, will have cast a glance at it.

In Hermite's scientific activity, shifts of emphasis rather than periods can be distinguished; 1843–1847, division and transformation of Abelian and elliptic functions; 1847–1851, arithmetical theory of quadratic forms and use of continuous variables; 1854–1864, theory of invariants; 1855, a connection of number theory with theta functions in the transformation of Abelian functions; 1858–1864, fifth-degree equations, modular equations, and class number relations; 1873, approximation of functions and transcendence of e; and 1877–1881, applications of elliptic functions and Lamé's equation.

In the 1840's, and even in the early 1850's, the inversion of integrals of algebraic functions was still a confusing problem, mainly because of the paradoxical occurrence of more than two periods. Jacobi reformulated the problem by simultaneously inverting p integrals—if the irrationality is a square root of a polynomial of the $(2p - 1)$th or $2p$th degree. In the early 1840's the young Hermite was one of the very few mathematicians who viewed Abelian functions clearly, owing to his acquaintance with Cauchy's and Liouville's ideas on complex functions. To come to grips with the new transcendents, he felt that one had to start from the periodicity properties rather than from Jacobi's product decomposition. This new approach proved successful in the case of elliptic functions, when Hermite introduced the theta functions of nth order as a means of constructing doubly periodic functions. In the hyperelliptic case he was less successful, for he did not find the badly needed theta functions of two variables. This was achieved in the late 1840's and early 1850's by A. Göpel and J. G. Rosenhain for $p = 2$; the more general case was left to Riemann. In 1855 Hermite took advantage of Göpel's and Rosenhain's work when he created his transformation theory (see below).

Meanwhile, Hermite turned to number theory. For definite quadratic forms with integral coefficients, Gauss had introduced the notion of equivalence by means of unimodular integral linear transformations; by a reduction process he had proved for two and three variables that, given the determinant, the class number is finite. Hermite generalized the procedure and proved the same for an arbitrary number of variables.

He applied this result to algebraic numbers to prove that given the discriminant of a number field, the number of norm forms is finite. By the same method he obtained the finiteness of a basis of units, not knowing that Dirichlet had already determined the size of the basis. Finally, he extended the theorem of the finiteness of the class number to indefinite quadratic forms, and he proved that the subgroup of unimodular integral transformations leaving such a form invariant is finitely generated.

Hermite did not proceed to greater depths in his work on algebraic numbers. He was an algebraist rather than an arithmetician. Probably he never assimilated the much more profound ideas that developed in the German school in the nineteenth century, and perhaps he did not even realize that the notion of algebraic integer with which he had started was wrong. Some of his arithmetical ideas were carried on with more success by Hermann Minkowski in the twentieth century.

In the reduction theory of quadratic and binary forms Hermite had encountered invariants. Later he made many contributions to the theory of invariants, in which Arthur Cayley, J. J. Sylvester, and F. Brioschi were active at that time. One of his most important contributions to the progress of the theory of invariants was the "reciprocity law," a one-to-one relation between the covariants of fixed degree of order p of an mth-degree binary form and those of order m of a pth-degree binary form. One of his invariant theory subjects was the fifth-degree equation, to which he later applied elliptic functions.

Armed with the theory of invariants, Hermite returned to Abelian functions. Meanwhile, the badly needed theta functions of two arguments had been found, and Hermite could apply what he had learned about quadratic forms to understanding the transformation of the system of the four periods. Later, Hermite's 1855 results became basic for the transformation theory of Abelian functions as well as for Camille Jordan's theory of "Abelian" groups. They also led to Hermite's own theory of the fifth-degree equation and of the modular equations of elliptic functions. It was Hermite's merit to use ω rather than Jacobi's $q = e^{\pi i \omega}$ as an argument and to prepare the present form of the theory of modular functions. He again dealt with the number theory applications of this theory, particularly with class number relations for quadratic forms. His solution of the fifth-degree equation by elliptic functions (analogous to that of third-degree equations by trigonometric functions) was the basic problem of this period.

In the 1870's Hermite returned to approximation problems, with which he had started his scientific career. Gauss's interpolation problem, Legendre functions, series for elliptic and other integrals, continued fractions, Bessel functions, Laplace integrals, and special differential equations were dealt with in this period, from which the transcendence proof for *e* and the Lamé equation emerged as the most remarkable results.

BIBLIOGRAPHY

I. ORIGINAL WORKS. Hermite's main works are *Oeuvres de Charles Hermite,* E. Picard, ed., 4 vols. (Paris, 1905–1917); *Correspondance d'Hermite et de Stieltjes,* B. Baillaud and H. Bourget, eds., 2 vols. (Paris, 1905); and "Briefe von Ch. Hermite an P. du Bois-Reymond aus den Jahren 1875–1888," E. Lampe, ed., in *Archiv der Mathematik und Physik,* 3rd. ser., **24** (1916), 193–220, 289–310. Nearly all his printed articles are in the *Oeuvres.* It is not known how complete an account the three works give of Hermite's activity as a correspondent. The letters to du Bois-Reymond are a valuable human document.

II. SECONDARY LITERATURE. The biographical data of this article are taken from G. Darboux's biography in *La revue du mois,* **1** (1906), 37–58, the most accurate and trustworthy source. Other sources are less abundant; the exception is P. Mansion and C. Jordan, "Charles Hermite (1822–1901)," in *Revue des questions scientifiques,* 2nd ser., **19** (1901), 353–396, and **20** (1901), 348–349; unfortunately, Mansion did not sufficiently account for the sources of his quotations.

An excellent analysis of Hermite's scientific work is M. Noether, "Charles Hermite," in *Mathematische Annalen,* **55** (1902), 337–385. Others, most of them superficial *éloges,* can be retraced from *Jahrbuch über die Fortschritte der Mathematik,* **32** (1901), 22–28; **33** (1902), 36–37; and **36** (1905), 22.

HANS FREUDENTHAL

HERO OF ALEXANDRIA (*fl.* Alexandria, A.D. 62)

Hero (or Heron) of Alexandria is a name under which a number of works have come down to us. They were written in Greek; but one of them, the *Mechanics,* is found only in an Arabic translation and another, the *Optics,* only in Latin. Apart from his works we know nothing at all about him.

His name is not mentioned in any literary source earlier than Pappus (A.D. 300), who quotes from his *Mechanics.*[1] Hero himself quotes Archimedes (*d.* 212 B.C.), which gives us the other time limit. Scholars have given different dates, ranging from 150 B.C. to A.D. 250, but the question has been settled by O. Neugebauer, who observed that an eclipse of the moon described by Hero in his *Dioptra* (chapter 35) as taking place on the tenth day before the vernal equinox and beginning at Alexandria in the fifth watch of the night, corresponds to an eclipse in A.D. 62 and to none other during the 500 years in question.[2] An astronomical date is the most reliable of all, being independent of tradition and opinion. The rather minute theoretical possibility that Hero might have lived long after this date I have discussed and dismissed, while I have elsewhere reviewed the whole controversy about his dates, which is now of historical interest only.[4]

The question of what sort of man he was has also been debated. H. Diels found that he was a mere artisan.[5] I. Hammer-Jensen took him to be an ignorant man who copied the chapters of his *Pneumatics* from works which he did not understand.[6] Although E. Hoppe attempted to defend Hero,[7] Hammer-Jensen maintained her opinion.[8] In 1925 J. L. Heiberg wrote: "Hero is no scientist, but a practical technician and surveyor. This view, which has been challenged in vain, was first put forth by H. Diels: [who called him] 'Ein reiner Banause.'"[9]

Such adverse judgment was based on a study of the *Pneumatics* at a time when neither the *Mechanics* nor the *Metrica* was known; and the *Pneumatics,* although by far the largest work (apart from the elementary textbooks) was neither by its contents nor form apt to inspire confidence in a serious scholar. The contents are almost exclusively apparatuses for parlor magic, and there is no discernible plan in the arrangement of the chapters. Apart from the introduction, there is no theoretical matter in the book, which consists entirely of practical descriptions.

But since then, the *Mechanics* has been published in Arabic, and a manuscript has come to light giving the *Metrica* in its original form; thus the image of Hero has changed. The *Mechanics* shows nothing of the disorder of the *Pneumatics,* consisting of an introduction, a theoretical part, and a practical part; the *Metrica* shows that Hero possessed all the mathematical knowledge of his time, while a chapter of the *Dioptra* indicates that he was familiar with astronomy. We also find that he quotes Archimedes by preference and has copied many chapters of a lost work of his on the statics of plane figures.

In the introduction to the *Pneumatics,* Diels found a quotation from Strato of Lampsacus (*fl.* 288 B.C.) and suggested that it was taken from Philo of Byzan-

HERO OF ALEXANDRIA

tium (*fl.* 250 B.C.), who probably took it from Ctesibius (*fl.* 270 B.C.);[10] but Philo's *Pneumatics,* which was discovered later, does not contain this passage, and a strictly accurate quotation is most likely to have been taken from the original work. The form of this theoretical introduction led I. Hammer-Jensen to assume that Hero was an ignoramus who did not understand what he copied from diverse sources; yet to me the freely flowing, rather discursive style suggests a man well-versed in his subject who is giving a quick summary to an audience that knows, or who might be expected to know, a good deal about it.

This discursive style, so very different from the concise style of the technical descriptions, is found again in the *Mechanics,* in which Hero, before giving the propositions from Archimedes' book *On Uprights,* presents the theory of the center of gravity as explained by Archimedes, not by Posidonius the Stoic, whose definition was not good enough.[11] Here again there is a strong suggestion of a teacher repeating swiftly a piece of knowledge which his students ought to know. Since we know the author as Hero of Alexandria, it seems reasonable to assume that he was appointed to the museum, that is, the University of Alexandria, where he taught mathematics, physics, pneumatics, and mechanics, and wrote textbooks on these subjects.

The *Pneumatics* can best be regarded as a collection of notes for such a textbook, of which only the introduction and the first six chapters have been given their final shape. All the chapters are uniform in style, even those taken from Philo, and eminently clear, so the idea of an ignorant compiler cannot be upheld. But there is more to be learned from the *Pneumatics.* While there is no order at all in the general arrangement of the chapters, we find here and there a short series of related chapters in which it is clear that Hero is searching for a better solution to a mechanical problem. This shows unmistakably that he was an inventor; it is therefore probable that he himself invented the dioptra, the screw-cutter, and the odometer, as well as several pneumatic apparatuses. This is all that can be learned about Hero himself.

The following works have survived under the name of Hero: *Automata, Barulkos, Belopoiica, Catoptrica, Cheirobalistra, Definitiones, Dioptra, Geometrica, Mechanica, De mensuris, Metrica, Pneumatica,* and *Stereometrica.* These can be divided into two categories, technical and mathematical. All the technical books, except the *Cheirobalistra,* seem to have been written by Hero; of the mathematical books only the *Definitiones* and the *Metrica* are direct from his hand. The others are, according to J. L. Heiberg, Byzantine schoolbooks with so many additions that it is impossible to know what is genuinely Heronian and what is not.[12]

The *Pneumatics* is by far the longest book, containing an introduction and two books of forty-three and thirty-seven chapters, respectively; but it is merely a collection of notes for a textbook on pneumatics. Only the introduction and the first six or seven chapters are finished. The introduction treats the occurrence of a vacuum in nature and the pressure of air and water; although it is written in a very prolix style with occasional digressions, the train of thought is never lost. It seems to have been written by a man very well versed in his subject, who is summarizing for students of pneumatics matters already known to them from their textbooks. Some of the theory is right, some is wrong (for instance, the *horror vacui* of nature), but it was the best theoretical explanation to be had at the time; a real understanding of the phenomenon had to wait for the experiments of Torricelli.

The first chapters, most of them taken from Philo's *Pneumatics,* describe experiments to show that air is a body, and that it will keep water out of a vessel unless it can find an outlet and will keep water in if it cannot enter. Hero goes on to siphons; but soon all order is lost, and the chapters appear haphazardly. Yet there is nothing haphazard about the chapters themselves, each of which—whether taken from Philo or a description of an apparatus seen by Hero—is written in the same concise style and according to a fixed plan, beginning with a description of the apparatus, with letters referring to a figure, then a description of how it works, then last (if necessary) an explanation. With very few exceptions it is evident that the chapters were written by Hero himself, and without exception they are very clear: each instrument can be reconstructed from the description and the figure.

The contents, on the other hand, have always been a source of puzzlement and despair for serious-minded scholars. Certainly Hero describes some useful implements—a fire pump and a water organ—but all the rest are playthings, puppet shows, or apparatuses for parlor magic. Trick jars that give out wine or water separately or in constant proportions, singing birds and sounding trumpets, puppets that move when a fire is lit on an altar, animals that drink when they are offered water—how can one respect an author who takes all these frivolities in earnest?

But Hero's treatment of these childish entertainments is quite matter-of-fact; he is interested in the way they work. In 1948 I explained this by the assumption that he was writing a handbook for the makers of pneumatic instruments, but this is not necessarily correct.[13] Hero was a teacher of physics, of which pneumatics is part. The book is a text for students, and Hero describes instruments the student needs to know, just as a modern physics textbook explains the laws governing the spinning top or the climbing monkey. Playthings take up so much of the book because such toys were very much in vogue at the time and the science of pneumatics was used for very little else. (Among the many toys of the *Pneumatics* there are even a few that use hot air or steam as a moving power, which has given rise to ill-founded speculations that the steam engine could have been invented at this time.) To this we must add that Hero was an inventor; and to a real inventor any clever apparatus is of interest, regardless of its purpose.

There is a slightly different text, found only in four manuscripts, that is generally designated Pseudo-Hero. Of seventy-eight chapters, seven have been radically changed; elsewhere the changes are only verbal corrections to clarify an already quite clear text. This text cannot have been written later than A.D. 500; therefore when the two texts agree, neither of them has been changed since then. For every chapter there is a figure, and the text in most cases begins with a reference to it, such as "Let *ABCD* be a base . . . ." Since Pseudo-Hero has the same figures as Hero, the figures cannot have been changed after A.D. 500; and there is every reason to believe that they were drawn by Hero himself. A complete set of these illustrations has been published in a reprint of Woodcroft's translation of the *Pneumatics.*[14] The *Pneumatics* was by far the most read of Hero's works during the Middle Ages and the Renaissance; more than 100 manuscripts of it have been found.

The *Mechanics,* preserved only in an Arabic version, was published in 1893 with a French translation and in 1900 with a German translation. A textbook for architects (that is, engineers, builders, and contractors), it is divided into three books. Book 1 deals with the theoretical knowledge and the practical skill necessary for the architect: the theory of the wheel, how to construct both plane and solid figures in a given proportion to a given figure, how to construct a toothed wheel to fit an endless screw, and the theory of motion. Drawing largely upon Archimedes, Hero then presents the theory of the center of gravity and equilibrium, the statics of a horizontal beam resting on vertical posts, and the theory of the balance.

Book 2 contains the theory of the five simple "powers": the winch, the lever, the pulley, the wedge, and the screw. The five "powers" are first described briefly, then the mechanical theory of each is presented and the results of a combination of the powers are calculated. Next is a chapter with answers to seventeen questions about physical problems, evidently inspired by Aristotle's *Mechanical Problems,* followed by seven chapters on the center of gravity in different plane figures and on the distribution of weight on their supports, once more from Archimedes. Book 3 describes sledges for transporting burdens on land, cranes and their accessories, other devices for transport, and wine presses; the last chapter describes a screw-cutter for cutting a female screw in a plank, which is necessary for direct screw presses.

Apart from the first chapter of book 1, which contains the *Barulkos,* the work proceeds in an orderly fashion; it shows nothing of the disorder of the *Pneumatics,* but the style is equally clear and concise, with a single exception. In book 1, chapter 24, Hero gives the theory of the center of gravity, and there he uses the same prolix and discursive style as in the introduction to the *Pneumatics.* This chapter would also seem to be a summary for students who should already know the subject. There are figures for most of the chapters; that they go back to the original Greek text can be seen from a mistake in the translation of a Greek work in one of the figures.[15] Editions of the work give only an interpretation of the figures; facsimilies have been published, with an English translation of many chapters, by A. G. Drachmann.[16] The fragments from Archimedes have been published in English with the manuscript figures.[17]

The *Dioptra* contains a description of an instrument for surveyors; it consists of a pointed rod to be planted in the ground, with two interchangeable instruments: a theodolite for staking out right angles and a leveling instrument. The description, which unfortunately is imperfect owing to a lacuna in the manuscript, covers six chapters; chapters 7–32 contain directions for the use of the two instruments in a great number of tasks. In chapter 33 Hero criticizes the *groma,* the instrument then used for staking out lines at right angles; chapter 34 describes an odometer actuated by the wheel of a car, used for measuring distances by driving slowly along a level road. Chapter 35 indicates the method for finding the distance between Alexandria and Rome by simultaneously observing a lunar eclipse in the two cities; this chapter has been thoroughly studied by O. Neugebauer.[18] There is no chapter 36, and chapter 37 is the *Barulkos,* which is also chapter 1 of book 1 of the *Mechanics;* it is out of place in both. Chapter 38 describes a ship's odometer and is certainly not by Hero.[19]

The *Belopoiika* contains the description of the *gastraphetes,* or stomach bow, a sort of crossbow in which the bowstring is drawn by the archer's leaning

HERO OF ALEXANDRIA

his weight against the end of the stock, and two catapults worked by winches; two bundles of sinews provide the elastic power to propel the arrow, bolt, or stone. The catapults are shaped like those described by Vitruvius and Philo.[20]

The *Automata,* or *Automatic Theater,* describes two sorts of puppet shows, one moving and the other stationary; both of them perform without being touched by human hands. The former moves before the audience by itself and shows a temple in which a fire is lit on an altar and the god Dionysus pours out a libation while bacchantes dance about him to the sound of trumpets and drums. After the performance the theater withdraws. The stationary theater opens and shuts its doors on the performance of the myth of Nauplius. The shipwrights work; the ships are launched and cross a sea in which dolphins leap; Nauplius lights the false beacon to lead them astray; the ship is wrecked; and Athena destroys the defiant Ajax with thunder and lightning. The driving power in both cases was a heavy lead weight resting on a heap of millet grains which escaped through a hole. The weight was attached by a rope to an axle, and the turning of this axle brought about all the movements by means of strings and drums. Strings and drums constituted practically all the machinery; no springs or cogwheels were used. It represents a marvel of ingenuity with very scant mechanical means.

The *Catoptrica,* found only in a Latin version, was formerly ascribed to Ptolemy, but is now generally accepted as by Hero. It deals with mirrors, both plane and curved, and gives the theory of reflection; it also contains instructions on how to make mirrors for different purposes and how to arrange them for illusions.

Barulkos, "the lifter of weights," is the name given by Pappus to his rendering of the *Dioptra,* chapter 37, and the *Mechanics,* book 1, chapter 1.[21] It is an essay describing how one can lift a burden of 1,000 talents by means of a power of five talents, that is, the power of a single man. The engine consists of parallel toothed wheels and is derived from the *Mechanics,* book 1, chapter 21; however, it is only a theoretical solution: parallel toothed wheels were not used for cranes during antiquity.[22] L. Nix takes *Barulkos* to be the name of the *Mechanics,* even though Pappus mentions the *Barulkos* and the *Mechanics* in the same sentence, because the Arabic name of the *Mechanics* is "Hero's Book About the Lifting of Heavy Things."[23] But since the essay is found as the first chapter of the *Mechanics* (where it does not belong), the translator would seem to have taken this title to be the title of the whole work. The *Cheirobalistra* was published in 1906 by Rudolf Schneider, who regarded it as a fragment of a dictionary dealing with catapults; it consists of six items, each describing an element that begins with the letter *K.*[24] E. W. Marsden has interpreted these chapters as a description of a sort of catapult, which he has reconstructed.[25] It is unlikely, however, that the *Cheirobalistra* is actually a work by Hero.

NOTES

1. Pappus of Alexandria, *Collectionis quae supersunt . . .,* Friedrich Hultsch, ed., III, pt. 1 (Berlin, 1878), 1060–1068.
2. O. Neugebauer, "Über eine Methode zur Distanzbestimmung Alexandria–Rom bei Heron," in *Kongelige Danske Videnskabernes Selskabs Skrifter,* **26,** no. 2 (1938), 21–24.
3. A. G. Drachmann, "Heron and Ptolemaios," in *Centaurus,* **1** (1950), 117–131.
4. A. G. Drachmann, *Ktesibios, Philon and Heron,* vol. IV of Acta historica Scientiarum naturalium et medicinalium (Copenhagen, 1948), pp. 74–77.
5. H. Diels, "Über das physikalische System des Straton," in *Sitzungsberichte der k. Preussischen Akademie der Wissenschaften zu Berlin,* no. 9 (1893), 110, n. 3.
6. I. Hammer-Jensen, "Die Druckwerke Herons von Alexandria," in *Neue Jahrbücher für das klassischen Altertum,* **25,** pt. 1 (1910), 413–427, 480–503.
7. Edmund Hoppe, "Heron von Alexandrien," in *Hermes* (Berlin), **62** (1927), 79–105.
8. I. Hammer-Jensen, "Die heronische Frage," *ibid.,* **63** (1928), 34–47.
9. J. L. Heiberg, *Geschichte der Mathematik und Naturwissenschaften im Altertum,* which is in Iwan von Müller, ed., *Handbuch der Altertumswissenschaft,* V, pt. 1, sec. 2 (Munich, 1925), 37.
10. Diels, *op. cit.,* pp. 106–110.
11. Hero, *Mechanics,* ch. 24.
12. Heiberg, *loc. cit.*
13. Drachmann, *Ktesibios . . .,* p. 161.
14. *The Pneumatics,* facs. of the 1831 Woodcroft ed., with intro. by Marie Boas Hall (London–New York, 1971).
15. A. G. Drachmann, *The Mechanical Technology of Greek and Roman Antiquity,* vol. XVII of Acta historica Scientiarum naturalium et medicinalium (Copenhagen, 1963), p. 110, text for fig. 44.
16. *Ibid.,* pp. 165 ff.
17. A. G. Drachmann, "Fragments from Archimedes in Heron's *Mechanics,*" in *Centaurus,* **8** (1963), 91–146.
18. Neugebauer, *op. cit.*
19. Drachmann, *The Mechanical Technology . . . .*
20. Vitruvius, *De architectura,* X, ch. 11; and Philo, *Belopoiika,* Greek and German versions by H. Diels and E. Schramm, in *Abhandlungen der Preussischen Akademie der Wissenschaften* for 1918, Phil.-hist. Kl., no. 16 (1919).
21. Pappus, *op. cit.,* pp. 1060 ff.
22. Drachmann, *The Mechanical Technology . . .,* p. 200.
23. Hero, *Mechanics,* introduction. pp. xxii ff.; Pappus, *op. cit.,* p. 1060.
24. Rudolf Schneider, ed. and trans., "Herons Cheirobalistra," in *Mitteilungen des kaiserlich deutschen archaeologischen Instituts,* Römische Abt., **21** (1906), 142–168.
25. E. W. Marsden, *Greek and Roman Artillery. Technical Treatises* (Oxford, 1971), pp. 206–233.

BIBLIOGRAPHY

I. Original Works. *Heronis Alexandrini Opera quae supersunt omnia,* 5 vols. (Leipzig, 1899–1914), contains all

Hero's works except the *Belopoiica. Automata* is published with *Pneumatica, Opera,* I. *Belopoiica* appeared as "Heron's Belopoiica Griechisch und Deutsch von H. Diels und E. Schramm," in *Abhandlungen der K. Preussischen Akademie der Wissenschaften,* Phil.-hist. Kl., no. 2 (1918); and in E. W. Marsden, *Greek and Roman Artillery. Technical Treatises* (Oxford, 1971), with English trans. and notes. *Catoptrica* is published with *Mechanica, Opera,* II, pt. 1. *Cheirobalistra,* edited and translated by Rudolf Schneider, is in *Mitteilungen des kaiserlich deutschen archaeologischen Instituts,* Römische Abt., **21** (1906), 142 ff.; and in Marsden, above. *Dioptra* is published with *Metrica, Opera,* III. *Definitiones* and *Geometrica* appear as *Heronis definitiones cum variis collectionibus Heronis quae feruntur Geometrica,* J. L. Heiberg, ed., *Opera,* IV. *Mechanica* is available as Carra de Vaux, "Les mécaniques ou l'élévateur de Héron d'Alexandrie," in *Journal asiatique,* 9th ser., **1** (1893), 386–472, and **2** (1893), 152–269, 420–514, consisting of Arabic text and French translation; and as *Herons von Alexandria Mechanik und Katoptrik,* edited and translated by L. Nix and W. Schmidt, *Opera,* II, pt. 1. *De mensuris* is published with *Stereometrica, Opera,* V. *Metrica* is available in three versions: *Herons von Alexandria Vermessungslehre und Dioptra,* Greek and German versions by Hermann Schöne, *Opera,* III: *Codex Constantinopolitanus Palatii Veteris,* no. 1, E. M. Bruins, ed., 3 pts. (Leiden, 1964)—pt. 1, reproduction of the MS; pt. 2, Greek text; pt. 3, translation and commentary; and *Heronis Alexandrini Metrica . . .,* E. M. Bruins, ed. (Leiden, 1964). *Pneumatica* can be found as *Herons von Alexandria Druckwerke und Automatentheater,* Greek and German versions edited by Wilhelm Schmidt, *Opera,* I; and *The Pneumatics of Hero of Alexandria,* translated for and edited by Bennet Woodcroft (London, 1851) and facs. ed. with intro. by Marie Boas Hall (London–New York, 1971). *Stereometrica* appears as *Heronis quae feruntur Stereometrica et De mensuris,* J. L. Heiberg, ed., *Opera,* V. *Fragmenta,* the commentary on Euclid's *Elements,* is found as *Codex Leidensis 399, 1. Euclidis Elementa ex interpretatione Al-Hadschdschadschii cum commentariis Al-Narizii,* Arabic and Latin edited by R. O. Besthorn and J. L. Heiberg, 3 vols. (Copenhagen, 1893–1911).

II. Secondary Literature. See A. G. Drachmann, *Ktesibios, Philon and Heron,* vol. IV in Acta historica Scientiarum naturalium et medicinalium (Copenhagen, 1948), on *Pneumatics;* and *The Mechanical Technology of Greek and Roman Antiquity,* vol. XVII in Acta historica Scientiarum naturalium et medicinalium (Copenhagen, 1963), on *Mechanics;* J. L. Heiberg, *Geschichte der Mathematik und Naturwissenschaften im Altertum,* in Iwan von Müller, ed., *Handbuch der Altertumswissenschaft,* V, pt. 2, sec. 1 (Munich, 1925), on the mathematical works; and O. Neugebauer, "Über eine Methode zur Distanzbestimmung Alexandria-Rom bei Heron," in *Kongelige Danske Videnskabernes Selskab Meddelelser,* **26,** no. 2 (1938), on *Dioptra.*

A. G. Drachmann

HERO OF ALEXANDRIA: Mathematics.

The historical evaluation of Hero's mathematics, like that of his mechanics, reflects the recent development of the history of science itself. Compared at first with figures like Archimedes and Apollonius, Hero appeared to embody the "decline" of Greek mathematics after the third century B.C. His practically oriented mensurational treatises then seemed to be the work of a mere "technician," ignorant or neglectful of the theoretical sophistication of his predecessors. As Neugebauer and others have pointed out, however, recovery of the mathematics of the Babylonians and greater appreciation of the uses to which mathematics was put in antiquity have necessitated a reevaluation of Hero's achievement.[1] In the light of recent scholarship, he now appears as a well-educated and often ingenious applied mathematician, as well as a vital link in a continuous tradition of practical mathematics from the Babylonians, through the Arabs, to Renaissance Europe.

The breadth and depth of Hero's mathematics are revealed most clearly in his *Metrica,* a mensurational treatise in three books that first came to the attention of modern scholars when a unique manuscript copy was found in Constantinople in 1896.[2] The prologue to the work gives a definition of geometry as being, both etymologically and historically, the science of measuring land. It goes on to state that out of practical need the results for plane surfaces have been extended to solid figures and to cite recent work by Eudoxus and Archimedes as greatly extending its effectiveness. Hero meant to set out the "state of the art," and the thrust of the *Metrica* is thus always toward practical mensuration, with a resulting ambiguity toward the rigor and theoretical fine points of classical Greek geometry. For example, Hero notes in regard to circular areas:

> Archimedes shows in the *Measurement of the Circle* that eleven squares on the diameter of the circle are very closely equal [ἴσα γίγνεται ὡς ἔγγιστα] to fourteen circles. . . . The same Archimedes shows in his *On Plinthides and Cylinders* that the ratio of the circumference of any circle to its diameter is greater than 211875 to 67441 and less than 197888 to 62351, but since these numbers are not easily handled, they are reduced to least numbers as 22 to 7 [*Metrica* I, 25, Bruins ed., p. 54].[3]

That is, Hero's use of approximating values for irrational quantities arose not out of ignorance of their irrationality or of theoretically more precise values, but out of the need for values that can be handled efficiently. In the case of $\sqrt{n}$ (n non-square) he set out an iterative technique for ever closer approximation, although he himself usually stopped at the first.[4]

Book I of the *Metrica* deals with plane figures and the surfaces of common solids. It proceeds in each case by numerical example (with no specified units of measure), presuming a knowledge of elementary geometry and supplying formal geometrical demonstrations where they might be unfamiliar. Beginning with rectangles and triangles, Hero gave, in proposition I.8, the famous "Heronic formula" for determining the area of a triangle from its three sides, $A = \sqrt{s(s-a)(s-b)(s-c)}$ (the proposition is actually derived from Archimedes). He then proceeded to treat general quadrilaterals by dividing them into rectangles and triangles. *Metrica* I. 17–25 treats the regular polygons of from three to twelve sides, directly deriving the relation of side to radius in all cases except 9 and 11, where Hero appeals to the "Table of Chords" (*τὰ περὶ τῶν ἐν κύκλῳ εὐθειῶν*). For $n = 5$, 6, and 7, the relations derived are the same as those found in the Babylonian texts at Susa.[5] After discussing the circle and annulus, Hero dealt extensively with the segment (but not the sector) of a circle, offering three approximating formulas, two "ancient" (which he criticized) and his own, which treats the segment as closely approximating a segment of a parabola (area = 4/3 inscribed triangle); Archimedes' *Method* is the explicit source for the latter. For the ellipse and parabola, and for the surfaces of a cone, sphere, and spherical segment, Hero did no more than cite Archimedes' results.

Book II moves on to solid figures. Beginning with the cone and the cylinder, Hero then dealt with prisms on various rectilinear bases and with regular and irregular frustra (including the famous *βωμίσκος*).[6] For the sphere he turned again to Archimedes; for the torus, to Dionysodorus. He concluded with the five "Platonic" solids (regular polyhedra).

In book III the treatment of the problem of dividing plane and solid figures into segments bearing fixed ratios to one another brought Hero's work more closely in line with the pure mathematical tradition. Very similar in style and content to Euclid's *On Divisions,* the subject matter forced Hero after proposition III.9 to give up numerical calculation in favor of geometrical construction of the lines and planes sought. Nonetheless, the problem of dividing the pyramid, cone, and conical frustrum required an approximating formula for the cube root of a number.[7]

Hero's concern in the *Metrica*—to extract from the works of such mathematicians as Archimedes only the results conducive to efficient mensuration—takes full effect in the other works that have come down to us bearing his name. *Geometrica* is essentially book I of the *Metrica; Stereometrica* is essentially book II. In both cases, numerical examples are used to eliminate geometrical derivations, concrete rather than general units of measure are employed, and the Greek mode of expressing fractions yields to the then more common and familiar Egyptian mode of unit fractions. *Geodaesia* and *De mensuris* contain nothing more than excerpts from the *Geometrica.* In all these texts, it is difficult to locate precisely Hero's original contribution, for they, rather than the *Metrica,* are the texts that circulated widely, were edited frequently, and were used for instruction. That their fate conformed at least in part to Hero's intention is indicated by his *Definitiones* and *Commentary on Euclid's Elements,* both of which show clear pedagogical concerns. As Heath notes,[8] the *Definitiones,* which contains 133 definitions of geometrical terms, is a valuable source of knowledge about alternative notions of geometry in antiquity and about what was taught in the classroom; it, like the others, shows the effect of many editors.

Hero's works enjoyed a wide audience. This is clear not only from what has been said above, but also in that fragments of his works can be found in the writings of several Arab mathematicians, including al-Nayrīzī and al-Khwārizmī.

NOTES

1. Otto Neugebauer, *Exact Sciences in Antiquity,* ed. 2 (New York, 1962), p. 146.
2. See Bibliography in section above for various modern editions.
3. Tannery has suggested correcting the numerators to read 211872 and 195882, respectively; *cf.* T. L. Heath, *History of Greek Mathematics,* I (Oxford, 1921), 232–233.
4. *Metrica* I, 8 (Bruins ed., p. 41): let $N = a^2 \pm r$;

   $a_1 = \frac{1}{2}\left(\frac{N}{a} + a\right)$ is a first approximation for $\sqrt{N}$,

   $a_2 = \frac{1}{2}\left(\frac{N}{a_1} + a_1\right)$ is a second, more accurate one, and so on.

   On the history of this method, see Heath, II, 324, note 2.
5. Neugebauer, p. 47.
6. For a discussion, see Heath, II, 332–333.
7. Heath, II, 341–342. Hero's method must be reconstructed from a single numerical example. The best conjecture (Wertheim's) seems to be that if $a^3 < N < (a+1)^3$, $d_1 = N - a^3$, and $d_2 = (a+1)^3 - N$, then

   $$\sqrt[3]{N} = a + \frac{(a+1)d_1}{(a+1)d_1 + ad_2}.$$
8. II, 314; pp. 314–316 present a summary of the contents of the *Definitiones.*

BIBLIOGRAPHY

T. L. Heath, *History of Greek Mathematics,* vol. II (Oxford, 1921), ch. 18, remains the most complete secondary account of Hero's mathematics and is the source of many of the details given above.

MICHAEL S. MAHONEY

HESSE, LUDWIG OTTO (*b.* Königsberg, Germany [now Kaliningrad, U.S.S.R.], 22 April 1811; *d.* Munich, Germany, 4 August 1874)

Hesse was the eldest son of Johann Gottlieb Hesse, a merchant and brewer, and his wife, Anna Karoline Reiter. He grew up in Königsberg, where he had his first contact with the sciences at the Old City Gymnasium. After obtaining his school certificate in 1832, he attended the University of Königsberg, specializing in mathematics and the natural sciences. Hesse studied mainly under C. G. J. Jacobi, who greatly stimulated his mathematical investigations. After taking the examination for headmaster in 1837 and spending a probationary year at the Kneiphof Gymnasium in Königsberg, Hesse made an educational journey through Germany and Italy. In the fall of 1838 he began to teach physics and chemistry at the trade school in Königsberg. In 1840 he graduated from the University of Königsberg and was made a lecturer there on the basis of his thesis, *De octo punctis intersectionis trium superficium secundi ordinis.* After this he lectured regularly, and in 1841 he resigned his position at the trade school. In the same year he married Maria Dulk, daughter of a chemistry professor; they had six children.

In 1845 Hesse was appointed extraordinary professor at Königsberg; he spent a total of sixteen years there as teacher and researcher. During this time nearly all his mathematical discoveries were made, and he published them in Crelle's *Journal für die reine und angewandte Mathematik.* Among those attending his lectures were Gustav Kirchhoff, Siegfried Heinrich Aronhold, Carl Neumann, Alfred Clebsch, and Sigismund Lipschitz.

Despite recognition of his scientific achievements, it was not until 1855 that Hesse received a call as ordinary professor to the University of Halle. Shortly thereafter he received an appointment to Heidelberg, which he gladly accepted, for Robert Bunsen and his former student Kirchhoff were there. From the winter of 1856 until 1868 Hesse taught in Heidelberg. During this period he wrote the widely read textbooks *Vorlesungen über analytische Geometrie des Raumes* and *Vorlesungen über analytische Geometrie.* According to Felix Klein, Hesse's methods of presenting material fortified and disseminated the feeling for elegant calculations expressed in symmetrical formulas. In 1868 Hesse accepted a call to the newly founded Polytechnicum at Munich. But only a few more years of activity were granted him, and he died in 1874 of a liver ailment. At his request, he was buried in Heidelberg, the city that had become his second home. The Bavarian Academy of Sciences, of which Hesse had become a member in 1868, arranged for the publication of his complete scientific works.

Hesse's mathematical works are important for the development of the theory of algebraic functions and of the theory of invariants. His achievements can be evaluated, however, only in close connection with those of his contemporaries. Hesse was indebted to Jacobi's investigations on the linear transformation of quadratic forms for the inspiration and starting point of his initial works on the theory of quadratic curves and planes. For proof (again influenced by Jacobi) he used the newly developed determinants, which allowed his presentation to reach an elegance not previously attained. Hesse again presented the results of these first researches when he developed his space geometry in his textbook.

In 1842 Hesse began his investigation on cubic and quadratic curves, which are closely linked to the development of basic concepts of algebra. The starting point was the paper "Über die Elimination der Variabeln aus drei algebraischen Gleichungen zweiten Grades mit zwei Variabeln." Again the problem can be traced to Jacobi. A treatise on the inflection points of cubic curves immediately followed this work. Within the framework of this treatise is the functional determinant that is named after Hesse and arises from the second partial derivative of a homogeneous function $f(x_1,x_2,x_3)$:

$$H = \begin{vmatrix} f_{11}\, f_{12}\, f_{13} \\ f_{21}\, f_{22}\, f_{23} \\ f_{31}\, f_{32}\, f_{33} \end{vmatrix}$$

This functional determinant has found many applications in algebraic geometry. In linear transformation of the variables x_1, x_2, x_3 into the variables y_1, y_2, y_3, $H' = A^2 \cdot H$, where A is the determinant of the matrix of the transformation and H is a covariant of f. Upon geometrically applying his first fundamental theory of homogeneous forms, Hesse obtained the result that the points of inflection of a curve C_n of the nth order are generally given as the intersection of this curve and a curve of the order $3(n - 2)$. These curves can be described by means of the Hessian determinant of C_n. Julius Plücker had previously obtained this result for C_3. With this work Hesse demonstrated how, by geometrical interpretation, the results of algebraic transformations could not only equal, but even surpass, the results of geometers.

Hesse devoted much research effort to the geometrical interpretation of algebraic transformations, admitting that he was stimulated primarily by the geometrical works of Jakob Steiner and by Plücker and Poncelet. Plücker had further discovered that the planar C_3 contains nine points of inflection, which lie on twelve straight lines in groups of three. Hesse proved that these twelve straight lines are arranged in four triple lines, each of which contains all nine points. He further demonstrated that for a complete mathematical solution of the problem an equation of the fourth degree is necessary; this was later confirmed by Aronhold.

A similar investigation of groupings was necessitated by the twenty-eight double tangents of the planar C_4. Here too Hesse's starting point was the so-called canonical representation of C_4 in the form of a symmetrical determinant of a quadruplc series. By this representation of the equation of the curve, the planar problem of the double tangent can be combined with a spatial problem: eight points in space are connected by twenty-eight straight lines. If a group of planes of the second order, infinite in both directions, is drawn through these eight fixed base points, then the parameters of the conical surfaces of this group are sufficient for a condition that can be understood as the given equation of this group. This connection led to the proof that the special case of the equation of C_4 can be represented in thirty-five other ways, all markedly different from the first.

From the beginning, Hesse always sought to arrange his calculations with homogeneous symmetrical starting points, so that the algebraic course of the calculation would be the counterpart of the geometric considerations. His student Alfred Clebsch in particular has used this concept in his own work and has further expanded on it.

In England, Cayley was also working on the theory of homogeneous forms. Rivalry arose when his "Mémoire sur les hyperdéterminants" appeared simultaneously with Hesse's paper.

Hesse's teaching was also influential. In his long years as a lecturer, he continually showed his enthusiasm for mathematics, and his textbooks on analytical geometry must be seen in this context. The special forms of linear equation and of planar equation that Hesse used in these books are called Hesse's normal form of the linear equation and of the planar equation in all modern textbooks in this discipline.

BIBLIOGRAPHY

I. ORIGINAL WORKS. Hesse's collected works were posthumously published by the Math.-phys. Kl. of the Bavarian Academy of Sciences as *Gesammelte Werke* (Munich, 1897). Individual works include "Über die Elimination der Variabeln aus drei algebraischen Gleichungen zweiten Grades mit zwei Variabeln," in *Journal für die reine und angewandte Mathematik,* **28** (1844), 68–96; *Vorlesungen über analytische Geometrie des Raumes* (Leipzig, 1861; 3rd ed., 1876); *Vorlesungen über analytische Geometrie der geraden Linie* (Leipzig, 1865; 4th ed., 1909); and "Sieben Vorlesungen aus der analytischen Geometrie der Kegelschnitte," in *Zeitschrift für Mathematik und Physik,* **19** (1874), 1–67.

II. SECONDARY LITERATURE. On Hesse or his work, see Gustav Bauer, "Gedächtnisrede auf Otto Hesse," in *Abhandlungen der Bayerischen Akademie der Wissenschaften;* Alexander Brill and Max Noether, "Die Entwicklung der Theorie der algebraischen Funktionen in älterer und neuerer Zeit," in *Jahresberichte der Deutschen Mathematikervereinigung,* **3** (1892–1893), 107–565; Moritz Cantor, "Otto Hesse," in *Allgemeine deutsche Biographie,* vol. XII (Leipzig, 1880); Felix Klein, *Vorlesungen über die Entwicklung der Mathematik im 19. Jahrhundert,* vol. XXIV in Die Grundlehren der mathematischen Wissenschaften (Berlin, 1926); Franz Meyer, "Bericht über den gegenwärtigen Stand der Invariantentheorie," in *Jahresberichte der Deutschen Mathematikervereinigung,* **1** (1890–1891), 79–281; and Max Noether, "Otto Hesse," in *Zeitschrift für Mathematik und Physik,* Hist.-lit. Abt., **20** (1875), 77–88.

KARLHEINZ HAAS

HEURAET, HENDRIK VAN (*b.* Haarlem, Netherlands, 1633; *d.* 1660 [?])

Van Heuraet entered the University of Leiden in March 1653 as a medical student and studied mathematics under Frans van Schooten. With Christian Huygens and Jan Hudde he formed a trio of highly talented students who, under van Schooten's leadership and in touch with René François de Sluse in Liège, devised methods for tangent determinations and quadratures of algebraic curves. In a letter of December 1657 to van Schooten he reported on his results in connection with the cubic parabola $y^2 = ax^2(a - x)$ and its generalization in the "pearls" of Sluse, $y^m = kx^n(a - x)^p$.

In 1658 van Heuraet, together with Hudde, was at the Protestant academy of Saumur, where he studied the novel subject of the rectification of curves, inspired by Huygens' discovery in 1657 that the arc length of a parabola can be measured by the quadrature of an equilateral hyperbola (in modern terms, it can be expressed by means of logarithms), reported to van Heuraet by van Schooten in a letter of 28 February 1658, but only in general terms. Van Heuraet then found his own general method of rectification, which he communicated to van Schooten in a letter of 13 January 1659. Van Schooten published this letter in the Latin translation of Descartes's *Géométrie,* then being prepared for publication, under the title "De transmutatione curvarum linearum in rectas," van Heuraet's only published work and the first publication of a general method of rectification, in principle the same as the present $\int \sqrt{1 + y'^2}\, dx$. It drew attention for breaking the spell of Aristotle's dictum that curved lines could not in principle be compared with straight ones.

Van Heuraet applied his method especially to the semicubic parabola and the parabola. In a letter of 7 February 1659 to van Schooten he mentioned that he could apply his method to rotation surfaces of quadrics. Huygens and Sluse were delighted but Wallis, in a letter to Huygens (answered 9 June 1659), claimed priority for William Neile, who, he said, rectified the cubic parabola in 1657. This assertion led to the customary priority struggle. Fermat published his general rectification method in 1660—independently, it seems, of van Heuraet.

After a trip to Burgundy and Switzerland, van Heuraet reentered Leiden as a medical student in February 1659. He is mentioned in a letter from Huygens to van Schooten, dated 6 December 1659, as "subtilissimus Heuratus," but after that nothing more is heard of him.

BIBLIOGRAPHY

I. ORIGINAL WORKS. Van Heuraet's paper is in *Geometria à Renato Des Cartes . . .*, Frans van Schooten, ed. (Leiden, 1659), pp. 517-520. On pp. 259-262 van Schooten gives a construction by van Heuraet of the inflection points of a conchoid. The correspondence between van Schooten, van Heuraet, Huygens, and Sluse is in C. Huygens, *Oeuvres complètes,* II (1889); for references in other volumes, see the index.

II. SECONDARY LITERATURE. A sketch of van Heuraet's life by C. de Waard is in *Nieuw Nederlandsch biographisch woordenboek,* I (Leiden, 1911), 1098-1099. On van Heuraet's rectifications see J. E. Hofmann, "Über die ersten logarithmischen Rektifikationen," in *Deutsche Mathematik,* **6** (1941), 283-304; and M. E. Baron, *The Origins of the Infinitesimal Calculus* (Oxford, 1969), pp. 223-236. On the priority question see C. Huygens, *Horologium oscillatorium* (1673), *Oeuvres complètes,* XVII, 123, and XVIII (1934), 208-210; J. Wallis, *Tractatus duo de cycloide et de cissoide* (Oxford, 1659), *Opera,* I (Oxford, 1695), 551-553; and S. A. Christensen, "The First Determination of the Length of a Curve," in *Bibliotheca mathematica,* n.s. **1** (1887), 76-80. On Fermat's rectification see Michael Mahoney, "Fermat," in *Dictionary of Scientific Biography,* IV (1971), 572-573.

D. J. STRUIK

HEYTESBURY, WILLIAM (*fl.* Oxford, England, *ca.* 1335)

Heytesbury was one of several scholars at Merton College, Oxford, during the second quarter of the fourteenth century whose writings formed the basis of the late medieval tradition of *calculationes,* the discussion of various modes of quantitative variation of qualities, motions, and powers in space and time. Other leading authors of the Merton group were Thomas Bradwardine, Richard Swineshead, and John of Dumbleton. The tradition they founded spread to the Continent in the second half of the fourteenth century and enjoyed a vogue in Italian universities during the fifteenth century and again at Paris and in the Spanish universities during at least the first third of the sixteenth century. Thereafter, however, it lost impetus with the shift of interests consequent upon the humanist movement. A question still under debate among historians of science is the precise extent of the later influence of Merton kinematics, and particularly of the Merton "mean-speed theorem," which can be used to prove that in uniformly accelerated motion starting from rest, the distances are in the duplicate ratio of the times. Other phases of the Mertonian discussions involving the mathematical concepts of limit, infinite aggregate, and the continuum as a dense set of points, as well as distinctions now treated in quantificational logic, seem to have fallen into oblivion after the sixteenth century but are anticipatory of nineteenth-century work in these areas.

Biographical information about Heytesbury, as about the other Mertonian scholars, is meager. His name, variously spelled, appears in the records of Merton College for 1330 and 1338-1339; he may have been the William Heightilbury who with other Mertonians was appointed fellow of Queen's College at its founding in 1340; in 1348, however, he was still—or once more—a fellow of Merton and by that year was a doctor of theology; finally, a William Heighterbury or Hetisbury was chancellor of the university in 1371.

Heytesbury's two best-known and most influential works—the only known ones of some length, the others being short discussions of particular questions—are his *Sophismata* and *Regule solvendi sophismata.* According to the explicit of an Erfurt manuscript (Wissenschaftliche Bibliothek, Amplon. F. 135, 17r), the *Regule* was "datus Oxonie a Wilhelmo de Hytthisbyri" in 1335; and it is probable that the *Sophismata* stems from about the same time, since the two works are closely related in content, one providing rules for the resolution of different classes of real or apparent logical fallacies and the other dealing intensively with thirty-two particular sophisms. The medieval discussion of sophisms grew out of Aristotle's *Sophistical Refutations;* but as we encounter it in Heytesbury, it has developed beyond the Aristotelian treatment in two directions. First, Heytesbury employs the *logica moderna,* a set of distinctions and word-order devices developed at the University of Paris during the thirteenth century. Second, he devotes much attention to cases and problems involving modes of purely quantitative variation in space and time.

The key innovation of the *logica moderna* was the theory of supposition, an analysis of the various ways in which a term is interpretable within a given proposition for some individual or individuals. For instance, in "That man disputes," the term "that man" is said to have discrete supposition, as referring to a single, definite individual, a *suppositum* to which one could point. In "Some man disputes" or "Every man disputes," on the other hand, the supposition of the subject term in either case is not discrete but common, although not in the same way. Thus, from "Some man disputes" it is permissible to descend to individual cases through an alternation: "This man disputes or this man disputes or . . .," there being no existent man who is not referred to in one of the members of the alternation. But from the statement "Every man disputes" it is permissible to descend to individual cases included under the term "man" only through a conjunction: "This man disputes, and this man disputes, and . . .," and so on. Finally, there are cases in which the descent is not possible through either an alternation or a conjunction, and in these cases the supposition is said to be confused only.

The kind of supposition of a term in any particular proposition is determined partly by the meaning of the predicate or subject term with which it is conjoined and partly by the "syncategorematic" terms included in the proposition—terms incapable of serving as subject or predicate but nevertheless influencing the supposition of the subject or predicate. Examples of syncategorematic terms are "any," "all," "some," "necessarily," "always," and "immediately."

This theory appeared, fully developed, in the works of William of Shyreswood in the middle of the thirteenth century. It seems to have derived in part from the analyses of grammarians (the first known use of the verb "to supposit" in the sense required by the theory occurs in the *Doctrinale* of the twelfth-century grammarian Alexander of Villa Dei) and in part from the Abelardian explication of universals: for Abelard a universal word gives rise only to a common and confused conception of many individuals and can come to determine a particular thing or particular things only in the context of a statement. Whatever its origins, the extensional analysis of the use of terms in discourse was much in vogue by Heytesbury's time and was used by him to reveal distinctions of structure that, in modern mathematical logic, are exhibited by means of the cross-references of quantifiers and variables.

For illustration, consider the distinction that Heytesbury makes in the *Regule* between the statement "Always some man will be" and the statement "Some man will be always." In the first statement the term "man" is preceded by the syncategorematic term "always," which according to Heytesbury has a "force of confounding" (*vim confundendi*) and thus confuses the supposition of the term that follows it. Hence the supposition of the term "some man" in the statement "Always some man will be" is confused only, and it is not permissible to descend either disjunctively or conjunctively to individual *supposita.* In the statement "Some man will be always," on the contrary, the term "some man" is not preceded by the term "always" and its supposition therefore remains determinate, so that some particular although unspecified individual is referred to. The first statement asserts the immortality of the race of mankind; the second asserts the immortality of some particular man. In the symbols of present-day mathematical logic, the first statement becomes

$$(x)\ (Ey)\ (Tx.My\colon \supset \colon Oyx).$$

(Read: "For all x there is a y such that, if x is a time and y is a man, then y occurs in x.") The second statement, on the other hand, becomes

$$(Ey)\ (x)\ (Tx.My\colon \supset \colon Oyx).$$

(Read: "There is a y such that for all x, if x is a time and y is a man, then y occurs in x.") Notationally, the distinction is one of the order of the universal and existential quantifiers, (x) and (Ey).

Because this distinction is crucial for the understanding of the modern definition of mathematical limit, it is of interest to find Heytesbury applying it to cases involving a mathematically conceived continuum. Thus, he distinguishes between the statement "Immediately after the present instant some instant will be" and the statement "Some instant will be immediately after the present instant." Once again, the distinction turns on the fact that the syncategorematic term "immediately" confounds the supposition of the term following it. Thus in the first statement the term "some instant," being preceded by the term "immediately," has confused supposition only; and it is not permissible to descend disjunctively or conjunctively to particular instants. In the second statement the term "some instant" is not preceded by "immediately" and thus has determinate supposition; the statement therefore means that, of the infinitely many instants following the present instant, there is a determinate one that will be first. Heytesbury concludes that this second statement is false, whereas the first statement is true if expounded as meaning that, whatever instant after the present instant be taken, between that instant and the present instant there is some instant. In modern symbols, with the range of the variables restricted to instants of time,

$$(i)\ (Ej)\ (Ai,i_0 \supset Bj,i_0,i).$$

(Read: "For all instants i, there is an instant j such that, if i is after the present instant i_0, then j lies between i_0 and i.") The false statement would reverse the order of the quantifiers. In effect, Heytesbury is insisting that instants in a time interval, like points on a line segment, form a dense set.

It is particularly in the two chapters of the *Regule* entitled "De incipit et desinit" and "De maximo et minimo" that Heytesbury's logical sophistication in dealing with limits and extrinsically or intrinsically bounded continua comes into play. In the first of these chapters he analyzes cases in which any thing or process or state may be said to begin or to cease to be. For instance, posing the case that Plato starts to move from rest with a constant acceleration, while at the same instant Socrates starts to move from rest with an acceleration that is initially zero but increases uniformly with time, Heytesbury concludes that "both Socrates and Plato infinitely slowly begin to be moved, and yet Socrates infinitely more slowly begins to be moved than Plato." As his explication shows, what is happening here is in effect a comparison of two infinitesimals of different order: if v_S is Socrates' velocity and v_P is Plato's, then

$$\lim_{t \to 0} \frac{v_S}{v_P} = 0.$$

The "De maximo et minimo" deals with the setting of boundaries to powers—for example, Socrates' power to lift weight or to see distant objects, or the power of a moving body to traverse a medium the resistance of which varies in some specified manner. Aristotle had flatly asserted that the boundary of a power or potency is a limiting maximum. The commentator Ibn Rushd emphasized that the incapacity of a power is bounded by a *minimum quod non;* later Schoolmen such as John of Jandun were thus faced with the question of the relation between the *maximum quod sic* and the *minimum quod non.* One thought that comes to play a role in the discussion is that no action or motion can proceed from a ratio of equality between power and resistance; this thought necessitates the assignment of the negative or extrinsic boundary, so that, for instance, Socrates' power to lift weights is to be bounded by the minimum weight that he is unable to lift. Heytesbury was not the first to consider the assignment of such extrinsic boundaries; but his formulation of rules and analysis of cases, compared with earlier discussions, shows a more exclusive concern with the mathematical and logical aspects of the problem.

An important last chapter of the *Regule* entitled "De tribus predicamentis" deals with the quantitative description of motion or change in the three Aristotelian categories of place, quantity, and quality. The principal aim of each of the three subchapters ("De motu locali," "De augmentatione," "De alteratione") is to establish the proper measure of velocity in the given category. In the case of augmentation, Heytesbury adopts a measure involving the exponential function, which had already played a role in Bradwardine's *Tractatus de proportionibus* (1328). All three subchapters exhibit the almost exclusive concern of the Mertonian *calculatores* with quantitative description of hypothetical cases.

This tendency to quantitative description had roots in earlier discussions of kinematics (as, for example, in the thirteenth-century *De motu* of Gerard of Brussels) and of what was known as "the intension and remission of forms," the variation in intensity of a quality or essence. Discussions of the latter topic prior to the fourteenth century had dealt primarily with the ontological nature of such variation; but by Heytesbury's time the Scotian assumption that intension is an additive increase had been generally accepted, and Schoolmen turned their attention to a logical or semantic question: how to denominate a subject in which the intensity of a quality varies from one point to another, or—a question treated as analogous—how to denominate or measure a motion in which the velocity varies from instant to instant of time or from point to point of the moved body. This question merges into the mathematical problems of describing different possible modes of spatial or temporal variation of intensity and of finding rules of equivalence between one distribution of intensities and another. Thus in Heytesbury's *Regule,* as in later fourteenth-century writings, any particular configuration or mode of variation of intensity in space or time is called a "latitude"; and latitudes are categorized as uniform (of constant intensity), uniformly nonuniform (the intensity varying linearly with spatial extension or time), and nonuniformly nonuniform (the intensity varying nonlinearly with spatial extension or time).

Heytesbury's *Regule* is the oldest datable writing in which we find the famous Merton rule: Every latitude uniformly nonuniform corresponds to its mean degree. Thus, if the whiteness or hotness of a body varies uniformly from an intensity of two degrees at one end of the body to an intensity of four degrees at the other end, then according to Heytesbury this latitude of whiteness or hotness is equivalent to a uniform latitude of three degrees extended over the same length. This assertion rests on the presupposition—unjustified for Heytesbury and his contemporaries by any empirical measurability—that intensities of a quality are intensities of some additive quantity. In application to local motion, since intensity of motion is measured in terms of distance traversed per unit time, and distance is an additive quantity, the Merton rule leads to testable empirical consequences. Heytesbury states the rule for local motion as follows:

> For whether it commences from zero degree or from some [finite] degree, every latitude [of velocity], provided that it is terminated at some finite degree, and is acquired or lost uniformly, will correspond to its mean degree. Thus the moving body, acquiring or losing this latitude uniformly during some given period of time, will traverse a distance exactly equal to what it would traverse in an equal period of time if it were moved continuously at its mean degree. For of every such latitude commencing from rest and terminating at some [finite] degree [of velocity], the mean degree is one-half the terminal degree of that same latitude (*Regule* [Venice, 1494], fol. 39).

The proposition implies, as Heytesbury notes, that in a uniformly accelerated motion starting from rest, the distance traversed in the second half of the time is three times that traversed in the first half—a consequence admitting of application in experimental tests. The first known assertion that the Merton theorem is applicable to free fall was made by Domingo de Soto, a Spanish Schoolman, in 1555; but it was not coupled with any attempt at empirical verification. The first experimental work on the assumption that free fall is uniformly accelerated with respect to time may have been that of Thomas Harriot, who within a few years before or after 1600 was finding the acceleration of free fall to be between 21 and 32.5 feet per second squared (for Harriot's theory of ballistics and his researches on free fall, see British Museum MS. Add. 6789, 19r–86v); in his discussion of projectile motion in the same manuscript Harriot explicitly refers to the 1494 volume that contains Heytesbury's works and commentaries thereon, so that a direct influence of the medieval treatises is here indicated.

In the case of Galileo, the evidence for direct medieval influence in his work on free fall is less clear and is still under debate. The *Juvenilia,* which may be the youthful Galileo's notes on lectures at the University of Pisa, contains references to Heytesbury and Calculator (Swineshead) and to such Mertonian distinctions as that between a *maximum quod sic* and a *minimum quod non,* and that between a uniformly nonuniform and a nonuniformly nonuniform variation in intensity (see *Le opere di Galileo Galilei,* A. Favaro, ed., I, 120, 136, 139 ff., 172). But from Galileo's letter of 1604 to Sarpi, it appears improbable that his thought on the mathematical characterization of naturally accelerated motion took its start from the Merton mean-speed theorem. According to Stillman Drake, "Galileo may have known the mean-speed rule and rejected it as inapplicable to the analysis of unbounded accelerated motion" (*British Journal for the History of Science,* **5** [1970], 42). It is at least a plausible suggestion, however, that a passing acquaintance with medieval discussions and *calculationes* involving instantaneous velocities, punctiform intensities, and different modes of variation of velocity or intensity in space or time, and also with the graphical representation of such variation that had been introduced by Oresme and was incorporated in the 1494 edition of Heytesbury's works, may have served as general preparation for the thinking that Galileo would have to do in founding his science of motion.

BIBLIOGRAPHY

I. Original Works. MSS giving the *Regule solvendi sophismata* in whole or in part are Biblioteca Antoniana, Padua, Scaff. XIX, MS.407, fols. 28–32, 53–56; library of the University of Padua, MS.1123, 14c, fols. 50–65; MS.1434, 15c, fols. 1–26; and MS.1570, 15c, fols. 131–137; Bodleian, Canon. Misc. MS.221, fols. 60–82; MS.376, 15c, fols. 30–32; MS.409, A.D. 1386, fols. 1–18; and MS.456, A.D. 1467, fols. 1–43; Bruges, Stadsbibliotheek, 497, 14c, fols. 46–59; and 500, 14c, fols. 33–71; Bibliotheca Marciana, Zanetti Latin MS.310, fols. 1–3; and VIII. 38 (XI, 14), a. 1391, fols. 40–54; Erfurt, Amplonian MS.135, fols. 1–17; and Vat. Lat. MS.2136, 14c, fols. 1–32; and MS.2138, 14c, fols. 89–109. It was published at Pavia in 1481 and at Venice in 1491 (fols. 4–21) and 1494 (fols. 7–52).

The *Sophismata* exists in the following MSS: Bibliotheca S. Johannis Baptistae, Oxford, MS.198, 14c, fols. 1–175; library of the University of Padua, MS.842, fols. 1–149; and MS.1123, 14c, fols. 97–172; Bodleian, Canon. Misc. MS.409, A.D. 1386, fols. 29–98; Bibliotheca Marciana,

Zanetti Latin MS.310, fols. 54–79; Paris, Bibliothèque Nationale, Latin MS.16134, 14c, fols. 81–146; and Vat. Lat. MS.2137, 14c, fol. 1 *et seq.;* and MS.2138, 14c, fols. 1-86. It was published at Pavia in 1481 and at Venice in 1491 (fols. 29-99) and 1494 (fols. 77–170).

De sensu composito et diviso is in following MSS: Biblioteca Nazionale, Florence, Cl. V, MS.43, 15c, fols. 38–44; library of the University of Padua, MS.1434, 15c, fols. 26–27; Bodleian, Canon. Misc. MS.219, A.D. 1395, fols. 4–6; Bologna University, MS.289.II.2, fols. 1–4; Bibliotheca Marciana, Zanetti Latin MS.310, fols. 49–53; and Vat. Lat. MS.2136, 14c, fols. 32–36; MS.3030, fols. 55–58; MS.3038, 14c, fols. 15–22; and MS.3065, 15c, fols. 140–143. It was published at Venice in 1491 (fols. 2–4), 1494 (fols. 2–4), and 1500 (fols. 1–23).

De veritate et falsitate propositionis was published at Venice in 1494 (fols. 183–188).

"Casus obligationis" is in MS: Bodleian, Canon. Latin MS.278, 14c, fol. 70; Bibliotheca Marciana, Zanetti Latin MS.310, fol. 96; and Vat. Lat. MS.3038, 14c, fols. 37–39.

"Tractatus de eventu futurorum" is in the MS Bibliotheca Marciana, MS.fa.300 (X,207), 14c, fols. 78–79.

"Tractatus de propositionum multiplicium significatione" is available as Bibliotheca Marciana, Latin MS.VI, 160 (X, 220), a. 1443, fols. 252–253.

The following are doubtful works: *Consequentie,* in MS as Corpus Christi College, Oxford, MS.293, fol. 337 *et seq.,* and published at Bologna; *Probationes conclusionum,* in MS as Vat. Lat. MS.2189, fols. 13–38, where the work is given the title "Anonymi conclusiones," and published at Venice in 1494 (fols. 188–203); "Regulae quaedam grammaticales," in MS as British Museum, Harleian MS.179; and "Sophismata asinina," available as: Biblioteca Nazionale, Florence, C1.V, MS.43, 15c, fols. 45–46; library of the University of Padua, MS.1123, 14c, fols. 18–22; and MS.1570, 15c, fols. 113–130; Bodleian, Canon. Latin MS.278, 14c, fols. 83–87; and Bibliotheca Marciana, Zanetti Latin MS.310, fols. 122–126.

II. SECONDARY LITERATURE. References to the relevant literature will be found in Marshall Clagett, *The Science of Mechanics in the Middle Ages* (Madison, Wis., 1959), pp. 683–698; and *Nicole Oresme and the Medieval Geometry of Qualities and Motions* (Madison, Wis., 1968), pp. 105–107; and Curtis Wilson, *William Heytesbury: Medieval Logic and the Rise of Mathematical Physics* (Madison, Wis., 1956), pp. 212–213.

A recent study of Heytesbury's work on the liar paradox is Alfonso Maierù, "Il problema della verità nelle opere di Guglielmo Heytesbury," in *Studi medievali,* 3rd ser., 7, fasc. 1 (Spoleto, 1966), 41–74.

CURTIS A. WILSON

HEYTING, AREND (*b.* Amsterdam, Netherlands, 9 May 1898; *d.* Lugano, Switzerland, 9 July 1980)

Heyting was the eldest child of Johannes Heyting and Clarissa Kok. Both parents were schoolteachers; his father, a man of considerable intellectual gifts, later became principal of a secondary school.

Originally Heyting was to become an engineer, but later it was decided that he should go to the university. In 1916 he enrolled as a student of mathematics at the University of Amsterdam. The funds to pay for his studies were earned by Heyting and his father by supervising the homework of high school students. Two of his teachers at the university, L. E. J. Brouwer and, to a lesser extent, Gerrit Mannoury, shaped and determined his future scientific interests: the greater part of Heyting's work is devoted to intuitionism, Brouwer's philosophy of mathematics, although at certain points his views are closer to the ideas of Mannoury.

After receiving the equivalent of the M.Sc. in 1922, Heyting became a teacher at two secondary schools in Enschede, an industrial town in the eastern Netherlands, far removed from any of the Dutch universities. In his leisure hours he worked on his dissertation, which dealt with the axiomatics of intuitionistic projective geometry. In 1925 he received his doctorate under Brouwer, cum laude.

Heyting's reputation grew rapidly, and in 1937 he was appointed lector at the University of Amsterdam, having been admitted the year before as *Privatdocent.* In 1948 he became a full professor, and in 1968 professor emeritus. In 1942 he was elected a member of the Royal Dutch Academy of Sciences.

Heyting was retiring and modest, lacking all ostentation. His interests were very wide-ranging and varied: music, literature, linguistics, philosophy, astronomy, and botany; he also was fond of walking, cycling, and gardening. As a teacher and lecturer he impressed his students and his international audiences at congresses with his exceptionally clear presentations. In 1929 Heyting married Johanne Friederieke Nijenhuis; they had eleven children. The couple were divorced in 1960, and in 1961 he married Joséphine Frédérique van Anrooy.

In 1927 the Dutch Mathematical Association published a prize question that asked for a formalization of Brouwer's intuitionistic theories. Heyting's answer was awarded the prize early in 1928; a revised and expanded version of his essay was published in 1930. This work made Heyting's name well known among logicians and philosophers of mathematics. It also marked the beginning of a lifelong friendship with Heinrich Scholz at Münster, not far from Enschede, who put his extensive library at Heyting's disposal. Scholz held the only chair of mathematical logic in Germany.

In Brouwer's intuitionism, mathematics consists in the mental construction of mathematical systems, an activity that is supposed to be carried out in the mind of an idealized mathematician, in principle without the use of language; language enters only in attempts to suggest similar constructions to other persons. Something is true in intuitionistic mathematics only if it can be shown to hold by means of a construction.

Brouwer's presentation of his views was deliberately antiformal, in a highly personal style, and often difficult to understand. Heyting's formalization, partially anticipated by V. Glivenko and Andrei N. Kolmogorov, made comparison with formalized traditional mathematics possible. Though Heyting's work has led some into the mistake of identifying intuitionism with his formalization, in the long run the study of intuitionistic formalisms has greatly helped the understanding of the basic intuitionistic concepts.

Around 1930 Heyting also formulated his explanation of the meaning of the intuitionistic logical operations, based on constructive proof or construction as a primitive notion. Though the germs of such an explanation can already be found in Brouwer's writings, this was an important step forward. (Kolmogorov independently gave, in 1932, a closely related interpretation of intuitionistic logic as a calculus of problems.)

Heyting also continued his work, begun with his dissertation, on Brouwer's program of the reconstruction of actual pieces of mathematics along intuitionist lines; in 1941 he published a pioneering paper on intuitionistic algebra, and in the 1950's he investigated the intuitionistic theory of Hilbert space. Some of his students who wrote dissertations under his direction also contributed to the program: J. G. Dijkman (theory of convergence, 1952), B. van Rootselaar (measure theory, 1954), D. van Dalen (affine geometry, 1963), Ashvinikumar (Hilbert space, 1966), A. S. Troelstra (general topology, 1966), and C. G. Gibson (Radon integral, 1967). In the period of his professorship Heyting also published textbooks in projective geometry, one of which was *Axiomatic Projective Geometry* (1963).

Heyting always saw the creation of a better understanding and appreciation of Brouwer's ideas as one of his principal tasks, and thus many of his talks at international meetings and his published writings are devoted to expositions and defense of the basic ideas of intuitionism, in a style that was never dogmatic or polemical.

There are differences in outlook between Brouwer and Heyting, however; in particular, Heyting frankly recognized the formal-theoretical element introduced into intuitionistic mathematics by the (in practice) inescapable use of language, an aspect suppressed in most of Brouwer's writings although Brouwer was aware of it. He also did not share Brouwer's pessimistic views on language as a means of communication, and accordingly he valued positively the use of formalization and axiomatization for intuitionism.

In 1934 Heyting wrote a short monograph titled *Intuitionism and Proof Theory*, a concise and well-written survey in which the viewpoints of intuitionism and formalism are clearly described and contrasted. In 1956 Heyting published his very successful *Intuitionism: An Introduction*, from which many logicians and mathematicians learned about intuitionism. It is certainly in large measure due to Heyting that intuitionism is still very much alive today; without his efforts the "intuitionistic revolution" might well have dwindled away and Brouwer's ideas would have become part of the past.

BIBLIOGRAPHY

I. Original Works. Heyting's writings include "Die formalen Regeln der intuitionistischen Logik," in *Sitzungsberichte der Preussischen Akademie der Wissenschaften*, Phys.-math. Kl. (1930), 42–56; "Die formalen Regeln der intuitionistischen Mathematik II, III," *ibid.*, 57–71, 158–169; *Mathematische Grundlagenforschung: Intuitionismus, Beweistheorie* (Berlin, 1934; repr. 1974), enl. French translation, *Les fondements des mathématiques: Intuitionisme, théorie de la démonstration*, P. Fevrier, trans. (Paris, 1955); "Untersuchungen über intuitionistische Algebra," in *Verhandelingen der Nederlandsche akademie van wetenschappen*, Afd. Natuurkunde, sec. 1, **18,** no. 2 (1941); *Intuitionism: An Introduction* (Amsterdam, 1956; 2nd, rev. ed., 1966; 3rd, rev. ed., 1971); *Axiomatic Projective Geometry* (New York, 1963; 2nd ed., 1980); "Intuitionistic Views on the Nature of Mathematics," in *Synthèse*, **27** (1974), 79–91.

II. Secondary Literature. Information on Heyting's life and work is in A. S. Troelstra, "Arend Heyting and His Contribution to Intuitionism," in *Nieuw archief voor wiskunde*, 3rd ser., **29** (1981), 1–23, and "Logic in the Writings of Brouwer and Heyting," in V. N. Abrusci, E. Casari, and M. Mugnai, eds., *Atti del Convengo internazionale di storia della logica, San Gimignano 4–8 dicembre 1982* (Bologna, 1983), 193–210; and J. Niekus, H. van Riemsdijk, and A. S. Troelstra, "Bibliography of A. Heyting," in *Nieuw archief voor wiskunde*, 3rd ser., **29** (1981), 24–35, with errata *ibid.*, 139.

A. S. Troelstra

HILBERT, DAVID (*b.* Königsberg, Germany [now Kaliningrad, R.S.F.S.R.], 23 January 1862; *d.* Göttingen, Germany, 14 February 1943)

Hilbert was descended from a Protestant middle-class family that had settled in the seventeenth century near Freiberg, Saxony. His great-grandfather, Christian David, a surgeon, moved to Königsberg, East Prussia. David's grandfather and father were judges in Königsberg. His father's Christian name was Otto; his mother's maiden name was Erdtmann. Hilbert's inclination to mathematics is said to have been inherited from his mother. From 1870 he attended the Friedrichskolleg in Königsberg; his last year of high school was spent at the Wilhelms-Gymnasium. In 1880 he took the examination for university admission. He studied at the University of Königsberg from 1880 to 1884, except for his second semester, when he went to Heidelberg. After his doctoral examination in 1884 and receipt of his Ph.D. in 1885, he traveled to Leipzig and Paris. In June 1886 he qualified as *Privatdozent* at Königsberg University. In 1892 Hilbert was appointed professor extraordinary to replace Adolf Hurwitz at Königsberg, and in the same year he married Käthe Jerosch. In 1893 he was appointed ordinary professor, succeeding F. Lindemann. He was appointed to a chair at Göttingen University in 1895, remaining there until his official retirement in 1930. In 1925 he fell ill with pernicious anemia, which at that time was considered incurable. New methods of treatment enabled him to recover, although he did not resume his full scientific activity. He died in 1943.

Königsberg, the university where Immanuel Kant had studied and taught, became a center of mathematical learning through Jacobi's activity (1827–1842). When Hilbert began his studies there, the algebrist Heinrich Weber, Dedekind's collaborator on the theory of algebraic functions, was a professor at Königsberg. In 1883 Weber left. His successor was Lindemann, a famous but muddle-headed mathematician who the year before had had the good luck to prove the transcendence of π. Lindemann displayed an astonishing seminar activity. (The notes of the Lindemann seminar are at present in the possession of Otto Volk.) Under his influence Hilbert became interested in the theory of invariants, his first area of research. At that time Königsberg boasted a brilliant student, Hermann Minkowski, two years younger than Hilbert but one semester ahead of him, who in 1883 received the Grand Prize of the Paris Academy. In 1884 Hurwitz, three years older than Hilbert and a mature mathematician at that time, was appointed professor extraordinary at Königsberg. For eight years he was Hilbert's guide in all of mathematics. In his obituaries of Minkowski and Hurwitz, Hilbert acknowledged the great influence of these two friends on his mathematical development. In 1892 Hurwitz left for Zurich and was soon followed by Minkowski. In 1902 Hilbert was reunited with Minkowski at Göttingen, where a new mathematics chair had been created for Minkowski at Hilbert's instigation.

The mathematician whose work most profoundly influenced Hilbert was the number theoretician Leopold Kronecker, although Hilbert took exception to Kronecker's seemingly whimsical dogmatism on methodological purity and hailed Georg Cantor's work in set theory, which had been criticized by Kronecker.

Hilbert's scientific activity can be roughly divided into six periods, according to the years of publication of the results: up to 1893 (at Königsberg), algebraic forms; 1894–1899, algebraic number theory; 1899–1903, foundations of geometry; 1904–1909, analysis (Dirichlet's principle, calculus of variations, integral equations, Waring's problem); 1912–1914, theoretical physics; after 1918, foundations of mathematics.

One should further mention his famous choice of mathematical problems which he propounded to the Second International Congress of Mathematicians at Paris in 1900.

At the end of a paper read at the International Mathematical Congress at Chicago in 1893, Hilbert said:

> In the history of a mathematical theory three periods can easily and clearly be distinguished: the naïve, the formal, and the critical ones. As to the theory of algebraic invariants, its founders Cayley and Sylvester are also representatives of the naïve period; when establishing the simplest invariant constructions and applying them to solving the equations of the first four degrees, they enjoyed their prime discovery. The discoverers and perfectioners of the symbolic calculus Clebsch and Gordan are the representatives of the second period, whereas the critical period has found its expression in the above mentioned theorems 6–13.

Whatever this historical tripartition means, it is obvious that Hilbert would have characterized his own numerous contributions to the theory of invariants from 1885 to 1888 as still belonging to the first two periods. Yet when he delivered his Chicago address, the theory of invariants was no longer what it had been five years before. Hilbert had perplexed his contemporaries by a revolutionary approach, nicknamed "theology" by Gordan, the "King of Invariants." What Hilbert had called Clebsch's and Gordan's formal period was the invention and the skillful handling of an apparatus, the symbolic method, which still can elicit the enjoyment of the historian who is faced with it. Hilbert's new approach was quite different: a direct, nonalgorithmic method, foreshadowing and preparing what would be called abstract algebra in the twentieth century. It has often been considered a mystery why, after his Chicago address, Hilbert left the field of invariants, never to return to it. But it should be pointed out that Hilbert was not the only mathematician to do so. It was said that Hilbert had solved all problems of the theory of invariants. This, of course, is not true. Never has a blooming mathematical theory withered away so suddenly. The theory of invariants died as a separate discipline. Hilbert had not finished the theory of invariants by solving all of its problems but, rather, by viewing invariants under a broader aspect. This often happens in mathematics. From a higher standpoint, paramount ideas can become futilities, profound facts trivialities, and sophisticated methods obsolete. Nevertheless, it is striking that the fortune of the theory of invariants changed so abruptly, that its fall was so great, and that it was caused by a single man.

In more modern terms, the theory of invariants dealt with linear groups G acting on N-space R and the polynomials on R, invariant under G. The groups actually studied at that time were mainly the linear representations of the special linear group of n-space by m-fold symmetric tensor products—in the terminology of the time, the invariants of an n-ary form of degree m. Up to that time much skill had been applied to finding and characterizing full systems of invariants. The invariants formed a ring with a finite basis, as far as one could tell from the examples available. Generally these basic invariants $I_1, \cdots, I_k$ are not algebraically independent; the polynomial relators, called syzygies, form an ideal, which again, according to the examples, has a finite ideal basis, $F_1, \cdots, F_l$. The $F_1, \cdots, F_l$ need not be ideal-independent; there can be relations $R_1F_1 + \cdots + R_lF_l = 0$ among them, so that one obtains an ideal of relators $R_1, \cdots, R_l$, or of "second-order syzygies," and so on.

When Hilbert started his work, the finiteness of a ring basis for invariants had been tackled by algorithmic methods which apply to very special cases only. Hilbert did not solve the total problem, and it still has not been solved. He also restricted himself to very special groups; explaining general methods through examples became one of the outstanding features of Hilbert's work. It is one of the reasons why he could build such a strong school.

It may be guessed that Hilbert started with the finiteness of the ideal basis of syzygies. In fact he proved the finiteness of the basis for any ideal in any polynomial ring. It was mainly this bold generalization and its straightforward proof which perplexed his contemporaries. The present formulation of Hilbert's basis theorem is as follows: The property of a ring R with one element of letting every ideal have a finite basis is shared by its polynomial ring $R[x]$. It has proved fundamental far outside the theory of invariants. Of course, it applied to the ideals of syzygies of any order as well. Moreover, Hilbert showed that the cascade of syzygies stops at last after m steps. This latter result looks like a nicety, and so it seems to have been considered for half a century, since no textbook used to mention it. Its revival in today's homological algebra is a new proof of Hilbert's prophetic vision.

Applied to the ring of invariants itself, Hilbert's basis theorem says that any invariant I can be presented in the form $A_1I_1 + \cdots + A_kI_k$ where $A_1, \cdots, A_l$ are polynomials which may be supposed of lower degree than I. If G is finite or compact, they can be changed into invariants by averaging over G. The new $A_1, \cdots, A_l$ can be expressed in the I $I_1, \cdots, I_k$ in the same way as I has been; this process is continued until the degrees of the coefficients have reached zero. This more modern averaging idea stems from Hurwitz. Hilbert himself used a differential operation, Cayley's Ω process, to reach the goal.

Further of Hilbert's results connected the invariants to fields of algebraic functions and algebraic varieties, in particular the *Nullstellensatz:* If a polynomial f vanishes in all zeros of a polynomial ideal M, then some power of f belongs to that ideal.

Other work from the same period dealt with the representation of definite polynomials or rational functions as terms of squares, a problem to which Artin made the definitive contribution thirty years later. There is also Hilbert's irreducibility theorem, which says that, in general, irreducibility is preserved if, in a polynomial of several variables with integral coefficients, some of the variables are replaced by integers. An isolated algebraic subject of later years is his investigation of the ninth-degree equation, solved by algebraic functions of four variables only and suggesting the still open problem of the most economic solving of algebraic equations.

There is no field of mathematics which by its beauty has attracted the elite of mathematicians with such an irresistible force as number theory—the "Queen of Mathematics," according to Gauss—has done. So from the theory of invariants Hilbert turned to algebraic number theory. At the 1893 meeting at Munich the Deutsche Mathematiker-Vereinigung, which Hilbert had presented with new proofs of the splitting of the prime ideal, charged Hilbert and Minkowski with preparing a report on number theory within two years. Minkowski soon withdrew, although he did read the proofs of what would be known as *Der Zahlbericht,* dated by Hilbert 10 April 1897. The *Zahlbericht* is infinitely more than a report; it is one of the classics, a masterpiece of mathematical literature. For half a century it was the bible of all who learned algebraic number theory, and perhaps it is still. In it Hilbert collected all relevant knowledge on algebraic number theory, reorganized it under striking new unifying viewpoints, reshaped formulations and proofs, and laid the groundwork for the still growing edifice of class field theory. Few mathematical treatises can rival the *Zahlbericht* in lucidity and didactic care. Starting with the quadratic field, Hilbert step by step increases the generality, with a view to a complete theory of relative Abelian fields; but from the beginning he chooses those methods which foreshadow the general principles.

At the end of the preface of the *Zahlbericht,* Hilbert said:

> The theory of number fields is an edifice of rare beauty and harmony. The most richly executed part of this building as it appears to me, is the theory of Abelian fields which Kummer by his work on the higher laws of reciprocity, and Kronecker by his investigations on the complex multiplication of elliptic functions, have opened up to us. The deep glimpses into the theory which the work of these two mathematicians affords, reveals at the same time that there still lies an abundance of priceless treasures hidden in this domain, beckoning as a rich reward to the explorer who knows the value of such treasures and with love pursues the art to win them.

It is hard, if not unfeasible, in a short account to evoke a faint idea of what Hilbert wrought in algebraic number theory. Even in a much broader context it would not be easy. Hilbert's own contributions to algebraic number theory are so overwhelming that in spite of the achievements of his predecessors, one gets the impression that algebraic number theory started with Hilbert—other than the theory of invariants, which he completed. So much has happened since Hilbert that one feels uneasy when trying to describe his work in algebraic number theory with his own terms, although it should be said that many modernizations of the theory are implicitly contained or foreshadowed in Hilbert's work.

Hilbert's work centers on the reciprocity law and culminates in the idea of the class field, where the ideals of the original field become principal ideals. The reciprocity law, as it now stands, has gradually developed from Gauss's law for quadratic residues. Hilbert interpreted quadratic residues as norms in a quadratic field and the Gauss residue symbol as a norm residue symbol. In this interpretation it can be generalized so as to be useful in the study of power residues in the most efficient way. The odd behavior of the even prime $p = 2$, which in general does not admit extending solutions of $x^2 = a \bmod p^k$ to higher values of k, is corrected by seeking solutions not in ordinary integers but in p-adic numbers, although before Hensel p-adic numbers could not occur explicitly in Hilbert's exposition. Likewise, the totality of prime spots, although not explicitly mentioned, is Hilbert's invention. In fact, to save the reciprocity law, he introduced the infinite prime spots. His formulation of the reciprocity law as $\Pi_p(\alpha/p) = 1$ foreshadowed *idèles,* and his intuition of the class field has proved an accurate guide for those who later tried to reach the goals he set.

Algebraic number theory was the climax of Hilbert's activity. He abandoned the field when almost everything had yet to be done. He left it to his students and successors to undertake the completion.

Hilbert turned to foundations of geometry. Traditional geometry was much easier than the highly sophisticated mathematics he had engaged in hitherto. The impact of his work in foundations of geometry cannot be compared with that of his work in the theory of invariants, in algebraic number theory, and in analysis. There is hardly one result of his *Grundlagen der Geometrie* which would not have been discovered in the course of time if Hilbert had not written this book. But what matters is that one man alone wrote this book, and that it is a fine book. *Grundlagen der Geometrie,* published in 1899, reached its ninth edition in 1962. This means that it is still being read, and obviously by more people than read Hilbert's other work. It has gradually been modernized, but few readers realize that foundations of geometry as a field has developed more rapidly than *Grundlagen der Geometrie* as a sequence of reeditions and that Hilbert's book is now a historical document rather than a basis of modern research or teaching.

The revival of mathematics in the seventeenth century had not included geometry. Euclid's choice of subjects and his axiomatic approach were seldom questioned before the nineteenth century. Then projective and non-Euclidean geometries were discovered, and the foundations of geometry were scrutinized anew by a differential geometry (Riemann) and the group theory approach (Helmholtz). G. K. C. von Staudt (1847) tried an axiomatic of projective geometry but, unaware of the role of continuity axioms, he failed. The first logically closed axiomatic system of projective and Euclidean geometry was Pasch's

(1882), modified and elaborated by the Italian school. Hilbert is often quoted as having urged: "It must be possible to replace in all geometric statements the words *point, line, plane* by *table, chair, mug.*" But Pasch had earlier said the same thing in other words. Moreover, this was not all that had to be done to understand geometry as a part of mathematics, independent of spatial reality; one needs to understand the relations between those points, lines, and planes in the same abstract way. The insight into the implicitly defining character of an axiomatic system had been reached in the *Grundlagen der Geometrie,* but at the end of the nineteenth century it was in the air; at least G. Fano had formulated it, even more explicitly, before Hilbert. It is true that this idea has become popular thanks to Hilbert, although quite slowly, against vehement resistance.

What Hilbert meant to do in his book, and actually did, is better characterized by the following statement at the end of the *Grundlagen:*

> The present treatise is a critical inquiry into the principles of geometry; we have been guided by the maxim to discuss every problem in such a way as to examine whether it could not be solved in some prescribed manner and by some restricted aids. In my opinion this maxim contains a general and natural prescription; indeed, whenever in our mathematical considerations we meet a problem or guess a theorem, our desire for knowledge would not be satisfied as long as we have not secured the complete solution and the exact proof or clearly understood the reason for the impossibility and the necessity of our failure.
>
> Indeed, the present geometrical inquiry tries to answer the question which axioms, suppositions or aids are necessary for the proof of an elementary geometric truth; afterwards it will depend on the standpoint which method of proof one prefers.

Hilbert's goals in axiomatics were consistency and independence. Both problems had been tackled before him. Non-Euclidean geometry was invented to show the independence of the axiom of parallel lines, and models of non-Euclidean geometry within Euclidean geometry proved its relative consistency. Hilbert's approach was at least partially different; his skillfully used tool was algebraization. Algebraic models and countermodels were invoked to prove consistency and independence.

Algebraization as a tool in foundations of geometry was not new at that time. It goes as far back as Staudt's "calculus of throws," although before Hilbert it seems not to have been interpreted as a relative consistency proof. For independence proofs, algebraization had been tried, just before Hilbert, in the Italian school; but Hilbert surpassed all his predecessors. In Hilbert's work and long afterward, algebraization of geometries has proved an important force in creating new algebraic structures. Isolation and interplay of incidence axioms and continuity axioms are reflected by analogous phenomena in the algebraic models. In Hilbert's work they led to structures which foreshadow the ideas of field and skew field, on the one hand, and topological space, on the other, as well as various mixtures of both. Indeed, Hilbert taught the mathematicians how to axiomatize and what to do with an axiomatic system.

In 1904 Hilbert perplexed the mathematical world by salvaging the Dirichlet principle, which had been brought into discredit by Weierstrass' criticism. Before Weierstrass it had been taken for granted in the theory of variations that the lower bound of a functional F is assumed and hence provides a minimum. If some integral along the curves joining two points was bounded from below, a minimum curve must exist. The boundary value problem for the potential equation was solved according to the Dirichlet principle by minimizing $F(u) = \int |\text{grad}\, u|^2\, d\omega$ under the given boundary conditions. After Weierstrass had shown that this argument was unjustified, the Dirichlet principle was avoided or circumvented.

Hilbert proved the Dirichlet principle by brute force, as straightforwardly as he had solved the finiteness problem of the theory of invariants. A sequence u_n is chosen such that $\lim_n F(u_n) = \inf_u F(u)$; the $|\text{grad}\, u_n|$ may be supposed bounded. Then a now-classic diagonal process yields a subsequence which converges first in a countable dense subset, and consequently everywhere and uniformly. Its limit solves the minimum problem. The method seems trivial today because it has become one of the most widely used tools of abstract analysis.

Hilbert also enriched the classical theory of variations, but his most important contribution to analysis is integral equations, dealt with in a series of papers from 1904 to 1910. In the course of the nineteenth century it had been learned that in integral equations the type $f - Af = g$ (where A is the integral operator and f the unknown function) is much more accessible than the type $Af = g$. Liouville (1837) once encountered such an equation and solved it by iteration. So did August Beer (1865), when trying to solve the boundary problem of potential theory by means of a double layer on the boundary; Carl Neumann mastered it (1877) by formal inversion of $1 - A$. The same method proved useful in Volterra's equations (1896). When Poincaré (1894) investigated the boundary problem $\Delta f + \lambda f = h$, turned into an integral equation $f - \lambda Af = g$ by means of Green's function, the parameter λ was analytically involved in the solution. This allowed analytic continuation through the λ plane except, of course, for certain polar singularities. To solve this kind of equation Fredholm (1900, 1902) devised a determinant method, but his greatest merit is to have more clearly understood the λ singularities as eigenvalues of the homogeneous problems.

At this point Hilbert came in. He deliberately turned from the inhomogeneous to the homogeneous equations, from the noneigenvalues to the eigenvalues—or, rather, he turned from the linear equation to the quadratic form, that is, to its transformation on principal axes. Fredholm's method told him how this transformation had to be approached from the finite-dimension case. It was a clumsy procedure and was soon superseded by Erhard Schmidt's much more elegant one (1905). With a fresh start Hilbert then coordinatized function space by means of an orthonormal basis of continuous functions and entered the space of number sequence with convergent square sums, or Hilbert space, as it has been called since. Here the transformation on principal axes was undertaken anew, first on the quadratic forms called "completely continuous" ("compact," in modern terminology) and then on bounded forms, where Hilbert discovered and skillfully handled the continuous spectrum by means of Stieltjes' integrals. The term "spectrum" was coined by Hilbert, who, indeed, must be credited with the invention of many suggestive terms. "Spectrum" was even a prophetic term; twenty years later physicists called upon spectra of operators, as studied by Hilbert, to explain optical spectra.

Hilbert's turn to the space of number sequences seems odd today, but at that time it was badly needed; Hilbert space in a modern sense was not thinkable before the Fischer-Riesz theorem (1907), and its abstract formulation dates from the late 1920's. Hilbert's approach to spectral resolution, utterly clumsy and suffering from the historical preponderance of the resolvent, was greatly simplified later, essentially by F. Riesz (1913); the theory was extended to unbounded self-adjoint operators by J. von Neumann and M. H. Stone about 1930.

Today the least studied and the most obsolete among Hilbert's papers are probably those on integral equations. Their value is now purely historical, as the most important landmark ever set out in mathematics: the linear space method in analysis, with its geometrical language and its numerous applications, quite a few of which go back to Hilbert himself.

From Hilbert's analytic period one rather isolated work, and the most beautiful of all he did, should not be overlooked: his proof of Waring's hypothesis that every positive integer can be represented as a sum of, at most, m l^{th} powers, m depending on l only.

From about 1909 Hilbert showed an ever increasing interest in physics, which, he asserted, was too difficult to be left to physicists. The results of this activity have only partially been published (kinetic gas theory, axiomatics of radiation, relativity). It is generally acknowledged that Hilbert's achievements in this field lack the profundity and the inventiveness of his mathematical work proper. The same is true of his highly praised work in the foundations of mathematics. (It is still a sacrilege to say so, but somebody has to be the first to commit this crime.) In this field even lesser merits have made people famous but, according to the standards set by Hilbert himself, his ideas in foundations of mathematics look poor and shallow. This has become clear with the passing of time. His contemporaries and disciples were much impressed, and even now it is difficult not to be impressed, by his introduction of the "transfinite" functor τ, which for every predicate A chooses an object τA such that $A(\tau A) \rightarrow A(x)$—the so-called Aristides of corruptibility, who, if shown to be corruptible, would prove the corruptibility of all Athenians. Indeed, it is a clever idea to incorporate all transfinite tools of a formal system, such as the universal and the existential quantifier, and the choice axiom into this one symbol τ and afterward to restore the finitistic point of view by systematically eliminating it. For many years the delusive profundity of that artifice led investigators the wrong way. But how of all people could Hilbert, whose intuitions used to come true like prophecies, ever believe that this tool would work? Asking this question means considering the tremendous problem of Hilbert's psychological makeup.

One desire of Hilbert's first axiomatic period was still unfulfilled: after the relative consistency of geometry he wanted to prove the consistency of mathematics itself—or, as he put it, the consistency of number theory. This desire, long suppressed, finally became an obsession. As long as mathematics is no more than counting beans, its consistency is hardly a problem. It becomes one when mathematicians start to treat infinities as though they were bags of beans. Cantor had done so in set theory, and the first to reap glory by the same kind of boldness in everyday mathematics was Hilbert. Is it to be wondered that he was haunted by the need to justify these successes?

He conceived the idea of formalism: to reduce mathematics to a finite game with an infinite but finitely defined treasure of formulas. This game must be consistent; it is the burden of metamathematics to prove that while playing this game, one can never hit on the formula $0 \neq 0$. But if a vicious circle is to be avoided, metamathematics must restrict itself to counting beans. If some chain of the game delivered $0 \neq 0$, one should try to eliminate all links involving the transfinite τ and to reduce the chain to one in which simple beans were counted—this was Hilbert's idea of a consistency proof.

From the outset there were those who did not believe this idea was feasible. Others rejected it as irrelevant. The most intransigent adversary was L. E. J. Brouwer, who from 1907 held that it is truth rather than consistency that matters in mathematics. He gradually built up a new mathematics, called intuitionism, in which many notions of classic mathematics became meaningless and many classic theorems were disproved. In the early 1920's Hermann Weyl, one of Hilbert's most famous students, took Brouwer's side. Both Hilbert and Brouwer were absolutists; for both of them mathematics was no joking matter. There must have been tension between them from their first meeting; although disguised, it can be felt in the discussions of the 1920's between a crusading Brouwer and a nervous Hilbert.

The mathematical world did not have to decide whether formalism was relevant. The catastrophe came in 1931, when Kurt Gödel proved that Hilbert's approach was not feasible. It was a profound discovery, although there had been intimations, such as the Löwenheim-Skolem paradox. Had Hilbert never doubted the soundness of his approach? All he published in this field is so naïve that one would answer "yes." But how was it possible?

Hilbert, as open-minded as a mathematician could be, had started thinking about foundations of mathematics with a preconceived idea which from the outset narrowed his attitude. He thought that something he wished to be true was true indeed. This is not so strange as it seems. It is quite a different thing to know whether mathematics is consistent, or whether some special mathematical hypothesis is true or not. There seems to be so much more at stake in the first case that it is difficult to deal with it as impartially as with the second.

At closer look, 1931 is not the turning point but the starting point of foundations of mathematics as it has developed since. But then Hilbert can hardly be counted among the predecessors, as could Löwenheim and Skolem. This is a sad statement, but it would be a sadder thing if those who know nothing more about Hilbert than his work in foundations of mathematics judged his genius on this evidence.

In 1900 Hilbert addressed the International Congress of Mathematicians on mathematical problems, saying: "This conviction of the solvability of any mathematical problem is a strong incentive in our work; it beckons us: *this is the problem, find its solutions. You can find it by pure thinking since in mathematics there is no Ignorabimus!* [*Gesammelte Abhandlungen,* III, 298]." With these words Hilbert introduced twenty-three problems which have since stimulated mathematical investigations:

1. *The cardinality of the continuum.* After a great many unsuccessful attempts the problem was solved in 1963 by Paul J. Cohen, although in another sense than Hilbert thought: it has been proved unsolvable. In the same connection Hilbert mentions well-ordering, which was accomplished by Zermelo.

2. *The consistency of the arithmetic axioms.* The history of this problem has already been dealt with.

3. *The existence of tetrahedrons with equal bases and heights that are not equal in the sense of division and completion.* The question was answered affirmatively shortly afterward by Max Dehn.

4. *The straight line as the shortest connection.* The problem is too vague.

5. *The analyticity of continuous groups.* The analyticity has been proved by small steps, with the final result in 1952.

6. *The axioms of physics.* Even today axiomatics of physics is hardly satisfactory. The best example is R. Giles's *Mathematical Foundations of Thermodynamics* (1964), but in general it is not yet clear what axiomatizing physics really means.

7. *Irrationality and transcendence of certain numbers.* From C. L. Siegel (1921) and A. O. Gelfond (1929) to A. Baker (1966–1969), problems of this kind have been tackled successfully.

8. *Prime number problems.* Riemann's hypothesis is still open, despite tremendous work. In algebraic fields it has been answered by E. Hecke (1917). Goldbach's hypothesis has successfully been tackled by L. Schnirelmann (1930), I. M. Vinogradov (1937), and others.

9. *Proof of the most general reciprocity law in arbitrary number fields.* The problem has been successfully tackled from Hilbert himself to Artin (1928) and I. R. Šafarevič (1950).

10. *Decision on the solvability of a Diophantine equation.* A rather broad problem, this has often been dealt with—for instance, by Thue (1908) and by C. L. Siegel (1929). The general problem was answered negatively by J. V. Matijasevič in 1969.

11. *Quadratic forms with algebraic coefficients.* Important results were obtained by Helmuth Hasse (1929) and by C. L. Siegel (1936, 1951). Connections to *idèles* and algebraic groups were shown by A. Weil and T. Ono (1964–1965).

12. *Kronecker's theorem on Abelian fields for arbitrary algebraic fields.* This relates to finding the functions which for an arbitrary field play the same role

as the exponential functions for the rational field and the elliptic modular functions for imaginary quadratic fields. Much has been done on this problem, but it is still far from being solved.

13. *Impossibility of solving the general seventh-degree equation by functions of two variables.* Solved by V. I. Arnold (1957), who admits continuous functions, this is still unsolved if analyticity is required.

14. *Finiteness of systems of relative integral functions.* This was answered in the negative by Masayoshi Nagata (1959).

15. *Exact founding of Schubert's enumerative calculus.* Although enumerative geometry has been founded in several ways, the justification of Schubert's calculus as such is still an open problem.

16. *Topology of real algebraic curves and surfaces.* The results are still sporadic.

17. *Representation of definite forms by squares.* This was solved by Artin (1926).

18. *Building space from congruent polyhedrons.* The finiteness of the number of groups with fundamental domain was proved by Ludwig Bieberbach (1910). A Minkowski hypothesis on the covering of space with cubes was proved by Georg Hajos (1941).

19. *The analytic character of solutions of variation problems.* A few special results have been obtained.

20. *General boundary value problems.* Hilbert's own salvage of the Dirichlet problem and many other investigations have been conducted in this area.

21. *Differential equations with a given monodromy group.* This was solved by Hilbert himself (1905).

22. *Uniformization.* For curves, this was solved by Koebe and others.

23. *Extension of the methods of variations calculus.* Hilbert himself and many others dealt with this.

> If I were a painter, I could draw Hilbert's portrait, so strongly have his features engraved themselves into my mind, forty years ago when he stood on the summit of his life. I still see the high forehead, the shining eyes looking firmly through the spectacles, the strong chin accentuated by a short beard, even the bold Panama hat, and his sharp East Prussian voice still sounds in my ears [F. W. Levi, *Forscher und Wissenschaftler im heutigen Europa,* p. 337].

This description by Levi is confirmed by many others. People who met Hilbert later were gravely disappointed.

Hilbert was a strong personality, and an independent thinker in fields other than mathematics. As an East Prussian he was inclined to political conservatism, but he abhorred all kinds of nationalist emotions. During World War I he refused to sign the famous Declaration to the Cultural World, a series of "it-is-not-true-that" statements; and when the French mathematician Darboux died during the war, he dared to publish an obituary.

Biographical sketches written during Hilbert's lifetime are more or less conventional but never Byzantine. The oral tradition is more characteristic; it has been collected by Constance Reid, who in her biography of Hilbert gives a truthful and understanding image of the man and his world. Her biography also contains a reprint of Weyl's obituary, which is the most expert analysis of his work and reflects Hilbert's personal influence on his students and collaborators: "the sweet flute of the Pied Piper that Hilbert was, seducing so many rats to follow him into the deep river of mathematics." There are more witnesses concerning Hilbert: Hilbert himself, telling about his friend Minkowski; and the list of sixty-nine theses written under his guidance, many of them by students who became famous mathematicians.

BIBLIOGRAPHY

I. Original Works. Hilbert's *Gesammelte Abhandlungen,* 3 vols. (Berlin, 1932–1935; 2nd ed., 1970), includes analyses of his work and a biography by Otto Blumenthal. Not included are his *Grundlagen der Geometrie* (Leipzig, 1899; 9th ed., Stuttgart, 1962) and *Grundzüge einer allgemeinen Theorie der Integralgleichungen* (Leipzig 1912; 2nd ed. 1924).

II. Secondary Literature. The best analysis of Hilbert's work as a whole is in Hermann Weyl, "David Hilbert and His Work," in *Bulletin of the American Mathematical Society,* **50** (1944), 612–654. See also F. W. Levi, *Forscher und Wissenschaftler im heutigen Europa, Weltall und Erde* (Oldenburg, 1955), pp. 337–347.

An analysis of his work in foundations of geometry is Hans Freudenthal, "Zur Geschichte der Grundlagen der Geometrie," in *Nieuw archief voor wiskunde,* 4th ser., **5** (1957), 105–142. The history of Hilbert's problems is discussed in P. Alexandrov, ed., *Problemy Gilberta* (Moscow, 1969); and Ludwig Bieberbach, "Über den Einfluss von Hilbert's Pariser Vortrag über 'Mathematische Probleme' auf die Entwicklung der Mathematik in den letzten dreissig Jahren," in *Naturwissenschaften,* **18** (1930), 1101–1111.

Biographical writings are Paul Bernays, "David Hilbert," in *Encyclopedia of Philosophy,* III (New York, 1967), 496–504; Otto Blumenthal, O. Toeplitz, Max Dehn, Richard Courant, Max Born, and Paul Bernays, in *Naturwissenschaften,* **10** (1922), 67–99; Constantin Carathéodory, "Hilbert," in *Sitzungsberichte der Bayerischen Akademie der Wissenschaften zu München,* Math.-nat. Abt. (1943), 350–354; Constantin Carathéodory and Arnold Sommerfeld, "Hilbert," in *Naturwissenschaften,* **31** (1943), 213–214; G. Polya, "Some Mathematicians I Have Known," in *American Mathematical Monthly,* **76** (1969), 746–753; and Constance Reid, *Hilbert* (Berlin–Heidelberg–New York, 1970).

Hans Freudenthal

HILL, GEORGE WILLIAM (*b.* New York, N.Y., 3 March 1838; *d.* West Nyack, New York, 16 April 1914)

In the opinion of Simon Newcomb, Hill was destined to rank "as the greatest master of mathematical astronomy during the last quarter of the nineteenth century." In 1903 Hill was ranked second after E. H. Moore by the leading mathematicians in the United States and first, tied with Newcomb, by the leading astronomers. He was honored in his lifetime by the bestowal of advanced degrees and medals and by honorary memberships in the most prestigious professional scientific societies and institutions throughout the world. Yet throughout all of this recognition he remained a simple man of the country.

Hill's father, John William Hill, was born in England while his mother, Catherine Smith, was descended from an old Huguenot family. His grandfather had been a successful engraver in London before emigrating to Philadelphia in 1816. Both Hill's father and younger brother were painters, and in 1846 his father retired to a farm in Nyack Turnpike (now West Nyack), New York. Country residence during Hill's youth was likely to carry with it grave drawbacks in the education of the young; teaching was frequently restricted to a few subjects on an elementary level. Hill was extremely fortunate, while at Rutgers College, to come under the influence of Theodore Strong, a friend of Nathaniel Bowditch, who had translated Laplace's *Mécanique céleste* into English. Strong's deep respect for tradition was reflected in the contents of his library. Hill relates that under Strong he read Sylvestre Lacroix's *Traité du calcul différential et intégral,* Poisson's *Traité de mécanique,* Philippe de Pontécoulant's *Théorie analytique du système du monde,* Laplace's *Mécanique céleste,* Lagrange's *Mécanique analytique,* and Legendre's *Fonctions elliptiques.* Hill quoted Strong as saying that "Euler is our great Master" and noted that Strong "scarcely had a book in his library published later than 1840." Poincaré said that to Strong Euler was "the god of mathematics" whose death marked the beginning of the decline of mathematics.

Hill's knowledge of the techniques of the old masters strengthened his ingenuity in the creation of new methodology. The extent of the Eulerian influence is evident in his "Researches in the Lunar Theory" (1878), which is based on an Eulerian method in its use of moving rectangular axes and the same first approximation. This device led to Hill's variational curve, the reference orbit in describing lunar motion. E. W. Brown developed the work still further for the preparation of lunar ephemerides.

After receiving the B.A. from Rutgers in 1859, Hill went to Cambridge, Massachusetts, to further his mathematical knowledge. In 1861 he joined the staff of scientists working in Cambridge on the *American Ephemeris and Nautical Almanac.* He had already begun to publish in 1859, while still at college, and his third paper, "On the Conformation of the Earth," in J. D. Runkle's *Mathematical Monthly* (1861) brought him a prize and the attention of Runkle as well. R. S. Woodward, president of the Royal Society at the time he wrote Hill's obituary notice, counted the paper as still worthy of reading and considered Hill as having become the leading contributor to the advances in dynamic astronomy during the half-century after its publication. At the *Almanac* office Hill was assigned the task of calculating the American ephemeris, work he was later authorized to continue at his home in West Nyack.

When Simon Newcomb became director of the *American Ephemeris* in 1877, he undertook the reconstruction of the theories and tables of lunar and planetary motion. Hill was induced to work on the theories of Jupiter and Saturn, known to be exceptionally difficult in the determination of their mutual perturbations. Because the *Nautical Almanac* office had meanwhile been transferred to Washington to be under the more immediate jurisdiction of the Navy Department, Hill resided there for a ten-year period beginning in 1882. His success with the Newcomb assignment represented one of the most important contributions to nineteenth-century mathematical astronomy. The calculation of the effects of the planets on the moon's motion was a particular case of the famous three-body problem, which dates back to Newton (1686).

Hill's "Researches in the Lunar Theory," published in the first issue of *American Journal of Mathematics* (1878), had, through its introduction of the periodic orbit, initiated a new approach to the study of three mutually attracting bodies. F. R. Moulton wrote in 1914 that no earlier work had approached it in practical application and no subsequent work had then surpassed it. The article became fundamental in the development of celestial mechanics.

The memoir of 1877 entitled *On the Part of the Motion of the Lunar Perigee Which Is a Function of the Mean Motions of the Sun and Moon* contains the incontrovertible evidence of Hill's mathematical genius. He was led to a differential equation, now called Hill's equation, that is equivalent to an infinite number of algebraic linear equations. Hill showed how to develop the infinite determinant corresponding to these equations.

Hill's procedures reflect his preference for the methodology of Charles Delaunay, as developed in the two-volume *Théorie du mouvement de la lune* (1860–1867), and he is said to have perfected it. Yet the methods adopted in the *Nautical Almanac* work were essentially those of P. A. Hansen, the other lunar theorist of eminence at that time.

Hill's many honors included membership in the National Academy of Sciences (1874), presidency of the American Mathematical Society (1894–1896), and the gold medal of the Royal Astronomical Society for his researches on lunar theory (1887). He was a foreign member of the Royal Society, the Paris Academy, and the Belgian Academy.

In 1898 J. K. Rees, who held the Rutherfurd chair of astronomy at Columbia University, persuaded Hill to accept the newly created lectureship in celestial mechanics. Since few students were qualified to comprehend work on that level, Hill objected to receiving pay and finally resigned in 1901. He was urged to write out his lectures, which he did very painstakingly; he gave them to Columbia but insisted on returning the money that had been paid to him.

Hill remained a recluse in West Nyack, devoted to his researches and to his large scientific library, which he bequeathed to Columbia University. Illness during the last years reduced his physical activity and a failing heart brought his career to a close.

BIBLIOGRAPHY

The Collected Mathematical Works of George William Hill, 4 vols. (Washington, D.C., 1905–1907), includes eighty-three papers and has a biographical intro. by H. Poincaré, pp. vii–xviii. A complete bibliography of Hill's papers is in Ernest W. Brown, "Biographical Memoir of George William Hill, 1838–1914," in *Biographical Memoirs. National Academy of Sciences,* **8** (1916), 275–309; and "History of the N.Y. Mathematical Society," in *American Mathematical Society Semicentennial Publications,* I (New York, 1938), 117–124, with 101 items and a complete list of his honors (p. 118).

A condensed version of Brown's memoir (see above), entitled "G. W. Hill, 1838–1914," is in *Obituary Notices of Fellows of the Royal Society,* **91A** (1915), xlii–li, repr. in *Bulletin of the American Mathematical Society,* **21** (1915), 499–511. See also E. W. Brown, "George William Hill, Mathematician and Astronomer," in *Nation,* **98,** no. 2549 (7 May 1914), 540–541; J. W. L. Glaiser, "Address Delivered by the President . . . on Presenting the Gold Medal of the Society to Mr. G. W. Hill," in *Monthly Notices of the Royal Astronomical Society,* **47** (Feb. 1887), 203–220; Harold Jacoby, "George William Hill," in *Columbia University Quarterly,* **16** (Sept. 1914), 439–442; F. R. Moulton, "George William Hill," in *Popular Astronomy,* **22,** no. 7 (Aug.–Sept. 1914), 391–400; Simon Newcomb, "The Work of George W. Hill," in *Nation,* **85,** no. 2209 (1907), 396, a letter to the editor; and R. S. Woodward, "George William Hill," in *Astronomical Journal,* **28,** no. 20 (5 June 1914), 161–162.

Columbia University Bulletin, no. 8 (July 1894), 24–25, contains a list of the materials in the course of thirty lectures on celestial mechanics given by Hill; on p. 63 of the same issue is the citation accompanying his honorary degree.

The following contain references important to Hill's work: G. D. Birkhoff, "Fifty Years of American Mathematics," in *American Mathematical Society Semicentennial Publications,* II (New York, 1938), 270–315; F. R. Moulton, *Differential Equations* (New York, 1930), pp. 224, 318, 353–354; Felix Klein, inaugural address at the general session of the Congress of Mathematics and Astronomy, Chicago, in *Bulletin of the New York Mathematical Society,* **3** (Oct. 1893), 1–3, also in *Monist,* **4** (Oct. 1893), 1–4; C. S. Peirce, "Note on Mr. G. W. Hill's Moon Theory," in *Nation,* **81** (19 Oct. 1905), 321; and review of Hill's *Collected Works, ibid.,* **85** (17 Oct. 1907), 355; E. H. Roberts, "Note on Infinite Determinants," in *Annals of Mathematics,* **10** (1896), 35–50; and D. E. Smith and J. Ginsburg, *History of Mathematics in America Before 1900* (Chicago, 1934), *passim.*

Further references are in *Dictionary of American Biography,* IX (New York, 1932), 32–33; *National Cyclopedia of American Biography* (New York, 1918), p. 388; Poggendorff, III, 631–632; IV, 639; V, 538; and *American Men of Science,* I (1906), 146.

Additional citations are found in *Encyklöpedie der mathematischen Wissenschaften,* VI (Leipzig, 1912–1926); J. J. [erwood], in *Monthly Notices of the Royal Astronomical Society,* **75** (1915); S. Newcomb, *Reminiscences of an Astronomer* (London, 1903); T. Muir, *Theory of Determinants in the Historical Order of Development,* III (London, 1920); and F. Schlesinger, "Recollections of George William Hill," in *Publications of the Astronomical Society of the Pacific,* **49** (1937).

CAROLYN EISELE

HILL, LESTER SANDERS (*b.* New York, N.Y., 19 January 1890; *d.* Bronxville, New York, 9 January 1961)

The son of James Edward Hill and the former Ellen Sheehan, Hill attended Columbia University, receiving the B.A. *summa cum laude* in 1911 and the M.A. in 1913. He taught mathematics at the University of Montana and at Princeton until 1916, when he joined the U.S. Naval Reserve. In 1921–1922 Hill was an associate professor of mathematics at the University of Maine; in 1922 he was appointed an instructor at Yale, where he was awarded the Ph.D. in 1926 with a dissertation entitled "Properties of Certain Aggregate Functions." In 1927 Hill went to Hunter College in New York City, where he remained until his retirement except for 1945–1946, when he was a member of the faculty of the U.S. Army University at Biarritz, France.

Hill is probably best known for his mathematical approaches to cryptography and cryptanalysis, having been among the first to apply the theories and methods of matrices and linear transformations to the construction of secret codes. His work in this field, called the Hill system by A. A. Albert, was analyzed by Luigi Sacco in his *Manuale di crittografia.* Only after his death did the U.S. government reveal his associations with the code systems of the army, navy, and State Department during and after World War II. Most of his research in developing a modular algebraic cipher-code system is still unpublished and is classed as highly confidential material. It is described by H. C. Bruton, director, naval communications, as "ingenious, detailed, and complete."

BIBLIOGRAPHY

I. ORIGINAL WORKS. Hill's published writings include "Concerning Huntington's Continuum and Other Types of Serial Order," in *American Mathematical Monthly,* **24** (1917), 345–348; "Cryptography in an Algebraic Alphabet," *ibid.,* **36** (1929), 306–312; "Concerning Certain Linear Transformation Apparatus of Cryptography," *ibid.,* **38** (1931), 135–154; "Probability Functions and Statistical Parameters," *ibid.,* **40** (1933), 505–532; "A Mathematical Checking System for Telegraphic Sequences," in *Telegraph and Telephone Age,* **24** (October 1926); **25** (April 1927); **25** (July 1927); "Properties of Certain Aggregate Functions," in *American Journal of Mathematics,* **49** (1937), 419–432, written with M. D. Darkow; and "An Algebraic Treatment of Geometry on a Spherical Surface," in *Scripta mathematica,* **3** (1935), 234–246, 327–336.

II. SECONDARY LITERATURE. See Luigi Sacco, *Manuale di crittografia* (Rome, 1936); *New York Times* (10 January 1961); *New York Journal-American* (10 January 1961); *New York World-Telegram & Sun* (10 January 1961); and *Who's Who in the East* (1959), 422.

MARY E. WILLIAMS

HINDENBURG, CARL FRIEDRICH (*b.* Dresden, Germany, 13 July 1741; *d.* Leipzig, Germany, 17 March 1808)

The son of a merchant, Hindenburg was privately tutored at home. He later attended the Gymnasium in Freiberg, and in 1757 he entered the University of Leipzig, where he studied medicine, philosophy, classical languages, physics, mathematics, and aesthetics. Through the assistance of C. F. Gellert, one of his tutors, Hindenburg became tutor to a young man named Schoenborn, whom he accompanied to the universities of Leipzig and Göttingen. His student's distinct interest in mathematics inspired Hindenburg to become increasingly occupied with mathematical studies, and he befriended A. G. Kaestner. In 1771 he received the M.A. at Leipzig, where he became a private lecturer and, in 1781, extraordinary professor of philosophy. In 1786 he was made professor of physics at Leipzig, a post he held until his death.

Hindenburg's first scientific publications were in philology (1763, 1769); his dissertation as professor of physics was on water pumps. His earliest mathematical investigations, in which he described a method of determining by denumerable methods the terms of arithmetic series, were published in 1776.

In 1778 Hindenburg's first publication on combinatorials appeared. Through a series of papers on this subject, as well as through his teaching, he became the founder of the "combinatorial school" in Germany. Combinatorial mathematics was not new at that time: Pascal, Leibniz, Wallis, the Bernoullis, De Moivre, and Euler, among others, had contributed to it. Hindenburg and his school attempted, through systematic development of combinatorials, to give it a key position within the various mathematical disciplines. Combinatorial considerations, especially appropriate symbols, were useful in the calculations of probabilities, in the development of series, in the inversion of series, and in the development of formulas for higher differentials.

This utility led Hindenburg and his school to entertain great expectations: they wanted combinatorial operations to have the same importance as those of arithmetic, algebra, and analysis. They developed a complicated system of symbols for fundamental combinatorial concepts, such as permutations, variations, and combinations. Various authors developed this system along different lines, but its cumbersomeness soon made it outmoded. The following "central problem" of Hindenburg might be taken as characteristic of the efforts of his school: Represent a random coefficient, b_i, explicitly by means of $a_i (k = 0, 1, \cdots, m)$ in the equation

$$(a_0 + a_1x + a_2x^2 + \cdots + a_mx^m)^n = b_0 + b_1x + \cdots + b_{mn}x^{mn}.$$

The importance that Hindenburg attached to his investigations is shown by the title of the work that summarized his unified system: *Der polynomische Lehrsatz, das wichtigste Theorem der ganzen Analysis* (1796).

None of these great expectations has been realized,

perhaps because Hindenburg and his followers were concerned more with the formal transformation of known results than with new discoveries. Thus the combinatorial school did not contribute to the development of the theory of determinants (Binet, Cauchy, Jacobi), although the latter made much use of the fundamental combinatorial concepts. The school's influence was limited to Germany, and no leading contemporary mathematician was a member.

Apart from founding the combinatorial school, Hindenburg was the first in Germany to publish professional journals for mathematics and allied fields. From 1781 to 1785, with C. B. Funck and N. G. Leske, he published the *Leipziger Magazin für Naturkunde, Mathematik und Ökonomie* and, from 1786 to 1789, with Johann III Bernoulli, the *Leipziger Magazin für angewandte und reine Mathematik.* From 1795 to 1800 he edited the *Archiv der reinen und angewandten Mathematik* and the *Sammlung Kombinatorisch-analytischer Abhandlungen.*

BIBLIOGRAPHY

I. Original Works. Hindenburg's writings include *Beschreibung einer neuen Art nach einem bekannten Gesetz fortgehende Zahlen durch Abzählen oder Abmessen bequem zu finden* (Leipzig, 1776); *Infinitionomii dignitatum indeterminarum leges ac formulae* (Göttingen, 1778; enl. ed., 1779); *Methodus nova et facilis serierum infinitarum ehibendi dignitates exponentis indeterminati* (Göttingen, 1778); *Novi systematis permutationum, combinationum ac variationum primae lineae* (Leipzig, 1781); and *Der polynomische Lehrsatz, das wichtigste Theorem der ganzen Analysis* (Leipzig, 1796).

II. Secondary Literature. See M. Cantor, *Vorlesungen über Geschichte der Mathematik,* IV (Leipzig, 1908); E. Netto, in *Enzyklopädie der mathematischen Wissenschaften,* I, pt. 1 (Leipzig, 1898–1904); H. Oettinger, "Über den Begriff der Kombinationslehre und die Bezeichnungen in derselben," in (J. A. Grunert's) *Archiv der Mathematik und Physik,* **15** (1850), 271–374; and I. C. Weingärtner, *Lehrbuch der kombinatorischen Analysis, nach der Theorie des Herrn Professor Hindenburg ausgearbeitet,* 2 vols. (Leipzig, 1800–1801), which contains a list of all the important writings of the "combinatorial school" to 1800.

Karlheinz Haas

HIPPARCHUS (*b.* Nicaea, Bithynia [now Iznik, Turkey], first quarter of second century B.C.; *d.* Rhodes [?], after 127 B.C.)

The only certain biographical datum concerning Hipparchus is his birthplace, Nicaea, in northwestern Asia Minor. This is attested by several ancient sources[1] and by Nicaean coins from the second and third centuries of the Christian era that depict a seated man contemplating a globe, with the legend ΙΠΠΑΡΧΟΣ. His scientific activity is dated by a number of his astronomical observations quoted in Ptolemy's *Almagest.* The earliest observation indubitably made by Hipparchus himself is of the autumnal equinox of 26/27 September 147 B.C.[2] The latest is of a lunar position on 7 July 127 B.C.[3] Ptolemy reports a series of observations of autumnal and vernal equinoxes taken from Hipparchus, ranging from 162 to 128 B.C., but it is not clear whether the earliest in the series had been made by Hipparchus himself or were taken from others; Ptolemy says only that "they seemed to Hipparchus to have been accurately observed." We can say, then, that Hipparchus' activity extended over the third quarter of the second century B.C., and may have begun somewhat earlier. This accords well with the calculations of H. C. F. C. Schjellerup and H. Vogt concerning the epoch of the stellar positions in Hipparchus' commentary on Aratus.[4]

It is probable that Hipparchus spent the whole of his later career at Rhodes: observations by him ranging from 141 to 127 B.C. are specifically attributed to Rhodes by Ptolemy. In Ptolemy's *Phases of the Fixed Stars*, however, it is stated that the observations taken from Hipparchus in that book were made in Bithynia (presumably Nicaea). We may infer that Hipparchus began his scientific career in Bithynia and moved to Rhodes some time before 141 B.C. The statement found in some modern accounts that he also worked in Alexandria is based on a misunderstanding of passages in the *Almagest* referring to observations made at Alexandria and used by or communicated to Hipparchus.[5] The only other biographical information we have is an utterly untrustworthy anecdote that Hipparchus caused amazement by sitting in the theater wearing a cloak, because he had predicted a storm.[6]

Hipparchus is a unique figure in the history of astronomy in that, while there is general agreement that his work was of profound importance, we are singularly ill-informed about it. Of his numerous works only one (the commentary on Aratus) survives, and that a comparatively slight one (although valuable in the absence of the others). We derive most of our knowledge of Hipparchus' achievements in astronomy from the *Almagest*; and although Ptolemy obviously had studied Hipparchus' writings thoroughly and had a deep respect for his work, his main concern was not to transmit it to posterity but to use it and, where possible, improve upon it in constructing his own astronomical system. Most of his references to Hipparchus are quite incidental; and some of them are obscure to us, since we cannot consult the originals. Some supplementary information can be gathered from remarks by other ancient writers; but for the most part they were not professional astronomers, and they frequently misunderstood or misrepresented what Hipparchus said (a typical example is the elder Pliny). Since the evidence is so scanty, the following account necessarily contains much that is uncertain or conjectural. Painstaking analysis of that evidence, however, which has begun only in recent years,[7] has revealed, and will reveal, a surprising amount. It also has demonstrated the groundlessness of the assumption, stated or tacit, of most modern accounts of Hipparchus: that everything in the *Almagest* that Ptolemy does not expressly claim as his own work is derived from Hipparchus. The truth is more complicated and more interesting. A further difficulty is that although we know the titles of a good many of Hipparchus' works, much of our information on his opinions and achievements cannot be assigned with certainty to any known title. Moreover, while we can make some inferences about the chronology of his work (it is certain, for instance, that his discovery of precession belongs to the end of his career), in general the dates and order of composition of his works are unknown. This discussion is therefore arranged by topics rather than by titles (the latter are mentioned under the topics that they are known or conjectured to have treated).

Mathematical Methods. In Greek astronomy the positions of the heavenly bodies were computed from geometrical models to which numerical parameters had been assigned. An essential element of the computation was the solution of plane triangles; Greek trigonometry was based on a table of chords. We are informed that Hipparchus wrote a work on chords,[8] and we can reconstruct his chord table. It was based on a circle in which the circumference was divided, in the normal (Babylonian) manner, into 360 degrees of 60 minutes, and the radius was measured in the same units; thus R, the radius, expressed in minutes, is

$$R = \frac{360 \cdot 60'}{2\pi} \approx 3438'.$$

This function is related to the modern sine function (for α in degrees) by

$$\frac{\text{Crd } 2\alpha}{2} = 3438 \sin \alpha.$$

Hipparchus computed the function only at intervals of 1/48 of a circle (7-1/2°), using linear interpolation between the computed points for other values. Thus he was able to construct the whole table on a very simple geometrical basis: it can be computed from the values of Crd 60° (= R), Crd 90° (= $\sqrt{2}R$), and the following two formulas (in which d is the diameter of the base circle and s is the chord of the angle α):

$$(1) \quad \text{Crd}\,(180° - \alpha) = \sqrt{d^2 - s^2}.$$

$$(2) \quad \text{Crd}\,\frac{1}{2}\alpha = \sqrt{\frac{1}{2}\left(d^2 - d\sqrt{d^2 - s^2}\right)}.$$

The first is a trivial application of Pythagoras' theorem, and the second was already known to Archimedes.

This chord table survives only in the sine table commonly found in Indian astronomical works, with $R = 3438'$ and values computed at intervals of 3-3/4°, which is derived from it. But its use by Hipparchus can be demonstrated from calculations of his preserved in *Almagest* IV, 11. Otherwise, apart from a couple of stray occurrences of its use,[9] it vanishes from Greek astronomy, being superseded by Ptolemy's improved chord table based on the unit circle ($R = 60 = 1,0$ in Ptolemy's sexagesimal system) and calculated to three sexagesimal places at intervals at ½°. The results of trigonometrical calculations based on Hipparchus' chord table, although less accurate than those based on Ptolemy's, are adequate in the context of ancient astronomy. The main disadvantage of its use, in contrast with Ptolemy's, is the constant intrusion of the factor 3438 in the calculations. It has the compensating advantage, however, that for small angles (up to 7-1/2°), the chord can be replaced by the angle expressed in minutes (in this respect it is analogous to modern radian measure), which greatly simplifies computations (for an example, see below on the distances of the sun and moon).

Given the chord function, Hipparchus could solve any plane triangle by using the equivalent of the modern sine formula:

$$\frac{\text{Crd } 2\alpha}{a} = \frac{\text{Crd } 2\beta}{b}.$$

No doubt, like Ptolemy, he usually computed with right triangles, breaking down other triangles into two right triangles. In the absence of a tangent function, he had to use the chord function combined with Pythagoras' theorem; but his methods were as effective as, if more cumbersome than, those of modern trigonometry. Particular trigonometrical problems had been solved before Hipparchus by Aristarchus of Samos (early third century B.C.) and by Archimedes, using approximation methods; but it seems highly probable that Hipparchus was the first to construct a table of chords and thus provide a general solution for trigonometrical problems.[10] A corollary of this is that, before Hipparchus, astronomical tables based on Greek geometrical methods did not exist. If this is so, Hipparchus was not only the founder of trigonometry but also the man who transformed Greek astronomy from a purely theoretical into a practical, predictive science.

In Greek astronomy most problems arising from computations of the positions of the heavenly bodies were either problems in plane trigonometry or could be reduced to such by replacing the small spherical triangles involved by plane triangles. The principal exception was those problems in which the earth is no longer treated as a point—that is, those in which the position of the observer on the earth must be taken into account, notably those concerned with parallax and rising times. Exact mathematical treatment of these requires spherical trigonometry. Since Hipparchus did treat these subjects, the question arises whether he used spherical trigonometry. In the *Almagest* spherical trigonometry is based on a theorem of Menelaus (late first century of the Christian era),[11] and there is no evidence for the existence of the trigonometry of the surface of the sphere before Menelaus. It was possible for Hipparchus to solve the problems he encountered in other ways, however, and there is considerable evidence that he did so.

The problem of the rising times of arcs of the ecliptic at a given latitude was usually connected in ancient astronomy with the length of daylight. The usual method of reckoning time in antiquity was to divide both the daylight and the nighttime into twelve hours. These "seasonal hours" (ὧραι καιρικαί) varied in length throughout the year, depending on the season and the latitude of the place. In order to convert them into hours of equal length ("equinoctial hours," ὧραι ἰσημεριναί), one needs to know the length of daylight on the date and at the place in question. This is given by the time it takes the 180° of the ecliptic following the longitude of the sun on that date to cross the horizon at that latitude (or, in spherical terms, the arc of the equator that rises with those 180°). For most purposes it is sufficient to know the rising times of the individual signs of the zodiac. This problem was solved in Babylonian astronomy by a simple arithmetical scheme that, although only approximately correct, produced remarkably good results.

If we number the rising times of the signs of the ecliptic, beginning with Aries, $\alpha_1, \alpha_2, \ldots, \alpha_{12}$, then, for the first six signs, it is assumed that the increment d between the rising time of a sign and the preceding sign is constant: $\alpha_2 = \alpha_1 + d$, $\alpha_3 = \alpha_2 + d = \alpha_1 + 2d$, and so on. The rising times of the signs of the second half of the ecliptic are equal to those of the corresponding signs of the first half according to the symmetry relations $\alpha_7 = \alpha_6$, $\alpha_8 = \alpha_5$, and so on. The length of the longest daylight, M, is the sum of the six arcs α_4 to α_9 inclusive; that of the shortest day, m, is the sum of the remaining six arcs. Thus, if the ratio M/m is given, the value of α_1 and d—and hence of all the rising times—can be computed arithmetically. For, in degrees of the equator, $M + m = 360°$, $M = 6\alpha_1 + 24d$, $m = 6\alpha_1 + 6d$. In Babylonian astronomy the ratio M/m was always taken as 3/2, which is approximately correct for Babylon. A contemporary of Hipparchus, Hypsicles of Alexandria, in his extant work Ἀναφορικός ("On Rising-times"), expounds exactly the same method, but for Alexandria, taking M/m as 7/5. It seems that Hipparchus extended the scheme to a number of different latitudes (probably the seven standard "climata" characterized by longest daylights extending from thirteen hours to sixteen hours at half-hour intervals, which Hipparchus used in his geographical treatise), for Pappus mentions a work by Hipparchus entitled "On the Rising of the Twelve Signs of the Zodiac" (Ἐν τῷ περὶ τῆς τῶν ιβ′ ζῳδίων ἀναφορᾶς) in which he proved a certain proposition "arithmetically" (δι' ἀριθμῶν).[12]

Other examples of the employment of arithmetical schemata for problems that would require spherical trigonometry if solved strictly can be inferred from Strabo's quotations from Hipparchus' geographical treatise. For instance, Hipparchus gave the following information: for the region where the longest daylight is sixteen hours, the maximum altitude of the sun above the horizon at winter solstice is nine cubits; for M = seventeen hours, it is six cubits, for M = eighteen hours, four cubits, and for M = nineteen hours, three cubits.[13] The altitudes form a series with constant second-order difference. Strabo also excerpted from Hipparchus' treatise the distance in stades between parallels with a given longest daylight. Here too the relationship is based on a constant difference, of third order.[14] Thus problems involving the relationship between geographical latitude and the length of daylight, which Ptolemy solved by spherical trigonometry at *Almagest* II, 2–5, were solved arithmetically by Hipparchus in every case for which there is evidence.

It does not seem possible, however, that Hipparchus solved arithmetically every problem that would normally require spherical trigonometry. Moreover, he himself said that he had written a work enabling one to determine "for almost every part of the inhabited world" which fixed stars rise and set simultaneously.[15] Theoretically one could solve such problems approximately by suitable manipulation of a celestial globe (see below on instruments). Hipparchus, however, stated that he had solved a particular problem of this type "in the general treatises we have composed on this subject [presumably the same as the above] geometrically" (διὰ τῶν γραμμῶν).[16] It is a plausible conjecture that at least one of the methods Hipparchus used for the solution of such problems was that known in antiquity as "analemma" and in modern times as descriptive geometry. This is best explained by an actual example, in which a numerical result given by Hipparchus is recomputed.[17] In the commentary on Aratus he said that a certain star is 27-1/3° north of the equator, and therefore (15/24 − 1/20 · 1/24) of the parallel circle through that star is above the horizon.[18] The horizon in question is Rhodes, with latitude $\phi = 36°$; the star's declina-

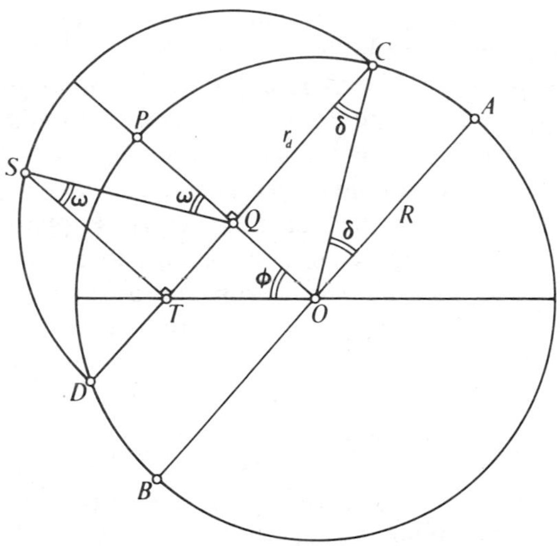

FIGURE 1

tion, δ, is 27-1/3°. In Figure 1 the circle *ACDB* represents the meridian at latitude 36°, *OT* the trace of the local horizon, *AB* the trace of the equator, and *CD* the trace of the parallel circle on which the star lies. Half of the parallel circle *CSD* is then drawn (rotated through 90° to lie in the plane of the meridian). It is required to find arc *SC* (= 90° + ω), which is the portion of the parallel circle lying between meridian and horizon. The radius of the parallel circle, r_d, is computed by

$$r_d = CQ = \frac{1}{2}\,\text{Crd}\,(180° - 2\delta),$$

and

$$OQ = \text{Crd}\,2\delta.$$

Then

$$QT = \frac{\text{Crd}\,2\phi \cdot OQ}{\text{Crd}\,(180° - 2\phi)} = \frac{\text{Crd}\,2\phi\,\text{Crd}\,2\delta}{\text{Crd}\,(180° - 2\phi)},$$

and, in triangle *STQ*,

$$\text{Crd}\,2\omega = \frac{QT \cdot R}{SQ} = \frac{QT \cdot R}{r_d}$$
$$= \frac{\text{Crd}\,2\phi\,\text{Crd}\,2\delta \cdot 2R}{\text{Crd}\,(180° - 2\phi)\,\text{Crd}\,(180° - 2\delta)}$$
$$= \frac{4039 \cdot 3156 \cdot 2 \cdot 3438}{5559 \cdot 6105} \approx 2583,$$

giving $2\omega = 44\text{-}1/8°$ and the part of the circle above the horizon as 224-1/8° (Hipparchus' result was equivalent to 224-1/4°).

The method we assume here is not attested for Hipparchus, but his use of small circles (such as the parallel circle here) is alien to the spherical astronomy of the *Almagest*, which uses only great circles, while it is exactly parallel to the methodology of Indian astronomical texts in which the analemma is implicit.[19] On the other hand, for computation of simultaneous risings and settings of fixed stars, stereographic projection would be more convenient; and we shall see, in connection with the astrolabe, that there is evidence that Hipparchus used stereographic projection too.

Theory of the Sun and Moon. Geometrical models that would in principle explain the anomalistic motion of the heavenly bodies had been developed before Hipparchus. Ptolemy attests the use of both epicycle and eccentric by Apollonius (*ca.* 200 B.C.),[20] and it is clear from his discussion that Apollonius was fully aware of the equivalence between the two models. Hipparchus used both models, and is known to have discussed their equivalence. What was new was (in all probability) his attempt to determine numerical parameters for the models on the basis of observations. We are comparatively well-informed about his solar theory, since Ptolemy adopted it virtually unchanged. Having established the lengths of the four seasons, beginning with the spring equinox, as 94-1/2,

92-1/2, 88-1/8, and 90-1/8 days, respectively, and assuming a single anomaly (in Greek terms, an eccentric with fixed apogee or the equivalent epicycle model), he was able to determine the eccentricity (1/24) and the position of the apogee (Gemini 5-1/2°) from the first two season lengths combined with a value for the length of the year.[21] We do not know what value Hipparchus adopted for the latter (his treatise "On the Length of the Year," in which he arrived at the value 365-1/4 – 1/300 days, belongs to the end of his career, after his discovery of precession, whereas he must have established a solar theory much earlier), but for this purpose the approximate value of 365-1/4 days (established by Callippus in the fourth century B.C.) is adequate. Hipparchus presumably then constructed a solar table similar to (but not identical with) that at *Almagest* III, 6, giving the equation as a function of the anomaly; the astrological writer Vettius Valens claimed to have used Hipparchus' table for the sun.[22]

In attempting to construct a lunar theory Hipparchus was faced with much greater difficulties. Whereas (in ancient theory) the sun has a single anomaly, the period of which is the same as that of its return in longitude (one year), for the moon one must distinguish three separate periods: the period of its return in longitude, the period of its return to the same velocity ("anomalistic month"), and the period of its return to the same latitude ("dracontic month"). Related to the return in longitude and the solar motion is the "synodic month" (the time between successive conjunctions or oppositions of the sun and moon). Hipparchus enunciated the following relationships: (1) In 126,007 days, 1 hour, there occur 4,267 synodic months, 4,573 returns in anomaly, and 4,612 sidereal revolutions, less 7-1/2° (hence the length of the mean synodic month is 29; 31, 50, 8, 20 days); (2) In 5,458 synodic months there occur 5,923 returns in latitude.

According to Ptolemy, *Almagest* IV, 2, Hipparchus established these relationships "from Babylonian and his own observations." Had he in fact arrived at these remarkably accurate periods merely by comparison of eclipse data, he would indeed be worthy of our marvel. In fact, as F. X. Kugler showed,[23] all the underlying parameters can be found in Babylonian astronomical texts. The second relationship can be derived directly from those texts, while the first is a result of purely arithmetical manipulation of the following Babylonian parameters: (a) 251 synodic months = 269 anomalistic months; (b) 1 mean synodic month = 29; 31, 50, 8, 20 days; (c) 1 year = 12; 22, 8 synodic months. One finds the first relationship by multiplying relationship (a) by 17. Hipparchus did this because he wanted to produce an eclipse period; and 17 is the smallest multiplier of (a) that will generate a period in which the moon can be near a node and the sun is in approximately the same position, at both beginning and end.[24] He wanted an eclipse period because he wished to confirm the Babylonian parameters by comparison of Babylonian and his own eclipse data; we can identify some of the eclipses that he used for this observational confirmation. Since one is the eclipse of 27 January 141 B.C., we have a *terminus post quem* for the establishment of the lunar theory.

The revelation of Hipparchus' dependence on Babylonian sources raises the question of what material was available to him, and in what form. We can infer that he possessed a complete or nearly complete list of lunar eclipses observed at Babylon since the reign of Nabonassar (beginning 747 B.C.). This list was available to Ptolemy. Hipparchus also had a certain number of Babylonian observations of planets (see below). Furthermore, he had access to some texts (apparently unknown to Ptolemy) that gave the fundamental parameters listed above. It seems highly improbable that he derived them from the type of texts in which they have come down to us, the highly technical lunar ephemerides. Rather, they must have been excerpted and translated by someone in Mesopotamia who was well acquainted with Babylonian astronomical methods. But when and how the transmission occurred is unknown. Hipparchus is the first Greek known to have used this material. Without it his lunar theory, and hence his eclipse theory, would not have been possible.

To represent the lunar anomaly Hipparchus used a simple epicycle model in which the center of the epicycle C moves at constant distance about the earth O with the mean motion in longitude, while the moon M moves about the center of the epicycle with the mean motion in anomaly. To determine the parameters of this model (that is, the size of the radius of the epicycle r relative to the radius of the deferent R), he devised an ingenious method involving only the observation of the times of three lunar eclipses. By calculating the position of the sun at the three eclipses (presumably from his solar table), he found the true longitude of the moon at the middle of each eclipse (180° away from the true sun). From the time intervals between the three eclipses he found the travel in mean longitude and mean anomaly between the three points. In Figure 2 points M_1, M_2, M_3 repre-

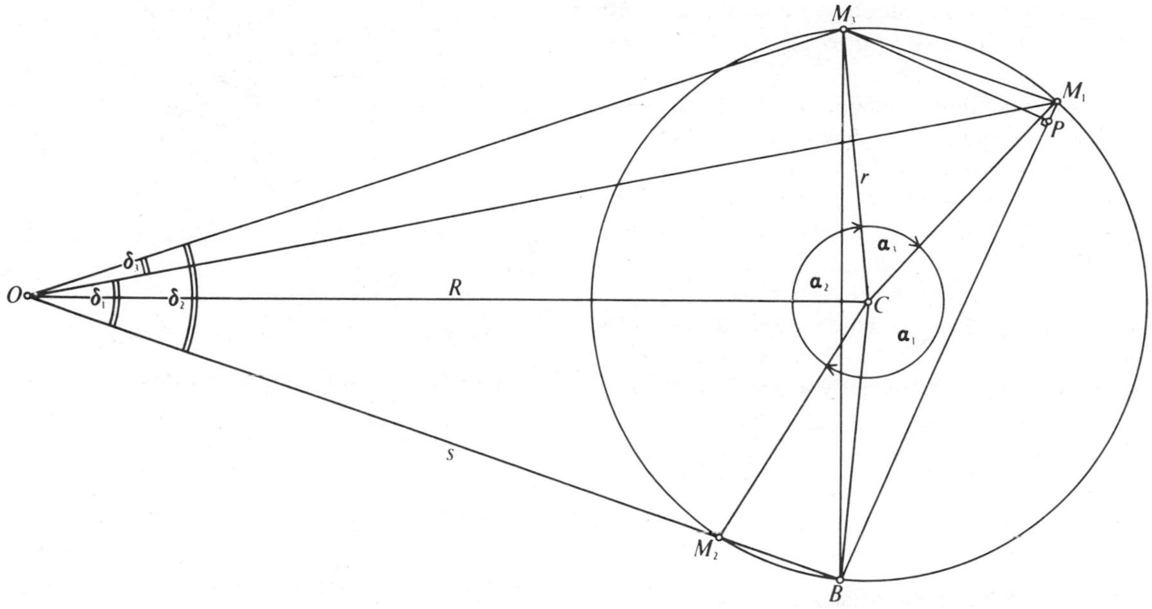

FIGURE 2

sent the positions of the moon on the epicycle at the three eclipses. The angles α at the center of the epicycle are given by the travel in mean anomaly (modulo 360°); the angles δ at the earth are the equational differences, found by comparing the intervals in mean longitude with the intervals in true longitude. Then, by solving a series of triangles, he found, first r in terms of $OB = s$, then M_2B in terms of s, and finally r in terms of R from

$$R^2 - r^2 = (R + r)(R - r) = s \cdot M_2O = s(s - M_2B).$$

Hipparchus performed this calculation twice, with two different sets of eclipses, using the epicycle model for one and the equivalent eccentric model for the other. Unfortunately the elegance of his mathematical approach was not matched by the accuracy of his calculations, so that carelessness in computing the intervals in time and longitude produced widely differing results from the two calculations, as Ptolemy demonstrates at *Almagest* IV, 11. The parameters that he found were $R:r$ = 3122-1/2:247-1/2 for the epicycle model, and $R:e$ = 3144:327-2/3 for the eccentric model.[25] We do not know how Hipparchus dealt with the discrepancy (he may have considered the possibility of a variation in the size of the epicycle), but we do know that he adopted the value 3122-1/2:247-1/2 (which is distinctly too small for the epicycle) in his work "On Sizes and Distances."

Ptolemy shows (*Almagest* V, 1–5) that a lunar model of the type developed by Hipparchus, with a single anomaly, works well enough at syzygies (oppositions and conjunctions) but that for other elongations of the moon from the sun, one must assume a second anomaly that reaches its maximum near quadrature (elongation of 90° or 270°). We can infer from material used here by Ptolemy that, toward the end of his career, Hipparchus had at least an inkling that his lunar theory was not accurate outside syzygies, and that he was systematically making observations of the moon at various elongations. Three of his latest observations that Ptolemy quotes (5 August 128 B.C., 2 May 127 B.C., and 7 July 127 B.C.) are of elongations of about 90°, 315°, and 45° respectively.[26] Hipparchus, however, seems never to have reached any firm conclusions as to the nature of the discrepancies with theory that he must have found; and it was left to Ptolemy to devise a model that would account for them mathematically.

In order to construct a theory of eclipses (one of the ultimate goals of his theory of the moon), Hipparchus had to take account of its motion in latitude. We have seen that he accepted a Babylonian parameter for the mean motion in latitude. He confirmed this by comparing two eclipses at as great an interval as possible.[27] He established the maximum latitude of the moon as 5° (*Almagest* V, 7) and devised a method of finding its epoch in latitude from an observation of the magnitude of an eclipse, combined with the data (obtained by measurement with the diopter; see below) that the

HIPPARCHUS

apparent diameter of the moon at mean distance is 1/650 of its circle (that is, 360°/650) and 2/5 of the shadow.

Sizes, Distances, and Parallax of the Sun and Moon. These last data are connected with another topic on which Hipparchus wrote. In order to predict the circumstances of a solar eclipse, one must know the relative sizes and distances of the bodies concerned: sun, moon, and earth (for lunar eclipses it suffices to know the apparent sizes; but in solar eclipses parallax, which depends on the distances of the moon and sun, is very important). Hipparchus devoted a treatise "On Sizes and Distances" (Περὶ μεγέθων καὶ ἀποστημάτων),[28] in two books, to the topic. By combining the remarks of Ptolemy and Pappus,[29] we can infer that Hipparchus proceeded as follows. By measurement with the diopter he had established the following data:

(1) The moon at mean distance measures its own circle 650 times.
(2) The moon at mean distance measures the earth's shadow (at the moon) 2-1/2 times.
(3) The moon at mean distance is the same apparent size as the sun.

He also had established by observation that the sun has no perceptible parallax. But from this he could deduce only that the sun's parallax was less than a certain amount, which he set at seven minutes of arc.

In book I, Hipparchus assumed that the solar parallax was the least possible—that is, zero. He then derived the lunar distance from two observations of a solar eclipse (which can be identified as the total eclipse of 14 March 190 B.C.),[30] in which the sun's disk was totally obscured near the Hellespont and four-fifths obscured at Alexandria. The assumption that the sun has zero parallax means that we can take the whole shift in the obscured amount of the sun's disk (a fifth of its diameter) as due to lunar parallax. Assuming that the eclipse was in the meridian at both Alexandria and the Hellespont, we have the situation of Figure 3, where M represents the center of the moon, O the earth's center, H the observer at the Hellespont, A the observer at Alexandria, Z the direction of the zenith at the Hellespont, and POQ the equator of the earth, the radius of which is $r_{\oplus}$. Since Hipparchus knew ϕ_H and ϕ_A, the latitudes of the Hellespont and Alexandria (about 41° and 31° respectively), and could find the moon's declination δ at the time of the eclipse (about $-3°$) from his tables, he could calculate the distance of the moon (OM in Figure 3):

$$AH = r_{\oplus} \cdot \text{Crd}\,\widehat{AOH} = r_{\oplus} \cdot \text{Crd}(\phi_H - \phi_A) \approx r_{\oplus} \cdot \text{Crd}\,10°.$$

The zenith distance of the moon at H, ζ', is approximately equal to ζ; and $\zeta = \phi_H - \delta \approx 44°$.

$$\theta = 180° - \zeta' - \widehat{OHA} \approx 51°.$$

μ is one-fifth of the apparent diameter of the sun, or $21600'/(5 \cdot 650)$ (from [1] and [3] above). From AH, ϑ, and μ the triangle AHM is determined (in terms of $r_{\oplus}$); and we find

$$AM = D' \approx 70r_{\oplus}, \text{ and } D \approx D' + r_{\oplus} \approx 71r_{\oplus}.$$

This is the distance of the moon at the time of the eclipse. To find the least distance of the moon, we have to reduce it by one or two earth radii. Hipparchus found $71r_{\oplus}$ as the least distance. The small discrepancy is no doubt due to the approximations (in ϕ_H, ϕ_A, and ζ') made above. By applying the ratio $R:e$ = 3122-1/2:247-1/2, derived from his lunar model, Hipparchus found the greatest distance as $83r_{\oplus}$. The assumption that the eclipse took place in the meridian (which Hipparchus knew to be false) implies, however, that the distances must be greater than those computed (for as the moon moves away from the meridian, the angle ϑ, and hence D', increases), so that $71r_{\oplus}$ represents the minimum possible distance of the moon.

Whereas in book I, Hipparchus had assumed that the solar parallax was the least possible, in book II he assumed that it was the greatest possible (consistent with the fact that it was not great enough to be observed)—that is, 7′. This immediately gives the solar distance, for since the angle is small, we can substitute the angle for the chord and say that the sun's distance is $3438/7 \approx 490r_{\oplus}$. In Figure 4, S, M, O, U are the centers of the sun, moon, earth, and shadow, respectively, and $OU = OM$. From the similar triangles with bases UA, OB, and MD, it follows that

$$MD = 2OB - UA.$$

From (2) $\quad UA = 2\tfrac{1}{2}MC.$

Therefore $\quad CD = MD - MC = 2OB - 3\tfrac{1}{2}MC$

and $\quad OB - CD = 3\tfrac{1}{2}MC - OB.$

From (1), and substituting angles for chords,

$$MC = \frac{1}{2} \cdot \frac{21600}{650} \cdot \frac{OM}{3438}.$$

And from the similar triangles OMC, OSE and OBE, CDE

$$\frac{OM}{OS} = \frac{OC}{OE} = \frac{OB - CD}{OB} = \frac{\dfrac{3\frac{1}{2} \cdot 21600\, OM}{2 \cdot 650 \cdot 3438} - OB}{OB}.$$

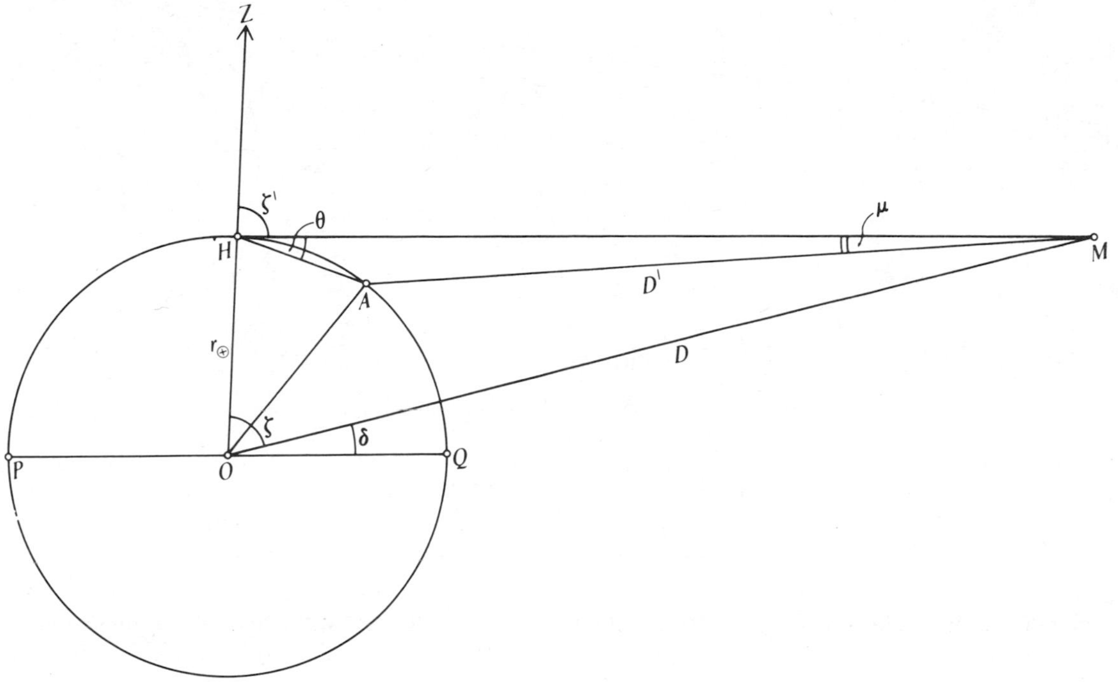

FIGURE 3

Since $OS = 490\ OB$,

$$(4)\quad OM = \frac{490}{\frac{490 \cdot 3\frac{1}{2} \cdot 21600}{2 \cdot 650 \cdot 3438} - 1}\ OB \approx 67\tfrac{1}{5}\ OB.$$

Hipparchus found the mean distance of the moon as 67-1/3$r_{\oplus}$, and the distance of the sun as 490$r_{\oplus}$. These too were computed under an extremal assumption however: that the solar parallax was the maximum possible (the solar distance was the minimum possible). This in turn implies that the resultant lunar distance is a maximum, for it is easily seen from equation (4) that as the sun's distance (490 in the expression) increases, the moon's distance decreases. Moreover, it does not decrease indefinitely, for as the sun's distance tends to infinity, the expression in (4) tends to the limit $(2 \cdot 650 \cdot 3438)/(3\text{-}1/2 \cdot 21600) \approx 59 r_{\oplus}$. Although it is not explicitly attested, there is little doubt that Hipparchus realized this, and stated that the mean distance of the moon lay between the bounds 67-1/3 and 59 earth radii.[31] He thus arrived at a value for the lunar mean distance that was not only greatly superior to earlier estimates but was also stated in terms of limits that include the true value (about 60 earth radii). His methods must be regarded as a tour de force in the use of crude and scanty observational data to achieve a result of the right order of magnitude.

Ptolemy criticized Hipparchus' procedure (unjustifiably, if the above reconstruction is correct), on the ground that it starts from the solar parallax, which is too small to be observed.[32] He himself used Hipparchus' second method (with different data) but started from the lunar distance (derived from an observation of the moon's parallax), whence he found the solar distance. This modified procedure became standard in later astronomical works, and was used by Copernicus.

Hipparchus also computed the true sizes of sun and moon (relative to the earth), which are easily found from the distances and apparent diameters. Theon of Smyrna stated that Hipparchus said that the sun was about 1,880 times the size of the earth, and the earth 27 times the size of the moon.[33] Since a lunar distance of about 60 earth radii implies that the earth's diameter is about 3 times the size of the moon's, Hipparchus must have been referring to comparative volumes. Hence the sun's diameter was, according to him, about 12-1/3 times the earth's; and therefore (by the method of book II) the sun's distance was about 2,500 earth radii and the moon's about 60-1/2 earth radii. These may have been the figures he finally decided on for the purposes of parallax computation.

In any case, his investigation of the distances furnished Hipparchus with a horizontal parallax that, for the moon, was approximately correct. For

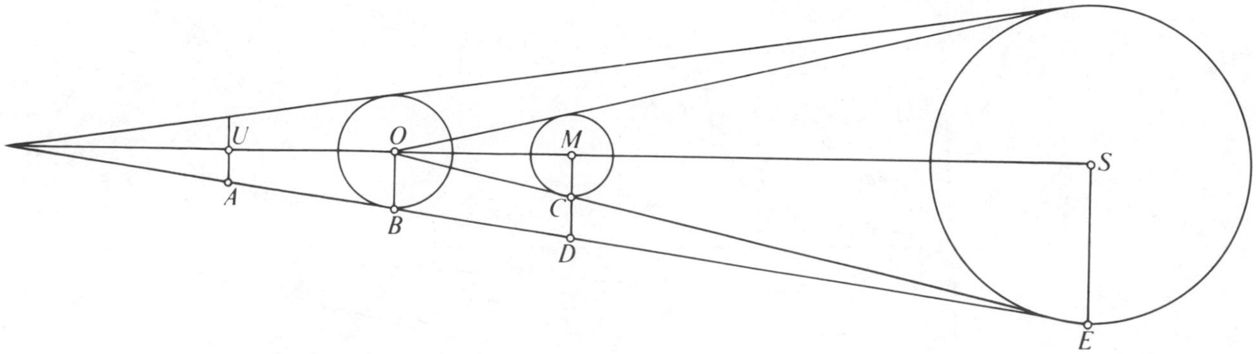

FIGURE 4.

computation of the circumstances of solar eclipses, and to correct observations of the moon with respect to fixed stars, he had to find the lunar parallax for a given lunar longitude and terrestrial latitude and time. This is a very unpleasant problem in spherical astronomy. We know that Hipparchus solved it; but we know very little about his solution, although it is certain that it was not carried out with full mathematical rigor. We can infer from a criticism made by Ptolemy[34] that Hipparchus wrote a work on parallax in at least two books. The details of Ptolemy's criticism are quite obscure to me; and the only safe inference is that in converting the total parallax into its longitudinal and latitudinal components, Hipparchus treated spherical triangles as plane triangles (some of these triangles are too large for the procedure to be justifiable, but one can apply the same criticism to Ptolemy).[35] The actual corrections for parallax that Hipparchus is known to have applied to particular lunar observations are, however, reasonably accurate.[36] One might guess that the methods of computing parallax found in Indian astronomical texts (which are quite different from Ptolemy's) are related to Hipparchus' procedures, but at present this is mere speculation.

Eclipses. Mastery of the above topics enabled Hipparchus to predict eclipses of both sun and moon for a given place; and we may presume, although there is no specific evidence, that he compiled eclipse tables for this purpose. The elder Pliny tells us that he predicted eclipses of the sun and moon for a period of 600 years[37]; and this has been taken seriously by some modern scholars, who envisage Hipparchus producing a primitive "Oppolzer." Although utterly incredible as it stands, the story must have some basis; and O. Neugebauer makes the plausible suggestion that what Hipparchus did was to arrange the eclipse records available to him from Babylonian and other sources (which, as we have seen, covered a period of 600 years from Nabonassar to his own time) in a form convenient for astronomical use. If this was so, we can explain more easily how Ptolemy was able to select eclipses with very special circumstances to suit a particular demonstration[38]: he was using material already digested by Hipparchus.

Pliny provides another valuable piece of information about Hipparchus' work on eclipses. He says that Hipparchus discovered that lunar eclipses can occur at five-month intervals, solar eclipses at seven-month intervals, and solar eclipses at one-month intervals—but in the last case only if one eclipse is seen in the northern hemisphere and the other in the southern.[39] Hipparchus, then, had discussed eclipse intervals; and we see from Ptolemy's discussion of the topic at *Almagest* VI, 5–6, how Hipparchus must have approached the problem. Babylonian astronomers were aware that lunar eclipses could occur at intervals of five synodic months as well as the usual six. Ptolemy showed that five-month intervals are possible for lunar eclipses but seven-month intervals are not, that both five- and seven-month intervals are possible for solar eclipses, and that one-month intervals are not possible for solar eclipses "in our part of the world." Hipparchus must have proved all this, and also that solar eclipses at one-month intervals are possible for different hemispheres. The essential elements in the proof (besides the apparent sizes of sun, moon, and shadow) are parallax (for solar eclipses) and the varying motion of the moon in latitude in a true synodic month. It is to this topic that we must refer the work "On the Monthly Motion of the Moon in Latitude" (Περὶ τῆς κατὰ πλάτος μηνιαίας τῆς σελήνης κινήσεως), the title of which is preserved in the *Suda*.[40] Presumably Achilles Tatius is referring to Hipparchus' work on eclipse intervals when he names him as one of those who have written treatises on solar eclipses in the seven "climata,"[41] for the geographical latitude is one of the most important elements in the discussion.

Fixed Stars. Hipparchus devoted much time and several works to topics connected with the fixed stars. His observations of them must have extended over many years. On these points there is general agreement among modern scholars. On all other points confusion reigns, although Hipparchus' sole surviving work, "Commentary on the Phaenomena of Aratus and Eudoxus" (Τῶν Ἀράτου καὶ Εὐδόξου Φαινομένων ἐξήγησις), in three books, is concerned with the fixed stars. Nevertheless, it is possible, if we look at the evidence without formulating prior hypotheses, to come to some conclusions.

In the mid-fourth century B.C., Eudoxus wrote a pioneering work naming and describing the constellations. This is now lost (Hipparchus is the main source of our knowledge of it). In the early third century B.C., Aratus wrote a poem based on Eudoxus, called "Phaenomena," which became immensely popular and is still extant. Not long before Hipparchus a mathematician, Attalus of Rhodes, wrote a commentary on Aratus (now lost). Hipparchus' treatise is a critique of all three works. None of the three contained any mathematical astronomy, only descriptions of the relative positions of stars, simultaneous risings and settings, and the like; and much of Hipparchus' criticism in books 1 and 2 is of the same qualitative kind. But even from this, one can see that he had fixed the positions of a number of stars according to a mathematical system (he incidentally notes some polar distances, declinations, and right ascensions). The last part of book 2 and the whole of book 3 are devoted to his own account of the risings and settings of the principal constellations for a latitude where the longest day is 14-1/2 hours. Whereas his predecessors had merely reported the stars or constellations that rise and set together with a given constellation, Hipparchus gave the corresponding degrees of the ecliptic (for risings, settings, and culminations). At the end of book 3 is a list of bright stars that lie on or near twenty-four-hour circles, beginning with the hour circle through the summer solstice. Hipparchus says that the purpose of this is to enable one to tell the time at night when making astronomical observations.

In this treatise Hipparchus indicates the position of a star in various ways. We have already mentioned declination (which he calls "distance from the equator along the circle through the pole") and polar distance (the complement of declination). He frequently uses an odd form of right ascension. Thus he says that a star "occupies three degrees of Leo along its parallel circle." This means that each small circle parallel to the equator is divided into twelve "signs" of 30°, and thus the right ascension of the star is 123°. The assignment of the stars to the hour circles at the end of book 3 is also a form of right ascension. Besides these equatorial coordinates, we find in the section on simultaneous risings and settings a mixture of equatorial and ecliptic coordinates: Hipparchus names the point of the ecliptic that crosses the meridian together with a given star. In other words, he gives the point at which the declination circle through the star cuts the ecliptic. It is significant that this, the "polar longitude," is one of the standard coordinates for fixed stars in Indian astronomical texts. There are no purely ecliptic coordinates (latitude and longitude) in Hipparchus' treatise.

Far from being a "work of his youth," as it is frequently described, the commentary on Aratus reveals Hipparchus as one who has already compiled a large number of observations, invented methods for solving problems in spherical astronomy, and developed the highly significant idea of mathematically fixing the positions of the stars (Aristyllus and Timocharis recorded a few declinations in the early third century, but we know of nothing else before Hipparchus). There is no hint of a knowledge of precession in the work; but, as we shall see, that discovery falls at the end of his career. The treatise is probably subsequent to Hipparchus' catalog of fixed stars.

The nature of this catalog (presumably "On the Compilation of the Fixed Stars and of the [?] Catasterisms") to which the *Suda* refers[42] is puzzling. The worst excess of the modern notion of the strict dependence of the *Almagest* on Hipparchus is the belief that we can obtain Hipparchus' catalog simply by taking Ptolemy's catalog in *Almagest* VII and VIII and lopping 2-2/3° (to account for precession) off the longitudes. This was conclusively refuted by Vogt, who showed by a careful analysis of the coordinates of 122 stars derived from the commentary on Aratus that in almost every case there was a significant difference between Hipparchus' and Ptolemy's data. The most explicit statement about Hipparchus' star catalog is found in Pliny, who says that Hipparchus noticed a new star and, because it moved, began to wonder whether other fixed stars move; he therefore decided to number and name the fixed stars for posterity, inventing instruments to mark the positions and sizes of each.[43] This confused notice could be a description of a star catalog like Ptolemy's, but it could equally well refer to an account of the number and relative positions of the stars in each constellation (without coordinates). In fact Ptolemy, wishing to show that the positions of the fixed stars relative to each other had not changed since the time of Hipparchus, reported a number of star alignments that Hipparchus seemed to have recorded for just the purpose alleged by Pliny; to allow posterity to determine whether the fixed stars have a proper motion.[44] Naturally no coordinates were given.

Apparent excerpts from Hipparchus' star catalog that are found in late Greek and Latin sources merely give the total number of stars in each constellation. These suggest that Hipparchus counted a large number of stars,[45] but they do not prove that he assigned coordinates to all—or, indeed, to any. Ptolemy quoted the declinations of a few bright stars mentioned by Hipparchus; but in every case he compared the declination with that recorded by Aristyllus and Timocharis, in order to determine the precession. These declinations may well have been taken not from Hipparchus' catalog but from one of his works on precession. There is one text, however, that does appear to preserve coordinates from Hipparchus' star catalog. In late Latin scholia on Aratus[46] there are found, for the circumpolar constellations, polar distances and what must be interpreted as polar longitudes, which are approximately correct for the time of Hipparchus. Whether Hipparchus gave such coordinates for every star in the catalog or only for some selected stars remains uncertain. The only thing we know for certain about the catalog is that the coordinates employed were not latitude and longitude: Ptolemy (*Almagest* VII, 3) would not have chosen such a roundabout way (conversion of declinations) to prove that latitudes of fixed stars remain constant, had he been able to cite the latitudes from Hipparchus' catalog. It is a plausible conjecture that the star coordinates given in the commentary on Aratus are taken directly from the catalog; at the very least, they are a good indication of the ways in which the position of a star was described in that work.

Precession and the Length of the Year. Hipparchus is most famous for his discovery of the "precession of the equinoxes," the slow motion of the solstitial and equinoctial points from east to west through the fixed stars. This topic is intimately connected with the length of the year, for precession implies both that the coordinates of the fixed stars (such as right ascension and declination) change over a period of time, and also that the tropical year (return of the sun to the same equinox or solstice) is shorter than the sidereal year (return of the sun to the same star). We do not know what phenomenon first led Hipparchus to suspect precession, but we do know that he confirmed his suspicion by both the above approaches. According to Ptolemy, the first hypothesis that he suggested was that only the stars in the zodiac move.[47] Later, in "On the Change in Position of the Solstitial and Equinoctial Points" (Περὶ τῆς μεταβάσεως τῶν τροπικῶν καὶ ἰσημερινῶν σημείων), he formulated the hypothesis that all the fixed stars move with respect to the equinoxes (or, rather, vice versa). He supported this hypothesis in two ways. First he compared the distance of the star Spica (α Virginis) from the autumnal equinox in the time of Timocharis (observations of 294 and 283 B.C.) and his own time. Unfortunately this involved considerable uncertainty, since Timocharis' observations were simply occultations of Spica by the moon, which had to be reduced to longitudes by means of the lunar theory; and Hipparchus' own observations of elongations of Spica from the moon at two lunar eclipses led to results differing by 3/4°.[48] He concluded that the longitudes of Spica had increased by about 2° in the 160-odd years since Timocharis, but he was well aware that his data were too shaky to allow any confidence in the precise amount.

Hipparchus' other approach was to try to find the length of the tropical year. For this purpose he set out a series of equinox observations (listed by Ptolemy at *Almagest* III, 1) ranging from 162 to 128 B.C. (the latter date is probably close to that of the composition of the book, as is confirmed by Hipparchus' observation of the longitude of Regulus in the same year [*Almagest* VII, 2]). Unfortunately, these seemed to indicate a variation in the length of the year, which Hipparchus evidently was prepared to consider at this point. We do not know what conclusion, if any, he reached in this work; but he must already have assumed some value for the length of the sidereal year (see below), for otherwise there would have been no point in investigating the length of the tropical year in order to determine the amount of precession. Hipparchus reverted to the topic in a later work, "On the Length of the Year" (Περὶ ἐνιαυσίου μεγέθους). In this he came to more definite conclusions. He determined that the tropical and equinoctial points move at least 1/100° a year backward through the signs of the ecliptic, and that the length of the tropical year is 365-1/4 days, less at least 1/300 of a day.[49] These two formulations are of course related. The basis of his proof was comparison of the solstice observed by himself in 135 B.C. with those observed by Aristarchus in 280 B.C. and Meton in 432 B.C. Having thus found a (maximum) value for the tropical year, Hipparchus subtracted it from his value for the sidereal year, thus producing a (minimum) value for precession.[50] From his figures for the tropical year and precession we can deduce the value he assigned to the sidereal year: 365-1/4 + 1/144 days, a very accurate estimate. There is independent evidence that he used this value, and that it is of Babylonian origin. In "On the Length of the Year" Hipparchus also assumed (correctly) that precession takes place about the poles of the ecliptic, and not of the equator, but still expressed uncertainty on that matter. He also realized that one must define the solar year as the tropical year.[51]

Having established the length of the tropical year, Hipparchus wrote "On Intercalary Months and Days" (Περὶ ἐμβολίμων μηνῶν τε καὶ ἡμερῶν), in which he proposed a lunisolar intercalation cycle that was a modification of the Callippic cycle:[52] it contained 304 tropical years, 112 with 13 synodic months and 292 with 12, and a total of 111,035 days. This produces very good approximations to Hipparchus' values for both the tropical year and the mean synodic month. There is no evidence that it was ever used, even by astronomers.

Planetary Theory. Ptolemy tells us (*Almagest* IX, 2) that Hipparchus renounced any attempt to devise a theory to explain the motions of the five planets, but contented himself with showing that the hypotheses of the astronomers of his time could not adequately represent the phenomena. We may infer from Ptolemy's discussion that Hipparchus showed that the simple epicycle theory propounded by Apollonius produced constant arcs of retrogradation, whereas observation showed that they vary in length. Ptolemy further informs us that Hipparchus assembled observations of the planets "in a more convenient form." He mentions Hipparchus specifically in connection with an observation of Mercury of 262 B.C. according to the strange "Dionysian era,"[53] and it is probable that all observations in that era preserved in the *Almagest* are derived from his collection; the same may be true of Babylonian observations of Mercury and Saturn according to the Seleucid era. Ptolemy mentions no planetary observations made by Hipparchus himself, and it is probable that he made few. Ptolemy does, however, ascribe to him the following planetary period relations (*Almagest* IX, 3):

Saturn in 59 years makes 57 revolutions in anomaly and 2 in the ecliptic.

Jupiter in 71 years makes 65 revolutions in anomaly and 6 in the ecliptic.

Mars in 79 years makes 37 revolutions in anomaly and 42 in the ecliptic.

Venus in 8 years makes 5 revolutions in anomaly and 8 in the ecliptic.

Mercury in 46 years makes 145 revolutions in anomaly and 46 in the ecliptic.

These are well-known relations in Babylonian astronomy, occurring in the so-called "goal-year" texts.

The only other indication of Hipparchus' interest in the planets is a passage in Ptolemy's *Planetary Hypotheses*[54] reporting an attempt to determine minimum values for the apparent diameters of the heavenly bodies. Hipparchus stated that the apparent diameter of the sun is thirty times that of the smallest star and ten times that of Venus.

Instruments. The only observational instrument that Ptolemy specifically ascribes to Hipparchus is the "four-cubit diopter" with which he observed the apparent diameters of the sun and moon and arrived at the estimates given above (*Almagest* V, 14). The instrument is described by Pappus and Proclus.[55] It consisted of a wooden rod of rectangular cross section some six feet in length. The observer looked through a hole in a block at one end of the rod, and moved a prism that slid in a groove along the top of the rod until the prism exactly covered the object sighted. The ratio of the breadth of the prism to its distance from the sighting hole gave the chord of the apparent diameter of the object.

As J. B. J. Delambre remarked,[56] certain observations of Hipparchus' seem to imply use of the "armillary astrolabe" described by Ptolemy at *Almagest* V, 1, and used by him to observe the ecliptic distance between heavenly bodies, particularly between sun and moon. These are observations of the elongation of the moon from the sun reported in *Almagest* V, 5. In particular, the observation of 7 July 127 B.C.[57] seems to indicate that Hipparchus observed not merely the elongation but also, and at the same time, the ecliptic position of the sun (which is given by the shadow on the armillary astrolabe). It seems odd, however, that Ptolemy should describe the instrument so carefully (and claim it as his own) if in fact it were old and well known. Furthermore, for one of the observations Ptolemy says Hipparchus used instruments (plural).[58] It is possible that Hipparchus used one instrument to determine the sun's position and another to measure the elongation, but use of the astrolabe cannot be excluded.

Hipparchus determined the times of equinox and solstice, and perhaps measured the inclination of the ecliptic, confirming Eratosthenes' estimation that the distance between the solstices was 11/83 of the circle.[59] For these observations he must, like Ptolemy, have measured the altitude or zenith distance of the sun at meridian transit. Much of his data on fixed stars also seem to imply observation of the meridian altitude. We can only speculate about the instrument(s) he used. One might conjecture that one was a primitive form of the diopter described by Hero, which could be used for both meridian and elongation observations.

An incidental remark of Ptolemy's implies that Hipparchus (like Ptolemy at *Almagest* VIII, 3) gave instructions for constructing a celestial globe and marking the constellations on it.[60] Such globes existed before Hipparchus, probably as early as the fourth century B.C., but more as artistic than scientific objects. Presumably Hipparchus mentioned the globe in connection with his star catalog. If the stars were marked on it according to a coordinate system, and if, like Ptolemy's, it were furnished with a ring indicating the local horizon to which its axis of rotation was inclined at the correct angle, it could be used not merely for demonstration purposes but also to read off simultaneous risings and settings directly.

There is evidence that Hipparchus invented the plane astrolabe. Our authority for this, Synesius, is late (A.D. 400) and his account confused. But the whole necessary theory of stereographic projection is set out in Ptolemy's *Planisphaerium*; and use of such projection would explain, among other things, how Hipparchus computed simultaneous risings and settings. The balance of probability is that Hipparchus used (and perhaps invented) stereographic projection. If that is so, there is no reason to deny his invention of the plane astrolabe, which provides an easy solution to the problems of the rising times of arcs of the ecliptic and simultaneous risings of stars at a given latitude.

Geography. Hipparchus wrote a work in (at least) three books entitled "Against the Geography of Eratosthenes" (Πρὸς τὴν 'Ερατοσθένους γεωγραφίαν). In the mid-third century Eratosthenes had given a description of the known world, in which he attempted to delineate crudely the main outlines of a world map by means of imaginary lines (including, but not restricted to, meridians and parallels of latitude) drawn through fixed points, and to establish distances along such lines in absolute terms (stades). This was related to astronomical geography in the sense that Eratosthenes had made an estimate of the circumference of the earth (252,000 stades), and had taken some account of the ratios of the shadow to the gnomon at various latitudes. Hipparchus' work was a detailed criticism of Eratosthenes' data, showing that the distances and relationships given were inconsistent with each other and with other geographical data. He evidently supplied numerous corrections and supplements to Eratosthenes; but, as we have seen, his astronomical geography is based on simple arithmetical schemes, and although he enunciated the principle that longitudes should be determined by means of eclipses,[61] this was merely an expression of an ideal. The only evidence that Hipparchus used astronomical observations to improve geographical studies is the statement of Ptolemy (*Geography* I, 4) that he gave the latitudes of "a few cities." Nor does he seem to have contributed anything to mathematical geography, which emerges from infancy only with the work of Marinus of Tyre and Ptolemy.

Other Works. Extant astrological works refer to Hipparchus as an authority on astrology; but we know almost nothing about the content of his writings on this subject, except that the topics attested are all well-worn astrological themes, such as "astrological geography," in which the various regions of the world are assigned to the influence of a zodiacal sign or part of a sign.[62] His work on weather prognostication from the risings and settings of fixed stars, known from numerous citations in Ptolemy's "Phases of the Fixed Stars," also belonged to a traditional genre of Greek "scientific" literature. Chance quotations mention a work on optics,[63] in which he endorsed the theory of vision that "visual rays" emanate from the eye; a book "On Objects Carried Down by Their Weight" (Περὶ τῶν διὰ βαρύτητα κάτω φερομένων);[64] and a work on combinatorial arithmetic. The last is almost the only reference we have to the topic in antiquity, but this merely illustrates how little we know of Greek mathematics outside the "classical" domain of geometry.

Both in antiquity and in modern times Hipparchus has been highly praised and misunderstood. Since Delambre modern scholarship has tended to treat Hipparchus as if he had written a primitive *Almagest*, and to extract his "doctrine" by discarding from the extant *Almagest* what are thought to be Ptolemy's additions. This unhistorical method has obscured Hipparchus' real achievement. Greek astronomy before him had conceived the idea of explaining the motions of the heavenly bodies by geometrical models, and had developed models that represented the motions well qualitatively. What Hipparchus did was to transform astronomy into a quantitative science. His main contributions were to develop mathematical methods enabling one to use the geometrical models for practical prediction, and to assign numerical parameters to the models. For the second, his use of observations and of constants derived from Babylonian astronomy was crucial (without them his lunar theory would not have been possible). His own observations were also important (he and Ptolemy are the only astronomers in antiquity known to have observed systematically). Particularly remarkable is his open-mindedness, his willingness to abandon traditional views, to examine critically, and to test by observation his own theories as well as those of others (Ptolemy's most frequent epithet for him is φιλαληθής, "lover of truth"). Remarkable too, in antiquity, was his attitude toward astronomy as an evolving science that would require observations over a much longer period before it could be securely established. Related to this were his attempts to assemble observational material for the use of posterity.

Hipparchus acquired a high reputation in antiquity (he was extravagantly praised by the elder Pliny, and later was depicted on the coins of his native city), but it seems likely that his works were little read. From Ptolemy's citations, one can see why. They were in the form of numerous writings discussing different, often highly specialized, topics. It seems that Hipparchus never gave an account of astronomical theory, or even part of it, starting from first principles (Ptolemy often inferred Hipparchus' opinion on a topic from incidental remarks). Hipparchus did not, then, construct an astronomical system: he only made such a system possible and worked out some parts of it. When Ptolemy, using Hipparchus' work as one of his essential foundations, did construct such a system, which became generally accepted, interest in Hipparchus' works declined further. It is not surprising that all are lost except the commentary on Aratus (which survived because of the popularity of Aratus' poem). Pappus, in the fourth century, still knew some works by Hipparchus, but there is no certain instance of firsthand knowledge of the lost works after him (the astrological treatise by Hipparchus referred to in Arabic sources was certainly pseudonymous). In Western tradition, then, the influence of Hipparchus was channeled solely through the *Almagest*. But there is much evidence that Indian astronomy of the *Siddhāntas* preserves elements of Hipparchus' theories and methods. These presumably come from some pre-Ptolemaic Greek astronomical work(s) based in part on Hipparchus (there are elements in Indian astronomy, notably in planetary theory, that are also of Greek origin but cannot have been derived from Hipparchus). The task of analyzing the Indian material from this point of view has hardly begun.

NOTES

1. For instance, *Suidae Lexicon*, Ada Adler, ed., II (Leipzig, 1931), 657, no. 521; Aelian, *De natura animalium*, R. Hercher, ed. (Leipzig, 1864), 175.
2. *Almagest* III, 1, Manitius ed., I, 142.
3. *Ibid.*, V, 5, Manitius ed., I, 274.
4. H. C. F. C. Schjellerup, "Recherches sur l'astronomie. . .," 38–39 (–140); H. Vogt, "Versuch einer Wiederherstellung . . .," cols. 25, 31–32 (different dates from different data: –138, –150, –130, –156).
5. The three eclipses of 201–200 B.C. (*Almagest* IV, 11, Manitius ed., I, 251–252) are obviously too early to have been seen by Hipparchus. For the equinox of 24 March 146 B.C. (*Almagest* III, 1, Manitius ed., I, 135), the observation made on the ring in Alexandria is stated to have differed by five hours from that made by Hipparchus himself.
6. See note 1. The text as printed by Hercher says that it was "Hieron the tyrant" who was amazed; presumably this is meant to be the tyrant of Syracuse in the early fifth century. This is, however, Valesius' emendation of "Nero the tyrant," which is equally impossible chronologically.
7. See the contributions of A. Aaboe, O. Neugebauer, N. Swerdlow, and G. J. Toomer in the bibliography. A notable exception from an earlier period is the article by Vogt in the bibliography.
8. A. Rome, *Commentaires . . . sur l'Almageste*, I (Rome, 1931), 451. The expression ἡ πραγματεία τῶν ἐν κυκλῷ εὐθειῶν (treatment of straight lines in a circle"; that is, chords) is not the title of the work, as is commonly supposed, but Theon's description of its contents, repeating verbatim the words Ptolemy applied to his own treatment (*Almagest* I, 9, Heiberg ed., I, 31, ll. 4–5). For a conjecture about the origin of Theon's incredible statement that Hipparchus' treatment was in twelve books see G. J. Toomer, "The Chord Table of Hipparchus . . .," 19–20.
9. Ptolemy, *Geography*, I, 20, C. F. A. Nobbe, ed., I (Leipzig, 1843), 42, ll. 26–30; Pappus, *Collectio* VI, F. Hultsch, ed., II (Berlin, 1877), 546, ll. 24–27. On this see G. J. Toomer, in *Zentralblatt für Mathematik*, **274** (1974), 7 (author's summary of article, "The Chord Table of Hipparchus . . .").
10. For a refutation of the argument of J. Tropfke that Archimedes had already constructed a chord table, see Toomer, "The Chord Table of Hipparchus . . .," 20–23.
11. See G. J. Toomer, "Ptolemy," *DSB*, XI, 189.
12. Pappus, *Collectio* VI, Hultsch ed., 600, ll. 10–11. The phrase "arithmetically" is implicitly opposed to "geometrically" (διὰ τῶν γραμμῶν), and in this context implies that Hipparchus was using not Euclidean geometry but Babylonian methods.
13. Strabo, *Geography* 75 and 135, H. L. Jones, ed., I, 282, 514–516. A "cubit" in the astronomical sense is 2°; it is known from cuneiform texts, and its use here and elsewhere by Hipparchus is another indication of his heavy debt to Babylonian astronomy.
14. See O. Neugebauer, *History of Ancient Mathematical Astronomy*, I, 304–306.

HIPPARCHUS

15. *Commentary on Aratus* II, 4, Manitius ed., 184. Ptolemy explains how to calculate simultaneous risings and settings trigonometrically at *Almagest* VIII, 5.
16. *Ibid.*, 2, Manitius ed., 150, ll. 14–17.
17. See Neugebauer, *op. cit.*, 301–302.
18. *Commentary on Aratus* II, 2, Manitius ed., 148–150.
19. See, for instance, O. Neugebauer and D. Pingree, *The Pañcasiddhāntikā of Varāhamihira (Kongelige Danske Videnskabernes Selskab. Historisk-Filosofiske Skrifter*, **6**, no. 1), II (Copenhagen, 1970), 41–42, 85. Use of the analemma is not attested before the first century B.C. (Diodorus of Alexandria) and is mainly, but not exclusively, associated with sundial theory in extant Greek texts (notably Ptolemy's *Analemma*). I believe that it was invented before Hipparchus for purely graphical purposes in sundial theory, and adapted by him to numerical solutions in spherical astronomy (whence it is found in Indian astronomy). But it must be admitted that this is all conjectural.
20. *Almagest* XII, 1. For a detailed discussion of the theories and their equivalence see Toomer, "Ptolemy," 190.
21. *Ibid.*, 190–191. It is likely that Hipparchus found only the first two season lengths by observation; the last two were then derived from the eccentric model after he had calculated the eccentricity.
22. Vettius Valens, *Anthologiae*, W. Kroll, ed. (Berlin, 1908), 354.
23. Kugler, *Die Babylonische Mondrechnung*, 21, 24, 40, 46, 108.
24. On all this see A. Aaboe, "On the Babylonian Origin of Some Hipparchian Parameters."
25. For details see Toomer, "The Chord Table of Hipparchus . . .," 7–16.
26. *Almagest* V, 3, Manitius ed., I, 266; V, 5, Manitius ed., I, 271, 274.
27. *Ibid.*, VI, 9, Manitius ed., I, 394–395.
28. On the exact title of the work see G. J. Toomer, "Hipparchus on the Distances of the Sun and Moon," 126, n. l.
29. *Almagest* V, 11, Manitius ed., I, 294–295; Rome, *op. cit.*, 67–68.
30. For the identification see Toomer, "Hipparchus on the Distances of the Sun and Moon," 131–138.
31. If so, it can hardly be a coincidence that Ptolemy establishes the mean distance of the moon as exactly $59r_{\oplus}$. See *ibid.*, 131, n. 25.
32. *Almagest* V, 11, Manitius ed., I, 294–295.
33. Theon of Smyrna, E. Hiller, ed. (Leipzig, 1878), 197.
34. *Almagest* V, 19, Manitius ed., I, 329–330.
35. Pappus' "explanation" of this passage, Rome, *op cit.*, 150–155, appears to be a completely fictitious reconstruction. I therefore ignore it here and in the account of Hipparchus' trigonometry (it is not credible that Hipparchus took the sides of large spherical triangles proportionate to the opposite angles).
36. Notably that for his observation of 2 May 127 B.C. (*Almagest* V, 5, Manitius ed., I, 271).
37. Pliny, *Naturalis historia* II, 54, Beaujeu ed., 24.
38. For instance, *Almagest* IV, 9; VI, 5.
39. Pliny, *op. cit.*, II, 57, Beaujeu ed., 25.
40. See note 1.
41. Maass, *Commentariorum in Aratum reliquiae*, 47.
42. See note 1. The Greek title is Περὶ τῆς τῶν ἀπλανῶν ἀστέρων συντάξεως καὶ τοῦ †καταστηριγμοῦ† (the last word should perhaps be emended to καταστερισμου).
43. Pliny, *op. cit.*, II, 95, Beaujeu ed., 41–42. The "new star" is commonly identified with a nova Scorpii of 134 B.C., alleged from Chinese records. The identification is of the utmost uncertainty (Pliny seems rather to refer to a comet).
44. *Almagest* VII, 1, Manitius ed., II, 5–8.
45. About 850, according to F. Boll, "Die Sternkataloge des Hipparch . . .," 194; but his calculations rest on no secure basis.
46. Maass, *op. cit.*, 183–189.
47. *Almagest* VII, 1, Manitius ed., II, 4. We do not know to what work of Hipparchus he refers.
48. *Ibid.* III, 1, Manitius ed., I, 137. Compare *ibid.*, VII, 2, Manitius ed., II, 12, where Hipparchus seems to have settled on a mean value between his two discrepant results.
49. *Ibid.*, III, 1, Manitius ed., I, 145 (this quotation is in fact from the later work "On Intercalary Months and Days"), and VII, 2, Manitius ed., II, 15.
50. That he did so is certain from his calculation of the precession over 300 years (that is, between his time and Meton's), which Ptolemy reports from this work at *Almagest* VII, 2, Manitius ed., II, 15.
51. Very interesting verbatim quotation of Hipparchus at *Almagest* III, 1, Manitius ed., I, 145–146.
52. See G. J. Toomer, "Meton," *DSB*, IX, 337–338. The details of the cycle are known from Censorinus, *De die natali* 18, O. Jahn, ed. (Berlin, 1845), 54.
53. *Almagest* IX, 7, Manitius ed., II, 134
54. Goldstein ed., 8. It is not clear whether the values for the apparent diameters of the other planets that Ptolemy adopts are also taken from Hipparchus.
55. Proclus, *Hypotyposis* . . ., Karl Manitius, ed. (Leipzig, 1909), 126–130; Rome, *op. cit.*, 90–92. The latter appears more reliable.
56. *Histoire de l'astronomie ancienne*, I, 117, 185; II, 185.
57. Manitius ed., I, 274–275.
58. That of 2 May 127 B.C., Manitius, ed., I, 271.
59. *Almagest* I, 12, Manitius ed., I, 44.
60. *Ibid.*, VII, 1, Heiberg ed., II, 11, ll. 23–24: ταῖς κατα τὸν τοῦ Ἱππάρχου τῆς στερεᾶς σφαίρας ἀστερισμὸν διατυπώσεσιν.
61. Strabo, *Geography* 7, H. L. Jones, ed., I, 22–24.
62. Hephaestion, *Apotelesmatica*, D. Pingree, ed., I (Leipzig, 1973), 4, 22.
63. *Doxographi Graeci*, H. Diels, ed. (Berlin, 1879), 404.
64. Simplicius. *Commentary on Aristotle's De caelo*, J. L. Heiberg, ed. (Berlin, 1894), which is *Commentaria in Aristotelem Graeca*, VII, 264–265.

BIBLIOGRAPHY

The only general account of Hipparchus that is at all adequate is O. Neugebauer, *A History of Ancient Mathematical Astronomy*, 3 vols. (New York, 1975) (which is Studies in the History of Mathematics and the Physical Sciences, no. 1), I, 274–343, on which I have drawn heavily. Still worth reading, despite their assumption of Ptolemy's servile dependence on Hipparchus, are J. B. J. Delambre, *Histoire de l'astronomie ancienne*, I (Paris, 1817), 106–189, and II (Paris, 1819) (the section on the *Almagest*); and Paul Tannery, *Recherches sur l'histoire de l'astronomie ancienne* (Paris, 1893). A. Rehm, "Hipparchos 18," in Pauly-Wissowa, *Real-Encyclopädie der classischen Altertumswissenschaft*, VIII, 2 (Stuttgart, 1913), cols. 1666–1681, is useful only for the references to Hipparchus in ancient sources that it assembles. No attempt can be made here to mention all the scattered references to Hipparchus in ancient sources (the more important are cited in text and notes). Our chief source, Ptolemy's *Almagest*, was edited by J. L. Heiberg, *Claudii Ptolemaei Opera quae extant omnia*, I, *Syntaxis mathematica*, 2 vols. (Leipzig, 1898–1903). Most of my references are to the German trans. by K. Manitius: *Ptolemäus, Handbuch der As-*

tronomie, 2nd ed., 2 vols., with corrections by O. Neugebauer (Leipzig, 1963). The references to Hipparchus by name can be found from the index in Manitius or that in J. L. Heiberg, *Ptolemaei Opera . . . omnia*, II, *Opera astronomica minora* (Leipzig, 1907).

Pliny the elder gives some important information in bk. II of his *Naturalis historia*, J. Beaujeu, ed. (Paris, 1950). For bibliography of the coins of Nicaea representing Hipparchus, see W. Ruge, "Nikaia 7," in Pauly-Wissowa, *Real-Encyclopädie*, XVII, 1 (Stuttgart, 1936), col. 237. Also see *British Museum Catalogue of Greek Coins, Pontus*, W. Wroth, ed. (London, 1889), 167 and pl. xxxiii.9; and *Sylloge nummorum graecorum, Deutschland, Sammlung v. Aulock, Pontus* (Berlin, 1957), nos. 548 (pl. 549), 717. There is a good photograph in Karl Schefold, *Die Bildnisse der antiken Dichter Redner und Denker* (Basel, 1943), 173, no. 30. Ptolemy's "Phases of the Fixed Stars" is printed in Heiberg's ed. of Ptolemy's *Opera astronomica minora*, 3–67. On Hipparchus' trigonometry, see G. J. Toomer, "The Chord Table of Hipparchus and the Early History of Greek Trigonometry," in *Centaurus*, **18** (1973), 6–28. On arithmetical methods for rising times, see O. Neugebauer in V. de Falco and M. Krause, *Hypsikles, Die Aufgangszeiten der Gestirne*, which is *Abhandlungen der Akademie der Wissenschaften zu Göttingen*, Phil.-hist. Kl., 3rd ser., no. 62 (1966), 5–17.

On arithmetical methods in Hipparchus' geography, see O. Neugebauer, *History of Ancient Mathematical Astronomy*, I, 304–306. On the "seven climata" see E. Honigmann, *Die sieben Klimata und die ΠΟΛΕΙΣ ΕΠΙΣΗΜΟΙ* (Heidelberg, 1929). On analemma methods, see Neugebauer, *History of Ancient Mathematical Astronomy*, II, 839–856. On Ptolemy's *Analemma* in particular, see P. Luckey, "Das Analemma von Ptolemäus," in *Astronomische Nachrichten*, **230** (1927), 17–46. On Hipparchus' equinox observations and solar theory see A. Rome, "Les observations d'équinoxes et de solstices dans le chapitre 1 du livre 3 du Commentaire sur l'*Almageste* de Théon d'Alexandrie," I and II, in *Annales de la Société scientifique de Bruxelles*, **57**, no. 1 (1937), 219–236, and **58**, no. 1 (1938), 6–26; and "Les observations d'équinoxes de Ptolémée," in *Ciel et terre*, **59** (1943), 1–15; and Viggo Petersen and Olaf Schmidt, "The Determination of the Longitude of the Apogee of the Orbit of the Sun According to Hipparchus and Ptolemy," in *Centaurus*, **12** (1968), 73–95.

The derivation of Hipparchus' lunar parameters from Babylonian astronomy was discovered by F. X. Kugler, in *Die Babylonische Mondrechnung* (Freiburg im Breisgau, 1900), and fully explained by A. Aaboe, "On the Babylonian Origin of Some Hipparchian Parameters," in *Centaurus*, **4** (1955), 122–125. On Hipparchus' derivation of the radius of the moon's epicycle, see G. J. Toomer, "The Chord Table of Hipparchus . . .," 8–16; and "The Size of the Lunar Epicycle According to Hipparchus," *ibid.*, **12** (1967), 145–150. For an explanation of his method of finding the moon's epoch in latitude, see Olaf Schmidt, "Bestemmelsen af Epoken for Maanens Middelbevaegelse i Bredde hos Hipparch og Ptolemaeus," in *Matematisk Tidsskrift*, ser. B (1937), 27–32 (whence Neugebauer, *History of Ancient Mathematical Astronomy*, I, 313). Our most detailed information about "On Sizes and Distances" comes from Pappus' commentary on *Almagest* V, in A. Rome, ed., *Commentaires de Pappus et de Théon d'Alexandrie sur l'Almageste*, I (which is Studi e Testi, no. 54) (Rome, 1931), 67–68. This passage was edited and discussed by F. Hultsch, "Hipparchos über die Grösse und Entfernung der Sonne," in *Berichte der Königlich sächsischen Gesellschaft der Wissenschaft zu Leipzig*, Phil.-hist Kl., **52** (1900), 169–200; but Hultsch failed to understand the text and, misled by the size of the sun given by Theon of Smyrna, "emended" the distance 490 earth radii to 2,490. The correct explanation of Hipparchus' procedure in bk. II was given by N. Swerdlow, "Hipparchus on the Distance of the Sun," in *Centaurus*, **14** (1969), 287–305; and a reconstruction of the whole of Hipparchus' procedure by G. J. Toomer, "Hipparchus on the Distances of the Sun and Moon," in *Archive for History of Exact Sciences*, **14** (1975), 126–142. The commentary on Aratus was edited by Karl Manitius, *Hipparchi in Arati et Eudoxi Phaenomena commentariorum libri tres* (Leipzig, 1894), with German trans. and often misleading notes. A brilliant analysis of the fixed-star data contained therein was made by H. Vogt, "Versuch einer Wiederherstellung von Hipparchs Fixsternverzeichnis," in *Astronomische Nachrichten*, **224** (1925), 17–54. A comparison of the stars on the hour circles with modern data was made by H. C. F. C. Schjellerup, "Recherches sur l'astronomie des anciens I. Sur le chronomètre céleste d'Hipparque," in *Urania*, **1** (1881), 25–39.

On the "new star" allegedly observed by Hipparchus, see J. K. Fotheringham, "The New Star of Hipparchus and the Dates of Birth and Accession of Mithridates," in *Monthly Notices of the Royal Astronomical Society*, **79** (1918–1919), 162–167. The excerpt from Hipparchus' star catalog is published and discussed by F. Boll, "Die Sternkataloge des Hipparch und des Ptolemaios," in *Bibliotheca mathematica*, 3rd ser., **2** (1901), 185–195. Related texts are printed in E. Maass, *Commentariorum in Aratum reliquiae* (Berlin, 1898), 128, 137–139, 177–275. There may be some connection between Hipparchus' catalog and a list of stars in late Latin MSS published and discussed by W. Gundel, *Neue astrologische Texte des Hermes Trismegistos* (Munich, 1936), which is *Abhandlungen der Bayerischen Akademie der Wissenschaften*, Phil.-hist. Abt., n.s. **12**, but most of Gundel's conclusions are to be rejected. The evidence for the value adopted by Hipparchus for the length of the sidereal year is discussed by O. Neugebauer, "Astronomical Fragments in Galen's Treatise on Seven-Month Children," in *Rivista degli studi orientali*, **24** (1949), 92–94. On his intercalation cycle see F. K. Ginzel, *Handbuch der mathematischen und technischen Chronologie*, II (Leipzig, 1911), 390–391.

On Babylonian "goal-year" texts see A. Sachs, "A

Classification of the Babylonian Astronomical Tablets of the Seleucid Period," in *Journal of Cuneiform Studies*, **2** (1948), 282–285. The section of Ptolemy's "Planetary Hypotheses" mentioning Hipparchus is found only in the ed. of the Arabic text by B. R. Goldstein, "The Arabic Version of Ptolemy's Planetary Hypotheses," in *Transactions of the American Philosophical Society*, n.s. **57**, pt. 4 (1967). The instruments mentioned are well described and illustrated by D. J. Price and A. G. Drachmann in *A History of Technology*, Charles Singer *et al.*, eds., III (Oxford, 1957), 586–614. On the four-cubit diopter also see F. Hultsch, "Winkelmessungen durch die Hipparchische Dioptra," in *Abhandlungen zur Geschichte der Mathematik*, **9** (1899), 193–209; on the armillary astrolabe see A. Rome, "L'astrolabe et le météoroscope d'après le commentaire de Pappus sur le 5e livre de l'*Almageste*," in *Annales de la Société scientifique de Bruxelles*, ser. A, **47**, no. 2 (1927), "Mémoires," 77–102, with good illustration on 78. On the history of the celestial globe in antiquity, see A. Schlachter, *Der Globus* (Leipzig–Berlin, 1927), which is ΣΤΟΙΧΕΙΑ, no. 8. There are good illustrations of the most famous surviving example, the globe borne by the Farnese Atlas, in Georg Thiele, *Antike Himmelsbilder* (Berlin, 1898), pls. II–VI. The (defective) text of Hero's work on the diopter is in *Heronis Alexandrini Opera quae supersunt omnia*, H. Schöne, ed., III (Leipzig, 1903), 188–315. On the evidence for the invention of stereographic projection and the astrolabe by Hipparchus, see O. Neugebauer, "The Early History of the Astrolabe," in *Isis*, **40** (1949), 240–256; and *A History of Ancient Mathematical Astronomy*, II, 868–869. The fragments of Hipparchus' geographical treatise are available in two eds. (both inadequate): H. Berger, *Die geographischen Fragmente des Hipparch* (Leipzig, 1869); and D. R. Dicks, *The Geographical Fragments of Hipparchus* (London, 1960). Our knowledge of the work is derived almost entirely from Strabo, cited here in the ed. by H. L. Jones, 8 vols., Loeb Classical Library (London–New York, 1917–1932).

On Hipparchus as an astrologer, see W. and H. G. Gundel, *Astrologumena* (Wiesbaden, 1966), which is *Sudhoffs Archiv* . . ., supp. 6, 109–110, with references to most relevant texts. The astrological work falsely ascribed to him in Arabic bibliographical works was called "The Secrets of the Stars" (*Kitāb asrār al-nujūm*): see Ibn al-Qifṭī, *Ta'rīkh al-ḥukamā'*, J. Lippert, ed. (Leipzig, 1903), 69; and Abu'l Faraj (Bar Hebraeus), *Chronography*, E. A. Wallis Budge, trans., I (London, 1932), 29. The description of the contents (*ibid.*) proves that this work originated in Islam. On Hipparchus' arithmetical work, see (for what little is known) T. L. Heath, *A History of Greek Mathematics*, II (Oxford, 1921). 256. An inconclusive attempt to reconstruct his procedure was made by Kurt R. Biermann and Jurgen Mau, "Überprüfung einer frühen Anwendung der Kombinatorik in der Logik," in *Journal of Symbolic Logic*, **23** (1958), 129–132. On combinatorial arithmetic in antiquity, see A. Rome, "Procédés anciens de calcul des combinaisons," in *Annales de la Société scientifique de Bruxelles*, ser. A., **50** (1930), "Mémoires," 97–104.

G. J. TOOMER

HIPPIAS OF ELIS (*b.* Elis, Greece; *fl.* 400 B.C.)

Elis was a small state in the northwest of the Peloponnesus whose inhabitants had charge of the Olympic festival. Hippias' father was named Diopeithes,[1] but his ancestry is otherwise unknown.[2] In the Platonic dialogue *Hippias Major*[3] he is made to say that he was young when Protagoras was old, and in the *Protagoras* Plato represents him as present at a philosophic discussion with that eminent Sophist about 432 B.C.[4] The date of the birth of Protagoras is uncertain but is usually placed from 488 to 485. In Plato's *Apology,*[5] set in 399, Hippias is mentioned as a teacher of youth along with Gorgias and other famous Sophists, and may then be presumed to have been at the height of his fame. He was therefore a contemporary of Plato. His wife Platane bore him three sons; and when she was left a widow, the orator Isocrates in extreme old age took her in marriage and adopted her youngest son, Aphareus,[6] who achieved some fame as a tragic poet. Isocrates died in 338. These facts would suggest that Hippias had a long life; and the belief is made certain if, with Mario Untersteiner, the preface to the *Characters* of Theophrastus is attributed to Hippias, for he is there made to say that he has reached ninety-nine years of age.[7] The old notion that he was killed while weaving plots against his native land must be abandoned now that the correct name in the text of Tertullian has been established as Icthyas.[8]

Hippias was taught by an otherwise unknown Aegesidamus, and he emerged as a polymath who wrote and lectured over a wide range of disciplines: rhetoric, politics, poetry, music, painting, sculpture, and astronomy, as well as the philosophy and mathematics on which his fame chiefly rests.[9] The secret of his wide knowledge appears to have been an exceptional memory. According to Philostratus, he had a system of mnemonics such that if he once heard a string of fifty names, he could repeat them in correct order.[10] Most of what is known about Hippias' life and character comes from a dialogue between Socrates and Hippias recorded by Xenophon[11] and from the two Platonic dialogues that bear his name, the *Hippias Major* and *Hippias Minor.* Their authenticity has been disputed, but even if not genuine they still correctly reflect Plato's attitude; in these dialogues Hippias is represented as a naïve and humorless boaster who cannot stand up to the remorseless logic

HIPPIAS OF ELIS

of Socrates. Xenophon's portrait is not so ruthless, but there also Hippias is reduced to silence by Socrates' arguments. Hippias was a second-generation Sophist, and Plato had no love for the Sophists as a class. Apart from more fundamental differences, Plato's aristocratic soul was offended by their professional teaching; and Hippias was especially successful in negotiating lecture fees, particularly in Sicily, although he received none in Sparta, where the law forbade a foreign education.[12]

The picture in the Platonic dialogues is no doubt a caricature; but in the light of Plato's more sympathetic treatment of other individual Sophists, there must have been enough truth in the caricature for it to be recognizable as a portrait.[13] Hippias is made to accept flattery even when laid on with a trowel, acknowledging that he had never found any man to be his superior in anything.[14] At the Olympic festival it was his custom to offer to discourse on any subject proposed to him out of those which he had prepared and to answer any questions.[15] He once appeared at the festival with everything that he wore made by himself, not merely his clothes but also a ring, an oil flask, and an oil scraper—which bears out the statement in the *Suda Lexicon* that he made self-sufficiency the end of life—and he brought with him poems, epics, tragedies, dithyrambs, and all kinds of prose works.[16]

Hippias could not have been such a figure of fun as the Platonic dialogues make him out to be, for he was frequently asked to represent his native state on missions to other states, notably Sparta.[17] He was widely traveled—two visits to Athens are recorded—and in Sicily his influence was lasting if, as Untersteiner believes, he was the mentor of Dionysius the Younger and inspired the work known as the *Dissoi logoi.*[18]

The *Suda Lexicon* tersely records that Hippias "wrote many things." None of his voluminous works has survived, but some of the titles and hints of the contents are known. His *Synagoge,* known through Athenaeus, has usually been thought, on the strength of a passage in Clement of Alexandria which seems to refer to it, to have been merely a miscellany in which he put together sayings of poets and prose writers, both Greek and foreign.[19] But Bruno Snell has advanced the theory that through this work Aristotle derived his knowledge of Thales; that the views of Thales about the All being water and about the souls of inanimate objects are thereby shown to be derived from earlier mythological speculations; and that the *Synagoge* is to be looked upon as the earliest work in both the history of Greek philosophy and the history of Greek literature.[20] If this is so, it encourages the thought that Hippias' *Nomenclature of Tribes*[21] may not have been a mere catalog but an expression of his belief in the fundamental unity of all mankind. His *Register of Olympic Victors* was no doubt a piece of Elian patriotism. It was the first such list to be drawn up; and Plutarch notes that, since it came so late after the events recorded, too much authority should not be attached to it.[22] Among his epideictic or set speeches, the one known as *The Trojan* may have been in dialogue form; in it Nestor suggests to Neoptolemus many lawful and beautiful pursuits by which he might win fame.[23] Hippias wrote an elegiac inscription for the statues made by Calon at Olympia in memory of a boys' choir from Messina drowned in crossing to Rhegium.[24] More important in its ultimate significance than any of these compositions is a work on the properties of the geometrical curve he discovered, since known as the quadratrix.

Hippias' teaching has to be reconstructed from the scattered references to him in Greek and Latin authors. Untersteiner has argued that Hippias was the author not only of the preface to Theophrastus' *Characters* but also of a spurious chapter in Thucydides (III, 84) dealing with events in Corcyra and of the epideictic speech known as the *Anonymus Iamblichi;* that the *Dissoi logoi,* a work drawing on Pythagorean and Sophistic sources, reflects the teaching of Hippias; and that the philosophical digression in Plato's seventh letter is an attack upon Hippias' doctrines.[25] If this were established, it would enable a clearer picture of Hippias' philosophy to be drawn; but Untersteiner's theories are too conjectural for any conclusions to be based on them. It is therefore to the dialogues between Socrates and Hippias as recorded by Xenophon and Plato, and to a passage in Plato's *Protagoras* which may well be an imitation of the Sophist's style, that we must look in the main for Hippias' teaching.[26]

The core of it would appear to be a distinction between *νόμος* and *φύσις*,[27] that is, between positive law and nature, with a corresponding belief in the existence of unwritten natural laws which are the same for all men in all places and at all times. Reverence for the gods and honor for parents are among such natural laws.[28] It was one of Hippias' fundamental beliefs that like is kin to like by nature, and he extended it to mean that men are neighbors and kinsmen. Positive law is a matter of human agreement and can be altered; it can be a great tyrant doing violence to human nature. It is a pity that Hippias' teaching has to be seen through the distorting mirrors of Plato and Xenophon, for he would appear to have been a progenitor of the doctrine of natural law, of the social-contract theory of the state, and of the essential unity of all mankind—in fact, no mean thinker.

It is clear from Plato's raillery that Hippias claimed proficiency in arithmetic, geometry, and astronomy,[29] and one important discovery is attributed to him: the transcendental curve known as the quadratrix.

The evidence comes from two passages in Proclus which are probably derived from Geminus. The first is "Nicomedes trisected every rectilineal angle by means of the conchoidal curves. . . . Others have done the same thing by means of the quadratrices of Hippias and Nicomedes, making use of the mixed curves which are called quadratices."[30] The second is "In the same manner other mathematicians are accustomed to treat of curves, setting forth the characteristic property of each type. Thus Apollonius shows what is the characteristic for each of the conic sections, Nicomedes for the conchoids, Hippias for the quadratrices, and Perseus for the spiric curves."[31]

Who is this Hippias? The natural assumption is that he is Hippias of Elis, who is mentioned in an earlier passage by Proclus,[32] this time in the summary of geometry derived from Eudemus, as having recorded that Mamercus (or perhaps Ameristus), brother of the poet Stesichorus, acquired a reputation for geometry. No other Hippias is mentioned by Proclus; and it is in accordance with his practice, having once referred to a person in full, to omit the patronymic on subsequent mention.[33] Hippias of Elis, as shown by the references of Plato and Xenophon, had mathematical qualifications; and among the many bearers of the name Hippias in antiquity there is no other of whom this can be said.[34] It is therefore natural to identify the Hippias who is mentioned in connection with quadratrices as Hippias of Elis; and most historians of Greek mathematics, from J. E. Montucla to B. L. van der Waerden, have done so.[35]

The objections made can easily be discounted.

1. If he made so important a discovery as the quadratrix, it has been argued, Hippias would be recorded in Proclus' "Eudemian Summary"; but the omission is accounted for by the Platonic prejudice against the Sophists, and the omission of Democritus is even more remarkable.

2. Diogenes Laertius says that Archytas was the first to use an instrument for the description of a curve,[36] and the quadratrix requires an instrument for its description. Yet, on the one hand, an indefinite number of points on the quadratrix can be obtained by the ruler and compass and, on the other hand, Diogenes is not a trustworthy guide in this matter, since (a) there is no suggestion of an instrument in Eutocius' description of the curve found by Archytas to solve the problem of doubling the cube;[37] and (b) Eratosthenes specifically states that Archytas was not able to realize his solution mechanically.[38]

3. Hippias is not mentioned by Pappus and Iamblichus in their accounts of curves used for squaring the circle;[39] but this is explained if, as seems probable, Hippias did not use the curve for that purpose but only for trisecting an angle.

It may therefore be taken that the Hippias who is mentioned by Proclus in connection with the quadratrix is Hippias of Elis; and, if so, he was its discoverer, since he preceded Nicomedes. But did he use it for squaring the circle? And did he give it the name quadratrix? This is more doubtful. Proclus implies that the curve was used by Hippias for trisecting an angle, saying nothing about squaring the circle; and those Greek authors who write about the squaring of the circle do not mention Hippias. A fundamental and obvious property of the curve is that it can be used to divide an angle in any given ratio, and therefore to trisect it; but to use it for squaring the circle is a more sophisticated matter and might not be obvious to the original discoverer. This can be seen from the way the curve is generated, as described by Pappus.[40]

Let $ABCD$ be a square and BED a quadrant of a circle with center A. If the radius of the circle moves uniformly from AB to AD and in the same time the line BC moves parallel to its original position from BC to AD, then at any given time the intersection

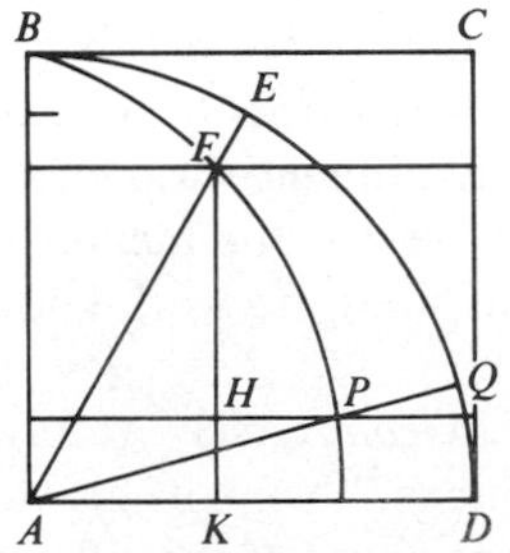

FIGURE 1

of the moving radius and the moving straight line will determine a point F. The path traced by F is the curve. If it is desired to trisect the angle EAD, let H be taken on the perpendicular FK to AD such that $FK = 3HK$. Let a straight line be drawn through H parallel to AD, and let it meet the curve at P. Let AP be produced to meet the circle at Q. Then, by the definition of the curve,

$$\angle EAD : \angle QAD = \text{arc } ED : \text{arc } QD$$
$$= FK : HK,$$

and therefore $\angle QAD$ is one-third of $\angle EAD$. It is obvious that the curve can be used not merely to trisect an angle but also to divide an angle in any given ratio; trisection is specified because this was one of the great problems of Greek mathematics when Hippias flourished.

If a is the length of a side of the square, ρ is any radius vector AF, and ϕ is the angle EAD, the equation of the curve is

$$\frac{\rho \sin \phi}{a} = \frac{\phi}{\frac{1}{2}\pi}$$

or

$$\pi\rho \sin \phi = 2a\phi.$$

The use of the quadratrix to square the circle is a more complicated matter, requiring the position of G to be known and an indirect proof *per impossibile.* (For this the article on Dinostratus may be consulted.)

The ancient witnesses can therefore be reconciled if Hippias discovered the curve and used it to trisect an angle, but its utility for squaring the circle was perceived only by such later geometers as Dinostratus and Nicomedes. In that case Hippias could not have called his curve the quadratrix, and we do not know what name he gave it. It is no objection that Proclus refers to "the quadratrices of Hippias and Nicomedes," for we have no hesitation in saying that Menaechmus discovered the parabola and hyperbola, although these terms did not come into use until Apollonius; Menaechmus would have called them "section of a right-angled cone" and "section of an obtuse-angled cone." There is, however, a more serious objection. From the second of the Proclus passages quoted above it could, without straining the sense, be inferred that Hippias wrote a whole treatise on the curve, setting forth its special properties; and in that case the probability increases that he was aware of its use for squaring the circle. Paul Tannery was of this opinion, and T. L. Heath thinks it "not impossible"; but on balance it seems preferable to hold, with C. A. Bretschneider and Moritz Cantor, that the circle-squaring property was discovered, and the name quadratrix given, later than Hippias.[41]

The citation of Hippias as the authority for Mamercus' mathematical proficiency has led some to suppose that Hippias wrote a history of geometry.[42] If so, it would be the first, antedating Eudemus by perhaps three-quarters of a century. But this is to read too much into the Greek word ἱστόρησεν, translated above as "related." It does not necessarily imply a full-scale treatise, but only that Hippias mentioned the fact in one of his many works.

NOTES

1. *Suda Lexicon,* "Ἱππίας," Adler ed., pt. 2 (Leipzig, 1931), Iota 543, p. 659.
2. Apuleius, *Florida* 9, Helm ed., p. 12.1.
3. Plato, *Hippias Major,* 282D–E.
4. Plato, *Protagoras,* 337C6–338B1. The scene is usually assigned to 432 B.C. but—as Athenaeus, V.218C–D, Gulick ed. (Loeb), II (London–New York, 1928), 428, points out—in antiquity Hippias could not have safely stayed in Athens until an annual truce was concluded in the archonship of Isarchus (423), and the chronology of what is presumably a fictitious gathering cannot be pressed.
5. Plato, *Apology,* 19E1–4.
6. [Plutarch], *Lives of the Ten Orators,* 838A–839C, Fowler ed. (Loeb); and *Moralia* 10, pp. 376–385 (the author makes Platane the daughter and not the widow of Hippias); Harpocration, *Lexicon,* "Ἀφαρεύς," Dindorf ed., I (Oxford, 1853), 68.18; Zosimus, *Historia nova* V, Mendelssohn ed. (Leipzig, 1887). Isocrates' marriage followed his liaison—when already an old man—with the courtesan Lagisca; hence "in extreme old age."
7. Theophrastus, *Characters,* pref. 2, Diels ed. (Oxford, 1909). See Mario Untersteiner, "Il proemio dei 'Caratteri' di Teofrasto e un probabile frammento di Ippia," in *Rivista di filologia classica,* n.s. **26** (1948), 1–25. In *I sofisti,* 2nd ed., fasc. 2, p. 115, translated by Kathleen Freeman in *The Sophists,* p. 274, he says the preface is "definitely a work of Hippias." But it is incredible that the author should have been still writing—even banalities—at the age of ninety-nine; and the figure must be treated with reserve. Perhaps there is a textual error. The preface is certainly not the work of Theophrastus; but the only reason for attributing it to Hippias is that it is such a work as the boastful Hippias of Plato's dialogues might have written, which is not a sufficiently strong ground.
8. The printed texts of Tertullian, *Apologeticum,* 46.16, until 1937 read: "et Hippias, dum civitati insidias disponit, occiditur." There was some dispute whether this referred to Hippias, son of Pisistratus; but since Tertullian is cataloging the misdeeds of pagan philosophers, there can be little doubt that the reading, if correct, would refer to Hippias of Elis. But H. Emonds, "Die Oligarchenrevolte zu Megara im Jahre 375 und der Philosoph Icthyas bei Tertullian *Apol.* 46.16," in *Rheinisches Museum für Philologie,* n.s. **86** (1937), 180–191, shows that the reading "et Hippias" has no MS authority and that "Icthyas" (Icthyas of Megara) should be substituted. Emonds has been followed by H. Hoppe (Vienna, 1939) and E. Dekkers (Tournai, 1954) in their subsequent eds.

   If the reading "Hippias" had been correct, the event could be referred, as in Untersteiner, to the war waged in 343 by the democrats of Elis, among whom Hippias might be numbered, in alliance with the surviving soldiers of the Phocian adventurer Phalaecus. With this peg gone, the case for giving Hippias an exceptionally long life is weakened, particularly if Platane is regarded as daughter and not wife of Hippias (see note 6) and the evidence for ascribing the Theophrastian preface to Hippias is regarded as unconvincing.
9. *Suda Lexicon,* "Ἱππίας." Otto Apelt, *Beiträge zur Geschichte der griechischen Philosophie,* pp. 382–384, 391–392, gives no convincing reasons for thinking that Aegesidamus is a mistake for Hippodamus of Miletus.

   Xenophon, *Memorabilia* IV.6, has Socrates apply the word "polymath" to Hippias; and Plato, *Hippias Minor,* 368B, makes Socrates call him, no doubt sarcastically, "the wisest of men in the greatest number of arts."
10. Philostratus, *Lives of the Sophists* I.11, Kayser ed., II (Leipzig, 1871), 13.27–30. See also Xenophon, *Symposium* 4.62; Plato, *Hippias Major,* 285E. According to Cicero, *De oratore* 2.86.351–354, the first to work out a mnemonic was Simonides, who is mentioned along with Hippias by Aelian, *On the Characteristics of Animals* VI.10, Scholfield ed. (Loeb), II (London–Cambridge, Mass., 1959), 22.9–13. Ammianus Marcellinus

HIPPIAS OF ELIS

XVI.5.8, Clark ed., I (Berlin, 1910), 76.17–20, notes the belief of some writers that his feats of memory, like those of King Cyrus and Simonides, were due to the use of drugs.
11. Xenophon, *Memorabilia* IV.4.19–20.
12. *Hippias Major,* 282D–E, 283B–284C. In the former passage Hippias boasts that although Protagoras was in Sicily at the time, he made more than 150 minas—at one small place, Inycus, taking in more than 20 minas.
13. See W. K. C. Guthrie, *A History of Greek Philosophy,* III (Cambridge, 1969), 280.
14. Plato, *Hippias Minor* 364A; compare *Hippias Major* 281D.
15. Plato, *Hippias Minor* 363C.
16. *Ibid.,* 368B–C; Apuleius, *Florida* 9, Helm ed., pp. 12.3–13.6.
17. Plato, *Hippias Major* 281A–B; Xenophon, *Memorabilia* IV.4.5.
18. The visits are recorded in Plato, *Hippias Major* 281A; and Xenophon, *Memorabilia* IV.4.5. See Mario Untersteiner, "Polemica contra Ippia nella settima epistola di Platone," in *Rivista di storia della filosofia,* 3 (1948), 101–119. The text of the *Dissoi logoi* is given in Diels-Kranz, *Vorsokratiker,* II, 90, pp. 405-416, and by Untersteiner, *Sofisti,* fasc. 3, pp. 148–191.
19. Athenaeus, XIII.608F–609A, Gulick ed. (Loeb), VI (London-Cambridge, Mass., 1937), 280; Clement of Alexandria, *Stromata* VI.C.2, 15.2, Stählin ed., *Clemens Alexandrinus* (in the series *Die Griechischen Christlichen Schriftsteller*), 3rd ed., II (Berlin, 1960), 434.23–435.5. Clement is making the point that the Greeks were incorrigible plagiarists, as shown by Hippias.
20. Bruno Snell, in *Philologus,* **96** (1944), 170–182. G. B. Kerferd, in *Proceedings of the Classical Association,* **60** (1963), 35-36, has adopted and extended Snell's views, and in particular has attributed to Hippias the doctrine of "continuous bodies" mentioned in *Hippias Major* 301B–E. (This passage would seem to have anticipations of Smuts's "holism"—τὰ ὅλα τῶν πραγμάτων.)
21. Scholium to Apollonius of Rhodes, III.1179, *Scholia in Apollonium Rhodium vetera,* Wendel ed. (Berlin, 1935), p. 251.13-14.
22. Plutarch, *Numa* 1.6, Ziegler ed., *Vitae parallelae,* III, pt. 2 (Leipzig, 1926), 55.7-9.
23. Plato, *Hippias Major* 286A.
24. Pausanias, V.25.4, Spiro ed. (Teubner), II (Leipzig, 1903), 78.4-13. Another statue made by Calon is dated 420–410 B.C.; but this does not have much bearing on Hippias' date, since his verses were added some time after the statues were made, in place of the original inscription.
25. See final paragraph of Bibliography. The *Anonymus Iamblichi* is reproduced in Diels-Kranz, *Vorsokratiker,* II, 89, 400-404.
26. Xenophon, *Memorabilia* IV.4.5-25. This passage purports to record a discussion between Socrates and Hippias in which Socrates identifies the just with the lawful—a view difficult to reconcile with Plato's Socrates—and discomfits Hippias.

    In *Protagoras* 337C–338B, Hippias mediates between Socrates and Protagoras, urging Socrates not to insist on brief questions and answers, and Protagoras not to sail off into an ocean of words. This pleases the company. In the opening sentence Plato would appear to have packed the main tenets of Hippias' thought: "Gentlemen, I look upon you all as kinsmen and neighbors and fellow citizens by nature, not by law; for by nature like is akin to like, but law, tyrant of men, often constrains us against nature."
27. Regarding these as key words, and in the fourth and fifth centuries as catch words, W. K. C. Guthrie devotes a chapter to the antithesis in *A History of Greek Philosophy,* III, 55–134.
28. Xenophon, *Memorabilia* IV.4.19–20.
29. Plato, *Protagoras* 318E; *Hippias Major* 366C–368A. The former passage deserves citation because it implies that Hippias believed in compulsory education in the quadrivium at the secondary level. Protagoras is the speaker: "The other [Sophists] mistreat the young, for when they have escaped from the arts they bring them back against their will and plunge them once more into the arts, teaching them arithmetic, astronomy, geometry and music—and here he looked at Hippias—whereas if he comes to me he will not be obliged to learn anything except what he has come for."
30. Proclus, *In primum Euclidis,* Friedlein ed. (Leipzig, 1873; repr., 1967), 272.3-10.
31. *Ibid.,* p. 356.6-12.
32. *Ibid.,* p. 65.11-15. The objection by W. K. C. Guthrie, *op. cit.,* III. 284, that it is "nearly 200 Teubner pages" earlier is not convincing.
33. He so treats Leodamas of Thasos, Oenopides of Chios, and Zeno of Sidon; and if he departs from this practice in the case of Hippocrates of Chios, it is only to avoid confusion with Hippocrates of Cos.
34. The Hippias described by the pseudo-Lucian in *Hippias seu Balneum* as a skillful mechanician and geometer is a fictional character.
35. J. E. Montucla, *Histoire des mathématiques,* I, 181; B. L. van der Waerden, *Science Awakening,* 2nd ed. (Groningen, n.d.), p. 146. Also C. A. Bretschneider, *Die Geometrie und die Geometer vor Euklides,* pp. 194–196; but H. Hankel, *Zur Geschichte der Mathematik,* p. 151, note, thought him "sicherlich nicht der Sophist Hippias aus Elis." After initial disbelief in the identification, G. J. Allman, *Greek Geometry From Thales to Euclid,* pp. 92–94, 189–193, was converted by Paul Tannery, in *Bulletin des sciences mathématiques et astronomiques,* 2nd ser., **7** (1883), 278–284; and by Moritz Cantor, *Vorlesungen über Geschichte der Mathematik,* 3rd ed., I, 193–197. After a thorough examination, A. A. Björnbo, in Pauly-Wissowa, VIII, cols. 1706–1711, accepted the identification; but Gino Loria, *Le scienze esatte nell' antica Grecia,* 2nd ed., p. 69, would say only: "Pesando dunque gli argomenti pro e contro l'identificazione, sembra a noi che i primi vincono per valore i secondi." T. L. Heath, *A History of Greek Mathematics,* I, 2, 23, 225, takes the identification for granted; but U. von Wilamowitz, *Platon,* I, 136, note, thinks that the name is so common that it is a matter of discretion; and W. K. C. Guthrie, *loc. cit.,* is undecided.
36. Diogenes Laertius VIII.iv, Cobet ed., p. 224.
37. Archimedes, Heiberg ed., 2nd ed., III, 84.12–88.2.
38. *Ibid.,* p. 90.4–11.
39. Pappus, *Collection,* Hultsch ed., pp. 250.33-252.3: "For the quadrature of the circle a certain curve was assumed by Dinostratus and Nicomedes and certain others more recent, and it takes its name from its property, for it is called by them quadratrix."

    Iamblichus as recorded by Simplicius, *In Aristotelis Categorias,* Kalbfleisch ed., p. 192.19–24: "Archimedes succeeded by means of the spiral-shaped curve, Nicomedes by means of the curve known by the special name quadratrix, Apollonius by means of a certain curve which he himself terms 'sister of the cochloid' but which is the same as the curve of Nicomedes, and lastly Carpus by means of a certain curve which he simply calls 'the curve arising from a double motion.'" When W. K. C. Guthrie, *op. cit.,* III, 284, note 2, finds significance in "the silence of Simplicius, who at *Physics* 54 ff (Diels ed.) seems to be giving as complete an account as he can of attempts to square the circle," it must be objected that Simplicius' aim in that passage was much more limited: the efforts of Alexander and Hippocrates.
40. Pappus, *op. cit.,* p. 252.5-25.
41. For references see Bibliography.
42. Kerferd, *op. cit.,* appears to hold this view.

BIBLIOGRAPHY

I. ORIGINAL WORKS. None of Hippias' many works has survived. The titles of the following are known: Ἐθνῶν ὀνομασίαι, *Nomenclature of Tribes;* Ὀλυμπιανικῶν ἀναγράφη, *Register of Olympic Victors;* Συναγωγή, *Collection;* and Τρωικός (*sc.* λόγος or διάλογος), *The Trojan.* Hippias is also known to have composed an elegiac inscription for the statues at Olympia in memory of a boys' choir from Messina drowned in crossing to Rhegium. He probably wrote a treatise on the quadratrix, of which he was the discoverer.

References to these works, and other witnesses to Hippias, are collected in H. Diels and W. Kranz, *Die Fragmente der Vorsokratiker,* 6th ed., II (Dublin-Zurich, 1970), 86, 326–334; and Mario Untersteiner, *Sofisti: Testimonianze e frammenti,* vol. VI in Biblioteca di Studi Superiori, fasc. 3 (Florence, 1954), 38–109.

It is conjectured by Untersteiner that Hippias was also the author of the preface to the *Characters* of Theophrastus; the *Anonymus Iamblichi;* and a spurious chapter in the third book of Thucydides' history, III, 84.

II. SECONDARY LITERATURE. In Greek literature the main secondary sources for Hippias are Plato, *Protagoras* 315C, 337C–338B; Plato (?), *Hippias Major* and *Hippias Minor,* Burnet ed., III (Oxford, 1903; repr., 1968); and Xenophon, *Memorabilia* IV.4.5-25, Marchant ed. (as *Commentarii*), in vol. II of Xenophon's *Works* (Oxford, 1901; 2nd ed., 1921). Other scattered references will be found in the notes.

The best recent accounts of Hippias as a philosopher are W. K. C. Guthrie, *A History of Greek Philosophy,* III (Cambridge, 1969), 280-285; and Mario Untersteiner, *I sofisti* (Milan, 1948; 2nd ed., 1967), II, 109–158, translated by Kathleen Freeman, *The Sophists* (Oxford, 1954), pp. 272–303.

Hippias' mathematical work may be studied in G. J. Allman, *Greek Geometry From Thales to Euclid* (Dublin, 1889), pp. 92–94, 189–193; A. A. Björnbo, "Hippias 13," in Pauly-Wissowa, *Real-Encyclopädie,* VIII (Stuttgart, 1913), cols. 1706–1711; C. A. Bretschneider, *Die Geometrie und die Geometer vor Euklides* (Leipzig, 1870), pp. 94–97; Moritz Cantor, *Vorlesungen über Geschichte der Mathematik,* 3rd ed., I (Leipzig, 1907), 193–197; James Gow, *A Short History of Greek Mathematics* (Cambridge, 1884), pp. 162–164; T. L. Heath, *A History of Greek Mathematics,* I (Oxford, 1921), 225-230; Gino Loria, *Le scienze esatte nell' antica Grecia,* 2nd ed. (Milan, 1914), pp. 67–72; and Paul Tannery, "Pour l'histoire des lignes et surfaces courbes dans l'antiquité," in *Bulletin des sciences mathématiques et astronomiques,* 2nd ser., **7** (1883), 278–291, repr. in his *Mémoires scientifiques,* II (Toulouse–Paris, 1912), 1–18.

Among other noteworthy assessments of Hippias are the following, listed chronologically: J. Mahly, "Der Sophist Hippias von Elis," in *Rheinisches Museum für Philologie,* **15** (1860), 514-535, and **16** (1861), 38–49; O. Apelt, *Beiträge zur Geschichte der griechischen Philosophie,* VIII, "Der Sophist Hippias von Elis" (Leipzig, 1891), 367–393; W. Zilles, "Hippias aus Elis," in *Hermes,* **53** (1918), 45–56; D. Viale (Adolfo Levi), "Ippia di Elide e la corrente naturalistica della sofistica," in *Sophia* (1942), pp. 441-450; Bruno Snell, "Die Nachrichten über die Lehren des Thales und die Anfänge der griechischen Philosophie- und Literaturgeschichte," in *Philologus,* **96** (1944), 170–182; and G. B. Kerferd, in *Proceedings of the Classical Association,* **60** (1963), 35–36.

Mario Untersteiner has put forward his conjectures about Hippias in "Un nuovo frammento dell' Anonymus Iamblichi. Identificazione dell' Anonimo con Ippia," in *Rendiconti dell' Istituto lombardo di scienze e lettere,* classe di lettere, **77,** fasc. II (1943–1944), 17; "Polemica contro Ippia nella settima epistola di Platone," in *Rivista di storia della filosofia,* **3** (1948), 101–119; and "Il proemio dei 'Caratteri' di Teofrasto e un probabile frammento di Ippia," in *Rivista di filologia classica,* n.s. **26** (1948), 1–25.

IVOR BULMER-THOMAS

HIPPOCRATES OF CHIOS (*b.* Chios; *fl.* Athens, second half of the fifth century B.C.)

The name by which Hippocrates the mathematician is distinguished from the contemporary physician of Cos[1] implies that he was born in the Greek island of Chios; but he spent his most productive years in Athens and helped to make it, until the foundation of Alexandria, the leading center of Greek mathematical research. According to the Aristotelian commentator John Philoponus, he was a merchant who lost all his property through being captured by pirates.[2] Going to Athens to prosecute them, he was obliged to stay a long time. He attended lectures and became so proficient in geometry that he tried to square the circle. Aristotle's own account is less flattering.[3] It is well known, he observes, that persons stupid in one respect are by no means so in others. "Thus Hippocrates, though a competent geometer, seems in other respects to have been stupid and lacking in sense; and by his simplicity, they say, he was defrauded of a large sum of money by the customs officials at Byzantium." Plutarch confirms that Hippocrates, like Thales, engaged in commerce.[4] The "Eudemian summary" of the history of geometry reproduced by Proclus states that Oenopides of Chios was somewhat younger than Anaxagoras of Clazomenae; and "after them Hippocrates of Chios, who found out how to square the lune, and Theodore of Cyrene became distinguished in geometry. Hippocrates is the earliest of those who are recorded as having written Elements."[5] Since Anaxagoras was born about 500 B.C. and Plato went to Cyrene to hear Theodore after the death of Socrates in 399 B.C., the active life of Hippocrates may be placed in the second half of the fifth century B.C. C. A. Bretschneider has pointed out that the accounts of Philoponus and Aristotle could be reconciled by supposing that Hippocrates' ship was captured by Athenian pirates during the Samian War of 440 B.C., in which Byzantium took part.[6]

Paul Tannery, who is followed by Maria Timpanaro Cardini, ventures to doubt that Hippocrates needed to learn his mathematics at Athens.[7] He thinks it more likely that Hippocrates taught in Athens what he had already learned in Chios, where the fame of Oenopides suggests that there was already a flourishing school of mathematics. Pointing out the proximity of Chios to Samos, the birthplace of Pythagoras, Timpanaro Cardini makes a strong case for regarding Hippocrates as coming under Pythagorean influence even though he had no Pythagorean teacher in the formal sense. Although Iamblichus does not include Hippocrates' name in his catalog of Pythagoreans, he, like Eudemus, links him with Theodore, who was undoubtedly in the brotherhood.[8]

Mathematics, he notes, advanced after it had been published; and these two men were the leaders. He adds that mathematics came to be divulged by the Pythagoreans in the following way: One of their number lost his fortune, and because of this tribulation he was allowed to make money by teaching geometry. Although Hippocrates is not named, it would, as Allman points out, accord with the accounts of Aristotle and Philoponus if he were the Pythagorean in question.[9] The belief that Hippocrates stood in the Pythagorean tradition is supported by what is known of his astronomical theories, which have affinities with those of Pythagoras and his followers. He was, in Timpanaro Cardini's phrase, a para-Pythagorean, or, as we might say, a fellow traveler.[10]

When Hippocrates arrived in Athens, three special problems—the duplication of the cube, the squaring of the circle, and the trisection of an angle—were already engaging the attention of mathematicians, and he addressed himself at least to the first two. In the course of studying the duplication of the cube, he used the method of reduction or analysis. He was the first to compose an *Elements of Geometry* in the manner of Euclid's famous work. In astronomy he propounded theories to account for comets and the galaxy.

Method of Analysis. Hippocrates is said by Proclus to have been the first to effect the geometrical reduction of problems difficult of solution.[11] By reduction (ἀπαγωγή), Proclus explains that he means "a transition from one problem or theorem to another, which being known or solved, that which is propounded is also manifest."[12] It has sometimes been supposed, on the strength of a passage in the *Republic,* that Plato was the inventor of this method; and this view has been supported by passages from Proclus and Diogenes Laertius.[13] But Plato is writing of philosophical analysis, and what Proclus and Diogenes Laertius say is that Plato "communicated" or "explained" to Leodamas of Thasos the method of analysis (ἀνάλυσις)—the context makes clear that this is geometrical analysis—which takes the thing sought up to an acknowledged first principle. There would not appear to be any difference in meaning between "reduction" and "analysis," and there is no claim that Plato invented the method.

Duplication of the Cube. Proclus gives as an example of the method the reduction of the problem of doubling the cube to the problem of finding two mean proportionals between two straight lines, after which the problem was pursued exclusively in that form.[14] He does not in so many words attribute this reduction to Hippocrates; but a letter purporting to be from Eratosthenes to Ptolemy Euergetes, which is preserved by Eutocius, does specifically attribute the discovery to him.[15] In modern notation, if $a:x = x:y = y:b$, then $a^3:x^3 = a:b$; and if $b = 2a$, it follows that a cube of side x is double a cube of side a. The problem of finding a cube that is double a cube with side a is therefore reduced to finding two mean proportionals, x, y, between a and $2a$. (The pseudo-Eratosthenes observes with some truth that the problem was thus turned into one no less difficult.)[16] There is no reason to doubt that Hippocrates was the first to effect this reduction; but it does not follow that he, any more than Plato, invented the method. It would be surprising if it were not in use among the Pythagoreans before him.

The suggestion was made by Bretschneider, and has been developed by Loria and Timpanaro Cardini,[17] that since the problem of doubling a square could be reduced to that of finding one mean proportional between two lines,[18] Hippocrates conceived that the doubling of a cube might require the finding of two mean proportionals. Heath has made the further suggestion that the idea may have come to him from the theory of numbers.[19] In the *Timaeus* Plato states that between two square numbers there is one mean proportional number but that two mean numbers in continued proportion are required to connect two cube numbers.[20] These propositions are proved as Euclid VII.11, 12, and may very well be Pythagorean. If so, Hippocrates had only to give a geometrical adaptation to the second.

Quadrature of Lunes. The "Eudemian summary" notes that Hippocrates squared the lune—so called from its resemblance to a crescent moon—that is, he found a rectilineal figure equal in area to the area of the figure bounded by two intersecting arcs of circles concave in the same direction.[21] This is the achievement on which his fame chiefly rests. The main source for our detailed knowledge of what he did is a long passage in Simplicius' commentary on Aristotle's *Physics*.[22] Simplicius acknowledges his debt to Eudemus' *History of Geometry* and says that he

 HIPPOCRATES OF CHIOS

will set out word for word what Eudemus wrote, adding for the sake of clarity only a few things taken from Euclid's *Elements* because of Eudemus' summary style. The task of separating what Simplicius added has been attempted by many writers from Allman to van der Waerden. When Simplicius uses such archaic expressions as τὸ σημεῖον ἐφ' ὧ (or ἐφ' οὗ) *A* for the point *A*, with corresponding expressions for the line and triangle, it is generally safe to presume that he is quoting; but it is not a sufficient test to distinguish the words of Hippocrates from those of Eudemus, since Aristotle still uses such pre-Euclidean forms. Another stylistic test is the earlier form which Eudemus would have used, δυνάμει εἶναι ("to be equal to when square"), for the form δύνασθαι, which Simplicius would have used more naturally. Although there can be no absolute certainty about the attribution, what remains is of great interest as the earliest surviving example of Greek mathematical reasoning; only propositions are assigned to earlier mathematicians, and we have to wait for some 125 years after Hippocrates for the oldest extant Greek mathematical text (Autolycus).

Before giving the Eudemian extract, Simplicius reproduces two quadratures of lunes attributed to Hippocrates by Alexander of Aphrodisias, whose own commentary has not survived. In the first, *AB* is the diameter of a semicircle, *AC*, *CB* are sides of a square inscribed in the circle, and *AEC* is a semicircle inscribed on *AC*. Alexander shows that the lune *AEC* is equal to the triangle *ACD*.

In the second quadrature *AB* is the diameter of a semicircle; and on *CD*, equal to twice *AB*, a semi-

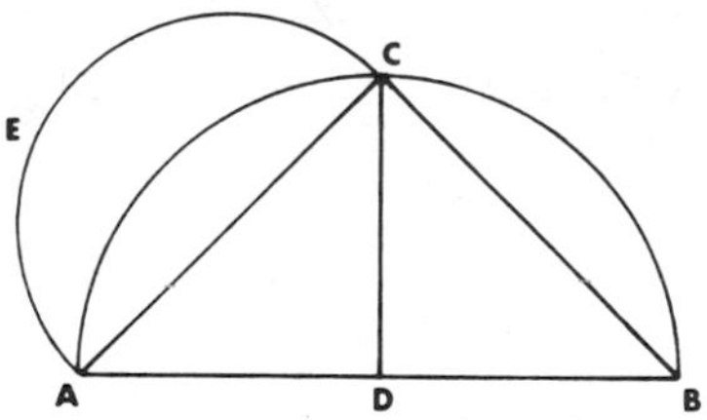

FIGURE 1

circle is described. *CE*, *EF*, *FD* are sides of a regular hexagon; and *CGE*, *EHF*, *FKD* are semicircles. Alexander proves that the sum of the lunes *CGE*, *EHF*, *FKD* and the semicircle *AB* is equal to the trapezium *CEFD*.

Alexander goes on to say that if the rectilinear figure equal to the three lunes is subtracted ("for a rectilinear figure was proved equal to a lune"), the circle will be squared. There is an obvious fallacy here, for the lune which was squared was one standing on the side of a square and it does not follow that the lune standing on the side of the hexagon can be squared. John Philoponus, as already noted, says that Hippocrates tried to square the circle while at Athens. There is confirmation in Eutocius, who in his commentary on Archimedes' *Measurement of a Circle* notes that Archimedes wished to show that a circle would be equal to a certain rectilinear area, a matter investigated of old by eminent philosophers before him.[23] "For it is clear," he continues, "that the subject of inquiry is that concerning which Hippocrates of Chios and Antiphon, who carefully investigated it, invented the paralogisms which, I think, are accurately known to those who have examined the *History of Geometry* by Eudemus and have studied the *Ceria* of Aristotle." This is probably a reference

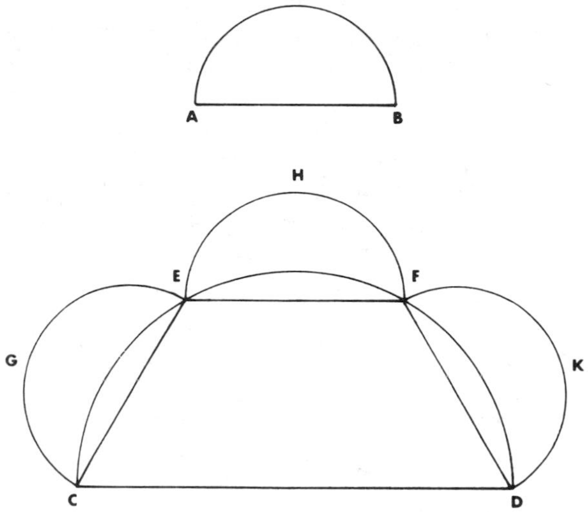

FIGURE 2

to a passage in the *Sophistici Elenchi* where Aristotle says that not all erroneous constructions are objects of controversy, either because they are formally correct or because they are concerned with something true, "such as that of Hippocrates or the quadrature by means of lunes."[24] In the passage in Aristotle's *Physics* on which both Alexander and Simplicius are commenting,[25] Aristotle rather more clearly makes the point that it is not the task of the exponent of a subject to refute a fallacy unless it arises from the accepted principles of the subject. "Thus it is the business of the geometer to refute the quadrature of a circle by means of segments but it is not his business to refute that of Antiphon."[26]

The ancient commentators are probably right in identifying the quadrature of a circle by means of segments with Hippocrates' quadrature of lunes; mathematical terms were still fluid in Aristotle's time,

HIPPOCRATES OF CHIOS

and Aristotle may well have thought there was some fallacy in it. We may be confident, though, that a mathematician of the competence of Hippocrates would not have thought that he had squared the circle when in fact he had not done so. It is likely that when Hippocrates took up mathematics, he addressed himself to the problem of squaring the circle, which was much in vogue; it is evident that in the course of his researches he found he could square certain lunes and, if this had not been done before him, probably effected the two easy quadratures described by Alexander as well as the more sophisticated ones attributed to him by Eudemus. He may have hoped that in due course these quadratures would lead to the squaring of the circle; but it must be a mistake on the part of the ancient commentators, probably misled by Aristotle himself, to think that he claimed to have squared the circle. This is better than to suppose, with Heiberg, that in the state of logic at that time Hippocrates may have thought he had done so; or, with Björnbo, that he deliberately used language calculated to mislead; or, with Heath, that he was trying to put what he had discovered in the most favorable light.[27] Let us turn to what Hippocrates actually did, according to Eudemus, who, as Simplicius notes, is to be preferred to Alexander as being nearer in date to the Chian geometer.

Hippocrates, says Eudemus, "made his starting point, and laid down as the first of the theorems useful for the discussion of lunes, that similar segments of circles have the same ratio as the squares on their bases; and this he showed from the demonstration that the squares on the diameters are in the same ratio as the circles." (This latter proposition is Euclid XII.2 and is the starting point also of Alexander's quadratures; the significance of what Eudemus says

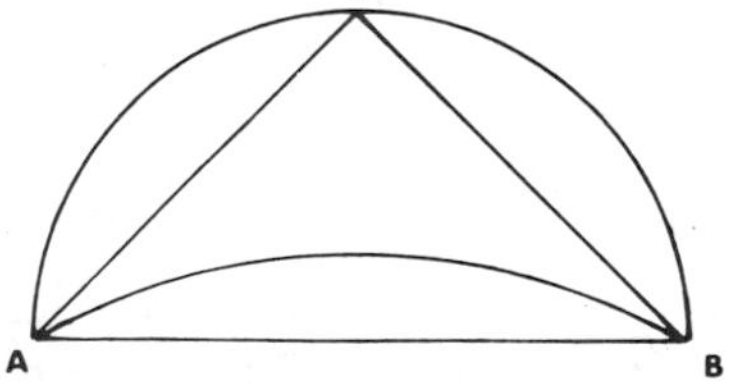

FIGURE 3

is discussed below.) In his first quadratuie he takes a right-angled isosceles triangle *ABC*, describes a semicircle about it, and on the base describes a segment of a circle similar to those cut off by the sides. Since $AB^2 = AC^2 + CB^2$, it follows that the segment about the base is equal to the sum of those about the sides; and if the part of the triangle above the segment about the base is added to both, it follows that the lune *ACB* is equal to the triangle.

Hippocrates next squares a lune with an outer circumference greater than a semicircle. *BA*, *AC*, *CD* are equal sides of a trapezium; *BD* is the side parallel to *AC* and $BD^2 = 3AB^2$. About the base *BD* there is described a segment similar to those cut off by the equal sides. The segment on *BD* is equal to the sum of the segments on the other three sides; and by adding the portion of the trapezium above the segment about the base, we see that the lune is equal to the trapezium.

Hippocrates next takes a lune with a circumference less than a semicircle, but this requires a preliminary construction of some interest, it being the first known example of the Greek construction known as a νεύσις, or "verging."[28] Let *AB* be the diameter of a circle and *K* its center. Let *C* be the midpoint of *KB* and let *CD* bisect *BK* at right angles. Let the straight line *EF* be placed between the bisector *CD* and the circumference "verging toward *B*" so that the square on *EF* is 1.5 times the square on one of the radii, that is, $EF^2 = 3/2\ KA^2$. If $FB = x$ and $KA = a$, it can easily be shown that $(x + \sqrt{3/2}\,a)\,x = a^2$, so that

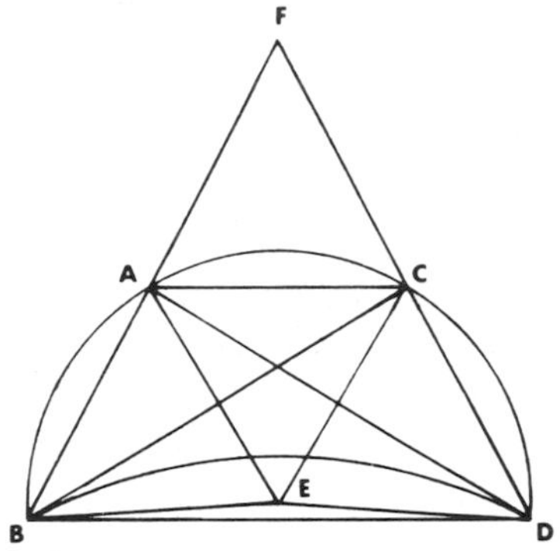

FIGURE 4

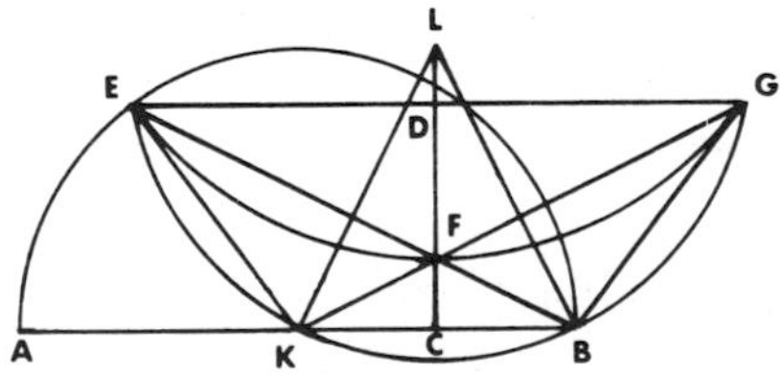

FIGURE 5

the problem is tantamount to solving a quadratic equation. (Whether Hippocrates solved this theoretically or empirically is discussed below.)

After this preliminary construction Hippocrates circumscribes a segment of a circle about the trapezium *EKBG* and describes a segment of a circle

HIPPOCRATES OF CHIOS

about the triangle *EFG*. In this way there is formed a lune having its outer circumference less than a semicircle, and its area is easily shown to be equal to the sum of the three triangles *BFG, BFK, EKF*.

Hippocrates finally squares a lune and a circle together. Let *K* be the center of two circles such that the square on the diameter of the outer is six times the square on the diameter of the inner. *ABCDEF* is a regular hexagon in the inner circle. *GH, HI* are sides of a regular hexagon in the outer circle. About *GI* let there be drawn a segment similar to that cut off by *GH*. Hippocrates shows that the lune *GHI* and the inner circle are together equal to the triangle *GHI* and the inner hexagon.

This last quadrature, rather than that recorded by Alexander, may be the source of the belief that Hippocrates had squared the circle, for the deduction is not so obviously fallacious. It would be easy for someone unskilled in mathematics to suppose that because Hippocrates had squared lunes with outer circumferences equal to, greater than, and less than a semicircle, and because he had squared a lune and a circle together, by subtraction he would be able to

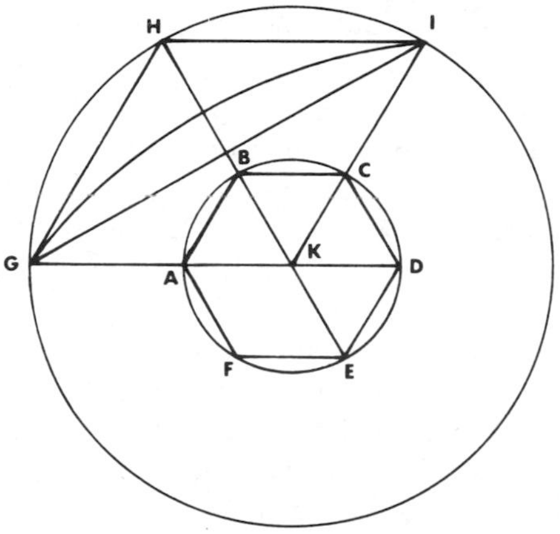

FIGURE 6

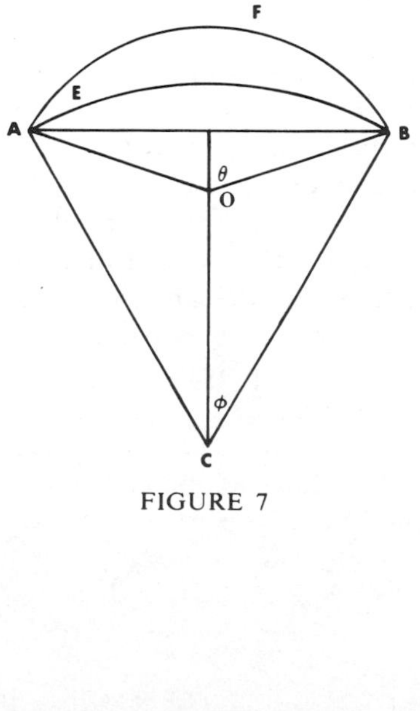

FIGURE 7

square the circle. The fallacy, of course, is that the lune which is squared along with the circle is not one of the lunes previously squared by Hippocrates; and although Hippocrates squared lunes having outer circumferences equal to, greater than, and less than a semicircle, he did not square all such lunes but only one in each class.

What Hippocrates succeeded in doing in his first three quadratures may best be shown by trigonometry. Let *O, C* be the centers of arcs of circles forming the lune *AEBF*, let *r, R* be their respective radii and θ, ϕ the halves of the angles subtended by the arcs at their centers.

$$\begin{aligned}\text{Then lune } AEBF &= \text{segment } AFB - \text{segment } AEB\\ &= (\text{sector } OAFB - \triangle\, OAB)\\ &\quad - (\text{sector } CAEB - \triangle\, CAB)\\ &= (\text{sector } OAFB - \text{sector } CAEB)\\ &\quad + (\triangle\, CAB - \triangle\, OAB)\\ &= r^2\theta - R^2\phi\\ &\quad + 1/2(R^2 \sin 2\phi - r^2 \sin 2\theta).\end{aligned}$$

It is a sufficient condition for the lune to be squarable that sector *OAFB* = sector *CAEB*, for in that case the area will be equal to $\triangle\, CAB - \triangle\, OAB$, that is, the quadrilateral *AOBC*. In trigonometrical notation, if $r^2\theta = R^2\phi$, the area of the lune will be $1/2(R^2 \sin 2\phi - r^2 \sin 2\theta)$. Let $\theta = k\phi$. Then $R = \sqrt{k}r$ and the area of the lune is $1/2\ r^2(k \sin 2\phi - \sin 2k\phi)$. Now $r \sin \theta = 1/2AB = R \sin \phi$, so that $\sin k\phi = \sqrt{k} \sin \phi$. This becomes a quadratic equation in $\sin \phi$, and therefore soluble by plane methods, when $k = 2, 3, 3/2, 5,$ or $5/3$. Hippocrates' three solutions correspond to the values 2, 3, 3/2 for *k*.[29]

Elements of Geometry. Proclus explains that in geometry the elements are certain theorems having to those which follow the nature of a leading principle and furnishing proofs of many properties; and in the summary which he has taken over from Eudemus he names Hippocrates, Leon, Theudius of Magnesia, and Hermotimus of Colophon as writers of elements.[30] In realizing the distinction between theorems which are merely interesting in themselves and those which lead to something else, Hippocrates made a significant discovery and started a famous tradition; but so complete was Euclid's success in this field that all the earlier efforts were driven out of circulation. What Proclus says implies that Hippocrates' book had the shortcomings of a pioneering work, for he tells us that Leon was able to make a collection of the elements in which he was more careful, in respect both of the number and of the utility of the things proved.

Although Hippocrates' work is no longer extant, it is possible to get some idea of what it contained.

HIPPOCRATES OF CHIOS

It would have included the substance of Books I and II of Euclid's *Elements,* since the propositions in these books were Pythagorean discoveries. Hippocrates' research into lunes shows that he was aware of the following theorems:

1. In a right-angled triangle, the square on the side opposite the right angle is equal to the sum of the squares on the other two sides (Euclid I.47).

2. In an obtuse-angled triangle, the square on the side subtending the obtuse angle is greater than the sum of the squares on the sides containing it (*cf.* II.12).

3. In any triangle, the square on the side opposite an acute angle is less than the sum of the squares on the sides containing it (*cf.* II.13).

4. In an isosceles triangle whose vertical angle is double the angle of an equilateral triangle (that is, 120°), the square on the base is equal to three times the square on one of the equal sides.

5. In equiangular triangles, the sides about the equal angles are proportional.

Hippocrates' *Elements* would have included the solution of the following problems:

6. To construct a square equal to a given rectilinear figure (II.14).

7. To find a line the square on which shall be equal to three times the square on a given line.

8. To find a line such that twice the square on it shall be equal to three times the square on a given line.

9. To construct a trapezium such that one of the parallel sides shall be equal to the greater of two given lines and each of the three remaining sides equal to the less.

The "verging" encountered in Hippocrates' quadrature of lines suggests that his *Elements* would have included the "geometrical algebra" developed by the Pythagoreans and set out in Euclid I.44, 45 and II.5, 6, 11. It has been held that Hippocrates may have contented himself with an empirical solution, marking on a ruler a length equal to $\sqrt{3/2}\ KA$ in Figure 5 and moving the ruler about until the points marked lay on the circumference and on *CD*, respectively, while the edge of the ruler also passed through *B*. In support, it is pointed out that Hippocrates first places *EF* without producing it to *B* and only later joins *BF*.[31] But it has to be admitted that the complete theoretical solution of the equation $x^2 + \sqrt{3/2}x = r^2$, having been developed by the Pythagoreans, was well within the capacity of Hippocrates or any other mathematician of his day. In Pythagorean language it is the problem "to apply to a straight line of length $\sqrt{3/2}\ a$ a rectangle exceeding by a square figure and equal to a^2 in area," and it would be solved by the use of Euclid II.6.

Hippocrates was evidently familiar with the geometry of the circle; and since the Pythagoreans made only a limited incursion into this field, he may himself have discovered many of the theorems contained in the third book of Euclid's *Elements* and solved many of the problems posed in the fourth book. He shows that he was aware of the following theorems:

1. Similar segments of a circle contain equal angles. (This implies familiarity with the substance of Euclid III.20–22.)

2. The angle of a semicircle is right, that of a segment greater than a semicircle is acute, and that of a segment less than a semicircle is obtuse. (This is Euclid III.31, although there is some evidence that the earlier proofs were different.)[32]

3. The side of a hexagon inscribed in a circle is equal to the radius (IV.15, porism). He knew how to solve the following problems: (1) about a given triangle to describe a circle (IV.5); (2) about the trapezium drawn as in problem 9, above, to describe a circle; (3) on a given straight line to describe a segment of a circle similar to a given one (*cf.* III.33).

Hippocrates would not have known the general theory of proportion contained in Euclid's fifth book, since this was the discovery of Eudoxus, nor would he have known the general theory of irrational magnitudes contained in the tenth book, which was due to Theaetetus; but his *Elements* may be presumed to have contained the substance of Euclid VI–IX, which is Pythagorean.

It is likely that Hippocrates' *Elements* contained some of the theorems in solid geometry found in Euclid's eleventh book, for his contribution to the Delian problem (the doubling of the cube) shows his interest in the subject. It would be surprising if it did not to some extent grapple with the problem of the five regular solids and their inscription in a sphere, for this is Pythagorean in origin; but it would fall short of the perfection of Euclid's thirteenth book. The most interesting question raised by Hippocrates' *Elements* is the extent to which he may have touched on the subjects handled in Euclid's twelfth book. As we have seen, his quadrature of lunes is based on the theorem that circles are to one another as the squares on their diameters, with its corollary that similar segments of circles are to each other as the squares on their bases. The former proposition is Euclid XII.2, where it is proved by inscribing a square in a circle, bisecting the arcs so formed to get an eight-sided polygon, and so on, until the difference between the inscribed polygon and the circle becomes as small as is desired. If similar polygons are inscribed in two circles, their areas can easily be proved to be in the ratio of the squares on the diameters; and when the number of the sides is increased and the polygons approximate more and more closely to the circles, this suggests that the areas of the two circles are in the ratio of the squares on their diameters.

But this is only suggestion, not proof, for the ancient Greeks never worked out a rigorous procedure for taking the limits. What Euclid does is to say that if the ratio of the squares on the diameters is not equal to the ratio of the circles, let it be equal to the ratio of the first circle to an area *S* which is assumed in the first place to be less than the second circle. He then lays down that by continually doubling the number of sides in the inscribed polygon, we shall eventually come to a point where the residual segments of the second circle are less than the excess of the second circle over *S*. For this he relies on a lemma, which is in fact the first proposition of Book X: "If two unequal magnitudes be set out, and if from the greater there be subtracted a magnitude greater than its half, and from the remainder a magnitude greater than its half, and so on continually, there will be left some magnitude which is less than the lesser magnitude set out." On this basis Euclid is able to prove rigorously by *reductio ad absurdum* that *S* cannot be less than the second circle. Similarly, he proves that it cannot be greater. Therefore *S* must be equal to the second circle, and the two circles stand in the ratio of the squares on their diameters.

Could Hippocrates have proved the proposition in this way? Here we must turn to Archimedes, who in the preface to his *Quadrature of the Parabola*[33] says that in order to find the area of a segment of a parabola, he used a lemma which has accordingly become known as "the lemma of Archimedes" but is equivalent to Euclid X.1: "Of unequal areas the excess by which the greater exceeds the less is capable, when added continually to itself, of exceeding any given finite area."[34] Archimedes goes on to say:

> The earlier geometers have also used this lemma. For it is by using this same lemma that they have proved (1) circles are to one another in the same ratio as the squares on their diameters; (2) spheres are to one another as the cubes on their diameters; (3) and further that every pyramid is the third part of the prism having the same base as the pyramid and equal height; and (4) that every cone is a third part of the cylinder having the same base as the cone and equal height they proved by assuming a lemma similar to that above mentioned.

In his *Method* Archimedes states that Eudoxus first discovered the proof of (3) and (4) but that no small part of the credit should be given to Democritus, who first enunciated these theorems without proof.[35]

In the light of what has been known since the discovery of Archimedes' *Method,* it is reasonable to conclude that Hippocrates played the same role with regard to the area of a circle that Democritus played with regard to the volume of the pyramid and cone; that is, he enunciated the proposition, but it was left to Eudoxus to furnish the first rigorous proof. Writing before the discovery of the *Method,* Hermann Hankel thought that Hippocrates must have formulated the lemma and used it in his proof; but without derogating in any way from the genius of Hippocrates, who emerges as a crucial figure in the history of Greek geometry, this is too much to expect of his age.[36] It is not uncommon in mathematics for the probable truth of a proposition to be recognized intuitively before it is proved rigorously. Reflecting on the work of his contemporary Antiphon, who inscribed a square (or, according to another account, an equilateral triangle) in a circle and kept on doubling the number of sides, and the refinement of Bryson in circumscribing as well as inscribing a regular polygon, and realizing with them that the polygons would eventually approximate very closely to the circle, Hippocrates must have taken the further step of postulating that two circles would stand to each other in the same ratio as two similar inscribed polygons, that is, in the ratio of the squares on their diameters.

A question that has been debated is whether Hippocrates' quadrature of lunes was contained in his *Elements* or was a separate work. There is nothing about lunes in Euclid's *Elements,* but the reason is clear: an element is a proposition that leads to something else; but the quadrature of lunes, although interesting enough in itself, proved to be a mathematical dead end. Hippocrates could not have foreseen this when he began his investigations. The most powerful argument for believing the quadratures to have been contained in a separate work is that of Tannery: that Hippocrates' argument started with the theorem that similar segments of circles have the same ratio as the squares on their bases. This depends on the theorem that circles are to one another as the squares on their bases, which, argues Tannery, must have been contained in another book because it was taken for granted.[37]

Astronomy. What is known of Oenopides shows that Chios was a center of astronomical studies even before Hippocrates; and he, like his contemporaries, speculated about the nature of comets and the galaxy. According to Aristotle,[38] certain Italians called Pythagoreans said that the comet—it was apparently believed that there was only one—was a planet which appeared only at long intervals because of its low elevation above the horizon, as was the case with Mercury.[39] The circle of Hippocrates and his pupil Aeschylus[40] expressed themselves in a similar way save in thinking that the comet's tail did not have a real existence of its own; rather, the comet, in its wandering through space, occasionally assumed the appearance of a tail through the deflection of our sight toward the sun by the moisture drawn up by the comet when in the neighborhood of the sun.[41] A second reason for the rare appearance of the comet, in the view of Hippocrates, was that it retrogressed so slowly in relation to the sun, and therefore took a long time to get clear of the sun. It could get clear of the sun to the north and to the south, but it was only in the north that the conditions for the formation of a tail were favorable; there was little moisture to attract in the space between the tropics, and although there was plenty of moisture to the south, when the comet was in the south only a small part of its circuit was visible. Aristotle proceeds to give five fairly cogent objections to these theories.[42]

After recounting the views of two schools of Pythagoreans, and of Anaxagoras and Democritus on the Milky Way, Aristotle adds that there is a third theory, for "some say that the galaxy is a deflection of our sight toward the sun as is the case with the comet." He does not identify the third school with Hippocrates; but the commentators Olympiodorus and Alexander have no hesitation in so doing, the former noting that the deflection is caused by the stars and not by moisture.[43]

NOTES

1. The similarity of the names impressed itself upon at least one ancient commentator, Olympiodorus. *In Aristotelis Meteora,* Stuve ed., 45.24–25: Ἱπποκράτης, οὐχ ὁ Κῷος, ἀλλ' ὁ Χῖος.
2. John Philoponus, *In Aristotelis Physica,* Vitelli ed., 31.3–9.
3. Aristotle, *Ethica Eudemia H* 14, 1247a17, Susemihl ed., 113.15–114.1.
4. Plutarch, *Vita Solonis* 2, *Plutarchi vitae parallelae,* Sintenis ed., I, 156.17–20.
5. Proclus, *In primum Euclidis,* Friedlein ed., 65.21–66.7.
6. C. A. Bretschneider, *Die Geometrie und die Geometer vor Eukleides,* p. 98.
7. Paul Tannery, *La géometrie grecque,* p. 108; Maria Timpanaro Cardini, *Pitagorici,* fasc. 2, pp. 29–31.
8. Iamblichus, *De vita Pythagorica* 36, Deubner ed., 143.19–146.16; and, for the link with Theodore, *De communi mathematica scientia* 25, Festa ed., 77.24–78.1. The same passage, with slight variations, is in *De vita Pythagorica* 18, Deubner ed., 52.2–11, except for the sentence relating to Hippocrates.
9. G. J. Allman, *Greek Geometry From Thales to Euclid,* p. 60.
10. Timpanaro Cardini, *op. cit.,* fasc. 2, p. 31.
11. Proclus, *op. cit.,* 213.7–11. He adds that Hippocrates also squared the lune and made many other discoveries in geometry, being outstanding beyond all others in his handling of geometrical problems.
12. *Ibid.,* 212.25–213.2.
13. Plato, *Republic* VI, 510B–511C, Burnet ed.; Proclus, *op. cit.,* 211.18–23; Diogenes Laertius, *Vitae philosophorum* III.24, Long ed., 1.131.18–20.
14. Proclus, *op. cit.,* 213.2–6.
15. *Archimedis opera omnia,* Heiberg ed., 2nd ed., III, 88.4–96.27.
16. *Ibid.,* 88.17–23.
17. Bretschneider, *op. cit.,* p. 97; Gino Loria, *Le scienze esatte nell' antica Grecia,* 2nd ed., pp. 77–78; Timpanaro Cardini, *op. cit.,* fasc. 2, pp. 34–35.
18. If $a:x = x:2a$, the square with side x is double the square with side a. The problem of doubling a square of side x is thus reduced to finding a mean proportional between a and $2a$.
19. Thomas Heath, *A History of Greek Mathematics,* I, 201.
20. Plato, *Timaeus* 32 A,B, Burnet ed. With the passage should be studied *Epinomis* 990b5–991b4, Burnet ed.; and the note by A. C. Lloyd in A. E. Taylor, *Plato: Philebus and Epinomis,* p. 249.
21. Proclus, *op. cit.,* 66.4–6, in fact mentions the squaring of the lune as a means of identifying Hippocrates.
22. Simplicius, *In Aristotelis Physica,* Diels ed., 53.28–69.35.
23. *Archimedis opera omnia,* Heiberg ed., 2nd ed., III, 228.11–19.
24. Aristotle, *Sophistici Elenchi* 11, 171b12–16. Toward the end of the third century Sporus of Nicaea compiled a work known as Κηρία, or Ἀριστοτελικὰ κηρία, which was used by Pappus, Simplicius, and Eutocius; but Heiberg sees here a reference to the *Sophistici Elenchi* of Aristotle. Grammatically it is possible that "the quadrature by means of lunes" is to be distinguished from "that of Hippocrates"; but it is more likely that they are to be identified, and Diels and Timpanaro Cardini are probably right in bracketing "the quadrature by means of lunes" as a (correct) gloss which has crept into the text from 172a2–3, where the phrase is also used.
25. Aristotle, *Physics* A 2, 185a14, Ross ed.
26. Aristotle does an injustice to Antiphon, whose inscription of polygons with an increasing number of sides in a circle was the germ of a fruitful idea, leading to Euclid's method of exhaustion; Aristotle no doubt thought it contrary to the principles of geometry to suppose that the side of the polygon could ever coincide with an arc of the circle.
27. J. L. Heiberg, *Philologus,* **43,** p. 344; A. A. Björnbo, in Pauly-Wissowa, VIII, cols. 1787–1799; Heath, *op. cit.,* I, 196, note. Montucla, *Histoire des recherches sur la quadrature du cercle,* pp. 21–22, much earlier (1754) had given the correct interpretation: "Hippocrate ne vouloit point proposer un moyen qu'il jugeoit propre à conduire quelque jour à la quadrature du cercle?"
28. There is a full essay on this subject in T. L. Heath, *The Works of Archimedes,* pp. c–cxxii.
29. It was shown by M. J. Wallenius in 1766 that the lune can be squared by plane methods when $x = 5$ or $5/3$ (Max Simon, *Geschichte der Mathematik im Altertum,* p. 174). T. Clausen gave the solution of the last four cases in 1840, when it was not known that Hippocrates had solved more than the first. ("Vier neue mondförmige Flachen, deren Inhalt quadrirbar ist," in *Journal für die reine und angewandte Mathematik,* **21** 375–376). E. Landau has investigated the cases where the difference between $r^2\theta$ and $R^2\phi$ is not zero but equal to an area that can be squared, although this does not lead to new squarable lunes: "Ueber quadrirbare Kreisbogen zweiecke," in *Sitzungsberichte der Berliner mathematischen Gesellschaft,* **2** (1903).
30. Proclus, *op. cit.,* 72.3–13, 66.7–8, 66.19–67.1, 67.12–16, 20–23. Tannery (*Mémoires scientifiques,* I, 46) is not supported either in antiquity or by modern commentators in discerning a written Pythagorean collection of *Elements* preceding that of Hippocrates.
31. Heath, *op. cit.,* I, 196.
32. See Aristotle, *Posterior Analytics* Π 11, 94a28–34; *Metaphysics* Θ 9, 1051a 26–29; and the comments by W. D. Ross, *Aristotle's Metaphysics,* pp. 270–271; and Thomas Heath, *Mathematics in Aristotle,* pp. 37–39, 71–74.
33. *Archimedis opera omnia,* Heiberg ed., 2nd ed., II, 264.1–22.
34. More strictly, "the lemma of Archimedes" is equivalent to Euclid V, def. 4—"Magnitudes are said to have a ratio one to another if they are capable, when multiplied, of exceeding one another"—and this is used to prove Euclid X.1. Archimedes not infrequently uses the lemma in Euclid's form.

HIPPOCRATES OF CHIOS

35. *Archimedis opera omnia,* Heiberg ed., 2nd ed., II, 430.1–9. In the preface to Book I of his treatise *On the Sphere and Cylinder* Archimedes attributes the proofs of these theorems to Eudoxus without mentioning the part played by Democritus.
36. Hermann Hankel, *Zur Geschichte der Mathematik in Alterthum und Mittelalter,* p. 122.
37. Tannery, *op. cit.,* I, 354–358. Loria, *op. cit.,* p. 91, inclines to the same view; but Timpanaro Cardini, *op. cit.,* fasc. 2, p. 37, is not persuaded.
38. *Meteorologica* A6, 342b30–343a20, Fobes ed., 2nd ed.
39. Because, like Mercury, it can be seen with the naked eye only when low on the horizon before dawn or after sunset, since it never sets long after the sun and cannot be seen when the sun is above the horizon.
40. Nothing more is known of Aeschylus. This and references by Aristotle to *οἱ περὶ Ἱπποκράτην* imply that Hippocrates had a school.
41. It is not clear how Aristotle thought the appearance to be caused, and the commentators and translators—Thomas Heath, *Aristarchus of Samos,* p. 243; E. W. Webster, *The Works of Aristotle,* III, *Meteorologica, loc. cit.;* H. D. P. Lee, *Aristotle, Meteorologica* in the Loeb Library, pp. 40–43; Timpanaro Cardini, *op. cit.,* fasc. 2, pp. 66–67—give only limited help. It is clear that Hippocrates, like Alcmaeon and Empedocles before him, believed that rays of light proceeded from the eye to the object; and it seems probable that he thought visual rays were *refracted* in the moisture around the comet toward the sun (the sun then being in a position in which this could happen), and *reflected* from the sun back to the moisture and the observer's eye (hence the choice of the neutral word "deflected"). Hippocrates believed that somehow this would create the appearance of a tail in the vapors around the comet; but since this is not the correct explanation, it is impossible to know exactly what he thought happened. It is tempting to suppose that he thought the appearance of the comet's tail to be formed in the moisture in the same way that a stick appears to be bent when seen partly immersed in water, but the Greek will not bear this simple interpretation.

    Olympiodorus, *op. cit.,* Stuve ed., 45.29–30, notes that whereas Pythagoras maintained that both the comet and the tail were made of the fifth substance, Hippocrates held that the comet was made of the fifth substance but the tail out of the sublunary space. This is anachronistic. It was Aristotle who added the "fifth substance" to the traditional four elements—earth, air, fire, water.
42. Aristotle, *Meteorologica, A*6, 343a21–343b8, Fobes ed., 2nd ed.
43. Olympiodorus, *op. cit.,* Stuve ed., 68.30–35; he reckons it a "fourth opinion," presumably counting the two Pythagorean schools separately. Alexander, *In Aristotelis Meteorologica,* Hayduck ed., 38.28–32.

BIBLIOGRAPHY

No original work by Hippocrates has survived, but his arguments about the squaring of lunes and possibly his *ipsissima verba* are embedded in Simplicius, *In Aristotelis Physicorum libros quattuor priores commentaria,* H. Diels ed., *Commentaria in Aristotelem Graeca,* IX (Berlin, 1882). In the same volume, pp. xxiii–xxxi, is an *appendix Hippocratea* by H. Usener, "De supplendis Hippocratis quas omisit Eudemus constructionibus."

The ancient references to Hippocrates' speculations on comets and the galaxy are in Aristotle, *Meteorologicorum libri quattuor* A6, 342a30–343a20 and A8, 345b9, Fobes ed. (Cambridge, Mass., 1918; 2nd ed., Hildesheim, 1967); and in the following volumes of *Commentaria in Aristotelem Graeca:* XII, pt. 2, *Olympiodori in Aristotelis Meteora commentaria,* Stuve ed. (Berlin, 1900), 45.24–46.24, 68.30–69.26; and *Alexandri in Aristotelis Meteorologicorum libros commentaria,* III, pt. 2, Hayduck ed. (Berlin, 1899), 38.28–38.32.

The chief ancient references to Hippocrates are collected in Maria Timpanaro Cardini, *Pitagorici, testimonianze e frammenti,* fasc. 2, Bibliotheca di Studi Superiori, XLI (Florence, 1962), 16(42), pp. 38–73, along with an Italian translation and notes, and an introductory note, pp. 28–37. A less comprehensive collection is in Diels and Kranz, *Die Fragmente der Vorsokratiker,* 14th ed. (Dublin–Zurich, 1969), I, 42 (3), 395–397.

For the mathematical work of Hippocrates generally, the best secondary literature is George Johnston Allman, *Greek Geometry From Thales to Euclid* (Dublin–London, 1889), pp. 57–77, reproducing a paper which first appeared in *Hermathena,* **4,** no. 7 (Apr. 1881), 180–228; and Thomas Heath, *A History of Greek Mathematics,* I (Oxford, 1921), 182–202.

The quadrature of lunes is the subject of papers by Paul Tannery: "Hippocrate de Chio et la quadrature des lunes," in *Mémoires de la Société des sciences physiques et naturelles de Bordeaux,* 2nd ser., **2** (1878), 179–184; and "Le fragment d'Eudème sur la quadrature des lunes," *ibid.,* **5** (1883), 217–237, which may be more conveniently studied as reproduced in Tannery, *Mémoires scientifiques,* I (Paris, 1912), 46–52, 339–370. Another paper by a leading historian of early mathematics is that of J. L. Heiberg, who gave his views on the passage of Simplicius in the course of his *Jahresberichte* in *Philologus,* **43** (1884), 336–344. F. Rudio, after papers in *Bibliotheca mathematica,* 3rd ser., **3** (1902), 7–62; **4** (1903), 13–18; and **6** (1905), 101–103, edited the Greek text of Simplicius with a German translation, introduction, full notes, and appendixes as *Der Bericht des Simplicius über die Quadraturen des Antiphon und Hippokrates* (Leipzig, 1907); but Heath's criticisms, *op. cit.,* pp. 187–190, must be studied with it. There are excellent notes in W. D. Ross, *Aristotle's Physics* (Oxford, 1936), pp. 463–467. A new attempt to separate the Eudemian text from Simplicius was made by O. Becker, "Zur Textgestaltung des Eudemischen Berichts über die Quadratur der Möndchen durch Hippocrates von Chios," in *Quellen und Studien zur Geschichte der Mathematik, Astronomie und Physik,* Abt. B, **3** (1936), 411–418. The same author later dealt specifically with the passage in Simplicius, Diels ed., 66.14–67.2, in "Zum Text eines mathematischen Beweises im Eudemischen Bericht über die quadraturen der 'Möndchen' durch Hippokrates von Chios bei Simplicius," in *Philologus,* **99** (1954–1955), 313–316. A still later attempt to separate the Eudemian text from that of Simplicius is in Fritz Wehrli, *Die Schule des Aristoteles, Texte und Kommentar,* VIII, *Eudemos von Rhodos,* 2nd ed. (Basel, 1969), 59.28–66.6

Two medieval versions of Hippocrates' quadratures are given in Marshall Clagett, "The *Quadratura circuli per lunulas,*" Appendix II, *Archimedes in the Middle Ages,* I (Madison, Wis., 1964), pp. 610–626.

IVOR BULMER-THOMAS

HOBBES, THOMAS (*b.* Malmesbury, England, 5 April 1588; *d.* Hardwick, Derbyshire, England, 4 December 1679)

Thomas Hobbes, author of *Leviathan* and one of England's most penetrating philosophers, was born into an impoverished family in Wiltshire. His father, for whom he was named, was vicar of St. Mary's Church in Westport. His mother came of a yeoman family named Middleton. According to John Aubrey, the elder Thomas Hobbes was a semiliterate man: "One of the Clergie of Queen Elizabeth's time, a little learning went a great way with him and many other ignorant Sir Johns in those days."[1] We know at least that he was not a discreet individual; after a night of card playing he fell asleep in his church and was heard to utter, "Clubs is trumps." Later a more serious indiscretion caused an upheaval in the family; its effect on the child Thomas can only be guessed. Standing in front of his church, the father quarreled with a fellow parson, struck him, and was obliged in consequence to flee from Malmesbury, never to return. Thus, before he reached the age of seven, Thomas Hobbes was deprived of the society of his father; and salt was rubbed in the wound when the man his father had struck became the new vicar.

The care of the Hobbes family passed to an uncle, Francis Hobbes, a glover and an intelligent man who recognized signs of precocity in his nephew and underwrote the cost of his education. When he was seven, Hobbes was sent to school at the house of Richard Latimer, described by Aubrey as "a good Grecian." He was given a solid grounding in Latin and Greek; and at age fourteen he matriculated at Magdalen Hall (later called Hertford College), Oxford, where, however, he chafed under the restrictions of a scholastic curriculum. He preferred to "prove things after my own sense,"[2] and he read deeply in areas not prescribed by his tutors. Astronomy and geography were his favorite subjects at this time.

In 1608 Hobbes, now bachelor of arts, was recommended by the principal of his college to be tutor to the son of William Cavendish, Baron Hardwicke, who later became the second earl of Devonshire. The significance of Hobbes's appointment to the Cavendish household cannot be exaggerated. The young graduate was introduced to a cultured, aristocratic world. Although his duties at first were almost menial, he was able with the passage of time to mingle with his master's guests on terms of some intimacy. In this way he came to know Ben Jonson, Lord Falkland, Sir Robert Ayton, Lord Herbert of Cherbury, and, some time later, the poet Edmund Waller, who became a particular friend. Moreover, in Chatsworth and Hardwick Hall, the great houses of the Cavendish family, Hobbes had at his disposal an excellent library in which, he said, he found the university he had missed at Oxford.

To a second branch of the Cavendish family residing at Welbeck Abbey, Hobbes owed the awakening of his interest in natural science. Sir Charles Cavendish was a skilled mathematician; and his more famous brother William, duke of Newcastle, was a scientific amateur who maintained a private laboratory and whose scientific speculations issued in such odd conclusions as that the sun is "nothing else but a very solid body of salt and sulphur, inflamed by its own motion upon its own axis."[3] Both men accepted Hobbes as a friend; and Newcastle, who had a passion for horses as well as a curiosity about optics and geometry, persuaded Hobbes to combine these interests in a curious treatise entitled "Considerations Touching the Facility or Difficulty of the Motions of a Horse on Straight Lines, or Circular," a work printed from manuscript in 1903 and described by its editor as "an irrelevant superfluity of reasoning" such as was produced by "the tailor in *Gulliver's Travels* who measures his men with the help of a sextant and other mathematical instruments."[4] It was on Newcastle's behalf that Hobbes searched the London bookshops in vain for a copy of Galileo's *Dialogues.*

In 1610 Hobbes set out on a grand tour of the Continent with his pupil. It was the year of the assassination of Henry IV of France, an event which impressed itself on Hobbes's mind as an extreme example of the chaos that follows from the abolition of sovereignty. On this first tour, through France, Germany, and Italy, Hobbes perfected his knowledge of foreign tongues and resolved, on his return, to become a scholar. In the library at Chatsworth he immersed himself in classical studies and in 1628–1629 published a brilliant translation of Thucydides' *Peloponnesian War.*

For a brief period before the Thucydides was published, Hobbes served as secretary to Francis Bacon, to whom he had been introduced by the younger Cavendish, one of Bacon's friends. Bacon had by this time been deposed as lord chancellor and was living in retirement at Gorhambury, where Hobbes accompanied him on his "delicious walkes" and where he acted as amanuensis and editorial assistant in the Latin translation of several of Bacon's *Essaies.* The connection between these two personalities is inherently interesting, but it should not be read as evidence of a Baconian influence on Hobbes's thought. Although they held some points in common, the two philosophers had worked out their ideas independently and essentially along different lines.

In June of 1628 Hobbes's master and friend, the second earl of Devonshire, died. Hobbes accepted a new appointment as tutor and cicerone to the son of Sir Gervase Clinton of Nottinghamshire, with whom he embarked, in 1629, on a second tour of Europe, to Paris, Orléans, Geneva, and Venice. It was in a library in Geneva that he first read Euclid; he was ever afterward enamored of geometry.[5] In particular, as Aubrey reports, he was attracted to the propositional character of geometry; it was a form of reasoning that fit in well with the conception of "truth" he was later to develop: that "truth" is the product of an analytical process in which definitions are placed in their proper order.

By November of 1630 Hobbes was recalled to the Cavendish family to serve as tutor in Latin and rhetoric to the next earl of Devonshire. With this young man, Hobbes, now in his forties, made his third grand tour of the Continent, the one which had the most important consequences for the development of his interest in natural science. That interest had not previously been dormant, since as Hobbes himself tells us, he had formulated a theory of light and sound as early as 1630;[6] a short manuscript tract giving a theory of sense and appetite is assigned by Dr. Frithiof Brandt to 1630. But on the third journey—to France and Italy—Hobbes made personal contact with scientific minds. In Arcetri, near Florence, he visited Galileo, whom he ever afterward held in veneration as "the first that opened to us the gate of natural philosophy universal"; and in Paris he met Marin Mersenne, the Franciscan monk in whose cell informal scientific meetings, attended by some of the best scientists of the age, took place. He also met Gassendi and Roberval; he read Descartes; and everywhere he went, he meditated on the problems of motion, which he conceived to be the principle by which a wholly material universe is to be understood.

Hobbes's deepest scientific interest was in optics. Probably this interest was awakened in him by his contact with the Cavendish circle, especially with Charles Cavendish, Walter Warner, and John Pell. A large part of the short tract of 1630 on sensation and appetite was devoted to optics; in that early work Hobbes adopted an emission or "corpuscular" theory of light, according to which there is a movement of particles of matter from the luminous source to the eye. But a letter of 1636 to William Cavendish shows that Hobbes had by this time abandoned the emission theory in favor of a mediumistic theory—light is propagated by a motion or pressure of the medium intervening between the source and the eye—and a letter of May 1640 shows that he developed the idea of the expansion and contraction of the medium as a way of accounting for the motion of the light and of the medium. He later rejected the idea of expansion and contraction because it demanded the presence of a vacuum, and a vacuum was precluded by the doctrine of plenitude in which Hobbes had come to believe.

The subtlest part of Hobbes's theory of light is his definition of a ray as "the path through which the motion from the luminous body is propagated through the medium."[7] He conceived of the propagated line of light as always normal to the sides of the ray; hence it may be thought of as a "ray front," on the analogy of a wave front.[8] What distinguishes Hobbes's conception of the ray from earlier conceptions—from that, for instance, of Descartes, who shows in his criticism of Hobbes that he entirely miscomprehended Hobbes's theory—is that for Hobbes the ray has infinitesimal elements. He accepted that light has physical dimensions but he argued that the significant feature of light, from a mathematical point of view, is its impulse or endeavor to motion; and this impulse is to be understood as the motion of infinitesimal elements. By taking this infinitesimal approach, by arguing that "we consider the width of the ray smaller than any given magnitude,"[9] Hobbes made the important transition from physical rays to mathematical rays. He himself perceived only gradually that he had introduced a new concept; but when he recognized that a shift had taken place, he abandoned the term "ray" (*radius*) and adopted the new term "radiation" (*radiatio*).[10]

These views were expressed in three manuscript treatises by Hobbes, one in English and two in Latin. The first of the Latin treatises, "Tractatus opticus," was communicated to Mersenne, who published it as book VII of the "Optics" in his *Universae geometriae* (Paris, 1644).[11] Mersenne had also published an optical treatise by Walter Warner which Hobbes had given him in Paris, and in 1641 he had published the *Objectiones ad Cartesii Meditationes,* the third "objection" of which was by Hobbes. When he returned to Chatsworth in 1637, after his third journey abroad, Hobbes continued to correspond with Mersenne on questions of physics and optics. He was now forty-nine: time, he thought, to put his ideas in order. He therefore formulated the outline of a large philosophical system, to be composed of three parts—body, man, and citizenship—and to be described in that order, since for Hobbes body or matter is the ultimate constituent of all things, including human society. Hobbes's early scientific manuscripts may be considered as preparation for *De corpore,* his formal account of the first principles of science, which he intended to put first in his system but which the pressure of events forced him to lay aside and not publish until 1655.

In the late 1630's political passions in England were boiling. Hobbes's inclinations were royalist, but he appears mainly to have been concerned by the imminent breakdown of civil order. In 1640, while Parliament and king were locked in political combat but before the outbreak of military hostilities in the Civil War, Hobbes considered it prudent for his safety to return to France. He did so and remained there for eleven years, part of that time with the duke of Newcastle in Paris. In Paris, Hobbes renewed his scientific contacts and almost immediately corresponded with Descartes about questions raised by the latter's *Méditations* and *Dioptriques.* Relations between these two proud thinkers were strained because neither was willing to concede any originality in the thought of the other.

The impulse to say something to his countrymen about politics in the hour of their travail deflected Hobbes's scientific preoccupations. In the spring of 1640, while still in England, he wrote a short treatise on politics which circulated widely in manuscript and was published in 1650 in two parts under the titles *Humane Nature* and *De corpore politico, or the Elements of Law.* In Paris he wrote *De cive,* published in 1642, a book which enjoyed international success. But *De cive* was written in Latin; and although it was separately translated into French by Samuel Sorbière and du Verdus, two of Hobbes's friends, it remained inaccessible to the general English reader. Hobbes therefore set to work on an English treatise, *Leviathan,* published in 1651. This work is justly celebrated for the brilliance, breadth, and coherence of its philosophical vision and for its concise, vigorous, and eloquent prose style.

The outlook of *Leviathan* is nominalist, materialist, and anticlerical. Hobbes believed that the universe is a great continuum of matter. It was created and set in motion by God, who is himself a material being, since the universe is utterly devoid of spirit. Of God's other attributes virtually nothing can be known. Our knowledge of the external world is derived, either directly or ultimately, from our sense impressions; and since sensory knowledge is the only knowledge we can ever have, we have no grounds for believing in the independent existence of universals or absolute ideas, or classes of things as separate entities. Human language consists of names of things and names of names, all joined by predicates. Names of names, or universals, must not be confused with names of things; universals exist in the mind and things exist in the external world; but universals are not therefore to be despised, because, being rooted in language, they play their part in the reasoning process. "Truth" for Hobbes is analytic, a product of the correct reasoning about names.

Hobbes was uncompromising in the application of his nominalist principles to ethics. He argued that ethical judgments are the products of human thought and culture. "For these words of good, evil and contemptible, are ever used with relation to the person that useth them: there being nothing simply and absolutely so; nor any common rule of good and evil, to be taken from the nature of the objects themselves." The same kind of analysis was given to the notion of justice, which Hobbes believed to have no independent or absolute existence. In Hobbes's view, justice is a function of positive law, and all law is essentially positive law. "Where there is no common power, there is no law; where no law, no injustice." Justice and injustice "are qualities that relate to men in society, not solitude," and they draw their meaning from the declared intentions and enforcements of the civil magistrate.

Such a doctrine of ethical relativism and legal positivism was profoundly offensive to orthodox opinion in the seventeenth century; in particular, it ran counter to traditional conceptions of natural law, which were conceived of as laws of eternal and immutable morality, antecedent to positive civil law, originating, as Richard Hooker had put it, "in the bosom of God." Modern scholars disagree about the meaning of Hobbes's natural law doctrine. Some commentators, such as A. E. Taylor and Howard Warrender, argue that certain obligations of the citizen and all the obligations of the sovereign to his subjects are, according to Hobbes, grounded in a natural law antecedent to civil law; on the other hand, Michael Oakeshott believes that all those prerogatives of the citizen which are immune to sovereign authority, such as the citizen's right of self-preservation, and the obligations of the sovereign himself, are rational, not moral, obligations. In this view natural law is prudential. Whichever view is correct, there can be no doubt that Hobbes cast his natural law doctrine in a secular mold.

In the same secular spirit Hobbes developed his ideas of human nature. Man is a part of material nature, so his behavior, including the behavior of his mind, can ultimately be understood by reference to physical laws. Viewed from a shorter perspective, human behavior is seen by Hobbes to be grounded in self-interest, especially in the fundamental desire to survive. Hobbes did not argue that human nature was an entity separate from human culture, but he asked his readers to imagine what life would be like in the absence of culture—in the absence, that is, of social conventions and civil restraint. This is Hobbes's famous hypothetical picture of the "state of nature." Men in this condition are rapacious and predatory; and since they are equal in the things they want and equal in their capacities to satisfy their desires, they live in a state of continuous warfare or, at the very least, in a condition of fear, their lives being then "solitary, poor, nasty, brutish, and short." The grimness of this picture is relieved for the modern reader by his discovery that Hobbes believed very strongly in the doctrine of human equality; and although Hobbes chose not to develop the democratic implications of this doctrine, his sense of human equality is wholly at variance with the precepts and practices of the modern totalitarian state.

What Hobbes feared more than the tyranny of a sovereign was anarchy, and so he constructed a model of the state in which he thought anarchy would be impossible. Moved by their fears and passions, and instructed by their reason, men would come to realize that they can be delivered from the state of nature only by the generation of a stable commonwealth. The process by which the state comes into being was not intended by Hobbes to be construed historically; in general he believed that men will come first to recognize the significance and utility of the "laws of nature"—or some twenty theorems of conduct conducive to peace which Hobbes enumerated, and which he said are summed up in the golden rule. But at this stage these theorems of peace are merely comprehended; what is required is the power to enforce them, and this power resides only in a commonwealth—and then only in its "soul," the sovereign, who must rule with absolute sway.

To achieve this condition of enforceable peace, men will make a sort of contract among themselves (but not between themselves and the sovereign) to transfer their individual powers to a central sovereign authority. Hobbes did not insist that the sovereign be a single individual; although he favored monarchy, he thought that a body of men, a parliament, or even a king and parliament working in concert could achieve the same results. The main point was that the power of the sovereign be absolute, for the slightest diminution of his power would erode the security of the citizens; and it was for their security from each other that the sovereign was brought into being. Hobbes reserves to the citizens the right of rebellion if the sovereign fails to protect their security, but he treats this question warily.

The argument of *Leviathan* does not end with these views; fully one-third of the book examines the implications of Hobbes's political philosophy in a Christian society. Hobbes recognized that a seventeenth-century audience would demand to know whether his principles conformed to the teaching of Scripture. He himself knew the Bible well, and he was able to find passages in it supporting his doctrine of absolute sovereignty; but other passages were inconvenient and there remained the question, particularly vexing in an age of religious warfare, of which of several interpretations of Scripture was the correct one. Ultimately, said Hobbes, all Scripture is subject to interpretation, there being nothing about it except its existence that is agreeable to all minds. His solution to the problem of conflicting interpretation was both political and philosophical. On the political side he adopted the ultra-Erastian position that the only interpretation of Scripture that may be publicly espoused by citizens in a commonwealth is the interpretation of the sovereign authority. The natural right which citizens, by agreement among themselves, had transferred to the sovereign included the natural right of scriptural interpretation; should they retain that right, the commonwealth would inevitably lapse into a state of nature.

Moreover, Hobbes remained philosophically skeptical about the truth of Scripture. He conceded that a core of mystery in Scripture must be accepted on faith; but the greater part of the Bible is immune to human reason. His skepticism took the form of a surprisingly modern biblical criticism in which he anticipated Richard Simon and Spinoza by calling in question the number, scope, authorship, and general authenticity of the books of the Bible.

The relationship between Hobbes's scientific ideas and outlook on the one hand and his political philosophy on the other is hard to define. The question has provoked disagreement among Hobbes's commentators. Croom Robertson thought that the whole of Hobbes's political doctrine "had its main lines fixed when he was still a mere observer of men and manners, and not yet a mechanical philosopher." Leo Strauss accepts this view, but he believes that Hobbes had cast his mature political philosophy into an alien scientific mold, which resulted in a distortion of the politics but not in any significant change of its essentially prescientific, humanistic character.

Clearly Hobbes's materialism and physics do not imply his political theory in any simple linear connection; but, as was pointed out by J. W. N. Watkins, the science implies the civil philosophy in the same way, for example, that the law of evidence has important implications for statements made by witnesses in law courts, although the law of evidence does not entail any of those statements. Watkins' treatment of this whole question is illuminating. He has shown how Hobbes came to abandon his earliest political views, set down in the introduction to his Thucydides. Those views were "inductivist"; they advocated the study of history as a guide to rational conduct. Under the shaping influence of the new scientific outlook, however, Hobbes adopted the method called resolutive-compositive, which he derived partly from Galileo, partly from Harvey, but primarily from the philosophers and scientists of the school of Padua. (Hobbes was personally acquainted with a disciple of this school, Berigardus, author of *Circulus Pisanus.*) The method is described by Hobbes in *De corpore.* It has a large Aristotelian component. Put in its simplest form, it consists of resolving whole conceptions into their constituent parts or first principles and then recomposing them. It can be seen that this method is not an instrument of discovery in any modern sense of the idea of "science"; it appears to have more usefulness in social enquiries. Hobbes assimilated it into his political theory—as in the striking example of the break-up of society into its constituent parts called the state of nature and its recomposition into a commonwealth.

Not unexpectedly, Hobbes's views in *Leviathan,* taken altogether, raised a storm of opposition. He was embroiled in controversy for the rest of his life—more, in fact, than any English thinker before or since. The first signs of opposition appeared in France before *Leviathan* was published. On the recommendation of Newcastle, Hobbes was appointed tutor in mathematics to the prince of Wales, the future Charles II. Because of fears expressed by clergymen that the prince would be contaminated with atheism, Hobbes was obliged to promise that he would teach mathematics only, and not politics or religion. And when *Leviathan* was published, no one of the English court in France liked it. Although it was absolutist, it expressed no particular bias in favor of monarchy; and it appeared to favor the Puritan regime in England when it insisted that a citizen submit to any government that can secure internal peace. Moreover, its anticlericalism and attacks on the papacy offended French Jesuits and English Catholics. For these reasons Charles ordered Hobbes to leave the English colony in France, and in 1652 the philosopher returned to England.

He stayed in London for a year and then retired to Chatsworth, where the Cavendish family treated him with affection and even a certain deference, as befitted a philosopher of international renown. But the shock inflicted by *Leviathan* on clerical and lay opinion produced a rising tide of hostile criticism, some of it intelligent and philosophical but much of it in the form of abuse.[12] Hobbes was pronounced atheist, heretic, and libertine. He was the "Monster of Malmesbury," "a pander to bestiality" whose "doctrines have had so great a share of the debauchery of his Generation, that a good Christian can hardly hear his name without saying of his prayers."[13] It is true that Hobbes had his admirers and defenders, both on the Continent and in England, including such perceptive opponents as Samuel von Pufendorf and James Harrington, who understood that *De cive* and *Leviathan* were works to be reckoned with; but the clergy of all persuasions, as well as the common lawyers and university dons, united in their opposition to Hobbes. Indeed, his doctrines were cited by the House of Commons as a probable cause of the Great Fire of 1666.

Part of Hobbes's difficulties can be traced to a controversy between himself and John Bramhall, bishop of Derry (Londonderry) and later archbishop of Armagh. The two had met in 1645 at Paris, where they debated the subject of free will. Bramhall committed his ideas to paper; Hobbes wrote a rejoinder. Both agreed not to publish what they had written, but Hobbes's side of the question was put into print without his permission in a little treatise called *Of Liberty and Necessity* (1654). Bramhall, outraged by what he considered to be Hobbes's discourtesy in ignoring his side, published in 1655 all that had passed between them. Thus was launched a controversy which continued until Hobbes had the last word with the posthumous publication of *An Answer to a Book by Dr Bramhall Called The Catching of the Leviathan* (1682). Hobbes's views were strictly determinist. A man, he said, is "free" to do anything he desires if there are no obstacles in his way; but his desire to do anything has necessary and material causes. To Bramhall this doctrine was the essence of impiety; it would deny any meaning to rewards for good actions or punishments for evil ones, thus overturning the whole apparatus of religious worship. For his part Hobbes admitted that piety might not be promoted by his doctrine, but "truth is truth" and he would not be silent.

Hobbes was not molested personally during this last period of his life because he enjoyed the protection of Charles II, although he was deeply alarmed when, sometime in the 1660's, a committee of bishops in the House of Lords moved that he be burned for heresy. He wrote, but did not publish, a short treatise in the form of a legal brief showing that the law of heresy had been repealed in the time of Elizabeth and had never been revived, so that there could be no legal grounds for executing him.[14] Nothing came of the episcopal agitation; but the king refused to license a history in English by Hobbes of the Long Parliament, published posthumously as *Behemoth,* and the crown prohibited Hobbes from publishing any other works in English on the subject of politics or religion. Not included in this ban was the Latin translation of *Leviathan,* made by Henry Stubbe and first published at Amsterdam in 1668 and at London in 1678.

A second controversy, even more absorbing of Hobbes's energy than his debate with Bramhall, was his dispute with John Wallis on questions of geometry. Wallis was a vastly superior mathematician who made important contributions to the development of the calculus. But he was an acrimonious, coarse-tempered man; in a controversy that lasted almost twenty-five years, Wallis pressed his mathematical advantage with ferocious zeal, also attacking Hobbes for what he thought were errors in Greek, for having a West Country manner of speech, for being a rustic, for disloyalty to the crown, and so on. Hobbes's replies were better mannered, but he too was capable of losing his temper. The issue between the two men was whether Hobbes had succeeded, as he claimed, both in squaring the circle and in duplicating the cube. Hobbes boldly announced success in both enterprises, although he modified his claim slightly in some of the later books written against Wallis. It should be observed that neither Hobbes nor Wallis doubted the possibility of a quadrature, a proof of its impossibility not having been discovered until the nineteenth century; moreover, the problem of the quadrature was not only venerable but had a particular vitality in the seventeenth century. Nevertheless, Wallis was able to show that Hobbes's claim of success was unfounded. Hobbes made no original contributions to geometry but, as A. De Morgan has written, though Hobbes was "very wrong in his quadrature . . . he was not the ignoramus in geometry that he is sometimes supposed. His writings, erroneous as they are in many things, contain acute remarks on points of principle."[15] Hobbes's passion for geometry derived from his analytic conception of truth. He appreciated the unity and logical structure of geometry, its freedom from verbal confusion, and its reasoning from definitions placed in their proper order.

Algebra, on the other hand, failed to attract Hobbes. He grossly underestimated its scope and was suspicious of all attempts to "arithmetize" geometry. He thought of algebra as a minor branch of arithmetic; Wallis' "scab of symbols" simply disfigured the page, "as if a hen had been scraping there."[16] Nor did he appreciate the significance of Wallis' contributions, published in *Arithmetica infinitorum* (1655), toward the development of the differential calculus, although Hobbes's speculations in optics of an earlier stage in his life seemed to be leading him in the direction Wallis was taking.

In fact, Hobbes, in his sixties when he began his dispute with Wallis, was out of touch with the generation of rising young scientists and mathematicians. He was not opposed to experimentalism on principle, but he had no natural sympathy for it and considered that most of the experiments performed by fellows and correspondents of the Royal Society were either ill-conceived and poorly executed, or else they reached conclusions long ago arrived at by Hobbes through the use of his unaided reason. In this spirit he wrote "Dialogus physicus, sive de natura aeris" (1661), a brief but barbed attack on Robert Boyle's experiments on the vacuum pump, to which Boyle replied calmly, though forcefully, in *Examen of Mr. Hobbes, His Dialogus* (1662) and *Dissertation on Vacuum Against Mr. Hobbes* (1674). Not surprisingly, Hobbes was excluded from membership in the Royal Society, a fact which he resented, although he publicly declared that he was lucky to be out of it.

Hobbes's last years were thus clouded with controversy, but they were not without their simple pleasures and rewards. He lived comfortably on the Cavendish estates in Chatsworth and Hardwick Hall and, more frequently, in the duke of Devonshire's house on the Strand in London. He enjoyed long walks; he played tennis until he was seventy-five; and he had an abiding love of music, listening to it whenever he could and playing on his own bass viol. Capable as he was of holding his own in public controversy, and sparkling with wit in table talk, he was always gentle with people of lower rank or inferior education. He was a bachelor, but according to Aubrey he was not a "woman-hater"; and it is possible that he had a natural daughter whom he cherished.

In his eighties, mostly to amuse himself, Hobbes published translations of the *Iliad* and the *Odyssey.* And when he was ninety he published *Decameron physiologicum,* a set of dialogues on physical principles containing also a last salvo fired off against Wallis. He died of a stroke at the age of ninety-one.

NOTES

1. John Aubrey, *Brief Lives,* A. Clark, ed. (Oxford, 1898), I, 390.
2. Hobbes, *Life . . . Written by Himself* (London, 1680), p. 3.

3. Margaret Cavendish, *Philosophical and Physical Opinions* (London, 1663), p. 463; Jean Jacquot, "Sir Charles Cavendish and His Learned Friends," in *Annals of Science,* **8** (1952), 13–27, 175–191.
4. S. Arthur Strong, *A Catalogue of Letters and Documents at Welbeck* (London, 1903), p. vii.
5. G. R. De Beer, "Some Letters of Hobbes," in *Notes and Records. Royal Society of London,* **7** (1950), 205.
6. Hobbes, *Latin Works,* Molesworth, ed., V, 303.
7. *Ibid.,* pp. 221–222.
8. See, on this point, Alan E. Shapiro, "Rays and Waves," doctoral dissertation, Yale University, 1970. Dr. Shapiro has made a full study of Hobbes's optics.
9. Hobbes, *Latin Works,* V, 228.
10. Hobbes, "Tractatus opticus," British Museum, Harleian MS. 6796, ch. 2, sec. 1.
11. The two other optical MSS are "A Minute or First Draught of the Optiques," British Museum, Harleian MS 3360; and a second Latin treatise also called "Tractatus opticus," British Museum, Harleian MS 6796.
12. See Samuel I. Mintz, *The Hunting of Leviathan* (Cambridge, 1962).
13. Bishop John Vesey, "The Life of Primate Bramhall," in John Bramhall, *Works* (Dublin, 1677).
14. Samuel I. Mintz, "Hobbes on the Law of Heresy; A New Manuscript," in *Journal of the History of Ideas,* **29** (1968), 409–414; "Hobbes's Knowledge of the Law," *ibid.,* **31** (1970), 614–616.
15. A. De Morgan, *A Budget of Paradoxes* (London, 1915), p. 110.
16. Hobbes, "Six Lessons to the Professors of the Mathematics," in *Works,* VII, 316.

BIBLIOGRAPHY

I. Original Works. Hobbes's works include *De cive* (Paris, 1642); *De corpore politico, or the Elements of Law* (London, 1650); *Leviathan* (London, 1651); *De corpore* (London, 1655); *Problemata physica* (London, 1662); *Lux mathematica* (London, 1672); *Decameron physiologicum* (London, 1678); and *Behemoth* (London, 1679). The standard ed. of Hobbes's works is by William Molesworth, 16 vols. (London, 1839–1845), but it has inaccuracies and omissions. A comprehensive modern ed., to be published at Oxford, is being prepared by Howard Warrender. The standard bibliography of Hobbes's works is by Hugh Macdonald (London, 1952). Important modern eds. of *Leviathan* are by Michael Oakeshott (Oxford, 1946) and by C. B. Macpherson (Baltimore, 1968). A modern translation particularly valuable for its full annotations and attention to textual problems is François Tricaud, *Leviathan: Traité de la matière, de la forme et du pouvoir de la république ecclésiastique et civile* (Paris, 1971).

II. Secondary Literature. Contemporary biographies of Hobbes are John Aubrey, *Brief Lives,* A. Clark, ed. (Oxford, 1898); and Richard Blackbourne, in *Vitae Hobbianae auctarium* (London, 1681). The most important nineteenth- and early twentieth-century studies of Hobbes, in which biography is mingled with commentary and criticism, are G. Croom Robertson, *Hobbes* (Edinburgh, 1886); and Ferdinand Tönnies, *Hobbes, der Mann und der Denker,* 2nd ed. (Leipzig, 1912). Later twentieth-century studies of Hobbes are numerous. They include the following, listed chronologically: Frithiof Brandt, *Thomas Hobbes' Mechanical Conception of Nature* (Copenhagen, 1928); Leo Strauss, *Political Philosophy of Thomas Hobbes* (Oxford, 1936); Howard Warrender, *Political Philosophy of Hobbes* (Oxford, 1957); C. B. Macpherson, *The Political Theory of Possessive Individualism: Hobbes to Locke* (Oxford, 1962); Samuel I. Mintz, *The Hunting of Leviathan* (Cambridge, 1962); Keith Brown, ed., *Hobbes Studies* (Oxford, 1965); J. W. N. Watkins, *Hobbes's System of Ideas* (London, 1965); M. M. Goldsmith, *Hobbes's Science of Politics* (New York, 1966); and R. Kosselleck and R. Schnur, eds., *Hobbes-Forschungen* (Berlin, 1969).

SAMUEL I. MINTZ

HOBSON, ERNEST WILLIAM (*b.* Derby, England, 27 October 1856; *d.* Cambridge, England, 19 April 1933)

Hobson was the eldest of six children of William Hobson, a prominent citizen of Derby, the founder and editor of the *Derbyshire Advertiser.* His mother was Josephine Atkinson. His brother, J. A. Hobson, became a well-known economist. Hobson went to Derby School and did well in languages and music as well as mathematics and science. He was brought up in a strictly religious atmosphere, from which he later broke away.

In 1874 he won a mathematical scholarship to Christ's College, Cambridge, and in January 1878 he was placed first in order of merit (the senior wrangler) in the mathematical tripos. He was elected a fellow of Christ's in the same year and spent the rest of his life in teaching and research at Cambridge. In 1883 he was elected one of the first university lecturers (as distinct from college lecturers) in Cambridge. Hobson married Selina Rosa, the daughter of a Swiss merchant, in 1882; they had four sons.

Until 1910 the mathematical life of Cambridge was unduly dominated by the famous tripos examination. The undergraduates were coached in the solving of problems, and much of the college teachers' energy went into this coaching. Many of the teachers, therefore, made no effort to break new ground in their subject. There were, indeed, famous pure mathematicians, notably Cayley and Sylvester, but they worked largely in isolation. Moreover, their interests were in formal algebra. The theory of functions, actively developed in Germany and France since the 1850's, only began to be recognized in England in the 1890's.

In 1891 Hobson published *A Treatise on Trigonometry,* which, except for Chrystal's *Algebra* (Edinburgh–London, 1886–1889), is the first English textbook of mathematical analysis. His early interests were mainly in the functions of mathematical physics, and the first of the papers on which his reputation rests, on general spherical harmonics, appeared in 1896. During the next ten years he became aware of the work of the French school (Baire, Borel, Lebesgue), realizing that this school formed the necessary foundation of the systematic theory of trigonometrical and other special functions. His *Theory of Functions of a Real Variable* (1907), together with W. H. Young's *Theory of Sets of Points* (Edinburgh-London, 1906), introduced to English readers the vital Borel-Lebesgue concepts of measure and integration. In addition, this work incorporated Hobson's own research on the general convergence theorem and convergence of series of orthogonal functions. By the age of fifty Hobson had developed into a pure mathematician. This unusually late maturity is a reflection of the existing academic conditions at Cambridge.

In 1910 Hobson succeeded A. R. Forsyth in the Sadleirian chair of pure mathematics; he was recognized as one of the leaders of English mathematics. He resigned in 1931. He had few research pupils and did not found a school. Toward the end of his life his influence was overshadowed by the rise of younger men of great analytical power, notably G. H. Hardy and J. E. Littlewood.

Hobson was a distinguished figure in the university and served on the central administrative committees. His views were progressive and, appropriately enough, he was one of the leaders in reforming the mathematical tripos and abolishing the order of merit.

BIBLIOGRAPHY

I. ORIGINAL WORKS. Hobson's works include *A Treatise on Trigonometry* (Cambridge, 1891); *Theory of Functions of a Real Variable* (Cambridge, 1907), later eds. in 2 vols; *Squaring the Circle* (Cambridge, 1913), with six excellent lectures on this classical problem; *The Domain of Natural Science* (Cambridge, 1923), the Gifford lectures in Aberdeen; and *Spherical and Ellipsoidal Harmonics* (Cambridge, 1931), with Hobson's early researches of the 1890's.

II. SECONDARY LITERATURE. See G. H. Hardy, in *Obituary Notices of Fellows of the Royal Society of London,* no. 3 (1934), with portrait; and *Dictionary of National Biography* (Oxford, 1931–1940), pp. 433–434.

J. C. BURKILL

HODGE, WILLIAM VALLANCE DOUGLAS (*b.* Edinburgh, Scotland, 17 June 1903; *d.* Cambridge, England, 7 July 1975)

Hodge came from a solid middle-class background. His father, Archibald James Hodge, was a searcher of records (an office concerned with land titles), and his mother, Janet Vallance, the daughter of a prosperous proprietor of a confectionery business. He was educated at George Watson's Boys College, Edinburgh University (1920–1923, M.A.), and St. John's College, Cambridge (1923–1926, B.A.). On 27 July 1929 he married Kathleen Anne Cameron; they had one son and one daughter. A fellow of the Royal Society since 1938, Hodge was physical secretary between 1957 and 1965 and was a foreign associate of many academies, including the U.S. National Academy of Sciences. He was a vice president of the International Mathematical Union (1954–1958) and master of Pembroke College, Cambridge (1958–1970). He also was responsible for organizing the International Congress of Mathematicians at Edinburgh in 1958. A cheerful and energetic person, he was both popular and effective in his numerous administrative roles.

On leaving Cambridge, where he had already started to specialize in algebraic geometry, Hodge took up his first teaching appointment at Bristol in 1926, and, influenced by a senior colleague, Peter Fraser, he made strenuous efforts to master the work of the Italian algebraic geometers. In the course of his reading, he soon came across a problem that determined the course of his work for years to come.

In one of his papers, Francesco Severi mentioned the importance of knowing whether a nonzero double integral of the first kind could have all its periods zero. By a stroke of luck, Hodge saw a paper by Solomon Lefschetz in the 1929 *Annals of Mathematics* in which purely topological methods were used to obtain the period relations and inequalities for integrals on a curve. It was clear to Hodge that Lefschetz's methods could be extended to surfaces to solve Severi's problem, and he found it incredible that this should have escaped Lefschetz's notice. It did not take Hodge long to work out the details and write "On Multiple Integrals Attached to an Algebraic Variety." This was the turning point in his career, and therefore it is perhaps appropriate to describe the essence of his proof and its relation to Lefschetz's paper.

If $\omega_1, \cdots, \omega_g$ are a basis of the holomorphic differentials on a curve X of genus g, we have $\omega_i \wedge \omega_j = 0$ for simple reasons of complex dimension. If $[\omega_i]$ denotes the 1-dimensional cohomology class defined by ω_i (that is, given by its periods), it follows that the cup product $[\omega_i] \cup [\omega_j] = 0$. If we spell this out in terms of the periods, we obtain the Riemann bilinear relations for the ω_i. This is the modern approach and the essential content of Lefschetz's 1929 paper, though it must be borne in mind that cohomology had not yet appeared and that the argument had to be expressed in terms of cycles and intersection theory. It was Lefschetz himself who led the developments in algebraic topology that enable us to express his original proof so succinctly.

Similarly, the Riemann inequalities arise from the fact that, for any holomorphic differential $\omega \neq 0$, $i\omega \wedge \overline{\omega}$ is a positive volume and thus $i \int_X \omega \wedge \overline{\omega} > 0$. In cohomological terms this implies in particular that $[\omega] \cup [\omega] \neq 0$, and hence that $[\omega] \neq 0$; in other words ω cannot have all its periods zero. If we now replace X by an algebraic surface and ω by a nonzero holomorphic 2-form (a "double integral," in the classical terminology), exactly the same argument applies and disposes of Severi's question.

In addition to the primitive state of topology at this time, complex manifolds (other than Riemann surfaces) were not conceived of in the modern sense. The simplicity of the proof indicated above owes much to Hodge's work in later years, which made complex manifolds familiar to the present generation of geometers. All this must have had something to do with Lefschetz's surprising failure to see what Hodge saw. In fact, however, this was no simple omission on Lefschetz's part, and he took a great deal of convincing on this point. At first he insisted publicly that Hodge was wrong, and he wrote to him demanding that the paper be withdrawn. In May 1931 Lefschetz and Hodge had a meeting in Max Newman's rooms at Cambridge. There was a lengthy discussion leading to a state of armed neutrality and an invitation to Hodge to spend the next academic year at Princeton. After Hodge had been at Princeton for a month, Lefschetz conceded defeat and, with typical generosity, publicly retracted his criticisms of Hodge's paper. Thereafter Lefschetz became one of Hodge's strongest supporters and fully made up for his initial skepticism. His support proved crucial when in 1936 Hodge was elected to the Lowndean chair of astronomy and geometry at Cambridge.

The publication of "On Multiple Integrals . . ." opened many doors for Hodge. In November 1930 he was elected to a research fellowship at St. John's College, Cambridge, and shortly afterward was awarded an 1851 Exhibition Scholarship. He was thus in a position to take up Lefschetz's invitation to spend a year in Princeton.

In 1931 Princeton was a relatively small university with a very distinguished academic staff. In mathematics, pioneering work was being done in the new field of topology by Oswald Veblen, James W. Alexander, and Lefschetz. Although Hodge never became a real expert in topology, he regularly attended the Princeton seminars and picked up enough general background for his subsequent work.

Lefschetz was, without doubt, the mathematician who exerted the strongest influence on Hodge's work. In Bristol, after his early encounter with Lefschetz's *Annals* paper, Hodge had proceeded to read his Borel tract, *L'analyse situs et la géométrie algébrique*, and was completely won over to the use of topological methods in the study of algebraic integrals. At Princeton, Lefschetz propelled Hodge further along his chosen path. They had frequent mathematical discussions in which Lefschetz's fertile imagination would produce innumerable ideas, most of which would turn out to be false but the rest of which would be invaluable.

Hodge in due course became Lefschetz's successor in algebraic geometry. Whereas the Princeton school inherited and developed Lefschetz's contributions in topology, his earlier fundamental work on the homology of algebraic varieties was somewhat neglected, probably because it was ahead of its time. Hodge's work was complementary or dual to that of Lefschetz, providing an algebraic description of the homology instead of a geometric one. The fact that Lefschetz's theory has now been restored to a central place in modern algebraic geometry is entirely due to the interest aroused by its interactions with Hodge's theory.

Recognizing that he was no longer an expert on algebraic geometry, Lefschetz persuaded Hodge to spend a few months at Johns Hopkins, where Oscar Zariski was the leading light. The visit had a great impact on Hodge's future. In the first place he and his wife formed a close lifelong friendship with the Zariskis. He also was impressed with the new algebraic techniques that Zariski was developing, and in later years he devoted much time and effort to mastering them. Although their technical involvement with algebraic geometry was different, Zariski and Hodge felt a common love for the subject and had serious mathematical discussions whenever they met. They also maintained an intermittent correspondence for more than forty years.

Princeton. By the time Hodge came to Princeton, his mathematical ideas, arising from "On Multiple Integrals . . . ," had already progressed very significantly. In studying integrals in higher dimensions, he soon put his finger on the crucial point. Whereas for the Riemann surface of a curve the number of holomorphic 1-forms is half the first Betti number, there is no corresponding relation in higher dimensions for holomorphic p-forms with $p > 1$. Hodge discussed this point on a number of occasions with

Peter Fraser until one day Fraser pointed out Georges de Rham's dissertation, which had just arrived in the Bristol University library. In later years Hodge described this as a stroke of good fortune; although it did not solve his problem, it helped him to see what was involved. In de Rham's theory, valid on any real differentiable manifold, the main result is that there always exists a closed p-form ω with prescribed periods, and that ω is unique modulo derived forms. On a Riemann surface there are natural choices given by the real and imaginary parts of the holomorphic differentials, and Hodge was looking for an appropriate generalization to higher-dimensional algebraic varieties. He saw that the real and imaginary parts of a holomorphic 1-form on a Riemann surface are in some sense duals of one another, and he had a hunch that there should be an analogous duality in general. More precisely, for each p-form ω there should be an $(n\text{-}p)$-form $*\omega$ (n being the dimension of the manifold); the preferred forms, later called harmonic, would be those satisfying $d\omega = 0$ and $d(*\omega) = 0$. The main theorem to be proved would be the existence of a unique harmonic form with prescribed periods.

Once established at Princeton, Hodge tried to clarify and develop these vague ideas. He soon realized that the relationship of ω to $*\omega$ was a kind of orthogonality and was able to make this precise in euclidean space and, more generally, on a conformally flat manifold. He then attempted to prove the existence theorem by generalizing the classical Dirichlet methods. The next stage was to try to remove the restriction of conformal flatness, but for this Hodge needed to become familiar with classical Riemannian geometry. This was his major preoccupation and achievement during his stay in Baltimore. At the same time he also came across a paper by the Dutch mathematician Gerrit Mannoury in which an explicit and convenient metric was introduced on complex projective space, and hence on any projective algebraic manifold. This metric proved of fundamental importance for all of Hodge's subsequent work.

Cambridge, 1932–1939. On returning to Cambridge, Hodge continued his efforts to prove the existence theorem for harmonic forms on a general Riemannian manifold. His first version was, in his words, "crude in the extreme"; Hermann Weyl found it hard to judge whether the proof was complete or, rather, how much effort would be needed to make it complete. Nevertheless, Hodge was convinced that he was on the right track, and his next step was to apply his theory in detail to algebraic surfaces. Using the Mannoury metric, he proceeded to study the harmonic forms and found the calculations much simpler than he had expected. Finally, to his great surprise, he discovered that his results gave a purely topological interpretation of the geometric genus (the number of independent holomorphic 2-forms).

This was a totally unexpected result; and when it was published ("The Geometric Genus of a Surface as a Topological Invariant," 1933), it created quite a stir among algebraic geometers. In particular it convinced even the most skeptical of the importance of Hodge's theory and became justly famous as "Hodge's signature theorem." Twenty years later it played a key role in Friedrich Hirzebruch's work on the Riemann-Roch theorem, and it remains one of the highlights of the theory of harmonic forms. It is intimately involved in the spectacular results (1983–1988) of Simon Donaldson on the structure of four-dimensional manifolds. Essentially Donaldson's work rests on a nonlinear generalization of the Hodge theory.

After his success with the signature theorem, Hodge worked steadily, polishing his theory and developing its applications to algebraic geometry. He also began to organize a connected account of all his work as an essay for the Adams Prize. He was awarded that prize in 1937, but the magnum opus took another three years to complete and finally appeared in book form (*The Theory and Applications of Harmonic Integrals*) in 1941. In the meantime he had published another approach to the existence theorem that had been suggested to him by Hans Kneser. It involved the use of the parametrix method of F. W. Levi and David Hilbert and was, as Hodge said, superior in all respects to his first attempt. Unfortunately this version, reproduced in his book, contained a serious error that was pointed out by Bohnenblust. The necessary modifications to provide a correct proof were made by Hermann Weyl at Princeton and independently by Kunihiko Kodaira in Japan.

Hodge freely admitted that he did not have the technical analytical background necessary to deal adequately with his existence theorem. He was only too pleased when others, better-qualified analysts than himself, completed the task. This left him free to devote himself to the applications in algebraic geometry, which was what really interested him.

In retrospect it is clear that the technical difficulties in the existence theorem required not significant new ideas but a careful extension of classical methods. The real novelty, which was Hodge's major contribution, was in the conception of harmonic integrals and their relevance to algebraic geometry. This triumph of concept over technique is reminiscent of a similar episode in the work of Hodge's great predecessor Bernhard Riemann.

Wartime Cambridge. By the spring of 1940, Hodge had completed the manuscript of his book on harmonic integrals and felt he had exhausted his ideas in that area for the time being. He was therefore looking for a new field. On the other hand, his increasing administrative commitment to Pembroke College and Cambridge University left him less time and energy to devote to mathematics. These two factors help to explain the shift in his interests over the next decade. For some time he had been aware of the powerful algebraic techniques that had been introduced into algebraic geometry by Bartel L. van der Waerden and Zariski. These ideas had had little impact on British geometers, so Hodge felt a duty to interpret and explain the new material to his colleagues. In this he was motivated by a desire to make amends to the Baker school of geometry at Cambridge for the sharp change of direction that his work on harmonic integrals had produced. He thus conceived the idea of writing a book that would replace Henry Baker's *Principles of Geometry*. Although not as demanding as original research, this task soon proved too much for his unaided effort. He therefore enlisted the assistance of Daniel Pedoe, thus beginning a collaborative enterprise that lasted for ten years and led to their three-volume *Methods of Algebraic Geometry*.

Although this book discharged Hodge's obligations to classical algebraic geometry and contained much useful material, it did not achieve its main objective of converting British geometers to modern methods, principally because it was overtaken by events. By the time it appeared, algebraic geometry was exploding with new ideas, and entirely new foundations were being laid. In addition, Hodge did not have the elegance and fluency of style that make algebra palatable. He recognized his limitations as an algebraist, however, and despite his admiration for, and interest in, Zariski's work, he eventually returned to his "first love," the transcendental theory.

Postwar Cambridge. Stimulated by a visit to Harvard in 1950, Hodge directed his research interests back to harmonic integrals. He wrote a number of papers that, though not sensational, were a steady development of his original ideas. In particular his paper "A Special Type of Kähler Manifold" led, a few years later, to Kodaira's final characterization of projective algebraic manifolds. The manifolds singled out by Hodge were, for a few years, known as Hodge manifolds; ironic ally, Kodaira's proof that Hodge manifolds are algebraic led to their disappearance.

Hodge also took an interest in the theory of characteristic classes and wrote a paper ("The Characteristic Classes on Algebraic Varieties") to bridge the gap between the algebraic-geometric classes of John A. Todd and the topological classes introduced by Shiing Shen Chern. He clearly saw the significance of this work at an early stage, and subsequent developments have fully justified him.

The early 1950's saw a remarkable influx of new topological ideas into algebraic geometry. In the hands of Henri Cartan, Jean-Pierre Serre, Kodaira, Donald Spencer, and Hirzebruch, these led in a few years to spectacular successes and the solution of many classical problems, such as the Riemann-Roch theorem in higher dimensions. The great revival of transcendental methods provided by sheaf theory and its intimate connection with harmonic forms naturally aroused Hodge's interest. He made strenuous efforts to understand the new methods and eventually saw that they could be applied to the study of integrals of the second kind. At this time (early 1954) he was busy preparing a talk to be delivered at Princeton in honor of Lefschetz's seventieth birthday, so he suggested that the present author, one of his research students, might try to develop the ideas further and see if they led to a complete treatment of integrals of the second kind. It did not take long to see that one obtained a very elegant and satisfactory theory in this way, and Hodge was given a complete manuscript a few days before his departure for Princeton. He was thus able to describe the results at the Princeton conference ("Integrals of the Second Kind on an Algebraic Variety").

Mathematical Assessment. Hodge's mathematical work centered so much on the one basic topic of harmonic integrals that it is easy to assess the importance of his contributions and to measure their impact. The theory of harmonic integrals can be roughly divided into two parts, the first dealing with real Riemannian manifolds and the second dealing with complex, and particularly algebraic, manifolds. These will be considered separately.

For a compact Riemannian manifold (without boundary), Hodge defined a harmonic form as one satisfying the two equations $d\phi = 0$ and $d^*\phi = 0$, where d is the exterior derivative and d^* its adjoint with respect to the Riemannian metric. An equivalent definition, proposed later by André Weil, is $\Delta\phi = 0$, where $\Delta = dd^* + d^*d$. Hodge's basic theorem asserts that the space $\mathcal{H}^q$ of harmonic q-forms is naturally isomorphic to the q-dimensional cohomology of X (or dual to the q-dimensional homology). The beauty and simplicity of this theorem made a

HODGE

deep impression. As mentioned earlier, Hermann Weyl, the foremost mathematician of the time, was so impressed that he assisted Hodge with the technicalities of the proof. At the International Congress of Mathematicians in 1954, Weyl said that in his opinion, Hodge's *Harmonic Integrals* was "one of the great landmarks in the history of science in the present century."

As an analytical result in differential geometry, one might have expected Hodge's theorem to have been discovered by an analyst, a differential geometer, or even a mathematical physicist (since in Minkowski space the equations $d\omega = d^*\omega = 0$ are simply Maxwell's equations). In fact Hodge knew little of the relevant analysis, no Riemannian geometry, and only a modicum of physics. His insight came entirely from algebraic geometry, where many other factors enter to complicate the picture.

The long-term impact of Hodge's theory on differential geometry and analysis was substantial. In both cases it helped to shift the focus from purely local problems to global problems of geometry and analysis "in the large." Together with Marston Morse's work on the calculus of variations, it set the stage for the new and more ambitious global approach that has dominated much of mathematics ever since.

One of the most attractive applications of Hodge's theory is to compact Lie groups, in which, as Hodge showed in his book, the harmonic forms can be identified with the bi-invariant forms. Another significant application, due to Salomon Bochner, showed that suitable curvature hypotheses implied the vanishing of appropriate homology groups, the point being that the corresponding Hodge-Laplacian Δ was positive definite.

If we turn now to a complex manifold X with a Hermitian metric, we can decompose any differential r-form ϕ in the form

$$\phi = \sum_{p+q=r} \phi^{p,q},$$

where $\phi^{p,q}$ involves, in local coordinates $(z_1, \cdots, z_n)$, p of the differentials dz_i and q of the conjugate differentials $d\bar{z}_i$ (and is said to be of type (p, q)). In general, if $\Delta\phi = 0$, so that ϕ is harmonic, the components $\phi^{p,q}$ need not be harmonic. It was one of Hodge's remarkable discoveries that for the Mannoury metric on a projective algebraic manifold (induced by the standard metric on projective space), the $\phi^{p,q}$ are in fact harmonic. This property of the Mannoury metric is a consequence of what is now known as the Kähler condition: that the 2-form ω (of type (1, 1)) associated to the metric ds^2 by the formula

$$ds^2 = \sum g_{ij} dz_i d\bar{z}_j, \quad \omega = \frac{i}{2\pi} \sum g_{ij} dz_i \wedge d\bar{z}_j$$

is closed (that is, $d\omega = 0$).

As a consequence we obtain a direct sum decomposition

$$\mathcal{H}^r = \sum_{p+q=r} \mathcal{H}^{p,q}$$

of the space of harmonic forms and consequently, by Hodge's main theorem, a corresponding decomposition of the cohomology groups. In particular the Betti numbers $h^r = \dim \mathcal{H}^r(X, C)$ are given by

$$h^r = \sum_{p+q=r} h^{p,q},$$

where $h^{p,q} = \dim \mathcal{H}^{p,q}$. Moreover, as Hodge showed, the numbers $h^{p,q}$ depend only on the complex structure of X and not on the particular projective embedding (which defines the metric).

In this way Hodge obtained new numerical invariants of algebraic manifolds. As the $h^{p,q}$ satisfy certain symmetries, namely

$$h^{p,q} = h^{q,p} \quad \text{and} \quad h^{p,q} = h^{n-p,n-q},$$

various simple consequences are immediately deduced for the Betti numbers. Thus h^{2k+1} is always even, generalizing the well-known property of a Riemann surface but also showing that many even-dimensional real manifolds cannot carry a complex algebraic structure.

The fact that one obtains in this way the new intrinsic invariants $h^{p,q}$ is a first vindication of the Hodge theory as applied to algebraic manifolds. It shows that the apparently strange idea of introducing an auxiliary metric into algebraic geometry does in fact produce significant new information. For Riemann surfaces the complex structure defines a conformal structure, and hence the Riemannian metric is not far away; but in higher dimensions this relation with conformal structures breaks down and makes Hodge's success all the more surprising. Only in the 1950's, with the introduction of sheaf theory, was an alternative and more intrinsic definition given for the Hodge numbers, namely

$$h^{p,q} = \dim H^q(X, \Omega^p),$$

where Ω^p is the sheaf of holomorphic p-forms.

A further refinement of Hodge's theory involved the use of the basic 2-form ω, which is itself harmonic. Hodge showed that every harmonic r-form ϕ has a further decomposition of the form

$$\phi = \sum_s \phi_s \omega^s,$$

where ϕ_s is an "effective" harmonic $(r - 2s)$ form.

This decomposition is the analogue of the results of Lefschetz that relate the homology of X to the homology of its hyperplane sections, ω playing the role of a hyperplane.

The theory of harmonic forms thus provides a remarkably rich and detailed structure for the cohomology of algebraic manifolds. This "Hodge structure" has been at the basis of a vast amount of work since the mid-1930's, and it has become abundantly clear that it will in particular play a key role in future work on the theory of moduli.

One problem that Hodge recognized as of fundamental importance is the characterization of the homology classes carried by algebraic subvarieties of X. For divisors (varieties of dimension $n - 1$) this problem had been settled by Émile Picard and Lefschetz, and Hodge saw what the appropriate generalization should be. For many years he attempted to establish his conjecture, but it eluded all his efforts. The conjecture is that a rational cohomology class in $H^{2q}(X, Q)$ is represented by an algebraic subvariety if and only if its harmonic form is of type (q, q). The necessity of this condition is easy; the difficulty lies in the converse, which asserts the existence of a suitable algebraic subvariety. This "Hodge conjecture" has achieved a considerable status, almost on a par with the Riemann hypothesis or the Poincaré conjecture. Its central importance is fully recognized, but no solution is in sight.

BIBLIOGRAPHY

I. ORIGINAL WORKS. Hodge's writings include "On Multiple Integrals Attached to an Algebraic Variety," in *Journal of the London Mathematical Society*, **5** (1930), 283–290; "The Geometric Genus of a Surface as a Topological Invariant," *ibid.*, **8** (1933), 312–319; "A Special Type of Kähler Manifold," in *Proceedings of the London Mathematical Society*, 3rd ser., **1** (1951), 104–117; "The Characteristic Classes on Algebraic Varieties," *ibid.*, 138–151; *The Theory and Applications of Harmonic Integrals* (Cambridge, 1941; 2nd ed., 1952; repr. 1959); *Methods of Algebraic Geometry*, 3 vols. (Cambridge, 1947–1954; vol. I repr. 1959; vol. II repr. 1968), written with Daniel Pedoe; and "Integrals of the Second Kind on an Algebraic Variety," in *Annals of Mathematics*, **62** (1955), 56–91, written with Michael F. Atiyah.

II. SECONDARY LITERATURE. Michael F. Atiyah, "William Vallance Douglas Hodge," in *Biographical Memoirs of Fellows of the Royal Society*, **22** (1976), 169–192, includes an extensive bibliography. Hodge's work is treated in Phillip Griffiths and Joseph Harris, *Principles of Algebraic Geometry* (New York, 1978).

MICHAEL ATIYAH

HODGKINSON, EATON (*b.* Anderton, near Great Budworth, Cheshire, England, 26 February 1789; *d.* Manchester, England, 18 June 1861)

Hodgkinson was one of the largely self-taught British mathematicians of the eighteenth and nineteenth centuries who turned their attention to applied mathematics and applied mechanics. His research and publications were confined almost entirely to the experimental and analytical study of the theory of elasticity and the strength of materials, and he became the foremost British authority in these fields during the second quarter of the nineteenth century.

His early education was first directed toward the study of Latin, Greek, and Hebrew in preparation for the university and a clerical career. He soon displayed a strong distaste for these studies, however, and suffered severely at the hands of a stern schoolmaster. As a result, he was transferred to another elementary school, where his mathematical ability was recognized and fostered. These episodes constituted the full extent of his formal education for he was compelled to devote himself to the assistance of his widowed mother, first in working the family farm in Cheshire, and later, beginning in 1811, when the family moved to Manchester, in operating a pawnbrokerage. Hodgkinson extended his knowledge of mathematics and mechanics through private study, largely of the works of William Emerson and Thomas Simpson. In Manchester he was guided and encouraged by John Dalton; together they studied the work of Euler, Lagrange, and Laplace. Hodgkinson had no sectarian affiliations and displayed no interest in religion.

At the age of thirty-three Hodgkinson read his first paper (published two years later), a study of beam flexure. Although a correct understanding of the distribution of stresses in a flexed beam had been reached by Parent and Coulomb during the eighteenth century, the solution had remained generally unnoticed. In Great Britain it had been presented only by Robison in his *Encyclopaedia Britannica* article, "Strength of Materials," and it was from this source that Hodgkinson derived the key principle, namely that in a transversely loaded beam the summation of the tensile and compressive stresses across any section must equal zero. Only with the publication of Hodgkinson's paper in 1824 did the solution become generally known.

In a later paper (1831) Hodgkinson examined the flexural characteristics of cast iron and showed that the tensile and compressive strengths of that material are unequal; and, accordingly, for the most economical cast-iron I beam and tension and compression flanges should be unequal. His further publications covered a variety of problems in structural mechanics, including dynamical loading of beams, column theory, structural characteristics of wrought iron, and hollow girders. In general, his research was relevant to many engineering problems encountered in the rapidly developing railroad industry and, appropriately, he became in 1847 one of the commissioners appointed to study the application of iron to railway structures. The results of his investigations constituted the primary documents in the "Report of the Iron Commissioners," which appeared in 1849. During this period he also collaborated with Robert Stephenson and William Fairbairn on the design of the Britannia and Conway tubular bridges.

Hodgkinson became one of the first British autodidacts to receive a university appointment when, in 1847, he was made professor of the mechanical principles of engineering at University College, London.

BIBLIOGRAPHY

I. ORIGINAL WORKS. Hodgkinson's most influential works include "On the Transverse Strain and Strength of Materials," in *Memoirs of the Manchester Literary and Philosophical Society,* 2nd ser., **4** (1824); "Theoretical and Experimental Researches to Ascertain the Strength and Best Forms of Iron Beams," *ibid.,* **5** (1831); the two investigations he contributed to the *Report of the Commissioners Appointed to Inquire into the Application of Iron to Railway Structures* (London, 1849); and *Experimental Researches on the Strength and Other Properties of Cast Iron* (London, 1846).

A list of many of Hodgkinson's publications is given in *Royal Society of London, Catalogue of Scientific Papers (1800–1863)* (London, 1869).

II. SECONDARY LITERATURE. Extensive reviews of many of Hodgkinson's publications are contained in Isaac Todhunter, *A History of the Theory of Elasticity and the Strength of Materials,* 2 vols. (Cambridge, 1886). For a long biographical article, see Robert Rawson, "Memoir of Eaton Hodgkinson," in *Memoirs of the Manchester Literary and Philosophical Society,* 3rd ser., **2** (1865), 145–204, repr. in *Annual Report of the Smithsonian Institution* (1868), pp. 203–230.

HAROLD DORN

HOËNÉ-WROŃSKI (or **HOEHNE**), **JÓZEF MARIA** (*b.* Wolsztyn, Poland, 23 August 1776; *d.* Neuilly, near Paris, France, 8 August 1853)

Hoehne was the son of Antoni Hoehne, the municipal architect of Poznań, and Elżbieta Pernicka. Educated in Poznań and Warsaw, he took part as a young artillery officer in the national uprising of 1794, commanding a battery during the siege of Warsaw by the Prussian army. In the same year he was taken prisoner by the Russian army, which he joined for a short period. He was released about 1797 and, living on money left to him by his father, spent the next few years studying philosophy at several German universities. In 1800 Hoehne settled in Marseilles, where he became a French citizen and addressed himself to scientific research. At first he took occasional jobs in scientific institutions, working at the Marseilles astronomical observatory and as secretary of the local medical association. In later years he earned his living by giving private lessons in science and philosophy. At various periods he was supported by patrons who had been converted to his philosophical doctrine and thus obtained the funds for his prolific publishing activity.

About 1810 Hoehne married Victoire Henriette Sarrazin de Montferrier, sister of the mathematician Alexandre Montferrier. At approximately the same time he adopted the surname Wroński, which he used alternatively with Hoehne; but most of his writings are signed Hoëné-Wroński, without a first name.

In 1810 Hoëné-Wroński moved to Paris and submitted to the Institut his first memoir on the foundations of mathematics, "Premier principe des méthodes analytiques." The paper received a rather sketchy review by Lacroix and Lagrange, and the ensuing polemic initiated by Hoëné-Wroński quickly led to a break in relations with the Institut. During his first years in Paris, he conducted intensive research in mathematical analysis, subsidized by the financier Pierre Arson, who was at first a devoted disciple. Their relations dissolved in a violent quarrel over financial arrangements that resulted in a trial, famous at the time, in 1819.

From 1820 to 1823 Hoëné-Wroński tried unsuccessfully to obtain the award of the British Board of Longitude for research on the determination of longitude at sea. He also failed in attempts to interest the Royal Society in his writings on hydrodynamics. In both cases Hoëné-Wroński became embroiled in polemics that quickly extended to extrascientific matters. He continued his mathematical research after returning to Paris, although his main interest had turned to the explication of his Messianic philosophy. In the 1830's Hoëné-Wroński investigated locomotion and sought to build vehicles that could compete both technically and economically with the newly developing railways, but the caterpillar vehicles that he designed did not progress beyond the model stage. His last years were spent in poverty.

Hoëné-Wroński's extant manuscripts and published writings cover a wide range of knowledge. His philosophy, which is central, forms the basis for reforming various branches of the exact and social sciences. Hoëné-Wroński's philosophical notions were formed under Kant's influence; and his first published work, *Philosophie critique découverte par Kant* (Marseilles, 1803), was the first exhaustive presentation of Kant's teachings in French. Hoëné-Wroński's philosophical system was based on the sudden revelation of the "Absolute," a concept never made precise, from which all aspects of existence evolve. This universal and rationalistic "absolute philosophy" could, according to its author, solve all theoretical and practical problems. Three main concepts constitute its framework: the "highest law," the foundation of reality independent of human influence; the "universal problem," man's supplementing of the Creation by introducing new realities; and the "final concordance," that harmony among various aspects of reality which is humanity's ultimate aim.

Hoëné-Wroński applied his philosophy to mathematics in a series of works that began with *Introduction à la philosophie des mathématiques*. In these writings rigorous mathematical proof retreated before arguments of the absolute philosophy—which, with the specific nomenclature introduced, made the reception and evaluation of his works difficult. Hoëné-Wroński criticized the standpoint taken by Lagrange in his *Théorie des fonctions analytiques*, disagreeing with both Lagrange's insufficient grounds for the use of the series development and his opposition to the introduction of infinite quantities in analysis. According to Hoëné-Wroński, the "highest law" in mathematics consisted in the development of any function in the series

$$F(x) = A_0\Omega_0(x) + A_1\Omega_1(x) + A_2\Omega_2(x) + \cdots,$$

where Ω_i denotes any function of the variable x. The "highest law" was to constitute the basis of the entire theory of differential equations. The lack of proof and imprecise range of applicability rendered its evaluation difficult; it is functional analysis that can determine the scope of Hoëné-Wroński's theorem. The determinants used to compute the coefficients A_i are known as Wronskians, a term introduced by Thomas Muir in 1882.

In 1812 Hoëné-Wroński published his universal solution of algebraic equations, *Résolution générale des équations de tous les degrés*. Althrough Ruffini's research had already demonstrated that this solution cannot be correct, it is applicable in particular cases. Several errors were found in Hoëné-Wroński's papers in other branches of sciences, for instance, in his treatment of the laws of hydrodynamics. His celestial mechanics—although based on a law allegedly more general than Newton's—was in fact equivalent to it. On the other hand, his method of resolving perturbative functions contained new ideas and was later found to be feasible.

A recurrent pattern in Hoëné-Wroński's relations with various institutions, both academic and social, indicates a marked psychopathic tendency: grandiose exaggeration of the importance of his own research, violent reaction to the slightest criticism, and repeated recourse to nonscientific media as allies against a supposed conspiracy. His aberrant personality, as well as the thesis of his esoteric philosophy (based on a revelation received on 15 August 1803 or, according to his other writings, 1804), tempt one to dismiss his work as the product of a gigantic fallacy engendered by a troubled and deceived mind. Later investigation of his writings, however, leads to a different conclusion. Hidden among the multitude of irrelevancies are important concepts that show him to have been a highly gifted mathematician whose contribution, unfortunately, was overshadowed by the imperative of his all-embracing absolute philosophy.

BIBLIOGRAPHY

I. ORIGINAL WORKS. A bibliography of Hoëné-Wroński's writings and a catalog of MSS preserved at the library of the Polish Academy of Sciences at Kórnik is in S. Dickstein, *Hoene Wroński. Jego życie i prace* (". . . His Life and Works"; Cracow, 1896). Subsequent literature is in B. J. Gawecki, *Wroński i o Wrońskim. Katalog prac filozoficznych Hoene Wrońskiego oraz literatury dotyczącej jego osoby i życia* ("Wroński and About Wroński. Catalog of Philosophical Works by Hoëné-Wroński and of Works on the Man and His Philosophy"; Warsaw, 1958). An incomplete ed. of Hoëné-Wroński's philosophical works is F. Warrain, ed., *L'oeuvre philosophique de Hoene Wroński*, 2 vols. (Paris, 1933–1936). A selection of philosophical works published in Italian is *Collezione italiana degli scritti filosofici di Hoene Wronski*, 4 pts. (Vicenza, 1870–1878). The mathematical works appeared as J. M. Wroński, *Oeuvres mathématiques*, 4 vols. (Paris, 1925).

II. SECONDARY LITERATURE. An introduction to Hoëné-Wroński's philosophy is P. d'Arcy, *Hoëné-Wroński, une philosophie de la création* (Paris, 1970). On the mathematical "supreme law" see S. Banach, "Über das 'loi suprême' von J. Hoene Wroński," in *Bul-*

letin international de l'Académie polonaise des sciences et des lettres, ser. A (1939), 1–10; and C. Lagrange, "Démonstration élémentaire de la loi suprême de Wroński," in *Mémoires couronnés . . . publiés par l'Académie royale des sciences . . . de Belgique*, **47**, no. 2 (1886). His astronomy is discussed in F. Koebcke, "Über Hoëné-Wroński's Überlegungen zur Himmelsmechanik," in *Acta astronomica*, ser. C, **3** (Feb. 1938), 73–81.

JERZY DOBRZYCKI

HÖLDER, OTTO LUDWIG (*b.* Stuttgart, Germany, 22 December 1859; *d.* Leipzig, Germany, 29 August 1937)

Hölder came from a Württemberg family of public officials and scholars. His father, Otto Hölder, was professor of French at the Polytechnikum in Stuttgart; his mother was the former Pauline Ströbel. In Stuttgart, Hölder attended one of the first Gymnasiums devoted to science and there he studied engineering for a short time. A colleague of his father's suggested that the best place to study mathematics was Berlin, where Weierstrass, Kronecker, and Kummer were teaching. When Hölder arrived at the University of Berlin in 1877, Weierstrass, lecturing on the theory of functions, had already covered the fundamentals of analysis. Hölder caught up to the class with the aid of other students' notes and was thus led to his first independent studies in mathematics.

Influenced by the rigorous foundation of analysis given by Weierstrass, Hölder developed the continuity condition for volume density that bears his name. It appeared in his dissertation (*Beiträge zur Potentialtheorie*), which he presented at Tübingen in 1882; his referee was Paul du Bois-Reymond. The Hölder continuity is sufficient for the existence of all the second derivatives of the potential and for the validity of the Poisson differential equation. These derivatives, as Arthur Korn later showed, possess exactly the same continuity properties as the density. Hölder's work on potential theory was continued on a larger scale by Leon Lichtenstein, O. D. Kellogg, P. J. Schauder, and C. B. Morrey, Jr.

Next Hölder investigated analytic functions and summation procedures by arithmetic means. He provided the first completely general proof of Weierstrass' theorem that an analytic function comes arbitrarily close to every value in the neighborhood of an essential singular point. He showed that it might be possible to compute, by repetition of arithmetic means (Hölder means), the limit of an analytic function the power series of which diverges at a point of the circle of convergence. This technique is equivalent to the one introduced by Cesàro, as Walter Schnee demonstrated.

In his *Habilitationsschrift* submitted in 1884 at Göttingen, Hölder examined the convergence of the Fourier series of a function that was not assumed to be either continuous or bounded; for such functions the Fourier coefficients had first to be defined in a new fashion as improper integrals. After qualifying as a lecturer, Hölder discovered the inequality named for him. This advance involved an extension of Schwarz's inequality to general exponents as well as to inequalities for convex functions of the type that were later treated by J. L. Jensen. After unsuccessful attempts to find an algebraic differential equation for the gamma function, Hölder inverted the method of posing the question and proved the impossibility of such a differential equation.

Hölder owed his interest in group theory and Galois theory primarily to Kronecker, but also to Felix Klein, in whose seminar at Leipzig Hölder participated soon after receiving his doctorate. To these fields he contributed "Zurückführung einer algebraischen Gleichung auf eine Kette von Gleichungen," in which he reduced an algebraic equation by using simple groups and by introducing the concept of "natural" irrationals. Here Hölder extended C. Jordan's theorem (stated in his *Commentary* on Galois) of the uniqueness of the indexes of such a "composition series," to the uniqueness of the "factor groups" that Hölder had introduced. This new concept and the Jordan-Hölder theorem are today fundamental to group theory.

With the help of these methods Hölder solved the old question of the "irreducible case." A solution of the cubic equation is given by the so-called Cardano formula, in which appear cube roots of a square root $\sqrt{D}$. For three distinct real roots $D < 0$, and therefore the quantities under the cube root sign are imaginary. The real solution is thus obtained as the sum of imaginary cube roots. Hölder showed that in this case it is impossible to solve the general cubic equation through real radicals, except where the equation decomposes over the base field.

Hölder turned his attention first to simple groups. Besides the simple groups of orders 60 and 168 already known at the time, he found no new ones with a composite order less than 200. Nevertheless, he considered his method to be "of some interest so long as we do not possess a better one suitable for handling the problem generally." Such a general method is still lacking, despite the progress and great efforts of recent years.

In further works Hölder treated the structure of composite groups having the following orders: p^3,

pq^2, pqr, p^4, where p, q, r are primes, and n, where n is square-free. Finally, he studied the formation of groups constructed from previously given factor groups and normal subgroups.

While an associate professor at Tübingen, Hölder verified (in "Über die Prinzipien von Hamilton und Maupertuis") that the variational principles of Hamilton are valid for nonholonomic motions—their applicability in these cases had been questioned by Heinrich Hertz. Physicists are indebted to Hölder for this confirmation of the Hamiltonian principle, which has often been used since then in deriving differential equations of physics.

The first third of Hölder's career in research was the most fruitful. A period of depression seems to have occurred at Königsberg, where he succeeded Minkowski in 1894. He was happy to leave that city in 1899, when he accepted an offer from Leipzig to succeed Sophus Lie. In the same year he married Helene Lautenschlager, who also came from Stuttgart.

At Leipzig, Hölder turned to geometrical questions, beginning with his inaugural lecture *Anschauungen und Denken in der Geometrie* (1900). He became interested in the geometry of the projective line and undertook investigations published in his paper "Die Axiome der Quantität und die Lehre vom Mass" (1901). The topics covered in this work were, in his view, important for physics. Moreover, in 1911 he published an article on "Streckenrechnung und projektive Geometrie."

Between 1914 and 1923 this work led to the logico-philosophical studies of the foundations of mathematics which are included in *Die mathematische Methode* (1924). These philosophical inquiries attracted less attention than Hilbert's axiomatic method, but Hölder saw connections between Brouwer's intuitionism and Weyl's logical investigations and his own ideas. P. Lorenzen's recent work on logic contains ideas which are in essence similar to those of Hölder's. In his obituary on Hölder, B. L. van der Waerden wrote:

> According to Hölder one of the essential features of the mathematical method consists in constructing for given concepts, concepts of higher order in such a way that concepts and methods of proof of one stage are taken as objects of mathematical investigation of the next higher stage. This is done, for example, by first developing a method of proof and afterward counting the steps of the proof or by letting them correspond to other objects, or by combining them by means of relations [p. 161].

On the basis of this conception Hölder concluded—and recent logical investigations of Gödel fully justify his position—that "one can never grasp the whole of mathematics by means of a logical formalism, because the new concepts and syllogism that are applied to the formulas of the formalism necessarily go beyond the formalism and yet also belong to mathematics."

In his last years one of Hölder's favorite topics was elementary number theory—his third great teacher in Berlin had been Kummer. Hölder's contributions in this area appeared mainly in the *Bericht. Sächsische Gesellschaft* (later *Akademie) der Wissenschaften.* From 1899 he was active in the academy and for several years served as president. He was also a member of the Prince Jablonowski Society. In 1927 Hölder became a corresponding member of the Bavarian Academy of Sciences.

BIBLIOGRAPHY

I. ORIGINAL WORKS. Hölder's books include *Anschauungen und Denken in der Geometrie* (Leipzig, 1900; Darmstadt, 1968); *Die Arithmetik in strenger Begründung. Programmabhandlung der philosophischen Fakultät* (Leipzig, 1914; 2nd ed., Berlin, 1929); and *Die mathematische Methode. Logisch-erkenntnis-theoretische Untersuchungen im Gebiet der Mathematik, Mechanik und Physik* (Berlin, 1924).

Among his papers are the following: *Beiträge zur Potentialtheorie* (Stuttgart, 1882), his diss.; "Beweis des Satzes, dass eine eindeutige analytische Funktion in unendlicher Nähe einer wesentlich singulären Stelle jedem Wert beliebig nahe kommt," in *Mathematische Annalen,* **20** (1882), 138–142; "Grenzwerte von Reihen an der Konvergenzgrenze," *ibid.,* 535–549; "Über eine neue hinreichende Bedingung für die Darstellbarkeit einer Funktion durch die Fouriersche Reihe," in *Bericht der Preussischen Akademie* (1885), 419–434; "Über die Eigenschaft der Gammafunktion, keiner algebraischen Differentialgleichung zu genügen," in *Mathematische Annalen,* **28** (1886), 1–13, "Zurückführung einer beliebigen algebraischen Gleichung auf eine Kette von Gleichungen," *ibid.,* **34** (1889), 26–56; "Über einen Mittelwertsatz," in *Nachrichten von der Gesellschaft der Wissenschaften zu Göttingen,* **2** (1889), 38–47; "Über den Casus irreducibilis bei der Gleichung dritten Grades," in *Mathematische Annalen,* **38** (1891), 307–312; "Die einfachen Gruppen im ersten und zweiten Hundert der Ordnungszahlen," *ibid.,* **40** (1892), 55–88; "Die Gruppen der Ordnungen p^3, pq^2, pqr, p^4," *ibid.,* **43** (1893), 301–412; "Bildung zusammengesetzter Gruppen," *ibid.,* **46** (1895), 321–422; "Die Gruppen mit quadratfreier Ordnungszahl," in *Nachrichten von der Gesellschaft der Wissenschaften zu Göttingen,* **2** (1895), 211–229; "Uber die Prinzipien von Hamilton und Maupertuis," *ibid.,* 122–157; "Galoissche Theorie mit Anwendungen," in *Encyklopädie der mathematischen Wissenschaften,* I (1898–1904), 480–520; "Die Axiome der Quantität und die Lehre vom Mass," in *Bericht. Sächsische Akademie der Wissenschaften,* Math.-nat. Klasse, **53** (1901), 1-64; "Die Zahlenskala auf der projektiven Geraden und die independente Geometrie dieser Geraden," in *Mathematische Annalen,* **65** (1908), 161-260; and "Streckenrechnung und projektive Geometrie," in *Bericht. Sächsische Akademie der Wissenschaften,* Math.-nat. Klasse, **63** (1911), 65-183.

II. SECONDARY LITERATURE. The main source is the obituary by B. L. van der Waerden, "Nachruf auf Otto Hölder," in *Mathematische Annalen,* **116** (1939), 157-165, with bibliography; it also appeared in *Bericht. Sächsische Akademie der Wissenschaften,* Math.-nat. Klasse, **90** (1938), without the bibliography. See also Poggendorff, IV, 651; V, 547; VI, 1136; VIIa, 509.

ERNST HÖLDER

HOLMBOE, BERNT MICHAEL (*b.* Vang, Norway, 23 March 1795; *d.* Christiania [now Oslo], Norway, 28 March 1850)

Holmboe was the son of a minister. After graduating from the Cathedral School in Christiania, he joined the student volunteer corps for service in the brief conflict with Sweden in 1814. In 1815 he became assistant to Christopher Hansteen, professor of astronomy at the newly created University of Christiania. He was appointed teacher at the Cathedral School in 1818; here he made his greatest contribution to mathematics by discovering and nurturing the genius of his pupil Niels Henrik Abel. Together they explored the whole mathematical literature in a quest in which the pupil soon became the leader.

In 1826 Holmboe was appointed lecturer in mathematics at the university, a move which was later criticized because it blocked the possibility of a position for Abel. Nevertheless, the friendship between the two remained undisturbed.

After Abel's death Holmboe edited his works at the request of the government; otherwise his own mathematical contributions were undistinguished. He published a number of elementary school texts which appeared in several editions. A later, more advanced calculus text was evidently influenced by Abel's research.

Holmboe was lecturer at the military academy in Christiania from 1826 until his death; during Hansteen's absence in 1828-1830 on a geomagnetic expedition to Siberia, Holmboe gave his lectures in astronomy. In 1834 he became professor of pure mathematics at the university.

BIBLIOGRAPHY

Holmboe edited Abel's writings as *Oeuvres complètes de N. H. Abel, mathématicien, avec des notes et développements* (Christiania, 1839). His advanced calculus text is *Laerebog i den höiere mathematik* (Christiania, 1849).

OYSTEIN ORE

HOPF, HEINZ (*b.* Breslau, Germany [now Wrocław, Poland], 19 November 1894; *d.* Zollikon, Switzerland, 3 June 1971)

Hopf attended school and started his university study of mathematics in his birthplace, but his studies were soon interrupted by a long period of military service during World War I. A fortnight's leave in the summer of 1917 determined his mathematical future: he ventured into Erhard Schmidt's set theory course at the University of Breslau and became fascinated by Schmidt's exposition of L. E. J. Brouwer's proof of the dimension invariance by means of the degree of continuous mappings.

In 1920 Hopf followed Schmidt to Berlin where, with topological research, he earned his Ph.D. in 1925 and his *Habilitation* in 1926. At Göttingen in 1925 he became acquainted with Emmy Noether and met the Russian mathematician P. S. Alexandroff, with whom he formed a lifelong friendship. Rockefeller fellowships enabled the two friends to spend the academic year 1927-1928 at Princeton University, where topology was fostered by O. Veblen, S. Lefschetz, and J. W. Alexander. In 1931 Hopf was appointed a full professor at the Eidgenössische Technische Hochschule in Zurich, assuming the chair of Weyl, who had gone to Göttingen.

The greater part of Hopf's work was algebraic topology, motivated by vigorous geometric intuitions. Although the number of his papers was relatively small, no topologist of that period inspired as great a variety of important ideas, not only in topology, but also in quite varied domains. He was awarded many honorary degrees and memberships in learned societies. From 1955 to 1958 he was the president of the International Mathematical Union.

Hopf was a short, vigorous man with cheerful, pleasant features. His voice was well modulated, and his speech slow and strongly articulated. His lecture style was clear and fascinating; in personal conversation he conveyed stimulating ideas. With his wife Anja, he extended hospitality and support to persecuted people and exiles.

After Brouwer created his profound "mixed" method in topology, Hopf was the first to continue Brouwer's work on a large scale. He focused on the mapping degree and the mapping class (homotopy class), which had been mere tools in Brouwer's work. Hopf set out to prove that Brouwer's mapping degree was a sufficient homotopy invariant for mappings of spheres of equal dimension (2, nos. 5, 11, 14) and in this context he studied fixed points (2, no. 8) and singularities of vector fields (2, no. 6). His initially crude and too directly geometric methods underwent gradual refinement, first by Emmy Noether's abstract algebraic influence, then through the combinatorial ideas of the American school. In 1933 his efforts culminated in the development of a complete homotopy classification by homology means of mappings of n-dimensional polytopes into the n-dimensional sphere S^n (2, no. 24).

Hopf's study of vector fields led to a generalization of and a formula about the integral curvature (2, no. 2), as a mapping degree of normal fields (1925). An extension of Lefschetz' fixed point formula (2, no. 9) was the result of work done in 1928. As a new and powerful tool to investigate mappings of manifolds, Hopf defined the inverse homomorphism (2, no. 16) using the Cartesian product of the related manifolds—a device he took from Lefschetz. In fact Hopf's 1930 paper on this subject goes back to his stay at Princeton. Not until the arrival of cohomology and the cohomology products was the inverse homomorphism better understood and more firmly integrated into algebraic topology (5).

Hopf's next great topological feat was the 1931 publication (2, no. 18) on an infinity of homotopy classes of S^3 into S^2, and the definition of the "Hopf invariant" for these mappings. As early as 1927 Hopf conjectured that the "Hopf fiber map" was homotopically essential, but the tool to prove this conjecture had still to be created: the idea of considering inverted mappings. Hopf's work on this subject was influential in W. Hurewicz' shaping the concept of homotopy groups, and in particular in his investigation (1935–1936) of homotopy groups of fiber spaces (4). H. Freudenthal, by a synthesis of Hopf's and Hurewicz' work, proved the completeness of Hopf's classification and discovered the suspension (6). From these beginnings homotopy of spheres developed after World War II into a growing field of research, to which Hopf himself had contributed (1935) the investigation of the case of mappings of S^{2n-1} into S^n (2, no. 26).

Vector fields and families of vector fields remained a concern of Hopf's. He stimulated Stiefel's work (7), which led to the discovery of what is now called Stiefel-Whitney classes, and that of B. Eckmann as well (8, 9). Hopf's 1941 paper on bilinear forms (2, no. 38) fits into the same context, as does his influential discovery (1948) of the concept of almost complex manifolds (2, no. 52), which, among other things, led to his 1958 paper with F. Hirzebruch (2, no. 66). Hopf's most important contribution to this area of mathematics is his paper, published in 1941, but begun in 1939, on the homology of group manifolds (2, no. 40), in which he proved the famous theorem that compact manifolds with a continuous multiplication with unit (now called H-manifolds) have a polynomial cohomology ring with all generators of odd dimension. The theorem had already been known by Lie groups methods for the four big classes. Hopf formulated the theorem in terms of homology; his tool was again the inverse homomorphism—Hopf did not like and never became fully acquainted with cohomology. He wrote a few more papers on this subject (2, nos. 41, 46) and instigated H. Samelson's 1942 investigations (10).

In 1936 Hurewicz (4) had proved that in polytopes with trivial higher homotopy groups the fundamental group uniquely determines the homology groups, raising the question of how the one determines the others. Hopf tackled the problem in his papers (2, nos. 40, 45, 49) of 1942 and 1944, which led to independent investigations of Eckmann (11), S. Eilenberg and S. MacLane (12), and Freudenthal (13). The result was the cohomology of groups, the first instance of cohomological algebra, which has since developed into a broad new field of mathematics.

Another beautiful idea of Hopf's was transferring Freudenthal's concept of ends of topological groups to spaces possessing a discontinuous group with a compact fundamental domain (2, no. 47), which Freudenthal in turn converted into a theory on ends of discrete groups with a finite number of generators (14).

Hopf was also interested in global differential geometry. With W. Rinow he contributed the concept of a complete surface (2, no. 20); with Samelson (2, no. 32) a proof of the congruence theorem for convex surfaces; with H. Schilt (2, no. 34) a paper on isometry and deformation; and he studied relations between the principal curvatures (2, no. 57).

Two beautiful papers of Hopf's that should be mentioned are one on the turning around of the tangent of a closed plane curve (2, no. 27) and one on the set of chord lengths of plane continua (2, no. 31), published in 1935 and 1937 respectively. Hopf was also interested in number theory, which he enjoyed teaching and to which he devoted a few papers.

BIBLIOGRAPHY

(1) P. Alexandroff and H. Hopf, *Topologie I* (Berlin, 1935).

(2) H. Hopf, *Selecta* (Berlin, 1964), contains an almost complete bibliography.

(3) H. Hopf, "Ein Abschnitt aus der Entwicklung der Topologie," in *Jahresbericht der Deutschen Mathematiker-vereinigung,* **68** (1966), 182–192.

(4) W. Hurewicz, "Beiträge zur Topologie der Deformationen. I–IV," in *Proceedings. K. Nederlandse akademie van wetenschappen,* **38** (1935), 113–119, 521–528; **39** (1936), 117–125, 215–224.

(5) H. Freudenthal, "Zum Hopfschen Umkehrhomomorphismus," in *Annals of Mathematics,* **38** (1937), 847–853.

(6) H. Freudenthal, "Über die Sphärenabbildungen, I," in *Compositio mathematica,* **5** (1937), 300–314.

(7) E. Stiefel, "Richtungsfelder und Fernparallelismus in *n*-dimensionalen Mannigfaltigkeiten," in *Commentarii mathematici helvetici,* **8** (1935–1936), 305–353.

(8) B. Eckmann, "Zur Homotopietheorie gefaserter Räume," *ibid.,* **14** (1942), 141–192.

(9) B. Eckmann, "Systeme von Richtungsfeldern in Sphären und stetige Lösungen komplexer linearer Gleichungen," *ibid.,* **15** (1943), 1–26.

(10) H. Samelson, "Beiträge zur Topologie der Gruppenmannigfaltigkeiten," in *Annals of Mathematics,* **42** (1941), 1091–1137.

(11) B. Eckmann, "Der Cohomologie-Ring einer beliebigen Gruppe," in *Commentarii mathematici helvetici,* **18** (1946), 232–282.

(12) S. Eilenberg and S. MacLane, "Relations Between Homology and Homotopy Groups of Spaces," in *Annals of Mathematics,* **46** (1945), 480–509.

(13) H. Freudenthal, "Der Einfluss der Fundamentalgruppe auf die Bettischen Gruppen," *ibid.,* **47** (1946), 274–316.

(14) H. Freudenthal, "Über die Enden diskreter Räume und Gruppen," in *Commentarii mathematici helvetici,* **17** (1944), 1–38.

(15) B. Eckmann, "Zum Gedenken an Heinz Hopf," in *Neue Züricher Zeitung* (18 June 1971).

(16) P. Alexandroff, "Die Topologie in und um Holland in den Jahren 1920–1930," in *Nieuw archief voor wiskunde,* **17** (1969), 109–127.

HANS FREUDENTHAL

HOPKINS, WILLIAM (*b.* Kingston-on-Soar, Derbyshire, England, 2 February 1793; *d.* Cambridge, England, 13 October 1866)

The only son of a gentleman farmer, Hopkins had a desultory early education which included some practical farming in Norfolk. Later his father gave him a small estate near Bury St. Edmunds, but he found the task of management both uncongenial and unprofitable. After the death of his wife he sold the estate to pay off debts and to provide the means wherewith in 1822, at the age of thirty, he entered St. Peter's College (Peterhouse), Cambridge. Here he married again and his mathematical talent shone. He took the B.A. in 1827, placing as seventh wrangler, and then became a very successful private tutor of mathematics. Among his many pupils who attained high distinction were George Stokes, William Thomson (Lord Kelvin), P. G. Tait, Henry Fawcett, James Clerk Maxwell, and Isaac Todhunter. In the 1830's he was appointed a syndic for the building of the Fitzwilliam Museum.

Hopkins became intensely interested in geology about 1833, after excursions with Adam Sedgwick near Barmouth, in northern Wales. He decided that he would place the physical aspects of geology on a firmer basis, would free it from unverified ideas, and "support its theories upon clear mathematical demonstrations." [1] His mathematical models and propositions greatly impressed contemporary geologists, and in 1850 he was awarded the Wollaston Medal of the Geological Society of London for his application of mathematics to physics and geology. In 1851 and 1852 he was elected president of that society and in 1853 presided over the British Association for the Advancement of Science. He became a fellow of the Royal Society, and following his death the Cambridge University Philosophical Society founded in his honor a prize which was first awarded in 1867 and triennially thereafter.

The main written product of Hopkins' interest in pure mathematics is the two-volume *Elements of Trigonometry* (London, 1833–1847). His applications of mathematics to geology were expressed mainly in articles, the contents of which may be grouped under the following topics: crustal elevation and its effect on surface fracturing, the transport of erratic boulders, the nature of the earth's interior, and the causes of climatic change.

Hopkins attempted to explain dislocations or fractures at the earth's surface by estimating the effects of an elevatory force acting at every point beneath extensive portions of the earth's crust. From his consideration of the pressures exerted by explosive gases, vapors, and other subterranean forces upon the crust, he concluded that during crustal extension and fracturing there must originate in nearly all cases first a series of longitudinal parallel fractures and second, with continued uplift, a series of transverse dislocations at right angles to the first. This rectangular pattern of faults provided the fundamental directive lines during the elevation and formation of continents and of mountain systems. On this assumption Hopkins discussed the elevation and denudation of the English Weald and Lake District and of the Bas Boulonnais in northern France. In the Weald, a land of wide longitudinal vales at the foot of steep escarpments that are breached transversally by narrow river valleys, Hopkins concluded that the main vales and scarps were associated with longitudinal parallel fractures and that the transverse valleys were formed by dislocations at right angles to them. He admitted that he could not find true geological evidence of fracturing except perennial springs, which he assumed to be thrown out at faultlines. Today, as by the more perceptive geologists then, the Weald valleys and scarps are considered to be typical products of subaerial erosion and not of crustal fracturing.

Hopkins played an important and equally unfortunate part in the contemporary debate on the transport of erratic boulders. The aura of mathematical conclusiveness that surrounded his work caused his opinions to make a lasting impression and to be hailed as incontrovertible by his followers. At first he rejected glacial or ice transport as an explanation of the movement of erratic boulders, since it often involved "such obvious mechanical absurdities that the author considers it totally unworthy of the attention of the Society."[2] In his studies of the Lake District Hopkins postulated sudden upheavals during each of which a great mass of water, or "wave of translation," rushed down the rift valleys, rolling and sliding great boulders for long distances. The idea was welcomed by antiglacialists in Britain and by leading geologists in America, including H. D. Rogers, who in 1844 wrote:

> It has been shown by Mr. Hopkins, of Cambridge, reasoning from the experimental deductions of Mr. Scott Russell upon the properties of waves, that "there is no difficulty in accounting for a current of twenty-five or thirty miles an hour, if we allow of paroxysmal elevation of from one hundred to two hundred feet," and he further proves that a current of twenty miles an hour ought to move a block of three hundred and twenty tons, and since the force of the current increases in the ratio of the square of the velocity, a very moderate addition to this speed is compatible with the transportation of the very largest erratics anywhere to be met with, either in America or Europe.[3]

Although Hopkins' idea was wrong when applied to the transport of glacial erratics—as he himself later half admitted—in presenting it he added detail which, when applied to hydraulic work, was to prove of great value and is today known as Gilbert's sixth-power law. Assuming, as Playfair had shown, that the force of a current increases in the ratio of the square of its velocity, Hopkins calculated that "if a certain current be just able to move a block of given weight and form, another current of double the velocity of the former would move a block of a similar form, whose weight should be to that of the former in the ratio of $2^6:1$ *i.e.* of 64 to 1."[4]

Hopkins' theoretical investigations into the constitution of the interior of the earth made him "one of the most famous champions of the theory of the earth's rigidity."[5] Assuming that the earth was originally molten, he calculated from the varying effects of the sun's and moon's attraction (and especially of precession and nutation) that the solid crust of the earth had a thickness of at least one-quarter or one-fifth of its radius. This thickness, he concluded, virtually prohibited direct heat or matter transference from the molten interior to the earth's surface; and therefore volcanoes must draw their molten material from reservoirs of moderate size within the solid crust. The largely solid and rigid state of the earth was considered to be due to cooling and to great internal pressure, an opinion supported by the work of Poisson, Ampère, George H. Darwin, and Lord Kelvin. Indeed, it was on the advice of Kelvin that Hopkins in 1851 undertook at Manchester, with the help of Joule and Fairbairn, experiments that showed effectively that the fusion temperature of strata increased considerably with depth and pressure.

Hopkins' theoretical studies on the motion of glaciers and on climatic change contained nothing new except their praiseworthy quantitative precision. For example, his deductions that the most probable cause of changes of climate during geological time was the influence of alterations in the various configurations of land and sea and in ocean currents were already held by Lyell and others, but none had hitherto expressed the details in precise mathematical terms. Thus, except in the popularization of quantification and in the broader field of geophysics, Hopkins' effect on contemporary geology was frequently retrogressive rather than progressive. He was often lacking in geological insight; and it is not entirely through misfortune that his valuable sixth-power law of hydraulic traction is usually attributed to G. K. Gilbert, who applied it firmly to river flow and not to mighty waves caused by paroxysmal uplifts of mountains.

NOTES

1. W. W. Smyth, in *Quarterly Journal of the Geological Society of London,* **23** (1867), xxx.
2. "On the Elevation and Denudation of the District of the Lakes of Cumberland and Westmoreland," p. 762.
3. Address to the Association of American Geologists and Naturalists, in *American Journal of Science,* **47** (1844), 244–245; see also R. J. Chorley, A. J. Dunn, and R. P. Beckinsale, *The History of the Study of Landforms,* I, 278.
4. *Op. cit.* (1842), pp. 764–765; (1849), p. 233.
5. K. A. von Zittel, *History of Geology and Palaeontology,* p. 178.

BIBLIOGRAPHY

I. Original Works. Hopkins' writings were published, often successively in enlarged form, mainly as articles in

Transactions of the Cambridge Philosophical Society, Proceedings and *Quarterly Journal of the Geological Society of London, Philosophical Transactions of the Royal Society,* and *Report of the British Association for the Advancement of Science.* The most important are "Researches in Physical Geology," in *Transactions of the Cambridge Philosophical Society,* **6** (1838), 1-84, mainly on crustal elevation and fracturing; "Researches in Physical Geology," in *Philosophical Transactions of the Royal Society,* **129** (1839), 381-423; **130** (1840), 193-208; **132** (1842), 43-55, on precession and nutation and their probable effect on the nature of the earth's crust and interior—see also *Report of the British Association for the Advancement of Science* for 1847 (1848), pp. 33-92; and for 1853 (1854), pp. xli-lvii; "On the Geological Structure of the Wealden District and of the Bas Boulonnais," in *Proceedings of the Geological Society of London,* **3** (1841), 363-366; "On the Elevation and Denudation of the District of the Lakes of Cumberland and Westmoreland," *ibid.* (1842), pp. 757-766, repr. in full, with map, in *Quarterly Journal of the Geological Society of London,* **4** (1848), 70-98; "On the Motion of Glaciers," in *Transactions of the Cambridge Philosophical Society,* **8** (1849), 50-74, 159-169, which favors a rigid sliding, fracturing motion; "On the Transport of Erratic Blocks," *ibid.,* pp. 220-240; "Presidential Address," in *Quarterly Journal of the Geological Society of London,* **8** (1852), xxi-lxxx, mainly on glacial drift and temperature changes; "On the Granitic Blocks of the South Highlands of Scotland," *ibid.,* pp. 20-30, which considers that striations on rocks are due to half-floating ice; "On the Causes Which May Have Produced Changes in the Earth's Superficial Temperature," *ibid.,* pp. 56-92, a detailed paper with a map of isotherms; and "Anniversary Address," *ibid.,* **9** (1853), xxii-xcii, which attacks Élie de Beaumont's ideas on pentagonal fracturing during crustal uplift and fracturing. See also "On the External Temperature of the Earth . . .," in *Monthly Notices of the Royal Astronomical Society,* **17** (1856-1857), 190-195, which makes use of H. W. Dove's world isothermal map.

II. Secondary Literature. See R. E. Anderson, in *Dictionary of National Biography,* XXVII (1891), 339-340; R. J. Chorley, A. J. Dunn, and R. P. Beckinsale, *The History of the Study of Landforms,* I (London, 1964), *passim,* with a portrait; J. W. Clark and T. M. Hughes, *Life and Letters of the Rev. Adam Sedgwick,* II (Cambridge, 1890), 74, 154, 323; Henry Rogers Darwin, address to the Association of American Geologists and Naturalists, in *American Journal of Science,* **47** (1844), 244-245; W. W. Smyth, in *Quarterly Journal of the Geological Society of London,* **23** (1867), xxix-xxxii; *The Times* (London) (16 Oct. 1866), p. 4; and K. A. von Zittel, *History of Geology and Palaeontology,* M. M. Ogilvie-Gordon, trans. (London, 1901), pp. 168, 178, 303.

Robert P. Beckinsale

HORNER, WILLIAM GEORGE (*b.* Bristol, England, 1786; *d.* Bath, England, 22 September 1837)

The son of William Horner, a Wesleyan minister, Horner was educated at the Kingswood School, Bristol, where he became an assistant master (stipend £40) at the age of fourteen. After four years he was promoted to headmaster, receiving an additional £10 annually. According to an account given by an "old scholar" in *The History of Kingswood School . . . By Three Old Boys* [A. H. L. Hastings, W. A. Willis, W. P. Workman] (London, 1898), p. 88, the educational regime in his day was somewhat harsh. In 1809 Horner left Bristol to found his own school at Grosvenor Place, Bath, which he kept until his death. He left a widow and several children, one of whom, also named William, carried on the school.

Horner's only significant contribution to mathematics lay in the method of solving algebraic equations which still bears his name. Contained in a paper submitted to the Royal Society (read by Davies Gilbert on 1 July 1819), "A New Method of Solving Numerical Equations of All Orders by Continuous Approximation," it was published in the *Philosophical Transactions* (1819) and was subsequently republished in *Ladies' Diary* (1838) and *Mathematician* (1843). Horner found influential sponsors in J. R. Young of Belfast and Augustus de Morgan, who gave extracts and accounts of the method in their own publications. In consequence of the wide publicity it received, Horner's method spread rapidly in England but was little used elsewhere in Europe.

Throughout the nineteenth and early twentieth centuries Horner's method occupied a prominent place in standard English and American textbooks on the theory of equations, although, because of its lack of generality, it has found little favor with modern analysts. With the development of computer methods the subject has declined in importance, but some of Horner's techniques have been incorporated in courses in numerical analysis.

Briefly, when a real root of an equation has been isolated by any method, it may be calculated by any one of several arithmetical processes. A real root r, of $f(x) = 0$, is isolated when one finds two real numbers a, b, between which r lies and between which lies no other root of $f(x) = 0$. Horner's method consists essentially of successively diminishing the root by the smaller members of successive pairs of positive real numbers.

If

$$f_1(x) \equiv a_0x^n + a_1x^{n-1} + a_2x^{n-2} + \cdots + a_n,$$

and if $x = h + y$, we have (expanding by Taylor's theorem)

$$f(h + y) \equiv f(h) + yf'(h) + \frac{y^2}{2!}f''(h)$$

$$+ \cdots + \frac{y^n f^{(n)}(h)}{n!},$$

$$f(h+y) \equiv f(h) + (x-h)f'(h) + \frac{(x-h)^2}{2!}f''(h) + \cdots + \frac{(x-h)^n f^{(n)}(h)}{n!}.$$

If this is written

$$f_2(x-h) \equiv c_n + c_{n-1}(x-h) + c_{n-2}(x-h)^2 + \cdots + c_0(x-h)^n,$$

the coefficients $c_n, c_{n-1}, c_{n-2}, \ldots, c_0$ in the reduced equation are given by the successive remainders when the given polynomial is divided by $(x-h)$, $(x-h)^2$, $(x-h)^3$, . . ., $(x-h)^n$. In the original account of the method Horner used Arbogast's derivatives ($D\phi R$, $D^2\phi R$, . . ., $D^n\phi R$). Later he dispensed altogether with the calculus and gave an account of the method in entirely algebraic terms. Successive transformations were carried out in a compact arithmetic form, and the root obtained by a continuous process was correct to any number of places. The computational schema adopted is often referred to as synthetic division. Horner suggested, correctly, that his method could be applied to the extraction of square and cube roots; but his claims that it extended to irrational and transcendental equations were unfounded.

Although Horner's method was extremely practical for certain classes of equations, the essentials were by no means new; a similar method was developed by the Chinese in the thirteenth century (see J. Needham, *Science and Civilisation in China,* I [Cambridge, 1959], p. 42). The iterative method devised by Viète (1600) and developed extensively by Newton (1669), which came to be known as the Newton-Raphson method, is applicable also to logarithmic, trigonometric, and other equations. The numerical solution of equations was a popular subject in the early nineteenth century, and in 1804 a gold medal offered by the Società Italiana delle Scienze for an improved solution was won by Paolo Ruffini (. . . *Sopra la determinazione delle radici* . . . [Modena, 1804]). Ruffini's method was virtually the same as that developed independently by Horner some years later.

BIBLIOGRAPHY

I. ORIGINAL WORKS. Horner's writings include "A New Method of Solving Numerical Equations of All Orders by Continuous Approximation," in *Philosophical Transactions of the Royal Society,* **109** (1819), 308–335; "Horae arithmeticae," in T. Leybourn, ed., *The Mathematical Repository,* V, pt. 2 (London, 1830); and "On Algebraic Transformations," in *Mathematician* (1843).

II. SECONDARY LITERATURE. Accounts of the method are given by J. R. Young in *An Elementary Treatise on Algebra* (London, 1826); and *The Theory and Solution of Algebraical Equations* (London, 1843). Augustus de Morgan described the method in sundry articles, including "On Involution and Evolution," in *The Penny Cyclopaedia,* vol. XIII (London, 1839); and "Notices of the Progress of the Problem of Evolution," in *The Companion to the Almanack* (London, 1839). See also Florian Cajori, "Horner's Method of Approximation Anticipated by Ruffini," in *Bulletin of the American Mathematical Society,* **17** (1911), 409–414.

MARGARET E. BARON

HOÜEL, GUILLAUME-JULES (*b.* Thaon, Calvados, France, 7 April 1823; *d.* Périers, near Caen, France, 14 June 1886)

Born into one of the older Protestant families of Normandy, Hoüel studied at Caen and the Collège Rollin before entering the École Normale Supérieure in 1843. He received his doctorate from the Sorbonne in 1855 for research in celestial mechanics and held the chair of pure mathematics at the Faculty of Sciences in Bordeaux from 1859 until his death.

Hoüel's reputation rests primarily on the quality and quantity of his activities in mathematical exposition. His gift for languages was used to evaluate and frequently to expound or translate important foreign mathematical writings. In the theory of complex numbers Hoüel introduced many of his countrymen to the researches of William R. Hamilton, Hermann Grassmann, Giusto Bellavitis, and Bernhard Riemann through his *Théorie élémentaire des quantités complexes* and other writings. Of greater importance were his successful efforts to overcome the long-standing failure of mathematicians to appreciate the significance of non-Euclidean geometry. Led by his own research to doubt the necessity of the parallel postulate and by Richard Baltzer to the writings of Lobachevski, Hoüel published in 1866 a translation of one of the latter's essays along with excerpts from the Gauss–Schumacher correspondence. By 1870 he had published translations of the classic writings in this area of János Bolyai, Beltrami, Helmholtz, and Riemann as well as his own proof of the impossibility of proving the parallel postulate. Hoüel also compiled logarithmic tables, worked on planetary perturbation theory, was an editor of the *Bulletin des sciences mathématiques et astronomiques,* and wrote a major text in analysis, *Cours de calcul infinitésimal.*

BIBLIOGRAPHY

I. ORIGINAL WORKS. A bibliography of 131 items is given in Brunel (see below). His books include *Théorie élémentaire des quantités complexes* (Paris, 1874); and *Cours de calcul infinitésimal,* 4 vols. (Paris, 1878–1881).

II. SECONDARY LITERATURE. Most useful is G. Brunel, "Notice sur l'influence scientifique de Guillaume-Jules Hoüel," in *Mémoires de la Société des sciences physiques et naturelles de Bordeaux,* 3rd ser., **4** (1888), 1–78. Obituary notices are *Leopoldina,* **22** (1886), 167–168; and G. Lespiault, in *Mémorial de l'Association des anciens élèves de l'Ecole normale supérieure* (Paris, 1887). See also Paul Barbarin, "La correspondance entre Hoüel et de Tilly," in *Bulletin des sciences mathématiques,* 2nd ser., **50** (1926), 50–64, 74–88.

MICHAEL J. CROWE

HUDDE, JAN (*b.* Amsterdam, the Netherlands, May 1628; *d.* Amsterdam, 15 April 1704)

Jan (or Johann) Hudde, the son of a merchant and patrician, Gerrit Hudde, and Maria Witsen, was christened on 23 May 1628. He studied law at the University of Leiden around 1648, at which time—perhaps even earlier—he was introduced to mathematics by Frans van Schooten. Besides acquainting his students with the classic works of the ancient mathematicians, Schooten gave them a thorough knowledge of Descartes's mathematical methods, as published in his *Géométrie* (1637).

Hudde's contributions to mathematics were probably made between 1654 and 1663, for there is no evidence of further mathematical work after the latter year. From then on, he devoted himself to the service of Amsterdam, as a member of the city council, juror, and chancellor. In 1673 he married Debora Blaw, a widow; they had no children. On 15 September 1672 Hudde was chosen by Stadtholder Wilhelm III as one of Amsterdam's four burgomasters. He held this office until 1704, serving altogether for twenty-one of those years (intermittently with one-year hiatuses required by law). Between his terms as burgomaster, Hudde was chancellor and deputy of the admiralty. In 1680 he received the Magnifikat for his services in the administration of the civic government. His anonymous biographer depicts him as "unselfish, honest, well-educated in the sciences, with his eyes open to the general welfare."

Hudde's teacher, Frans van Schooten, often incorporated the results of his students' work in his own books. Thus, in his *Exercitationes mathematicae* (1657) there are three essays by Hudde, including a treatise written in 1654 on the determination of the greatest width of the folium of Descartes. In 1657 Hudde participated in a correspondence among R. F. de Sluse, Christiaan Huygens, and Schooten on the questions of quadrature, tangents, and the centroids (centers of gravity) of certain algebraic curves.

Schooten's edition of the *Géométrie* (1659–1661) contains two other works by Hudde. The first, *De reductione aequationum,* may have been written in 1654–1655, according to a note in the foreword. Presented in the form of a letter to Schooten, it is dated 15 July 1657. The second, *De maximis et minimis,* is dated 26 February 1658. There also exists an exchange of letters between Hudde and Huygens (1663) on problems dealing with games of chance. This enumeration comprises all of Hudde's known mathematical works; but it is recorded in the notes of Leibniz, who visited Hudde in Amsterdam in November 1676, that Hudde still had many unpublished mathematical writings, which are now lost.

In Hudde's extant mathematical works two main problems can be recognized: the improvement of Descartes's algebraic methods with the intention of solving equations of higher degree by means of an algorithm; and the problem of extreme values (maxima and minima) and tangents to algebraic curves. In the latter Hudde accomplished the algorithmizing of Fermat's method, with which he had become acquainted through Schooten.

The solution, that is, the reduction, of algebraic equations was a central problem at that time. In 1545 Ludovico Ferrari had reduced the solution of a fourth-degree equation to the solution of a cubic equation. In the *Géométrie* Descartes had combined equations of the fifth and sixth degrees into one genre and had given a method for the graphic determination of the roots. The contents of *De reductione aequationum* indicate that Hudde had originally tried to solve equations of the fifth and sixth degrees algebraically. Although unsuccessful in his attempt—and totally unaware of the reason for his failure—he at least compiled the cases in which a reduction of the degree is possible by separation of a factor. Correspondingly, Hudde also dealt with equations of the third and fourth degrees because their general solution presents great analytical difficulties. He gave the solution of the reduced cubic equation $x^3 = qx + r$ by means of the substitution $x = y + z$; he also gave the determination of the greatest common divisor of two polynomials by the process of elimination.

Hudde's rule of extreme values and tangents can be traced to Fermat. Expressed in modern terms, Fermat starts with the proposition that in the proximity of the maximum or minimum position x_0 of the function $f(x)$, $f(x_0 + h)$ is approximately equal to $f(x_0 - h)$. By expansion in terms of powers of h the linear member must, therefore, be omitted. For a rational function, which disappears at x_0, this means that x_0 is a "double" zero of the function. Proceeding from this proposition, Hudde was seeking an algorithmically usable rule for rational functions. His law states that if the polynomial $f(x) = \Sigma\, a_k x^{n-k}$ has the "double" zero of the function, then the polynomial $\Sigma\,(p + kq)a_k x^{n-k}$, with p,q arbitrary natural numbers, also has x_0 as the zero of the function. Fully stated (in Latin), the rule can be translated as "If in an equation two roots are equal and the equation is multiplied by an arithmetic progression to whatever degree is desired—that is, the first term of the equation is multiplied by the first term of the progression, the second term of the equation by the second term of the progression, and so on in regular order—then I say that the product will be an equation in which one of the mentioned roots will be found." The "double" zero of the function is, then, the zero of the greatest common divisor of the two polynomials. The greatest common divisor is found by the process of elimination that represents a variation of the well-known Euclidean algorithm. Hudde extended his dealings to include fractionalized rational functions, his method amounting to the expression (in modern terms)

$$\frac{f(x)}{g(x)} = \frac{f'(x)}{g'(x)}.$$

His rule of tangents stands in direct relation to his process of extreme values, just as most of his other works represent applications of the results of his theory of equations, that is, the rule of tangents and extreme values.

Hudde was also interested in physics and astronomy. He spent much time with the astronomer Ismael Boulliau and reported his comet observations to Huygens in 1665. In 1663 he produced microscopes with spherical lenses; in 1665 he worked with Spinoza on the construction of telescope lenses. That he also had assembled a small *dioptrica* is seen from his correspondence with Spinoza. In 1671 he sent to Huygens mortality tables for the calculation of life annuities. During the next two years Hudde was charged by the city of Amsterdam with appraising DeWitt's formulas for the calculation of life annuities.

Perhaps the most gifted of Schooten's students, Hudde was also the most strongly influenced by him. At the time of Schooten's death in 1660, Hudde felt that he commanded a comprehensive view of the basic contemporary mathematical problems. Like Descartes he held as meaningful only such mathematical problems as could be handled through algebraic equations. After 1663 he pursued mathematics only as an avocation apart from—for him—more important civic activities.

His contemporaries saw him as a mathematician of great ability. Leibniz wrote, even as late as 1697, that one could expect a solution to the difficult problem of the brachistochrone only from L'Hospital, Newton, the Bernoullis, and Hudde "had he not ceased such investigations long ago."

BIBLIOGRAPHY

I. ORIGINAL WORKS. Frans van Schooten's *Exercitationum mathematicarum libri quinque* (Leiden, 1657) contains three essays by Hudde; see Schooten's ed. of Descartes's *Géométrie, Geometria Renati Cartesii,* I (Amsterdam, 1659), for Hudde's *De reductione aequationum* and *De maximis et minimis.* Hudde's correspondence with Huygens is in the latter's *Oeuvres complètes,* 22 vols. (The Hague, 1888–1950).

II. SECONDARY LITERATURE. On Hudde and his contributions, see Karlheinz Haas, "Die mathematischen Arbeiten von Johann Hudde," in *Centaurus,* **4** (1956), 235–284—the app. contains an extensive bibliography; Joseph E. Hofmann, *Geschichte der Mathematik,* pt. 2, (Berlin, 1957), pp. 45–46, 54, 74; and P. C. Molhuysen and P. J. Blok, eds., *Nieuw Neederlandsch biografisch Woordenboek* (Leiden, 1911–1937).

KARLHEINZ HAAS

HUGH OF ST. VICTOR (*d.* Paris, France, 11 February 1141)

Probably from Saxony or Flanders originally, Hugh came to Paris at an early age and joined the canons regular of the abbey of St. Victor. He lectured on theology in the famous school attached to this monastery, and was its greatest representative. He wrote a very large number of exegetical, philosophical, and theological works which exercised a profound influence on the scholasticism of the twelfth and thirteenth centuries. The most famous of them is the *De sacramentis christianae fidei.*

Preoccupied with giving a scientific basis to the teaching of theology, Hugh wrote an introductory treatise to the sacred sciences, the *Didascalicon* or *De studio legendi,* composed before 1125. Book II of this work contains a division of philosophy which is a classification of the sciences, inspired by that of Boethius. According to Hugh, philosophy encompasses four parts: *theorica, practica* (that is, moral philosophy), *mechanica,* and *logica. Theorica* in turn is divided into *theologia, mathematica,* and *physica* or *physiologia.* The *Didascalicon* says little about *physica,* limiting itself to indicating that it is the science of nature and that it examines the causes of things in their effects and their effects in their causes. Hugh lingers a great deal longer on mathematics, to which he gives a preponderant place; it is indispensable to the knowledge of physics and ought to be studied before the latter. The word *mathematica* has two senses: When the *t* is not aspirated, this term designates "the superstition of those who place the destiny of men in the constellations" of the heavens; when the *t* is aspirated, it designates, on the contrary, the science of "abstract quantity," itself identified with the *intellectibile,* as opposed to the *intelligibile,* the object of theology. *Mathematica* thus defined is divided into four sciences, in which are recognized the four disciplines of the Carolingian quadrivium: arithmetic, the science of numbers and their properties; music, divided into music of the world (the study of the harmony of the elements, the planets, and the divisions of time), human music (the study of the body and its functions and humors, of the soul and its powers, and of the relations of the body and the soul), and instrumental music; geometry, which is subdivided into *planimetria, altimetria,* and *cosmimetria;* and finally astronomy, the subject matter of which is identical in part with that of the preceding sciences, but which is a study of the stars from the point of view of movement and time. The classification of the sciences in the *Didascalicon* gives a place not only to *theorica,* but to *mechanica* as well, that is, to the mechanical arts (the arts of clothing, armament, navigation, agriculture, hunting, medicine, and the theater). Hugh was thus the first to raise technology to the dignity of science. In this regard he was the first of a great number of the authors of the twelfth and thirteenth centuries.

The division of the sciences in the *Didascalicon* was resumed a short time later in a dialogue entitled *Epitome Dindimi in philosophiam.* The interest that he had shown for mathematics reappeared in *Practica geometriae,* the authenticity of which, sometimes contested, is now well established. Composed at about the same time as the *Didascalicon,* this treatise, which shows the influence of Macrobius and especially of Gerbert (Gerbert d'Aurillac), testifies to the state of geometry in the West before the great diffusion of Arabic science. In it Hugh presented the methods of calculating and measuring used in *altimetria* (the measurement of heights and depths), in *planimetria* (the measurement of the lengths and widths of surfaces), and in *cosmimetria,* a discipline intermediate between geometry and astronomy which is concerned with the measurement of the dimensions of the terrestrial sphere and of the celestial sphere. His descriptions of these sciences involve chiefly the properties of triangles and more precisely those of the right-angled triangle, but Hugh also described the methods that can be employed for these mensurations: surveying, measurement of shadows, use of mirrors or the astrolabe, etc. At the end of his *Practica geometriae* he alluded to an astronomical treatise which was supposed to follow, but it is not known if this is a reference to a lost work or simply to a project that Hugh never carried out.

BIBLIOGRAPHY

I. ORIGINAL WORKS. Hugh's writings, frequently published, have been reproduced by Migne, in *Patrologia latina,* CLXXV–CLXXVII (Paris, 1854), following the ed. produced in Rouen in 1658 by the canons regular of St. Victor. This ed. sins by default and by excess; it is incomplete and contains apocryphal works, but it may still be used if one takes as a guide D. van den Eynde's *Essai sur la succession et la date des écrits de Hugues de S.-V.,* in Spicilegium Pontificii Athenaei Antoniani, XIII (Rome, 1960).

Recent editions of the scientific works are *Didascalicon, de studio legendi: A Critical Text,* C. H. Buttimer, ed., in The Catholic University of America: Studies in Medieval and Renaissance Latin, X (Washington, 1939); "Epitome Dindimi in philosophiam," R. Baron, ed., in *Traditio,* **11** (1955), 105–119; "Practica geometriae," R. Baron, ed., in *Osiris,* **12** (1956), 176–224; and *Hugonis de Sancto Victore opera propedeutica: Practica geometriae, De grammatica, Epitome Dindimi in philosophiam,* R. Baron, ed., in Publications in Mediaeval Studies. The University of Notre Dame, XX (Notre Dame, Ind., 1966).

For recent translations of his work, see *On the Sacraments of the Christian Faith* (*De sacramentis*), English vers. by R. J. Deferrari (Cambridge, Mass., 1951); J. Taylor, *The Didascalicon of Hugh of St. Victor, Translated From the Latin With Introduction and Notes,* in Records of Civilization, Sources and Studies, no. 64 (New York, 1961).

II. SECONDARY LITERATURE. Information on Hugh's work and life is in R. Baron, *Science et sagesse chez Hugues de S.-V.* (Paris, 1957); and *Études sur Hugues de S.-V.* (Paris, 1963); F. E. Croydon, "Notes on the Life of Hugh of St. Victor," in *Journal of Theological Studies,* **40** (1939), 232–253; J. Taylor, *The Origins and Early Life of Hugh of St. Victor* (Notre Dame, Ind., 1957); and R. Javelet, "Les origines de Hugues de S.-V.," in *Revue des sciences religieuses,* **34** (1960), 74–83.

Hugh's scientific thought is discussed in M. Curtze, "Practica geometriae. Ein anonymer Traktat aus dem Ende des zwölften Jahrhunderts," in *Monatshefte für Mathematik und Physik,* **8** (1897), 193–220; P. Tannery, *Mémoires scientifiques,* J. L. Heiberg, ed., vol. V, *Sciences exactes au moyen âge* (*1887–1921*) (Toulouse–Paris, 1922), 308–313, 326–328, 357–358, 361–368; R. Baron, "Hugues de S.-V. auteur d'une *Practica geometriae,*" in *Mediaeval Studies,*

17 (1955), 107–116; "Sur l'introduction en Occident des termes 'geometria, theorica et practica,'" in *Revue d'histoire des sciences et de leurs applications,* **8** (1955), 298–302; and "Note sur les variations au XIIe siècle de la triade géométrique altimetria, planimetria, cosmimetria," in *Isis,* **48** (1957), 30–32; L. Thorndike, "Cosmimetria or Steriometria," *ibid.,* p. 458; and J. Châtillon, "Le Didascalicon de Hugues de S.-V.," in *Cahiers d'histoire mondiale,* **9** (1966), 539–552.

JEAN CHÂTILLON

HUMBERT, MARIE-GEORGES (*b.* Paris, France, 7 January 1859; *d.* Paris, 22 January 1921)

A brilliant representative of the French school of mathematics at the end of the nineteenth century, Humbert distinguished himself primarily through his work in fields pioneered by Poincaré and Hermite.

Orphaned at a very young age, Humbert was brought up by his grandparents, industrialists in Franche-Comté. First a boarder at the Oratorian *collège* in Juilly, where he studied classics, he completed his secondary studies at the Collège Stanislas in Paris and entered the École Polytechnique in 1877. For several years he worked as a mining engineer: first in Vesoul and then in Paris, where the École Polytechnique and the École des Mines were quick to add him to their teaching corps.

Humbert earned his doctorate in mathematics in 1885. In 1891–1892 he was a laureate of the Academy of Sciences, and from then on he was well known. Elected president of the Mathematical Society of France in 1893 and named professor of analysis at the École Polytechnique in 1895, he was elected in 1901 to the Academy, filling the seat left vacant by the death of Hermite. From 1904 to 1912 he was Camille Jordan's assistant in the Collège de France and on occasion lectured in his place. Humbert then succeeded to Jordan's chair and continued the teaching of higher mathematics in that institution.

Humbert married in 1890, but his wife died a short time after the birth of their son Pierre; he remarried in 1900. A man of high moral character and intellectual rigor, Humbert was remarkably gifted not only in mathematics but also in clarity of expression and intellectual cultivation. He exerted a great influence and was able, by his discretion and objectivity, to assure respect for his religious convictions during a period of some hostility toward religion in French scientific circles.

Besides his two pedagogical works, it was through numerous memoirs (approximately 150, which have been collected) that Humbert held a major place in the mathematical discovery and production of his time. His writings were inspired by his interest in the study of algebraic curves and surfaces and were marked by the lucidity with which he related the problems encountered in this area to questions of analysis and number theory.

In his doctoral dissertation Humbert completed Clebsch's work by providing the means of determining whether a curve of which the coordinates are elliptic functions of a parameter is actually of type one. He soon noted the advantage for algebraic geometry obtained from a very general technique of representation gained by using Fuchsian functions.

Humbert familiarized himself with the work of Abel, whose theorem concerning the rational sums of certain systems of algebraic differentials he made the subject of important developments and elegant geometric applications. He then derived every possible advantage from the use of Abelian functions in geometry. In his memoir on this subject, submitted for the Academy's prize in 1892, Humbert solved the difficult problem of classifying left curves traced on hyperelliptic surfaces of type two (Kummer surfaces); but his solution excluded the case in which the four periods of the function which defines the surface are joined by a relationship with integral coefficients. Next, Humbert studied Abelian functions presenting singularities of this type and showed that these singularities are characterized by an integer.

He thus enriched analysis and gave the complete solution of the two great questions of the transformation of hyperelliptic functions and of their complex multiplication. He also pointed out the resulting consequence: the existence of a group of transformations of certain surfaces into themselves constitutes an essential difference between the geometry of surfaces and that of curves. But, most important, he completed the work of Hermite by pursuing the applications to number theory throughout his life.

The progressive alliance of geometry, analysis, and arithmetic in Humbert's works is a splendid example of how a broad mathematical education can assist discovery. The results he obtained, and with which his name remains linked, have survived the revolution of modern mathematics, although they belong to a very specialized field.

BIBLIOGRAPHY

I. ORIGINAL WORKS. All of Humbert's memoirs and articles were collected in *Oeuvres de Georges Humbert,* Pierre Humbert and Gaston Julia, eds., 2 vols. (Paris, 1929–1936), with a pref. by Paul Painlevé. Among his writings are *Sur les courbes de genre un* (Paris, 1885), his doctoral thesis; *Application de la théorie des fonctions fuchsiennes à l'étude des courbes algébriques* (Paris, 1886), repr. from *Journal de mathématiques pures et appliquées,* 4th ser., **2** (1886); and three separate notices, on C. Saint-Saëns, I.-J. Paderewski, and G. Doret, in *Fêtes musicales* (Vevey, 1913).

II. SECONDARY LITERATURE. See Emile Borel, *Notice sur la vie et les travaux de Georges Humbert* (Paris, 1922); Camille Jordan and Maurice Croiset, *Discours prononcés aux funérailles de Georges Humbert le 25 janvier 1921* (Paris, 1921); and Maurice d'Ocagne, *Silhouettes de mathématiciens* (Paris, 1928), pp. 167–172.

PIERRE COSTABEL

HUMBERT, PIERRE (*b.* Paris, France, 13 June 1891; *d.* Montpellier, France, 17 November 1953)

Humbert was the son of the mathematician Georges Humbert and, like his father, attended the École Polytechnique, entering in 1910. He soon directed himself to scientific research and from 1913 to 1914 he was a member of the research class of the University of Edinburgh. The scientific and philosophical conceptions of Edmund Whittaker, the director of the class, were in accord with his own inclinations and made a deep impression on him throughout his career. Humbert's health was delicate and during World War I he was removed from combat after being wounded. He earned his doctorate in mathematics in 1918 and then began his academic career, which he spent almost entirely in the Faculty of Science at Montpellier, but which consumed only a portion of his energies.

Humbert combined his father's mathematical ability with the temperament of a humanist. He demonstrated a highly refined sensitivity to culture, devoting attention to literature and music as well as to science. Moreover, he was unsatisfied with the simple juxtaposition of knowledge and religious faith. A talented lecturer, he traveled a good deal in France and abroad. He also possessed remarkable ability for organization, which he displayed mainly in the French Association for the Advancement of Sciences and in the Joseph Lotte Association (a society of Catholic public school teachers).

The multiplicity of subjects in which Humbert was interested, and about which he contributed stimulating articles in the most diverse periodicals, is characteristic of his highly personal vocation: to promote the awakening of the intellect. In pursuit of this goal he was willing to sacrifice a certain intellectual rigor in the interest of his wide-ranging curiosity. Thus Humbert's scientific work provides no definitive advances, although it remains a valuable reference source.

In the field of mathematics, Humbert, faithful to Whittaker, directed his efforts chiefly toward the development of symbolic calculus. He also began to undertake scholarly research in the history of science, specializing in the study of seventeenth-century astronomy. He was partially influenced in this choice by his father-in-law, the astronomer Henri Andoyer. His articles on the Provençal school, whose members included Peiresc and Gassendi, revealed the resources held by the archives in Aix, Carpentras, Digne, and other localities in the south of France.

Beyond these two major areas, Humbert should be remembered for his other writings, numerous and highly varied, that remain capable of inspiring new investigations.

BIBLIOGRAPHY

I. ORIGINAL WORKS. Humbert's works in mathematics include *Sur les surfaces de Poincaré* (Paris, 1918), doctoral thesis; *Introduction à l'étude des fonctions elliptiques* (Paris, 1922); "Fonctions de Lamé et fonctions de Mathieu," Mémorial des sciences mathématiques, no. 10 (1926); "Le calcul symbolique," *Actualités scientifiques,* no. 147 (1934); "Potentiels et prépotentiels," *Cahiers scientifiques,* no. 15 (1936); "Le calcul symbolique et ses applications à la physique mathématique," Mémorial des sciences mathématiques, no. 105 (1947), rev. and enl. in a sep. pub. (Paris, 1965); *Formulaire pour le calcul symbolique* (Paris, 1950), written with N. W. McLachlan; and *Supplément au formulaire pour le calcul symbolique* (Paris, 1952), also written with McLachlan and L. Poli.

For Humbert's publications in the history of astronomy and mathematics, see "Histoire des mathématiques, de la mécanique et de l'astronomie," in Gabriel Hanotaux, ed., *Histoire de la nation française,* tome XIV, vol. 1 (Paris, 1924), written with Henri Andoyer; *Pierre Duhem* (Paris, 1932); *Un amateur: Peiresc (1580–1637)* (Paris, 1933); "L'oeuvre astronomique de Gassendi," in *Actualités scientifiques,* no. 378 (1936); *De Mercure à Pluton, planètes et satellites* (Paris, 1937); "Histoire des découvertes astronomiques," in *Revue des jeunes,* no. 16 (1948); *Blaise Pascal, cet effrayant génie* (Paris, 1947); and "Les mathématiques de la Renaissance à la fin du XVIIIe siècle," in Maurice Daumas, ed., *Histoire de la science* (Paris, 1957), 537–688.

On his contribution to the philosophy of science, see *Philosophes et savants* (Paris, 1953); and Edmund Whittaker, *Le commencement et la fin du monde, suivi de hasard, libre arbitre et nécessité dans la conception scientifique de l'univers* (Paris, 1953), translated from English by Humbert.

Articles by Humbert include "Les astronomes français de 1610 à 1667. Étude d'ensemble et répertoire alphabétique," in *Mémoires de la Société d'études scientifiques de Draguignan,* **63** (1942); "Les erreurs astronomiques en littérature"; "La mesure de la méridienne de France," in *Mémoires de l'Académie des sciences et lettres de Montpellier,* **20** (1924); **25** (1930); **27** (1932); "Spongia solis," in *Annales* *de l'université de Montpellier,* **1** (1943); "Claude Mydorge (1585–1647)," *ibid.,* **3** (1945); "La première carte de la lune," in *Revue des questions scientifiques,* **108** (1931); "Le baptême des satellites de Jupiter," *ibid.,* **117** (1940); and "L'observation des halos," in *Atti dell'Accademia pontificia dei Nuovi Lincei* (1931).

Humbert wrote many other articles and memoirs which may be found in *Archives internationales d'histoire des sciences,* and *Revue d'histoire des sciences et de leurs applications,* two journals on which he collaborated.

II. SECONDARY LITERATURE. For information on Humbert, see P. Sergescu, "Notice sur Pierre Humbert," in *Archives internationales d'histoire des sciences,* **7,** no. 27 (1954), 181–183; B. Rochot, "Notice sur Pierre Humbert," in *Revue d'histoire des sciences,* **7,** no. 1, 79–80; and Jacques Devisme, *Sur l'équation de M. Pierre Humbert* (Paris–Toulouse, 1933), doctoral thesis.

PIERRE COSTABEL

HUNTINGTON, EDWARD VERMILYE (*b.* Clinton, New York, 26 April 1874; *d.* Cambridge, Massachusetts, 25 November 1952)

Huntington was the son of Chester Huntington and the former Katharine Hazard Smith. He received his A. B. and A. M. from Harvard in 1895 and 1897, and his Ph.D. from the University of Strasbourg in 1901. In 1909 he married Susie Edwards Van Volkenburgh. Almost all of Huntington's professional career was spent at Harvard University, where he was an enthusiastic and innovative teacher; one of his interests is indicated by the title—unusual in a department of mathematics—of professor of mechanics, which he held from 1919 until his retirement in 1941. His interest in teaching was also reflected in his improvement of the format of the mathematical tables that he compiled or edited.

Huntington's major scientific work was in the logical foundations of mathematics. It is now commonplace to present a mathematical theory as consisting of the logical consequences of a set of axioms about unspecified objects, assumed to satisfy the axioms and nothing more. In spite of the example of Euclid, who tried to develop geometry in this way but did not completely succeed, the thorough axiomatization of a branch of mathematics was a novelty when Huntington's career began. He constructed sets of axioms for many branches of mathematics, one of which was Euclidean geometry, and developed techniques for proving their independence (that is, that no axiom is deducible from the others) and their completeness (that is, that they describe precisely the mathematical system that they are supposed to describe). His book *The Continuum* was for many years the standard introduction to the theory of sets of points and transfinite numbers.

Huntington was interested in the applications of mathematics to many different subjects. His most influential contribution was a mathematical theory of the apportionment of representatives in Congress. The Constitution states that "Representatives shall be apportioned among the several States according to their respective numbers" but does not specify how this is to be done. In the 1920's Huntington analyzed the problem and recommended the so-called method of equal proportions; in 1941 this method was adopted by Congress.

BIBLIOGRAPHY

Huntington's writings include *The Continuum, and Other Types of Serial Order, With an Introduction to Cantor's Transfinite Numbers* (Cambridge, Mass., 1917), repr. from *Annals of Mathematics,* **6** (1905), 151–184; **7** (1905), 15–43; and "The Apportionment of Representatives in Congress," in *Transactions of the American Mathematical Society,* **30** (1928), 85–110.

R. P. BOAS, JR.

HURWITZ, ADOLF (*b.* Hildesheim, Germany, 26 March 1859; *d.* Zurich, Switzerland, 18 November 1919)

Hurwitz, the son of a manufacturer, attended the Gymnasium in Hildesheim. His mathematics teacher, H. C. H. Schubert, was known as the inventor of a dazzling calculus for enumerative geometry. He discovered Hurwitz, gave him private lessons on Sundays, and finally persuaded Adolf's father, who was not wealthy, to have his son study mathematics at the university, financially supported by a friend. Before leaving the Gymnasium, Hurwitz published his first paper, jointly with Schubert, on Chasles's theorem (*Werke,* paper no. 90).

In the spring term of 1877 he enrolled at the Munich Technical University, recommended to Felix Klein by Schubert. From the fall term of 1877 through the spring term of 1879 he was at Berlin University, where he attended courses given by Kummer, Weierstrass, and Kronecker. Then he returned to Munich, only to follow Klein in the fall of 1880 to Leipzig, where he took his Ph.D. with a thesis on modular functions. In 1881-1882, according to Meissner, he turned anew to Berlin to study with Weierstrass and Kronecker. (Hilbert did not know of a second stay in Berlin.) In the spring of 1882 he qualified as *Privatdozent* at Göttingen University, where he came into close contact with the mathematician M. A. Stern and the physicist Wilhelm Weber. In 1884 Hurwitz accepted Lindemann's invitation to fill an extraordinary professorship at Königsberg University, which was then a good place for mathematics. Among its students were Hilbert and Minkowski. Hurwitz, a few years their elder, became their guide to all mathematics and their lifelong friend. Hilbert always acknowledged his indebtedness to Hurwitz. In 1892 Hurwitz was offered Frobenius' chair at the Zurich Polytechnical University and H. A. Schwarz's at Göttingen University. He had already accepted the first offer when the second arrived. He went to Zurich and remained there for the rest of his life. He married the daughter of Professor Samuel, who taught medicine at Königsberg.

Hurwitz' health was always poor. Twice he contracted typhoid fever, and he often suffered from migraine. In 1905 one kidney had to be removed; and the second did not function normally. Although seriously ill, he continued his research.

Hurwitz' papers reveal a lucid spirit and a love of good style and perspicuous composition. Hilbert depicted him as a harmonious spirit; a wise philosopher; a modest, unambitious man; a lover of music and an amateur pianist; a friendly, unassuming man whose vivid eyes revealed his spirit.

His papers were collected by his Zurich colleagues, particularly G. Polya. Although entitled *Werke,* the edition does not include his book on the arithmetic of quaternions and his posthumous function theory. The *Werke* lists his twenty-one Ph.D. students and contains an obituary written by Hilbert in 1919 and Ernst Meissner's eulogy. All present biographical data were extracted from these contributions. Hilbert's obituary is rather disappointing—even more so if it is compared with Hilbert's commemoration of Minkowski, which rings of high enthusiasm and deep regret. Certainly Hilbert had esteemed Hurwitz as a kind man, an erudite scholar, a good mathematician, and a faithful guide. But one may wonder whether he appreciated Hurwitz' mathematics as sincerely as he appreciated its creator. Of course it is easier to write a brilliant biography if the subject is as brilliant as was Minkowski. Hurwitz was anything but brilliant, although he was as good a mathematician as Minkowski. Or, if that was not the reason, was it perhaps because Hilbert himself had changed in the ten years since he wrote Minkowski's biography, and his own productivity had come to a virtual standstill. Anyhow, because Hilbert wrote his biography, Hurwitz never got the one he deserved.

In a large part of Hurwitz' work the influence of Klein is overwhelming. Among Klein's numerous Ph.D. students Hurwitz was second to none except, perhaps, Furtwängler. Much of Klein's intuitiveness is found again in Hurwitz, although the latter was superior in the rationalization of intuitive ideas. Klein was at the peak of his creativity when Hurwitz studied with him and Klein's best work was that in which Hurwitz took a share. Klein's new view on modular functions, uniting geometrical aspects such as the fundamental domain with group theory tools such as the congruence subgroups and with topological notions such as the genus of the Riemann surface, was fully exploited by Hurwitz. In his thesis he worked out Klein's ideas to reach an independent reconstruction of the theory of modular functions and, in particular, of multiplier equations by Eisenstein principles (*Werke,* paper no. 2). Modular functions were applied by Hurwitz to a classical subject of number theory—relations between the class numbers of binary quadratic forms with negative discriminant—which had been tackled long before by Kronecker and Hermite, and afterward by J. Gierster, another student of Klein's.

The problem of how to derive class number relations from modular equations and correspondences was put in general form by Hurwitz, although the actual execution was restricted to particular cases (*Werke,* papers no. 46, 47). The problem has long remained in the state in which Hurwitz had left it; but in the last few years it has been revived in C. L. Siegel's school although, strangely enough, no attention whatsoever has been paid to Hurwitz' other, unorthodox approach to class numbers (*Werke,* papers no. 56, 62, 69, 77). It is, first, a reduction of quadratic forms by means of Farey fractions and so-called Farey polygons: on the conic defined by $x:y:z = 1:-\lambda:\lambda^2$, a pair of points $\lambda = p/q$, r/s (p, q, r, s are integers) is called an elementary chord if $ps - qr = 1$, and such chords are taken to form elementary triangles; the reduction is carried by a systematic transition from one triangle to the next. The splitting of the conic surface into such triangles led Hurwitz in 1905 to a curious nonarithmetic infinite sum for class numbers, generalized in 1918 to ternary forms. Hurwitz also refashioned the classical expressions for class numbers into fast-converging infinite series, which, together with congruence arguments, provide easy means of computation (*Werke,* paper no. 59).

More direct products of Hurwitz' collaboration with Klein were his remarkable investigations on the most general correspondences on Riemann surfaces (*Werke,* paper no. 10), in particular Chasles's correspondence principle, and his work on elliptic σ products and their behavior under the transformation of the periods (Klein's elliptic normal curves, *Werke,* paper no. 11). For Dirichlet series occurring in class number formulas, Hurwitz derived transformations like those of the ζ function (*Werke,* paper no. 3). By means of complex multiplication he studied the development coefficients of the lemniscatic function, which look much like the Bernoulli numbers (*Werke,* paper no. 67). He also investigated the automorphic groups of algebraic Riemann surfaces of genus > 1; showed that they were finite; estimated the maximal order of automorphisms as $\leqslant 10(p - 1)$, the best value, according to A. Wiman, being $2(2p + 1)$; estimated the group order as $\leqslant 84(p - 1)$; and constructed Riemann surfaces from group theory or branching data (*Werke,* papers no. 12, 21, 22, 23, 30). Hurwitz' formula $p' - 1 = w/2 + n(p - 1)$ for the genus p' of a surface w times branched over a surface of genus p is found in *Werke,* paper no. 21, p. 376. Automorphic functions of several variables were also among Hurwitz' subjects (*Werke,* paper no. 36).

In general complex-function theory Hurwitz studied arithmetic properties of transcendents which generalize those of the exponential function (*Werke,* papers no. 6, 13), the roots of Bessel functions and other transcendents (*Werke,* papers no. 14, 17), and difference equations (*Werke,* paper no. 26). Giving a solution of the isoperimetric problem, he became interested in Fourier series, to which he devoted several papers (*Werke,* papers no. 29, 31, 32, 33). Hurwitz was the author of a condition, very useful in stability theory, on a polynomial having all its roots in the left half-plane, expressed by the positivity of a sequence of determinants (see also I. Schur, "Über algebraische Gleichungen"). He gave a proof of Weierstrass' theorem that an everywhere locally rational function of n variables should be globally rational (*Werke,* paper no. 8). He was much interested in continuous fractions, to which he devoted several papers (*Werke,* papers no. 49, 50, 52, 53, 63). He also gave a remarkable proof of Minkowski's theorem on linear forms (*Werke,* paper no. 65).

In algebraic number theory Hurwitz devised new proofs for the fundamental theorem on ideals (*Werke,* papers no. 57, 58, 60, 66). He studied the binary unimodular groups of algebraic number fields of finite degree and proved that they were finitely generated. (A survey on modern extensions of this result is found in Borel's "Arithmetic Properties of Linear Algebraic Groups.") He discovered the "correct" definition of integrity in quaternions (*Werke,* paper no. 64). In the theory of invariants he wrote several papers, among them a new proof for Franz Mertens' theorems on the resultant of n forms in n variables, in which he introduced the notion of the inertia form (*Werke,* paper no. 86). To obtain orthogonal invariants he devised the invariant volume and integration in the orthogonal groups (*Werke,* paper no. 81), which, generalized to compact groups by I. Schur and H. Weyl and complemented by the invention of Haar's measure, have become extremely powerful tools in modern mathematics.

This was one of the fundamental discoveries for which Hurwitz' name will be remembered. The other is the theorem on the composition of quadratic forms (*Werke,* papers no. 82, 89), which concerns the search for algebras over the reals with a nondegenerate quadratic form Q such that $Q(xy) = Q(x)Q(y)$. The complex numbers had been known as an example of dimension 2 for centuries; in 1843 W. R. Hamilton had discovered the quaternions, of dimension 4; and in 1845 Cayley and J. T. Graves independently hit upon the octaves, of dimension 8. Attempts to go further failed. In 1898 Hurwitz proved that the classical examples exhausted the algebras over the reals with a quadratic norm. With the increasing importance of quaternions and octaves in the theory of algebras, in foundations of geometry, in topology, and in exceptional Lie groups, Hurwitz' theorem has become of fundamental importance. Many new proofs have been given; and it has been extended several times, with the final result by J. W. Milnor that algebras over the reals without zero divisors exist in dimensions 1, 2, 4, and 8 only.

BIBLIOGRAPHY

I. ORIGINAL WORKS. Hurwitz' papers were brought together as *Mathematische Werke* (Basel, 1932). His books are *Vorlesungen über die Zahlentheorie der Quaternionen* (Berlin, 1919); and *Vorlesungen über allgemeine Funktionentheorie und elliptische Funktionen,* R. Courant, ed. (Berlin, 1922; 2nd ed., 1925), with a section on geometrical function theory by Courant.

II. SECONDARY LITERATURE. For additional information see F. van der Blij, "History of the Octaves," in *Simon Stevin,* **34** (1961), 106–125; A. Borel, "Arithmetic Properties of Linear Algebraic Groups," in *Proceedings of the [9th] International Congress of Mathematicians. Stockholm 1962* (Djursholm, 1963), pp. 10–22; A. Haar, "Der Massbegriff in der Theorie der kontinuierlichen Gruppen," in *Annals of Mathematics,* 2nd ser., **34** (1933), 147–169, also in his *Gesammelte Arbeiten* (Budapest, 1959), pp. 600–622; G. Polya, "Some Mathematicians I Have Known," in *American Mathematical Monthly,* **76** (1969), 746–753; I. Schur, "Über algebraische Gleichungen, die nur Wurzeln mit negativen Realteilen besitzen," in *Zeitschrift für angewandte Mathematik und Mechanik,* **1** (1922), 307–311; and "Neue Anwendung der Integralrechnung auf Probleme der Invariantentheorie," in *Sitzungsberichte der Preussischen Akademie der Wissenschaften zu Berlin* (1924), 189-208, 297-321, 346-355; and H. Weyl, "Theorie der Darstellung kontinuierlicher halbeinfacher Gruppen durch lineare Transformationen," in *Mathematische Zeitschrift,* **23** (1925), 271-309, and **24** (1926), 328-395, 789-791, also in his *Selecta* (Basel, 1956), pp. 262-366.

HANS FREUDENTHAL

HUTTON, CHARLES (*b.* Newcastle-upon-Tyne, England, 14 August 1737; *d.* London, England, 27 January 1823)

Hutton was the son of a colliery worker. Largely self-educated, he rapidly acquired enough knowledge of mathematics to establish himself as a schoolmaster in Newcastle. His pupils, drawn from the families of local landowners and leading citizens, included John Scott (earl of Eldon) and Hutton's future wife, Elizabeth Surtees. Hutton carried cut a local land survey (1770) and wrote a tract on the equilibrium of bridges (1772), an elementary textbook on arithmetic (1764), and a more elaborate treatise on mensuration that was illustrated by Thomas Bewick (1767).

In 1773 Hutton was appointed professor of mathematics at the Royal Military Academy at Woolwich, where he remained for thirty-four years. He was elected to the Royal Society in 1774 and served as foreign secretary from 1779 to 1783. Hutton's resignation from office, requested by Sir Joseph Banks (then president of the Society) on the grounds that he failed to carry out his duties efficiently, led to a major attack by Horsley, F. Masères, Maskelyne, P. H. Maty, and others on Banks's management of the affairs of the Society.

Hutton wrote many papers and received the Copley Medal of the Royal Society for "The Force of Fired Gunpowder and the Velocities of Cannon Balls," published in 1778. That year he also presented a report to the Society on the mean density of the earth, deduced from Maskelyne's observations at Mount Schiehallion in Perthshire. With George Shaw and Richard Pearson he edited an abridgment of the *Philosophical Transactions* for the years 1665 to 1680.

Hutton was an indefatigable worker and his mathematical contributions, if unoriginal, were useful and practical. Throughout his life, he contributed assiduously to scientific periodicals through notes, problems, criticism, and commentary. He wrote textbooks for his pupils in Newcastle and the cadets at Woolwich; edited a great many almanacs, including the *Ladies' Diary* (1773-1818); and compiled several volumes of mathematical tables, one of which contained a comprehensive historical introduction (1785). In addition he translated from the French Montucla's four-volume edition (1778) of Ozanam's 1694 work *Recreations in Mathematics and Natural Philosophy* (London, 1803).

The *Mathematical and Philosophical Dictionary* (1795) is probably the best known of Hutton's works. Although it was criticized as unbalanced in content, unduly cautious in tone, and sometimes lacking judgment, the dictionary has served as a valuable source for historians of mathematics.

BIBLIOGRAPHY

I. ORIGINAL WORKS. Many of Hutton's contributions to the *Ladies' Diary* are included in the *Diarian Miscellany* (London, 1775). His land survey, *Plan of Newcastle and Gateshead* (1770), is now in the City Library, Newcastle-upon-Tyne. Of his scientific papers the most important are "A New and General Method of Finding Simple and Quickly Converging Series," in *Philosophical Transactions of the Royal Society of London,* **66** (1776), 476-492; "The Force of Fired Gunpowder and the Velocities of Cannon Balls," *ibid.,* **68** (1778), 50-85; "An Account of the Calculations Made From the Survey and Measures Taken at Mount Schiehallion, in Perthshire, in Order to Ascertain the Mean Density of the Earth," *ibid.,* 689-778; "Calculations to Determine at What Point in the Side of a Hill Its Attraction Will be the Greatest," *ibid.,* **70** (1780), 1-14; "On Cubic Equations, and Infinite Series," *ibid.,* 387-450; and "Project for a New Division of the Quadrant," *ibid.,* **74** (1784), 21-34.

These works and other papers, including the tract *The Principles of Bridges* (Newcastle, 1772), are brought together in *Tracts, Mathematical and Philosophical* (London, 1786) and *Tracts on Mathematical and Philosophical Subjects,* 3 vols. (London, 1812). His textbooks include *The Schoolmaster's Guide* (Newcastle, 1764); *A Treatise on Mensuration* (Newcastle, 1767-1770); *The Compendious Measurer* (London, 1784); *The Elements of Conic Sections* (London, 1787); and *A Course of Mathematics for the Cadets of the Royal Military Academy* (London, 1798-1801). See also *Mathematical and Philosophical Dictionary,* 2 vols. (London, 1795); *The Philosophical Transactions to 1800 Abridged With Notes,* 18 vols. (London, 1809); and the historical introduction to *Mathematical Tables* (London, 1785).

II. SECONDARY LITERATURE. An adequate account of Hutton's life and work is that of R. E. Anderson in *Dictionary of National Biography,* XXVIII, 351-353. Background information is in J. Bruce, *A Memoir of Charles Hutton* (Newcastle, 1823). A lengthy and eulogistic account is Olinthus Gregory, "Brief Memoir of Charles Hutton, L.L.D., F.R.S.," in *Imperial Magazine,* **5** (1823), 202-227. The local history collection in the City Library, Newcastle-upon-Tyne, contains many portraits of Hutton. A bust, executed before his death, stands in the Literary and Philosophical Society of Newcastle.

Many pamphlets (mostly anonymous) relate to the Royal Society controversy in 1784; see A. Kippis, *Observations on the Late Contests in the Royal Society* (London, 1784); *'A Friend to Dr Hutton' Writes An Appeal to the Fellows. . .* (London, 1784), anonymous; and *An Authentic Narrative of the Dissensions and Debates in the Royal Society* (London, 1785), anonymous.

MARGARET E. BARON

HUYGENS, CHRISTIAAN (also **Huyghens, Christian**) (*b.* The Hague, Netherlands, 14 April 1629; *d.* The Hague, 8 July 1695)

Huygens belonged to a prominent Dutch family. His grandfather, also Christiaan Huygens, served William the Silent and Prince Maurice as secretary. In 1625 his father, Constantijn, became a secretary to Prince Frederic Henry and served the Orange family for the rest of his life, as did Christiaan's brother Constantijn.

Along with this tradition of diplomatic service to the house of Orange, the Huygens family had a strong educational and cultural tradition. The grandfather took an active part in the education of his children, and thus Huygens' father acquired great erudition in both literature and the sciences. He corresponded with Mersenne and Descartes, the latter often enjoying his hospitality in The Hague. Constantijn was a man of taste in the fine arts, talented in drawing, a musician and fertile composer, and, above all, a great poet; his Dutch and Latin verse gained him a lasting place in the history of Dutch literature.

Like his father, Constantijn was actively committed to the education of his children. Christiaan and his brother Constantijn were educated at home up to the age of sixteen by both their father and private teachers. They acquired a background in music (Christiaan sang well and played the viola da gamba, the lute, and the harpsichord), Latin, Greek, French, and some Italian, and logic, mathematics, mechanics, and geography. A highly talented pupil, Christiaan showed at an early age the combination of theoretical interest and insight into practical applications and constructions (at thirteen he built himself a lathe) which characterized his later scientific work.

From May 1645 until March 1647 Christiaan studied law and mathematics at the University of Leiden, the latter with Frans van Schooten. He studied classical mathematics as well as the modern methods of Viète, Descartes, and Fermat. During this period his father called Mersenne's attention to his son's study on falling bodies, and this opened up a direct correspondence between Christiaan and Mersenne. Descartes, whose work in these years had a great influence on young Huygens, also showed an interest in and an appreciation of Christiaan's work. From March 1647 until August 1649 Christiaan studied law at the newly founded Collegium Arausiacum (College of Orange) at Breda, of which his father was a curator and where Pell taught mathematics.

Huygens did not, after his studies, choose the career in diplomacy which would have been natural for a man of his birth and education. He did not want such a career, and in any event the Huygens family lost its main opportunities for diplomatic work as a result of the death of William II in 1650. Huygens lived at home until 1666, except for three journeys to Paris and London. An allowance supplied by his father enabled him to devote himself completely to the study of nature. These years (1650–1666) were the most fertile of Huygens' career.

Huygens at first concentrated on mathematics: determinations of quadratures and cubatures, and algebraic problems inspired by Pappus' works. In 1651 the *Theoremata de quadratura hyperboles, ellipsis et circuli* [1] appeared, including a refutation of Gregory of St. Vincent's quadrature of the circle. The *De circuli magnitudine inventa* [2] followed in 1654. In the subsequent years Huygens studied the rectification of the parabola, the area of surfaces of revolution of parabolas, and tangents and quadratures of various curves such as the cissoid, the cycloid (in connection with a problem publicly posed by Pascal in 1658), and the logarithmica. In 1657 Huygens' treatise on probability problems appeared, the *Tractatus de ratiociniis in aleae ludo* [4].

A manuscript on hydrostatics [20] had already been completed in 1650, and in 1652 Huygens formulated the rules of elastic collision and began his studies of geometrical optics. In 1655 he applied himself, together with his brother, to lens grinding. They built microscopes and telescopes, and Huygens, in the winter of 1655–1656, discovered the satellite of Saturn and recognized its ring, as reported in his *De Saturni lunâ observatio nova* [3] and *Systema Saturnium* [6], respectively.

In 1656 Huygens invented the pendulum clock. This is described in 1658 in the *Horologium* [5] (not to be confused with the later *Horologium oscillatorium*) and formed the occasion for the discovery of the tautochronism of the cycloid (1659), and for the studies on the theory of evolutes and on the center of oscillation. Huygens' study of centrifugal force also dates from 1659. In these years he corresponded with increasing intensity with many scholars, among them Gregory of St. Vincent, Wallis, van Schooten, and Sluse. Studies on the application of the pendulum clock for the determination of longitudes at sea occupied much of his time from 1660 onward.

Of the journeys mentioned above, the first, from July until September 1655, brought Huygens to Paris, where he met Gassendi, Roberval, Sorbière, and Boulliau—the circle of scholars which later formed the Académie Royale des Sciences. He used the opportunity of the stay in France to buy, as did his brother, a doctorate "utriusque juris" in Angers. During his second stay in Paris, from October 1660 until March 1661, he met Pascal, Auzout, and Desargues. Afterward he was in London (until May 1661). There Huygens attended meetings in Gresham College, and met Moray, Wallis, and Oldenburg, and was impressed by Boyle's experiments with the air pump. A third stay in Paris, from April 1663 to May 1664, was interrupted by a journey to London (June to September 1663), where he became a member of the newly founded Royal Society. He then returned to Paris where he received from Louis XIV his first stipend for scientific work.

In 1664 Thévenot approached Huygens to offer him membership in an academy to be founded in Paris; Colbert proposed giving official status and financial aid to those informal meetings of scholars which had been held in Paris since Mersenne's time. In 1666 the Académie Royale des Sciences was founded. Huygens accepted membership and traveled to Paris in May of that year. Thus began a stay in Paris that lasted until 1681, interrupted only by two periods of residence in The Hague because of ill health. Huygens' health was delicate, and in early 1670 he was afflicted by a serious illness. In September, partially recovered, he left for The Hague and returned to Paris in June 1671. The illness recurred in the autumn of 1675, and from July 1676 until June 1678 Huygens again was in The Hague.

As the most prominent member of the Academy, Huygens received an ample stipend and lived in an apartment in the Bibliothèque Royale. In the Academy, Huygens encouraged a Baconian program for the study of nature. He participated actively in astronomical observations (of Saturn, for example) and in experiments with the air pump. He expounded his theory of the cause of gravity in 1669, and in 1678 he wrote the *Traité de la lumière* [12], which announced the wave, or more accurately, the pulse theory of light developed in 1676–1677. In the years 1668–1669 he investigated, theoretically and experimentally, the motion of bodies in resisting media. In 1673 he cooperated with Papin in building a *moteur à explosion*, and from that year onward he was also in regular contact with Leibniz. Huygens began his studies of harmonic oscillation in 1673 and designed clocks regulated by a spring instead of a pendulum, about which a controversy with Hooke ensued. In 1677 he did microscopical research.

In 1672 war broke out between the Dutch republic and Louis XIV and his allies. William III of Orange came to power and Huygens' father and brother assumed prominent positions in Holland. Huygens stayed in Paris, and, although he was deeply concerned with the Dutch cause, proceeded with his work in the Academy under the protection of Colbert. In 1673 he published the *Horologium oscillatorium* [10]. It was his first work to appear after he entered a position financed by Louis XIV, and he dedicated it to the French king. This gesture served to strengthen his position in Paris but occasioned some disapproval in Holland.

Huygens left Paris in 1681, again because of illness. He had recovered by 1683, but Colbert had died meanwhile, and without his support Huygens' nationality, his Protestantism, and his family's ties with the house of Orange would have engendered such strong opposition in Paris that he decided to stay in Holland. His financial position was thus not as secure but he did have an income from his family's landed property. Huygens never married. In the relative solitude of his residence in The Hague and at Hofwijck, the family's country house near Voorburg, he continued his optical studies, constructed a number of clocks, which were tested on several long sea voyages, and wrote his *Cosmotheoros* [14]. From June until September 1689 he visited England, where he met Newton. The *Principia* aroused Huygens' admiration but also evoked his strong disagreement. There is evidence of both in the *Traité de la lumière* [12] and its supplement, the *Discours de la cause de la pesanteur* [13]. Discussions with Fatio de Duillier, correspondence with Leibniz, and the interest created by the latter's differential and integral calculus drew Huygens' attention back to mathematics in these last years.

In 1694 Huygens again fell ill. This time he did not recover. He died the following summer in The Hague.

Mathematics. The importance of Huygens' mathematical work lies in his improvement of existing methods and his application of them to a great range of problems in natural sciences. He developed no completely new mathematical theories save his theory of evolutes and—if probability may be considered a mathematical concept—his theory of probability.

Huygens' mathematics may be called conservative in view of the revolutionary innovations embodied in the work of such seventeenth-century mathematicians as Viète, Descartes, Newton, and Leibniz.

A marked tension is often apparent between this conservatism and the new trends in the mathematics of Huygens' contemporaries. Whereas, for example, Huygens fully accepted Viète's and Descartes's application of literal algebra to geometry, he rejected Cavalieri's methods of indivisibles. In his earlier works he applied rigorous Archimedean methods of proof to problems about quadratures and cubatures. That is, he proved equality of areas or contents by showing, through consideration of a sequence of approximating figures, that the supposition of inequality leads to a contradiction. On the other hand, he accepted Fermat's infinitesimal methods for extreme values and tangents, freely practicing division by "infinitely small"—his terminology—differences of abscissae, which subsequently are supposed equal to zero. Eventually the tediousness of the Archimedean methods of proof forced him to work directly with partition of figures into "infinitely small" or very small component figures; he considered this method to be inconclusive but sufficient to indicate the direction of a full proof. He long remained skeptical about Leibniz' new methods, largely because of Leibniz' secrecy about them.

In his first publication, *Theoremata de quadratura hyperboles,* Huygens derived a relation between the quadrature and the center of gravity of segments of circles, ellipses, and hyperbolas. He applied this result to the quadratures of the hyperbola and the circle. In the *De circuli magnitudine inventa* he approximated the center of gravity of a segment of a circle by the center of gravity of a segment of a parabola, and thus found an approximation of the quadrature; with this he was able to refine the inequalities between the area of the circle and those of the inscribed and circumscribed polygons used in the calculations of π. The same approximation with segments of the parabola, in the case of the hyperbola, yields a quick and simple method to calculate logarithms, a finding he explained before the Academy in 1666–1667.

In an appendix to the *Theoremata,* Huygens refuted the celebrated proof by Gregory of St. Vincent (*Opus geometricum* [1647]) of the possibility of the quadrature of the circle. Huygens found the crucial mistake in this very extensive and often obscure work. Gregory had applied Cavalierian indivisible methods to the summation of proportions instead of to line segments. The language of proportions was still sufficiently close to that of arithmetic for Gregory's error not to be a simple blunder, but Huygens was able to show by a numerical example that the application was faulty.

Having heard in Paris about Pascal's work in probability problems, Huygens himself took up their study in 1656. This resulted in the *Tractatus de ratiociniis in aleae ludo,* a treatise that remained the only book on the subject until the eighteenth century. In his first theorems Huygens deduced that the "value of a chance," in the case where the probabilities for a and b are to each other as $p:q$, is equal to

$$\frac{pa + qb}{p + q}.$$

He thus introduced as a fundamental concept the expectation of a stochastic variable rather than the probability of a process (to put it in modern terms). Subsequent theorems concern the fair distribution of the stakes when a game is broken off prematurely. The treatise closes with five problems, the last of which concerns expected duration of play.

In 1657 Huygens found the relation between the arc length of the parabola and the quadrature of the hyperbola. His method cannot be extended to a general rectification method, for it depends on a special property of the parabola: if a polygon is tangent to the parabola, and if the tangent points have equidistant abscissae, the polygon can be moved in the direction of the axis of the parabola to form an inscribed polygon. Huygens also employed this property to find the surface area of a paraboloid of revolution. From correspondence he learned about the general rectification method of Heuraet (1657). He found, in 1658, the relation which in modern notation is rendered by $yds = ndx$ (s: arc length; n: normal to the curve (y, x)), with which he could reduce the calculation of surface areas of solids of revolution to the quadrature of the curve $z = n(x)$; he used this relation also in a general rectification method. Some of

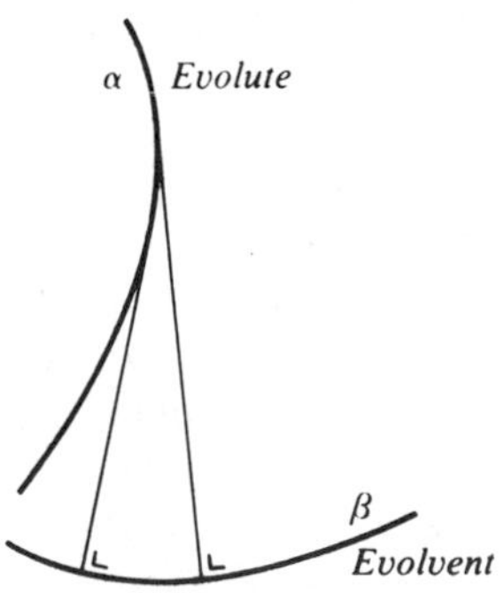

FIGURE 1

these results were published in part 3 of the *Horologium oscillatorium* [10].

In 1659 Huygens developed, in connection with the pendulum clock, the theory of evolutes (Fig. 1). The curve β described by the end of a cord which is wound off a convex curve α is called the evolvent of α, and conversely α is called the evolute of β. In part 3 of the *Horologium oscillatorium* Huygens showed, by rigorous Archimedean methods, that the tangents to the evolute are perpendicular to the evolvent, and that two curves which exhibit such a relation of tangents and perpendiculars are the evolute and evolvent of one another. Further, he gives a general method (proved much less rigorously) of determining from the algebraic equation of a curve the construction of its evolute; the method is equivalent to the determination of the radius of curvature (although Huygens only later interested himself in this as a measure of curvature) and implies, accordingly, a twice repeated determination of tangents by means of Sluse's tangent rule.

Huygens' study on the logarithmica dates from 1661; the results were published in the *Discours.* Huygens introduced this curve (modern $y = ae^x$) as the one in which every arithmetical series of abscissae corresponds to a geometrical series of ordinates. He noted its connection both with the quadrature of the hyperbola and with logarithms and pointed out that its subtangent is constant.

In the last decade of his life Huygens became convinced of the merits of the new Leibnizian differential and integral calculus through the study of articles by the Bernoullis, L'Hospital, and Leibniz, and through correspondence with the latter two. In 1691 he learned how to apply calculus in certain simple cases. Nevertheless, Huygens continued to use the old infinitesimal geometrical methods—which he applied with such virtuosity that he was able to solve most of the problems publicly posed in this period, including Leibniz' isochrone problem (1687), Johann Bernoulli's problem (1693-1694), the tractrix problem (1693), and the catenary problem (1691-1693). His final solution (1693) of this last problem may serve as an example of the force and style of Huygens' mathematics.

In dealing with the catenary problem, Huygens conceived the chain as a series of equal weights, connected by weightless cords of equal length. It follows from statics that every four subsequent weights A, B, C, D (Fig. 2) in the chain are disposed such that the extensions of AB and CD meet at H on the vertical that bisects BC. (Huygens had already found this result in 1646 and used it to refute Galileo's assertion that the catenary is a parabola.) By simple geometry it may now be seen that the tangents of the angles of subsequent cords to the horizontal are in arithmetical progression. Huygens further conceived (Fig. 2) the chain $C_1C_2C_3C_4 \cdots$ (the lowest link being horizontal) stretched along the horizontal axis, to become $C_1D_2D_3D_4 \cdots$. Point P on the vertical through C_1 is chosen such that $\angle C_1PD_2 = \angle C_2C_1B_1$. (As Huygens knew, it can be proved that in the limit C_1P is equal to the radius of curvature in the vertex of the chain.) As the tangents of $\measuredangle D_iC_1P$ are obviously in arithmetical progression, $\angle D_iC_1P$ must be equal to $\angle C_{i+1}C_iB_i$. Introducing normals D_iE_i on $D_{i+1}P$, it follows that the triangles $D_iD_{i+1}E_i$ are congruent with $C_iC_{i+1}B_i$, so that the chain is stretched, as it were, together with its series of characteristic triangles.

Considering the abscissa C_1B and the ordinate BC of a point C on the catenary, it is clear that

$$C_1B = \sum C_iB_i = \sum D_iE_i$$

and that

$$BC = \sum B_iC_{i+1} = \sum E_iD_{i+1}.$$

Huygens now imagines the interstices to be "infinitely small," so that C_1 coincides with the vertex O of the catenary, and he takes $OD = \widehat{OC}$. It is then clear that $\Sigma E_iD_{i+1} = QD$, if $PQ = PO$, so that the ordinate BC is equal to QD. To evaluate the abscissa OB, Huygens extends the normals D_iE_i and remarks that they are the tangents of a curve $\widehat{OS}$, which has the property that the normals PD_i on its tangents D_iE_i meet in one point. This determines the curve $\widehat{OS}$ as a parabola; by the theory of evolutes ΣD_iE_i is equal to the arc length $\widehat{OS}$ of the parabola minus the tangent SD, so that the abscissa OB is equal to $\widehat{OS} - SD$. This result, in combination with the previously found equality $BC = QD$, makes possible the geometrical construction of corresponding ordinates and abscissae of the curve. The construction presupposes the rectification of the parabola, which, as Huygens knew, depends on the quadrature of the hyperbola. Thus his solution of the catenary problem is the geometrical equivalent of the analytical solution of the problem, namely, the equation of the curve involving exponentials.

Statics and Hydrostatics. In the treatment of problems in both statics (the catenary problem, for example) and hydrostatics, Huygens proceeded from the axiom that a mechanical system is in equilibrium if its center of gravity is in the lowest possible position with respect to its restraints. In 1650 he brought together the results of his hydrostatic studies in a manuscript, *De iis quae liquido supernatant* [20]. In this work he derived the law of Archimedes from the basic axiom and proved that a floating body is in a position of equilibrium when the distance between

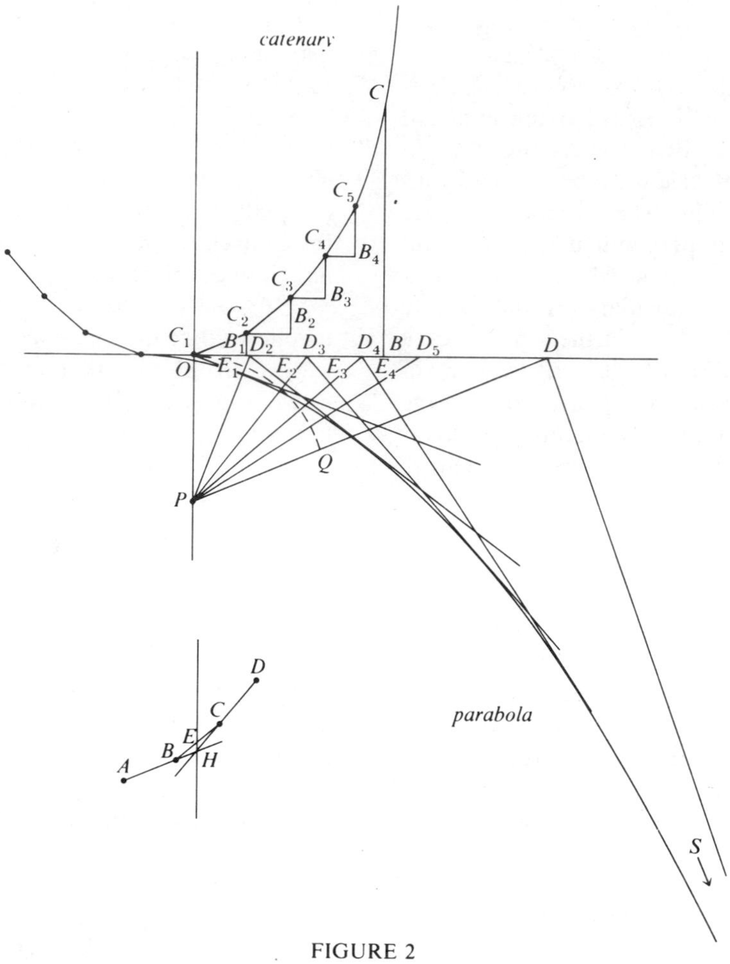

FIGURE 2

the center of gravity of the whole body and the center of gravity of its submerged part is at a minimum. The stable position of a floating segment of a sphere is thereby determined, as are the conditions which the dimensions of right truncated paraboloids and cones must satisfy in order that these bodies may float in a vertical position. Huygens then deduced how the floating position of a long beam depends on its specific gravity and on the proportion of its width to its depth, and he also determined the floating position of cylinders. The manuscript is of further mathematical interest for its many determinations of centers of gravity and cubatures, as, for example, those of obliquely truncated paraboloids of revolution and of cones and cylinders.

Impact. Huygens started his studies on collision of elastic bodies in 1652, and in 1656 he collected his results in a treatise *De motu corporum ex percussione* [18]. He presented the most important theorems to the Royal Society in 1668, simultaneously with studies by Wren and Wallis; they were published, without proofs, in the *Journal des sçavans* in 1699 [9]. Since Huygens' treatise is a fundamental work in the theory of impact and exhibits his style at its best, it is worth describing in some detail.

Huygens' theory amounted to a refutation of Descartes's laws of impact. Indeed, Huygens' disbelief in these laws was one of the motivations for his study. Descartes supposed an absolute measurability of velocity (that is, a reference frame absolutely at rest). This assumption is manifest in his rule for collision of equal bodies. If these have equal velocities, they rebound; if their velocities are unequal, they will move on together after collision. Huygens challenged this law and in one of his first manuscript notes on the question, remarked that the forces acting between colliding bodies depend only on their relative velocity. Although he later abandoned this dynamical approach to the question, the relativity principle remained fundamental. It appeared as hypothesis III of *De motu corporum,* which asserts that all motion is measured against a framework that is only assumed to be at rest, so that the results of speculations about motion should not depend on whether this frame is at rest in any absolute sense. Huygens' use of this principle in his impact theory may be described algebraically (although Huygens himself, of course, gave a geometrical treatment) as follows: If bodies A and B with velocities v_A and v_B acquire, after collision, velocities u_A and u_B, then the same bodies with velocities $v_A + v$ and $v_B + v$ will acquire, after collision, the velocities $u_A + v$ and $u_B + v$. Huygens discussed the principle at great length and as an illustration used collision processes viewed by two observers—one on a canal boat moving at a steady rate and the other on the bank.

In the treatise, Huygens first derived a special case of collision (prop. VIII) and extended it by means of the relativity principle to a general law of impact, from which he then derived certain laws of conservation. This procedure is quite contrary to the method of derivation of the laws of impact from the axiomatic conservation laws, which has become usual in more recent times; but it is perhaps more acceptable intuitively. In the special case of prop. VIII the magnitudes of the bodies are inversely proportional to their (oppositely directed) velocities ($m_A : m_B = |v_B| : |v_A|$), and Huygens asserts that in this case the bodies will simply rebound after collision ($u_A = -v_A$, $u_B = -v_B$). To prove this, Huygens assumed two hypotheses. The first, hypothesis IV, states that a body A colliding with a smaller body B at rest transmits to B some of its motion—that is, that B will acquire some velocity and A's velocity will be reduced. The second, hypothesis V, states that if in collision the motion of one of the bodies is not changed (that is, if the absolute value of its velocity remains the same), then the motion of the other body will also remain the same.

The role of the concept of motion (*motus*) as used here requires some comment. Descartes had based his laws of impact partly on the theorem that motion is conserved, whereby he had quantified the concept of motion as proportional to the magnitude of the body and to the absolute value of its velocity ($m|v|$). Huygens found that in this sense the *quantitas motus* is not conserved in collision. He also found that if the velocities are added algebraically, there is a law of conservation (namely, of momentum) which he formulated as conservation of the velocity of the center of gravity. But for Huygens the vectorial quantity $\overrightarrow{mv}$ was apparently so remote from the intuitive concept of motion that he did not want to assume its conservation as a hypothesis. Nor could he take over Descartes's quantification of the concept, and thus he used a nonvectorial concept of motion, without quantifying it, restricting himself to one case in which motion is partly transferred, and to another in which it remains unchanged.

Huygens now deduced from hypotheses III, IV, and V that the relative velocities before and after collision are equal and oppositely directed: $v_A - v_B = u_B - u_A$ (prop. IV). To derive proposition VIII, he drew upon three more assertions: namely, Galileo's results concerning the relation between velocity and height in free fall; the axiom that the center of gravity of a mechanical system cannot rise under the influence of gravity alone; and the theorem that elastic collision is a reversible process, which he derived from proposition IV. Huygens considered the velocities v_A and v_B in proposition VIII as acquired through free fall from heights h_A and h_B, and supposed that the bodies after collision are directed upward and rise to heights h'_A and h'_B. Because the collision is reversible, the centers of gravity of the systems (A, B, h_A, h_B) and (A, B, h'_A, h'_B) must be at the same height, from which it can be calculated that $u_A = -v_A$ and $u_B = -v_B$. Proposition VIII is now proved, and by means of the relativity principle the result of any elastic collision can be derived, as Huygens showed in proposition IX. Finally, he deduced from this general law of impact the proposition that before and after collision the sum of the products of the magnitudes and the squares of the velocities of the bodies are equal (conservation of $\Sigma\ mv^2$).

Optical Techniques. Working with his brother, Huygens acquired great technical skill in the grinding and polishing of spherical lenses. The lenses that they made from 1655 onward were of superior quality, and their telescopes were the best of their time. In 1685 Huygens summarized his technical knowledge of lens fabrication in *Memorien aengaende het slijpen van glasen tot verrekijckers* [17]. In *Astroscopia compendiaria* [11], he discussed the mounting of telescopes in which, to reduce aberration, the objective and ocular were mounted so far apart (up to twenty-five meters) that they could not be connected by a tube but had to be manipulated separately.

Geometrical Optics. As early as 1653 Huygens recorded his studies in geometrical optics in a detailed manuscript, *Tractatus de refractione et telescopiis* [16]. He treated here the law of refraction, the determination of the focuses of lenses and spheres and of refraction indices, the structure of the eye, the shape of lenses for spectacles, the theory of magnification, and the construction of telescopes. He applied his theorem that in an optical system of lenses with collinear centers the magnification is not changed if the object and eye are interchanged to his theory of telescopes. He later used the theorem in his calculations for the so-called Huygens ocular, which has two lenses. He began studying spherical aberration in 1665, determining for a lens with prescribed aperture and focal length the shape which exhibits minimal spherical aberration of parallel entering rays. He further investigated the possibility of compensating for spherical aberration of the objective in a telescope by the aberration of the ocular, and he studied the relation between magnification, brightness, and resolution of the image for telescopes of prescribed length. These results were checked experimentally in 1668, but the experiments were inconclusive, because in the overall aberration effects the chromatic aberration is more influential than the spherical.

About 1685 Huygens began to study chromatic aberration. He did not start from his own experiments, as he usually did, but rather began with the results of Newton's work; he had first heard of Newton's theory of colors in 1672. Huygens confirmed the greater influence of chromatic as compared with spherical aberration, and he thereby determined the most advantageous shapes for lenses in telescopes of prescribed length.

About 1677 Huygens studied microscopes, including aspects of their magnification, brightness, depth of focus, and lighting of the object. Under the influence of Leeuwenhoek's discoveries, with his microscope he observed infusoria, bacteria, and spermatozoa. In consequence he became very skeptical about the theory of spontaneous generation.

Astronomy. With the first telescope he and his brother had built, Huygens discovered, in March 1655, a satellite of Saturn, later named Titan. He determined its period of revolution to be about sixteen days, and noted that the satellite moved in the same plane as the "arms" of Saturn. Those extraordinary appendages of the planet had presented astronomers since Galileo with serious problems of interpretation; Huygens solved these problems with the hypothesis that Saturn is surrounded by a ring. He arrived at this solution partly through the use of better observational equipment, but also by an acute argument based on the use of the Cartesian vortex (the whirl of "celestial matter" around a heavenly body supporting its satellites).

Huygens' argument began with the premise that it is a general feature of the solar system that the period of rotation of a heavenly body is much shorter than the periods of revolution of its satellites, and that the periods of inner satellites are smaller than those of outer satellites. This is the case with the sun and the planets, with the earth and the moon, and with Jupiter and its satellites. In the same way the "celestial matter" between Saturn and its satellite must move so that the parts near the planet—including the "arms"—will have a period of revolution about equal to the period of rotation of the planet and much shorter than the sixteen days assigned to the satellite. In the period of Huygens' observations in 1655–1656, no alteration was observed in the aspects of the "arms," a phenomenon which could be explained only if the matter forming the "arms" was distributed with cylindrical symmetry around Saturn, with its axis of symmetry—the axis of the vortex—perpendicular to the plane of the satellite and of the "arms" themselves. Therefore, the "arms" must be considered as the aspect of a ring around Saturn. In his further calculations, Huygens established that this hypothesis could also be used to explain the observed long-term variations in the aspect of the "arms."

In March 1656 Huygens published his discovery of Saturn's satellite in the pamphlet *De Saturni lunâ observatio nova* [3], in which, to secure priority, he also included an anagram for the hypothesis of the ring. (After decoding, this anagram reads "Annulo cingitur, tenui, plano, nusquam cohaerente, ad eclipticam inclinato"—"It is surrounded by a thin flat ring, nowhere touching, and inclined to the ecliptic.") The full theory was published, after some delay (1659), in *Systema Saturnium* [6], together with many other observations on the planets and their satellites, all contributing to an emphatic defense of the Copernican system.

Of Huygens' further astronomical work, one should mention the determination of the period of Mars and the observation of the Orion nebula. He described the latter, in *Systema Saturnium,* as the view through an opening in the dark heavens into a brighter region farther away. He also developed micrometers for the determination of angular diameters of planets.

Pendulum Clock. In the winter of 1656–1657 Huygens developed the idea of using a pendulum as a regulator for clockworks. Galileo had strongly maintained the tautochronism of the pendulum movement and its applicability to the measurement of time. Pendulums were so used in astronomical observations, sometimes connected to counting mechanisms. In cogwheel clocks, on the other hand, the movement was regulated by balances, the periods of which were strongly dependent on the source of motive power of the clock and hence unreliable. The necessity for accurate measurement of time was felt especially in navigation, since good clocks were necessary to find longitude at sea. In a seafaring country like Holland, this problem was of paramount importance. Huygens' invention was a rather obvious combination of existing elements, and it is thus not surprising that his priority has been contested, especially in favor of Galileo's son, Vincenzio.

There is no question of Huygens' originality, however, if one acknowledges as the essential point in his clock the application of a freely suspended pendulum, whose motion is transmitted to the clockwork by a handle and fork. The first such clock dates from 1657, and was patented in the same year. In the *Horologium* Huygens described his invention, which had great success; many pendulum clocks were built and by 1658 pendulums had been applied to the tower clocks of Scheveningen and Utrecht.

Huygens made many theoretical studies of the pendulum clock in the years after 1658. The problem central to such mechanisms is that the usual simple pendulum is not exactly tautochronous. Its period depends on the amplitude, although when the amplitudes are small this dependence may be neglected. (This problem was recognized in the first applications of Galileo's proposal.) There are three possible solutions. A constant driving force would secure constant amplitude, but this is technically very difficult. The amplitude may be kept small, a remedy Huygens applied in the clock he described in the *Horologium,* but then even a small disturbance can stop the clock. The best method, therefore, is to design the pendulum so that its bob moves in such a path that the dependence of period on amplitude is entirely eliminated. Huygens tried this solution in his first clock, applying at the suspension point of the pendulum two bent metal laminae, or cheeks, along which the cord wrapped itself as the pendulum swung. Thus the bob did not move in a circle but in a path such that—it could be argued qualitatively—the swing was closer to being tautochronous than in the usual pendulum.

In 1659 Huygens discovered that complete independence of amplitude (and thus perfect tautochronism) can be achieved if the path of the pendulum bob is a cycloid. The next problem was what form to give the cheeks in order to lead the bob in a cycloidal path. This question led Huygens to the theory of evolutes of curves. His famous solution was that the cheeks must also have the form of a cycloid, on a scale determined by the length of the pendulum.

Huygens also studied the relation between period and length of the pendulum and developed the theory of the center of oscillation. By this theory the notion of "length" of a pendulum is extended to compound pendulums, so that Huygens could investigate how the period of a pendulum can be regulated by varying the position of an additional small weight on the arm. These studies form the main contents of Huygens' magnum opus, the *Horologium oscillatorium* [10] (1673). After 1673 Huygens studied harmonic oscillation in general, in connection with the tautochronism of the cycloid. He developed the application of springs instead of pendulums as regulators of clocks—a question on which he engaged in priority disputes with Hooke and others. Huygens also designed many other tautochronous balances for clocks.

Huygens considered the determination of longitudes at sea to be the most important application of the pendulum clock. Here the main difficulty was maintaining an undisturbed vertical suspension. Huygens designed various apparatus to meet this problem, some of which were tested on sea voyages after 1663. Huygens discussed these experiments in *Kort Onderwijs aengaende het gebruyck der Horologien tot het vinden der Lenghten van Oost en West,* a manual for seamen on how to determine longitudes with the help of clocks. Clocks tested on later expeditions (for example, to Crete in 1668–1669 and to the Cape of Good Hope in 1686–1687 and 1690–1692) were not really successful.

Simple Pendulum: Tautochronism of the Cycloid. In 1659, in a study done on the ordinary simple pendulum, Huygens derived a relation between the period and the time of free fall from rest along the length of the pendulum. His result, which he published in part 4 of the *Horologium oscillatorium,* is equivalent to $T = 2\pi \sqrt{l/g}$. In deriving the relation, Huygens used a certain approximation which discards the dependence of the period on the amplitude. The error thus introduced is negligible in the case of a small amplitude. In a subsequent investigation, Huygens posed the question of what form the path of the pendulum bob should have, so that the approximative assumption would cease to be an approximation and would describe the real situation. He found a condition for the form of the path related to the position of the normals to the curve with respect to the axis; and he recognized this as a property of the cycloid, which he had studied in the previous year in connection with a problem set by Pascal. He thus discovered the tautochronism of the cycloid—"the most fortunate finding which ever befell me," he said later. He published his discovery, with a scrupulously rigorous Archimedean proof, in the second part of *Horologium oscillatorium.*

Center of Oscillation. Huygens began his studies on the center of oscillation in 1659 as part of his work on the pendulum clock. By 1669 he had formulated a general computation rule applicable to all sorts of compound pendulums (*Horologium oscillatorium,* part 4). He showed that the period of a compound pendulum depends on the form of the pendulous body and on the position of the axis (Fig. 3). The theory of the center of oscillation determines this dependence by establishing the length λ of the simple pendulum that oscillates isochronously with the compound pendulum. The center of oscillation of the compound pendulum is the point O which lies at distance λ from the axis on the line through the center of gravity Z, perpendicular to the axis. If one assumes all the mass of the pendulum to be concentrated in O, the simple pendulum thus formed (with the same axis) will have the same period as the compound one.

In determining centers of oscillation Huygens proceeded from two hypotheses. The first, which he also used in deriving laws of impact, asserts that the center of gravity of a system, under the sole influence of gravity, cannot rise; the second, that in the absence of friction the center of gravity of a system will, if the component parts are directed upward after a descent, rise again to its initial height. Huygens further supposed that the latter hypothesis also applies if during the movement the links between the component parts are severed.

Huygens' determination of centers of oscillation can now be represented as follows: The compound pendulum (Fig. 3) consists of small parts with weight g_i, whose distances to the axis are α_i. The center of gravity Z has distance ζ to the axis; λ is the length of the isochronous simple pendulum, whose bob in initial position (the amplitudes of both pendulums being equal) is at height h above its lowest position; passing this lowest position it has velocity v. It is now obvious that in moving from the initial to the lowest position, the center of gravity Z descends over $\frac{\zeta}{\lambda}h$, a height to which it will therefore ascend again. Huygens now imagines that at the moment of passing the lowest position, all the linkages between the parts are severed. These parts then have velocities

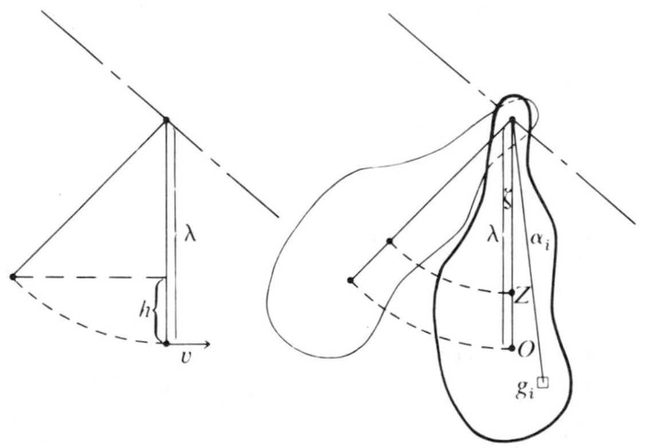

FIGURE 3

$v_i = \frac{\alpha_i}{\lambda} v$, with which they can, when directed upward, ascend to heights h_i. Now according to Galileo's law of falling bodies, v_i^2 is proportional to h_i; velocity v corresponds to height h, so that

$$h_i = \frac{v_i^2}{v^2} h - \frac{\alpha_i^2}{\lambda^2} h.$$

If all the parts are directed upward and arrested at their highest positions, the center of gravity will be at height $\frac{\Sigma g_i h_i}{\Sigma g_i}$; the second hypothesis asserts that this height is equal to $\frac{\zeta}{\lambda} h$.

Thus, $$\frac{\zeta}{\lambda} h = \frac{\Sigma\, g_i \frac{\alpha_i^2}{\lambda^2} h}{G},$$

with $$G = \Sigma g_i,$$

hence $$G\zeta\lambda = \Sigma g_i \alpha_i^2.$$

This, then, is Huygens' general computation rule for the center of oscillation. More recently, the final term $\Sigma g_i \alpha_i^2$, rendered as $\Sigma m_i \alpha_i^2$, has been called the "moment of inertia," but Huygens did not give it a separate name. Huygens determined the centers of oscillation of compound pendulums of many types; he applied complicated geometrical transformations to interpret $\Sigma g_i \alpha_i^2$ as being a quadrature, a cubature, or dependent on the center of gravity of certain curvilinear areas or bodies. He also derived the general theorem which asserts that with respect to different parallel oscillation axes of one pendulum, the product $\zeta(\lambda\text{-}\zeta)$ is constant and that, consequently, if the center of oscillation and the axis are interchanged, the period remains the same.

In the fourth part of *Horologium oscillatorium*, Huygens also discussed the possibility of defining a universal measure of length by using the length of a simple pendulum having a period of one second, an idea he had first developed in 1661. The advantage of such a method of measurement is that it is not affected in the case of bodies subject to wear or decay, while the theory of the center of oscillation makes it easy to verify the measure itself. In this connection Huygens again mentioned the relation between period and time of fall along the pendulum length, which he had determined as being equivalent to $T = 2\pi \sqrt{l/g}$. He does not, however, touch upon the possibility that the acceleration of free fall is dependent on the geographical position because of the centrifugal force of the earth's rotation. Strangely, he had in 1659 already recognized this possibility, which invalidates his definition of a universal measure of length. But he apparently did not think that the effect occurred in reality, a view which he sustained even after having heard about Richer's observations in Cayenne; indeed, it was only by reports on experiments in 1690–1692 that Huygens was convinced of the actual occurrence of this effect.

Centrifugal Force. In 1659 Huygens collected in a manuscript, *De vi centrifuga* [19] (1703), the results of his studies on centrifugal force, which he had taken up in that year in his investigations on the cause of gravity. He published the most important results, without proofs, in *Horologium oscillatorium.* The fundamental concept in Huygens' treatise is the conatus of a body, which is its tendency to motion and the cause of the tension in a cord on which the body is suspended or on which it is swung around. The conatus of a body is measured by the motion that arises if the restraints are removed; that is, in the case of bodies suspended or swung, if the cords are cut. If these motions are similar—if, for instance, both are uniformly accelerated—then the two conatus are similar and therefore comparable. If the motions that arise are the same, then the two conatus are equal.

Huygens showed that for bodies suspended on cords and situated on inclined planes, the conatus, measured in this way, are indeed proportional to the forces which the theory of statics assigns in these cases. He remarked that the motions arising when the restraints are removed must be considered for only a very short interval after this removal, since a body on a curved plane has the same conatus as a body on the corresponding tangent plane; this obtains although the motions which they would perform are approximately the same only in the first instants after release. What was probably the most important result of this study for Huygens himself was his conclusion that centrifugal force and the force of gravity are similar, as is evidenced by the property of horizontal circular motion. After the cutting of the cord, the body will proceed along the tangent with a uniform motion, so that with respect to an observer participating in the circular motion, it will recede in the direction of the cord; it will recede in such a way that, in subsequent equal short-time intervals, the distance between observer and body will increase with increments approximately proportional to the odd numbers $1, 3, 5, \cdots$.

The motion of the swung body when released is thus similar to the motion of free fall, and the conatus of suspended and swung bodies are therefore similar and comparable. Huygens compared them by calculating for a given radius (length of cord) r, the velocity v with which a body must traverse the horizontal circle to cause in its cord the same tension as if it were suspended from it. For this to be the case, the spaces traversed in subsequent equal short increments of time in free fall and in release from circular motion must be the same (that is, the conatus must be the same).

Using the law of falling bodies in the form of the relation $v(t) = 2s(t)/t$, it can be deduced that the required velocity v must be the velocity acquired by a body after free fall along distance $s = r/2$. Huygens then deduced from geometrical arguments that the centrifugal conatus is proportional to the square of the velocity and inversely proportional to the radius. These results were later summarized in the formula $F = \frac{mv^2}{r}$—which formula, however, differs significantly in its underlying conceptions from Huygens' result, since its standard derivation involves a measure of the force of gravity by the Newtonian expression mg and since it assimilates centrifugal to gravitational force by the common measure involving the second derivative of the distance-time function. In Huygens' treatment, the notion of "acceleration" as a measurable quantity is entirely absent, and the similarity of the two different forces is a demonstrandum rather than an axiom.

Fall and Projectiles. In the second part of *Horologium oscillatorium* Huygens gave a rigorous derivation of the laws of unresisted descent along inclined planes and curved paths, these being the laws which he applied in his proof of the tautochronism of the cycloid. In this derivation he made use of an earlier investigation (1646), in which he had dealt with Galileo's law of falling bodies, by considering that such a law has to be scale-free. He also made use of a study of 1659 in which he derived the law of falling bodies from the principles of relativity of motion.

In 1659 Huygens also made experiments concerning the distance which a freely falling body traverses from rest over a period of one second. This is the form in which the physical constant now indicated by the gravitational acceleration g occurs in the work of Huygens and his contemporaries. By means of the relation between period and length of the simple pendulum, derived in the same year, he found for this distance the value of fifteen Rhenish feet, seven and one-half inches, which is very close to the correct value. Huygens published this result in *Horologium oscillatorium,* part 4.

In 1668 Huygens studied fall and projectile motion in resisting media, a subject on which he had already made short notes in 1646 and 1659. He supposed the resistance, that is, the change of velocity induced by the medium in a short time interval, to be proportional to the velocity. By considering a figure in which the velocity was represented by an area between a time axis and a curve, Huygens was able to interpret vertical segments of the area perpendicular to the axis as the changes in velocity in the corresponding time interval. These changes are calculated as combinations of the acceleration of gravity and the deceleration by the medium. Thus a certain relation between the area and ordinates of the curve is known, and Huygens recognized this relation as a property of the logarithmica which he had studied extensively in 1661. In that way he found the velocity-time relation (and consequently the distance-time relation) in this type of retarded motion without having explicitly introduced acceleration as a distinct quantity.

But by 1669 Huygens had become convinced by experiments that the resistance in such media as air and water is proportional to the square of the velocity. This induced him to make a new theoretical study of motion in resisting media. Huygens derived a property of the tangents of the curve which represented the velocity-time relation in this case. The determination of the curve was now a so-called inverse tangent problem (equivalent to a first-order differential equation). Huygens reduced it to certain quadratures, but no solution as simple as that for the other case of resistance could be found. Huygens published these results in 1690 in a supplement to the *Discours.*

Concepts of Force. Huygens' study of resisted motion shows that, although he did not accept a Newtonian force concept as a fundamental mechanical principle, he was quite able to perform complicated calculations in which this concept occurs implicitly. In that study, however, he left undiscussed the question of the cause of the forces. His researches on harmonic oscillation (1673–1674) illustrate how unnatural it was for Huygens to disregard this question. Huygens' starting point was the tautochronism of the cycloid. He remarked that a force directed along the tangent, which can keep a body at a certain point *P* on a cycloid in equilibrium, is proportional to the arc length between *P* and the vertex of the cycloid. He concluded from this that, in general, if the force exerted on a body is proportional to its distance to a certain center and directed toward that center, the body will oscillate tautochronously (that is, harmonically) around that center.

Before coming to this conclusion, however, Huygens stated emphatically that in such an instance the force exerted has to be independent of the velocity of the body (otherwise the property of the force in the case of the cycloid cannot be extended to the case of bodies moving along the curve). He added that this condition of independence will be satisfied if the agent that causes the force (gravity, elasticity, or magnetism, for example) has infinite or very great velocity. This argument appears again in his studies on the cause of gravity. He also expressly formulated the hypothesis that equal forces produce equal motions regardless of their causes. Only under these presuppositions could Huygens accept the conclusion that proportionality of force and distance yields harmonic oscillation. He applied the argument to springs and torsion balances, and he designed numerous ingenious apparatus for tautochronous balances for clocks. He further studied in this connection the vibration of strings.

Huygens also took a critical position toward Leibniz' concept of force. Although in his collision theory he had found that the sum of the products of the quantity of matter and the square of the velocity is conserved, he did not consider mv^2 to be the quantification of a fundamental dynamical entity (what Leibniz called *vis viva*). In Huygens' opinion, Leibniz failed to prove both the existence of a constant *vis viva* and the proportionality of this entity to mv^2. On the other hand, Huygens liked the idea that a force, or "power to lift," is conserved in mechanical systems, as is indicated by a note in his manuscripts of 1693. This is not surprising since the principle on which most of his mechanical theories are founded—namely, that the center of gravity of a mechanical system cannot rise of its own force—can be shown to be equivalent to the principle of conservation of energy. In support of his principle, Huygens sometimes argued that a mechanical *perpetuum mobile* would otherwise be possible, a conclusion he considered absurd. This view is understandable in its turn because (as we have seen) so many of Huygens' basic ideas in mechanics derived from the pendulum and from the Galilean notion of constrained fall.

Mechanistic Philosophy. Huygens' studies on light and gravity (as well as his few researches on sound, magnetism, and electricity) were strongly influenced by his mechanistic philosophy of nature. In the preface of his *Traité de la lumière,* Huygens described a "true philosophy" as one "in which one conceives the causes of all natural effects by reasons of mechanics." In his view, the motions of various particles of matter and their interactions by direct contact are the only valid starting points for philosophizing about natural phenomena. In this he was following Descartes, and if one wants to view this as the essence of Descartes's thought, then Huygens may be called a Cartesian.

There are marked differences between Huygens and Descartes in the actual working out of this philosophy, however. Of these, the most important is that Huygens rejected Descartes's complete trust in the power of reason to attain truth. Complete certainty, according to Huygens, cannot be achieved in the study of nature, although there are degrees of probability; the determination of these degrees requires that the philosopher use good sense. Huygens assigned a most important role to experience and experiment in the discovery and verification of theoretical explanations. He also accepted the intercorpuscular vacuum—in regard to which his philosophy is nearer to Gassendi's than to Descartes's.

According to Huygens, the particles of matter move in the vacuum. These particles are homogeneous, being one kind of matter and differing from each other only in shape and size. The *quantitas materiae* is therefore proportional to the content of the particles or, equivalently, to the space occupied by them. The weight of ordinary bodies is proportional to their *quantitas materiae* because the collisions of ethereal particles that cause gravity have effects proportional to the magnitudes of the colliding particles. This may be considered to mark one of the first insights into the difference between mass and weight.

Huygens explained differences in specific gravity of ordinary bodies as differences in the density of matter. The great variety of specific gravities in nature led him to suppose large interspaces, or "pores," between the component particles of bodies and to attribute an important role to the forms of these interspaces. In Huygens' view the particles are completely hard and, in collision, completely elastic. They are indivisible and keep the form in which they were created. They move in right lines or, in the case of vortices, in circles; they can influence each other's motions only by direct contact.

Huygens' mechanistic explanations of natural phenomena thus consisted in showing that, given a certain combination of shapes, magnitudes, number, and velocities of particles, processes occur which manifest themselves macroscopically as the phenomena under consideration.

In the course of working out a pattern of size relations between particles, Huygens came to the conclusion that four or five discrete classes of particles exist. Particles of the same class are approximately equal in form and magnitude. The classes are differentiated by the magnitudes of the particles, those of one class being much smaller than those of the preceding class and much larger than those of the class following.

The particles of the first class are the components of the ordinary bodies and of the air. They move slowly, and Huygens used suppositions about their forms in his explanations of cohesion and coagulation. He considered sound to be vibrations in ordinary bodies and in the air. The particles of the second class form the "ether," and the phenomena of light may be explained by shock waves in this medium. In some ordinary bodies, the spaces between the particles of the first class are so formed that the ether particles can traverse them freely: these bodies are transparent. The particles of the third class are the carriers of magnetic phenomena, and those of the fourth class form the "subtle matter" which causes gravity. (It is not clear whether Huygens supposed a fifth class between the third and the fourth classes to account for electrical phenomena.) Particles of the fourth class move very rapidly in circular paths around the earth; they are so small that they can pass through the "pores" of all ordinary bodies and are scarcely hindered by the particles of the other classes. In Huygens' explanation of gravity as caused by the motion of these particles, as well as in his explanation of magnetism, the concept of vortex plays a fundamental role.

Huygens' adherence to a strongly geometrical approach to problems in infinitesimal mathematics prevented him from making the definitive innovations in the infinitesimal calculus that Newton and Leibniz did. Similarly, his strict adherence to mechanistic principles prevented his achieving results in mechanics comparable to Newton's revolutionary work. Huygens immediately realized the importance of Newton's *Principia,* but he also strongly opposed Newton's use of attractive force as a fundamental explanatory principle. Force, in the Newtonian sense, could never count as a fundamental mechanical principle for Huygens. The occurrence of such forces always required a further, mechanistic explanation for him.

It is important to emphasize the role of Huygens' mechanistic vision in his studies and the reasons which led him to defend this vision so strongly against Newton. First of all, it is remarkable that in Huygens' early work the mechanistic point of view is of importance only as a source of inspiration rather than as a principle of explanation. The special hypotheses on which Huygens based his studies on collision, centrifugal force, motion of pendulums, and statics were not substantiated by mechanistic arguments, nor did Huygens seem to think this should be done. There is no mechanistic philosophy in the *Horologium oscillatorium.*

It would seem that only after his removal to Paris (1666) did Huygens come to emphasize strongly the necessity for strict mechanistic explanations and to combat the supposition of occult qualities—among which he counted attraction—that some of the members of the Academy applied rather freely. His most important reason for taking this position was, no doubt, that he simply could not accept a phenomenon as properly explained if he could not imagine a mechanistic process causing it. As further reasons we must consider the impressive results that he gained precisely by applying this mechanistic point of view. Huygens' discovery of Saturn's ring was directly connected with the vortex theories; and his study of centrifugal force, which showed that the centrifugal tendency (conatus) of particles moving in circles is indeed similar to the centripetal tendency of heavy bodies, supported the explanation of gravity as the effect of a vortex. Finally, Huygens formulated the wave theory of light, which constituted a mechanistic explanation of refraction and reflection, and which he applied in a masterly fashion to the refractive properties of Iceland spar.

The publication, in 1690, of the *Traité de la lumière* and its supplement, the *Discours,* must be seen as Huygens' answer to Newton's *Principia.* In these works Huygens opposed his mechanistic philosophy to Newton's *Philosophia naturalis.* The wave theory of light and its application to the refraction in Iceland spar are an effective mechanistic explanation of natural phenomena, equal in mathematical sophistication and elegance to Newton's explanation of the motion of the planets. Huygens' explanation of gravity dealt with fundamental problems that Newton avoided and left unsolved. Finally, Huygens' treatment of motion in resisting media proved that he could achieve the same results as Newton in this difficult subject although with different methods.

Wave Theory of Light. Light, according to Huygens, is an irregular series of shock waves which proceeds with very great, but finite, velocity through the ether. This ether consists of uniformly minute, elastic particles compressed very close together. Light, therefore, is not an actual transference of matter but rather of a "tendency to move," a serial displacement similar to a collision which proceeds through a row of balls. Because the particles of the ether lie not in rows but irregularly, a colliding particle will transfer its tendency to move to all those particles which it touches in the direction of its motion. Huygens therefore concluded that new wave fronts originate around each particle that is touched by light and extend outward from the particle in the form of hemispheres. Single wave fronts originating at single points are infinitely feeble; but where infinitely many of these fronts overlap, there is light—that is, on the envelope of the fronts of the individual particles. This is "Huygens' principle."

About 1676 Huygens found the explanation of reflection and refraction by means of this principle; his theory connected the index of refraction with the velocities of light in different media. He became completely convinced of the value of his principle on 6 August 1677, when he found the explanation of the double refraction in Iceland spar by means of his wave theory. His explanation was based on three hypotheses: (1) There are inside the crystal two media in which light waves proceed. (2) One medium behaves as ordinary ether and carries the normally refracted ray. (3) In the other, the velocity of the waves is dependent on direction, so that the waves do not expand in spherical form, but rather as ellipsoids of revolution; this second medium carries the abnormally refracted ray. By studying the symmetry of the crystal Huygens was able to determine the direction of the axis of the ellipsoids, and from the refraction properties of the abnormal ray he established the proportion between the axes. He also calculated the refraction of rays on plane sections of the crystal other than the natural crystal sides, and verified all his results experimentally.

Although the completeness of Huygens' analysis is impressive, he was unable to comprehend the effect that we now recognize as polarization, which occurs if the refracted ray is directed through a second crystal of which the orientation is varied. Huygens described this effect in his first studies on the crystal, but he could never explain it. These results are included in the *Traité de la lumière,* which was completed in 1678; Huygens read parts of it to the Academy in 1679.

Gravity. Huygens' explanation of gravity developed the ideas of Descartes. He presupposed a vortex of particles of subtle matter to be circling the earth with great velocity. Because of their circular movement these particles have a tendency (conatus) to move away from the earth's center. They can follow this tendency if ordinary bodies in the vortex move toward the center. The centrifugal tendency of the vortex particles thus causes a centripetal tendency in ordinary bodies, and this latter tendency is gravity. The space which a body of matter vacates, under the influence of gravity, can be taken by an equal quantity of subtle matter. Hence the gravity of a body is equal to the centrifugal conatus of an equal quantity of subtle matter moving very rapidly around the earth.

This argument led Huygens to study centrifugal force in 1659. In his investigations he proved the similarity of the centrifugal and the gravitational conatus, a result that strengthened his conviction of the validity of the vortex theory of gravity. The study also enabled him to work out this theory quantitatively, since given the radius of the earth and the acceleration of gravity he could calculate the velocity of the particles; he found that they circle the earth about seventeen times in twenty-four hours.

Huygens developed this theory further in a treatise presented to the Academy in 1669. Since the cylindrically symmetrical vortices posited by Descartes could explain only a gravity toward the axis, Huygens imagined a multilaterally moving vortex—in which the particles circle the earth in all directions—by which a truly centrally directed gravity could be explained. The particles are forced into circular paths because the vortex is held within a sphere enveloping the earth, and bounded by "other bodies," such that the particles cannot leave this space. The boundary of the gravitational vortex was supposed to be somewhere between the earth and the moon, because Huygens thought the moon to be carried around the earth by a uniaxial vortex (the so-called *vortex deferens*). Later, convinced by Newton of the impossibility of such vortices, he supposed the gravity vortex to extend beyond the moon.

Galileo's law of falling bodies requires that the acceleration which a falling body acquires in a unit of time be independent of the velocity of the body. This independence is the greatest obstacle for any mechanistic explanation of gravity, for the accelerations must be acquired during collisions, but the change of velocity of colliding bodies is dependent on their relative velocities. On this problem Huygens argued that, because the velocity of the vortex particles is very great with respect to the velocity of the falling body, their relative velocity can be considered constant. Thus, in effect he argued that Galileo's law of falling bodies holds only approximately for small velocities of the falling body.

Huygens never discussed the fundamental question raised by this explanation of gravity—namely, how, by means of collisions, a centrifugal tendency of the particles of the subtle matter can transfer a centripetal tendency to heavy bodies.

In the *Discours*, the treatise of 1669 is reiterated almost verbatim, but Huygens added a review of Newton's theory of gravitation, which caused him to revise his own theories somewhat. He resolutely rejected Newton's notion of universal attraction, because, as he said, he believed it to be obvious that the cause of such an attraction cannot be explained by any mechanical principle or law of motion. But he was convinced by Newton of the impossibility of the *vortices deferentes*, and he accepted Newton's explanation of the motion of satellites and planets by a force varying inversely with the square of the distance from the central body. According to Huygens, however, this gravity is also caused by a vortex, although he did not dwell on the explanation of its dependence on the distance.

Cosmotheoros. Huygens did not believe that complete certainty could be achieved in the study of nature, but thought that the philosopher must pursue the highest degree of probability of his theories. Clearly Huygens considered this degree to be adequate in the case of his explanations of light and gravity. It is difficult for the historian to assert how plausible, in comparison with those explanations, Huygens considered his theories about life on other planets and about the existence of beings comparable to man. These theories were expounded in his Κοσμοθεωρος, *sive de terris coelestibus, earumque ornatu, conjecturae* [14].

The argument of the book is very methodically set forth, and its earnestness suggests that Huygens did indeed assign a very high degree of probability to these conjectures. Huygens' reasoning is that it is in the creation of life and living beings that the wisdom and providence of God are most manifest. In the Copernican world system—which is sufficiently proved as agreeing with reality—the earth holds no privileged position among the other planets. It would therefore be unreasonable to suppose that life should be restricted to the earth alone. There must be life on the other planets and living beings endowed with reason who can contemplate the richness of the creation, since in their absence this creation would be senseless and the earth, again, would have an unreasonably privileged position. In further discussion of the different functions of living organisms and rational beings, Huygens came to the conclusion that, in all probability, the plant and animal worlds of other planets are very like those of the earth. He also surmised that the inhabitants of other planets would have a culture similar to man's and would cultivate the sciences.

In the second part of *Cosmotheoros*, Huygens discussed the different movements of the heavenly bodies and how they must appear to the inhabitants of the planets. He took the occasion to mention new advances in astronomy. In contrast to most other Huygensian writings, *Cosmotheoros* has had wide appeal and a broad readership, and has been translated into several languages.

Conclusion. In the period bounded on one side by Viète and Descartes and on the other by Newton and Leibniz, Huygens was Europe's greatest mathematician. In mechanics, in the period after Galileo and before Newton, he stood for many years on a solitary height. His contributions to astronomy, time measurement, and the theory of light are fundamental, and his studies in the many other fields to which his universal interest directed him are of a very high order.

But Huygens' work fell into relative oblivion in the eighteenth century, and his studies exerted little influence. There is thus a marked discrepancy between Huygens' actual stature as a natural philosopher and the influence he exerted. This is due in part to his extreme reluctance to publish theories which he considered insufficiently developed or which did not meet his high standards of adequacy and significance. For this reason his work on hydrostatics, collision, optics, and centrifugal force were published too late to be fully influential. It is also clear that Huygens did not attract disciples: he was essentially a solitary scholar.

Other reasons for Huygens' limited influence must be sought in the character of his work. His infinitesimal-geometrical mathematics and his studies in mechanics and the theory of light, inspired by his mechanistic philosophy, were culminations that defined limits rather than opening new frontiers. Even his early studies in mechanics, based on hypotheses that we can recognize as equivalent to conservation of energy, served as a basis for later work to only a limited extent—although it is true that one may consider the eighteenth-century researches in mechanics, so far as they were centered around the Leibnizian concept of *vis viva,* to be continuations of Huygens' approach. The Newtonian notion of force became the fundamental concept in mechanics after publication of the *Principia;* Huygens' work could not easily be incorporated into this new mechanics, and it was only much later that the two different concepts could be synthesized.

Huygens' work nonetheless forms a continuously impressive demonstration of the explanatory power of the mathematical approach to the study of natural phenomena, and of the fertility of its application to the technical arts. His magnum opus, *Horologium oscillatorium,* stands as a solid symbol of the force of the mathematical approach and was recognized as such by Huygens' contemporaries. Compared to the relatively simple mathematical tools which Galileo used in his works, the wealth of mathematical theories and methods that Huygens was able to apply is significant, and herein lies the direct and lasting influence of his work.

BIBLIOGRAPHY

I. ORIGINAL WORKS. For a complete list of the works of Huygens which appeared before 1704, see *Oeuvres* XXII, 375-381 (see below). Here we recapitulate the writings discussed above:

1. *Theoremata de quadratura hyperboles, ellipsis et circuli ex dato portionum gravitatis centro, quibus subjuncta est Ἐξέτασις Cyclometriae Cl. Viri Gregorii à St. Vincentio,* Leiden, 1651 (*Oeuvres* XI).

2. *De circuli magnitudine inventa. Accedunt ejusdem problematum quorundam illustrium constructiones,* Leiden, 1654 (*Oeuvres* XII).

3. *De Saturni lunâ observatio nova,* The Hague, 1656 (*Oeuvres* XV).

4. *Tractatus de ratiociniis in aleae ludo,* in F. van Schooten, *Exercitationum mathematicarum libri quinque,* Leiden, 1657 (Latin trans. of [7] by van Schooten).

5. *Horologium,* The Hague, 1658 (*Oeuvres* XVII).

6. *Systema Saturnium, sive de causis mirandorum Saturni phaenomenôn, et comite ejus planeta novo,* The Hague, 1659 (*Oeuvres* XV).

7. *Tractaet handelende van Reeckening in Speelen van Geluck,* in F. van Schooten, *Mathematische Oeffeningen begrepen in vijf boecken,* Amsterdam, 1660 (also published separately in the same year; *Oeuvres* XIV).

8. *Kort onderwijs aengaende het gebruyck der Horologien tot het vinden der Lenghtèn van Oost en West,* 1665 (*Oeuvres* XVII).

9. *Règles du mouvement dans la rencontre des corps,* in *Journal des sçavans,* 1669 (*Oeuvres* XVI).

10. *Horologium oscillatorium, sive de motu pendulorum ad horologia aptato demonstrationes geometricae,* Paris, 1673 (*Oeuvres* XVIII); a German trans. in the series *Ostwald's Klassiker der Exakten Wissenschaften,* no. 192 (Leipzig, 1913).

11. *Astroscopia compendiaria, tubi optici molimine liberata,* The Hague, 1684 (*Oeuvres* XXI);

12. *Traité de la lumière, où sont expliquées les causes de ce qui lui arrive dans la Reflexion & dans la Refraction, et particulièrement dans l'étrange Refraction du Cristal d'Islande.* (*Avec un Discours de la Cause de la Pesanteur*), Leiden, 1690 (*Oeuvres* XIX); there is a German trans. in *Ostwald's Klassiker,* no. 20 (Leipzig, 1903).

13. *Discours de la cause de la Pesanteur* appears in [12] (*Oeuvres* XXI).

14. Κοσμοθεωρος, *sive de terris coelestibus, earumque ornatu, conjecturae,* The Hague, 1698 (*Oeuvres* XXI).

15. B. de Volder and B. Fullenius, ed., *Christiani Hugenii Opuscula Posthuma* (Leiden, 1703).

16. *Tractatus de refractione et telescopiis,* MS originating from 1653, was later changed and amplified many times. One version is published under the title *Dioptrica* in the Volder and Fullenius edition and another version in *Oeuvres* XIII.

17. *Memorien aengaende het slijpen van glasen tot verrekijckers,* MS originating from 1685, published in *Oeuvres* XXI. A Latin trans. was published in Volder and Fullenius.

18. *De motu corporum ex percussione,* MS originating from 1656, published in *Oeuvres* XVI. A German trans. appeared in *Ostwald's Klassiker,* no. 138 (Leipzig, 1903).

19. *De vi centrifuga,* MS originating from 1659, published in *Oeuvres* XVI, a German trans. existing in *Ostwald,* no. 138, Leipzig, 1903. Like [18] this is also found in Volder and Fullenius.

20. *De iis quae liquido supernatant,* MS originating from

1650, appears in *Oeuvres* XI.

In his will, Huygens asked Volder and Fullenius to edit some not yet published MSS, which resulted in their posthumous edition [15].

Two further publications of Huygens' writings, edited by G. J. 'sGravesande, are [21] *Christiani Hugenii Opera Varia* (Leiden, 1724) and [22] *Christiani Hugenii Opera Reliqua* (Leiden, 1728). Little more than a century later, P. J. Uylenbroek edited Huygens' correspondence with L'Hospital and Leibniz in [23] *Christiani Hugenii aliorumque seculi XVII virorum celebrium exercitationes mathematicae et philosophicae* (The Hague, 1833).

In 1882, the Netherlands Academy of Sciences at Amsterdam organized a preparatory committee for a comprehensive ed. of Huygens' works. In 1885 it was agreed that the Society of Sciences of Holland at Haarlem would take responsibility for the publication. The undertaking resulted, after more than sixty years of editorial commitment, in what may be considered the best edition of the works of any scientist, the *Oeuvres complètes de Christiaan Huygens, publiées par la Société Hollandaise des Sciences,* 22 vols. (The Hague, 1888–1950).

The first ten vols. comprise Huygens' correspondence, the subsequent ones his published and unpublished scholarly writings, of which the most important are accompanied by a French trans. Vol. XXII contains a detailed biography of Huygens by J. A. Vollgraff.

The editors in chief were, successively, D. Bierens de Haan, J. Bosscha, D. J. Korteweg, and J. A. Vollgraff. Among the many collaborators, C. A. Crommelin, H. A. Lorentz, A. A. Nijland, and E. J. Dijksterhuis may be mentioned. The editors adopted a strict code of anonymity, which was broken only in the last volume.

II. SECONDARY LITERATURE. While Huygens' work is easily accessible in the *Oeuvres,* there exists relatively little secondary literature about him. We may mention [24] P. Harting, *Christiaan Huygens in zijn leven en werken geschetst* (Groningen, 1868); [25] H. L. Brugmans, *Le séjour de Christiaan Huygens à Paris et ses relations avec les milieux scientifiques français, suivi de son journal de voyage à Paris et à Londres* (Paris, 1935); and [26] A. Romein-Verschoor, "Christiaen Huygens, de ontdekker der waarschijnlijkheid," in *Erflaters van onze beschaving* (Amsterdam, 1938–1940), written with J. Romein.

The only recent separately published scientific biography of Huygens is [27] A. E. Bell, *Christian Huygens and the Development of Science in the Seventeenth Century* (London, 1947). On the occasion of the completion of the *Oeuvres* edition, there appeared [28] E. J. Dijksterhuis, *Christiaan Huygens* (Haarlem, 1951).

J. A. Vollgraff, who by editing the last seven vols. of the *Oeuvres* acquired a thorough knowledge of Huygens' life and works, has written a book about Huygens which has not been published. The private typescript will be transferred to the Leiden University Library.

H. J. M. BOS.

HYPATIA (*b.* Alexandria, Egypt, *ca.* 370; *d.* Alexandria, 415)

Hypatia, the first woman in history to have lectured and written critical works on the most advanced mathematics of her day, was the daughter and pupil of the mathematician Theon of Alexandria. It is believed that she assisted him in writing his eleven-part treatise on Ptolemy's *Almagest* and possibly in formulating the revised and improved version of Euclid's *Elements* that is the basis of all modern editions of the work. According to Suidas she composed commentaries not only on the *Almagest* but also on Diophantus' *Arithmetica* and Apollonius' *Conic Sections.* None of them survives.

Although accurate documentation of Hypatia's activities is lacking, it is known that she lectured in her native city on mathematics and on the Neoplatonic doctrines of Plotinus and Iamblichus and that about A.D. 400 she became head of the Neoplatonic school in Alexandria. Her classes attracted many distinguished men, among them Synesius of Cyrene, later bishop of Ptolemais. Several of his letters to Hypatia are extant. They are full of chivalrous admiration and reverence. In one he asks her how to construct an astrolabe and a hydroscope.

In spite of her association with Synesius and other Christians, Hypatia's Neoplatonic philosophy and the freedom of her ways seemed a pagan influence to the Christian community of Alexandria. Prejudice was strengthened by her friendship with Orestes, Roman prefect of the city and political enemy of Cyril, bishop of Alexandria. The mounting hostility culminated in her murder by a fanatic mob. None of her writings was preserved; but the general loss of Hellenic sources must be blamed on repeated book-burning episodes rather than on lynching. The great Alexandrian library had been burned by Roman soldiers long before Hypatia's day, and during her lifetime the valuable library in the temple of Serapis was sacked by an Alexandrian mob.

Hypatia has been the subject of much romantic drama and fiction, including the 1853 novel *Hypatia, or New Foes With an Old Face,* by Charles Kingsley. Such works have perpetuated the legend that she was not only intellectual but also beautiful, eloquent, and modest.

BIBLIOGRAPHY

See T. L. Heath, *History of Greek Mathematics,* II (Oxford, 1921), 528–529; A. W. Richeson, "Hypatia of Alexandria," in *National Mathematics Magazine,* **15,** no. 2 (Nov. 1940), 74–82; Socrates Scholasticus, *Ecclesiastical History,*

HYPSICLES OF ALEXANDRIA

VII (London, 1853), 15; *Suidae Lexicon,* Ada Adler, ed., I (Leipzig, 1928), 618; B. L. van der Waerden, *Science Awakening* (New York, 1961), 290.

EDNA E. KRAMER

HYPSICLES OF ALEXANDRIA (*fl.* Alexandria, first half of second century B.C.)

Hypsicles is attested, by the more definitive manuscripts, to be the author of what has come to be printed as book XIV of Euclid's *Elements.* In the preface to that book he states that Basilides of Tyre came to Alexandria, where he engaged in mathematical discussions with Hypsicles' father. Together they studied a tract by Apollonius of Perga on the dodecahedron and the icosahedron inscribed in the same sphere, and found the treatment unsatisfactory.

Later, presumably after his father's death, Hypsicles himself found what would appear to have been a revised, more accurate version in wide circulation. Taken together, these facts suggest that Hypsicles' father was an older contemporary of Apollonius, living at Alexandria. As Apollonius died early in the second century B.C., the middle point of Hypsicles' activities may be placed at about 175 B.C.

The so-called book XIV, like book XIII, is concerned with the inscription of regular solids in a sphere. Hypsicles proves a proposition, which he attributes to Aristaeus (who was probably not the author of *Five Books Concerning Solid Loci*), that the same circle can be described about the pentagonal face of a regular dodecahedron and the triangular face of a regular icosahedron inscribed in the same sphere. He proves, as had Apollonius before him, that the volume of the dodecahedron bears the same relation to the volume of the icosahedron as the surface of the former bears to the surface of the latter, because the perpendiculars to the respective faces are equal; and that both the ratios are equal to the ratio of the side of the inscribed cube to the side of the dodecahedron.

Arabic traditions suggest that Hypsicles also had something to do with the so-called book XV of the *Elements,* whether he wrote it, edited it, or merely discovered it. But this is clearly a much later and much inferior book, in three separate parts, and this speculation appears to derive from a misunderstanding of the preface to book XIV.

One other work by Hypsicles survives, the *Anaphorikos* (Ἀναφορικός), or *On the Ascension of Stars.* Although quite brief, probably truncated, and based on a false assumption, it is noteworthy in being the first work in which the ecliptic is divided into 360 parts or degrees. He writes,

> The circle of the zodiac having been divided into 360 equal arcs, let each of the arcs be called a spatial degree, and likewise, if the time taken by the zodiac circle to return from a point to the same point is divided into 360 equal times, let each of the times be called a temporal degree [*Die Aufgangszeiten der Gestirne* 55–59, De Falco, ed., p. 36].

This division into 360 parts was almost certainly borrowed from Babylonia, and the *Anaphorikos* is therefore testimony to the existence of links between Greek and Babylonian astronomy in the second century B.C.

Hypsicles posits for himself two problems. Given the ratio of the longest day to the shortest day at any place, how long does it take any given sign of the zodiac to rise there? Second, how long does it take any given degree in a sign to rise? The practical object of this investigation may have been, as T. L. Heath conjectures, to tell the time at night. But the problem came really within the province of spherical trigonometry, which was not developed until Hipparchus. Ptolemy later solved it with the help of his table of sines (*Syntaxis mathematica,* bk. 2, J. L. Heiberg, ed. [Leipzig, 1898], ch. 8, pp. 134–141); and Hipparchus had no doubt solved it before Ptolemy, for Pappus of Alexandria (*Collection* VI 109, Hultsch ed., 600.9–13) refers to calculations "by means of numbers" appearing in Hipparchus' book *On the Rising of the Twelve Signs of the Zodiac.* This method of solution was not open to Hypsicles, which is further confirmation of his date.

The longest day, Hypsicles says, is the time during which Cancer, Leo, Virgo, Libra, Scorpio, and Sagittarius rise (14 hours at Alexandria), and the shortest is the time in which Capricornus, Aquarius, Pisces, Aries, Taurus, and Gemini rise (10 hours); and as their ratio is 7:5, the former signs take 210 temporal degrees and the latter 150. He assumes that the quadrants Cancer-Virgo and Libra-Sagittarius take equal times to rise, 105 temporal degrees, and that the quadrants Capricornus-Pisces and Aries-Gemini each require 75 degrees. He further assumes that the times taken by Virgo, Leo, Cancer, Gemini, Taurus, and Aries form a descending arithmetical series, and that the times for Libra, Scorpio, Sagittarius, Capricornus, Aquarius, and Pisces are in the same series.

With the help of three lemmas concerning arithmetical progressions which he has proved at the outset of his book, Hypsicles shows that Virgo and Libra take 38° 20′ to rise, Leo and Scorpio 35°, and so on, the common difference being 3° 20′. He goes on to prove that each spatial degree takes 0° 0′ 13″ 20‴ less (or more) than its predecessor to rise.

As Hypsicles' assumption that the times of rising

form an arithmetical progression was erroneous, his results were correspondingly in error. But his tract was a gallant attempt to solve the problem before trigonometry provided the right way. The *Anaphorikos* has probably survived by reason of having been included in the collection of ancient Greek texts known as *The Little Astronomy*. It was translated into Arabic toward the end of the ninth century; the translation is variously ascribed to Qustā ibn Lūqā and Ishāq ibn Ḥunayn, but it was in any case considerably altered by later writers. From Arabic it was translated into Latin by Gerard of Cremona (*ca.* 1150) as *Liber Esculei De ascensionibus.* The first printed edition, in Greek and Latin, by Jacobus Mentelius (Paris, 1657) remained the only one until that of K. Manitius in 1888, and this has in turn been superseded by the critical edition of De Falco and Krause (1966).

Hypsicles is cited by Diophantus of Alexandria in *De polygonis numeris* (*Diophanti Alexandrini opera omnia,* I, P. Tannery, ed. [Leipzig, 1893–1895], 470.27–472.4) as the author of the following definition:

> If there be as many numbers as we please beginning from 1 and increasing by the same common difference, then, when the common difference is 1 the sum of all the numbers is a triangular number; when 2, a square number; when 3, a pentagonal number, and so on, the number of angles being called after the number which exceeds the common difference by 2 and the sides after the number of terms, including 1.

In modern notation, the nth a-gonal number (1 being the first) is

$$\frac{1}{2}n\{2 + (n-1)(a-2)\}.$$

From this reference by Diophantus it is presumed that Hypsicles must have written a book, since lost, on numbers. According to Achilles Tatius (*Introductio in Aratum,* E. Maass, ed., *Commentariorum in Aratum reliquiae,* Berlin, 1898, p. 43.9), Hypsicles also wrote a book on the harmony of the spheres; it has not survived.

BIBLIOGRAPHY

I. ORIGINAL WORKS. *Hypsiclis liber, sive Elementorum liber XIV qui fertur, Euclidis opera omnia,* J. L. Heiberg and H. Menge, eds., V (Leipzig, 1888), 1–67; *Des Hypsikles Schrift Anaphorikos nach Überlieferung und Inhalt kritisch behandelt* (Programm des Gymnasiums zum heiligen Kreuz in Dresden), Karl Manitius, ed. (Dresden, 1888), including an introduction, Greek text, and Gerard of Cremona's Latin translation; V. De Falco and M. Krause, eds., *Hypsikles: Die Aufgangszeiten der Gestirne,* in *Abhandlungen der Akademie der Wissenshaften zu Göttingen,* Phil.-hist. Klasse, 3rd ser., no. 62 (1966), with an introduction and valuable interpretation by O. Neugebauer; this has Greek text, scholia, and translation by De Falco, and Arabic text and German translation by Krause.

II. SECONDARY LITERATURE. A. A. Bjørnbo, "Hypsikles 2," in Pauly-Wissowa, IX (1914), cols. 427–433. See also T. L. Heath, *The Thirteen Books of Euclid's Elements,* 2nd ed. (Cambridge, 1925; repr. New York, 1956), I, 5–6; III, 512–519; and *A History of Greek Mathematics* (Oxford, 1921), I, 419–420; II, 213–218; and Jürgen Mau, "Hypsikles," in *Der kleine Pauly,* II (Stuttgart, 1967), cols. 1289–1290.

IVOR BULMER-THOMAS

IBRĀHĪM IBN SINĀN IBN THĀBIT IBN QURRA (*b.* Baghdad [?], 908; *d.* Baghdad, 946)

Born into a family of celebrated scholars, Ibn Sinān was the son of Sinān ibn Thābit, a physician, astronomer, and mathematician, and the grandson of Thābit ibn Qurra. Although his scientific career was brief—he died at the age of thirty-eight—he left a notable body of work, the force and perspicuity of which have often been underlined by biographers and historians. This work covers several areas, such as tangents of circles, and geometry in general; the apparent motions of the sun, including an important optical study on shadows; the solar hours; and the astrolabe and other astronomical instruments.

Since it would hardly be feasible to give even a summary sketch of Ibn Sinān's entire work in a brief article, the best course will be to concentrate attention on two important contributions: his discussions of the quadrature of the parabola and of the relations between analysis and synthesis.

His study of the parabola followed directly out of the treatment given the problem in the work of his grandfather. Thābit ibn Qurra had already resolved this problem in a different way from that of Archimedes. Although his method may have been equivalent to that of summing integrals, the approach was

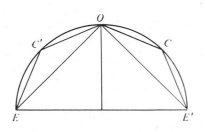

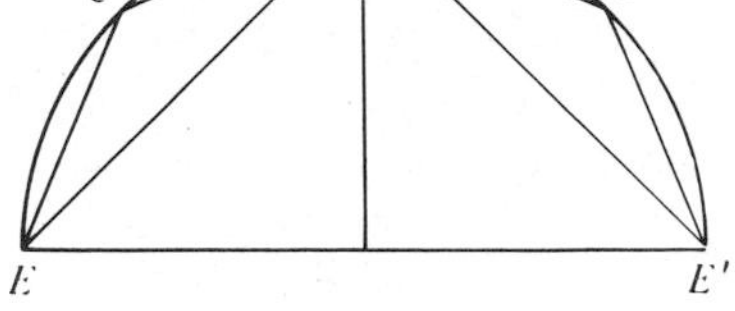

FIGURE 1

more general than that of Archimedes in that the intervals of integration were no longer divided into equal subintervals. Thābit's demonstration was lengthy, however, containing twenty propositions. Another mathematician, one al-Mahānni, had given a briefer one but Ibn Sinān felt it to be unacceptable that (as he wrote) "al Mahānni's study should remain more advanced than my grandfather's unless someone of our family (the Ibn Qurra) can excel him" (*Rāsa'ilu Ibn-i-Sinān*, p. 69). He therefore sought to give an even more economical demonstration, one that did not depend upon reduction to the absurd. The proposition on which Ibn Sinān founded his demonstration, and which he took care to prove beforehand, is that the proportionality of the areas is invariant under affine transformation.

His method considers the polygon a_n to be composed of $2^n - 1$ triangles and inscribed in the area a of the parabola. The polygon a_1 is the triangle EOE', a_2 is the polygon $ECOC'E'$, etc. Ibn Sinān demonstrated that if a_n and a'_n are two polygons inscribed, respectively, in the two areas a and a' of the parabola, then

$$\frac{a_n}{a'_n} = \frac{a_1}{a'_1}.$$

Actually, he derived an expression equivalent to

$$\frac{a}{a'} = \lim_{n\to\infty} \frac{a_n}{a'_n} = \frac{a_1}{a'_1},$$

from which he obtained

$$\frac{\frac{1}{2}(a - a_1)}{a} = \frac{\frac{1}{2}(a_2 - a_1)}{a_1} = \frac{1}{8},$$

and finally derived

$$a = \frac{4}{3}a_1.$$

Ibn Sinān's originality in this investigation is manifest. It was with that same independence of mind that he intended to revive classical geometric analysis in order to develop it in a separate treatise. By virtue of that study, the author may be considered one of the foremost Arab mathematicians to treat problems of mathematical philosophy. His attempt has the form of a critique of the practical geometry in his own times. "I have found," he wrote, "that contemporary geometers have neglected the method of Apollonius in analysis and synthesis, as they have in most of the things I have brought forward, and that they have limited themselves to analysis alone in so restrictive a manner that they have led people to believe that this analysis did not correspond to the synthesis effected" (*ibid.*, p. 66).

In this work, Ibn Sinān proposed two tasks simultaneously, the one technical and the other epistemological. On the one hand, the purpose was to provide those learning geometry with a method (*tarīq*) which could furnish what they needed in order to solve geometrical problems. On the other hand, it was equally important to think about the procedures of geometrical analysis itself and to develop a classification of geometrical problems according to the number of the hypotheses to be verified, explaining the bearing, respectively, of analysis and synthesis on each class of problems.

Considering both the problem of infinitesimal determinations and the history of mathematical philosophy, it is obvious that the work of Ibn Sinān is important in showing how the Arab mathematicians pursued the mathematics they had inherited from the Hellenistic period and developed it with independent minds. That is the dominant impression left by his work.

BIBLIOGRAPHY

I. ORIGINAL WORKS. The *Rāsa'ilu Ibn-i-Sinān* (Hyderabad, 1948) comprises *Fī'l astrolāb* ("On the Astrolabe"), *Al-Tahlīl wa'l-Tarkīb* ("Analysis and Synthesis"), *Fī Ḥarakati'š-Šams* ("On Solar Movements"), *Rasm al-qutū' aṭṭalāta* ("Outline of Three Sections"), *Fī misāḥat qat'al-Maḥrūṭ al-mukāfī* ("Measurement of the Parabola"), and *Al-Handasa wa'n-Nujūm* ("Geometry and Astronomy").

II. SECONDARY LITERATURE. See Ibn al-Qifti, *Ta'riḥ al-Ḥukamā'*, J. Lippert, ed. (Leipzig, 1903); Ibn al-Nadīm, *Kitāb al-Fihrist*, Flugel, ed. (Leipzig, 1871–1872), p. 272; C. Brockelmann, *Geschichte der arabischen Literatur*, I (Leiden, 1943), 245; H. Suter, *Die Mathematiker und Astronomer der Araber und ihre Werke* (Leipzig, 1900), pp. 53–54; "Abhandlung über die Ausmessung der Parabel von Ibrahim ben Sinan ben Thabit ben Kurra," in *Vierteljahrsschrift der Naturforschenden Gesellschaft in Zürich*, **63** (1918), 214 ff.; A. P. Youschkevitch, "Note sur les déterminations infinitésimales chez Thabit ibn Qurra," in *Archives internationales d'histoire des sciences*, no. 66 (January–March 1964), pp. 37–45.

ROSHDI RASHED

ISIDORUS OF MILETUS (*b.* Miletus; *fl.* Constantinople, sixth century)

Isidorus of Miletus was associated with Anthemius of Tralles (a neighboring town of Asia Minor) in the construction of the church of Hagia Sophia at Constantinople. The church begun by Constantine was destroyed in the Nika sedition on 15 January 532.[1] Justinian immediately ordered a new church to be built on the same site, and it was begun the next month.[2] Procopius names Anthemius as the man who organized the tasks of the workmen and made models of the future construction, adding: "With him was associated another architect, Isidorus by name, a Milesian by birth, an intelligent man and in other ways also worthy to execute Justinian's designs."[3] Paul the Silentiary concurs in his labored hexameters: "Anthemius, a man of great ingenuity and with him Isidorus of the all-wise mind—for these two, serving the wills of lords intent on beauty, built the mighty church."[4] It is commonly held that Anthemius died in or about 534,[5] when Isidorus was left in sole charge, but this must be regarded as unproved. The church was dedicated on 27 December 537.[6]

In the astonishing space of five years Anthemius and Isidorus erected one of the largest, most ingenious, and most beautiful buildings of all time. The ground plan is a rectangle measuring seventy-seven by seventy-one meters, but the interior presents the appearance of a basilica terminating in an apse, flanked by aisles and galleries, and surmounted by a dome greater than any ecclesiastical dome ever built. The dome rests upon four great arches springing from four huge piers; the pendentives between the arches were at that time a novel device. As in the church of SS. Sergius and Bacchus in the same city, the stresses of the central dome are shared by half domes to the west and east, and the general similarity of plan has led to conjectures that the same architects built the earlier church. The dome nevertheless exerted a greater outward thrust on the piers supporting it than was safe, and when it had to be reconstructed after an earthquake twenty years later it was made six meters higher; but in general the applied mathematics of the architects (no doubt applied instinctively rather than consciously) have proved equal to the exacting demands of fourteen centuries. The decoration of the building was worthy of its artifice; the empire was ransacked to adorn it with gold, silver, mosaics, fine marbles, and rich hangings. Its ambo excited particular admiration.

Anthemius and Isidorus were consulted by Justinian when the fortifications at Daras in Mesopotamia were damaged by floods; but on this occasion the advice of Chryses, the engineer in charge, was preferred.[7]

Isidorus probably died before 558, for when a section of the dome and other parts of Hagia Sophia were destroyed by an earthquake at the end of the previous year, it was his nephew, called Isidorus the Younger, who carried out the restoration.[8] No doubt he had learned his art in his uncle's office. Essentially what is extant is the church of Anthemius and Isidorus, as repaired by the latter's nephew and patched after no fewer than thirty subsequent earthquakes, in addition to the ordinary ravages of time.

Isidorus was a mathematician of some repute as well as an architect. Notes at the end of Eutocius' commentaries on Books I and II of Archimedes' *On the Sphere and the Cylinder* and *Measurement of the Circle* indicate that Isidorus edited these commentaries.[9] The first such note reads, "The commentary of Eutocius of Ascalon on the first of the books of Archimedes *On the Sphere and the Cylinder*, the edition revised by Isidore of Miletus, the engineer (μηχανικός), our teacher"; and, *mutatis mutandis*, the other two are identical. It was formerly supposed on the strength of these notes that Eutocius was a pupil of Isidorus; but other considerations make this impossible, and it is now agreed that the three notes must be interpolations by a pupil of Isidorus.[10] A similar note added to Eutocius' second solution to the problem of finding two mean proportionals—"The parabola is traced by the *diabetes* invented by Isidorus of Miletus, the engineer, our teacher, having been described by him in his commentary on Hero's book *On Vaultings*"—must also be regarded as an interpolation by a pupil of Isidorus.[11] The nature of the instrument invented by Isidorus can only be guessed—the Greek word normally means "compass"—and nothing is otherwise known about Hero's book or Isidorus' commentary on it.

The third section of the so-called Book XV of Euclid's *Elements* shows how to determine the angle of inclination (dihedral angle) between the faces meeting in any edge of any one of the five regular solids. The procedure begins with construction of an isosceles triangle with vertical angle equal to the angle of inclination. Rules are given for drawing these isosceles triangles, and the rules are attributed to "Isidorus our great teacher."[12] It may therefore be presumed that at least the third section of the book was written by one of his pupils.

The above passages are evidence that Isidorus had a school, and it would appear to have been in this school that Archimedes' *On the Sphere and the Cylinder* and *Measurement of the Circle*—in which Eutocius had revived interest through his commentaries—were translated from their original Doric into the vernacular, with a number of changes designed to make them more easily understood by beginners. It is evident from a comparison of Eutocius' quotations with the text of extant manuscripts that the text of these treatises which Eutocius had before him differed in many respects from that which we have today, and the changes in the manuscripts must therefore have been made later than Eutocius.[13]

NOTES

1. "Chronicon Paschale," in *Corpus scriptorum historiae Byzantinae*, X (Bonn, 1832), 621.20–622.2.
2. Zonaras, *Epitome historiarum*, XIV.6, in the edition by Dindorf, III (Leipzig, 1870), 273.23–29.
3. Procopius, *De aedificiis*, I.1.24, in his *Opera omnia*, Haury, ed., IV (Leipzig, 1954), 9.9–16. In another passage Procopius says that "Justinian and the architect Anthemius along with Isidorus employed many devices to build so lofty a church with security" (*ibid.*, I.1.50; *Opera omnia*, IV, 13.12–15) and in yet another reference he relates how Anthemius and Isidorus, alarmed at possible collapse, referred to the emperor, who in one instance ordered an arch to be completed and in another ordered the upper parts of certain arches to be taken down until the moisture had dried out—in both cases with happy results (*ibid.*, I.1.66–77; *Opera omnia*, IV, 15.17–17.7). The word translated "architect" in these passages (μηχανοποιός) might equally be rendered "engineer." There was no sharp distinction in those days. Perhaps "master builder" would be the best translation.
4. Paul the Silentiary, *Description of the Church of the Holy Wisdom*, ll. 552–555, Bekker, ed., *Corpus scriptorum historiae Byzantinae*, XL (Bonn, 1837), 28. Agathias, *Historiae*, V.9, R. Keydell, ed. (Berlin, 1967), 174.17–18, mentions Anthemius alone, but this is not significant; in his account of the church, Evagrius Scholasticus—*Ecclesiastical History*, Bidez and Parmentier, eds. (London, 1898), 180.6–181.14—mentions neither.
5. F. Hultsch, "Anthemius 4," in Pauly-Wissowa, I (Stuttgart, 1894), col. 2368, "um 534"; followed more precisely by G. L. Huxley, *Anthemius of Tralles* (Cambridge, Mass., 1959), "in A.D. 534." But Agathias, V.9, on which Hultsch relies, cannot be made to furnish this date; and the latest editor, R. Keydell, in his *Index nominum*, merely deduces from the passage *pridem ante annum 558 mortuus*.
6. Marcellinus Comes, "Chronicon," in J. P. Migne, ed., *Patrologia latina*, LI (Paris, 1846), col. 943D.
7. Procopius, *op. cit.*, II.3.1–15; *Opera omnia*, IV, 53.20–55.17.
8. Agathias, *op. cit.*, 296. Procopius records that the younger Isidorus had previously been employed by Justinian, along with John of Byzantium, in rebuilding the city of Zenobia in Mesopotamia (*op. cit.*, II.8.25; *Opera omnia*, IV, 72.12–18).
9. *Archimedis opera omnia*, J. L. Heiberg ed., 2nd ed., III (Leipzig, 1915), 48.28–31, 224.7–10, 260.10–12. The Greek will bear the interpretation that it was the treatises of Archimedes, rather than the commentaries by Eutocius, which Isidorus revised. This was the first opinion of Heiberg—*Jahrbuch für classische Philologie*, supp. **11** (1880), 359—but he was converted by Tannery to the view given in the text: *Archimedis opera omnia*, III, xciii.
10. Paul Tannery, "Eutocius et ses contemporains," in *Pulletin des sciences mathématiques*, 2nd ser., **8** (1884), 315–329, repr. in *Mémoires scientifiques*, II (Toulouse–Paris, 1912), 118–136.
11. *Archimedis opera omnia*, III, 84.8–11.
12. *Euclidis opera omnia*, J. L. Heiberg and Menge, eds., V (Leipzig, 1888), 50.21–22. See also T. L. Heath, *The Thirteen Books of Euclid's Elements*, 2nd ed., III (Cambridge, 1926), 519–520.
13. J. L. Heiberg, "Philologische Studien zu griechischen Mathematikern II. Ueber die Restitution der zwei Bücher des Archimedis περὶ σφαίρας καὶ κυλίνδρου," in *Neues Jahrbuch für Philologie und Pädagogik*, supp. **11** (1880), 384–385; *Quaestiones Archimedeae* (Copenhagen, 1879), pp. 69–77; *Archimedis opera omnia*, III, xciii. The delight with which Eutocius found an old book which preserved in part Archimedes' beloved Doric dialect—ἐν μέρει δὲ τὴν Ἀρχιμήδει φίλην Δωρίδα γλῶσσαν ἀπέσωζον—shows that there had been a partial loss of Doric forms even before his time.

BIBLIOGRAPHY

I. Original Works. Isidorus edited the commentaries of Eutocius on Archimedes' *On the Sphere and the Cylinder* and *Measurement of the Circle*. These survive—with subsequent editorial changes—and are in *Archimedis opera omnia*, J. L. Heiberg, ed., 2nd ed., III (Leipzig, 1915). A commentary which Isidorus wrote on an otherwise unknown book by Hero, *On Vaultings*, has not survived.

II. Secondary Literature. The chief ancient authorities for the architectural work of Isidorus are Procopius, *De aedificiis*, in *Opera omnia*, Haury, ed., IV (Leipzig, 1954); Paul the Silentiary, *Description of the Church of the Holy Wisdom*, Bekker, ed., *Corpus scriptorum historiae Byzantinae*, XL (Bonn, 1837); and Agathias Scholasticus, *Historiae*, R. Keydell, ed. (Berlin, 1967). One of the best modern books is W. R. Lethaby and Harold Swainson, *The Church of Sancta Sophia Constantinople* (London, 1894). A more recent monograph is E. H. Swift, *Hagia Sophia* (New York, 1940). There are good shorter accounts in Cecil Stewart, *Simpson's History of Architectural Development*, II (London, 1954), 66–72; and Michael Maclagan, *The City of Constantinople* (London, 1968), pp. 52–62.

For Isidorus' contribution to the study of the five regular solids, see T. L. Heath, *The Thirteen Books of Euclid's Elements*, 2nd ed. (Cambridge, 1926; repr. New York, 1956), III, 519–520.

Ivor Bulmer-Thomas

IVORY, JAMES (*b.* Dundee, Scotland, 17 February 1765; *d.* London, England, 21 September 1842)

The son of James Ivory, a watchmaker, Ivory was educated at the universities of St. Andrews (1779–1785) and Edinburgh (1785–1786). After taking the M.A. degree (1783) he studied theology, with a view to entering the Church of Scotland. His studies in divinity were not pursued further, for immediately on leaving the university he was appointed teacher of mathematics and natural philosophy in Dundee. After three years he became the manager of a flax-spinning company in Forfarshire (now Angus). In 1804 the company was dissolved, and Ivory took up a mathematical professorship at the Royal Military College at Great Marlow (subsequently at Sandhurst). He held this office until 1819, when ill health compelled an early retirement. During the remainder of his life Ivory lived in London, devoting himself entirely to mathematical investigations, the results of which he made available in a long series of articles published in scientific journals. Sixteen of his papers were printed in the *Philosophical Transactions of the Royal Society* (he was elected a fellow of the Society in 1815). He was awarded the Copley Medal in 1814 and received the Royal Medal in 1826 and 1839.

Ivory's interests lay mainly in the application of mathematics to physical problems, and his principal contributions may be summarized under six categories.

1. The attraction of homogeneous ellipsoids upon points situated within or outside them. His paper "On the Attractions of Homogeneous Ellipsoids," containing the well-known theorem which bears his name, in which the attraction of an ellipsoid upon a point exterior to it is made to depend upon the attraction of another ellipsoid upon a point interior to it, was printed in the *Philosophical Transactions* for 1809 (pp. 345–372). Although Laplace had already reduced this problem to a similar form, Ivory's solution was regarded as simpler and more elegant.

2. Critical commentaries on the methods used by Laplace in the third book of the *Mécanique céleste* for computing the attraction of spheroids differing little from spheres and the substitution of analytical methods for some of Laplace's geometrical considerations (1812, 1822). Although some of Ivory's criticisms seem to have been unjustified, Laplace himself paid tribute to Ivory's work.

3. The investigation of the orbits of comets (1814).

4. Atmospheric refraction (1823, 1838).

5. The equilibrium of fluid bodies (1824, 1831, 1834, 1839).

6. The equilibrium of a homogeneous ellipsoid with three unequal axes rotating about one of its axes, based on a theorem of Jacobi and Liouville (1838).

Ivory's scientific reputation, for which he was accorded many honors during his lifetime, including knighthood of the Order of the Guelphs, Civil Division (1831), was founded on the ability to understand and comment on the work of the French analysts rather than on any great originality of his own. At a time when few in England were capable of understanding the work of Laplace, Ivory not only grasped its significance but also showed himself capable, in many cases, of substituting a clearer and more direct process for the original. Ivory's work, conducted with great industry over a long period, helped to foster in England a new interest in the application of analysis to physical problems.

BIBLIOGRAPHY

A list of ninety papers published by Ivory is in the Royal Society, *Catalogue of Scientific Papers*, III, 502–505. These include brief notes, comments and corrections, correspondence from the *Philosophical Magazine* (1821–1828), and his most important papers in the *Philosophical Transactions of the Royal Society*.

Biographical notices include R. E. Anderson in *Dictionary of National Biography*, XXIX, 82–83; and W. Norrie in *Dundee Celebrities* (Dundee, 1878), pp. 70–73. An informed critique of Ivory's work is in *Proceedings of the Royal Society*, n.s. **55** (1842), 406–513. Isaac Todhunter discusses Ivory's contribution to the theory of attraction in *A History of the Mathematical Theories of Attraction and the Figure of the Earth*, 2 vols. (London, 1873), II, 221–224, and *passim*.

MARGARET E. BARON

JĀBIR IBN AFLAḤ AL-ISHBĪLĪ, ABŪ MUḤAMMAD (*fl.* Seville, first half of the twelfth century)

Usually known in the West by the Latinized name Geber, Jābir has often been confused with the alchemist Jābir ibn Ḥayyān and occasionally with the astronomer Muḥammad ibn Jābir al-Battānī. He should also be distinguished from Abū Aflaḥ ha-Saraqosṭī, the author of the mystical *Book of the Palm*, and from the Baghdad poet Abu'l Qāsim ʿAlī ibn Aflaḥ. Almost nothing is known of Jābir ibn Aflaḥ's life. He can be roughly dated by Maimonides' citation in his *Guide of the Perplexed:* ". . . Ibn Aflaḥ of Seville, whose son I have met . . . ."[1] That he came from Seville is deduced from the name "al-Ishbīlī" in manuscripts of his works and in the above quotation from Maimonides.

Jābir's most important work was a reworking of Ptolemy's *Almagest* in nine books. Its title in one Arabic manuscript (Berlin 5653) is *Iṣlāḥ al-Majisṭī* ("Correction of the *Almagest*"), but it had no fixed title in the West—Albertus Magnus calls it *Flores*, presumably short for *Flores Almagesti*, in his *Speculum astronomiae*.[2] According to the contemporary historian Ibn al-Qifṭī,[3] the text was revised by Maimonides and his pupil Joseph ibn ʿAqnīn. This revision seems to have been done about 1185, and so it was almost certainly from the unrevised text that Gerard of Cremona made his Latin translation. The *Iṣlāḥ* was translated from Arabic into Hebrew by Moses ibn Tibbon in 1274 and again by his nephew Jacob ben Māḥir; the latter translation was revised by Samuel ben Judah of Marseilles in 1335.

Jābir describes the principal differences between the *Iṣlāḥ* and the *Almagest* in the prologue: Menelaus' theorem is everywhere replaced by theorems on right spherical triangles, so that a proportion of four quantities is substituted for one of six; further, Jābir does not present his theorems in the form of numerical examples, as Ptolemy did. So far the changes seem to be the same as those made by Abu'l Wafā', but Jābir's spherical trigonometry is less elaborate. It occupies theorems 12–15 of book

I and follows a theorem giving criteria for the sides of a spherical triangle to be greater or less than a quadrant (so that the sides may be known from their sines). In modern notation it may be summarized as follows:

Theorem 12. If all the lines in the figure are arcs of great circles, then

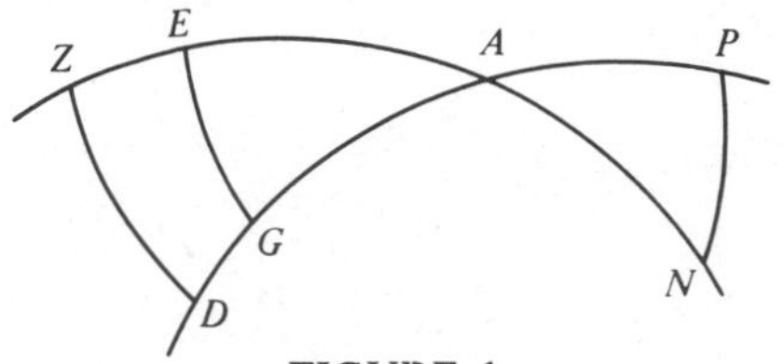

FIGURE 1

$$\text{Sin } AG\text{:Sin } GE = \text{Sin } AD\text{:Sin } DZ$$
$$= \text{Sin } AN\text{:Sin } NP.$$

Theorem 13. In any spherical triangle ABG, Sin BG:Sin $\hat{A}$ = Sin GA:Sin $\hat{B}$ = Sin AB:Sin $\hat{G}$.

Theorem 14. If in spherical triangle ABG, $\hat{B}$ is right, then Sin $\hat{A}$:Sin $\hat{B}$ = Cos $\hat{G}$:Cos AB.

Theorem 15. If in spherical triangle ABG, $\hat{B}$ is right, then Cos AG:Cos BG = Cos AB:Sin (quadrant).

Theorems 13 and 15 are the most frequently used. Because of the differences in treatment it is unreasonable to suppose that Jābir copied directly from Abu'l Wafā', whose writings have survived. They may both have derived their fundamental theorems from Thābit ibn Qurra's tract on Menelaus' theorem, or all three may depend upon some source that in turn depends upon the third book of Menelaus' *Spherics*. As a trigonometer Jābir is important only because he was translated into Latin, whereas works such as Abu'l Wafā''s—which carried an equivalent, or a better, trigonometry—were not.

Jābir criticized Ptolemy—sometimes very violently—on a number of astronomical matters. Ptolemy's "errors" are listed in the prologue of the *Iṣlāḥ*. The most substantial, and most famous, deviation from the *Almagest* concerns Venus and Mercury. Ptolemy placed them beneath the sun, claiming that they were never actually on the line joining the eye of the observer and the sun. Jābir contradicted this justification, putting Venus and Mercury above the sun. The *Iṣlāḥ* is the work of a theorist. The demonstrations are free of all numbers and there are no tables. Jābir does, however, describe a torquetum-like instrument, which he says replaces all the instruments of the *Almagest*.

Although Jābir was quoted in the twelfth century by al-Biṭrūjī and by the author of the compendium of the *Almagest* ascribed to Ibn Rushd, and although the *Iṣlāḥ* was epitomized by Quṭb al-Dīn al-Shīrāzī in the thirteenth century, Jābir was better known in the West through Gerard of Cremona's translation. His name was used as that of an authority who criticized Ptolemy. But more serious was his influence on Western trigonometry. For instance, Richard of Wallingford cited him several times in the *Albion* and in the *De sectore* (a variant of the *Quadripartitum*); Simon Bredon took a great deal from Jābir in his commentary on the *Almagest;* and part of a commentary on the *Iṣlāḥ* in which Jābir's theorems are made more general is extant. But his most important influence was upon Regiomontanus' *De triangulis,* written in the early 1460's and printed in 1533, which systematized trigonometry for the Latin West. The core of the fourth book of this treatise is taken from Jābir without acknowledgment; the plagiarism was the subject of several pungent remarks by Cardano. Jābir was still quoted in the sixteenth and seventeenth centuries—for instance, by Sir Henry Savile and Pedro Nuñez. Copernicus' spherical trigonometry is of the same general type, but we have no reason to believe it was taken straight from the *Iṣlāḥ*. He called Jābir an "egregious calumniator of Ptolemy."

NOTES

1. Pt. II, ch. 9. See *The Guide of the Perplexed*, Schlomo Pines, trans. (Chicago, 1963), p. 268.
2. See Erfurt, Wissenschaftliche Bibliothek, MS Q223, fols. 106r–106v, and other MSS. The 1891 ed. is somewhat corrupt at this point.
3. *Ta'rīkh al-ḥukamā'*, J. Lippert, ed. (Leipzig, 1903), pp. 319, 392–393. The text is the abridgment by Muḥammad ibn 'Alī al-Zawzānī (1249); the original is lost.

BIBLIOGRAPHY

I. Original Works. *Iṣlāḥ al-Majisṭī* is in the following Arabic MSS: Berlin 5653; Escorial 910 and 930; Paris, B.N. héb. 1102 (fragment of bk. V in Arabic but in Hebrew script). Hebrew MSS are Moses ibn Tibbon, trans., Bodleian Opp. Add. fol. 17 (Neubauer 2011); and Jacob ben Māḥir, trans., rev. by Samuel ben Judah, Paris, B.N. héb. 1014, 1024, 1025, 1036. At the end of the text Samuel describes the circumstances of the translation. This passage is transcribed by Renan with a French paraphrase in "Les écrivains juifs français," in *Histoire littéraire*, **31** (Paris, 1893), 560–563.

There are some 20 Latin MSS plus five fragments; the text was published by Peter Apian (Nuremberg, 1534) together with his *Instrumentum primi mobilis*. There is a description of a different but similar instrument in the Latin version, but the original diagrams remain. Jacob ben Māḥir describes both instruments.

The commentary on Thābit ibn Qurra's tract on Menelaus' theorem and the commentary on Menelaus'

Spherics (fragment) occur together and are extant only in Hebrew. MSS are Bodleian Hunt. 96 (Neubauer 2008), fols. 40v–42v, and Bodleian Heb. d.4 (Neubauer 2773), fols. 165r–177v. Berlin Q 747 (Steinschneider catalog no. 204) contains part of this text.

The anonymous Latin commentary on the *Iṣlāḥ* is in Paris, B.N. Lat. 7406, fols. 114ra–135rb.

The six-book *Parvum Almagestum*, which exists only in Latin, is almost certainly not by Jābir, as has sometimes been held—see Lorch (below), ch. 3, pt. 1.

II. SECONDARY LITERATURE. See H. Bürger and K. Kohl, "Zur Geschichte des Transversalensatzes des Ersatztheorems, der Regel der vier Grössen und des Tangentensatzes," in *Abhandlungen zur Geschichte der Naturwissenschaften und der Medizin*, 7 (1924), a substantial article following Axel Björnbo's ed. of Thābit ibn Qurra's tract on Menelaus' theorem; J. B. J. Delambre, *Histoire de l'astronomie du moyen âge* (Paris, 1819; repr. 1965), esp. pp. 179–185—Delambre is very hostile to Jābir; and R. P. Lorch, "Jābir ibn Aflaḥ and His Influence in the West" (Manchester, 1970), a Ph.D. thesis concerned mainly with spherical trigonometry.

For further references, see G. Sarton, *Introduction to the History of Science*, II (Washington, D.C., 1931), 206.

R. P. LORCH

JACOBI, CARL GUSTAV JACOB (*b.* Potsdam, Germany, 10 December 1804; *d.* Berlin, Germany, 18 February 1851)

The second son of Simon Jacobi, a Jewish banker, the precocious boy (originally called Jacques Simon) grew up in a wealthy and cultured family. His brother Moritz, three years older, later gained fame as a physicist in St. Petersburg. His younger brother, Eduard, carried on the banking business after his father's death. He also had a sister, Therese.

After being educated by his mother's brother, Jacobi entered the Gymnasium at Potsdam in November 1816. Promoted to the first (highest) class after a few months in spite of his youth, he had to remain there for four years because he could not enter the university until he was sixteen. When he graduated from the Gymnasium in the spring of 1821, he excelled in Greek, Latin, and history and had acquired a knowledge of mathematics far beyond that provided by the school curriculum. He had studied Euler's *Introductio in analysin infinitorum* and had attempted to solve the general fifth-degree algebraic equation.

During his first two years at the University of Berlin, Jacobi divided his interests among philosophical, classical, and mathematical studies. Seeing that time would not permit him to follow all his interests, he decided to concentrate on mathematics. University lectures in mathematics at that time were at a very elementary level in Germany, and Jacobi therefore in private study mastered the works of Euler, Lagrange, and other leading mathematicians. (Dirichlet, at the same time, had gone to Paris, where Biot, Fourier, Laplace, Legendre, and Poisson were active. Apart from the isolated Gauss at Göttingen, there was no equal center of mathematical activity in Germany.)

In the fall of 1824 Jacobi passed his preliminary examination for *Oberlehrer*, thereby acquiring permission to teach not only mathematics but also Greek and Latin to all high school grades, and ancient and modern history to junior high school students. When—in spite of being of Jewish descent—he was offered a position at the prestigious Joachimsthalsche Gymnasium in Berlin in the following summer, he had already submitted a Ph.D. thesis to the university. The board of examiners included the mathematician E. H. Dirksen and the philosopher Friedrich Hegel. Upon application he was given permission to begin work on the *Habilitation* immediately. Having become a Christian, he was thus able to begin a university career as *Privatdozent* at the University of Berlin at the age of twenty.

Jacobi's first lecture, given during the winter term 1825–1826, was devoted to the analytic theory of curves and surfaces in three-dimensional space. He greatly impressed his audience by the liveliness and clarity of his delivery, and his success became known to the Prussian ministry of education. There being no prospect for a promotion at Berlin in the near future, it was suggested that Jacobi transfer to the University of Königsberg, where a salaried position might be available sooner. When he arrived there in May 1826, the physicists Franz Neumann and Heinrich Dove were just starting their academic careers, and Friedrich Bessel, then in his early forties, occupied the chair of astronomy. Joining these colleagues, Jacobi soon became interested in applied problems. His first publications attracted wide attention among mathematicians. On 28 December 1827 he was appointed associate professor, a promotion in which Legendre's praise of his early work on elliptic functions had had a share. Appointment as full professor followed on 7 July 1832, after a four-hour disputation in Latin. Several months earlier, on 11 September 1831, Jacobi had married Marie Schwinck, the daughter of a formerly wealthy *Kommerzienrat* who had lost his fortune in speculative transactions. They had five sons and three daughters.

For eighteen years Jacobi was at the University of Königsberg, where his tireless activity produced amazing results in both research and academic instruction. Jacobi created a sensation among the mathematical world with his penetrating investigations into the theory of elliptic functions, carried out in competition with Abel. Most of Jacobi's fundamental research articles in the theory of elliptic functions, mathematical analysis, number theory, geometry, and mechanics were published in Crelle's *Journal für die reine und angewandte Mathematik*. With an average of three articles per volume, Jacobi was one of its most active contributors and quickly helped to establish its international fame. Yet his tireless occupation with research did not impair his teaching. On the contrary—never satisfied to lecture along trodden paths, Jacobi presented the substance of his own investigations to his students. He would lecture up to eight or ten hours a week on his favorite subject, the theory of elliptic functions, thus demanding the utmost from his listeners. He also inaugurated what was then a complete novelty in mathematics—research seminars—assembling the more advanced students and attracting his nearest colleagues.

Such were Jacobi's forceful personality and sweeping enthusiasm that none of his gifted students could escape his spell: they were drawn into his sphere of thought, worked along the manifold lines he suggested, and soon represented a "school." C. W. Borchardt, E. Heine, L. O. Hesse, F. J. Richelot, J. Rosenhain, and P. L. von Seidel belonged to this circle; they contributed much to the dissemination not only of Jacobi's mathematical creations but also of the new research-oriented attitude in university instruction. The triad of Bessel, Jacobi, and Neumann thus became the nucleus of a revival of mathematics at German universities.

In the summer of 1829 Jacobi journeyed to Paris, visiting Gauss in Göttingen on his way and becoming acquainted with Legendre (with whom he had already been in correspondence), Fourier, Poisson, and other eminent French mathematicians. In July 1842 Bessel and Jacobi, accompanied by Marie Jacobi, were sent by the king of Prussia to the annual meeting of the British Association for the Advancement of Science in Manchester, where they represented their country splendidly. They returned via Paris, where Jacobi gave a lecture before the Academy of Sciences.

Early in 1843 Jacobi became seriously ill with diabetes. Dirichlet, after he had visited Jacobi for a fortnight in April, procured a donation (through the assistance of Alexander von Humboldt) from Friedrich Wilhelm IV, which enabled Jacobi to spend some months in Italy, as his doctor had advised. Together with Borchardt and Dirichlet and the latter's wife, he traveled in a leisurely manner to Italy, lectured at the science meeting in Lucca (but noticed that none of the Italian mathematicians had really studied his papers), and arrived in Rome on 16 November 1843. In the stimulating company of these friends and of the mathematicians L. Schläfli and J. Steiner, who also lived in Rome at that time, and further blessed by the favorable climate, Jacobi's health improved considerably. He started to compare manuscripts of Diophantus' *Arithmetica* in the Vatican Library and began to resume publishing mathematical articles. By the end of June 1844 he had returned to Berlin. He was granted royal permission to move there with his family because the severe climate of Königsberg would endanger his health. Jacobi received a bonus on his salary to help offset the higher costs in the capital and to help with his medical expenses. As a member of the Prussian Academy of Sciences, he was entitled, but not obliged, to lecture at the University of Berlin. Because of his poor health, however, he lectured on only a very limited scale.

In the revolutionary year of 1848 Jacobi became involved in a political discussion in the Constitutional Club. During an impromptu speech he made some imprudent remarks which brought him under fire from monarchists and republicans alike. Hardly two years before, in the dedication of volume I of his *Opuscula mathematica* to Friedrich Wilhelm IV, he had expressed his royalist attitude; now he had become an object of suspicion to the government. A petition of Jacobi's to become officially associated with the University of Berlin, and thus to obtain a secure status, was denied by the ministry of education. Moreover, in June 1849 the bonus on his salary was retracted. Jacobi, who had lost his inherited fortune in a bankruptcy years before, had to give up his Berlin home. He moved into an inn and his wife and children took up residence in the small town of Gotha, where life was considerably less expensive.

Toward the end of 1849 Jacobi was offered a professorship in Vienna. Only after he had accepted it did the Prussian government realize the severe blow to its reputation which would result from his departure. Special concessions from the ministry and his desire to stay in his native country finally led Jacobi to reverse his decision. His family, however, was to remain at Gotha for another year, until the eldest son graduated from the Gymnasium. Jacobi, who lectured on number theory in the summer term of 1850, joined his family during vacations and worked on an astronomical paper with his friend P. A. Hansen.

Early in 1851, after another visit to his family, Jacobi contracted influenza. Hardly recovered, he fell ill with smallpox and died within a week. His close friend Dirichlet delivered the memorial lecture at the Berlin Academy on 1 July 1852, calling Jacobi the greatest mathematician among the members of the Academy since Lagrange and summarizing his eminent mathematical contributions.

The outburst of Jacobi's creativity at the very beginning of his career, combined with his self-conscious attitude, early caused him to seek contacts with some of the foremost mathematicians of his time. A few months after his arrival at Königsberg he informed Gauss about some of his discoveries in number theory, particularly on cubic residues, on which he published a first paper in 1827. Jacobi had been inspired by Gauss's *Disquisitiones arithmeticae* and by a note on the results which Gauss had recently presented to the Göttingen Academy, concerning biquadratic residues. Obviously impressed, Gauss asked Bessel for information on the young mathematician and enclosed a letter for Jacobi, now lost—as are all subsequent letters from Gauss to Jacobi. No regular correspondence developed from this beginning.

Another contact, established by a letter from Jacobi on 5 August 1827, initiated an important regular mathematical correspondence with Legendre that did not cease until Legendre's death. Its topic was the theory of elliptic functions, of which Legendre had been the great master until Abel and Jacobi came on the scene. Their first publications in this subject appeared in September 1827—Abel's fundamental memoir "Recherches sur les fonctions elliptiques" in Crelle's *Journal* (**2**, no. 2) and Jacobi's "Extraits de deux lettres . . ." in *Astronomische Nachrichten* (**6**, no. 123). From these articles it is clear that both authors were in possession of essential elements of the new theory. They had developed these independently: Abel's starting point was the multiplication, Jacobi's the transformation, of elliptic functions; both of them were familiar with Legendre's work.

The older theory centered on the investigation of elliptic integrals, that is, integrals of the type $\int R(x, \sqrt{f(x)})\,dx$, where R is a rational function and $f(x)$ is an integral function of the third or fourth degree. Examples of such integrals had been studied by John Wallis, Jakob I and Johann I Bernoulli, and in particular G. C. Fagnano. Euler continued this work by investigating the arc length of a lemniscate, $\int \frac{dx}{\sqrt{1-x^4}}$; by integrating the differential equation

$$\frac{dx}{\sqrt{1-x^4}} + \frac{dy}{\sqrt{1-y^4}} = 0$$

he was led to the addition formula for this integral (elliptic integral of the first kind). When he extended these investigations—for example, to the arc length of an ellipse (elliptic integral of the second kind)—he concluded that the sum of any number of elliptic integrals of the same kind (except for algebraic or logarithmic terms, which may have to be added) may be expressed by a single integral of this same kind, of which the upper limit depends algebraically on the upper limits of the elements of the sum. This discovery shows Euler to be a forerunner of Abel.

The systematic study of elliptic integrals and their classification into the first, second, and third kinds was the work of Legendre, who had cultivated this field since 1786. The leading French mathematicians of his day were interested in the application of mathematics to astronomy and physics. Therefore, although Legendre had always emphasized the applicability of his theories (for instance, by computing tables of elliptic integrals), they did not appreciate his work. Gauss, on the other hand, was well aware of the importance of the subject, for he had previously obtained the fundamental results of Abel and Jacobi but had never published his theory. Neither had he given so much as a hint when Legendre failed to exploit the decisive idea of the inverse function.

It was this idea, occurring independently to both Abel and Jacobi, which enabled them to take a big step forward in the difficult field of transcendental functions. Here Abel's investigations were directed toward the most general question; Jacobi possessed an extraordinary talent for handling the most complicated mathematical apparatus. By producing an almost endless stream of formulas concerning elliptic functions, he obtained his insights and drew his conclusions about the character and properties of these functions. He also recognized the relation of this theory to other fields, such as number theory.

When Legendre first learned of the new discoveries of Abel and Jacobi, he showed no sign of envy. On the contrary, he had nothing but praise for them and expressed enthusiasm for their creations. He even reported on Jacobi's first publications (in the *Astronomische Nachrichten*) to the French Academy and wrote to Jacobi on 9 February 1828:

> It gives me a great satisfaction to see two young mathematicians such as you and him [Abel] cultivate with success a branch of analysis which for so long a time has been the object of my favorite studies and which has not been received in my own country as well as it would deserve. By these works you place yourselves in the ranks of the best analysts of our era.

Exactly a year later Legendre wrote in a letter to Jacobi:

> You proceed so rapidly, gentlemen, in all these wonderful speculations that it is nearly impossible to follow you—above all for an old man who has already passed the age at which Euler died, an age in which one has to combat a number of infirmities and in which the spirit is no longer capable of that exertion which can surmount difficulties and adapt itself to new ideas. Nevertheless I congratulate myself that I have lived long enough to witness these magnanimous contests between two young athletes equally strong, who turn their efforts to the profit of the science whose limits they push back further and further.

Jacobi, too, was ready to acknowledge fully the merits of Abel. When Legendre had published the third supplement to his *Traité des fonctions elliptiques et des intégrales eulériennes*, in which he presented the latest developments, it was Jacobi who reviewed it for Crelle's *Journal* (**8**[1832], 413–417):

> Legendre to the transcendental functions $\int \frac{f(x)\,dx}{\sqrt{X}}$, where X exceeds the fourth degree, gives the name "hyperelliptical" [*ultra-elliptiques*]. We wish to call them *Abelsche Transcendenten* (Abelian transcendental functions), for it was Abel who first introduced them into analysis and who first made evident their great importance by his far-reaching theorem. For this theorem, as the most fitting monument to this extraordinary genius, the name "Abelian theorem" would be very appropriate. For we happily agree with the author that it carries the full imprint of the depth of his ideas. Since it enunciates in a simple manner, without the vast setup of mathematical formalism, the deepest and most comprehensive mathematical thought, we consider it to be the greatest mathematical discovery of our time although only future—perhaps distant—hard work will be able to reveal its whole importance.

Jacobi summarized his first two years' research, a good deal of which had been obtained in competition with Abel, in his masterpiece *Fundamenta nova theoriae functionum ellipticarum*, which appeared in April 1829. His previous publications in *Astronomische Nachrichten* and in Crelle's *Journal* were here systematically collected, greatly augmented, and supplemented by proofs—he had previously omitted these, thereby arousing the criticism of Legendre, Gauss, and others.

The *Fundamenta nova* deals in the first part with the transformation, and in the second with the representation, of elliptic functions. Jacobi took as his starting point the general elliptic differential of the first kind and reduced it by a second-degree transformation to the normal form of Legendre. He studied the properties of the functions U (even) and V(odd) in the rational transformation $Y = U/V$ and gave as examples the transformations of the third and fifth degrees and the pertinent modular equations. By combining two transformations he obtained the multiplication of the elliptic integral of the first kind, a remarkable result. He then introduced the inverse function $\varphi = am\, u$ into the elliptic integral

$$u(\varphi, k) = \int_0^\varphi \frac{d\varphi}{\sqrt{1 - k^2 \sin^2 \varphi}};$$

hence

$$x = \sin \varphi = \sin am\, u.$$

Further introducing $\cos am\, u = am\,(K - u)$ $\left(\text{with } K = u\left[\frac{\pi}{2}, k\right]\right)$,

$$\Delta\, am\, u = \sqrt{1 - k^2 \sin^2 am\, u},$$

he collected a large number of formulas. Using the substitution $\sin \varphi = i \tan \psi$, he established the relation

$$\sin am\,(iu,k) = i \tan am\,(u,k');$$

the moduli k and k' are connected by the equation $k^2 + k'^2 = 1$. He thus obtained the double periodicity, the zero values, the infinity values, and the change of value in half a period for the elliptic functions. This introduction of the imaginary into the theory of elliptic functions was another very important step which Jacobi shared with Abel. Among his further results is the demonstration of the invariance of the modular equations when the same transformation is applied to the primary and secondary moduli. Toward the end of the first part of his work Jacobi developed the third-order differential equation which is satisfied by all transformed moduli.

The second part of the *Fundamenta nova* is devoted to the evolution of elliptic functions into infinite products and series of various kinds. The first representation of the elliptic functions $\sin am\, u$, $\cos am\, u$, $\Delta\, am\, u$, which he gave is in the form of quotients of infinite products. Introducing $q = e^{-\frac{\pi K'}{K}}$, Jacobi expressed the modulus and periods in terms of q, as for instance

$$k = 4\sqrt{q}\left\{\frac{(1+q^2)(1+q^4)(1+q^6)\cdots}{(1+q)(1+q^3)(1+q^5)\cdots}\right\}^4.$$

Another representation of the elliptic functions and their nth powers as Fourier series leads to the sums (in terms of the moduli) of various infinite series in q. Integrals of the second kind are treated after the function

$$Z(u) = \frac{F^1E(\varphi) - E^1F(\varphi)}{F^1} \quad (\varphi = am\, u)$$

has been introduced. Jacobi reduced integrals of the third kind to integrals of the first and second kinds and a third transcendental function which also depends on two variables only. In what follows, Jacobi's function

$$\Theta(u) = \Theta(0) \cdot \exp\left(\int_0^u Z(u)\, du\right)$$

played a central role. It is then supplemented by the function $H(u)$ such that $\sin am\, u = \frac{1}{\sqrt{k}} \cdot \frac{H(u)}{\Theta(u)}$. $\Theta(u)$ and $H(u)$ are represented as infinite products and as Fourier series. The latter yield such remarkable formulas as

$$\sqrt{\frac{2kK}{\pi}} = 2\sqrt[4]{q} + 2\sqrt[4]{q^9} + 2\sqrt[4]{q^{25}} + 2\sqrt[4]{q^{49}} + \cdots.$$

After a number of further summations and identities Jacobi closed this work with an application to the theory of numbers. From the identity

$$\left(\frac{2K}{\pi}\right)^2 = (1 + 2q + 2q^4 + 2q^9 + 2q^{16} + \cdots)^4$$
$$= 1 + 8 \sum \varphi(p)(q^p + 3q^{2p} + 3q^{4p} + 3q^{8p} + \cdots),$$

where $\varphi(p)$ is the sum of the divisors of the odd number p, he drew the conclusion that any integer can be represented as the sum of at most four squares, as Fermat had suggested.

Jacobi lectured on the theory of elliptic functions for the first time during the winter term 1829–1830, emphasizing that double periodicity is the essential property of these functions. The theta function should be taken as foundation of the theory; the representation in series with the general term $e^{-(an+b)^2}$ ensures convergence and makes it possible to develop the whole theory. In his ten hours a week of lecturing in the winter of 1835–1836 Jacobi for the first time founded the theory on the theta function, proving the famous theorem about the sum of products of four theta functions and defining the kinds of elliptic functions as quotients of theta functions. He continued this work in his lectures of 1839–1840, the second part of which is published in volume I of his *Gesammelte Werke*. Volume II contains a historical summary, "Zur Geschichte der elliptischen und Abel'schen Transcendenten," composed by Jacobi probably in 1847, which documents his view of his favorite subject toward the end of his life.

Some of Jacobi's discoveries in number theory have already been mentioned. Although he intended to publish his results in book form, he was never able to do so. The theory of residues, the division of the circle into n equal parts, the theory of quadratic forms, the representation of integers as sums of squares or cubes, and related problems were studied by Jacobi. During the winter of 1836–1837 he lectured on number theory, and some of his methods became known through Rosenhain's lecture notes. In 1839 Jacobi's *Canon arithmeticus* on primitive roots was published; for each prime and power of a prime less than 1,000 it gives two companion tables showing the numbers with given indexes and the index of each given number.

Most of Jacobi's work is characterized by linkage of different mathematical disciplines. He introduced elliptic functions not only into number theory but also into the theory of integration, which in turn is connected with the theory of differential equations where, among other things, the principle of the last multiplier is due to Jacobi. Most of his investigations on first-order partial differential equations and analytical mechanics were published posthumously (in 1866, by Clebsch) as *Vorlesungen über Dynamik*. Taking W. R. Hamilton's research on the differential equations of motion (canonical equations) as a starting point, Jacobi also carried on the work of the French school (Lagrange, Poisson, and others). He sought the most general substitutions that would transform canonical differential equations into such equations. The transformations are to be such that a canonical differential equation (of motion) is transformed into another differential equation which is again canonical. He also developed a new theory for the integration of these equations, utilizing their relation to a special Hamiltonian differential equation. This method enabled him to solve several very important problems in mechanics and astronomy. In some special cases Clebsch later improved Jacobi's results, and decades later Helmholtz carried Jacobi's mechanical principles over into physics in general.

Among Jacobi's work in mathematical physics is research on the attraction of ellipsoids and a surprising discovery in the theory of configurations of rotating liquid masses. Maclaurin had shown that a homogeneous liquid mass may be rotated uniformly about a fixed axis without change of shape if this shape is an ellipsoid of revolution. D'Alembert, Laplace, and Lagrange had studied the same problem; but it was left for Jacobi to discover that even an ellipsoid of three different axes may satisfy the conditions of equilibrium.

The theory of determinants, which begins with Leibniz, was presented systematically by Jacobi early in 1841. He introduced the "Jacobian" or functional determinant; a second paper—also published in Crelle's *Journal*—is devoted entirely to its theory, including relations to inverse functions and the transformation of multiple integrals.

Jacobi was also interested in the history of mathematics. In January 1846 he gave a public lecture on Descartes which attracted much attention. In the same year A. von Humboldt asked him for notes on the mathematics of the ancient Greeks as material for his *Kosmos* and Jacobi readily complied—but Humboldt later confessed that some of the material went beyond his limited mathematical knowledge. In the 1840's Jacobi became involved in the planning of an edition of Euler's works. He corresponded with P. H. von Fuss, secretary of the St. Petersburg Academy and great-grandson of the famous mathematician, who had discovered a number of Euler's unpublished papers. Jacobi drew up a very detailed plan of distributing the immense number of publications among the volumes of the projected edition. Unfortunately, the project could be realized only on a much reduced scale. It was not until 1911 that the first volume of *Leonhardi Euleri opera omnia*—still in progress—appeared.

Jacobi's efforts to promote an edition of Euler were prompted by more than the ordinary interest a mathematician might be expected to take in the work of a great predecessor. Jacobi and Euler were kindred spirits in the way they created their mathematics. Both were prolific writers and even more prolific calculators; both drew a good deal of insight from immense algorithmical work; both labored in many fields of mathematics (Euler, in this respect, greatly surpassed Jacobi); and both at any moment could draw from the vast armory of mathematical methods just those weapons which would promise the best results in the attack on a given problem. Yet while Euler divided his energies about equally between pure and applied mathematics, Jacobi was more inclined to investigate mathematical problems for their intrinsic interest. Mathematics, as he understood it, had a strong Platonic ring. For the disputation at his inauguration to a full professorship in 1832 Jacobi had chosen as his first thesis "Mathesis est scientia eorum, quae per se clara sunt."

BIBLIOGRAPHY

I. ORIGINAL WORKS. Jacobi's works have been collected twice. *Opuscula mathematica* is in 3 vols. (Berlin, 1846–1871). Vol. I was edited by Jacobi himself; vol. II, also prepared by him, was published posthumously by Dirichlet; vol. III was published by his pupil C. W. Borchardt.

The standard ed., 7 vols. and supp., was issued by the Prussian Academy of Sciences as *C. G. J. Jacobi's Gesammelte Werke*, C. W. Borchardt, A. Clebsch, and K. Weierstrass, eds. (Berlin, 1881–1891). Vol. I contains, among other works, the *Fundamenta nova theoriae functionum ellipticarum* (Königsberg, 1829). The supp. vol. is *Vorlesungen über Dynamik*, first published by A. Clebsch (Leipzig, 1866). *Gesammelte Werke* has been repr. (New York, 1969).

Jacobi's only other publication in book form, the *Canon arithmeticus* (Berlin, 1839), is not in the *Gesammelte Werke* but appeared in a 2nd ed. recomputed by W. Patz and edited by H. Brandt (Berlin, 1956).

Kurt-R. Biermann has published "Eine unveröffentlichte Jugendarbeit C. G. J. Jacobis über wiederholte Funktionen," in *Journal für die reine und angewandte Mathematik*, **207** (1961), 96–112.

A list of Jacobi's publications and of his lectures is in *Gesammelte Werke*, VII, 421–440. See also Poggendorff, I, 1178–1181, 1576; III, 681; IV, 688; VIIa, Supp. 302–303.

Brief information on 16 vols. of manuscript material, in the archives of the Deutsche Akademie der Wissenschaften in Berlin, is in *Gelehrten- und Schriftstellernachlässe in den Bibliotheken der DDR*, I (Berlin, 1959), 50, no. 315, "Jakobi" [*sic*].

II. SECONDARY LITERATURE. The main secondary sources are J. P. G. Lejeune Dirichlet, "Gedächtnisrede" (1852), repr. in *Gesammelte Werke*, I; and Leo Koenigsberger, *Carl Gustav Jacob Jacobi. Festschrift zur Feier der hundertsten Wiederkehr seines Geburtstages* (Leipzig, 1904); and *Carl Gustav Jacob Jacobi. Rede zu der von dem Internationalen Mathematiker-Kongress in Heidelberg veranstalteten Feier der hundertsten Wiederkehr seines Geburtstages, gehalten am 9. August 1904* (Leipzig, 1904), also in *Jahresbericht der Deutschen Mathematikervereinigung*, **13** (1904), 405–433. For further secondary literature see Poggendorff, esp. VIIa Supp.

CHRISTOPH J. SCRIBA

JAGANNĀTHA (*fl.* India, *ca.* 1720–1740)

According to legend, Jagannātha Samrāṭ was discovered by Jayasiṃha of Amber during a campaign against the Marāṭha chief Śivājī in 1664–1665; Jagannātha was then supposed to be twenty years old. Unfortunately for the story, it was Jayasiṃha I, known as Mirjā, who was involved with Śivājī; the patron of Jagannātha was Jayasiṃha II, known as Savāī, who ruled Amber from 1699 to 1743. For Jayasiṃha II, Jagannātha translated Euclid's *Elements* and Ptolemy's *Syntaxis Mathēmatikē* (both in the recensions of Naṣīr al-Dīn al-Ṭūsī) from Arabic into Sanskrit as a part of Jayasiṃha's program to revitalize Indian astronomy and Indian culture in general.

Jagannātha translated Euclid's *Elements* under the

title *Rekhāgaṇita* shortly before 1727, the date of the earliest manuscript copied at his command by Lokamaṇi. He translated Ptolemy's *Syntaxis Mathēmatikē* in 1732 under the title *Siddhāntasamrāṭ*. This contains not only a translation of al-Ṭūsī's Arabic recension but also notes of his own referring to Ulugh Beg and al-Kāshī of Samarkand as well as to Muḥammad Shāh, the Mogul emperor to whom Jayasiṃha dedicated his *Zīj-i-jadīd-i Muḥammad-Shāhī* in 1728; these additions closely link Jagannātha's translation with the work of the other astronomers assembled by Jayasiṃha. (See essays on Indian science in Supplement.)

BIBLIOGRAPHY

The *Rekhāgaṇita* was edited by H. H. Dhruva and K. P. Trivedi as Bombay Sanskrit series no. 61–62, 2 vols. (Bombay, 1901–1902); the *Siddhāntasamrāṭ* was edited by Rāmasvarūpa Śarman, 3 vols. (New Delhi, 1967–1969).

Secondary literature includes Sudhākara Dvivedin, *Gaṇakataraṅginī* (Benares, 1933), repr. from *Pandit*, n.s. **14** (1892), 102–110; and L. J. Rocher, "Euclid's Stoicheia and Jagannātha's Rekhāgaṇita," in *Journal of the Oriental Institute, Baroda*, **3** (1953–1954), 236–256.

DAVID PINGREE

JANISZEWSKI, ZYGMUNT (*b.* Warsaw, Poland, 12 June 1888; *d.* Lvov, Poland [now U.S.S.R.], 3 January 1920)

Janiszewski founded, with Stefan Mazurkiewicz and Wacław Sierpiński, the contemporary Polish school of mathematics and its well-known organ *Fundamenta mathematicae*, devoted to set theory and allied fields (topology, foundations of mathematics, and other areas).

Janiszewski's father Czesław, a licentiate of the University of Warsaw and a financier by profession, was director of the Société du Crédit Municipal in Warsaw; his mother was Julia Szulc-Chojnicka. He completed his secondary education in his native city in 1907 and immediately began studying mathematics at Zurich. There, along with several of his colleagues, including Stefan Straszewicz, he organized a group of Polish students. He continued his studies in Munich, Göttingen, and Paris. Among his professors were the mathematicians Burkhardt, H. K. Brunn, Hilbert, H. Minkowski, Zermelo, Goursat, Hadamard, Lebesgue, Picard, and Poincaré, and the philosophers Foerster, Bergson, and Durkheim.

Janiszewski received a doctorate from the Sorbonne in 1911 for his thesis on a topic proposed by Lebesgue. The bold notions that he introduced in it and the results it contained became an important part of set theory (see, for example, F. Hausdorff, *Mengenlehre*, 2nd ed. [Berlin–Leipzig, 1927]). Beginning in the same year he taught mathematics at the Société des Cours des Sciences, which had replaced the Polish university in Warsaw, banned by the czarist regime. In 1913 he obtained the *agrégation* in mathematics from the University of Lvov, where until World War I he lectured on the theory of analytic functions and functional calculus.

At the outbreak of the war Janiszewski enlisted in the legion fighting for Polish independence. A soldier in the artillery, he participated in the costly winter campaign (1914–1915) in the Carpathians. A year later, refusing with a substantial part of the legion to swear allegiance to the Central Powers, he took refuge under the pseudonym of Zygmunt Wicherkiewicz at Boiska, near Zwoleń, and at Ewin, near Włoszczowa. At Ewin he directed a refuge for homeless children, which he founded and supported. In 1918, when the University of Warsaw, which had again become Polish, offered him a chair in mathematics, he began to engage in notable scientific, teaching, and editorial activities. But these were suddenly cut short by his death two years later at Lvov, following a brief illness.

For Janiszewski teaching was a mission and the student a comrade, and his attitude was shared by the other mathematicians of the Polish school. In order to better prepare his courses, he took up residence in a small isolated house in Klarysew, near Warsaw. By applying mathematical logic, he wished methodically to unmask the defects and confusions in the structure of fundamental mathematical concepts. His first research works (1910–1912) dealt with the concepts of arc, curve, and surface, which had not yet been defined precisely. In 1912, in a communication to the International Congress of Mathematicians in Cambridge, England, he sketched the first construction of a curve without arcs (that is, without homeomorphic images of the segment of a straight line).

Three topological theorems are especially associated with his name:

1. If a continuum C has points in common with a set E and with the complement of this set, then each component of the set $C \cdot \bar{E}$ (where $\bar{}$ designates closure) has points in common with the boundary $Fr(E)$.

2. If a continuum is irreducible between two points and does not contain subcontinua which are nondense on it, then it is an arc. This intrinsic topological characterization of the notion of arc is due to Janiszewski.

3. In order that the sum of two continua, neither

of which is a cut of the plane which contains them, be a cut of this plane, it is necessary and sufficient that their common part is not connected (that is, that it has more than one component). This theorem abridged and simplified considerably the demonstration of the Jordan curve theorem. Moreover, it constitutes the most essential part of the topological characterization of the plane—a success all the more remarkable because the problem of a topological characterization of Euclidean spaces of more than two dimensions still remains unsolved.

When Poland became independent in 1918, the Committee of the Mianowski Foundation in Warsaw, an important social institution patronizing scientific research, invited Polish scientists to give their views on the needs of the various disciplines in Poland. In his article in *Nauka polska*, the organization's yearbook, Janiszewski advocated the concentration of mathematical research in a special institution (now the Institute of Mathematics of the Polish Academy of Sciences) and the foundation of a periodical devoted solely to a single branch of mathematics having in Poland sufficiently numerous and capable practitioners; the latter criterion would assure its value and worldwide importance and, at the same time, create a favorable mathematical climate for youth. Such was the origin of *Fundamenta mathematicae*.

Through a series of articles on philosophy and the various branches of mathematics in volume I of *Poradnik dla samouków* ("Adviser for Autodidacts"), of which he was the principal author, Janiszewski exerted an enormous influence on the development of mathematics in Poland. He was aware of social problems. As a student in Paris he had been strongly influenced by Marc Sangnier, founder of the "Sillon" group, a Christian-democrat movement, and author of *Vie profonde*. Thus when chevrons were initiated in the Polish Legion, Janiszewski refused to accept this distinction for himself, contending that it introduced inequality. He donated for public education all the money he received for scientific prizes and an inheritance from his father. Before he died he willed his possessions for social works, his body for medical research, and his cranium for craniological study, desiring even to be "useful after his death."

BIBLIOGRAPHY

I. Original Works. Janiszewski's works include "Contribution à la géométrie des courbes planes générales," in *Comptes rendus hebdomadaires des séances de l'Académie des sciences*, **150** (1910), 606–609; "Sur la géométrie des lignes cantoriennes," *ibid.*, **151** (1910), 198–201; "Nowy kierunek w geometryi," in *Wiadomości matematyczne*, **14** (1910), 57–64; *Sur les continus irréductibles entre deux points* (Paris, 1911), also in *Journal de l'École polytechnique*, **16** (1912), 79–170, and *Comptes rendus hebdomadaires des séances de l'Académie des sciences*, **152** (1911), 752–755, his thesis; "Über die Begriffe 'Linie' und 'Fläche,'" in *Proceedings. International Congress of Mathematicians* (Cambridge, 1912), pp. 1–3; "Démonstration d'une propriété des continus irréductibles entre deux points," in *Bulletin de l'Académie des sciences de Cracovie* (Cracow, 1912), pp. 906–914; and "Sur les coupures du plan faites par des continus," in *Prace matematyczno-fizyczne*, **26** (1913), in Polish with French summary.

Among his articles in *Poradnik dla samouków*, I (Warsaw, 1915), are "Wstep ogólny" ("General Introduction"), 3–27; "Topologia," 387–401; and "Zakończenie" ("Conclusion"), 538–543. These have also been published, with French trans., in Janiszewski's *Oeuvres choisies* (Warsaw, 1962). See also "O realizmie i idealizmie w matematyce," in *Przegląd filozoficzny*, **19** (1916), 161–170; and "Sur les continus indécomposables," in *Fundamenta mathematicae*, **1** (1920), 210–222, written with C. Kuratowski.

II. Secondary Literature. For information on Janiszewski, see S. Dickstein, "Przemówienie ku uczczeniu Zygmunta Janiszewskiego," in *Wiadomości matematyczne*, **25** (1921), 91–98, with portrait; B. Knaster, "Zygmunt Janiszewski," *ibid.*, **74** (1960), 1–9, with portrait and bibliography; K. Kuratowski, "10 lat Instytutu Matematycznego," in *Nauka polska*, **7**, no. 3 (1959), 29–48, English trans. in *Review of the Polish Academy of Sciences*, **4**, no. 3 (1959), 16–32; H. Lebesgue, "À propos d'une nouvelle revue mathématique: *Fundamenta Mathematicae*," in *Bulletin des sciences mathématiques*, 2nd ser., **46** (1921), 1–3; and E. Marczewski, *Rozwój matematyki w Polsce*, Historia Nauki Polskiej, I (Cracow, 1948), 18–21, 33–34, 40; "Uwagi o środowisku naukowyn" ("Remarks on the Scientific Milieu"), in *Życie nauki*, no. 4 (1951), 352–370, Czech trans. in *Časopis pro pěstování matematiky a fysiky*, **78** (1953), 31–45; and "Zygmunt Janiszewski," in *Polski Słownik Biograficzny*, X (Warsaw, 1962–1964), 527–530.

See also obituaries by J. Ryglówna, "Dr. Zygmunt Janiszewski," in *Dziennik Ludowy*, no. 7 (1920); W. Sierpiński, "Śp. profesor Zygmunt Janiszewski," in *Kurier warszawski* (7 Jan. 1920); H. Steinhaus, "Wspomnienie pośmiertne o Zygmuncie Janiszewskim," in *Przegląd filozoficzny*, **22** (1920), 113–117, and obituary in *Fundamenta mathematicae*, **1** (1920), p. v, with list of nine works and portrait, repr. (1937), with preface, pp. iv–vi; and J. D. Tamarkin, "Twenty-five Volumes of *Fundamenta Mathematicae*," in *Bulletin of the American Mathematical Society*, **42** (1936), 300.

B. Knaster

AL-JAWHARĪ, AL-ʿABBĀS IBN SAʿĪD (*fl.* Baghdad *ca.* 830).

Al-Jawharī was one of the astronomers in the service of the ʿAbbāsid Caliph al-Maʾmūn (813–833). He participated in the astronomical observations which took place in Baghdad in 829–830 and in those which took place in Damascus in 832–833. Ibn al-Qifṭī (*d.* 1248) describes him as an expert in the art of *tasyīr* (ἄφεσις, "prorogation"), the complex astrological theory concerned with determining the length of life of individuals (Ptolemy, *Tetrabiblos* III, 10), and adds that he was in charge of (*qayyim ʿlā*) the construction of astronomical instruments. According to Ibn al-Nadīm (*fl.* 987), he worked mostly (*al-ghālib ʿalayh*) in geometry.

Ibn al-Nadīm lists two works by al-Jawharī: *Kitāb Tafsīr Kitāb Uqlīdis* ("A Commentary on Euclid's Elements") and *Kitāb al-Ashkāl allatī zādahā fi 'l-maqāla 'l-ūlā min Uqlīdis* ("Propositions Added to Book I of Euclid's Elements"). To this list Ibn al-Qifṭī adds *Kitāb al-Zīj* ("A Book of Astronomical Tables"), which, he says, was well known among astronomers, being based on the observations made in Baghdad. None of these works has survived.

Naṣīr al-Dīn al-Ṭūsī (*d.* 1274), in his work devoted to Euclid's theory of parallels, *al-Risāla 'l-shāfiya ʿan al-shakk fi 'l-khuṭūṭ al-mutawāziya*, ascribes to al-Jawharī an "Emendation of the Elements" (*Iṣlāḥ li-Kitāb al-Uṣūl*), which may be identical with the "Commentary" (*Tafsīr*) mentioned by Ibn al-Nadīm and Ibn al-Qifṭī. According to al-Ṭūsī, this work included additions by al-Jawharī to the premises and the theorems of the *Elements*, the added theorems totaling "nearly fifty propositions." From among these al-Ṭūsī quotes six propositions constituting al-Jawharī's attempt to prove Euclid's parallels postulate.

Al-Jawharī's is the earliest extant proof of the Euclidean postulate written in Arabic. As a premise (which his book included among the common notions) al-Jawharī lays down a rather curious version of the so-called Eudoxus-Archimedes axiom: If from the longer of two unequal lines a half is cut off, and from the [remaining] half another half is cut off, and so on many times; and if to the shorter line an equal line is added, and to the sum a line equal to it is added, and so on many times, there will remain of the halves of the longer line a line shorter than the multiples (*aḍʿāf*) of the shorter line. The axiom, which in different forms became a common feature of many Arabic proofs of the postulate, had already been applied in the same context in a demonstration attributed by Simplicius to an associate (*ṣāḥib*) of his named Aghānīs or Aghānyūs (Agapius [?]). This demonstration was known to mathematicians in Islam through the Arabic translation of a commentary by Simplicius on the premises of Euclid's *Elements*. The exact date of this translation is unknown, but it was available to al-Nayrīzī (*fl.* 895) and could have been made early in the ninth century.

The six propositions making up al-Jawharī's proof are the following:

(1) If a straight line falling on two straight lines makes the alternate angles equal to one another, then the two lines are parallel to one another; and if parallel to one another, then the distance from every point on one to the corresponding (*naẓīra*) point on the other is always the same, that is, the distance from the first point in the first line to the first point in the second line is the same as that from the second point in the first line to the second point in the second line, and so on.

(2) If each of two sides of any triangle is bisected and a line is drawn joining the dividing points, then the remaining side will be twice the joining line.

(3) For every angle it is possible to draw any number of bases (sing. *qāʿida*).

(4) If a line divides an angle into two parts (*biqismayn*) and a base to this angle is drawn at random, thereby generating a triangle, and from each of the remainders of the sides containing the angle a line is cut off equal to either side of the generated triangle, and a line is drawn joining the dividing points, then this line will cut off from the line dividing the given angle a line equal to that which is drawn from the [vertex of the] angle to the base of the generated triangle.

(5) If any angle is divided by a line into two parts and a point is marked on that line at random, then a line may be drawn from that point on both sides [of the dividing line] so as to form a base to that given angle.

(6) If from one line and on one side of it two lines are drawn at angles together less than two right angles, the two lines meet on that side.

Proposition (6) is, of course, Euclid's parallels postulate. Proposition (5) is, essentially, an attempt to prove a statement originally proposed by Simplicius, as we learn from a thirteenth-century document, a letter from ʿAlam al-Dīn Qayṣar to Naṣīr al-Dīn al-Ṭūsī, which is included in manuscripts of the latter's *al-Risāla 'l-shāfiya*. The attempted proof, which makes use of the Eudoxus-Archimedes axiom, rests on proposition (4) and ultimately depends on (1) and (2). Proposition (3), used in the deduction of (4), also formed part of Simplicius' attempted demonstration. The first part of proposition (1) is the same as Euclid I, 27, and does not depend on the parallels postulate. To prove the second part al-Jawharī takes $HO = TQ$ on the two parallel lines cut by the transversal HT (Figure 1). The alternate angles AHT, HTD being equal, it follows that the corresponding angles and sides in the triangles OHT, HTQ are equal. He then takes $HL = TS$ and similarly proves the

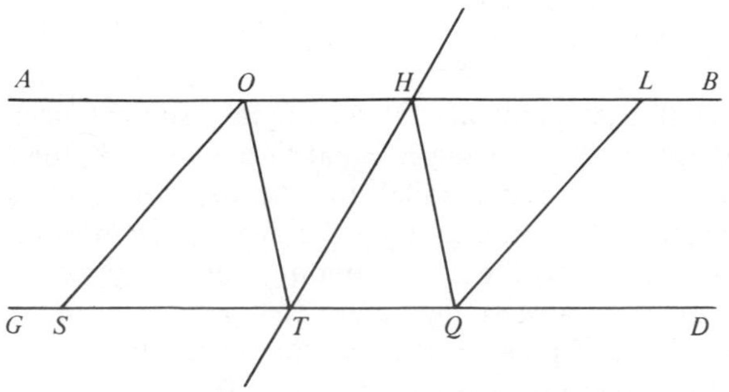

FIGURE 1

congruence of the triangles *OST*, *QLH*, and hence the equality of the corresponding sides *OS*, *QL*. As the lines *OS*, *QL* join the extremities of the equal segments *OL*, *SQ*, they may be said to join "corresponding points" of the latter, parallel lines, and they have been shown to be equal.

As al-Ṭūsī remarked, the proof fails to establish the intended general case: it does not establish the equality of lines joining "corresponding points" on the same side of the transversal or at unequal distances on either side of the transversal, nor does it show the equality of either *OS* or *LQ* to the transversal *HT* itself, even if one takes $HL = TQ = OH = ST$. It is this failure which is overlooked in proving proposition (2), which, in turn, forms the basis of (4).

It seems clear that al-Jawharī took his starting point from Simplicius, although he himself appears to have been responsible for propositions (1) and (2). His attempt should therefore be grouped with those Arabic proofs clustered round Simplicius' propositions. Another proof belonging to this group was one proposed in the thirteenth century by Muḥyi 'l-Dīn al-Maghribī, and still another is the anonymous treatise on parallel lines in Istanbul MS Carullah 1502, fols. 26v-27r, dated A.H. 894 (A.D. 1488–1489).

Also extant by al-Jawharī are some "additions" (*ziyādāt*) to book V of the *Elements*. Istanbul MS Feyzullah 1359, fols. 239v-240v, dated A.H. 868 (A.D. 1464–1465), contains only a fragment consisting of three propositions taken either from a longer work on that part of Euclid's book or, probably, from al-Jawharī's comprehensive commentary on or emendation of the *Elements*. The first of these propositions "proves" Euclid's definition of proportionals (book V, def. 5), the second is the counterpart of the first, and the third is the same as Euclid's definition of "to have a greater ratio" (book V, def. 7). Further, al-Ṭūsī quotes from the "Emendation" one proposition which al-Jawharī added after Euclid I, 13: If three straight lines are drawn from any point in different directions, the three angles thus contained by the three lines are together equal to four right angles.

BIBLIOGRAPHY

Naṣīr al-Dīn al-Ṭūsī's *al-Risāla 'l-shāfiya 'an al-shakk fi 'l-khuṭūṭ al-mutawāziya*, which contains al-Jawharī's proof of Euclid's parallels postulate and the letter of 'Alam al-Dīn Qayṣar to al-Ṭūsī, is published in *Majmū' Rasā'il al-Ṭūsī*, II (Hyderabad, A.H. 1359), *Risāla* no. 8, see esp. pp. 17–26. A Russian trans. of al-Ṭūsī's *Risāla* by B. A. Rosenfeld with introduction and notes by B. A. Rosenfeld and A. P. Youschkevitch is in *Istoriko-matematicheskie issledovaniya*, **13** (1960), 475–532. MS Feyzullah 1359, containing what is left of al-Jawharī's additions to bk. V of the *Elements*, is listed in M. Krause, "Stambuler Handschriften islamischer Mathematiker," in *Quellen und Studien zur Geschichte der Mathematik, Astronomie und Physik*, Abt. B, Studien, **3** (1936), 446. See also C. Brockelmann, *Geschichte der arabischen Literatur*, Supp. I (Leiden, 1937), 382.

Brief biobibliographical notices on al-Jawharī are in Ibn al-Nadīm, *al-Fihrist*, G. Flügel, ed., I (Leipzig, 1871), 266, 272; and in Ibn al-Qifṭī, *Ta'rikh*, J. Lippert, ed. (Leipzig, 1903), pp. 64, 219. On al-Jawharī's participation in the astronomical observations under al-Ma'mūn, see Ibn Yūnus, *al-Zīj al-Ḥākimī*, in *Notices et extraits des manuscrits de la Bibliothèque Nationale. . .* , VII (Paris, 1803), pp. 57, 167.

For questions of the identity of "Aghānīs," and for references to his demonstration of Euclid's postulate, see A. I. Sabra, "Thābit ibn Qurra on Euclid's Parallels Postulate," in *Journal of the Warburg and Courtauld Institutes*, **31** (1968), 12–32, esp. 13. On the proof attributed to Simplicius and the related proof by al-Maghribī, see A. I. Sabra, "Simplicius's Proof of Euclid's Parallels Postulate," in *Journal of the Warburg and Courtauld Institutes*, **32** (1969), 1–24.

A. I. SABRA

AL-JAYYĀNĪ, ABŪ 'ABD ALLĀH MUḤAMMAD IBN MU'ĀDH (*b.* Córdoba[?], Spain, *ca.* 989/990; *d.* after 1079)

"Jayyānī" means from Jaén, the capital of the Andalusian province of the same name. The Latin form of his name is variously rendered in the manuscripts as Abenmoat, Abumadh, Abhomadh, or Abumaad, corresponding to either Ibn Mu'ādh or Abū . . . Mu'ādh.

Very little is known about al-Jayyānī. Ibn Bashkuwāl (*d.* 1183) mentions a Koranic scholar of the same name who had some knowledge of Arabic philology, inheritance laws (*farḍ*), and arithmetic. Since in his treatise *Maqāla fi sharḥ al nisba* (*On Ratio*) al-Jayyānī is called *qāḍī* (judge) as well as *faqīh* (jurist), he is thought to be identical with this scholar, who was born in Córdoba in 989/990 and lived in Cairo from the beginning of 1012 until the end of 1017. The date of al-Jayyānī's death must be later than 1079, for he wrote a treatise ("On the Total Solar Eclipse") on an eclipse which occurred in Jaén on 1 July 1079. This means that he took the real astronomical and not the average date according to the ordinary Islamic lunar calendar (3 July 1079). In *Tabulae Jahen* he explains that the difference between these two dates may amount to as much as two days.

"On the Total Solar Eclipse" was translated into Hebrew by Samuel ben Jehuda (*fl. ca.* 1335), as was a treatise entitled "On the Dawn." A Latin translation of the latter work, *Liber de crepusculis*, was made by Gerard of Cremona. The Arabic texts of these two works are not known to be extant.

The *Liber de crepusculis*, a work dealing with the phenomena of morning and evening twilights, was for a long time attributed to Ibn al-Haytham, probably because in some manuscripts it comes immediately after his *Perspectiva* or *De aspectibus*, sometimes without any mention of the name of the author of the second work. In it al-Jayyānī gives an estimation of the angle of depression of the sun at the beginning of the morning twilight and at the end of the evening twilight, obtaining the reasonably accurate value of 18°. On the basis of this and other data he attempts to calculate the height of the atmospheric moisture responsible for the phenomena of twilights. The work found a wide interest in the Latin Middle Ages and in the Renaissance.

Liber tabularum Iahen cum regulis suis, the Latin version of the *Tabulae Jahen*, was also translated from the Arabic by Gerard of Cremona. A printed edition of the *Regulae*, lacking the tables, appeared in 1549 at Nuremberg as *Saraceni cuiusdam de Eris*. These tables were based on the tables of al-Khwārizmī, which were converted to the longitude of Jaén for the epoch of midnight, 16 July 622 (the date of the *hijra*), completed and simplified. For the daily needs of the *qāḍī* a practical handbook without much theory was sufficient. The *Tabulae Jahen* contains clear instructions for determining such things as the direction of the meridian, the time of day, especially the time and direction of prayer, the calendar, the visibility of the new moon, the prediction of eclipses, and the setting up of horoscopes. Finally al-Jayyānī deals critically with previous astrological theories. He rejects the theories of al-Khwārizmī and Ptolemy on the division of the houses and the theory of Abū Maʿshar on ray emission (*ἀκτινοβολία; emissio radiorum*); his astrological chronology refers to Hindu sources.

In the *Libros del saber* (II, 59, 309), al-Jayyānī is quoted as considering the twelve astrological houses to be of equal length. Other astronomical works by al-Jayyānī are the *Tabula residuum ascensionum ad revolutiones annorum solarium secundum Muhad Arcadius*, preserved in Latin translation (possibly a fragment of the *Tabulae Jahen*), and *Maṭraḥ shuʿāʿāt al-kawākib* ("Projection of the Rays of the Stars").

Several mathematical works by al-Jayyānī are extant in Arabic. His treatise *Kitāb majhūlāt qisiyy al-kura* ("Determination of the Magnitudes of the Arcs on the Surface of a Sphere"), which is also cited in *Saraceni cuiusdam de Eris*, is a work on spherical trigonometry.

Ibn Rushd mentions the Andalusian mathematician Ibn Muʿādh as one of those who consider the angle to be a fourth magnitude along with body, surface, and line (*Tafsīr* II, 665). Although he finds the argument not very convincing, he regards Ibn Muʿādh as a progressive and high-ranking mathematician. This Ibn Muʿādh is presumably al-Jayyānī, especially since in *On Ratio* an even more elaborate point of view is found. Here al-Jayyānī defines five magnitudes to be used in geometry: number, line, surface, angle, and solid. The un-Greek view of considering number an element of geometry is needed here because al-Jayyānī bases his definition of ratio on magnitudes.

The treatise *On Ratio* is a defense of Euclid. Al-Jayyānī, a fervent admirer of Euclid, says in his preface that it is intended "to explain what may not be clear in the fifth book of Euclid's writing to such as are not satisfied with it." The criticism of Euclid, to which al-Jayyānī objected, was a general dissatisfaction among Arabic mathematicians with Euclid V, definition 5. The cool, abstract form in which the Euclidean doctrine of proportions was presented did not appeal to the Arabic mind, since little or nothing could be deduced regarding the way in which it had come into being. So from the ninth century on, the Arabs tried either to obtain equivalent results more in accord with their own views, or to find a relation between their views and the unsatisfying theory. Those who chose the second way, such as Ibn al-Haytham, al-Khayyāmī, and al-Ṭūsī, tried to explain the Greek technique of equimultiples in terms of more basic, better-known concepts and methods.

The most successful among them was al-Jayyānī. To establish a common base he assumes that a right-thinking person has a primitive conception of ratio and proportionality. From this he derives a number of truths characteristic of proportional magnitudes, without proofs, since "There is no method to make clear what is already clear in itself." He then makes the connection by converting Euclid's multiples into parts, so that magnitudes truly proportional according to his own view also satisfy Euclid's criterion. The converse is proved by an indirect proof much resembling the one of Ibn al-Haytham, being based on the existence of a fourth proportional and the unlimited divisibility of magnitudes. In the third part al-Jayyānī deals with unequal ratios.

Al-Jayyānī shows here an understanding comparable with that of Isaac Barrow, who is customarily regarded as the first to have really understood Euclid's Book V.

BIBLIOGRAPHY

I. Original Works. Lists of MSS, which may not be complete, are in C. Brockelmann, *Geschichte der arabischen Literatur*, supp. I (Leiden, 1937), 860; and F. J. Carmody, *Arabic Astronomical and Astrological Sciences in Latin Translation* (Berkeley, 1956), p. 140. Extant MSS are "On the Total Solar Eclipse"—see Hermelink (below); "Tabula residuum ascensionum," Madrid 10023, fol. 66r—see J. M. Millás Vallicrosa, *Las traducciones orientales de la Biblioteca Catedral de Toledo* (Madrid, 1942), p. 246; and "Kitāb majhūlāt qisiyy al-kura" ("Determination of the Magnitudes of the Arcs on the Surface of a Sphere"), Escorial 955 and in a codex in the Biblioteca Medicea-Laurenziana, Or. 152—the latter also contains "Maṭraḥ shuʿāʿ [marg., shuʿāʿāt] al-kawākib" ("Projection of the Ray[s] of the Stars").

Published works are *De crepusculis* (Lisbon, 1541); *On Ratio*, with English trans., in E. B. Plooij, *Euclid's Conception of Ratio* (Rotterdam, 1950); and *Tabulae Jahen* (Nuremberg, 1549)—see H. Hermelink, "Tabulae Jahen," in *Archives for History of Exact Sciences*, **2**, no. 2 (1964), 108–112.

II. Secondary Literature. A survey of al-Jayyānī's work is in A. I. Sabra, "The Authorship of the *Liber de Crepusculis*, an Eleventh-Century Work on Atmospheric Refraction," in *Isis*, **58** (1967), 77–85. Biographical references are in M. Steinschneider, *Die hebräischen Übersetzungen des Mittelalters* (Berlin, 1893), pp. 574–575; H. Suter, *Die Mathematiker und Astronomen der Araber und ihre Werke* (Leipzig, 1900), pp. 96 and 214, *n.* 44; and "Nachträge und Berichtigungen zur *Die Mathematiker* . . .," in *Abhandlungen zur Geschichte der Mathematik*, **14** (1902), 170; and Sabra and Hermelink (see above). On the Arabic title of the *Liber de crepusculis*, see P. Kunitzsch, "Zum Liber Alfadhol eine Nachlese," in *Zeitschrift der Deutschen morgenländischen Gesellschaft*, **118** (1968), 308, *n.* 28. The conception of ratio in the Middle Ages is discussed in J. E. Murdoch, "The Medieval Language of Proportions," in A. C. Crombie, ed., *Scientific Change* (Oxford, 1961), pp. 237–272. See also Ibn Rushd, *Tafsīr Mā baʿd aṭ-ṭabīʿat*, M. Bouyges, ed., II (Beirut, 1942), 665.

Yvonne Dold-Samplonius
Heinrich Hermelink

JENSEN, JOHAN LUDVIG WILLIAM VALDEMAR (*b.* Nakskov, Denmark, 8 May 1859; *d.* Copenhagen, Denmark, 5 March 1925)

Jensen's career did not follow the usual pattern for a mathematician. He was essentially self-taught and never held an academic position. His father was an educated man of wide cultural interests but unsuccessful in a series of ventures, and pecuniary problems were frequent. At one time the family moved to northern Sweden, where for some years the father managed an estate, and Jensen considered these years the most wonderful of his life. After they returned to Denmark he finished school in Copenhagen and, at the age of seventeen, entered the College of Technology, where he studied mathematics, physics, and chemistry. He soon became absorbed in mathematics and decided to make it his sole study; his first papers date from this time.

In 1881 Jensen's life took an unexpected turn. In order to support himself, he became an assistant at the Copenhagen division of the International Bell Telephone Company, which in 1882 became the Copenhagen Telephone Company. His exceptional gifts and untiring energy soon made Jensen an expert in telephone technique, and in 1890 he was appointed head of the technical department of the company. He held this position until the year before his death. He was extremely exacting, and it was largely through his influence that the Copenhagen Telephone Company reached a high technical level at an early time. He continued his mathematical studies in his spare time and acquired extensive knowledge, in particular, of analysis. Weierstrass was his ideal, and his papers are patterns of exact and concise exposition.

Jensen's most important mathematical contribution is the theorem, named for him, expressing the mean value of the logarithm of the absolute value of a holomorphic function on a circle by means of the distances of the zeros from the center and the value at the center. This was communicated in a letter to Mittag-Leffler, published in *Acta mathematica* in 1899. Jensen thought that by means of this theorem he could prove the Riemann hypothesis on the zeros of the zeta function. This turned out to be an illusion, but in occupying himself with the Riemann hypothesis he was led to interesting results on algebraic equations and, from such results, to generalizations on entire functions.

Another important contribution by Jensen is his study of convex functions and inequalities between mean values, published in *Acta mathematica* in 1906; he showed there that a great many of the classical inequalities can be derived from a general inequality for convex functions. Among other subjects studied by Jensen is the theory of infinite series. In 1891 he published an excellent exposition of the theory of the gamma function, an English translation of which appeared in *Annals of Mathematics* in 1916.

BIBLIOGRAPHY

A list of Jensen's papers is contained in the obituaries mentioned below.

Obituaries by N. E. Nørlund appear in *Oversigt over det K. Danske Videnskabernes Selskabs Forhandlinger Juni 1925–Maj 1926* (1926), pp. 43–51, and in *Matematisk Tidsskrift B* (1926), pp. 1–7 (in Danish). See also G. Pólya, "Über die algebraisch-funktionentheoretischen Untersuchungen von J. L. W. V. Jensen," in *Mathematisk-fysiske Meddelelser*, VII, **17** (1927), 1–33.

BØRGE JESSEN

JERRARD, GEORGE BIRCH (*b.* Cornwall, England, 1804; *d.* Long Stratton, Norfolk, England, 23 November 1863)

George Jerrard was the son of Major General Joseph Jerrard. Although he entered Trinity College, Dublin, where he was a pupil of T. P. Huddart, on 4 December 1821, he did not take his B.A. until the spring of 1827. Jerrard's name is remembered for an important theorem in the theory of equations, relating to the reduction of algebraic equations to normal forms. In 1824 Abel had shown that the roots of the general quintic equation cannot be expressed in terms of its coefficients by means of radicals. E. W. Tschirnhausen had previously generalized the technique of Viète, Cardano, and others of removing terms from a given equation by a rational substitution. Then, in 1786, E. S. Bring reduced the quintic to a trinomial form

$$x^5 + px + q = 0$$

by a Tschirnhausen-type transformation with coefficients expressible by one cube root and three square roots (that is, the coefficients defined by equations of degree three or less). Jerrard also obtained this result, independently, and in a more general form, reducing any equation of degree n to an equation in which the coefficients of x^{n-1}, x^{n-2}, and x^{n-3} are all zero.

When Hermite found a solution for quintic equations in terms of elliptic modular functions, he cited only Jerrard. Unaware that Bring had found the result for the case $n = 5$, Hermite stated that Jerrard's theorem was the most important step taken in the algebraic theory of equations of the fifth degree since Abel. Bring's partial priority, later brought to light by C. J. D. Hill in 1861, did not entirely detract from the importance of Jerrard's research.

BIBLIOGRAPHY

Apart from his *Mathematical Researches*, 3 vols. (Bristol–London, 1832–1835), in which his theorem was first given, Jerrard wrote *An Essay on the Resolution of Equations*, 2 vols. (London, 1858). On his earlier work, see W. R. Hamilton, "Inquiring Into the Validity of a Method Recently Proposed by George B. Jerrard . . .," in *British Association Report*, **5** (1837), 295–348. On the question of Bring's priority, see Felix Klein, *Vorlesungen über die Ikosaeder* (Leipzig, 1884), pt. 2, ch. 1, sec. 2, Eng. trans. (London, 1913), pp. 156–159, English repr. (New York, 1956).

Jerrard wrote extensively in the *Philosophical Magazine*; references to these articles are in Klein, *op. cit.*; and the Royal Society, *Catalogue of Scientific Papers, 1800–1863*, **3** (1869), 547–548. For a useful bibliography on the theory of equations and its history, see G. Loria, *Bibliotheca mathematica*, **5** (1891), 107–112. A short obituary is in *Gentleman's Magazine*, **1** (1864), 130; sparse personal details are in the registers of Trinity College, Dublin.

J. D. NORTH

JEVONS, WILLIAM STANLEY (*b.* Liverpool, England, 1 September 1835; *d.* Hastings, England, 13 August 1882)

Jevons' name is purportedly of Welsh origin, akin to Evans. His father, Thomas, was a notable iron merchant with an inventive trait, and his mother, Mary Anne Roscoe, belonged to an old Liverpool family of bankers and lawyers with a literary bent. The ninth of eleven children, Jevons was brought up, and always in spirit remained, a Unitarian. He was a timid, clever boy and not narrowly studious, showing unusual mechanical aptitude. At University College, London, he took science courses, and his prowess in chemistry was such that he was recommended, while still an undergraduate and only eighteen years of age, for the job of assayer at the newly established Australian mint. In part to help ease a shrunken family budget, he decided to interrupt his education and to accept the post, which carried the handsome remuneration of over £600 a year. In Sydney he cultivated his interests in meteorology, botany, and geology and published papers in these fields. After five years he renounced a prosperous future in Australia and went back to England to further his education with a view to becoming an academic; he was already saying that "my forte will be found to lie . . . in the moral and logical sciences."

The first subject Jevons concentrated on was political economy, which he felt he could transform. His early and sustained interest in economics must have owed something to two disjoint features of his youth: a family bankruptcy caused by a trade slump, and his having been involved in the physical creation of money. The fluctuations of the national economy always fascinated him.

Having earned his master's degree at University College in 1863, Jevons was appointed junior lecturer at Owens College, Manchester, thus beginning a long association with that city. Two years later he became a part-time professor of logic and political economy at Queen's College, Liverpool, and in 1866 the Manchester institution raised him to a full-time double professorship of "logic and mental and moral philosophy," and of political economy. The following year Jevons married Harriet Ann Taylor, daughter of the founder and first editor of the *Manchester Guardian*, and the couple was soon enjoying the lively intellectual atmosphere of Victorian Manchester. They had three children, of whom one, Herbert Stanley, became a well-known economist. Jevons was made a fellow of the Royal Society in 1872.

In 1876, tired of his teaching chores (he was a poor lecturer and hated to speak in public), Jevons moved to a less onerous but more prestigious professorship at University College. Four years later, he resigned, anxious to spend all his time writing, but his health had begun to deteriorate, despite many long recuperative vacations in England and Norway. A few weeks before his forty-seventh birthday he drowned (possibly as the result of a seizure) while swimming off the Sussex coast.

Jevons had a strong and almost visionary sense of his own destiny as a thinker, and he worried about its fulfillment. A prodigious worker, he sustained many side interests and was passionately fond of music. Among his tributary writings are articles on the Brownian movement, the spectrum, communications, muscular exertion, pollution, skating, and popular entertainment. He tried hard and successfully to improve his literary style, and his later writings are more concise and readable than his earlier ones.

Whether economics or the rationale of scientific methodology benefited more from Jevons' attention is still arguable, but it was certainly as an economist that he became a public figure. Ironically, his popular fame rested on two achievements that now seem slight or even misguided. The first was his book *The Coal Question* (1865), a homily about dwindling English fuel supplies in relation to rocketing future demands. The work was Malthusian in the sense that he discussed industry and coal in much the terms that the earlier author had discussed population and food. It was a tract and obviously, as Keynes remarked, *épatant*. Gladstone, then chancellor of the Exchequer, was deeply impressed by the book, whose "grave conclusions" influenced his fiscal policy. A royal commission was subsequently appointed to look into the matter. Jevons' second achievement was the thesis, developed in the late 1870's from tentative suggestions made by earlier writers, that trade cycles could be correlated with sunspot activity through agrometeorology and, at a further remove, through the price of wheat. It was an ingenious and inherently plausible argument, but the data could not be manipulated to yield convincing evidence and the theory has no standing today.

Jevons brought to economic theory a fruitful insistence on a mathematical framework with an abundance of statistical material to fill out the structure. He was a diligent collector and sifter of statistics, and his methods of presenting quantitative data showed insight and skill. He strongly advocated the use of good charts and diagrams (colored, if possible), which, he said, were to the economist what fine maps are to the geographer. (At one time he toyed with a project to sell illustrated statistical information bulletins to businessmen.) He clarified certain concepts, particularly that of value, which he regarded as a function of utility, a property he wrote about with luminance. Indeed, this was his major contribution, and one that led to the explicit use of the calculus and other mathematical tools by economists.

Utility, said Jevons, "is a circumstance of things arising out of their relation to man's requirements and that normally diminishes." One of his favorite examples concerns bread, a daily pound of which, for a given person, has the "highest conceivable utility," and he went on to show that extra pounds have progressively smaller utilities, illustrating that the "final degree of utility" declines as consumption rises. In effect he was arguing that the second derivative of the function $U_a = U(Q_a)$, where U_a is the total utility or satisfaction derived from the consumption of a in the amount Q_a, is negative. This simple proposition was quite new, for the classical theorists, including Marx, had analyzed value from the supply side only, whereas Jevons' analysis was from demand. Later writers were to recognize the necessity of both approaches. Incidentally, Jevons' approach was the forerunner of the idea of "marginal utility," the first of the "marginal" concepts on which modern economics may be said to rest.

Jevons' work on price index-numbers deserves mention, as his setting them on a sound statistical footing enormously advanced understanding of changes in price and in the all-important value of gold.

Although some of Jevons' ideas can be found inchoate in the works of his predecessors Augustus Cournot and H. H. Gossen, and of his contemporaries Karl Menger and Léon Walras, he arrived at his theories independently and can be seen as a pathbreaker in modern economics. His stress on the subject as essentially a mathematical science was judicious, and he held no exaggerated notions about the role of mathematics—he had observed, he said slyly, that mathematical students were no better than any others when faced with real-life problems.

Economics and logic have traditionally been associated in England, and Jevons belongs to the chain of distinguished thinkers, from John Stuart Mill to Frank Ramsey, who are linked to both disciplines. He was opposed to Mill in divers particulars, and at times he looked upon the older man's deep influence on the teaching of logic as hardly short of disastrous. Mill's mind, he once averred, was "essentially illogical," and Jevons eagerly seized on Boole's remarkable new symbolic logic to show up what he deemed the vastly inferior warmed-over classical logic of Mill. Jevons actually improved on Boole in some important details, as, for instance, in showing that the Boolean operations of subtraction and division were superfluous. Whereas Boole had stuck to the mutually exclusive "either-or," Jevons redefined the symbol $+$ to mean "either one, or the other, or both." This change, which was at once accepted and became permanent, made for greater consistency and flexibility. The expression $a + a$, which was an uninterpretable nuisance in the Boolean scheme, now fell into place, the sum being a.

At the same time Jevons deprecated certain aspects of Boole's work. He thought it too starkly symbolic and declared that "the mathematical dress into which he [Boole] threw his discoveries is not proper to them, and his quasi-mathematical processes are vastly more complicated than they need have been"—an extravagant statement, even in the light of Jevons' own logic. Indeed, some of Jevons' writings about Boole's system, and especially his worries about the discrepancies between orthodox and Boolean algebras, suggest that he did not fully grasp Boole's originality, potential, and abstractness. Nevertheless, he can certainly be reckoned a leading propagandist for Boole, particularly among those who could not understand, or who would not brook, Boole's logic. Moreover, Jevons was led through Boole's ideas to some original work on a logical calculus.

Jevons' logic of inference was dominated by what he called the substitution of similars, which expressed "the capacity of mutual replacement existing in any two objects which are like or equivalent to a sufficient degree." This became for him "the great and universal principle of reasoning" from which "all logical processes seem to arrange themselves in simple and luminous order." It also allowed him to develop a special equational logic, with which he constructed various truth-tablelike devices for handling logical problems. He did not foresee that a truth-table calculus could be developed as a self-contained entity, but he was able to devise a logic machine—a sort of motional form of the later diagrammatic scheme of John Venn. Jevons' "logical piano" (as he eventually called it in preference to his earlier terms "abacus," "abecedarium," and "alphabet") was built for him by a Salford clockmaker. It resembled a small upright piano, with twenty-one keys for classes and operations in an equational logic. Four terms, A, B, C, and D, with their negations, in binary combinations, were displayed in slots in front and in back of the piano; and the mechanism allowed for classification, retention, or rejection, depending upon what the player fed in via the keyboard. The keyboard was arranged in an equational form, with all eight terms on both left and right and a "copula" key between them. The remaining four keys were, on the extreme left, "finis" (clearance) and the inclusive "or," and, on the extreme right, "full stop" (output) and the inclusive "or again." In all 2^{16} (65,536) logical selections were possible.

The machine earned much acclaim, especially after its exhibition at the Royal Society in 1870. At present it is on display in the Oxford Museum of the History of Science. Although its principal value was as an aid to the teaching of the new logic of classes and propositions, it actually solved problems with superhuman speed and accuracy, and some of its features can be traced in modern computer designs.

Jevons' various textbooks on logic sold widely for many decades, and his *Elementary Lessons in Logic* (London, 1870) was still in print in 1972. Moreover, he considered his ambitious work on the rationale of science to be an extension of his logic into a special field of human endeavor. His biggest and most celebrated book, *The Principles of Science*, is firmly rooted in Jevonian logic and contains practically all his ideas on, and contributions to, the subject. Inescapably, the matter of induction, the basis of scientific method and the bugbear of scientific philosophy, is lengthily explored and analyzed. Jevons confidently declared that "induction is, in fact, the inverse operation of deduction." Such a statement—in one sense a truism and in another a travesty—might be thought a feeble beginning for a study of the how and why of science, but Jevons acquits himself admirably. He does not confuse the formal logic of induction with the problems of inductive inference in the laboratory, and he is obviously under no illusions about the provisional nature of all scientific "truth."

Nineteenth-century English scholars, inspired by the phenomenal explicatory and material success of science, had been taking an increasing interest in its philosophy. John Stuart Mill and William Whewell are particularly associated with these early studies; and in Jevons' view their work contained serious flaws. He thought that Mill, first, expected too much of science as a key to knowledge of all kinds and, second, that he was overly respectful of Bacon's view of science as primarily the collection and sortation of data. His criticism of Whewell centered on that writer's apparent assumption that exact knowledge is a reality attainable by scientific patience.

Jevons was perhaps the first writer to insist that absolute precision, whether of observation or of correspondence between theory and practice, is necessarily beyond human reach. Taking a thoroughly modern position, Jevons held that approximation was of the essence, adding that "in the measure of continuous quantity, perfect correspondence must be accidental, and should give rise to suspicion rather than to satisfaction." He also felt that causation was an overrated if not dangerous concept in science, and that what we seek are logically significant interrelations. All the while, he said, the scientist is framing hypotheses, checking them against existing information, and then designing experiments for further support. There can be no cut-and-dried conclusion to most investigations and no guarantee that correct answers can be issued. The scientist must act in accordance with the probabilities associable with rival hypotheses, which probabilities, or, as many would prefer to say today, likelihoods, constitute the decision data. Thus "the theory of probability is an essential part of logical method, so that the logical value of every inductive result must be determined consciously or unconsciously, according to the principles of the inverse method of probability." An entire chapter of *The Principles* is devoted to direct probability and another to inverse probability.

As a probabilist Jevons was fundamentally a disciple of Laplace, or at least of Laplace as reshaped by Jevons' own college teacher and mentor Augustus De Morgan—that is to say, he was a subjectivist. Probability, he maintained, "belongs wholly to the mind" and "deals with quantity of knowledge." Yet he was careful to emphasize that probability is to be taken as a measure, not of an individual's belief, but of rational belief—of what the perfectly logical man would believe in the light of the available evidence. In espousing this view, Jevons sidestepped Boole's disturbing reservations about subjectivism—mainly because he had difficulty grasping them. Writing to Herschel, he stated, frankly: "I got involved in Boole's probabilities, which I did not thoroughly understand. . . . The most difficult points ran in my mind, day and night, till I got alarmed. The result was considerable distress of head a few days later, and some signs of indigestion." In general Jevons was silent about the movement toward a frequential theory of probability that was growing out of the work of Leslie, Ellis, and Poisson, as well as that of his contemporary, Venn.

To the modern reader, however, Jevons may seem altogether too self-assured in this notoriously treacherous field. For example, he wholeheartedly accepted Laplace's controversial rule of succession and offered a naive illustration of its applicability: Observing that of the sixty-four chemical elements known to date (Jevons was writing in 1873) fifty are metallic, we say that the quantity $(50 + 1)/(64 + 2) = 17/22$ is the probability that the next element discovered will be a metal. To the frequentist, insistent on a clearly delineated sample space, this statement is almost wholly devoid of meaning. Another, more bizarre example of his naive Laplaceanism is his contention that the proposition "a platythliptic coefficient is positive" has, because of our complete ignorance, a probability of correctness of 1/2. Boole had rightly objected to this sort of thing and would agree with Charles Terrot that such a probability has the numeric but wholly indeterminate value of 0/0. To understand Jevons' position, however, we must bear in mind that the prestige of Laplace, especially in this area, was then enormous.

Curiously, in discoursing on what he calls "the grand object of seeking to estimate the probability of future events from past experience," Jevons made only one casual and unenlightening reference to Thomas Bayes, who, a century earlier, had been the first to attempt a coherent theory of inverse probability. Today the implications of Bayes's work form the subject of lively discussion among probabilists.

Some of the most illuminating sections of *The Principles of Science* are those dealing with technical matters, such as the methodology of measurement, the theory of errors and means, and the principle of least squares. Yet the book offers only a shallow treatment of the logic of numbers and arithmetic, and it has been criticized for the absence of any serious discussion of the social and biological sciences. By and large, however, *The Principles* is something of a landmark in the bleak country of nineteenth-century philosophy of science.

BIBLIOGRAPHY

I. ORIGINAL WORKS. According to Harriet Jevons' bibliography (see below), Jevons' first appearance in print was a weather report (24 Aug. 1856) in the *Empire*, a Sydney, Australia, newspaper, for which he wrote weekly reports until 1858. His first publication in a scholarly journal was "On the Cirrus Form of Cloud, With Remarks on Other Forms of Cloud," in *London, Edinburgh and Dublin Philosophical Magazine*, **14** (July 1857), 22–35. His account of the logical piano is "On the Mechanical Performance of Logical Inference," in *Philosophical Transactions of the Royal Society*, **160** (1870), 497–518.

His books, all published in London, include *Pure Logic* (1863); *The Coal Question* (1865); *The Theory of Political Economy* (1871); *The Principles of Science* (1874); *Studies in Deductive Logic* (1880); *The State in Relation to Labour* (1882); *Methods of Social Re-Form* (1883); *Investigations in Currency and Finance* (1884); and *Principles of Economics* (1905). The last three were published posthumously, and the very last is a fragment of a large work that he was writing at the time of his death. *The Principles of Science, A Treatise on Logic and Scientific Method*, the frontispiece of which is an engraving of the logical piano, is available as a paperback reprint (New York, 1958).

For information on the 1952 exhibition of Jevons' works at the University of Manchester, see *Nature*, **170** (1952), 696. The library of that university has Jevons' economic and general MSS, and Wolfe Mays of the Department of Philosophy owns the philosophic and scientific MSS; much of this material is still unpublished.

II. SECONDARY LITERATURE. No full biography exists. The primary source is Harriet A. Jevons, *Letters and Journal of W. Stanley Jevons* (London, 1886), with portrait and bibliography. See also the obituary by the Reverend Robert Harley in *Proceedings of The Royal Society*, **35** (1883), i–xii. Jevons' granddaughter, Rosamund Könekamp, contributed "Some Biographical Notes" to *Manchester School of Economics and Social Studies*, **30** (1962), 250–273. For a modern view of his logic, see W. Mays and D. P. Henry, "Jevons and Logic," in *Mind*, **62** (1953), 484–505. The logic contrivances are described and placed in historic perspective in Martin Gardner, *Logic Machines and Diagrams* (New York, 1958). Jevons' economics is reviewed in J. M. Keynes, *Essays in Biography*, 2nd ed. (London, 1951); and, more formally, in E. W. Eckard, *Economics of W. S. Jevons* (Washington, D.C., 1940); both of the foregoing also contain biographical material. His contemporary influence is discussed in R. D. C. Black, "W. S. Jevons and the Economists of His Time," in *Manchester School of Economics and Social Studies*, **30** (1962), 203–221. Ernest Nagel has written a preface on Jevons' philosophy of science for the paperback ed. of *Principles of Science*. See also W. Mays, "Jevons's Conception of Scientific Method," in *Manchester School of Economics and Social Studies*, **30** (1962), 223–249.

NORMAN T. GRIDGEMAN

JOACHIMSTHAL, FERDINAND (*b.* Goldberg, Germany [now Złotoryja, Poland], 9 March 1818; *d.* Breslau, Germany [now Wrocław, Poland], 5 April 1861)

Son of the Jewish merchant David Joachimsthal and Friederike Zaller, Joachimsthal attended school in Liegnitz (now Legnica, Poland), where he had the good fortune to have Kummer as his teacher. In 1836 after completing his studies there, he went to Berlin for three semesters, where his mathematics teachers were Dirichlet and Jacob Steiner.

Starting with the summer semester of 1838, he spent another four semesters as a student at the University of Königsberg (now Kaliningrad, U.S.S.R.). Most notable among his teachers there were Jacobi, Germany's leading mathematician after Gauss, and Bessel, foremost German astronomer of his day. Joachimsthal thus received the best available mathematical training.

After completion of these studies, he went to Halle to work for his doctorate under Otto Rosenberger, obtaining his Ph.D. on 21 July 1840. His dissertation, "De lineis brevissimis in superficiebus rotatione ortis," was graded *docta*, and he passed his oral examinations *cum laude*.

As was then still generally customary, Joachimsthal took the *Examen pro facultate docendi* and in 1844 joined the teaching staff of the Königliche Realschule in Berlin. Starting in 1847, he taught in Berlin at the Collège Royal Français, after 1852 with the rank of full professor. In 1845 he applied to the school of philosophy at the University of Berlin for accreditation to teach there. Prior to this time, after taking his doctor's degree, Joachimsthal had become a convert from Judaism to the Protestant faith.

After being accepted as an applicant for university teaching credentials, on 7 August 1845 he delivered before the assembled department a trial lecture entitled *Über die Untersuchungen der neueren Geometrie, welche sich der Lehre von den Brennpunkten anschliessen* and on 13 August a public trial lecture entitled "De curvis algebraicis." The *Venia legendi* was conferred upon him that day.

From the winter semester of 1845–1846 to that of 1852–1853, in addition to his teaching, Joachimsthal lectured as *Privatdozent* at the University of Berlin to beginners in analytic geometry and differential and integral calculus; to advanced students of the theory of surfaces and calculus of variations; and to special students on statics, analytic mechanics, and the theory of the most important curves encountered in architecture. Profiting from his experience in Jacobi's seminar, he also held mathematical drill sessions, a relative novelty at Berlin. His effective teaching won the unanimous approval of the department. His lectures attracted more students than did those of Eisenstein, his brilliant colleague in the same field.

Meanwhile, Joachimsthal's prospects in Berlin were not at all promising. On 7 May 1853 he was finally promoted to full professor by the Prussian Ministry of Culture, after repeated urgings and commendations from his department at the university, and received an appointment in Halle as successor to Sohnke. By 1855 he had received a new offer and went as Kummer's successor to Breslau, where his lectures were very popular. He taught, among other things, analytic geometry, differential geometry, and the theory of surfaces, in which—exceptional for the time—he operated with determinants and parameters. He gave special lectures on geometry and mechanics for students of mining engineering and metallurgy.

The average number of his listeners exceeded that of Kummer, who with Weierstrass was later to become one of the most sought-after teachers of mathematics. In 1860, for example, Joachimsthal had an audience of sixty-six attending his mechanics lectures. By the time of his death, at the age of forty-three, he had acquired a wide reputation as an excellent teacher and kind person.

His *Cours de géométrie élémentaire à l'usage des élèves du Collège Royal Français* (1852) had demonstrated his talent as a textbook writer through its clear logical structure and insight (rarely found in accomplished mathematicians) into the difficulties facing beginners, and he was naturally expected to turn out equally valuable university texts.

Jacobi persuaded him to write an *Analytische Geometrie der Ebene* as a supplement to the *Geometrie des Raumes* that he himself was planning. It was published posthumously in 1863. A printed version of his lecture during the winter semester of 1856–1857 on the application of infinitesimal calculus to surfaces and lines of double curvature was also published posthumously in 1872. Reprinted several times, both books were in use for some thirty years, due largely to their clear, simple exposition and to the general applicability of their conclusions.

But the reputation of a teacher tends to be transitory, and Joachimsthal's contributions would have receded into oblivion had it not been for his outstanding original research. Those qualities of clarity, rigor, and elegance that made him one of the most eminent teachers of his day were also characteristic of his own work. One of his favorite fields of study was the theory of surfaces. He dealt repeatedly with the problem of normals to conic sections and second-degree surfaces.

His published writings (the first of which appeared in 1843) show him to have been influenced primarily by Jacobi, Dirichlet, and Steiner. Although never prolific, he always went deeply into a subject, seeking to discover connections between isolated, ostensibly unrelated phenomena. In treating a problem of attraction, for example, he gave a solution constituting an application of the Abel method for defining a tautochrone.

His striving for general validity and his critical acumen emerged also in treatises in which he took up problems dealt with by other mathematicians, such as Bonnet, La Hire, Carl Johann Malmsten, Heinrich Schröter, Steiner, Jacques Charles Sturm, whose solutions he strengthened. As in his lectures, he was primarily concerned in his writings with analytic applications in geometry. Not only did he use determinants himself but explicitly indicated their possible applications in geometry. His use of oblique coordinates also deserves special mention.

Today his name is associated with Joachimsthal surfaces, which possess a family of plane lines of curvature within the planes of a pencil; the Joachimsthal theorem concerning the intersection of two surfaces in three-dimensional real Euclidean space along a common line of curvature; and a theorem on the four normals to an ellipse from a point inside it.

Joachimsthal's contributions were substantial and lucid. His marked predilection for mature, polished exposition was expressed in constant recasting, revising, and rewriting; so that many planned works never reached completion. In addition, during the few years of his greatest potential, when he was teaching in Berlin as *Privatdozent*, he lived surrounded by an unprecedented galaxy of luminaries within his field (Dirichlet, Jacobi, Steiner, Eisenstein, and Borchardt).

BIBLIOGRAPHY

I. ORIGINAL WORKS. Most of Joachimsthal's writings not published independently appeared in the *Journal für die reine und angewandte Mathematik* between 1843 and 1871. A bibliography of most of his published works is given in Poggendorff, I, 1196, and III, 692. Works not mentioned there are found in *Nouvelles annales de mathématiques*, **6** (1847); **9** (1850); and **12** (1853); and in *Abhandlungen zur Geschichte der Mathematik*, **20** (1905), 76–79. See also Royal Society, *Catalogue of Scientific Papers*, III,

548–549, and VIII, 27. Also worthy of mention is his "Mémoire sur les surfaces courbes," in *Collège Royal Français, Programme* (Berlin, 1848), pp. 3–20; and his foreword in Friedrich Engel, *Axonometrische Projectionen der wichtigsten geometrischen Flächen* (Berlin, 1854).

Some of the works listed in Poggendorff appeared as preprints in school and university publications before reaching a wider public in the *Journal für die reine und angewandte Mathematik*.

A collection of Joachimsthal's papers is to be found partly in the archives of Humboldt University, Berlin, German Democratic Republic, and in those of the Martin Luther University of Halle-Wittenberg in Halle, German Democratic Republic.

II. SECONDARY LITERATURE. Borchardt published a brief obituary in the *Journal für die reine und angewandte Mathematik*, **59** (1861), 124. The only detailed biography, by Moritz Cantor, in *Allgemeine deutsche Biographie*, XIV (Leipzig, 1881), 96–97, is the source of most biographic references to Joachimsthal, such as those in Karl Gustav Heinrich Berner, *Schlesische Landsleute* (Leipzig, 1901), p. 221; and S. Wininger, *Grosse jüdische National-Biographie*, III (Chernovtsy, 1928), 317.

Additional information is given in Rudolf Sturm, "Geschichte der mathematischen Professuren im ersten Jahrhundert der Universität Breslau 1811–1911," in *Jahresberichte der Deutschen Matematikervereinigung*, **20** (1911), 314–321; this appeared in virtually the same form in *Festschrift zur Feier des hundertjährigen Bestehens der Universität Breslau*, II, *Geschichte der Fächer* (Breslau, 1911), 434–440.

Joachimsthal is mentioned also in Wilhelm Lorey, *Das Studium der Mathematik an den deutschen Universitäten seit Anfang des 19. Jahrhunderts* (Leipzig–Berlin, 1916), pp. 87, 88, 120; Max Lenz, *Geschichte der Königlichen Friedrich-Wilhelms-Universität zu Berlin*, II, pt. 2 (Halle, 1918), pp. 155 and 156; Heinrich Brandt, "Mathematiker in Wittenberg und Halle," in *450 Jahre Martin-Luther-Universität Halle-Wittenberg*, II (Halle, 1952), 449–455.

KURT-R. BIERMANN

JOHN OF GMUNDEN (*b.* Gmunden am Traunsee, Austria, *ca.* 1380–1384; *d.* Vienna, Austria, 23 February 1442)

John of Gmunden's origins were long the subject of disagreement. Gmunden am Traunsee, Gmünd in Lower Austria, and Schwäbisch Gmünd were all thought to be possible birthplaces; and Nyder (Nider), Schindel, Wissbier, and Krafft possible family names. Recent research in the records of the Faculty of Arts of the University of Vienna, however, appears to have settled the question. The Vienna matriculation register records the entrance, on 13 October 1400, of an Austrian named "Johannes Sartoris de Gmundin," that is, of the son of a tailor from Gmunden.[1] He was surely the "Johannes de Gmunden" who was admitted to the baccalaureate examination on 13 October 1402.[2] If he was the astronomer John of Gmunden, who was accepted as master into the Faculty of Arts on 21 March 1406, along with eight other candidates, then he spent all his student years at Vienna.[3] His birthplace could only have been Gmunden am Traunsee, since Gmünd and Schwäbisch Gmünd were then known only as "Gamundia"; the locality on the Traunsee, which even in Latin sources, is called "Gmunden" (Gemunden until 1350).[4] Schwäbisch Gmünd must be eliminated from consideration because our John of Gmunden was an examiner of Austrian students, which means he had to be of Austrian birth. The family names Nyder and Schindel can be excluded, but that of Krafft is better established. In his writings and the records of his deanship of the Arts faculty, carefully written in his own hand, he calls himself Johannes de Gmunden exclusively, thus clearly he never used a family name.[5]

John of Gmunden's career can be divided into four periods. In the first (1406–1416) his early lectures —besides one given in 1406 on "Theorice"—were devoted to nonmathematical subjects: "Physica" (1408), "Metheora" (1409, 1411), "Tractatus Petri Hyspani" (1410), and "Vetus ars" (1413).[6] On 25 August 1409 he became *magister stipendiatus* and received an appointment at the Collegium Ducale.[7] He gave his first mathematics lecture in 1412. He was also interested in theology, the study of which he completed in 1415 as "Baccalaureus biblicus formatus in theologia." Two lectures in this field concerned the Exodus (1415) and the theology of Peter Lombard (1416).

In 1416–1425 John of Gmunden lectured exclusively on mathematics and astronomy, which led to the first professorship in these fields at the University of Vienna; the position became permanent under Maximilian I. When John became ill in 1418, he lost his salary, since only someone actively teaching (*magister stipendiatus legens*) could be paid; but, at the request of the faculty, the duke removed this hardship. John obtained permission to hold lectures in his own house—a rarely granted privilege.[8] During his years at the university he held many honorary offices. He was dean twice (1413 and 1423) and examiner of Saxon (1407), Hungarian (1411), and Austrian (1413) students.[9] In 1410 he was named *publicus notarius*.[10] In 1414 he was receiver (bursar) of the faculty treasury and member of the dormitory committee[11] for the bylaws for the *burse*. In 1416 he was "Conciliarius of the Austrian nation," and from 1423 to 1425 he was entrusted with supervising the university's new building program.[12]

The third period (1425–1431) began when John of Gmunden retired from the Collegium Ducale and, on

14 May 1425, became canon of the chapter of St. Stephen.[13] Previously he had been ordained priest (1417) and delivered sermons.[14] He was also vice-chancellor of the university, which had long been closely associated with St. Stephen's Gymnasium.[15] Henceforth John devoted himself to writings on astronomy, astronomical tables, and works on astronomical instruments. He also lectured on the astrolabe.[16]

In the last period (1431–1442) John became *plebanus* in Laa an der Thaya, an ecclesiastical post that yielded an income of 140 guldens.[17] In 1435 he wrote his will, in which he bequeathed his books (particularly those he himself had written) and instruments to the library of the Faculty of Arts. He also gave precise instructions for their use.[18] We note the absence from his list of those books on which his own works were based, but these undoubtedly were in the Faculty of Arts library. John died on 23 February 1442 and was probably buried in St. Stephen's cathedral; no monument indicates where he was laid to rest. Moreover, we possess no likeness of him except for an imaginative representation that shows him wearing a full-bottomed wig.[19]

John of Gmunden's work reflects the goal of the instruction given in the Scholastic universities: to teach science from existing books, not to advance it. He was above all a teacher and an author. His mathematics lectures were entitled "Algorismus de minutiis" (1412, 1416, 1417), "Perspectiva" (1414), "Algorismus de integris" (1419), and "*Elementa* Euclidis" (1421).[20] In this series one does not find a lecture on *latitudines formarum*, which was already part of the curriculum and a topic on which John's teacher, Nicolaus of Dinkelsbühl, had lectured in 1391. John's main concerns, however, lay in astronomy, and thus even in his mathematical writings he treated only questions of use to astronomers. Tannstetter cites three mathematical treatises by him: an arithmetic book with sexagesimal fractions, a collection of tables of proportions, and a treatise on the sine.[21] Only the first of these was printed, appearing in a compendium containing a series of writings that provided the basis for mathematics lectures.[22] In this area John introduced no innovations.[23] For example, in extracting the square root of a sexagesimal number, he first transformed the latter into seconds, quarters, and so forth (therefore into minutes with even index), added an even number of zeros (*cifras*) in order to achieve greater accuracy, then extracted the root, divided through the *medietates cifrarum*, and expressed the result sexagesimally (thus $\sqrt{a} = \frac{1}{10^n}\sqrt{a \cdot 10^{2n}}$). Even the summation of two zodiac signs of thirty degrees into a *signum physicum* of sixty degrees had appeared earlier.[24] The treatise on the sine was recently published.

John's other mathematical works are contained in manuscript volumes that he himself dated (Codex Vindobonensis 5151, 5268).[25] From his writings on angles, arcs, and chords it is clear that Arabic sine geometry was known in Vienna. Yet it is doubtful whether—as has been asserted[26]—John was also acquainted with the formula (corresponding to the cosine law) $\frac{\sin h}{\sin H} = \frac{\sin \text{vers}\, b - \sin \text{vers}\, t}{\sin \text{vers}\, b}$.[27] The formula, which was employed in calculating the sun's altitude for every day of the year, was discovered by Peurbach with "God's help."[28]

John of Gmunden's work in astronomy was of greater importance than his efforts in mathematics. It was through his teaching and writings that Vienna subsequently became the center of astronomical research in Europe. His astronomy lectures were entitled "Theoricae planetarum" (1406, 1420, 1422, 1423), "Sphaera materialis" (1424), and "De astrolabio" (1434).[29] He probably did not himself make any systematic observations of the heavens, but his students are known to have done so. The instruments that he had constructed according to his own designs were used only in teaching and to determine time.[30] He was no astrologer, as can be seen from a letter of September 1432 to the prior Jacob de Clusa, who had made predictions on the basis of planetary conjunctions.[31] Although his library contained numerous astrological writings, the stringent directions in his will pertaining to the lending of these dangerous works show what he thought of this pseudoscience. If occasionally he spoke of the properties of the zodiac signs and of bloodletting, it was because these subjects were of particular interest to purchasers of almanacs.[32]

The great number of extant manuscripts of John of Gmunden's works attests his extensive literary activity, which began in 1415 and steadily intensified until his death. Many of the manuscripts are in his own hand, such as those in Codex Vindobonensis 2440, 5151, 5144, and 5268.[33] Most of those done by students and other scribes date from the fifteenth century. Only a small portion (about twenty of the total of 238 manuscripts that Zinner located in the libraries of Europe) are from a later period. This indicates that his works were superseded by those of Peurbach and Regiomontanus. John's writings can be divided into tables, calendars, and works on astronomical instruments.

John of Gmunden produced five versions of his tabular works, which contained tables of the motions of the sun, the moon, and the planets, as well as of eclipses and new and full moons. They also included explanatory comments (*tabulae cum canonibus*). They are all enumerated in his deed of gift. Regiomontanus

JOHN OF GMUNDEN

studied the first of the tabular works (in Codex Vindobonensis 5268) and found an error in it that he noted in the margin.[34] John was also the author of many individual writings on astronomy that were not made part of the tabular works. Shorter than the latter (with the exception of the tables of eclipses), they contained tables of planetary and lunar motions, of the true latitudes of the planets (with explanations), and of the true new and full moons, as well as tables of eclipses.[35] Further astronomical writings can be found in his works on astronomical instruments.

Along with elaborating and improving the values of his tables, John of Gmunden was especially concerned with the preparation of calendars, which provided in a more usable form the information contained in the tabular works. In addition to such astronomical data, they included the calendar of the first year of a cycle with saints' days and feast days, dominical letter, and the golden numbers, so that the calendar could be used during all nineteen years of a cycle.[36] He brought out four editions of the calendar: the first covered 1415–1434; the second, 1421–1439; the third, 1425–1443; and the fourth, 1439–1514.[37] The fourth edition was printed on Gutenberg's press in 1448.[38] Two other calendars bearing John's name were published later. From one of them, a xylographic work, there remains only a woodblock; of the other, a peasants' calendar, only a single copy is extant.[39]

John of Gmunden's third area of interest was astronomical instruments; he explained how they operated and gave directions for making them. In his deed of gift he mentioned two works in this field: a volume bound in red parchment containing *Astrolabium Alphonsi* and a little book written by himself, entitled *Astrolabii quadrantes*.[40] In his will he lists the following instruments: a celestial globe (*sphaera solida*), an "equatorium" of Campanus with models taken from the *Albion* (devised and written about by Wallingford), an astrolabe, two quadrants, a *sphaera materialis*, a large cylindrical sundial, and four "*theorice lignee*."[41] He stipulated that these instruments should be kept well and seldom loaned out—the equatorium only very seldom (*rarissime*). Of all this apparatus nothing remains in Vienna.[42] On the other hand, about 100 manuscripts of his treatises on astronomical instruments have been preserved. To date no one has made a study of these manuscripts (which contain other works on astronomy) thorough enough to establish, in detail, what John took from his predecessors and what he himself contributed. The instruments he discussed, with regard to both their theoretical basis and their production and use, were the following:

1. The astrolabe. The text is composed of fourteen manuscripts.[43] The star catalog joined to one of them indicates that the first version dates from 1424.[44]

2. The quadrant. John's treatise on the quadrant exists in three versions.

Quadrant I: Fifteen manuscripts are extant of this version of the work, which dates from 1424–1425.[45] Here he drew on a revision from 1359 of the *Quadrans novus* of Jacob Ibn Tibbon (also known as Jacob ben Maḥir or Profatius Judaeus) from 1291–1292 and on a revision from 1359.[46] To these John appended an introduction and remarks on measuring altitudes.[47] Several of the manuscripts also contain additional data that he presented in 1425: a table of the true positions of the sun at the beginnings of the months, star catalogs, and a table of the sun's entrance into the zodiac signs.[48]

Quadrant II: A second, more elaborate version of the work on the quadrant exists in only one manuscript; it no doubt stems from a student, who speaks of a "tabula facta a Johanne de Gmunden, 1425."[49]

Quadrant III: This version, which is independent of John's other writings on the topic, is known in thirteen manuscripts.[50] One of them is dated 1439.[51] Many of the manuscripts contain tables of solar altitudes for every half month and for various localities (calculated or taken from the celestial globe) as well as tables for the shadow curves of cylindrical sundials.[52]

3. The albion. This universal device ("all-by-one"), which combined the properties of the instruments used for reckoning time and location, was devised and built by Richard of Wallingford.[53] His treatise on it (1327) was revised by John of Gmunden, to whom it is often incorrectly attributed. Several manuscripts contain further additions by John, such as a star catalog for 1430 and also (most probably by him) instructions (1433) on the use of the albion in the determination of eclipses.[54] He had earlier used the instrument for this purpose for 1415–1432.[55]

4. The equatorium. This instrument, made of either metal or paper, could represent the motions of the planets.[56] It is found in the thirteenth century in the writings of Campanus and in those of John of Lignères and Ibn Tibbon.[57] John called the device "instrumentum solemne."[58] Following Campanus, he set forth its theoretical basis and described how to make and use it in a work published at the University of Vienna that was highly regarded by Peurbach and Regiomontanus.[59] The manuscripts occasionally also present tables of the mean motion of the sun and moon for 1428.[60]

5. The torquetum. This instrument, whose origin is uncertain, was the subject of a treatise by a Master Franco de Polonia (Paris, 1284); it exists in manu-

 JOHN OF GMUNDEN

scripts of the fourteenth and fifteenth centuries.[61] John completed the treatise with an introduction and a conclusion. In the latter he stated that with the "turketum" one can determine the difference in longitude between two localities.

6. The cylindrical sundial. The origin of this instrument is likewise unknown; it is described as early as the thirteenth century in an Oxford manuscript.[62] John introduced it to Vienna. His work on it, *Tractatus de compositione et usi cylindri*, exists in nineteen manuscripts.[63] From these it can be inferred that he composed his treatise between 1430 and 1438. He calculated the shadow curves at Vienna, taking the latitude as $\varphi = 47°46'$; in the Oxford manuscript φ is taken as $51°50'$. Shadow curves for other localities also appear in the manuscripts.[64]

A further work on sundials and nocturnals was written by John or by one of his students.[65]

The study of mathematics and astronomy beyond what was offered in the quadrivium first became possible at Vienna through the efforts of Henry of Hesse, who brought back from Paris knowledge of the recent advances in mathematics (as is reported by Petrus Ramus[66]). The first evidence of this is found in the work of Nicolaus of Dinkelsbühl, who taught, besides Sacrobosco's astronomy and Euclid's *Elements*, Oresme's "latitudines formarum." His last lecture (1405), on theories of the planets,[67] may have stimulated the young John of Gmunden to study astronomy. In any case, John studied the relevant available writings, transcribed them, and frequently added to them. Although he seldom mentioned his predecessors, his sources can be inferred to some extent. He was acquainted with the Alphonsine and Oxford tables and knew Euclid from the edition prepared by Campanus, to whose ideas on planetary theories he subscribed.[68] In his first tabular work John cited Robert the Englishman.[69] Moreover, his *Algorismus de minuciis phisicis* undoubtedly follows the account of John of Lignères. In 1433 he transcribed and completed John of Murs's treatise on the tables of proportions; hence many manuscripts name him as the author.[70] It is not clear to what extent his treatise on the sine, arc, and chord depended on the work of his predecessors (Levi ben Gerson, John of Murs, John of Lignères, and Dominic de Clavasio). His dependence on earlier authors is most evident in his writings on astronomical instruments (Campanus' equatorium, Ibn Tibbon's new quadrants, Richard of Wallingford's albion, and Franco de Polonia's torquetum). In his will he also mentions a work entitled *Astrolabium Alphonsi*.

John of Gmunden was influential both through his teaching and, long after his death, through his writings. Among his students Tannstetter mentions especially Georg Pruner of Ruspach. There are transcriptions (in London) by the latter of John's works with remarks by Regiomontanus.[71] John's co-workers included Johann Schindel, Ioannes Feldner, and Georg Müstinger, prior of the Augustinian monastery in Klosterneuburg.[72] Fridericus Gerhard (*d.* 1464–1465), of the Benedictine monastery of St. Emmeran in Regensburg, also had connections with the Vienna school; however, they were indirect, being based on his contacts with Master Reinhard of Kloster-Reichenbach, who worked at Klosterneuburg. Gerhard was a compiler of manuscript volumes that reflected the mathematical knowledge of the age; in them he included works by John of Gmunden, drawn partially from a lecture notebook of 1439.[73] Gerhard was particularly interested in geography; and geographical coordinates play a role in astronomy. Thus it is quite possible that his knowledge in this area also came from Vienna.[74]

John of Gmunden greatly influenced Peurbach. To be sure, the latter cannot be considered a direct student of John's since Peurbach was nineteen when John died. Nevertheless, he undoubtedly knew John personally, and he studied his writings thoroughly. The same is known of Regiomontanus, who in his student years at Vienna made critical observations in copies of John's works.[75] He also bought a copy of the treatise on the albion.[76]

The outstanding achievements of Peurbach and Regiomontanus resulted in John of Gmunden's being overshadowed, as can be seen from the small number of manuscripts of his works that date from after the fifteenth century. Yet it was he who initiated the tradition that was established with Peurbach, whose scientific reputation caused the young Regiomontanus to come to Vienna (1450) instead of staying longer at Leipzig.

NOTES

1. *Matrikel der Universität Wien*, I, p. 57. Another John Sartoris de Gmunden is listed in the register for 14 April 1403 (I, p. 65). He cannot yet have been a master in 1406. He may have been the son of another tailor, or it may be a second matriculation.
2. *Acta Facultatis artium Universitatis Viennensis 1385–1416*, p. 212. (Cited below as *AFA*.)
3. *AFA*, p. 261. John of Gmunden is the only one of all the candidates for whom no family name is given; but if it is true (letter from P. Uiblein) that the lectures were distributed to the *magistri legentes* in the same sequence in which they received their *magisterium*, then John is identical with Krafft. Johannes Wissbier of Schwäbisch Gmünd studied at Ulm in 1404. See M. Curtze, "Über Johann von Gmunden," in *Bibliotheca mathematica*, **10**, no. 2 (1896), 4.
4. R. Klug, *Johann von Gmunden*, p. 14. Several variants exist in the MSS, including Gmund, Gmunde, Gmundt,

and Gmundia. Concerning the two dots over the "u" in "Gmünden" see *ibid.*, p. 16. It is not an *Umlaut* but a vowel mark; on this point see H. Rosenfeld, in *Studia neophilologica*, **37** (1965), 126 ff., 132 f.

5. The name Nyder does not appear, as has been asserted, in the obituaries of the canons of St. Stephen. See J. Mundy, "John of Gmunden," p. 198, n. 29. Regarding Schindel, it is a matter of a change of name in the Vienna MSS. See Klug, *op. cit.*, p. 17, Curtze, *op. cit.*, p. 4. In 1407 this scholar left Prague for Vienna, where he taught privately for several years. He is mentioned with praise along with Peurbach and Regiomontanus by Kepler in the preface to the *Rudolphine Tables*. A Master Johannes Krafft lectured on the books of Euclid in 1407 (*AFA*, p. 281). Others also lectured on Euclid around this time (*AFA*, pp. 253, 292, 453).
6. *AFA*, pp. 292, 325, 365, 338, and 401.
7. *AFA*, p. 324: "magistro Iohanni de Gmunden data fuit regencia"; Klug, pp. 18 f.
8. J. Aschbach, *Geschichte der Wiener Universität im ersten Jahrhundert ihres Bestehens*, p. 457.
9. On his deanship see *AFA*, p. 405; Aschbach, *op. cit.*, p. 458. On his posts as examiner see *AFA*, pp. 284, 370, 402. In 1413 he was also examiner of candidates for the licentiate (*AFA*, p. 391).
10. *AFA*, p. 345.
11. *AFA*, p. 421.
12. *AFA*, p. 472; Aschbach, *loc. cit.*
13. *AFA*, p. 530.
14. Mundy, *op. cit.*, p. 199; Klug, *op. cit.*, pp. 20 f.
15. Aschbach, *op. cit.*, p. 459; *AFA*, p. 530.
16. Klug, *op. cit.*, p. 18. Even if he retired in 1434, he was already a clergyman in Laa.
17. *AFA*, p. 530; Klug, *op. cit.*, p. 21.
18. The text of the will is given in Mundy, *op. cit.*, p. 198; Klug, *op. cit.*, pp. 90 ff.
19. E. Zinner, *Leben und Wirken des Johann Müller von Königsberg, genannt Regiomontanus*, p. 196, n. 16. (Cited below as *ZR*.)
20. *AFA*, pp. 381, 430; Klug, *op. cit.*, p. 18. See also Note 5.
21. G. Tannstetter, in *Tabulae eclypsium Magistri Georgii Peurbachii*, wrote: "Libellum de arte calculandi in minuciis phisicis, Tabulas varias de parte proporcionali, Tractatum sinuum" (fol. aa 3v).
22. The title of the compendium is *Contenta in hoc libello*; on this point see D. E. Smith, *Rara arithmetica*, p. 118.
23. See Simon Stevin, *De thiende*, H. Gericke, K. Vogel, ed., in Ostwald's Klassiker der Exacten Wissenschaften, n.s. 1 (Braunschweig, 1965), pp. 47 ff.
24. Mundy, *op. cit.*, p. 199.
25. The treatise on tables of proportions, along with explanatory comments, is cited in E. Zinner, *Verzeichnis der astronomischen Handschriften des deutschen Kulturgebietes*, nos. 3585, 3586, 3695, and 3696 (dated for 1433 and 21 May 1440); two treatises on the sine, chord, and arc are noted in this work by Zinner (cited below as *ZA*) as nos. 3591 and 3592; the letter (from Codex Vindobonensis 5268) was published by Busard (Vienna, 1971); then follows a work on Euclid, also by John of Gmunden.
26. Klug, *op. cit.*, p. 50.
27. Here H = meridian altitude, b = semidiurnal arc, and t = horary angle.
28. Codex Vindobonensis 5203, fol. 54r; *ZR*, p. 25—here $\cos b$ should be altered to $(\cos b - 1)$.
29. Klug, *op. cit.*, p. 18.
30. *ZR*, p. 15. The *Tabula de universo* undoubtedly was also conceived for use at the university; on this point see Mundy, *op. cit.*, p. 206; Klug, *op. cit.*, pp. 63 ff.
31. *ZA*, no. 3584.
32. *ZA*, no. 3732; Mundy, *op. cit.*, p. 204.
33. *ZR*, p. 16.
34. The MSS of the tabular works are as follows:
 Version I: Codex Vindobonensis 5268, fols. 1v–34r (*ZA*, no. 3587; *ZA*, no. 3588 is an extract), with explanation in *ZA*, no. 3589 (from 10 August 1437); the tables were valid for Vienna during 1433, 1436, and 1440, among other years. For a marginal notation by Regiomontanus ("non valet. Nam in alio circulo sumitur declinatio et in alio latitudo") see *ZR*, p. 43.
 Version II: *ZA*, no. 3709 (for 1400).
 Version III: *ZA*, nos. 3710–3716, also *ZA*, no. 3719. MS 3711 (in Codex Vindobonensis 5151) was written by John of Gmunden himself, as was *ZA*, no. 3694 (of 20 May 1440).
 Version IV: *ZA*, nos. 3717, 3718. A student's transcription in a MS at the British Museum is dated 1437; on this point see Mundy, *op. cit.*, p. 202, n. 73.
 Version V: *ZA*, nos. 3691–3693, with explanatory material at nos. 3688–3690 (for 1440, 1444, 1446).
35. On planetary and lunar motions see *ZA*, nos. 3496, 3720, 3721, 3723; moreover, the tables in *ZA*, nos. 11203, 11204, and 11207 ("quamvis de motibus mediis . . .") stem from John of Gmunden (*ZA*, p. 523). On the true planetary latitudes see *ZA*, nos. 3697, 3699 (from 21 and 25 May 1440), 3698, 3700. On the true new and full moons see *ZA*, nos. 3702, 3707, 3708, 3733, 3734. Tables of eclipses are at *ZA*, nos. 3498, 3701, 3703–3706, 3735 (for 1433 and 1440). Further works by him are undoubtedly *ZA*, nos. 3590 (astronomy), 3725 (position of the heavenly spheres), and 3729 (intervals between heavenly bodies). Codex latinus monaiensis 10662, fols. 99v–102r, contains a "Tabula stellarum per venerabilem Joh. de Gmunden" for 1430, and Codex latinus monaiensis 8950, fols. 81r–92v, a treatise on the "radices" of the sun, moon, and "Caput draconis." See Mundy, *op. cit.*, p. 201, n. 72.
36. Tannstetter (fol. aa 3v) records that he left to the library a "Kalendarium quod multis sequentibus annis utile erat et jucundissimum" (perhaps *ZA*, no. 3606).
37. 1st calendar: *ZA*, nos. 3499–3502 (four MSS).
 2nd calendar (nine MSS): *ZA*, nos. 3503–3511, 5378. This was the calendar for whose publication John of Gmunden obtained permission. See Mundy, *op. cit.*, p. 201, n. 71; Klug, *op. cit.*, p. 91.
 3rd calendar (fifteen MSS): *ZA*, nos. 3512–3526; no. 3513 dates from 1431.
 4th calendar: Exists in eighty MSS (Zinner, in 1938, knew of ninety-nine copies [*ZR*, p. 15]): *ZA*, nos. 3606–3687, of which three date from 1439; this calendar was announced at the University of Vienna (*ZA*, p. 425). An extract with explanation by John of Gmunden exists in MS 12118 (*ZA*, p. 536).
38. J. Bauschinger and E. Schröder, "Ein neu entdeckter astronomischer Kalender für das Jahr 1448."
39. Mundy, *op. cit.*, p. 203; Klug, *op. cit.*, pp. 79 ff. (with illustrations on p. 81 and plates VIII and IX); Aschbach, *op. cit.*, pp. 465 ff.
40. Each astronomical instrument served to "grasp the stars" (λαμβάνειν τὰ ἄστρα).
41. Tannstetter (fol. aa 3v) simply groups Campanus' instrument ("equatorium motuum planetarum ex Campano transsumptum") and almost all the others as "Compositio Astrolabii & utilitates eiusdem & quorundam aliorum instrumentorum."
42. An ivory quadrant in the Kunsthistorisches Museum in Vienna was undoubtedly designed by John of Gmunden. See *ZR*, p. 16; Klug, *op. cit.*, p. 26.
43. *ZA*, nos. 3593, 3593a–3605.
44. *ZA*, no. 3593; *ZA*, no. 3602 contains still another star catalog as well as tables for the rising of the signs and for the entrance of the sun into the signs for the year 1425.
45. *ZA*, nos. 3555–3569.
46. *ZA*, p. 424. On Ibn Tibbon see R. T. Gunther, *Early Science in Oxford*, II, 164.
47. *ZA*, p. 468.
48. *ZA*, nos. 3556, 3557, 3569 for the table of true positions;

ZA, nos. 3557, 3559, 3561, 3562 for the star catalogs; and for the sun's entrance into the zodiac signs *ZA*, nos. 3557 and 3564 for 1424; no. 3568 for 1425; and no. 3569.
49. *ZA*, no. 3570; additional material in *ZA*, no. 3724 contains tables of equatorial altitudes. In the same volume of MSS there is also an essay on solar quadrants that is by either John of Gmunden or a student of his (*ZA*, no. 3731).
50. *ZA*, nos. 3571–3583.
51. *ZA*, no. 3578.
52. For solar attitudes see *ZA*, nos. 3572, 3578, 3580 for Vienna, Nuremberg, Klosterneuburg, Prague, Venice, Rome, and the town of "Cöppt"; for tables of shadow curves see *ZA*, no. 3578 for the places named and for Regensburg. In addition, nos. 3577, 3579, 3583 have tables for Vienna; and no. 3576 has them for Vienna and Nuremberg.
53. Gunther, *op. cit.*, pp. 49 f., 349 ff.; *ZA*, nos. 11584–11586; p. 52 g.
54. *ZA*, nos. 11590–11593, 11596, and p. 529.
55. *ZA*, no. 3498.
56. Perhaps the wooden instruments (*theorice lignee*) named in the will are such equatoria.
57. Gunther, *op. cit.*, p. 234.
58. *ZA*, no. 3527–3535; s. 2A p. 423.
59. John of Gmunden's explanation of Campanus' work is *ZA*, no. 1912; construction and use of the instrument is at *ZA*, p. 423.
60. *ZA*, nos. 3527, 3531.
61. *ZA*, nos. 2787–2800 and p. 416. See also G. Sarton, *Introduction to the History of Science*, II, 1005 and III, 1846; and Gunther, *op. cit.*, pp. 35, 370 ff.
62. Gunther, *op. cit.*, p. 123. There had been a MS in Germany since the fourteenth century.
63. *ZA*, nos. 3536–3554.
64. Venice, Rome, Nuremberg, Prague, and Klosterneuburg; they stem in part from John of Gmunden and in part from Prior Georg. Moreover, tables of solar altitudes for Vienna, Nuremberg, and Prague are appended to some of the MSS (*ZA*, p. 424).
65. *ZA*, nos. 3722, 3726, 3727, 3730.
66. Petrus Ramus, *Mathematicarum scholarum, libri duo* (Basel, 1569), p. 64: "Henricus Hassianus . . . primo mathematicas artes Lutetia Viennam transtulit" (Aschbach, *op. cit.*, p. 386, n. 3).
67. *AFA*, p. 253.
68. A star catalog is completed in *ZA*, no 452. See also *ZA*, p. 390. The tables of the planetary latitudes in *ZA*, no. 3700 were taken from the Oxford tables (*ZA*, p. 426). On Campanus' edition of Euclid, see *ZA*, no. 1912 and p. 405.
69. *ZR*, p. 14; Mundy, *op. cit.*, p. 200.
70. *ZA*, no. 7423; on his being considered the author, see *ZA*, p. 475.
71. *ZR*, pp. 15, 43; Mundy, *op. cit.*, pp. 197, 202, n. 73.
72. *ZA*, p. 529: "Selder"; Mundy, *op. cit.*, p. 197. Tannstetter, fol. aa 3^v: Schinttel.
73. *ZR*, pp. 50 f.; see also *ZA*, nos. 3565, 3578, 10979, 11198, 11205, 11206.
74. D. B. Durand, "The Earliest Modern Maps of Germany and Central Europe," p. 498; Mundy, *Eine Schrift über Orts Koordinaten*, in *ZA*, 3728.
75. *ZR*, p. 43.
76. *ZR*, pp. 53, 218; here one can find references to other works by John of Gmunden that Regiomontanus studied (and in part copied).

BIBLIOGRAPHY

I. ORIGINAL WORKS. The only works by John of Gmunden to be printed, except for the posthumous calendars mentioned above, were the treatise on the sine (see below on Busard) and the "Algorithmus Magistri Joannis de Gmunden de minuciis phisicis," which appeared in a compendium prepared by Joannes Sigrenius, entitled *Contenta in hoc libello* (Vienna, 1515). A facsimile of the title page is given in Smith, *Rara arithmetica*, p. 117. An extract on the finding of roots is in C. J. Gerhardt, *Geschichte der Mathematik in Deutschland* (Munich, 1877), pp. 7 f. John of Gmunden's will is published in Mundy, "John of Gmunden," p. 198; and in Klug, "Johann von Gmunden," p. 90 ff., with a facsimile of the first page. All his other writings are preserved only in MS; they were compiled by Zinner in *ZA*.

Three MSS are obtainable in microfilm or photostatic reproduction (Document 1645 of the American Documentation Institute, 1719 N Street, N.W., Washington, D.C.; in this regard see Mundy, *op. cit.*, p. 196):

1. Codex latinus Monaiensis 7650, fols. 1r–8r (the calendar cited at *ZA*, no. 3524).

2. Cod. lat. Mon. 8950, fol. 81v ("Proprietates signorum," *ZA*, no. 3732).

3. Cod. St. Flor. XI, 102, 1rv (letter to Jacob de Clusa, *ZA*, no. 3584; this letter was published in Klug, *op. cit.*, pp. 61 ff.).

II. SECONDARY LITERATURE. See *Acta Facultatis artium Universitatis Viennensis 1385–1416*, P. Uiblein, ed. (Vienna, 1968), a publication of the Institut für Österreichische Geschichtsforschung, 6th ser., Abt. 2; J. Aschbach, *Geschichte der Wiener Universität im ersten Jahrhundert ihres Bestehens* (Vienna, 1865), pp. 455–467; J. Bauschinger and E. Schröder, "Ein neu entdeckter astronomischer Kalender für das Jahr 1448," in *Veröffentlichungen der Gutenberg-Gesellschaft*, **1** (1902), 4–14; D. B. Durand, "The Earliest Modern Maps of Germany and Central Europe," in *Isis*, **19** (1933), 486–502; R. T. Gunther, *Early Science in Oxford*, II, *Astronomy* (Oxford, 1923); R. Klug, "Johann von Gmunden, der Begründer der Himmelskunde auf deutschem Boden. Nach seinen Schriften und den Archivalien der Wiener Universität," Akademie der Wissenschaften Wien, Phil.-hist. Kl., Sitzungsberichte, **222**, no. 4 (1943), 1–93; *Die Matrikel der Universität Wien*, I, *1377–1435*, ed. by the Institut für Österreichische Geschichtsforschung (Vienna, 1956); J. Mundy, "John of Gmunden," in *Isis*, **34** (1942–1943), 196–205; G. Sarton, *Introduction to the History of Science*, III (Baltimore, 1948), 1112 f.; D. E. Smith, *Rara arithmetica* (Boston–London, 1908, 117, 449); G. Tannstetter, *Tabulae eclypsium Magistri Georgii Peurbachii. Tabula primi mobilis Joannis de Monteregio* (Vienna, 1514), which contains *Viri mathematici quos inclytum Viennense gymnasium ordine celebres habuit*, fol. aa 3^v; L. Thorndike and P. Kibre, *A Catalogue of Incipits of Mediaeval Scientific Writings in Latin* (London, 1963), index, p. 1838; and E. Zinner, *Verzeichnis der astronomischen Handschriften des deutschen Kulturgebietes* (Munich, 1925), 119–126; and *Leben und Wirken des Johann Müller von Königsberg, genannt Regiomontanus* (Munich, 1938), pp. 14 ff. and index, p. 284.

See also H. H. Busard, "Der Traktat De sinibus, chordis et arcubus von Johannes von Gmunden," in

Denkschriften der Akademie der Wissenschaften, **116** (Vienna, 1971), 73–113.

KURT VOGEL

JOHN OF LIGNÈRES, or **Johannes de Lineriis** (*fl.* France, first half of fourteenth century)

Originally from the diocese of Amiens, where any of several communes could account for his name, John of Lignères lived in Paris from about 1320 to 1335. There he published astronomical and mathematical works on the basis of which he is, with justice, credited with diffusion of the Alfonsine tables in the Latin West.[1]

In astronomy the work of John of Lignères includes tables and canons of tables, a theory of the planets, and treatises on instruments. The tables and the canons of tables have often been confused among themselves or with the works of other contemporary Paris astronomers named John: John of Murs, John of Saxony, John of Sicily, and John of Montfort. There are three canons by John of Lignères.

1. The canons beginning *Multiplicis philosophie variis radiis* . . . are sometimes designated as the *Canones super tabulas magnas;* they provide the daily and annual variations of the mean motions and mean arguments of the planets in a form which, although not the most common, is not exceptional. The tables of equations, on the other hand, are completely original: one enters them with both mean argument and mean center at the same time and reads off directly a single compound equation, the sum of the equation of center and the corrected equation of argument; it is sufficient to add this compound equation to the mean motion in order to obtain the true position. The tables also permit the calculation of the mean and true conjunctions and oppositions of the sun and the moon; but there is no provision for the determination of the eclipses and for planetary latitudes. The radix of the mean motions is of the time of Christ, but the longitude is not specified (in all probability that of Paris); nevertheless, since the list of apogees is established by reckoning from 1320, *Tabule magne* may be dated approximately to that year.

The canons are dedicated, as is the treatise on the saphea (see below), to Robert of Florence, dean of Glasgow in 1325.[2] It is not certain whether these tables were calculated on the basis of the Alfonsine tables, which John of Lignères would therefore already have known.[3] Although certain characteristics (the use of physical signs of thirty degrees and not of natural signs of sixty degrees) are not decisive, the tables of the equations of Jupiter and Venus appear to be calculated following neither those of the Alfonsine tables nor the Ptolemaic eccentricities:[4] insofar as one can judge on the basis of tables from which it is difficult to derive the equation of center and the equation of argument, the eccentricities used are not the customary ones.

The text of the canons of John of Lignères is very concise. It was the object of an explanatory effort by John of Speyer, *Circa canonem de inventione augium*. . ., which may have been written in 1348, since it contains an example calculated for that year.[5]

2. In 1322[6] John of Lignères composed a set of tables completely different from the preceding. (One cannot tell, however, if they are earlier or later than the *Tabule magne*.) These tables, and especially their canons, are in three parts often found separately, particularly the first. The canons of the *primum mobile* (*Cujuslibet arcus propositi sinum rectum* . . .), in forty-four chapters, correspond to the trigonometric part of the tables and consider the problems linked to the daily movement of the sun: trigonometric operations, the determination of the ascendant and of the celestial houses, of equal and unequal hours, and so on. Three of the canons describe the instruments used in astronomical observation: Ptolemaic parallactic rulers and a quadrant firmly fixed in the plane of the meridian. The corresponding part of the tables is thus made up of a table of sines, a table of declinations (the maximum declination is 23°33′30″), and tables of right and oblique ascensions for the latitude of Cremona and of Paris (seventh clima). This portion of the canons is not dated, and the contents do not provide any chronological information whatever; but it is reasonable to suppose that the canons were published at the same time as the tables and the canons of the movements of the planets, with which they form a harmonious ensemble.

The canons of the *primum mobile* were the object of a commentary, accompanied by many worked-out examples, by John of Saxony (*ca.* 1335): *Quia plures astrologorum diversos libros fecerunt* . . . . One of the canons of the *primum mobile*, no. 37, concerning the equation of the celestial houses, was printed at the end of the canons by John of Saxony that were appended to the edition of the Alfonsine tables published by Erhard Ratdolt in 1483.

The canons of the movements of the planets form the second part of the treatise whose first part comprises the canons of the *primum mobile: Prior s astrologi motus corporum celestium* . . . . They treat the conversion of eras (very briefly), the determination of the true positions of the planets and of their latitudes, the mean and true conjunctions and oppositions of the sun and the moon and their eclipses, the coor-

 JOHN OF LIGNÈRES

dinates of the stars, and the revolution of the years. The corresponding tables give (*a*) chronological schemes which permit the conversion from one era to another with a sexagesimal computation of the years; (*b*) the mean motions and mean arguments of the planets for groups of twenty years (*anni collecti*), single years (*anni expansi*), months, and days—both for the epoch of the Christian era and 31 December 1320 at the meridian of Paris; and (*c*) the tables of equations according to the usual presentation.

These canons, which are usually dated by their explicit references to 1322, allude to the Alfonsine tables, to which the tables of John of Lignères are certainly related, if only by the adoption of the motion compounded from precession and accession and recession for the planetary auges. Yet the longitudes of the stars, established by adding a constant to Ptolemy's longitudes, are not the same as those of Alfonso X. Nor are the tables of equations of Jupiter and Venus those ordinarily found in the Alfonsine tables or those of the *Tabule magne* but, rather, the equations of the Toledan tables. On the other hand, John of Lignères used the physical signs of thirty degrees and not the natural signs of sixty degrees. J. L. E. Dreyer observed that the Castilian canons of the Alfonsine tables in their original version, as they were published by Rico y Sinobas, do not correspond at all to the tables commonly designated as Alfonsine; he believed he had found them in a state closer to the original in the Oxford tables constructed by William Reed with the year 1340 as radix.[7] It is reasonable to suppose that the tables of John of Lignères represent, twenty years before Reed, an analogous effort to reduce the Castilian tables to the meridian of Paris; he preserved their general structure, and notably three characteristics: the compound motion of the auges (precession and accession and recession), physical signs of thirty degrees, and tables of periodic movements presented on the basis of twenty-year *anni collecti*.

The part of the canons of 1322 dealing with the determination of eclipses frequently appears separately (*Diversitatem aspectus lune in longitudine et latitudine*), despite the many references made to the preceding canons—references that thereby lose all significance.

In 1483 some of the canons on the planetary motions were included in the edition of the Alfonsine tables and with the canons of John of Saxony: canons 21–23, concerning the determination of the latitudes of the three superior planets and of Venus and Mercury, and canons 38 and 40, on eclipses.

3. Finally, John of Lignères wrote canons beginning *Quia ad inveniendum loca planetarum* . . . in order to treat the tabular material ordinarily designated as Alfonsine tables.[8] The signs are the natural signs of sixty degrees, and the tables of the mean motions and mean arguments of the planets consist of the sexagesimal multiples of the motions during the day. The chronological portion has, obviously, had to be increased since with this system, in order to enter the tables of mean motions, it is necessary to transform a date expressed in any given calendar into a number of days in sexagesimal numeration. As it is certain that the sexagesimal form of the Alfonsine tables does not represent their original state, there is firm evidence for believing that the transformation which they underwent was carried out at Paris in the 1320's, either by John of Lignères himself, under his direction, or under the direction of John of Murs. The date of these very succinct new canons cannot be determined from the text; but it is certainly later than that of the canons *Priores astrologi* . . . (1322) and may perhaps be earlier than 1327, when John of Saxony produced a new version of the canons of the Alfonsine tables.

For those who are aware of the almost universal diffusion of the Alfonsine tables at the end of the Middle Ages, almost to the exclusion of any other tables, there is no need to emphasize John of Lignères's exceptional role in the history of astronomy. The magnitude of the work that he and his collaborators accomplished in so few years is admirable. Although there is no formal proof of the existence of a team of workers, the terms in which John of Saxony expressed his admiration for his "maître" bear witness to the enthusiasm that John of Lignères evoked.

In order to complete the account of John of Lignères's work on astronomical tables, we must notice the execution of an almanac conceived, like that of Ibn Tibbon (Profacius), on the principle of the "revolutions" of each planet and therefore theoretically usable in perpetuity, provided a correction is applied based on the number of revolutions intervening since the starting date (1321) of the almanac. The work appears to be preserved in only one manuscript, unfortunately incomplete, with a short canon: *Subtrahe ab annis Christi 1320 annos Christi* . . . .

John of Lignères's theory of the planets, *Spera concentrica vel circulus concentricus dicitur* . . ., represents the theoretical exposition of the principles of the astronomy of planetary motions, the application of which is furnished by the Alfonsine tables. In particular this theory provides a detailed justification of the compound motion of the eighth sphere; in it the author strives to demonstrate at length the inanity of the solution recommended by Thābit ibn Qurra (a motion of simple accession and recession). Furthermore, he promises to return, in a work which it is not known whether he wrote, to certain difficulties remaining under the Alfonsine theory. John of Lignères provided no indication of the values of the planetary eccentricities, of the lengths of the radii of the epicycles, or of the values of the various motions at any particular date. The only precise information, the reference to the position of the star Alchimech in 1335, allows the text to be dated about that year.

John of Lignères's astronomical work also included treatises on three instruments: the saphea, the equatorium, and the directorium. The saphea is an astrolabe with a peculiar system of stereographic projection: the pole of projection is one of the points of intersection of the equator and the ecliptic, and the plane of projection is that of the colure of the solstices. Following a rather clumsy effort by William the Englishman in 1231 to reconstruct the principle of an instrument attributed to al-Zarqāl that he no doubt had never seen, the saphea was introduced in the West by the translation, done by Ibn Tibbon in 1263, of al-Zarqāl's treatise. The saphea described by John of Lignères (*Descriptiones que sunt in facie instrumenti notificate . . .*) presents technically several improvements over al-Zarqāl's instruments.[9] The most notable is the use of a kind of rete, the *circulus mobilis*, consisting of a graduated circle of the same diameter as the face and an arc of circle bearing the stereographic projection of the northern half of the zodiac, as in the classic astrolabe. The diameter that subtends this projection of the zodiac carries a graduation similar to almucantars on the meridian line of the astrolabe's tablet; a rule graduated in the same manner can be mounted on the *circulus mobilis*, forming a given angle with the diameter of the latter. On such an instrument one may consider either (1) one of the diameters of the face as a horizon, in the projection which characterizes the saphea: the diameter of the *circulus mobilis* then serves to refer to this horizon every position located in the unique system of the almucantars and of the azimuths traced on the instrument for the diameter of the horizon (this is the principle used in al-Zarqāl's canons); or (2) the almucantars of the face as the horizons of a tablet of the horizons in a classic stereographic projection bounded by the equator: the half of the ecliptic traced on the *circulus mobilis* then plays the same role as the ordinary rete. The judicious alternate use of both systems allowed John of Lignères to offer simpler and more rapid solutions to the problems dealt with in al-Zarqāl's canons without losing any of the saphea's advantages.

John of Lignères wrote two treatises on the equatorium. The first, *Quia nobilissima scientia astronomie non potest . . .*, is an adaptation of Campanus' instrument.[10] In order to find the true positions of the planets, Campanus recommended a series of three disks, that is, six "instruments" (one on each face of one disk), which reproduced fairly closely the schema of the geometric analysis of the planetary motions. John of Lignères maintained this principle but simplified the construction by adopting a common disk to bear the equants of all the planets (but not the moon). To avoid difficulties in reading, the equants are represented by a circle without graduations; and these ones, which begin at a different point for each planet, are replaced by a graduated ring which is superposed on the equant in the position suitable to the planet for which one is operating. The radii of the deferents are represented by a small rule bearing, on one side, a nail to be fixed in the center of the deferent of the planet, and on the other, an epicycle at the center of which is turning another small rule bearing, at appropriate distances, the "bodies" of the planets. Two threads represent the radius of the equant which measures the mean center and the radius of the zodiac which passes through the planet.

The other treatise on the equatorium (uses: *Primo linea recta que est in medio regule . . .*; construction: *Fiat primo regula de auricalco seu cupro . . .*[11]) is fundamentally different from the first. The problem is no longer to reproduce the geometric construction of a planet's true position but, rather, to calculate graphically, so to speak, the angular corrections (equation of center and equation of argument) that, added to the mean motion of a planet, determine its true position. The sole function of the instrument's five parts (the so-called ruler of the center of the epicycle, the disk of the centers, the epicycle, the square carrying the "bodies" of the planets, and the rule for reading off) therefore is to furnish and to position in relation to each other the parameters of the planets (eccentricities, epicycle radii). Successively determined—exactly as in a calculation carried out with the Alfonsine tables—are the equation of center on the basis of the mean center, then the equation of argument on the basis of the true center and the true argument; the true position is obtained by adding the two equations to the mean motion.

The astrologer Simon de Phares, whose account of John of Lignères is otherwise fairly correct, attributes to him a directorium the incipit of which ("*Accipe tabulam planam rotundam cujus . . .*") corresponds very closely to that of a text on this instrument preserved in at least four anonymous manuscripts: "Accipe tabulam planam mundam super cujus extremitatem . . . ."[12] The directorium was used only for astrology: it served to "direct" a planet or a point in the zodiac having a particular astrological value, that is, to lead it to another point in the zodiac by counting the degrees of the equator corresponding to this course. In fact, it is very similar to the astrolabe, except that the fixed celestial reference sphere, represented only by the horizon of the place and by the meridian line, is made to turn above the sphere of the stars and of the zodiac. Since, in a good calculation of "direction," the latitude of the planets must be taken into account, the zodiac is represented by a wide band on which are traced its almucantars and its azimuths, as far as six degrees on either side of the ecliptic. John of Lignères's directorium presents no special features.

Finally, a Vatican manuscript attributes to John of Lignères an "armillary instrument" that is difficult to define (*Rescriptiones* [read *Descriptiones*] *que sunt in facie instrumenti notificare. Trianguli equilateri ex tribus quartis arcus circuli magni* . . .): in the absence of a section on its construction, the uses and the brief description that precede them give a very imperfect idea of the instrument, which appears to derive from the new quadrant. John of Lignères's idea seems to have been to replace the rotation of the margarites (which, in the new quadrant, compensated for the immobility in which this instrument held the rete of the astrolabe because of the reduction of the latter to one of its quarters)[13] by the rotation of another quarter-disk bearing the oblique horizon. This conception amounted to a return to what had constituted the justification of the stereographic projection characterizing the astrolabe, that is, to the rotation of the sphere of the stars and of the zodiac on the celestial sphere used for reference but with a reversal, as in the directorium, of the respective roles of the spheres.[14]

None of John of Lignères's treatises on astronomical instruments is dated or contains information from which a date can be established. Nevertheless, the preface to the canons of the *Tabule magne*, addressed to Robert of Florence, notes the simultaneous sending, along with the tables, of an equatorium and a "universal astrolabe." The latter should be identified with the saphea; as for the equatorium, defined as suitable to furnish "easily and rapidly the equations of the planets," it is more likely to be the second of the instruments described above.[15]

We have seen the development that John of Lignères gave to sexagesimal numeration in the astronomical tables, since the tables of the regular movements of the planets in the Alfonsine tables have been modified so as to permit the systematic use of this type of numeration. He was so aware of the astronomer's need for its use that he introduced, at the beginning of the canons of the *Tabule magne*, a long section on the technique of working on the "physical minutes." He took up the question again and expounded it in the *Algorismus minutiarum*, in which he simultaneously treated physical fractions and vulgar fractions. Its great success is attested to by the number of manuscripts in which the *Algorismus* is preserved.

NOTES

1. P. Duhem, *Le système du monde*, IV (Paris, 1916), 578–581, following G. Bigourdan, maintains that John of Lignères was alive after 1350; he bases this on a letter from Wendelin to Gassendi that mentions the positions of the stars determined by John of Lignères and reproduced by John of Speyer in his *Rescriptum super canones J. de Lineriis.* As long as John of Speyer's work had not been found, one could—just barely—give credence to this tale. But the *Rescriptum* of John of Speyer, identified through MS Paris lat. 10263—see E. Poulle, *La bibliothèque scientifique d'un imprimeur humaniste au XVe siècle* (Geneva, 1963), p. 49—and dating from about 1348, makes no reference to any table of stars.
2. G. Sarton, *Introduction to the History of Science*, III (Baltimore, 1947), 649*n.*
3. Despite the title of the MS Paris lat. 7281, fol. 201v: *Canones super tabulas magnas per J. de Lineriis computatas ex tabulis Alfonsii* (in another hand: *ad meridianum Parisiensem*).
4. The equations of Jupiter and Venus given in the Alfonsine tables use simultaneously two values for the eccentricities of these planets. See E. Poulle and O. Gingerich, "Les positions des planètes au moyen âge: application du calcul électronique aux tables alphonsines," in *Comptes rendus des séances de l'Académie des inscriptions et belles-lettres* (1967), pp. 531–548, esp. 541.
5. See note 1.
6. Some MSS, notably MS Paris lat. 7281, fol. 201v, which Duhem used in constructing his account, give the date as 1320: it corresponds to the epoch of the tables (31 Dec. 1320), that is, to the beginning of the first year following the closest leap year to the date of composition of the tables and canons.
7. J. L. E. Dreyer, "On the Original Form of the Alfonsine Tables," in *Monthly Notices of the Royal Astronomical Society*, **80** (1919–1920), 243–262. M. Rico y Sinobas, *Libros del saber del rey d. Alfonso X de Castilla*, IV (Madrid, 1866), 111–183; the tables actually published by Rico y Sinobas, in facs. (*ibid.*, pp. 185 ff.), are spurious, as J.-M. Millás Vallicrosa has shown in *Estudios sobre Azarquiel* (Madrid–Granada, 1943–1950), pp. 407–408.
8. The Alfonsine tables reorganized at the time of John of Lignères are shorter than those published in 1483, which were completed by tables of ascensions, by tables of proportion and by tables for the calculation of eclipses. A portion of this supplement, but not the whole of it, is borrowed from John of Lignères's tables of the *primum mobile* and from the part of the tables of 1322 dealing with the calculation of eclipses; but the canons *Quia ad inveniendum* . . . are silent on the use of this part of the tables and give no special attention to eclipses. In the medieval MSS the list of the tables forming the Alfonsine tables varies considerably from one MS to another, and it is very difficult to reconstruct the original core of the text; one can rely on little more than the uses specified by the canons.
9. John of Lignères's treatise on the saphea contains only uses, preceded by a chapter of description. But the MS Paris lat. 7295, which preserves the text of the treatise (fols. 2–14), also included (fols. 18v–19) two incomplete and unidentified drawings; these must be compared with John of Lignères's text, which they illustrate most pertinently.

   On the saphea, see G. García Franco, *Catalogo crítico de astrolabios existentes en España* (Madrid, 1945), pp. 64–

 JOHN OF LIGNÈRES

65; M. Michel, *Traité de l'astrolabe* (Paris, 1947), pp. 95–97; and E. Poulle, "Un instrument astronomique dans l'occident latin, la saphea," in *A Giuseppe Ermini* (Spoleto, 1970), pp. 491–510, esp. pp. 499–502.

10. In MS Oxford, Digby 57, fols. 130–132v, the same incipit introduces another treatise on the equatorium, composed at Oxford with 31 December 1350 as the radix. MS Paris fr. 2013, fols. 2–8v, preserves a text in French ("Pour composer l'equatoire des sept planètes . . .") presented as the translation, in 1415, of a treatise on the equatorium by John of Lignères written in 1360; besides the fact that the date cannot be accepted, the instrument, although similar to John of Lignères's first equatorium, is not identical.
11. The part dealing with its construction is found in only one of the two MSS of the texts, and there it is placed after the uses. The incipit "Descriptiones (eorum) que sunt in equatorio . . ." noted by L. Thorndike and P. Kibre in *Catalogue of Incipits*, 2nd ed. (Cambridge, Mass., 1963), col. 402, is the title of the descriptive chapter that broaches the section on the uses.
12. E. Wickersheimer, ed., *Recueil des plus célèbres astrologues et quelques hommes doctes faict par Symon de Phares* (Paris, 1929), p. 214.
13. On the new quadrant, see E. Poulle, "Le quadrant nouveau médiéval," in *Journal des savants* (1964), pp. 148–167, 182–214.
14. MS Berlin F. 246, fol. 155, preserves extracts from a *Tractatus de mensurationibus* by John of Lignères: they are actually several of the chapters from the section on geometric uses in the treatise on the armillary instrument, a section extremely similar, in terms of its contents, to the treatise on the ancient quadrant by Robert the Englishman.
15. Paris lat. 7281, fol. 202: "Post multas excogitatas vias, feci instrumentum modici sumptus, levis ponderis, quantitate parvum et continentia magnum quod planetarium equatorium nuncupavi, eo quod in eo faciliter et prompte eorum equationes habetur; . . . unum composui instrumentum omnium predictorum instrumentorum [astrolabe, saphea, solid sphere] vires et excellentias continens quod merito universale astrolabium nuncupatur, eo quod unica superficie tota celi machina continetur et illa eadem cunctis regionibus applicatur . . .. Suscipiatis, o domine decane, instrumenta et tabulas que vobis . . . offero."

BIBLIOGRAPHY

I. Original Works. Of the canons and tables written by John of Lignères, only the canons of the *primum mobile* (the first part of the canons of 1322) have been published in part: M. Curtze, "Urkunden zur Geschichte der Trigonometrie im christlichen Mittelalter," in *Bibliotheca mathematica*, ser. 3, **1** (1900), pt. 7, 321–416, pp. 390–413: "Die canones tabularum primi mobilis des Johannes de Lineriis"; there are the first nineteen canons (pp. 391–403), followed by the titles of the succeeding canons, as well as by the tables of sines and chords and of shadows and the *tabula proportionis* (pp. 411–413); canon 9 of the *canones super tabulas latitudinum planetarum et etiam eclipsium* (the second part of the canons of 1322) is also included (pp. 403–404). See also J.-M. Millás Vallicrosa (note 7), p. 414. To study John of Lignères's work on astronomical tables recourse to the MSS is therefore necessary.

The almanac of 1321 is in MS Philadelphia Free Library 3, fols. 3–10 (the beginning is incomplete).

The *Tabule magne* are very rare. The canons are in Erfurt 4° 366, fols. 28–32v; Paris lat. 7281, fols. 201v–205v; and Paris lat. 10263, fols. 70–78. The tables are in Erfurt F.388, fols. 1–42; and (tables of equations only) Lisbon Ajuda 52-VI-25, fols. 67–92v.

The tables and the canons of 1322, on the other hand, are fairly common; but the tables themselves are seldom complete, probably because those among them that duplicated the Alfonsine tables were not so well accepted as the latter and hence only the tables for the *primum mobile*, those for the latitudes, and those for the eclipses were preserved: Basel F.II.7, fols. 38–57v, 62–77v (incomplete canons and tables in part); Catania 85, fols. 144–173 (canons), 192–201v (partial tables); Erfurt 4° 366, fols. 1–25v (canons only); Paris lat. 7281, fols. 178v–201v (canons only); Paris lat. 7282, fols. 46v–52v (canons), 113–128v (partial tables); Paris lat. 7286 C, fols. 9–58v (tables and canons), etc. The canons of the *primum mobile* often appear alone: Paris lat. 7286, fols. 35–42v (unfinished canons and partial tables); Paris lat. 7290 A, fols. 66–75v; Paris lat. 7292, fols. 1–12v; Paris lat. 7378 A, fols. 46–52. The canons of the planetary movements likewise are frequently found by themselves: Cusa 212, fols. 74–108 (with tables); Paris lat. 7295 A, fols. 155–181v (with tables); Paris lat. 7407, fols. 40–63, etc. Those of John of Lignères's tables and canons that, for the latitudes and the eclipses, complete the Alfonsine tables are sometimes integrated into the latter, as in Paris lat. 7432, fols. 224–358v. The portion of the canons that treats eclipses can be found separately: Paris lat. 7329, fols. 127–131v.

See also Cracow 557, fols. 58–96 v (canons and partial tables).

John of Lignères's canons on the Alfonsine tables, while much less common than those of John of Saxony, are nevertheless not rare: Cusa 212, fols. 65–66v; Oxford, Digby 168, fols. 145–146; Oxford, Hertford College 4, fols. 148v–155; Paris lat. 7281, fols. 175–178; Paris lat. 7286, fols. 1–3v; Paris lat. 7405, fols. 1–4v. Moreover, they often duplicate those of John of Saxony.

John of Lignères's other astronomical works do not seem to have had as great a diffusion. The theory of the planets is preserved in Cambridge Mm.3.11, fols. 76–80v; Paris lat. 7281, fols. 165–172. Another Cambridge MS, Gg.6.3, fols. 237v–260, also preserves this text in a version that appears to be quite different, but this MS is very mutilated and practically unusable.

The saphea can be found (the incipit of which is very similar to the one in Ibn Tibbon's translation of al-Zarqāl's treatise) in Erfurt 4° 355, fols. 73–81v; Erfurt 4° 366, fols. 40–49; Paris lat. 7295, fols. 2–14. The first chapter (description) was published in L. A. Sédillot, "Mémoire sur les instruments astronomiques des Arabes," in *Mémoires présentés par divers savants à l'Académie des inscriptions et belles-lettres*, ser. 1, **1** (1844), 1–220, see 188–189n.

The first treatise on the equatorium was published by D. J. Price as an appendix to the treatise attributed to Chaucer: *The Equatorie of the Planetis* (Cambridge, 1955), pp. 188–196, but the text is very defective and it is still necessary to refer to the MSS: Cambridge Gg.6.3, fols. 217v–220v; Cracow 555, fols. 11–12v; Cracow 557, fols. 11–12v; Oxford, Digby 168, fols. 65v–66; and Vatican

Palat. 1375, fols. 8v–10v. The treatise on the equatorium preserved in Oxford, Digby 57, fols. 130–132v, under the same incipit, is not the one by John of Lignères. The second equatorium is unpublished: Vatican Urbin. lat. 1399, fols. 16–21 (uses and construction); Oxford, Digby 228, fols. 53v–54v (uses only).

The treatise on the directorium, *Accipe tabulam planam* . . ., is found only anonymously in Florence, Magl. XX.53, fols. 35–37; Oxford, Digby 48, fols. 91v–94; Salamanca 2621, fols. 21v–23; Wolfenbuttel 2816, fols. 125–126v. The armillary instrument is attributed to John of Lignères in Vatican Urbin. lat. 1399, fols. 2–15.

The *Algorismus minutiarum* (*Modum representationis minutiarum vulgarium* . . .) was published very early: Padua, 1483 (Klebs 167.1) and Venice, 1540. See A. Favaro, "Intorno alla vita ed alle opere di Prosdocimo de' Beldomandi," in *Bullettino di bibliografia e di storia delle scienze matematiche e fisiche*, **12** (1879), 115–125; D. E. Smith, *Rara arithmetica* (Boston, 1908), pp. 13–15; and H. L. L. Busard, "Het rekenen met breuken in de middeleeuwen, in het bijzonder bij Johannes de Lineriis," in *Mededelingen van de K. academie voor wetenschappen, letteren en schoone kunsten van België* (1968). There are a great many MSS of this work.

II. SECONDARY LITERATURE. Pierre Duhem, *Le système du monde*, IV (Paris, 1916), 60–69, 578–581; and L. Thorndike, *A History of Magic and Experimental Science*, III (New York, 1934), 253–262, although they supersede most of the earlier works—see G. Sarton, *Introduction to the History of Science*, III (Baltimore, 1947), 649–652— do not really bring John of Lignères's work into clear focus; the canons of the tables, especially, have been confused with each other and with the treatises on the instruments. Moreover, Duhem's hypothesis that the *Algorismus minutiarum* ought to be attributed to John of Sicily rather than to John of Lignères is not based on any serious evidence: the medieval attribution is unanimously to John of Lignères.

EMMANUEL POULLE

JOHN OF MURS (*fl.* France, first half of the fourteenth century)

Originally from the diocese of Lisieux in Normandy, John of Murs was active in science from 1317 until at least 1345. He wrote most of his works in Paris, at the Sorbonne, where he was already a master of arts in 1321. Between 1338 and 1342 he was among the clerks of Philippe III d'Évreux, king of Navarre, and in 1344 he was canon of Mézières-en-Brenne, in the diocese of Bourges.[1] The date of his death is not known. His letter to Clement VI on the conjunctions of 1357 and 1365 must have been sent before the pope's death in 1352; on the other hand, the chronicler Jean de Venette prefaced his account of the year 1340 with two prophecies, one for the year 1315 and the other, no date given, attributed to John of Murs, of whom he speaks in the past tense.[2] But this prophecy is probably not by John of Murs.[3] Moreover, Jean de Venette, whose information is not necessarily firsthand, wrote his chronicle at different times and probably made corrections and additions which do not permit the assignment of a definite year to the composition of the account of the year 1340.[4] There has been an attempt to argue that John of Murs's life extended beyond the accession of Philippe de Vitry to the see of Meaux in 1351, but there is no ground for accepting this assertion.

John of Murs wrote a great deal, but certain of his works appear not to have been preserved. Among the missing are one on squaring the circle and a "genealogia astronomie," both cited at the end of the *Canones tabule tabularum* as composed in 1321. The other writings are devoted to music, mathematics, and astronomy.

John of Murs's musical works include *Ars nove musice*, composed in 1319, according to the explicit of one of the manuscripts; *Musica speculativa secundum Boetium*, dating from 1323 and written at the Sorbonne; *Libellus cantus mensurabilis;* and *Questiones super partes musice*, which takes up again, in the form of questions and answers, the material of the *Libellus*. We do not know whether to this list should be added the *Artis musice noticia* cited by the *Canones tabule tabularum* among the works composed in 1321, or whether this text is the same as the *Ars nove musice* mentioned above. The *Musica speculativa* is a commentary on Boethius. The other treatises bear witness to a scientific conception of music, new at the beginning of the fourteenth century: it is as a mathematician that John of Murs views musical problems. In addition to its fundamental originality, his work reveals the pedagogic qualities that assured his musical writings a wide diffusion until the end of the Middle Ages.

It was in mathematics that John of Murs's learned work received its greatest development. The *Canones tabule tabularum* mentions a squaring of the circle which does not seem to have been preserved; it is therefore not known whether he was acquainted at that time with Archimedes' *De mensura circuli* in the translation of William of Moerbeke, which he mentions knowing twenty years later. This quadrature aside, the earliest mathematical work of John of Murs is the *Tabula tabularum* with its canons "Si quis per hanc tabulam tabularum proportionis . . ." It is a table giving, for the numbers one to sixty inscribed as both abscissas and ordinates, the product of their multiplication expressed directly in sexagesimal notation. The year of this table, 1321, and its title clearly reveal the preoccupations which led John of Murs to construct it, since he was associated at that time with the project of recasting the astronomical tables of Alfonso X of Castile in a strictly sexagesimal presentation. This systematic conversion of the chronological elements into the number of days expressed in sexagesimal numeration presupposed great suppleness in the mental gymnastics involved in such a conversion.

In addition to calculations in sexagesimal numeration, knowledge of trigonometry was necessary in astronomy. Hence it is not surprising to find, under the name of John of Murs, a short treatise on trigonometry entitled *Figura inveniendi sinus kardagarum* ("Omnes sinus recti incipiunt a dyametro orthogonaliter . . ."), which concerns the construction of a table of sines.

Yet it would be wholly incorrect to consider John of Murs's mathematical work as only a sort of handmaiden to astronomy. About 1344[5] he completed *De arte mensurandi* ("Quamvis plures de arte mensurandi inveniantur tractatus . . ."), in twelve chapters —of which the first four chapters and the beginning of the fifth had already been written by another author and deal precisely with the mathematical knowledge necessary for astronomy (operations on sexagesimal fractions and trigonometry). Going beyond these elementary notions, John of Murs utilized Archimedes' treatises on spirals, on the measurement of the circle, on the sphere and the cylinder, and on the conoids and spheroids, which he knew in the translations of William of Moerbeke. Moreover, he inserted in this work, as the eighth chapter, a squaring of the circle which is sometimes found separately ("Circulo dato possibile est accipere . . .") and which is dated 1340. The propositions of the *De arte mensurandi* appeared, without the demonstrations, under the title *Commensurator* or as *Problemata geometrica omnimoda*, long attributed to Regiomontanus.[6]

John of Murs's most famous mathematical work is his *Quadripartitum numerorum* ("Sapiens ubique sua intelligit . . ."), which takes its name from its division into four books. They are preceded by a section in verse ("Ante boves aratrum res intendens...") and completed by a *semiliber* interpolated between books III and IV. The arithmetical portions of this treatise derive from al-Khwārizmī, with no evidence of any great advance over the original. Yet the appearance, in book III, of the use of decimal fractions in a particular case, that of the extraction of square roots, is noteworthy; but reference to their use is almost accidental and is not developed. The sections on algebra, both in the versified portion and in book III, draw on the *Flos super solutionibus* of Leonardo Fibonacci. Since book IV is devoted to practical applications of arithmetic, John of Murs uses this occasion to introduce a discussion on music (*De sonis musicis*) and two treatises on mechanics (*De movimentis et motis* and *De ponderibus*), the second of which reproduces long extracts from the *Liber Archimedis de incidentibus in humidum*.[7]

The *Quadripartitum* is dated 13 November 1343, and the versified part is addressed to Philippe de Vitry. Since the Paris manuscripts of this text note that this celebrated poet and musician was also the bishop of Meaux,[8] it has been claimed that the versified part cannot be prior to 1351, the year in which Philippe de Vitry assumed his episcopal functions; in fact, the part in verse was indeed written after the prose part, but the date of the former is certainly not much later than that of the latter (see note 5). The reference to the bishopric of Meaux is made by the copyist of the Paris manuscript, not by John of Murs.

In astronomy John of Murs's name is associated, as is that of John of Lignères, with the introduction of the Alfonsine tables into medieval science. Yet his first astronomical writing, a critique of the ecclesiastical computation of the calendar ("Autores calendarii nostri duo principaliter tractaverunt . . ."), in 1317, is that of a convinced partisan of the Toulouse tables, which he declares to be the best. The attribution of this text to John is proposed only by a fifteenth-century manuscript, but there is no reason to contest it; moreover, the author's style, very critical and impassioned, is definitely that of John of Murs when, later on, he attacked the defects of the calendar. The reference to the Toulouse tables would then demonstrate that, whatever P. Duhem may have believed, the introduction of the Alfonsine tables among the Paris astronomers was not yet complete in 1317.

Nor is that introduction established for 1318. In fact, we possess the report of the observation of the equinox and of the calculation of the hour of the entry of the sun into Aries, both made in that year at Évreux by John of Murs. Since the report invokes the authority of Alfonso X and his tables, Duhem saw in it proof that those tables were then in current use; but his account rests on an erroneous subdivision of a poorly identified text, the *Expositio intentionis regis Alfonsii circa tabulas ejus*, preserved in the manuscript Paris lat. 7281 ("Alfonsius Castelle rex illustris florens . . ."). Duhem made two different texts from it, dating the first 1301 and proposing to attribute it to William of Saint-Cloud, and assigning to John of Murs only the second, reduced to the account of the observation of 1318. In truth, the references to 1300 (*anno perfecto*, that is to say 1301) are found in both texts, and therefore cannot signify the year in which the texts were composed, for they accompany the results of the observation of 1318; the latter, moreover, is not described as a very recent event but as evidence invoked a posteriori to confirm the excellence of the Alfonsine tables. This *Expositio*, including the account of 1318, must correspond to the *Expositio tabularum Alfonsi regis Castelle* mentioned in John's *Canones tabule tabularum* as being among the works that he composed in 1321. It must, consequently, have been between 1317 and 1321 that John learned of the Alfonsine tables. These dates may be compared with those of the first two tables of John of Lignères: those from around 1320, which appear to be independent of the Alfonsine tables, and those from 1322, which present the Alfonsine tables in a first draft. This *Expositio* is presented as a technical study of the values given by the Alfonsine tables for the composite movement of the apogees of the planets and for the mean movement of the sun; as the copyist of manuscript Paris lat. 7281 remarks in a final note, nothing appears about the eccentricities of the planets.[10] It was not until 1339 that John of Murs composed, after John of Lignères and John of Saxony, canons of the Alfonsine tables in their definitive version: "Prima tabula docet differentiam unius ere . . ."[11]

We have seen that John of Murs had observed the sun at Évreux in 1318, on the occasion of the vernal equinox. This was not his only observation: a manuscript in the Escorial preserves abundant autograph notes by him dealing with his observations at Bernay, Fontevrault, Évreux, Paris, and Mézières-en-Brenne between 1321 and 1344, notably at the time of the solar eclipse of 3 March 1337.[12] They attest to the scientific character of an outstanding mind, for the records of medieval astronomical observations are quite exceptional.

An informed practitioner very closely associated with the diffusion of the Alfonsine tables, John of Murs was not unaware of the extent to which astronomical tables based on the calculation of the mean movements and mean arguments of the planets, and on the corresponding equations, however satisfying they might be theoretically, contained snares and difficulties when put to practical use. An important part of his work was therefore devoted to perfecting the tables and the calculating procedures in order to lighten the task of determining planetary positions on a given date.

Thus the tables of 1321, bearing the canons "Si vera loca planetarum per presentes tabulas invenire...," represent one of the most original productions of medieval astronomy. They are based on the generalization to all the planets of the principle ordinarily applied in calculating solar and lunar conjunctions and oppositions. This calculation rests on the determination of a mean conjunction or opposition, a unique moment in which the two bodies have the same mean movement and, consequently, the equation of the center of the moon is null. Likewise, John of Murs provided, for the sixty years beginning on 1 January 1321, the list of dates on which the sun and each of the planets have the same mean movement; the argument of the planet and the equation of the argument are then null. Next, a *contratabula* gives directly the equation to be added to the mean movement in order to obtain the true position, partly as a function of the difference between the date for which the true position of the planet and that of its "mean conjunction" with the sun are sought and partly as a function of the mean center of the planet at the moment of the "mean conjunction."

For the particular case of the sun and the moon, John of Murs proposed to simplify further the calculation of their conjunctions and oppositions by means of new tables, termed *tabule permanentes*, and of their canon "Omnis utriusque sexus armoniam celestem . . .": knowing the date of a mean conjunction or opposition of the two bodies (it is determined very easily with the aid of the table of mean elongation of the sun and the moon, which is included among the tables of mean movements and mean arguments of the planets), John of Murs presented directly the difference in time which separates the mean conjunction or opposition from the true conjunction or opposition in a double-entry table, where the sun's argument is given as the abscissa and that of the moon as the ordinate.

Maintaining the goal of a rapid determination of the conjunctions and oppositions of the sun and the moon, the *Patefit* (so designated after the first word of its canon: "Patefit ex Ptolomei disciplinis in libro suo . . .") offers a complete solution that is limited to the period 1321–1396.[13] A series of tables gives, without the necessity of calculation, the dates of the mean conjunctions and oppositions, the true positions of the two bodies at the times of the mean conjunctions, and the data needed to calculate rapidly, from this information, their actual positions at the times of the true conjunctions. Other tables deal with the determination of those conjunctions and oppositions which eclipse one of the two bodies and also with the calculation of the duration of the eclipse. All these tables form an annex to a calendar of which the originality consists in providing, in addition to the true daily position of the sun during the years of a bissextile cycle, the correction to be employed after the years 1321–1324 of the first cycle. Here John of Murs's concern to replace the ecclesiastical calendar, frozen in a nonscientific conservatism (the faults of which already were revealed in 1317),

JOHN OF MURS

by a chronological instrument conforming to astronomical reality becomes fully apparent.

John of Murs expressed that concern again on two occasions in texts on the calendar and on the reforms that should be made in it. One of these ("De regulis computistarum quia cognite sunt a multis . . ."), by the violence of its style, almost seems to be a pamphlet against the traditional *computus* and the computists;[14] it nevertheless offers some constructive solutions, such as suppressing, for forty years, the intercalation of the bissextile or shortening eleven months of any given year by one day each, so that at the end of the period thus treated the calendar will have lost the eleven-day advance that it then would have recorded over the astronomical phenomena whose rhythm it should have reproduced. Another of its suggestions was to adopt a lunar cycle of four times nineteen years, a better one than the ordinary cycle of nineteen years. One of the manuscripts of the *De regulis computistarum* preserved at Erfurt assigns to the text the date of 1337.[15]

The other text on the calendar has a more official character; in fact, in 1344, John of Murs and Firmin de Belleval were called to Avignon by Pope Clement VI to give their opinion on calendar reform.[16] The result of this consultation was, in 1345, a memoir ("Sanctissimo in Christo patri ac domino . . .") in which the experts proposed two arrangements: the suppression of a bissextile year every 134 years to correct the solar calendar (after applying a suitable correction to compensate for the gap of eleven days between the date of the equinox of the computists and the true date), and the adoption of a new table of golden numbers to correct the lunar calendar.[17] It was suggested that the reform begin in 1349, which offered the advantage of being the first year after a bissextile and of having "1" for its golden number according to the ancient *computus*. This advice was not followed, and the Julian calendar retained its errors for more than two centuries.[18]

It was perhaps to follow up on these matters that John of Murs again sent to Clement VI, at an unknown date but necessarily before the pope's death in 1352, an opinion concerning the anticipated conjunction of Saturn and Jupiter on 30 October 1365 and of Saturn and Mars on 8 June 1357 ("Sanctissimo et reverendissimo patri et domino . . ."). In it he informed the pope of the particularly favorable conditions which were to conjoin in 1365 for the success of a crusade against the Muslims, but he beseeched him at the same time to use the weight of his authority to prevent the wars between the Christian states inscribed in the very unfavorable conjunction of 1357. Analogous astrological concern had elicited, at the time of the triple conjunction of 1345, parallel commentaries by Leo of Balneolis (his commentary was translated into Latin by Peter of Alexandria), by Firmin de Belleval, and by John of Murs ("Ex doctrina mirabili sapientium qui circa noticiam . . ."); the conjunctions were predicted for 1 March between Jupiter and Mars, for 4 March between Saturn and Mars, and for 20 March between Saturn and Jupiter, all in the sign of Aquarius. An autograph note by John of Murs on the same conjunction is found in one of the manuscripts of *De arte mensurandi.*[19]

NOTES

1. L. Gushee, "New Sources for the Biography of Johannes de Muris," in *Journal of the American Musicological Society*, **22** (1969), 3–26, esp. 19, 26.
2. "Quam, ut fertur, fecit magister Johannes de Muris qui temporibus suis fuit magnus astronomus," in H. Géraud, *Chronique latine de Guillaume de Nangis de 1113 à 1300 avec les continuations de cette chronique de 1300 à 1368*, II (Paris, 1843; Société de l'histoire de France), 181. This prophecy is completely independent of the texts on the conjunction of 1345 and the conjunctions of 1357 and 1365.
3. This prophecy appears elsewhere than in Jean de Venette's chronicle: see H. L. D. Ward, *Catalogue of Romances in the Department of Manuscripts in the British Museum*, I (London, 1883), 302, 314, 316–319, 321. It is taken up again by the fifteenth-century historian Thedericus Pauly, in *Speculum historiale*, edited by W. Focke in his inaugural dissertation, *Theodericus Pauli ein Geschichtsschreiber des XV. Jahrhunderts* (Halle, 1892), pp. 47–48, but only Jean de Venette attributes it to John of Murs; it is generally given under the name of Hemerus, the equivalent of Merlin.
4. A. Coville, "La chronique de 1340 à 1368 dite de Jean de Venette," in *Histoire littéraire de la France*, **38** (1949), 333–354, esp. 344–346.
5. The *De arte mensurandi* was completed after the prose part of the *Quadripartitum numerorum*, to which it alludes in several places, but before the epistle in verse which accompanies the *Quadripartitum* and in which there is an allusion to the *De arte mensurandi.*
6. M. Clagett, "A Note on the Commensurator Falsely Attributed to Regiomontanus," in *Isis*, **60** (1969), 383–384.
7. E. A. Moody and M. Clagett, *The Medieval Science of Weights* (Madison, Wis., 1960), pp. 35–53. It was published by Clagett in *The Science of Mechanics in the Middle Ages*, pp. 126–135.
8. The allusion to the bishopric of Meaux is not found in either of the two Vienna MSS.
9. The announcement of the observation is made in a quite solemn and perhaps parodic manner, according to a formulation borrowed from the charters: "Noverint preterea presentes et futuri . . ."; similarly at the end there is a prohibitive clause against the ignorant and the jealous.
10. Paris lat. 7281, fol. 160: after the explicit of the *Expositio* the copyist has added: "Per Joh. de Muris credo; mirum videtur quod iste non determinavit de quantitate eccentricitatum deferentis solis et aliorum planetarum et de quantitate epiciclorum, consequenter de quantitate equationum argumenti solis, centri et argumenti etc. ceteris planetis convenientium secundum intentionem regis Alfonsii quia alias et differentes posuit ab antiquis, prospecto quod de istis fuit semper diversitas inter consideratores."
11. These canons are not very frequently found in the MSS and often appear only in a fragmentary state, which explains why John of Murs is constantly credited with canons on the

eclipses that Duhem assigned to the year 1339, distinguishing them from the canons of the Alfonsine tables that he thought dated from 1321, having confused them with the *Canones tabule tabularum* that he had not read; in fact, the canons on the eclipses form the last part of the canons of the Alfonsine tables. MS Oxford Hertford Coll. 4, fols. 140–147, appears to preserve the totality of these canons, but its text is constantly interrupted by explicits, anonymous or referring to John of Murs.

12. G. Beaujouan (who is preparing an ed. of these notes), in *École pratique des hautes études, IVe section, Sciences Historiques et Philologiques, Annuaire*, 1964–1965, pp. 259–260; these notes were partially used by L. Gushee (see note 1).
13. In the London MS, the *Patefit* is designated as *Calendarium Beccense* and includes a long explicit in which the author, who does not identify himself, dedicates his work to Geoffroy, abbot of Bec-Hellouin. A problem results from the fact that the abbot of Bec in 1321 was Gilbert de St.-Étienne; Geoffroy Fare did not become abbot until 1327. It is perhaps for this reason that an annotator of the Metz MS, in which the tables are attributed to John of Murs, has corrected them thus: "Falsum, et quidam dicunt quia fuit cujusdam monachi Beccensis."
14. The computists were reproached in particular for never stating whether their dates were "completo" or "incompleto anno" and for calculating the life of Christ in solar years rather than in lunar years.
15. Erfurt 4° 371, fol. 45. It is this MS, which is undoubtedly the source of the information on John of Murs's calendrical work before 1345, on which Duhem relied—*Le système du monde*, IV (Paris, 1916), 51—following a work by Schubring (1883) cited by M. Cantor, *Vorlesungen über die Geschichte der Mathematik*, II, 2nd ed. (Leipzig, 1900), 125, which no one has been able to locate.
16. The papal letters addressed to John of Murs and Firmin de Belleval were published in E. Deprez, "Une tentative de réforme du calendrier sous Clément VI: Jean de Murs et la chronique de Jean de Venette," in *École française de Rome, Mélanges d'archéologie et d'histoire*, **19** (1889), 131–143, republished in Clement VI, *Lettres closes, patentes et curiales se rapportant à la France*, E. Deprez, ed., I (Paris, 1901–1925), nos. 1134, 1139, 1140.
17. The summary found at the end of the text is an integral part of it and is in all the MSS.
18. A London MS—Sloane 3124, fols. 2–8v—preserves a calendar whose brief canon ("Canon autem tabule ita scripte ut supra apparet est de renovatione lune . . .") attributes it to John of Murs and to the other experts who composed it at the request of Clement VI; but this calendar was established for a classical cycle of nineteen years beginning in 1356.
19. Paris lat. 7380, fol. 38v.

BIBLIOGRAPHY

I. Original Works. Almost all of John of Murs's musical work has been published: The *Ars nove musice* was included by M. Gerbert in his *Scriptores ecclesiastici de musica sacra*, III (St.-Blaise, 1784), but it was fragmented under various titles (pp. 256–258, 312–315, 292–301), as were the *Musica speculativa* (*ibid.*, pp. 249–255, 258–283; also printed in Cologne, *ca.* 1500, in a collection entitled *Epitoma quadrivii practica* [Klebs 554.1]) and the *Questiones super partes musice* (*ibid.*, pp. 301–308). The *Questiones* was reproduced, under the title of *Accidentia musice*, by E. De Coussemaker in *Scriptorum de musica medii aevi nova series*, III (Paris, 1869), 102–106; Coussemaker also published the *Libellus cantus mensurabilis* (*ibid.*, pp. 46–58). U. Michels, "Die Musiktraktate des Johannes de Muris," in *Beihefte zum Archiv für Musikwissenschaft*, **8** (1970). The *Summa musice*, published under the name of John of Murs by Gerbert (*op. cit.*, pp. 190–248), and the *Speculum musice*, published in part by Coussemaker (*op. cit.*, II [Paris, 1867], 193–433), although long attributed to John, are not by him.

Of John of Murs's mathematical works, the only ones which have been published are an abridgment of Boethius' *Arithmetica* (Vienna, 1515; Mainz, 1538), dealt with in A. Favaro, "Intorno alla vita ed alle opere di Prosdocimo de' Beldomandi," in *Bullettino di bibliografia e di storia delle scienze matematiche e fisiche*, **12** (1879), 231, D. E. Smith, *Rara arithmetica* (Boston, 1908), pp. 117–119, and H. L. L. Busard, "Die 'Arithmetica speculativa' des Johannes de Muris," in *Scientiarum historia*, **13** (1971), 103–132; and the short treatise on trigonometry, M. Curtze, ed., "Urkunden zur Geschichte der Trigonometrie im christlichen Mittelalter," in *Bibliotheca mathematica*, 3rd ser., **1** (1900), 321–416, no. 8, pp. 413–416: "Die Sinusrechnung des Johannes de Muris." A partial ed. of *De arte mensurandi* is in preparation: M. Clagett, *Archimedes in the Middle Ages*, III; it will be based on MS Paris lat. 7380, of which the parts composed by John of Murs are autograph—see S. Victor, "Johannes de Muris' Autograph of the *De Arte Mensurandi*," in *Isis*, **61** (1970), 389–394. Other MSS are Florence, Magliab. XI-2, fols. 1–89, and XI-44, fols. 2–26v.

The *Canones tabule tabularum* are in the following MSS: Berlin F.246, fols. 79v–81; Brussels 1022–47, fols. 41–43v, 154v–158v; Erfurt F.377, fols. 37–38; Paris lat. 7401, pp. 115–124; Vienna 5268, fols. 35–39. Of the MSS cited, only those of Paris and Vienna contain the table itself.

Extracts of bk. II of the *Quadripartitum* were published in A. Nagl, "Das Quadripartitum des Johannes de Muris," in *Abhandlungen zur Geschichte der Mathematik*, **5** (1890), 135–146; and extracts of the versified portion and of bk. III were published in L. C. Karpinski, "The Quadripartitum numerorum of John of Meurs," in *Bibliotheca mathematica*, 3rd ser., **13** (1912–1913), 99–114. The second tract of bk. IV was published in M. Clagett, *The Science of Mechanics in the Middle Ages* (Madison, Wis., 1959; 1961), pp. 126–135. The *Quadripartitum* is preserved in four MSS: Paris lat. 7190, fols. 21–100v; Paris lat. 14736, fols. 23–108; Vienna 4770, fols. 174–324v; Vienna 10954, fols. 4–167. MS Paris lat. 14736, which begins with bk. II and has a lacuna in bk. IV, was completed by its copyist with the *De elementis mathematicis* of Wigandus Durnheimer, which replaces bk. I, and with the text of the versified portion, inserted in the middle of bk. IV. This MS served as the model for MS Paris lat. 7190; but since Durnheimer's text was incomplete in it, it was completed, in the sixteenth century, by the MS now cited as Paris lat. 7191, where it was wrongly baptized "Residuum primi libri Quadripartiti numerorum Johannis de Muris." In MS Vienna 10954, the epistle in verse appears after bk. IV.

The only text of John of Murs's astronomical *oeuvre* which has been published is that on the triple conjunction of 1345: H. Pruckner, *Studien zu den astrologischen Schriften des Heinrich von Langenstein* (Leipzig, 1933), pp. 222–226. The letter to the pope on the conjunctions of 1357 and 1365 is translated in P. Duhem, *Le système du monde*, IV (Paris, 1916), 35–37; the original text can be found in MS Paris lat. 7443, fols. 33–34v.

The criticism of the *computus* of 1317 is in MSS Vienna 5273, fols. 91–102; and Vienna 5292, fols. 199–209v. The treatise on the calendar, *De regulis computistarum*, is in MSS Brussels 1022–47, fols. 40–40v, 203–204v; Erfurt 4° 360, fols. 51v–52; Erfurt 4° 371, fols. 44v–45. The letter to Clement VI on calendar reform is in Paris lat. 15104, fols. 114v–121v (formerly fols. 50v–58v, or fols. 208v–215v, the MS having three simultaneous foliations); Vienna 5226, fols. 73–77v; Vienna 5273, fols. 111–122; and Vienna 5292, fols. 221–230.

The *Expositio tabularum Alfonsii* is preserved in only one MS, Paris lat. 7281, fols. 156v–160.

The tables of 1321 and their canons are in MSS Lisbon, Ajuda 52-VI-25, fols. 24–66; Oxford, Canon. misc. 501, fols. 54–106v. The *Canones tabularum permanentium* are in MSS Munich lat. 14783, fols. 198v–200v; London, Add. 24070, fols. 55, 57v; Vatican, Palat. lat. 1354, fols. 60–60v; Vienna 5268, fols. 45v–48v. None of the MSS cited in L. Thorndike and P. Kibre, *A Catalogue of Incipits*, 2nd ed. (London, 1963), col. 1004, appears to contain the tables, which are found only in the Vienna MS. The Alfonsine canons of 1339 are in MSS Erfurt 4° 366, fols. 52–52v; Oxford, Hertford Coll. 4, fols. 140–147; Paris lat. 18504, fols. 209–209v.

The *Patefit* is in MSS Erfurt 4° 360, fols. 35–51, 52–55; Erfurt 4° 371, fols. 2–42v; London, Royal 12.C.XVII, fols. 145v–190, 203–210; Metz 285. In MS Lisbon, Ajuda 52-VI-25, fols. 1–14v, is an extract of the *Patefit:* the list of mean and true conjunctions and oppositions for 1321–1396, with the canon "In canone hujus operis continentur medie et vere conjonctiones . . . Deus dat bona hominibus qui sit benedictus . . ." This extract seems to have been printed in 1484; see O. Mazal, "Ein unbekannter astronomischer Wiegendruck," in *Gutenberg Jahrbuch*, 1969, 89–90.

Duhem, *op. cit.*, p. 33, has called attention to a MS of *Fractiones* or *Arbor Boetii*, written in 1324; and L. Thorndike, *A History of Magic and Experimental Science*, III (New York, 1934), 301, mentions a *Figura maris aenei Salomonis*, also of 1324, the nature of which is uncertain.

A Cambridge MS attributes to John of Murs a short memoir refuting the Alfonsine tables in 1347–1348, "Bonum mihi quidem videtur omnibus nobis . . .," in Cambridge, Trinity Coll. 1418, fols. 55–57v; this attribution, which contradicts John of Murs's actions during the same period, cannot be upheld. This text is sometimes also attributed to Henri Bate, despite the chronological improbability. Duhem (*op. cit.*, pp. 22–24) resolved this difficulty by very subtle but unconvincing artifices. Also very suspect are the attributions to John of Murs of a geomancy according to a Venetian MS—see Thorndike, *op. cit.*, III, 323–324—and of a poem in French on the philosophers' stone, the "Pratique de maistre Jean de Murs parisiensis"—Florence, Laurenz. Acq. e Doni 380, fols. 83–86v.

II. Secondary Literature. John of Murs's work has interested historians of music. The article in *Grove's Dictionary of Music and Musicians*, 5th ed., V (London, 1954), 1005–1008, is now completely outdated; that by H. Besseler, *Die Musik in Geschichte und Gegenwart*, VII (Kassel, 1958), cols. 105–115, is excellent and contains an abundant bibliography. For John of Murs's astronomical work, however, it is dependent on Duhem, *op. cit.*, pp. 30–38, 51–60; and Thorndike, *op. cit.*, pp. 268–270, 294–324, which should be used—especially the former—with caution. L. Gushee, "New Sources for the Biography of Johannes de Muris," in *Journal of the American Musicological Society*, **22** (1969), 3–26, is presented as a restatement, with new documentation, of Besseler's article but likewise remains tied to Duhem's information.

Emmanuel Poulle

JOHNSON, WILLIAM ERNEST (*b.* Cambridge, England, 23 June 1858; *d.* Northampton, England, 14 January 1931)

Johnson's father, William Henry Johnson, was headmaster of a school in Cambridge, and Johnson first studied there. In 1879 he entered King's College, Cambridge, where he was eleventh wrangler in the mathematics tripos of 1882 and placed in the first class in the moral sciences tripos of 1883. For the next nineteen years he held a variety of temporary positions around Cambridge. During that period he published three technical papers on Boolean logic and one on the rule of succession in probability theory. In 1902 Johnson was appointed to the Sidgwick lectureship in moral science and was awarded a fellowship at King's College. He held these positions until shortly before his death. Although shy and sickly, he was a popular, respected teacher. Indeed, it was his students, especially Naomi Bentwich, who persuaded him to publish his three-volume *Logic* (1921–1924). A fourth volume, on probability, was never finished, but the first few chapters were published posthumously in *Mind.* This book won Johnson fame, honorary degrees from Manchester (1922) and Aberdeen (1926), and election as a fellow of the British Academy (1923).

Johnson made some technical contributions to logic. In "On the Logical Calculus" he developed an elegant version of Boolean propositional and functional logic, using conjunction and negation as his primitive symbols. He even attempted to define the quantifiers in terms of these connectives. In "Sur la théorie des équations logiques" and in his later writings on probability, he developed various rules of succession for the theory of probability. His primary contributions were, however, in the foundations of logic and of probability theory.

Johnson made many worthwhile, although not major, contributions to the philosophy of logic. Perhaps the most important were his distinction between determinables and determinates, his theory of ostensive definition, and his distinction between primary and secondary propositions. On all of these topics his ideas influenced, directly or indirectly, many contemporary logicians.

Johnson was one of the first to expound the view that probability claims should be interpreted as expressing logical relationships between evidence propositions and hypothesis propositions, relationships determined in each case by the content of these propositions. This view, also adopted by J. M. Keynes, Harold Jeffreys, and Rudolf Carnap, is one of the main contemporary alternatives to the frequency interpretation of probability claims. Although Keynes and Jeffreys published their books before the appearance of Johnson's "Probability," Keynes freely admitted his indebtedness to Johnson's ideas.

BIBLIOGRAPHY

Johnson's main writings are "The Logical Calculus," in *Mind*, **1** (1892), 3–30, 235–250, 340–347; "Sur la théorie des équations logiques," in *Bibliothèque du Congrès international de philosophie* (1901); *Logic*, 3 vols. (Cambridge, 1921–1924); and "Probability," in *Mind* (1932).

BARUCH BRODY

JONES, WILLIAM (*b.* Llanfihangel Tw'r Beird, Anglesey, Wales, 1675; *d.* London, England, 3 July 1749)

According to Welsh custom Jones, the son of a small farmer, John George, took the Christian name of his father (John) as his own surname (Jones). His mother was Elizabeth Rowland. Although Jones has little claim to eminence as a mathematician in his own right, his name is well-known to historians of mathematics through his association with the correspondence and works of many seventeenth-century mathematicians, particularly Newton.

In his early schooling Jones showed enough promise to secure the patronage of a local landowner (Bulksley of Baron Hill) who helped him to enter the countinghouse of a London merchant. Subsequently he traveled to the West Indies and taught mathematics on a man-of-war. Upon his return to London, Jones established himself as a teacher of mathematics; tutorships in great families followed. One of his pupils, Philip Yorke (afterward first earl of Hardwicke), later became lord chancellor; Jones traveled with him on circuit and was appointed "secretary for peace." He also taught Thomas Parker, afterward first earl of Macclesfield, and his son George, who became president of the Royal Society. For many years Jones lived at Shirburn Castle, Tetsworth, Oxfordshire, with the Parker family. There he met and married Maria Nix, daughter of a London cabinetmaker; they had two sons and a daughter.

In 1702 Jones published *A New Compendium of the Whole Art of Navigation*, a practical treatise concerned with the application of mathematics to astronomy and seamanship. His second book, *Synopsis palmariorum matheseos* (1706), attracted the attention of Newton and Halley. Although the book was designed essentially for beginners in mathematics, it contained a fairly comprehensive survey of contemporary developments, including the *method of fluxions* and the *doctrine of series*. Of the binomial theorem he wrote: ". . . and in a word, there is scarce any *Inquiry* so Sublime and Intricate, or any *Improvement* so Eminent and Considerable, in *Pure Mathematics*, but by a *Prudent application* of this *Theorem*, may easily be exhibited and deduced." Although all the symbols used by Jones are sensible and concise, in only one respect does he appear to have been an innovator: he introduced π for the ratio of the circumference of a circle to the diameter.

From 1706 on, Jones remained in close touch with Newton and was one of the privileged few who obtained access to his manuscripts. About 1708 he acquired the papers and correspondence of John Collins, a collection that included a transcript of Newton's *De analysi* (1669). In 1711 Newton permitted Jones to print the tracts *De analysi per aequationes numero terminorum infinitas* and *Methodus differentialis* (along with reproductions of his tracts on quadratures and cubics) as *Analysis per quantitatum series, fluxiones ac differentias; cum enumeratione linearum tertii ordinis*. In the same year Jones was appointed a member of the committee set up by the Royal Society to investigate the invention of the calculus. With John Machin and Halley, he was responsible for the preparation of the printed report. On 30 November 1712 he was elected a fellow of the Royal Society and subsequently became vice-president. He contributed sundry papers to the *Philosophical Transactions*, mostly of a practical character.

At his death Jones left a voluminous collection of manuscripts and correspondence which he had assembled mainly through his connections with Newton and the Royal Society. It seems that he intended to publish an extensive work on mathematics and, to this end, made copious notes and transcripts from manuscripts lent by Newton. This material became inextricably mixed with the original manuscripts and the transcripts of others, including those of John Collins and James Wilson. John Coulson (1736) used a transcript made by Jones as the basis for an English version of Newton's 1671 tract, *The Method of Fluxions and Infinite Series*. Subsequently Samuel Horsley (Newton's *Opera omnia*, I [1779]) retained Jones's title for the tract on fluxions (1671) and copied the "dot" notation inserted by Jones. D. T. Whiteside (*Newton Papers*, I, xxxiii) remarks that the sections of the Portsmouth collection relating to fluxions are "choked with irrelevant, fragmentary transcripts by Jones and Wilson." After Jones's death most of the manuscript collection passed into the hands of the second earl of Macclesfield. Two volumes of correspondence from this collection were published by Rigaud in 1841. The task of separating the mass of material compiled by Jones from Newton's original manuscripts has only recently been completed by Whiteside.

BIBLIOGRAPHY

I. Original Works. Jones's books are *A New Compendium of the Whole Art of Navigation* (London, 1702), with tables by J. Flamsteed; and *Synopsis palmariorum matheseos, or a New Introduction to the Mathematics* (London, 1706). Charles Hutton, *The Mathematical and Philosophical Dictionary*, 2 vols. (London, 1795), I, 672, lists the papers (mostly slight) published by Jones in the *Philosophical Transactions of the Royal Society* and gives some account of the disposal of his library of MSS after his death. F. Maseres, *Scriptores logarithmici* (London, 1791), contains a paper by Jones on compound interest. D. T. Whiteside, *The Mathematical Papers of Isaac Newton*, I–II (Cambridge, 1967–1968), makes numerous references to Jones and his connection with the Newton MSS. A number of letters written by and received by Jones were printed in S. J. Rigaud, *Correspondence of Scientific Men of the Seventeenth Century*, 2 vols. (Oxford, 1841).

II. Secondary Literature. Biographical material is available in Hutton's *Mathematical Dictionary* (see above) and in John Nichols, *Biographical and Literary Anecdotes of William Bowyer, Printer, F.S.A.* (London, 1782), pp. 73–74. See also Lord Teignmouth, *Memoirs of the Life, Writings and Correspondence of Sir William Jones* (London, 1804); and David Brewster, *Memoirs of the Life, Writings and Discoveries of Sir Isaac Newton*, 2 vols. (Edinburgh, 1855), I, 226, II, 421.

M. E. Baron

JONQUIÈRES, ERNEST JEAN PHILIPPE FAUQUE DE (*b.* Carpentras, France, 3 July 1820; *d.* Mousans-Sartoux, near Grasse, France, 12 August 1901)

Jonquières entered the École Navale at Brest in 1835 and subsequently joined the French navy, in which he spent thirty-six years. He achieved the rank of vice-admiral in 1879, and retired in 1885. He traveled all over the world, particularly to Indochina. In 1884 he was named member of the Institut de France.

In the 1850's Jonquières became acquainted with the geometric work of Poncelet and Chasles, which stimulated his own work in the field of synthetic geometry. In 1862 he was awarded two-thirds of the Grand Prix of the Paris Academy for his work in the theory of fourth-order plane curves. Geometry remained his main scientific interest. He was outstanding in solving elementary problems, for which, besides traditional methods, he used projective geometry. In addition to elementary problems Jonquières studied then-current questions of the general theory of plane curves, curve beams, and the theory of algebraic curves and surfaces, linking his own work with that of Salmon, Cayley, and Cremona. In his studies he generalized the projective creation of curves and tried to obtain higher-order curves with projective beams of curves of lower order. In 1859–1860 (before Cremona), he discovered the birational transformations (called by him "isographic"), which can be considered as a special case of Cremona's transformations; in nonhomogeneous coordinates they have the form:

$$x' = x \qquad y' = \frac{\alpha y + \beta}{\gamma y + \delta}$$

where α, β, γ, δ are functions of x and $\alpha\delta - \beta\gamma$ does not equal zero.

A number of Jonquières's results were in the field of geometry which Schubert called "abzählende Geometrie."

Besides geometry, Jonquières studied algebra and the theory of numbers, in which he continued the tradition of French mathematics. Here again his results form a series of detailed supplements to the work of others and reflect Jonquières's inventiveness in calculating rather than a more profound contribution to the advancement of the field.

BIBLIOGRAPHY

An autobiographical work is *Notice sur la carrière maritime, administrative et scientifique du Vice-Amiral de Jonquières, Grand officier de la Légion d'honneur, Directeur général du Dépôt des cartes et plans de la marine, Vice-Président de la Commission des phares, Membre de la Commission de l'Observatoire* (Paris, 1883).

On Jonquières's work, see Gino Loria, "L'oeuvre mathématique d'Ernest de Jonquières," in *Bibliotheca mathematica*, 3rd ser., **3** (1902), 276–322, and "Elenco delle pubblicazioni matematiche di Ernesto de Jonquières," in *Bullettino di bibliografia e storia delle scienze matematiche e fisiche*, **5** (1902), 72–82. See also H. G. Zeuthen, "Abzählende Methoden"; L. Berzolari, "Allgemeine Theorie der höheren ebenen algebraischen Kurven"; and L. Berzolari, "Algebraische Transformationen und Korrespondenzen"; all in *Encyklopädie der mathematischen Wissenschaften*, III, *Geometrie*.

L. Nový
J. Folta

JORDAN, CAMILLE (*b*. Lyons, France, 5 January 1838; *d*. Paris, France, 22 January 1921)

Jordan was born into a well-to-do family. One of his granduncles (also named Camille Jordan) was a fairly well-known politician who took part in many events from the French Revolution in 1789 to the beginning of the Bourbon restoration; a cousin, Alexis Jordan, is known in botany as the discoverer of "smaller species" which still bear his name ("jordanons"). Jordan's father, an engineer, was a graduate of the École Polytechnique; his mother was a sister of the painter Pierre Puvis de Chavannes. A brilliant student, Jordan followed the usual career of French mathematicians from Cauchy to Poincaré: at seventeen he entered the École Polytechnique and was an engineer (at least nominally) until 1885. That profession left him ample time for mathematical research, and most of his 120 papers were written before he retired as an engineer. From 1873 until his retirement in 1912 he taught simultaneously at the École Polytechnique and the Collège de France. He was elected a member of the Academy of Sciences in 1881.

Jordan's place in the tradition of French mathematics is exactly halfway between Hermite and Poincaré. Like them he was a "universal" mathematician who published papers in practically all branches of the mathematics of his time. In one of his first papers, devoted to questions of "analysis situs" (as combinatorial topology was then called), he investigated symmetries in polyhedrons from an exclusively combinatorial point of view, which was then an entirely new approach. In analysis his conception of what a rigorous proof should be was far more exacting than that of most of his contemporaries; and his *Cours d'analyse*, which was first published in the early 1880's and had a very widespread influence, set standards which remained unsurpassed for many years. Jordan took an active part in the movement which started modern analysis in the last decades of the nineteenth century: independently of Peano, he introduced a notion of exterior measure for arbitrary sets in a plane or in n-dimensional space. The concept of a function of bounded variation originated with him; and he proved that such a function is the difference of two increasing functions, a result which enabled him to extend the definition of the length of a curve and to generalize the known criteria of convergence of Fourier series. His most famous contribution to topology was to realize that the decomposition of a plane into two regions by a simple closed curve was susceptible of mathematical proof and to imagine such a proof for the first time.

Although these contributions would have been enough to rank Jordan very high among his mathematical contemporaries, it is chiefly as an algebraist that he reached celebrity when he was barely thirty; and during the next forty years he was universally regarded as the undisputed master of group theory.

When Jordan started his mathematical career, Galois's profound ideas and results (which had remained unknown to most mathematicians until 1845) were still very poorly understood, despite the efforts of A. Serret and Liouville to popularize them; and before 1860 Kronecker was probably the only first-rate mathematician who realized the power of these ideas and who succeeded in using them in his own algebraic research. Jordan was the first to embark on a systematic development of the theory of finite groups and of its applications in the directions opened by Galois. Chief among his first results were the concept of composition series and the first part of the famous Jordan-Hölder theorem, proving the invariance of the system of indexes of consecutive groups in any composition series (up to their ordering). He also was the first to investigate the structure of the general linear group and of the "classical" groups over a prime finite field, and he very ingeniously applied his results to a great range of problems; in particular, he was able to determine the structure of the Galois group of equations having as roots the parameters of some well-known geometric configurations (the twenty-seven lines on a cubic surface, the twenty-eight double tangents to a quartic, the sixteen double points of a Kummer surface, and so on).

Another problem for which Jordan's knowledge of these classical groups was the key to the solution, and to which he devoted a considerable amount of effort from the beginning of his career, was the general study of solvable finite groups. From all we know today (in particular about p-groups, a field which was started, in the generation following Jordan, with the Sylow theorems) it seems hopeless to expect a complete classification of all solvable groups which would characterize each of them, for instance, by a system of numerical invariants. Perhaps Jordan realized this; at any rate he contented himself with setting up the machinery that would automatically yield all solvable groups of a given order n. This in itself was no mean undertaking; and the solution imagined by Jordan was a gigantic recursive scheme, giving the solvable groups of order n when one supposes that the solvable groups of which the orders are the exponents of the prime factors of n are all known. This may have no more than a theoretical value; but in the process of developing his method, Jordan was led to many important new concepts, such as the minimal normal subgroups of a group and the orthogonal groups over a field of characteristic 2 (which he called "hypoabelian" groups).

In 1870 Jordan gathered all his results on permutation groups for the previous ten years in a huge volume, *Traité des substitutions,* which for thirty years was to remain the bible of all specialists in group theory. His fame had spread beyond France, and foreign students were eager to attend his lectures; in particular Felix Klein and Sophus Lie came to Paris in 1870 to study with Jordan, who at that time was developing his researches in an entirely new direction: the determination of all groups of movements in three-dimensional space. This may well have been the source from which Lie conceived his theory of "continuous groups" and Klein the idea of "discontinuous groups" (both types had been encountered by Jordan in his classification).

The most profound results obtained by Jordan in algebra are his "finiteness theorems," which he proved during the twelve years following the publication of the *Traité*. The first concerns subgroups G of the symmetric groups $\mathfrak{S}_n$ (group of all permutations of n objects); for such a group G, Jordan calls "class of G" the smallest number $c > 1$ such that there exists a permutation of G which moves only c objects. His finiteness theorem on these groups is that there is an absolute constant A such that if G is primitive and does not contain the alternating group $\mathfrak{A}_n$, then $n \leqslant Ac^2 \log c$ (in other words, there are only finitely many primitive groups of given class c other than the symmetric and alternating groups).

The second, and best-known, finiteness theorem arose from a question which had its origin in the theory of linear differential equations: Fuchs had determined all linear equations of order 2 of which the solutions are all algebraic functions of the variable. Jordan reduced the similar problem for equations of order n to a problem in group theory: to determine all finite subgroups of the general linear group $GL(n, \mathbf{C})$ over the complex field. It is clear that for $n \geqslant 1$ there are infinitely many such groups, but Jordan discovered that for general n the infinite families of finite subgroups of $GL(n, \mathbf{C})$ are of a very special type. More precisely, there exists a function $\varphi(n)$ such that any finite group G of matrices of order n contains a normal subgroup H which is conjugate in $GL(n, \mathbf{C})$ to a subgroup of diagonal matrices, and such that the index $(G : H)$ is at most $\varphi(n)$ (equivalently, the quotient group G/H can only be one of a finite system of groups, up to isomorphism).

Jordan's last finiteness theorem is a powerful generalization of the results obtained earlier by Hermite in the theory of quadratic forms with integral coefficients. Jordan considered, more generally, the vector space of all homogeneous polynomials of degree m in n variables, with complex coefficients; the unimodular group $SL(n, \mathbf{C})$ operates in this space, and Jordan considered an orbit for this action (that is, the set of all forms equivalent to a given one F by unimodular substitutions). Within that orbit he considered the forms having (complex) integral coefficients (that is, coefficients which are Gaussian integers), and he placed in the same equivalence class all such forms which are equivalent under unimodular substitutions having (complex) integral coefficients. His fundamental result was then that the number of these classes is finite, provided $m > 2$ and the discriminant of F is not zero.

BIBLIOGRAPHY

Jordan's papers were collected in *Oeuvres de Camille Jordan*, R. Garnier and J. Dieudonné, eds., 4 vols (Paris, 1961–1964). His books are *Traité des substitutions et des équations algébriques* (Paris, 1870; repr. 1957) and *Cours d'analyse de l'École Polytechnique*, 3 vols. (3rd ed., 1909–1915).

A detailed obituary notice is H. Lebesgue, in *Mémoires de l'Académie des sciences de l'Institut de France*, 2nd ser., **58** (1923), 29–66, repr. in Jordan's *Oeuvres*, IV, x–xxxiii.

J. DIEUDONNÉ

JORDANUS DE NEMORE (*fl. ca.* 1220)

Although Jordanus has been justly proclaimed the most important mechanician of the Middle Ages and one of the most significant mathematicians of that period, virtually nothing is known of his life. That he lived and wrote during the first half of the thirteenth century, and perhaps as early as the late twelfth century, is suggested by the inclusion of his works in the *Biblionomia*, a catalogue of Richard de Fournival's library compiled sometime between 1246 and 1260.[1]

JORDANUS DE NEMORE

In all, twelve treatises are ascribed to Jordanus de Nemore, whose name is cited four times in this form.[2] Since most of his genuine treatises are included, it seems reasonable to infer that Jordanus' productive career antedated the *Biblionomia.*

The appellation "Jordanus de Nemore" is also found in a number of thirteenth-century manuscripts of works attributed to Jordanus. The meaning and origin of "de Nemore" are unknown. It could signify "from" or "of Nemus," a place as yet unidentified (the oft-used alternative "Nemorarius," frequently associated with Jordanus, is apparently a later derivation from "Nemore"), or it may have derived from a corruption of "de numeris" or "de numero" from Jordanus' arithmetic manuscripts.[3]

Identification of Jordanus de Nemore with Jordanus de Saxonia (or Jordanus of Saxony), the master general of the Dominican order from 1222 to 1237, has been made on the basis of a statement by Nicholas Trivet (in a chronicle called *Annales sex regum Angliae*) that Jordanus of Saxony was an outstanding scientist who is said to have written a book on weights and a treatise entitled *De lineis datis.*[4] Although a late manuscript of a work definitely written by Jordanus de Nemore is actually ascribed to "Jordanus de Alemannia" (Jordanus of Germany, and therefore possibly Jordanus of Saxony), no mathematical or scientific works can be assigned to Jordanus of Saxony, whose literary output was seemingly confined to religion and grammar. At no time, moreover, was Jordanus of Saxony called Jordanus de Nemore or Nemorarius. Finally, if Jordanus de Nemore lectured at the University of Toulouse, as one manuscript indicates,[5] this could have occurred no earlier than 1229, the year of its foundation. As master general of the Dominican order during the years 1229–1237, the year of his death, Jordanus of Saxony could hardly have found time to lecture at a university. For all these reasons it seems implausible to suppose that Jordanus of Saxony is identical with Jordanus de Nemore.

It was in mechanics that Jordanus left his greatest legacy to science. The medieval Latin "science of weights" (*scientia de ponderibus*), or statics, is virtually synonymous with his name, a state of affairs that has posed difficult problems of authorship. So strongly was the name of Master Jordanus identified with the science of weights that manuscripts of commentaries on his work, or works, were frequently attributed to the master himself. Since the commentaries were in the style of Jordanus, original works by him are not easily distinguished. At present only one treatise, the *Elementa Jordani super demonstrationem ponderum,* may be definitely assigned to Jordanus. Whether he inherited the skeletal frame of the *Elementa* in the form of its seven postulates and the enunciations of its nine theorems, for which he then supplied proofs, is in dispute.[6] Indisputable, however, is the great significance of the treatise. Here, under the concept of "positional gravity" (*gravitas secundum situm*), we find the introduction of component forces into statics. The concept is expressed in the fourth and fifth postulates, where it is assumed that "weight is heavier positionally, when, at a given position, its path of descent is less oblique" and that "a more oblique descent is one in which, for a given distance, there is a smaller component of the vertical."[7] In a constrained system the effective weight of a suspended body is proportional to the directness of its descent, directness or obliquity of descent being measured by the projection of any segment of the body's arcal path onto the vertical drawn through the fulcrum of the lever or balance. It is implied that the displacement which measures the positional gravity of a weight can be infinitely small. Thus, by means of a principle of virtual displacement (since actual movement cannot occur in a system in equilibrium, positional gravity can be measured only by "virtual" displacements) Jordanus introduced infinitesimal considerations into statics.

These concepts are illustrated in Proposition 2, where Jordanus demonstrates that "when the beam of a balance of equal arms is in horizontal position, then if equal weights are suspended from its extremities, it will not leave the horizontal position; and if it should be moved from the horizontal position, it will revert to it."[8] If the balance is depressed on the side of *B* (see Figure 1), Jordanus argues that it will return to a

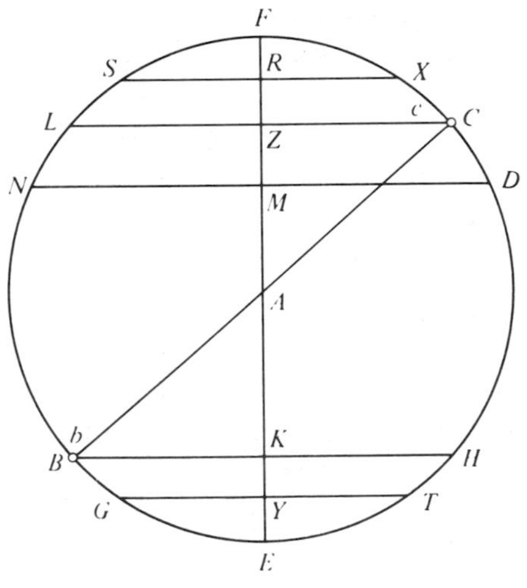

FIGURE 1

JORDANUS DE NEMORE

horizontal position because weight c at C will be positionally heavier than weight b at B, a state of affairs which follows from the fact that if any two equal arcs are measured downward from C and B, they will project unequal intercepts onto diameter $FRZMAKYE$. If the equal arcs are CD and BG, Jordanus can demonstrate (by appeal to his *Philotegni*, or *De triangulis*, as it was also called) that the intercept of arc CD—ZM—is greater than the intercept of arc BG—KY—and the "positionally" heavier c will cause C to descend to a horizontal position. The concept of positional heaviness, although erroneous when applied to arcal paths, may have derived ultimately from application of an idea in the pseudo-Aristotelian *Mechanica*, where it was argued that the further a weight is from the fulcrum of a balance, the more easily it will move a weight on the other side of the fulcrum, since "a longer radius describes a larger circle. So with the exertion of the same force the motive weight will change its position more than the weight which it moves, because it is further from the fulcrum."[9] It was by treating the descent of b independently from the ascent of c that Jordanus fell into error. A comparison of the ratio of paths formed by a small descent of b and an equal ascent of c with the ratio of paths formed by a small descent of c and an equal ascent of b would have revealed the equality of these ratios and demonstrated the absence of positional advantage. As we shall see below, however, when the concept of positional gravity was applied to rectilinear, rather than arcal, constrained paths, perhaps by Jordanus himself, it led to brilliant results.

More important than positional gravity is Jordanus' proof of the law of the lever by means of the principle of work. In Figure 2, ACB is a balance beam and

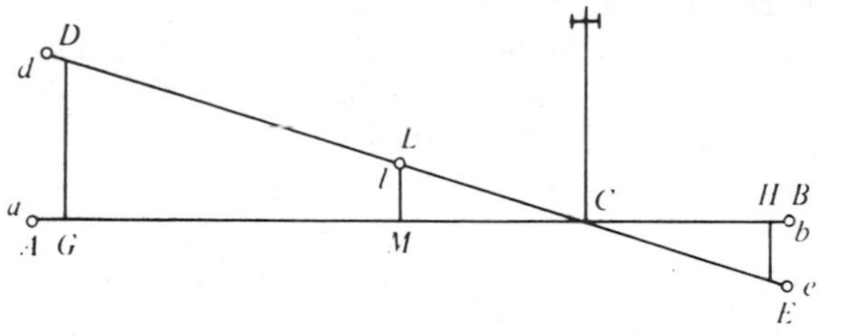

FIGURE 2

a and b are suspended weights. If we assume that $b/a = AC/BC$, no movement of the balance will occur. The demonstration takes the form of an indirect proof. It is assumed that the balance descends on B's side so that as b descends through vertical distance HE, it lifts a through vertical distance DG. If a weight l, equal to b, is now suspended at L, Jordanus shows, on the basis of similar triangles DCG and ECH, that $DG/EH = b/a$. On the assumption that $CL = CB$ and drawing perpendicular LM, he concludes that $LM = EH$. Therefore $DG/LM = b/a = l/a$. At this point the principle of work is applied, for "what suffices to lift a to D, would suffice to lift l through the distance LM. Since therefore l and b are equal, and LC is equal to CB, l is not lifted by b; and, as was asserted, a will not be lifted by b."[10] If a weight is thus incapable of lifting an equal weight the same distance that it descends, it cannot raise a proportionally smaller weight a proportionally greater distance.

The principles of positional gravity and work were superbly employed in the *De ratione ponderis*, which contains forty-five propositions and is probably the most significant of all medieval statical treatises. If, as the manuscripts indicate, it was by Jordanus himself[11] (although there is some doubt about this),[12] not only did Jordanus extend his own concept of positional gravity to rectilinear paths (the incorrect application to arcal paths was, however, retained in a few propositions) but he also applied that concept, in conjunction with the principle of work, to a formulation of the first known proof—long before Galileo—of the conditions of equilibrium of unequal weights on planes inclined at different angles. Paradoxically, in Book I, Proposition 2, the *De ratione ponderis* included reasoning which, if rigorously applied, would have destroyed the notion that an elevated weight has greater positional gravity with which to restore the equilibrium of a balance.[13]

In Book I, Proposition 9, Jordanus (for convenience we shall assume his authorship) shows that positional gravity—the heaviness or force of a weight—along an inclined plane (see Figure 3) is the same at any

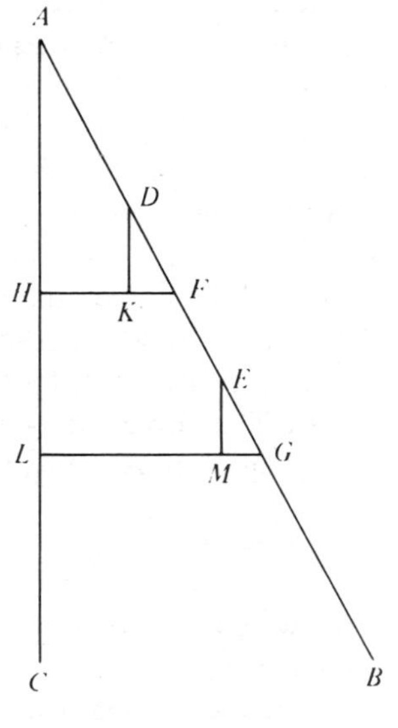

FIGURE 3

JORDANUS DE NEMORE

point. Thus a given weight at *D* or *E* will possess equal force, since for equal segments of the inclined path *AB*—*DF* and *EG*—equal segments of the vertical *AC* will be intercepted—*DK* and *EM*.

On the basis of Postulates 4 and 5 of the *Elementa*, which are also Postulates 4 and 5 of the *De ratione ponderis*, and Book I, Proposition 9, the inclined plane proof is enunciated in Book I, Proposition 10, as follows: "If two weights descend along diversely inclined planes, then, if the inclinations are directly proportional to the weights, they will be of equal force in descending."[14] Jordanus demonstrates that weights *e* and *h*, on differently inclined planes, are of

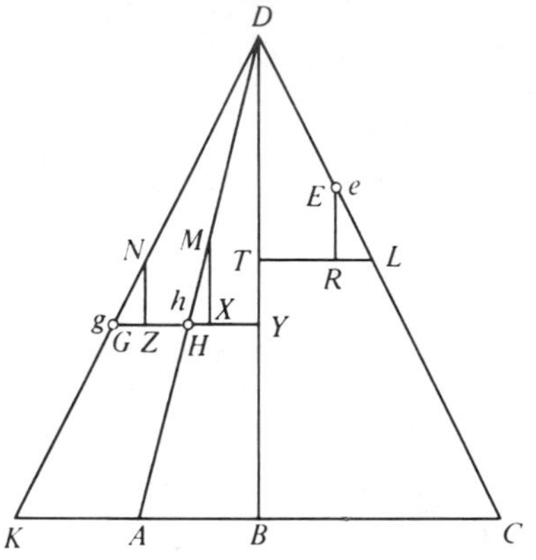

FIGURE 4

equal force. He first assumes that a weight *g*, equal to *e*, is on another plane, *DK*, whose obliquity is equal to that of *DC* and then assumes that if *e* moves to *L* through vertical distance *ER*, it will also draw *h* up to *M*. Should this occur, however, it would follow by the principle of work that what is capable of moving *h* to *M* can also move *g* to *N*, since it can be shown that $MX/NZ = g/h$. But *g* is equal to *e* and at the same inclination; hence, by Book I, Proposition 9, they are of equal force because they will intercept equal segments of vertical *DB*. Therefore *e* is incapable of raising *g* to *N* and, consequently, unable to raise *h* to *M*. By substituting a straight line for an arcal path and utilizing Postulate 5 of the *Elementa* (see above), Jordanus was, in modern terms, measuring the obliquity of descent, or ascent, by the sine of the angle of inclination. The force along the rectilinear oblique path, or incline, is thus equivalent to

$$F = W \sin a,$$

where *W* is the free weight and *a* is the angle of inclination of the oblique path.

The principle of work, which was but a vague concept prior to Jordanus, was not only used effectively in the proof of the inclined plane and, as indicated above, in the proof of the law of the lever in the *Elementa*, a proof repeated in Book I, Proposition 6, of the *De ratione ponderis*, but was also applied successfully to the first proof of the bent lever in Book I, Proposition 8, of the *De ratione ponderis*, which reads: "If the arms of a balance are unequal, and form an angle at the axis of support, then, if their ends are equidistant from the vertical line passing through the axis of support, equal weights suspended from them will, as so placed, be of equal heaviness."[15] In this proof there is also an anticipation of the concept of static moment, that the effective force of a weight is dependent on the weight and its horizontal distance from a vertical line passing through the fulcrum.[16]

Over and above his specific contributions to the advance of statics, Jordanus marks a significant departure in the development of that science. He joined the dynamical and philosophical approach characteristic of the dominant Aristotelian physics of his day with the abstract and rigorous mathematical physics of Archimedes. Thus the postulates of the *Elementa* and *De ratione ponderis* were derived from, and consistent with, Aristotelian dynamical concepts of motion but were arranged in a manner that permitted the derivation of rigorous proofs within a mathematical format modeled on Archimedean statics and Euclidean geometry.

The extensive commentary literature on the statical treatises ascribed to Jordanus began in the middle of the thirteenth century and continued into the sixteenth. Through printed editions of the sixteenth century, the content of this medieval science of weights, identified largely with the name of Jordanus, became readily available to mechanicians of the sixteenth and seventeenth centuries. Dissemination was facilitated by works such as Peter Apian's *Liber Iordani Nemorarii . . . de ponderibus propositiones XIII et earundem demonstrationes* (Nuremberg, 1533); Nicolo Tartaglia's *Questii ed invenzioni diverse* (Venice, 1546, 1554, 1562, 1606; also translated into English, German, and French), which contained a variety of propositions from Book I of the *De ratione ponderis*; and *Jordani Opusculum de ponderositate* (Venice, 1565), a version of the *De ratione ponderis* published by Curtius Trojanus from a copy owned by Tartaglia, who had died in 1557.

Concepts such as positional gravity, static moment, and the principle of work, or virtual displacement, were now available and actually influenced leading mechanicians, including Galileo, although some preferred to follow the pure Greek statical tradition of Archimedes and Pappus of Alexandria. In commenting on Guido Ubaldo del Monte's *Le mechaniche* (1577), which he himself had translated into Italian, Filippo Pigafetta remarked that Guido Ubaldo's more immediate predecessors

> . . . are to be understood as being the modern writers on this subject cited in various places by the author [Guido Ubaldo], among them Jordanus, who wrote on weights and was highly regarded and to this day has been much followed in his teachings. Now our author [Guido Ubaldo] has tried in every way to travel the road of the good ancient Greeks, . . . in particular that of Archimedes of Syracuse . . . and Pappus of Alexandria . . .[17]

Guido Ubaldo's attitude was costly, for it led him to reject Jordanus' correct inclined-plane theorem in favor of an erroneous explanation by Pappus.

Since few editions of his mathematical treatises have been published, and critical studies and evaluations are largely lacking, Jordanus' place in the history of medieval and early modern mathematics has yet to be determined. Treatises on geometry, algebra, proportions, and theoretical and practical arithmetic have been attributed to him.

The *Liber Philotegni de triangulis*, a geometrical work extant in two versions, represents medieval Latin geometry at its highest level. In the four books of the treatise we find propositions concerned with the ratios of sides and angles; with the division of straight lines, triangles, and quadrangles under a variety of given conditions; and with ratios of arcs and plane segments in the same circle and in different circles. The fourth book contains the most significant and sophisticated propositions. In IV.20 Jordanus presents three solutions for the problem of trisecting an angle, and IV.22 offers two solutions for finding two mean proportionals between two given lines. A proof of Hero's theorem on the area of a triangle—$A = \sqrt{s(s-a)(s-b)(s-c)}$, where s is the semiperimeter and a, b, and c are the sides of the triangle—may also have been associated with the *De triangulis*. Jordanus drew his solutions largely from Latin translations of Arabic works, which were themselves based on Greek mathematical texts. He did not always approve of these proofs and occasionally displayed a critical spirit, as when he deemed two proofs of the trisection of an angle based on mechanical means inadequate and uncertain (although no source is mentioned, they were derived from the *Verba filiorum* of the Banū Mūsā) and offered what is apparently his own demonstration,[18] in which a proposition from Ibn al-Haytham's *Optics* is utilized. In IV.16 a non-Archimedean proof of the quadrature of the circle may have been original. It involves finding a third continuous proportional. Here is the proof.[19]

> To Form a Square Equal to a Given Circle.
> For example, let the circle be A [see Figure 5].
> Disposition: Let another circle B with its diameter be added; let a square be described about each of those circles. And the circumscribed square [in each case] will be as a square of the diameter of the circle. Hence, by [Proposition] XII.2 [of the *Elements*], circle A/circle B = square DE/square FG. Therefore, by permutation, $DE/A = FG/B$. Let there be formed a third surface C, which is a [third] proportional [term] following DE and A. Now C will either be a circle or a surface of another kind, like a rectilinear surface. In the first place, let it be a circle which is circumscribed by square HK. And so, $DE/A = A/C$ but also, by [Proposition] XII.2 [of the *Elements*], $DE/A = HK/C$. Therefore, HK as well as A is a mean proportional between DE and C. Therefore, circle A and square HK are equal, which we proposed.
>
> Next, let C be some [rectilinear] figure other than a circle. Then let it be converted into a square by the last [proposition] of [Book] II [of the *Elements*], with its angles designated as R, S, Y, and X. And so, since DE is the larger extreme [among the three proportional terms], DE is greater than square RY, and a side [of DE] is greater than a side [of RY]. Therefore, let MT, equal to RX, be cut from MD. Then a parallelogram MN—contained by ME and MT—is described. Therefore, MN is the mean proportional between DE and RY, which are the squares of its sides, since a rectangle is the mean proportional between the squares of its sides. But circle A was the mean proportional between them [i.e., between square DE and C (or square RY)]. Therefore, circle A and parallelogram MN are equal. Therefore, let MN be converted to a square by the last [proposition] of [Book] II [of the *Elements*], and this square will be equal to the given circle A, which we proposed.

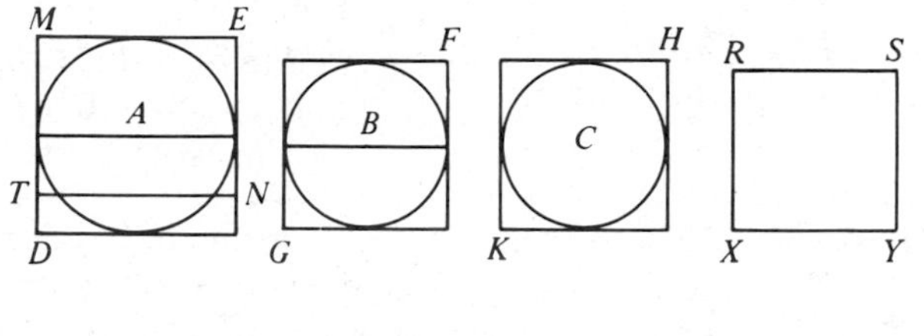

FIGURE 5

JORDANUS DE NEMORE

The *De numeris datis*, Jordanus' algebraic treatise in four books, which was praised by Regiomontanus, was more formal and Euclidean than the algebraic treatises derived from Arabic sources. Indeed it has recently been claimed[20] that in the *De numeris datis* Jordanus anticipated Viète in the application of analysis to algebraic problems. This may be seen in Jordanus' procedure, where he regularly formulated problems in terms of what is known and what is to be found (this is tantamount to the construction of an equation), and subsequently transforms the initial equation into a final form from which a specific computation is made with determinate numbers that meet the general conditions of the problem.

The general pattern of every proposition is thus (1) formal enunciation of the proposition; (2) proof; and (3) a numerical example, which is certainly non-Euclidean and was perhaps patterned after Arabic algebraic treatises. In this wholly rhetorical treatise, Jordanus used letters of the alphabet to represent numbers. An unknown number might be represented as *ab* or *abc*, which signify $a + b$ and $a + b + c$ respectively. Occasionally, when two unknown numbers are involved, one would be represented as *ab*, the other as *c*.

Typical of the propositions in the *De numeris datis* are Book I, Proposition 4, and Book IV, Proposition 7. In the first of these, a given number, say s,[21] is divided into numbers x and y, whose values are to be determined. It is assumed that g, the sum of x^2 and y^2, is also known. Now $s^2 - g = 2xy = e$ and $g - e = h = (x - y)^2$. Therefore $(x - y) = \sqrt{h} = d$. Since d is the difference between the unknown numbers x and y, their values can be determined by Book I, Proposition 1, where Jordanus demonstrated that "if a given number is divided in two and their difference is given, each of them will be given." The numbers are found from their sum and difference. Since $x + y = s$ and $x - y = d$, it follows that $y + d = x$ and, therefore, $2y + d = x + y = s$; hence $2y = s - d$, $y = (s - d)/2$, and $x = s - y$. Should we be given the ratio between x and y, say r, and the product of their sum and difference, say p, the values of x and y are determinable by Book IV, Proposition 7, as follows: since $x/y = r$, $x^2/y^2 = r^2$; moreover, since $(x + y)\ (x - y) = p$, therefore $x^2 - y^2 = p$. Now $x^2 = r^2y^2$, so that $(r^2 - 1)y^2 = p$ and $y = \sqrt{p/(r^2 - 1)}$. In the numerical example $r = 3$ and $p = 32$, which yields $y = 2$ and $x = 6$.

In the *Arithmetica*, the third and probably most widely known of his three major mathematical works, Jordanus included more than 400 propositions in ten books which became the standard source of theoretical arithmetic in the Middle Ages. Proceeding by definitions, postulates, and axioms, the *Arithmetica* was modeled after the arithmetic books of Euclid's *Elements*, a treatise which Jordanus undoubtedly used, although the proofs frequently differ. Jordanus' *Arithmetica* contrasts sharply with the popular, non-formal, and often philosophical *Arithmetica* of Boethius. A typical proposition, which has no counterpart in Euclid's *Elements*, is Book I, Proposition 9:

> *The* [*total sum or*] *result of the multiplication of any number by however many numbers you please is equal to* [*est quantum*] *the result of the multiplication of the same number by the number composed of all the others.*
>
> Let A be the number multiplied by B and C to produce D and E [respectively]. I say that the composite [or sum] of D and E is produced by multiplying A by the composite of B and C. For it is obvious by Definition [7] that B measures [*numerat*] D A times and that C measures E by the same number, namely, A times. By the sixth proposition of this book, you will easily be able to argue this.[22]

Thus Jordanus proves that if $A \cdot B = D$ and $A \cdot C = E$, then $D + E = A(B + C)$. By Definition 7, $D/B = A$ and $E/C = A$. And since D and E are equimultiples of B and C, respectively, then, by Proposition 6, it follows that $B + C = \frac{1}{n}(D + E)$ and, assuming $n = A$, we obtain $A(B + C) = D + E$.

The Arabic number system also attracted Jordanus' attention—if the *Demonstratio Jordani de algorismo* and a possible earlier and shorter version of it, the *Opus numerorum*, are actually by Jordanus. Once again Jordanus proceeded by definitions and propositions in a manner that differed radically from Johannes Sacrobosco's *Algorismus vulgaris*, or *Common Algorism*. Unlike Sacrobosco, Jordanus described the arithmetic operations and extraction of roots succinctly and formally and without examples. Among the twenty-one definitions of the *Demonstratio Jordani* are those for addition, doubling, halving, multiplication, division, extraction of a root (these definitions are illustrated as propositions), simple number, composite number, digit, and article (which is ten or consists of tens). Propositions equivalent to the following are included:

3. If $a : b = c : d$, then $a \cdot 10^n : b = c \cdot 10^n : d$
12. $1 \cdot 10^n + 9 \cdot 10^n = 1 \cdot 10^{n+1}$
19. $a \cdot 10^n + b \cdot 10^n = (a + b)10^n$
32. If $a_1 = a \cdot 10$, $a_2 = a \cdot 100$, $a_3 = a \cdot 1{,}000$, then $(a \cdot a_1)/a^2 = (a_1 \cdot a_2)/a_1^2 = (a_2 \cdot a_3)/a_2^2 = \cdots$

An algorithm of fractions, called *Liber* or *Demonstratio de minutiis* in some manuscripts, may also have been written by Jordanus. It describes in general terms arithmetic operations with fractions alone and with

JORDANUS DE NEMORE

fractions and integers. He also composed a *Liber de proportionibus*, a brief treatise containing propositions akin to those in Book V of Euclid's *Elements*.

NOTES

1. Marshall Clagett, *The Science of Mechanics in the Middle Ages*, pp. 72–73.
2. Leopold Delisle, *Le cabinet des manuscrits de la Bibliothèque nationale*, II (Paris, 1874), 526, 527.
3. This has been suggested by O. Klein, "Who Was Jordanus Nemorarius?," in *Nuclear Physics*, **57** (1964), 347.
4. Maximilian Curtze, "Jordani Nemorarii Geometria vel De triangulis libri IV," in *Mitteilungen des Coppernicus-Vereins*, **6** (1887), iv, n. 2.
5. *Ibid.*, p. vi.
6. Clagett, *op. cit.*, p. 73.
7. Translated by E. A. Moody and M. Clagett, *The Medieval Science of Weights*, p. 129.
8. *Ibid.*, p. 131.
9. 850b.4–6 in the translation of E. S. Forster (Oxford, 1913).
10. Moody and Clagett, trans., *op. cit.*, pp. 139, 141.
11. A position adopted by Moody, *ibid.*, pp. 171–172.
12. Joseph E. Brown, *The Scientia de ponderibus in the Later Middle Ages*, pp. 64–66.
13. Clagett, *op. cit.*, pp. 76–77.
14. Moody and Clagett, trans., *op. cit.*, p. 191.
15. *Ibid.*, pp. 185, 187.
16. Clagett, *op. cit.*, p. 82.
17. Translated by Stillman Drake in *Mechanics in Sixteenth-Century Italy*, trans. and annotated by Stillman Drake and I. E. Drabkin (Madison, Wis., 1969), p. 295.
18. Marshall Clagett, *Archimedes in the Middle Ages*, I, 675.
19. Trans. by Clagett, *ibid.*, pp. 573–575.
20. Barnabas B. Hughes (ed. and trans.), *The De numeris datis of Jordanus de Nemore*, pp. 50–52.
21. In his ed. of the *De numeris datis*, Curtze altered the letters in presenting the analytic summaries of the propositions; in a few instances I have altered Curtze's letters.
22. My translation from Edward Grant, ed., *A Source Book in Medieval Science* (in press).

BIBLIOGRAPHY

I. Original Works. In Richard Fournival's *Biblionomia* twelve works are attributed to Jordanus. In codex 43 we find (1) *Philotegni*, or *De triangulis*; (2) *De ratione ponderum*; (3) *De ponderum proportione*; and (4) *De quadratura circuli*. In codex 45 three works are listed: (5) *Practica*, or *Algorismus;* (6) *Practica de minutiis;* and (7) *Experimenta super algebra*. Codex 47 contains the lengthy (8) *Arithmetica*. Codex 48 includes (9) *De numeris datis;* (10) *Quedam experimenta super progressione numerorum;* and (11) *Liber de proportionibus*. Codex 59 includes a treatise called (12) *Suppletiones plane spere*.

Numbers (2) and (3) are obviously statical treatises. The *De ratione ponderum* is probably the *De ratione ponderis* edited and translated by E. A. Moody in E. A. Moody and M. Clagett, *The Medieval Science of Weights* (*Scientia de ponderibus*) (Madison, Wis., 1952); its attribution to Jordanus has been questioned by Joseph E. Brown, *The Scientia de ponderibus in the Later Middle Ages* (Ph.D. diss., University of Wis., 1967), pp. 64–66. In the same volume Moody has also edited and translated the *Elementa Jordani super demonstrationem ponderum*, a genuine work of Jordanus, which perhaps corresponds to the *De ponderum proportione* of the *Biblionomia*.

The *Philotegni*, or *De triangulis*, exists in two versions. The longer, and apparently later, version was published by Maximilian Curtze, "Jordani Nemorarii Geometria vel De triangulis libri IV," in *Mitteilungen des Coppernicus-Vereins für Wissenschaft und Kunst zu Thorn*, **6** (1887), from MS Dresden, Sächsische Landesbibliothek, Db 86, fols. 50r–61v. Utilizing additional MSS, Marshall Clagett reedited and translated Props. IV.16 (quadrature of the circle), IV.20 (trisection of an angle), and IV.22 (finding of two mean proportionals) in his *Archimedes in the Middle Ages*, I, *The Arabo-Latin Tradition* (Madison, Wis., 1964), 572–575, 672–677, and 662–663, respectively. A shorter version, which lacks Props. II.9–12, 14–16, and IV.10 and terminates at IV.9 or IV.11, has been identified by Clagett. Both versions will be reedited by Clagett in vol. IV of his *Archimedes in the Middle Ages*. Of the 17 MSS of the two versions which Clagett has found thus far, we may note, in addition to the Dresden MS used by Curtze, the following: Paris, BN lat. 7378A, 29r–36r; London, Brit. Mus., Sloane 285, 80r–92v; Florence, Bibl. Naz. Centr., Conv. Soppr. J. V. 18, 17r–29v; and London, Brit. Mus., Harley 625, 123r–130r.

The *De quadratura circuli* attributed to Jordanus as a separate treatise in Fournival's *Biblionomia* may be identical with Bk. IV, Prop. 16 of the *De triangulis*, which bears the title "To Form a Square Equal to a Given Circle" (quoted above; for the Latin text, see Clagett, *Archimedes in the Middle Ages*, I, 572, 574). In at least one thirteenth-century MS (Oxford, Corpus Christi College 251, 84v) the proposition stands by itself, completely separated from the rest of the *De triangulis*, an indication that it may have circulated independently (for other MSS, see Clagett, *Archimedes*, I, 569).

The *De numeris datis* has been edited three times. It was first published on the basis of a single fourteenth-century MS, Basel F.II.33, 138v–145v, by P. Treutlein, "Der Traktat des Jordanus Nemorarius 'De numeris datis,' " in *Abhandlungen zur Geschichte der Mathematik*, no. 2 (Leipzig, 1879), pp. 125–166. Relying on MS Dresden Db86, supplemented by MS Dresden C80, Maximilian Curtze reedited the *De numeris datis* and subdivided it into four books in "Commentar zu dem 'Tractatus de numeris datis' des Jordanus Nemorarius," in *Zeitschrift für Mathematik und Physik*, hist.-lit. Abt., **36** (1891), 1–23, 41–63, 81–95, 121–138. In MS Dresden C80 Curtze found additional propositions (IV.16–IV.35) beyond the concluding proposition in Treutlein's ed. The additional propositions included no proofs but only the enunciations of the propositions followed immediately by a single numerical example for each. That these extra propositions formed a genuine part of the *De numeris datis* was verified by MSS Vienna 4770 and 5303, which included not only the additional propositions but also their proofs. Using MS Vienna 4770, from which 5303 was copied, R. Daublebsky von Sterneck published complete versions of Props. IV.15–IV.35 and also

JORDANUS DE NEMORE

supplied corrections and additions to a few propositions in Bk. I in "Zur Vervollständigung der Ausgaben der Schrift des Jordanus Nemorarius: 'Tractatus de numeris datis,'" in *Monatshefte für Mathematik und Physik*, **7** (1896), 165–179. A third ed., with the first English trans., has been completed by Barnabas Hughes: *The De numeris datis of Jordanus de Nemore, a Critical Edition, Analysis, Evaluation and Translation* (Ph.D. diss., Stanford University, 1970). Hughes's thorough study also includes (pp. 104–126) a history of previous editions, as well as a description of twelve MSS, whose relationships are discussed in detail.

A Russian translation from Curtze's edition was made by S. N. Šreĭder, "The Beginnings of Algebra in Medieval Europe in the Treatise De numeris datis of Jordanus de Nemore," in *Istoriko-Matematicheskie issledovaniya*, **12** (1959), 679–688.

As yet there is no ed. of the ten-book *Arithmetica*, although the enunciations of the propositions were published by Jacques Lefèvre d'Étaples (Jacobus Faber Stapulensis), who supplied his own demonstrations and comments in *Arithmetica (Iordani Nemorarii) decem libris demonstrata* (Paris, 1496, 1503, 1507, 1510, 1514). At least sixteen complete or partial MSS of it are presently known, among which are two excellent and complete thirteenth-century MSS: Paris, BN 16644, 2r–93v; and Vat. lat., Ottoboni MS 2069, 1r–51v.

The Latin text of the definitions and enunciations of the 34 propositions of the *Demonstratio Jordani de algorismo* were published by G. Eneström, "Über die 'Demonstratio Jordani de algorismo,'" in *Bibliotheca mathematica*, 3rd ser., **7** (1906–1907), 24–37, from MSS Berlin, lat. 4° 510, 72v–77r (Königliche Bibliothek, renamed Preussische Staatsbibliothek in 1918; the fate of this codex after World War II, when the basic collection was divided between East and West Germany, is unknown to me) and Dresden Db 86, 169r–175r. The *Demonstratio* appears to be an altered version of a similar and earlier work beginning with the words "Communis et consuetus . . .," which Eneström called *Opus numerorum*. The Latin text of its introduction and a comparison of its propositions with those of the *Demonstratio Jordani* were published by Eneström as "Über eine dem Jordanus Nemorarius zugeschriebene kurze Algorismusschrift," in *Bibliotheca mathematica*, 3rd ser., **8** (1907–1908), 135–153. He relied primarily on MS Vat. lat. Ottob. 309, 114r–117r, supplemented by MSS Vat. lat. Reg. Suev. 1268, 69r–71r; Florence, Bibl. Naz. Centr., Conv. Soppr. J.V. 18 (cited by Eneström as San Marco 216, its previous designation), 37r–39r; and Paris, Mazarin 3642, 96r and 105r. Since the *Demonstratio Jordani* was definitely ascribed to Jordanus, and the *Opus numerorum* seemed an earlier version of it, Eneström conjectured that the *Opus* was a more likely candidate for Jordanus' original work, while the *Demonstratio Jordani*, which omits most of the introduction but expands the text itself, may have been revised by Jordanus or someone else.

Each of these two treatises has associated with it a brief work, attributed in some MSS to Jordanus, on arithmetic operations with fractions. The treatise associated with the *Opus numerorum*, which Eneström calls *Tractatus minutiarum*, contains an introduction and 26 highly abbreviated propositions; the work on fractions associated with the *Demonstratio Jordani de algorismo*, which Eneström calls *Demonstratio de minutiis*, consists of an introduction and 35 propositions. Although the introductions differ, all 26 propositions of the *Tractatus minutiarum* have, according to Eneström, identical counterparts in the longer *Demonstratio de minutiis*. In "Das Bruchrechnen des Jordanus Nemorarius," in *Bibliotheca mathematica*, 3rd ser., **14** (1913–1914), 41–54, Eneström includes a list of MSS for both treatises (pp. 41–42), the Latin texts of the introductions, the texts of the enunciations of the propositions, and analytic representations of the propositions. By analogy with his reasoning about the relations obtaining between the *Opus numerorum* and *Demonstratio Jordani de algorismo*, Eneström conjectures that Jordanus is the author of the *Tractatus minutiarum*, the briefer treatise associated with the *Opus numerorum*. One of the MSS is Bibl. Naz. Centr., Conv. Soppr. J.V. 18, 39r–42v, which follows immediately after the *Opus numerorum* in the same codex cited above; correspondingly, MS Berlin, lat. 4° 510, 72v–77r, of the *Demonstratio Jordani de algorismo* is followed immediately by a version of the *Demonstratio de minutiis* on fols. 77r–81v, a relation which also seems to obtain in Bibl. Naz. Centr., Conv. Soppr. J.I. 32, 113r–118v, 118v–124r. Whether the two algorithm treatises and the two associated treatises on fractions bear any relation to works (5), (6), (7), or (10), cited above from the *Biblionomia*, has yet to be determined and may, indeed, be impossible to determine. The *Algorismus demonstratus* published in 1534 by J. Schöner and formerly ascribed to Jordanus, was composed by a Master Gernardus, who is perhaps identical with Gerard of Brussels.

The *Liber de proportionibus*, mentioned in the *Biblionomia*, is probably a brief work by Jordanus beginning with the words "Proportio est rei ad rem determinata secundum quantitatem habitudo . . . ." A seemingly complete MS of it is Florence, Bibl. Naz. Centr., Conv. Soppr. J.V. 30, 8r–9v. Other MSS are listed in L. Thorndike and P. Kibre, *A Catalogue of Incipits of Mediaeval Scientific Writings in Latin*, rev. ed. (Cambridge, Mass., 1963), col. 1139. The *Suppletiones plane spere* of the *Biblionomia* is probably a commentary on Ptolemy's *Planisphaerium*. According to G. Sarton, *Introduction to the History of Science*, 3 vols. in 5 pts., II, pt. 2 (Baltimore, 1931), 614, it is "a treatise on mathematical astronomy, which contains the first general demonstration of the fundamental property of stereographic projection—i.e., that circles are projected as circles (Ptolemy had proved it only in special cases)." In Thorndike and Kibre, *op. cit.*, Jordanus' *Planisphaerium* is listed under three separate and different incipits (see cols. 1119, 1524, and 1525, where MSS are listed for each). An edition appeared at Venice in 1558, under the title *Ptolemaei Planisphaerium: Iordani Planisphaerium; Federici Commandi Urbinatis in Ptolemaei Planisphaerium commentarius.* A work on isoperimetric figures, *De figuris ysoperimetris*, is also attributed to Jordanus: MSS Florence, Bibl. Naz. Centr., Conv. Soppr. J.V. 30, 12v (a fragment) and

Vienna 5203, 142r–146r, the latter actually copied by Regiomontanus, who was also acquainted with Jordanus' *De triangulis*, *Planisphaerium*, *Arithmetica*, *De numeris datis*, and *De proportionibus;* the enunciations of the eight propositions in the Vienna MS were published by Maximilian Curtze, "Eine Studienreise," in *Zentralblatt für Bibliothekswesen*, **16** (1899), 264–265.

II. SECONDARY LITERATURE. The most significant studies on Jordanus are monographic in character and have been cited above, since they are associated with editions and translations of his works. No general appraisal and evaluation of his scientific works has yet been published. To what has already been cited, the following may be added: O. Klein, "Who Was Jordanus Nemorarius?," in *Nuclear Physics*, **57** (1964), 345–350; Benjamin Ginzberg, "Duhem and Jordanus Nemorarius," in *Isis*, **25** (1936), 341–362, which seeks to refute Duhem's claims for medieval science and for Jordanus' statics in particular (Ginzberg seriously misread Duhem and was also ignorant of Jordanus' subsequent impact on later statics, believing mistakenly that all of it was rediscovered); M. Clagett, *The Science of Mechanics in the Middle Ages* (Madison, Wis., 1959), ch. 2, which is a summary of medieval contributions in statics, including source selections from the works of Jordanus; Joseph E. Brown, *The Scientia de ponderibus in the Later Middle Ages* (Ph.D. diss., University of Wis., 1967), which includes summaries and evaluations of the major principles in Jordanus' statical treatises and their subsequent influence in the commentary literature; and G. Wertheim, "Über die Lösung einiger Aufgaben in *De numeris datis*," in *Bibliotheca mathematica*, **1** (1900), 417–420. Additional bibliography is given in Sarton, *op. cit.*, II, pt. 2, 614–616.

EDWARD GRANT

JUEL, SOPHUS CHRISTIAN (*b.* Randers, Denmark, 25 January 1855; *d.* Copenhagen, Denmark, 24 January 1935)

Juel's father, a judge, died the year after his son was born. The boy spent his youth in the country and attended the Realschule in Svendborg. At the age of fifteen he went to Copenhagen, where in 1871 he entered the Technical University. In January 1876, being more interested in pure science, he took the examinations for admission to the University of Copenhagen. Completing his university studies in 1879 with the state examination, he received his doctor's degree in 1885. From 1894 he was lecturer at the Polytechnic Institute, where in 1907 he became full professor. He occasionally lectured at the University of Copenhagen.

From 1889 to 1915 he was editor of the *Matematisk Tidsskrift*. In 1925 he became an honorary member of the Mathematical Association and in 1929 received an honorary doctorate from the University of Oslo. He married a daughter of T. N. Thiele, professor of mathematics and astronomy. Failing eyesight plagued him in later years.

Juel's writings include schoolbooks, textbooks, and essays. He made substantial contributions to projective geometry for the cases of one and two complex dimensions, and to the theory of curves and surfaces. His book on projective geometry is very similar in approach to that of Staudt but is easier to understand; his treatment of autocollineations goes beyond Staudt's. Segré arrived at similar results independently.

In 1914 Juel devised the concept of an elementary curve, which is in the projective plane without straight-line segments and has the topological image of a circle and a tangent at every point. Outside these points a convex arc can be described on each side. Thus an elementary curve consists of an infinite number of convex arcs passing smoothly one into another.

Juel, whose treatment of his subject was loose and incomplete, dealt mainly with fourth-order curves, developing the concept of the order of an elementary curve and setting up a correspondence principle and theory of inflection points. His third-order elementary curve is very close to a third-order algebraic curve but no longer has three points of inflection on one straight line.

Juel worked also on the theory of finite equal polyhedra, on cyclic curves, and on oval surfaces.

BIBLIOGRAPHY

I. ORIGINAL WORKS. Juel's textbooks include *Vorlesungen über Mathematik für Chemiker* (Copenhagen, 1890); *Elementar stereometri* (Copenhagen, 1896); *Analytisk stereometri* (Copenhagen, 1897); *Ren og anvendt aritmetik* (Copenhagen, 1902); *Forlaesinger over rational mekanik* (Copenhagen, 1913; enl. ed., 1920); and *Vorlesungen über projektive Geometrie mit besonderer berücksichtigung der von staudtschen Imaginärtheorie* (Berlin, 1934).

His articles and essays include *Inledning i de imaginaer linies og den imaginaer plans geometrie* (Copenhagen, 1885), his dissertation; "Grundgebilde der projektiven geometrie," in *Acta mathematica*, **14** (1891); and "Parameterbestimmung von Punkten auf Kurven 2. und 3. Ordnung," in *Mathematische Annalen*, **47** (1896), written with R. Clebsch; and three that appeared in *Kongelige Danske Videnskabernes Selskabs Skrifter:* "Inledning i laeren om de grafiske kurver" (1899); "Caustiques planes" (1902); "Égalité par addition de quelques polyèdres" (1902).

The following articles appeared in *Matematisk Tidsskrift:* "Kegelsnitskorder des fra et fast punkt ses under ret vinkel" (1886); "Korder i en kugel, der fra et fast punkt ses under ret vinkel" (1887); "Vivianis theorem" (1891); "Transformationer af Laguerre" (1892); "Polyeder, der ere kongruente med deres speilbilleder uden at vaere selvsymmetriske" (1895); "Konstrukter af dobbelpunktstangenterne ved en rumkurve af 4. order" (1897); and "Arealer ot voluminere" (1897).

II. SECONDARY LITERATURE. Details concerning Juel's work can be found in David Fog, "The Mathematician C. Juel—Commemorative Address Delivered Before the Mathematical Association on March 18, 1935," in *Matematisk Tidsskrift*, **B** (1935), 3–15.

HERBERT OETTEL

JUNGIUS, JOACHIM (*b.* Lübeck, Germany, 22 October 1587; *d.* Hamburg, Germany, 23 September 1657)

Jungius was the son of Nicolaus Junge, a professor at the Gymnasium St. Katharinen in Lübeck who died in 1589, and Brigitte Holdmann, who later married Martin Nortmann, another professor at St. Katharinen. Jungius attended that Gymnasium, where he commented on the *Dialectic* of Petrus Ramus, as well as writing on logic and composing poetry, then entered the Faculty of Arts of the University of Rostock in May 1606.

At Rostock Jungius studied with Johann Sleker, from whom he learned metaphysics in the tradition of Francisco Suarez and his school. In general, however, he preferred to concentrate on mathematics and logic. In May 1608 Jungius went to the new University of Giessen to continue his studies. He took the M.A. at Giessen on 22 December 1608, and remained there until 1614 as professor of those disciplines then generally designated as mathematics. His inaugural dissertation was the famous oration on the didactic significance, advantage, and usefulness of mathematics for all disciplines, which he later repeated at Rostock and Hamburg and which revealed the idea that guided his lifework. He ardently pursued mathematical studies. He copied a book by F. Viète, although which one is not known, and in 1612 and 1613, while on a journey to Frankfurt, observed sunspots, the existence of which had been confirmed by Johann Fabricius and Christoph Scheiner.

At this time Jungius was attracted to pedagogy. In 1612 he traveled to Frankfurt with Christoph Helvich of the University of Giessen to attend the coronation of the emperor Matthias; there he met Wolfgang Ratke, who was trying to revive the "Lehrkunst." Jungius resigned his post at Giessen in 1614 and devoted himself to educational reform in Augsburg and Erfurt, but by the time of his return to Lübeck, on 27 July 1615, he had changed his mind in favor of the natural sciences. He began to study medicine at the University of Rostock in August 1616 and received the M.D. at Padua on 1 January 1619.

The years between 1619 and 1629 were a peak in Jungius' scientific life. He deepened his knowledge in the natural sciences while practicing medicine at Lübeck (1619–1623) and at Brunswick and Wolfenbüttel (1625) and during his tenure as a professor of medicine at the University of Helmstedt. He improved his abilities in mathematics as a professor of mathematics at Rostock in 1624–1625 and again from 1626 until 1628. He utilized this practical experience in the intensive private research that he conducted at the same time. This is particularly apparent in his "Protonoeticae philosophiae sciagraphia" and in his "Heuretica." In addition, he founded in about 1623 the Societas Ereunetica, a short-lived group dedicated to scientific research and perhaps modeled on the Accademia dei Lincei, with which Jungius had become acquainted in Italy. Finally, he was appointed professor of natural science and rector of the Akademisches Gymnasium at Hamburg, a post he held until his death.

Two tragic features characterized this last period of Jungius' life. His wife, Catharina, the daughter of Valentin Havemann of Rostock, whom he had married on 10 February 1624, died on 16 June 1638. During the 1630's, too, he became subject to the envy of his colleagues and even to attacks by the clergy, despite his devout Protestantism. He was thereafter reluctant to publish his writings and left some 75,000 pages in manuscript at the time of his death, of which two-thirds were destroyed in a fire in 1691, while the remainder have been little studied. Indeed, the primary source of Jungius' influence on his disciples and contemporaries must be sought in his correspondence and in his composition of some forty disputations.

Jungius tried to apply his mathematical training in two ways. First, he used it to solve problems, as, for example, in proving that the catenary is not, as Galileo had assumed, a parabola. Many of his problems in arithmetic and geometry, including those set out in his *Geometria numerosa* and *Mathesis specialis*, have not been found. He was one of the first to use exponents to represent powers. His experiments and views on the laws of motion are also mathematical in nature, as was explicit in the *Phoranomica*, which in part set out the instruction given by Jungius to Charles Cavendysshe, Jr., of Newcastle-upon-Tyne, when the latter mathematician was staying at Hamburg, from 8 July 1644 to February 1645, as a refugee from Cromwell's regime. In this complete, but lost, *Phoranomica* Jungius also wrote on such topics as "De impetu," "De intensione motus" (on velocity), "De tempore," and "De tendentia motuum." A specimen of this work, containing the titles of single chapters, was sent to the

Royal Society of London in December 1669. Astronomy was at that time comprised in mathematics, and an account of Jungius' observations of the variable star Mira (Omicron) Ceti, made in 1647, was also sent to the Royal Society by Heinrich Sivers in a letter of 23 June 1673. While Jungius made other astronomical observations and calculations, they remained unpublished, as did his optical researches.

Second, Jungius used mathematics as a model on which to base a theory of science in general. He outlined this principle in the "Protonoeticae philosophiae sciagraphia," of which a copy was sent by Samuel Hartlib to Robert Boyle in 1654. In this paper and in his orations in praise of mathematics and his "Analysis heuretica," Jungius worked out a scientific method analogous to the mathematical mode of proof that he called "ecthesis." These works were composed more than eight years before Descartes's *Discours* appeared. In other writings Jungius rejected such Scholastic devices as single syllogisms and consequences and advocated the "clear and distinct" methodological principle of Galen. He further elaborated a theory of mathematical operations ("zetetica") that continued in more detail the "general mathematics" of the school of Proclus, Conrad Dasypodius, and Johann Heinrich Alsted. Jungius thought that this methodology was closely connected with the logical doctrine of proof that he presented in 1638 in the fourth book of his *Logica Hamburgensis*, in which he for the first time also treated such mathematical principles as "problems," "regulas," and "theorems"; abandoned distinctions in favor of exact nominal definitions; recommended a "geometric style" ("stylus protonoeticus"); and defined a systematic science ("scientia totalis"). His method of scientific inference as here set forth was based upon "demonstrations" from principles (including definitions) and upon both complete and incomplete induction.

Jungius' taste for systematizing led him to morphological studies in botany and to a corpuscular theory of chemistry, among other things. All his arguments were based on observations that he put in writing as "protonoetical papers." In botany he built his system on what Andrea Cesalpino had defined as plant morphology; some of his work was incorporated by John Ray in *Catalogus plantarum circa Cantabrigiam nascentium* (1660) and was communicated to the Royal Society of London by John Beale on 6 May 1663.

Jungius' chemical system was elaborated before 1630 and was published in two *Disputationes* (1642) and in the *Doxoscopiae physicae minores* (1662). It was based upon planned experiment and closely related to the medical tradition of the corpuscular hypothesis, as opposed to atomism. Jungius explained the apparent homogeneity of a natural body, the mechanism of chemical reaction, and the conservation of matter and weight through the assumption of invisible particles of no fixed size or shape. This enabled him to elucidate the precipitation of copper by iron in solution as an exchange of individual particles at the metal and in the solution, as opposed to the "transubstantiation" suggested by Andreas Libavius, the mere extraction from solution proposed by Nicolas Guibert and Angelo Sala, and the simple disappearance of iron particles in the solution postulated by J. B. van Helmont.

Jungius stressed that the parts of a body should be reducible to their original states with the same weights that they had originally had. In keeping with his analytical point of view he defined an element a posteriori, that is as experimentally separable. He found that gold, silver, sulfur, mercury, saltpeter, common salt, soda, and some other substances had existed as discrete elements before separation. He distinguished the bodies arrived at after separation, that is, those "exactly simple bodies," from the substantial parts, that is, "elements," in the natural body. He chose to emphasize the former, and stated that each consisted of like particles—although he did not specify how the particles of one such exactly simple body might be told from those of another. He further recognized spontaneous reactions, but referred them to attraction, and so he did not believe that any motion is inherent to the corpuscles. Like Galileo, he tried to objectify the properties of bodies and studied the transitions between their solid, liquid, and vapor phases. He was opposed to the Peripatetic notions of substantial forms and inseparable matter and fought strongly against the ideas of inherent qualities and a single principle of combustion.

Jungius' systems for botany and chemistry—cited here as an example—were products of his methodological program for all sciences, with its emphasis on observation and mathematical demonstration.

BIBLIOGRAPHY

I. Original Works. A complete bibliography of Jungius' printed works is in Hans Kangro, *Joachim Jungius' Experimente und Gedanken zur Begründung der Chemie als Wissenschaft, ein Beitrag zur Geistesgeschichte des 17. Jahrhunderts* (Wiesbaden, 1968), pp. 350–394, with photographic reproductions of nearly all title pages.

Important works published during Jungius' lifetime are *Kurtzer Bericht von der Didactica, oder Lehrkunst Wolfgangi Ratichii . . . durch Christophorum Helvicum . . . und*

Joachimum Jungium (Frankfurt am Main, 1613); *Geometrica empirica* (Rostock, 1627); *Logica Hamburgensis*, bks. I–III (Hamburg, 1635), bks. I–VI (Hamburg, 1638); *Verantwortung wegen desjenigen was neulich vor und in den Pfingsten wegen des griechischen Neuen Testaments und anderer Schulsachen von öffentlicher Kanzel fürgebracht*, in Johannes Geffcken, "Joachim Jungius, Über die Originalsprache des Neuen Testaments vom Jahre 1637," in *Zeitschrift des Vereines für hamburgische Geschichte*, **5** (n.s. **2**) (1866), 164–183; *Candido lectori salutem* (Hamburg, 1639), with the incipit "Pervenit tandem hestierno die . . .," Jungius' answer to an attack by Johannes Scharff of Wittenberg; *De stilo sacrarum literarum, et praesertim Novi Testamenti Graeci* (n.p., 1639); *Compendium Logicae Hamburgensis* (Hamburg, 1641); a pamphlet (Hamburg, 1642), with the incipit "L. S. P. Philosophiae studium . . .," Jungius' invitation to the oration of his disciple Caspar Westermann; some forty *Disputationes* printed between 1607 and 1652, in which Jungius was "respondens," afterward "praesidens," the exact dates of which may be found in Kangro's bibliography (cited above); *Dokt. Joach. Jungius Reisskunst* (n.p., n.d.), only fols. A1–D4 plus one page, a free German translation from the Latin *Geometria empirica*.

Important works published after Jungius' death are *Doxoscopiae physicae minores*, Martin Fogel, ed. (Hamburg, 1662); 2nd ed., entitled *Praecipuae opiniones physicae*, M. Fogel and Johann Vaget, eds. (Hamburg, 1679), also contains *Harmonica* (n.p., n.d.) and *Isagoge phytoscopica* (preface dated 1678); *Germania Superior*, J. Vaget, ed. (Hamburg, 1685); *Mineralia*, Christian Buncke and J. Vaget, eds. (Hamburg, 1689); *Historia vermium*, J. Vaget, ed. (Hamburg, 1691); and *Phoranomica, id est De motu locali* (n.p., n.d., but perhaps not earlier than 1699, since it first appears in Johann Adolph Tassius, *Opuscula mathematica* [Hamburg, 1699]). Selections from Jungius' voluminous correspondence were published—although the collection is not perfect, some letters being presented only in extract or translation—by Robert C. B. Avé-Lallement, *Des Dr. Joachim Jungius aus Lübeck Briefwechsel mit seinen Schülern und Freunden* (Lübeck, 1863); the incipit "Quod iis evenire solet . . ." to Jungius' oration on the propaedeutic use of mathematics in studying liberal arts, presented 19 March 1629 at his inauguration in Hamburg, was edited by J. Lemcke and A. Meyer [-Abich] in *Beiträge zur Jungius-Forschung* (*Festschrift der Hamburgischen Universität anlässlich ihres zehnjährigen Bestehens*), A. Meyer [-Abich], ed. (Hamburg, 1929), pp. 94–120, with German trans. There is also "Protonoeticae philosophiae sciagraphia," the first four sheets of a copied or dictated MS, edited by H. Kangro in *Joachim Jungius' Experimente . . .*, pp. 256–271, with German trans.

A reprint, arranged by Jungius, of *Auctarium epitomes physicae . . . Dn. Danielis Sennerti* (author unknown; Wittenberg, 1635) appeared at Hamburg in 1635.

The main collection of MSS, including orations and correspondence, is in the Staats- und Universitätsbibliothek Hamburg; these include nearly all the MSS on botany, as well as part of Jungius' correspondence with John Pell. The rest of the Jungius–Pell letters are in London, BM Sloane 4279 and 4280. Other MSS are "Phoranomica" ("praelecta . . . 1644"), perhaps addressed to Charles Cavendysshe, in the Niedersächsische Landesbibliothek Hannover, MS IV, 346; "Definitiones geometricae inservientes Phoranomicae," written down by Cavendysshe, London BM Harl. 6083, fols. 246–265; and "Isagoge phytoscopica," copied or dictated before 1660, in MSS of Samuel Hartlib in the possession of Lord Delamere. Also in the Niedersächsische Landesbibliothek Hannover are Jungius' "Heuretica," partly copied by Leibniz under the title "Logica did. [actica]," LH Phil. VII C, fols. 139r–145r; "Texturae contemplatio," LH XXXVIII, fols. 26–29; "De dianoea composita lectiones," LH Phil. VII C, fols. 149r–150r, which is fragmentary; and sheets on various topics interspersed in MSS XLII 1923 of Jungius' disciple Martin Fogel.

II. SECONDARY LITERATURE. The best biography, although an old one, is Martin Fogel, *Memoriae Joachimi Jungii mathematici summi . . .* (Hamburg, 1657), 2nd ed., entitled *Historia vitae et mortis Joachimi Jungii . . .* (Strasbourg, 1658). There are relevant additions by J. Moller in his *Cimbria literata* (Copenhagen, 1744), III, 342–348.

On Jungius' philosophy see G. E. Guhrauer, *Joachim Jungius und sein Zeitalter* (Stuttgart–Tübingen, 1850), original but in need of updating. His corpuscular hypothesis and chemistry are discussed in E. Wohlwill, "Joachim Jungius und die Erneuerung atomistischer Lehren im 17. Jahrhundert," in *Festschrift zur Feier des fünfzigjährigen Bestehens des Naturwissenschaftlichen Vereins in Hamburg* (Hamburg, 1887), paper II, which presents a positivistic point of view; a new view of Wohlwill's theses is given in R. Hooykaas, "Elementenlehre und Atomistik im 17. Jahrhundert," in *Die Entfaltung der Wissenschaft* (Hamburg, n. d. [1958]), pp. 47–65; and H. Kangro, *Joachim Jungius' Experimente und Gedanken zur Begründung der Chemie als Wissenschaft, ein Beitrag zur Geistesgeschichte des 17. Jahrhunderts* (Wiesbaden, 1968). An original sketch of Jungius' botany is W. Mevius, "Der Botaniker Joachim Jungius und das Urteil der Nachwelt," in *Die Entfaltung der Wissenschaft* (Hamburg, n. d. [1958]), pp. 67–77. Texts of original MSS concerning Jungius' conflict with the clergy are Erich von Lehe, "Jungius-Archivalien aus dem Staatsarchiv," in *Beiträge zur Jungius-Forschung*, A. Meyer[-Abich], ed. (Hamburg, 1929), pp. 62–87.

On other topics see the following by H. Kangro: "Heuretica (Erfindungskunst) und Begriffskalkül—ist der Inhalt der Leibnizhandschrift Phil. VII C 139r–145r Joachim Jungius zuzuschreiben?," in *Sudhoffs Archiv, Vierteljahrsschrift für Geschichte der Medizin und der Naturwissenschaften, der Pharmazie und der Mathematik*, **52** (1968), 48–66; "Joachim Jungius und Gottfried Wilhelm Leibniz, ein Beitrag zum geistigen Verhältnis beider Gelehrten," in *Studia Leibnitiana*, **1** (1969), 175–207; "Die Unabhängigkeit eines Beweises: John Pells Beziehungen zu Joachim Jungius und Johann Adolph Tassius (aus unveröffentlichten MSS)," in *Janus*, **56** (1969), 203–209; "Martin Fogel aus Hamburg als Gelehrter des 17. Jahrhunderts," in

Ural-Altaische Jahrbücher, **41** (1969), 14–32, containing many relations between Fogel and Jungius; and "Organon Joachimi Jungii ad demonstrationem Copernici hypotheseos Keppleri conclusionibus suppositae," in *Organon* (in press).

HANS KANGRO

KAESTNER, ABRAHAM GOTTHELF (*b.* Leipzig, Germany, 27 September 1719; *d.* Göttingen, Germany, 20 June 1800)

Kaestner's father, a professor of jurisprudence, began early preparing him to enter that field but the young man's interests turned to philosophy, mathematics, and physics. After his *Habilitation* at the University of Leipzig in 1739, Kaestner lectured there on mathematics, logic, and natural law, as privatdocent until 1746, and then as extraordinary professor. In 1756 he was appointed professor of mathematics and physics at the University of Göttingen, where he remained for the rest of his life, becoming an influential figure through his teaching and writing; Göttingen's reputation as a center of mathematical studies dates from that time. Kaestner is also known in German literature, notably for his epigrams. He was a devout Lutheran. Kaestner married twice and had a daughter by his second wife.

Kaestner owes his place in the history of mathematics not to any important discoveries of his own but to his great success as an expositor and to the seminal character of his thought. His output as a writer in mathematics and its applications (optics, dynamics, astronomy), in the form of long works and hundreds of essays and memoirs, was prodigious. Most popular was his *Mathematische Anfangsgründe*, which appeared in four separately titled parts, each going through several editions (Göttingen, 1757–1800). Of lesser significance was his other four-volume work, *Geschichte der Mathematik* (Göttingen, 1796–1800).

From today's point of view Kaestner's historical significance lies mostly in the interest he promoted in the foundations of parallel theory. His own search for a proof of Euclid's parallel postulate culminated in his sponsorship of, and contribution of a postscript to, a dissertation by G. S. Klügel (1763) in which thirty purported proofs of that postulate are examined and found defective. This influential work prompted J. H. Lambert's important researches on parallel theory. The three men who independently founded non-Euclidean (hyperbolic) geometry in the early nineteenth century were all directly or indirectly influenced by Kaestner: Gauss had studied at Göttingen during Kaestner's tenure there; Johann Bolyai's father, Wolfgang, who personally taught his son geometry, had studied under Kaestner and had tried his own hand at proving Euclid's postulate; Lobachevsky studied mathematics at the University of Kazan under J. M. C. Bartels, a former student of Kaestner's.

As a student, Gauss is said to have shunned Kaestner's lectures as too elementary. Yet the *princeps mathematicorum* shows the influence of Kaestner, not only in the matter of parallelism but in other areas as well. Kaestner opposed, as did Gauss, the concept of actual infinity in mathematics (see, for example, Kaestner and G. S. Klügel, *Philosophische-mathematische Abhandlungen* [Halle, 1807]); and he felt the need, later clearly expressed by Gauss (*Werke* [Göttingen, 1870–1927], VIII, 222), for postulates of order in geometry. Indeed, Kaestner anticipated M. Pasch in explicitly postulating the division of the plane, by a line, into two parts, and in enunciating the needed assumptions concerning the intersections of a circle with a line or another circle (*Anfangsgründe*, I).

BIBLIOGRAPHY

I. ORIGINAL WORKS. Most of Kaestner's scientific publications are listed in the article on him in Poggendorff, I, cols. 1217–1219. Also valuable is the bibliography in the article on Kaestner in the *Biographie universelle* (Paris, 1852–1868), XXI, which includes literary works. Neither of these two bibliographies cites Kaestner's sponsorship of and contribution to the dissertation by G. S. Klügel, *Conatuum praecipuorum theoriam demonstrandi recensio, quam publico examini submittent Abrah. Gotthelf Kaestner et auctor respondens Georgius Simon Klügel* (Göttingen, 1763). For details of Kaestner's life, see his autobiography, *Vita Kestneri* (Leipzig, 1787).

II. SECONDARY LITERATURE. References to Kaestner's preparatory role in the development of non-Euclidean geometry are found in Friedrich Engel and Paul Stäckel, *Theorie der Parallelinien von Euclid bis auf Gauss* (Leipzig, 1895), pp. 138–140; and in Roberto Bonola, *Non-Euclidean Geometry: A Critical and Historical Study of Its Developments*, trans. by H. S. Carslaw (New York, 1955), pp. 50, 60, 64, 66. For Kaestner's anticipations of Pasch, see George Goe, "Kaestner, Forerunner of Gauss, Pasch, Hilbert," in *Proceedings of the 10th International Congress of the History of Science*, II (Paris, 1964), 659–661.

GEORGE GOE

KAGAN, BENJAMIN FEDOROVICH (*b.* Shavli, Kovno [Kaunas] district [now Siauliai, Lithuanian S.S.R.], 10 March 1869; *d.* Moscow, U.S.S.R., 8 May 1953)

The son of a clerk, Kagan entered Novorossysky

University, Odessa, in 1887, but was expelled in 1889 for participating in the democratic students' movement and was sent to Ekaterinoslav (now Dnepropetrovsk). In 1892 he passed the examinations in the department of physics and mathematics of Kiev University. He passed the examinations for the master's degree at St. Petersburg (1895), becoming lecturer at Novorossysky in 1897 and professor in 1917. Besides teaching at Novorossysky, Kagan gave higher education classes for women and presented courses at a Jewish high school. He edited *Vestnik opytnoi fiziki i elementarnoi matematiki* ("Journal of Experimental Physics and Elementary Mathematics") in 1902–1917 and was a director of a large scientific publishing house, Mathesis.

Kagan's first important work was devoted to a very original and ingenious exposition of Lobachevsky's geometry. Next he considered problems of the foundations of geometry, proposing in 1902 a system of axioms and definitions considerably different from all previously suggested, and particularly different from that of Hilbert. This system was based on the notion of space as a set of points in which to every two points there corresponds a nonnegative number—distance—invariant in respect to a system of point transformations (movements) in this space; the point, the principal element from which other figures are generated, is not defined. A very complete construction of Euclid's geometry on such a basis is in the first volume of Kagan's master's thesis, defended in 1907; the second volume contains a detailed history of the doctrines of the foundations of geometry. In 1903 Kagan presented a new demonstration, remarkable in its simplicity, of Dehn's well-known theorem on equal polyhedrons (1900). Since he was interested in Einstein's theory of relativity, Kagan also began studies in tensor differential geometry which he pursued intensively in Moscow, to which he moved in 1922.

For almost ten years Kagan was in charge of the science department of the state publishing house, and for many years he supervised the department of mathematical and natural sciences of the *Great Soviet Encyclopedia*. But his principal efforts were directed to Moscow University, where he was elected professor in 1922; in 1927 he organized a seminar on vector and tensor analysis, and from 1934 he held the chair of differential geometry. At Moscow, Kagan created a large scientific school with considerable influence on the development of contemporary geometrical thought; his disciples include Y. S. Dubnov, P. K. Rashevsky, A. P. Norden, and V. V. Wagner. Kagan himself was concerned mainly with the theory of subprojective spaces, a generalization of Riemannian spaces of constant curvature.

Kagan also wrote studies on the history of non-Euclidean geometry and published a detailed biography of Lobachevsky. He was the general editor of the five-volume edition of Lobachevsky's complete works (1946–1951).

In 1926 Kagan was raised to the rank of honored scientist of the Russian Federation; in 1943 he was awarded the U.S.S.R. State Prize.

BIBLIOGRAPHY

I. ORIGINAL WORKS. A bibliography of Kagan's writings is in Lopshitz and Rashevsky (see below). They include "Ocherk geometricheskoy systemy Lobachevskogo" ("Outline of Lobachevsky's Geometrical System"), in *Vestnik opytnoi fiziki i elementarnoi matematiki* (1893–1898), also published separately (Odessa, 1900); "Ein System von Postulaten, welche die euklidische Geometrie definieren," in *Jahresbericht der Deutschen Mathematiker-vereinigung*, **11** (1902), 403–424; "Über die Transformation der Polyeder," in *Mathematische Annalen*, **57** (1903), 421–424; *Osnovania geometrii* ("Foundations of Geometry"), 2 vols. (Odessa, 1905–1907); "Über eine Erweiterung des Begriffes vom projectiven Raume und dem zugehörigen Absolut," in *Trudy seminara po vektornomu i tensornomu analysu* ("Transactions of the Seminar on Vector and Tensor Analysis"), I (Moscow–Leningrad, 1933), 12–101, repr. in Kagan's *Subproektivnye prostranstva* ("Subprojective Spaces"; Moscow, 1960); *Lobachevsky* (Moscow–Leningrad, 1944; 2nd ed., 1948); *Osnovy teorii poverkhnostey v tensornom izlozhenii* ("Foundations of the Theory of Surfaces Exposed by Means of Tensor Calculus"), 2 vols. (Moscow–Leningrad, 1947–1948); *Osnovania geometrii* ("Foundations of Geometry"), 2 vols. (Moscow–Leningrad, 1949–1956); and *Ocherki po geometrii* ("Essays on Geometry"; Moscow, 1963), a volume of collected papers and discourses.

II. SECONDARY LITERATURE. See A. M. Lopshitz and P. K. Rashevsky, *Benjamin Fedorovich Kagan* (Moscow, 1969); I. Z. Shtokalo, ed., *Istoria otechestvennoy matematiki* ("History of Native Mathematics"), II-III (Kiev, 1967–1968), see index; and A. P. Youschkevitch, *Istoria matematiki v Rossii do 1917 goda* ("History of Mathematics in Russia Until 1917"; Moscow, 1968), see index.

A. P. YOUSCHKEVITCH

KALMÁR, LÁSZLÓ (*b.* Edde, Hungary, 27 March 1905; *d.* Mátraháza, Hungary, 2 August 1976)

László Kalmár was the youngest child of Zsigmond Kalmár and Róza Krausz Kalmár. His father was an estate bailiff on a manor situated in Transdanubia, about 30 kilometers from Lake Balaton. About the beginning of World War I, Kalmár moved with his widowed mother to Budapest, where he attended secondary school. His outstanding mathematical abilities were already evident: he had read and understood Cesàro's calculus text when he was only thirteen. He studied mathematics and physics at the University of Budapest between 1922 and 1927. Despite unhappy circumstances (his mother had died earlier), he was very successful in his studies and was considered by his fellow students as their master in mathematics. During his university years he studied under such eminent mathematicians as József Kürschák and Lipót Fejér. After obtaining a Ph.D. he accepted a faculty position at the University of Szeged, where he remained until his retirement in 1975. He was an assistant to Alfréd Haar and Frigyes Riesz from 1930 to 1947. He was promoted in 1947 to full professor. He married Erzsébet Árvay in 1933. Three of their four children survived him.

Kalmár was elected a corresponding member of the Hungarian Academy of Sciences in 1949 and as a full member in 1961. He was awarded the highest orders in Hungary for scientific activity: the Kossuth Prize in 1950 and the State Prize in 1975. He was honorary president of the János Bolyai Mathematical Society and the John von Neumann Society for Computer Science. In spite of his age, he continued his research with full energy until the last day of his life.

One of the fields in which his contribution is of greatest importance is mathematical logic. His interest in logic was aroused on a visit to Göttingen in 1929. He gave simplified proofs of several fundamental results: Bernays and Post's theorem on the completeness of the propositional calculus, Gentzen's theorem on the consistency of elementary number theory, Löwenheim's theorem on the satisfiability of any first-order sentence in a countable set, and Post and Markov's theorem on the algorithmic unsolvability of the word problem of associative systems. He analyzed carefully the possibilities for stating generally and proving straightforwardly Gödel's celebrated incompleteness theorem. He studied the interrelations and significance of the incompleteness results of Church and Gödel. Concerning Church's famous thesis in which the heuristic concept of effective calculability is identical to the precise notion of general recursivity, he advocated the view that the limits of effective calculability become ever broader, and that therefore this concept cannot be identified permanently with an unalterably fixed notion. He wrote, partly with János Surányi, a series of articles on the reduction theory of the so-called *Entscheidungsproblem* (the decision problem of mathematical logic).

Kalmár also was extensively involved in theoretical computer science. He concerned himself from the mid 1950's with the mathematics of planning and programming electronic computers. He dealt with adapting the usual mathematical formula language and the programming languages to each other and with questions of mathematical linguistics. In addition, he wrote papers on defining the field of cybernetics, the use of computers, and the applicability of cybernetical ideas in various sciences.

It is common knowledge that mathematics can be applied widely in more practical fields. Kalmár often expressed his conviction that the connection with other domains of science is important to both sides, because the influence of more empirical sciences may be the source of permanent inspiration for the development of mathematics. He wrote a large number of articles popularizing mathematics. Some of his articles, written in Hungarian, are so constructed that the paper begins with a broad survey of a branch of logic before concluding with his own results.

Kalmár's scholarly personality was vivid and well rounded. His work cannot be discussed adequately by considering only his published works. He was enthusiastically inclined toward various sorts of personal contacts in his profession: regular teaching of university students, informal discussions with colleagues, lectures to general audiences. He taught primarily calculus, beginning with integral and then continuing with differential calculus, and foundations of mathematics (set theory and mathematical logic). His ideas on teaching calculus were explained in a posthumous book compiled by his pupils.

In the Department of Mathematics at the University of Szeged, he was the founder and first occupant of the Chair for Foundations of Mathematics and Computer Science. He also founded the Cybernetical Laboratory, which bears his name, and the Research Group for Mathematical Logic and Automata Theory at the university.

He was member of several scientific committees and editorial boards of scientific journals. The journals *Acta cybernetica* and *Alkalmazott matematikai lapok* were founded by him.

The names of Hungarian mathematicians whose scientific activity was essentially promoted by Kalmár would fill a long list. Of these, the following four persons are most noteworthy. Rózsa Péter was Kalmár's contemporary. Her basic contributions to the theory of recursive functions was close to one of the research areas of Kalmár. Among his younger colleagues, he was the teacher of the set theorist Géza Fodor. The algebraists Tibor Szele and Andor Kertész were also extensively encouraged and guided by him.

From the viewpoint of the development of the sciences in Hungary, Kalmár will probably be remembered most for his ceaseless effort in promoting the development of computer science and the use of computers in his country.

BIBLIOGRAPHY

I. Original Works. "A Hilbert-féle bizonyításelmélet célkitüzései, módszerei és eredményei" (The purposes, methods, and results of the Hilbertian Proof Theory), in *Matematikai és fizikai lapok*, **48** (1941), 65–119; "Quelques formes genérales du théorème de Gödel," in *Comptes rendus de l'Academie des sciences* (Paris), **229** (1949), 1047–1049; "Ein direkter Beweis für die allgemein-rekursive Unlösbarkeit des Entscheidungsproblems des Prädikatenkalküls der ersten Stufe mit Identität," in *Zeitschrift für mathematische Logik und Grundlagen der Mathematik*, **2** (1956), 1–14; "An Argument Against the Plausibility of Church's Thesis," in A. Heyting, ed., *Constructivity in Mathematics* (Amsterdam, 1959), 72–80; "Über einen Rechenautomaten, der eine mathematische Sprache versteht," in *Zeitschrift für angewandte Mathematik und Mechanik*, **40** (1960), T64–T65; "A kvalitatív, információelmélet problémái" (The problems of qualitative information theory), in *Magyar tudományos akadémia Matematikai és fizikai*, **12** (1962), 293–301; "Foundations of Mathematics—Whither Now?" in Imre Lakatos, ed., *Problems in the Philosophy of Mathematics* (Amsterdam, 1967), 187–207; "Meaning, Synonymy, and Translation," in *Computational Linguistics*, **6** (1967), 27–39; *Bevezetés a matematikai analízisbe* (Introduction to mathematical analysis; Budapest, 1982).

II. Secondary Literature. For a systematic treatment of the reduction theory of the *Entscheidungsproblem*, including a number of Kalmár's results in this area, see János Surányi, *Reduktionstheorie des Entscheidungsproblems im Prädikatenkalkül der ersten Stufe* (Budapest, 1959). See also R. Péter, "Kalmár László matematikai munkássága" (The mathematical activity of László Kalmár), in *Matematikai lapok*, **6** (1955), 138–150; A. Ádám, "Kalmár László matematikai munkásságáról" (On the mathematical activity of László Kalmár), *ibid.*, **26** (1975), 1–10, which includes a detailed bibliography. Brief obituaries appeared in *Acta scientiarum mathematicarum*, **38** (1976), 221–222, and *Alkalmazott matematikai lapok*, **2** (1976), 151–155 (with bibliography).

András Ádám

KALUZA, THEODOR FRANZ EDUARD (*b.* Ratibor, Germany [now Raciborz, Poland], 9 November 1885; *d.* Göttingen, Germany, 19 January 1954)

Theodor Kaluza was the only child of the German Anglicist Max Kaluza, whose works on phonetics and Chaucer were widely read in his day. The Kaluza family tree may be traced back to 1603, the family having been in Ratibor for over three centuries.

Kaluza was a bright student at school. Beginning his mathematical studies at the age of eighteen at the University of Königsberg, he prepared a doctoral dissertation on Tschirnhaus transformation[1] under Professor F. W. F. Meyer and qualified to lecture there in 1909. He married in the same year and remained a meagerly remunerated privatdocent in Königsberg for two decades.[2]

By the time Kaluza was past forty, Einstein, recognizing his worth and finding him in a position far below his merits, recommended him warmly for something better.[3] At last, in 1929, Kaluza obtained a professorship at the University of Kiel. In 1935 he moved to the University of Göttingen, where he became a full professor. Two months before he was to be named professor emeritus, Kaluza died after a very brief illness.

By the close of the nineteenth century, the concept of ether had become an integral part of physics. It was generally expected that the ether, and perhaps even the electromagnetic equations themselves, would explain all of physics, including gravitation. But when Einstein developed his general relativity theory (1910–1920), in which gravitational effects are traced to changes in the structure of a four-dimensional Riemannian manifold, the question arose as to whether the electromagnetic field could be incorporated into such a manifold. The aim was to give a unified picture of the gravitational and electromagnetic phenomena. This was referred to as the unitary problem.

Kaluza's essentially mathematical mind was attracted to the problem. He initiated a line of attack by introducing into the structure of the universe a fifth dimension which would account for the electromagnetic effects. When he communicated his ideas to Einstein, the latter encouraged him to pursue such an approach, submitting that this was an entirely original point of view.[4] Kaluza's major paper on this question appeared in 1921.[5] Here he combined the ten gravitational potentials, which arise in Einstein's general relativity theory as the components of the metric tensor of a four-dimensional space-time continuum, with the four components of the electromagnetic potential. He did this by means of his fifth dimension, which had the characteristic restriction that in it the trajectory of a particle is always a closed curve. This makes the universe essentially filiform with respect to the fifth dimension.

Mathematically, the five-dimensional manifold may be defined in terms of the metric

$$d\sigma^2 = \gamma^{mn} dx^m dx^n \qquad (m, n = 1, 2, 3, 4, 5),$$

in which the coefficients γ^{mn} are assumed to be independent of the fifth coordinate x^5. With the additional restriction that γ^{55} is a constant, Kaluza could deduce that the charge-mass ratio is a constant for the electron. The motion of electrically charged particles in an electromagnetic field is described by the equations of the geodesics in such a space.

If one were to assume that the periodicity of the fifth dimension is a "quantum effect"—indeed, that it is the physical source of Planck's constant—then the radius of the curves in the fifth dimension which would give the empirical value of the electron's charge would be on the order of 10^{-30} cm, and would thus be beyond the reach of experiment. (This result is due to O. Klein.)

Kaluza's theory was criticized on the ground that the fifth dimension is a purely mathematical artifice, with only a formalistic significance and no physical meaning whatever. Nevertheless, the five-dimensional idea was explored by several mathematical physicists.[6]

Kaluza also worked on models of the atomic nucleus, applying the general principles of energetics. He wrote on the epistemological aspects of relativity and was sole author of or collaborator on several mathematical papers. In 1938 a text on higher applied mathematics written by Kaluza and G. Joos was published; in this work he showed himself as a mathematician rather than as a mathematical physicist.[7]

Kaluza was a man of wide-ranging interests. Although mathematical abstraction delighted him tremendously, he was also deeply interested in languages, literature, and philosophy. He studied more than fifteen languages, including Hebrew, Hungarian, Arabic, and Lithuanian. He had a keen sense of humor. A nonswimmer, he once demonstrated the power of theoretical knowledge by reading a book on swimming, then swimming successfully on his first attempt (he was over thirty when he performed this feat). Kaluza loved nature as much as science and was also fond of children.

He was liked and respected by his students and had extremely good relations with his colleagues. He never used notes while lecturing, except on one occasion, when he had to copy down a fifty-digit number which showed up in number theory.

NOTES

1. The dissertation was published in *Archiv der Mathematik und Physik*, **16** (1910), 197–206.
2. Privatdocents did not have a definite salary; they were merely allowed the privilege of giving lectures. If a privatdocent gave x hours of lectures a week and had y students, he would earn about $5xy$ gold marks per semester, an inconsiderable sum.
3. In a note written to a colleague in November 1926 Einstein praised Kaluza's "schöpferische Begabung." He considered it unfortunate that "Kaluza unter schwierigen äusseren Bedingungen arbeitet" and added, "Es würde mich sehr freuen, wenn er einen passenden Wirkungskreis bekäme."
4. In his first reaction to Kaluza's private communication of the five-dimensional idea, Einstein wrote, ". . . der Gedanke, dies (elektrischen Feldgrössen) durch eine fünfdimensionale Zylinderwelt zu erzielen, ist mir nie gekommen und dürfte überhaupt neu sein. Ihr Gedanke gefällt mir zunächst ausserordentlich" (letter dated 21 Apr. 1919).
5. "Zum Unitärsproblem der Physik," in *Sitzungsberichte der Preussischen Akademie der Wissenschaften*, **54** (1921), 966–972. The communication was delivered by Einstein on 8 December 1921.
6. The most important of these were O. Klein, L. de Broglie, Einstein, E. P. Jordan, and Y. R. Thiry. For a detailed bibliography on these extensions the reader may consult the treatise by Tonnelat cited in the bibliography.
7. *Höhere Mathematik für die Praktiker* (Leipzig, 1938).

BIBLIOGRAPHY

I. ORIGINAL WORKS. A bibliography of Kaluza's works is found in Poggendorff, VIIA, pt. 2 (1958), 684. I am indebted to Theodor Kaluza, Jr., for letting me see the scientific correspondence of his father, especially that with Einstein, and for relating personal details.

II. SECONDARY LITERATURE. Good discussions of Kaluza's five-dimensional theory may be found in P. G. Bergmann, *An Introduction to the Theory of Relativity* (New York, 1942); and M. A. Tonnelat, *Les théories unitaires de l'électro-magnétisme et de la gravitation* (Paris, 1965).

VARADARAJA V. RAMAN

KAMĀL AL-DĪN ABU'L ḤASAN MUḤAMMAD IBN AL-ḤASAN AL-FĀRISĪ (*d.* Tabrīz [?], Iran, 1320)

Kamāl al-Dīn was the disciple of the famous Qutb al-Dīn al-Shīrāzī, mathematician, astronomer, and commentator on Ibn Sīnā.[1] Scholars since Wiedemann and Sarton have linked the names of the two, and some questions of priority have arisen, as will be seen below. Although Kamāl al-Dīn produced a number of writings in different branches of mathematics—particularly arithmetic and geometry—his essential contribution was in optics. It was in response to a question addressed to him on the principles of refraction that al-Shīrāzī recommended to Kamāl al-Dīn that he study the *Kitāb al-manāẓir* ("Book of Optics") of Ibn al-Haytham. Once Kamāl al-Dīn had undertaken this study, al-Shīrāzī, who was at this time occupied in commenting on the *Canon* of Ibn Sīnā, suggested further that Kamāl al-Dīn write his own commentary on Ibn al-Haytham's book.

Kamāl al-Dīn chose to extend the task set him to other works of Ibn al-Haytham as well, so that his *Tanqīḥ al-manāẓir li-dhawi 'l-abṣār wa'l-basā'ir* contains, in addition to the originally planned study of the *Kitāb al-manāẓir*, essays on Ibn al-Haytham's *The Burning Sphere*, *The Halo and the Rainbow*, *Shadows*, *The Shape of Eclipse*, and the *Discourse on Light*. He was also led, in the course of this work, to study Ibn al-Haytham's *The Solar Rays*, although he did not comment upon it. Kamāl al-Dīn was thus dealing with the essential optical works of Ibn al-Haytham, and with this group we must also consider his own work on optics, *Al-baṣā'ir fī 'ilm al-manāẓir* ("Insights Into the Science of Optics"). This is basically a textbook for students of optics, presenting the conclusions of the *Tanqīḥ* without the proofs or experiments.

In order to grasp the meaning and scope of Kamāl al-Dīn's contribution, it must first be understood that his work was more properly a revision (*tanqīḥ*) than a commentary (*sharḥ*), as the title itself indicates. To Kamāl al-Dīn "to comment" meant a reconsideration and reinterpretation, rather than the medieval notion of a return to the original sources for a more faithful reading. In the course of his revision, Kamāl al-Dīn did not hesitate to refute certain of Ibn al-Haytham's theories, such as the analogy between impact and the propagation of light, an essential element of the explanation of reflection and refraction. He further had no reluctance in developing other of Ibn al-Haytham's ideas, notably the example of the camera obscura, refraction in two transparent spheres, and the numerical tabulation of refraction (air to glass); indeed, from time to time he simply set aside Ibn al-Haytham's doctrine to substitute one of his own. An important instance is the theory of the rainbow.

This profound change in the notion of a commentary is directly attributable to the new stage reached by Ibn al-Haytham in his optics, which may be briefly characterized as the systematic introduction of new norms—mathematical and experimental—to treat traditional problems in which light and vision are united. Until then light had been considered to be the instrumentality of the eye and to see an object was to illuminate it. In order to construct a theory of light, it was necessary to begin with a theory of vision; but to establish a theory of vision required taking a position on the propagation of light. Each task immediately involved the other and each theory borrowed the language of the other. The optics of Aristotle, like that of Euclid and even that of Ptolemy, comprised both factors. In order to introduce the new norms systematically, a better differentiation forced itself on Ibn al-Haytham. But the distinction between seeing and illuminating had to allow the transfer of the notions of a physical doctrine to an experimental situation and thus to bring about a realization of the initial project.

The essential and most representative part of Kamāl al-Dīn's work, however, is his study of the rainbow. The question of Kamāl al-Dīn's originality here has been raised; recalling that Kamāl al-Dīn had borrowed the idea of studying the rainbow from his teacher, Carl Boyer writes, "Hence the discovery of the theory presumably should be ascribed to the latter [al-Shīrāzī], its elaboration to the former [Kamāl al-Dīn]."[2] Although the same notion is supported by Crombie and many subsequent authors, it remains unconvincing, despite a manuscript text on the rainbow attributed to al-Shīrāzī (at the end of his commentary on Ibn Sīnā's *Canon*, in a manuscript kept at Paris). The manuscript, written before 1518, is incomplete, and the text dealing with the rainbow occurs after several pages on alchemy that are irrelevant to the rest of the book, and in a different hand. The text on the rainbow itself is in yet another hand; after examining this manuscript and comparing it with one of the same book in the National Library at Cairo, Naẓīf suggested that the passage is an interpolation.[3] The Cairo manuscript has in turn been compared with a complete version of the same book, copied in an elegant handwriting and dating from 1785.[4] In confirmation of Naẓīf's theory, this last altogether lacks the passage on the rainbow.

Even were this text on the rainbow to be accepted as being by al-Shīrāzī, no doubt would be cast on Kamāl al-Dīn's originality, since we have seen that Kamāl al-Dīn drew upon a new interpretation of Ibn al-Haytham's optics. The theory of the rainbow elucidated in the text in question deals with the reflection of light on droplets of water dispersed in the atmosphere, a traditional conception that does not agree with Kamāl al-Dīn's (although it is not too unlike al-Shīrāzī's, since the latter, following in the path of such geometers as al-Ṭūsī, was still concerned with visual rays). The disputed manuscript reveals a further fundamental difference from the work of Kamāl al-Dīn in its optical terminology.

Ibn al-Haytham, on the other hand, had in his discussion of the rainbow dealt specifically with the problem of reflection; that is, in order to explain the form of the arc, he had proposed that the light from the sun is reflected on the cloud before reaching the eye. He sought the condition under which a ray emanating from a source of light—the sun—and reflected on a concave spherical surface, outside the axis, passes through the eye after its reflection. Admitting, as did the Aristotelian tradition before him, the possibility of a direct study of the arc, Ibn al-Haytham did not attempt to construct an experimental situation in order to verify the geometrical hypotheses. But the direct study of the rainbow did not lend itself to this sort of proof, even though Ibn al-Haytham called for it.

Kamāl al-Dīn took up Ibn al-Haytham's project at this point. Despite Ibn al-Haytham's authority, Kamāl al-Dīn began by submitting his predecessor's attempt to a severe criticism that, essentially, showed the need of a better physics which, when joined with geometry, would allow him to reach the goal formulated but unattained by Ibn al-Haytham.

Thus Kamāl al-Dīn returned to the doctrine of the rainbow proposed by Ibn Sīnā, who conceived of the arc as being produced by reflection from a totality of the water droplets dispersed in the atmosphere at the moment when the clouds dissolve into rain. Ibn Sīnā's improvement justified an analogy—important for the explanation of the rainbow—between a drop of water and a transparent sphere filled with water.

Having stated the analogy, Kamāl al-Dīn wished to introduce two refractions between which one or several reflections occur. He benefited here from the results obtained by Ibn al-Haytham in *The Burning Sphere*, in which the latter showed that the paths followed by the light propagated between the two refractions are a function of the relationships of the increase in the angles of incidence and those of the increase in the angles of deviation.

Ibn al-Haytham established that for two rays to intersect inside the circle—that is, for the points of the second refraction to approach O' instead of moving away from each other—it is necessary that $D' - D > 1/2\ (i' - i)$ (compare Kamāl al-Dīn's diagram, Figure 1). While it is true that this relationship is valid for the passage from air to glass, it can be easily demonstrated that it is independent of n. Drawing upon this relationship, however, Ibn al-Haytham was able to show by a simple geometric demonstration that the angle beginning with which this intersection occurs is 50° for the case in which

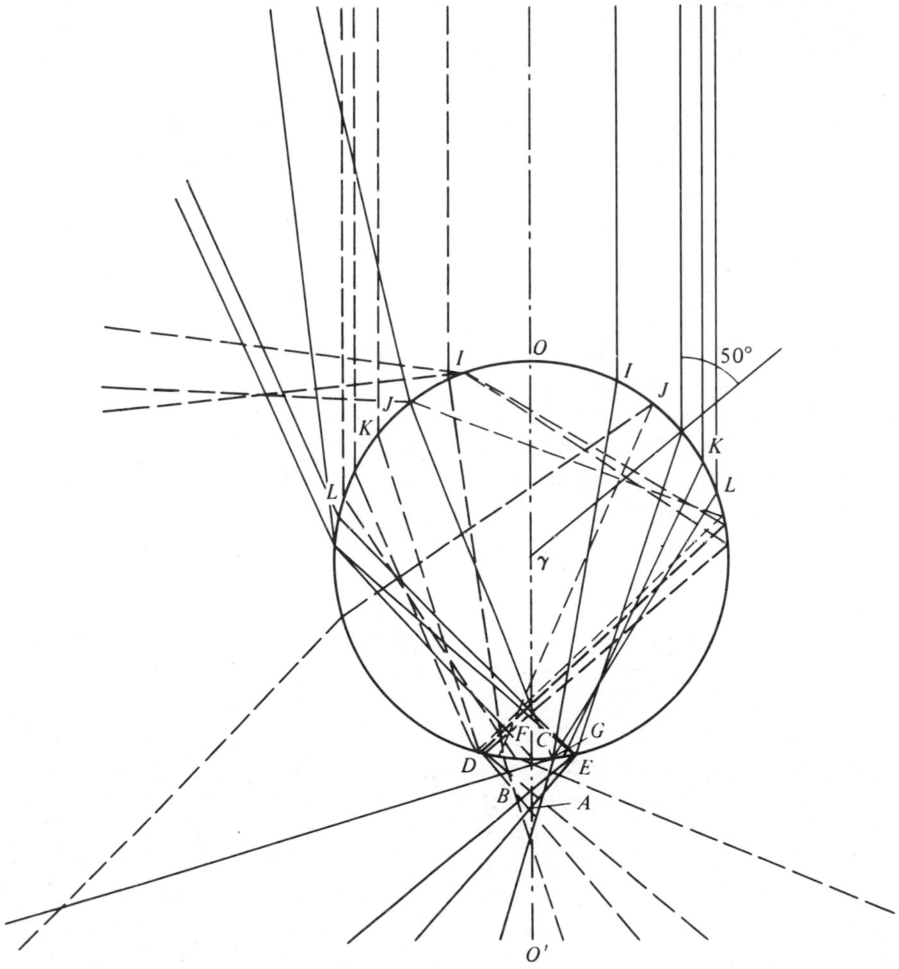

FIGURE 1

$n = 3/2$ (from air to glass). This can be verified by the relation $\frac{dD}{di} = 1 - \frac{\cos i}{n \cos r}$. It should be noted that Ibn al-Haytham thought that with the incident ray at 90°, the second point of refraction was on the same side of the axis as the point of the first refraction; this was not verified in the air-to-glass case that he was considering. In the water-to-air case that Kamāl al-Dīn studied, on the other hand, this was easily verifiable, so that in taking up Ibn al-Haytham's results, Kamāl al-Dīn did not encounter the same difficulty.

Kamāl al-Dīn thus considered the incident rays to be parallel to the axis OO'. These rays intersect the sphere at points increasingly removed from O and are refracted in it at points distant from O' on the opposite portion of the sphere up to the angle of incidence of 50°. For an angle of incidence greater than 50°, the points of the second refraction successively approach O'. Concerning the propagation of rays at their exit from the sphere, Ibn al-Haytham had already demonstrated spherical aberration.

With these results Kamāl al-Dīn attempted to show how, following double refraction in the sphere and depending on whether rays near to or distant from the axis are considered, one or several images of a luminous object as well as different forms can be obtained—an arc or a ring in the case of a circular object. Before treating in detail double refraction in the sphere, however, Kamāl al-Dīn eliminated a difficulty resulting from the fact that, unlike the sphere, the drop does not have a glass envelope and that there are therefore four refractions, not two, in the sphere. In order to guarantee the correspondence between the manufactured object—the sphere—and the natural object—the drop of water—Kamāl al-Dīn employed an approximation furnished by the study of refraction and justified by the consideration that the indexes of the two mediums are quite close, which allowed him, finally, to disregard the glass envelope.

Kamāl al-Dīn considered the circle of center γ and the rays that form angles of incidence of 10°, 20°,..., 90° with it. He divided the rays into two groups. The first five form angles of incidence of less than 50°; the four others, of more than 50°. (See Figure 2.) He divided the arc DE into two equal parts at O' and took F and G equidistant from O'. Let SJ be the ray with the angle of incidence 50° and SJ' its symmetric counterpart in relation to the axis OO'. These two rays are refracted along the lines JE and $J'D$ and meet after the second refraction at point A, exterior to the sphere on the axis. Following the first refraction, all the rays of incidence of less than 50° are contained in the interior of the trunk of the cone generated by JE and $J'D$, called the "central cone" by Kamāl al-Dīn. Following the second refraction, these same rays are contained within the cone generated by EA and DA, the "burning cone." The rays that constitute the second group—with angle of incidence greater than 50°—are refracted, some between JE and LG and others symmetrically between $J'D$ and $L'F$, which generate the two exterior cones, or "hollow cones." These rays are refracted a second time, some between GB and EA and some between FC and DA; they generate the exterior refracted cones or "hollow opposites." These rays intersect on the axis at points H and A.

At this stage, Kamāl al-Dīn's problem was to produce, under certain conditions, several possible images of the same object placed before the sphere. He could then vary their respective positions, causing them to become more distant from each other or superimposing them. Kamāl al-Dīn sought, in fact, to place himself outside what are today called Gauss's approximation conditions in order to produce this multiplicity of images.

He then returned to his model and complicated it with new, precise details. He examined the propagation of rays inside the sphere between two refractions and also treated the different types of reflection. Kamāl al-Dīn believed that a bundle of parallel rays falling on the drop of water is transformed, following a certain number of reflections in the sphere, into a divergent bundle. He knew, moreover, that the rays refracted in the drop of water after one or several reflections in its interior are not sent equally in all directions but produce a mass of rays in certain regions of space. This mass—and Kamāl al-Dīn's text allows no doubt on this point—is in the vicinity of the point of emergence of the ray which corresponds to the maximum (actually maximum or minimum) of deviation.[6] He stated, in addition, that the intensities of the lights join together, producing a greater illumination. He expressed these ideas in the complicated language of "cones" of rays that have been refracted after having undergone one or two reflections in the interior of the sphere and also in the concept of a greater illumination at the edges of the "cones." In the case of one reflection between two refractions, he distinguished two bundles of rays coming from the exterior cones and the central cone (see Figure 2); in the case of two reflections, he obtained two groups of rays that were more divergent than in the case of one reflection and that also gave one or two images. If the eye receives the rays coming from the central cone, Kamāl al-Dīn stated, a single image will be seen in a single position; and if the eye

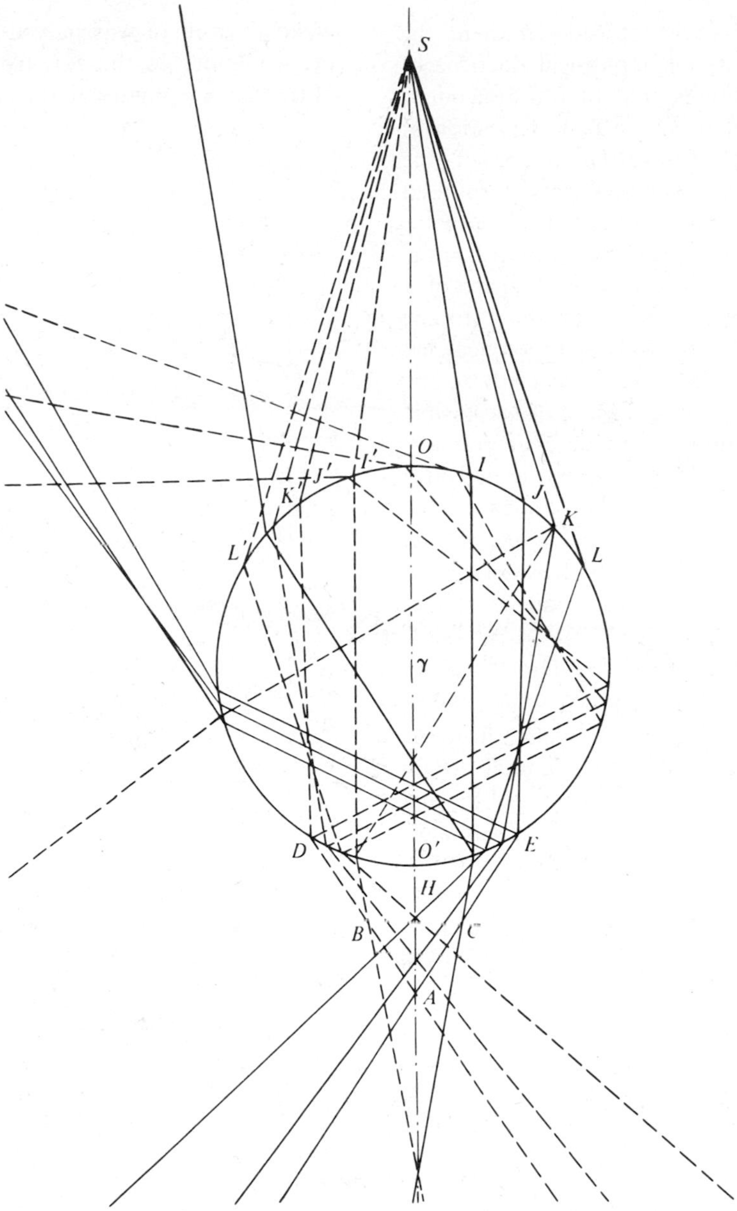

FIGURE 2

is placed in the region where the rays issuing from the central cone and the exterior cone intersect, two images will be seen in two positions.

In order to test the completed model, Kamāl al-Dīn employed an experimental procedure that was independently rediscovered by Descartes. He constructed a dark chamber with one opening, and placed inside it a transparent sphere illuminated by the rays of the sun. He masked half of the sphere with a dense white body and observed the face on the side toward the sphere: on it he saw an arc whose center was on the axis leading from the center of the sphere to the sun. This arc was formed from light rays that had undergone a refraction, a reflection, and another refraction. The inside of the arc was brighter than the outside because it contained rays emitted by both the central cone and the exterior cone. Kamāl al-Dīn next placed another white body, less dense than the first, before the sphere and again observed the face turned toward the sphere. This time he saw a complete ring that always displayed the colors of the rainbow. This ring was formed from the rays refracted a second time after having been reflected in the sphere. He noted the variation in the intensity of the colors according to the position of the screen, then employed the same dark chamber to consider the case of two reflections between two refractions.

This introduced into the study an important

KAMĀL AL-DĪN

possibility that had not been considered then: the transfer through geometry of a physical doctrine of this phenomenon—essentially that of Ibn Sīnā—into the realm of experiment. It was in fact a question of restoration, contrary to Ibn al-Haytham, of the latter's own style of optics. The new optics promised to respect the norms of the combination of geometry and physics. But to follow the new norms with some prospect of success necessarily led, in the case of a phenomenon as complicated as the rainbow, to the abandonment of direct study. This abandonment led to research on phenomena better mastered by the contemporary optical knowledge and more accessible to experimental verification—to the use of practical analogy. The analogue could be subjected to objective observation, and the resulting data applied to the study of the proposed natural object. Thus, Kamāl al-Dīn's spherical glass vial filled with water served to demonstrate the natural phenomenon of refraction.

On the problem of color, Kamāl al-Dīn turned to a commentary by al-Shīrāzī on the text of Ibn Sīnā's *Canon.*[5] His work soon began to diverge from its older model, however. In particular, Kamāl al-Dīn chose to treat four colors instead of three and to treat the problem of color by a reformulation of al-Shīrāzī's method. Kamāl al-Dīn set forth the doctrine of color, then limited its scope so as to consider only the colors formed on the screen in front of the sphere after the combination of reflections and refractions. He wrote:

> The colors of the arc are different but related, between the blue, the green, the yellow, and the dark red, and come from a strong luminous source reaching the eye by a reflection or a refraction or a combination of the two [*Tanqīḥ* . . ., p. 337].

Thus varying the respective positions of the images in the different cones formed by the refracted rays, Kamāl al-Dīn declared that he perceived the different colors gradually as the two images were superposed. The bright blue was produced by the approach, without superposition, of two images; the bright yellow resulted from the superposition of two images; and the darkish red appeared at the edge of the bundle of rays. It was no longer, therefore—as in a traditional doctrine of color—the mixture of light and darkness that produced color, but the bringing together or the superposition of two or more images—or, still better, "forms"—of light on a background of darkness that explained the formation and diversity of colors.

Kamāl al-Dīn thought that he finally could explain how the rainbow should be observed. He showed that when the sphere was moved up and down along the perpendicular to the axis from the eye to the center of the sun (see Figure 3), then according to the position

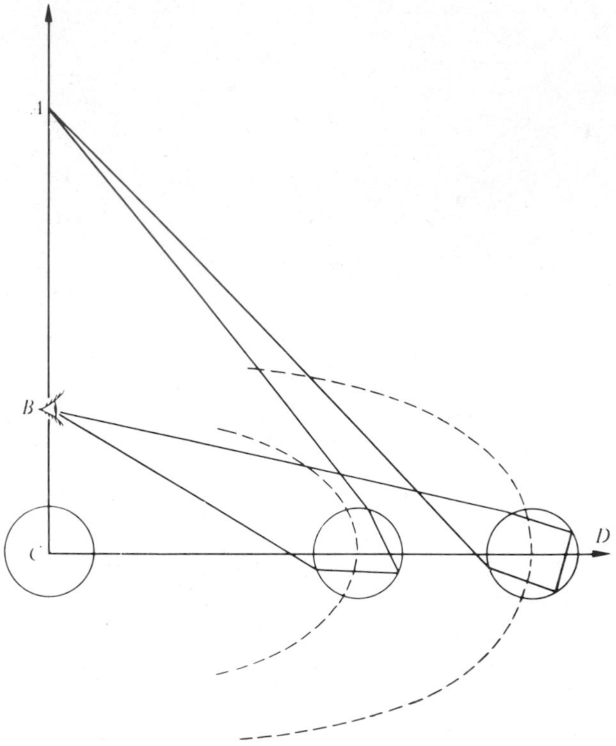

FIGURE 3

of the sphere the image of the sun could be produced by simple reflection between two refractions. In other words, depending on the angle formed by the rays of sun meeting the sphere, the well-placed observer will perceive either the rays refracted after one reflection or the rays refracted after two reflections. Then the colors of the first arc and those of the second are obtained successively. It must be noted that Kamāl al-Dīn employed here—as elsewhere—the principle of reversibility. Thus he imagined the cones of the rays refracted after one or two reflections, by putting, in the first step, the light source where the eye had been. In the second step he reversed the situation in order to consider the displacement of the sun in relation to these cones of rays, the eye being returned to its initial position. He wrote:

> Let us suppose that *B*, the center of the eye, is between *A*, the center of the sun, and *C*, the center of a polished transparent sphere. *ABC* is a straight line. Draw a perpendicular, *CD*, from *C* and suppose that the sphere is moved away from the line *ABC* in such a manner that its center remains on the perpendicular. If its center is moved away from *ABC*, the cone of rays refracted after one reflection will incline toward the sun

KAMĀL AL-DĪN

while the latter, proportionally to the displacement of the sphere from *ABC*, will continue to approach the edge of the cone in the direction of the movement of the sphere and will appear in two images, at two positions on the sphere. . . . To the extent that the sphere is displaced, the two images draw closer until they become tangent. It is then that the light becomes stronger and produces an *isfanjūnī* blue if it blends with the darkness or with the green. If the images then interpenetrate, the light is again intensified and produces a bright yellow. Next, the blended image diminishes and becomes a darker and darker red until it disappears when the sun is outside the cone of rays refracted after one reflection.

If the sphere continues to become more distant from the line *ABC*, the cone of rays refracted after two reflections approaches closer and closer to the sun until the sun is contained within this cone, and then what had disappeared in the beginning reappears in inverse order, beginning with the purple red, then the bright yellow, then the pure blue, and finally a light that is not really perceived because of the disappearance of one of the images or because of their mutual separation. If there are a great many drops of water massed in the air, these, arranged in a circle—each drop giving one of the images mentioned according to its size—produce the image of two arcs, as one may see: the small one is red on its exterior circumference, then yellow, then blue. The same colors appear in inverse order on the superior arc, hiding what is behind it by the colors and lights that appear in it. The air between the two arcs is darker than the air above and below them, because the portions between the two arcs are screened from the light of the sun [*Tanqīḥ* . . ., pp. 340–342].

In order to bring the combination of geometry and physics as in Ibn al-Haytham's optics to the study of the rainbow—that is, to arrive at a valid proof through geometrical deduction and experimental verification—Kamāl al-Dīn was led to reject as a starting point the notion of direct study, used by Ibn al-Haytham and by a whole tradition. He therefore elaborated a mode of explanation by reduction by establishing a group of correspondences between a natural object and a synthetic object, which he then systematically reduced by the geometry of the propagation of light in the first object to its propagation in the second.

Appearing in the wake of Ibn al-Haytham's reform, this achievement was a means of extending that reform to an area where it was not yet operative. It is in this way that the importance of Kamāl al-Dīn's contribution is to be understood.

It remains for us to consider Kamāl al-Dīn's work on the rainbow in conjunction with that of Dietrich von Freiberg. Dietrich's *De iride et radialibus impressionibus* was written between 1304 and 1311;[6] Krebs found the direct influence of Ibn al-Haytham in this work: "However, it seems very likely," he wrote, "that Dietrich used fully the great work of the Arabic father of modern optics. . . ."[7] Würschmidt, too, stated, "that Dietrich, by his own testimony, used in the treatment of this problem of the rainbow ... the optics of Ibn al-Haytham."[8]

Wiedemann concluded that Kamāl al-Dīn completed the definitive version of his work between 1302 and 1311,[9] during Dietrich's lifetime. In support of this thesis he offered the arguments that the book was written during al-Shīrāzī's lifetime (that is, before 1311), and that in it Kamāl al-Dīn refers to a lunar eclipse that, according to Wiedemann, occurred in 1302. This evidence has been accepted by other historians; Naẓīf, however, took exception to it.

In his research on the rainbow included in the appendix to the *Tanqīḥ*, al-Fārisī [Kamāl al-Dīn] borrowed from al-Shīrāzī's commentary to the *Canon* the latter's conception of the manner in which colors originate; the passage containing al-Shīrāzī's remarks clearly indicates that the commentary had not been completed. This is tantamount to saying that al-Fārisī had completed the *Tanqīḥ* before al-Shīrāzī finished the commentary to the *Canon*. As for the lunar eclipse that Wiedemann emphasizes, if the year 1304 is accepted for its occurrence (Wiedemann gives 1302), the fact remains that the eclipse is not mentioned either in the main portion of the *Tanqīḥ*, in its conclusion, or in the appendix. The eclipse is referred to only in al-Fārisī's commentary on one of Ibn al-Haytham's treatises that al-Fārisī appended to his own book. This is *Shadows*, and it is conceivable that these treatises were added to the book after publication or that the reference to the eclipse was added at a later date.

At least one can speculate; I do not believe that it is mistaken to say that al-Fārisī had completed the research on which he would base his two theories of the rainbow before al-Shirazi had finished his commentary. This is not to generalize and include the entire *Tanqīḥ*—corpus, conclusion, appendixes, and excursus—in this chronology. Thus, I am not suggesting what is probable but, rather, what is certain, in alleging that al-Fārisī had completed the research on the rainbow that is included in the appendix to the *Tanqīḥ* at least ten years before Theodoricus [Dietrich] wrote his treatise between the years 1304 and 1311 [M. Naẓīf, "Kamāl al-Dīn al-Fārisī . . .," p. 94].

Naẓīf went on to posit the possibility of Kamāl al-Dīn's influence upon Dietrich. Such influence would seem tenuous at best, however; no trace has been found of Kamāl al-Dīn's work in Latin, and Dietrich himself did not cite him. The influence of Ibn al-Haytham on Dietrich is another matter. As Würschmidt wrote:

. . . a comparison of these works [those of Kamāl al-Dīn] with those of Master Dietrich indicates that the latter definitely did not know Kamāl al-Dīn's commentary; Kamāl al-Dīn avoided a succession of errors which occur with Dietrich as well as with earlier Arab scholars, and saw clearly especially the returned rays so important later in Descartes's rainbow theory.[10]

It may thus be seen that Kamāl al-Dīn's priority in no way implies his influence upon Dietrich, but, rather, that both Kamāl al-Dīn and Dietrich were disciples of Ibn al-Haytham and, relying upon the same source for their essential ideas, independently arrived at the model of the transparent sphere to explain the rainbow.

NOTES

1. See R. Rashed, "Le modèle de la sphère . . .," p. 114.
2. *The Rainbow: From Myth to Mathematics*, p. 125.
3. The Paris MS is Bib. Nat., Fonds arabe, MS 2517; that at Cairo, written in 1340 at Mossoul, is National Library MS 7797.
4. Paris, Bib. Nat., Fonds arabe, MS 2518.
5. *Tanqīḥ*, p. 331 *et seq.*
6. See E. Krebs, "Meister Dietrich (Theodoricus Teutonicus de Vriberg), sein Leben, seine Werke, seine Wissenschaft," in *Beiträge zur Geschichte der Philosophie und Theologie des Mittelalters*, V, pts. 5–6 (Münster in Westfalen, 1906), 105 ff.; and P. Duhem, *Le système du monde*, III (Paris, 1915), 383 ff.
7. See Krebs, *op. cit.*, p. 40.
8. "Dietrich von Freiberg; Über den Regenbogen und die durch Strahlen erzeugten Eindrücke," in *Beiträge zur Geschichte der Philosophie und Theologie des Mittelalters*, XII, pts. 5–6 (Münster in Westfalen, 1906), p. 1.
9. "Zu Ibn al-Haitams Optik," in *Archiv für die Geschichte der Naturwissenschaften und der Technik*, no. 3 (1912), pp. 3-4.
10. *Op. cit.*, p. 2, note 8.

BIBLIOGRAPHY

I. ORIGINAL WORKS. The *Tanqīḥ al-manāẓir*, 2 vols. (Hyderabad, 1928–1929), contains, at the end of vol. II, commentaries on the following works of Ibn al-Haytham: *The Halo and the Rainbow*, trans. by E. Wiedemann as "Theorie des Regenbogens von Ibn al-Haitam," in *Sitzungsberichte der Physikalisch-medizinische Sozietät in Erlangen*, **46** (1919), 39–56; *The Burning Sphere*, trans. by Wiedemann as "Über die Brechung des Lichtes in Kugeln nach Ibn al-Haitam und Kamal al-Din al-Farisi," *ibid.*, **42** (1910), 15–58; *Shadows*, trans. by Wiedemann as "Über eine Schrift von Ibn al-Haitam, über die Beschaffenheit der Schatten," *ibid.*, **39** (1907), 226–248; *The Shape of Eclipses*; and *Discourse on Light*, trans. by R. Rashed in *Revue d'histoire des sciences*, **21**, no. 3 (1968), 197–224.

Works still in MS are *Al-Basā'ir fī 'ilm al-manāẓir fi'l ḥikma*; *Asās al-gawā'id fī uṣūl al'fawa'id*; *Taḍhirat al-aḥhāb fī bayān al-tahābb*; and "Treatise on a Geometrical Proposition of Nasīr al-Dīn al-Ṭūsi." See C. Brockelmann, *Geschichte der arabischen Literatur*, supp. II (Leiden, 1938), p. 295; and H. Suter, *Die Mathematiker und Astronomen der Araber und ihre Werke* (Leipzig, 1900), p. 159.

II. SECONDARY LITERATURE. On Kamāl al-Dīn or his work, see Carl Boyer, *The Rainbow: From Myth to Mathematics* (New York, 1959), pp. 127–129; M. Schramm, "Steps Towards the Idea of Function: A Comparison Between Eastern and Western Science of the Middle-Ages," in *History of Science*, **4** (1956), 70–103, esp. 81–85; M. Naẓif, "Kamāl al-Dīn al-Fārisī wa ba'ḍ buḥūṭuhu fī 'ilm al-ḍaw'," in *La société égyptienne et histoire des sciences*, no. 2 (Dec. 1958), 63–100 (in Arabic); R. Rashed, "Le modèle de la sphère transparente et l'explication de l'arc-en-ciel: Ibn al-Haytham—al-Fārisī," in *Revue d'histoire des sciences*, **22** (1970), 109–140; and J. Würschmidt, "Über die Brennkugel," in *Monatshefte für den naturwissenschaftlichen Unterricht*, **4** (1911), 98–113.

ROSHDI RASHED

AL-KARAJĪ (or **AL-KARKHĪ**), **ABŪ BAKR IBN MUḤAMMAD IBN AL ḤUSAYN** (or **AL-ḤASAN**) (*fl.* Baghdad, end of tenth century/beginning of eleventh)

Virtually nothing is known of al-Karajī's life; even his name is not certain. Since the translations by Woepcke and Hochheim he has been called al-Karkhī, a name adopted by historians of mathematics.[1] In 1933, however, Giorgio Levi della Vida rejected this name for that of al-Karajī.[2] This debate would have been pointless if certain authors had not attempted to use the name of this mathematician to deduce his origins: Karkh, a suburb of Baghdad, or Karaj, an Iranian city. In the present state of our knowledge della Vida's argument is plausible but not decisive. On the basis of the manuscripts consulted it is far from easy to decide in favor of either name.[3] Turning to the "commentators" does not take us any further.[4] For example, the *al-Bāhir fi'l jabr* of al-Samaw'al cites the name al-Karajī, as indicated in MS Aya Sofya 2718. On this basis some authors have sought to derive a definitive argument in favor of this name.[5] On the other hand, another hitherto unknown manuscript of the same text (Esat Efendi 3155) gives the name al-Karkhī.[6] Because the use of the name al-Karajī is beginning to predominate—for no clear reasons—and because we do not wish to add to the already great confusion in the designation of Arab authors, we shall use the name al-Karajī—refraining from any speculation designed to infer our subject's origins from this name. It is sufficient to know that he lived and produced the bulk of his work in Baghdad at the end of the tenth century and the beginning of the eleventh and that he probably left that city for the "mountain countries,"[7] where he appears to have ceased writing mathematical works in order to devote himself to composing works on engineering, as indicated by his book on the drilling of wells.

Al-Karajī's work holds an especially important place in the history of mathematics. Woepcke remarked that it "offers first the most complete or rather the only theory of algebraic calculus among the Arabs known to us up to the present time."[8] It is true that al-Karajī employed an approach entirely new in the tradition of the Arab algebraists—al-Khwārizmī, Ibn al-Fatḥ, Abū Kāmil—commencing with an exposition of the theory of algebraic calculus.[9] The more or less explicit aim of this exposition was to find means of realizing the autonomy and specificity of algebra, so as to be in a position to reject, in particular, the geometric representation of algebraic operations. What was actually at stake was a new beginning of algebra by means of the systematic application of the operations of arithmetic to the interval $[0, \infty]$. This arithmetization of algebra was based both on algebra, as conceived by al-Khwārizmī and developed by Abū Kāmil and many others, and on the translation of the *Arithmetica* of Diophantus, commented on and developed by such Arab mathematicians as Abu'l Wafā' al-Būzjānī.[10] In brief, the discovery and reading of the arithmetical work of Diophantus, in the light of the algebraic conceptions and methods of al-Khwārizmī and other Arab algebraists, made possible a new departure in algebra by al-Karajī, the author of the first account of the algebra of polynomials.

In his treatise on algebra, *al-Fakhrī*, al-Karajī first presented a systematic study of algebraic exponents, then turned to the application of arithmetical operations to algebraic terms and expressions, and concluded with a first account of the algebra of polynomials. He studied[11] the two sequences $x, x^2, \cdots, x^9, \cdots; 1/x, 1/x^2, \cdots, 1/x^9, \cdots$ and, successively, formulated the following rules:

$$(1)\quad \frac{1}{x} : \frac{1}{x^2} = \frac{1}{x^2} : \frac{1}{x^3} = \cdots$$

$$(2)\quad \frac{1}{x} : \frac{1}{x^2} = \frac{x^2}{x} = \cdots = \frac{1}{x^{n-1}} : \frac{1}{x^n} = \frac{x^n}{x^{n-1}}$$

$$(3)\quad \frac{1}{x} \cdot \frac{1}{x} = \frac{1}{x^2},\quad \frac{1}{x^2} \cdot \frac{1}{x} = \frac{1}{x^3}, \cdots,\quad \frac{1}{x^n} \cdot \frac{1}{x^m} = \frac{1}{x^{n+m}}$$

$$(4)\quad \frac{1}{x} \cdot x^2 = \frac{x^2}{x},\quad \frac{1}{x} \cdot x^3 = \frac{x^3}{x}, \cdots,\quad \frac{1}{x^n} \cdot x^m = \frac{x^m}{x^n}$$

$$m = 1, 2, 3, \cdots \qquad n = 1, 2, 3, \cdots$$

In order to appreciate the importance of this study, it is necessary to see how al-Karajī's more or less immediate successors exploited it. For example, al-Samaw'al[12] was able, on the basis of al-Karajī's work, to utilize the isomorphism of what would now be called the groups $(Z, +)$ and $([x^n; n \in Z], \times)$ in order to give for the first time, in all its generality, the rule equivalent to $x^m x^n = x^{m+n}$, where $m, n \in Z$.

In applying arithmetical operations to algebraic terms and expressions, al-Karajī first considered the application of these rules to monomials before taking up "composed quantities," or polynomials. For multiplication he thus demonstrated the following rules: (1) $(a/b) \cdot c = ac/b$ and (2) $a/b \cdot c/d = ac/bd$, where a, b, c, and d are monomials. He then treated the multiplication of polynomials, for which he gave the general rule. He proceeded in the same manner and with the same concern for the symmetry of the operations of addition and subtraction. Yet this algebra of polynomials was uneven. In division and the extraction of roots al-Karajī did not achieve the generality already attained for the other operations. Hence he considered only the division of one monomial by another and of a polynomial by a monomial. Nevertheless, these results permitted his successors—notably al-Samaw'al—to study, for the first time to our knowledge, divisibility in the ring $[Q(x) + Q(1/x)]$ and the approximation of whole fractions by elements of the same ring.[13] As for the extraction of the square root of a polynomial, al-Karajī succeeded in giving a general method—the first in the history of mathematics—but it is valid only for positive coefficients. This method allowed al-Samaw'al to solve the problem for a polynomial with rational coefficients or, more precisely, to determine the root of a square element of the ring $[Q(x) + Q(1/x)]$.[14] Al-Karajī's method consisted in giving first the development of $(x_1 + x_2 + x_3)^2$—where x_1, x_2, and x_3 are monomials—for which he proposed the canonical form

$$x_1^2 + 2x_1x_2 + (x_2^2 + 2x_1x_3) + 2x_2x_3 + x_3^2.$$

This last expression is itself, in this case, a polynomial ordered according to decreasing powers. Al-Karajī then posed the inverse problem: finding the root of a five-term polynomial. He therefore considered this polynomial to be of the canonical form and proposed two methods. The first consisted in taking the sum of the roots of two extreme terms—if these exist—and the quotient of either the second term divided by twice the root of the first or of the fourth term divided by twice the root of the last.[15] The second method consisted in subtracting from the third term twice the product of the root of the first term times the root of the last term, then the root of the remainder from the subtraction is added to the roots of the extreme terms. Great care must be exercised here. This form is not restricted to the particular example, and al-Karajī's method, as can be seen in *al-Badī*ʿ, is general.[16]

Again with a view to extending algebraic computation al-Karajī pursued the examination of the application of arithmetical operations to irrational terms and expressions.

"How multiplication, division, addition, subtraction, and the extraction of roots may be used [on irrational algebraic quantities]."[17] This was the problem posed by al-Karajī and used by al-Samawʾal as the title of the penultimate chapter of his work on the use of arithmetical tools on irrational quantities. The problem marked an important stage in al-Karajī's whole project and therefore also in the extension of the algebraic calculus. Just as he had explicitly and systematically applied the operations of elementary arithmetic to rational quantities, al-Karajī, in order to achieve his objectives, wished to extend this application to irrational quantities in order to show that they still retained their properties. This project, while conceived as purely theoretical, led to a greatly increased knowledge of the algebraic structure of real numbers. Clear progress indeed, but to make it possible it was necessary to risk a setback—a risk at which some today would be scandalized—in that it did not base the operation on the firm ground of the theory of real numbers. The arithmetician-algebraists were only interested in what we might call the algebra of R and did not attempt to construct the field of real numbers. Here progress was made in another algebraic field, that of geometrical algebra, later revived by al-Hayyām and Šaraf al-Dīn al-Tusī.[18] In the tradition of this algebra al-Karajī and al-Samawʾal could extend their algebraical operations to irrational quantities without questioning the reasons for their success or justifying the extension. Because an unfortunate lack of any such justification gave the sense of a setback al-Karajī simultaneously adopted the definitions of books VII and X of the *Elements*. While he borrowed from book VII the definition of number as "a whole composed of unities" and of unity—not yet a number—as that which "qualifies by an existing whole," it is in conformity with book X that he defined the concepts of incommensurability and irrationality. For Euclid, however, as for his commentators, these concepts apply only to geometrical objects or, in the expression of Pappus, they "are a property which is essentially geometrical."[19] "Neither incommensurability nor irrationality," he continued, "can exist for numbers. Numbers are rational and commensurable."[20]

Since al-Karajī explicitly used the Euclidean definitions as a point of departure, it would have been useful if he could have justified his use of them on incommensurable and irrational quantities. His works may be searched in vain for such an explanation. The only justification to be found is extrinsic and indirect and is based on his conception of algebra. Since algebra is concerned with both segments and numbers, the operations of algebra can be applied to any object, be it geometrical or arithmetical. Irrationals as well as rationals may be the solution of the unknown in algebraic operations precisely because they are concerned with both numbers and geometrical magnitudes. The absence of any intrinsic explanation seems to indicate that the extension of algebraic calculation—and therefore of algebra—needed for its development to forget the problems relative to the construction of R and to surmount any potential obstacle, in order to concentrate on the algebraic structure. An unjustified leap, indeed, but a fortunate one for the development of algebra. This is the exact meaning of al-Karajī when he writes, without transition immediately after referring to the definitions of Euclid, "I show you how these quantities [incommensurables, irrationals] are transposed into numbers."[21]

One of the consequences of this project, and not the least important, is the reinterpretation of book X of the *Elements*.[22] This had until then been considered by most mathematicians, even by one so important as Ibn al-Haytham, as merely a geometry book. For al-Karajī its concepts concerned magnitudes in general, both numerical and geometric, and by algebra he classified the theory in this book in what was later to be known as the theory of numbers. To extend the concepts of book X of the *Elements* to all algebraic quantities al-Karajī began by increasing their number. "I say that the monomials are infinite: the first is absolutely rational, five for example, the second is potentially rational, as the root of ten, the third is defined by reference to its cube as the *côté* of twenty, the fourth is the *médiale* defined by reference to the square of its square, the fifth is the square of the quadrato-cube, then the *côté* of the cubo-cube and so on to infinity."[23] In the same way binomials can also be split infinitely. In this field, as in so many others, al-Samawʾal is continuing the work of al-Karajī. At the same time one contribution belongs to him alone and that is his generalization of the division of a polynomial with irrational terms.[24] He thus developed the calculus of radicals introduced by his predecessors. At the beginning of *al-Badī*ʿ[25] is a statement—for the monomials x_1, x_2 and the strictly positive natural integers m, n—of the rules that make it possible to calculate the following:

$$x_1 \sqrt[n]{x_2};\ \sqrt[n]{x_1}/\sqrt[m]{x_2};\ \sqrt[n]{x_1}\cdot\sqrt[m]{x_2}$$
$$\sqrt[n]{x_1}/\sqrt[n]{x_2};\ \sqrt[n]{x_1}/\sqrt[m]{x_2}$$
$$\sqrt[n]{x_1} \pm \sqrt[n]{x_2}.$$

Al-Karajī next discussed the same operations carried out on polynomials and gave, among others, rules that allow calculation of expressions such as

$$\frac{\sqrt{x_1}}{\sqrt{x_2}-\sqrt{x_3}};\ \frac{x_1}{4\sqrt{x_2}+4\sqrt{x_3}};$$
$$\sqrt{x_1+\sqrt{x}};\ \sqrt{\sqrt{x_1}+\sqrt{x_2}}.$$

In addition he attempted, unsuccessfully, to calculate

$$\frac{x_1}{\sqrt{x_2}+\sqrt{x_3}+\sqrt{x_4}}.$$

In the same spirit al-Karajī took up binomial developments. In *al-Fakhrī*[26] he gives the development of $(a+b)^3$, and in *al-Badī*ʿ[27] he presents those of $(a-b)^3$ and $(a+b)^4$. In a long text of al-Karajī reported by al-Samawʾal are the table of binomial coefficients, its formation law $C_n^m = C_{n-1}^{m-1} + C_{n-1}^m$, and the expansion $(a+b)^n = \sum_{m=0}^{n} C_n^m\, a^{n-m}\, b^n$ for integer n.[28]

To demonstrate the preceding proposition as well as the proposition $(ab)^n = a^n b^n$, where a and b are commutative and for all $n \in N$, al-Samawʾal uses a slightly old-fashioned form of mathematical induction. Before proceeding to demonstrate the two propositions he shows that multiplication is commutative and associative—$(ab)(cd) = (ac)(bd)$—and recalls the distributivity of multiplication with respect to addition —$(a+b)\lambda = a\lambda + b\lambda$. He then uses the expansion of $(a+b)^{n-1}$ to prove the identity for $(a+b)^n$ and that of $(ab)^{n-1}$ to prove the identity for $(ab)^n$. It is the first time, as far as we know, that we find a proof that can be considered the beginning of mathematical induction.

Turning to the theory of numbers, al-Karajī pursued further the task of extending algebraic computation. He demonstrated the following theorems:[29]

$$\sum_{i=1}^{n} i = (n^2+n)/2 = n(\tfrac{1}{2}+n/2) \qquad (1)$$

$$\sum_{i=1}^{n} i^2 = \sum_{i=1}^{n} i(2n/3+\tfrac{1}{3}). \qquad (2)$$

Actually al-Karajī did not demonstrate this theorem; he only gave the equivalent form

$$\sum_{i=1}^{n} i^2 \Big/ \sum_{i=1}^{n} i = (2n/3+\tfrac{1}{3}).$$

The algebraic demonstration appeared for the first time in al-Samawʾal:[30]

$$\sum_{i=1}^{n-1} i(i+1) = \left(\sum_{i=1}^{n} i\right)(2n/3-\tfrac{2}{3}) \qquad (3)$$

$$\sum_{i=1}^{n} i^3 = \left(\sum_{i=1}^{n} i\right)^2 \qquad (4)$$

$$\sum_{i=0}^{n-1}(2i+1)(2i+3) + \sum_{i=1}^{n} 2i(2i+2) \qquad (5)$$
$$= \left(\sum_{i=1}^{2n+2} i\right)(\tfrac{2}{3}[2n+2]-\tfrac{5}{3}) + 1$$

$$\sum_{i=1}^{n-2} i(i+1)(i+2) = \sum_{i=1}^{n-1} i^3 - \sum_{i=1}^{n-1} i \qquad (6)$$
$$= \left(\sum_{i=1}^{n-1} i\right)^2 - \sum_{i=1}^{n-1} i.$$

For al-Karajī, the "determination of unknowns starting from known premises" is the proper task of algebra.[31] The aim of algebra is to show how unknown quantities are determined by known quantities through the transformation of the given equations. This is obviously an analytic task, and algebra was already identified with the science of algebraic equations. One can thus understand the extension of algebraic computation and why al-Karajī's followers[32] did not hesitate to join algebra to analysis and, to a certain extent, to oppose it to geometry, thus affirming its autonomy and its independence. Since al-Khwārizmī the unity of the algebraic object was no longer founded in the unity of mathematical entities but in that of operations. It was a question, on the one hand, of the operations necessary to reduce an arbitrary problem to one form of equation—or, more precisely, to one of the canonical types stated by al-Khwārizmī—and, on the other hand, of the operations necessary to give particular solutions, that is, the "canons." In the same fashion al-Karajī took up the six canonical equations[33]—$ax = b$, $ax^2 = bx$, $ax^2 = b$, $ax^2 + bx = c$, $ax^2 + c = bx$, $bx + c = ax^2$

—in order to solve equations of higher degree: $ax^{2n} + bx^n = c$, $ax^{2n} + c = bx^n$, $bx^n + c = ax^{2n}$, $ax^{2n+m} = bx^{n+m} + cx^m$.

Next, following Abū Kāmil in particular, al-Karajī studied systems of linear equations[34] and solved, for example, the system $x/2 + w = s/2$, $2y/3 + w = s/3$, $5z/6 + w = s/6$, where $s = x + y + z$ and $w = 1/3(x/2 + y/3 + z/6)$.

The translation of the first five books of Diophantus' *Arithmetica* revealed to al-Karajī the importance of at least two fields. Yet, unlike Diophantus, he wished to elaborate the theoretical aspect of the fields under consideration. Therefore al-Karajī benefited from both a conception of algebra renewed by al-Khwārizmī and a more developed theory of algebraic computation, and he was able, through his reading of Diophantus, to state in a general form propositions still implicit in Diophantus and to add to them others not initially foreseen. In *al-Fakhrī*, as in *al-Badī*ʿ, by indeterminate analysis (*istiqrāʾ*)[35] al-Karajī meant "to put forward a composite quantity [that is, a polynomial or algebraic expression] formed from one, two, or three successive terms, understood as a square but the formulation of which is nonsquare and the root of which one wishes to extract."[36] By the solution in q of a polynomial with rational coefficients al-Karajī proposed to find the values of x in q such that $P(x)$ will be the square of a rational number. In order to solve in this sense, for example, $A(x) = ax^{2n} + bx^{2n-1}$, where $n = 1, 2, 3, \cdots$, divide by x^{2n-2} to arrive at the form $ax^2 + b$, which should be set equal to a square polynomial of which the monomial of maximum degree is ax^2, such that the equation has a rational root.

Al-Karajī noted that problems of this type have an infinite number of solutions and proposed to solve many of them, some of which were borrowed from Diophantus while others were of his own devising. An exhaustive enumeration of these problems cannot be given here. We shall present only the principal types of algebraic expressions or polynomials that can be set equal to a square.[37]

1. Equations in one unknown:

$ax^n = u^2$

$ax^2 + bx = u^2$ and in general $ax^{2n} + bx^{2n+1} = u^2$

$ax^2 + b = u^2$ and in general $ax^{2n} + bx^{2n-2} = u^2$

$ax^2 + bx + c = u^2$ and in general
$ax^{2n} + bx^{2n-1} + cx^{2n-2} = u^2$

$ax^3 + bx^2 = u^2$ and in general $ax^{2n+1} + bx^{2n} = u^2$ for $n = 1, 2, 3 \cdots$.

2. Equations in two unknowns:

$x^2 + y^2 = u$, $x^3 \pm y^3 = u^2$, $(x^2)^{2m} \pm (y^3)^{2m+1} = u^2$
$(x^{2m+1})^{2m+1} - (y^{2m})^{2m} = u^2$.

3. Equation in three unknowns:

$x^2 + y^2 + z^2 \pm (x + y + z) = u^2$.

4. Two equations in one unknown:

$$\begin{cases} a_1x + b_1 = u_1^2 \\ a_2x + b_2 = u_2^2 \end{cases} \text{ and in general } \begin{cases} a_1x^{2n+1} + b_1x^{2n} = u_1^2 \\ a_2x^{2n+1} + b_2x^{2n} = u_2^2 \end{cases}$$

$$\begin{cases} a_1x^2 + b_1x + c_1 = u_1^2 \\ a_2x^2 + b_2x + c_2 = u_2^2. \end{cases}$$

5. Two equations in two unknowns:

$$\begin{cases} x^2 + y = u^2 \\ x + y^2 = v^2 \end{cases} \begin{cases} x^2 - y = u^2 \\ x^2 - x = v^2 \end{cases} \begin{cases} x^3 + y^2 = u^2 \\ x^3 - y^2 = v^2 \end{cases}$$

$$\begin{cases} x^2 - y^3 = u^2 \\ x^2 + y^3 = v^2 \end{cases} \begin{cases} x^2 + y^2 = u^2 \\ x^2 + y^2 \pm (x + y) = v^2 \end{cases}$$

$$\begin{cases} x + y + x^2 = u^2 \\ x + y + y^2 = v^2. \end{cases}$$

6. Two equations in three unknowns:

$$\begin{cases} x^2 + z = u^2 \\ y^2 + z = v^2. \end{cases}$$

7. Three equations in two unknowns:

$$\begin{cases} x^2 + y^2 = u^2 \\ x^2 + y = v^2 \\ x + y^2 = w^2. \end{cases}$$

8. Three equations in three unknowns:

$$\begin{cases} x^2 + y = u^2 \\ x + z = v^2 \\ z^2 + x = w^2 \end{cases} \begin{cases} x^2 - y = u^2 \\ y^2 - z = v^2 \\ z^2 - x = w^2 \end{cases}$$

$$\begin{cases} (x + y + z) - x^2 = u^2 \\ (x + y + z) - y^2 = v^2 \\ (x + y + z) - z^2 = w^2. \end{cases}$$

In al-Karajī's work there are other variations on the number of equations and of unknowns, as well as a study of algebraic expressions and of polynomials that may be set equal to a cube. From a comparison of the problems solved by al-Karajī and those of Diophantus it was found that "more than a third of the problems of the first book of Diophantus, the problems of the second book starting with the eighth, and virtually all the problems of the third book were included by al-Karajī in his collection."[38] It should be noted that al-Karajī added new problems.

Two sorts of preoccupations become evident in al-Karajī's solutions: to find methods of ever greater generality and to increase the number of cases in which the conditions of the solution should be examined. Hence, for the equation $ax^2 + bx + c = u^2$—although he supposed that its solution requires that a and c be positive squares—he considered the various possibilities: a is a square, b is a square, neither a nor b is a square in $ax^2 + b = u^2$ but $-b/a$ is a square. In addition he showed that $\pm(bx - c) - x^2 = u^2$ has no rational solution unless $b^2/4 \pm c$ is the sum of two squares.[39] Another example is that of the solution of the system $ax + b = u^2$ and $ax + c = v^2$ where he set up $b - c = a \cdot (b - c)/\alpha$ and took $ax + b = (a + [b - c]/a)^2/4$.

The same preoccupation appears in his solution of the system $x^2 + y = u^2$ and $y^2 + x = v^2$, where he sought first to transform $x = at$ and $y = bt$, $a > b$, in order to posit $(a - b)t = \lambda$; $a^2 + t^2 + bt = u$; $b^2t^2 + at = v$, and to solve the problem by means of the demonstrated identity

$$\frac{1}{4}\left[\left(\frac{u - v}{\lambda} + \lambda\right)^2 - \left(\frac{u - v}{\lambda} - \lambda\right)^2\right] = u - v.$$

This concern with generality is also evident in the following two examples: (1) $x^3 + y^3 = u^2$, where he set $y = mx$ and $u = nx$, with $n, m \in q$ and derived $x = n^2/1 + m^2$—a method applicable to more general rational problems of the form $ax^n + by^n = cu^{n-1}$—and $x^3 + ax^2 = u^2$; $x^3 - bx^2 = v^2$, where a and b are integers; he set $u = mx$, $v = nx \Rightarrow x = m^2 - a = n^2 + b$, from which he showed that the condition that m and n should fulfill is $m^2 - n^2 = a + b$. He set $m = n + t$ and obtained $2nt + t^2 = a + b \Rightarrow n = a + b - t^2/2t$.

A great many other examples could be cited to illustrate al-Karajī's incontestable concern with generality and with the study of solutions, as well as a considerable number of other mathematical investigations and results. His most important work, however, remains this new start he gave to algebra, an arithmetization elicited by the discovery of Diophantus by a mathematician already familiar with the algebra of al-Khwārizmī. This new impetus was understood perfectly and extended by al-Karajī's direct successors, notably al-Samaw'al. It is this tradition, as all the evidence indicates, of which Leonardo Fibonacci had some knowledge, as perhaps did Levi ben Gerson.[40]

NOTES

1. F. Woepcke, *Extrait du Fahri, traité d'algèbre* (Paris, 1853); A. Hochheim, *Al-Kāfī fil Ḥisāb*, 3 pts. (Halle, 1877–1880).
2. G. Levi della Vida, "Appunti e quesiti di storia letteraria araba, IV," in *Rivista degli studi orientali*, **14** (1933), 264 ff.
3. No claim for completeness is made for this table, because of the dispersion of the Arabic MSS and their insufficient classification.

Title	al-Karkhī	al-Karajī
al-Fakhrī	BN Paris 2495 Esat Efendi Istanbul 3157 Cairo Nat. Lib., 21	Köprülü Istanbul 950
al-Kāfī	Gotha 1474 Alexandria 1030	Topkapi Sarayī, Istanbul A. 3135 Damat, Istanbul no. 855 Sbath Cairo 111
al-Badī'		Barberini Rome 36, 1
'ilal-ḥisāb al-jabr	Hūsner pasha, Istanbul 257	Bodleian Library I, 968, 3
Inbat al-miyāh al-khafiyyat	Publ. Hyderabad, 1945, on the basis of the MSS. of the library of Aya Sofya and of the library of Bankipore.	

4. One encounters the same difficulties when one considers the MSS of the later Arab commentators and scholars. Thus in the commentaries of al-Shahrazūrī (Damat 855) and of Ibn al-Shaqqāq (Topkapi Sarayī A. 3135), both of which refer to *al-Kāfī*, one finds the name al-Karajī, whereas in MS Alexandria 1030 one finds al-Karkhī.
5. See A. Anbouba, *L'algèbre al-Badī' d'al-Karajī* (Beirut, 1964), p. 11; this work has an introduction in French.
6. This MS was classified as anonymous until the present author identified it as being the *al-Bāhir* of al-Samaw'al. See R. Rashed, "L'arithmétisation de l'algèbre au 11ème siècle," in *Actes du Congrès de l'histoire des sciences* (Moscow, in press); and R. Rashed and S. Ahmad, *L'algèbre al-Bāhir d'al-Samaw'al* (Damascus, 1972).
7. In Arab dictionaries the "mountain countries" include the cities located between "Ādharbayjān, Arab Iraq, Khourestan, Persia, and the land of Deïlem (a land bordering the Caspian Sea)."
8. Woepcke, *op. cit.*, p. 4.
9. See R. Rashed, "Algèbre et linguistique: L'analyse combinatoire dans la science arabe," in R. Cohen, ed., *Boston Studies in the Philosophy of Science*, X (Dordrecht).
10. See M. I. Medovoi, "Mā yaḥtāj ilayh al-Kuttāb wa'l-'ummāl min sinā'at al-ḥisab," in *Istoriko-mathematicheskie issledovaniya*, **13** (1960), pp. 253–324.
11. *Al-Fakhrī*; see Woepcke, *op. cit.*, p. 48.
12. See al-Samaw'al, *op. cit.*, pp. 20 ff. of the Arabic text.
13. *Ibid.*
14. *Ibid.*, p. 60 of the Arabic text.
15. For example, for the first method, to find the root of $x^6 + 4x^5 + (4x^4 + 6x^3) + 12x^2 + 9$; one takes the roots of x^3 and of 9; one then divides $4x^5$ by x^3 or $12x^2$ by 3; in both cases one obtains $4x^2$. The root sought is thus $(x^3 + 2x^2 + 3)$. For the second method, take

$$x^8 + 2x^6 + 11x^4 + 10x^2 + 25.$$

One finds the roots of x^8 and of 25; x^4 and 5, then subtracts as indicated to obtain x^4, the root of which is x^2. The root sought is thus $(x^4 + x^2 + 5)$. See *al-Fakhrī*, p. 55; and *al-Badī'*, p. 50 of the Arabic text.

16. Al-Samaw'al, *op. cit.*
17. *Al-Badī'*, p. 31 of the Arabic text.

18. See Šaraf al-Dīn al Tusī, MSS India office 80th 767 (I.O. 461) and the important work on decimal numbers.
19. See *The Commentary of Pappus on Book X of Euclid's Elements*, W. Thomson, ed. (Cambridge, Mass., 1930), p. 193.
20. *Ibid.*
21. Al-Karajī, *op. cit.*, p. 29 of the Arabic text.
22. For Euclid, book X, see Van der Waerden, *Erwachende Wissenschaft* (Basel-Stuttgart, 1956), J. Vuillemin, *La philosophie de l'algèbre* (Paris, 1962), and P. Dedron and J. Itard, *Mathématiques et mathématisation* (Paris, 1959).
23. *Al-Badī'*, p. 29 of the Arabic text.
24. See the introduction to the present author's edition of al-Bāhir, cited above (note 7).
25. See Anbouba, *op. cit.*, pp. 32 ff. of the Arabic text and pp. 36 ff. of the French intro.
26. See *al-Fakhrī*, in Woepcke, *op. cit.*, p. 58.
27. See *al-Badī'*, in Anbouba, *op. cit.*, p. 33 of the Arabic text.
28. See the chapter on numerical principles in al-Samaw'al, *op. cit.*
29. See *al-Fakhrī*, in Woepcke, *op. cit.*, pp. 59 ff.
30. See al-Samaw'al, *op. cit.*, pp. 64 ff.
31. See *al-Fakhrī*, in Woepcke, *op. cit.*, p. 63, with the trans. improved by comparison with MSS of the Bibliothèque Nationale, Paris.
32. See al-Samaw'al, *op. cit.*, pp. 71 ff. of the Arabic text.
33. See *al-Fakhri*, in Woepcke, *op. cit.*, pp. 64 ff.
34. *Ibid.*, pp. 90–100.
35. *Ibid.*, p. 72; *Al-Badī'*, in Anbouba, *op. cit.*, p. 62 of the Arabic text.
36. *Al-Fakhrī*, with trans. improved by comparison with the MSS of the Bibliothèque Nationale.
37. See *al-Fakhrī* and *al-Badī'*.
38. See *al-Fakhrī*, *op. cit.*, p. 21.
39. *Ibid.*, p. 8.
40. See the comparison made by Woepcke, *op. cit.*; and G. Sarton, *Introduction to the History of Science (1300–1500)*, p. 596.

BIBLIOGRAPHY

I. Original Works. In addition to the works cited in note 3, all of which have been published except *'ilal ḥisāb al-jabr*, the Arabic bibliographies and al-Karajī himself mention other texts that seem to have been lost. Those mentioned in the bibliographies are *Kitāb al 'uqūd wa'l abniyah* ("Of Vaults and Buildings") and *Al-madkhal fi 'ilm al-nujūm* ("Introduction to Astronomy"). Cited by Karajī in *al-Fakhrī* are *Kitāb nawādir al-ashkāl* ("On Unusual Problems") and *Kitāb al dūr wa'l wiṣāyā* ("On Houses and Wills"); and in *al-Badi'*, "On Indeterminate Analysis" and *Kitāb fi'l-hisāb al-hindi* ("On Indian Computation"). Finally, al-Samaw'al mentions a book by al-Karajī from which he has extracted his text on binomial coefficients and expansion.

II. Secondary Literature. Besides the works cited in the notes, see Amir Moez, "Comparison of the Methods of Ibn Ezra and Karhi," in *Scripta mathematica*, **23** (1957); and L. E. Dickson, *History of the Theory of Numbers* (New York, 1952).

See also R. Rashed, "L'induction mathématique-al-Karajī et As-Samaw'al," in *Archive for History of Exact Sciences*, **1** (1972), 1–21.

Roshdi Rashed

AL-KĀSHĪ (or AL-KĀSHĀNĪ), GHIYĀTH AL-DĪN JAMSHĪD MAS'ŪD (*b.* Kāshān, Iran; *d.* Samarkand [now in Uzbek, U.S.S.R], 22 June 1429)

The biographical data on al-Kāshī are scattered and sometimes contradictory. His birthplace was a part of the vast empire of the conqueror Tamerlane and then of his son Shāh Rukh. The first known date concerning al-Kāshī is 2 June 1406 (12 Dhū'l-Hijja, A.H. 808), when, as we know from his *Khaqānī zīj*, he observed a lunar eclipse in his native town.[1] According to Suter, al-Kāshī died about 1436; but Kennedy, on the basis of a note made on the title page of the India Office copy of the *Khaqānī zīj*, gives 19 Ramaḍān A.H. 832, or 22 June 1429.[2] The chronological order of al-Kāshī's works written in Persian or in Arabic is not known completely, but sometimes he gives the exact date and place of their completion. For instance, the *Sullam al-samā'* ("The Stairway of Heaven"), a treatise on the distances and sizes of heavenly bodies, dedicated to a vizier designated only as Kamāl al-Dīn Maḥmūd, was completed in Kāshān on 1 March 1407.[3] In 1410–1411 al-Kāshī wrote the *Mukhtaṣar dar 'ilm-i hay'at* ("Compendium of the Science of Astronomy") for Sultan Iskandar, as is indicated in the British Museum copy of this work. D. G. Voronovski identifies Iskandar with a member of the Tīmūrid dynasty and cousin of Ulugh Bēg, who ruled Fars and Iṣfahān and was executed in 1414.[4] In 1413–1414 al-Kāshī finished the *Khaqānī zīj*. Bartold assumes that the prince to whom this *zīj* is dedicated was Shāh Rukh, who patronized the sciences in his capital, Herat;[5] but Kennedy established that it was Shāh Rukh's son and ruler of Samarkand, Ulugh Bēg. According to Kennedy, in the introduction to this work al-Kāshī complains that he had been working on astronomical problems for a long time, living in poverty in the towns of Iraq (doubtless Persian Iraq) and mostly in Kāshān. Having undertaken the composition of a *zīj*, he would not be able to finish it without the support of Ulugh Bēg, to whom he dedicated the completed work.[6] In January 1416 al-Kāshī composed the short *Risāla dar sharḥ-i ālāt-i raṣd* ("Treatise on . . . Observational Instruments"), dedicated to Sultan Iskandar, whom Bartold and Kennedy identify with a member of the Kārā Koyunlū, or Turkoman dynasty of the Black Sheep.[7] Shishkin mistakenly identifies him with the above-mentioned cousin of Ulugh Bēg.[8] At almost the same time, on 10 February 1416, al-Kāshī completed in Kāshān *Nuzha al-ḥadāiq* ("The Garden Excursion"), in which he described the "Plate of Heavens," an astronomical instrument he invented. In June 1426, at Samarkand, he made some additions to this work.

Dedicating his scientific treatises to sovereigns or

magnates, al-Kāshī, like many scientists of the Middle Ages, tried to provide himself with financial protection. Although al-Kāshī had a second profession—that of a physician—he longed to work in astronomy and mathematics. After a long period of penury and wandering, al-Kāshī finally obtained a secure and honorable position at Samarkand, the residence of the learned and generous protector of science and art, Sultan Ulugh Bēg, himself a great scientist.

In 1417–1420 Ulugh Bēg founded in Samarkand a *madrasa*—a school for advanced study in theology and science—which is still one of the most beautiful buildings in Central Asia. According to a nineteenth-century author, Abū Ṭāhir Khwāja, "four years after the foundation of the *madrasa,*" Ulugh Bēg commenced construction of an observatory; its remains were excavated from 1908 to 1948.[9] For work in the *madrasa* and observatory Ulugh Bēg took many scientists, including al-Kāshī, into his service. During the quarter century until the assassination of Ulugh Bēg in 1449 and the beginning of the political and ideological reaction, Samarkand was the most important scientific center in the East. The exact time of al-Kāshī's move to Samarkand is unknown. Abū Ṭāhir Khwāja states that in 1424 Ulugh Bēg discussed with al-Kāshī, Qāḍī Zāde al-Rūmī, and another scientist from Kāshān, Muʿin al-Dīn, the project of the observatory.[10]

In Samarkand, al-Kāshī actively continued his mathematical and astronomical studies and took a great part in the organization of the observatory, its provision with the best equipment, and in the preparation of Ulugh Bēg's *Zīj*, which was completed after his (al-Kāshī's) death. Al-Kāshī occupied the most prominent place on the scientific staff of Ulugh Bēg. In his account of the erection of the Samarkand observatory the fifteenth-century historian Mirkhwānd mentions, besides Ulugh Bēg, only al-Kāshī, calling him "the support of astronomical science" and "the second Ptolemy."[11] The eighteenth-century historian Sayyīd Raqīm, enumerating the main founders of the observatory and calling each of them *maulanā* ("our master," a usual title of scientists in Arabic), calls al-Kāshī *maulanā-i ālam* (*maulanā* of the world).[12]

Al-Kāshī himself gives a vivid record of Samarkand scientific life in an undated letter to his father, which was written while the observatory was being built. Al-Kāshī highly prized the erudition and mathematical capacity of Ulugh Bēg, particularly his ability to perform very difficult mental computations; he described the prince's scientific activity and once called him a director of the observatory.[13] Therefore Suter's opinion that the first director of the Samarkand observatory was al-Kāshī, who was succeeded by Qāḍī Zāde, must be considered very dubious.[14] On the other hand, al-Kāshī spoke with disdain of Ulugh Bēg's nearly sixty scientific collaborators, although he qualified Qāḍī Zāde as "the most learned of all."[15] Telling of frequent scientific meetings directed by the sultan, al-Kāshī gave several examples of astronomical problems propounded there. These problems, too difficult for others, were solved easily by al-Kāshī. In two cases he surpassed Qāḍī Zāde, who misinterpreted one proof in al-Bīrūnī's *al-Qānūn al-Masʿūdī* and who was unable to solve one difficulty connected with the problem of determining whether a given surface is truly plane or not. Nevertheless his relations with Qāḍī Zāde were amicable. With great satisfaction al-Kāshī told his father of Ulugh Bēg's praise, related to him by some of his friends. He emphasized the atmosphere of free scientific discussion in the presence of the sovereign. The letter included interesting information on the construction of the observatory building and the instruments. This letter and other sources characterize al-Kāshī as the closest collaborator and consultant of Ulugh Bēg, who tolerated al-Kāshī's ignorance of court etiquette and lack of good manners.[16] In the introduction to his own *Zīj* Ulugh Bēg mentions the death of al-Kāshī and calls him "a remarkable scientist, one of the most famous in the world, who had a perfect command of the science of the ancients, who contributed to its development, and who could solve the most difficult problems."[17]

Al-Kāshī wrote his most important works in Samarkand. In July 1424 he completed *Risāla al-muḥīṭīyya* ("The Treatise on the Circumference"), a masterpiece of computational technique resulting in the determination of 2π to sixteen decimal places. On 2 March 1427 he finished the textbook *Miftāḥ al-ḥisāb* ("The Key of Arithmetic"), dedicated to Ulugh Bēg. It is not known when he completed his third chef d'oeuvre, *Risāla al-watar wa'l-jaib* ("The Treatise on the Chord and Sine"), in which he calculated the sine of $1°$ with the same precision as he had calculated π. Apparently he worked on this shortly before his death; some sources indicate that the manuscript was incomplete when he died and that it was finished by Qāḍī Zāde.[18] Apparently al-Kāshī had developed his method of calculation of the sine of $1°$ before he completed *Miftāḥ al-ḥisāb*, for in the introduction to this book, listing his previous works, he mentions *Risāla al-watar wa'l-jaib*.

As was mentioned above, al-Kāshī took part in the composition of Ulugh Bēg's *Zīj*. We cannot say exactly what he did, but doubtless his participation was considerable. The introductory theoretical part of the *Zīj* was completed during al-Kāshī's lifetime, and he translated it from Persian into Arabic.[19]

Mathematics. Al-Kāshī's best-known work is *Miftāḥ al-ḥisāb* (1427), a veritable encyclopedia of elementary mathematics intended for an extensive range of students; it also considers the requirements of calculators—astronomers, land surveyors, architects, clerks, and merchants. In the richness of its contents and in the application of arithmetical and algebraic methods to the solution of various problems, including several geometric ones, and in the clarity and elegance of exposition, this voluminous textbook is one of the best in the whole of medieval literature; it attests to both the author's erudition and his pedagogic ability.[20] Because of its high quality the *Miftāḥ al-ḥisāb* was often recopied and served as a manual for hundreds of years; a compendium of it was also used. The book's title indicates that arithmetic was viewed as the key to the solution of every kind of problem which can be reduced to calculation, and al-Kāshī defined arithmetic as the "science of rules of finding numerical unknowns with the aid of corresponding known quantities."[21] The *Miftāḥ al-ḥisāb* is divided into five books preceded by an introduction: "On the Arithmetic of Integers," "On the Arithmetic of Fractions," "On the 'Computation of the Astronomers'" (on sexagesimal arithmetic), "On the Measurement of Plane Figures and Bodies," and "On the Solution of Problems by Means of Algebra [linear and quadratic equations] and of the Rule of Two False Assumptions, etc." The work comprises many interesting problems and carefully analyzed numerical examples.

In the first book of the *Miftāḥ*, al-Kāshī describes in detail a general method of extracting roots of integers. The integer part of the root is obtained by means of what is now called the Ruffini–Horner method. If the root is irrational, $a < \sqrt[n]{a^n + r} < a + 1$ (a and r are integers), the fractional part of the root is calculated according to the approximate formula $\frac{r}{(a+1)^n - a^n}$.[22] Al-Kāshī himself expressed all rules of computation in words, and his algebra is always purely "rhetorical." In this connection he gives the general rule for raising a binomial to any natural power and the additive rule for the successive determination of binomial coefficients; and he constructs the so-called Pascal's triangle (for $n = 9$). The same methods were presented earlier in the *Jāmiʿ al-ḥisāb biʾl takht waʾl-tuzāb* ("Arithmetic by Means of Board and Dust") of Naṣīr al-Dīn al-Ṭūsī (1265). The origin of these methods is unknown. It is possible that they were at least partly developed by al-Khayyāmī; the influence of Chinese algebra is also quite plausible.[23]

Noteworthy in the second and the third book is the doctrine of decimal fractions, used previously by al-Kāshī in his *Risāla al-muḥīṭīyya*. It was not the first time that decimal fractions appeared in an Arabic mathematical work; they are in the *Kitāb al-fuṣūl fīʾl-ḥisāb al-Hindī* ("Treatise of Arithmetic") of al-Uqlīdisī (mid-tenth century) and were used occasionally also by Chinese scientists.[24] But only al-Kāshī introduced the decimal fractions methodically, with a view to establishing a system of fractions in which (as in the sexagesimal system) all operations would be carried out in the same manner as with integers. It was based on the commonly used decimal numeration, however, and therefore accessible to those who were not familiar with the sexagesimal arithmetic of the astronomers. Operations with finite decimal fractions are explained in detail, but al-Kāshī does not mention the phenomenon of periodicity. To denote decimal fractions, written on the same line with the integer, he sometimes separated the integer by a vertical line or wrote in the orders above the figures; but generally he named only the lowest power that determined all the others. In the second half of the fifteenth century and in the sixteenth century al-Kāshī's decimal fractions found a certain circulation in Turkey, possibly through ʿAlī Qūshjī, who had worked with him at Samarkand and who sometime after the assassination of Ulugh Bēg and the fall of the Byzantine empire settled in Constantinople. They also appear occasionally in an anonymous Byzantine collection of problems from the fifteenth century which was brought to Vienna in 1562.[25] It is also possible that al-Kāshī's ideas had some influence on the propagation of decimal fractions in Europe.

In the fifth book al-Kāshī mentions in passing that for the fourth-degree equations he had discovered "the method for the determination of unknowns in . . . seventy problems which had not been touched upon by either ancients or contemporaries."[26] He also expressed his intention to devote a separate work to this subject, but it seems that he did not complete this research. Al-Kāshī's theory should be analogous to the geometrical theory of cubic equations developed much earlier by Abu'l-Jūd Muḥammad ibn Laith, al-Khayyāmī (eleventh century), and their followers: the positive roots of fourth-degree equations were constructed and investigated as coordinates of points of intersection of the suitable pairs of conics. It must be added that actually there are only sixty-five (not seventy) types of fourth-degree equations reducible to the forms considered by Muslim mathematicians, that is, the forms having terms with positive coefficients on both sides of the equation. Only a few cases of fourth-degree equations were studied before al-Kāshī.

Al-Kāshī's greatest mathematical achievements are

Risāla al-muḥīṭīyya and *Risāla al-watar wa'l-jaib*, both written in direct connection with astronomical researches and especially in connection with the increased demands for more precise trigonometrical tables.

At the beginning of the *Risāla al-muḥīṭīyya* al-Kāshī points out that all approximate values of the ratio of the circumference of a circle to its diameter, that is, of π, calculated by his predecessors gave a very great (absolute) error in the circumference and even greater errors in the computation of the areas of large circles. Al-Kāshī tackled the problem of a more accurate computation of this ratio, which he considered to be irrational, with an accuracy surpassing the practical needs of astronomy, in terms of the then-usual standard of the size of the visible universe or of the "sphere of fixed stars."[27] For that purpose he assumed, as had the Iranian astronomer Quṭb al-Dīn al-Shīrāzī (thirteenth-fourteenth centuries), that the radius of this sphere is 70,073.5 times the diameter of the earth. Concretely, al-Kāshī posed the problem of calculating the said ratio with such precision that the error in the circumference whose diameter is equal to 600,000 diameters of the earth will be smaller than the thickness of a horse's hair. Al-Kāshī used the following old Iranian units of measurement: 1 parasang (about 6 kilometers) = 12,000 cubits, 1 cubit = 24 inches (or fingers), 1 inch = 6 widths of a medium-size grain of barley, and 1 width of a barley grain = 6 thicknesses of a horse's hair. The great-circle circumference of the earth is considered to be about 8,000 parasangs, so al-Kāshī's requirement is equivalent to the computation of π with an error no greater than $0.5 \cdot 10^{-17}$. This computation was accomplished by means of elementary operations, including the extraction of square roots, and the technique of reckoning is elaborated with the greatest care.

Al-Kāshī's measurement of the circumference is based on a computation of the perimeters of regular inscribed and circumscribed polygons, as had been done by Archimedes, but it follows a somewhat different procedure. All calculations are performed in sexagesimal numeration for a circle with a radius of 60. Al-Kāshī's fundamental theorem—in modern notation—is as follows: In a circle with radius r,

$$r(2r + crd\ \alpha^\circ) = crd^2\left(\alpha^\circ + \frac{180^\circ - \alpha^\circ}{2}\right),$$

where $crd\ \alpha^\circ$ is the chord of the arc α° and $\alpha^\circ < 180^\circ$. Thus al-Kāshī applied here the "trigonometry of chords" and not the trigonometric lines themselves. If $\alpha = 2\varphi$ and $d = 2$, then al-Kāshī's theorem may be written trigonometrically as

$$\sin\left(45^\circ + \frac{\varphi^\circ}{2}\right) = \sqrt{\frac{1 + \sin\varphi^\circ}{2}},$$

which is found in the work of J. H. Lambert (1770). The chord of 60° is equal to r, and so it is possible by means of this theorem to calculate successively the chords $c_1, c_2, c_3, \cdots$ of the arcs 120°, 150°, 165°, $\cdots$; in general the value of the chord c_n of the arc $\alpha_n^\circ = 180^\circ - \dfrac{360^\circ}{3 \cdot 2^n}$ will be $c_n = \sqrt{r(2r + c_{n-1})}$. The chord c_n being known, we may, according to Pythagorean theorem, find the side $a_n = \sqrt{d^2 - c_n^2}$ of the regular inscribed $3 \cdot 2^n$-sided polygon, for this side a_n is also the chord of the supplement of the arc α_n° up to 180°. The side b_n of a similar circumscribed polygon is determined by the proportion $b_n : a_n = r : h$, where h is the apothem of the inscribed polygon. In the third section of his treatise al-Kāshī ascertains that the required accuracy will be attained in the case of the regular polygon with $3 \cdot 2^{28} = 805{,}306{,}368$ sides.

He resumes the computation of the chords in twenty-eight extensive tables; he verifies the extraction of the roots by squaring and also by checking by 59 (analogous to the checking by 9 in decimal numeration); and he establishes the number of sexagesimal places to which the values used must be taken. We can concisely express the chords c_n and the sides a_n by formulas

$$c_n = r\sqrt{2 + \sqrt{2 + \cdots + \sqrt{2 + \sqrt{3}}}}$$

and

$$a_n = r\sqrt{2 - \sqrt{2 + \cdots + \sqrt{2 + \sqrt{3}}}},$$

where the number of radicals is equal to the index n. In the sixth section, by multiplying a_{28} by $3 \cdot 2^{28}$, one obtains the perimeter p_{28} of the inscribed $3 \cdot 2^{28}$-sided polygon and then calculates the perimeter P_{28} of the corresponding similar circumscribed polygon. Finally the best approximation for $2\pi r$ is accepted as the arithmetic mean $\dfrac{p_{28} + P_{28}}{2}$, whose sexagesimal value for $r = 1$ is $6\ 16^{I}\ 59^{II}\ 28^{III}\ 1^{IV}\ 34^{V}\ 51^{VI}\ 46^{VII}\ 14^{VIII}\ 50^{IX}$, where all places are correct. In the eighth section al-Kāshī translates this value into the decimal fraction $2\pi = 6.2831853071795865$, correct to sixteen decimal places. This superb result far surpassed all previous determinations of π. The decimal approximation $\pi \approx 3.14$ corresponds to the famous boundary values found by Archimedes, $3\frac{10}{71} < \pi < 3\frac{1}{7}$; Ptolemy used the sexagesimal value $3\ 8^{I}\ 30^{II}$ (≈ 3.14166), and the results of al-Kāshī's predecessors in the Islamic countries were not much better. The most accurate value of π obtained before al-Kāshī by the Chinese scholar Tsu Ch'ung-chih (fifth century) was correct to six decimal places. In Europe in 1597 A. van Roomen approached al-Kāshī's result by calculating π to fifteen decimal places; later Ludolf van Ceulen calculated π to twenty and then to thirty-two places (published 1615).

In his *Risāla al-watar wa'l-jaib* al-Kāshī again calculates the value of sin 1° to ten correct sexagesimal places; the best previous approximations, correct to four places, were obtained in the tenth century by Abu'l-Wafā' and Ibn Yūnus. Al-Kāshī derived the equation for the trisection of an angle, which is a cubic equation of the type $px = q + x^3$—or, as the Arabic mathematicians would say, "Things are equal to the cube and the number." The trisection equation had been known in the Islamic countries since the eleventh century; one equation of this type was solved approximately by al-Bīrūnī to determine the side of a regular nonagon, but this method remains unknown to us. Al-Kāshī proposed an original iterative method of approximate solution, which can be summed up as follows: Assume that the equation

$$x = \frac{q + x^3}{p}$$

possesses a very small positive root x; for the first approximation, take $x_1 = \frac{q}{p}$; for the second approximation, $x_2 = \frac{q + x_1^3}{p}$; for the third, $x_3 = \frac{q + x_2^3}{p}$, and generally

$$x_n = \frac{q + x_{n-1}^3}{p}, \qquad x_0 = 0.$$

It may be proved that this process is convergent in the neighborhood of values of x, $\frac{3x^2}{p} < r < 1$. Al-Kāshī used a somewhat different procedure: he obtained x_1 by dividing q by p as the first sexagesimal place of the desired root, then calculated not the approximations $x_2, x_3, \cdots$ themselves but the corresponding corrections, that is, the successive sexagesimal places of x. The starting point of al-Kāshī's computation was the value of sin 3°, which can be calculated by elementary operations from the chord of 72° (the side of a regular inscribed pentagon) and the chord of 60°. The sin 1° for a radius of 60 is obtained as a root of the equation

$$x = \frac{900 \sin 3^\circ + x^3}{45 \cdot 60}.$$

The sexagesimal value of sin 1° for a radius of 60 is $1\ 2^{\mathrm{I}}\ 49^{\mathrm{II}}\ 43^{\mathrm{III}}\ 11^{\mathrm{IV}}\ 14^{\mathrm{V}}\ 44^{\mathrm{VI}}\ 16^{\mathrm{VII}}\ 26^{\mathrm{VIII}}\ 17^{\mathrm{IX}}$; and the corresponding decimal fraction for a radius of 1 is 0.017452406437283571. All figures in both cases are correct.

Al-Kāshī's method of numerical solution of the trisection equation, whose variants were also presented by Ulugh Bēg, Qāḍī Zāde, and his grandson Maḥmūd ibn Muḥammad Mīrīm Chelebī (who worked in Turkey),[28] requires a relatively small number of operations and shows the exactness of the approximation at each stage of the computation. Doubtless it was one of the best achievements in medieval algebra. H. Hankel has written that this method "concedes nothing in subtlety or elegance to any of the methods of approximation discovered in the West after Viète."[29] But all these discoveries of al-Kāshī's were long unknown in Europe and were studied only in the nineteenth and twentieth centuries by such historians of science as Sédillot, Hankel, Luckey, Kary-Niyazov, and Kennedy.

Astronomy. Until now only three astronomical works by al-Kāshī have been studied. His *Khāqānī Zīj,* as its title shows, was the revision of the *Īlkhānī Zīj* of Naṣīr al-Dīn al-Ṭūsī. In the introduction to al-Kāshī's *zīj* there is a detailed description of the method of determining the mean and anomalistic motion of the moon based on al-Kāshī's three observations of lunar eclipses made in Kāshān and on Ptolemy's three observations of lunar eclipses described in the *Almagest.* In the chronological section of these tables there are detailed descriptions of the lunar Muslim (Hijra) calendar, of the Persian solar (Yazdegerd) and Greek-Syrian (Seleucid) calendars, of al-Khayyāmī's calendar reform (Malikī), of the Chinese-Uigur calendar, and of the calendar used in the Il-Khan empire, where Naṣīr al-Dīn al-Ṭūsī had been working. In the mathematical section there are tables of sines and tangents to four sexagesimal places for each minute of arc. In the spherical astronomy section there are tables of transformations of ecliptic coordinates of points of the celestial sphere to equatorial coordinates and tables of other spherical astronomical functions.

There are also detailed tables of the longitudinal motion of the sun, the moon, and the planets, and of the latitudinal motion of the moon and the planets. Al-Kāshī also gives the tables of the longitudinal and latitudinal parallaxes for certain geographic latitudes, tables of eclipses, and tables of the visibility of the moon. In the geographical section there are tables of geographical latitudes and longitudes of 516 points. There are also tables of the fixed stars, the ecliptic latitudes and longitudes, the magnitudes and "temperaments" of the 84 brightest fixed stars, the relative distances of the planets from the center of the earth, and certain astrological tables. In comparing the tables with Ulugh Bēg's *Zīj*, it will be noted that the last tables in the geographical section contain coordinates of 240 points, but the star catalog contains coordinates of 1,018 fixed stars.

In his *Miftāḥ al-ḥisāb* al-Kāshī mentions his *Zīj al-tashīlāt* ("Zīj of Simplifications") and says that he also composed some other tables.[30] His *Sullam al-samā'*, scarcely studied as yet, deals with the determination of the distances and sizes of the planets.

In his *Risāla dar sharḥ-i ālāt-i raṣd* ("Treatise on the Explanation of Observational Instruments") al-Kāshī briefly describes the construction of eight astronomical instruments: triquetrum, armillary sphere, equinoctial ring, double ring, Fakhrī sextant, an instrument "having azimuth and altitude," an instrument "having the sine and arrow," and a small armillary sphere. Triquetra and armillary spheres were used by Ptolemy; the latter is a model of the celestial sphere, the fixed and mobile great circles of which are represented, respectively, by fixed and mobile rings. Therefore the armillary sphere can represent positions of these circles for any moment; one ring has diopters for measurement of the altitude of a star, and the direction of the plane of this ring determines the azimuth. The third and seventh instruments consist of several rings of armillary spheres. The equinoctial ring (the circle in the plane of the celestial equator), used for observation of the transit of the sun through the equinoctial points, was invented by astronomers who worked in the tenth century in Shīrāz, at the court of the Buyid sultan ʿAḍūd al-Dawla. The Fakhrī sextant, one-sixth of a circle in the plane of the celestial meridian, used for measuring the altitudes of stars in this plane, was invented about 1000 by al-Khujandī in Rayy, at the court of the Buyid sultan Fakhr al-Dawla. The fifth instrument was used in the Marāgha observatory directed by Naṣīr al-Dīn al-Ṭūsī. The sixth instrument, al-Kāshī says, did not exist in earlier observatories; it is used for determination of sines and "arrows" (versed sines) of arcs.

In *Nuzha al-ḥadāiq* al-Kāshī describes two instruments he had invented: the "plate of heavens" and the "plate of conjunctions." The first is a planetary equatorium and is used for the determination of the ecliptic latitudes and longitudes of planets, their distances from the earth, and their stations and retrogradations; like the astrolabe, which it resembles in shape, it was used for measurements and for graphical solutions of problems of planetary motion by means of a kind of nomograms. The second instrument is a simple device for performing a linear interpolation.

NOTES

1. See E. S. Kennedy, *The Planetary Equatorium* . . ., p. 1.
2. H. Suter, *Die Mathematiker und Astronomen* . . ., pp. 173–174; Kennedy, *op. cit.*, p. 7.
3. See M. Krause, "Stambuler Handschriften . . .," p. 50; M. Ṭabāṭabā'i, "Jamshīd Ghiyāth al-Dīn Kāshānī," p. 23.
4. D. G. Voronovski, "Astronomy Sredney Azii ot Muhammeda al-Havarazmi do Ulugbeka i ego shkoly (IX–XVI vv.)," pp. 127, 164.
5. See V. V. Bartold, *Ulugbek i ego vremya*, p. 108.
6. Kennedy, *op. cit.*, pp. 1–2.
7. Bartold, *op. cit.*, p. 108; Kennedy, *op. cit.*, p. 2.
8. V. A. Shishkin, "Observatoriya Ulugbeka i ee issledovanie," p. 10.
9. See T. N. Kary-Niyazov, *Astronomicheskaya shkola Ulugbeka*, 2nd ed., p. 107; see also Shishkin, *op. cit.*
10. See Kary-Niyazov, *loc. cit.*
11. See Bartold, *op. cit.*, p. 88.
12. *Ibid.*, pp. 88–89.
13. E. S. Kennedy, "A Letter of Jamshīd al-Kāshī to His Father," p. 200.
14. Suter, *op. cit.*, pp. 173, 175; E. S. Kennedy, "A Survey of Islamic Astronomical Tables," p. 127.
15. Kennedy, "A Letter . . .," p. 194.
16. See Bartold, *op. cit.*, p. 108.
17. See *Zīj-i Ulughbeg*, French trans., p. 5.
18. See Kennedy, *The Planetary Equatorium* . . ., p. 6.
19. See *Taʿrīb al-zīj*; Kary-Niyazov, *op. cit.*, 2nd ed., pp. 141–142.
20. See P. Luckey, *Die Rechenkunst* . . .; A. P. Youschkevitch; *Geschichte der Mathematik im Mittelalter*, p. 237 ff.
21. al-Kāshī, *Klyuch arifmetiki* . . ., p. 13.
22. See P. Luckey, "Die Ausziehung des *n*-ten Wurzel . . . ."
23. P. Luckey, "Die Ausziehung des *n*-ten Wurzel . . ."; Juschkewitsch, *op. cit.*, pp. 240–248.
24. See A. Saidan, "The Earliest Extant Arabic Arithmetic . . ."; Juschkewitsch, *op. cit.*, pp. 21–23.
25. H Hunger and K. Vogel, *Ein byzantinisches Rechenbuch des 15. Jahrhunderts*, p. 104.
26. al-Kāshi, *Klyuch arifmetiki* . . ., p. 192.
27. *Ibid.*, p. 126.
28. Kary-Niyazov, *op. cit.*, 2nd ed., p. 199; Qāḍī Zāde, *Risāla fī istikhrāj jaib daraja wāhida*; Mīrīm Chelebī, *Dastūr al-ʿamal wa taṣḥīḥ al-jadwal.*
29. H. Hankel, *Zur Geschichte der Mathematik* . . ., p. 292.
30. al-Kāshī, *Klyuch arifmetiki* . . ., p. 9.

BIBLIOGRAPHY

I. ORIGINAL WORKS. Al-Kāshī's writings were collected as *Majmū'* ("Collection"; Teheran, 1888), an ed. of the original texts; "Matematicheskie traktaty," in *Istoriko-matematicheskie issledovaniya*, **7** (1954), 9–439, Russian trans. by B. A. Rosenfeld and commentaries by Rosenfeld and A. P. Youschkevitch; and *Klyuch arifmetiki. Traktat of okruzhnosti* ("The Key of Arithmetic. A Treatise on Circumference"), trans. by B. A. Rosenfeld, ed. by V. S. Segal and A. P. Youschkevitch, commentaries by Rosenfeld and Youschkevitch, with photorepros. of Arabic MSS.

His individual works are the following:

1. *Sullam al-samā' fī ḥall ishkāl waqaʿa li'l-muqaddimīn fi'l-abʿād wa'l-ajrām* ("The Stairway of Heaven, on Resolution of Difficulties Met by Predecessors in the Determination of Distances and Sizes"; 1407). Arabic MSS in Lon-

don, Oxford, and Istanbul, the most important being London, India Office 755; and Oxford, Bodley 888/4.

2. *Mukhtaṣar dar 'ilm-i hay'at* ("Compendium on the Science of Astronomy") or *Risāla dar hay'at* ("Treatise on Astronomy"; 1410–1411). Persian MSS in London and Yezd.

3. *Zīj-i Khaqānī fī takmīl-i Zīj-i Īlkhānī* ("Khaqānī Zīj—Perfection of Īlkhānī Zīj"; 1413–1414). Persian MSS in London, Istanbul, Teheran, Yezd, Meshed, and Hyderabad-Deccan, the most important being London, India Office 2232, which is described in E. S. Kennedy, "A Survey of Islamic Astronomical Tables," pp. 164–166.

4. *Risāla dar sharḥ-i ālāt-i raṣd* ("Treatise on the Explanation of Observational Instruments"; 1416). Persian MSS in Leiden and Teheran, the more important being Leiden, Univ. 327/12, which has been pub. as a supp. to V. V. Bartold, *Ulugbek i ego vremya;* and E. S. Kennedy, "Al-Kāshī's Treatise on Astronomical Observation Instruments," pp. 99, 101, 103. There is an English trans. in Kennedy, "Al-Kāshī's Treatise . . .," pp. 98–104; and a Russian trans. in V. A. Shishkin, "Observatoriya Ulugbeka i ee issledovanie," pp. 91–94.

5. *Nuzha al-ḥadāiq fī kayfiyya ṣan'a al-āla al-musammā bi ṭabaq al-manāṭiq* ("The Garden Excursion, on the Method of Construction of the Instrument Called Plate of Heavens"; 1416). Arabic MSS are in London, Dublin, and Bombay, the most important being London, India Office Ross 210. There is a litho. ed. of another MS as a supp. to the Teheran ed. of *Miftāḥ al-ḥisāb;* see also *Risāla fi'l-'amal bi ashal āla min qabl al-nujūm;* G. D. Jalalov, "Otlichie 'Zij Guragani' ot drugikh podobnykh zijey" and "K voprosu o sostavlenii planetnykh tablits samarkandskoy observatorii"; T. N. Kary-Niyazov, *Astronomicheskaya shkola Ulugbeka;* and E. S. Kennedy, "Al-Kāshī's 'Plate of Conjunctions.' "

6. *Risāla al-muḥīṭiyya* ("Treatise on the Circumference"; 1424). Arabic MSS are in Istanbul, Teheran, and Meshed, the most important being Istanbul, Ask. müze. 756. There is an ed. of another MS in *Majmū'* and one of the Istanbul MS with German trans. in P. Luckey, *Der Lehrbrief über den Kreisumfang von Ǧamšīd b. Mas'ūd al-Kāšī.* Russian trans. are in "Matematicheskie traktaty," pp. 327–379; and in *Klyuch arifmetiki*, pp. 263–308, with photorepro. of Istanbul MS on pp. 338–426.

7. *Ilkaḥāt an-Nuzha* ("Supplement to the Excursion"; 1427). There is an ed. of a MS in *Majmū'*.

8. *Miftāḥ al-ḥisāb* ("The Key of Arithmetic") or *Miftāḥ al-ḥussāb fi 'ilm al-ḥisāb* ("The Key of Reckoners in the Science of Arithmetic"). Arabic MSS in Leningrad, Berlin, Paris, Leiden, London, Istanbul, Teheran, Meshed, Patna, Peshawar, and Rampur, the most important being Leningrad, Publ. Bibl. 131; Leiden, Univ. 185; Berlin, Preuss. Bibl. 5992 and 2992a, and Inst. Gesch. Med. Natur. I.2; Paris, BN 5020; and London, BM 419 and India Office 756. There is a litho. ed. of another MS (Teheran, 1889). Russian trans. are in "Matematicheskie traktaty," pp. 13–326; and *Klyuch arifmetiki*, pp. 7–262, with photorepro. of Leiden MS on pp. 428–568. There is an ed. of the Leiden MS with commentaries (Cairo, 1968). See also P. Luckey, "Die Ausziehung des *n*-ten Wurzel . . ." and "Die Rechenkunst bei Ǧamšīd b. Mas'ūd al-Kāšī . . . ."

9. *Talkhiṣ al-Miftāḥ* ("Compendium of the Key"). Arabic MSS in London, Tashkent, Istanbul, Baghdad, Mosul, Teheran, Tabriz, and Patna, the most important being London, India Office 75; and Tashkent, Inst. vost. 2245.

10. *Risāla al-watar wa'l-jaib* ("Treatise on the Chord and Sine"). There is an ed. of a MS in *Majmū'*.

11. *Ta'rīb al-zij* ("The Arabization of the Zij"), an Arabic trans. of the intro. to Ulugh Bēg's *Zīj.* MSS are in Leiden and Tashkent.

12. *Wujūh al-'amal al-ḍarb fi'l-takht wa'l-turāb* ("Ways of Multiplying by Means of Board and Dust"). There is an ed. of an Arabic MS in *Majmū'*.

13. *Natā'ij al-ḥaqā'iq* ("Results of Verities"). There is an ed. of an Arabic MS in *Majmū'*.

14. *Miftāḥ al-asbāb fī 'ilm al-zij* ("The Key of Causes in the Science of Astronomical Tables"). There is an Arabic MS in Mosul.

15. *Risāla dar sakht-i asṭurlāb* ("Treatise on the Construction of the Astrolabe"). There is a Persian MS in Meshed.

16. *Risāla fī ma'rifa samt al-qibla min dāira hindiyya ma'rūfa* ("Treatise on the Determination of Azimuth of the Qibla by Means of a Circle Known as Indian"). There is an Arabic MS at Meshed.

17. Al-Kāshī's letter to his father exists in 2 Persian MSS in Teheran. There is an ed. of them in M. Ṭabāṭabā'ī, "Nāma-yi pisar bi pidar," in *Amūzish wa parwarish*, **10**, no. 3 (1940), 9–16, 59–62. An English trans. is E S. Kennedy, "A Letter of Jamshīd al-Kāshī to His Father"; English and Turkish trans. are in A. Sayili, "Ghiyāth al-Dīn al-Kāshī's Letter on Ulugh Bēg and the Scientific Activity in Samarkand," in *Türk tarih kurumu yayinlarinden*, 7th ser., no. 39 (1960).

II. Secondary Literature. See the following: V. V. Bartold, *Ulugbek i ego vremya* ("Ulugh Bēg and His Time"; Petrograd, 1918), 2nd ed. in his *Sochinenia* ("Works"), II, pt. 2 (Moscow, 1964), 23–196, trans. into German as "Ulug Beg und seine Zeit," in *Abhandlungen für die Kunde des Morgenlandes*, **21**, no. 1 (1935); L. S. Bretanitzki and B. A. Rosenfeld, "Arkhitekturnaya glava traktata 'Klyuch arifmetiki' Giyas ad-Dina Kashi" ("An Architectural Chapter of the Treatise 'The Key of Arithmetic' by Ghiyāth al-Dīn Kāshī"), in *Iskusstvo Azerbayjana*, **5** (1956), 87–130; C. Brockelmann, *Geschichte der arabischen literatur*, 2nd ed., II (Leiden, 1944), 273 and supp. II (Leiden, 1942), 295; Mīrīm Chelebī, *Dastūr al-'amal wa taṣḥīḥ al-jadwal* ("Rules of the Operation and Correction of the Tables"; 1498), Arabic commentaries to Ulugh Bēg's *Zīj*, contains an exposition of al-Kāshī's *Risāla al-watar wa'l-jaib*—Arabic MSS are in Paris, Berlin, Istanbul, and Cairo, the most important being Paris, BN 163 (a French trans. of the exposition is in L. A. Sédillot, "De l'algèbre chez les Arabes," in *Journal asiatique*, 5th ser., **2** [1853], 323–350; a Russian trans. is in *Klyuch arifmetiki*, pp. 311–319); A. Dakhel, *The Extraction* *of the n-th Root in the Sexagesimal Notation. A Study of Chapter 5, Treatise 3 of Miftāḥ al Ḥisāb*, W. A. Hijab and E. S. Kennedy, eds. (Beirut, 1960); H. Hankel, *Zur Geschichte der Mathematik im Altertum und Mittelalter* (Leipzig, 1874); and H. Hunger and K. Vogel, *Ein byzantinisches Rechenbuch des 15. Jahrhunderts* (Vienna, 1963), text, trans., and commentary.

See also G. D. Jalalov, "Otlichie 'Zij Guragani' ot drugikh podobnykh zijey" ("The Difference of 'Gurgani Zīj' from Other Zījes"), in *Istoriko-astronomicheskie issledovaniya*, **1** (1955), 85–100; "K voprosu o sostavlenii planetnykh tablits samarkandskoy observatorii" ("On the Question of the Composition of the Planetary Tables of the Samarkand Observatory"), *ibid.*, 101–118; and "Giyas ad-Din Chusti (Kashi)—krupneyshy astronom i matematik XV veka" ("Ghiyāth al-Dīn Chūstī [Kāshī]—the Greatest Astronomer and Mathematician of the XV Century"), in *Uchenye zapiski Tashkentskogo gosudarstvennogo pedagogicheskogo instituta*, **7** (1957), 141–157; T. N. Kary-Niyazov, *Astronomicheskaya shkola Ulugbeka* (Moscow–Leningrad, 1950), 2nd ed. in his *Izbrannye trudy* ("Selected Works"), VI (Tashkent, 1967); and "Ulugbek i Savoy Jay Singh," in *Fiziko-matematicheskie nauki v stranah Vostoka*, **1** (1966), 247–256; E. S. Kennedy, "Al-Kāshī's 'Plate of Conjunctions,' " in *Isis*, **38**, no. 2 (1947), 56–59; "A Fifteenth-Century Lunar Eclipse Computer," in *Scripta mathematica*, **17**, no. 1–2 (1951), 91–97; "An Islamic Computer for Planetary Latitudes," in *Journal of the American Oriental Society*, **71** (1951), 13–21; "A Survey of Islamic Astronomical Tables," in *Transactions of the American Philosophical Society*, n.s. **46**, no. 2 (1956), 123–177; "Parallax Theory in Islamic Astronomy," in *Isis*, **47**, no. 1 (1956), 33–53; *The Planetary Equatorium of Jamshid Ghiyāth al-Dīn al-Kāshī* (Princeton, 1960); "A Letter of Jamshīd al-Kāshī to His Father. Scientific Research and Personalities of a Fifteenth Century Court," in *Commentarii periodici pontifici Instituti biblici, Orientalia*, n.s. **29**, fasc. 29 (1960), 191–213; "Al-Kāshī's Treatise on Astronomical Observation Instruments," in *Journal of Near Eastern Studies*, **20**, no. 2 (1961), 98–108; "A Medieval Interpolation Scheme Using Second-Order Differences," in *A Locust's Leg. Studies in Honour of S. H. Tegi-zadeh* (London, 1962), pp. 117–120; and "The Chinese-Uighur Calendar as Described in the Islamic Sources," in *Isis*, **55**, no. 4 (1964), 435–443; M. Krause, "Stambuler Handschriften islamischer Mathematiker," in *Quellen und Studien zur Geschichte der Mathematik, Astronomie und Physik*, Abt. B, **3** (1936), 437–532; P. Luckey, "Die Ausziehung des *n*-ten Wurzel und der binomische Lehrsatz in der islamischen Mathematik," in *Mathematische Annalen*, **120** (1948), 244–254; "Die Rechenkunst bei Ǧamšīd b. Mas'ūd al-Kāšī mit Rückblicken auf die ältere Geschichte des Rechnens," in *Abhandlungen für die Kunde des Morgenlandes*, 31 (Wiesbaden, 1951); and *Der Lehrbrief uber den Kreisumfang von Ǧamšīd b. Mas'ūd al-Kāšī*, A. Siggel, ed. (Berlin, 1953); *Risāla fī'l-'amal bi ashal āla min qabl al-nujūm* ("Treatise on the Operation With the Easiest Instrument for the Planets"), a Persian exposition of al-Kāshī's *Nuzha*—available in MS as Princeton, Univ. 75; and in English trans. with photorepro. in E. S. Kennedy, *The Planetary Equatorium;* B. A. Rosenfeld and A. P. Youschkevitch, "O traktate Qāḍī-Zāde ar-Rūmī ob opredelenii sinusa odnogo gradusa" ("On Qāḍī-Zāde al-Rūmī's Treatise on the Determination of the Sine of One Degree"), in *Istoriko-matematicheskie issledovaniya*, **13** (1960), 533–556; and Mūsā Qāḍī Zāde al-Rūmī, *Risāla fī istikhrāj jaib daraja wāhida* ("Treatise on Determination of the Sine of One Degree"), an Arabic revision of al-Kāshī's *Risāla al-watar wa'l-jaib*—MSS are Cairo, Nat. Bibl. 210 (ascribed by Suter, p. 174, to al-Kāshī himself) and Berlin, Inst. Gesch. Med. Naturw. I.1; Russian trans. in B. A. Rosenfeld and A. P. Youschkevitch, "O traktate Qāḍī-Zāde . . ." and descriptions in G. D. Jalalov, "Giyas ad-Din Chusti (Kashi) . . ." and in Ṣālih Zakī Effendī, *Athār bāqiyya*, I.

Also of value are A. Saidan, "The Earliest Extant Arabic Arithmetic. *Kitāb al-fuṣūl fi al-ḥisāb al-Hindī* of . . . al-Uqlīdisī," in *Isis*, **57**, no. 4 (1966), 475–490; Ṣālih Zakī Effendī, *Athār bāqiyya*, I (Istanbul, 1911); V. A. Shishkin, "Observatoriya Ulugbeka i ee issledovanie" ("Ulugh Bēg's Observatory and Its Investigations"), in *Trudy Instituta istorii i arkheologii Akademii Nauk Uzbekskoy SSR*, V, *Observatoriya Ulugbeka* (Tashkent, 1953), 3–100; S. H. Sirazhdinov and G. P. Matviyevskaya, "O matematicheskikh rabotakh shkoly Ulugbeka" ("On the Mathematical Works of Ulugh Bēg's School"), in *Iz istorii epokhi Ulugbeka* ("From the History of Ulugh Bēg's Age"; Tashkent, 1965), pp. 173–199; H. Suter, *Die Mathematiker und Astronomen der Araber und ihre Werke* (Leipzig, 1900); M. Ṭabāṭabā'ī, "Jamshīd Ghiyāth al-Dīn Kāshānī," in *Amuzish wa Parwarish*, **10**, no. 3 (1940), 1–8 and no. 4 (1940), 17–24; M. J. Tichenor, "Late Medieval Two-Argument Tables for Planetary Longitudes," in *Journal of Near Eastern Studies*, **26**, no. 2 (1967), 126–128; D. G. Voronovski, "Astronomy Sredney Azii ot Muhammeda al-Havarazmi do Ulugbeka i ego shkoly (IX–XVI vv.)" ("Astronomers of Central Asia from Muḥammad al-Khwārizmī to Ulugh Bēg and His School, IX–XVI Centuries"), in *Iz istorii epokhi Ulugbeka* (Tashkent, 1965), pp. 100–172; A. P. Youschkevitch, *Istoria matematiki v srednie veka* ("History of Mathematics in the Middle Ages"; Moscow, 1961), trans. into German as A. P. Juschkewitsch, *Geschichte der Mathematik in Mittelalter* (Leipzig, 1964); and *Zīj-i Ulughbēg* ("Ulugh Bēg's Zīj") or *Zīj-i Sulṭānī* or *Zīj-i jadīd-i Guragānī* ("New Guragānī Zīj"), in Persian, the most important MSS being Paris, BN 758/8 and Tashkent, Inst. Vost. 2214 (a total of 82 MSS are known)—an ed. of the intro. according to the Paris MS and a French trans. are in L. A. Sédillot, *Prolegomènes des tables astronomiques d'Oloug-Beg* (Paris, 1847; 2nd ed., 1853), and a description of the Tashkent MS is in T. N. Kary-Niyazov, *Astronomicheskaya shkola Ulugbeka* (2nd ed., Tashkent, 1967), pp. 148–325.

A. P. YOUSCHKEVITCH

B. A. ROSENFELD

KECKERMANN, BARTHOLOMEW (*b.* Danzig [now Gdansk], Poland, 1571/73; *d.* Danzig, 25 July 1609)

Keckermann, the son of George and Gertrude Keckermann, was educated by Jacob Fabricius, rector of the Danzig Gymnasium, who imbued him with strict Calvinist doctrine and a detestation of Anabaptists and Catholics. In 1590 he was sent to Wittenberg University, then to Leipzig for a semester (1592), and finally to Heidelberg (1592). In the latter city he obtained his M.A. in 1595, afterward being appointed tutor and then lecturer in philosophy. The chair of Hebrew was conferred on him in 1600. Keckermann's growing reputation had resulted in an invitation in 1597 from the Danzig senate to return to that city's Gymnasium. Although he declined this offer, preferring to work toward his doctorate of divinity at Heidelberg (obtained 1602), Keckermann accepted a later invitation and became professor of philosophy at Danzig in 1602. There he remained until he died, "worn out with mere scholastic drudgery," in 1609.

At the Danzig Gymnasium, Keckermann tried to implement a Ramist reform of the curriculum with a scheme intended to give youths an encyclopedic education within three years. In this new *cursus philosophicus* the first year was devoted to logic and physics, the second year to mathematics and metaphysics, and the third to ethics, economics, and politics. The key to this syllabus was Keckermann's systematic method, which was influenced by the view of Petrus Ramus that the correct approach to a discipline is topical and analytical, rather than merely historical or narrative.

Keckermann was not a pure Ramist, however, and was most sympathetic to the progressive Aristotelian views outlined in Jacopo Zabarella's *De methodis*. Like Zabarella, Keckermann believed that much of the effort being devoted to the textual analysis of Aristotle (effort that led to the prolonging of the *cursus philosophicus*) could be better diverted to developing new Aristotelian methods and analytical systems. He thus drew heavily on both Aristotelian and Ramist ideas for his philosophical and logical *Praecognita*, in which he gave the first theoretical discussion of systems (the set of precepts characterizing each science).

In his lectures at Danzig, he made abundant use of his systematic method. In its published form the typical lecture course is entitled *Systema* .... Among the published *systeme* are treatments of logic, politics, physics, metaphysics, ethics, theology, Hebrew, geography, geometry, astronomy, and optics. These works are philosophical and pedagogical in character and contain little material of any scientific value; certainly there is no scientific originality in them. Their main interest lies perhaps in their illustration of the content of university courses in mathematics and natural philosophy in the early years of the seventeenth century.

Keckermann's *Systema physicum*, a set of lectures delivered in 1607 and published in 1610, discussed physics, astronomy, and natural philosophy, all in largely Aristotelian terms. The author differed from most Peripatetics by describing the four elements as less complete and perfect in form than the mixed bodies. Since elements are not completely and individually sui generis, Keckermann found it plausible that they should be capable of rapid transmutation into one another.

The long discussion of comets has a theological flavor, which is not surprising in view of Keckermann's religious training and devotion. Comets are conventionally defined as terrestrial exhalations produced by action of the planets in the supreme aerial region. God then encourages angels, or permits demons, to join with the comet in producing extraordinary terrestrial effects. God's unpredictable choice of angels or demons for the task explains the good and bad effects of comets, although some allowance must be made for the comet's relation to the stars and planets. Predominantly, however, the effects of comets are malign and indicate divine wrath.

There are serious gaps and errors in the *Systema physicum*. The vacuum is not adequately discussed in terms of Aristotelian motion and place. Keckermann also maintained that water contracts when frozen. This mistake was criticized in 1618 by Isaac Beeckman, who remarked that either a simple experiment or common sense would have exposed the fallacy. Keckermann's use of experiment—or, rather, of experience—is in fact very crude and imprecise.

The *Systema compendiosum totius mathematices* (1617) consists of lectures, read in 1605 and other unspecified years, on geometry, optics, astronomy, and geography; it was intended to form the second year of the *cursus philosophicus*. The geometry section is elementary, although it describes the duplication of the cube and other problems. The main influence of this section—and of the whole *Systema*—seems to have been Ramus, *Scholarum mathematicarum* (1569). Among the geometrical authors cited are Regiomontanus, Albrecht Dürer, and Wilhelm Xylander. For the section on optics Keckermann drew on Arab writers, Witelo, and Peter Apian. The astronomical section follows Regiomontanus and Georg Peurbach but also cites Copernicus, Erasmus Reinhold's *Prutenic Tables*, and Tycho Brahe. Keckermann remarks that while the Ptolemaic theory of the *primum mobile* is certain, the theory of the planets has defects which compelled Copernicus and Brahe to try to reduce the planetary motions to "greater certainty and superior method" (1621 ed., p. 349). Keckermann disappointingly failed to follow up this interesting statement, although later (p. 357) he cites with approval Copernicus' criticism (*De revolutionibus*, III, cap. 13) of the Ptolemaic treatment of the solar year. There is, however, no real examination of the Copernican system.

BIBLIOGRAPHY

I. ORIGINAL WORKS. The collected ed. of Keckermann's works is *Operum omnium quae extant*, 2 vols. (Geneva, 1614), which includes his religious works as well as the *Systeme* and *Praecognita*. The *Systema physicum septem libris adornatum* . . . first appeared at Danzig in 1610. A 3rd ed. was published at Hanau in 1612. The various parts of the *Systema mathematices* were published separately soon after Keckermann's death. They were collected into the *Systema compendiosum totius mathematices* . . . (Hanau, 1617, 1621; Oxford, 1661).

II. SECONDARY LITERATURE. The main source for Keckermann's life is the nearly contemporary biography (1615) by Melchior Adam, *Vitae Germanorum philosophorum* (3rd ed., Frankfurt, 1706), pp. 232–234. The work of Keckermann is surveyed in Bronisław Nadolski, *Zycie i działalność naukowa uczenego gdańskiego Bartlomieja Keckermanna; studium z dziejów Odrodzenia na Pomorzu* (Torun, 1961). W. H. van Zuylen, *Bartholomäus Keckermann: Sein Leben und Wirken*, Tübingen dissertation (Leipzig, 1934), concentrates on the theological works.

For notes on Keckermann's physics, see Lynn Thorndike, *A History of Magic and Experimental Science*, 8 vols. (New York, 1923–1958), VII, 375–379. For Keckermann as a systematist, see Otto Ritschl, *System und systematische Methode in der Geschichte des wissenschaftlichen Sprachgebrauchs und der philosophischen Methodologie* (Bonn, 1906), pp. 26–31; and Neal W. Gilbert, *Renaissance Concepts of Method* (New York, 1960), pp. 214–220. Beeckman's criticism appears in Cornelis de Waard, ed., *Journal tenu par Isaac Beeckman de 1604 à 1634*, I (The Hague, 1939), 215; see also II, 253.

PAUL LAWRENCE ROSE

KEILL, JOHN (*b.* Edinburgh, Scotland, 1 December 1671; *d.* Oxford, England, 31 August 1721)

Keill's early education was at Edinburgh, where he also attended the university, studying under David Gregory, the first to teach pupils on the basis of the newly published Newtonian philosophy. He graduated M.A. before going to Oxford with Gregory, who had been made Savilian professor of astronomy there. Keill was incorporated M.A. at Balliol in 1694 and in 1699 became deputy to Thomas Millington, Sedleian professor of natural philosophy. After a short absence from Oxford he became Savilian professor of astronomy there in 1712, and a year later a public act made him doctor of physic. He remained as Savilian professor until his death.

Keill was one of the very important disciples gathered around Newton who transmitted his principles of philosophy to the scientific and intellectual community, thereby influencing the directions and emphases of Newtonianism. As one of the few around Newton with High Church patronage, Keill apparently tried to counter the Low Church influences of such spokesmen as Richard Bentley and William Whiston. While agreeing with them that the discoveries and doctrine of universal attraction of Newtonianism should play a crucial role in fighting "atheistic" Cartesianism and mechanical thinking, he rejected the notion that this should be accomplished exclusively or primarily by means of natural theology. Rather, natural theology should be subordinated to the Scripture, while natural philosophy should acknowledge the important role played not only by Providence but also by outright miracles. These arguments are made in Keill's first work, *An Examination of Dr Burnet's Theory of the Earth. Together With Some Remarks on Mr. Whiston's New Theory* . . . (1698). This was probably written before he had met Newton, and was an attack on the cosmogonical treatises about the world's creation then being widely debated by many members of the Royal Society. Although supposedly written specifically against the unscientific methods of the theories of Thomas Burnet and William Whiston, in substance it amounted to a very hostile attack—in the name of orthodoxy—on the delusions of "world-making" which were caused, Keill claimed, by Cartesian natural philosophy. As an antidote Keill prescribed the more modest and exact Newtonian philosophy, based solidly on mathematical reasoning, even though Newton himself was known at the time to have sympathies with the cosmogonical theories. Besides those of Burnet and Whiston, Keill attacked the ideas of Richard Bentley, who had tried to use Newtonian principles as the foundation for his physicotheology in his famous Boyle lectures in 1692.

In effect, Keill's work offered itself to Newton as an alternative Newtonian theology, different from that of the Low Church disciples. Newton's public acceptance of Keill's basic criticism against "world-making" was incorporated in 1706 in what was to be the famous 31st Query of the *Opticks*.

Keill's role as propagator of Newtonian philosophy was carried out primarily through his major work, *Introductio ad veram physicam* . . . (1701), based on the series of experimental lectures on Newtonian natural philosophy he had been giving at Oxford since 1694. The first such lectures ever given, their attempt to derive Newton's laws experimentally did much to influence later publications. Although Keill makes the decidedly anti-Newtonian principle of the infinite divisibility of matter in nature a fundamental axiom, the *Introductio* again unfavorably contrasts Cartesian mechanism, with its dangers of atheism, and Newtonianism. Descartes's insufficient use of geometry, his attempt to define the essences of things rather than being content merely to describe their major properties, and his desire to explain the complex before he can adequately deal with the simple distinguish his fictions from the true principles of Newton. An appendix to the *Introductio* gives a proof for the law of centrifugal "force," whose magnitude had been announced in 1673 by Christiaan Huygens. Several years after the *Introductio*, Keill published an article on the laws of attraction, dealing mainly with short-range forces between small particles, in which he elaborated on Newtonian hypotheses that Newton himself had been unable to pursue.

Some of Keill's writings also brought hostile attacks against Newtonianism from the Continent. For example, his charge that Leibniz had plagiarized from Newton's invention of the calculus gave rise to a major dispute between English and Continental natural philosophers, in which Keill served as Newton's "avowed Champion." Keill's article on the laws of attraction also brought criticisms from the Continent against the employment in Newtonianism of such dubious philosophical concepts as attraction.

In 1700 Keill was elected fellow of the Royal Society. Support from Henry Aldrich, dean of Christ Church College, Oxford, helped Keill's preferment, particularly in becoming deputy to Millington in 1699, just after the attack on Burnet, Whiston, and Bentley. In 1709 Robert Harley helped Keill become treasurer for the refugees from the Palatinate, in which connection he traveled to New England. From 1712 to 1716, with Harley's help, he was a decipherer to Queen Anne.

Keill's uncle was John Cockburn, a controversial Scottish clergyman with Jacobin sympathies. His brother, James, with help from John, tried to apply Newtonian principles to medicine; at his death James left a large sum of money to John. John's marriage in 1717 to Mary Clements, many years his junior and of lesser social standing, was the cause of some scandal. Besides her, Keill was survived by a son, who became a linen draper in London.

BIBLIOGRAPHY

I. Original Works. *Introductio ad veram physicam, accedunt Christiani Hugenii theoremata de vi centrifuga et motu circulari demonstrata* ... (Oxford, 1701) was translated as *An Introduction to Natural Philosophy, or Philosophical Lectures Read in the University of Oxford* ... (London, 1720); when Newtonianism began to make inroads in France, it was translated into French. *An Examination of Dr Burnet's Theory of the Earth. Together With Some Remarks on Mr Whiston's New Theory of the Earth* (Oxford, 1698) includes, in the 1734 ed., Maupertuis's *Dissertation on the Celestial Bodies.* Keill answered Burnet's and Whiston's defenses in *An Examination of the Reflections on the Theory of the Earth. Together With a Defence of the Remarks on Mr Whiston's New Theory* (Oxford, 1699). *Introductio ad veram astronomiam, seu lectiones astronomicae* ... (Oxford, 1718) was translated as *An Introduction to the True Astronomy; or, Astronomical Lectures* ... (London, 1721) and also appeared in French. "On the Laws of Attraction and Other Principles of Physics" is in *Philosophical Transactions of the Royal Society*, no. 315 (1708), p. 97. "Response aux auteurs des remarques, sur le différence entre M. de Leibnitz et M. Newton," in *Journal litéraire de la Haye*, **2** (1714), 445–453, is one of several articles by Keill on the calculus controversy. He edited the *Commercium epistolicum D. Johannis Collins, et aliorum, de analysi promota* ... (London, 1712), which contains the original documents bearing on the Newton–Leibniz controversy. Samuel Halkett and John Laing, *Dictionary of Anonymous and Pseudonymous English Literature*, II (Edinburgh, 1926), 202, cite a contemporary MS note in attributing authorship of Martin Strong [pseud.], *An Essay on the Usefulness of Mathematical Learning. In a Letter From a Gentleman in the City to His Friend at Oxford* (London, 1701), to John Arbuthnot and Keill. "Theoremata quaedam infinitam materiae divisibilitatem spectantia, quae ejusdem raritatem et tenuem compositionem demonstrans, quorum ope plurimae in physica tolluntur difficultates" is in *Philosophical Transactions of the Royal Society*, no. 339 (1714), p. 82. There are letters from Keill in *Correspondence of Sir Isaac Newton and Professor Cotes*, J. Edleston, ed. (London, 1850). Two boxes of Keill MSS, including some letters, drafts of lectures, notebooks, and an inventory of his library are in the Lucasian Papers at Cambridge University Library.

II. Secondary Literature. There has been very little attention given to Keill by historians of science, and mention of him generally is found only in connection with the controversy over the calculus. Among Newton's biographers, Sir David Brewster, *Memoirs of the Life, Writings, and Discoveries of Sir Isaac Newton*, I (Edinburgh, 1855), pp. 335, 341–342, II, pp. 43–44, 53, 69; and Frank Manuel, *Portrait of Isaac Newton* (Cambridge, Mass., 1968), pp. 271–278, 321–323, 329, 335–338, 351, 399, 456, discuss Keill. There is a section on Keill's approach to natural philosophy in E. W. Strong, "Newtonian Explications of

Natural Philosophy," in *Journal of the History of Ideas*, **18** (1957), 49–83. Ernst Cassirer, *Das Erkenntnisproblem in der Philosophie und Wissenschaft der neueren Zeit*, II (Berlin, 1907), pp. 404–406, has a brief discussion of Keill. Pierre Brunet, *L'introduction des théories de Newton en France au XVIIIe siècle. Avant 1738* (Paris, 1931), p. 79 f., briefly deals with Keill. See Arnold Thackray, " 'Matter in a Nut-Shell': Newton's Opticks and Eighteenth Century Chemistry," in *Ambix*, **15** (1968), 29–53, for Keill's ideas on the infinite divisibility of matter and *Atoms and Powers. An Essay on Newtonian Matter-Theory and the Development of Chemistry* (Cambridge, Mass., 1970). A chapter on Keill in David Kubrin, "Providence and the Mechanical Philosophy: The Creation and Dissolution of the World in Newtonian Thought," unpub. diss. (Cornell University, 1968), discusses Keill's attack on Burnet and Whiston. See also Robert Schofield, *Mechanism and Materialism. British Natural Philosophy in an Age of Reason* (Princeton, 1969), pp. 15n, 25–30, 42, 42n, 43–44, 55, 80.

DAVID KUBRIN

KERÉKJÁRTÓ, BÉLA (*b.* Budapest, Hungary, 1 October 1898; *d.* Gyöngyos, Hungary, 26 June 1946)

In 1920 Kerékjártó took the Ph.D. degree at Budapest University. He became a privatdocent at Szeged University in 1922, extraordinary professor in 1925, and professor ordinarius in 1929. In 1938 he became professor ordinarius at Budapest University. From 1922 to 1926 he had also traveled abroad: in 1922–1923 he stayed at Göttingen University where he gave lectures on topology and mathematical cosmology; in 1923 he taught geometry and function theory at the University of Barcelona; and from 1923 to 1925 he was at Princeton University, where he lectured on topology and continuous groups. When he returned to Europe he lectured in Paris. Kerékjártó was a corresponding member of the Hungarian Academy of Sciences from 1934 and a full member from 1945. He was a coeditor of *Acta litterarum ac scientiarum Regiae Universitatis hungarica* . . ., Sectio scientiarum mathematicarum, beginning with volume 6 (1932–1934).

After Max Dehn and P. Heegaard's article "Analysis situs" (1907), in *Encyklopädie der mathematischen Wissenschaften* and Schönflies' *Die Entwicklung der Lehre von den Punktmannigfaltigkeiten* (1908), the first three monographs on topology to appear were Veblen's "Analysis situs," in American Mathematical Society Colloquium Publications (1922), Kerékjártó's (1923), and S. Lefschetz's "L'analysis situs et la géométrie algébrique" (1924). Kerékjártó's probably sold best and was the most widely known, but it has exerted much less (if any) influence than the two others. One reason is the restriction of subject and method to two dimensions, at a time when all efforts were directed to understanding higher dimensions. The other, decisive reason is that everyone knew Kerékjártó's *Vorlesungen über Topologie* was not a good book and, therefore, nobody read it. The present author has held this opinion for many years and now feels obliged to make a closer examination of Kerékjártó's works.

The book opens with a proof which is unintelligible and probably wrong. This, indeed, is the worst possible beginning, but it continues the same way. The greater part of Kerékjártó's own contributions are hardly intelligible and most are apparently wrong. The work of others is often taken over almost literally or in a way which proves that Kerékjártó had not really assimilated the material. The level of the book is far below that of topology at that time, and the organization is chaotic. When referring to a concept, a notation, or an argument, he often quotes a proof, a page, or an entire chapter—but often the material quoted is not found where he cites it; sometimes footnotes serve to fill gaps in arguments. For many years this also was the style of Kerékjártó's papers. They are full of mistakes or gaps which should have been filled by other papers which never appeared.

Kerékjártó's papers written around 1940 make a more favorable impression. In general they are correct. They deal with his earlier problems on topological groups but use methods which in the meantime had become obsolete. It is quite probable that he did not know the developments in topology after 1923. The strangest feature is that he never used set-theory symbols, such as the signs for belonging to a set, inclusion, union, and intersection. Apparently he did not know of their existence.

Kerékjártó mainly continued the work of Brouwer and Hilbert on mappings of surfaces and topological groups acting upon surfaces. The undeniable merits of his work are obscured by the manner of presentation. The classification of open surfaces is usually ascribed to Kerékjártó, but the exposition of this subject in his book hardly justifies this claim. It was probably his greatest accomplishment that he became interested in groups of locally equicontinuous mappings (of a surface), although his definition of this notion did not match the way in which it was applied; strangely enough, he did not notice that this notion had already been fundamental in Hilbert's work. The best result in studying such groups with Kerékjártó's methods has recently been achieved by I. Fary, who proved that equicontinuous, orientation-preserving groups of the plane are essentially subgroups of the Euclidean or of the hyperbolic group.

In addition to the work on topology in German and a work on foundations of geometry in Hungarian, which has been translated into French, Kerékjártó wrote some sixty papers, most of them comprising only a few pages. The bibliography is restricted to the more mature ones.

BIBLIOGRAPHY

Kerékjártó's works include *Vorlesungen über Topologie* (Berlin, 1923); "Sur le caractère topologique du groupe homographique de la sphère," in *Acta mathematica*, **74** (1941), 311-341; "Sur le groupe des homographies et des antihomographies d'une variable complexe," in *Commentarii mathematici helvetici*, **13** (1941), 68–82; "Sur les groupes compacts de transformations topologiques des surfaces," in *Acta mathematica*, **74** (1941), 129–173; "Sur le caractère topologique du groupe homographique de la sphere," in *Journal de mathématiques pures et appliquées*, 9th ser., **2** (1942), 67–100; and *A geometria alapjai*, 2 vols. (I, Szeged, 1937; II, Budapest, 1944), translated into French as *Les fondements de la géométrie euclidienne*, 2 vols. (Budapest, 1955–1956).

See also I. Fary, "On a Topological Characterization of Plane Geometries," in *Cahiers de topologie et géométrie différentielle*, **7** (1964), 1–33. There is also an obituary in *Acta Universitatis szegediansis, Acta scientiarum mathematicarum*, **11** (1946–1948), v–vii.

HANS FREUDENTHAL

KEYNES, JOHN MAYNARD (*b.* Cambridge, England, 5 June 1883; *d.* Firle, Sussex, England, 21 April 1946)

His father, John Nevile Keynes, was the author of *Formal Logic* (1884) and *Scope and Method of Political Economy* (1890). Both were thoroughly up-to-date in their day and remained standard texts for a number of years. John Nevile was a lifelong fellow of Pembroke College, Cambridge, and registrary (chief administrative officer) of Cambridge University from 1910 to 1925. Maynard's mother was Florence Ada, daughter of John Brown, who wrote what was for long regarded as the standard life of John Bunyan, the author of *The Pilgrim's Progress*. She was an authoress and an ardent worker for social causes and in local government, eventually becoming the mayor of Cambridge.

Keynes went to the Perse School Kindergarten, Cambridge (1890), and to St. Faith's Preparatory School, Cambridge (1892). He won a scholarship at Eton College (1897) and at Kings College, Cambridge (1902). For his degree he studied mathematics only and in 1905 was twelfth wrangler (i.e., twelfth on the list of those offering mathematics in that year). This was sufficiently distinguished but not eminently so. The fact is that he did little work at academic studies when an undergraduate, devoting his time to wide reading, some political activity (he was president of the Cambridge Union) and, more particularly, to the cultivation of literary friends (Lytton Strachey and others) who were destined to play a notable part in the intellectual life of England.

He spent the next year (1905–1906) as a graduate at Cambridge, not working for a degree but enlarging his reading, including that in economics, in which he had instruction from Alfred Marshall and A. C. Pigou, and which he had also imbibed in early boyhood from his father.

In 1906 he took the British Civil Service examination and was second on the list for all England. There happened to be only one vacancy in the Treasury in that year, and he opted for the India Office as his second preference. He remained there for two years. During those years and in the three years that followed, he devoted the greater part of his time to work on the theory of probability.

His *Treatise on Probability* was not published until 1921, owing to the interruption of the war, but had been almost completed by 1911. This was at once a work of great learning and also an exposition of important original ideas. Its bibliography of the literature is one of the most comprehensive that has ever been made.

In regard to the original ideas, his ambition was to provide a firm mathematical basis for the probability theory on lines comparable to those of the *Principia Mathematica*, in which Russell and Whitehead laid the foundations of symbolic deductive logic. Of Keynes's book Bertrand Russell afterward wrote, "The mathematical calculus is astonishingly powerful, considering the very restricted premises which form its foundation . . . the book as a whole is one which it is impossible to praise too highly" (*Mathematical Gazette* [July 1922]).

While Keynes was an innovator in expressing probability theory in terms of modern-type symbolism, and in this respect his book constituted a landmark, two of its central doctrines have not been widely accepted since.

(1) Keynes thought it proper to postulate that probability is a concept that is capable of being apprehended by direct intuition and requires no definition. This approach was due to the influence of the Cambridge philosopher G. E. Moore but no longer finds favor.

(2) Keynes translated into his own symbolism the central proposition of Bayes. The Bayes-type approach demonstrates how favorable instances can increase

KEYNES

the probability of a given premise. For this reasoning to work, the premise must have some prior probability of its own. The trouble is that in the very beginning of the inductive process there are no empirical propositions with any intrinsic probability of their own. So how to make a start? This is, of course, the crux of the problem of induction. Keynes thought it proper to overcome this difficulty by postulating the principle of limited independent variety, meaning that there is a finite number of "ultimate generator properties" in the universe. This would enable one to assign a positive probability to the proposition that one (or another) of the ultimate properties was operating in a given case. The objection was then made that to get any significant probability for a conclusion it would not be enough to postulate a finite number of ultimate generator properties, but a specific number. The impossibility of doing this is clearly a stumbling block for the Keynes-type approach.

In 1908 he resigned from the India Office and went to Cambridge, without official appointment, on the invitation of Alfred Marshall to assist the new Department of Economics there. Shortly afterwards he was awarded a fellowship at Kings College, open to competition, on the strength of his thesis on probability.

Meanwhile he was also at work on his book *Indian Currency and Finance* (1913), which included a description of what is called a "gold exchange standard." He had also been invited to serve on a royal commission on Indian finance and currency. He contributed much to the report and also appended an annex of his own, recommending a central bank. At that time this was a revolutionary idea for a less-developed country.

He was in the British Treasury from 1915 to 1919, in the later years as head of the department looking after foreign exchange controls. In 1919 he went to the Paris Peace Conference as principal representative of the British Treasury and deputy for the chancellor of the exchequer. In June 1919 he resigned, on the ground that the proposals put forward for German reparations payments were impractical and unjust. In December 1919 he published *The Economic Consequences of the Peace*, which won him a worldwide reputation for its brilliant writing and character sketches, its humane and liberal outlook, and the cogency of its arguments about the German reparations problem.

He returned to Kings College, Cambridge. For a period his primary interest was in German reparations. *A Revision of the Treaty* was published in 1922. Other economic matters began to engage his attention, namely the evils of deflation, which became severe both in the United States and the United Kingdom in 1920, and the unemployment question.

On the monetary side he published *A Tract on Monetary Reform* (1923), which was a lucid exposition of monetary theory partly on traditional lines. He departed from those lines, however, in advocating that there should not be a return to a fixed parity between the pound and the dollar but that a floating exchange rate should be regarded as normal. When, despite his advocacy, the United Kingdom returned to the gold standard in 1925, he wrote a devastating pamphlet entitled *The Economic Consequences of Mr. Churchill.*

On the side of unemployment he began at an early date to advocate public works, mainly in articles in *The Nation*. Orthodoxy claimed that public works would not decrease unemployment, on the ground that money spent on them would entail that private enterprise had that much less money to spend, so that there would be no net gain of employment at all. This was sometimes known as the "Treasury view." It was the intellectual challenge presented by this view which drove him to the conclusion that quite a considerable part of economics would have to be rethought, and to that he devoted his main powers for the next dozen years. The fruits of his thinking were published in *A Treatise on Money* (December 1930), when his intellectual journey was half complete, and in *The General Theory of Employment, Interest and Money* (January 1936). Note should also be made of his membership (1929–1931) of the official Macmillan committee of enquiry into finance and industry. He gave that committee the benefit of a statement of his views on money which lasted for five days. A rescript of this is due eventually to be published in his collected works.

Of the two books, the *Treatise* is the more comprehensive volume and contains much vital material not to be found elsewhere. For knowledge of Keynes the *General Theory* is compulsory reading, because it contains his final synthesis; but this has had the unfortunate effect that the *Treatise* has not been read as much as it should be by those who wish to understand Keynes in depth over a wide range of subjects.

This is not the place to summarize Keynes's theory. His position in the history of economic thought may be described by saying that he was the first economist to provide a systematic "macrostatics." Traditional economics had had a considerable measure of success in what is known as "microstatics"; this refers to the analysis of the supply and demand for particular commodities, the allocation of productive resources among different uses, the distribution of income, decisions by firms, etc.; but there was lacking a systematic account of what determines the level of activity in the economy as a whole, and the balance between saving and investment requirements. Whatever criticisms have been or may in due course be made in detail, Keynes's work will remain a landmark in the history of theories relating to these topics.

Mention should be made of his influence during World War II in getting the British government first to compile, and later to publish, national income statistics, which give the factual material required for the practical application of his theories. Most countries have come to think it needful to compile such statistics.

Keynes had a serious illness in 1937 and was never thereafter restored to full health. In 1940 he was invited into the British Treasury in an honorary capacity. Although he did not have responsibilities such as he had in World War I, his advice was constantly sought on all matters relating to the economics of the war. Then he began, as early as 1941, to acquire a position of leadership in matters relating to Anglo-American cooperation for postwar world reconstruction. At this point mention should be made of his booklet *The Means to Prosperity* (1933), which he published shortly before the World Economic Conference in London and which contained some of the ideas to which he began to give a more elaborate form in his Clearing Union plan in 1941, which was the British contribution to the Anglo-American-Canadian effort leading to the Bretton Woods Conference (1944) and the foundation of the International Monetary Fund.

Prior to his illness he devoted much time to practical finance, on his own behalf, on that of Kings College, Cambridge, of which he was bursar for many years, and of certain insurance and investment companies with which he was associated. He was joint editor of the *Economic Journal* from 1912 to 1945. He also made important collections of old books and of modern paintings. He was the founder of the Arts Theatre in Cambridge. During the war he became chairman of the British Arts Council. In 1925 he married Lydia Lopokova, the famous Russian ballerina.

In his book collecting, he specialized in the philosophers and thinkers of the seventeenth and eighteenth centuries and, later, in the general English literature, including drama and poetry, of the sixteenth century. He had an exceptionally important collection of Newton manuscripts. It was this, doubtless, that caused him to prepare an essay on "Newton, the Man" for the tricentenary celebrations (1942).

He pays tribute to Newton's world preeminence as a scientist. "His peculiar gift was his power of holding continuously in his mind a mental problem until he had seen straight through it. I fancy his pre-eminence is due to his muscles of intuition being the strongest and most enduring with which a man has ever been gifted." But he gives more space to Newton's other interests—alchemy and apocalyptic writings, to which, so the manuscripts suggest, he devoted as much time as he did to physics.

Had Keynes completed his work, he would doubtless have inserted the fact (of relevance to Keynes's own work!) that Newton became Master of the Mint and established a new bimetallic parity for Britain (1717). Alexander Hamilton was responsible for the original parity of the U. S. gold and silver dollars, and expressed indebtedness to Newton's writings on the topic.

In 1942 Keynes was made a member of the House of Lords, where he sat on the Liberal benches.

The Royal Society paid him the honor, rare for a nonscientist, of making him a fellow, doubtless in recognition of his basically scientific approach to all things.

He died in his country home, Tilton, on 21 April 1946, shortly after his return from a meeting in Savannah, which was concerned with details relating to the setting up of the International Monetary Fund and the International Bank for Reconstruction and Development.

BIBLIOGRAPHY

For a list of Keynes's writings see British Museum *General Catalogue of Printed Books*, CXXII, cols. 706–710.

Recent works in English on Keynes are Dudley Dillard, *The Economics of John Maynard Keynes* (New York, 1948), with bibliography, pp. 336–351; Seymour E. Harris, *The New Economics* (London, 1960), with bibliography, pp. 665–686; Roy Forbes Harrod, *The Life of John Maynard Keynes* (New York–London, 1951; repr. 1969); and the obituary by A. C. Pigou in *Proceedings of the British Academy*, **32** (1946), 395–414, with portrait.

ROY FORBES HARROD

AL-KHALĪLĪ, SHAMS AL-DĪN ABŪ ᶜABDALLĀH MUḤAMMAD IBN MUḤAMMAD (*fl.* Damascus, Syria, *ca.* 1365)

Al-Khalīlī (Suter, no. 418) was an astronomer associated with the Umayyad Mosque in the center of Damascus. A colleague of the astronomer Ibn al-Shāṭir, he was also a *muwaqqit*—that is, an astronomer concerned with *ʿilm al-mīqāt*, the science of timekeeping by the sun and stars and regu-

AL-KHALĪLĪ

lating the astronomically defined times of Muslim prayer. Al-Khalīlī's major work, which represents the culmination of the medieval Islamic achievement in the mathematical solution of the problems of spherical astronomy, was a set of tables for astronomical timekeeping. Some of these tables were used in Damascus until the nineteenth century, and they were also used in Cairo and Istanbul for several centuries. The main sets of tables survive in numerous manuscripts, but they were not investigated in modern times until the 1970's.

Al-Khalīlī's tables can be categorized as follows: tables for reckoning time by the sun, for the latitude of Damascus; tables for regulating the times of Muslim prayer, for the latitude of Damascus; tables of auxiliary mathematical functions for timekeeping by the sun for all latitudes; tables of auxiliary mathematical functions for solving the problems of spherical astronomy for all latitudes; a table displaying the *qibla*, that is, the direction of Mecca, as a function of terrestrial latitude and longitude; and tables for converting lunar ecliptic coordinates to equatorial coordinates.

The first two sets of tables correspond to those in the large corpus of spherical astronomical tables computed for Cairo that are generally attributed to the tenth-century Egyptian astronomer Ibn Yūnus. They are recomputed for Ibn al-Shāṭir's parameters: 33;30° for the latitude of Damascus and 23;31° for the obliquity of the ecliptic. Al-Khalīlī does not mention any of his Egyptian predecessors. We know, however, that an elder colleague of his, the instrument maker al-Mizzī (*d. ca.* 1350; Suter, no. 406), who spent the first part of his life in Egypt and then moved to Damascus, had already compiled a set of hour-angle tables and prayer tables similar to those used in Egypt and based on 33;27° for the latitude of Damascus and 23;33° for the obliquity, a pair of parameters used by earlier Syrian astronomers. Al-Khalīlī's first and second tables were thus intended to replace al-Mizzī's set. These tables were used in Damascus until the nineteenth century. The Damascus *muwaqqit* Muḥammad ibn Muṣṭafā al-Ṭanṭāwī, who died in 1889, was one of the last to use them; he also converted the entries from equatorial degrees and minutes to equinoctial hours and minutes.

The third set of tables compiled by al-Khalīlī consisted of auxiliary tables for timekeeping by the sun and a table of the solar azimuth as a function of the solar meridian altitude and instantaneous altitude. The auxiliary tables, which contain over 9,000 entries, are intended specifically for facilitating the computation of the hour angle for given solar altitude and solar longitude, and any terrestrial latitude. They were plagiarized by later astronomers in both Egypt and Tunis.

Al-Khalīlī's fourth set of tables was designed to solve all the standard problems of spherical astronomy, and they are particularly useful for those problems that, in modern terms, involve the use of the cosine rule for spherical triangles. Al-Khalīlī tabulated three functions and gave detailed instructions for their application. The functions are the following (the capital notation indicates that the medieval trigonometric functions are computed to base $R = 60$, thus $\text{Sin}\,\vartheta = R\ \text{Sin}\,\vartheta$, and so on):

$$f_\varphi(\vartheta) = \frac{R\ \text{Sin}\,\vartheta}{\text{Cos}\,\varphi},\quad g_\varphi(\vartheta) = \frac{\text{Sin}\,\vartheta\ \text{Tan}\,\varphi}{R},$$

and

$$G(x,y) = \text{arc Cos}\left\{\frac{R\,x}{\text{Cos}\,y}\right\},$$

computed for the domains

$\vartheta = 1°, 2°, \cdots, 90°$

$\varphi = 1°, 2°, \cdots, 55°$, as well as 21;30° (Mecca) and 33;30° (Damascus)

$x = 1, 2, \cdots, 59$

$y = 0°, 1°, \cdots, n(x)$,

where $n(x)$ is the largest integer such that

$$R\,x \leqslant \text{Cos}\,n(x).$$

The entries in these tables, which number over 13,000, were computed to two sexagesimal digits and are invariably accurate. An example of the use of these functions is the rule outlined by al-Khalīlī for finding the hour angle t for given solar or stellar altitude h, declination δ, and terrestrial latitude ϕ. This may be represented as

$$t(\text{h},\delta,\varphi) = G\{[f_\varphi(h) - g_\varphi(\delta)], \delta\},$$

and it is not difficult to show the equivalence of al-Khalīlī's rule to the modern formula

$$t = \text{arc cos}\left\{\frac{\sin h - \sin\delta\,\sin\varphi}{\cos\delta\,\cos\varphi}\right\}.$$

These auxiliary tables were used for several centuries in Damascus, Cairo, and Istanbul, the three main centers of astronomical timekeeping in the Muslim world.

Al-Khalīlī's computational ability is best revealed by his *qibla* table. The determination of the *qibla* for a given locality is one of the most complicated problems of medieval Islamic trigonometry. If (L, φ) and (L_M, φ_M) represent the longitude and latitude of a given locality and of Mecca, respectively, and $\Delta L = |\,L - L_M\,|$, then the modern formula for $q(L, \varphi)$, the direction of Mecca for the locality, measured from the south, is

$$q = \text{arc cot}\left\{\frac{\sin\varphi\cos\Delta L - \cos\varphi\tan\varphi_M}{\sin\Delta L}\right\}.$$

Al-Khalīlī computed $q(\varphi, L)$ to two sexagesimal digits for the domains $\varphi = 10°, 11°, \cdots, 56°$ (also 33;30°) and $\Delta L = 1°, 2°, \cdots, 60°$; the vast majority of the 2,880 entries are either accurately computed or in error by ±0;1° or ±0;2°. He states that he used the method for finding the *qibla* expounded by the late thirteenth-century Cairo astronomer Abū ʿAlī al-Marrākushī (Suter, no. 363); and it seems that he used his universal auxiliary tables to compute the *qibla* values, although they are generally more accurate than can be derived from the auxiliary tables in their present form. Several other *qibla* tables based on approximate formulas are known from the medieval period. Al-Khalīlī's table does not appear to have been widely used by later Muslim astronomers.

The last set of tables known to have been compiled by al-Khalīlī is for converting lunar ecliptic coordinates to equatorial coordinates, in order to facilitate computations relating to the visibility of the lunar crescent.

Al-Khalīlī wrote at least one treatise on the use of the quadrant with a trigonometric grid (*al-rubʿ al-mujayyab*), but his writings on this instrument have not yet been studied.

BIBLIOGRAPHY

I. Original Works. MS Paris B.N. ar. 2558, copied in 1408, contains all of the tables in al-Khalīlī's major set (nos. 1, 2, 4, and 5). MS Berlin Ahlwardt 5753–6 (Wetzstein 1138) contains all but the hour-angle tables. MS Oxford Bodleian Seld. sup. 100 contains the prayer tables and the hour-angle tables; MS Oxford Marsh 39 contains the hour-angle tables. MSS Oxford Marsh 95 and Escorial ar. 931 contain only the universal auxiliary tables; and MS Gotha Forschungsbibliothek A1406, only the prayer tables. MSS Damascus Ẓāhiriyya 3116 and 10378 also contain tables from the corpus. MS Cairo Ṭalaat *mīqāt* 228 contains al-Khalīlī's universal auxiliary tables and hour-angle tables for Damascus, as well as an anonymous set of prayer tables for the latitude of Tripoli (Lebanon). MS Cairo Dār al-Kutub *mīqāt* 71M contains al-Khalīlī's tables of the hour angle and time since sunrise, plus tables of the solar azimuth computed by al-Ḥalabī (*d.* 1455; Suter, no. 434). Egyptian copies of the auxiliary tables exist in MSS Princeton Yahuda 861, 2 and Cairo Dār al-Kutub *mīqāt* 43M. MS Istanbul Aya Sofya 2590 consists of a recension of the auxiliary tables by the Ottoman astronomer Muḥammad ibn Kātib Sinān (*ca.* 1500; Suter, no. 455). Al-Ṭanṭāwī's prayer tables and hour-angle tables are extant in MSS Damascus Ẓāhiriyya 9233, and Cairo Taymūr *riyāḍiyyāt* 129 and Dār al-Kutub *mīqāt* 1007.

MS Dublin Chester Beatty 4091 is an apparently unique copy of al-Khalīlī's auxiliary tables for timekeeping by the sun and azimuth tables. Later Egyptian and Tunisian copies of the auxiliary tables are MSS Cairo Dār al-Kutub *mīqāt* 644 and Istanbul S. Esad Ef. Madresesi 119,2 and MS Cairo Dār al-Kutub *mīqāt* 689, respectively.

Al-Khalīlī's tables for crescent visibility are in the treatise entitled *ʿIqd al-durar*, by the later Egyptian astronomer Ibn al-Majdī (Suter, no. 432), and his criteria for crescent visibility are outlined in the writings of his nephew Sharaf al-Dīn al-Khalīlī (Suter, no. 427).

Al-Khalīlī's treatise on the quadrant with trigonometric grid is in MSS Cairo Dār al-Kutub *mīqāt* 138,9 and 201M. Another treatise of considerable interest on the same subject, preserved in MS Cairo Dār al-Kutub *mīqāt* 167M,8, may be by al-Khalīlī. A treatise describing a horizontal sundial is attributed in MS Princeton Yahuda 373, fols. 131v–135r, to Abū ʿAbd Allāh al-Khalīlī, and in MS Manchester 361G to the later Egyptian astronomer ʿAbd al-ʿAzīz ibn Muḥammad al-Wafāʾī (Suter, no. 437).

II. Secondary Literature. See D. A. King, "Al-Khalīlī's Auxiliary Tables for Solving Problems of Spherical Astronomy," in *Journal for the History of Astronomy*, **4** (1973), 99–110; and "Al-Khalīlī's *Qibla* Table," in *Journal of Near Eastern Studies*, **34** (1975), 81–122; and H. Suter, *Die Mathematiker und Astronomen der Araber und ihre Werke* (Leipzig, 1900), 169.

David A. King

AL-KHAYYĀMĪ (or **KHAYYĀM**), **GHIYĀTH AL-DĪN ABU'L-FATḤ ʿUMAR IBN IBRĀHĪM AL-NĪSĀBŪRĪ** (or **AL-NAYSĀBŪRĪ**), also known as **Omar Khayyam** (*b.* Nīshāpūr, Khurasan [now Iran], 15 May 1048 [?]; *d.* Nīshāpūr, 4 December 1131 [?])

As his name states, he was the son of Ibrāhīm; the epithet "al-Khayyāmī" would indicate that his father or other forebears followed the trade of making tents. Of his other names, "ʿUmar" is his proper designation, while "Ghiyāth al-Dīn" ("the help of the faith") is an honorific he received later in life and "al-Nīsābūrī" refers to his birthplace. Arabic sources of the twelfth to the fifteenth centuries[1] contain only infrequent and sometimes contradictory references to al-Khayyāmī, differing even on the dates of his birth and death. The earliest birthdate given is approximately 1017, but the most probable date (given above) derives from the historian Abu'l-Ḥasan al-Bayhaqī (1106–1174), who knew al-Khayyāmī personally and left a record of his horoscope. The most probable deathdate is founded in part upon the account of Niẓāmī ʿArūḍī Samarqandī (1110–1155) of a visit he paid to al-Khayyāmī's tomb in A.H. 530 (A.D. 1135/1136), four years after the latter's death.[2] This date is confirmed by the fifteenth-century writer Yār-Aḥmed Tabrīzī.[3]

At any rate, al-Khayyāmī was born soon after Khurasan was overrun by the Seljuks, who also conquered Khorezm, Iran, and Azerbaijan, over which they established a great but unstable military empire. Most sources, including al-Bayhaqī, agree that he came from Nīshāpūr, where, according to the thirteenth/fourteenth-century historian Faḍlallāh Rashīd al-Dīn, he received his education. Tabrīzī, on the other hand, stated that al-Khayyāmī spent his boyhood and youth in Balkh (now in Afghanistan), and added that by the time he was seventeen he was well versed in all areas of philosophy.

Wherever he was educated, it is possible that al-Khayyāmī became a tutor. Teaching, however, would not have afforded him enough leisure to pursue science. The lot of the scholar at that time was, at best, precarious, unless he were a wealthy man. He could undertake regular studies only if he were attached to the court of some sovereign or magnate, and his work was thus dependent on the attitude of his master, court politics, and the fortunes of war. Al-Khayyāmī gave a lively description of the hazards of such an existence at the beginning of his *Risāla fiʾl-barāhīn ʿalā masāʾil al-jabr waʾl-muqābala* ("Treatise on Demonstration of Problems of Algebra and Almuqabala"):

> I was unable to devote myself to the learning of this *al-jabr* and the continued concentration upon it, because of obstacles in the vagaries of Time which hindered me; for we have been deprived of all the people of knowledge save for a group, small in number, with many troubles, whose concern in life is to snatch the opportunity, when Time is asleep, to devote themselves meanwhile to the investigation and perfection of a science; for the majority of people who imitate philosophers confuse the true with the false, and they do nothing but deceive and pretend knowledge, and they do not use what they know of the sciences except for base and material purposes; and if they see a certain person seeking for the right and preferring the truth, doing his best to refute the false and untrue and leaving aside hypocrisy and deceit, they make a fool of him and mock him.[4]

Al-Khayyāmī was nevertheless able, even under the unfavorable circumstances that he described, to write at this time his still unrecovered treatise *Mushkilāt al-ḥisāb* ("Problems of Arithmetic") and his first, untitled, algebraical treatise, as well as his short work on the theory of music, *al-Qāwl ʿalā ajnās allatī biʾl-arbaʿa* ("Discussion on Genera Contained in a Fourth").

About 1070 al-Khayyāmī reached Samarkand, where he obtained the support of the chief justice, Abū Ṭāhir, under whose patronage he wrote his great algebraical treatise on cubic equations, the *Risāla* quoted above, which he had planned long before. A supplement to this work was written either at the court of Shams al-Mulūk, *khaqan* of Bukhara, or at Isfahan, where al-Khayyāmī had been invited by the Seljuk sultan, Jalāl al-Dīn Malik-shāh, and his vizier Niẓām al-Mulk, to supervise the astronomical observatory there.

Al-Khayyāmī stayed at Isfahan for almost eighteen years, which were probably the most peaceful of his life. The best astronomers of the time were gathered at the observatory and there, under al-Khayyāmī's guidance, they compiled the *Zīj Malik-shāhī* ("Malik-shāh Astronomical Tables"). Of this work only a small portion—tables of ecliptic coordinates and of the magnitudes of the 100 brightest fixed stars—survives. A further important task of the observatory was the reform of the solar calendar then in use in Iran.

Al-Khayyāmī presented a plan for calendar reform about 1079. He later wrote up a history of previous reforms, the *Naurūz-nāma*, but his own design is known only through brief accounts in the astronomical tables of Naṣīr al-Dīn al-Ṭūsī and Ulugh Beg. The new calendar was to be based on a cycle of thirty-three years, named "Malikī era" or "Jalālī era" in honor of the sultan. The years 4, 8, 12, 16, 20, 24, 28, and 33 of each period were designated as leap years of 366 days, while the average length of the year was to be 365.2424 days (a deviation of 0.0002 day from the true solar calendar), a difference of one day thus accumulating over a span of 5,000 years. (In the Gregorian calendar, the average year is 365.2425 days long, and the one-day difference is accumulated over 3,333 years.)

Al-Khayyāmī also served as court astrologer, although he himself, according to Niẓāmī Samarqandī, did not believe in judicial astrology. Among his other, less official activities during this time, in 1077 he finished writing his commentaries on Euclid's theory of parallel lines and theory of ratios; this book, together with his earlier algebraical *Risāla*, is his most important scientific contribution. He also wrote on philosophical subjects during these years, composing in 1080 a *Risāla al-kawn waʾl-taklīf* ("Treatise on Being and Duty"), to which is appended *Al-Jawab ʿan thalāth masāʾil: ḍarūrat al-taḍadd fiʾl-ʿālam waʾl-jabr waʾl baqāʾ* ("An Answer to the Three Questions: On the Necessity of Contradiction in the

World, on the Necessity of Determinism, and on Longevity"). At about the same time he wrote, for a son of Mu'ayyid al-Mulk (vizier in 1095–1118), *Risāla fī'l kulliyat al-wujūd* ("Treatise on the Universality of Being"). (His two other philosophical works, *Risāla al-ḍiyā' al-ʿaqlī fi mawḍūʿ al-'ilm al-kullī* ["The Light of Reason on the Subject of Universal Science"] and *Risāla fī'l wujūd* ["Treatise on Existence"] cannot be dated with any certainty.)

In 1092 al-Khayyāmī fell into disfavor, Malik-shāh having died and his vizier Niẓām al-Mulk having been murdered by an Assassin. Following the death of Malik-shāh his second wife, Turkān-Khātūn, for two years ruled as regent, and al-Khayyāmī fell heir to some of the hostility she had demonstrated toward his patron, Niẓām al-Mulk, with whom she had quarreled over the question of royal succession. Financial support was withdrawn from the observatory and its activities came to a halt; the calendar reform was not completed; and orthodox Muslims, who disliked al-Khayyāmī because of the religious freethinking evident in his quatrains, became highly influential at court. (His apparent lack of religion was to be a source of difficulty for al-Khayyāmī throughout his life, and al-Qifṭī [1172–1239] reported that in his later years he even undertook a pilgrimage to Mecca to clear himself of the accusation of atheism.)

Despite his fall from grace al-Khayyāmī remained at the Seljuk court. In an effort to induce Malik-shāh's successors to renew their support of the observatory and of science in general, he embarked on a work of propaganda. This was the *Naurūz-nāma*, mentioned above, an account of the ancient Iranian solar new year's festival. In it al-Khayyāmī presented a history of the solar calendar and described the ceremonies connected with the Naurūz festival; in particular, he discussed the ancient Iranian sovereigns, whom he pictured as magnanimous, impartial rulers dedicated to education, building edifices, and supporting scholars.

Al-Khayyāmī left Isfahan in the reign of Malik-shāh's third son, Sanjar, who had ascended the throne in 1118. He lived for some time in Merv (now Mary, Turkmen S.S.R.), the new Seljuk capital, where he probably wrote *Mizān al-ḥikam* ("Balance of Wisdoms") and *Fi'l-qusṭas al-mustaqīm* ("On Right *Qusṭas*"), which were incorporated by his disciple al-Khāzinī (who also worked in Merv), together with works of al-Khayyāmī's other disciple, al-Muẓaffar al-Isifīzarī, into his own *Mīzān al-ḥikam*. Among other things, al-Khayyāmī's *Mizān* gives a purely algebraic solution to the problem (which may be traced back to Archimedes) of determining the quantities of gold and silver in a given alloy by means of a preliminary determination of the specific weight of each metal. His *Fī'l-qusṭas* deals with a balance with a mobile weight and variable scales.[5]

Arithmetic and the Theory of Music. A collection of manuscripts in the library of the University of Leiden, Cod. or. 199, lists al-Khayyāmī's "Problems of Arithmetic" on its title page, but the treatise itself is not included in the collection—it may be surmised that it was part of the original collection from which the Leiden manuscript was copied. The work is otherwise unknown, although in his algebraic work *Risāla fi'l-barāhīn ʿalā masā'il al-jabr wa'l-muqābala*, al-Khayyāmī wrote of it that:

> The Hindus have their own methods for extracting the sides of squares and cubes based on the investigation of a small number of cases, which is [through] the knowledge of the squares of nine integers, that is, the squares of 1, 2, 3, and so on, and of their products into each other, that is, the product of 2 with 3, and so on. I have written a book to prove the validity of those methods and to show that they lead to the required solutions, and I have supplemented it in kind, that is, finding the sides of the square of the square, and the quadrato-cube, and the cubo-cube, however great they may be; and no one has done this before; and these proofs are only algebraical proofs based on the algebraical parts of the book of Elements.[6]

Al-Khayyāmī may have been familiar with the "Hindu methods" that he cites through two earlier works, *Fī uṣul ḥisāb al-hind* ("Principles of Hindu Reckoning"), by Kushyār ibn Labbān al-Jīlī (971–1029), and *Al-muqniʿ fi'l-ḥisāb al-hindī* ("Things Sufficient to Understand Hindu Reckoning"), by ʿAlī ibn Aḥmad al-Nasawī (*fl.* 1025). Both of these authors gave methods for extracting square and cube roots from natural numbers, but their method of extracting cube roots differs from the method given in the Hindu literature and actually coincides more closely with the ancient Chinese method. The latter was set out as early as the second/first centuries B.C., in the "Mathematics in Nine Books," and was used by medieval Chinese mathematicians to extract roots with arbitrary integer exponents and even to solve numerical algebraic equations (it was rediscovered in Europe by Ruffini and Horner at the beginning of the nineteenth century). Muslim mathematics—at least the case of the extraction of the cube root—would thus seem to have been influenced by Chinese, either directly or indirectly. Al-Jīlī's and al-Nasawī's term "Hindu reckoning" must then be understood in the less restrictive sense of reckoning in the decimal positional system by means of ten numbers.

The earliest Arabic account extant of the general method for the extraction of roots with positive integer exponents from natural numbers may be found in the *Jāmiʿ al-ḥisāb bi'l-takht wa'l-turāb* ("Collection on Arithmetic by Means of Board and Dust"), compiled by al-Ṭūsī. Since al-Ṭūsī made no claims of priority of discovery, and since he was well acquainted with the work of al-Khayyāmī, it seems likely that the method he presented is al-Khayyāmī's own. The method that al-Ṭūsī gave, then, is applied only to the definition of the whole part a of the root $\sqrt[n]{N}$, where

$$N = a^n + r, \qquad r < (a + 1)^n - a^n.$$

To compute the correction necessary if the root is not extracted wholly, al-Ṭūsī formulated—in words rather than symbols—the rule for binomial expansion

$$(a + b)^n = a^n + na^{n-1} + \cdots + b^n,$$

and gave the approximate value of $\sqrt{a^n + r}$ as $a + \dfrac{r}{(a + 1)^n - a^n}$, the denominator of the root being reckoned according to the binomial formula. For this purpose al-Ṭūsī provided a table of binomial coefficients up to $n = 12$ and noted the property of binomials now expressed as

$$C_n^m = C_{n-1}^{m-1} + C_{n-1}^m.$$

Al-Khayyāmī applied the arithmetic, particularly the theory of commensurable ratios, in his *al-Qawl ʿalā ajnās allatī bi'l-arbaʿa* ("Discussion on Genera Contained in a Fourth"). In the "Discussion" al-Khayyāmī took up the problem—already set by the Greeks, and particularly by Euclid in the *Sectio canonis*—of dividing a fourth into three intervals corresponding to the diatonic, chromatic, and enharmonic tonalities. Assuming that the fourth is an interval with the ratio 4:3, the three intervals into which the fourth may be divided are defined by ratios of which the product is equal to 4:3. Al-Khayyāmī listed twenty-two examples of the section of the fourth, of which three were original to him. Of the others, some of which occur in more than one source, eight were drawn from Ptolemy's "Theory of Harmony"; thirteen from al-Fārābī's *Kitāb al-mūsikā al-kabīr* ("Great Book of Music"); and fourteen from Ibn Sīnā, either *Kitāb al-Shifāʾ* ("The Book of Healing") or *Dānish-nāmah* ("The Book of Knowledge"). Each example was further evaluated in terms of aesthetics.

Theory of Ratios and the Doctrine of Number. Books II and III of al-Khayyāmī's commentaries on Euclid, the *Sharḥ ma ashkala min muṣādarāt kitāb Uqlīdis*, are concerned with the theoretical foundations of arithmetic as manifested in the study of the theory of ratios. The general theory of ratios and proportions as expounded in book V of the *Elements* was one of three aspects of Euclid's work with which Muslim mathematicians were particularly concerned. (The others were the theory of parallels contained in book I and the doctrine of quadratic irrationals in book X.) The Muslim mathematicians often attempted to improve on Euclid, and many scholars were not satisfied with the theory of ratios in particular. While they did not dispute the truth of the theory, they questioned its basis on Euclid's definition of identity of two ratios, $a/b = c/d$, which definition could be traced back to Eudoxus and derived from the quantitative comparison of the equimultiples of all the terms of a given proportion (*Elements*, book V, definition 5).

The Muslim critics of the Euclid-Eudoxus theory of ratios found its weakness to lie in its failure to express directly the process of measuring a given magnitude (a or c) by another magnitude (b or d). This process was based upon the definition of a proportion for a particular case of the commensurable quantities a, b, and c, d through the use of the so-called Euclidean algorithm for the determination of the greatest common measure of two numbers (*Elements*, book VII). Beginning with al-Māhānī, in the ninth century, a number of mathematicians suggested replacing definition 5, book V, with some other definition that would, in their opinion, better express the essence of the proportion. The definition may be rendered in modern terms by the continued fraction theory: if $a/b = (q_1, q_2, \cdots, q_n, \cdots)$ and $c/d = (q_1', q_2', \cdots, q_n', \cdots)$, then $a/b = c/d$ under the condition that $q_k' = q_k$ for all k up to infinity (for commensurable ratios, k is finite). Definitions of inequality of ratios $a/b > c/d$ and $a/b < c/d$, embracing cases of both commensurable and incommensurable ratios and providing criteria for the quantitative comparison of rational and irrational values, are introduced analogously. In the Middle Ages it was known that this "anti-phairetical" theory of ratios existed in Greek mathematics before Eudoxus; that it did was discovered only by Zeuthen and Becker. The proof that his theory was equivalent to that set out in the *Elements* was al-Khayyāmī's greatest contribution to the theory of ratios in general. Al-Khayyāmī's proof lay in establishing the equivalence of the definitions of equality and inequalities in both theories, thereby obviating the need to deduce all the propositions of book V of the *Elements* all over again. He based his demonstration on an important theorem of the existence of the fourth proportional d with the three given magnitudes a, b, and c; he tried to prove it by means of the principle of the infinite divisibility of magnitudes, which was, however, insufficient for his purpose.

His work marked the first attempt at a general demonstration of the theorem, since the Greeks had not treated it in a general manner. These investigations are described in book II of the *Sharḥ*.

In book III, al-Khayyāmī took up compound ratios (at that time most widely used in arithmetic, as in the rule of three and its generalizations), geometry (the doctrine of the similitude of figures), the theory of music, and trigonometry (applying proportions rather than equalities). In the terms in which al-Khayyāmī, and other ancient and medieval scholars, worked, the ratio a/b was compounded from the ratios a/c and c/b—what would in modern terms be stated as the first ratio being the product of the two latter. In his analysis of the operation of compounding the ratios, al-Khayyāmī first set out to deduce from the definition of a compound ratio given in book VI of the *Elements* (which was, however, introduced into the text by later editors) the theorem that the ratio a/c is compounded from the ratios a/b and b/c and an analogous theorem for ratios a/c, b/c, c/d, and so on. Here, cautiously, al-Khayyāmī had begun to develop a new and broader concept of number, including all positive irrational numbers, departing from Aristotle, whose authority he nonetheless respectfully invoked. Following the Greeks, al-Khayyāmī properly understood number as an aggregate of indivisible units. But the development of his own theory—and the development of the whole of calculation mathematics in its numerous applications—led him to introduce new, "ideal" mathematical objects, including the divisible unit and a generalized concept of number which he distinguished from the "absolute and true" numbers (although he unhesitatingly called it a number).

In proving this theorem for compound ratios al-Khayyāmī first selected a unit and an auxiliary quantity g whereby the ratio $1/g$ is the same as a/b. He here took a and b to be arbitrary homogeneous magnitudes which are generally incommensurable; $1/g$ is consequently also incommensurable. He then described the magnitude g:

> Let us not regard the magnitude g as a line, a surface, a body, or time; but let us regard it as a magnitude abstracted by reason from all this and belonging in the realm of numbers, but not to numbers absolute and true, for the ratio of a to b can frequently be non-numerical, that is, it can frequently be impossible to find two numbers whose ratio would be equal to this ratio.[7]

Unlike the Greeks, al-Khayyāmī extended arithmetical language to ratios, writing of the equality of ratios as he had previously discussed their multiplication. Having stated that the magnitude g, incommensurable with a unit, belongs in the realm of numbers, he cited the usual practice of calculators and land surveyors, who frequently employed such expressions as half a unit, a third of a unit, and so on, or who dealt in roots of five, ten, or other divisible units.

Al-Khayyāmī thus was able to express any ratio as a number by using either the old sense of the term or the new, fractional or irrational sense. The compounding of ratios is therefore no different from the multiplication of numbers, and the identity of ratios is similar to their equality. In principle, then, ratios are suitable for measuring numerically any quantities. The Greek mathematicians had studied mathematical ratios, but they had not carried out this function to such an extent. Al-Khayyāmī, by placing irrational quantities and numbers on the same operational scale, began a true revolution in the doctrine of number. His work was taken up in Muslim countries by al-Ṭūsī and his followers, and European mathematicians of the fifteenth to seventeen centuries took up similar studies on the reform of the general ratios theory of the *Elements*. The concept of number grew to embrace all real and even (at least formally) imaginary numbers; it is, however, difficult to assess the influence of the ideas of al-Khayyāmī and his successors in the East upon the later mathematics of the West.

Algebra. Eastern Muslim algebraists were able to draw upon a mastery of Hellenistic and ancient Eastern mathematics, to which they added adaptations of knowledge that had come to them from India and, to a lesser extent, from China. The first Arabic treatise on algebra was written in about 830 by al-Khwārizmī, who was concerned with linear and quadratic equations and dealt with positive roots only, a practice that his successors followed to the degree that equations that could not possess positive roots were ignored. At a slightly later date, the study of cubic equations began, first with Archimedes' problem of the section by a plane of a given sphere into two segments of which the volumes are in a given ratio. In the second half of the ninth century, al-Māhānī expressed the problem as an equation of the type $x^3 + r = px^2$ (which he, of course, stated in words rather than symbols). About a century later, Muslim mathematicians discovered the geometrical solution of this equation whereby the roots were constructed as coordinates of points of intersection of two correspondingly selected conic sections—a method dating back to the Greeks. It was then possible for them to reduce a number of problems, including the trisection of an angle, important to astronomers, to the solution of cubic equations. At the same time devices for numerical approximated solutions were created, and a systematic theory became necessary.

Al-Khayyāmī's construction of such a geometrical theory of cubic equations may be accounted the most successful accomplished by a Muslim scholar. In his first short, untitled algebraic treatise he had already reduced a particular geometrical problem to an equation, $x^3 + 200x = 20x^2 + 2{,}000$, and had solved it by an intersection of circumference $y^2 = (x - 10) \cdot (20 - x)$ and equilateral hyperbola $xy = 10\sqrt{2}\,(x - 10)$. He also noted that he had found an approximated numerical solution with an error of less than 1 percent, and he remarked that it is impossible to solve this equation by elementary means, since it requires the use of conic sections. This is perhaps the first statement in surviving mathematical literature that equations of the third degree cannot be generally solved with compass and ruler—that is, in quadratic radicals—and al-Khayyāmī repeated this assertion in his later *Risāla.* (In 1637 Descartes presented the same supposition, which was proved by P. Wantzel in 1837.)

In his earlier algebraic treatise al-Khayyāmī also took up the classification of normal forms of equations (that is, only equations with positive coefficients), listing all twenty-five equations of the first, second, and third degree that might possess positive roots. He included among these fourteen cubic equations that cannot be reduced to linear or quadratic equations by division by x^2 or x, which he subdivided into three groups consisting of one binomial equation ($x^3 = r$), six trinomial equations ($x^3 + px^2 = r$; $x^3 + r = qx$; $x^3 + r = px^2$; $x^3 + qx = r$; $x^3 = px^2 + r$; and $x^3 = qx + r$), and seven quadrinomial equations ($x^3 = px^2 + qx + r$; $x^3 + qx + r = px^2$; $x^3 + px^2 + r = qx$; $x^3 + px^2 + qx = r$; $x^3 + px^2 = qx + r$; $x^3 + qx = px^2 + r$; and $x^3 + r = px^2 + qx$). He added that of these four types had been solved (that is, their roots had been constructed geometrically) at some earlier date, but that "No rumor has reached us of any of the remaining ten types, neither of this classification,"[8] and expressed the hope that he would later be able to give a detailed account of his solution of all fourteen types.

Al-Khayyāmī succeeded in this stated intention in his *Risāla.* In the introduction to this work he gave one of the first definitions of algebra, saying of it that, "The art of *al-jabr* and *al-muqābala* is a scientific art whose subject is pure number and measurable quantities insofar as they are unknown, added to a known thing with the help of which they may be found; and that [known] thing is either a quantity or a ratio . . ."[9] The "pure number" to which al-Khayyāmī refers is natural number, while by "measurable quantities" he meant lines, surfaces, bodies, and time; the subject matter of algebra is thus discrete, consisting of continuous quantities and their abstract ratios. Al-Khayyāmī then went on to write, "Now the extractions of *al-jabr* are effected by equating . . . these powers to each other as is well known."[10] He then took up the consideration of the degree of the unknown quantity, pointing out that degrees higher than third must be understood only metaphorically, since they cannot belong to real quantities.

At this point in the *Risāla* al-Khayyāmī repeated his earlier supposition that cubic equations that cannot be reduced to quadratic equations must be solved by the application of conic sections and that their arithmetical solution is still unknown (such solutions in radicals were, indeed, not discovered until the sixteenth century). He did not, however, despair of such an arithmetical solution, adding, "Perhaps someone else who comes after us may find it out in the case, when there are not only the first three classes of known powers, namely the number, the thing, and the square."[11] He then also repeated his classification of twenty-five equations, adding to it a presentation of the construction of quadratic equations based on Greek geometrical algebra. Other new material here appended includes the corresponding numerical solution of quadratic equations and constructions of all the fourteen types of third-degree equations that he had previously listed.

In giving the constructions of each of the fourteen types of third-degree equation, al-Khayyāmī also provided an analysis of its "cases." By considering the conditions of intersection or of contact of corresponding conic sections, he was able to develop what is essentially a geometrical theory of the distribution of (positive) roots of cubic equations. He necessarily dealt only with those parts of conic sections that are located in the first quadrant, employing them to determine under what conditions a problem may exist and whether the given type manifests only one case—or one root (including the case of double roots, but not multiple roots, which were unknown)—or more than one case (that is, one or two roots). Al-Khayyāmī went on to demonstrate that some types of equations are characterized by a diversity of cases, so that they may possess no roots at all, or one root, or two roots. He also investigated the limits of roots.

As far as it is known, al-Khayyāmī was thus the first to demonstrate that a cubic equation might have two roots. He was unable to realize, however, that an equation of the type $x^3 + qx = px^2 + r$ may, under certain conditions, possess three (positive) roots; this constitutes a disappointing deficiency in his work. As F. Woepcke, the first editor of the *Risāla*, has shown, al-Khayyāmī followed a definite system in selecting the curves upon which he based the construction of the roots of all fourteen types of third-degree equations; the conic sections that he preferred were circumferences, equilateral hyperbolas of which the axes, or asymptotes, run parallel to coordinate axes; and parabolas of which the axes parallel one of the coordinate axes. His general geometrical theory of distribution of the roots was also applied to the analysis of equations with numerical coefficients, as is evident in the supplement to the *Risāla*, in which al-Khayyāmī analyzed an error of Abū'l-Jūd Muḥammad ibn Layth, an algebraist who had lived some time earlier and whose work al-Khayyāmī had read a few years after writing the main text of his treatise.

His studies on the geometrical theory of third-degree equations mark al-Khayyāmī's most successful work. Although they were continued in oriental Muslim countries, and known by hearsay in Moorish countries, Europeans began to learn of them only after Descartes and his successors independently arrived at a method of the geometrical construction of roots and a doctrine of their distribution. Al-Khayyāmī did further research on equations containing degrees of a quantity inverse to the unknown ("part of the thing," "part of the square," and so on) including, for example, such equations as $1/x^3 + 3\ 1/x^2 + 5\ 1/x = 3\ 3/8$, which he reduced by substituting $x = 1/z$ in the equations that he had already studied. He also considered such cases as $x^2 + 2x = 2 + 2\ 1/x^2$, which led to equations of the fourth degree, and here he realized the upper limit of his accomplishment, writing, "If it [the series of consecutive powers] extends to five classes, or six classes, or seven, it cannot be extracted by any method."[12]

The Theory of Parallels. Muslim commentators on the *Elements* as early as the ninth century began to elaborate on the theory of parallels and to attempt to establish it on a basis different from that set out by Euclid in his fifth postulate. Thābit ibn Qurra and Ibn al-Haytham had both been attracted to the problem, while al-Khayyāmī devoted the first book of his commentaries to the *Sharḥ* to it. Al-Khayyāmī took as the point of departure for his theory of parallels a principle derived, according to him, from "the philosopher," that is, Aristotle, namely that "two convergent straight lines intersect and it is impossible that two convergent straight lines should diverge in the direction of convergence."[13] Such a principle consists of two statements, each equivalent to Euclid's fifth postulate. (It must be noted that nothing similar to al-Khayyāmī's principle is to be found in any of the known writings of Aristotle.)

Al-Khayyāmī first proved that two perpendiculars to one straight line cannot intersect because they must intersect symmetrically at two points on both sides of the straight line; therefore they cannot converge. From the second statement the principle follows that two perpendiculars drawn to one straight line cannot diverge because, if they did, they would have to diverge on both sides of the straight line. Therefore, two perpendiculars to the same straight line neither converge nor diverge, being in fact equidistant from each other.

Al-Khayyāmī then went on to prove eight propositions, which, in his opinion, should be added to book I of the *Elements* in place of the proposition 29 with which Euclid began the theory of parallel lines based on the fifth postulate of book I (the preceding twenty-eight propositions are not based on the fifth postulate). He constructed a quadrilateral by drawing two perpendicular lines of equal length at the ends of a given line segment AB. Calling the perpendiculars AC and BD, the figure was thus bounded by the segments AB, AC, CD, and BD, a birectangle often called "Saccheri's quadrilateral," in honor of the eighteenth-century geometrician who used it in his own theory of parallels.

In his first three propositions, al-Khayyāmī proved that the upper angles C and D of this quadrilateral are right angles. To establish this theorem, he (as Saccheri did after him) considered three hypotheses whereby these angles might be right, acute, or obtuse; were they acute, the upper line CD of the figure must be longer than the base AB, and were they obtuse, CD must be shorter than AB—that is, extensions of sides AC and BD would diverge or converge on both ends of AB. The hypothetical acute or obtuse angles are therefore proved to be contradictory to the given equidistance of the two perpendiculars to one straight line, and the figure is proved to be a rectangle.

In the fourth proposition al-Khayyāmī demonstrated that the opposite sides of the rectangle are of equal length, and in the fifth, that it is the property of any two perpendiculars to the same straight line that any perpendicular to one of them is also the perpendicular to the other. The sixth proposition states that if two straight lines are parallel in Euclid's sense—that is, if they do not intersect—they are both perpendicular to one straight line. The seventh proposition adds that if two parallel straight lines are intersected by a third straight line, alternate and corresponding angles are equal, and the interior angles of one side are two right angles, a proposition coinciding with Euclid's book I, proposition 29, but one that al-Khayyāmī reached by his own, noncoincident methods.

Al-Khayyāmī's eighth proposition proves Euclid's fifth postulate of book I: two straight lines intersect if a third intersects them at angles which are together less than two right angles. The two lines are extended and a straight line, parallel to one of them, is passed through one of the points of intersection. According to the sixth proposition, these two straight lines—being one of the original lines and the line drawn parallel to it—are equidistant, and consequently the two original lines must approach each other. According to al-Khayyāmī's general principle, such straight lines are bound to intersect.

Al-Khayyāmī's demonstration of Euclid's fifth postulate differs from those of his Muslim predecessors because he avoids the logical mistake of *petitio principi*, and deduces the fifth postulate from his own explicitly formulated principle. Some conclusions drawn from hypotheses of acute or obtuse angles are essentially the same as the first theorems of the non-Euclidean geometries of Lobachevski and Riemann. Like his theory of ratios, al-Khayyāmī's theory of parallels influenced the work of later Muslim scholars to a considerable degree. A work sometimes attributed to his follower al-Ṭūsī influenced the development of the theory of parallels in Europe in the seventeenth and eighteenth centuries, as was particularly reflected in the work of Wallis and Saccheri.

Philosophical and Poetical Writings. Although al-Khayyāmī wrote five specifically philosophical treatises, and although much of his poetry is of a philosophical nature, it remains difficult to ascertain what his world view might have been. Many investigators have dealt with this problem, and have reached many different conclusions, depending in large part on their own views. The problem is complicated by the consideration that the religious and philosophical tracts differ from the quatrains, while analysis of the quatrains themselves is complicated by questions of their individual authenticity. Nor is it possible to be sure of what in the philosophical treatises actually reflects al-Khayyāmī's own mind, since they were written under official patronage.

His first treatise, *Risālat al-kawn wa'l-taklīf* ("Treatise on Being and Duty"), was written in 1080, in response to a letter from a high official who wished al-Khayyāmī to give his views on "the Divine Wisdom in the Creation of the World and especially of Man and on man's duty to pray."[14] The second treatise, *Al-Jawab ʿan thalāth masā'il* ("An Answer to the Three Questions"), closely adheres to the formula set out in the first. *Risāla fi'l kulliyat al-wujūd* ("Treatise on the Universality of Being") was written at the request of Mu'ayyid al-Mulk, and, while it is not possible to date or know the circumstances under which the remaining two works, *Risālat al-ḍiyā' al-ʿaqlī fi mawḍūʿ al-ʿilm al-kullī* ("The Light of Reason on the Subject of Universal Science") and *Risāla fi'l wujūd* ("Treatise on Existence"), were written, it would seem not unlikely that they had been similarly commissioned. Politics may therefore have dictated the contents of the religious tracts, and it must be noted that the texts occasionally strike a cautious and impersonal note, presenting the opinions of a number of other authors, without criticism or evaluation.

It might also be speculated that al-Khayyāmī wrote his formal religious and philosophical works to clear his name of the accusation of freethinking. Certainly strife between religious sects and their common aversion to agnosticism were part of the climate of the time, and it is within the realm of possibility that al-Khayyāmī's quatrains had become known to the religious orthodoxy and had cast suspicion upon him. (The quatrains now associated with his name contain an extremely wide range of ideas, ranging from religious mysticism to materialism and almost atheism; certainly writers of the thirteenth century thought al-Khayyāmī a freethinker, al-Qifṭī calling the poetry "a stinging serpent to the Sharīʿa" and the theologian Abū Bakr Najm al-Dīn al-Rāzī characterizing the poet as "an unhappy philosopher, materialist, and naturalist.")[15]

Insofar as may be generalized, in his philosophical works al-Khayyāmī wrote as an adherent of the sort of eastern Aristotelianism propagated by Ibn Sīnā—that is, of an Aristotelianism containing considerable amounts of Platonism, and adjusted to fit Muslim religious doctrine. Al-Bayhaqī called al-Khayyāmī "a successor of Abū ʿAli [Ibn Sīnā] in different domains of philosophical sciences,"[16] but from the orthodox point of view such a rationalistic approach to the dogmas of faith was heresy. At any rate, al-Khayyāmī's philosophy is scarcely original, his most interesting works being those concerned with the analysis of the problem of existence of general concepts. Here al-Khayyāmī—unlike Ibn Sīnā, who held views close to Plato's realism—developed a position similar to that which was stated simultaneously in Europe by Abailard, and was later called conceptualism.

As for al-Khayyāmī's poetical works, more than 1,000 quatrains, written in Persian, are now published under his name. (Govinda counted 1,069.) The poems were preserved orally for a long time, so that many of them are now known in several variants. V. A. Zhukovsky, a Russian investigator of the poems, wrote of al-Khayyāmī in 1897:

> He has been regarded variously as a freethinker, a subverter of Faith, an atheist and materialist; a pantheist and a scoffer at mysticism; an orthodox Musulman; a true philosopher, a keen observer, a man of learning; a bon vivant, a profligate, a dissembler, and a

hypocrite; a blasphemer—nay, more, an incarnate negation of positive religion and of all moral beliefs; a gentle nature, more given to the contemplation of things divine than the wordly enjoyments; an epicurean skeptic; the Persian Abū'l-'Alā, Voltaire, and Heine. One asks oneself whether it is possible to conceive, not a philosopher, but merely an intelligent man (provided he be not a moral deformity) in whom were commingled and embodied such a diversity of convictions, paradoxical inclinations and tendencies, of high moral courage and ignoble passions, of torturing doubts and vacillations?[17]

The inconsistencies noted by Zhukovsky are certainly present in the corpus of the poems now attributed to al-Khayyāmī, and here again questions of authenticity arise. A. Christensen, for example, thought that only about a dozen of the quatrains might with any certainty be considered genuine, although later he increased this number to 121. At any rate, the poems generally known as al-Khayyāmī's are one of the summits of philosophical poetry, displaying an unatheistic freethought and love of freedom, humanism and aspirations for justice, irony and skepticism, and above all an epicurean spirit that verges upon hedonism.

Al-Khayyāmī's poetic genius was always celebrated in the Arabic East, but his fame in European countries is of rather recent origin. In 1859, a few years after Woepcke's edition had made al-Khayyāmī's algebra—previously almost unknown—available to Western scholars, the English poet Edward FitzGerald published translations of seventy-five of the quatrains, an edition that remains popular. Since then, many more of the poems have been published in a number of European languages.

The poems—and the poet—have not lost their power to attract. In 1934 a monument to al-Khayyāmī was erected at his tomb in Nīshāpūr, paid for by contributions from a number of countries.

NOTES

1. V. A. Zhukovsky, *Omar Khayyam i "stranstvuyushchie" chetverostishia*; Swami Govinda Tirtha, *The Nectar of Grace*; and Niẓāmī 'Arūḍī Samarqandī, *Sobranie redkostei ili chetyre besedy.*
2. Samarqandī, *op. cit.*, p. 97; in the Browne trans., p. 806, based on the later MSS, "four years" is "some years."
3. Govinda, *op. cit.*, pp. 70–71.
4. *Risāla fi'l-barāhīn 'alā masā'il al-jabr wa'l-muqābala*, Winter-'Arafat trans., pp. 29–30.
5. I. S. Levinova, "Teoria vesov v traktatakh Omara Khayyama i ego uchenika Abu Hatima al-Muzaffara ibn Ismaila al-Asfizari."
6. *Risāla*, Winter-'Arafat trans., pp. 34 (with correction), 71.
7. *Omar Khayyam, Traktaty*, pp. 71, 145.
8. First algebraic treatise, Krasnova and Rosenfeld trans., p. 455; omitted from Amir-Moéz trans.
9. *Risāla*, Winter-'Arafat trans., p. 30 (with correction).
10. *Ibid.*, p. 31.
11. *Ibid.*, p. 32 (with correction).
12. *Ibid.*, p. 70.
13. *Omar Khayyam, Traktaty*, pp. 120–121; omitted from *Sharḥ mā ashkala min muṣādarāt kitāb Uqlīdis*, Amir-Moéz trans.
14. *Omar Khayyam, Traktaty*, p. 152.
15. Zhukovsky, *op. cit.*, pp. 334, 342.
16. Govinda, *op. cit.*, pp. 32–33.
17. Zhukovsky, *op. cit.*, p. 325.

BIBLIOGRAPHY

I. ORIGINAL WORKS. The following are al-Khayyāmī's main writings:

1. The principal ed. is *Omar Khayyam, Traktaty* ("... Treatises"), B. A. Rosenfeld, trans.; V. S. Segal and A. P. Youschkevitch, eds.; intro. and notes by B. A. Rosenfeld and A. P. Youschkevitch (Moscow, 1961), with plates of the MSS. It contains Russian trans. of all the scientific and philosophical writings except the first algebraic treatise, *al-Qawl 'alā ajnās allātī bi'l-arba'a*, and *Fī'l-qusṭas al-mustaqīm*.

2. The first algebraic treatise. MS: Teheran, Central University library, VII, 1751/2. Eds.: Arabic text and Persian trans. by G. H. Mossaheb (see below), pp. 59–74, 251–291; English trans. by A. R. Amir-Moéz in *Scripta mathematica*, **26**, no. 4 (1961), 323–337; Russian trans. with notes by S. A. Krasnova and B. A. Rosenfeld in *Istoriko-matematicheskie issledovaniya*, **15** (1963), 445–472.

3. *Risāla fi'l-barāhīn 'alā masā'il al-jabr wa'l-muqābala* ("Treatise on Demonstration of Problems of Algebra and Almuqabala"). MSS: Paris, Bibliothèque Nationale, Ar. 2461, 2358/7; Leiden University library, Or. 14/2; London, India Office library, 734/10; Rome, Vatican Library, Barb. 96/2; New York, collection of D. E. Smith.

Eds.: F. Woepcke, *L'algèbre d'Omar Alkhayyâmî* (Paris, 1851), text of both Paris MSS and of the Leiden MS, French trans. and ed.'s notes—reedited by Mossaheb (see below), pp. 7–52, with Persian trans. (pp. 159–250) ed. by the same author earlier in *Jabr-u muqābala-i Khayyām* (Teheran, 1938); English trans. by D. S. Kasir, *The Algebra of Omar Khayyam* (New York, 1931), trans. from the Smith MS, which is very similar to Paris MS Ar. 2461, and by H. J. J. Winter and W. 'Arafat, "The Algebra of 'Umar Khayyam," in *Journal of the Royal Asiatic Society of Bengal Science*, **16** (1950), 27–70, trans. from the London MS; and Russian trans. and photographic repro. of Paris MS 2461 in *Omar Khayyam, Traktaty*, pp. 69–112; 1st Russian ed. in *Istoriko-matematicheskie issledovaniya*, **6** (1953), 15–66.

4. *Sharḥ mā ashkala min muṣādarāt kitāb Uqlīdis* ("Commentaries to Difficulties in the Introductions to Euclid's Book"). MSS: Paris, Bibliothèque Nationale, Ar. 4946/4; Leiden University library, Or. 199/8.

Eds.: T. Erani, *Discussion of Difficulties of Euclid by Omar Khayyam* (Teheran, 1936), the Leiden MS, reed. by J. Humai (see below), pp. 177–222, with a Persian trans. (pp. 225–280); *Omar Khayyam, Explanation of the Difficulties in Euclid's Postulates*, A. I. Sabra, ed. (Alexandria,

1961), the Leiden MS and text variants of Paris MS; an incomplete English trans. by A. R. Amir-Moéz, in *Scripta mathematica*, **24**, no. 4 (1959), 275–303; and Russian trans. and photographic repro. of Leiden MS in *Omar Khayyam, Traktaty*, pp. 113–146; 1st Russian ed. in *Istoriko-matematicheskie issledovaniya*, **6** (1953), 67–107.

5. *Al-Qawl 'alā ajnās allatī bi'l-arba'a* ("Discussion on Genera Contained in a Fourth"). MS: Teheran, Central University library, 509, fols. 97–99.

Ed.: J. Humai (see below), pp. 341–344.

6. *Mizān al-ḥikam* ("The Balance of Wisdoms") or *Fī ikhtiyāl ma'rafa miqdāray adh-dhahab wa-l-fiḍḍa fī jism murakkab minhumā* ("On the Art of Determination of Gold and Silver in a Body Consisting of Them"). Complete in Abdalraḥmān al-Khāzinī, *Kitāb mizān al-ḥikmu* ("Book of the Balance of Wisdom"). MSS: Leningrad, State Public Library, Khanykov collection, 117, 57b–60b; also in Bombay and Hyderabad. Incomplete MS: Gotha, State Library, 1158, 39b–40a.

Eds. of the Bombay and Hyderabad MSS: Abdalraḥmān al-Khāzinī, *Kitāb mizān al-ḥikma* (Hyderabad, 1940), pp. 87–92; S. S. Nadwi (see below), pp. 427–432. German trans. by E. Wiedemann in *Sitzungsberichte der Physikalisch-medizinischen Sozietät in Erlangen*, **49** (1908), 105–132; Russian trans. and repro. of the Leningrad MS in *Omar Khayyam, Traktaty*, pp. 147–151; 1st Russian ed. in *Istoriko-matematicheskie issledovaniya*, **6** (1953), 108–112.

Eds. of the Gotha MS: Arabic text in Rosen's ed. of the *Rubā'ī* (see below), pp. 202–204), in Erani's ed. of the *Sharḥ* (see above), and in M. 'Abbasī (see below), pp. 419–428; German trans. by F. Rosen in *Zeitschrift der Deutschen morgenländischen Gesellschaft*, **4(79)** (1925), 133–135; and by E. Wiedemann in *Sitzungsberichte der Physikalisch-medizinischen Sozietät in Erlangen*, **38** (1906), 170–173.

7. *Fī'l-qusṭas al-mutaqīm* ("On Right *Qusṭas*"), in al-Khāzinī's *Mīzān* (see above), pp. 151–153.

8. *Zīj Malik-shāhī* ("Malik-shāh Astronomical Tables"). Only a catalogue of 100 fixed stars for one year of the Malikī era is extant in the anonymous MS Bibliothèque Nationale, Ar. 5968.

Eds.: Russian trans. and photographic repro. of the MS in *Omar Khayyam, Traktaty*, pp. 225–235; same trans. with more complete commentaries in *Istoriko-astronomicheskie issledovaniya*, **8** (1963), 159–190.

9–11. *Risāla al-kawn wa'l-taklīf* ("Treatise on Being and Duty"), *Al-Jawab 'an thalāth masā'il: ḍarūrat al-taḍadd fī'l-'ālam wa'l-jabr wa'l-baqā'* ("Answer to Three Questions: On the Necessity of Contradiction in the World, on Determinism and on Longevity"), *Risāla al-ḍiyā' al-'aqlī fi mawḍū' al-'ilm al-kullī* ("The Light of Reason on the Subject of Universal Science"). MSS belonging to Nūr al-Dīn Muṣṭafā (Cairo) are lost.

Arabic text in *Jāmi' al-badā'i'* ("Collection of Uniques"; Cairo, 1917), pp. 165–193; text of the first two treatises published by S. S. Nadwī (see below), pp. 373–398; and S. Govinda (see below), pp. 45–46, 83–110, with English trans.; Persian trans., H. Shajara, ed. (see below), pp. 299–337; Russian trans. of all three treatises in *Omar Khayyam, Traktaty*, pp. 152–171; 1st Russian ed. in S. B. Morochnik and B. A. Rosenfeld (see below), pp. 163–188.

12. *Risāla fī'l-wujūd* ("Treatise on Existence"), or *al-Awṣāf wa'l-mawṣūfāt* ("Description and the Described"). MS: Berlin, former Prussian State Library, Or. Petermann, B. 466; Teheran, Majlis-i Shurā-i Millī, 9014; and Poona, collection of Shaykh 'Abd al-Qādir Sarfaraz.

The Teheran MS is published by Sa'īd Nafīsī in *Sharq* ("East"; Sha'bān, 1931); and by Govinda (see below), pp. 110–116; Russian trans. in *Omar Khayyam, Traktaty*, pp. 172–179; 1st Russian ed. in S. B. Morochnik and B. A. Rosenfeld (see below), pp. 189–199.

13. *Risāla fī kulliyat al-wujūd* ("Treatise on the Universality of Existence"), or *Risāla-i silsila al-tartīb* ("Treatise on the Chain of Order"), or *Darkhwāstnāma* ("The Book on Demand"). MSS: London, British Museum, Or. 6572; Paris, Bibliothèque Nationale, Suppl. persan, 139/7; Teheran, Majlis-i Shurā-i Millī, 9072; and al-Khayyāmī's library. London MS reproduced in B. A. Rosenfeld and A. P. Youschkevitch (see below), pp. 140–141; the Paris MS is reproduced in *Omar Khayyam, Traktaty*; the texts of these MSS are published in S. S. Nadwi (see below), pp. 412–423; the Majlis-i Shurā-i Millī MS is in Nafīsī's *Sharq* (see above) and in M. 'Abbasī (see below), pp. 393–405; the al-Khayyāmī library MS is in *'Umar Khayyām, Darkhwāstnāma*, Muḥammad 'Alī Taraqī, ed. (Teheran, 1936). Texts of the London MS and the first Teheran MS are published by Govinda with the English trans. (see below), pp. 47–48, 117–129; French trans. of the Paris MS in A. Christensen, *Le monde orientale*, I (1908), 1–16; Russian trans. from the London and Paris MSS, with repro. of the Paris MS in *Omar Khayyam, Traktaty*, pp. 180–186—1st Russian ed. in S. B. Morochnik and B. A. Rosenfeld (see below), pp. 200–208.

14. *Naurūz-nāma*. MS: Berlin, former Prussian State Library, Or. 2450; London, British Museum, Add. 23568.

Eds. of the Berlin MS: *Nowruz-namah*, Mojtaba Minovi, ed. (Teheran, 1933); by M. 'Abbasī (see below), pp. 303–391; Russian trans. with repro. of the Berlin MS in *Omar Khayyam, Traktaty*, pp. 187–224.

15. *Rubāiyāt* ("Quatrains"). Eds. of MS: *Rubāiyāt-i hakīm Khayyām*, Sanjar Mirzā, ed. (Teheran, 1861), Persian text of 464 *ruba'i*; Muhammad Sadīq 'Alī Luknawī, ed. (Lucknow, 1878, 1894, 1909), 762 (1st ed.) and 770 (2nd and 3rd eds.) *ruba'i*; Muḥammad Raḥīm Ardebili, ed. (Bombay, 1922); Husein Danish, ed. (Istanbul, 1922, 1927), 396 quatrains with Turkish trans.; Jalāl al-Dīn Aḥmed Jafrī, ed. (Damascus, 1931; Beirut, 1950), 352 quatrains with Arabic trans.; Sa'īd Nafisī, ed. (Teheran, 1933), 443 quatrains; B. Scillik, ed., *Les manuscrits mineurs des Rubaiyat d'Omar-i-Khayyam dans la Bibliothèque National* (Paris-Szeged, 1933–1934)—1933 MSS containing 95, 87, 75, 60, 56, 34, 28, 8, and 6 *ruba'i* and 1934 MSS containing 268, 213, and 349 *ruba'i*; Maḥfūz al-Ḥaqq, ed. (Calcutta, 1939) repro. MS containing 206 *ruba'i* with minatures; Muḥammad 'Ali Foroughī, ed. (Teheran, 1942, 1956, 1960), 178 selected *ruba'i* with illustrations; R. M. Aliev, M. N. Osmanov, and E. E. Bertels, eds. (Moscow, 1959), photographic repro. of MS containing 252 *ruba'i* and Russian prose trans. of 293 selected *ruba'i*.

English trans.: Edward FitzGerald (London, 1859, 1868, 1872, 1879) a poetical trans. of 75 (1st ed.) to 101 (4th ed.) quatrains, often repr. (best ed., 1900); E. H. Whinfield (London, 1882, 1883, 1893), a poetical trans. of 253 (1st ed.), 500 (2nd ed.), and 267 (3rd ed.) *ruba'i* from the MS published by Luknawi, in the 2nd ed. with the Persian text; E. Heron-Allen (London, 1898), a prose trans. and repro. of MS containing 158 *ruba'i;* S. Govinda (see below), pp. 1–30, a poetical trans. and the text of 1,069 *ruba'i;* A. J. Arberry (London, 1949), a prose trans. and the Persian text of MS containing 172 *ruba'i* with FitzGerald's and Whinfield's poetical trans., 1952 ed., a poetical trans. of 252 *ruba'i* from the MS published in Moscow in 1959. French trans.: J. B. Nicolas (Paris, 1867), prose trans. and the Persian text of 464 *ruba'i* from the Teheran ed. of 1861; German trans.: C. H. Rempis (Tübingen, 1936), poetical trans. of 255 *ruba'i*; Russian trans.: O. Rumer (Moscow, 1938), poetical trans. of 300 *ruba'i;* V. Derzhavin (Dushanbe, 1955), verse trans. of 488 *ruba'i;* and G. Plisetsky (Moscow, 1972), verse trans. of 450 *ruba'i*, with commentaries by M. N. Osmanov.

II. Secondary Literature. The works listed below provide information on al-Khayyāmī's life and work.

1. Muḥammad 'Abbasī, *Kulliyāt-i athār-i parsi-yi hakīm 'Umar-i Khayyām* (Teheran, 1939), a study of al-Khayyāmī's life and works. It contains texts and translations of *Mizān al-ḥikam*, *Risālat al-kawn wa'l-taklif*, *Al-Jawab 'an thalāth masā'il*, *Risālat al-ḍiyā'* . . ., *Risāla fi'l-wujūd*, and *Risāla fi kulliyat al-wujūd* and the quatrains.

2. C. Brockelmann, *Geschichte der arabischen Literatur*, I (Weimar, 1898), 471; supp. (Leiden, 1936), 855–856; III (Leiden, 1943), 620–621. A complete list of all Arabic MSS and their eds. known to European scientists; supp. vols. mention MSS and eds. that appeared after the main body of the work was published.

3. A. Christensen, *Recherches sur les Rubâiyât de 'Omar Hayyâm* (Heidelberg, 1904), an early work in which the author concludes that since there are no criteria for authenticity, only twelve quatrains may reasonably be regarded as authentic.

4. A. Christensen, *Critical Studies in the Rubaiyát of 'Umar-i-Khayyám* (Copenhagen, 1927). A product of prolonged study in which a method of establishing the authenticity of al-Khayyāmī's quatrains is suggested; 121 selected quatrains are presented.

5. J. L. Coolidge, *The Mathematics of Great Amateurs* (Oxford, 1949; New York, 1963), pp. 19–29.

6. Hâmit Dilgan, *Büyük matematikci Omer Hayyâm* (Istanbul, 1959).

7. F. K. Ginzel, *Handbuch der mathematischen und technischen Chronologie*, I (Leipzig, 1906), 300–305, information on al-Khayyāmī's calendar reform.

8. Swami Govinda Tirtha, *The Nectar of Grace*, *'Omar Khayyām's Life and Works* (Allahabad, 1941), contains texts and trans. of philosophical treatises and quatrains and repros. of MSS by al-Bayhaqī and Tabrīzī giving biographical data on al-Khayyāmī.

9. Jamāl al-Dīn Humāī, *Khayyām-nāmah*, I (Teheran, 1967). A study of al-Khayyāmī's commentary to Euclid; text and Persian trans. of *Sharḥ mā ashkala min muṣādarāt kitāb Uqlīdis* and text of *al-Qawl 'alā ajnās allatī bi'l-arba'a* are in the appendix.

10. U. Jacob and E. Wiedemann, "Zu Omer-i-Chajjam," in *Der Islam*, **3** (1912), 42–62, critical review of biographical data on al-Khayyāmī and a German trans. of al-Khayyāmī's intro. to *Sharḥ mā ashkala min muṣādarāt kitāb Uqlīdis*.

11. I. S. Levinova, "Teoria veso v traktatakh Omara Khayyama i ego uchenika Abu Hatima al-Muzaffara ibn Ismaila al-Asfizari," in *Trudy XV Nauchnoy Konferencii . . . Instituta istorii estestvoznaniya i tekhniki, sekoiya istorii matematiki i mekhaniki* (Moscow, 1972), pp. 90–93.

12. V. Minorsky, "'Omar Khayyām," in *Enzyklopädie des Islams*, III (Leiden–Leipzig, 1935), 985–989.

13. S. B. Morochnik, *Filosofskie vzglyady Omara Khayyama* ("Philosophical Views of Omar Khayyam"; Dushanbe, 1952).

14. S. B. Morochnik and B. A. Rosenfeld, *Omar Khayyam—poet, myslitel, uchenyi* (". . . Thinker, Scientist"; Dushanbe, 1957).

15. C. H. Mossaheb, *Hakim Omare Khayyam as an Algebraist* (Teheran, 1960). A study of al-Khayyāmī's algebra; text and trans. of the first algebraic treatise and *Risāla fi'l-barāhīn 'alā masā'il al-jabr wa'l muqābala* are in appendix.

16. Seyyīd Suleimān Nadwī, *Umar Khayyam* (Azamgarh, 1932), a study of al-Khayyāmī's life and works, with texts of *Mizān al-ḥikam Risālat al-kawn wa'l taklīf*, *Al-Jawab 'an thalāth masā'il*, *Risālat al-ḍiyā'* . . ., *Risāla fi'l-wujūd*, and *Risāla fi kulliyat al-wujūd* in appendix.

17. B. A. Rosenfeld and A. P. Youschkevitch, *Omar Khayyam* (Moscow, 1965), consisting of a biographical essay, analysis of scientific (especially mathematical) works, and detailed bibliography.

18. Niẓāmī 'Arūḍī Samarqandī, *Sobranie redkostei ili chetyre besedy* ("Collection of Rarities or Four Discourses"), S. I. Bayevsky and Z. N. Vorosheikina, trans., A. N. Boldyrev, ed. (Moscow, 1963), pp. 97–98; and "The Chahár Maqála" ("Four Discourses"), E. G. Browne, English trans., in *Journal of the Royal Asiatic Society*, n. s. **31** (1899), 613–663, 757–845, see 806–808. Recollections of a contemporary of al-Khayyāmī's regarding two episodes in the latter's life.

19. G. Sarton, *Introduction to the History of Science*, I (Baltimore, 1927), 759–761.

20. Husein Shajara, *Tahqiq-i dar rubā'iyāt-i zindagānī-i Khayyām* (Teheran, 1941). A study of al-Khayyāmī's life and work; Persian trans. of *Risālat al-kawn wa'l-taklīf* and *Al-Jawab 'an thalāth masā'il* are in appendix.

21. D. E. Smith, "Euclid, Omar Khayyam and Saccheri," in *Scripta mathematica*, **3**, no. 1 (1935), 5–10, the first critical investigation of al-Khayyāmī's theory of parallels in comparison with Saccheri's.

22. D. J. Struik, "Omar Khayyam, Mathematician," in *Mathematical Teacher*, no. 4 (1958), 280–285.

23. H. Suter, *Die Mathematiker und Astronomen der Araber und ihre Werke* (Leipzig, 1900), pp. 112–113.

24. A. P. Youschkevitch, "Omar Khayyam i ego Alge-

bra," in *Trudy Instituta istorii estestvoznaniya*, **2** (1948), 499–534.

25. A. P. Youschkevitch, *Geschichte der Mathematik im Mittelalter* (Leipzig, 1964), pp. 251–254, 259–269, 283–287.

26. A. P. Youschkevitch and B. A. Rosenfeld, "Die Mathematik der Länder des Osten im Mittelalter," in G. Harig, ed., *Sowjetische Beiträge zur Geschichte der Naturwissenschaften* (Berlin, 1960), pp. 119–121.

27. V. A. Zhukovsky, "Omar Khayyam i 'stranstvuyuschie' chetverostishiya" ("Omar Khayyam and the 'Wandering' Quatrains"), in *al-Muẓaffariyya* (St. Petersburg, 1897), pp. 325–363. Translated into English by E. D. Ross in *Journal of the Royal Asiatic Society*, n. s. **30** (1898), 349–366. This paper gives all principal sources of information on al-Khayyāmī's life and presents the problem of "wandering" quatrains, that is, *ruba'i* ascribed to both al-Khayyāmī and other authors.

A. P. YOUSCHKEVITCH
B. A. ROSENFELD

AL-KHĀZIN, ABŪ JA'FAR MUḤAMMAD IBN AL-ḤASAN AL-KHURĀSĀNĪ (*d.* 961/971)

Al-Khāzin, usually known as Abū Ja'far al-Khāzin, was a Sabaean of Persian origin. The *Fihrist* calls him al-Khurāsānī, meaning from Khurāsān, a province in eastern Iran. He should not be confused with 'Abd al-Raḥmān al-Khāzinī (*ca.* 1100), the probable author of *Kitāb al-ālāt al'ajība al-raṣdiyya*, on observation instruments, often attributed to al-Khāzin. (E. Wiedemann attributed this work, inconsistently, to al-Khāzin in the *Enzyklopaedie des Islam*, II [Leiden–Leipzig, 1913], pp. 1005–1006, and to al-Khāzinī in *Beiträge*, **9** [1906], 190. De Slane confounded these two astronomers in his translation of Ibn Khaldūn's *Prolegomena*, I, 111.)

Abū Ja'far al-Khāzin, said to have been attached to the court of the Buwayhid ruler Rukn al-Dawla (932–976) of Rayy, was well known among his contemporaries. In particular his *Zīj al-ṣafā'iḥ* ("Tables of the Disks [of the astrolabe]"), which Ibn al-Qifṭī calls the best work in this field, is often cited; it may be related to manuscript "Liber de sphaera in plano describenda," in the Laurentian library in Florence (Pal.-Med. 271).

Al-Bīrūnī's *Risāla fī fihrist kutub Muḥammad b. Zakariyyā' al-Rāzī* ("Bibliography") of 1036 lists several texts (written in cooperation with Abū Naṣr Manṣūr ibn 'Irāq), one of which is *Fī taṣḥīḥ mā waqa'a li Abī Ja'far al-Khāzin min al-sahw fī zīj al-ṣafā'iḥ* ("On the Improvement of What Abū Ja'far Neglected in His Tables of the Disks"). In *Tamhīd al-mustaqarr li-taḥqīq ma'nā al-mamarr* ("On Transits"), al-Bīrūnī criticizes Abū Ja'far al-Khāzin for not having correctly handled two equations defining the location of a planet but remarks that the *Zīj al-ṣafā'iḥ* is correct on this matter. Abū Ja'far al-Khāzin criticized the claim of Abū Ma'shar that, unlike many others, he had fully determined the truth about the planets, which he had included in his *Zīj*. Abū Ja'far al-Khāzin regarded this work as a mere compilation. Al-Bīrūnī compared Abū Ja'far al-Khāzin very favorably with Abū Ma'shar, and in his *al-Āthār al-bāqiya min al-qurūn al-khāliya* ("Chronology of Ancient Nations") he refers to *Zīj al-ṣafā'iḥ* for a good explanation of the progressive and retrograde motion of the sphere.

An anonymous manuscript in Berlin (*Staatsbibliothek*, *Ahlwardt Cat. No.* 5857) contains two short chapters on astronomical instruments from a work by Abū Ja'far al-Khāzin, probably the *Zīj al-ṣafā'iḥ*. The MS Or. 168(4) in Leiden by Abū'l-Jūd quotes Abū Ja'far al-Khāzin's remark in *Zīj al-ṣafā'iḥ* that he would be able to compute the chord of an angle of one degree if angle trisection were possible.

In *Kitāb fī isti'āb*, dealing with constructions of astrolabes, al-Bīrūnī cites Abū Ja'far al-Khāzin's work "Design of the Horizon of the Ascensions for the Signs of the Zodiac." And in his *Chronology* he describes two methods for finding the *signum Muharrami* (the day of the week on which al-Muḥarram, the first month of the Muslim year, begins) described by Abū Ja'far al-Khāzin in *al-Madkhal al-kabīr fī'ilm al-nujūm* ("Great Introduction to Astronomy"). Neither work is extant.

Also treated in al-Bīrūnī's *Chronology* is Abū Ja'far al-Khāzin's figure, different from the eccentric sphere and epicycle, in which the sun's distance from the earth is always the same, independent of the rotation. This treatment gives two isothermal regions, one northern and one southern. Ibn Khaldūn gives a precise exposition of Abū Ja'far al-Khāzin's division of the earth into eight climatic girdles.

Al-Kharaqī (*d.* 1138/1139), in *al-Muntahā*, mentions Abū Ja'far al-Khāzin and Ibn al-Haytham as having the right understanding of the movement of the spheres. This theory was perhaps described in Abū Ja'far al-Khāzin's *Sirr al-'ālamīn* (not extant).

In *Taḥdīd nihāyāt al-amākin* . . ., al-Bīrūnī criticizes the verbosity of Abū Ja'far al-Khāzin's commentary on the *Almagest* and objects to Ibrāhīm ibn Sīnān and Abū Ja'far al-Khāzin's theory of the variation of the obliquity of the ecliptic; al-Bīrūnī himself considered it to be constant. The obliquity was measured by al-Harawī and Abū Ja'far al-Khāzin at Rayy (near modern Teheran) in 959/960, on the order of Abu'l Faḍl ibn al-'Amīd, the vizier of Rukn al-Dawla. The determination of this quantity by "al-Khāzin and his collaborators using a ring of about 4 meters" is recorded by al-Nasawī.

Abū Ja'far al-Khāzin was, according to Ibn al Qifṭī, an expert in arithmetic, geometry, and *tasyīr* (astrological computations based on planetary trajectories). According to al-Khayyāmī, he used conic sections to give the first solution of the cubic equation by which al-Māhānī represented Archimedes' problem of dividing a sphere by a plane into two parts whose volumes are in a given ratio (*Sphere and Cylinder* II, 4) and also gave a defective proof of Euclid's fifth postulate.

Abū Ja'far al-Khāzin wrote a commentary on Book X of the *Elements*, a work on numerical problems (not extant), and another (also not extant) on spherical trigonometry, *Maṭālib juz'iyya mail al-muyūl al-juz' iyya wa 'l-maṭāli' fi'l-kura al-mustaqīma.* From the latter, al-Ṭūsī, in *Kitāb šakl al-qaṭṭā'* ("On the Transversal Figure"), quotes a proof of the sine theorem for right spherical triangles. Al-Ṭūsī also added another proof of Hero's formula to the *Verba filiorum* of the Banū Mūsā (in *Majmū' al-rasā'il*, II [Hyderabad, 1940]), attributing it to one al-Khāzin. This proof, closer to that of Hero than the proof by the Banū Mūsā, and in which the same figure and letters are used as in Hero's *Dioptra*, is not found in the Latin editions of the *Verba filiorum*.

BIBLIOGRAPHY

I. ORIGINAL WORKS. Not many of al-Khāzin's writings are extant. The available MSS are listed in C. Brockelmann, *Geschichte der arabischen Literatur, Supplementband*, I (Leiden, 1943), 387. The commentary on Book X of the *Elements* is discussed by G. P. Matvievskaya in *Uchenie o chisle na srednevekovom Blizhnem i Srednem Vostoke* ("Studies About Number in the Medieval Near and Middle East"; Tashkent, 1967), ch. 6.

II. SECONDARY LITERATURE. Biographical and bibliographical references can be found in Ya'qub al-Nadim, *al-Fihrist*, G. Flügel, ed. (Leipzig, 1871–1872), pp. 266, 282; Ibn al-Qifṭī, *Ta'rikh-al-ḥukamā'*, J. Lippert, ed. (Leipzig, 1903), 396; Hājjī Khalifa, *Lexicon bibliographicum* (repr. New York, 1964), I, 382, II, 584, 585, III, 595, VI, 170; H. Suter, *Die Mathematiker und Astronomen der Araber ubd ihre Werke* (Leipzig, 1900), p. 58, and *Nachträge*, p. 165; and A. Sayili, *The Observatory in Islam* (Ankara, 1960), pp. 103–104, 123, 126, which emphasizes the observations at Rayy. For Abū Ja'far al-Khāzin's astronomical theories and activities, see Ibn Khaldūn, *Prolegomena*, I, M. de Slane, trans. (repr. Paris, 1938), p. 111; and al-Bīrūnī, *Chronology of Ancient Nations*, C. E. Sachau, ed. (London, 1879), pp. 183, 249; *On Transits*, M. Saffouri and A. Ifram, trans. with a commentary by E. S. Kennedy (Beirut, 1959), pp. 85–87, and *Taḥdīd nihāyāt al-amākin* (Cairo, 1962), pp. 57, 95, 98, 101, 119.

M. Clagett, *Archimedes in the Middle Ages*, I, *The Arabo-Latin Tradition* (Madison, Wis., 1964), p. 353; and H. Suter, "Über die Geometrie der Söhne des Mūsā ben Schākir," in *Bibliotheca mathematica*, 3rd ser., **3**, no. 1 (1902), p. 271, mention the proof of Hero's formula. For the cubic equation of al-Māhānī, see F. Woepcke, *L'algèbre d'Omar Alkhayyāmi* (Paris, 1851), pp. 2–3; for the sine theorem, see Naṣīr al-Dīn al-Ṭūsī, *Traité du quadrilatère*, A. Carathéodory, ed. (Constantinople, 1891), pp. 148–151; for the fifth postulate, see G. Jacob and E. Wiedemann, "Zu 'Omer-i-Chajjâm," in *Der Islam*, **3** (1912), p. 56. Other articles by E. Wiedemann containing information on Abū Ja'far al-Khāzin are in *Beiträge* **60** (1920–1921) and **70** (1926–1927), of *Sitzungsberichte der Physikalisch-Medizinischen Sozietät zu Erlangen*. Now available in E. Wiedemann, *Aufsätze zur arabischen Wissenschaftsgeschichte*, II (Hildesheim, 1970), pp. 498, 503, 633.

YVONNE DOLD-SAMPLONIUS

KHINCHIN, ALEKSANDR YAKOVLEVICH (*b.* Kondrovo, Kaluzhskaya guberniya, Russia, 19 July 1894; *d.* Moscow, U.S.S.R., 18 November 1959)

The son of an engineer, Khinchin graduated from a technical high school in Moscow in 1911 and, from 1911 until 1916, studied at the Faculty of Physics and Mathematics of Moscow University. In 1916 he was retained by the university to prepare for professorship. From 1918 Khinchin taught at various colleges in Moscow and Ivanovo; in 1927 he became a professor at Moscow University. He was elected an associate member of the Soviet Academy of Sciences in 1939 and a member of the Academy of Pedagogical Sciences of the R.S.F.S.R. in 1944. He received the State Prize in 1940 for his scientific achievements. With A. N. Kolmogorov, Khinchin was one of the founders of the Moscow school of probability theory, one of the most influential in the twentieth century.

Khinchin's interest in mathematics was awakened in high school. Other strong interests of his youth were poetry and the theater. At the university Khinchin became an active member of the group of gifted young mathematicians guided by N. N. Luzin, the passionate propagandist of the modern theory of functions. In this group Khinchin began to work on the metric theory of functions. His first paper (1916), on a generalization of the Denjoy integral, began a series of works dealing with the properties of functions which remain after the removal of a set of density 0 at a given point (asymptotic derivative, asymptotic monotonicity).

After 1922 Khinchin turned to the theory of numbers and to probability theory. First he studied metric problems of the theory of Diophantine approximations and of the theory of continuous fractions. These problems, which deal with properties true for almost all real numbers, are naturally connected with the asymptotic properties of functions mentioned above. Later Khinchin studied classical Diophantine approximations, which hold true for all numbers; in particular he established the so-called principle of transposition. Another topic of the theory of numbers was studied in his works on the density of sequences.

In 1923 Khinchin established the so-called law of the iterated logarithm, strengthening the results obtained by G. H. Hardy and John Littlewood on the frequency of zeros in the binary expansion of real numbers. In the probabilistic interpretation this law improves the strengthened law of large numbers established by Borel. Probability theory proved to be an auspicious field for the application of the methods of the metric theory of functions, and Khinchin was drawn more and more into the problems of the summation of independent random variables. During the 1920's and 1930's this classical branch of probability theory assumed its present form in the closely related works of Kolmogorov, P. Lévy, Khinchin, and others. Khinchin's contribution included results on the applicability of the law of large numbers to equally distributed random variables with finite mathematical expectations, on the coincidence of the class of all limit distributions with the class of all infinitely divisible laws, on the convergence of series of random variables (jointly with Kolmogorov), and on the structure of stable laws (jointly with Lévy).

In a series of papers written between 1932 and 1934, Khinchin laid the foundation of the general theory of stationary random processes, revealed the spectral representation of their correlation functions, and generalized G. D. Birkhoff's ergodic theorem, which is a strengthened law of large numbers for such processes.

In other works Khinchin dealt with the convergence of discrete Markov chains to continuous diffusion, with large deviations, with the arithmetic of distribution laws, and with the method of arbitrary functions. In the 1940's Khinchin's interest shifted to statistical mechanics. With the aid of local limit theorems, he substantiated the possibility of replacing means in time by means in the phase space both for classical and quantum statistics. In the last years of his life Khinchin studied information theory and queuing theory.

Khinchin also wrote several popular books on the theory of numbers and published articles devoted to pedagogic and philosophic questions of mathematics.

BIBLIOGRAPHY

I. Original Works. Khinchin's writings include "Über dyadische Brüche," in *Mathematische Zeitschrift*, **18** (1923), 109–116, on the law of the iterated logarithm; "Recherches sur la structure des fonctions mesurables," in *Fundamenta mathematica*, **9** (1927), 212–279, a summary work on the theory of functions; *Osnovnye zakony teorii veroyatnostey* ("Basic Laws of Probability Theory"; Moscow, 1927, 2nd ed., rev., 1932), on the summation of independent random variables; *Asymptotische Gesetze der Wahrscheinlichkeitsrechnung* (Berlin, 1933), a monograph on the convergence of Markov chains to diffusion processes; "Korrelationstheorie der stationären stochastischen Prozesse," in *Mathematische Annalen*, **109** (1934), 604–615, the principal work on stationary processes; *Predelnye raspredelenia dlya summ nezavisimykh sluchaynykh velichin* ("Limit Distributions for Sums of Independent Random Variables"; Moscow, 1938); *Matematicheskie osnovania statisticheskoy mekhaniki* ("Mathematical Foundations of Statistical Mechanics"; Moscow, 1943), also in English (New York, 1949); *Matematicheskie osnovania kvantovoy statistiki* ("Mathematical Foundations of Quantum Statistics"; Moscow, 1951); *Pedagogicheskie stati* ("Pedagogical Articles"; Moscow, 1963), English trans., *The Teaching of Mathematics* (London, 1968); and *Raboty po matematicheskoy teorii massovogo obsluzhivania* ("Works on the Mathematical Theory of Queuing"; Moscow, 1963).

II. Secondary Literature. A biography of Khinchin by B. V. Gnedenko is in *Pedagogicheskie stati* (see above, pp. 180–196); there is also an article by A. I. Markushevich in the same volume (pp. 173–179; both are in the English ed.). See also Gnedenko's article in *Uspekhi matematicheskikh nauk*, **10**, no. 3 (1955), 197–212; and the obituary by Gnedenko and Kolmogorov, *ibid.*, **15**, no. 4 (1960), 97–110. Each of these articles has a full bibliography of Khinchin's works up to the time of publication.

See also *Nauka v SSR za pyatnadtsat let. Matematika* ("Fifteen Years of Science in the U.S.S.R. Mathematics"; Moscow-Leningrad, 1932), 150–151, 166–169; *Matematika v SSSR za tridtsat let* ("Thirty Years of Mathematics in the U.S.S.R."; Moscow-Leningrad, 1948), 57, 60–61, 259–260, 509, 706–713, 724–727; and *Matematika v SSR za sorok let* ("Forty Years of Mathematics in the U.S.S.R."), I (Moscow-Leningrad, 1959), 129–130, 789, 795.

A. A. Youschkevitch

AL-KHUJANDĪ, ABŪ MAḤMŪD ḤĀMID IBN AL-KHIḌR (*d.* 1000)

Little is known of al-Khujandī's life. Nāṣir al-Dīn al-Ṭūsī states that he had the title of khan, which would lead one to believe that he was one of the khans of Khujanda on the Syr Darya, or Jaxartes, in Transoxania. For a time he lived under the patronage of the Buwayhid ruler Fakhr al-Dawla (976–997). He died in 1000.

Ḥājjī Khalīfa, Suter, and Brockelmann ascribe the following scientific works to al-Khujandī: *Risāla fi'l mayl wa'arḍ balad* ("On the Obliquity of the Ecliptic and the Latitude of the Lands"), a text on geometry, and *Fi'amal al-āla al-'amma* or *al-āla al-shāmila* ("The Comprehensive Instrument").

According to Nāṣir al-Dīn al-Ṭūsī, al-Khujandī discovered *qānūn al-haiya*, the sine theorem relative to spherical triangles; it displaced the so-called theorem of Menelaus. Abu'l-Wafā' and Abū Naṣr ibn 'Alī ibn 'Irāq (tenth century) also claimed to have discovered the sine theorem.

Al-Ṭūsī, in his *Shakl al-qaṭṭā'*, gives al-Khujandī's solution related to the sine theorem.

Given the spherical triangle ABC whose sides AC and AB are completed into quadrants. RA, RD, RE, and RB are joined and form radii of the sphere.

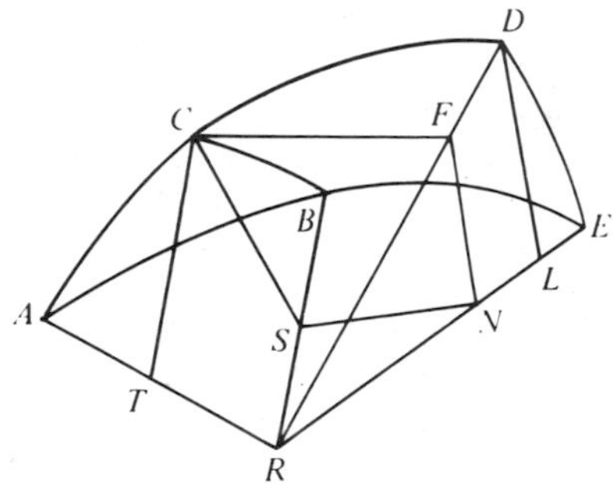

FIGURE 1

$$RA \perp \text{plane of the circle } DE$$

At the same time

$$RA \perp \text{radii } RE \text{ and } RD$$

Erect the perpendicular CF on the plane of the circle DE. The perpendiculars FN and CS are erected on the plane ABE. $CFNS$ is a rectangle, and $DE \parallel FN$.

$$\overset{\triangle}{DER} \sim \overset{\triangle}{FNR}.$$

The perpendicular CT is erected on the plane of the circle AR and is parallel to RS,

$$\text{angle } R = \text{angle } T = 90^\circ$$

$$CF \perp RH$$

$$\text{angle } CFR = 90^\circ$$

Therefore

$$CFRT \text{ forms a rectangle}$$

$$\frac{RF = CT = \sin AC}{FN = CS = \sin CB} = \frac{RH = \sin 90^\circ}{FE = \sin A}$$

In geometry al-Khujandī proved (imperfectly) that the sum of two cubic numbers cannot be a cubic number.

Under the patronage of Fakhr al-Dawla, al-Khujandī constructed, on a hill called *jabal Tabrūk*, in the vicinity of Rayy, an instrument called *al-suds al-Fakhrī* ("sixth of a circle") for the measurement of the obliquity of the ecliptic. The instrument can be described as follows.

Two walls, parallel to the meridian and 40 *zira'* in height, are constructed. Near the southern wall, there is an arched ceiling with an aperture about three inches in diameter.

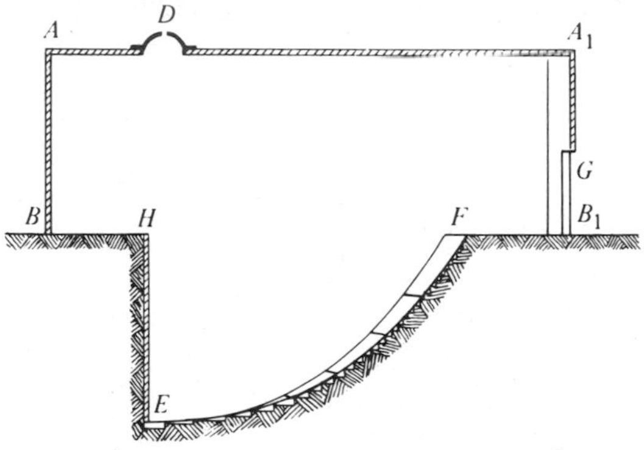

FIGURE 2

The floor directly underneath this aperture is excavated to a depth of forty *zira'*. A wooden arc of 60°, forty *zira'* in diameter and covered with sheets of copper, is placed between the two walls. Each degree of the arc is divided into sixty minutes and each minute into ten parts.

Since the sun's rays projected through the aperture form a cone, an instrument is needed to find the center of its base. This instrument, a circle with two diameters intersecting at right angles, coincides with the base of the cone. It is moved as the cone moves until its center is at the meridian. The arc between the plumb-line and the altitude of the sun is equal to the cosine of the altitude of the sun.

Al-Khujandī says that this instrument is his own invention and adds, "We have attained to the degrees, minutes, and seconds with this instrument." According to Al-Bīrūnī, on this instrument each degree was subdivided into 360 equal parts and each ten-second portion was distinguished on the scale. It should be noted that before al-Khujandī the instruments did not indicate the seconds.

Before al-Khujandī a domed building was used to make solar measurements. According to Al-Bīrūnī, Abū Sahl al-Kūhī (tenth century), at the Sharaf al-

Dawla observatory (built in 988) constructed a domed building with an aperture on the top. This structure was a section of a sphere with a radius of 12.5 meters. Solar rays entered through the aperture and traced the daily trajectory of the sun.

After al-Khujandī, an instrument like *suds al-Fakhrī* was constructed at the Marāgha observatory (built in 1261). The huge meridian arc of the Samarkand observatory (built in 1420) apparently was similar to al-Khujandī's *suds al-Fakhrī.*

The astronomers of Islam tried to increase the precision of their instruments and to make it possible to read the smaller fractions of a degree. For this purpose they increased the size of the instruments. Al-Khujandī and Ulugh Beg represent the extreme examples of this tendency. Increased size, however, causes slight displacement. Al-Bīrūnī says that the aperture of *suds al-Fakhrī* sank by about one span because of the weight of the instrument. Experience with several large instruments proved disappointing and may have led to some doubts about the advisability of continuing to build them.

For the observations of the planets al-Khujandī constructed an armillary sphere and other instruments. He also built a universal instrument called *al-āla al-shāmila* (comprehensive instrument), which was used instead of the astrolabe or the quadrant. It could, however, be used for only one latitude. Al-Badī al-Aṣṭurlābī al-Baghdadī al-Isfahanī (first half of the twelfth century) constructed an astrolabe used for all latitudes.

Al-Khujandī observed the sun and the planets and determined the obliquity of the ecliptic and the latitude of Rayy. He says that these observations were made in the presence of a group of distinguished astronomers and that they gave their written testimony concerning the observations. Using these observations, he compiled his *Zīj al-Fakhrī.* There is in the Library of the Iranian Parliament (Teheran MS 181) an incomplete copy of a *zīj* written in Persian about two centuries after the death of al-Khujandī, which may have been based on his observations.

Al-Khujandī observed the meridian altitude of the sun on two consecutive days, 16 and 17 June 994, and found it to be 77°57′40″. According to this result the entrance of the sun into the summer solstice must have taken place at midnight.

He then observed the sun on 14 December 994 and found the meridian altitude to be 30°53′35″. On the following two days the weather was cloudy, and on the third day he found the meridian altitude of the sun to be 30°53′32″. The entrance of the sun into the winter solstice must have taken place between these two observations. But the second observation is 3″ less than the first. Al-Khujandī calculated from them that its least meridian altitude must have been 30°53′2.30″ (the least altitude of the sun).

Half of the difference between the greatest and the least altitudes of the sun is equal to the obliquity of the ecliptic:

$$1/2(77°57'40'' - 30°53'2'') = 23°32'19''.$$

Al-Khujandī says that the Indians found the greatest obliquity of the ecliptic, 24°; Ptolemy, 23°51′; and he himself, 23°32′19″. These divergent values cannot be due to defective instruments. Actually the obliquity of the ecliptic is not constant; it is a decreasing quantity.

Al-Khujandī calculated the latitude of Rayy by adding the obliquity of the ecliptic (23°32′18.45″) to the least altitude of the sun (30°53′2.30″) and subtracting the result from 90°(90° − 54°25′21.15″ = 35°34′38.45″).

BIBLIOGRAPHY

I. ORIGINAL WORKS. Editions of al-Khujandī's writings are L. Cheiko, *Risāla al-Khujandī fi'l mayl wa'ard balad, al-machriq*, II (Beirut, 1908), 60–68; E. Wiedemann, "Über den Sextant des al-Chogendī," in *Archiv für die Geschichte der Naturwissenschaften*, **2** (1919), 148–151; and "Avicennas Schrift über ein von ihm ersonnenes Beobachtungsinstrument," in *Acta orientalia*, **5** (1926), 81–167; and O. Schirmer, "Studien zur Astronomie der Araber," in *Sitzungsberichte der Physikalisch-medizinische Sozietät in Erlangen*, **58–59** (1926–1927), 43–79.

II. SECONDARY LITERATURE. See C. Brockelmann, *Geschichte der arabischen Literatur*, supp. I (Leiden, 1937), 390; M. Cantor, *Vorlesungen über Geschichte der Mathematik*, 2 vols. (Leipzig, 1880–1892); A. P. Carathéodory, *Traité du quadrilatère attribué à Nassiruddin-el-Toussy* (Constantinople, 1891), pp. 108–120; J. Frank, "Über zwei astronomische arabische Instrumente," in *Zeitschrift für Instrumentenkunde*, **41** (1921), 193–200; Ḥājjī Khalīfa, *Kashf al-zunuh*, S. Yaltkaya, ed., 2 vols. (Istanbul, 1941–1943); E. S. Kennedy, "A Survey of Islamic Astronomical Tables," in *Transactions of the American Philosophical Society*, n.s. **46** (1956), 123–177; J. A. Repsold, *Zur Geschichte der astronomischen Messwerkzeuge von Purbach bis Reinach, 1450 bis 1830*, I (Leipzig, 1908), 8–10; G. Sarton, *Introduction to the History of Science*, I (Baltimore, 1927), 667; A. Sayili, *The Observatory in Islam and Its Place in the General History of the Observatory* (Ankara, 1960), pp. 118–120; A. L. Sédillot, "Mémoire sur les instruments astronomiques des Arabes," in *Mémoires de l'Académie des inscriptions et belles-lettres*, **1** (1884), 202–206; H. Suter, *Die Mathematiker und Astronomen der Araber und ihre Werke* (Leipzig, 1900), p. 74; S. Tekeli, "Nasirüddin, Takiyüddin ve Tycho Brahe'nin Rasataletlerinin Mukayesesi," in *Ankara üniversitesi Dil ve* *tarih-cografya fakültesi dergisi*, **16**, no. 3–4 (1958), 301–393; E. Wiedemann, "Al-Khujandī," in *Encyclopédie de l'Islam*, II; and Sālih Zakī, *Athār-i bāqiyya*, I (Istanbul, 1911), 165.

SEVIM TEKELI

AL-KHWĀRIZMĪ, ABŪ JAʿFAR MUḤAMMAD IBN MŪSĀ (*b.* before 800; *d.* after 847)

Only a few details of al-Khwārizmī's life can be gleaned from the brief notices in Islamic bibliographical works and occasional remarks by Islamic historians and geographers. The epithet "al-Khwārizmī" would normally indicate that he came from Khwārizm (Khorezm, corresponding to the modern Khiva and the district surrounding it, south of the Aral Sea in central Asia). But the historian al-Ṭabarī gives him the additional epithet "al-Quṭrubbullī," indicating that he came from Quṭrubbull, a district between the Tigris and Euphrates not far from Baghdad,[1] so perhaps his ancestors, rather than he himself, came from Khwārizm; this interpretation is confirmed by some sources which state that his "stock" (*aṣl*) was from Khwārizm.[2] Another epithet given to him by al-Ṭabarī, "al-Majūsī," would seem to indicate that he was an adherent of the old Zoroastrian religion. This would still have been possible at that time for a man of Iranian origin, but the pious preface to al-Khwārizmī's *Algebra* shows that he was an orthodox Muslim, so al-Ṭabarī's epithet could mean no more than that his forebears, and perhaps he in his youth, had been Zoroastrians.

Under the Caliph al-Ma'mūn (reigned 813–833) al-Khwārizmī became a member of the "House of Wisdom" (Dār al-Ḥikma), a kind of academy of scientists set up at Baghdad, probably by Caliph Harūn al-Rashīd, but owing its preeminence to the interest of al-Ma'mūn, a great patron of learning and scientific investigation. It was for al-Ma'mūn that al-Khwārizmī composed his astronomical treatise, and his *Algebra* also is dedicated to that ruler. We are told that in the first year of his reign (842) Caliph al-Wāthiq sent al-Khwārizmī on a mission to the chief of the Khazars, who lived in the northern Caucasus.[3] But there may be some confusion in the source here with another "Muḥammad ibn Mūsā the astronomer," namely, one of the three Banū Mūsā ibn Shākir. It is almost certain that it was the latter, and not al-Khwārizmī, who was sent, also by al-Wāthiq, to the Byzantine empire to investigate the tomb of the Seven Sleepers at Ephesus.[4] But al-Khwārizmī survived al-Wāthiq (*d.* 847), if we can believe the story of al-Ṭabarī that he was one of a group of astronomers, summoned to al-Wāthiq's sickbed, who predicted on the basis of the caliph's horoscope that he would live another fifty years and were confounded by his dying in ten days.

All that can be said concerning the date and order of composition of al-Khwārizmī's works is the following. The *Algebra* and the astronomical work, as we have seen, were composed under al-Ma'mūn, in the earlier part of al-Khwārizmī's career. The treatise on Hindu numerals was composed after the *Algebra*, to which it refers. The treatise on the Jewish calendar is dated by an internal calculation to 823–824. The *Geography* has been tentatively dated by Nallino ("al-Khuwārizmī," p. 487) to soon after 816–817, since one of the localities it mentions is Qiman, an Egyptian village of no importance whatever except that a battle was fought there in that year; but the inference is far from secure. The *Chronicle* was composed after 826, since al-Ṭabarī quotes it as an authority for an event in that year.[5]

The *Algebra* is a work of elementary practical mathematics, whose purpose is explained by the author (Rosen trans., p. 3) as providing "what is easiest and most useful in arithmetic, such as men constantly require in cases of inheritance, legacies, partition, lawsuits, and trade, and in all their dealings with one another, or where the measuring of lands, the digging of canals, geometrical computations, and other objects of various sorts and kinds are concerned." Indeed, only the first part of the work treats of algebra in the modern sense. The second part deals with practical mensuration, and the third and longest with problems arising out of legacies. The first part (the algebra proper) discusses only equations of the first and second degrees. According to al-Khwārizmī, all problems of the type he proposes can be reduced to one of six standard forms. These are (here, as throughout, we use modern notation, although al-Khwārizmī's exposition is always rhetorical) the following:

(1) $ax^2 = bx$

(2) $ax^2 = b$

(3) $ax = b$

(4) $ax^2 + bx = c$

(5) $ax^2 + c = bx$

(6) $ax^2 = bx + c,$

where a, b, and c are positive integers. Such an elaboration of cases is necessary because he does not recognize the existence of negative numbers or zero as a coefficient. He gives rules for the solution of each of the six forms—for instance, form (6) is solved by

$$x^2 = (b/a)\,x + c/a,$$

AL-KHWĀRIZMĪ

$$x = \sqrt{\left[\frac{1}{2}\left(\frac{b}{a}\right)\right]^2 + \frac{c}{a}} + \frac{1}{2}\left(\frac{b}{a}\right).$$

He also explains how to reduce any given problem to one of these standard forms. This is done by means of the two operations *al-jabr* and *al-muqābala*. *Al-jabr*, which we may translate as "restoration" or "completion," refers to the process of eliminating negative quantities. For instance, in the problem illustrating standard form (1) (Rosen trans., p. 36), we have

$$x^2 = 40x - 4x^2.$$

By "completion" this is transformed to

$$5x^2 = 40x.$$

Al-muqābala, which we may translate as "balancing," refers to the process of reducing positive quantities of the same power on both sides of the equation. Thus, in the problem illustrating standard form (5) (Rosen trans., p. 40), we have

$$50 + x^2 = 29 + 10x.$$

By *al-muqābala* this is reduced to

$$21 + x^2 = 10x.$$

These two operations, combined with the arithmetical operations of addition, subtraction, multiplication, and division (which al-Khwārizmī also explains in their application to the various powers), are sufficient to solve all types of problems propounded in the *Algebra*. Hence they are used to characterize the work, whose full title is *al-Kitāb al-mukhtaṣar fī ḥisāb al-jabr wa'l-muqābala* ("The Compendious Book on Calculation by Completion and Balancing"). The appellation *al-jabr wa'l-muqābala*, or *al-jabr* alone, was commonly applied to later works in Arabic on the same topic; and thence (via medieval Latin translations from the Arabic) is derived the English "algebra."

In his *Algebra* al-Khwārizmī employs no symbols (even for numerals) but expresses everything in words. For the unknown quantity he employs the word *shay'* ("thing" or "something"). For the second power of a quantity he employs *māl* ("wealth," "property"), which is also used to mean only "quantity." For the first power, when contrasted with the second power, he uses *jidhr* ("root"). For the unit he uses *dirham* (a unit of coinage). Thus the problem

$$(x/3 + 1)(x/4 + 1) = 20$$

and the first stage in its resolution,

$$x^2/12 + x/3 + x/4 + 1 = 20,$$

appear, in literal translation, as follows:

> A quantity: I multiplied a third of it and a *dirham* by a fourth of it and a *dirham:* it becomes twenty. Its computation is that you multiply a third of something by a fourth of something: it comes to a half of a sixth of a square (*māl*). And you multiply a *dirham* by a third of something: it comes to a third of something; and [you multiply] a *dirham* by a fourth of something to get a fourth of something; and [you multiply] a *dirham* by a *dirham* to get a *dirham*. Thus its total, [namely] a half of a sixth of a square and a third of something and a quarter of something and a *dirham*, is equal to twenty *dirhams*.[6]

After illustrating the rules he has expounded for solving problems by a number of worked examples, al-Khwārizmī, in a short section headed "On Business Transactions," expounds the "rule of three," or how to determine the fourth member in a proportion sum where two quantities and one price, or two prices and one quantity, are given. The next part concerns practical mensuration. He gives rules for finding the area of various plane figures, including the circle, and for finding the volume of a number of solids, including cone, pyramid, and truncated pyramid. The third part, on legacies, consists entirely of solved problems. These involve only arithmetic or simple linear equations but require considerable knowledge of the complicated Islamic law of inheritance.

We are told that al-Khwārizmī's work on algebra was the first written in Arabic.[7] In modern times considerable dispute has arisen over the question of whether the author derived his knowledge of algebraic techniques from Greek or Hindu sources. Both Greek and Hindu algebra had advanced well beyond the elementary stage of al-Khwārizmī's work, and none of the known works in either culture shows much resemblance in presentation to al-Khwārizmī's. But, in favor of the "Hindu hypothesis," we may note first that in his astronomical work al-Khwārizmī was far more heavily indebted to a Hindu work than to Greek sources; second, that his exposition is completely rhetorical, like Sanskrit algebraic works and unlike the one surviving Greek algebraic treatise, that of Diophantus, which has already developed quite far toward a symbolic representation; third that the "rule of three" is commonly enunciated in Hindu works but not explicitly in any ancient Greek work; and fourth that in the part on mensuration two of the methods he gives for finding the circumference of the circle from its diameter are specifically Hindu.[8]

On the other hand, in his introductory section al-Khwārizmī uses geometrical figures to explain equations, which surely argues for a familiarity with Book II of Euclid's *Elements*. We must recognize that he was a competent enough mathematician to select and adapt material from quite disparate sources in order to achieve his purpose of producing a popular handbook. The question of his sources is further complicated by the existence of a Hebrew treatise, the *Mishnat ha-Middot*, which is closely related in content and arrangement to the part of al-Khwārizmī's work dealing with mensuration. If we adopt the conclusion of Gandz, the last editor of the *Mishnat ha-Middot*, that it was composed about A.D. 150,[9] then al-Khwārizmī must be the borrower, either through an intermediary work or even directly—his treatise on the Jewish calendar (see below) shows that he must have been in contact with learned Jews. But the Hebrew treatise may be a later adaptation of al-Khwārizmī's work. Gad Sarfatti (*Mathematical Terminology in Hebrew Scientific Literature of the Middle Ages*, Jerusalem, 1968, 58–60) argues on linguistic grounds that the *Mishnat ha-Middat* belongs to an earlier Islamic period.

Al-Khwārizmī wrote a work on the use of the Hindu numerals, which has not survived in Arabic but has reached us in the form of a Latin translation (probably much altered from the original). The Arabic title is uncertain; it may have been something like *Kitāb ḥisāb al-ʿadad al-hindī* ("Treatise on Calculation With the Hindu Numerals"),[10] or possibly *Kitāb al-jamʿ waʾl-tafrīq bi ḥisāb al-hind* ("Book of Addition and Subtraction by the Method of Calculation of the Hindus").[11] The treatise, as we have it, expounds the use of the Hindu (or, as they are misnamed, "Arabic") numerals 1 to 9 and 0 and the place-value system, then explains various applications. Besides the four basic operations of addition, subtraction, multiplication, and division, it deals with both common and sexagesimal fractions and the extraction of the square root (the latter is missing in the unique manuscript but is treated in other medieval works derived from it). In other words, it is an elementary arithmetical treatise using the Hindu numerals. Documentary evidence (eighth-century Arabic papyri from Egypt) shows that the Arabs were already using an alphabetic numeral system similar to the Greek (in which 1, 2, 3, . . . 9, 10, 20, 30, . . . 90, 100, 200, . . . 900 are each represented by a different letter). The sexagesimal modified place-value system used in Greek astronomy must also have been familiar, at least to learned men, from the works such as Ptolemy's *Almagest* which were available in Arabic before 800. But it is likely enough that the decimal place-value system was a fairly recent arrival from India and that al-Khwārizmī's work was the first to expound it systematically. Thus, although elementary, it was of seminal importance.

The title of al-Khwārizmī's astronomical work was *Zīj al-sindhind.*[12] This was appropriate, since it is based ultimately on a Sanskrit astronomical work brought to the court of Caliph al-Manṣūr at Baghdad soon after 770[13] by a member of an Indian political mission. That work was related to, although not identical with, the *Brāhmasphuṭasiddhānta* of Brahmagupta. It was translated into Arabic under al-Manṣūr (probably by al-Fazārī), and the translation was given the name *Zīj al-sindhind. Zīj* means "set of astronomical tables"; and *sindhind* is a corruption of the Sanskrit *siddhānta*, which presumably was part of the title of the Hindu source work. This translation formed the basis of astronomical works (also called *Zīj al-sindhind*) by al-Fazārī and Yaʿqūb ibn Ṭāriq in the late eighth century. Yet these astronomers also used other sources for their work, notably the *Zīj al-shāh*, a translation of a Pahlavi work composed for the Sassanid ruler Khosrau I (Anūshirwān) about 550, which was also based on Hindu sources.

Al-Khwārizmī's work is another "revision" of the *Zīj al-sindhind.* Its chief importance today is that it is the first Arabic astronomical work to survive in anything like entirety. We are told that there were two editions of it; but we know nothing of the differences between them, for it is available only in a Latin translation made by Adelard of Bath in the early twelfth century. This translation was made not from the original but from a revision executed by the Spanish Islamic astronomer al-Majrīṭī (*d.* 1007–1008) and perhaps further revised by al-Majrīṭī's pupil Ibn al-Ṣaffār (*d.* 1035).[14] We can, however, get some notions of the original form of the work from extracts and commentaries made by earlier writers.[15] Thus from the tenth-century commentary of Ibn al-Muthannā we learn that al-Khwārizmī constructed his table of sines to base 150 (a common Hindu parameter), whereas in the extant tables base 60 (more usual in Islamic sine tables) is employed. From the same source we learn that the epoch of the original tables was era Yazdegerd (16 June 632) and not the era Hijra (14 July 622) of al-Majrīṭī's revision.[16]

The work as we have it consists of instructions for computation and use of the tables, followed by a set of tables whose form closely resembles that made standard by Ptolemy. The sun, the moon, and each of the five planets known in antiquity have a table of mean motion(s) and a table of equations. In addition there are tables for computing eclipses, solar declination and right ascension, and various trigonometrical tables. It is certain that Ptolemy's tables, in their revision by Theon of Alexandria, were already known to some Islamic astronomers; and it is highly likely that they influenced, directly or through intermediaries, the form in which al-Khwārizmī's tables were cast.

AL-KHWĀRIZMĪ

But most of the basic parameters in al-Khwārizmī's tables are derived from Hindu astronomy. For all seven bodies the mean motions, the mean positions at epoch, and the positions of the apogee and the node all agree well with what can be derived from the *Brāhmasphuṭasiddhānta*. The maximum equations are taken from the *Zīj al-shāh*. Furthermore, the method of computing the true longitude of a planet by "halving the equation" prescribed in the instructions is purely Hindu and quite alien to Ptolemaic astronomy.[17] This is only the most notable of several Hindu procedures found in the instructions. The only tables (among those that can plausibly be assigned to the original *Zīj*) whose content seems to derive from Ptolemy are the tables of solar declination, of planetary stations, of right ascension, and of equation of time. Nowhere in the work is there any trace of original observation or of more than trivial computation by the author. This appears strange when we learn that in the original introduction (the present one must be much altered) al-Khwārizmī discussed observations made at Baghdad under al-Ma'mūn to determine the obliquity of the ecliptic.[18] The value found, 23° 33′, was fairly accurate. Yet in the tables al-Khwārizmī adopts the much worse value of 23° 51′ from Theon. Even more inexplicable is why, if he had the Ptolemaic tables available, he preferred to adopt the less accurate parameters and obscure methods of Hindu astronomy.

The *Geography*, *Kitāb ṣūrat al-arḍ* ("Book of the Form of the Earth"), consists almost entirely of lists of longitudes and latitudes of cities and localities. In each section the places are arranged according to the "seven climata" (in many ancient Greek geographical works the known world was divided latitudinally into seven strips known as "climata," each clima being supposed to enjoy the same length of daylight on its longest day), and within each clima the arrangement is by increasing longitude. Longitudes are counted from an extreme west meridian, the "shore of the western ocean." The first section lists cities; the second, mountains (giving the coordinates of their extreme points and their orientation); the third, seas (giving the coordinates of salient points on their coastlines and a rough description of their outlines); the fourth, islands (giving the coordinates of their centers, and their length and breadth); the fifth, the central points of various geographical regions; and the sixth, rivers (giving their salient points and the towns on them).

It is clear that there is some relationship between this work and Ptolemy's *Geography*, which is a description of a world map and a list of the coordinates of the principal places on it, arranged by regions. Many of the places listed in Ptolemy's work also occur in al-Khwārizmī's, with coordinates that are nearly the same or systematically different. Yet it is very far from being a mere translation or adaptation of Ptolemy's treatise. The arrangement is radically different, and the outline of the map which emerges from it diverges greatly from Ptolemy's in several regions. Nallino is surely right in his conjecture that it was derived by reading off the coordinates of a map or set of maps based on Ptolemy's but was carefully revised in many respects. Nallino's principal argument is that al-Khwārizmī describes the colors of the mountains in a way which could not possibly represent their physical appearance but might well represent their depiction on a map. To this we may add that in those areas where al-Khwārizmī agrees, in general, with Ptolemy, the coordinates of the two frequently differ by 10, 15, 20, or more minutes, up to one degree of arc; such discrepancies cannot be explained by scribal errors but are plausible by supposing a map as intermediary. The few maps accompanying the sole manuscript of al-Khwārizmī's *Geography* are crude things; but we know that al-Ma'mūn had had constructed a world map, on which many savants worked. According to al-Mas'ūdī, the source of this information, al-Ma'mūn's map was superior to Ptolemy's.[19] Nallino makes the plausible suggestion that al-Khwārizmī's *Geography* is based on al-Ma'mūn's world map (on which al-Khwārizmī himself had probably worked), which in turn was based on Ptolemy's *Geography*, which had been considerably revised.

The map which emerges from al-Khwārizmī's text is in several respects more accurate than Ptolemy's, particularly in the areas ruled by Islam. Its most notable improvement is to shorten the grossly exaggerated length of the Mediterranean imagined by Ptolemy. It also corrects some of the distortions applied by Ptolemy to Africa and the Far East (no doubt reflecting the knowledge of these areas brought back by Arab merchants). But for Europe it could do little more than reproduce Ptolemy; and it introduces errors of its own, notably the notion that the Atlantic is an inland sea enclosed by a western continent joined to Europe in the north.

The only other surviving work of al-Khwārizmī is a short treatise on the Jewish calendar, *Istikhrāj ta'rīkh al-yahūd* ("Extraction of the Jewish Era"). His interest in the subject is natural in a practicing astronomer. The treatise describes the Jewish calendar, the 19-year intercalation cycle, and the rules for determining on what day of the week the first day of the month Tishrī shall fall; calculates the interval between the Jewish era (creation of Adam) and the Seleucid era; and gives rules for determining the mean longitude of the sun and moon using the Jewish calendar. Although a slight work, it is accurate, well informed, and of importance as evidence for the antiquity of the present Jewish calendar.

Al-Khwārizmī wrote two works on the astrolabe, *Kitāb ʿamal al-asṭurlāb* ("Book on the Construction of the Astrolabe") and *Kitāb al-ʿamal biʾl-asṭurlāb* ("Book on the Operation of the Astrolabe"). Probably from the latter is drawn the extract found in a Berlin manuscript of a work of the ninth-century astronomer al-Farghānī. This extract deals with the solution of various astronomical problems by means of the astrolabe—for instance, determination of the sun's altitude, of the ascendant, and of one's terrestrial latitude. There is nothing surprising in the content, and it is probable that al-Khwārizmī derived it all from earlier works on the subject. The astrolabe was a Greek invention, and we know that there were once ancient Greek treatises on it. Astrolabe treatises predating al-Khwārizmī survive in Syriac (by Severus Sebokht, seventh century) and in Arabic (now only in Latin translation, by Māshāʾllāh, late eighth century).

The *Kitāb al-taʾrīkh* ("Chronicle") of al-Khwārizmī does not survive, but several historians quote it as an authority for events in the Islamic period. It is possible that in it al-Khwārizmī (like his contemporary Abū Maʿshar) exhibited an interest in interpreting history as fulfilling the principles of astrology.[20] In that case it may be the ultimate source of the report of Ḥamza al-Iṣfahānī about how al-Khwārizmī cast the horoscope of the Prophet and showed at what hour Muḥammad must have been born by astrological deduction from the events of his life.[21] Of a book entitled *Kitāb al-rukhāma* ("On the Sundial") we know only the title, but the subject is consonant with his other interests.

Al-Khwārizmī's scientific achievements were at best mediocre, but they were uncommonly influential. He lived at a time and in a place highly favorable to the success of his works: encouraged by the patronage of the caliphs, Islamic civilization was beginning to assimilate Greek and Hindu science. The great achievements of Islamic science lay in the future, but these early works which transmitted the new knowledge ensured their author's lasting fame. Between the ninth and twelfth centuries algebra was developed to a far more sophisticated level in Islamic lands, aided by the spread of knowledge of Diophantus' work. But even such advanced algebraists as al-Karajī (*d.* 1029) and ʿUmar al-Khayyāmī (*d.* 1123–1124) still used the rhetorical exposition popularized by al-Khwārizmī.

Al-Khwārizmī's *Algebra* continued to be used as a textbook and praised highly (see, for instance, the quotations in Hajī Khalfa, V, 67–69). The algebraic part proper was twice translated into Latin in the twelfth century (by Robert of Chester and by Gerard of Cremona) and was the chief influence on medieval European algebra, determining its rhetorical form and some of its vocabulary (the medieval *cossa* is a literal translation of Arabic *shayʾ*, and *census* of *māl*). The treatise on Hindu numerals, although undoubtedly important in introducing those useful symbols into more general use in Islamic lands, achieved its greatest success only when introduced to the West through Latin translation in the early twelfth century (occasional examples of the numerals appeared in the West more than a century earlier, but only as isolated curiosities). The work quickly spawned a number of adaptations and offshoots, such as the *Liber alghoarismi* of John of Seville (*ca.* 1135), the *Algorismus* of John of Sacrobosco (*ca.* 1250), and the *Liber ysagogarum Alchorizmi* (twelfth century). In fact, al-Khwārizmī's name became so closely associated with the "new arithmetic" using the Hindu numerals that the Latin form of his name, *algorismus*, was given to any treatise on that topic. Hence, by a devious path, is derived the Middle English "augrim" and the modern "algorism" (corrupted by false etymology to "algorithm").

The other works did not achieve success of such magnitude; but the *Zīj* continued to be used, studied, and commented on long after it deserved to be superseded. About 900 al-Battānī published his great astronomical work, based on the *Almagest* and tables of Ptolemy and on his own observations. This is greatly superior to al-Khwārizmī's astronomical work in nearly every respect, yet neither al-Battānī's opus nor the other results of the prodigious astronomical activity in Islamic lands during the ninth and tenth centuries drove al-Khwārizmī's *Zīj* from the classroom. In fact it was the first such work to reach the West, in Latin translation by Adelard of Bath in the early twelfth century. Knowledge of this translation was probably confined to England (all surviving manuscripts appear to be English), but many of al-Khwārizmī's tables reached a wide audience in the West via another work, the *Toledan Tables*, a miscellaneous assembly of astronomical tables from the works of al-Khwārizmī, al-Battānī, and al-Zarqāl which was translated into Latin, probably by Gerard of Cremona, in the late twelfth century and which, for all its deficiencies, enjoyed immense popularity throughout Europe for at least 100 years.

The *Geography* too was much used and imitated in Islamic lands, even after the appearance of good

AL-KHWĀRIZMĪ

Arabic translations of Ptolemy's *Geography* in the later ninth century caused something of a reaction in favor of that work. For reasons rather obscure the medieval translators of Arabic scientific works into Latin appear to have avoided purely geographical treatises, so al-Khwārizmī's *Geography* was unknown in Europe until the late nineteenth century. But some of the data in it reached medieval Europe via the lists of longitudes and latitudes of principal cities, which were commonly incorporated into ancient and medieval astronomical tables.[22]

NOTES

1. Al-Ṭabarī, de Goeje ed., III, 2, 1364.
2. E.g., *Fihrist*, Flügel ed., I, 274; followed by Ibn al-Qifṭī, Lippert, ed., p. 286.
3. Al-Muqaddasī, de Goeje ed., p. 362.
4. The story is found in several sources, all of which call the envoy "Muḥammad ibn Mūsā the astronomer." Only one, al-Mas'ūdī, *Kitāb al-tanbīh*, de Goeje ed., p. 134, adds "ibn Shākir." For the full story see Nallino, "Al-Khuwārizmī," pp. 465–466.
5. Al-Ṭabarī, de Goeje ed., III, 2, 1085.
6. Rosen, text, p. 28, somewhat emended. The translation is mine.
7. E.g., Hajī Khalfa, Flügel ed., V, 67, no. 10012.
8. These are $c = \sqrt{10d^2}$ and $c = 62832d/20000$. See Rosen's note on pp. 198–199 of his ed. The second value, which is very accurate, is attested for the later *Pauliśasiddhānta* and also, significantly, for Ya'qūb ibn Ṭāriq, al-Khwārizmī's immediate predecessor, by al-Bīrūnī, *India*, Sachau trans., I, 168–169. Pauliśa presumably derived it from the *Āryabhaṭīya* (see the *Āryabhaṭīya*, Clark ed., p. 28).
9. See Gandz's ed. of the *Mishnat ha-Middot*, pp. 6–12.
10. Some such title seems to be implied by Ibn al-Qifṭī, Lippert ed., pp. 266–267.
11. As conjectured by Ruska, "Zur ältesten arabischen Algebra," pp. 18–19.
12. *Fihrist*, Flügel ed., I, 274.
13. See, e.g., al-Bīrūnī, *India*, Sachau trans., II, 15.
14. For the latter revision see Ibn Ezra, *Libro de los fundamentos*, p. 109.
15. For a list of these see Pingree and Kennedy, commentary on al-Hāshimī's *Book of the Reasons Behind Astronomical Tables*, sec. 11; see also in biblio. (below).
16. For the value 150 see, e.g., Goldstein, *Ibn al-Muthannâ*, p. 178. For the epoch, *ibid.*, p. 18.
17. On "halving the equation" see Neugebauer, *al-Khwārizmī*, pp. 23–29.
18. Ibn Yūnus, quoted by Nallino, "Al-Khuwārizmī," p. 469.
19. Al-Mas'ūdī, *Kitāb al-tanbīh*, de Goeje ed., p. 33.
20. On Abū Ma'shar see especially Pingree, *The Thousands of Abū Ma'shar*.
21. Ḥamza, *Ta'rīkh*, Beirut ed., p. 126. However, Ḥamza quotes this not directly from the *Chronicle* (which he uses elsewhere, *ibid.*, p. 144) but from Shādhān's book of Abū Ma'shar's table talk, so the ultimate source might be a conversation between al-Khwārizmī and Abū Ma'shar.
22. The list in the *Toledan Tables*, which is certainly in part related to al-Khwārizmī's *Geography*, is printed with commentary in Toomer, "Toledan Tables," pp. 134–139.

BIBLIOGRAPHY

The principal medieval Arabic sources for al-Khwārizmī's life and works are Ibn al-Nadīm, *Kitāb al-fihrist*, Gustav Flügel, ed., 2 vols. (Leipzig, 1872; repr. Beirut, 1964), I, 274—trans. by Heinrich Suter, "Das Mathematiker-Verzeichniss im Fihrist des Ibn Abî Ja'ḳûb an-Nadîm," which is Abhandlungen zur Geschichte der Mathematik, VI, 29, supp. to *Zeitschrift für Mathematik und Physik*, 37 (1892); Ibn al-Qifṭī, *Ta'rīkh al-ḥukamā'*, Julius Lippert, ed. (Leipzig, 1903; repr. Baghdad, n.d.), p. 286, a mere repetition of the *Fihrist* but with more information under the entry "Kanka," p. 266; Ṣâ'id al-Andalusî, *Kitâb ṭabaḳât al-umam* (*Livre des catégories des nations*), which is Publications de l'Institut des Hautes Études Marocaines, XXVIII, Régis Blachère, trans. (Paris, 1935), pp. 47–48, 130; Hajī Khalfa, *Lexicon bibliographicum*, G. Flügel, ed., V (London, 1850; repr. London–New York, 1964), 67–69, no. 10012; *Annales quos scripsit Abu Djafar Mohammed ibn Djarir at-Tabari*, M. J. de Goeje, ed., III, 2 (Leiden, 1881; repr. Leiden, 1964), 1364; *Descriptio imperii moslemici auctore al-Mokaddasi*, M. J. de Goeje, ed. (Leipzig, 1876–1877), p. 362; al-Mas'ūdī, *Kitāb al-tanbīh wa'l-ishrāf*, which is Bibliotheca Geographorum Arabicorum, VIII, M. J. de Goeje, ed. (Leiden, 1894; repr. 1967), pp. 33, 134. The best modern account of his life is C. A. Nallino, "Al-Khuwārizmī e il suo rifacimento della Geografia di Tolomeo," in his *Raccolta di scritti editi e inediti*, V (Rome, 1944), 458–532 (an amended repr. of his article in *Atti dell'Accademia nazionale dei Lincei. Memorie*, Classe di scienze morali, storiche e filologiche, 5th ser., II, pt. 1), and sec. 2, 463–475, where references to further source material may be found.

The Arabic text of the *Algebra* was edited with English trans. by Frederic Rosen as *The Algebra of Mohammed ben Musa* (London, 1831; repr. New York, 1969). Editing and trans. are careless. A somewhat better Arabic text is provided by the ed. of 'Alī Muṣṭafā Masharrafa and Muḥammad Mursī Aḥmad (Cairo, 1939), which is Publications of the Faculty of Science, no. 2. Both eds. are based only on the MS Oxford Bodleian Library, I 918, 1, but other MSS are known to exist. I owe the refs. to the following to Adel Anbouba: Berlin 5955 no. 6, ff. 60r–95v; also a MS at Shibin el-Kom (Egypt) mentioned in *Majalla Ma'had al-Makhṭūṭāt al-'Arabiyya* (Cairo, 1950), no. 19. The section of the *Algebra* concerning mensuration is published with an English trans. by Solomon Gandz, together with his ed. of the *Mishnat ha-Middot*, which is *Quellen und Studien zur Geschichte der Mathematik, Astronomie und Physik*, Abt. A, **2** (1932). A useful discussion of the *Algebra* is given by Julius Ruska, "Zur ältesten arabischen Algebra und Rechenkunst," in *Sitzungsberichte der Heidelberger Akademie der Wissenschaften*, Phil.-hist. Kl. (1917), sec. 2, where further bibliography will be found. On the section dealing with legacies, see S. Gandz, "The Algebra of Inheritance," in *Osiris*, **5** (1938), 319–391. The Latin trans. by Robert of Chester was edited with English trans. by Louis Charles Karpinski, *Robert of Chester's Latin Translation of the Algebra of al-Khowa-*

rizmi (Ann Arbor, 1915); repr. as pt. I of Louis Charles Karpinski and John Garrett Winter, *Contributions to the History of Science* (Ann Arbor, 1930). The editor perversely chose to print a sixteenth-century reworking rather than Robert's original translation, but his introduction and commentary are occasionally useful. The anonymous Latin version printed by G. Libri in his *Histoire des sciences mathématiques en Italie*, I (Paris, 1858), 253–297, is probably that of Gerard of Cremona, but the problem is complicated by the existence of another Latin text which is a free adaptation of al-Khwārizmī's *Algebra*, whose translation is expressly ascribed to Gerard of Cremona. This is printed by Baldassarre Boncompagni in *Atti dell'Accademia pontificia dei Nuovi Lincei*, **4** (1851), 412–435. A. A. Björnbo, "Gerhard von Cremonas Übersetzung von Alkwarizmis Algebra und von Euklids Elementen," in *Bibliotheca mathematica*, 3rd ser., **6** (1905), 239–241, argues that the version printed by Libri is the real Gerard translation. On al-Karaji's *Algebra* see Adel Anbouba, *L'algèbre al-Badi' d'al-Karagi* (Beirut, 1964), which is Publications de l'Université Libanaise, Section des Études Mathématiques, II. On 'Umar al-Khayyāmī's *Algebra* see F. Woepcke, *L'algèbre d'Omar al-Khayyâmi* (Paris, 1851); and, for discussion and further bibliography, Hâmit Dilgan, *Büyük matematikci Ömer Hayyâm* (Istanbul, 1959), in the series Istanbul Technical University Publications. On Hindu values of π see *Alberuni's India*, Edward C. Sachau, trans., I (London, 1910), 168–169; and *The Āryabhaṭiya of Āryabhaṭa*, Walter Eugene Clark, trans. (Chicago, 1930), p. 28.

The Latin text of the treatise on Hindu numerals was first published, carelessly, *Algoritmi de numero indorum* (Rome, 1857), which is Trattati d'aritmetica, B. Boncompagni, ed., I. A facs. text of the unique MS was published by Kurt Vogel, *Mohammed ibn Musa Alchwarizmi's Algorismus* (Aalen, 1963), which is Milliaria, III. Vogel provides a transcription as inaccurate as his predecessor's and some useful historical information. Of the numerous medieval Latin works named *Algorismus* the following have been published: John of Seville's *Alghoarismi de practica arismetrice*, B. Boncompagni, ed. (Rome, 1857), which is Trattati d'aritmetica, II; John of Sacrobosco's *Algorismus*, edited by J. O. Halliwell as "Joannis de Sacro-Bosco tractatus de arte numerandi," in his *Rara mathematica*, 2nd ed. (London, 1841), pp. 1–31; and Alexander of Villa Dei (*ca.* 1225), "Carmen de algorismo," *ibid.*, pp. 73–83. See also M. Curtze, "Über eine Algorismus-Schrift des XII Jahrhunderts," in *Abhandlungen zur Geschichte der Mathematik*, **8** (1898), 1–27.

The Latin version of al-Khwārizmī's *Zīj* was edited by H. Suter, *Die astronomischen Tafeln des Muḥammed ibn Mūsā al-Khwārizmī* (Copenhagen, 1914), which is Kongelige Danske Videnskabernes Selskabs Skrifter, 7. Raekke, Historisk og filosofisk Afd., III, 1. Suter has a useful commentary, but an indispensable supplement is O. Neugebauer, *The Astronomical Tables of al-Khwārizmī* (Copenhagen, 1962), Kongelige Danske Videnskabernes Selskabs, Historisk-filosofiske Skrifter, IV, 2, which provides a trans. of the introductory chapters and an explanation of the basis and use of the tables. Important information on al-Khwārizmī's *Zīj* will be found in the forthcoming ed. of al-Hāshimī's *Book of the Reasons Behind Astronomical Tables* (*Kitāb fī 'Ilal al-Zījāt*), ed. and trans. by Fuad I. Haddad and E. S. Kennedy, with a commentary by David Pingree and E. S. Kennedy. The Arabic text of Ibn al-Muthannā's commentary is lost, but one Latin and two Hebrew versions are preserved. The Latin version has been miserably edited by E. Millás Vendrell, *El comentario de Ibn al-Mutannā a las Tablas astronómicas de al-Jwārizmī* (Madrid–Barcelona, 1963). It is preferable to consult Bernard R. Goldstein's excellent ed., with English trans. and commentary, of the Hebrew versions, *Ibn al-Muthannâ's Commentary on the Astronomical Tables of al-Khwârizmî* (New Haven–London, 1967). On the origin of the *Sindhind* and early versions of it, see David Pingree, "The Fragments of the Works of al-Fazārī," in *Journal of Near Eastern Studies*, **29** (1970), 103–123; "The Fragments of the Works of Ya'qūb ibn Ṭāriq," *ibid.*, **26** (1968), 97–125; and *The Thousands of Abū Ma'shar* (London, 1968). On Maslama and Ibn al-Ṣaffār's revision of al-Khwārizmī's *Zīj* see Ibn Ezra, *El libro de los fundamentos de las tablas astronómicas*, J. M. Millás Vallicrosa, ed. (Madrid-Barcelona, 1947), pp. 75, 109–110. The relationship of the mean motions in al-Khwārizmī's *Zīj* to the *Brāhmasphuṭasiddhānta* was demonstrated by J. J. Burckhardt, "Die mittleren Bewegungen der Planeten im Tafelwerk des Khwârizmî," in *Vierteljahrsschrift der Naturforschenden Gesellschaft in Zürich*, **106** (1961), 213–231; and by G. J. Toomer, review of O. Neugebauer's *The Astronomical Tables of al-Khwārizmī*, in *Centaurus*, **10** (1964), 203–212. Al-Battānī's *Zīj* was edited magisterially by C. A. Nallino, *Al-Battānī sive Albatenii opus astronomicum*, 3 vols. (Milan, 1899–1907), which is Pubblicazioni del Reale Osservatorio di Brera in Milano, XL (vols. I and II repr. Frankfurt, 1969; vol. III repr. Baghdad [?], 1970 [?] [n.p., n.d.]). The *Toledan Tables* have never been printed in their entirety, but they are extensively analyzed by G. J. Toomer, "A Survey of the Toledan Tables," in *Osiris*, **15** (1968), 5–174.

The text of the *Geography* was published from the unique MS by Hans von Mžik, *Das Kitāb Ṣūrat al-Arḍ des Abū Ǧa'far Muḥammad ibn Mūsā al-Ḫuwārizmī* (Leipzig, 1926). The classic study of the work is that by C. A. Nallino mentioned above. See also Hans von Mžik, "Afrika nach der arabischen Bearbeitung der *Γεωγραφικὴ ὑφήγησις* des Claudius Ptolemaeus von Muḥammad ibn Mūsā al-Ḫwārizmī," which is *Denkschriften der K. Akademie der Wissenschaften* (Vienna), Phil.-hist. Kl., **59**, no. 4 (1916); and "Osteuropa nach der arabischen Bearbeitung der *Γεωγραφικὴ ὑφήγησις* des Klaudios Ptolemaios von Muḥammad ibn Mūsā al-Ḫuwārizmī," in *Wiener Zeitschrift für die Kunde des Morgenlandes*, **43** (1936), 161–193; and Hubert Daunicht, *Der Osten nach der Erdkarte al-Ḫuwārizmīs* (Bonn, 1968), with further bibliography.

The treatise on the Jewish calendar is printed as the first item in *al-Rasā'il al-mutafarriqa fī'l-hay'a* (Hyderabad [Deccan], 1948). See E. S. Kennedy, "Al-Khwārizmī on the Jewish Calendar," in *Scripta mathematica*, **27** (1964),

55–59. The extract from the treatise on the astrolabe survives in MSS Berlin, Arab. 5790 and 5793. A German trans. and commentary was given by Josef Frank, *Die Verwendung des Astrolabs nach al Chwârizmi* (Erlangen, 1922), which is Abhandlungen zur Geschichte der Naturwissenschaften und der Medizin, no. 3. Severus Sabokht's treatise was edited by F. Nau, "Le traité sur l'astrolabe plan de Sévère Sabokt," in *Journal asiatique*, 9th ser., **13** (1899), 56–101, 238–303, also printed separately (Paris, 1899). The Latin trans. of Māshā'llāh's treatise was printed several times in the sixteenth century; a modern ed. is in R. T. Gunther, *Chaucer and Messehalla on the Astrolabe*, which is *Early Science in Oxford*, V (Oxford, 1929), 133–232. For the *Chronicle* the principal excerptor is Elias of Nisibis, in his *Chronography*, written in Syrian and Arabic. See the ed. of the latter, with trans. and commentary, by Friedrich Baethgen, *Fragmente syrischer und arabischer Historiker*, which is Abhandlungen für die Kunde des Morgenlandes, VIII, 3 (Leipzig, 1884; repr. Nendeln, Lichtenstein, 1966), esp. pp. 4–5. A fuller ed., with Latin trans., is given in E. W. Brooks and J.-B. Chabot, *Eliae metropolitae Nisibeni opus chronologicum*, 2 vols. (Louvain, 1910), which is Corpus Scriptorum Christianorum Orientalium, Scriptores Syri, vols. XXIII and XXIV. See also the French trans. by L.-J. Delaporte, *La chronographie d'Élie bar-Šinaya* (Paris, 1910). See also Ḥamza al-Ḥasan al-Iṣfahānī, *Ta'rikh sini mulūk al-arḍ wa l-anbiyā'* (Beirut, 1961), pp. 126, 144. Other excerptors are listed by Nallino, "Al-Khuwārizmī," pp. 471–472.

G. J. TOOMER